THE OFFICIAL

# Music Master

# JAZZ CATALOGUE



**EVERY JAZZ & BLUES RECORDING ON THE MUSIC MASTER DATABASE – OVER 25,000 ENTRIES!**

# MUSIC MASTER JAZZ CATALOGUE

First published by John Humphries in 1990.

Published by John Humphries (Publishing) Ltd, 1 De Cham Avenue, Hastings, Sussex, England. TN37 6HE. Telephone: 0424 715181. Fax: 0424 422805.

ISBN 0 904520 48 X

General editor: John Humphries.



**Book trade enquiries:** Harrap Publishing Group Ltd, Chelsea House, 26 Market Square, Bromley, Kent. BR1 1NA. Telephone: 081 313 3484. Fax: 081 313 0702.

**Record trade and private enquiries:** John Humphries (Publishing) Ltd, Music House, 1 De Cham Avenue, Hastings, Sussex. England. TN37 6HE. Telephone: 0424 715181. Fax: 0424 422805.

**Record trade enquiries:** Arabesque Ltd, Network House, 29-39 Stirling Road, London. W3 8DJ. Telephone: UK Sales: 081 992 7732. International Sales: 081 992 0098. Fax: 081 992 0340.

A full list of our distributors worldwide is printed on pages 13 and 14 of this book.

Printed and bound in Great Britain.

# MUSIC MASTER JAZZ CATALOGUE

## CONTENTS



## FOREWORD

The Music Master Jazz Catalogue is the latest in the Music Master series of paperbacks, and with the resurgence in popularity of jazz music, ought to be a must for all music enthusiasts, whether jazz buffs or not. This is new ground for Music Master, and we must thank Graham Langley of the British Institute of Jazz Studies, without whose expert assistance we would have not been able to produce this book. Graham's introductory article on the following pages explains why certain information has been included or excluded. We have tried, by conducting a thorough editing job, to minimise errors, duplications or inaccuracies. If any occur, we do apologise, but as this a new title from our range, we feel sure the experience gained from producing this book can only help to raise the standard of future Music Master publications.
It has been impossible to go through each artist's individual recordings and delete any because they are not considered to be in the 'jazz' category. It is appreciated that it may appear to be the case that recordings listed under an artist we have included such as *Bing Crosby* are not jazz, but some are included due to that artist's connections with jazz. We hope our readers will realise the reasons for including all these artists' recordings, regardless of their specific music classifications. All the artists included in this book are considered to have connections with jazz, but for reasons already mentioned, the arguments will doubtless rage on forever!
G.R.

# INTRODUCTION

When John Humphries first asked for my help in compiling this current **Music Master Jazz Catalogue**, I blithely accepted without giving real thought to the task that lay ahead.
If the first problem was one of scale, the second was one of knowledge. I have been listening to and reading about jazz for the last thirty years as well as having access to probably the finest jazz reference library available in the UK. So what was the problem? Almost immediately, I was faced with names that I half recognised, half remembered, but from where?

## What Is Jazz?

Then came the third and biggest problem of all. What is *jazz*? Ask ten genuine enthusiasts and likely as not you will recieve ten different answers. The recorded history of jazz music spans over seventy years and in that time has evolved, changed and mutated in a seemingly never ending series of progressions so that the 'jazz' of today appears to bear little relationship to that first *Original Dixieland Jazz Band* recording of 1917. For many years there have been factional fights between supporters of various styles, and the placing of artists into 'pigeon holes' has become a national sport. Periodicals have flourished, catering for differing tastes and frequently using an inordinate amount of space, (particularly in the letters columns), in criticising all those who do not follow the 'true way'. Ironically, publications which were once established to cover the latest sounds, eventually find themselves overtaken by events and relegated to the middle ground as even newer developments take over. So, how to resolve the dilemma? As an individual I naturally have my own likes and dislikes, styles and artists I prefer and others that I really do not care for. However, the aim of this volume is to offer as complete a picture as possible and reflect the broad spectrum of music available under the jazz banner, so I have attempted to put prejudice to one side and this is the finished article. There will of course be criticism. 'Why is *X* in?' and 'Why was *Y* left out?', so I will try to explain the criteria that I have used.

## Jazz & Blues

My original brief was to produce a Jazz Catalogue, but I immediately suggested that it should be amended to include jazz and blues, though retaining the title of Music Master Jazz Catalogue. To my mind, the two musics are indelibly linked and would hardly exist without each other. So *Blues* was in!
I have delved into the pre-history to include *Ragtime*, which was such an influence on early jazz stylists, and *Spirituals* and *Minstrelsy* which helped the evolution of vocal traditions in *Gospel* music and *Blues*. The whole range of 'core' jazz activity is of course represented: *New Orleans; Chicago; Swing; Bop; West Coast; Boogie Woogie; Avant Garde* , etc (sorry, there are these 'pigeon holes' again), from the finest artists of America and Europe. I have also included the predominantly British *Dance Bands* of the 30's and 40's which still have such a following today. A contentious area for some will be the inclusion of vocalists. *Billie Holiday* is a *Jazz* singer isn't she? So is *Ella* and *Sarah*, but what about .........? The list is endless. The same can be said for the males as well, so this is an area where personal opinion has to apply. *Crosby* and *Sinatra* are both in; their roots are in jazz with *Whiteman* and *Dorsey*. *Joe Williams* is in of course, but so is *Tony Bennett* - he has also made

some albums with *Basie*. If you don't approve, please turn the page. The same mus be said of a limited number of entries that offer the overall 'feel' of *Jazz* but purist may well object to. The *Temperance Seven*, who amused and entertained from th sixties on are a prime example.That is what is in - so what is left out? There are a number of musics that are often associated with *Jazz* and *Blues* which I hav excluded, like *Cajun, Zydeco* and *Salsa*. I have also ommitted ethnic recordings tha are frequently given a *'jazz'* tag like some examples of African regional popula music. However, musicians from that continent who have entered the *Jazz* main-stream like Hugh Masekela and Abdullah Ibrahim (Dollar Brand) are included.The greatest area of difficulty has been with the sector commonly designated *Rhythm 'n Blues*. Definitions differ according to the listener and a single artist could be classifie as *R 'n' B, Soul, Rock 'n' Roll* or even *Blues* depending on who you talk to. I have therefore excluded this whole area with the exception of a few seminal figures like *Fats Domino*, *Johnny Otis* and *Chuck Berry*, just to give a flavour.

So there you have it. Look for your favourites and more than anything else expanc your horizons. If it is listed here it falls under the overall *Jazz* and *Blues* umbrella, sc experiment with your listening and above all - enjoy!

*Graham Langley, 1990.*

## BRITISH INSTITUTE OF JAZZ STUDIES

The B.I.J.S. is run by Graham Langley, 45 years of age and married with a teenage daughter. By profession he is a 'headhunter' with one of the country's leading executive recruitment consultants and in his spare time he runs the British Institute of Jazz Studies. Established in the sixties, the B.I.J.S., a registered charity, set about building a library of all written material on jazz and related musics and now has probably the largest collection available in the U.K. As a part-time activity and seriously underfunded, progress has been fairly slow, but the archive now consists of some 1,600 books, around 10,000 periodicals and countless ephemeral items like concert brochures, newscuttings, etc. Access to the material is open to researchers, authors, students and publishers. Users of the library can usually rely on a fair degree of help from Graham himself who will act as a guide round the sheives pointing out sources of information most suitable for the project in hand. Being a glutton for punishment, and a confirmed bibliophile, Graham Langley is also on the committee of the recently formed National Jazz Foundation Archive being set up at Lougton Library, Essex, with the assistance of Essex County Council. The two organisations will work in tandem to provide an unequalled information source to jazz enthusiasts of every persuasion.

# ILLUSTRATIONS' INDEX

**Front cover:**



**Back cover:**



**Inside the book:**

# RECORD TRADE DISTRIBUTION

*Record trade orders for Music Master books should be sent to the following companies:-*

**France:**
WOTRE MUSIC DISTRIBUTION, Les Carreaux, Route de Niort, 79410 St. Gelais, France. Telephone: 49 33 45 64. Fax: 49 24 97 47.

**Canada:**
RECORD PEDDLER, 12 Brant Street, Toronto, Ontario, Canada. M5V 2MI. Telephone: 416 364 5507.

**Germany:**
BELLA MUSICA TONTRAEGER GmbH, Rheinstrasse 26, 7580 Buhl, Germany. Telephone: 07223 27009. Fax: 07223 30109.

**Greece:**
MUSI COMPACT, Shopping Centre 'Phinikas', 293 Kifissias Avenue, Athens, Greece. Telephone: 01 8015 794. Fax: 01 8016 425.

**Holland:**
DIGITAL SOUNDS, Post Bus 6118, 1005 E C, Amsterdam, Netherlands. Telephone: 010 3120 12 00 85. Fax: 010 3120 12 00 85.
HOME ENTERTAINMENT SERVICES BV, Klokhoek 1, 3833 GW, Leusden, Netherlands. Telephone: 033 948300. Fax: 033 948709.

**Iceland:**
SKIFAN H.F, P.O. Box 8120, 128 Reykjavik, Iceland. Telephone: 354 (1) 600900. Telex: 3033 SKIFAN IS. Fax: 354 (1) 687670.

**Indonesia:**
INDY PARAMADELLA, Prince Centre II, 3rd Floor, Room 306, J1 Jenderal Sudirman 3-4, Jakarta, Indonesia. Telephone: 583901. Fax: 5704544.

**Italy:**
SOUND & VISION, PO Box 3196 00121, Ostia, Rome, Italy. Telephone: 06 561 11088.

**Japan:**
UNITED PUBLISHERS SERVICES LTD, Kenkyu-sha Bldg., 9, Kanda Surugadai 2-chome, Chiyoda-ku, Tokyo, Japan. Telephone: 03 292 7160. Telephone: 03 291 4541. Fax: 03 292 8610.

**Norway:**
AKERS MIC 2A/S, Kongensgi 25, N-0153, Oslo, Norway. Telephone: 472 33 0330.

**Singapore:**
AUDIO MUSICAL PTE LTD, 162 Rangoon Road, Singapore 0821. Telephone: 292 9896. Fax: 291 6009.

**South Africa:**
MUSICA CAPE, Techno Square 42, Morningside, Ndabeni, Capetown. Telephone: 021 531 1150.
MUSIC TEAM, 33 Scott Street, Waverley, Johannesburg, South Africa. Telephone: 011 887 7313. Fax: 011 887 7357.

**Spain and Portugal:**
DISCOBI, Luchana 1-4 Dpto 2, 48008, Bilbao, Spain. Telephone: 416 42 31. Fax: 443 0024. (Also at Rafael Harrera 11, 28036, Madrid. 34-1-314-2114.)

**Sweden:**
BLITZ RECORDS AB, PO Box 347, S-10124, Stockholm 1, Sweden. Telephone: 46 8 28 28 90. Fax: 46 8 29 01 22.

**Switzerland:**
DISQUES-OFFICE S.A, CH-1700 Fribourg, Route de La Glane 31, Switzerland.

Telephone: 037 24 62 61. Fax: 037 24 37 63.

**United Kingdom**

ARABESQUE RECORDS LTD, Network House, 29-39 Stirling Road, London. W3 8DJ. Telephone: UK Sales: 081 992 7732. International Sales: 081 992 0098. Fax: 081 992 0340

CAROLINE EXPORTS, 56 Standard Road, London, England. NW10 6ES. Telephone: 081 961 2919.

JOHN HUMPHRIES (PUBLISHING) LTD., 1 De Cham Avenue, Hastings, Sussex, England. TN37 6HE. Telephone: 0424 715181. Fax: 0424 422805.

LASGO LTD., Unit 2, Chapmans Park Industrial Estate, 378-388 High Road, Willesden, London, England. NW10 2DY. Telephone: 081 459 8800.

**United States of America:**

MUSIC/NH, WAYNE GREEN ENTERPRISES, Hancock, New Hampshire 03449, USA. Telephone: 603 525 4201.

## BOOK TRADE DISTRIBUTION

*Book trade orders for Music Master books should be sent to the following companies:*

**All Countries (except United States of America)**

Harrap Publishing Group Ltd, Chelsea House, 26 Market Square, Bromley, Kent. BR1 1NA. Telephone: 081 313 3484. Fax: 081 313 0702.

**United States of America**

Last Gasp of San Francisco, 2180 Bryant Street, San Francisco, CA 94110, USA. Telephone (415) 824 6636. Fax: (415) 824 1836.

## INDEX OF ADVERTISERS

**Accordion For All (International) Ltd,**
146 Birmingham Road, Kidderminster, Worcestershire. DY10 2SL.

**Acorn Music,**
Grove Hill, Victoria Road, Barnstaple, North Devon. EX32 8DS.

**Jazz Music,**
12 Regent Street, Haslingden, Lancashire. BB4 5HQ.

**Just Jazz,**
2A Orton Avenue, Woodston, Peterborough, Cambridgeshire.

**Lake Records,**
Fellside Road, 15 Banklands, Workington, Cumbria. CA14 3EW.

**Mainly Big Bands,**
21B Kings Road, Sutton Coldfield, West Midlands. B74 2LD.

**Mole Jazz,**
291 Pentonville Road, London. N1 9NP.

# A

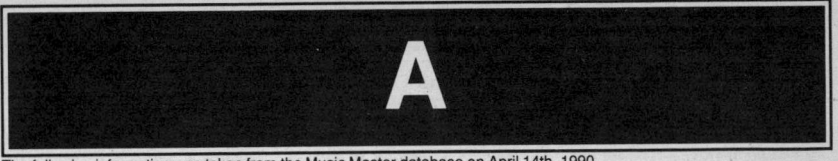

The following information was taken from the Music Master database on April 14th, 1990.

## Abercrombie, John

**ANIMATO**
Tracks: / Right now / Single moon / Agitato / First light / Last light / For hope of hope / Bright reign / Ollie Mention.
**CD:** Released Mar '90, on New Note Catalogue no: **841 779 2**
**Album:** Released Mar '90, on New Note Catalogue no: **ECM 1411**

**CURRENT EVENTS**
Tracks: / Clint / Alice In Wonderland / Ralph's piano waltz / Lisa / Hippityville / Killing time / Still.
**Album:** Released Jun '86, on ECM Deleted '88. Catalogue no: **ECM 1311**
**CD:** Released Aug '86, on ECM Deleted '88. Catalogue no: **827 770-2**

**GATEWAY**
**CD:** on ECM Deleted '88. Catalogue no: **829 192 2**

**GETTING THERE**
Tracks: / Sidekick / Upon a time / Getting there / Remember hymn / Thalia / Furs on ice / Chance / Labour day.
Note: For this album, John has added to his Trio (with Marc Johnson,Peter Erskine) a fourth member: Mike Brecker, one of the leading and most sought-after saxophonists on the scene. PERSONNEL: John Abercrombie-electric & acoustic guitars, guitar synthesizer / Marc Johnson - bass / Peter Erskine-drums / Special guest: Michael Brecker-tenor saxophone.
**CD:** Released Feb '88, on ECM Catalogue no: **8334942**
**Album:** Released Feb '88, on ECM Catalogue no: **ECM 1321**

**JOHN ABERCROMBIE TRIO (Abercrombie, John Trio)**
Tracks: / Furs on ice / Alice in Wonderland / Innerplay / Drum solo / Samurai hee-haw / Stella by starlight / Beautiful love / Light beam / Four on one / Haunted heart.
Note: This live recording by John Abercrombie, Marc Johnson and Peter Erskine will be a sought after document of this innovative trio. Recorded in concert at Boston's Nightstage in April '88, the trio explores space, density and dynamics. Pieces from their repertoire are presented in new transformations and four standards associated with Bill Evans are given resplendant treatment. Personnel: John Abercrombie (guitar, guitar synth), Marc Johnson (bass), Peter Erskine (drums).
**Album:** Released Apr '89, on ECM Catalogue no: **ECM 1390**
**CD:** Released Apr '89, on ECM Catalogue no: **837 756-2**

**M (Abercrombie Quartet)**
**Album:** Released Jun '81, on ECM Catalogue no: **ECM 1191**

**NIGHT**
Tracks: / Etherreggae / Night / 3 East / Look around / Believe you me / Four on one.
Note: American guitarist John Abercrombie has come up with a real winner on this LP. The opening track, an infectious reggae influenced piece is ideal for mainstream radio plays. Excellent support from Jan Hammer on keyboards, Jack DeJohnette drums, and Mike Brecker tenor saxophone. Digital Stereo.
**Album:** Released Nov '84, on ECM Deleted '88. Catalogue no: **ECM 1272**
**CD:** on ECM Deleted '88. Catalogue no: **823 212-2**

**SARGASSO SEA (see Towner, Ralph) (Abercrombie, John & Ralph Towner)**
**Album:** Released Oct '76, on ECM Deleted '88. Catalogue no: **ECM 1080**

**TIMELESS**
Tracks: / Lungs / Love song / Ralph's piano waltz / Red and orange / Remembering / Timeless.
**CD:** Released '87, on ECM Catalogue no: **829 114 2**

**WORKS: JOHN ABERCROMBIE**
Tracks: / Red and orange / Night / Ralph's piano waltz / Backward glance / Nightlake / Dreamstalker / Isla / Sing song.
Note: Personnel: John Abercrombie, Jack Hammer, Jack DeJohnette, Mike Brecker, Lester Bowie, Eddie Gomez, Dave Holland.
**Album:** Released Jun '89, on ECM Catalogue no: **837 275-1**
**CD:** Released Jun '89, on ECM Catalogue no: **837 275-2**

## Abrams, Muhal Richard

**Biographical details:** Muhal Richard Abrams was born in Chicago in 1930; the composer and pianist turned pro at 18; gigged with visitors to Chicago including Miles Davis and Sonny Rollins; he formed his Experimental Band in 1961, which included Eddie Harris; he was founder and director from 1967 of the Association for the Advancement of Creative Musicians (AACM), which included members of the Art Ensemble of Chicago and the trio Air (including Henry Threadgill, now a celebrated leader of his one Sextett). Abrams' importance as a guru for scores of fine musicians cannot be overestimated. (Donald Clarke 21 July 1988.).

**1-0 QA + 19**
**Album:** Released Jul '78, on Black Saint (Italy) Deleted '88. Catalogue no: **BSR 0017**

**BLUES FOREVER**
**CD:** Released Jun '86, on Black Saint (Italy) Catalogue no: **BSR 0061**

**DUET WITH AMINA CLAUDINE MYERS**
**Album:** Released Jul '82, on Black Saint (Italy) Deleted '88. Catalogue no: **BSR 0051**

**LEVELS AND DEGREES OF LIGHT**
**Album:** on Delmark (USA) by Delmark Records (USA). Catalogue no: **DS 413**

**SIGHT SONG**
**Album:** Released Jul '78, on Black Saint (Italy) Deleted '88. Catalogue no: **BSR 003**

**VIEW FROM WITHIN**
**CD:** Released Jun '86, on Black Saint (Italy) Catalogue no: **BSR 0081**

**YOUNG AT HEART**
**Album:** on Delmark (USA) by Delmark Records (USA). Catalogue no: **DS 423**

## Acceleration

**ACCELERATION**
Note: "More and more new impulses seem to come from Switzerland. Here one finds some new and radical statements. Last year ECM released Red Twist And Tuned Arrow, the trio with Fredy Studer on drums and the two guitarists Christy Doran and Stephan Wittwer. Whereas their concept was based to a large extent on balancing fixed structures and rough free playing, heavily relying on electronics, Acceleration has its deeper roots in the jazz tradition. The music, all composed by Hans Koch, the band's reed player, injects new life into a trio line-up. With large expressivity and, at the same time, control, the free improvisational backgrounds of the individual musicians are focussed by the well-structured compoisitional outlines. This is the trio's debut album." (IMS Records, May 1988.)
**CD:** Released May '88, on ECM Catalogue no: **833 473-2**
**Album:** Released May '88, on ECM Catalogue no: **ECM 1357**

## AC/DC Blues...

**AC/DC BLUES GAY JAZZ REISSUES (Various artists)**
**Album:** Released '87, on Stash (USA) Catalogue no: **ST 106**

## Acid Jazz

**ACID JAZZ & OTHER ILLICIT GROOVES (Various artists)**
Tracks: / Introduction: *Ace Of Clubs* / Ace of clubs: *Ace Of Clubs* / Jalal: *Jalal* / Push: *Traffic* / Shaft in action: *Acid Jazz* / Galliano: *Six Sharp Fists* / And now we have rhythm: *Night Trains* / Doin' it naturally: *Rhythm Blades* / Jazz renegades: *Various artists.*
**Cass:** Released 16 Sep '88, on Urban by Polydor Ltd. Catalogue no: **URBMC 16**
**CD:** Released 16 Sep '88, on Urban by Polydor Ltd. Catalogue no: **837 347-2**
**Album:** Released 16 Sep '88, on Urban by Polydor Ltd. Catalogue no: **URBLP 16**

**ACID JAZZ & OTHER ILLICIT GROOVES VOL 2 (Freedom principle) (Various artists)**
**Album:** Released 27 Feb '89, on Urban by Polydor Ltd. Catalogue no: **837 925-1**
**CD:** Released 27 Feb '89, on Urban by Polydor Ltd. Catalogue no: **837 925-2**
**Cass:** Released 27 Feb '89, on Urban by Polydor Ltd. Catalogue no: **837 925-4**

**ACID JAZZ VOL.1 (Various artists)**
Tracks: / Better Half: *Funk Inc* / Got Myself A Good Man: *Pucho* / Houston Express, The: *Houston Person* / Grits and gravy: *Kloss,Eric* / Hoochie Coo Chickie: *Jones, Ivan "Boogaloo Joe"* / Lady Mama: *Ammons, Gene* / Hipshaker: *Spencer, Leon* / Psychedelic Sally: *Various artists.*
**Album:** Released Sep '88, on BGP by Ace Records. Catalogue no: **BGP 1015**
**Album:** Released Sep '88, on BGP by Ace Records. Catalogue no: **ACE 1015**

**ACID JAZZ VOL.2 (Various artists)**
Tracks: / Super bad: *Muhammad, Idris* / Cold sweat: *Purdie, Bernard* / Wildfire: *Bryant, Rusty* / Hot barbecue: *McDuff, Jack* / Reelin' with the feelin': *Kynard, Charles* / Spinky: *Earland, Charles* / Who's gonna take the weight: *Sparks,Melvin.*
**Album:** Released Oct '88, on BGP by Ace Records. Catalogue no: **BGP 1017**

**ACID JAZZ VOL.3 (Various artists)**
Tracks: / I want you back: *Mabern, Harold* / Psychedelic pucho: *Pucho* / Zebra walk: *Kynard, Charles* / Akilah: *Sparks,Melvin* / What it is: *Jones, Ivan "Boogaloo Joe"* / Bad montana: *Parker, Maynard* / Dig on it: *Smith, Johnny "Hammond"* / Bowlegs: *Funk Inc.*
**Album:** Released 28 Mar '89, on BGP by Ace Records. Catalogue no: **BGP 1025**

**ACID JAZZ VOL.4 (Various artists)**
Tracks: / Soul dance: *Person, Houston* / Sing a simple song: *Earland, Charles* / Twang thang, The: *Butler, Billy* / Shaft, Theme from: *Purdie, Bernard* / Sure 'nuff, sure 'nuff: *Phillips, Sonny* / Mambues: *Tjader, Cal & Bernard Purdie* / Haw right now: *Rushen, Patrice* / Life is funky: *Round Robin Monopoly.*
**Album:** Released 3 Jul '89, on BGP by Ace Records. Catalogue no: **BGP 1029**

**BEST OF ACID JAZZ, THE**
Tracks: / Chicken lickin' / Zebra walk / Reelin' with the feelin' / Dig on it / Got myself a good man / Super bad / Who's gonna take the weight / Sure 'nuff, sure 'nuff / Cold sweet / Psychadelic Sally / Soul dance / Houston Express, The / Smokin' at Tiffany's.
**Cass:** Released 5 Jun '89, on BGP by Ace Records. Catalogue no: **BGPC 921**
**CD:** Released 5 Jun '89, on BGP by Ace Records. Catalogue no: **CDBGP 921**

## Adams, George

**Biographical details:** George Adams was born in Covington, Georgia in 1940. He plays jazz tenor sax, also flute and bass clarinet, and also sings. He played in R&B bands and backed singers; he first came to fame with Charles Mingus in 1973-4; when they were playing opposite Manhattan Transfer at Max's Kansas City, Mingus told Adams to sing and he created 'Devil Woman' (nothing to do with Cliff Richard's song). As well as fine albums of his own he has been co-leader of a quartet with the ex-Mingus pianist Don Pullen. (Donald Clarke July 1988.)

**ALL THAT FUNK (Adams, George & Don Pullen)**
Tracks: / Alfie / Intentions / Big Alice.
Note: Cameron Brown, Danny Richmond (Recorded live at Ciak, Milano, Italy, 2nd November, 1979.
**Album:** Released Nov '79, on Palcoscenico (Italy) Deleted '88. Catalogue no: **PAL 15002**

**CITY GATES (Adams, George & Don Pullen Quartet)**
**Album:** Released Feb '84, on Timeless by Timeless Records. Deleted '88. Catalogue no: **SJP 181**

**DON'T LOSE CONTROL (Adams, George & Don Pullen Quartet)**
**CD:** Released Jan '87, on Soul Note Catalogue no: **SNCD 1004**

**EARTH BEAMS (Adams, George & Don Pullen Quartet)**
Tracks: / Magnetic love / Dionysus / Saturday nite in the cosmos / More flowers / Sophisticated Alice.
Note: Adams tenor; flute; Pullen piano; Cameron Brown bass; Dennis Richmond drums.
**Cass:** Released Oct '86, on Timeless by Timeless Records. Catalogue no: **SJP 1147**
**Album:** Released Apr '81, on Timeless by Timeless Records. Catalogue no: **SJP 147**
**CD:** Released Mar '90, on Timeless by Timeless Records. Catalogue no: **CDSJP 147**

**GEORGE ADAMS & THE DON PULLEN QUARTET (Adams, George & Don Pullen Quartet)**
**Album:** Released '88, on Timeless by Timeless Records. Catalogue no: **SFP 154**
**Album:** Released '88, on Timeless by Timeless Records. Catalogue no: **SJP 181**

**HAND TO HAND (Adams, George & Danny Richmond Quartet)**
**CD:** Released Jun '86, on Soul Note Catalogue no: **SNCD 1007**

**LIVE AT MONMARTRE (Adams, George & Don Pullen Quartet)**
**CD:** Released 16 Jan '88, on Timeless by Timeless Records. Catalogue no: **CDSJP 219**
**Album:** Released 16 Jan '88, on Timeless by Timeless Records. Catalogue no: **SJP 219**

**LIVE AT VILLAGE VANGUARD (Adams, George & Don Pullen Quartet)**
Tracks: / Necessary blues, The / Solitude / Intentions / Diane.
**CD:** Released May '85, on Soul Note Catalogue no: **SNCD 1094**
**Album:** Released May '85, on Soul Note Catalogue no: **SN 1094**

**MELODIC EXCURSIONS**
Tracks: / Calling, The / God has smiled on me / Kahji / Playground uptown and downtown / Decisions / Reflexions inward / Resolution of conflicts.
**Album:** Released Jun '82, on Timeless by Timeless Records. Catalogue no: **SJP 166**

**MORE FUNK (Adams, George & Don Pullen)**
Tracks: / Metamorphosis for Charles Mingus.
Note: Recorded live at Ciak, Milano, Italy, 3rd November, 1979.
**Album:** Released Nov '79, on Palcoscenico (Italy) Catalogue no: **PAL 15003**

**MORE SIGHTINGS (Adams, George, Hannibal & friends)**
**Album:** Released Feb '85, on Enja (Germany) by Enja Records (West Germany). Catalogue no: **ENJA 4084**

**NIGHTINGALE**
Tracks: / Bridge over troubled water / What a wonderful world / Nightingale sang in Berkley Square, A / Moon River / Precious Lord, take my hand / Ol' man river / Going home.
**CD:** Released Jul '89, on Blue Note by EMI Records. Catalogue no: **CDP 791 984 2**
**Album:** Released Jul '89, on Blue Note by EMI Records. Catalogue no: **B1 91984**

**PARADISE SPACE SHUTTLE (Adams, George Quintet)**
Tracks: / Paradise space shuttle / Intentions / Send in the clowns / Metamorthesis for Mingus / City of peace / Funk-roonie-peacock.
**Album:** Released Jan '85, on Timeless by Timeless Records. Catalogue no: **SJP 127**

## Adams, John

**CHAIRMAN DANCES, THE**
Tracks: / Chairman dances, The / Christian zeal and activity / Two fanfares for orchestra / Tromba lontana / Short ride in a fast machine / Common tones in simple time.

**Album:** Released Sep '87, on Nonesuch (USA) by Nonesuch Records (USA). Catalogue no: **K 979144 1**
**Cass:** Released Sep '87, on Nonesuch (USA) by Nonesuch Records (USA). Catalogue no: **K 979144 4**

**FEARFUL SYMMETRIES (Wound dresser)**
**Cass:** Released Nov '89, on Elektra by Elektra Records (UK). Catalogue no: **979 218 4**
**CD:** Released '89, on Elektra by Elektra Records (UK). Catalogue no: **979 218 2**
**Album:** Released Nov '89, on Elektra by Elektra Records (UK). Catalogue no: **979 218 1**

**HARMONIE LEHRE**
**Album:** Released Mar '86, on Nonesuch (USA) by Nonesuch Records (USA). Deleted '88. Catalogue no: **979115-1**

**HARMONIUM**
Tracks: / Negative love (part one) / Because I could not stop for death - Wild nights (part 2) / Negative love (Poem by John Donne) / Because I could not stop for death (Poem by Emily Dickinson) / Wild nights / Why do I / Laughin' and clownin' / If I ever had a good time / Scarred knees / Your love is so dogonne good / We don't see eye to eye / Road block / Teach me to forget.
Note: San Francisco Symphony Orchestra Chorus / Edo de Waart Vance George - chorus director, John Adams is currently the Composer-in-residence with the San Fransisco Symphony and has played a large role in the creation of its New and Unusual Music series. Mr. Adams continues to serve the New Music Adviser to Director Edo de Waart.
**Album:** Released Nov '84, on ECM Catalogue no: **ECM 1277**
**CD:** Released Apr '87, on ECM Catalogue no: **821 465-2**

**MUSIC FROM NIXON IN CHINA**
**CD:** Released Oct '88, on Nonesuch Catalogue no: **979193 2**
**Album:** Released Oct '88, on Nonesuch Catalogue no: **979193 1**
**Cass:** Released Oct '88, on Nonesuch Catalogue no: **979193 4**

**NIXON IN CHINA**
Tracks: / Opera in three acts.
**CD Set:** Released Jul '88, on Nonesuch Catalogue no: **979177 2**
**LP Set:** Released Jul '88, on Nonesuch Catalogue no: **979177 1**
**Cass set:** Released Jul '88, on Nonesuch Catalogue no: **979177 4**

**STRIP THIS HEART**
Tracks: / Strip this heart / Precious one.
Note: Available on 7" and 4-track 12" re-mixed by D.J. mixer Bruce Forest.
**12" Single:** Released Jul '87, on A&M by A&M Records. Deleted Mar '88. Catalogue no: **AMY 398**
**7" Single:** Released Jul '87, on A&M by A&M Records. Deleted Mar '88. Catalogue no: **AM 398**

**THROUGH THE EYES OF LOVE**
Tracks: / Through the eyes of love / Don't turn and walk away.
**12" Single:** Released Sep '85, on Parlophone by EMI Records. Deleted '88. Catalogue no: **12R 6108**
**7" Single:** Released Sep '85, on Parlophone by EMI Records. Deleted '88. Catalogue no: **R 6108**

## Adams, Pepper

**Biographical details:** Pepper Adams the baritone saxist was born in 1930 in Detroit and died in 1986 in New York City of cancer. Nicknamed 'The Knife' for authoritative, slashing attack, he was central to the important Detroit scene of the early 1950s; he could not play an uninteresting solo. Apart from many fine albums of his own, his uncounted dates as a sideman include John Coltrane's darkly beautiful *Dakar* in 1957, many others; his last appearance on record was with the young guitarist Joshua Breakstone on Contemporary. He also played bassoon on a couple of Enja albums in the 1970s. Donald Clarke 21 July 1988..

**10 TO 4 AT THE 5-SPOT (Adams, Pepper Quintet)**
**Album:** Released Jun '86, on Original Jazz Classics (USA) by Fantasy Inc (USA). Catalogue no: **OJC 031**

**EPHEMERA**
Tracks: / Ephemera / Bouncing with Bud / Civilization and its discontents / Jitterbug waltz / Quiet lady / Patrice / Hellure.
Note: With Roland Hanna, George Mraz and Mel Lewis.
**Album:** Released '87, on Spotlite by Spotlite Records. Catalogue no: **SPJ PA6**

**JULIAN**
**Album:** Released Jan '82, on Enja (Germany) by Enja Records (West Germany). Catalogue no: **ENJA 2060**

**MASTER, THE**
Tracks: / Enchilada / Chelsea Bridge / Bossallegro / Rue Serpente / Lovers of their time / My shining hour.
Note: Adams on bassoon; Tommy Flanagan on piano; George Mraz on bass; Leroy Williams on drums. Recorded March 11, 1980.
**Album:** Released Apr '81, on Muse by Black & Blue Records. Catalogue no: **MR 5213**

**PURE PEPPER**
**Album:** Released Feb '85, on Savoy (France) Deleted Nov '89. Catalogue no: **WL 70514**

**REFLECTORY**
Tracks: / Reflectory / Sophisticated lady / Etude diabolique / Claudette's way / I carry your heart / That's all.
Note: Roland Hanna on piano; George Mraz on bass; Billy Hart on drums; Adams on bassoon. Recorded on June 14, 1978.
**Album:** Released Apr '81, on Muse by Black & Blue Records. Catalogue no: **MR 5182**

**TWELFTH AND PINGREE**
**Album:** Released Jan '82, on Enja (Germany) by Enja Records (West Germany). Catalogue no: **ENJA 2074**

**URBAN DREAMS**
**Album:** Released Jul '86, on Palo Alto Catalogue no: **PA 8009**
**Cass:** Released Jul '86, on Palo Alto Catalogue no: **PAC 8009**

## Adderley, Cannonball

**Biographical details:** Julian 'Cannonball' Adderley was born in 1928 in Tampa, Florida; he died suddenly of a heart attack in 1975 in Gary, Indiana. He played alto and later soprano sax, was a composer and a bandleader. He directed a high school band in Florida from 1948 as well as US Army bands in the early '50s; he recorded for Savoy in 1955, formed a quintet with brother Nat in 1956, made *Somethin' Else* in 1958 with guest Miles Davis, and played in Davis's group in 1958-9 with John Coltrane; he then reformed with Nat and his combo became one of the most successful in the history of jazz. Personnel passing through included pianists Bobby Timmons, then Jow Zawinul (who wrote *Mercy! Mercy! Mercy!*, their biggest hit); the group became a sextet with the addition of Yusef Lateef in 1961, replaced by Charles Lloyd in 1963; then a quintet again from mid-'65; Zawinul was succeeded by George Duke. The group's album with Nancy Wilson was a hit in 1962. The title track on *Why Am I Treated So Bad* was written by Roebuck Staple and featured Zawinul's electric piano, a pre-taste of funk. His style was rooted in the tradition of his generation - influenced by Charlie Parker and Benny Carter - but was communicated with rare skill and still has many fans. Donald Clarke 21 July 1988.

**ACCENT ON AFRICA (Adderley, Cannonball Quintet)**
Tracks: / Ndo Lima / Hamba nami / Dikhutsana / Up and at it / Gumba Gumba / Marabi / Gun-Jah / Lehadima.
Note: Licensed from EMI Records Ltd. This compilation P 1986 C 1976 Charly Records Ltd.
**Album:** Released Apr '86, on Affinity by Charly Records. Catalogue no: **AFF 148**
**Cass:** Released Apr '86, on Affinity by Charly Records. Catalogue no: **TCAFF 148**

**AFRICAN WALTZ**
Tracks: / African waltz / Barefoot sunday blues / Kelly blue.
**Album:** Released Mar '87, on Original Jazz Classics (USA) by Fantasy Inc (USA). Catalogue no: **OJC 258**

**ALABAMA/AFRICA**
Tracks: / African waltz / Kelly blue / Smoke gets in your eyes / West Coast blues / Letter from home / Something different / Blue brass groove / I'll close my eyes / Stockholm sweetnin / Uptown, The / This here / John Benson Brooks / Alabama concerto (in four movements).
**2 LP Set:** Released Dec '81, on Milestone by Ace Records. Deleted '88. Catalogue no: **M 47059**

**ALTO GIANT**
Tracks: / Scavenger / Sweet Emma / Ballads Medley / This here / Manha De Carnival / Walk tall.
Note: Nat Adderley on cornet; Joe Zawinul on piano; Victor Gaskin on bass; Louis Hayes on drums. Recorded live in Milan Italy in 1969, and previously unissued.
**Album:** Released Sep '87, on Lotus Catalogue no: **LOP 14 070**

**AT THE LIGHTHOUSE**
Note: With Victor Feldman, Nat Adderley.
**CD:** Released Jul '88, on Landmark (USA) by Fantasy Inc (USA). Catalogue no: **LCD 13052**
**Album:** Released Jul '88, on Landmark (USA) by Fantasy Inc (USA). Catalogue no: **LLP 1305**

**BOSSA NOVA**
Note: Featuring Sergio Mendes.
**Album:** Released Sep '88, on Landmark (USA) by Fantasy Inc (USA). Catalogue no: **LLP 1302**
**CD:** Released Jul '88, on Landmark (USA) by Fantasy Inc (USA). Catalogue no: **LCD 13022**

**CANNONBALL & 8 GIANTS**
**2 LP Set:** Released '74, on Milestone by Ace Records. Deleted '88. Catalogue no: **ML 47001**

**CANNONBALL ADDERLEY**
**Album:** Released Dec '75, on Milestone by Ace Records. Deleted '88. Catalogue no: **M 47029**

**CANNONBALL ADDERLEY AND THE POLL WINNERS**
Tracks: / Chant, The / Azwle scrape / Heart alone / Lolita / Au privave / Never will I marry.
Note: With Wes Montgomery, Victor Feldman etc.
**CD:** Released Jul '88, on Landmark (USA) by Fantasy Inc (USA). Catalogue no: **LCD 13042**
**Album:** Released Jul '88, on Landmark (USA) by Fantasy Inc (USA). Catalogue no: **LLP 1304**

**CANNONBALL IN EUROPE**
Note: A live performance from 1962, featuring Nat Adderley, Yusef Lateef, Joe Zawinul.
**CD:** Released Jul '88, on Landmark (USA) by Fantasy Inc (USA). Catalogue no: **LCD 13072**
**Album:** Released Jul '88, on Landmark (USA) by Fantasy Inc (USA). Catalogue no: **LLP 1307**

**CANNONBALL TAKES CHARGE**
Note: With Wynton Kelly.
**CD:** Released Jul '88, on Landmark (USA) by Fantasy Inc (USA). Catalogue no: **LCD 13062**
**Album:** Released Jul '88, on Landmark (USA) by Fantasy Inc (USA). Catalogue no: **LLP 1306**

**CANNONBALL'S BOSA NOVA VOL.2**
Tracks: / Clouds (take 7) / Groovy samba / Joyce's samba / Corcovado / Sambop / Batida diferente / Once I loved / Minha Suadade / Clouds.
Note: Personnel: Julian Adderley - alto sax Bossa Rios Sextet: Sregio Mendes - poano/Durval Ferreira - guitar/Octavio Bailly, Jnr. - bass/Dom Um Romao - drums/Pedro Paulo - trumpet/Paulo Moura - alto sax. Recorded in New York in 1962 Recommended tracks: *Once I loved, Clouds, Groovy Samba*
**Cass:** Released Jun '86, on Fantasy (import) by Fantasy Inc (USA). Deleted '88. Catalogue no: **LLP 51302**
**CD:** Released Jan '89, on JVC/Fantasy Catalogue no: **VDJ 1599**
**Album:** Released Jun '86, on Fantasy (import) by Fantasy Inc (USA). Deleted '88. Catalogue no: **LLP 1302**

**COAST TO COAST**
Tracks: / This hare / Spontaneous combustion / High fly / Straight no chaser / You got it / Gemini / Planet earth / Dizzy's business / Syn anthesia / Scotch and water / Cannonball's theme.
**2 LP Set:** Released Mar '81, on Milestone by Ace Records. Deleted '88. Catalogue no: **M 47039**

**DREAMWEAVERS, THE/ SUITE BEAT (Adderley, Cannonball/ John Coltrane)**
**CD:** Released '88, on Import (label unknown) Catalogue no: **SBCD 2003**

**IN JAPAN (Adderley, Cannonball Quintet)**
Tracks: / Work song / Mercy mercy mercy / This here / Money in the pocket / Sticks, The / Jive samba.
**CD:** Released Apr '90, on Pacific Jazz by EMI Records. Catalogue no: **CDP 793 560 2**
**CD:** Released Apr '90, on Pacific Jazz by EMI Records. Catalogue no: **CZ 300**

**IN SAN FRANCISCO (Adderley Cannonball Quintet)**
**CD:** Released Apr '86, on JVC/Fantasy Deleted '88. Catalogue no: **VDJ 1530**

**JAZZ WORKSHOP REVISITED**
Tracks: / Opening comment by Cannonball, An / Pimitiva / Jessica's day / Unit 7 / Another few words / Jive samba / Marney / Mellow buno / Time to go now - really.
Note: Julian Cannonball Adderley, alto sax; Nat Adderley, cornet; Yusef Lateef, flute, oboe, tenor sax; Joe Zawinful, piano; Sam Jones, bass; Louis Hayes, drums. Recorded live in San Francisco in 1962.
**Album:** Released Jul '88, on Landmark (USA) by Fantasy Inc (USA). Catalogue no: **LLP 1303**
**CD:** Released Jul '88, on Landmark (USA) by Fantasy Inc (USA). Catalogue no: **LCD 13032**

**JUST FRIENDS (See panel below)**
Tracks: / Ease it / Just friends / I got rhythm / Julie Ann / Awful mean / There is no greater love.
Note: As a jazz bass player, Paul Laurence Dunbar Chambers, Jr, just about had it all. For one thing, he had a huge, resonant sound. Superb articulation, too. Acute harmonic knowledge, coupled with great melodic strength. An ability to anchor any group with which he was associated in prescribed classic

**Cannonball Adderley - Just Friends (Charly)**

style. Chambers was also an impressive, if not positively outstanding soloist, who mixed a basic walking style with more horn like qualities. There were occasions, it is true, when he suffered intonation problems with his alto bowing - something not unknown to many other jazz bassists. But all in all, he was a formidable musician who, during the 1950's and up to his sad premature death in January 1969, helped continue to elevate the stature of the bassist in jazz in a profound and highly individual way.

The homogenous quality of the group assembled under Chambers' leadership for the bassist's first of two dates for the Vee Jay label is most easily explained by the fact, Freddie Hubbard apart; all the participating musicians were either currently members of the Miles Davis Sextet - working at the time of this recording at the Sutherland Hotel, Chicago - or, in the case of Philly Joe Jones, had worked with Miles in the not-too-distant past, Jones who appeared a the second of the two dates needed to complete the contents of this LP, had been Davis' regular drummer between 1955 and the summer of 1958. At which the latter time he had been succeeded by Washington - born Wilbur 'Jimmy' Cobb who'd already put in excellent timekeeping service with numerous bands, including those fronted by such luminaries as Dinah Washington, Stan Getz, Dizzy Gillespie, and Cannonball Adderley.

But, as of February '59, there was more than sufficient action, recording wise. For one thing, at the conclusion of the second of the two consecutive sessions required to complete the recording of the contents of this fine LP, Messrs. Chambers, Cobb, Kelly, Cannonball Adderley, linking up with Davis colleague John Coltrane, were to record a separate date for Mercury Records, to which Adderley was contracted at that time and made unter the altoist's leadership. (A fine session, too, reissued subsequently on a couple of occasions at least). Cannon, whose impassioned alto enhances each and every track of the *Just Friends* LP, was, like his colleagues in the Davis combo, to take part in another record date a month hence - and one that was to have far-reaching consequences for the future of jazz. This was the first of two dates that were to comprise the awesome contents of the immortal King of Blue collection. Wynton Kelly, who appeared on only one of the KOB selections (Freddie Freeloader - Bill Evans made his final on - record appearances with Miles for the rest of the LP), was a new member of the Davis aggregation at the time of the Chambers and Adderley dates in Chicago. Chambers himself was well and truly into his third year as rhythmic pivot with Miles Davis. During which period he had consolidated an enviable position as one of jazz' premier bassists - Chambers was to rank second only to Ray Brown in the 1959 *Down beat* Annual Readers' Poll - even though he still hadn't celebrated his 24th birthday. (He had been a *Down Beat* New Star winner with the jazz critics in 1956). It's Chambers' big-as-a-barn-door bass that opens proceedings. Adderley plays the theme of the leader's *Awful mean*, an attractive blues line, with Kelly demonstrating for the umpteenth time just how superlative an all round keyboard player he was. And, in this case, that does include his abilities in the area of blues-playing. Philly Joe lays down a very basic beat, in prescribed fashion. As for Cannonball, well there never was any doubt, at any period of his career, as to his affinity with the blues. Here, he's as basic as you'd wish. He dirties his tone to splendid advantage, and the overall feeling he imparts is tremendous. Paced by Jones' typically magnificent brush-work, Paul bows himself a much too short solo, before handing over to the drummer who produces his own brand of solo magic. The lilting *Julie Ann* - titled by Chambers for one of Adderley's daughters - contains another strong, superbly articulated solo by its composer.

Appropriately, Adderley is at his most melodic - yet never, at any time, losing his emotional commitment Kelly too, sparkles eloquently. *Julie Ann* also contains a flaring, effortless Hubbard solo, a self-contained proof-positive demonstration of just what kind of chops he had in this, his 21st year. Although he'd settled in the Big Apple, from his native Indianapolis, Ind., less than a year when this recording took place, the youthful Hubbard's reputation was already growing - and fast. His work throughout the Chambers date did absolutely nothing to diminish his upward-spiralling career.

It's Hubbard whose fiery, intense playing almost - but not quite - makes even Adderley take second place during a fast and furious *I got rhythm*. But, then, Kelly's sparkling pianistics just about tops everything, solowise. Chambers is a real tower of strength here, underpinning all the individual action with awesome power. His arco playing, too, is impressive. Cobb takes full advantage of a solo outing - his speed around the kit is as adroit as his all-round technique - and, thankfully, he doesn't outstay his welcome. There are more superior solos all round (except for Cobb) during a fresh sounding reworking of that fine piece of standard pop *Just friends* (with what seems to be applause for Hubbard's uplifting statement by one of the other cats). But if anything, the Hubbard less *there is no greater love* has an even finer set of improvisations, with Adderley in unsurpassable form. The altoist sounds particularly happy and relaxed here, and truly inspired. He uses the full range of his instrument, and that big sound is amply in evidence, Jones, back in the drum seat, really cooks throughout, and the rhythm team is a total unit at all times. Adderley's joint predilection for both Bird and Carter is readily apparent during Chambers' title tune - a solid piece of bebop that has Hubbard coruscating trumpet returning once more, and a Wynton Kelly contribution that dances the light fantastic in the most delightful way (with Cobb's four-in-the-bar rimshot accents adding further helpful dynamics).

It is perhaps a sobering thought that Paul Chambers has been dead now for almost 15 years. And that of his colleagues, both Adderley and Kelly have likewise, sadly departed. *Ease it* represents the bassist's penultimate opportunity to host his own record date (the final session, some 15 months after this one, was also for Vee Jay). It's a credit to the combined efforts of all the participants - certainly, this was no run of the mill blowing session - and it's good to have *Ease it* back in circulation again. Listen and learn ... (Stan Britt, The Wire)

**CD:** Released Jan '87, on Charly by Charly Records. Catalogue no: **CDCHARLY 58**

## KNOW WHAT I MEAN? (Adderley, Cannonball with Bill Evans)

**Album:** Released Aug '84, on Riverside (USA) by Fantasy Inc (USA). Deleted '88. Catalogue no: **OJC 105**

**CD:** Released Apr '86, on JVC/Fantasy Catalogue no: **VDJ 1518**

## MERCY, MERCY, MERCY

**Album:** Released Aug '83, on EMI (Germany) by EMI Records. Deleted '88. Catalogue no: **IC 048 50710**

## SOMETHIN' ELSE

Tracks: / Autumn leaves / Love for sale / Something else / One for Daddy O / Dancing in the dark / Alison's uncle.

**CD:** Released Sep '87, on Blue Note by EMI Records. Catalogue no: **CDP 746 338 2**

**CD:** Released Sep '87, on Blue Note by EMI Records. Catalogue no: **BNZ 1**

**Album:** Released '79, on Blue Note by EMI Records. Deleted '84. Catalogue no: **BNS 40036**

**Album:** Released Jul '82, on Blue Note by EMI Records. Deleted Nov '88. Catalogue no: **BST 81595**

**Cass:** Released Mar '86, on Blue Note by EMI Records. Catalogue no: **TC BST 81595**

## SPONTANEOUS COMBUSTION

Tracks: / Still talkin' to ya / Little taste, A / Caribbean cutie / Bohemia after dark / Chasm / Willow weep for me / Late entry / Spontaneous combustion / Flamingo / Hear me talkin' to ya / With apologies to Oscar / We'll be together again.

**CD:** Released Nov '86, on RCA by BMG Records (UK). Deleted Nov '89. Catalogue no: **ZD 70816**

**Cass Set:** Released Jun '86, on Savoy (France) Catalogue no: **WK 70531**

**2 LP Set:** Released Jun '86, on Savoy (France) Deleted May '89. Catalogue no: **WL 70531**

## SPONTANEOUS COMBUSTION, THE SAVOY SESSION

**Album:** Released Mar '85, on Savoy Jazz (USA) by Malaco Records (USA). Catalogue no: **SJL 2206**

## STICKS AND SOUL

Tracks: / Sticks / Games / I'm on my way / Mercy mercy mercy / Mini man / Why am I treated so bad / Walk tall (baby that's what I need) / Country preacher.
**Album:** Released Nov '86, on Affinity by Charly Records. Catalogue no: **AFF 162**

**THEM DIRTY BLUES**
Tracks: / Dat dere / Del sasser / Soon / Work song / Jeannine / Easy living / Them dirty blues.
Note: Julian Cannonball Adderley, alto sax; Nat Adderley, cornet; Bobby Timmons, Barry Harris, piano; Sam Jones, bass; Louis Hayes, drums. Recorded in Chicago in 1960.
**CD:** Released Jan '89, on JVC/Fantasy Catalogue no: **VDJ 1598**
**Album:** Released Jul '88, on Landmark (USA) by Fantasy Inc (USA). Catalogue no: **LLP 1301**
**CD:** Released Jul '88, on Landmark (USA) by Fantasy Inc (USA). Catalogue no: **LCD 13012**

**THINGS ARE GETTING BETTER (Adderley, Cannonball with Milt Jackson)**
**Album:** Released Feb '88, on Riverside (USA) by Fantasy Inc (USA). Catalogue no: **RSLP 286**

**WHAT I MEAN**
Tracks: / Arriving soon / Well, you needn't / New Delhi / Winetone star eyes / Lisa / Waltz for Debby / Goodbye / Who cares? / Elsa / Toy / Nancy / Venice / Know what I mean?.
**2 LP Set:** Released Apr '80, on Milestone by Ace Records. Deleted '85. Catalogue no: **M 47053**

**WHAT IS THIS THING CALLED SOUL? (Adderley, Cannonball Quintet)**
Tracks: / Azule serape / Big 'p' / One for daddy-o / Chant, The / What is this thing called love? / Cannonball's theme.
Note: Personnel: Nat Adderley / Vic Feldman / Sam Jones and Louis Hayes. Recorded live in Europe 1960.
**Cass:** Released May '84, on Pablo Jazz (USA) by Pablo Records (USA). Catalogue no: **K 08 238**
**Album:** Released May '84, on Pablo Jazz (USA) by Pablo Records (USA). Catalogue no: **230 8238**

**WORKSHOP**
**CD:** Released '88, on Fantasy (import) by Fantasy Inc (USA). Catalogue no: **LCD 1303**

## Adderley, Nat

**Biographical details:** Nat Adderley was born in 1931 in Tampa, Florida; he began on trumpet in 1946 influenced by his father and his brother Cannonball, but switched to cornet in 1950. He shared his brother's stunning success from 1959 to 1975, and has made many fine albums of his own, as well as writing tunes that have become standards, such as *Work Song* and *Sermonette*. He also plays mellophone and French horn. Donald Clarke 21 July 1988..

**ART FORD'S JAZZ PARTY (August 1958)**
Note: With Cootie Williams/Kai Winding / Coleman Hawkins/Cannonball Adderley / Rolf Khun / Billy Taylor / Harry Sheppard / Al Casey / Barry Miles / Lil Greenwood. Tracks include: Body and soul / Cootie's blues / I got it bad / Fine and Dandy / Bugle call rag / Airmail special.
**Album:** Released Oct '87, on Jazz Connoisseur by Spotlite Records. Catalogue no: **AFJP 5**

**BLUE AUTUMN (Adderley Quintet, Nat)**
**Album:** Released 7 Nov '87, on Theresa (USA) by Theresa Records (USA). Catalogue no: **TR 122**
**CD:** Released Oct '87, on Theresa (USA) by Theresa Records (USA). Catalogue no: **TRCD 122**

**DON'T LOOK BACK**
**Album:** Released Mar '77, on Steeplechase (USA) Deleted '88. Catalogue no: **SCS 1059**

**NAT ADDERLEY QUARTET (VIDEO) (Adderley, Nat Quartet)**
**VHS:** Released '88, on Kay Jazz (video) by Kay Jazz. Catalogue no: **KJ 060**

**NAT & JULIAN CANNONBALL ADDERLEY (Adderley, Nat & Julian Cannonball Adderley)**
Tracks: / Stay on it / Autumn leaves / This here / Prelude / Gemini.
Note: Recorded New York City 13th August, 1960.
**Album:** Released '81, on Kings Of Jazz Deleted '88. Catalogue no: **KLJ 20024**

**SAYIN' SOMETHING / THAT'S JAZZ**
**Album:** Released '88, on Atlantic Jazz by WEA Records. Catalogue no: **K 50246**

**THAT'S NAT**
Note: Artists include: Nat Adderley - cornet / Jerome Richardson - flute, tenor sax / Hank Jones - piano / Wendell Marshall - bass / Kenny Clarke - drums. Nat, brother of Cannonball, says now of this album:- "For 1955, I think it was a reasonably good album. Playing with that rhythm section was a major thrill for me at the time". Since he made this, Nat has experimented with funk, electronics and 'out' music, but recently he's returned to a style of playing not dissimilar to this straight-ahead hard-bop album. Recorded in New Jersey in 1955.
**Album:** Released Dec '85, on Savoy (France) Deleted '88. Catalogue no: **WL 70506**

**WORK SONGS**
Tracks: / Work song / Pretty memory / I've got a crush on you / Mean to me / Fallout / Sack o' woe / My heart stood still / Violets for your furs / Scrambled eggs.
**CD:** Released May '87, on JVC/Fantasy Catalogue no: **VDJ 1539**
**Album:** Released Feb '88, on Riverside (USA) by Fantasy Inc (USA). Catalogue no: **RSLP 318**
**2 LP Set:** Released '79, on Prestige Deleted '84. Catalogue no: **M 47047**

## Akiyoshi, Toshiko

**Biographical details:** Toshiko Akiyoshi was born in 1929 in Manchuria; she is a very highly regarded pianist, arranger and composer and has made both small-group and big band albums, many winning prizes, especially in Japan. She went to the USA in 1956 but has spent much time in Japan; she was married to saxist Charlie Mariano and worked with him; also with Charles Mingus in 1962; then she married another reedman, Lew Tabackin, who has worked and toured with the big band; they formed their own Ascent label in the USA. (Donald Clarke 21 July 1988).

**INSIGHTS (Akiyoshi, Toshiko and Lew Tabackin)**
**Album:** Released '83, on RCA (France) by BMG Records (France). Catalogue no: **PL 45363**

**INTERLUDE**
Tracks: / Interlude / I know who loves you / Blue and sentimental / I ain't gonna ask no more / Pagliacci / Solitude / So in love / You stepped out of a dream.
**Album:** Released Sep '87, on Concord Jazz by Concord Jazz Records (USA). Catalogue no: **CJ 324**
**CD:** Released Oct '87, on Concord Jazz by Concord Jazz Records (USA). Catalogue no: **CCD 4324**
**Cass:** Released Sep '87, on Concord Jazz by Concord Jazz Records (USA). Catalogue no: **CJC 324**

**LIVE AT NEWPORT '77**
**Album:** Released Feb '85, on RCA (France) by BMG Records (France). Catalogue no: **NL 70579**

**SUMI-E (Akiyoshi, Toshiko and Lew Tabackin)**
**Album:** Released '83, on RCA (France) by BMG Records (France). Catalogue no: **PL 37537**

**TOSHIKO AKIYOSHI (VIDEO)**
**VHS:** Released '88, on Kay Jazz (video) by Kay Jazz. Catalogue no: **KJ 006**

**TOSHIKO AT THE TOP OF THE GATE**
Tracks: / Introduction / Opus 0 / First night / Phrygian waterfall / Let's roll in sake / How insensitive / Morning of the carnival / Night song, The / Willow weep for me / My elegy.
Note: Musicians: Toshiko Akiyoshi (piano), Kenny Dorham (trumpet), Lew Tabackin (tenor sax / flute), Ron Carter (bass), Mickey Roker (drums).
**CD:** on Denon Deleted '88. Catalogue no: **C38-7874**

## Akkerman, Jan

**Biographical details:** Jan Akkerman plays electric and acoustic guitar, also lute. He was born in 1946 in Amsterdam. He played in bands including Brainbox, then jazz/rock band Focus (with Thijs Van Leer on organ, flute, occasional vocals; Martin Dresden on bass, various drummers, other occasional personnel incl. Philip Catherine on guitar in 1976; there was an album with P.J. Proby and Catherine in 1978). Akkerman formed Eli with Kaz Lux (vocals) and drummer Pierre Van der Linden, both ex-Brainbox (Van der Linden also played on a couple of Focus LPs). Akkerman has made several albums of his own and rejoined Focus in 1985 for an album on Vertigo. (Donald Clarke 1988)..

**CAN'T STAND NOISE**
Tracks: / Pietons / Everything must change / Back to the factory / Journey (A real elegant gypsy) / Heavy treasure / Just because / Who knows.
**Album:** Released May '86, on Charly by Charly Records. Catalogue no: **CR 30250**

**COMPLETE GUITARIST, THE**
Tracks: / Old tennis shoes / Come closer / Funkology / It could happen to you / Pietons / Journey (a real elegant gypsy).
**CD:** Released Jun '86, on Charly by Charly Records. Catalogue no: **CDCHARLY 17**

**GOLDEN HIGHLIGHTS OF AKKERMAN & OGERMAN (Akkerman & Ogerman)**
**Cass:** Released Jun '86, on CBS (import) by CBS Records. Catalogue no: **40 54730**
**Album:** Released Jun '86, on CBS (import) by CBS Records. Catalogue no: **54730**

**IT COULD HAPPEN TO YOU**
Tracks: / Old tennis shoes / Come closer / Funkology / It could happen to you.
**Album:** Released Dec '85, on Charly by Charly Records. Catalogue no: **CR 30246**

**JAN AKKERMAN 3**
**Album:** Released Jan '80, on Atlantic by WEA Records. Catalogue no: **K 50664**

**LIVE! (Akkerman, Jan & Joachim Kuhn)**
Note: Live in Kiel and Stuttgart - Parts 1 & 2.
**CD:** Released '88, on Inak Catalogue no: **INAK 868 CD**

**PLEASURE POINT**
Tracks: / Valdez / Heavy pleasure / Cool in the shadow / Visions of blue / C.S. / Bird Island.
Note: Licensed from Joe Sweetinburgh. (P)1987 Charly Records Ltd. (C)1987 Charly Records Ltd.
**Cass:** Released Jul '87, on Decal by Charly Records. Catalogue no: **TCLIK 13**
**CD:** Released Jul '87, on Charly by Charly Records. Catalogue no: **CDCHARLY 90**
**Album:** Released Jul '87, on Decal by Charly Records. Catalogue no: **LIK 13**

**PROFILE: JAN AKKERMAN**
**Album:** Released Aug '84, on EMI (Holland) by EMI Records. Catalogue no: **5C 038 24707**

**SHE'S SO DIVINE**
Tracks: / She's so divine / Spy dancer.
**7" Single:** Released Jan '80, on Atlantic by WEA Records. Deleted Jan '85. Catalogue no: **K11374**

## Alabama Blues

**ALABAMA BLUES (1927-31) (Various artists)**
**Album:** Released Dec '88, on Yazoo (USA) by Shanachie Records (USA). Catalogue no: **L 1006**

**ALABAMA BLUES (1927-51) (Various artists)**
**Album:** Released Dec '88, on HK Catalogue no: **HK 4004**

## Alabama Country Blues

**ALABAMA COUNTRY BLUES (Various artists)**
**Album:** Released Oct '88, on Roots (Germany) Catalogue no: **RL 325**

## Alabama Harmonica Kings

**ALABAMA HARMONICA KINGS 1927-30**
Note: Jaybird Coleman, Ollis Marin, George Bullet Williams.
**Album:** Released Sep '87, on Wolf Catalogue no: **WSE 127**

## Alabama Singers

**NEGRO SPIRITUAL MUSIC**
Tracks: / Battle of Jericho, The / Poor pilgrim of sorrow / Talk about Jesus / Jesus met the woman at the well / Daniel saw the stone / He'll never let go your hand / Come home / Yes indeed / Go down, Moses / I could do better than that / Soldier's plea / Motherless child / I remember the time / Walk around.
**Album:** Released '79, on Joker (USA) by Lifetime Records (USA). Catalogue no: **SM 3342**

## Albam, Manny

**Biographical details:** Manny Albam was born in 1922 in the Dominican Republic, emigrating to the USA as an infant. His arranging, composing and sax playing began with big bands from 1940, and was a priceless asset to mainstream jazz in the ensuing decades, both in small-group and big band contexts. His studio work for RCA in the '50s was often done in the excellent company of Al Cohn and Ernie Wilkins. (Donald Clarke 21 July 1988).

**JAZZ WORKSHOP, THE**
Tracks: / Anything goes / Headstrong / Black bottom / Changing scene, The / Turning point / Charmaine / Diga diga doo / Royal Garden blues / Swingin' on a star / Intermezzo / Ferris wheel urbanity.
**Album:** Released '83, on RCA (France) by BMG Records (France). Catalogue no: **PM 43551**

**MANNY ALBAM AND THE GREATS OF OUR TIME VOL.1**
Tracks: / Blues for neither coast / Latined fracture / Poor Doctor Millmoss / Minor matters / My sweetie went away / All too soon / See here Miss Bromley.
**Album:** Released Feb '83, on Jasmine by Hasmick Promotions. Deleted Feb '88. Catalogue no: **JASM 1010**

**WEST SIDE STORY (Albam, Manny/his Jazz Greats)**
Tracks: / Prologue and jet song / Something's coming (could be) / Cool / Maria / Tonight / I feel pretty / Somewhere / Finale.
**Album:** Released Feb '83, on Jasmine by Hasmick Promotions. Deleted Feb '88. Catalogue no: **JASM 1003**

## Albany, Joe

**Biographical details:** Joe Albany (1924-88) was an American bop pianist who disappeared into obscurity, partly because he walked out of many jobs (for example, with Charlie Parker) over musical and other differences, yet he made several fine albums. Donald Clarke 21 July 1988).

**AT HOME: JOE ALBANY**
Tracks: / What's new / You're blase / Why was I born / Jitterbug waltz / Night and day / What are you doing the rest of your life / Barbados / Can't we be friends / Everything happens to me / You've changed / Birdtown birds / Isn't it romantic.
Note: Solo piano recorded in Hollywood
**Album:** Released '83, on Spotlite by Spotlite Records. Catalogue no: **SPJ JA1**

**BIRD LIVES**
**CD:** Released Feb '90, on Storyville by Storyville Records AB. Catalogue no: **STCD 4164**
**Album:** Released Jun '79, on Interplay (USA) by Interplay Records (USA). Catalogue no: **IP-7723**

**PORTRAIT OF AN ARTIST**
Tracks: / Autumn in New York / Guess I'll hang my tears out to dry / For the little guy / They say it's wonderful / Too late now / Confirmation / Ruby, my dear / Conversation with Joe Albany.
**Album:** Released Oct '82, on Elektra (Musician) by Elektra Records (USA). Deleted Oct '87. Catalogue no: **K 52390**

**PROTO-BOPPER**
Tracks: / When lights are low / Our love affair is over / You don't know what love is / For heaven's sake / Getting sentimental over you / Yardbird suite / Imagination / Like someone in love / C.C. rider / You're blase / Suddenly it's spring.
Note: Solo and trio performances by the legendary Albany
**Album:** Released '83, on Spotlite by Spotlite Records. Catalogue no: **SPJ JA3**

**RIGHT COMBINATION, THE**
Tracks: / Daahoud / I love you / It's you or no one / Nearness of you, the / Angel eyes / Body and soul / All the things you are.
**Album:** Released Feb '88, on Riverside (USA) by Fantasy Inc (USA). Catalogue no: **RSLP 270**

## Alcorn, Alvin

**ALVIN ALCORN & HIS NEW ORLEANS JAZZ BAND(Alcorn, Alvin & His New Orleans Jazz Band)**
**Album:** Released Sep '86, on New Orleans Catalogue no: **NOR 7205**

## Alexander, Monty

**COBILIMBO**
**Album:** Released '81, on MPS Jazz Catalogue no: **MPS 68 188**

**DUKE ELLINGTON SONG BOOK**
Tracks: / I let a song go out of my heart / Sophisticated lady / Things ain't what they used to be / Love you madly / Eastside Westside / In a mellow tone / In a sentimental mood / C jam blues.
Note: This new album with bass player John Clayton features ten of the most popular compositions by the late-great Duke Ellington.
**CD:** Released '84, on MPS Jazz (Germany) Deleted Aug '87. Catalogue no: **821 151-2**
**Album:** Released '84, on MPS Jazz (Germany) Catalogue no: **821 151-1**

**FULL STEAM AHEAD**
Tracks: / Freddie freeloader / Once I loved / Ray's idea / Because you're mine / Satisfaction / Happy talk / Estate / Hi-fly / Just friends.
**CD:** Released Nov '86, on Concord Jazz by Concord Jazz Records (USA). Catalogue no: **CCD 4287**
**Cass:** Released Dec '85, on Concord Jazz by Concord Jazz Records (USA). Catalogue no: **CJC 287**
**Album:** Released Dec '85, on Concord Jazz by Concord Jazz Records (USA). Catalogue no: **CJ 287**

**IVORY AND STEEL**
**CD:** Released Jul '88, on Concord Jazz by Concord Jazz Records (USA). Catalogue no: **CCD 4124**

**JAMBOREE (Alexander, Monty Ivory & Steel)**
Note: The sequel to 'Ivory & Steel' finds Monty Alexander returning to his Jamaican roots. Featured in this Jamboree are Trinidad's top steel drummers- Othello Molineaux & Len 'Boogsie' Sharp- along with Monty's red hot rhytm section. An exciting fusion of Jamaican folk songs, calypso, reggae & jazz. Personel: Monty Alexander(piano), Othello Molineaux (steel drums), Len 'Boogsie' Sharp (steel drums), Marshall Wood (bass), Robert Thomas Jnr.(hand drums), Marvin 'Smitty' Smith (drums).
**CD:** Released Oct '88, on Concord Jazz by Concord Jazz Records (USA). Catalogue no: **CCD 4359**
**Cass:** Released Oct '88, on Concord Jazz by Concord Jazz Records (USA). Catalogue no: **CJP 359 C**
**Album:** Released Oct '88, on Concord Jazz by Concord Jazz Records (USA). Catalogue no: **CJP 359**

**JAMENTO (Alexander, Monty Seven)**
Tracks: / Accompong / Slippery / Sugar loaf at twilight / Weekend in L.A. / Jamento / Mango rengue.
**Cass:** Released '82, on Pablo Jazz (USA) by Pablo Records (USA). Catalogue no: **K10 826**
**Album:** Released '82, on Pablo Jazz (USA) by Pablo Records (USA). Catalogue no: **231 0826**

**MONTREUX ALEX**
Tracks: / Nite mist blues / Feelings / Satin doll / Work song / Drown in my own tears / Battle hymn of the Republic.
**CD:** Released Apr '84, on Pablo Jazz (USA) by Pablo Records (USA). Deleted Jul '88. Catalogue no: **817 487-2**
**Album:** Released '81, on MPS Jazz Catalogue no: **MPS 68 170**

**MONTY ALEXANDER IN TOKYO**
Tracks: / Broadway / Just in time / Sweet lady / Tricrotism / Never let me go / Montevideo / Pawnbroker / See see rider.
**Cass:** Released '82, on Pablo Jazz (USA) by Pablo Records (USA). Catalogue no: **K10 836**
**Album:** Released '82, on Pablo Jazz (USA) by Pablo Records (USA). Catalogue no: **231 0836**

**MONTY STRIKES AGAIN**
**Album:** Released '81, on MPS Jazz Catalogue no: **MPS 68 044**

**OVERSEAS SPECIAL**
Tracks: / But not for me / Time for love, A / Orange in pain / F S R / For all we know / C.C. rider.
Note: "Overseas Special" marks Monty Alexander, Ray Brown and Herb Ellis third collaboration for Concord Records. This superb trio exites the live audience while pushing itself to its swinging best with a concert of great standards and finely tailored original compostions. Personnel: Monty Alexander - piano/ Ray Brown - bass/ Herb Ellis - guitar.
**CD:** Released '84, on Concord Jazz by Concord Jazz Records (USA). Deleted '88. Catalogue no: **CJ 253**

**PERCEPTION**
**Album:** Released '81, on MPS Jazz Catalogue no: **MPS 68 042**

**SATURDAY NIGHT (Alexander, Monty Quartet)**
Note: Amazing inspired performance recorded live at Valentyne's Club, Florida October '85. A sequel to the earlier Friday Night album, this set features popular/jazz compositions from such notable writers as Johnny Mandel - Close enough, Milt Jackson - SKJ and Ceder Walton - Bolivia to name but a few. Personnel: Monty Alexander (piano), Ed Thigpen (drums), Reggie Johnson (bass), Robert Thomas (hand drums).
**Album:** Released May '89, on Timeless by Timeless Records. Catalogue no: **MLP 024**
**CD:** Released May '89, on Timeless by Timeless Records. Catalogue no: **MCD 024**

**TRIO (Alexander / Brown / Ellis)**
**Album:** Released Mar '81, on Concord Jazz by Concord Jazz Records (USA). Catalogue no: **CJ 136**

**TRIPLE TREAT (Alexander, Monty/ Ray Brown/ Herb Ellis)**
Tracks: / Flintstones, The / Body and soul / Small fry / When lights are low / Triple treat blues / Fungi mama / Sweet lady / But not for me.
**CD:** Released Jul '88, on Concord Jazz by Concord Jazz Records (USA). Catalogue no: **CCD 4193**
**Album:** Released '82, on Concord Jazz by Concord Jazz Records (USA). Catalogue no: **CJ 193**

**TRIPLE TREAT II (Alexander, Monty/ Ray Brown/ Herb Ellis)**
Tracks: / Lined with a groove / Straighten up and fly right / It might as well be spring / Seven come eleven / Smile / I'll remember April / Polka dots and moonbeams / Lester leaps in.
Note: "This supercharged reunion of old friends was captured live at The Loa in Santa Monica, California. To further enhance the treat violinist John Frigo joins the group on four selections. Annotator Ken Franckling (UPI) sums up the flavour of this special album: 'Pull up a chair and kick off your shoes. This musical conversation among friends is something to savour'. Monty Alexander, piano; Ray Brown, bass; Herb Ellis, guitar; John Fridfo, violin." (IMS Records, May 1988.)
**Cass:** Released May '88, on Concord Jazz by Concord Jazz Records (USA). Catalogue no: **CJC 338**
**CD:** Released May '88, on Concord Jazz by Concord Jazz Records (USA). Catalogue no: **CCD 4338**
**Album:** Released May '88, on Concord Jazz by Concord Jazz Records (USA). Catalogue no: **CJ 338**

**TRIPLE TREAT III (Alexander, Monty/ Ray Brown/ Herb Ellis)**
**Cass:** Released '89, on Concord by Concord Jazz Records (USA). Catalogue no: **CJ 394C**
**CD:** Released '89, on Concord by Concord Jazz Records (USA). Catalogue no: **CCD 4394**

**WAY IT IS,THE**
**Album:** Released '81, on MPS Jazz Catalogue no: **MPS 68 223**

## Alexander, Texas

**TEXAS ALEXANDER VOL 1 (1927-28)**
Tracks: / Range in my kitchen blues / Long lonesome day blues / Corn bread blues / Section gang blues / Levee camp moan blues / Mama I heard you brought it right back home / Farm hand blues / Evil woman blues / Sabine River blues / Death bed blues / Yellow girl blues / West Texas blues / Bantam rooster blues / Deep blue sea blues / No more woman blues / Don't you wish your baby was built up like mine / Bell cow blues.
**Album:** Released '82, on Matchbox (Bluesmaster) by Saydisc Records. Catalogue no: **MSE 206**

**TEXAS ALEXANDER VOL 2**
Tracks: / Sittin' on a log / Mam's bad luck

child / Bo hog blues / Work ox blues / Risin' sun,The / Penitentiary moan blues / Blue devil blues / Tell me woman blues / Frisco train blues / St. Louis fair blues / I am calling blues / Double crossing blues / Ninety-eight degree blues / Some day baby your troubles is gonna be like mine / Water bound blues / Awful moaning blues part 1&2.
**Album:** Released '83, on Matchbox by Flyright Records. Catalogue no: **MSE 214**

**TEXAS ALEXANDER VOL 3 (1929-30)**
Tracks: / Gold tooth blues / Johnny Behren's blues / Rolling mill blues / Broken yo yo / Texas special, The / When you get to thinking / Thirty day blues / Peaceful blues / Days is lonesome / Last stage blues / See better days / Stealing to her man / She's so fair / Rolling and stumbling blues / Frost Texas tornado blues / Texas troublesome blues.
Note: The complete recorded output of one of the most influential and enigmatic country blues singers will run to 4 vols. This 3rd vol. shows again the variety of accompanists that he attracted. He was unusual amongst blues singers in that he didn't play an instrument and his individual style was a challenge to some of the great blues and jazz instrumentalists. MONO
**Album:** Released Aug '86, on Matchbox by Flyright Records. Catalogue no: **MSE 220**

**TEXAS ALEXANDER VOL 4 (1934-50)**
**Album:** Released '88, on Matchbox by Flyright Records. Catalogue no: **MSE 224**

## Alexandria, Lorez

**ALEXANDRIA THE GREAT**
Tracks: / Show me / I've never been in love before / Satin doll / My one and only love / Over the rainbow / Get me to the church on time / Best is yet to come, The / I've grown accustomed to his face / Give me the simple life / I'm through with love / But beautiful / Little boat / Dancing on the ceiling / It might as well be spring / Once / Wildest gal in town, The / Angel eyes / This could be the start of something big / No more / That far away look.
**CD:** Released Jan '90, on MCA (Impulse Jazz) Catalogue no: **MCAD 33116**

**BAND SWINGS LOREZ**
Tracks: / You're my thrill / Don't blame me / Ain't misbehavin' / What is this thing called love / Dancing on the ceiling / Love is just around the corner / I'm gonna sit right down / Just you, just me / All the things you are / Thrill is gone, The / My baby just cares for me.
**Album:** Released '88, on Sing Catalogue no: **SING 657**

**HOW WILL I REMEMBER YOU?**
Tracks: / Make someone happy / You light up my life / Greatest love of all, The / Until its time for you to go / While we're young.
Note: Lorez Alexandria-vocals, Gildo Mahones Quintet.
**Cass:** Released '88, on Discovery (USA) by Discovery Records (USA). Catalogue no: **DSC 782**
**Album:** Released '88, on Discovery (USA) by Discovery Records (USA). Catalogue no: **DS 782**

**LOREZ SINGS PRES (Late session at an intimate club)**
Tracks: / Fine and dandy / Fooling myself / D.B. blues / You're driving me crazy / Easy living / Polka dots and moonbeams / This year's kisses / There will never be another you / No eyes blues / Jumpin' with symphony Sid.
Note: A tribute to the great tenor sax star Lester ("Pres") Young.
**CD:** Released Mar '90, on King Catalogue no: **KCD 565**
**Album:** Released May '88, on Sing Catalogue no: **SING 565**

**SINGING SONGS EVERYONE KNOWS**
**CD:** Released Oct '88, on King 1 Catalogue no: **KLP 676**

**SINGS THE SONGS OF JOHNNY MERCER (Alexandria, Lorez & The Mike Wofford Quartet)**
Tracks: / I remember you / My shining hour / Days of wine and roses / I thought about you / Early Autumn / Dearly beloved / Travellin' light / When a woman loves a man / Fools rush in.
**Album:** Released '88, on Discovery (USA) by Discovery Records (USA). Catalogue no: **DS 826**
**Album:** Released '84, on Discovery (USA) by Discovery Records (USA). Catalogue no: **DS 905**
**CD:** Released Sep '86, on Discovery (USA) by Discovery Records (USA). Catalogue no: **DSCD 905**
**Cass:** Released '88, on Discovery (USA) by Discovery Records (USA). Catalogue no: **DSC 905**

**STANDARDS WITH A SLIGHT TOUCH OF**
Tracks: / Just one of those things / Then I'll be tired of you / Lush life / Sometimes I'm happy / Long ago and far away / But beautiful / I'm beginning to see the light / I can't believe that you're in love with me / Spring is here / Angel eyes / Better luck next time / I didn't know what time it was.
**CD:** Released Mar '90, on King Catalogue no: **KCD 676**
**Album:** Released Dec '87, on Sing Catalogue no: **SING 676**

**TANGERINE (Alexandria, Lorez / Gildo Mahones Quintet)**
Tracks: / Bittersweet / I'm old fashioned / When the world was young / Any place I hang my hat / That old black magic / Namely you / Midnight sun / I'm building up to an awful let-down / Day in, day out / Days of wine and roses / Travellin' light / When a woman loves a man / I remember you / My shining hour.
**CD:** on Trend (USA) by Trend Records (USA). Catalogue no: **TRCD 538**
**Album:** Released '88, on Trend (USA) by Trend Records (USA). Catalogue no: **TR 538**

## All...

**ALL AROUND BLUEGRASS (Various artists)**
Tracks: / On the southbound: *Various artists* / Chalk up another one: *Various artists* / Blue moon of Kentucky: *Various artists* / You can't go in the red playing bluegrass: *Various artists* / Carolina breakdown: *Various artists* / Have you come to say goodbye: *Various artists* / It's only a phonograph record: *Various artists* / I'll go steppin' too: *Various artists* / Windy mountain: *Various artists* / Save it, save it: *Various artists* / Cuttin the grass: *Various artists* / Corn cob blues: *Various artists* / Kentucky ridgerunner: *Various artists* / Bringin in the Georgia mail: *Various artists* / I won't be hanging around: *Various artists* / Nashville grass breakdown: *Various artists* / Kentucky: *Various artists* / Special: *Various artists* / When it's peach pickin time in Georgia: *Various artists* / Williams lake stampede: *Various artists.*
**Cass:** Released May '84, on RCA International by BMG Records (UK). Deleted Jul '89. Catalogue no: **NK 89139**
**Album:** Released May '84, on RCA International by BMG Records (UK). Deleted Jul '89. Catalogue no: **NL 89139**
**Album:** Released Sep '82, on RCA by BMG Records (UK). Deleted Jan '88. Catalogue no: **INTS 5188**

**ALL THAT TRAD (Various artists)**
**Cass set:** Released Mar '83, on Ditto by Pickwick Records. Catalogue no: **DTO 10050**

**ALL THAT'S JAZZ/JUBILEE JAZZ (Various artists)**
**Cass:** Released Jun '87, Catalogue no: **BARX-SAM 001**

## All American...

**ALL AMERICAN SWING GROUPS-VOL.5 (Various artists)**
**Album:** Released Sep '79, on Rarities Catalogue no: **RARITIES 61**

## All Star...

**ALL STAR SWING (Various artists)**
**2 LP Set:** Released Oct '85, on Savoy (France) Catalogue no: **WL 70533**

**ALL STAR TROMBONE SPECTACULAR (Various artists)**
**Album:** Released Aug '82, on Progressive (USA) by Jazzology Records (USA). Catalogue no: **PRO 7018**

**ALL STAR TRUMPET SPECTACULAR (Various artists)**
**Album:** Released Apr '81, on Progressive (USA) by Jazzology Records (USA). Catalogue no: **PRO 7015**

**SWING FEVER (All Star Swing)**
Tracks: / In the swing / Swingin' easy / Swing's the thing / Swing with swing / Swing, swing, swing, swing and sway / Swing with the king.
**Album:** Released Dec '82, on CBS by CBS Records. Deleted Dec '87. Catalogue no: **CBS 25042**

## All Star Jazz Show

**ALL STAR JAZZ SHOW (Mahogany hall stomp) (Various artists)**
**Cass:** Released '89, on Jasmine by Hasmick Promotions. Catalogue no: **JASMC 2530**
**Album:** Released Jan '88, on Sounds Great Catalogue no: **SG 8017**
**Album:** Released '89, on Jasmine by Hasmick Promotions. Catalogue no: **JASM 2530**

**ALL STAR JAZZ SHOW, NO 3 (I love jazz) (Various artists)**
Note: Teletext, 10 November, 1958. Third in a series of one hour jazz specials sponsored by Timex in the 50's. Co-hosted by Hoagy Carmichael and Bob Crosby, this telecast features names such as Louis Armstrong, Gene Krupa, Lionel Hampton and Anita O'Day. Highlights include I Love Jazz.
**Album:** Released Apr '88, on Sounds Great Catalogue no: **SG 8011**

**ALL-STAR JAZZ SHOW (Various artists)**
Note: Telecast, 30 December, 1957. The 50's ushered in the Jazz Age on television. Among the visual products of this period were the one-hour jazz specials sponsored by Timex. Here is the first in the series, hosted by pianist/composer Steve Allen. Among musicians featured are Louis Armstrong, Duke Ellington, Woody Herman, Gene Krupa and Jack Teagarden and musical highlights include Mahogany Hall Stomp, Dark Eyes, Apple Honey and Ol' Rockin' Chair.
**Album:** Released Apr '88, on Sounds Great Catalogue no: **SG 8005**

## All Star Six

**MY BABY LIKE TO BE BOP**
Note: Artists are Reg Arnold/Terry Pollard/Aubrey Franks/Ralph Sharon/Kenny Baker/John Dankworth.
**Album:** Released Dec '87, on Esquire by Titan Int. Prod.. Catalogue no: **ESQ 337**

## All Stars...

**ALL STAR SAX SPECTACULAR (Various artists)**
**Album:** Released Apr '81, on Progressive (USA) by Jazzology Records (USA). Catalogue no: **PRO 7019**

**ALL STAR'S AT NEWPORT (Various artists)**
**Album:** Released Aug '81, on Verve Catalogue no: **2304 369**

**ALL STARS EUROPEAN CONCERT (Various artists)**
**Album:** Released '88, on Unique Jazz by Spotlite Records. Catalogue no: **UJ 28**

**ALL STAR'S VOL 1 (Various artists)**
**12" Single:** Released Jul '88, on Black Scorpio Catalogue no: **BSLP 8803**
**Cass:** Released Apr '81, on Gold by Gold Records. Catalogue no: **GL 1961**

**ALL STAR'S VOL 2 (Various artists)**
**Cass:** Released Apr '81, on Gold by Gold Records. Catalogue no: **GL 1962**

**LIVE EUROPEAN CONCERT**
Tracks: / Bauhaus / Tenderly / Makin' whoppee / C jam blues / Yardbird suite / Sunday / Willow weep for me.
**Album:** Released Apr '81, on Unique Jazz by Spotlite Records. Catalogue no: **UJ 25**

**NEWPORT JAZZ FESTIVAL**
**Album:** Released Aug '86, on Avan-Guard Catalogue no: **BVL 011**

## All That Trad

**ALL THAT TRAD (Various artists)**
Tracks: / Kansas city stomp: *Welsh, Alex* / Mama don't allow it: *Kelly, George & Mick Mulligan* / Sweet Georgia Brown: *Barber, Chris* / Lazy river: *Ball, Kenny.*
**CD:** Released Mar '88, on Pickwick by Pickwick Records. Catalogue no: **PWK 054**

## Allen, Henry 'Red'

**AND FRIENDS, 1932-56 (Volume 1) (See panel below)**
Tracks: / Swingin' at the Lido / Swingin' at the Lido (2nd try) / Swingin' at the Lido (3rd try) / Havin' a ball / Havin' a ball (4th try) / Sheridan square, A / Travelin' light / Ride, red, ride / Riffin' / Dark eyes / Sweet Lorraine / Indiana / Frankie & Johnny / Maryland, my, Maryland.
**Album:** Released Sep '87, on Meritt (USA) Catalogue no: **MERITT 26**

**ART FORD'S JAZZ PARTY (November 1958)**
Note: With Dicky Wells/Coleman Hawkins/Buster Bailey/Willie the lion Smith / Danny Barker/Vinnie Burk/Sonny Greer / Modern Jazz Quartet / Mae Barnes. Tracks include: Runnin' wild/Stompin at the savoy / Somebody loves me / True blue lou / Charleston / China boy / Memphis blues, etc
**Album:** Released Oct '87, on Jazz Connoisseur by Spotlite Records. Catalogue no: **AFJP 8**

**AT NEWPORT FESTIVAL 1957 (Allen, Henry Red / Kid Ory & Jack Teagarden)**
Tracks: / Struttin' with some barbecue / St. James infirmary / China boy / Basin Street blues / Muskrat ramble / High society.
Note: All-star jam session in celebration of Louis Armstrong's 57th Birthday.
**Album:** Released Apr '84, on Verve (France) Catalogue no: **8177 921**

**BLUEGRASS COUNTRY**
**Album:** Released 18 Jun '87, on Fundamental by Fundamental Music Records. Catalogue no: **SAVE 029**

**HENRY ALLEN AND ORCHESTRA (Allen, Henry 'Red' & his Orchestra)**
**Album:** Released '88, on Collector's Classics Catalogue no: **CC 13**

**HENRY ALLEN AND ORCHESTRA, VOL.3 1936**
**Album:** Released '88, on Collector's Classics Catalogue no: **CC 51**

**HENRY ALLEN AND ORCHESTRA, VOL.5 1932-7**

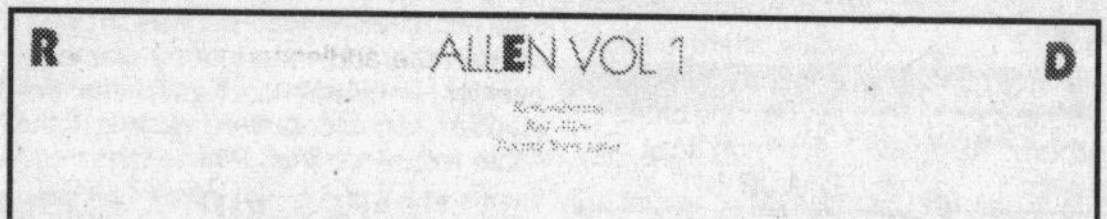

Henry 'Red' Allen - And Friends 1932-56 (Meritt(USA))

**Henry 'Red' Allen - Live 1965 (Meritt (USA))**

**Album:** Released '88, on Collector's Classics Catalogue no: **CC 55**

**HENRY 'RED' ALLEN**
Tracks: / That's a plenty / Tin roof blues / Royal garden blues / Way down yonder in New Orleans / Beale street blues / Muskrat ramble / I've found a new baby / Basin street blues / Wolverine blues.
**Album:** Released Jul '82, on Jazz Reactivation Catalogue no: **JR 161**

**HENRY 'RED' ALLEN (TAX)**
**CD:** Released '89, on Tax Catalogue no: **TAXCD S-3-2**

**HENRY 'RED' ALLEN 1933-41**
**Album:** Released '88, on Meritt (USA) Catalogue no: **MERITT 13-14**

**HENRY 'RED' ALLEN 1939-41**
**Album:** Released Jul '82, on Everybody's (Sweden) Catalogue no: **E 1000**

**HENRY RED ALLEN & MILLS BLUE RHYTHM BAND (Allen, Henry 'Red' & Mills Blue Rhythm Band)**
**Album:** Released Jan '88, on Gaps Catalogue no: **GAPS 170**

**LIVE 1965 (Allen, Red Quartet) (See panel above)**
Tracks: / Canal Street blues / Mack the knife / Blue spruce boogie / Muskrat ramble / Crazy blues / Lover, come back to me / St.Louis blues / Caravan / Pleasin' Paul / Hello Dolly / Memphis blues / Satin doll / Never on Sunday / New Orleans medley.
Note: Henry 'Red' Allen (trumpet & vocal), Lannie Scott and / or Sammy Price (piano), Bennie Moten (bass), George Reed (drums).
Toward the end of the Spring of 1965 Henry 'Red' Allen was booked into the beautiful Blue Spruce Inn in Roslyn, Long Island. The original booking was for a two week period. Red was so popular with the audience that he was held over for two full months. Early during this stand arrangements were made to make some test recordings. These tapes survived and were found recently in the basement (not mine) of a collector on Long Island. It should be noted here that the results of two nights of recording at the Blue Spruce Inn encouraged a major record company to come in later and record. The album was released in 1966. Many of the titles found on the commericial album release were on our tapes (different versions). It was our feeling that collectors of Red Allen's work would prefer and enjoy hearing numbers that did not duplicate those made around the same time. There is over twenty-eight minutes of musical excitement and beauty on each side of this Meritt record release. Along with the record you will find an insert sheet with some background on Red Allen and the Blue Spruce Inn from an interview I did with David 'Red' Metzger while this album was going into production. It is a happy celebration for us all remembering Henry 'Red' Allen twenty years later. (Jerry Valburn)
**Album:** Released Sep '87, on Meritt (USA) Catalogue no: **MERITT 27**

**NICE**
Tracks: / Theme / Red jump / Ride red, ride / Dark eyes / Dear old southland / Get the mop / Just a feeling / Wild man blues / Rosetta / Memphis blues / Yellow dog blues / Cherry / Fidgety feet.
Note: Allen tpt.vcl./ J.C. Higginbotham tbn./ Don Stovall alt./ Al Williams pn./ Clarence Moten bs./ Alvin Burroughs d./ Rex Stewart cor./ Vic Dickerson tbn./ Pee Wee Russel clnt./ Coleman Hawkins ten./ Nat Pierce pn./ Danny Parker gt./ Milt Hinton bs./ Jo Jones d./ TV show July 12th 1957: Cutty Cutshall tbn./ Tony Parent clnt.
**Album:** Released Apr '81, on Phoenix (USA) by All Star Talent Inc.(USA). Catalogue no: **LP 24**

**RED ALLEN (Allen, Henry 'Red'/James P Johnson)**
**Album:** Released '88, on Meritt (USA) Catalogue no: **MERITT 5**

**RED ALLEN & BLUES SINGERS Vol. 1 (Allen, Henry 'Red' & The Blues Singers)**
**Album:** Released '88, on Jass Catalogue no: **JA 47**

**RED ALLEN & GEORGE LEWIS (With George Lewis Quartet)**
**Album:** Released Dec '82, on Hot Society Catalogue no: **HSLP 1002**

**RED ALLEN MEETS KID ORY (Allen, Red & Kid Ory)**
**Album:** Released Oct '82, on Verve (France) Catalogue no: **2304 544**

**RED ALLEN & THE BLUES SINGERS (Allen, Henry 'Red' & The Blues Singers)**
**Album:** Released Jul '86, on Jazz Archives (USA) by Jazz Archives Inc.(USA). Catalogue no: **JA 46**

**TRUMPET ALBUM (Allen, Henry 'Red' & Mills Blue Rhythm Band)**
**Album:** Released '88, on Meritt (USA) Catalogue no: **MERITT 8**

**VERY GREAT HENRY 'RED' ALLEN WITH 'KID' ORY'S CREOLE, THE**
Tracks: / Peoria / Basin street blues / St. James infirmary blues / Wolverine blues / Savoy blues / Tin roof blues / That's a plenty / Aunt Hagar's blues / Panama rag / At the Jazz Band Ball.
Note: Personnel: Henry 'Red' Allen, tpt., vcls., Edward 'Kid' Ory, tmbn., Bob McCracken, cl., Cedric Haywood, pno., Alton Redd, dms., Squire Gersh, Bass.
**Album:** Released Apr '81, on Rarities Catalogue no: **RARITIES 60**

**VERY GREAT HENRY 'RED' ALLEN - VOL.1**
Tracks: / Sometimes I'm happy / Ol' man river / Siesta at the Fiesta / Jack the bellboy / Ride, red ride / Dark eyes / Dear old Southland / Red jump / Crawl,The / Buzz me / Drink hearty / Get the mop / Count me out / Check up / If it's love you want / Let me miss you.
Note: Personnel: Features Red Allen, J.C. Higginbotham, Don Stovall, Benny Moten, Bill Thompson, Ed Hall.
**Album:** Released Apr '81, on Rarities Catalogue no: **RARITIES 14**

## Allen, Pete

**DIXIE DATE (Allen, Pete Band)**
Tracks: / Clarinet marmalade / At the Devil's ball / Sailing down Chesapeake Bay / St. Phillip street breakdown / Fidgety feet / Mama's gone / Do you know what it means to miss New Orleans? / There's yes yes in your eyes / I found a new baby.
**Album:** Released Jul '88, on Black Lion Catalogue no: **BLM 51107**

**DOWN IN HONKY TONK TOWN**
Tracks: / Royal Garden blues / Black and fan 'antasy / Down in honky tonk town / South rampart street parade / I'm gonna sit right down and write myself a letter / Cornet chop suey / Rent party blues / Ole miss rag / Black lion rag / Riverboat shuffle.
**Album:** Released Jan '80, on Black Lion Deleted Jan '85. Catalogue no: **BLP 12185**

**GONNA BUILD A MOUNTAIN (Allen, Pete Jazz Band)**
Tracks: / Gonna build a mountain / Livery stable blues / I ain't gonna give nobody none of my jelly roll / Seagull strut / My little bimbo / Louisiana / Chimes blues / Snake rag / I've got a feeling I'm falling / Potato head blues / I'm slapping Seventh Avenue with the sole of my shoe / T'ain't no sin to take off your skin (Full title: T'ain't no sin to take off your skin and dance around in you) / West End blues / 1919 march.
**Album:** Released '82, on Platform Catalogue no: **PAJB 1**
**Cass:** Released '82, on Platform Catalogue no: **TC PAJB 1**

**JAZZIN' AROUND II (Allen, Pete Band)**
**Album:** Released Nov '85, on ARB by ARB Records. Catalogue no: **ARB 853**

**MARTINIQUE (Allen, Pete Jazz Band)**
**Album:** Released Nov '88, on ARB by ARB Records. Catalogue no: **ARB 831**

**ONE FOR THE ROAD (Allen, Pete Jazz Band)**
Tracks: / Honeysuckle rose / Hiding place, The / Drop me off in Harlem / Sensation rag / Potato rag / Potato head blues.
**Cass:** Released Nov '87, on P.A.R. Catalogue no: **PAR 187**
**Album:** Released Nov '87, on P.A.R. Catalogue no: **PAR 187 S**

**TURKEY TROT (Allen, Pete Jazz Band)**
**Album:** Released Apr '79, on Black Lion Deleted Apr '84. Catalogue no: **BLP 12174**

**WHILE WE DANCED AT THE MARDI (Allen, Pete Jazz Band)**
**Album:** Released Mar '87, on Jazz Club Catalogue no: **JLP 5501**

**WILD CAT BLUES (Allen, Pete Jazz Band)**
Tracks: / Hiawatha rag / Chips are down, The / Apex blues / Tea for two / Sweet Georgia Brown / Petite fleur / Wild cat blues / Until the real thing comes along / Sentimental journey / Froggie Moore / I'm putting all my eggs in one basket / Concord blues.
**Album:** Released Jul '88, on Pete Allen Catalogue no: **PAR 288**

## Allen, Steve

**ALL STAR JAZZ CONCERT VOL.1**
Tracks: / I want to be happy / Sweet Georgia Brown / I can't get started / Big noise from Winnetka / Love me or leave me / Swing that music / Big town boogie / That's a plenty / Long gone.
**Album:** Released Dec '83, on Jasmine by Hasmick Promotions. Deleted Feb '88. Catalogue no: **JASM 1030**

**ALL STAR JAZZ CONCERT VOL 2**
Tracks: / When the saints / Blues / Basin street blues / Lover / St james infirmary / At sundown / Whistling cow blues / Only man blues / South rampart street parade.
**Album:** Released Jun '84, on Jasmine by Hasmick Promotions. Deleted Feb '88. Catalogue no: **JASM 1042**

**JAZZ FOR TONIGHT**
Tracks: / S'posin I should fall in love with you / Chicken wire blues / Body and soul / I thought about you / Limehouse blues / Tea for two / Lover man / Poor butterfly.
**Album:** Released Jun '83, on Jasmine by Hasmick Promotions. Deleted Feb '88. Catalogue no: **JASM 1018**

**LOVE IS IN THE AIR**
Tracks: / Love is in the air.
**7" Single:** Released May '87, on WEA by WEA Records. Deleted Jan '88. Catalogue no: **YZ 126**
**12" Single:** Released May '87, on WEA by WEA Records. Deleted Jul '88. Catalogue no: **YZ 126T**

**STEVE ALLEN AT THE ROUNDTABLE**
**Album:** Released 7 Nov '87, on Fresh Sounds (Spain) by Fresh Sounds Records (Spain). Catalogue no: **FS 253**

## Allison, Mose

**Biographical details:** ALLISON, Mose was born in 1927 in Mississippi; as a white child he was influenced by the blues on the juke box in a filling station, and became a uniquely blues-tinged singer - songwriter and pianist, usually leading a piano trio. His first album *Back Country Suite* in 1957 on Prestige remains a classic; his latest, *Ever Since The World Ended*, was his first studio album in several years, released on Blue Note to high praise from critics and fans.
Donald Clarke 21 July 1988
This US pianist and singer achieved just one week on the British album chart in 1966 with the *Mose Alive* LP. (Bob Macdonald)..

**BACK COUNTRY SUITE**
Tracks: / Back country suite / New ground / Train / Warm night / Blues / Saturday / Scamper / January / Promised land / Spring song / Highway 49 / Blueberry Hill / I thought about you / In Salah / You won't let me go / One room country shack.
**Album:** Released Feb '84, on Prestige (USA) by Fantasy Inc (USA). Catalogue no: **OJC 075**

**EVER SINCE THE WORLD ENDED**
Tracks: / Ever since the world ended / Top Forty / Puttin' up with me / Josephine / I looked in the mirror / Gettin' there / Tai chi life / What's you movie / Trouble in mind / I'm alive / Tumblin' tumbleweeds.
**Album:** Released Feb '88, on Blue Note by EMI Records. Deleted Nov '88. Catalogue no: **BLJ 48015**
**CD:** Released Jul '89, on Blue Note by EMI Records. Catalogue no: **CDP 748 015 2**

**LESSONS IN LIVING**
Tracks: / Lost mind / Wild man on the loose / Your mind is on vacation / You are my sunshine / Seventh son / Everybody is cryin' mercy / Middle class white boy / I don't worry about a thing / Night club.
**Album:** Released '84, on Elektra (Musician) by Elektra Records (USA). Catalogue no: **96-0237-1**

**MOSE ALIVE**
Tracks: / Smashed / Seventh son / Fool's paradise / I love the life I live / Since I fell for you / Love for sale / Baby please don't go / That's alright / Parchman farm / Tell me somethin' / Chaser, The.
**Album:** Released Jun '66, on Atlantic by WEA Records. Catalogue no: **587-007**
**Album:** Released Jul '85, on Edsel by Demon Records. Catalogue no: **ED 153**

**MOSE ALLISON SINGS THE SEVENTH SON**
Tracks: / Seventh son / Eyesight to the blind / Do nothing till you hear from me / Lost mind / I got a right to cry baby / Baby let me hold your hand / Parchman farm / If you live / Don't get round much anymore / One room country shack / I hadn't anyone till you / Young man, A / That's alright.
**Album:** Released Mar '88, on Prestige Catalogue no: **PR 7279**
**Cass:** Released Mar '88, on Prestige Deleted Jan '90. Catalogue no: **PRC 7279**
**Album:** Released May '84, on Prestige (USA) by Fantasy Inc (USA). Catalogue no: **OJC 3003**

## Almeida, Laurindo

**ARTISTRY IN RHYTHM (Almeida, Laurindo Trio)**
Tracks: / Chariots of fire / Astronauta / Andante / Te amo / Artistry in rhythm / Always on my mind / Slaughter on Tenth

Avenue / Up where we belong / Almost a farewell / Liza / Puka shells in a whirl.
Note: This is a beautiful collection of melodies performed in the soft and serious manner that Brazilian guitarist Laurindo Almeida is known for. Artistry in rhythm is an appropriate name for this recording...Laurindo was a member of the Stan Kenton orchestra in 1947 when he just came to North America in 1953, this album is latin-laced with samba rhythms. A true listening delight.
**Album:** Released Apr '84, on Concord Jazz by Concord Jazz Records (USA). Catalogue no: **CJ 238**

**BRAZILIAN SOUL (Almeida, Laurindo & Charlie Byrd)**
**Album:** Released May '81, on Concord Jazz by Concord Jazz Records (USA). Catalogue no: **CJP 150**

**BRAZILIAN SOUND (Almeida, Laurindo & Charlie Byrd)**
**CD:** Released Jul '88, on Concord Jazz by Concord Jazz Records (USA). Catalogue no: **CCD 4150**

**LATIN ODYSSEY (Almeida, Laurindo & Charlie Byrd)**
Tracks: / Memory / Zum and ressurection / El nino / Gitanerias / Adios / El cavilan / Estrellita / Turbilhao / Intermezzo malinconico.
Note: More offerings from two of the greatest exponents of Brazillian/jazz guitar
**Cass:** Released May '83, on Concord Jazz by Concord Jazz Records (USA). Catalogue no: **CJPC 211**
**CD:** Released Jan '90, on GRP by GRP Records (USA). Catalogue no: **CCD 4211**

**MUSIC OF THE BRAZILIAN MASTERS (Almeida, Laurindo & Charlie Byrd)**
**CD:** Released Oct '89, on New Note Catalogue no: **CCD 4389**

**NEW DIRECTIONS**
Tracks: / Stuff like that / Feels so good / Just the way you are / Copacabana / Tomorrow / You needed me.
**Album:** Released Dec '80, on Crystal Clear Catalogue no: **CCS 8007**

**NEW DIRECTIONS OF VIRTUOSO**
Tracks: / Stuff like that / Feels so good / Just the way you are / What are you doing the rest of your life / Copacabana / Tomorrow / You needed me / All my love / Yesterday / Jazz-tuno at the mission / Late last night / I write the songs / Hey Jude.
**CD:** Released Nov '87, on Teldec (Germany) by ASV (Academy Sound & Vision). Catalogue no: **8.26517**

**SELECTED CLASSICAL WORKS FOR (Almeida, Laurendo / Bud Shank)**
**Album:** Released Jul '82, on Concord Jazz by Concord Jazz Records (USA). Catalogue no: **CC 2003**

**TANGO (Almeida, Laurindo & Charlie Byrd)**
Tracks: / Orchids in the moonlight / Blue tango / Jalousie / Los enamorados / La Rosita / Tanog alegre / La cumparsita / Moon was yellow, The / Hernando's hideaway / Tanguero.
**Cass:** Released Dec '85, on Concord Jazz by Concord Jazz Records (USA). Catalogue no: **CJPC 290**
**CD:** Released Jul '88, on Concord Jazz by Concord Jazz Records (USA). Catalogue no: **CCD 4290**
**Album:** Released Dec '85, on Concord Jazz by Concord Jazz Records (USA). Catalogue no: **CJP 290**

**VIRTUOSO GUITAR**
Note: Direct cut
**Album:** Released Aug '78, on Crystal Clear Catalogue no: **CCS 8001**

## Alvin, Phil

**UNSUNG STORIES**
Tracks: / Somebody stole Gabriel's horn / Next week sometime / Ballad of Smoky Joe, The / Death in the morning / Old man of the mountain, The / Daddy rollin' stone / Titanic blues / Brother can you spare a dime / Collins cave / Gangsters blues.
Note: Phil Alvin is best known for his work as lead vocalist with the Slash band *The Blasters*, who have built up a small UK following. This solo album is very jazz influenced and features *Sun Ra & The Arkestra* as well as *The Dirty Dozen Brass Band*
**Album:** Released Sep '86, on Slash by London Records Ltd. Deleted Oct '88. Catalogue no: **SLAP 12**

## Ambrose

**1929 SESSIONS (Ambrose & His Orchestra)**
**Album:** Released Dec '82, on Halcyon (USA) by Submarine Records. Catalogue no: **HAL 19**
**Cass:** Released Sep '87, on Halcyon (USA) by Submarine Records. Catalogue no: **CHAL 19**

**AMBROSE 1928-1932 (Ambrose & His Orchestra)**
**Album:** Released Jan '74, on Retrospect by EMI Records. Catalogue no: **SHB 21**

**AMBROSE AND HIS ORCHESTRA (Ambrose & His Orchestra)**
**Album:** Released '88, on GNP Crescendo (USA) by GNP Crescendo Records (USA). Catalogue no: **GNPS 9020**
**Album:** Released Mar '79, on Monmouth Evergreen Catalogue no: **MES 7032**

**AMBROSE (HARLEQUIN) 1935-37 (Ambrose & His Orchestra)**
Tracks: / Hors d'ouvres / B'wanga / Did you mean it / Night rides / Wood and ivory / Power house / Organ grinder's swing / Caravan / Embassy stomp / My red letter day / Swing patrol / Cotton picker's congregation / Bye bye baby / Champagne cocktail / Cuban Pete.
**Album:** Released Jan '88, on Harlequin by Interstate Music. Catalogue no: **HQ 3016**

**AMBROSE (LIVING ERA)**
Tracks: / Don't let that moon get away / Says my heart / Love bug will bite you, The / Two sleepy people / Rhythm's OK in Harlem / Blue skies are around the corner / Goodnight to you all / I've got a pocketful of dreams / Sailor, where art thou? / While a cigarette was burning / Lord and Lady Whoozis / Moon or no moon / Lambeth Walk / Chestnut tree, The / I may be poor but I'm honest / Oh, they're tough, mighty tough, in the west / Ten pretty girls / Organ, the monkey and me, The / In a little French casino / Fifty million robins can't be wrong / Smile when you say goodbye / Sympathy.
**Album:** Released 1 Feb '90, on Living Era by Academy Sound & Vision Records. Catalogue no: **AJA 5066**
**CD:** Released 1 Feb '90, on Living Era by Academy Sound & Vision Records. Catalogue no: **CD AJA 5066**
**Cass:** Released 1 Feb '90, on Living Era by Academy Sound & Vision Records. Catalogue no: **ZC AJA 5066**

**BODY & SOUL (Ambrose & His Orchestra)**
Tracks: / Stormy weather / There's a cabin in the pines / You've got me crying again / Punch and Judy show, The / Lazybones / I can't remember / Body and soul / Goodnight but not goodbye / Cupid / It's the talk of the town / Stay as sweet as you are / Last round-up, The / College rhythm / Willow weep for me / I couldn't be mean to you / Who's been polishing the sun.
**Cass:** Released Jan '86, on Conifer Happy Days by Conifer Records. Catalogue no: **MCHD 124**
**Album:** Released Jan '86, on Conifer Happy Days Catalogue no: **CHD 124**

**CHAMPAGNE COCKTAIL (Ambrose & His Orchestra)**
**Album:** Released '88, on GNP Crescendo (USA) by GNP Crescendo Records (USA). Catalogue no: **GNPS 9005**

**FAITHFULLY YOURS 1930-1932 (Ambrose & His Orchestra)**
Tracks: / Please / I'm just wearing out my heart for you / Have a little faith in me / If they ever had an income take on love / Till tomorrow / Livin' in the sunlight, lovin' in the moonligh / For you, just you my baby (28/7/32) / Laughing at the rain / Little girl / Just like in a story book / Loving you the way I do / Hummin' to myself / Kiss by kiss / Love, you funny thing / I'm in the market for you / What good am I without you / One little raindrop / Here lies love / Faithfully yours.
**Cass:** Released '86, on Saville by Conifer Records. Catalogue no: **CSVL 159**
**Album:** Released '86, on Saville by Conifer Records. Catalogue no: **SVL 159**

**GOLDEN AGE OF AMBROSE AND HIS ORCHESTRA, THE (Ambrose & His Orchestra)**
Tracks: / I don't know why (I just do) / Dancin in the dark / Soft lights and sweet music / When Yuba plays the rumba on

the tuba / Isn't it romantic / Pu-leeze Mr. Hemingway / Too many tears / Let's put out the lights / Leven thirsty Saturday night / Cryin' for the Carolines / Free & easy / Stardust / Blue again / Bye bye blues / Yes yes (my baby says yes) / Whistling in the dark.
Note: 16 great tracks from the man who went to become a great impresario, furthering the career of Kathy Kirby in the later years of his life. Recorded during his heyday in the late 20's and early 30's at the Ritzy nite spot in London this LP contains amongst other, "Stardust", "Dancin in the dark", "Isn't it romantic", and his theme tune "Leven thirty Saturday night". While reading the interesting sleeve note, take a listen to "Let's put out the lights" Surely a risky for 1932?
**Cass:** Released Apr '85, on Golden Age by EMI Records. Catalogue no: **GX 2525 4**
**Album:** Released Apr '85, on Golden Age by EMI Records. Catalogue no: **GX 41 2525 1**

**HAPPY DAYS, 1929-30 (Ambrose & His Orchestra)**
Tracks: / Precious little thing called love / You're the cream in my coffee / Breakaway / Makin' whoopee / Love me or leave me / For the likes of you and me / L.O.V.E / Who cares / If I had a talking picture of you / You want lovin' / Little by little / I'll be getting along / Blondy / Happy days are here again / High and low / I don't want your kisses / One I love just can't be bothered with me / I'm following you / Mona / I'm on a diet of love.
**Album:** Released Jul '82, on Saville by Conifer Records. Catalogue no: **SVL 147**
**Cass:** Released '86, on Saville by Conifer Records. Catalogue no: **CSVL 147**

**HITS OF 1931 (Ambrose & His Orchestra)**
Tracks: / Wrap your troubles in dreams / On a little balcony in Spain / I surrender dear / When your lover has gone / Out of nowhere / It must be true / Just one more chance / I'm an unemployed sweetheart / You can't stop me from lovin' you / For you / Smile darn ya smile / Nevertheless / You forgot your gloves / Love letters in the sand / Cuban love song / Longer that you linger in Virginia.
**Album:** Released Feb '84, on Retrospect by EMI Records. Deleted '86. Catalogue no: **SH 419**
**Cass:** Released Feb '84, on Retrospect by EMI Records. Catalogue no: **TC SH 419**

**I ONLY HAVE EYES FOR YOU (Ambrose & His Orchestra)**
Tracks: / It's an old southern custom / According to the moonlight / Top hat, white tie and tails / Isn't this a lovely day / How could we be wrong / Because it's love / Tick tock town / Stars fell on Alabama / I travel alone / Lost in a fog / I only have eyes for you / Dames / Winter wonderland / If I had a million dollars / If I love again / London on a rainy night / Maracas / Copenhagen.
**Cass:** Released Sep '86, on Old Bean by Submarine Records. Catalogue no: **COLD 9**
**Album:** Released Sep '86, on Old Bean by Submarine Records. Catalogue no: **OLD 9**

**LOVE IS THE SWEETEST THING (Ambrose & His Orchestra)**
**Album:** Released '88, on Joy by President Records. Catalogue no: **JOYD 280**

**MAKIN' WHOOPEE (Ambrose & His Orchestra)**
**Cass:** Released '88, on Saville by Conifer Records. Catalogue no: **CSVLD 007**
**2 LP Set:** Released Sep '87, on Saville by Conifer Records. Catalogue no: **SVLD 007**

**MIDNIGHT IN MAYFAIR (Ambrose & His Orchestra)**
**Album:** Released Mar '90, on Saville by Conifer Records. Catalogue no: **SVL 207**
**CD:** Released Mar '90, on Saville by Conifer Records. Catalogue no: **CDSVL 207**
**Cass:** Released Mar '90, on Saville by Conifer Records. Catalogue no: **CSVL 207**

**RECOLLECTIONS (Ambrose & His Orchestra)**
Tracks: / If I didn't care / What do we care / I'm in love for the last time / Let there be love / You made me care / No mama no / Two sleepy people / Continental, The / I threw a kiss in the ocean / My own / I have eyes / Sympathy / How about you / Cinderella / Sweetheart / I got love / That lovely weekend / Scatterbrain / Apple for teacher, An.
Note: Featuring Vera Lynn
**Album:** Released Jun '81, on Decca by Decca International. Deleted '88. Catalogue no: **RFL 10**

**'S WONDERFUL (Ambrose & His Orchestra)**
Tracks: / 'S wonderful / Roll away, clouds / Louise / Old Italian love song / I'll see you again / If love were all / Singin' in the rain / Too wonderful for words / Ain't misbehavin' / Am I blue / Love is a dreamer / Thought never entered my head, The / She's such a comfort to me / How am I to know / My sweeter than sweet / Piccolo Pete / Just you - just me / My love parade / Little kiss each morning a little kiss each night / Lucky me, lovable me.
**Cass:** Released Jan '87, on Saville by Conifer Records. Catalogue no: **CSVL 181**
**Album:** Released Jan '87, on Saville by Conifer Records. Catalogue no: **SVL 181**

**SOFT LIGHT AND SWEET MUSIC (Ambrose & His Orchestra)**
Tracks: / I'll guess I'll have to change my plan / Moon / You brought a new kind of love to me / After tonight we say goodbye / You forgot your gloves / When mother played her organ / I don't want to go to bed / Let's all sing like the birdies sing / Lullaby of the leaves / I'm an unemployed sweetheart / I'm gonna get you / You rascal you / Trees / All of me / Aboard the lugger.
**Album:** Released Apr '83, on Joy by President Records. Catalogue no: **JOYD 271**

**SUN HAS GOT HIS HAT ON, THE (Ambrose & His Orchestra)**
Tracks: / I can't believe it's true / After tonight we say goodbye / Sun has got his hat on, The / Day by day / At eventide / Clouds will soon roll by, The / Streamline strut / Dames / Big Ben is saying goodnight / Memphis blues / I only have eyes for you / Who's been polishing the Sun / La cucaracha / Home James and don't spare the horses / Yip Neddy / I'm gonna wash my hands of you / Stay as sweet as you are / No, no, a thousand times no.
**CD:** Released Sep '88, on Burlington (nostalgia) by Counterpoint Distribution. Catalogue no: **2 BUR 002**
**Album:** Released Jun '88, on Burlington (nostalgia) by Counterpoint Distribution. Catalogue no: **BUR 002**
**Cass:** Released Jul '88, on Burlington (nostalgia) by Counterpoint Distribution. Catalogue no: **4BUR 002**

**SWING IS IN THE AIR (Ambrose & His Orchestra)**
Tracks: / Jeepers creepers / Too marvellous for words / Woe is me / They can't take that away from me / No mama no / Careless / Lost my rhythm, lost my music, lost my man / Arm in arm / I'm all in / Swing is in the air / Let's call the whole thing off / Hurry home / I promise / Life begins when you're in love / Three little fishes / Lord & lady whoozles / Beer barrel polka / When day is done.
**Album:** Released '84, on Recollections (Decca) by Decca Records. Catalogue no: **RFL 35**

**TRIBUTE TO COLE PORTER (Ambrose & His Orchestra)**
Tracks: / Night and day / I get a kick out of you / I've got my eyes on you / Thank you so much, Mrs Lowsborough / Begin the beguine / After you / Anything goes / I've got you on my mind / Easy to love / I've got you under my skin / Just one of those things / My heart belongs to daddy / You're the top / You'd be so nice to come home to.
**Album:** Released Mar '83, on Jasmine by Hasmick Promotions. Deleted Jun '87. Catalogue no: **JASM 2017**

## American Folk Blues..

**AMERICAN FOLK BLUES FESTIVAL (Various artists)**
Note: Includes: Louisiana Red, Willie Mabon, Eddie Taylor.
**2 LP Set:** Released Oct '88, on L&R Catalogue no: **LR 42.013**
**2 LP Set:** Released Jun '84, on Musidisc by Musidisc Records (France). Catalogue no: **ALB 125**

**AMERICAN FOLK BLUES FESTIVAL (Various artists) 1962**
**Album:** Released Oct '88, on L&R Catalogue no: **LR 42.017**

**AMERICAN FOLK BLUES FESTIVAL 1963 (Various artists)**
Note: Featuring: Muddy Waters, Sonny Boy Williamson, Willie Dixon etc.
**Album:** Released Oct '88, on L&R Catalogue no: **LR 42.023**

**AMERICAN FOLK BLUES FESTIVAL (Various artists) 1964**
**Album:** Released Oct '88, on L&R Catalogue no: **LR 42.025**

**AMERICAN FOLK BLUES FESTIVAL (Various artists) 1966, VOL.1**
**Album:** Released Oct '87, on Amiga Catalogue no: **855 114**

**AMERICAN FOLK BLUES FESTIVAL (Various artists) 1966, VOL.2**
**Album:** Released Jul '87, on Amiga Catalogue no: **855 126**

**AMERICAN FOLK BLUES FESTIVAL (Various artists) 1970**
**2 LP Set:** Released Oct '88, on L&R Catalogue no: **LR 42.021**

**AMERICAN FOLK BLUES FESTIVAL (Various artists) 1972**
**2 LP Set:** Released Oct '88, on L&R Catalogue no: **LR 42.018**

**AMERICAN FOLK BLUES FESTIVAL (Various artists) 1981**
**Album:** Released Oct '88, on L&R Catalogue no: **LR 42.022**

**AMERICAN FOLK BLUES FESTIVAL (Various artists) 1982**
**2 LP Set:** Released Oct '88, on L&R Catalogue no: **LR 42.053**
**2 LP Set:** Released Oct '88, on L&R Catalogue no: **LR 42.052**

**AMERICAN FOLK BLUES FESTIVAL (Various artists) 1983**
**Album:** Released Oct '88, on L&R Catalogue no: **LR 50.001**
**Album:** Released Oct '88, on L&R Catalogue no: **LR 50.002**
**2 LP Set:** Released Oct '88, on L&R Catalogue no: **LR 42.063**

**AMERICAN FOLK BLUES FESTIVAL (Various artists) 1985**
**Album:** Released Oct '88, on L&R Catalogue no: **LR 42.065**
**Album:** Released Oct '88, on L&R Catalogue no: **LR 50.003**

## American Jazz

**AMERICAN JAZZ SERIES 11 (Various artists)**
Note: Includes: New Orleans Rhythm Kings etc.
**Cass:** Released Jul '86, on Emporium Cassettes Catalogue no: **043**

**AMERICAN JAZZ SERIES 12 (Various artists)**
Note: Includes: McKinneys Cotton Pickers etc.
**Cass:** Released Jul '86, on Emporium Cassettes Catalogue no: **048**

**AMERICAN JAZZ SERIES 13 (Various artists)**
Note: Includes: The Arcadian Seranaders/Fess Williams
**Cass:** Released Jul '86, on Emporium Cassettes Catalogue no: **050**

## American Jazz Festival

**AMERICAN JAZZ FESTIVAL IN LATIN (Various artists)**
Note: Performances recorded during July '61 at a jazz festival in Rio De Janeiro, Brazil. Featured artists include Chris Connor (vocals), Coleman Hawkins (tenor sax), Roy Eldridge (trumpet), Tommy Flanagan (piano) and Jo Jones (drums).
**CD:** Released May '89, on West Wind Catalogue no: **WWCD 2025**

## Americans In Europe

**AMERICANS IN EUROPE VOL.1 (Various artists)**
Tracks: / No smokin': *Kenny Clarke Trio* / Low life: *Idries Sulieman Quartet* / I can't get started: *Various artists* / Freeway: *Smith, Bill Quintet* / Pyramid: *Powell, Bud Trio* / Round midnight: *Various artists.*
**Album:** Released Mar '83, on Jasmine by Hasmick Promotions. Deleted Feb '88. Catalogue no: **JAS 64**

**AMERICANS IN EUROPE VOL.2 (Various artists)**
Tracks: / My buddy run rabbits: *Various artists* / My daughter how are you: *Various artists* / Rose room: *Various artists* / Wine, whiskey and gin head woman: *Various artists* / Lots of talk for you: *Various artists* / All things you are: *Various artists* / I remember Clifford: *Various artists.*
**Album:** Released Mar '83, on Jasmine by Hasmick Promotions. Deleted Feb '88. Catalogue no: **JAS 65**
**Album:** Released '88, on Tax Catalogue no: **TAX 8035**

## Ammons, Albert

**ALBERT AMMONS VOL 1 (King of the blues and boogie woogie)**
**Album:** Released '88, on Oldie Blues Catalogue no: **OL 2807**

**ALBERT AMMONS VOL 2 (King of the blues and boogie woogie)**
**Album:** Released '88, on Oldie Blues Catalogue no: **OL 2822**

**BOOGIE WOOGIE AND THE BLUES (Ammons, Albert & His Rhythm Kings)**
Tracks: / Bugle boogie (A-4717-1 Alternate choice - previously unissued) / Revelle boogie (A-4717-2 Alternate choice - previously unissued) / Blues in the groove (A-4718-2 Alternate choice - previously unissued) / Breaks, The (A-4719-2 Alternative choice - previously unissued) / Jammin the boogie (A-4720-1) / Bottom blues (A-4721-1) / Albert's special boogie (A-4714-1) / Boogie rocks, The (A-4715-2) / Blues on my mind (A-4716-2 Previously unissued).
**CD:** Released May '87, on Commodore Class Catalogue no: **824 297**
**Album:** Released Nov '86, on Teldec (Germany) by ASV (Academy Sound & Vision). Catalogue no: **6 24297**

**BOOGIE WOOGIE CLASSICS (Ammons, Albert & Pete Johnson)**
**Album:** Released Sep '84, on Blue Note by EMI Records. Catalogue no: **BLP 1209**

**BOOGIE WOOGIE WOOGIE PIANO**
Tracks: / Swanee River boogie / Boogie woogie at the Civic Opera / S.P.Blues / Sheik of Araby, The / St. Louis Blues / You are my sunshine / Shufflin' the boogie / Twelfth St. boogie.
Note: Artists include: Marvin Randolph/Gene Ammons/Ike Perkins/Israel Crosby/Al Burroughs/Jack Cooley. Recorded between 1947-1949
**Album:** Released Dec '83, on Mercury Jazz Masters Catalogue no: **6336 326**

**GIANTS OF BOOGIE WOOGIE (Ammons, Albert / Pete Johnson / Meade Lux Lewis)**
Tracks: / St. Louis blues / Mecca flat blues / Bass goin' crazy / Closing hour blues / Messin' around / Deep fives / Blues de luxe / Let 'em jump / Pete's blues / B & O blues.
**Album:** Released Apr '81, on Joker (USA) by Lifetime Records (USA). Catalogue no: **SM 3094**

**KING OF BOOGIE WOOGIE**
**Album:** Released '88, on Blues Classics(USA) by Arhoolie Records (USA). Catalogue no: **BC 27**

**WITH RHYTHM KINGS & PIANO SOLOS (Ammons, Albert & His Rhythm Kings)**
Tracks: / Blues in the groove / Breaks, The / Jammin' the boogie / Bottom blues / Albert's special boogie / Boogie rocks, The / Blues on my mind / Bugle boogie / Reveille boogie.
**Album:** Released Aug '82, on Commodore Class Catalogue no: **AG6 24297**

## Ammons, Gene

**ALL STARS SESSIONS (Ammons, Gene All Stars)**
**Album:** Released Jun '86, on Original Jazz Classics (USA) by Fantasy Inc (USA). Catalogue no: **OJC 014**

**BOSS TENOR**
Tracks: / Hittin' the jug / Close your eyes / My romance / Canadian Sunset / Blue Ammons / Confirmation / Savoy.
**Album:** Released May '88, on Prestige Catalogue no: **PR 7180**
**Cass:** Released May '88, on Prestige Catalogue no: **PRC 7180**

**EARLY VISIONS**
Tracks: / Swinging for Xmas / Talk of the town / Battle, The / Jam for boppers / Do you really mean it? / Bless you / Stuffy / Once in a while / Pennies from Heaven / Cha bootie / More moon / Last mile, The / Goodbye / Ten or eleven / It's you or no one / My foolish heart / Jug head ramble / You go to my head / Baby won't you please say yes / Don't do me wrong / Prelude to a kiss / Can anyone explain / You're not the kind / Happiness is just a thing called Joe.
**2 LP Set:** Released '88, on Chess by Vogue Records. Catalogue no: **GCH 2-6031**
**Cass:** Released Oct '84, on Chess Jazz

by Vogue Records. Catalogue no: **ZCCJD 6701**

**2 LP Set:** Released Oct '84, on Chess Jazz by Vogue Records. Catalogue no: **CXJD 6701**

### GENE AMMONS

**Album:** Released Jul '82, on Jazz Reactivation Catalogue no: **JR 150**

### GENE AMMONS STORY - ORGAN COMBOS

Tracks: / Twisting the jug / Born to be blue / Satin doll / Moten swing / Stormy Monday blues / Down the line / Velvet soul / In Sid's thing / Blue room / Water jug / Angel eyes / Gettin' around.

**2 LP Set:** Released '79, on Prestige Deleted '84. Catalogue no: **PR 24071**

### HAPPY BLUES, THE (Ammons, Gene All Stars)

**Album:** Released '88, on QJC Catalogue no: **QJC 7039**

**Album:** Released Jun '86, on Original Jazz Classics (USA) by Fantasy Inc (USA). Catalogue no: **OJC 013**

### IN SWEDEN

**Album:** Released Feb '82, on Enja (Germany) by Enja Records (West Germany). Catalogue no: **ENJA 3093**

### JAMMIN' WITH GENE (Ammons, Gene All Stars)

**Album:** Released Apr '86, on Original Jazz Classics (USA) by Fantasy Inc (USA). Catalogue no: **OJC 211**

### JUG & SONNY (Ammons, Gene & Sonny Stitt)

Tracks: / You're not that kind of girl / I cover the waterfront / Full moon / Jam from boppers / Don't do me wrong / Don't worry about me / Baby won't you please say yes / Cha bootie / Tenor eleven / Last mile, The.

**Album:** Released Aug '88, on Chess by Vogue Records. Catalogue no: **GCH 8091**

**Cass:** Released Aug '88, on Chess by Vogue Records. Catalogue no: **GCHK 78091**

### JUGANTHOLOGY

**2 LP Set:** Released May '74, on Prestige Catalogue no: **PR 24036**

### JUGGIN' AROUND (Ammons, Gene and Benny Green)

Tracks: / Juggin' around / Sermonette / Swinging for Benny / Little ditty / Going south / Jim dog.

**Album:** Released Dec '86, on Atlantis by Charly Records. Deleted '88. Catalogue no: **ATS 1**

**Cass:** Released Dec '86, on Atlantis by Charly Records. Catalogue no: **KATS 1**

### PUNKY

Tracks: / Pint size / Punky / Stella by starlight / King size.

**Album:** Released Jan '87, on Original Jazz Classics (USA) by Fantasy Inc (USA). Catalogue no: **OJC 244**

### UP TIGHT

Tracks: / Breeze and I, The / Moonglow / Five o'clock whistle / Lester leaps in / I sold my heart to the junkman / Uptight / Jug's blue blues.

**Album:** Released Nov '88, on Prestige Deleted Jan '90. Catalogue no: **PR 7208**

## Amstell, Billy

### JEWISH PARTY, DANCES & STORIES (Various artists)

**Album:** Released May '81, on Zodiac by Delta Records. Catalogue no: **ZR 1015**

### SESSION AFTER MIDNIGHT (Amstell, Billy, Dixielanders)

Tracks: / Blues in B flat / British grenadiers / Tishomingo blues / Paradise / Free'n'easy / Don't fuss / Washington and Lee sing / Tootin' around / My old Kentucky home / Sue, Sue / My bonnie lies over the ocean / Royal garden blues.

**Album:** Released May '81, on Zodiac by Delta Records. Catalogue no: **ZR 1010**

## Amy, Curtis

**Biographical details:** AMY, Curtis was born in 1929 in Texas. He recorded on tenor sax in a backing group in Houston, went to college in Kentucky, moved to Los Angeles in 1955 and was one of the excellent black musicians who should have been more successful commercially, but the media had decided that 'West Coast jazz' was a genre and that it was white. He also played flute and (later) soprano sax; of his several albums in the '60s *Katanga* is a fine example of West Coast post-bop jazz, also noteworthy for the presence of the excellent and mysterious trumpeter Dupree Bolton, who only every played on two albums (the other by Elmo Hope). Amy also sessioned on pop records: the Doors, Carole King etc. Donald Clarke 21 July 1988.

### CURTIS AMY & PAUL HORN (VIDEO) (Amy, Curtis & Paul Horn)

**VHS:** Released '88, on Kay Jazz (video) by Kay Jazz. Catalogue no: **KJ 038**

### KATANGA (Amy, Curtis & Dupree Bolton)

**Album:** Released Nov '84, on Affinity by Charly Records. Catalogue no: **AFF 128**

## Andersen, Arild

### BANDE A PARTE (Andersen, Arild Quintet)

Tracks: / 3 for 5 / Natt / Sort of / Vanilje / Bali / Tutte / No soap / Nyl.

Note: During his long association with EMC Norwegian bass player Arild Anderson has introduced a number of new young musicians from his country to an international audience.His new quintet Masquelero live up to this reputation, presenting one of the freshest, most exciting sounds in modern jazz. This music is for the head, heart and feet.Personnel: Nils Petter Molvaer-trumpet/Tore Brunborg-tenor & sop. sax/Jon Balke-acoustic & electric keyboards/Arild Anderson - acoustic & electric bass/Jon Christensen-drums,percussion

**Album:** Released Apr '86, on ECM Catalogue no: **ECM 1319**

**CD:** Released Apr '86, on ECM Catalogue no: **8290222**

### LIFELINES

**Album:** Released May '81, on ECM Catalogue no: **ECM 1188**

### MOLDE CONCERT, A

**Album:** Released Oct '82, on ECM Catalogue no: **ECM 1236**

## Anderson, Cat

### CAT ANDERSON & LES FOUR BONES

**Album:** Released Nov '79, on Barclay (France) by Decca Records. Catalogue no: **80715**

### PARIS - 1958 AND 1964 (Anderson, Cat & The Duke Ellington All Stars)

**Album:** Released Oct '86, on Ace by Ace Records. Catalogue no: **SW 8412**

## Anderson, Ernestine

### BE MINE TONIGHT

Tracks: / Sunday in New York / In a mellow tone / I'm comin' home again / Christopher Columbus / London by night / Little bird / Be mine (tonight) / Lend me your life / Sack full of dreams.

Note: Personnel: Ernestine Anderson - vocals / Ray Brown - bass / Benny Carter - alto sax / Ron Eschete - guitar / Marshall Otwell - piano / Jimmie Smith - drums.

**CD:** Released Jul '87, on Concord Jazz by Concord Jazz Records (USA). Catalogue no: **CCD 4319**

**Album:** Released Jul '87, on Concord Jazz by Concord Jazz Records (USA). Catalogue no: **CJ 319**

**Cass:** Released Jul '87, on Concord Jazz by Concord Jazz Records (USA). Catalogue no: **CJC 319**

### BIG CITY

Tracks: / All I need is you / 59th Street Bridge song / Spring is here / I'll never pass this way again / Big city / All blues / Welcome to the club / I didn't know what time it was.

Note: Ernestine Anderson -Vocals/Hank Jones -piano/Monty Budwig -Bass/Jeff Hamilton- Drums

**CD:** Released '89, on Concord Jazz by Concord Jazz Records (USA). Catalogue no: **CCD 4214**

**Cass:** Released May '83, on Concord Jazz by Concord Jazz Records (USA). Catalogue no: **CJC 214**

**Album:** Released May '83, on Concord Jazz by Concord Jazz Records (USA). Catalogue no: **CJ 214**

### HELLO LIKE BEFORE

Tracks: / Hello like before / Yes sir, that's my baby / Tain't nobody's bizness if I do / Send in the clowns / Bird of beauty / Time for love, A / Soft shoe / It don't mean a thing / I am his lady.

Note: Personnel: Ernestine Anderson, Hank Jones, Ray Brown, J. Smith.

**CD:** Released Jun '89, on Concord Jazz by Concord Jazz Records (USA). Catalogue no: **CCD 4031**

### MISS ERNESTINE ANDERSON

Tracks: / Let's get away from it all / End

of a love affair, The / So nice / Funny how time slips away / Talk to me baby / Tears have to fall / Big spender / What did I have that I don't have / On a clear day / I fall in love too easily / Feeling good / Make it another old fashioned please.
Note: Johnnie Scott & His Orchestra/Bill Oliver &His Orchestra. A good selection of classics on this, Ernestine Anderson's only British recorded album. This fine singer works her way through favourites such as 'Let's get away from it all','Big spender' and 'On a clear day you can see forever' in a style comparable to Sarah Vaughn. A good collectors album.
**Cass:** Released Jan '86, on Capitol by EMI Records. Deleted Jul '87. Catalogue no: **TCEMS 1141**
**Album:** Released Jan '86, on Capitol by EMI Records. Deleted Jan '88. Catalogue no: **EMS 1141**

### NEVER MAKE YOUR MOVE TOO SOON
**Album:** Released May '81, on Concord Jazz by Concord Jazz Records (USA). Catalogue no: **CJ 147**

### WHEN THE SUN GOES DOWN
Tracks: / Someone else is steppin' in / In the evening when the sun goes down / I love being here with you / Down home blues / I'm just a lucky so and so / Alone on my own / Mercy, mercy, mercy / Goin to Chicago blues.
Note: American singer Ernestine Anderson had to go to Sweden to gain sucess and recognition .Having formerly worked with Johnny Otis and Lionel Hampton, it wasn't until her album 'Hot Chicago' recorded in Sweden with the Harry Arnold Band wasreleased that she gained acceptance in her own country. She won the 'New Star' award in Down Beat's critics poll in 1959. This album, her seventh for concord, features blues and blues related songs, and includes pieces from Count Basie, Peggy Lee ,and Duke Ellington. Personnel: Ernestine Anderson -Vocals/Ray Brown - Bass/Gene Harris - Piano/Red Holloway - Tenor Saxophone/Gerryck King - Drums.
**Cass:** Released Apr '85, on Concord Jazz by Concord Jazz Records (USA). Catalogue no: **CJC 263**
**Album:** Released Apr '85, on Concord Jazz by Concord Jazz Records (USA). Catalogue no: **CJ 263**
**CD:** Released '88, on Concord Jazz by Concord Jazz Records (USA). Catalogue no: **CCD 4263**

## Anderson, Lew

### ALL AMERICAN BIG BAND
**Album:** Released Nov '88, on Sea Breeze Catalogue no: **SB 2032**

## Andrews, Inez

### IF JESUS CAME TO YOUR TOWN TODAY
Tracks: / Holding on with a smile / People get ready / If jesus came to town / Joy / No place but up / Praise the Lord / We've got work to do / Mind made up.
**Album:** Released Jun '88, on Ichiban by Ichiban Records (UK). Catalogue no: **MIR 5004**
**Cass:** Released Jun '88, on Ichiban by Ichiban Records (UK). Catalogue no: **ZCMIR 5004**

## Andrews Sisters

**Biographical details:** The close-harmony vocal trio from Minneapolis, Minnesota was one of the biggest acts of the 1940s, now rivalling Glenn Miller and Vera Lynn for period nostalgia; LaVerne, Maxene and Patti were born 1915-20; LaVerne was a contralto (died 1967), Maxene sang harmony, Patti lead. They had 90 hits on USA Decca (now MCA) 1938-51, taking up where the Boswell Sisters left off and inspiring '50s groups like the McGuire Sisters; they sold 60 million records, No. 1 hits including *'Bei Mir Bist Du Schon'* (1938), *'Rum And Coca-Cola'* (1945), *'I can dream, can't I?'* (1949); 23 hits with Bing Crosby (*'Pistol Packin' Mama'*, *'Don't Fence Me in'*); they also recorded with Guy Lombardo, Ernest Tubb, Carmen Miranda, etc. and appeared in many films. Bette Midler's top ten hit *'Boogie Woogie Bugle Boy'* in 1973 was a cover of their 1943 one. Patti and Maxene appeared in Broadway show *Over Here* in the mid-'70s; Maxene had a heart attack in 1982 after 11 concerts in Chicago, followed by heart bypass operation; made her first solo album in 1985: *Maxene* on the Bainbridge label had a sleeve note by Midler. (Donald Clarke, 21 July 1988)..

### 16 GOLDEN CLASSICS
Tracks: / I'll be with you in apple blossom time / Woody woodpecker / Near you / Shoo shoo baby / Underneath the arches / Ferryboat serenade / Toolie oolie doolie / East of the sun / In the mood / I wanna be loved / Civilisation / Rumours are flying / Strip polka / You call everybody darling / She wore a yellow ribbon / Don't be that way / Sing, sing, sing / If I had a boy like you / Piccolo Pete / Don't sit under the apple tree.
**Cass:** Released Nov '87, on Unforgettable by Castle Communications Records. Catalogue no: **UNMC 025**
**CD:** Released Nov '87, on Unforgettable by Castle Communications Records. Catalogue no: **UNCD 025**
**Album:** Released Nov '87, on Unforgettable by Castle Communications Records. Catalogue no: **UNLP 025**

### 16 ORIGINAL HITS
**Cass:** Released 7 Nov '87, on Timeless Treasures Catalogue no: **MC 1634**

### 20 GREATEST HITS: ANDREWS SISTERS
**Cass:** Released Dec '85, on Nostalgia (USA) by Sonic Arts Corporation (USA). Catalogue no: **42006**
**CD:** Released Sep '87, on Scana Catalogue no: **77019**
**Album:** Released Dec '85, on Nostalgia by Mainline Records. Catalogue no: **N 22006**

### ANDREWS SISTERS
Tracks: / Begin the beguine / I'll be with you in apple blossom time / Roll out the barrel / Don't sit under the apple tree / Don't bring Lulu.
**Cass:** Released '86, on MFP (Holland) by EMI Records. Catalogue no: **1A 222-58097**
**Album:** Released '83, on EMI (Holland) by EMI Records. Catalogue no: **1A 022 58097**
**Album:** Released Apr '85, on Magic (1) by Submarine Records. Catalogue no: **AWE 4**

### AT THE MICROPHONE
**Album:** Released Jun '87, on Take 2 Catalogue no: **TT 305**

### BEAT ME DADDY EIGHT TO THE BAR
Tracks: / Beat me daddy, eight to the bar / Boogie woogie bugle boy / I'll be with you in apple blossom time / Beer barrel polka / I can dream, can't I / Pennsylvania polka / Hold tight (want some sea food mama) / Oh Johnny, oh Johnny oh / Rum and coca cola / Down in the valley / Bei mir bist du schon / Shrine of St Cecilia / Rhumboogie / Joseph! Joseph! / South American way / Strip polka.
**Cass:** Released May '82, on MFP by EMI Records. Deleted '87. Catalogue no: **TCMFP 50556**
**Album:** Released May '82, on MFP by EMI Records. Deleted '87. Catalogue no: **MFP 50556**

### BEI MIR BIST DU SCHON
**LP Pic:** Released Oct '87, on Exclusive Picture Discs Catalogue no: **AR 30054**

### BEST OF THE ANDREWS SISTERS, THE
Tracks: / Joseph, Joseph / South American way / Oh Johnny, oh Johnny oh / Rum and coca cola / Strip polka / Sonny boy / Beat me daddy eight to the bar / Well all right / Pennsylvania polka / Beer barrel polka / Bei mir bist du schon / Tico tico / Oh ma ma / Don't sit under the apple tree / Hold tight / Ti-pi-tin / Boogie woogie bugle boy / I can dream, can't I / I'll be with you in Apple Blossom time / Rhumboogie / Say si si / Yes, my darling daughter / I wanna be loved / There will never be another you.
**2 LP Set:** Released Oct '81, on Coral by MCA Records. Catalogue no: **MCLD 604**

### BOOGIE WITH THE ANDREWS SISTERS
Tracks: / Boogie with the Andrews Sisters / In the mood.
**7" Single:** Released Aug '83, on MCA by MCA Records. Deleted '86. Catalogue no: **MCA 289**

### BOOGIE WOOGIE BUGLE BOY
Tracks: / Boogie woogie bugle boy.
**7" Single:** Released Jul '82, on Revival Catalogue no: **REV 6018**

### BOOGIE WOOGIE BUGLE BOY (OLD
Tracks: / Boogie woogie bugle boy / Bounce me brother with a solid four.
**7" Single:** Released Nov '83, on Old Gold by Old Gold Records. Catalogue no: **OG 9388**

### CHRISTMAS WITH THE AN-

### DREWS SISTERS
**Album:** Released Dec '88, on Hallmark by Pickwick Records. Catalogue no: **SHM 3253**
**Cass:** Released Dec '88, on Hallmark by Pickwick Records. Catalogue no: **HSC 3253**
**CD:** Released Dec '88, on Hallmark by Pickwick Records. Catalogue no: **PWK 082**

### EARLY YEARS, 1937-42
Tracks: / Just a simple melody / Why talk about love / I married an angel / Love is where you find it / When a prince of a fella meets a cinderella / Chico's love song / Let's have another one / I want my mama / Oh he loves me / I wish I had a dime / Music makers / Sleepy serenade / Why don't we do this more often / Honey / What to do / Zoot suit, A.
**Cass:** Released '88, on Official by Official Records. Catalogue no: **OFF 412005**
**Album:** Released '88, on Official by Official Records. Catalogue no: **OFF 12005**

### EARLY YEARS, VOL.2
Tracks: / Where have we met before? / It's easier said than done / From the land of the sky blue water / Oh, faithless maid / Lullaby to a little jitterbug / Goodbye, goodbye / You don't know how much you can suffer / Rock, rock, rock-a-bye baby / Cock-eyed mayor of Kaunakakai, The / Let's pack our things and trek / Hit the road / Sweet Molly Malone / Mean to me / Jack of all trades / Nickel serenade, The / He said, she said.
**Album:** Released '89, on Official by Official Records. Catalogue no: **OFF 12011**

### GOLDEN GREATS: ANDREWS SISTERS
Tracks: / Boogie woogie bugle boy / Bei mir bist du schon / Don't sit under the apple tree / Rum and coca cola / Beat me daddy eight to the bar / Booglie wooglie piggy, The / Rhumboogie / House of blue lights / Say si si / Oh Johnny, oh Johnny oh / Beer barrel polka / South American way / Shoo shoo baby / Strip polka / I'll be with you in apple blossom time / Blossom time / Hold tight (want some sea food mama).
**Album:** Released Jul '85, on MCA by MCA Records. Catalogue no: **MCM 5015**
**Cass:** Released Jul '85, on MCA by MCA Records. Catalogue no: **1CMC 5015**

### GREATEST HITS: ANDREWS SISTERS
**Album:** Released May '88, on Scana Catalogue no: **27019**
**Cass:** Released May '88, on Scana Catalogue no: **47019**

### GREATEST HITS: ANDREWS SISTERS (IMPORT)
Tracks: / Beer barrel polka / I can dream, can't I / When the midnight choo choo leaves for Alabama.
**Cass:** Released Sep '88, on Fun (Holland) Catalogue no: **FUNC 9004**
**Album:** Released Sep '88, on Fun (Holland) Catalogue no: **FUN 9004**

### HOLD TIGHT IT'S THE
**Cass:** Released Oct '87, on Dance Band Days by Prism Leisure. Catalogue no: **DBDC 12**
**CD:** Released Dec '88, on Dance Band Days by Prism Leisure. Catalogue no: **DBCD 12**
**Album:** Released Oct '87, on Dance Band Days by Prism Leisure. Catalogue no: **DBD 12**

### JUMPIN' JIVE
Tracks: / Jumpin' jive (jim, jam' jump), The / Tu-li-tulip time / Ooooo-boom / Tuxedo Junction / Johnny Peddler / Daddy / Coffee song, The / Straighten up and fly right / Three little sisters / I'll pray for you / Pennsylvania 6-5000 / Rainy night in Rio, A / Mister five by five / Money is the root of all evil / Rancho pillow / Massachusetts.
**Album:** Released Sep '86, on MCA by MCA Records. Catalogue no: **MCL 1789**
**Cass:** Released Sep '86, on MCA by MCA Records. Catalogue no: **MCLC 1789**

### RARITIES
**CD:** Released Jun '88, on MCA (USA) by MCA Records (USA). Catalogue no: **31036**

### SAYS MY HEART
Tracks: / Says my heart / Why talk about love? / Love is where you find it / It's easier said than done / Ooo Oo-oh boom / Oh faithless maid / Lullaby to a little jitterbug / Joseph Joseph / Tu-li-tulip time / Shortenin' bread / Bei mir bist du schhon / Just a simple melody / Billy boy / Where have we met before / Ti-pi-tin / From the land of sky-blu water / Sha sha / Oh mama / Hold tight (want some seafood, Mama) / Goodbye, goodbye.
**Cass:** Released Jun '88, on Conifer Happy Days by Conifer Records. Catalogue no: **MCHD 161**
**Album:** Released Jun '88, on Conifer Happy Days by Conifer Records. Catalogue no: **CHD 161**

### SING... AND WIN
Tracks: / Any bonds today? / You're a lucky fellow, Mr. Smith / Yi, yi, yi, yi / At Sonya's cafe / Helena / Boolie boolie boon / Hummingbird, The / East of the rockies / Here comes the navy / I've got a guy in Kalamazoo / When Johnny comes marching home / There'll be a jubilee / Great day / Smile, smile, smile / Welcome song, The / Put that ring on my finger.
**Album:** Released '89, on Official by Official Records. Catalogue no: **OFF 12008**
**Cass:** Released '89, on Official by Official Records. Catalogue no: **OFF 412008**

### SING, SING, SING
Tracks: / Beat me daddy eight to the bar / I'll be with you in apple blossom time / Oh Johnny, oh Johnny oh / Bei mir bist du schon / Sing, sing, sing / Pennsylvania 6-5000 / Joseph Joseph / In the mood / Boogie woogie bugle boy / Don't sit under the apple tree / Hold tight (want some sea food mama) / I can dream, can't I / I got a gal in Kalamazoo / Coffee song, The / Lullaby of Broadway / Elmers tune / Alexander's ragtime band (CD only.) / Don't be that way (CD only.) / Yes my darling daughter (CD only.) / Say si si (CD only.).
**CD:** Released Mar '89, on MFP by EMI Records. Catalogue no: **CDMFP 6044**
**Album:** Released Oct '88, on MFP by EMI Records. Catalogue no: **MFP 5841**
**Cass:** Released Oct '88, on MFP by EMI Records. Catalogue no: **TCMFP 5841**
**CD:** Released Mar '89, on MFP by EMI Records. Catalogue no: **CDB 791 536 2**

### SING THE DANCING 20'S
Tracks: / Last night on the back porch / When Francis dances with me / Back in your own back yard / Keep your skirts down / Mary Ann / Japanese Sandman / Show me the way to go home / Don't bring Lulu / Me too / That naughty waltz / Smile will go a long long way, A / Barney Google / Collegiate.
Note: Mono. Nostalgia existed even in the 50's. On this light-hearted album, the Andrews Sisters revive the carefree days of he 20's with tunes such as 'Don't Bring Lulu','Keep your skirts down, Mary Ann','When Francis Dances with me' and many more, all with orchestrarion by Billy May.
**Album:** Released May '85, on Capitol by EMI Records. Deleted Jan '90. Catalogue no: **ED 2604171**
**Cass:** Released Apr '85, on Capitol by EMI Records. Deleted Jun '89. Catalogue no: **ED 2604174**

### VERY BEST: ANDREWS SISTERS
**Album:** Released Jun '88, on Pickwick by Pickwick Records. Catalogue no: **SHM 3234**
**Cass:** Released Jun '88, on Pickwick by Pickwick Records. Catalogue no: **HSC 3234**

### VERY BEST OF THE ANDREW SISTERS
Tracks: / Booglie wooglie piggy, The / Beat me daddy eight to the bar / Rhumboogie / House of blue lights / Say si si / Oh Johnny, oh Johnny oh / Boogie woogie bugle boy / Don't sit under the apple tree / Rum and coca cola / Beer barrel polka / South American way / Bei mir bist du schon / Shoo shoo baby / Strip polka / I'll be with you in apple blossom time / Hold tight.
**CD:** on Pickwick by Pickwick Records. Catalogue no: **PWK 064**
**Album:** Released Dec '81, on MCA by MCA Records. Catalogue no: **MCL 1635**
**Cass:** Released '81, on MCA by MCA Records. Catalogue no: **MCLC 1635**

## Angelic Gospel Singers

### 40 YEARS
**Album:** Released '88, on Malaco Gospel by Malaco Records (UK). Catalogue no: **MAL 043 98**

### I'VE GOT VICTORY

**Album:** Released '88, on Malaco Gospel by Malaco Records (UK). Catalogue no: **MAL 04407**

### OUT OF THE DEPTHS
**Album:** Released Mar '89, on Malaco by Malaco Records (UK). Catalogue no: **MAL 4424**

## Anthony, Ray

**Biographical details:** This American orchestra leader first became known as a trumpeter in the Glenn Miller and Jimmy Dorsey bands. He hit No 7 on the UK chart in 1953 with *Dragnet*. After duetting with Frank Sinatra on a 1955 US Top Twenty hit, *Melody Of Love*, he reached the American Top Ten in '59 with his version of Henry Mancini's *Peter Gunn* theme, outstripping Duane Eddy. (Bob MacDonald, 1984.)
Ray Anthony was born in 1922 in Pennsylvania. He played trumpet with Glenn Miller and Jimmy Dorsey in the '40's, then had his own band with an unusual lineup: one trumpet, one French horn, five reeds, three rhythm. After US Navy service 1942-6, his more conventional dance band was the most successful Miller imitator in the early '50's, playing very well indeed and benefitting form the excellent technology of Capitol Records, at the time the most innovative and up to date in the world. Hit singles 1950-54 included *Dragnet*, TV cop show theme; co written pop novelty *The bunny hop*; single *Dancing in the dark* won award as best dance band record in '53. He was married to actress Mamie Van Doren. He bought the Billy May Band in 1954, hiring Sam Donahue to front it. He led smaller combos, had a band in Las Vegas in 1980, formed Big Bands in the '80's to furnish the traditional sound to school, radio. (Donald Clarke, July 1988).

### 1988 & ALL THAT JAZZ (Anthony, Ray & His Orchestra)
**Album:** Released Mar '90, on Aerospace Catalogue no: **RA1030**

### ARTHUR MURRAY DANCE PARTY
Tracks: / Swing / Shuffle my boogie / Guantanamera / Bunny hop cha cha / New York, New York / Last cheater's waltz, The / Don't cry for me Argentina / Coffee song, The / Riviera rumba / Tango, anyone?.
**Cass:** Released Jul '86, on Aerospace Catalogue no: **RA 1009C**
**Album:** Released Jul '86, on Aerospace Catalogue no: **RA 1009**
**CD:** Released Nov '88, on Aerospace Catalogue no: **RA 1009CD**

### BIG BAND JAZZ
Tracks: / Baby but you did / Roll 'em around / South Dakota / This may be the time / Every dog has his day / Why should I worry? / Why don't you want to come home? / You gotta get lucky sometime / Mr. Moon / Indubitably / You're the one for me / Lavender mood, A.
Note: Twelve jazz originals by Steve Allen: originally on Capitol titled Anthony plays Allen.
**Album:** Released Jul '86, on Aerospace Catalogue no: **RA 998**
**Cass:** Released Jul '86, on Aerospace Catalogue no: **RA 998C**

### BIG BAND SINGER
Tracks: / Swing dance / Just hooked on dancing / Singing in the rain / Moonlight saving time / Candy and cake / I've never been in love before / I let a song go out of my heart / Young at heart / Gloria / Jean / Your eyes / Count every star.
**Cass:** Released Jul '86, on Aerospace Catalogue no: **RA 1021C**
**Album:** Released Jul '86, on Aerospace Catalogue no: **RA 1021**

### BRASS GALORE
Tracks: / Annie Laurie / Deep river / Reuben, Reuben / Camptown races / Mockingbird / Bluebells of Scotland / Kerry dance, The / Dry bones / Comin' thro' the rye / American patrol / Swing low, sweet chariot / Chopsticks.
Note: Formerly a Capitol recording titled Sound spectacular.
**Album:** Released Jul '86, on Aerospace Catalogue no: **RA 997**
**Cass:** Released Jul '86, on Aerospace Catalogue no: **RA 997C**

### DANCERS' CHOICE
Tracks: / Anonimo Veneziano / Country bumpkin / Touch dancing / Cotton-eyed Joe / Country blues / Bunny hop disco / Chaputin / Early morning love / Leroy's back / Shadows, The / Fun dancers / Malibu sunset.
**Album:** Released Jul '86, on Aerospace Catalogue no: **RA 1006**

### DANCERS IN LOVE (Anthony, Ray & His Orchestra)
**Cass:** Released Nov '89, on Memoir by Memoir Records. Catalogue no: **CMOIR 210**
**Album:** Released Nov '89, on Memoir by Memoir Records. Catalogue no: **MOIR 210**

### DANCING ALONE TOGETHER
Tracks: / My funny valentine / Guess I'll hang my tears out to dry / To love and be loved / I should care / Party's over, The / Here's that rainy day / What's new / Misty / Like someone in love / Alone together / All the way.
**Album:** Released Jul '86, on Capitol by EMI Records. Deleted Jun '89. Catalogue no: **EMS 1156**
**Cass:** Released Jul '86, on Capitol by EMI Records. Deleted Aug '89. Catalogue no: **TCEMS 1156**

### DANCING IN THE DARK
Tracks: / Dancing in the dark / True blue Lou / Begin the beguine / Cheek to cheek / Dancing on the ceiling / I wonder what's become of Sally / Continental, The / You and the night and the music / Taking a chance on love / You're the cream in my coffee / It's de-lovely / I get a kick out of you.
**Album:** Released Jul '86, on Aerospace Catalogue no: **RA 995**
**Cass:** Released Jul '86, on Aerospace Catalogue no: **RA 995C**

### DRAGNET
Tracks: / Dragnet.
**7" Single:** on Capitol by EMI Records. Catalogue no: **CL 13983**

### DREAM DANCING AROUND THE WORLD
Tracks: / My way / Love story / Girl from Ipanema / Yesterday / Wonderland by night / It's impossible / Snowbird / To be the one you love / Japanese love song, A / Dreamtime for Jedda / Shadows, The / Royal Hawaiian sunset.
**Album:** Released Jul '86, on Aerospace Catalogue no: **RA 1007**

### DREAM DANCING MEDLEY
Tracks: / As time goes by / Soon / Where am I? / I'll string along with you / Of thee I sing / It had to be you / Auf wiedersehen, my dear / Can't we be friends? / Heaven can wait / Too marvellous for words / When your lover has gone / Love nest, The / Dancing on the ceiling / Sweet madness / 'S wonderful / With a song in my heart / Very thought of you, The / Boulevard of broken dreams / Autumn in New York / Man I love, The / Tis' autumn / Please be king / Ev'ry day / If there is someone lovelier than you / September in the rain / My heart stood still / Dancing in the dark / Something to remember you by / Oh! You crazy moon / Mine.
Note: The smooth, sentimental sound of Ray Anthony's Orchestra playing a lush medley of thirty famous tunes including, As time goes by , With a song in my heart , Autumn in New York , The man I love , Please be kind' and many more. Ideal for dancing!n
**Cass:** Released Mar '85, on Capitol by EMI Records. Deleted Nov '88. Catalogue no: **ED 2604314**
**Album:** Released Mar '85, on Capitol by EMI Records. Deleted Jun '89. Catalogue no: **ED 2604311**

### FOR DANCERS ONLY (Cheek to cheek) (Anthony, Ray & His Orchestra)
**Cass:** Released Dec '88, on Capitol (Specials) Catalogue no: **4XL 57009**

### GLENN MILLER - THEN AND NOW (Anthony, Ray & His Orchestra)
**Album:** Released '88, on Aerospace Catalogue no: **RA 1011**

### HITS OF RAY ANTHONY
Tracks: / Slaughter on Tenth Avenue / Man with the horn, The / Mr. Anthony's boogie / Oh mein papa / Bunny hop, The / Thunderbird / Dragnet / At last / Harlem nocturne / Stardust / Peter Gunn / Tenderly / When the saints go marching in.
**Album:** Released Jul '86, on Aerospace Catalogue no: **RA 999**
**Cass:** Released Jul '86, on Aerospace Catalogue no: **RA 999C**

### HOOKED ON BIG BANDS - LIVE FROM RADIO PROGS
**Cass:** Released Nov '88, on Aerospace Catalogue no: **RA 1012C**
**Album:** Released Nov '88, on Aerospace Catalogue no: **RA 1012**
**CD:** Released Nov '88, on Aerospace Catalogue no: **RA 1012CD**

**HOUSEPARTY HOP**
Tracks: / I get a kick out of you / Houseparty hop / Begin the beguine / Perdido / Bunny hop, The / Darktown strutters' ball / Dinah / Sentimental journey / My blue Heaven / Wagon wheels / Rockin' in rhythm / Bandstand matinee.
**Album:** Released Jul '85, on Capitol by EMI Records. Deleted Jan '88. Catalogue no: **EG 2606011**
**Cass:** Released Jul '85, on Capitol by EMI Records. Deleted Jan '88. Catalogue no: **EG 2606014**

**I GET THE BLUES WHEN IT RAINS**
**Album:** Released May '89, on Ranwood Catalogue no: **R 8082**

**I REMEMBER GLENN MILLER**
Tracks: / Tuxedo Junction / Chattanooga choo choo / Serenade in blue / Elmer's tune / Sunrise serenade / Song of the volga boatmen / In the mood / I know why (and so do you) / Sweet as apple cider / At last / Little Brown jug / Moonlight serenade.
**Album:** on Capitol (import) Catalogue no: **2C 068 86544**
**CD:** Released '89, on Aerospace Catalogue no: **RACD 1011**

**JAM SESSION AT THE TOWER - SOUNDS SPECTACULAR (Anthony, Ray & His Orchestra)**
**CD:** Released Oct '89, on Aerospace Catalogue no: **RACD 996**

**LET'S DANCE AGAIN**
**Cass set:** Released Jul '86, on Aerospace Catalogue no: **RA 1020C**
**LP Set:** Released Jul '86, on Aerospace Catalogue no: **RA 1020**

**LET'S GO DANCING**
Tracks: / All of me / Ain't misbehavin' / Always / Sleepy lagoon / Spaghetti rag / Swing dance / Similau / Al di la / Skokiaan / Tango for two / Petard mambo.
**Album:** Released Jul '86, on Aerospace Catalogue no: **RA 1028**
**Cass:** Released Jul '86, on Aerospace Catalogue no: **RA 1028C**

**MORE DREAM DANCING**
Tracks: / April in Paris / Blue Hawaii / There's a small hotel / I cover the waterfront / Meet me tonight in dreamland / Venezuela / East of the sun / Along the Sante Fe / Palm Springs / Home Monika / Dream while you dance.
**Cass:** on Pathe Marconi (France) Catalogue no: **PM 154 570 4**
**Album:** Released Sep '83, on Capitol (import) Deleted Sep '88. Catalogue no: **2C 068 54570**

**MUSIC OF YOUR MEMORIES**
Tracks: / What's new? / Here's that rainy day / Like someone in love / My funny valentine / To love and be loved / All the way / Misty / I should care / I'm through with love / Guess I'll hang my clothes out to dry / Alone together / Party's over, The.
**Cass:** Released Jul '86, on Aerospace Catalogue no: **RA 1019C**
**Album:** Released Jul '86, on Aerospace Catalogue no: **RA 1019**

**PLAYS FOR DREAM DANCING**
Tracks: / This love of mine / Dream dancing / I'll never smile again / Out of nowhere / I only have eyes for you / Embraceable you / Street of dreams / Stars fell on Alabama / I don't know why (I just do) / Laura / Moonlight in Vermont / September song.
Note: Ray Anthony, who served his apprenticeship with the Glen Miller Orchestra became famous for his Dream Dancing albums-collections of well known songs lushly arranged for dancing cheek to cheek. This is the classic first album of that series and has not been available for a number of years.
**Cass:** Released Feb '84, on Capitol by EMI Records. Deleted Jun '89. Catalogue no: **TCCAPS 2600014**
**Album:** Released Feb '84, on Capitol by EMI Records. Deleted Aug '89. Catalogue no: **CAPS 2600011**

**RAY ANTHONY**
**Album:** Released Sep '87, on Entertainers Deleted '88. Catalogue no: **ENT LP 13015**
**Cass:** Released Sep '87, on Entertainers Deleted '88. Catalogue no: **ENT MC 13015**

**SAMPLER, THE**
Tracks: / Mr. Anthony's boogie / Man with the horn, The / Dancing in the dark / Cheek to cheek / Baby but you did / Roll 'em around / Swingin' at the Tower / How high the moon / Country bumpkin / Leroy's back / Annie Laurie / Deep river.
Note: Two selections from each of six separate albums.
**Album:** Released Jul '86, on Aerospace Catalogue no: **RA 1000**

**SHOW AND DANCE AND PARTY**
Note: Combination package featuring dance music, the Book End Revue live show and Music for a Swingin' Party.
**Cass set:** Released Jul '86, on Aerospace Catalogue no: **RA 1027C**
**LP Set:** Released Jul '86, on Aerospace Catalogue no: **RA 1027**

**SWEET & SWINGIN' 1949-53**
**Album:** Released Dec '87, on Circle (USA) by Jazzology Records (USA). Catalogue no: **CLP 96**

**SWING**
Tracks: / Swing / Swing machine / Big band blast / Swingalong / Swinger, The / Movin' / Swing thing / Shuffle my boogie / Boogie on down / Heat Ray / Swingin' affair, A / Fanfare boogie.
**Album:** Released Jul '86, on Aerospace Catalogue no: **RA 1010**
**Cass:** Released Jul '86, on Aerospace Catalogue no: **RA 1010C**

**SWING GOES ON VOL 10**
Tracks: / What can I say / I wonder what's become of Sally / Idaho / Blue moon / Dancing over the waves / It's de-lovely / Man with the horn, The / For dancers only / Jeepers creepers / My blue Heaven / Amor / Dinah / Sentimental journey / Begin the beguine / I get a kick out of you / Houseparty hop.
**Album:** on EMI (Germany) by EMI Records. Catalogue no: **IC 054 52719**

**SWINGIN' AT THE TOWER**
Tracks: / Flying home / Night train / How high the moon / Perdido / One o'clock jump / Swingin' at the Tower.
Note: The first big band recording made at the Capitol Tower in Hollywood. Formerly titled Jam session at the Tower.
**Cass:** Released Jul '86, on Aerospace Catalogue no: **RA 996C**
**Album:** Released Jul '86, on Aerospace Catalogue no: **RA 996**

**SWINGIN' ON CAMPUS**
Tracks: / What can I say after I say I'm sorry / On the Alamo / I've found a new baby / Chloe / At sundown / Pick yourself up / Ain't misbehavin' / Lady is in love with you, The / Am I blue / If I had you / Undecided / Swing on campus.
Note: A good set of swinging standards in the same vein as Houseparty hop - the sucessful multi-tempo album.
**Album:** Released Dec '85, on Capitol by EMI Records. Deleted Jan '88. Catalogue no: **EMS 1137**
**Cass:** Released Dec '85, on Capitol by EMI Records. Deleted Jan '88. Catalogue no: **TCEMS 1137**

**TOUCH DANCING**
Tracks: / Touch dancing / Too much, too little, too late / Just a gigolo / How deep is your love? / Feelings / Closer I get to you, The / Dancing close together / Come dance with me / My way / Yesterday / Love story / It's impossible.
**Album:** Released Jul '86, on Aerospace Catalogue no: **RA 1008**
**Cass:** Released Jul '86, on Aerospace Catalogue no: **RA 1008C**

**TRIBUTE (Anthony, Ray & His Orchestra)**
**CD:** Released Oct '89, on Aerospace Catalogue no: **RACD 1012**

## Ardley, Neil

**HARMONY OF THE SPHERES**
Tracks: / Upstarts all / Leap in the dark / Glittering circles / Fair mirage / Soft stillness and the night / Headstrong, headlong / Toward tranquility.
**Album:** Released Feb '79, on Decca by Decca International. Deleted Feb '84. Catalogue no: **TXSR 133**

**KALEIDOSCOPE OF RAINBOWS**
Tracks: / Prologue / Rainbow one / Rainbow two / Rainbow three / Rainbow four / Rainbow five / Rainbow six / Rainbow seven / Epilogue.
**Album:** Released Sep '77, on Gull by Gull Records. Catalogue no: **GULP 9077**
**CD:** Released 5 Jun '89, on Line by Line Records (W.Germany). Catalogue no: **LICD 9.00351**

## Arkansas Blues

**ARKANSAS BLUES VOL.1 (Keep it yourself) (Various artists)**
**Album:** Released Oct '88, on Rooster (USA) Catalogue no: **R 7605**

## Armstrong, Lil

**BORN TO SWING 1936-37**

**Album:** Released '89, on Harlequin by Interstate Music. Catalogue no: **HQ 2069**

## Armstrong, Louis

**Biographical details:** When 'Satchmo' died in 1971, he was one of the best-known, best loved entertainers in the world, but many people had forgot (if they ever knew) that he was one of the most important stars in the history of popular music, having invented much of it. He traditionally gave his birth date as the fourth of July 1900, but was probably born a couple of years earlier; he may not have known when he was born, and may have fibbed about his age to avoid the draft during WW1. He came from utter poverty in New Orleans, where he was put in the Coloured Waif's Home for firing a pistol in the air on the fourth of July (USA Independence Day); he learned to play the cornet there. He played in local bands and was invited to Chicago in 1923 to play second cornet to King Oliver in his Creole Jazz Band, which made the first important jazz records that year, preserving the New Orleans style. Pushed by his then-wife, pianist Lillian Hardin, to strike out on his own, he joined Fletcher Henderson's band in New York for a year; it was just a good ragtimey dance band then, but he set it on fire and set New York on its ear. Back in the Midwest in 1925, as the new technology of electrical recording was being adopted, he made the first of his small group recordings, leading studio groups called the Hot Five and the Hot Seven, later editions including pianist Earl Hines; these records changed popular music forever, astonishing every musician who heard them. He set the soloist free from the constraints of the New Orleans style once and for all and did it with such complete mastery that he remains one of the most influential musicians of the century, rivalled only by Charlie Parker and John Coltrane. By the late 1920s he was an enormously popular theatre entertainer, and for the next 20 years he made delightful pop records with his travelling big band; the band itself was not up to much, but there was something magical on every record, and his singing was almost as influential as his playing. In the late '40s he began to play and record again with small groups; the famous Town Hall concert in New York in 1947 (with Hines, Jack Teagarden and other stars) was so successful that the big band was abandoned for good. The best of his later records include the small-group sides made for Victor and USA Decca (now MCA) during that period and a handful on CBS from the '50s, including *Ambassador Satch* (live on world tour) and albums of songs by W.C.Handy (which Handy loved) and Fats Waller. (Donald Clarke 21 July 1988)..

### 19 HISTORICAL TRACKS

**CD:** Released Apr '87, on Delta (1) by Delta Records. Deleted '88. Catalogue no: **11 063**

### 20 GOLDEN PIECES: LOUIS ARMSTRONG

Tracks: / Someday you'll be sorry / Heebie Jeebies / I can't give you anything but love baby / Muskrat ramble / Dear old Southland / That lucky old sun / Black & blue / Panama / Royal Garden blues / Chinatown my Chinatown / Swing that music / Tiger rag / Baby won't you please come home / Storyville blues / Jeepers creepers / Do you know what it means to miss New Orleans / Old rockin' chair / Way down yonder in New Orleans / I'm not so rough.

**Album:** Released Jul '82, on Bulldog Records by President Records. Catalogue no: **BDL 2007**

**Cass:** Released Jul '82, on Bulldog Records by President Records. Catalogue no: **BDC 2007**

### 20 GREATEST HITS: LOUIS ARMSTRONG

**Cass:** Released Nov '84, on Astan (USA) Catalogue no: **40123**

**Album:** Released Nov '84, on Astan (USA) Catalogue no: **20123**

### 20 HITS - LOUIS ARMSTRONG

**CD:** Released Sep '89, on Big Band Era Catalogue no: **2601752**

### 20 UNFORGETTABLE HITS (Armstrong, Louis / his Allstars)

**CD:** Released Sep '87, on Big Band Era Catalogue no: **70191**

**Cass:** Released Jun '86, on Astan (USA) Catalogue no: **40191**

### 1924 (Armstrong, Louis / Red Onion Jazz Babies / Freddie Keppard / Doc C)

Tracks: / Everybody loves my baby / Texas moaner blues / Of all the wrongs you've done to me / Terrible blues / Santa Claus blues / Nobody knows the way I feel this morning / Early every morn / Cake walking babies from home / Scissor grinder Joe / Lonely little wallflower / So this is Venice / Moanful man / Memphis maybe man, The / One I love belongs to somebody else, The / Stockyards strut / Salty dog.

**Album:** Released Jan '83, on Swaggie (Australia) Catalogue no: **804**

### 1940'S SMALL BANDS

Tracks: / I want a little girl / Sugar / Do you know what it means to miss New Orleans / Mahogany Hall stomp / Rockin' chair / Back o' town blues.

Note: Track's include the above.

**CD:** Released Jun '88, on Bluebird (2) by BMG Records (UK). Catalogue no: **ND 86378**

### 1944-4

Tracks: / Blues in the night / Pretty girl is like a melody, A / Baby don't you cry / Coquette / Dear old Southland / Lazy river / I've got a gal in Kalamazoo / Ain't misbehavin' / Is you is or is you ain't my baby / Perido / Accentuate the positive / Always.

**Album:** Released Apr '81, on Joker (USA) by Lifetime Records (USA). Catalogue no: **SM 3082**

### 1940-47

**Album:** Released Sep '87, on Giants of Jazz by Hasmick Promotions. Catalogue no: **LPJT 64**

### 1944-51

Tracks: / Blues in the night / Pretty girl is like a melody, A / Baby don't you cry / Coquette / Dear old Southland / Lazy river / I've got a gal in Kalamazoo / Ain't misbehavin' / Is you is or is you ain't my baby / Perdido / Accentuate the positive / Always / Back o' town blues / Basin street blues / Black & blue / Do you know what it means to miss New Orleans / I got a right to sing the blues / I'm confessin' / You rascal you / Someday you'll be sorry / Panama / Struttin' with some barbecue.

**2 LP Set:** Released Apr '81, on Joker (USA) by Lifetime Records (USA). Catalogue no: **SM 3764/2**

### ALL STARS VOL II

Tracks: / High society / I cried for you / Whispering / Me & Brother Bill / Don't fence me in / Basin Street blues / I gotta right to sing the blues / Jack Armstrong blues / Mop mop.

**Album:** Released Apr '81, on Unique Jazz by Spotlite Records. Catalogue no: **UJ 17**

### AMBASSADOR SATCH

**Cass:** Released May '85, on CBS (import) by CBS Records. Catalogue no: **40-21121**

**Album:** Released May '85, on CBS (import) by CBS Records. Catalogue no: **21121**

### AN EVENING WITH LOUIS ARSTRONG

**Cass:** Released '88, on GNP Crescendo (USA) by GNP Crescendo Records (USA). Catalogue no: **GNP5 9050**

**Album:** Released '88, on GNP Crescendo (USA) by GNP Crescendo Records (USA). Catalogue no: **GNPS 9050**

### ARMED FORCES RADIO SERVICE (Armstrong, Louis / his orchestra)

**Album:** Released Jun '86, on Duke by Melodisc Records. Catalogue no: **D 1021**

### ARMSTRONG & ALL STARS (Armstrong, Louis/his Allstars)

**Album:** Released '88, on Joker (USA) by Lifetime Records (USA). Catalogue no: **SM 3863**

### ARMSTRONG, LOUIS & JACK TEAGARDEN (See also under Teagarden, Jack) (Armstrong, Louis / Jack Teagarden)

**Album:** Released Mar '90, on Echo Jazz Catalogue no: **EJLP07**

### AT HIS RAREST OF ALL RARE PERFORMANCES VOL. 2

**Album:** Released Jul '82, on Kings Of Jazz Catalogue no: **KLJ 20026**

### AT THE EDDIE CONDON FLOOR SHOW

Tracks: / When it's sleepy time down South / Them there eyes / St. James infirmary / Sweets on parade / Do you know what it means to miss New Or-

leans / Sruttin' with some barbecue / Sweet Georgia Brown / After you've gone / Royal Garden blues / Back o' town blues / Me and Brother Bill / Blues in B flat.
**Album:** Released Apr '81, on Queendisc (Italy) Catalogue no: **QU 010**

**BACK O' TOWN BLUES**
Tracks: / Someday you'll be sorry / Sweethearts on parade / Jelly roll blues / Chimes blues / Dippermouth blues / Snake rag / New Orleans stomp / Bye and bye / Back o' town blues / I want a big butter and egg man.
**CD:** Released 10 Jul '89, on Vogue by Vogue Records. Catalogue no: **VGCD 670207**
**Album:** Released Feb '87, on Pathe Marconi (France) Catalogue no: **2400591**

**BASIN STREET BLUES**
**Album:** Released Jun '88, on Black Lion Catalogue no: **BLP 60128**
**Album:** Released Mar '84, on EMI (France) by EMI Records. Catalogue no: **2M 056 78139**
**CD:** Released Jun '88, on Black Lion Catalogue no: **BLCD7 60128**
**Cass:** Released Mar '84, on EMI (France) by EMI Records. Catalogue no: **2M 256 78139**

**BEST LIVE CONCERT 1965**
**Cass:** Released Dec '89, on Accord (France) by Musidisc Records (France). Catalogue no: **302002**
**CD:** Released Dec '89, on Accord (France) by Musidisc Records (France). Catalogue no: **302004**

**BEST OF LOUIS ARMSTRONG**
Tracks: / What a wonderful world / Hello Dolly / C'est si bon / Skokiaan.
Note: Tracks include the above
**Cass:** Released Apr '83, on MFP (Holland) by EMI Records. Catalogue no: **1A 222-58256**
**Album:** Released Apr '83, on MFP (Holland) by EMI Records. Catalogue no: **1A 022-58256**

**BEST OF SATCHMO**
Tracks: / On the sunny side of the street / Lazy river / Georgia on my mind / I surrender dear / Exactly like you / Some of these days / Kiss to build a dream on, A / La vie en rose / Blueberry Hill / Whiffenpoof song, The / Shadrack / When it's sleepy time down South / I can't give you anything but love / If I could be with you one hour tonight / When you're smiling.
**Cass:** Released Aug '81, on Coral by MCA Records. Catalogue no: **MCLC 1600**
**Album:** Released Aug '81, on Coral by MCA Records. Catalogue no: **MCL 1600**

**BIG BANDS 1928-1930**
**Album:** Released '88, on DRG (USA) by DRG Records (USA). Catalogue no: **SW 8450**

**BIG BANDS, THE**
**Album:** Released Jan '83, on Swaggie (Australia) Catalogue no: **S 1253**

**BIG BANDS VOL. 1 1930-31**
**CD:** Released Oct '88, on JSP by JSP Records. Catalogue no: **JSP CD 305**

**BIG BANDS VOL. 2 1931-32**
**CD:** Released Oct '88, on JSP by JSP Records. Catalogue no: **JSP CD 306**

**BLOW THAT HORN**
Tracks: / Ain't misbehavin' / I ain't got nobody / I'm confessin' / St. James Infirmary / Gut bucket blues / You can depend on me / Peanut vendor / You rascal you / Body and soul / Drop that sack / West End blues / Heebie jeebies / Up a lazy river / Dinah / Muskrat ramble / Struttin' with some barbecue / Mahogany Hall stomp / Got no blues / Georgia on my mind / Cornet chop suey / Knockin' on a jug / Ory's creole trombone / Chinatown my Chinatown / You're lucky to me.
**Cass set:** Released May '89, on Ditto by Pickwick Records. Catalogue no: **DTO 10310**

**CARNEGIE HALL CONCERT (February 8th, 1947)**
Tracks: / New Orleans function / Free as a bird / Oh didn't he ramble? / Dippermouth blues / Mahogany Hall stomp / Muskrat ramble / St. Louis blues / Rockin' chair / Tiger rag / Black and blue / I'm confessin' / Struttin' with some barbecue / Up a lazy river / You rascal you / Save it, pretty mama / Ain't misbehavin'.
**Album:** Released Apr '81, on Connoisseur Rarities Catalogue no: **CR 520**
**Album:** Released Apr '81, on Joker (USA) by Lifetime Records (USA). Catalogue no: **SM 3614**
**Album:** Released Apr '81, on Kings Of Jazz Catalogue no: **KLJ 20001**

**CHEEK TO CHEEK (Armstrong, Louis / Ella Fitzgerald)**
**Album:** Released Sep '87, on Entertainers Catalogue no: **ENT 13023**
**CD:** Released Sep '87, on Entertainers Catalogue no: **ENT CD 215**

**CHICAGO CONCERT 1956**
Tracks: / Memphis blues, The / Frankie and Johnny / Tiger rag / Do you know what it means to miss New Orleans / Basin Street blues / Black & blue / West End blues / On the sunny side of the street / Struttin' with some barbecue / Manhattan / When it's sleepy time down South / Indiana / Gypsy, The / Faithful hussar, The / Rockin' chair / Bucket's got a hole in it / Perdido / Clarinet marmalade / Mack the knife / Tenderly / You'll never walk alone / Stompin' at the Savoy / Margie / Mama's back in town / That's my desire / Ko ko mo (I love you so) / I love you so.
**Cass set:** Released '84, on CBS by CBS Records. Deleted '87. Catalogue no: **40 22106**
**2 LP Set:** Released '84, on CBS by CBS Records. Catalogue no: **22106**

**CHICAGO JAZZ (23-29) (Armstrong, Louis / Johnny Davis)**
**Album:** Released '88, on Swaggie (Australia) Catalogue no: **S 818**

**CHINATOWN MY CHINATOWN**
**Cass:** Released Nov '84, on Astan (USA) Catalogue no: **40073**
**Album:** Released Nov '84, on Astan (USA) Catalogue no: **20073**

**CLASSIC LOUIS ARMSTRONG**
**Cass set:** Released 7 Nov '87, on Warwick by Warwick Records. Catalogue no: **WW 6039**

**CLASSICS**
**Album:** Released Dec '79, on Boulevard by Boulevard Records. Deleted '84. Catalogue no: **BD 3001**

**COLLECTION : LOUIS ARMSTRONG (20 golden greats)**
Tracks: / Hello Dolly / Cabaret / Tiger rag / When it's sleepy time down South / Indiana / Muskrat ramble / Mack the knife / Blueberry Hill / St. James' Infirmary / Kiss to build a dream on, A / When the saints go marching in / Jeepers creepers / On the sunny side of the street / Ain't misbehavin' / Panama rag / Black and blue / Dear old Southland / Basin Street blues / Lazy river / Struttin' with some barbecue.
**Album:** on Deja Vu Catalogue no: **DVLP 2007**
**CD:** Released Jul '87, on Deja Vu Catalogue no: **DVCD 2007**
**Cass:** Released Aug '85, on Deja Vu Catalogue no: **DVMC 2007**

**COLLECTION: LOUIS ARMSTRONG & HIS ALLSTARS (Armstrong, Louis/his Allstars)**
**Cass:** Released Feb '89, on Giants of Jazz by Hasmick Promotions. Catalogue no: **MCJT 78**
**Album:** Released Feb '89, on Giants of Jazz by Hasmick Promotions. Catalogue no: **LPJT 78**

**COMPLETE LOUIS ARMSTRONG**
**Album:** Released '88, on RCA by BMG Records (UK). Deleted May '89. Catalogue no: **NK 89279**

**COMPLETE LOUIS ARMSTRONG - DUKE ELLINGTON (Armstrong, Louis / Duke Ellington)**
Tracks: / Duke's place / I'm just a lucky so and so / Cottontail / Mood indigo / Do nothin' till you hear from me / Beautiful American, The / Black and tan fantasy / Drop me off at Harlem / Mooche, The / In a mellow tone / It don't mean a thing (if it ain't got that swing) / Solitude / Don't get around much anymore / I'm beginning to see the light / Just squeeze me / I got it bad and that ain't good / Azalea.
**CD:** Released Feb '90, on Roulette (EMI) by EMI Records. Catalogue no: **CDP 793 844 2**

**COMPLETE TOWN HALL CONCERT, THE**
Tracks: / Cornet chop suey / Our Monday date / Dear old Southland / Big butter and egg man / Tiger rag / Struttin' with some barbecue / Sweethearts on parade / St. Louis blues / Pennies from Heaven / On the sunny side of the street / I can't give you anything but love / Back o' town blues / Ain't misbehavin' / Rockin' chair / Muskrat ramble / Save it

pretty mama / St. James Infirmary / Royal Garden blues / Do you know what it means to Miss New Orleans? / Jack Armstrong blues.
**Cass Set:** Released Mar '86, on RCA by BMG Records (UK). Deleted May '89. Catalogue no: **NK 89746**
**2 LP Set:** Released Mar '86, on RCA by BMG Records (UK). Catalogue no: **NL 89746**

**COUNTDOWN**
Tracks: / Way down yonder in New Orleans / Won't you come home Bill Bailey / Avalon / Honeysuckle rose / On the sunny side of the street / Sweet Georgia Brown / Bourbon street parade / Muskrat ramble / I got rhythm / Tiger rag / Jeepers creepers / Someday you'll be sorry.
**Cass:** Released '82, on Dakota (Countdown series) Catalogue no: **ZC CNT 7**
**Album:** Released '82, on Dakota (Countdown series) Catalogue no: **COUNT 7**

**DO YOU KNOW WHAT IT MEANS TO MISS NEW ORLEANS?**
**Cass:** Released 5 Jun '89, on Polydor by Polydor Ltd. Catalogue no: **837 919-4**
**CD:** Released 5 Jun '89, on Polydor by Polydor Ltd. Catalogue no: **837 919-2**
**Album:** Released 5 Jun '89, on Polydor by Polydor Ltd. Catalogue no: **837 919-1**

**ELLA AND LOUIS AGAIN VOL 1 (Armstrong, Louis/Ella Fitzgerald)**
Tracks: / Don't be that way / Makin' whoopee / They all laughed / Comes love / Autumn in New York / Let's do it / Stompin' at the Savou / I won't dance / Gee baby ain't I good to you.
**Album:** Released Jan '90, on Verve Catalogue no: **837 442 1**
**Album:** Released Aug '81, on Verve Catalogue no: **2304 501**

**ELLA AND LOUIS AGAIN, VOL 2 (Armstrong, Louis/Ella Fitzgerald)**
Tracks: / Let's call the whole thing off / These foolish things / I've got my love to keep me warm / I'm puttin' all my eggs... / Fine romance, A / I'll wind / Love is here to stay / I get a kick out of you / Learnin' the blues.
Note: For full information see Fitzgerald, Ella & Louis Armstrong
**Album:** Released Jan '90, on Verve Catalogue no: **837 443 1**

**ELLA FITZGERALD & LOUIS ARMSTRONG (Armstrong, Louis / Ella Fitzgerald)**
Tracks: / When the saints go marching in / West End blues / Jeepers creepers / On the sunny side of the street / Ain't misbehavin' / Swing that music / Undecided / Tisket a tasket, A / Got a pebble in my shoe / You'll have to swing it / Chew, chew, chew, chew (your bubble gum) / I found my yellow basket.
Note: Ella and Louis recorded separately in 1936, 1938, 1939.
**Album:** Released '81, on Joker (USA) by Lifetime Records (USA). Catalogue no: **SM 3099**

**ESSENCE OF LOUIS ARMSTRONG, THE**
**Album:** Released Jul '87, on Nostalgia by Mainline Records. Catalogue no: **NOST 7662**

**ESSENTIAL LOUIS ARMSTRONG, THE**
Tracks: / Bourbon street parade / Washington and Lee swing / Avalon / New Orleans / That's a plenty / Just a closer walk with thee / Dixie / Sheik of Araby / Wolverine blues / Sweet Georgia Brown / Limehouse blues / Back o' town blues / Sweethearts on parade / Sugar foot stomp / Canal street blues / Bill Bailey / Someday you'll be sorry / Struttin' with some barbecue / I ain't gonna give nobody none of my jelly roll / Cornet chop suey / My bucket's got a hole in it.
**Cass Set:** Released '87, on Audio Fidelity(USA) by Audio Fidelity (USA). Catalogue no: **ZCAFD 1042**
**2 LP Set:** Released '87, on Audio Fidelity(USA) by Audio Fidelity (USA). Catalogue no: **AFESD 1042**

**EVENING WITH LOUIS ARMSTRONG**
**CD Set:** Released May '89, on GNP Crescendo (USA) by GNP Crescendo Records (USA). Catalogue no: **GNPD 2-11001**
**Cass:** Released Oct '77, on Vogue by Vogue Records. Catalogue no: **ZCVJD 538**
**2 LP Set:** Released May '89, on GNP Crescendo (USA) by GNP Crescendo Records (USA). Catalogue no: **GNPS 2-11001**
**Cass set:** Released May '89, on GNP Crescendo (USA) by GNP Crescendo Records (USA). Catalogue no: **GNP5 2-11001**

**FABULOUS PARIS CONCERT VOL. 1 (March 2, 1948) (Armstrong, Louis/his Allstars)**
**Album:** Released Jan '88, on Two Flat Discs Catalogue no: **TFD 5.003**

**FABULOUS PARIS CONCERT VOL. 2 (March 2, 1948) (Armstrong, Louis/his Allstars)**
**Album:** Released Jan '88, on Two Flat Discs Catalogue no: **TFD 5.004**

**FAITHFUL HUSSAR, THE**
Tracks: / Faithful hussar, The.
**7" Single:** Released Jul '56, on Philips by Phonogram Ltd. Deleted Jul '61. Catalogue no: **PB 604**

**FIRST RECORDED CONCERT 1932/1933**
Tracks: / I cover the waterfront / Tiger rag / Chinatown / You rascal you / On the closest / Dinah / Harlem stomp / When it's sleepy time down South.
**Album:** Released May '85, on Jazz Anthology by Musidisc Records (France). Catalogue no: **JA 52238**

**FROM THE BIG BAND TO THE ALL STARS**
Tracks: / Long long journey / Linger in my arms / Back o' town blues / Where the blues were born in New Orleans / I believe / You don't learn that in school / Rockin' chair / I never saw a better day / Hobo you can't ride this train.
**Album:** Released Feb '86, on RCA (France) by BMG Records (France). Deleted May '89. Catalogue no: **NL 89279**

**GEORGIA ON MY MIND**
**CD:** Released Jun '88, on Dance Band Days by Prism Leisure. Catalogue no: **DBCD 17**
**Cass:** Released Jun '88, on Dance Band Days by Prism Leisure. Catalogue no: **DBDC 17**
**Album:** Released Jun '88, on Dance Band Days by Prism Leisure. Catalogue no: **DBD 17**

**GOLDEN GREATS: LOUIS ARMSTRONG**
Tracks: / What a wonderful world / Hello Dolly / Cabaret / On the sunny side of the street / Lazy river / Georgia on my mind / I surrender dear / Exactly like you / Some of these days / Kiss to build a dream on, A / La vie en rose / Blueberry Hill / Whiffenpoof song, The / Shadrack / When it's sleepy time down South / I can't give you anything but love / If I could be with you one hour tonight / When you're smiling.
**Cass:** Released Jul '85, on MCA by MCA Records. Catalogue no: **MCMC 5013**
**Album:** Released Jul '85, on MCA by MCA Records. Catalogue no: **MCM 5013**

**GOLDEN HIGHLIGHTS**
**Album:** Released '88, on CBS by CBS Records. Catalogue no: **CBS 54720**

**GOOD YEARS OF JAZZ VOL 1 (VIDEO)**
**VHS:** Released Feb '90, on Storyville by Storyville Records AB. Catalogue no: **SV3001**

**GREAT ENTERTAINER, THE**
Tracks: / Hello Dolly / Gone fishin' / Cabaret / Lazybones / High society / Basin Street blues / Confessin' / Skokiaan / Swing that music (CD only.) / Lazy river (CD only.) / Pretty little missy (CD only.) / I love jazz (CD only.) / What a wonderful world / Everybody loves my baby / When you're smiling / On the sunny side of the street / Ain't misbehavin' / Blueberry Hill / Shadrack / Among my souvenirs.
**Album:** Released Mar '89, on MFP by EMI Records. Catalogue no: **MFP 5857**
**CD:** Released Mar '89, on MFP by EMI Records. Catalogue no: **CDMFP 6056**
**Cass:** Released '89, on MFP by EMI Records. Catalogue no: **TCMFP 5857**
**CD:** Released Mar '89, on MFP by EMI Records. Catalogue no: **CDB 792 030 2**

**GREAT REUNION (Armstrong, Louis / Duke Ellington)**
**2 LP Set:** Released '88, on Vogue by Vogue Records. Catalogue no: **400505**
**CD:** Released '88, on Vogue by Vogue Records. Catalogue no: **VG 600 013**

**GREAT REUNION, THE (Armstrong, Louis / Duke Ellington)**
Tracks: / It don't mean a thing (if it ain't got that swing) / Solitude / Don't get around much anymore / I'm beginning to

see the light / Just squeeze me / I got it bad and that ain't good / Azalea.
**Album:** Released Feb '90, on Roulette (EMI) by EMI Records. Catalogue no: **ROU 1008**

## GREATEST CONCERT, THE
Tracks: / Rose room / Back o' town blues / C'est si bon / Way down yonder in New Orleans / Stardust / Rockin' chair / Where did you stay last night / Baby it's cold outside / C jam blues / Stompin' at the Savoy / I used to love you / La vie en rose / Lover / That's my desire / Royal Garden blues / Ain't misbehavin' / Love me or leave me / How high the moon / Tea for two / Hucklebuck, The.
Note: Louis Armstrong with all star band recorded live in Toronto during 1951. All the favourites are here.Collective Personnel Louis Armstrong-Trumpet & Vocals / Barney Bigard -Clarinet / Jack Teagarden -Trombone & Vocals / Arvell Shaw -String Bass / Cozy Cole -Drums / Earl "Fatha" Himes Piano / Velma Middleton -Vocals.
**Album:** Released Nov '84, on Festival (France) by Musidisc Records (France). Catalogue no: **ALB 154**

## GREATEST HITS 2
**Album:** Released May '88, on Music Power Catalogue no: **33002**
**Cass:** Released May '88, on Music Power Catalogue no: **63002**

## GREATEST HITS: LOUIS ARMSTRONG
**Album:** Released May '88, on Music Power Catalogue no: **33001**
**Cass:** Released May '88, on Music Power Catalogue no: **63001**

## GREATEST HITS: LOUIS
**Album:** Released Oct '88, on Fun (Holland) Catalogue no: **FUN 9018**
**Cass:** Released Oct '88, on Fun (Holland) Catalogue no: **FUNC 9018**

## GREATEST HITS: LOUIS ARMSTRONG
Tracks: / Mack the Knife / Back o' town blues / Black & blue / Ain't misbehavin' / Basin Street blues / Cabaret / Honeysuckle Rose / When it's sleepy time down South / All of me / West End blues / Struttin' with some barbecue / Indiana / Tin roof blues.
**Album:** Released May '83, on CBS by CBS Records. Catalogue no: **CBS 21058**
**Cass:** Released '84, on CBS by CBS Records. Catalogue no: **40 32030**
**Cass:** Released Aug '85, on K-Tel by K-Tel Records. Catalogue no: **CE 2306**
**Album:** Released '84, on CBS by CBS Records. Catalogue no: **CBS 32030**
**Album:** Released Aug '85, on K-Tel by K-Tel Records. Catalogue no: **NE 1306**
**Cass:** Released May '83, on CBS by CBS Records. Catalogue no: **40 21058**

## HALL OF FAME
Tracks: / When it's sleepy time down south / Indiana / Hello Dolly / St.James infirmary / Blueberry hill / Mack the knife / Cabaret / That's my desire / Ole miss / Kiss to build a dream on.
**Album:** Released Jan '77, on Black Lion Deleted '82. Catalogue no: **BLPS 20155**

## HELLO DOLLY
**Album:** Released Jun '64, on London-American Deleted '69. Catalogue no: **HAR 8190**

## HELLO DOLLY (SINGLE)
Tracks: / Hello dolly.
**7" Single:** Released Apr '64, on London-American Deleted Apr '69. Catalogue no: **HLR 9878**

## HIGH SOCIETY
Tracks: / Someday you'll be sorry / Dippermouth blues / Do you know what it means to miss New Orleans? / Honeysuckle rose / Panama / Save it, pretty mama / High society / Rockin' chair / Back o' town blues / Tin roof blues / You can depend on me.
**Album:** Released Jul '88, on Black Lion Catalogue no: **BLM 52035**

## HIS IMMORTAL CONCERT SERIES
Tracks: / Back o' town blues / Do you know what it means to miss New Orleans / Black & blue / Basin Street blues / I gotta right to sing the blues / I'm confessin' / You rascal you / Lazy river / Someday you'll be sorry / Panama / Struttin' with some barbecue.
**Album:** Released Apr '81, on Joker (USA) by Lifetime Records (USA). Catalogue no: **SM 3133**

## HIS LAST RECORDINGS - 1970
Tracks: / Boy from New Orleans / What a wonderful world / Mood indigo / Give peace a chance / My one and only love / Everybody's talkin' / His father wore long hair / This black cat has nine lives / We shall overcome.
**Album:** Released '83, on RCA (France) by BMG Records (France). Catalogue no: **PL 43553**

## HOT 5 & HOT 7 1925-1928
**CD:** Released Mar '90, on Giants of Jazz by Hasmick Promotions. Catalogue no: **GOJ CD 53001**

## HOT 5 & HOT 7 1926-28
**Album:** Released Sep '87, on Giants of Jazz by Hasmick Promotions. Catalogue no: **LPJT 15**

## HOT FIVE (1928)
**Album:** Released Jan '83, on Swaggie (Australia) Catalogue no: **S 1239**

## HOT FIVE (1925-26)
**Album:** Released Jan '83, on Swaggie (Australia) Catalogue no: **S 1230**

## HOT FIVES & SEVENS COMPLETE (2)
Tracks: / My heart / Yes I'm in the barrel / Gut bucket blues / Come back sweet papa / Georgia grind / Heebie jeebies / Cornet chop suey / Oriental strut / You're next / Muskrat ramble / Don't forget to mess around / I'm gonna getcha / Dropping shucks / Who's it? / King of the Zulus, The / Big fat ma and skinny pa / Lonesome blues / Sweet little papa / Jazz lips / Skid dat de dat / Big butter and egg man / Sunset cafe stomp / You made me love you / Irish black bottom / Willie the weeper / Wild man blues / Chicago breakdown / Alligator crawl / Potato head blues / Melancholy blues / Weary blues / Twelfth St. rag / Keyhole blues / SOL blues / Gully low blues / That's when I'll come back to you / Put 'em down blues / Ory's Creole trombone / Last time, The / Struttin' with some barbecue / Got no blues / Once in a while / I'm not rough / Hotter than that / Savoy blues / Fireworks / Skip the gutter / Monday date, A / Don't jive me / West End blues / Sugar foot strut / Two deuces / Squeeze me / Knee drops / Symphonic raps / Savoyagers' stomp / No papa no / Basin Street blues / No one else but you / Bean koo jack / Save it, pretty mama / Weather bird / Muggles / Heah me talkin' to ya / St. James' Infirmary / Tight like this / Knockin' a jug.
**Album:** Released Mar '81, on Retrospect by EMI Records. Deleted 31 Jul '88. Catalogue no: **SH 405**

## HOT FIVES & SEVENS COMPLETE (SET OF 4)
**LP Set:** Released Mar '81, on Retrospect by EMI Records. Catalogue no: **SHB 69**

## HOT FIVES & SEVENS, THE
Tracks: / Lonesome blues / Jazz lips / Big butter and egg man / You made me love you / Willie the weeper / Alligator crawl / Melancholy / Twelfth St. rag / Sweet little papa / Skid dat de dat / Sunset cafe stomp / Irish black bottom / Wild man blues / Potato head blues / Weary blues / Keyhole blues.
**CD:** Released Apr '89, on CBS (import) by CBS Records. Catalogue no: **463 052 2**
**Album:** Released Apr '89, on CBS (import) by CBS Records. Catalogue no: **463 052 1**
**Cass:** Released Apr '89, on CBS (import) by CBS Records. Catalogue no: **463 052 4**

## HOT FIVES & SEVENS, VOL.3
**Cass:** Released '88, on CBS by CBS Records. Catalogue no: **465 189 4**
**CD:** Released '88, on CBS by CBS Records. Catalogue no: **465 189 2**
**Album:** Released '88, on CBS by CBS Records. Catalogue no: **465 189 1**

## HOT FIVES VOL.1, THE
Tracks: / My heart / I'm in the barrel / Gut bucket blues / Come back sweet papa / Georgia grind / Heebie jeebies / Cornet chop suey / Oriental strut / You're next / Muskrat ramble / Don't forget to mess around / I'm gonna gitcha / Droppin' shucks / Whosit / King of the Zulus, The / Big fat Ma and skinny Pa.
Note: In 1925 Louis Armstrong's name meant little to the general public, even though his playing was revered by countless jazz musicians. Only the initiated were aware that he had already eclipsed the work of pioneer cornetists like Freddie Keppard and Joe 'King' Oliver. Three years earlier, King Oliver, realizing that young Louis was coming up fast on the inside lane, invited him to

Digitally Remastered Directly From The Original Analog Tapes
LOUIS ARMSTRONG
THE HOT FIVES
CBS JAZZ MASTERPIECES


**Louis Armstrong - The Hot Fives Vol. 1 (CBS)**

leave New Orleans to join the famous Creole Jazz Band in Chicago. Louis accepted, and made his recording debut with Oliver in 1923. Subsequently, Fletcher Henderson, the foremost of the black band leaders in New York, made a bid for Louis' services. As a result, in 1924, Louis moved East and demolished all the contenders for the title of the world's most exciting cornetist. But in those early years no one mounted a publicity campaign for Louis and, though he played on many recording sessions in New York for various leaders, he remained, in 1925, just a supremely talented sideman.

Fortunately Louis had an ambitious wife, Lillian; they had met as members of King Oliver's Band, in which Lil played piano. Each of them had previously been married, Louis to a New Orleans 'hostess' Daisy Parker and Lil to singer James Johnson. Lillian accompanied Louis to New York, but moved back to Chicago in 1925. There she developed ambitions for her husband, and suspicions that he was doing more than practicing the cornet during his off-duty hours. Accordingly, Lil obtained a residency at the Chicago Dreamland and then sent Louis an ultimatum: come home or else.

To restore domestic peace, and to benefit from a raise in pay that took him from fifty-five to seventy-five dollars a week, Louis moved back to Chicago. Within a week he was taking part in a freelance recording date with pianist Richard M Jones, and blues singer Bertha 'Chippie' Hill. On November 9 1925, these three cut two sides for Okeh a company, which issued material aimed principally at black buyers (known as race records). Jones (from New Orleans) was a local talent scout and recording manager for Okeh, and he suggested to Tommy Rockwell, the company's chief talent spotter, that Louis should record for them.

After listening to Louis, Tommy Rockwell whole heartedly endorsed Jones' suggestion but since Okeh did most of its band recordings early in the morning and Rockwell was a notoriously late riser, he turned the task of setting up the deal to another white executive of the company, Elmer A Fearn. Fearn tried to convince Louis that it would be advantageous, to capture some of the market then occupied by Paul Whiteman, but eventually went along with a plan to form an all star quintet featuring New Orleans musicians alreading working in Chicago. This was a revolutionary idea. Most previous jazz instrumental recordings had been made by bands whose personnel worked together regularly (such as the Original Dixieland Jazz Band, King Oliver's Band, and the New Orleans Rhythm Kings). It was half suggested that Richard M Jones should be the leader - for all Armstrong's immense talents, he had never regularly fronted a band. According to Jones, Louis modestly agreed with this idea, but Jones shrewdly decided that Okeh would gain a great deal by using the name of an up and coming star. Lillian quickly seconded that idea and followed up by insisting that she play on the dates. A budget was fixed for a five piece band, each partipant to receive a flat fee of fifty dollars per session. Kid Ory was recruited to play trombone, Johnny St. Cyr the banjo and Johnny Dodds, the clarinet - this line-up contained four musicians from Louisiana and one, Lil from Tennessee. The group approached its task conscientiously and rehearsed before making its recording debut on November 12, 1925. Most of the material waxed by Louis Armstrong's Hot Five had not been recorded before; four of the participating musicians contributed tunes (none of Johnny Dodds' compositions were used). The first cut, *My heart*, had been copyrighted by Lillian in July 1920; its full title was *My heart will always lead me back to you* and it was originally a waltz. The Hot Five's treatment of the tune is positively un-waltz like, as they effortlessly transform it into a swinging, four in a bar theme. Louis doesn't hag the proceedings, but even without a show of his solo strength, it's obvious from the sheer ingenuity of his lead playing that he is the supreme talent on the session..

Louis' superb timing graces, the sombre opening strain of his own composition, *(Yes) I'm in the barrel*. Having established an evocative minor mood over stop time chords, he cleverly changes tactics and stomps out the main theme. Dodds plays two heartfelt blues choruses, then the cohesive ensemble moves on, its phrases glowing like embers. Louis' final breaks are fierce and daring, acting like a gust of wind igniting a finale of flaming brilliance. Armstrong offers his talented colleagues vocal encouragement on another of his tunes, *Gut bucket blues*. Lil vigorously rolls out twelve bars, then Ory, placid and sonourous, blows effectively before handing over to Dodds whose spine tingling solo opens with a dramatic long note. Behind Louis' solo (full of exquisitely shaped phrases), Kid Ory's words urge the cornetist on. The front line re-gathers and pioneers the art of riffing, later an essential ingredient in the success of swing music. Johnny Dods, on alto saxophone, plays the opening melody of *Come back sweet Papa* (by Paul Barbarin and Luis Russell). Dodds was more gifted on Clarinet, but still manages to imbue the tune with an infectious lilt. The two brass players take over and blow with such impeccable accord that Dodds, who was putting down his saxophone and picking up his clarinet, is hardly missed; however he soon rejoins the front line and the perfect team is re-established. The success of the Hot Five's initial date meant that there was no change of policy or personnel when it met again in February 1926. The session opened with *Georgia Grind*, a medium paced blues, written by A Williams. A relaxed ensemble precedes a vinegary vocal from Lil; Louis sings the next two choruses much more effectively. In those days the gravel was only sprinkled lightly over his vocal chrods, but all the vigor and artistry of his later singing was

already obvious.
*Heebie jeebies* made jazz history by being the first proper recording of scat singing. Louis demonstrates the highly rhythmic art of wordless singing to perfection on a tune claimed by Boyd Atkins. Armstrong usually had a twinkle in his eye when telling how he had to improvise vocal sounds after dropping the lyric sheet on the recording. Both Lil and Kid Ory later expressed doubts about the move being impromptu, but what is certain that Louis' scatting was a big selling point for the record. On *Cornet chop suey* (a tune copyrighted by Louis in January 1924), Lil takes a full chorus, but the rest of the piece is a superb instrumental display by the composer, who demonstrates his flexible technique and his mental agility. Copying the recording became a test for thousands of aspiring jazz musicians. In Louis' home city, two young trumpeters, Henry 'Red' Allen and Edgar 'Guy' Kelly, locked horns in a cutting contest on *Cornet chop suey.* Allen won the day because his adversary forgot to play the ingenious coda that Louis fashioned on the original recording. Johnny St. Cyr's banjo is well featured on his composition *Oriental strut.* So too is the band's joyous ensemble sound. Ory's warm, full-toned trombone work and Dodds, at his most ebulient, precede some brilliant stop time soloing by Armstrong. Most of the Hot Five's repertoire was medium paced, but Lil's *You're next* is effectively taken at a majestically slow tempo.

Kid Ory's great moments, both ensemble and solo, occur on his tune *Muskrat ramble.* No subsequent version of this much recorded item ever measures up to the spirit and rhythmic invention of the original, with its flamboyantly syncopated final chorus. The great New Orleans reed-player, Sidney Bechet, vowed that the tune was an old Creole theme called *The old cow died,* but whatever its origins, Ory deserves full credit for introducing it to the jazz world. In June 1926, on further sessions by the group, it's obvious that Louis' upper register playing, always spectacular, had reached world beating proportions. It figures on the lively *Don't forget to mess around* (another Paul Barbarin composition); Dodds again flirts with the alto. sax and Louis shows how skillfully he was able to project his vocal exuberance. The next two tunes, *I'm gonna gitcha* and *Droppin' shucks* (written by Lil) feature telling vocals by Louis and more of his daring crystal clear cornet playing. Dodds is consistently brilliant and Ory dependable as ever.

*Who sit,* a bright composition by Richard M Jones, contains some amazingly novel tone colors, (created by Dodds and St. Cyr as they improvise around the lines that Louis produces from a 'slide whistle'. The excursion didn't affect Louis' chops; after the piano and clarinet solos he picks up his cornet and steers the band to an exciting finish. On *king of the Zulus* Ory blows sombre phrases over an ostinato rhythm, then a humourous interlude develops in which Clarence Babcock acts the part of a Jamaican at a soul food party. The hokum ceases and Louis begins a passionate musical exploration, soaring to wonderfully expressive high notes. St Cyr's banjo arpeggios create an effective coda which is sealed by a chord from the band. Just as this is fading, the bizarre Babcock emits afarewell shout. There's also an element of novelty about Richard M Jones' song *Big fat ma and skinny pa* in which Babcock plays the role of a dance caller. the band enters into the spirit and socks out a chorus full of rhythmic energy. Dodds solos effectively, then Louis takes a masterfully phrased vocal. Ory blows lustily before the inexorable swing of the full ensemble creates a superb ride-out.

Thus, the first sixteen titles of a series now revered as jazz classics were recorded. Years later Louis Armstrong described the Okeh dates as 'just a gig to us'. Posterity was not on the young musicians' minds as they recorded; they were totally unaware that their improvisations would help spread the New Orleans musical gospel throughout the world. Kid Ory gave his views: 'I think the reason those records came out so well was that the Okeh people left us alone and didn't try to expert us'. He then added an accolade that summarized the leader's immeasurable genius: 'You couldn't go wrong with Louis'. (John Chilton, 1988)

**Album:** Released 22 Aug '88, on CBS (import) by CBS Records. Catalogue no: **460 821 1**

**Cass:** Released 22 Aug '88, on CBS (import) by CBS Records. Catalogue no: **460 821 4**

**Louis Armstrong - Hot Five/Seven (1926-27) (Swaggie(USA))**

**HOT FIVE/SEVEN (1926-27) (See panel above)**

Tracks: / Lonesome blues / Sweet little papa / Jazz lips / Skid-dat-de-dat / I want a big butter and egg man / Sunset cafe stomp / You made me love you / Irish black bottom / Willie the weeper / Wild man blues / Chicago breakdown / Alligator crawl / Potato head blues / Melancholy blues / Weary blues / Twelfth street rag.

Note: The first side of this second set of classic Louis Armstrong records completes those made by the accoustic system; from the first track on Side 2 onwards, they were made by the remarkably good Western-Electric Sound System, and even today they could hardly be improved upon. Some doubt exists regarding the exact part played by Kid Ory on some of these. He is supposed, on his own evidence, to have missed a session about this time, but arguments still continue among collectors as to just which one this was. The trombone on the last accoustic date, stated by some to have featured one John Thomas, certainly sounds like Ory when compared with his work on *Oriental strut* (see Swaggie S1230) others state that the Ory-less date was one of the earliest electric sessions, and point to the fact of Ory's having been in New York with Joe Oliver at the time. *The Chicago defender* of May 14, 1927, says that Oliver was at that date in New York, and as Ory was a member of Oliver's band, by inference he was there too; hence, despite the Oryesque sound of the trombone on the second side of this set, it seems that the mysterious John Thomas was the man responsible, although an even stronger possibilty is Gerald Reeves. *Lonesome blues* has one of Dodd's most poignant soli; Louis' gruff but heart-searching vocal is also one of the rare occasions when he sings a traditional twelve-bar blues. *Sweet little papa*, by Kid Ory, is based on the famous Nick LaRocca-Larry Shields composition *Ostrich walk*, while *Jazz lips* is quite a technical excercise for the brass. We then come to another example of Louis' scat vocal work - and to one of the most moving of all instrumental blues, *Skid-dat-de-dat*. There is such perfect accord between all five musicians that there is not one fluff or hiatus anywhere (something which cannot be said for some of the other performances). Louis' voice is not so much singing as being used as an instrument on which he doubles. The girl with whom he sings *I want a big butter and egg man*, and who sings the rowdy vocal on *Sunset cafe stomp* (s tribute to the spot where Louis had his regular band at the time; the Hot Five never made a public appearance except at the Okeh artists' ball in Chicago on June 12, 1926), is May Alix. Both these and the last two on Side 1, are numbers that were featured by Louis as part of the floor-show at the Sunset. *You made me love you* is not the song written by James V. Monaco in 1913, with the refrain "I didn't want to do it" but an entirely different number by Percy Venable. *Irish black bottom* is a light comedy number which Louis sings with his tongue firmly in his cheek. It is, after all, a little difficult to believe him when he says "I was born in Ireland".

The first of the electric recordings, *Willie the weeper*, is one of the most magnificent. It features soli all round, including a beauty by St Cyr, which later became the basis of a ridiculous popular song, *You can't tell a waltz from a tango*. *Wild man blues*, apparently a collaboration between the piano genius "Jelly Roll" Morton and Louis Armstrong, had the distinction of appearing on Parlophone soon after its issue in America. Unfortunately, it includes a serious "clinker". Apart from this, its magestic melody and flowing line make it a classic indeed. John Dodds plays superbly. *Chicago breakdown* is another Morton composition which the master himself never recorded, alas. The band here is not the recording group hitherto, but the regular Sunset Cafe big band, led by Carroll Dickerson, and including, besides Armstrong, Bill Wilson (trumpet), Honore Dutrey (trombone), Darnell Howard (clarinet, soprano and alto sax), Joe Walker (alto sax), Al Washington (tenor sax), Earl Hines (piano), Rip Bassett (banjo), Tubby Hall (drums) and Pete Briggs (tuba), the only man apart from Louis common to all the others on this side. It is a typical Morton number, and particularly interesting in that it has Earl Hines, Armstrong's future collaborator on many classic discs at the piano. He fits the Mortonian mood very well, though his style is as far removed from Morton's delicate ragtime idiom as anything could be. *Alligator Crawl* is a Fats Waller number, recorded long before the composer did so, with some particularly powerful work from Armstrong. St Cyr has a short solo to relieve the truly shattering effect of the brass and Dodds' soaring clarinet. *Potato head blues* is another example of Louis' mastery of timing - his solo of stop chords towards the end is breathtaking. *Melancholy blues*, which owes much of its melodic line to *I ain't got nobody*, written some seventeen years before, also marks a new high level of understanding between Louis and his men; if it is John Thomas on this, it is a thousand pities we have noother known solos by this man. *Weary blues* is the old rag by Artie Matthews, dating from 1915 and recorded by hundreds of different (and indifferent) bands before and since this version; but none of them, from the delicate understatement of the New Orleans Rhythm Kings in 1923 to the ferocious onslaught by Ray Miller's Hotel Gibson Orchestra later in 1927, catch the spirit of the number as well as does this. Johnny Dodds in the low register is sheer delight. The last track in this set is *Twelfth street rag*, which was rejected for issue in 1927, and never saw the presses until 1940, when George Avakian, the eminent American critic, then working on some Armstrong reissues, discovered the master intact. It contains some rather odd high-register work by Louis, some very blue clarinet by Dodds, and some masterful, gruff trombone that I would have said could only have been by Ory, but I have already mentioned that problem. The slow deliberate tempo of the number makes a pleasing contrast with the nervous cacophony exhibited by most other versions, before and after. Brian Rust.

**Album:** Released Jan '83, on Swaggie (Australia) Catalogue no: **S 1233**

## HOT SEVEN/FIVE (1927-28)

**Album:** Released Jan '83, on Swaggie (Australia) Catalogue no: **S 1236**

## IMMORTAL CONCERTS (At Symphony Hall-Boston, November 30, 1947) (Armstrong, Louis/his All-stars)

Tracks: / Mahogany Hall stomp / Black and blue / Royal Garden blues / That's my desire / C jam blues / Stars fell on Alabama / I cried for you / On the sunny side of the street / Tea for two / Baby, won't you please come home / Muskrat ramble / Lover / Body and soul / Steak face / High society / Boff boff.

**CD:** Released Feb '88, on Entertainers Catalogue no: **ENTCD 235**

**CD:** Released '88, on Giants of Jazz by Hasmick Promotions. Catalogue no: **GOJCD 0235**

## IN CONCERT

**2 LP Set:** Released Oct '88, on Vogue by Vogue Records. Catalogue no: **426014**

## IN EAST EUROPE

**Album:** Released '88, on Joker (USA) by Lifetime Records (USA). Catalogue no: **SM 3864**

## IN NEW YORK

**Cass:** Released May '88, on Classic Jazz Masters Catalogue no: **42018**

**Album:** Released May '88, on Classic Jazz Masters Catalogue no: **22018**

## IN SWEDEN (1959)

**Album:** Released Oct '86, on Jazz Information (Sweden) Catalogue no: **CAH 4000**

## INTEGRAL NICE CONCERT 1948 - VOL. 1

Tracks: / Panama / Black and blue / Velma's blues / Monday date, 1 / Monday date, 2 / Royal Garden blues (part 1) / Royal Garden blues (part 2) / Someday / Muskrat ramble / I cried last night, 1 / I cried last night, 2.

**Album:** Released Jun '85, on Jazz Anthology by Musidisc Records (France). Catalogue no: **JA 5154**

## JACK ARMSTRONG BLUES

**Album:** Released Jun '89, on Jazz & Jazz Catalogue no: **JJ 601**

## JAZZ CLASSICS

**Album:** Released Oct '61, on Ace Of Hearts by Decca Records. Deleted '66. Catalogue no: **AH 7**

## JAZZ GREATS

Tracks: / St. Louis blues / Do you know what it means to miss New Orleans / Swing you cats.

**2 LP Set:** Released Jan '85, on RCA (Germany) Catalogue no: **NL 45217**

## JAZZ POTPOURRI

**Album:** Released '88, on Meritt (USA) Catalogue no: **MERITT 19**

## JAZZ TIME VOL.6

**Album:** Released '88, on Vogue (France) by Vogue Records. Catalogue no: **502706**

## JULY 4, 1900 - JULY 6, 1971

Tracks: / (You so and so) You'll wish you'd never been / Hustlin' and bustlin' for baby / Sittin' in the dark / He's a son of the south / Some sweet day / Honey don't you love me anymore / Mississippi basin / Tomorrow night / Dusky stevedore / Song was born, A / Lovely weather we're having / Please stop playing that blues, boy / Ain't misbehavin' / Pennies from heaven / Save it, pretty mama / Rain, rain / I never saw a better day / I wonder who / Don't play me cheap / Linger in my arms a little longer baby / Whatta ya gonna do / Joseph 'n' his brudders / No variety blues / Blues in the south / I want a little girl / Sugar (that sugar baby o' mine) / Blues are brewin', The / Endie / I believe / Why doubt my love / You don't learn that in school / Fifty fifty blues / Some day you'll be sorry.

**2 LP Set:** on RCA Victor by BMG Records (UK). Catalogue no: **DPM 2017**

**LA VOCE DEL JAZZ (Armstrong, Louis / his Allstars)**
**Album:** Released Nov '88, on Musica Jazz Catalogue no: **2MJP 1056**

**LAUGHIN' LOUIS**
Tracks: / That's my home / Hobo, you can't ride this train / Medley of Armstrong hits (part 2) / When you're smiling (the whole world smiles) / St James infirmary / Dinah / Medley of Armstrong hits (part 1) / I'll be glad when you're dead you rascal you / When it's sleepy time down south / Nobody's sweetheart / I've got the world on a string / I gotta right to sing the blues / High society / Basin Street blues / Mahogany Hall stomp / Laugin' Louis / Dusky stevedore / There's a cabin in the pines / Sweet Sue, just you / Don't play me cheap / St. Louis blues.
**Cass:** Released Nov '89, on Bluebird (2) by BMG Records (UK). Catalogue no: **NK 90404**
**CD:** Released Nov '89, on Bluebird (2) by BMG Records (UK). Catalogue no: **ND 90404**
**Album:** Released Nov '89, on Bluebird (2) by BMG Records (UK). Catalogue no: **NL 90404**

**LEGEND (Armstrong, Louis Hot Five & Hot Seven)**
Tracks: / My heart / Yes I'm in the barrel / Gut bucket blues / Come back sweet papa / Georgia grind / Heebie jeebies / Cornet chop suey / Oriental strut / You're next / Muskrat rumble / Don't forget to mess around / I'm gonna gitcha / Dropping shucks / Who'sit / King of the zulus / Big fat ma and skinny pa.
**Album:** Released Feb '84, on Retrospect by EMI Records. Deleted Jun '89. Catalogue no: **SH 404**

**LEGENDARY LOUIS ARMSTRONG, THE**
**Cass set:** Released Jun '88, on Spectrum (1) Catalogue no: **M 10224**

**LEGENDARY PERFORMER, A**
Tracks: / What a wonderful world / I gotta right to sing the blues / When you're smiling / St. James infirmary / Dinah / Basin Street blues / Mahogany Hall blues stomp / High society / Do you know what it means to miss New Orleans / Rockin' chair / Ain't misbehavin' / Some day you'll be sorry / You rascal you / When it's sleepytime down south / Nobody's sweetheart / St. Louis blues / Some sweet day.
**Album:** Released '79, on RCA Victor by BMG Records (UK). Deleted '82. Catalogue no: **PL 12659**
**Cass:** Released '79, on RCA Victor by BMG Records (UK). Deleted '82. Catalogue no: **PK 12659**

**LIVE & AT HIS BEST**
**CD:** Released May '88, on Jazz Life Catalogue no: **2473262**
**Cass:** Released May '88, on Jazz Life Catalogue no: **2173262**
**Album:** Released May '88, on Jazz Life Catalogue no: **2273262**

**LIVE FROM HOLLYWOOD 1949**
**Album:** Released Apr '79, on Swing House by Submarine Records. Catalogue no: **SWH 2**
**Cass:** Released Oct '84, on Swing House by Submarine Records. Catalogue no: **CSWH 2**

**LIVE IN YOKOHAMA**
Tracks: / When it's sleepy time down South / Indiana / Kiss to build a dream on, A / Tea for two / My bucket's got a hole in it / Margie / Velma's blues / C'est si bon / Stompin' at The Savoy.
**Album:** Released Apr '81, on Queendisc (Italy) Catalogue no: **QU 032**

**LOUIS ARMSTRONG (Compact / Walkman jazz)**
Tracks: / I gotta right to sing the blues / Moon song / Don't get around much anymore / Let's fall in love.
**Cass:** Released 27 Feb '88, on Verve Catalogue no: **833 293-4**
**CD:** Released Mar '88, on Verve Catalogue no: **833 293-2**

**LOUIS ARMSTRONG, 1959**
**CD:** Released '89, on Tax Catalogue no: **TAXCD 3712-2**

**LOUIS ARMSTRONG 1928-1931**
**CD:** Released Sep '88, on Hermes by Nimbus Records. Catalogue no: **HRM 6002**

**LOUIS ARMSTRONG ALL STARS 1948-49 VOL. 2**
**Album:** Released Apr '79, on Jazz Connoisseur by Spotlite Records. Catalogue no: **JC 110**

**LOUIS ARMSTRONG ALL STARS PHILADELPHIA (August 7 and 9, 1949)**
**Album:** Released Apr '79, on Jazz Connoisseur by Spotlite Records. Catalogue no: **JC 005**

**LOUIS ARMSTRONG AND DUKE ELLINGTON VOL. 1**
**Album:** Released Jan '82, on Jazz Reactivation Catalogue no: **JR 133**

**LOUIS ARMSTRONG AND GUESTS**
**Cass:** Released '88, on Entertainers Catalogue no: **ENT MC 13041**
**Album:** Released '88, on Entertainers Catalogue no: **ENT LP 13041**

**LOUIS ARMSTRONG AND HIS ALL STARS (Armstrong, Louis/his Allstars)**
**LP Set:** Released '88, on Joker (USA) by Lifetime Records (USA). Catalogue no: **C 65/4 BOX 4**
**2 LP Set:** Released Aug '81, on Joker (USA) by Lifetime Records (USA). Catalogue no: **SM 3806/2**

**LOUIS ARMSTRONG AND HIS ALL STARS 1961-2**
**CD:** Released Feb '89, on Storyville by Storyville Records AB. Catalogue no: **STCD 4012**
**Album:** Released May '86, on Storyville by Storyville Records AB. Catalogue no: **SLP 4012**
**Cass:** Released Mar '86, on Ditto by Pickwick Records. Catalogue no: **DTO 10234**

**LOUIS ARMSTRONG AND HIS ALL STARS (STORYVILLE) (Armstrong, Louis / his Allstars)**
Tracks: / When it's sleepy time down south / Hello dolly / Blueberry hill / Volare / St. James infirmary / Girl from Ipanema / Indiana / Muskrat ramble / Mack the knife / I love Paris / Time after time / Cabaret / Tiger rag / When the saints go marching in / This could be the start of something big / Please don't talk about me when I'm gone / Stompin' at the Savoy / That's my desire / Closer walk with thee, A / Them there eyes / Avalon / Kiss to build a dream on, A / Ole miss.
**Album:** Released May '86, on Storyville by Storyville Records AB. Catalogue no: **SLP 4095**
**CD:** Released Feb '89, on Storyville by Storyville Records AB. Catalogue no: **STCD 4095**

**LOUIS ARMSTRONG AND HIS ALL STARS VOL.1 (Armstrong, Louis/his Allstars)**
Tracks: / Sleepy time down south / Indiana / Someday / Ole miss / Tin roof blues / My buckets got a hole in it / Periddo / Dardanella.
**Album:** Released Jan '82, on Jazz Reactivation Catalogue no: **JR 110**

**LOUIS ARMSTRONG AND HIS ORCHESTRA 1935 - 44**
**Album:** Released Jan '83, on Swaggie (Australia) Catalogue no: **S 702**

**LOUIS ARMSTRONG AND JACK TEAGARDEN (Armstrong, Louis / Jack Teagarden)**
**CD:** Released '89, on Echo Jazz Catalogue no: **EJCD 05**
**Cass:** Released '89, on Echo Jazz Catalogue no: **EJMC 05**
**Album:** Released '89, on Echo Jazz Catalogue no: **EJLP 05**

**LOUIS ARMSTRONG AND KING OLIVER**
Tracks: / Just gone / Canal Street blues / Mandy Lee blues / I'm going to wear you off my mind / Chimes blues / Weather bird rag / Dipper mouth blues / Froggie Moore / Snake rag / Alligator hop / Zulu's ball / Working man blues / Krooked blues / Mabel's dreams (take 1) / Mabel's dreams (take 2) / Southern stomps (take 1) / Southern stomps (take 2) / Riverside blues / King Oliver / Jelly Roll Morton (King Porter stomp) / Tom cat blues / Terrible blues / Santa Claus blues / Texas moaner blues / Of all the wrongs you've done to me / Nobody knows the way I feel this morning / Early every morn / Cake walking babies from home.
**2 LP Set:** Released Aug '80, on Milestone by Ace Records. Catalogue no: **M 47017**

**LOUIS ARMSTRONG AT EDDIE CONDON FLOOR SHOW VOL. 1**
**Album:** Released '88, on Queen Catalogue no: **QUEEN 010**

**LOUIS ARMSTRONG AT EDDIE CONDON FLOOR SHOW VOL. 2**
**Album:** Released '88, on Queen Catalogue no: **QUEEN 011**

**LOUIS ARMSTRONG (AUDIO FIDELITY)**
**Cass:** Released '84, on Audio Fidelity(USA) by Audio Fidelity (USA). Catalogue no: **ZCGAS 725**

**LOUIS ARMSTRONG (CAMBRA)**
Tracks: / Hello Dolly / Sit down you're rockin' the boat / I'm confessin' / Jeepers creepers / Swing that music / On the sunny side of the street / When the saints go marching in / Cabaret / Heebie jeebies / I'll string along with you / West End blues / Down by the riverside / Among my souvenirs / 'S wonderful / Georgia on my mind / What a wonderful world / High society / Mahogany Hall stomp / Carry me back to old Virginny / When you're smiling / I can't give you anything but love / Alexander's ragtime band / Blueberry Hill / Naturally / That lucky old sun / Dippermouth blues / Ain't misbehavin' / Basin Street blues / When it's sleepy time down South.
**Cass set:** Released '83, on Cambra by Cambra Records. Deleted '88. Catalogue no: **CRT 010**

**LOUIS ARMSTRONG & EDMOND HALL'S ORCHESTRA (Live at Carnegie Hall, Feb 8 1947) (Armstrong, Louis/Edmond Hall's orchestra)**
Tracks: / New Orleans function / St. Louis blues / Muskrat ramble / Ain't misbehavin'.
**CD:** Released Mar '88, on Delta (1) by Delta Records. Catalogue no: **20 802**

**LOUIS ARMSTRONG (ENTERTAINERS)**
Tracks: / Cabaret / Mack the knife / Ramona / Gypsy, The / Only you / Blueberry hill / Hello Dolly.
**Album:** Released Sep '87, on Entertainers Catalogue no: **ENT LP 13007**
**Cass:** Released Sep '87, on Entertainers Catalogue no: **ENT MC 13007**

**LOUIS ARMSTRONG & FLETCHER HENDERSON 1924-25 (Armstrong, Louis / Fletcher Henderson Orchestra)**
**Album:** Released '79, on VJM (Vintage Jazz Music) by Vintage Jazz Music Society(VJM). Catalogue no: **VLP 60**

**LOUIS ARMSTRONG & HIS ALL STARS (1947-50) (Armstrong, Louis / his Allstars)**
**Album:** Released Jul '88, on Forlane Catalogue no: **99002**
**Album:** Released Jan '88, on Family Catalogue no: **SFR DP 692**
**CD:** Released Sep '88, on Giants of Jazz by Hasmick Promotions. Catalogue no: **CD 53032**
**CD:** Released Jul '88, on Forlane Catalogue no: **UCD 19002**

**LOUIS ARMSTRONG & HIS ORCHESTRA 1929 - 49 (Armstrong, Louis / his orchestra)**
**Album:** Released Sep '87, on Giants of Jazz by Hasmick Promotions. Catalogue no: **LPJT 53**

**LOUIS ARMSTRONG HOT FIVE & HOT SEVEN 1925-28 (Armstrong, Louis Hot Five & Hot Seven)**
Tracks: / Alligator crawl / Wild man blues / Melancholy blues / Willie the weeper / Ory's Creole trombone / Struttin' with some barbecue / Hotter than that / West End blues / Potato head blues / Keyhole blues / Gully low blues / Basin Street blues / SOL blues / Twelfth St. rag / Savoy blues / Muskrat ramble / Cornet chop suey / Skid dat de dat / Come back, sweet papa / Yes, I'm in the barrel / Weary blues / Put 'em down blues / Monday date, A.
**CD:** Released Jan '88, on Giants of Jazz by Hasmick Promotions. Catalogue no: **GOJCD 0242**

**LOUIS ARMSTRONG IN THE 1930'S**
**Album:** Released '88, on Collector's Classics Catalogue no: **CC 26**

**LOUIS ARMSTRONG & JACK TEAGARDEN (Armstrong, Louis / Jack Teagarden)**
**Album:** Released '88, on Joker (USA) by Lifetime Records (USA). Catalogue no: **SM 3873**

**LOUIS ARMSTRONG JULY 4 - JULY 6, 1971**
**2 LP Set:** Released Jan '85, on RCA (Germany) Catalogue no: **26 28109**

**LOUIS ARMSTRONG LEGEND**
**Album:** Released Mar '79, Catalogue no: **P 42**

**LOUIS ARMSTRONG LEGEND 1926-27**
Tracks: / Lonesome blues / Sweet little Papa / Jazz lips / Skid dat de dat / I want a big butter and egg man / Sunset cafe stomp / You made me love you / Irish black bottom / Willie the weeper / Wild man blues / Chicago breakdown / Alligator crawl / Potato head blues / Melancholy / Weary blues / Twelfth St. rag.
**Cass:** Released Mar '85, on Retrospect by EMI Records. Deleted Nov '88. Catalogue no: **EG 2604584**
**Album:** Released Mar '85, on Retrospect by EMI Records. Deleted Nov '88. Catalogue no: **EG 2604581**

**LOUIS ARMSTRONG LEGEND, THE 1927 - 28(Hot Fives & Sevens vol. 3)**
Tracks: / Put 'em down blues / Ory's creole trombone / Last time, The / Struttin' with some barbecue / Got no blues / Once in a while / I'm not rough / Hotter than that / Savoy blues / Fireworks / Skip the gutter / Monday date, A / Don't jive me / Keyhole blues / SOL blues / Gully low blues / That's when I'll come back to you.
Note: The third re-issue due to popular demand, from 'The Louis Armstrong Legend' collection - only latterly available in a four record box set.This album displays Armstrong's unquestionable talent and familiar style through from up tempo New Orleans jives to the ever popular sophisticated blues sound of the 20's, illustrating beautidully this important transitional period of his career.
**Album:** Released Jan '86, on Retrospect by EMI Records. Deleted Aug '89. Catalogue no: **SH 406**

**LOUIS ARMSTRONG LEGEND, THE 1928 - 29 (Hot Fives & Sevens complete vol. 4)**
Tracks: / West end blues / Sugar foot strut / Two deuces / Squeeze me / Knee drops / Symphonic raps / Savoyagers' stomp / No papa, no / Basin street blues / No one else but you / Beau koo Jack / Save it pretty mam / Weather bird / Muggles / Heah me talkin to ya / St. James infirmary / Tight like this / Knockin' a jug.
**Album:** Released Nov '86, on Retrospect by EMI Records. Deleted Aug '89. Catalogue no: **SH 407**
**Cass:** Released Nov '86, on Retrospect by EMI Records. Deleted 31 Jul '88. Catalogue no: **TC SH 407**

**LOUIS ARMSTRONG -- LIVE (February 24, 1962)**
Note: Hamburg concert featuring Louis with supporting musicians including Trummy Young, Joe Darensbourg and Billy Kyle. Jazz classics include Indiana, Mack The Knife and Struttin' With Some Barbecue plus a medley of Armstrong vocals.
**Album:** Released Apr '88, on Sounds Great Catalogue no: **SG 8008**

**LOUIS ARMSTRONG (LOTUS)**
**Album:** Released '88, on Lotus Catalogue no: **LOP 14,030**

**LOUIS ARMSTRONG & LUIS RUSSELL 1929 - 30**
Note: MONO
**Album:** Released Jan '83, on Swaggie (Australia) Catalogue no: **S 1267**

**LOUIS ARMSTRONG MEETS OSCAR PETERSON (Armstrong, Louis / Oscar Peterson)**
Tracks: / That old feeling / I'll never be the same / How long has this been going on / I was doing all right / Moon song / There's no you / Sweet Lorraine / Let's fall in love / Blues in the night / What's new / Just one of those things / You go to my head.
**Album:** Released Mar '83, on Verve (USA) by Polydor Ltd. Catalogue no: **2304 422**
**CD:** on Verve Catalogue no: **825 713-2**

**LOUIS ARMSTRONG & ORCHESTRA 1929-31 (Armstrong, Louis / his orchestra)**
**Album:** Released '88, on Swaggie (Australia) Catalogue no: **S 1402**

**IOUIS ARMSTRONG & ORCHESTRA 1931-32 (Armstrong, Louis / his orchestra)**
**Album:** Released '88, on Swaggie (Australia) Catalogue no: **S 1403**

**LOUIS ARMSTRONG REMEMBERED (VIDEO)(Various artists)**
**VHS:** Released '88, on Kay Jazz (video) by Kay Jazz. Catalogue no: **KJ 050**

**LOUIS ARMSTRONG STORY**
**Album:** Released Feb '85, on CBS (import) by CBS Records. Catalogue no: **66427**

**LOUIS ARMSTRONG STORY, THE**
Tracks: / When you're smiling / Some of these days / On the sunny side of the street / Solitude / When the saints go marching in / Ain't misbehavin' / Jeepers creepers / I want a little girl / Someday you'll be sorry / Lazy river / I love jazz / Mack the knife / Muskrat ramble / Tiger rag / When it's sleepy time down South / Cabaret / Volare / Indiana / Kiss to build a dream on, A / Hello Dolly / Blueberry hill / St. James Infirmary / Tenderly / You'll never walk alone / Mop mop.
**Cass:** Released May '89, on Deja Vu Catalogue no: **DVREMC 04**
**CD:** Released May '89, on Deja Vu Catalogue no: **DVRECD 04**

**LOUIS ARMSTRONG & THE ALL STARS (Philadelphia 1948)**
Tracks: / Just you, just me / Boogie woogie on St. Louis blues / Struttin' with some barbecue / St. Louis blues / Someday / Together / That's a plenty / East of the sun / St. James' Infirmary / Panama / Maybe you'll be there / Lazy river / Muskrat ramble.
Note: Line-up: Armstrong,Teagarden,Bigard,Hines,Shaw,Catlett,V.Middleton.
**Album:** Released '81, on Queendisc (Italy) Catalogue no: **QU 19**

**LOUIS ARMSTRONG (THE COLLECTION)**
**CD:** Released Aug '87, on The Collection by Object Enterprises. Catalogue no: **OR 0015**

**LOUIS ARMSTRONG (VERVE)**
**CD:** Released '88, on Verve Catalogue no: **821 988 2**

**LOUIS ARMSTRONG, VOL 1 (Muskrat ramble)**
Tracks: / My heart / Yes, I'm in the barrel / Gut bucket blues / Come back sweet Papa / Georgia grind / Heebie jeebies / Cornet chop suey / Oriental Strut / You're next / Muskrat ramble / Don't forget to mess around / I'm gonna gitcha.
**Album:** Released Apr '81, on Joker (USA) by Lifetime Records (USA). Catalogue no: **SM 3742**

**LOUIS ARMSTRONG, VOL 2 (Irish black bottom)**
Tracks: / Droppin' sucks / Who's it / Big fat ma & skinny pa / Lonesome blues / Sweet little papa / Jazz lips / King of the Zulus, The / Skid dat de dat / Big butter and egg man / Sunset Cafe stomp / You made me love you / Irish black bottom.
Note: Hot Five recordings from 1926: Louis Armstrong (cornet), Kid Ory (trombone), Johnny Dodds (clarinet), Lil Armstrong (piano), Johnny St. Cyr (banjo).
**Album:** on Joker (USA) by Lifetime Records (USA). Catalogue no: **SM 3743**

**LOUIS ARMSTRONG, VOL 3 (Potato head blues)**
Tracks: / Willie the weeper / Wild man blues / Chicago breakdown / Alligator crawl / Potato head blues / Melancholy blues / Weary blues / Twelfth St. rag / Keyhole blues / SOL blues / Gully low blues / That's when I'll come back to you.
Note: Hot Seven and Louis Armstrong Orchestra recordings from 1927.
**Album:** Released Apr '81, on Joker (USA) by Lifetime Records (USA). Catalogue no: **SM 3744**

**LOUIS ARMSTRONG, VOL 4 (Savoy blues)**
Tracks: / Put 'em down blues / Ory's Creole trombone / Last time, The / Struttin' with some barbecue / Got no blues / Once in a while / I'm not rough / Hotter than that / Savoy blues / Fireworks / Skip the gutter / Monday date / Don't jive me.
Note: Hot Five recordings from 1927 and 1928.
**Album:** Released Apr '81, on Joker (USA) by Lifetime Records (USA). Catalogue no: **SM 3745**

**LOUIS ARMSTRONG, VOL 5 (West End blues)**
Tracks: / West End blues / Sugarfoot strut / Kneedrops / Two deuces / Squeeze me / Symphonic raps / Savoyagers' stomp / No papa no / Basin Street blues / No one else but you / Beau Koo Jack / Save it, pretty mama / Weather bird / Muggles.
Note: Hot Five, Carroll Dickerson Orchestra and Savoy Ballroom Five recordings from 1928.
**Album:** Released Apr '81, on Joker (USA) by Lifetime Records (USA). Catalogue no: **SM 3746**

**LOUIS ARMSTRONG, VOL 6 (Savoy Ballroom Five and Louis Armstrong Orchestra)**
Tracks: / Hear me talkin' to ya / St. James' Infirmary / Tight like this / Ain't misbehavin' / Black and blue / That rhythm man / Sweet Savanah Sue / Some of these days / When you're smiling / After you've gone.
Note: Recordings from 1928 and 1929.
**Album:** Released Apr '81, on Joker (USA) by Lifetime Records (USA). Catalogue no: **SM 3747**

**LOUIS ARMSTRONG, VOL 7 (Orchestra, 1929-30)**
Tracks: / I ain't got nobody / Dallas blues / St. Louis blues / Rockin' chair / Song of the islands / Bessie couldn't help it / Blue turning grey over you / Dear old Southland / My sweet / I can't believe that you're in love with me / Indian cradle song / Exactly like you / Dinah / Tiger rag.
**Album:** on Joker (USA) by Lifetime Records (USA). Catalogue no: **SM 3748**

**LOUIS ARMSTRONG, VOL 8 (Sebastian New Cotton Club Orchestra)**
Tracks: / I'm a ding dong daddy / I'm in the market for you / I'm confessin' / If I could be with you / Body and soul / Memories of you / You're lucky to me / Sweethearts on parade / You're driving me crazy / Peanut vendor / Just a gigolo / Shine.
Note: Recordings from 1930 and 1931.
**Album:** Released Apr '81, on Joker (USA) by Lifetime Records (USA). Catalogue no: **SM 3749**

**LOUIS ARMSTRONG VOL 9: ORCHESTRA 1931**
Tracks: / Walkin' my baby back home / I surrender dear / When it's sleepy time down South / Blue again / Little Joe / You rascal you / Them there eyes / When your lover has gone / Lazy river / Chinatown, my Chinatown / Wrap your troubles in dreams / Stardust.
**Album:** Released Apr '81, on Joker (USA) by Lifetime Records (USA). Catalogue no: **SM 3750**

**LOUIS ARMSTRONG VOL 10: ORCHESTRA**
Tracks: / You can depend on me / Georgia on my mind / Lonesome road / I got rhythm / Between the devil and the deep blue sea / Kickin' the gong around / Home / All of me / Love, you funny thing / New tiger rag, The / Keepin' out of mischief now / Lawd, you made the night too long.
**Album:** Released Apr '81, on Joker (USA) by Lifetime Records (USA). Catalogue no: **SM 3751**

**LOUIS ARMSTRONG VOL 11: ORCHESTRA**
Tracks: / That's my home / Hobo you can't ride this train / I hate to leave you now / You'll wish you'd never been born / I've got the world on a string / I've got a right to sing the blues / Hustling and bustling for baby / Sittin' in the dark / High society / He's a son of the south.
Note: Medley:- When you're smiling; St. James' infirmary; Dinah, part 1; You rascal you; When it's sleepy time down south; Nobody's sweetheart;
**Album:** Released Apr '81, on Joker (USA) by Lifetime Records (USA). Catalogue no: **SM 3752**

**LOUIS ARMSTRONG VOL 12: ORCH.**
Tracks: / Basin street blues / Honey do / Snowball / Mahogany Hall stomp / Swing, you cats / Honey, don't you love me anymore / Mississippi basin / Laughing Louis / Tomorrow night / Dusky Stevedore / There's a cabin in the sky / Mighty river / Sweet Sue / I wonder who / St. Louis blues / Don't play me cheap.
**Album:** Released Apr '81, on Joker (USA) by Lifetime Records (USA). Catalogue no: **SM 3753**

**LOUIS ARMSTRONG VSOP SERIES (Volumes 3/4)**
**Cass:** Released '88, on CBS by CBS Records. Catalogue no: **40 88002**

**LOUIS ARMSTRONG VSOP SERIES (Volumes 5/6)**
**Cass:** Released '88, on CBS by CBS Records. Catalogue no: **40 88003**

**LOUIS ARMSTRONG/SIDNEY BECHET (Armstrong, Louis/Sidney Bechet)**
Tracks: / On the sunny side of the street / King Porter stomp (Featuring Sidney Bechet & Dutch Swing College Band) / Dutch Swing College blues (featuring Sidney Bechet & Dutch Swing College

Band) / St. Louis blues / Tiger rag / Pretty little missy / Bye'n'bye / Tyree's blues / Short but sweet / Tin roof blues / Circle of your arms, The / When the saints go marching in.
Note: Louis Armstrong & His Orchestra. Sidney Bechet featured on two tracks with the Dutch Swing College Band. Recorded:May 1951,November 1964,September 1964,October 1965,April 1966.
**Album:** Released '83, on Jazz Masters Catalogue no: **6499 355**

## LOUIS' BLUES
**Cass:** Released '84, on Astan (USA) Catalogue no: **40074**
**Album:** Released '84, on Astan (USA) Catalogue no: **20074**

## LOUIS & FRIENDS
**Album:** Released Jan '84, on MCA by MCA Records. Deleted Jan '89. Catalogue no: **MCL1772**

## LOUIS IN LOS ANGELES
**Album:** Released Jan '83, on Swaggie (Australia) Catalogue no: **S 1265**

## LOUIS' LOVE SONGS
Tracks: / Among my souvenirs / I'm confessin' / It's all in the game / Only you (and you only) / I'll string along with you / I'm in the mood for love / Dream a little dream of me / You are my lucky star / Gypsy, The / Be my life's companion / Your cheatin' heart / I guess I'll get the papers and go home / Ramona / April in Portugal / Them there eyes / Ain't misbehavin'.
**Cass:** Released Sep '86, on MCA by MCA Records. Catalogue no: **MCLC 1822**
**Album:** Released May '86, on MCA by MCA Records. Deleted Jan '88. Catalogue no: **MCL 1822**

## MACK THE KNIFE
Tracks: / Mack the knife.
**7" Single:** Released Nov '59, on Philips by Phonogram Ltd. Deleted Nov '64. Catalogue no: **PB 967**

## MAHOGANY HALL STOMP
Tracks: / Blueberry Hill / That's my desire / Dear old Southland / Struttin' with some barbecue / Jeepers creepers / St. Louis blues / Hello Dolly / Tiger rag.
**Album:** Released Jul '88, on Black Lion Catalogue no: **BLM 52015**

## MAHOGANY HALL STOMP (2)
Tracks: / Mahogany Hall stomp / I can't give you anything but love / Ain't misbehavin' / That rhythm man / Sweet Savannah Sue / Rockin' chair / Song of the islands / Blue, turning grey over you / I can't believe that you're in love with me / I'm in the market for you / Confessin' / Body and soul / You're driving me crazy / Them there eyes / Wrap your troubles in dreams / Star dust / I got rhythm / Between the devil and the deep blue sea.
**CD:** Released '88, on Saville by Conifer Records. Catalogue no: **CDSVL 198**
**Cass:** Released '88, on Saville by Conifer Records. Catalogue no: **CSVL 198**
**Album:** Released '88, on Saville by Conifer Records. Catalogue no: **SVL 198**

## MAHOGANY HALL STOMP (LIVING ERA)
Tracks: / Mahogany Hall stomp / Rockin' chair / Savoy blues / Sweethearts on parade / Swing that music / Lyin' to myself / Thankful / I come from a musical family / Eventide / Red nose / If we never meet again / Peanut vendor / You're lucky to me / St. James Infirmary / You rascal, you / Lazy river / I ain't got nobody / Ain't misbehavin'.
**Album:** Released 1 Nov '87, on Living Era by Academy Sound & Vision Records. Catalogue no: **AJA 5049**
**Cass:** Released 1 Nov '87, on Living Era by Academy Sound & Vision Records. Catalogue no: **ZC AJA 5049**

## MASTERS OF JAZZ
**Album:** Released '83, on RCA (Germany) Catalogue no: **CL 42327**

## MASTERS OF JAZZ VOL.1
**Album:** Released May '86, on Storyville by Storyville Records AB. Catalogue no: **SLP 4101**

## MEMORIAL
**Album:** Released Oct '88, on Vogue by Vogue Records. Catalogue no: **500 816**

## MET. OPERA HOUSE 1944 (Armstrong, Louis / Esquire All Stars)
**2 LP Set:** Released Aug '87, on Jazz Society Catalogue no: **AA 522/523**

## MORE FUN (Armstrong, Louis / Bing Crosby)
**Album:** Released '88, on Sounds Rare Catalogue no: **SR 5010**
**Cass:** Released 10 Jul '89, on Jasmine by Hasmick Promotions. Catalogue no: **JASC 2526**

## MUSIC FOR THE MILLIONS
Tracks: / Stompin' at the Savoy / Do nothing till you hear from me / Just one of those things / Foggy day, A / Uncle Satchmo's lullaby / When the saints go marching in / Someday you'll be sorry / Nobody knows the trouble I've seen / Top hat, white tie and tails / Blues in the night.
**Album:** Released Feb '86, on Mercury (Holland) Catalogue no: **245 9406**
**Cass:** Released Feb '86, on Mercury (Holland) Catalogue no: **319 2596**

## NEW ORLEANS FUNCTION
Tracks: / When it's sleepy time down South / Indiana / Give me a kiss to build a dream on / My bucket's got a hole in it / Mack the knife / Ole Miss / C'est si bon / La vie en rose / New Orleans function / Free as a bird / Oh didn't he ramble?.
**CD:** Released Sep '87, on Entertainers Catalogue no: **ENT CD 206**
**Album:** Released Oct '82, on Black Lion Catalogue no: **BLM 52005**
**Album:** Released '88, on Joker (USA) by Lifetime Records (USA). Catalogue no: **SM 3965**

## NEW ORLEANS JAZZ AT NEWPORT
**Album:** Released Sep '87, on Wolf Catalogue no: **WJS 1003**

## NEW ORLEANS MASTERS VOLUME 2
**Album:** Released '84, on Swing House by Submarine Records. Catalogue no: **SWH 44**
**Cass:** Released '84, on Swing House by Submarine Records. Catalogue no: **CSWH 44**

## NOONE 1941
**Album:** Released Jan '83, on Swaggie (Australia) Catalogue no: **S 1210**

## ON STAGE
Tracks: / Jubilee / Do you know what it means / I'm confessin' / Panama rag stomp / Struttin' with some barbecue / Muskrat ramble / High society / Basin street blues.
**Album:** Released Oct '86, on Jazz Live (Italy) Catalogue no: **BLJ 8041**

## ORIGINAL RECORDINGS 1936-39
Tracks: / Swing that music / Dippermouth blues / I've got a heart full of rhythm / On the sunny side of the street / Struttin' with some barbecue / When the Saints go marching in / Flat foot floogie / Ain't misbehavin' / Jeepers creepers / What is this thing called swing? / Savoy blues / West End blues.
Note: With Tommy Dorsey & The Mills Brothers
**Album:** Released '81, on Joker (USA) by Lifetime Records (USA). Catalogue no: **SM 3052**
**Cass:** Released '81, on Joker (USA) by Lifetime Records (USA). Catalogue no: **MC 3052**

## PASADENA CIVIC AUDITORIUM, THE
**Album:** Released Oct '88, on Vogue by Vogue Records. Catalogue no: **500 206**
**CD:** Released Oct '87, on Vogue by Vogue Records. Catalogue no: **VG 600 143**

## PASADENA CONCERT
Tracks: / Someday / Ole Miss / Tin roof blues / My bucket's got a hole in it / Dardanella / Gypsy, The / Undecided / Blues / That's my desire / Didn't he ramble / Sleepy time down south (2 takes) / Indiana.
**LP Set:** Released Oct '88, on Vogue by Vogue Records. Catalogue no: **000201**
**CD:** Released '84, on Vogue by Vogue Records. Catalogue no: **VG 600 007**

## PLAYS W.C.HANDY
**Cass:** Released Mar '88, on CBS (import) by CBS Records. Catalogue no: **450 981 4**
**Album:** Released 27 Feb '88, on CBS (import) by CBS Records. Catalogue no: **450 981 1**
**CD:** Released Mar '88, on CBS (import) by CBS Records. Catalogue no: **450 981 2**

## PORGY & BESS (Armstrong, Louis/Ella Fitzgerald)
Tracks: / Summertime / I got plenty o' nuttin' / My man's gone now / Bess, you

is my woman now / It ain't necessarily so / There's a boat that's leaving shortly for New York / Bess, oh where's my Bess? / I'm on my way / I loves you, Porgy / Woman is a sometime thing.
**CD:** on Polydor by Polydor Ltd. Catalogue no: **827 475-2**
**Cass:** Released Jan '78, on Verve Catalogue no: **3507 034**
**Cass:** Released Jun '89, on Verve Catalogue no: **350 150**
**CD:** Released '83, on Verve Catalogue no: **810 049-2**
**Cass:** Released May '85, on Verve Catalogue no: **100 7016**
**Album:** Released May '85, on Verve Catalogue no: **171 110 5**
**Album:** Released Jun '89, on Verve Catalogue no: **827 475 1**
**Album:** Released Jan '78, on Verve Catalogue no: **2632 052**

## RARE LOUIS ARMSTRONG VOLUME 3 (The Big Band 1943-44)
Tracks: / I can't give you anything but love / If I could be with you one hour tonight / I'm confessin' / In the mood / I never knew / What's the good word / Lost my sugar in Salt Lake City / Lazy river / On the sunny side of the street / King Porter stomp / It's love love love / Ain't misbehavin' / Barrelhouse Bessie from Basin Street / Peanut vendor / Slender, tender and tall / Coquette.
**Album:** Released Apr '81, on Rarities Catalogue no: **RARITIES 50**

## RARE PERFORMANCES OF THE 50'S & 60'S
Tracks: / T'aint what you do (it's the way that you do it) / Back o' town blues / Mack the knife / Mack the knife (inst) / Indiana / Six foot four / When the red, red robin comes bob, bob, bobbin' along / Way down yonder in New Orleans / Blueberry Hill / Mack the knife (concert version) / Tin roof blues / My bucket's got a hole in it / Whispering / Bugle blues - Ole Miss / Kokomo / Basin Street blues / Mahogany hall stomp / St. Louis blues / Rockin' chair / On the sunny side of the street / Nomad / Lonesome / You swing baby / Canal Street blues.
**Album:** Released Jul '86, on CBS by CBS Records. Deleted Aug '87. Catalogue no: **CBS 88669**

## REMINISCIN' WITH LOUIS
Tracks: / Ain't misbehavin' / When the saints go marching in / I cried for you / Boogie woogie on St. Louis / When it's sleepy time down South / I cried last night / Steak face.
**Album:** Released Apr '81, on Queendisc (Italy) Catalogue no: **QU 004**

## REPLAY ON LOUIS ARMSTRONG
**Album:** Released May '86, on Sierra by Sierra Records. Catalogue no: **FEDB 5028**
**Cass:** Released May '86, on Sierra by Sierra Records. Catalogue no: **CFEDB 5028**

## ROCKIN' CHAIR (Armstrong, Louis / his Allstars)
Tracks: / Rockin' chair / Where did you stay last night / Baby, it's cold outside / C Jam Blues / Stompin' at the Savoy / I used to love you / La vie en rose / Lover / I love the guy / That's my desire / Royal Garden blues / Ain't misbehavin' / Back o' town blues / Rose room / C'est ci bon / Way down yonder in New Orleans / Stardust.
**Cass:** Released Jan '85, on Topline by Charly Records. Catalogue no: **KTOP 119**
**Album:** Released Apr '87, on Topline by Charly Records. Catalogue no: **TOP 119**

## SATCH PLAYS FATS
Tracks: / Honeysuckle rose / Blue turning grey over you / I'm crazy 'bout my baby / I've got a feeling I'm falling / Keepin' out of mischief now / All that meat and no potatoes / Squeeze me / Black and blue / Ain't misbehavin'.
**Cass:** Released 27 Feb '88, on CBS (import) by CBS Records. Catalogue no: **450 980 4**
**Cass:** Released '84, on CBS by CBS Records. Deleted Aug '87. Catalogue no: **40 21103**
**Album:** Released 27 Feb '88, on CBS (import) by CBS Records. Catalogue no: **450 980 1**
**Album:** Released '84, on CBS by CBS Records. Catalogue no: **21103**
**CD:** Released 27 Feb '88, on CBS (import) by CBS Records. Catalogue no: **450 980 2**

## SATCHMO
Tracks: / What a wonderful world / Cabaret / Hello Dolly / Jeepers creepers / Georgia on my mind / Lazy river / When you're smiling / Wiffenpoof song, The / Blueberry Hill / La vie en rose / I can't give you... / I surrender dear / On the sunny side of the street / Some of these days / Exactly like you.
**Album:** Released Jul '88, on Vanstory Catalogue no: **VS 3404**
**Cass:** Released Jul '88, on Vanstory Catalogue no: **VSK 3404**

## SATCHMO '54
Note: Four radio programmes from 1954, broadcast live by a New York station, which show a cross section of Armstrong the showman, singer and jazz musician.
**CD:** Released Jan '90, on Jazz-Up Catalogue no: **JU 301**

## SATCHMO IN STOCKHOLM
Tracks: / When it's sleepy time down South / Indiana / Tin roof blues / Basin street blues / Sweet Georgia Brown / Struttin' with some barbecue / Gipsy, The / Pretty little missy / When the saints go marching in.
**Album:** Released '81, on Queendisc (Italy) Catalogue no: **QU 053**

## SATCHMO MEETS BIG T (Armstrong, Louis / Jack Teagarden)
**Album:** Released Feb '89, on Giants of Jazz by Hasmick Promotions. Catalogue no: **LPJT 69**

## SATCHMO (PICKWICK)
Tracks: / Back o' town blues / I want a big butter and egg man / (Back home in) Indiana / Tiger rag / Jelly roll blues / C'est si bon / St. James infirmiary / When the Saints go marching in / Someday you'll be sorry / Sweethearts on parade / (What did I have to do to get) black and blue / Chimes blue / Dipper mouth blues / Snake rag / New Orleans stomp / Bye and bye.
**Album:** Released '88, on Pickwick by Pickwick Records. Catalogue no: **PWK 009**
**Cass:** Released Jun '89, on Hallmark by Pickwick Records. Catalogue no: **HSC 3272**

## SATCHMO PLAYS KING OLIVER
**Album:** Released Oct '60, on Audio Fidelity(USA) by Audio Fidelity (USA). Deleted '65. Catalogue no: **AFLP 1930**

## SATCHMO STYLE
**Album:** Released '88, on DRG (USA) by DRG Records (USA). Catalogue no: **SW 8451**

## SATCHMO (VIDEO)
**VHS:** Released Oct '89, on CMV Enterprises (video) by CBS Records. Catalogue no: **490242**

## SATCHMO - WHAT A WONDERFUL WORLD
**Album:** Released 22 Aug '88, on Polydor by Polydor Ltd. Catalogue no: **835 895-1**
**Cass:** Released 22 Aug '88, on Polydor by Polydor Ltd. Catalogue no: **835 895-4**
**CD:** Released 22 Aug '88, on Polydor by Polydor Ltd. Catalogue no: **835 895-2**

## SATCHMO'S GREATEST HITS
Tracks: / I gotta right to sing the blues / High society / When you're smiling / St. James Infirmary / Dinah / Basin Street blues / You rascal you / Sleepy time down south / Nobody's sweetheart / Mahogany hall stomp / Do you know what it means to Miss New Orleans? / St. Louis blues / Sweet Sue / Back o' town blues / Jack Armstrong blues / Where the blues were born in New Orleans.
**Album:** Released Jun '86, on RCA by BMG Records (UK). Deleted Jul '89. Catalogue no: **CL 89799**
**Cass:** Released Jun '86, on RCA by BMG Records (UK). Catalogue no: **CK 89799**

## SATCHMO'S IMMORTAL PERFORMANCES
**CD:** Released Mar '90, on Giants of Jazz by Hasmick Promotions. Catalogue no: **GOJCD53088**

## SILVER COLLECTION, THE (Compilation)
Tracks: / Top hat white tie and tails / Have you met Miss Jones / I only have eyes for you / Stormy weather / Home / East of the sun (and west of the moon) / You're blase / Body and soul / When your lover has gone / You're the top / Nobody knows the trouble I've seen / We'll be together again / I've got the world on a string / Do nothing till you hear from me / I gotta right to sing the blues.
**CD:** Released Nov '84, on Verve Deleted May '89. Catalogue no: **823 446-2**

**SINGIN' N' PLAYIN'**
Tracks: / Hello Dolly / Mack the knife / Muskrat ramble / Blueberry Hill / That's my desire / Ole Miss / When it's sleepy time down South / Kiss to build a dream on ,A / St. James infirmary / Indiana.
Note: Personnel: Louis Armstrong (Trumpet / Vocal), Trummy Young (Trombone), Edmond Hall (Clarinet), Billy Kyle (Piano), Dale Jones (Bass), Barett Deems (Drums) and others.
**Cass:** Released Apr '89, on Denon Catalogue no: **MC 7685**
**CD:** Released '88, on Denon Catalogue no: **C38-7685**
**CD:** Released Apr '89, on Denon Catalogue no: **DC 8534**

**SOUNDTRACK NEW ORLEANS (Armstrong, Louis/Billie Holiday)**
**Album:** Released Jul '84, on Giants of Jazz by Hasmick Promotions. Catalogue no: **GOJ 1025**

**SPECIAL MAGIC (Armstrong, Louis/Ella Fitzgerald)**
**Cass:** Released Aug '76, on Verve Catalogue no: **3113 190**

**ST. LOUIS BLUES**
Tracks: / Tiger rag / Maine / So long dearie / Cheesecake / Pretty little miss / Short and sweet / When the saints go marching in / St. Louis blues / Circle of your arms, The / Tin roof blues / Tyrees blues / Bye n bye / On the sunny side of the street / Black and blue / I'm confessin' / Struttin' with some barbecue / Up a lazy river / Save it pretty mama / Ain't misbehavin' / St. Louis blues / Rockin' chair / Dippermouth blues / Mahogany hall stomp / Muskrat ramble.
**Cass:** Released '82, on Black Lion-Intercord Catalogue no: **CAS 427 035**
**Album:** Released '82, on Black Lion-Intercord Catalogue no: **INT 127 035**

**ST. LOUIS BLUES (1960'S)**
Tracks: / Tiger rag / Maine / So long dearie / Cheesecake / Pretty little miss / Short and sweet / When the saints go marching in / St. Louis blues / Circle of your arms / Tin roof blues / Tyrees blues / Bye n bye / On the sunny side of the street.
**Album:** Released Mar '83, on Mercury (USA) by PolyGram Rec.Inc.(USA). Catalogue no: **9279 254**
**Album:** Released Mar '83, on Mercury (USA) by PolyGram Rec.Inc.(USA). Catalogue no: **7259 154**

**ST. LOUIS BLUES (CBS)**
**Cass:** Released Feb '85, on CBS (import) by CBS Records. Catalogue no: **40 54612**
**Album:** Released Feb '85, on CBS (import) by CBS Records. Catalogue no: **54612**

**STRUTTIN' WITH SOME BARBECUE**
Tracks: / Struttin' with some barbecue / What is this thing called swing? / Jeepers creepers / Lyin' to myself / Shoe shine boy / I hope Gabriel likes my music / Perdido street blues / 2.19 blues / Swing that music / Down in honky tonk town / Coal cart blues / Eventide / Dippermouth blues / Solitude / Jubilee / Mahogany hall stomp.
**Album:** Released Jun '86, on Affinity by Charly Records. Catalogue no: **AFS 1024**

**SUNSHINE OF LOVE**
Tracks: / Sunshine of love.
**7" Single:** Released Jun '68, on Stateside by EMI Records. Deleted Jun '73. Catalogue no: **SS 2116**

**TAKE IT SATCH**
Tracks: / Take it Satch / Tiger rag / Mack the knife / Faithful hussar, The / Back o' town blues.
**7" EP:** Released Jun '56, on Philips by Phonogram Ltd. Deleted Jun '61. Catalogue no: **BBE 12035**

**TAKES TWO TO TANGO**
Tracks: / Takes two to tango.
**7" Single:** Released Dec '52, on Brunswick by Decca Records. Deleted Dec '57. Catalogue no: **04995**

**THAT OLD FEELING (Armstrong, Louis/Billie Holiday)**
**Album:** Released Feb '82, on Polydor (Import) by Polydor Ltd. Catalogue no: **2872 217**
**Cass:** Released Feb '82, on Polydor (Import) by Polydor Ltd. Catalogue no: **3472 217**

**THAT RHYTHM MAN**
Tracks: / All of me / Knockin' a jug / I'm confessin' / Dinah / St. Louis blues / St. James infirmary / Mahogany hall stomp / Chinatown / No papa no / Hear me talkin' to ya / New tiger rag / I ain't got nobody / Kickin' the gong around / Blue turning grey over you / That rhythm man / I'm in the market for you / After you've gone / Some of these days.
**Album:** Released Dec '84, on American Recollections by London Records Ltd. Catalogue no: **RAL 507**

**THEME FROM THE THREEPENNY OPERA**
Tracks: / Theme from the threepenny opera.
**7" Single:** Released Apr '56, on Philips by Phonogram Ltd. Deleted Apr '61. Catalogue no: **PB 574**

**TIGER RAG**
**CD:** Released May '89, on Object Enterprises Catalogue no: **ONN 44**

**TOGETHER AGAIN LIVE AT THE MONTREUX JAZZ FESTIVAL**
**CD:** Released May '86, on Pablo Jazz (USA) by Pablo Records (USA). Catalogue no: **CD 20005**

**TOGETHER FOR THE FIRST TIME (Armstrong, Louis/Duke Ellington)**
Tracks: / Duke's place / I'm just a lucky so and so / Cottontail / Mood indigo / Do nothin' till you hear from me / Beautiful American, The / Black and tan fantasy / Drop me off at Harlem / Mooche, The / In a mellow tone.
**Album:** Released Feb '90, on Roulette (EMI) by EMI Records. Catalogue no: **ROU 1007**

**TOWN HALL CONCERT PLUS**
Tracks: / Rockin' chair / Ain't misbehavin' / Back o' town blues / Long long journey / I want a little girl / Mahogany hall stomp / Pennies from Heaven / St. James Infirmary / Save it pretty mama / Someday you'll be sorry / Sugar / Snafu.
**Cass:** Released Nov '84, on RCA International by BMG Records (UK). Catalogue no: **NK 89419**
**Album:** Released Apr '81, on RCA International by BMG Records (UK). Deleted Apr '86. Catalogue no: **INTS 5070**
**Album:** Released Nov '84, on RCA International by BMG Records (UK). Catalogue no: **NL 80419**

**TWELFTH STREET RAG**
Tracks: / Baby it's cold outside / On the sunny side of the street / Gypsy, The / Mame / Old man Mose / 2.19 blues / I can't give you anything but love / Twelfth St. rag / Faithful hussar, The / After you've gone / What a wonderful world.
**Album:** Released Jul '88, on Black Lion Catalogue no: **BLM 52045**

**UNFORGETTABLE LOUIS ARMSTRONG**
**Cass:** Released '87, on Unforgettable by Castle Communications Records. Catalogue no: **UNMC 009**
**Album:** Released '87, on Unforgettable by Castle Communications Records. Catalogue no: **UNLP 009**

**V DISC ALL STARS (Armstrong, Louis/Jack Teagarden)**
**Album:** Released Apr '79, on Pumpkin Catalogue no: **PUMPKIN 103**

**VERY BEST OF LOUIS ARMSTRONG**
**Album:** Released Feb '82, on Warwick by Warwick Records. Deleted '87. Catalogue no: **WW 5512**

**WHAT A WONDERFUL WORLD (BMG)**
Tracks: / What a wonderful world / Everybody's talking (echoes) / Boy from New Orleans / We shall overcome / Creator has a master plan, The / Mood indigo / This black cat has nine lives / My one and only love / His father wore long hair / Give peace a chance.
**CD:** Released Nov '88, on Bluebird (2) by BMG Records (UK). Catalogue no: **ND 88310**

**WHAT A WONDERFUL WORLD (H.M.V.)**
Tracks: / What a wonderful world.
**7" Single:** Released Feb '68, on H.M.V. by EMI Records. Deleted '73. Catalogue no: **POP 1615**

**WHAT A WONDERFUL WORLD (MCA)**
Tracks: / What a wonderful world / Cabaret / Home fire, The / Dream a little dream of me / Give me your kisses(I'll give you my heart) / Sunshine of love / Hello brother / There must be a way / Fantastic, that's you / I guess I'll get the papers and go home / Hellzapoppin'.
Note: Louis Armstrong is about to be introduced to a whole new audience, not

Louis Armstrong - What a Wonderful World (Platinum Music)

only through this mid-line CD, but thanks to the release of the critically acclaimed movie, "Good morning, Vietnam", which features "What a Wonderful World". Considered by many to be the most influential jazz musician of all time, Louis Armstrong is a legend.
**CD:** Released Jul '88, on MCA by MCA Records. Catalogue no: **DMCL 1876**

**WHAT A WONDERFUL WORLD (OLD GOLD)**
Tracks: / What a wonderful world / Hello Dolly.
**7" Single:** Released Mar '90, on Old Gold by Old Gold Records. Catalogue no: **OG 9419**

**WHAT A WONDERFUL WORLD (PLATINUM) (See panel above)**
Tracks: / What a wonderful world / Jeepers creepers / Georgia on my mind / On the sunny side of the street / Cabaret / Hello Dolly / Lazy river / When you're smiling / Whiffenpoof song, The / Blueberry Hill / La vie en rose / Can't give you anything but love / When it's sleepy time down South / Surrender dear / Some of these days / Exactly like you.
Note: Twenty years after reaching No. 1 in the British charts, Louis Armstrong's recording of 'What a wonderful world' entered the US Charts for the first time. This belated good fortune was caused by the success of the soundtrack from the box office smash 'Good Morning Vietnam'. It may seem ironic that a vocal pop performance should bring mass recognition to an artist previously know as the undisputed maestro of jazz. A product of the Jazz Age, Louis was born on July 4 1900 in New Orleans. After three years at reform school, where he had learned the cornet, he joined King Oliver's band. With the closing down of the New Orlean's red-light district, Louis moved on to Chicago and New York, where he formed his own band in 1927. His international reputation was evidenced by successful tours of Europe in the early 1930's. The silver-screen enabled Louis to reach a broader audience, his Hollywood debut coming in *Pennies from heaven* in 1936. He is perhaps remembered best for his appearance in *High society* in which his broad grin, sense of humour and gravelly voice made such an indelible impression. Above all, stands his legacy of recordings stretching over an amazing forty-eight years. Fondly known to all his fans as Satchmo (derived from the expression 'satchel mouth'), he was undoubtedly one of the most influential of all jazz artists. This selection features many of the hits of which are always associated with him. Although he died in 1971, his appeal today has not diminished as the renewed success of *What a wonderful world* underlines. (Prism Leisure)
**CD:** Released Aug '88, on Platinum Music by Prism Leisure. Catalogue no: **PLATCD 304**
**Album:** Released Apr '88, on Platinum Music by Prism Leisure. Catalogue no: **PLAT 304**
**Cass:** Released Apr '88, on Platinum Music by Prism Leisure. Catalogue no: **PLAC 304**

**WHAT A WONDERFUL WORLD (SINGLE)**
Tracks: / What a wonderful world / Game of love.
**12" Single:** Released Mar '88, on A&M by A&M Records. Catalogue no: **AMY 435**
**7" Single:** Released Mar '88, on A&M by A&M Records. Catalogue no: **AM 435**

**WHAT A WONDERFUL WORLD**
**Album:** Released Nov '68, on Stateside by EMI Records. Deleted '73. Catalogue no: **SSL 10247**

**WHAT A WONDERFUL WORLD**
Tracks: / What a wonderful world / Hello Dolly.
**7" Single:** Released Jul '86, on MCA by MCA Records. Deleted '86. Catalogue no: **MCA 706**

**WHEN THE SAINTS GO MARCHING IN**
Tracks: / St. James' Infirmary / When the saints go marching in / I'm confessin' / Royal Garden blues / Black and blue / Up a lazy river / I'll be glad when you're dead, you rascal you / Ain't misbehavin' / Basin Street blues.
**Album:** Released Jul '88, on Black Lion Catalogue no: **BLM 52025**

**WONDERFUL WORLD OF LOUIS ARMSTRONG, THE**
**Album:** Released Nov '82, on MFP by EMI Records. Deleted '84. Catalogue no: **MFP 5584**
**Cass:** Released Nov '82, on MFP by EMI Records. Deleted '84. Catalogue no: **TCMFP 5584**

**WONDERFUL WORLD (VIDEO)**
**VHS:** Released '88, on Kay Jazz (video) by Kay Jazz. Catalogue no: **KJ 052**

**YOUNG LOUIS ARMSTRONG (1930-1933)**
Tracks: / Blue yodel no. 9 (Standing on the corner) / That's my home (2 takes) / Hobo, you can't ride this train / I hate to leave you now (2 takes) / You'll wish you'd never been born / When you're smiling / St. James' Infirmary / Dinah / You rascal, you / When it's sleepy time down South / Nobody's sweetheart / I've got the world on a string / I gotta right to sing the blues / Hustlin' and bustlin' for baby / Sittin' in the dark / High Society / Basin Street blues / He's a son of the south / Some sweet day / Honey do / Snowball / Mahogany hall stomp / Swing, you cats / Honey don't you love me anymore? / Mississippi basin / Laughin' Louie / Tomorrow night / Dusky stevedore / There's a cabin in the pines / Mighty river / Sweet Sue / I wonder who / St. Louis blues / Don't play me cheap.
**2 LP Set:** Released Jan '87, on RCA by BMG Records (UK). Deleted Jul '89. Catalogue no: **NL 89747**
**Cass set:** Released Jan '87, on RCA by BMG Records (UK). Deleted May '89. Catalogue no: **NK 89747**

**YOUNG LOUIS ARMSTRONG**
**Album:** Released '83, on RCA (France) by BMG Records (France). Catalogue no: **PM 43269**

## Arnold, Billy Boy

**Biographical details:** Arnold, Billy Boy Blues singer, guitarist, harmonica player, born in 1935 in Chicago. He worked as a child with Bo Diddley in a washboard trio at parties, etc; later with all the Chicago greats; recorded under his own name from 1954 and toured Europe in the '70s. Donald Clarke 21 July 1988.

### BLOW THE BACK OFF IT

Tracks: / I'm sweet on you baby / You got to love me baby / I wish you would / I was fooled / Don't stay out all night / I ain't got you / Hello stranger / Here's my picture / You've got me wrong / My heart is crying / Kissing at midnight / Prisoners plea / Rockinits.
**Album:** Released Sep '82, on Red Lightnin' by Red Lightning Records. Deleted Sep '86. Catalogue no: **RL 012**

### CHECKIN' IT OUT

Tracks: / Dirty mother fucker / Don't stay out all night / 1-2-99 / Riding the el / Just to know / Christmas time / I wish you would / Ah'w baby / Sweet Miss Bea / Blue & lonesome / Eldorado Cadillac / Mary Bernice.
**Album:** Released Sep '82, on Red Lightnin' by Red Lightning Records. Deleted Jun '89. Catalogue no: **RL 024**

### CRYING AND PLEADING

**Album:** Released Jul '88, on Charly R&B by Charly Records. Deleted Jul '88. Catalogue no: **CRB 1016**

### I WISH YOU WOULD

Tracks: / I wish you would.
**7" Single:** Released Jul '80, on Charly by Charly Records. Deleted '87. Catalogue no: **CTD 117**

### MORE BLUES ON THE SOUTH SIDE

Tracks: / School time / You don't love me no more / Oh baby / I love only you / I'll forget about you / You better cut that out / Going by the river / You're my girl / Evalena / Two drinks of wine / Billy Boy's blues / Get out of here.
**Album:** Released Jan '89, on Ace by Ace Records. Catalogue no: **CH 253**

### SINNERS PRAYER

Tracks: / I was fooled / High heel sneakers / Back door friend / Tomorrow night / Annie Lee / Ooh Wee / Blues in A natural / I'm gonna move / Sinners prayer.
**Album:** Released Sep '82, on Red Lightnin' by Red Lightning Records. Deleted Jun '89. Catalogue no: **RL 014**

### SUPERHARPS

Tracks: / Superharps.
**12" Single:** Released Oct '88, on Red Lightnin' by Red Lightning Records. Deleted Jun '89. Catalogue no: **RLEP 0027**

## Arnold, Kokomo

**Biographical details:** Arnold, Kokomo was born James Arnold in 1901 in Texas and died in 1968 in Chicago. The blues singer and guitarist made two sides for Victor in 1930 in Memphis under the name of Gitfiddle Jim, more for Decca in Chicago and NYC '34-8. He acquired his nickname from 'Old Original Kokomo Blues' '34 (Kokomo was a brand of coffee, as well as a town in Indiana). Highly regarded by critics and collectors, he made a comeback in Chicago during the folk-blues revival in the early '60s. (Donald Clarke 21 July 1988).

### KOKOMO ARNOLD & CASEY BILL (Arnold, Kokomo & Casey Bill Weldon)

**Album:** Released Dec '88, on Yazoo (USA) by Shanachie Records (USA). Catalogue no: **L 1049**

### KOKOMO ARNOLD - MASTER OF THE 1930-38

**Album:** Released Jul '87, on Document Catalogue no: **DLP 512**

## Art Ensemble Of Chicago

### A.A.C.M.: GREAT BLACK MUSIC, A

Tracks: / Waltz / Ericka / Song for Charles / Jackson in your house, A / Get in line / Waltz Ericka, The / Song for Charles.
**Album:** Released Feb '78, on Affinity by Charly Records. Deleted '88. Catalogue no: **AFF 9**
**CD:** Released Mar '87, on Charly by Charly Records. Catalogue no: **CDCHARLY 78**

### AMONG THE PEOPLE

**Album:** Released May '84, on Praxis (Greece) Catalogue no: **CM 103**

### FANFARE OF THE WARRIORS

Tracks: / Illistrum / Barnyard scuffel shuffel / Nonaah / Fanfare for the warriors / What's to say / Tnoona / Key, The.
**Album:** on Atlantic by WEA Records. Catalogue no: **K 50304**

### FULL FORCE

**CD:** Released Oct '86, on ECM Catalogue no: **829 197-2**

### JACKSON IN YOUR HOUSE, A (Message to our folks)

Tracks: / Jackson in your house, A / Get in line / Hey friend / Ericka / Song for Charles / Old time religion / Dexterity / Rock out / Brain for the Seine, A.
**CD:** Released Sep '89, on Affinity by Charly Records. Catalogue no: **CDAFF 752**

### KABBALABA LIVE AT MONTREUX

**Album:** Released May '81, on Aeco Catalogue no: **AECO 004**

### LES STANCES A SOPHIE

**Album:** Released Mar '79, on Nessa Deleted '84. Catalogue no: **N 4**

### LIVE: ART ENSEMBLE OF CHICAGO

**2 LP Set:** Released Feb '80, on Affinity by Charly Records. Deleted '88. Catalogue no: **AFFD 46**

### MESSAGE TO OUR FOLKS

Tracks: / Old time religion / Dexterity / Rock out / Brain for the Seine.
**Album:** Released Mar '83, on Affinity by Charly Records. Catalogue no: **AFF 77**

### NICE GUYS

Tracks: / Ja / Nice guys / Folkus / 597-59 / Cyp / Dreaming of the master.
**CD:** Released Jun '86, on ECM Catalogue no: **827 876-2**

### PARIS SESSION, THE

Tracks: / Tutankhamun / Ninth room that evening the sky fell through / Toro / Lori song / Tthinitthedalen / Spiritual freedom.
**2 LP Set:** Released Jun '79, on Freedom Catalogue no: **FLP 41106/7**

### PEOPLE IN SORROW

**Album:** Released Mar '79, on Nessa Deleted '83. Catalogue no: **N 3**

### REESE AND THE SMOOTH ONES

**Album:** Released May '79, on Affinity by Charly Records. Deleted '88. Catalogue no: **AFF 22**

### THIRD DECADE

**CD:** Released Apr '85, on ECM Catalogue no: **823 213-2**
**Album:** Released Feb '85, on ECM Catalogue no: **EXM 1273**

### TUTANKHAMUN

Tracks: / Tutankhamun / Ninth room, The.
**Album:** Released Sep '85, on Freedom Catalogue no: **FLP 40122**

### URBAN BUSHMEN

**Cass:** Released Jul '85, on ECM Catalogue no: **7579037**
**Album:** Released May '82, on ECM Catalogue no: **ECM 1211**

## At Pepper's Lounge...

### AT PEPPER'S LOUNGE,CHICAGO VOL.2 (Various artists)

Tracks: / Off the wall: *Various artists* / Pepper's other thing: *Various artists* / You're so fine: *Various artists* / Rocker: *Various artists* / Pepper's boogie woogie: *Various artists* / How long can this thing go on?: *Various artists* / These ole cotton pickin' blues: *Various artists* / Left me alone: *Various artists* / Everyday I have the blues: *Various artists* / Dynamite: *Various artists*.
Note: Personnel: Featuring Little Walter, Earl Hooker, Louis Myers, Dave Myers, Fred Bellow, Eddie Taylor, John 'Big Moose' Walker, Paul Askell, Geno Skaggs, Little Mac Roosevelt Shaw, B. B. King Junior (Andre Odom).
**Album:** Released Apr '81, on Rarities Catalogue no: **RARITIES 28**

## Atlantic Blues

### ATLANTA BLUES 1933 (Various artists)

**Album:** Released '88, on JEMF (USA) by Arhoolie Records (USA). Catalogue no: **JEMF 106**

### ATLANTIC BLUES (Various artists)

**Album:** Released Feb '87, on Atlantic by WEA Records. Catalogue no: **K 781 713 1**
**Cass:** Released Feb '87, on Atlantic by WEA Records. Catalogue no: **K 781 713 4**

### ATLANTIC BLUES: CHICAGO (Various artists)

Tracks: / Chicago blues: *Jones, Johnny* / Hoy hoy: *Jones, Johnny* / Play on little girl: *Walker, T-Bone* / T-Bone blues special: *Walker, T-Bone* / Poor man's plea: *Guy, Buddy & Junior Wells* / My baby she left me: *Guy, Buddy & Junior Wells* / T-Bone shuffle: *Guy, Buddy & Junior Wells* / I wonder why: *King, Freddie* / Play it cool: *King, Freddie* / Woke up this morning: *King, Freddie* / Gambler's blues: *Rush, Otis* / Feel so bad: *Rush, Otis* / Reap what you sow: *Various artists* / Highway 49: *Various artists* / Honey bee: *Waters, Muddy* / Wang dang doodle: *Taylor, Koko* / Dust my broom: *Shines, Johnny* / Going down: *King, Freddie* / Please send me someone to love: *Allison, Luther* / Walking the dog: *Allison, Luther* / Feel so good: *Hutto, J.B.*.

**Album:** Released '87, on Atlantic by WEA Records. Catalogue no: **UNKNOWN**

### ATLANTIC BLUES: GUITAR (Various artists)

Tracks: / Broke down engine: *McTell, Blind Willie* / Shake 'em on down: *McDowell, Mississippi Fred* / My baby don't love me: *Hooker, John Lee* / Tall pretty woman: *McGhee, Stick* / Blues rock: *Brown, Texas Johnny* / There goes the blues: *Brown, Texas Johnny* / Bongo boogie: *Brown, Texas Johnny* / Two bones and a pick: *Walker, T-Bone* / Mean old world: *Walker, T-Bone* / Let me know: *Norris, Chuck* / It hurts to love someone: *Guitar Slim* / Down through the years: *Guitar Slim* / Okie dokie stomp: *Dupree, Cornell* / Blues nocturne: *Dupree, Cornell* / T.V. mama: *Turner, Big* / Reconsider baby: *King, Al* / Midnight midnight: *Baker, Mickey* / I smell trouble: *Turner, Ike & Tina* / Why I sing the blues: *King, Albert* / Crosscut saw: *King, Albert* / Angels of mercy: *King, Albert* / Can't be satisfied: *Hammond, John* / Flood down in Texas: *Vaughan, Stevie Ray*.

**Album:** Released '87, on Atlantic by WEA Records. Catalogue no: **UNKNOWN**

### ATLANTIC BLUES: PIANO (Various artists)

Tracks: / Yancey special: *Yancey, Jimmy* / Talkin' boogie: *Montgomery, Little Brother* / Mournful blues: *Yancey, Jimmy* / Farish street jive: *Montgomery, Little Brother* / Salute to pinetop: *Yancey, Jimmy* / Vicksburg blues: *Montgomery, Little Brother* / Shave 'em dry: *Yancey, Jimmy* / Frankie and Johnny / T B blues / Strollin' / Boogie woogie: *Professor Longhair* / Tipitina: *Professor Longhair* / Blue sender: *Walls, Van* / After midnight: *Walls, Van* / Roll 'em Pete: *Turner, Big* / Fore day rider: *McShann, Jay* / Cherry red: *Turner, Big* / My chile: *McShann, Jay* / Cow cow blues: *Atlantic...* / Albert's blues: *Lewis, Meade Lux* / Honky tonk train: *Lewis, Meade Lux* / Ray's blues: *Charles, Ray* / Low society: *Charles, Ray* / Bit of soul, A: *Charles, Ray* / Hey bartender: *Dixon, Floyd* / Floyd's blues: *Dixon, Floyd* / After hours blues: *Brown, Texas Johnny* / Junco partner: *Atlantic...* / I don't know: *Mabon, Willie*.

**Album:** Released '87, on Atlantic by WEA Records. Catalogue no: **UNKNOWN**

### ATLANTIC BLUES: VOCALISTS (Various artists)

Tracks: / You got to know how: *Wallace, Sippie* / Suitcase blues: *Wallace, Sippie* / Mighty tight woman: *Wallace, Sippie* / How long blues: *Witherspoon, Jimmy* / In the evening: *Witherspoon, Jimmy* / Gimme a pigfoot and a bottle of beer: *Various artists* / Make me a pallet on the floor: *Yancey, Mama* / St. Louis blues: *Turner, Big* / Oke-she-moke-she-pop: *Turner, Big* / I've got that feelin: *Green, Lil* / Destination love: *Harris, Wynonie* / Tell a whale of a tale: *Harris, Wynonie* / Rain is a bringdown: *Brown, Ruth* / R.B. blues: *Brown, Ruth* / I don't want to be president: *Mayfield, Percy* / Nothing stays the same: *Mayfield, Percy* / River's invitation: *Taylor, Ted* / Just like a fish: *Phillips, Esther* / Pouring water on a drowning man: *Clay, Otis* / Did you ever love a woman: *Thomas, Rufus* / Baby girl (parts 1 & 2): *Turner, Titus* / Ain't that lovin' you: *Bland, Bobby* / It's my own tears: *Copeland, Johnny* / Cheatin' woman: *Holmes, Eldridge* / I had a dream: *Various artists* / Takin' another mans place: *Franklin, Aretha* / It's a hang up: *Hill, Z.Z.* / Home ain't home at suppertime: *Hill, Z.Z.*.

**Album:** Released '87, on Atlantic by WEA Records. Catalogue no: **UNKNOWN**

## Atlantic Honkers

### ATLANTIC HONKERS (Various artists)

Note: With Arnett Cobb, King Curtis, Tiny Grimes, Frank Culley.

**Album:** Released Jun '88, on Atlantic by WEA Records. Catalogue no: **81666**

## Atlantic Jazz

### ATLANTIC JAZZ (Various artists)

Tracks: / Bourbon Street Parade: *Barbarin, Paul* / Burgundy Street Blues: *Lewis, George* / My bucket's got a hole in it: *Robinson, Jim* / Cielito Lindo: *De Paris, Wilbur* / Salty dog: *Lewis, George* / Eh la bas: *Barbarin, Paul* / Maple leaf rag: *Murphy, Turk* / Eureka brass band, The: *Avery, Joe's Blues* / Nobody knows the way I feel this morning: *Miller, Ernest 'Punch'* / Shreveport Stomp: *De Paris, Wilbur* / Sing on: *Barbarin, Paul* / Shake it and break it: *Pierce, Joseph 'De De'* / Tiger rag: *Miller, Ernest 'Punch'* / You're driving me crazy: *Turner, Big* / Lamp is low, The: *Dickenson, Vic* / Hootie blues: *McShann, Jay* / E flat boogie: *Smith, Buster* / Confessin' the blues: *McShann, Jay* / Jumpin' at the woodside: *McShann, Jay* / Until the real thing comes along: *Turner, Big* / Undecided: *McShann, Jay* / Evenin': *Walker, T-Bone* / Buster's tune: *Smith, Buster* / Piney Brown blues: *Turner, Big* / Our love is here to stay: *Turner, Big* / Evidence: *Blakey, Art/Jazz Messengers/Thelonious Monk* / Bebop: *Blakey, Art/Jazz Messengers/Thelonious Monk* / Koko: *Stitt, Sonny* / Salt peanuts: *Jones, Philly Joe* / Almost like me: *Roach, Max* / Allen's alley: *Roach, Max* / Sa-Frantic: *Safranski, Eddie* / Not really the blues: *Rogers, Shorty* / Paradox: *Montrose, Jack* / Cheremoya: *Candoli, Conte* / Blues way up high: *Rogers, Shorty* / Song is you, The: *Giuffre, Jimmy* / Topsy: *Giuffre, Jimmy* / Triplin' awhile: *Mitchell, Red & Harold Land* / You name it: *Manne, Shelly* / I'll be seeing you: *Fruscella, Tony* / Ain't misbehavin': *Charles, Ray* / Stuffy: *Hawkins, Coleman & Milt Jackson* / Django: *Hawkins, Coleman & Milt Jackson* / Daphne: *Grappelli, Stephane* / Perdido: *Ellington, Duke* / Embraceable you: *Farmer, Art* / Four brothers: *Herman, Woody* / Everthing happens to me: *Sullivan, Ira* / Speedy reeds: *Clarke-Boland Big Band* / Lydian M-1: *Tentet, Charles 'The Teddy'* / I can't get started: *Konitz, Lee* / Bag's groove: *MJQ with Sonny Rollins, The* / This 'n' that: *Jazz Modes, The* / Giant steps: *MJQ with Sonny Rollins, The* / Sister salvation: *Slide Hampton Octet, The* / White sand: *Freeman, Von* / Misty: *Hubbard, Freddie* / Thoroughbred: *Evans, Gil* / Hard times (no one knows better than I): *Charles, Ray* / I want a little girl: *Turner, Big* / T'aint nobody's business if I do: *De Paris, Wilbur* / Have you met Miss Jones: *Monney, Joe* / Empty bed blues: *Various artists* / I can dream, can't I: *Brown, Ruth* / Any time: *Coleman, Earl* / Crazy he calls me: *Hunter, Lurean* / Love is a word for the blues: *Richards, Ann* / Your mind is on vacation: *Various artists* / Whisper not: *Hunter, Lurean* / T'aint nobody's business if I do: *Harrow, Nancy* / Desafinado: *Gilberto, Joao* / Good life: *Carter, Betty* / Salty papa blues: *Redd, Vi* / Confessin' the blues: *Phillips, Esther* / There's no you: *Coleman, Earl* / I got it bad and that ain't good: *McRae* / Do nothing till you hear from me: *Hibbler, Al & Kirk Roland* / Moody's Mood: *Franklin, Aretha* / Don't let me be lonely tonight: *Lee, Peggy* / Something: *Vaughan, Sarah* / Lonely woman: *Syms, Sylvia* / Sing joy Spring: *Manhattan Transfer* / Way you look tonight: *Garner, Erroll* / In the purple grotto: *Williams, Mary Lou* / Line up: *Tristano, Lennie* / Celia: *Newborn, Phineas Jr.* / Sweet sixteen bars: *Charles, Ray* / In walked Bud: *Blakey, Art/Jazz Messengers/Thelonious Monk* / Delaunay's dilemma: *Lewis, John* / One for fun: *Taylor, Billy* / Night in Tunisia: *Hanna, Sir Roland* / Lazy bird: *Tyner, McCoy* / Nirvana: *Mann, Herbie* / Blues for five reasons: *Weston, Randy* / Young soul: *Mitchell, Dwike* / My one and only love: *Zawinul, Joseph* / Sweet Georgia Brown: *Mance, Junior* / Ein bahn strasse: *Hancock, Herbie* / Blues 2: *Bryant, Ray* / Pardon my rags: *Jarrett, Keith* / Koto song: *Brubeck, Dave* / Last year's lies and tomorrow's promises: *Pullen, Don* / Acorn: *Jamal, Ahmad* / State trooper: *Wright, Leo* / Think: *Scott, Shirley J.* / Twist city: *Griffin, Johnny* /

Broasted or fried: *Wheeler, Clarence* / Wade in the water: *McDuff, Brother Jack* / How long blues: *Charles, Ray* / Comin' home baby: *Mann, Herbie* / Russell and Eliot: *Lateef, Yusef* / Burnin coal: *McCann, Les* / Listen here: *Ponty, Jean-Luc* / Compared to what: *McCann, Les* / You're the one: *Crawford, Hank* / Jive samba: *Adderley, Nat* / Money in the pocket: *Zawinul, Joseph* / Memphis soul stew: *Curtis, King* / Black mystery has been revealed: *Kirk, Roland* / Wednesday night prayer meeting: *Mingus, Charles* / Eventually: *Coleman, Ornette* / Cherryco: *Coleman, Ornette* / Countdown: *Coleman, Ornette* / Inflated tear, The: *Kirk, Roland* / Nonaah: *Kirk, Roland* / Yoruba: *Laws, Hubert* / Tones for Joan's bones: *Corea, Chick* / In a silent way: *Zawinul, Joseph* / Standing outside: *Zawinul, Joseph* / Chega De Saudade: *Burton, Gary* / Fortune smiles: *Burton, Gary* / Freedom jazz dance: *Vitous, Miroslav* / Beaux J. Pooboo: *McCann, Les* / Quadrant 4: *Cobham, Billy* / Beneath the earth: *Mouzon, Alphonse* / Homunculus: *Passport* / Egocentric molecules: *Ponty, Jean-Luc*.
Note: Of all the post-war labels involved in jazz, few can compete with Atlantic when it comes to the scope their recordings have covered or the number of sessions they have conducted. In its 39-year existence, Atlantic has built one of America's finest jazz catalogues. This sweeping retrospective, comprising three double and nine single albums (available as a 15-disc boxed set), is the first attempt by the company to anthologize its great wealth of material in this field. 141 cuts, recorded from the label's inception in 1947 up to this year, are arranged according to style in 12 volumes. Every major stylistic development is represented, from avant-garde to mainstream, from fusion to New Orleans. Digital re-mastering guarantees the best sound quality possible, while extensive liner notes and track-by-track credits will satisfy the most avid jazz buff. Rarely has America's classical music received such splendid treatment. Contains medley 'Forest flower/Sunrise'
**LP Set:** Released Feb '87, on Atlantic by WEA Records. Catalogue no: **K 781 712 1**
**Cass set:** Released Feb '87, on Atlantic by WEA Records. Catalogue no: **K 781 712 4**

**ATLANTIC JAZZ-AVANT GARDE**
**CD:** Released Dec '87, on WEA by WEA Records. Catalogue no: **781709 2**

**ATLANTIC JAZZ-BEBOP**
**CD:** Released Dec '87, on WEA by WEA Records. Catalogue no: **781702 2**

**ATLANTIC JAZZ-FUSION**
**CD:** Released Dec '87, on WEA by WEA Records. Catalogue no: **781711 2**

**ATLANTIC JAZZ-INTROSPECTION**
**CD:** Released Dec '87, on WEA by WEA Records. Catalogue no: **781710 2**

**ATLANTIC JAZZ-KANSAS (Various artists)**
**CD:** Released '88, on Atlantic by WEA Records. Catalogue no: **781 701-2**

**ATLANTIC JAZZ-MAINSTREAM (Various artists)**
**CD:** Released '87, on Atlantic by WEA Records. Catalogue no: **781 704-2**

**ATLANTIC JAZZ-NEW ORLEANS (Various artists)**
**CD:** Released '88, on Atlantic by WEA Records. Catalogue no: **781 700-2**

**ATLANTIC JAZZ-POST BEBOP (Various artists)**
**CD:** Released Dec '87, on WEA by WEA Records. Catalogue no: **781705 2**

## Auld, Georgie

**BY GEORGE**
**Album:** Released '84, on Swing House by Submarine Records. Catalogue no: **SWH 25**

**CANYOU PASSAGE (Auld, Georgie & His Orchestra)**
**CD:** Released '88, on Musicraft (USA) by Discovery Records (USA). Catalogue no: **MVSCD 57**

**GEORGIE AULD & HIS ORCHESTRA, (Auld, Georgie & His Orchestra/Sarah Vaughan)**
Tracks: / You're blase / I don't know why / Just you, just me / Blue moon / Route 66 / Hundred years from today / Canyon passage.
Note: A mid-1940 recording.
**Album:** Released '88, on Musicraft (USA) by Discovery Records (USA). Catalogue no: **MVS 509**

**GEORGIE PORGIE (Auld, Georgie & His Orchestra)**
**CD:** Released '88, on Musicraft (USA) by Discovery Records (USA). Catalogue no: **MVSCD 56**

**HOMAGE**
**Album:** Released '87, on Xanadu Catalogue no: **XANADU 190**

**I'VE GOT YOU UNDER MY SKIN**
Tracks: / I've got you under my skin / S'posin / I cover the waterfront / I didn't know what time it was / Stairway to the stars, A / Body and soul / I don't stand a ghost of a chance with you / Take care / Smoke gets in your eyes / All the things you are / Someone to watch over me.
**Album:** Released Feb '83, on Jasmine by Hasmick Promotions. Catalogue no: **JASM 1006**

**JUMP GEORGIE JUMP**
Tracks: / Short circuit / Mandrake root / Poinciana / Jivin with the jug / Yesterdays / I'll always be in love with you / Stompin' at the Savoy / Sentimental journey / Jump Georgie jump / I'm always chasing rainbows / I can't get started / Taps Miller / Concerto for tenor.
**Album:** Released Jan '83, on Hep Jazz by Hep Records. Catalogue no: **HEP 27**

## Avon Cities Jazz Band

**BLUE FUNK**
Tracks: / Stevedore stomp / Blue funk / Aquari us / Machine gun Kelly / Midnight sleighride / Pata pata / Godspell / Road to the Isles / Mercy mercy mercy / Superstar.
**Album:** Released '74, on Joy by President Records. Catalogue no: **JOY 249**

**CURRENT A/C**
Tracks: / Brazilian bounce / Fuse blues / Wabash blues / Ritual fire dance / Life raver / Doctor Caligari / Louisiana / Little 3/4 for God and co, A / Delta dawn.
**Album:** Released May '79, on Joy by President Records. Catalogue no: **JOYS 262**

**SILVER COLLECTION**
Tracks: / St. Thomas / El Condor Pasa / Sometime later / Bourbon Street parade / We believe in music / Heliotrope bouquet / Hi de ho / South / Tsar Paul.
**Album:** Released '86, on Joy by President Records. Catalogue no: **JOYS 261**

## Axidentals

**AXIDENTALS WITH THE KAI WINDING**
Tracks: / Day in, day out / I will come back / You don't know what love is / Gypsy in my soul / Close to you / No moon at all / Waiting for the Robert E. Lee / Walkin' / Rockaby bluebird / Flamingo / Out of this world / You gotta wail.
**Album:** Released Mar '84, on Jasmine by Hasmick Promotions. Catalogue no: **JASM 1507**

## Ayler, Albert

**ALBERT AYLER**
**Album:** Released Apr '81, on ESP by ESP Records. Catalogue no: **ESP 1020**

**ALBERT AYLER IN GREENWICH**
**Album:** Released May '85, on MCA by MCA Records. Deleted Dec '89. Catalogue no: **AS 9155**
**Cass:** Released May '85, on MCA by MCA Records. Deleted Dec '89. Catalogue no: **ASC 9155**
**CD:** Released May '85, on MCA by MCA Records. Deleted Dec '89. Catalogue no: **2546 352**

**AT SLUG'S SALOON (Ayler, Albert Quintet)**
**Album:** Released Oct '82, on Base Deleted '88. Catalogue no: **BASE 3031**

**AT SLUG'S SALOON VOL.2, MAY 1ST (Ayler, Albert Quintet)**
**Album:** Released Oct '82, on Base Deleted '88. Catalogue no: **BASE 3032**

**BLACK REVOLT (Ayler, Albert Quintet)**
**CD:** Released '88, on Crusader Catalogue no: **400 04**

**FIRST RECORDINGS, THE**
**Album:** Released '88, on GNP Crescendo (USA) by GNP Crescendo Records (USA). Catalogue no: **GNPS 9022**
**Album:** Released '88, on Sonet by Sonet Records. Catalogue no: **SNTF 604**

**LIVE IN GREENWICH VILLAGE**
Tracks: / For John Coltrane / Change has come / Truth is marching in / Our prayer.

Note: Recorded 1967 (two live dates). Personnel: Albert Ayler (alto sax), Joel Friedman (cello), Bill Folwell (bass), Beaver Harris (drums).
**CD:** Released Jun '89, on MCA (Impulse Jazz) Catalogue no: **MCAD 39123**
**Album:** Released Jun '89, on MCA (Impulse Jazz) Catalogue no: **MCA 39123**
**Album:** Released Mar '83, on Jasmine by Hasmick Promotions. Deleted Feb '88. Catalogue no: **JAS 70**

**NEW YORK EYE & EAR CONTROL**
**Album:** Released Apr '81, on ESP by ESP Records. Catalogue no: **ESP 1016**

**NUITS DE LA FONDATION**
**2 LP Set:** Released Mar '78, on Shandar Catalogue no: **SHAN 83503/4**

**PROPHECY**
**Album:** Released Apr '81, on UNI by MCA Records. Catalogue no: **ESP 3030**

**SPIRITUAL UNITY (Ayler, Albert Trio)**
**Album:** Released Apr '81, on ESP by ESP Records. Catalogue no: **ESP 1002**

**VIBRATIONS (Ayler, Albert & Don Cherry)**
Tracks: / Ghosts / Children / Holy spirit / Vibrations / Mothers.
**Album:** Released Sep '87, on Freedom Catalogue no: **FLP 41000**
**CD:** Released Sep '87, on Freedom Catalogue no: **FCD 41000**

**WITCHES AND DEVILS**
**Album:** Released Jan '79, on Freedom Catalogue no: **FLP 41018**

## Azymuth

**DEPART (Azymuth with Ralph Towner)**
**Album:** Released Nov '80, on ECM Catalogue no: **ECM 1163**

**TUDO BEN**
**CD:** Released 10 Jul '89, on Virgin by Virgin Records. Catalogue no: **CDENV 533**
**Album:** Released 10 Jul '89, on Virgin by Virgin Records. Catalogue no: **ENVLP 533**

# B

The following information was taken from the Music Master database on April 14th, 1990.

## Babs, Alice

**Biographical details:** Alice Babs was a rare example of a Swedish singer achieving British chart glory in pre-Abba days. But she had to be content with just a week: After You've Gone peaked at No 43 in 1963. (Bob MacDonald, 1984.) Born Alice Nilson in 1924 in Kalmar, Sweden, Babs has been a film and TV star in Europe, touring for some years with a trio including Sven Asmussen. She had a UK hit in 1963 with *After You've Gone*, and recorded with Duke Eillington the same year, later singing in his Sacred Concerts, as well as at the 1975 Newport Jazz Festival. Ellington said 'Alice Babs is a composer's dream, for with her he can forget all the limitations and just write his heart out'. (Donald Clarke 23 August 1988).

### AFTER YOU'VE GONE

Tracks: / After you've gone.
**7" Single:** Released Aug '63, on Fontana by Phonogram Ltd. Deleted '66. Catalogue no: **TF 409**

## Bahatia, Amin

### INTER STELLAR SUITE, THE

**CD:** Released Sep '87, on Blue Note by EMI Records. Deleted Nov '88. Catalogue no: **CDP 746 869-2**

## Bailey, Buster

### ALL ABOUT MEMPHIS

Tracks: / Bear wallow / Hatton Avenue and Gayoso Street / Sunday parade / Beale street blues / Memphis blues / Chicasaw bluff / Hot water ba you.
**CD:** Released Jan '88, on London by London Records Ltd. Catalogue no: **820 598 2**
**Album:** Released Oct '86, on Affinity by Charly Records. Catalogue no: **AFF 170**

### COMPLETE RECORDINGS 1934-1940

Tracks: / Call of the Delta / Shanghai shuffle / Afternoon in Africa / Dizzy debutante / Planters punch / Sloe Jam fizz / Chained to a dream / Light up / Man with a horn goes berzerk / Should I / Blue room / April in Paris / Am I blue / Seems like a month of Sundays / Fable of the rose / Pinetop's boogie woogie.
**Album:** Released '87, on Saydisc by Amon Ra Records. Catalogue no: **MSE 222**
**Album:** Released Apr '81, on Rarities Catalogue no: **RARITIES 17**

### VARSITY SESSIONS VOL 1, THE (Bailey, Buster & His Orchestra)

**Album:** Released Jul '81, on Storyville by Storyville Records AB. Catalogue no: **SLP 701**

## Bailey, Derek

**Biographical details:** Bailey, Derek The avant-garde guitarist and composer was born in 1930 in Sheffield. He played in theatres, dance halls etc. and began to improvise in 1965, now one of the most highly regarded artists on the contemporary scene: his demanding, abstract music contains considerable drama and wit. He co-formed Incus Records in 1970 with Evan Parker and Tony Oxley, the first independent in the UK owned by musicians. He has mostly played solo or duo with selected company such as Parker, Steve Lacy, Tony Coe and others; he has made more than 50 albums since 1968 recording with John Stevens, Trevor Watts, Dave Holland, John Zorn, George Lewis, Anthony Braxton, Lol Coxhill, Han Bennink, many more (Donald Clarke 23 August 1988).

### BARFIGURING

**CD:** Released Mar '90, on Incus by Incus Records. Catalogue no: **JJCD1**

### COMPANY 3 (Bailey, Derek & Hans Bennink)

**Album:** Released May '78, on Incus by Incus Records. Catalogue no: **INCUS 25**

### CONCERT... (Bailey, Derek & Tristan Honsinger)

**Album:** Released Nov '76, on Incus by Incus Records. Catalogue no: **INCUS 20**

### DROPS (Bailey, Derek & Andrea Centazzo)

**Album:** Released Dec '77, on Incus by Incus Records. Catalogue no: **INCUS 3**

### LIVE FROM VERITY'S PLACE (Bailey, Derek & Hans Bennink)

**Album:** Released Nov '76, on Incus by Incus Records. Catalogue no: **INCUS 9**

### LONDON CONCERT (Bailey, Derek & Evan Parker)

**Album:** Released Nov '76, on Incus by Incus Records. Catalogue no: **INCUS 16**

### LOT 74-SOLO IMPROVISATIONS

**Album:** Released Nov '76, on Incus by Incus Records. Catalogue no: **INCUS 12**

### SOLO

**Album:** Released Nov '76, on Incus by Incus Records. Catalogue no: **INCUS 2**

## Bailey, Mildred

**Biographical details:** Mildred was part American Indian; her brother, Al Rinker, was a member of Paul Whiteman's vocal trio the Rhythm Boys, which included Bing Crosby. Her unique high-pitched range, accuracy and jazz-influenced phrasing made her one of the best girl singers and a favourite with musicians. She was married to vibraharpist Red Norvo; they were billed as Mr & Mrs Swing, co-leading an excellent band which broadcast and recorded in the late '30s. Later she had her own radio shows and records. (Donald Clarke 23 August 1988).

### 1944

Tracks: / Please don't talk to me when I'm gone / I'll never be the same / St. Louis blues / Man I love / I'll get by / I dream of you / Someday sweetheart / Four in a bar / From the land of the sky blue water / Lover come back to me / I didn't know about you / I never knew / China boy / Evelina / Body and soul / It had to be you.
**Album:** Released '79, on London Records by London Records Ltd. Deleted '84. Catalogue no: **HMP 5056**

### ALL OF ME

**Album:** Released May '79, on Monmouth Evergreen Catalogue no: **MES 6814**

### HARLEM LULLABY (original recordings 1931-1939)

Tracks: / Georgia on my mind / Concentratin' / Harlem lullaby / Junk man / Ol' Pappy / Squeeze me / Downhearted blues / Porter's love song to a chambermaid, A / Smoke dreams / Rockin' chair / Moon got in my eyes, The / It's the natural thing to do / Worried over you / Thanks for the memory / More than ever / Please be kind / I let a song go out of my heart / Rock it for me / My melancholy baby / Lonesome road, The.
Note: 60 minutes. With Red Norvo, Bunny Berigan, Chuck Berry, Buck Clayton, Jimmy Dorsey, Tommy Dorsey, Benny Goodman, Coleman Hawkins, Johnny Hodges, Gene Krupa, Teddy Wilson, etc.
**Cass:** Released 1 Dec '89, on Living Era by Academy Sound & Vision Records. Catalogue no: **ZC AJA 5065**
**CD:** Released 1 Dec '89, on Living Era by Academy Sound & Vision Records. Catalogue no: **CD AJA 5065**
**Album:** Released 1 Dec '89, on Living Era by Academy Sound & Vision Records. Catalogue no: **AJA 5065**

### MILDRED BAILEY 1938/39

**Album:** Released Jul '82, on Jazz Document Catalogue no: **VA 7996**

### MILDRED BAILEY COLLECTION (20 golden greats)

Tracks: / Georgia on my mind / Stop the Sun, stop the Moon / Rockin' chair / Smoke dreams / Heaven help this heart of mine / Don't be that way / Old folks / Thanks for the memory / St. Louis blues

/ I thought about you / Gulf Coast blues / Ghost of a chance / There'll be some changes made / I'm nobody's baby / More than you know / Squeeze me / Honeysuckle rose / Summertime / I'll close my eyes / Lover come back to me.
**Cass:** Released Dec '87, on Deja Vu Catalogue no: **DVMC 2106**
**Album:** Released Dec '87, on Deja Vu Catalogue no: **DVLP 2106**

**MILDRED BAILEY WITH THE PAUL BARONS ORCHESTRA 1944**
**Album:** Released Oct '79, on London Records by London Records Ltd. Catalogue no: **HMA 5056**

**PAUL WHITEMAN YEARS 1931-1932**
**Album:** Released Mar '90, on Tono Catalogue no: **TJ6002**

**RAREST OF ALL RARE PERFORMANCES**
**Album:** Released Jul '82, on Kings Of Jazz Catalogue no: **KLJ 20035**

**UNCOLLECTED MILDRED BAILEY, THE (CBS Radio Show)**
Tracks: / Please don't talk about me / St. Louis blues / I'll get by / Someday, sweetheart / From the land of the sky blue water / Body and soul / China boy / It had to be you / I'll never be the same / Man I love, The / I dream of you / Four in a bar / Lover come back to me / I didn't know / Evelina / I never knew.
Note: Bailey had her own CBS radio show in 1944 with Paul Baron's full orchestra which featured such notable sidemen as Will Bradley, Yank Lawson, Oscar Pettiford, Teddy Wilson, Roy Eldridge, Red Norvo, etc. The LP consists of the best excerpts of the season edited into one long complete show, with introductions, announcements, opening, closing, etc. Liner notes are by Charles Rinker, Mildred's brother. This album demonstrates if there was ever a bond in music between two musicians, Mildred Bailey and Ned Norvo really had one. Produced by Wally Heider. (Hindsight Catalogue - 1989)
**Album:** Released May '79, on Hindsight Catalogue no: **HSR 133**

## Baker, Chet

**Biographical details:** Baker, Chet. The American trumpeter was born in Oklahoma in 1929; he died in Amsterdam in 1988 in a fall from a hotel room window. In the early '50s Charlie Parker told Miles Davis, 'You'd better watch out. There's a little white cat on the West Coast who's gonna eat you up.' In fact Baker never learned to read music well and had as much in common with Bix Beiderbecke as with Davis. But he achieved national fame with the Gerry Mulligan quartet in 1952, then led his own group with the excellent Russ Freeman on piano '53-4; his light, wistful tone and laid-back lyricism was at the centre of the West Coast 'cool jazz' scene; his occasional singing was derided by critics, but the meticulous reissue of his complete Pacific Jazz recordings by the USA Mosaic label in limited-edition box sets show the records to have much more than a period charm. Chet on Riverside is a beautiful set made in 1959 with Bill Evans on piano, others including an excellent rhythm section (no vocals). He was one of the most tragic victims of narcotics in popular music; he was beaten by hoodlums in San Fransisco in 1968, losing his teeth; he never beat the habit, yet he recovered and his playing since the mid-'70s was as lovely as ever. His death was thought to be a drug related accident. (Donald Clarke 23 August 1988).

**ALL TOGETHER (Baker, Chet, Lee Konitz & Keith Jarrett)**
**Album:** Released Apr '79, on Jazz Connoisseur by Spotlite Records. Catalogue no: **JC 113**

**ALMOST BLUE**
Tracks: / Almost blue.
**12" Single:** Released 24 Jul '89, on RCA by BMG Records (UK). Catalogue no: **PT 49371**

**AT RONNIE SCOTT'S (Baker, Chet (with Van Morrison))**
**CD:** Released Dec '87, on Hendring Deleted '88. Catalogue no: **HEN 6044 Y**

**BALLADS FOR TWO**
**Album:** Released Sep '79, on Sandra Catalogue no: **SMP 2102**

**BLUES FOR... (featuring Warne Marsh) (Baker, Chet Quartet)**
**Album:** Released '88, on Criss Cross Catalogue no: **CRISS 1010**

**CANDY**
**CD:** Released Jun '88, on Sonet by Sonet Records. Catalogue no: **SNTCD 946**
**Album:** Released Jan '87, on Sonet by Sonet Records. Catalogue no: **SNTF 946**

**CHET**
Tracks: / Alone together / How high the moon / It never entered my mind / 'Tis Autumn / If you could see me now / September song / You'd be nice to come home to / Time on my hands / You & the night & the music.
**Album:** Released Feb '84, on Riverside (USA) by Fantasy Inc (USA). Catalogue no: **OJC 087**

**CHET BAKER**
**Album:** Released Jan '78, on Horizon by A&M Records. Catalogue no: **AMLJ 726**

**CHET BAKER AND STRINGS: FEATURING ZOOT SIMS**
Tracks: / You don't know what love is / I'm through with love / Love walked in / You better go now / I married an angel / Love / I love you / What a difference a day made / Why shouldn't I? / Little duet, A / Wind, The / Trickledidlier.
**Album:** Released Jul '87, on CBS by CBS Records. Deleted Aug '88. Catalogue no: **CBS 21142**
**Cass:** Released Jul '87, on CBS by CBS Records. Catalogue no: **40 21142**

**CHET BAKER BIG BAND (Baker, Chet Big Band)**
**Album:** Released Feb '88, on Fresh Sounds (Spain) by Fresh Sounds Records (Spain). Catalogue no: **FS 89**

**CHET BAKER IN CONCERT (Baker, Chet & Lee Konitz)**
**Album:** Released May '84, on India Navigation Catalogue no: **IN 1052**

**CHET BAKER IN PARIS**
**CD Set:** Released May '88, on Fresh Sounds (Spain) by Fresh Sounds Records (Spain). Catalogue no: **FSR CD 1/2**
**LP Set:** Released Feb '88, on Fresh Sounds (Spain) by Fresh Sounds Records (Spain). Catalogue no: **FSBOX 1**

**CHET BAKER IN PARIS VOL 3**
**Album:** Released Nov '79, on Barclay (France) by Decca Records. Catalogue no: **80711**

**CHET BAKER IN TOKYO**
**Album:** Released Jul '89, on Concord Jazz by Concord Jazz Records (USA). Catalogue no: **K 28P6495**
**CD:** Released Jul '89, on Concord Jazz by Concord Jazz Records (USA). Catalogue no: **K 32Y6281**

**CHET BAKER INTRODUCES JOHNNY PACE (Baker, Chet & Johnny Pace)**
**Album:** Released Sep '88, on Riverside (1) Catalogue no: **RLP 292**

**CHET BAKER: LIVE AT RONNIE SCOTTS**
**CD:** Released Aug '87, on Hendring Catalogue no: **WHCD 003**

**CHET BAKER - SEXTET & QUARTET (JOKER) (Baker, Chet Sextet & Quartet)**
**Album:** Released '88, on Joker (USA) by Lifetime Records (USA). Catalogue no: **SM 3910**

**CHET BAKER SEXTET & QUARTET (UP INTERNATIONAL) (Baker, Chet Sextet & Quartet)**
Tracks: / Ladybird / Cheryl / Tune up / Line for Lyons / Pent up house / My old flame / Indian summer / Look for the silver lining.
**Album:** Released Apr '81, on Up International Catalogue no: **LPUP 5116**

**CHET BAKER SINGS AGAIN**
**CD:** Released Jun '86, on RCA Jazz (Japan) Catalogue no: **886 002**
**CD:** Released '89, on Timeless by Timeless Records. Catalogue no: **CDSJP 238**
**Album:** Released '88, on Timeless by Timeless Records. Catalogue no: **SJP 238**

**CHET IN PARIS - VOL. 1 (Featuring Dick Twardzik)**
**CD:** Released Jan '89, on Polygram (France) by PolyGram UK Ltd. Catalogue no: **837 474-2**

**CHET IN PARIS - VOL. 2 (Everything happens to me)**
**CD:** Released Jan '89, on Polygram (France) by PolyGram UK Ltd. Catalogue no: **837 475-2**

**CHET IN PARIS - VOL. 3 (Cheryl)**
**CD:** Released Jan '89, on Polygram (France) by PolyGram UK Ltd. Catalogue no: **837 476-2**

**CHET IN PARIS - VOL. 4 (Alterna-**

**tive takes)**
**CD:** Released Jan '89, on Polygram (France) by PolyGram UK Ltd. Catalogue no: **837 477-2**

**CHET IS BACK**
Tracks: / Well you needn't / Pent up house / Barbados.
**Album:** Released Oct '85, on RCA (France) by BMG Records (France). Catalogue no: **NL 70578**
**Album:** Released Jan '85, on RCA (Germany) Catalogue no: **CL 31649**

**CHET'S CHOICE (Baker, Chet Trio)**
**Album:** Released '88, on Criss Cross Catalogue no: **CRISS 1016**

**COOL BLUES (Unissued live recordings vol.2) (Baker, Chet Quintet)**
**Album:** Released Mar '87, on Replica Catalogue no: **RR 2**

**COOL CAT**
Tracks: / Swift shifting / Round midnight / Caravelle / For all we know / Blue moon / My foolish heart.
**Cass:** Released Mar '90, on Timeless by Timeless Records. Catalogue no: **MCSJP 262**
**CD:** Released Mar '90, on Timeless by Timeless Records. Catalogue no: **CDSJP 262**

**COOLS OUT (Baker, Chet Quintet)**
Tracks: / Extra mild / Halema / Jumpin' off a cliff / Route / Lucius lou / Pawnee junction.
**Album:** Released Feb '89, on Boplicity by Ace Records. Catalogue no: **BOP 013**

**DAYBREAK**
**Album:** Released Apr '81, on Steeplechase (USA) Catalogue no: **SCS 1142**

**DIANE (Baker, Chet / Paul Bley)**
**Album:** Released Jul '88, on Steeplechase (USA) Catalogue no: **SCS 1207**
**CD:** Released Jul '88, on Steeplechase (USA) Catalogue no: **SCCD 31207**

**DOWN HERE ON THE GROUND**
**CD:** Released Feb '89, on A&M by A&M Records. Catalogue no: **CDA 0805**

**EVERYTHING HAPPENS TO ME**
**Cass:** Released Oct '86, on Timeless by Timeless Records. Catalogue no: **SJP 1192**

**EXITUS (Unissued live recordings vol.1) (Baker, Chet Quintet)**
**Album:** Released Mar '87, on Replica Catalogue no: **RR 1**

**FOUR**
**CD:** Released Jun '89, on Paddlewheel/King Catalogue no: **K32Y 6281**
**Album:** Released Jun '89, on Paddlewheel/King Catalogue no: **K28P 6495**

**HEART OF THE BALLAD (Baker, Chet & Enrico Pieranunzi)**
**Album:** Released '88, on Philology Catalogue no: **214W 20**

**IN NEW YORK**
**Album:** Released Jun '86, on Original Jazz Classics (USA) by Fantasy Inc (USA). Catalogue no: **OJC 207**
**CD:** Released Apr '87, on Crusader Catalogue no: **CA 98956**

**JAMES DEAN STORY, THE (Baker, Chet & Bud Shank)**
**Album:** Released Feb '88, on Fresh Sounds (Spain) by Fresh Sounds Records (Spain). Catalogue no: **FS 110**

**JAZZ AT ANN ARBOR (Baker, Chet Quartet)**
**Album:** Released Feb '88, on Fresh Sounds (Spain) by Fresh Sounds Records (Spain). Catalogue no: **FS 26**

**KIRK LIGHTSEY TRIO & CHET BAKER (Baker, Chet & Kirk Lightsey Trio)**
**Album:** Released '88, on Timeless by Timeless Records. Catalogue no: **SJP 176**

**LET'S GET LOST**
**CD:** Released Mar '90, on Pacific Jazz by EMI Records. Catalogue no: **JJCD2**
**Album:** Released May '89, on RCA by BMG Records (UK). Catalogue no: **PL 83054**
**Cass:** Released May '89, on RCA by BMG Records (UK). Catalogue no: **PK 83054**
**CD:** Released May '89, on RCA by BMG Records (UK). Catalogue no: **PD 83054**

**LET'S GET LOST (2) (Best of Chet Baker sings)**
Tracks: / Thrill is gone, The / But not for me / Time after time / I get along without you very well / There will never be another you / Look for the silver lining / My funny valentine / I fall in love too easily / Daybreak / Just friends / I remember you / Let's get lost / Long ago (and far away) / You don't know what love is.
**CD:** Released Jan '90, on Pacific Jazz by EMI Records. Catalogue no: **CDP 792 932 2**
**Album:** Released Jan '90, on Pacific Jazz by EMI Records. Catalogue no: **B1 92932**
**CD:** Released Jan '90, on Pacific Jazz by EMI Records. Catalogue no: **CZ 259**
**Album:** Released Jan '90, on Pacific Jazz by EMI Records. Catalogue no: **792 932 1**

**LIVE AT NICK'S**
**Album:** Released Jul '87, on Criss Cross Catalogue no: **CRISS 1027**
**CD:** Released Mar '90, on Criss Cross Catalogue no: **CRISSCD1027**

**LIVE AT ROSENHEIMER**
Note: The last quartet recording before Chet Baker's tragic death in Amsterdam on May 13th 1988. Musically in top condition, Chet is heard on trumpet, vocals and piano. Personnel: Chet Baker (trumpet, vocals, piano), Nicola Stilo (guitar, flute), Marc Abrams (bass).
**CD:** Released May '89, on Timeless by Timeless Records. Catalogue no: **CDSJP 233**
**Album:** Released May '89, on Timeless by Timeless Records. Catalogue no: **SJP 233**

**LIVE FROM THE MOONLIGHT (Baker, Chet Trio)**
**2 LP Set:** Released '88, on Philology Catalogue no: **214W 10-11**

**LIVE IN PARIS 1960 & NICE 1975**
**CD:** Released Jun '89, on France's Concert Catalogue no: **FCD 123**
**Album:** Released Jun '89, on France's Concert Catalogue no: **FC 123**

**LIVE IN SWEDEN**
Tracks: / Lament / My ideal / Beatrice / You can't go home again / But not for me / Ray's idea / Milestones.
**CD:** Released Sep '89, on Dragon by Dragon Records. Catalogue no: **DRCD 178**
**Album:** Released Jun '86, on Dragon by Dragon Records. Catalogue no: **DRLP 56**

**MEMORIES**
**CD:** Released 12 Apr '89, on King Catalogue no: **K32Y 6270**
**Album:** Released 12 Apr '89, on Paddlewheel/King Catalogue no: **K28P 6491**

**MR B**
Tracks: / Dolphin dance / Ellen and David / Strollin' / In your own sweet way / Mister B / Beatrice.
**Album:** Released Aug '85, on Timeless by Timeless Records. Catalogue no: **SJP 192**

**MY FAVOURITE SONGS**
**Cass:** Released Sep '89, on Enja (Germany) by Enja Records (West Germany). Catalogue no: **ENJA 5097 4**
**Album:** Released Sep '89, on Enja (Germany) by Enja Records (West Germany). Catalogue no: **ENJA 5097 1**

**NEW BLUE HORNS (Baker, Chet / Kenny Dorham)**
Tracks: / New blue horns.
**Album:** Released Jan '87, on Original Jazz Classics (USA) by Fantasy Inc (USA). Catalogue no: **OJC 256**

**NIGHTBIRD (Live at Ronnie Scott's)**
Tracks: / But not for me / Arboway / If I should loose you / My ideal / Nightbird / Love for sale / Shifting down / You can't go home again / Send in the clowns.
**Cass:** Released Feb '90, on Essential by Castle Communications Records. Catalogue no: **ESMMC 015**
**CD:** Released Feb '90, on Essential by Castle Communications Records. Catalogue no: **ESMCD 015**

**NO PROBLEM (Baker, Chet Quartet)**
**CD Single:** Released '88, on Steeplechase (USA) Catalogue no: **SCCD 31131**

**PEACE**
**CD:** Released Jul '88, on Enja (Germany) by Enja Records (West Germany). Catalogue no: **ENJA 4016-04**
**Album:** Released Jul '88, on Enja (Germany) by Enja Records (West Germany). Catalogue no: **ENJA 4016**

**PLAYBOYS (Baker, Chet & Art**

**Pepper)**
Tracks: / For minors only / Original Pepper / Resonant emotions / Tynan time / Pictures of Heath / For miles and miles / C.T.A..
**Album:** Released Oct '83, on Boplicity by Ace Records. Deleted '88. Catalogue no: **BOP 003**

**PLAYS VLADIMIR COSMA**
**CD:** Released Apr '87, on Crusader Catalogue no: **96251**

**ROUTE, THE (Baker, Chet & Art Pepper)**
Tracks: / Tynan time / Route, The / Sonny boy / Minor yours / Little girl / Ol' croix / I can't give you anything but love / Great lie, The / Sweet Lorraine / If I should lose you / Younger than springtime.
**CD:** Released Mar '90, on Pacific Jazz by EMI Records. Catalogue no: **JJCD 3**
**CD:** Released Jan '90, on Pacific Jazz by EMI Records. Catalogue no: **CZ 258**
**CD:** Released Jan '90, on Pacific Jazz by EMI Records. Catalogue no: **CDP 792 931 2**

**SAKURA**
**CD:** Released '89, on GSR Catalogue no: **GSRCD 87**

**SILENT NIGHTS/CHRISTMAS JAZZ (Baker, Chet & Christopher Mason)**
**CD:** Released '88, on Varrick (USA) by Rounder Records (USA). Catalogue no: **CDVR 032**

**SINGS**
**Album:** Released Feb '88, on Fresh Sounds (Spain) by Fresh Sounds Records (Spain). Catalogue no: **FS 87**

**TOUCH OF YOUR LIPS, THE**
**Album:** Released Sep '79, on Steeplechase (USA) Catalogue no: **SCS 1122**

**WHEN SUNNY GETS BLUE**
**CD:** Released Jul '88, on Steeplechase (USA) Catalogue no: **SCCD 31221**
**Album:** Released Jul '88, on Steeplechase (USA) Catalogue no: **SCS 1221**
**Cass:** Released Jul '88, on Steeplechase (USA) Catalogue no: **SCM 51221**

**WITCH DOCTOR (Baker, Chet & Lighthouse All Stars)**
Tracks: / Loaded / I'll remember April / Winter wonderland / Pirouette / Witch doctor.
**Album:** Released Dec '86, on Contemporary by Ace Records. Catalogue no: **COP 033**

**YOU CAN'T GO HOME AGAIN**
Tracks: / Love for sale / Un poco loco / You can't go home again / El morro.
**CD:** Released 28 Nov '88, on A&M by A&M Records. Catalogue no: **CDA 0805**

## Baker, Duck

**FINGER STYLE JAZZ GUITAR**
Tracks: / Tintiyana / Summertime / White with foam / Take the 'A' train / Yes yes / Sweet and lovely / Wishes / Plain as the winter / Stompin' at the Savoy / Southern Cross / Everything that rises must converge / Good intentions / In a sentimental mood / You're a lady.
**Album:** Released Sep '79, on Kicking Mule by Sonet Records. Catalogue no: **SNKF 154**

**KING OF BONGO BONG, THE**
Tracks: / New righteous blues / Crazy rhythm / I found a new baby / No love / There'll be some changes made / See you in my dreams / I ain't go nobody / Mama's getting younger / Papa's getting older each day / Immaculate conception rag / River blues / Chicken ain't nothing but a bird / King of bongo bong / Business as usual.
**Album:** Released Jan '78, on Kicking Mule by Sonet Records. Catalogue no: **SNKF 137**

**THERE'S SOMETHING FOR EVERYONE**
Tracks: / Jackson stomp, The / Mission street blues, The / Allegheny county / Matty powell / Zebra blues / Wolverine blues / Melancholy baby / Medley / Take me out to the ball game (Medley (a)) / America (Medley (b)) / Temperence reel / Pineapple rag / Hicks farewell / Doctor jazz / Old folks polka, The / There'll be a happy meeting / Wreck of the old '97.
**Album:** Released '80, on Kicking Mule by Sonet Records. Catalogue no: **SNKF 116**

**WHEN YOU WORE A TULIP**
Tracks: / You took advantage of me / Grace street / Was / Liza (all the clouds will roll away) / Boys from Blue Hill / Back home again in Indiana / Rapid transit blues / Two cats with new shoes / Plymouth rock / Honeysuckle rose / Cousin / Lazy river / Drunken wagoner / When you wore a tulip / Thou swell / Angeline the baker.
**Album:** Released Jan '78, on Kicking Mule by Sonet Records. Catalogue no: **SNKF 123**

## Baker, Earl

**LEGENDARY EARL BAKER CYLANDERS, THE**
**Album:** Released Jan '80, on Jazz Archives (USA) by Jazz Archives Inc.(USA). Catalogue no: **JA 43**

## Baker, Kenny

**BAKER'S JAM (Baker, Kenny All Stars)**
**Album:** Released Jul '88, on 77 by 77 Records. Catalogue no: **77 S 56**

**DATE WITH THE DOZEN**
**Album:** Released '88, on Dormouse Catalogue no: **DM 9**

**KENNY BAKER HALF DOZEN (Baker, Kenny featuring George Chisolm)**
Tracks: / How's this / Love me or leave me / If I could be with you / Keepin' out of mischief now / How can you face me / Puttin' on the ritz / Mr. Paganini / Doodee / St. Louis blues / Honolulu blues.
**Album:** Released Feb '89, on Dormouse Catalogue no: **DMLP 19**

## Baker, Laverne

**Biographical details:** Baker, Laverne. The rhythm & blues singer was born in 1929 in Chicago. She began at 17 as 'Little Miss Sharecropper', was spotted by bandleader Fletcher Henderson; she recorded for CBS and King but achieved her greatest success on the young Atlantic label, unfortunately during her era of the white cover: she had 18 crossovers to the USA pop chart, but her biggest hit *Tweedle Dee* was beaten in the chart by Georgia Gibbs' cover. Baker later moved to Japan. (Donald Clarke 1988).

**HITS AND RARITIES**
Tracks: / Jim Dandy / Tweedle dee / So high so low / Soul on fire / Romance in the dark / Tomorrow night / Humpty dumpty heart / Manana / Harbor lights / Fool that I am / I can't love you enough / I'm living my life for you / I can't hold out any longer / I'll do the same for you / Game of love, The / Help each other romance, A.
**Album:** on Official by Official Records. Catalogue no: **OFF 6042**

**I'M GONNA GET YOU**
Tracks: / Love is ending / Born to lose / I need you so / Play it fair / Baby / One monkey don't stop no show / Batman to the rescue / Think twice (With Jackie Wilson.) / Call me darling / Nothing like being in love / I'm gonna get you / Pledging my love to you / Let me belong to you / I'm the one to do it / Baby don't you do it / please dont hurt me.
**Cass:** Released Nov '87, on C5 by C5 Records. Catalogue no: **C5K 510**
**Album:** Released Nov '87, on C5 by C5 Records. Catalogue no: **C5-510**

**LAVERNE BAKER SINGS BESSIE SMITH / THAT'S JAZZ**
Tracks: / Gimme a pigfoot and a bottle of beer / Baby doll / On revival day / Money blues / I ain't gonna play no second fiddle / Back water blues / Empty bed blues / There'll be a hot time in the old town tonight / Nobody knows / You when you're down and out / After you've gone / Young woman's blues / Preaching the blues.
**Album:** Released '88, on Atlantic by WEA Records. Catalogue no: **K 50241**

**REAL GONE GAL**
Tracks: / How can you leave a man like this / Jim Dandy / My happiness for ever / Fee fi fo fum / Jim Dandy got married / Substitute / Whipper snapper / Voodoo voodoo / I cried a tear / He's a real gone guy / I waited too long / Tiny Tim / Shake a hand / Bumble bee / Hey Memphis / See see rider.
Note: A sister release to our Ruth Brown compilation(CRB 1069).Lavern was Atlantic Record's other great female R&B star of the fifties,and this album presents 16 other humdingers from 1953-62, three or four of which have never previously appeared on album. They weren't all hits: despite her great popularity Lavern's chart sucess was erratic and, any way ,we have deliberately omitted some hit titles, some of the poppier items, in favour of grittier tracks; The result has much the same sort of musical

balance as the Ruth Brown album: one or two of her best ballad performances, one or two of her bouncy but brittle finger snappers, a bit of blues and a whole lotta good-time rock and rolling. Irrestible stuff then and now..t

**Album:** Released Apr '84, on Charly R&B by Charly Records. Deleted '88. Catalogue no: **CRB 1072**

**Cass:** Released '85, on Charly R&B by Charly Records. Deleted '88. Catalogue no: **TCCRB 1072**

### TWEEDLE DEE

Tracks: / Tweedle dee / Jim Dandy / Bumble bee.

**7" EP:** Released Jul '82, on Revival Catalogue no: **REV 6007**

## Baker, Shorty

**Biographical details:** Baker, Shorty Harold Baker (1913-66) was an underrated trumpeter, except by other musicians. He was once married to pianist Mary Lou Williams; he played in several bands, but was best-known with Duke Ellington from 1942. Among many fine solos, *Mood Indigo* on one of Duke's most beautiful albums *Ellington Indigos* was a feature vehicle for his lovely muted horn. He also freelanced extensively until he died of cancer. (Donald Clarke 23 August 1988).

### SUMMER CONCERT 1960 (Baker, Shorty & Bud Freeman)

**Album:** Released Jan '80, on Jazz Archives (USA) by Jazz Archives Inc.(USA). Catalogue no: **JA 38**

## Ball, Kenny

**Biographical details:** Born in Ilford in 1931, Kenny Ball took up the trumpet at the age of 16. Having played in various jazz bands, he formed Kenny Ball & His Jazzmen in 1958. Riding the crest of the early 60's trad jazz boom, Ball and his band scored a string of hit singles, beginning with Cole Porter's Samantha in early 1961. Their biggest success came at the end of that year when Midnight In Moscow went to No 2 in both Britain and, surprisingly, America. There were no further US hits but they continued at home with three more Top Tenners, March Of The Siamese Children, The Green Leaves Of Summer and Sukiyaki, which charted in advance of the original Japanese version by Kyu Sakamoto. In 1964, when Beatlemania was at its height and the trad boom was abating, the hits tailed off. Ball could no longer achieve success in either the singles chart or the albums list, where he had had a No 1 in '62 with a collaborative Best of Ball, Barber & Bilk (Chris and Acker respectively) plus a No 4 LP with Kenny Ball's Golden Hits. A very brief return to the charts came in summer '67 with a minor hit version of the Beatles' When I'm Sixty-Four. (Bob MacDonald, 1984.) The jazz trumpeter and bandleader born in 1931 in Ilford was one of the most successful during the trad boom: of 14 hits in the UK, three were top tens; *Midnight In Moscow* also reached no.2 in the USA. He is more highly regarded than that by some jazz fans, however; in their recent book 'The Jazz Companion', Ian Carr, Digby Fairweather and Brian Priestley gave Ball a longer entry than Chet Baker, and why not? Trad or 'dixieland' people, however talented, usually get short shrift in reference books. He toured the Soviet Union in 1985. (Donald Clarke 23 August 1988).

### ACAPULCO 1922 (Ball, Kenny & His Jazzmen)

Tracks: / Acapulco 1922.

**7" Single:** Released Aug '63, on Pye Jazz Today Deleted '66. Catalogue no: **7 NJ 2067**

### AT THE MOVIES

Tracks: / Raiders of the Lost Ark / Mrs. Robinson (From 'The Graduate') / As time goes by (from 'Casablanca') / Arthur's theme (from 'Arthur') / I love you, Samantha (from 'High Society') / Cavatina (Theme from 'The Deerhunter') / March of the Siamese children (from 'The King and I') / Mona Lisa / When you wish upon a star / Hello, Dolly / Green leaves of summer (from 'The Alamo') / Ben / Bare necessities (from 'The Jungle Book') / I wanna be like you (from 'The Jungle Book').

**Cass:** Released Sep '87, on MFP by EMI Records. Deleted Apr '90. Catalogue no: **TCMFP 5803**

**Album:** Released Sep '87, on MFP by EMI Records. Deleted Aug '89. Catalogue no: **MFP 5803**

### BALL PLAYS BRITISH

Tracks: / White cliffs of Dover / Eton boating song / Lincolnshire poacher / Men of Harlech / We'll keep a welcome in the hillside / British grenadiers, The / Ilkley Moor / Lambeth walk / O' Danny boy (Londonderry air) / When Irish eyes are smiling / Scarborough Fair / Sweet Afton / Scotland the brave / Greensleeves / English country garden (CD only.).

**CD:** Released Mar '90, on MFP by EMI Records. Catalogue no: **CDB 792 785 2**

**CD:** Released Mar '90, on MFP by EMI Records. Catalogue no: **CDMFP 6072**

**Cass:** Released Mar '90, on MFP by EMI Records. Catalogue no: **TCMFP 5864**

**Album:** Released Mar '90, on MFP by EMI Records. Catalogue no: **MFP 5864**

### CASABLANCA (Ball, Kenny & His Jazzmen)

Tracks: / Casablanca.

**7" Single:** Released Apr '63, on Pye Jazz Today Deleted '66. Catalogue no: **7 NJ 2064**

### CLAP TRAP (Ball, Kenny & His Jazzmen)

Tracks: / Clap trap.

**7" Single:** Released Jul '82, on Mont by Mont Music Records. Catalogue no: **MM 101**

### COLLECTION, THE

Tracks: / Midnight in Moscow / Alexander's ragtime band / Casablanca / Muskrat ramble / Samantha / Gavotte and rondo / Green leaves of summer, The / Wonderful world / Saturday night / From Russia with love / Someday / When the saints go marching in / March of the Siamese children / So do I / Cabaret / Pay off, The / Ace in the hole / Hello Dolly / Sukiyaki / When I'm sixty four / Acapulco 1922 / I still love you all / Maple leaf rag / I shall not be moved.

**Cass:** Released 5 Mar '90, on Castle Collector Series by Castle Communications Records. Catalogue no: **CCSMC 258**

**CD:** Released 5 Mar '90, on Castle Collector Series by Castle Communications Records. Catalogue no: **CCSCD 258**

### COTTON CLUB

Tracks: / Minnie the moocher (From the film 'Cotton Club') / Midnight in Moscow / I wanna be like you / Scorpio blues / March of the Siamese children / You are my sunshine / Sailing / Samantha / Eyes / It's life / So do I / One night stand / Annie's song / Is that the human thing to do.

**Cass:** Released Apr '86, on Conifer Catalogue no: **MCFRC 510**

**Album:** Released Apr '86, on Conifer Catalogue no: **CFRC 510**

### DIXIE (Ball, Kenny & His Jazzmen)

Tracks: / Aura Lee / Sophie's rag / Sunshine time / Nicole / Lighting up the town / Stepping along to the beat / Frankie and Johnny / My home town / Down Dixie Way / Southland blue / Kibbutz girl / Honky stonkin'.

**Album:** Released Jul '89, on Pickwick by Pickwick Records. Catalogue no: **HSC 3269**

**CD:** Released May '89, on Pickwick by Pickwick Records. Catalogue no: **PWK 106**

### GOLDEN HITS: KENNY BALL (Ball, Kenny & His Jazzmen)

Tracks: / Midnight in Moscow / So do I / March of the Siamese children / Someday you'll be sorry / 55 Days at Peking / Rondo alla turk / Sukiyaki / I still love you all / Green leaves of summer / I love you Samantha.

**Album:** Released Jul '86, on PRT Flashback Catalogue no: **FBLP 8104**

**Cass:** Released Jul '86, on PRT Flashback Catalogue no: **ZCFBL 8104**

### GOLDEN HOUR: KENNY BALL (Ball, Kenny & His Jazzmen)

**Cass:** Released '71, on Golden Hour Catalogue no: **ZCGH 512**

### GREENLEAVES OF SUMMER, THE (Ball, Kenny & His Jazzmen)

Tracks: / Green leaves of summer.

**7" Single:** Released May '62, on Pye Jazz Today Deleted '65. Catalogue no: **7 NJ 2054**

### GREENSLEEVES (Ball, Kenny & His Jazzmen)

Tracks: / Flow gently sweet Afton / No-

body knows you (when you're down and out) / I've got rhythm / Ostrich walk / I shall not be moved / St. Louis blues / Greensleeves / My mothers eyes / I wanna be like you / Mood indigo / Them there eyes / Old folks / Sweet Georgia Brown.
Note: Personnel: Kenny Ball- trumpet and vocals; John Fenner- guitar, banjo and vocals John Bennett- trombone and vocals; Ron Bowden- drums; Andy Cooper- clarinet and vocals; Duncan Swift- piano; John Benson- bass and vocal. Recorded November 1982.
**Album:** Released Sep '86, on Timeless by Timeless Records. Catalogue no: **TTD 505**
**Cass:** Released Sep '86, on Timeless by Timeless Records. Catalogue no: **TTD 5505**

**HAVE A DRINK ON ME (Ball, Kenny & His Jazzmen)**
**CD:** Released '88, on Pickwick by Pickwick Records. Catalogue no: **PWK 043**

**HELLO DOLLY**
**Album:** Released Sep '77, on Golden Hour Catalogue no: **GH 636**

**HELLO DOLLY (SINGLE) (Ball, Kenny & His Jazzmen)**
Tracks: / Hello Dolly.
**7" Single:** Released Jun '64, on Pye Jazz Today Deleted '67. Catalogue no: **7 NJ 2071**

**I STILL LOVE YOU ALL (Ball, Kenny & His Jazzmen)**
Tracks: / I Still love you all.
**7" Single:** Released May '61, on Pye Jazz Today Deleted '64. Catalogue no: **7 NJ 2042**

**I WANNA BE LIKE YOU (Ball, Kenny & His Jazzmen)**
Tracks: / I wanna be like you / Bare necessities.
**7" Single:** Released Oct '83, on PRT by Castle Communications Records. Catalogue no: **7P 289**

**IMAGES: KENNY BALL**
Tracks: / Green leaves of summer, The / 1919 march / Tie a yellow ribbon round the old oak tree / Tin roof blues / 55 days at Peking / From Russia with love / High society / Midnight in Moscow / Blue turning grey over you / Old miss rag / Sukiyaki / Rondo / Livery stables blues / March of the Siamese children.
**CD:** Released Feb '90, on Knight by Knight Records Ltd.. Catalogue no: **KNCD 16009**
**Cass:** Released Feb '90, on Knight by Knight Records Ltd.. Catalogue no: **KNMC 16009**

**KENNY BALL IN CONCERT (Live)**
**Album:** Released Jul '78, on Nevis Catalogue no: **NEVLP 139**

**KENNY BALL'S GOLDEN HITS**
**Album:** Released Sep '63, on Pye Deleted '68. Catalogue no: **GGL 0209**

**KENNY IN CONCERT IN THE USA (Vol. 1)**
**Album:** Released Aug '79, on Jazzology (USA) by Jazzology Records (USA). Catalogue no: **J 65**

**LIGHTING UP THE TOWN (Ball, Kenny & His Jazzmen)**
**Album:** Released Mar '90, on Intersound Catalogue no: **ISST199**

**LIVE AT THE ROYAL FESTIVAL HALL (Ball, Barber & Bilk)**
**Cass set:** Released Apr '85, on Cambra by Cambra Records. Deleted '88. Catalogue no: **CRT 5152**
**2 LP Set:** Released Apr '85, on Cambra by Cambra Records. Deleted '88. Catalogue no: **CR 5152**

**MARCH OF THE SIAMESE CHILDREN (Ball, Kenny & His Jazzmen)**
Tracks: / March of the Siamese children / If I could be with you.
**7" Single:** Released Jun '79, on Pye Deleted '82. Catalogue no: **7P 107**
**7" Single:** Released Feb '62, on Pye Jazz Today Deleted '65. Catalogue no: **7 NJ 2051**

**MIDNIGHT IN MOSCOW (Ball, Kenny & His Jazzmen)**
Tracks: / Midnight in Moscow.
**7" Single:** Released Nov '61, on Pye Jazz Today Deleted '64. Catalogue no: **7 NJ 2049**

**MIDNIGHT IN MOSCOW (2) (Ball, Kenny & His Jazzmen)**
Note: double cassette.
**Cass set:** Released '88, on Ditto by Pickwick Records. Catalogue no: **DTO 10209**

**MIDNIGHT IN MOSCOW (OLD GOLD) (Ball, Kenny & His Jazzmen)**
Tracks: / Midnight in Moscow / Cast your fate to the wind.
**7" Single:** Released Jul '82, on Old Gold by Old Gold Records. Deleted Jul '88. Catalogue no: **OG 9087**

**ON STAGE**
Tracks: / Midnight in Moscow / Rondo / Saturday night / Someday / I still love you all / Sukiyaki / Payoff, the / When I'm sixty four / Samantha / Green leaves of summer / So do I / Casablanca / Acapulco 1922 / 55 days at Peking / March of the siamese children / Hello dolly.
**Album:** Released Mar '88, on Start by Start Records Ltd.. Catalogue no: **STOL 102**
**CD:** Released Mar '88, on Start by Start Records Ltd.. Catalogue no: **STOCD 102**
**Cass:** Released Mar '88, on Start by Start Records Ltd.. Catalogue no: **STOC 102**

**PAY OFF, THE (Ball, Kenny & His Jazzmen)**
Tracks: / Pay off, The.
**7" Single:** Released Oct '62, on Pye Jazz Today Deleted '65. Catalogue no: **7 NJ 2061**

**RONDO (Ball, Kenny & His Jazzmen)**
Tracks: / Rondo.
**7" Single:** Released Jun '63, on Pye Jazz Today Deleted '66. Catalogue no: **7 NJ 2065**

**SAMANTHA (Ball, Kenny & His Jazzmen)**
Tracks: / Samantha.
**7" Single:** Released Feb '61, on Pye Jazz Today Deleted '64. Catalogue no: **7 NJ 2040**

**SATURDAY NIGHT AT THE MILL**
Tracks: / Saturday night at the mill / Sunday / Sweet painted lady / Feline stomp / Them there eyes / You can't get to Heaven by livin like hell / Lady of Spain / I've got plenty of nuttin / Bess you is my woman / T'aint what you do (it's the way that you do it) / Lili Marlene.
**Album:** Released May '77, on Spiral by President Records. Catalogue no: **SPJ 9000**

**SINGLES COLLECTION, THE (Ball, Kenny & His Jazzmen)**
Tracks: / Midnight in Moscow / Rondo / Saturday night / Someday you'll be sorry / I still love you all / Sukiyaki / Pay off, The / When I'm sixty four / Samantha / Green leaves of summer / So do I / Casablanca / Acapulco 1922 / 55 days at Peking / March of the Siamese children / Hello Dolly.
**Album:** Released Nov '87, on PRT by Castle Communications Records. Catalogue no: **PYL 6029**
**Cass:** Released Nov '87, on PRT by Castle Communications Records. Catalogue no: **PYM 6029**

**SO DO I (Ball, Kenny & His Jazzmen)**
Tracks: / So do I.
**7" Single:** Released Aug '62, on Pye Jazz Today Deleted '65. Catalogue no: **7 NJ 2056**

**SOAP**
**Cass:** Released Sep '81, on A.M.I.(USA) by American Music Corp.(USA). Catalogue no: **AMILP 101**

**SOAP (SINGLE)**
Tracks: / Soap .
**7" Single:** Released Nov '80, on AMI by AMI Records. Deleted Nov '83. Catalogue no: **AIS 109**

**SOMEDAY (Ball, Kenny & His Jazzmen)**
Tracks: / Someday.
**7" Single:** Released Aug '61, on Pye Jazz Today Deleted '64. Catalogue no: **7 NJ 2047**

**SUKIYAKI (Ball, Kenny & His Jazzmen)**
Tracks: / Sukiyaki.
**7" Single:** Released Jan '63, on Pye Jazz Today Deleted '66. Catalogue no: **7 NJ 2062**

**SUNSHINE**
Tracks: / Sunshine / Scorpio.
**7" Single:** Released Dec '84, on American Phonogram by American Phonogram Int.. Catalogue no: **APKB**

**TURTLE'S PROGRESS (Ball, Kenny & His Jazzmen)**
Tracks: / Turtle's progress / Swet Afton.
**7" Single:** Released Jun '79, on Breeze by Pinnacle Records. Deleted '82. Catalogue no: **BRE 501**

**WAY DOWN YONDER (Ball, Kenny & His Jazzmen)**
**Album:** Released Nov '80, on Nevis Catalogue no: **NEVLP 161**
**Cass:** Released Nov '80, on Nevis Catalogue no: **NEVC 161**

**WHEN I'M 64 (Ball, Kenny & His Jazzmen)**
Tracks: / When I'm sixty four.
**7" Single:** Released Jul '67, on Pye Deleted '70. Catalogue no: **7N 17348**

## Ballamy, Iain

**BALLOON MAN**
**Album:** Released Oct '89, on Editions EG by E.G. Records. Catalogue no: **EGED 63**

## Bang, Billy

**LIVE AT CARLOS**
**CD:** Released '88, on Soul Note Catalogue no: **121136-2**

## Banks, Bishop Jeff

**CAUGHT UP IN THE RAPTURE**
**Album:** Released Mar '89, on Savoy by Savoy Records. Catalogue no: **SL 14787**
**Cass:** Released Mar '89, on Savoy by Savoy Records. Catalogue no: **SC 14787**

## Barbarin, Paul

**STREETS OF THE CITY (Barbarin, Paul & His New Orleans Band 1950)**
**Cass:** Released Sep '86, on 504 Catalogue no: **TCS 9**
**Album:** Released Sep '86, on 504 Catalogue no: **LPS 9**

## Barbecue Bob

**BROWN SKIN GAL**
**LP Set:** Released Oct '88, on Agram Catalogue no: **AB 2001**

**REMAINING TITLES, THE 1927-30**
Tracks: / Good time rounder / Yo yo blues / Darktown gamblin' / Easy rider don't you deny my name / Cold wave blues.
**Album:** Released Apr '87, on Saydisc by Amon Ra Records. Catalogue no: **MSE 1009**

## Barber, Ball & Bilk

**BEST OF BARBER, BALL AND BILK VOL.1 (Barber, Chris/Acker Bilk / Kenny Ball)**
**Album:** Released May '61, on Pye Deleted '66. Catalogue no: **GGL 0075**

**BEST OF BARBER, BALL AND BILK VOL.2 (Barber, Chris/Acker Bilk / Kenny Ball)**
**Album:** Released Nov '61, on Pye Deleted '66. Catalogue no: **GGL 0096**

**BEST OF BARBER, BALL AND BILK VOL. 3 (Barber, Chris/Acker Bilk / Kenny Ball)**
**Album:** Released Aug '62, on Pye Deleted '67. Catalogue no: **GGL 0131**

**ULTIMATE, THE**
Tracks: / (I love you) Samantha / Panama rag / Midnight in Moscow / Nobody knows you (when you're down and out) / Avalon / I wanna be like you / Christopher Columbus / Spanish harlem / That da da strain / Them there eyes / Stranger on the shore / That's my home / Good Queen Bess / Perdido street blues / Harlem rag / Mood indigo / Mary had a little lamb / When the saints go marching in / St. Louis blues / So do I / Muskrat ramble / Auf wiedersehen.
**CD Set:** Released May '88, on Kaz by Kaz Records. Catalogue no: **KAZ CD 4**
**2 LP Set:** Released May '88, on Kaz by Kaz Records. Catalogue no: **KAZ LP 4**
**Cass set:** Released May '88, on Kaz by Kaz Records. Catalogue no: **KAZ MC 4**

## Barber, Chris

**Biographical details:** Barber, Chris The trombonist and trad jazzband leader was born in Welwyn Garden City in 1930. He joined the Ken Colyer band and took it over in 1954. It was the first UK combo to appear on the Ed Sullivan TV show in the USA in 1959. Their big transatlantic hit was *Petite Fleur*, a song by Sidney Bechet; ironically Barber did not play on it; it was a solo vehicle for clarinettist Monty Sunshine, who used a pretty vibrato similar to that of Bechet. Sunshine (born in 1928 in London) and Barber played in films including 'Look Back In Anger; Barber's various lineups remained popular with jazz fans, and he also recorded with Dr John (Mac Rebbenack) (Donald Clarke 23 August 1988) Born in Welwyn Garden City in 1930, Chris Barber formed his first band in 1949 with himself on trombone. This was the instrument he was to make his own. His new 1954 band included Lonnie Donegan on guitar and banjo and became a regular fixture at Humphrey Lyttelton's club in Oxford Street. In early '56 he scored a Top 10 hit on both sides of the Atlantic without anyone really knowing - the Chris Barber Band included in their act a skiffle on washboard and it was this outfit who played on Donegan's *Rock Island line* single. Once this 45 had become a major success, Donegan left Barber to begin his own string of hits. Chris Barber's jazz band scored a smash single in their own right in 1959 with *Petite fleur*, reaching No. 3 in the UK and No. 5 in the US. They never returned to the Top 20 in either country, but instead rode the early Sixties jazz boom with a series of UK hit albums. After charting with three LPs in the Autumn of 1960, Barber teamed with clarinet star Acker Bilk in '61 for a couple of big selling duet albums. Even more successful was the triumvirate LP *Best of Ball, Barber and Bilk*, a No. 1 album in 1962. While othaving the sinlges sales of Ball and Bilk, Barber kept busy by developing his interest in the blues. A number of American blues artists toured Britain with Barber's band and he helped to organise an important blues festival. While playing a mean jazz trombone, Chris Barber was also a quietly influential figure on Britain's burgeoning rhythm and blues scene. (Bob MacDonald).

**BARBER'S BEST**
Tracks: / Bobby Shaftoe / Martinique, The / Chimes blues / Merry down rag / Skokiaan / St. Louis blues / It's tight like that / Ice cream / Oh, didn't he ramble / Storyville blues / World is waiting for the sunshine, The / Reckless blues.
**Album:** Released Mar '85, on Jasmine by Hasmick Promotions. Deleted Jun '87. Catalogue no: **JASM 2028**

**BARBER'S CHOICE**
**Album:** Released Jul '84, on Teldec (Germany) by ASV (Academy Sound & Vision). Catalogue no: **6 28491**

**BARBICAN BLUES**
Tracks: / Bourbon Street Parade / Mary had a little Lamb / Perdido street blues / Spanish castles / Barbican blues / Bugle Boy March / Good Queen Bess / Wild cat blues / Rose room / Basin Street blues / Ice Cream.
Note: Recorded at Barbican Centre on April 20, 1982.
**2 LP Set:** Released Feb '83, on Black Lion Catalogue no: **BLM 61003/4**

**BEST OF CHRIS BARBER**
**Cass:** Released '86, on Decca by Decca International. Catalogue no: **KTBC 86**
**Album:** Released Nov '60, on Ace Of Clubs by Decca Records. Deleted '65. Catalogue no: **ACL 1037**
**Album:** Released Jun '85, on Decca by Decca International. Deleted '88. Catalogue no: **TAB 86**

**BEST OF CHRIS BARBER (PRT)**
Tracks: / Petite fleur / One sweet letter from you / Wabash blues / Texas moaner / Old rugged cross, The / Olga / Papa de da da / Thriller rag / When you and I were young, Maggie / Tishomingo blues / Sweet Georgia Brown / Big house blues / Just a closer walk with thee / Ugly child / Careless love.
**Album:** Released Mar '88, on PRT by Castle Communications Records. Catalogue no: **PYL 6031**
**Cass:** Released Mar '88, on PRT by Castle Communications Records. Catalogue no: **PYM 6031**

**BEST SELLERS (See also under Papa Bue)**
Note: Tracks include: Ice cream, Bonaza, Precious lord lead me on, Spinning wheel, Washington square
**CD:** Released Oct '87, on Storyville by Storyville Records AB. Catalogue no: **STCD 200**

**CAN'T WE GET TOGETHER (Barber, Chris Jazz & Blues Band)**
Tracks: / Holiday / Double check stomp / Here come my blackbird / I wish I could shimmy like my sister Kate / Over the waves / Everybody love my baby / Whistling Rufus / Can't we get together / Good time tonight / High Society / Bobby Shaftoe / New Orleans Ceremony / Just a little while to stay here / Oration by Chris Barber / Just a closer walk with thee / When the saints go marching in / At the jazz band ball / Good Queen Bess / Easter Parade / Isle of Capri / Wabas blues / Sheik of Araby, The / Going home / Old rugged cross, The / Too busy.
Note: Double Album. Personnel includes: Pat Halcox - trumpet / Chris Bar-

ber - trombone / Eddie Smith - banjo / Dick Smith - bass / Ron Bowden - drums with special guests Ottilie Patterson, Monty Sunshine, Ken Colyer and Dr John. Recordings made between November 1954 and October 1984.
**2 LP Set:** Released Sep '86, on Timeless by Timeless Records. Catalogue no: **TTD 517/18**
**Cass Set:** Released Sep '86, on Timeless by Timeless Records. Catalogue no: **TTD 5517/18**

**CHRIS BARBER BAND BOX NO.2**
**Album:** Released Sep '60, on Columbia by EMI Records. Deleted '65. Catalogue no: **33SCX 3277**

**CHRIS BARBER IN NEW ORLEANS**
Tracks: / Shake it or break it / Eh la bas / It's right here for you / High society / You can't depend on me / Hindustan / Mama's in the racket / Billies' boogie / Gulf coast blues / Dippermouth blues / Billie's blues / All of me / Love song of the Nile.
**Album:** Released Sep '79, on Hefty Jazz Catalogue no: **HJ 106**

**CHRIS BARBER STORY VOL.1 (In the beginning)**
Tracks: / Gatemouth / Mama's gone, goodbye / Sing on / How long blues / Martinique / Bobby Shafto / Stevedore stomp / Yellow dog blues / Original Charleston strut / Jazz lips / Over in the gloryland / Tiger rag / Baby won't you please come home / Doctor jazz.
**Album:** Released May '80, on Black Lion Deleted '85. Catalogue no: **BLM 51003**

**CHRIS BARBER STORY VOL.2**
Tracks: / When things go wrong with you / Highway to heaven / High society / I'm gonna move to the outskirts of town / Help me / Drat that fratle rat / Bone and bread / Just a sittin' and a rockin' / Couldn't keep it to myself / Mooche / Jenny's ball.
**Album:** Released May '80, on Black Lion Deleted '85. Catalogue no: **BLM 51004**

**CHRIS BARBER STORY VOL.3**
Tracks: / Everybody knows / Cortina run / Oro / I think it's going to rain today / Watcha gonna do / Jazz me blues / Give me an old fashioned swing in the evening / Shout 'em Aunt Tillie / I'm slapping Seventh Avenue with the sole of my shoe.
**Album:** Released May '80, on Black Lion Deleted '85. Catalogue no: **BLM 51006**

**CLASSICS CONCERT IN BERLIN 1959**
Tracks: / Climax rag / Gotta travel on / Chimes blues / Just a little white to stay here / S'wonderful / Lord, Lord, Lord / Revival.
**CD:** Released Oct '88, on Chris Barber Collection Catalogue no: **CBJBCD 4002**
**2 LP Set:** Released Oct '88, on Chris Barber Collection Catalogue no: **CBJBD 4002**
**Cass:** Released Oct '88, on Chris Barber Collection Catalogue no: **ZCBJB 4002**

**COME FRIDAY (Barber, Chris Jazz & Blues Band)**
Tracks: / Aligator hop / St. Louis blues / Wild cat blues / Come Friday / Sweet Sue / Stevedore stomp.
**Album:** Released Oct '80, on Black Lion Deleted Jan '88. Catalogue no: **BLM 51008**

**CONCERT FOR THE BBC (Barber, Chris Jazz & Blues Band)**
**2 LP Set:** Released Sep '86, on Timeless by Timeless Records. Catalogue no: **TTD 509/510**
**CD Set:** Released Sep '86, on Timeless by Timeless Records. Catalogue no: **CATTD 509/510**
**CD Set:** Released '86, on Timeless by Timeless Records. Catalogue no: **CDTTD 509/10**

**CREOLE LOVE CALL (Barber, Chris Band)**
Tracks: / Stevedore stomp / Come Friday / Sweet Sue / Wild cat blues / St. Louis blues / Alligator hop / Queen Bess / Creole love call / South Rampart street parade / Snag it / Easter parade.
**2 LP Set:** Released Sep '86, on Timeless by Timeless Records. Catalogue no: **TTD 502/503**

**ECHOES OF HARLEM**
**Album:** Released Nov '86, on Dormouse Catalogue no: **DM 8**

**ELITE SYNCOPATIONS**
**Album:** Released Nov '60, on Columbia by EMI Records. Deleted '65. Catalogue no: **33SX 1245**

**ENTERTAINER, THE (Barber, Chris Jazzband)**
Tracks: / New St.Louis blues / Bourbon Street parade / Sheik of Araby, The / Entertainer, The / Georgia catwalk / High society / When the saints go marching in / Burgundy Street blues / On the sunny side of the street / Down home rag / Baby won't you please come home / L'il Liza Jane / Stavedore stomp / When the saints go marching in / Ory's Creole trombone.
Note: A compilation of live & studio recordings made between 1955 & 1962.
**CD:** Released Feb '88, on Polydor (Europe) by Polydor Ltd. Catalogue no: **832 593-2**

**EVERYBODY KNOWS**
**CD:** Released Sep '87, on Compact Collection Catalogue no: **15015**

**GET YOURSELF TO JACKSON SQUARE**
**Album:** Released Nov '89, on Sonet by Sonet Records. Catalogue no: **SNTF 1018**
**CD:** Released Nov '89, on Sonet by Sonet Records. Catalogue no: **SNCD 1018**

**GETTING AROUND (Barber, Chris Jazz & Blues Band)**
Tracks: / Isle of Capri / Freight train blues / Magnolia's wedding day / I love my baby / Tishomingo blues / Strange things / See see rider / Tight like that / When my sugar walks down the street / Bonsoir mes souvenirs / Mack the knife / How to survive / Army song / Useless song / Great bear, The / O sole mio.
**Album:** Released '88, on Storyville by Storyville Records AB. Catalogue no: **SLP 423**

**ICE CREAM**
Tracks: / Wild cat blues / Old rugged cross, The / Over in the gloryland / Canal Street blues / Muskrat ramble / High society / Jazz me blues / New Orleans wiggle / London blues / Ice cream.
**Cass:** Released '82, on Black Lion-Intercord Catalogue no: **CAS 427 029**
**Album:** Released '82, on Black Lion-Intercord Catalogue no: **INT 127 029**

**IN BUDAPEST**
Tracks: / Lord lord lord / Mood indigo / Whistling Rufus / Some of these days / Mama he treats your daughter mean / Trad tavern.
**Album:** Released Jan '85, on Storyville by Storyville Records AB. Catalogue no: **SLP 4085**
**CD:** Released Jun '87, on Storyville by Storyville Records AB. Catalogue no: **STCD 408**

**JAZZ HOLIDAY (Meets Rod Mason's Hot Five) (Barber, Chris / Rod Mason's Hot Five)**
**Album:** Released Sep '86, on Timeless by Timeless Records. Catalogue no: **TTD 524**

**JUBILEE ALBUM**
Tracks: / Savoy blues / Doctor jazz / Baby won't you please come home / Star of the County Down / Bill Bailey won't you please come home / Please don't talk about me when I'm gone / Oro / Give me an old fashioned swing in the evening / It's tight like that / New Orleans wiggle / I'm slapping Seventh Avenue with the sole of my shoe / I think it's going to rain today / Jazz me blues / Whatcha gonna do? / Canal Street blues / Muskrat ramble / Ice cream / Goodbye, goodbye, goodbye.
Note: Personnel: Pat Halcox/John Crocker / John Slaughter / Stu Morrison / Jackie Flavelle / Graham Burbidge / Ottilie Patterson / Steve Hammond / Stig Praestvang / Johnny McCallum. Recorded: 1970-1974.
**Album:** Released '82, on Black Lion-Intercord Catalogue no: **INT 182 010**

**LIVE 54/55 (Barber, Chris Jazzband)**
**CD:** Released Jan '90, on Limelight Catalogue no: **8208782**
**Album:** Released Jan '90, on Limelight Catalogue no: **8208781**

**LIVE IN '85 (Barber, Chris Jazz & Blues Band)**
**Album:** Released Sep '86, on Timeless by Timeless Records. Catalogue no: **TTD 527**

**LONESOME (Barber, Chris Jazzband)**
Tracks: / Lonesome.
**7" Single:** Released Oct '59, on Colum-

bia by EMI Records. Deleted '62. Catalogue no: **DB 4333**

**MARDI GRAS AT THE MARQUEE (Barber, Chris & Dr John)**
Note: Chris Barber and his band join forces with legendary blues giant Dr John for a Mardi Gras celebration live at London' Marquee Club. This superb album features thirteen great tracks, eleven of which are Dr John original compositions. Personnel includes: Pat Halcox (trumpet), Chris Barber (trombone, baritone horn, trumpet), John Crocker (tenor sax, alto sax, clarinet), Ian Wheeler (clarinet, alto sax), Dr John (piano, vocals), Johnny McCallum (banjo, guitar), Roger Hill (guitar), Vic Pitt (bass), Norman Emberson (drums), Halcox/Barber/Crocker/Wheeler (vocal backing).
**CD:** Released May '89, on Timeless Traditional Catalogue no: **CDTTD 5546**
**Cass:** Released May '89, on Timeless Traditional Catalogue no: **TTD 5546**
**Album:** Released May '89, on Timeless Traditional Catalogue no: **TTD 546**

**MUSIC FROM THE LAND OF DREAMS**
Tracks: / Music from the land of dreams / Goin' up the river / Nobody knows you (when you're down and out) (Introducing'Down & out blues') / New Orleans Louisiana / Big bass drum (on a mardi gras day) / Beg,steal or borrow / Whose blues / New York town / Second line saints.
Note: Produced by Tony Atkins for Chris Barber Productions Personnel: Chris Barber-trombone & vocals/Pat Halcox-trumpet/Ian Wheeler-clarinet,alto,harmonica/John Crocker-tenor,alto ,"New York Town"/Roger Hill-guitar/Johnny McCalham -banjo,guitar/Vic Pitt-string bass,tuba/Norman Emberson-drums
**Album:** Released Sep '86, on Sonet by Sonet Records. Catalogue no: **SNTF 962**
**Cass:** Released Sep '86, on Sonet by Sonet Records. Catalogue no: **ZCSN 962**
**CD:** Released Nov '87, on Sonet by Sonet Records. Catalogue no: **SNTCD 962**

**MUSIC FROM THE LAND OF DREAMS (Barber, Chris Jazz & Blues Band & Dr John)**
**VHS:** Released Feb '90, on Storyville by Storyville Records AB. Catalogue no: **SV9000**

**MUSIC FROM THE LAND OF DREAMS**
Tracks: / Music from the land of dreams / Take me back to New Orleans.
**7" Single:** Released Oct '85, on Sonet by Sonet Records. Catalogue no: **SON 2293**

**PETITE FLEUR**
**Cass set:** Released '88, on Ditto by Pickwick Records. Catalogue no: **DTO 10226**

**PETITE FLEUR (SINGLE) (Barber, Chris Jazzband)**
Tracks: / Petite fleur.
**7" Single:** Released Feb '59, on Pye Jazz Today Deleted '62. Catalogue no: **NJ 2026**

**REUNION**
Tracks: / Bourbon Street parade / Saturday night function / Martinique, The / Isle of Capri / Hush-a-bye / It's tight like that / Fairfield reunion blues / Bobby Shaftoe / On a Monday / Bury my body / Long gone lost John / Jenny's ball / Chimes blues / Whistling Rufus / Jazz me blues / Just a sittin' and a rockin' / Stevedore stomp / Jack-ass blues / New Orleans stomp / Maryland my Maryland / When you wore a tulip / Panama rag.
**Album:** Released '82, on Black Lion-Intercord Catalogue no: **INT 182 014**

**REVIVAL (Barber, Chris Jazzband)**
Tracks: / Revival.
**7" Single:** Released Jan '62, on Columbia by EMI Records. Deleted '65. Catalogue no: **SCD 2166**

**SPECIAL**
Tracks: / Dardanella / Jazz lips / Original Charleston strut / Lonesome Road / Eh La bas / I wish I could shimmy like my sister Kate / Makin' whoopee / Clarinet Marmalade / Precious lord, take my hand / Colla voce / High society / I'm looking for a four leaf clover / Panama rag / From me to you / Money can't buy me love / Over in the gloryland / Tiger rag / South Rampart Street Parade / Easter Parade / All my loving.
**2 LP Set:** Released '82, on Black Lion-Intercord Catalogue no: **INT 157 004**

**STAR PORTRAIT: CHRIS BARBER**
Tracks: / Down by the riverside / Burgandy Street blues / Phil's late / Sweet Lorraine / Blueberry Hill / When the saints go marching in / Whistling Rufus / Lazy River / St. Georges rag / Creole song / Gonna build a mountain / Stevedore stomp / Ice cream / Baby won't you please come home / I can't escape from you / Canal Street blues / Running wild / Just a closer walk with thee / Muskrat ramble / Savoy blues / When you and I were young, Maggie / Bourbon Street Parade / Oh Didn't he ramble / Goodbye, goodbye, goodbye.
Note: Personnel: Pat Halcox/Ian Wheeler/Eddie Smith/Dick Smith/Graham Burbidge/ Ottilie Patterson/Morty Sunshine/Edmond Hall/Joe Marshall/Hanc Duncan/Hayes Alvis/John Crocker/Johnny McCallum/Dickie Hawdon/Ben Cohen/Brylo Ford.
**2 LP Set:** Released '82, on Black Lion-Intercord Catalogue no: **INT 156 502**

**STARDUST (Barber, Chris Jazz & Blues Band)**
Note: The ever popular and irrespressible Chris Barber Band with a brand new album featuring popular evergreens. Personnel: Chris Barber (trombone), Pat Halcox (trumpet), John Crocker (clarinet, tenor sax), Ian Wheeler (clarinet, alto sax, harmonica), John Slaughter (guitar), Johnny McCallum (guitar, banjo), Vic Pitt (bass), Norman Emberson (drums).
**Album:** Released May '89, on Timeless Traditional Catalogue no: **TTD 537**
**Cass:** Released May '89, on Timeless Traditional Catalogue no: **TTD 5537**
**CD:** Released May '89, on Timeless Traditional Catalogue no: **CDTTD 537**

**SWING IS HERE (Barber, Chris with John Lewis & Trummy Young)**
Tracks: / Home folks / Time / Mood indigo / T'aint what you do (it's the way that you do it) / Georgia / Someday you'll be sorry / Muskrat ramble / When the saints go marching in.
**Album:** Released Jan '80, on Black Lion Deleted Jan '85. Catalogue no: **BLP 12182**

**TAKE ME BACK TO NEW ORLEANS (Barber, Chris & Dr John)**
Tracks: / Take me back to New Orleans / Ti-pi-ti-na / Perdido street blues / New Orleans, Louisiana / Decatur drive / New Orleans / Meet me on the Levee / Harlem rag / Ride on / Big bass drum, The / At the cemetery / Concert on Canal Street / Bourbon Street scene / Basin Street / Just a little while to stay here / Oration by Dr. John / What a friend we have in Jesus / When the Saints go Marching In / Concert in Canal Street / When the saints go marching in / Buddy Bolden Blues / South Rampart Street Parade / Burgandy Street Blues / Canal Street Blues / Bourbon Street Parade / Do you know what it means to miss New Orleans / Professor Longhair's tip / Brass band blues / Basin Street Blues.
**2 LP Set:** Released Feb '83, on Black Lion Catalogue no: **BLM 61001/2**
**2 LP Set:** Released '82, on Black Lion-Intercord Catalogue no: **INT 157 007**

**TIMELESS TRADITIONAL JAZZ (Barber, Chris/Acker Bilk/Kenny Ball)**
**2 LP Set:** Released '88, on Timeless by Timeless Records. Catalogue no: **TTD 522-23**
**CD Set:** Released '89, on Timeless by Timeless Records. Catalogue no: **CDTTD 522-23**

**WHEN IT'S THURSDAY NIGHT IN EGYPT (Barber, Chris Band)**
Tracks: / When it's Thursday night in Egypt / I'm beginning to see the light / Sweet Sue / Under the bamboo tree / Lonesome Road / Goodnight sweeheart / All our tomorrows / Memphis blues / We'll meet again / One sweet letter again / Georgia on my mind / Just once for all time.
**Album:** Released Dec '87, on Sonet by Sonet Records. Catalogue no: **SNTF 996**
**CD:** Released 30 Apr '88, on Sonet by Sonet Records. Catalogue no: **SNTCD 996**

## Barber, Frank

**BARBER CUTS**
Tracks: / James Bond medley / If only I

could talk to you / Michel Le Grand Medley / Charlie Chalplin Medley / Richard Rodgers Medley / Henry Mancini Medley / I know I'm lucky / John Williams Medley / Where are you now / Dicing with disco / Bond medley.
Note: Following on Frank Barber's world success and his success with the Disco Bond 12" and 7" single, this album features many of the great film themes by some of the finest composers and four of Frank's own compositions. As always, Frank hasarranged all the tracks and the Orchestra features many of the top session musicians in the UK, including - Trombonist Don Lusher and Trumpeter Kenny Baker.
**Cass:** Released Oct '83, on PRT by Castle Communications Records. Catalogue no: **ZCN 149**
**Album:** Released Oct '83, on PRT by Castle Communications Records. Catalogue no: **N 149**

**BIG BANDS ARE BACK**
Tracks: / One o'clock jump / 9.20 special / Jumpin' at the Woodside / Lil' darlin' / Lester leaps in / Swingin' the blues / Li'l darlin' / Song on India / Marie / At the Fat Man's / Liebstraum / Chloe / Tuxedo Junction / String of pearls / When Johnny comes marching home / Serenade in blues / Song of the volga boatmen / On the Atchison, Topeka and Santa Fe / Woodchoppers ball / Four brothers / Your fathers moustache / Good earth, The / Northwest passage / Skyliner / Cherokee / Redskin rhumba / Pompton turnpike / Skyliner (reprise) / Artistry in rhythm / Intermission riff / Southern scandal / Eager beaver / Painted rhythm.
**Album:** Released Oct '82, on PRT by Castle Communications Records. Catalogue no: **N 144**
**Cass:** Released Oct '82, on PRT by Castle Communications Records. Catalogue no: **ZCN 144**

**DALLAS**
Tracks: / Dallas / Knots Landing.
**7" Single:** Released Jan '80, on BBC by BBC Records & Tapes. Deleted 31 Aug '88. Catalogue no: **RESL 87**

**DISCO BOND (Barber, Frank & His Orchestra)**
Tracks: / Disco bond.
**7" Single:** Released Jun '83, on PRT by Castle Communications Records. Deleted Jun '86. Catalogue no: **7P 276**
**12" Single:** Released Jun '83, on PRT by Castle Communications Records. Deleted Jun '86. Catalogue no: **12P 276**

**GLENN MILLER TODAY (Barber, Frank & His Orchestra)**
Tracks: / Glenn Miller today / Trad disco medley.
**7" Single:** Released Aug '81, on PRT by Castle Communications Records. Deleted Aug '84. Catalogue no: **7P 220**
**12" Single:** Released Aug '81, on PRT by Castle Communications Records. Deleted Aug '84. Catalogue no: **12P 220**

**GLENN MILLER TODAY (VOL 2)**
Tracks: / Glenn Miller today (vol 2) / Count Basie medley.
**12" Single:** Released Jan '83, on PRT by Castle Communications Records. Catalogue no: **12P 258**
**7" Single:** Released Jan '83, on PRT by Castle Communications Records. Catalogue no: **7P 258**

**MEDDLIN' WITH MILLER (Barber, Frank & His Orchestra)**
Tracks: / In the mood / Pennsylvania 6 5000 / I've got a gal in Kalamazoo / Moonlight serenade / Little brown jug / Chattanooga choo choo / At last / American patrol / Perdido / Take the 'A' train / C Jam blues / Satin doll / Things ain't what they used to be / I'm beginning to see the light / Begin the beguine / Back bay shuffle / What is this thing called love / Frenesi / My heart stood still / Johnson rag / Tangerine / So rare / I'm getting sentimental over you / On the sunny side of the street / Opus one / Hello dolly / When it's sleepy time down South / What a wondeful world / Struttin' with some barbecue / Rockin' chair / Mack the knife / Sing, sing, sing / Stompin' at the Savoy / Don't be that way / Jersey bounce / Christopher Columbus / And the angels sing.
**Album:** Released Mar '82, on PRT by Castle Communications Records. Catalogue no: **N 143**
**Cass:** Released Mar '82, on PRT by Castle Communications Records. Catalogue no: **ZCN 143**

## Barbieri, Gato

**Biographical details:** Barbieri, Gato The tenor saxist and composer was born in 1934 in Argentina; he played in Lalo Schifrin's band in 1953 and began travelling in the early '60s, ending up in the USA. He played with avant-gardists such as Don Cherry and Steve Lacy, and tried mixing Latin rhythms with free jazz, but gradually settled for a mainstream MOR style, his talent needing someone else to spark off of (e.g. on Tropic Appetites with Carla Bley). He won a Grammy for his score for the film 'Last Tango In Paris' in 1972, in which he also appeared. (Donald Clarke 23 August 1988).

**APASSIONADO**
Tracks: / Latin lovers / Que pasa / Last tango in Paris / Terra me siente / Angel / Tiempo buono / Habanera.
**CD:** Released Feb '84, on Polydor (Italy) by Polydor Ltd. Deleted '88. Catalogue no: **815 585-2**
**Album:** Released Feb '84, on Polydor (Italy) by Polydor Ltd. Catalogue no: **815 585-1**
**Cass:** Released Feb '84, on Polydor (Italy) by Polydor Ltd. Catalogue no: **815 585-4**

**CHAPTER FOUR - ALIVE IN NEW YORK**
Tracks: / Milonga triste / La China leoncia / Baihia / Lluvia azul.
**Cass:** Released Sep '82, on Jasmine by Hasmick Promotions. Catalogue no: **JAS C54**
**Album:** Released Sep '82, on Jasmine by Hasmick Promotions. Catalogue no: **JAS 54**

**CHAPTER ONE - LATIN AMERIC**
Tracks: / Encuentros / La China Leior cia arreo la / To be continued / India Nunca mas.
Note: Recorded 1973 in Buenos Aire and Rio de Janeiro. Personnel: Gat Barbieri (tenor sax), Dino Saluzzi (bar doneon), Osvaldo Bellingieri (piano), A berto Cevasco (bass), and loca musicians playing native and tradition instruments.
**CD:** Released Jun '89, on MCA (Impuls Jazz) Catalogue no: **MCAD 39124**
**Album:** Released Jun '89, on MCA (Im pulse Jazz) Catalogue no: **MCA 3912**

**CHAPTER THREE**
**Album:** Released Jan '87, on MCA b MCA Records. Deleted Dec '89. Cata logue no: **ASD 9279**
**Cass:** Released Jan '87, on MCA b MCA Records. Deleted Dec '89. Cata logue no: **ASCD 9279**

**CONFLUENCE (Barbieri, Gato & Dollar Brand)**
Tracks: / Aloe and the wild rose, The Hamba khale / To Elsa / Eighty firs street.
**Album:** Released Jul '88, on Black Lio Catalogue no: **BLM 52010**

**EL GATO**
**Album:** Released '83, on RCA (France by BMG Records (France). Catalogue no: **PL 13816**

**EUPHORIA**
Tracks: / Sophia / Carnavalito / Lions also cry / Firepower / Gods and astronauts / Secret fiesta / Speak law.
**Album:** Released '79, on A&M by A&M Records. Deleted '84. Catalogue no **AMLH 64774**

**GATO...PARA LOS AMIGOS!**
Tracks: / Llamerito tango / Carnavalito / Brazil / Viva Emilliano Zapata / Encuentros / Latino America / El arriero / Bolivia / Finale (medley).
**Cass:** Released Apr '84, on Doctor Jazz (USA) by CBS Records (USA). Catalogue no: **ZCASD 851**
**Album:** Released Apr '84, on Docto Jazz (USA) by CBS Records (USA). Catalogue no: **ASLD 851**

**HAMBA KHALE (Barbieri, Gato / Dollar Brand)**
Tracks: / Hamba khale / Aloe and the wild rose, The / To Elsa / 81st Street.
**CD:** Released Mar '87, on Charly by Charly Records. Catalogue no: **CDCHARLY 79**
**Album:** Released Oct '79, on Affinity by Charly Records. Catalogue no: **AFF 39**

**I WANT YOU**
Tracks: / I want you (2 parts).
**7" Single:** Released Jan '77, on A&M by A&M Records. Deleted '80. Catalogue no: **AMS 7269**

**IN SEARCH OF THE MYSTERY**
**Album:** Released '88, on ESP Base Catalogue no: **ESP 1049**

**OBSESSION**
**Album:** Released '78, on Affinity by

:harly Records. Deleted '88. Catalogue o: **AFF 12**

**'HIRD WORLD REVISITED, THE**
'racks: / Yesterdays / John Coltrane ılues, A / Marnie / Brasil / Carinhoso / El ırriero.
**:D:** Released Nov '88, on Bluebird (2) ıy BMG Records (UK). Deleted Jul '89. :atalogue no: **ND 86995**

**INDER FIRE**
'racks: / El parana / Yo le canto a la luna Antonico / Maria Domingas / El sertao.
**Album:** Released Sep '80, on Philips by 'honogram Ltd. Deleted Sep '85. Cataogue no: **632 111 6**

**'IVA EMILIANO ZAPATA**
**Album:** Released Oct '85, on Impulse ıy Impulse Records. Catalogue no: **AS 279**

## Barnard, Bob

**AT BIX FESTIVAL 1976 (Barnard, Bob & His Australian Jazz Band)**
**Album:** Released Apr '79, on BBMS :atalogue no: **BBMS 8**

**BIG BOB, LITTLE BEN**
**Album:** Released Aug '89, on Fly by Fly Records. Catalogue no: **EAGLELP 1**

**COUNT 'EM (Barnard, Bob, Jazz Orchestra)**
**Album:** Released Jan '83, on Swaggie Australia) Catalogue no: **S 1353**

**FIRST UP (1975-76) (Barnard, Bob & His Jazz Band)**
**Album:** Released Jan '83, on Swaggie Australia) Catalogue no: **S 1369**

**NED KELLY JAZZ SUITE (Barnard, Bob & Friends)**
**Album:** Released Jan '83, on Swaggie Australia) Catalogue no: **S 1374**

**RIVERBOAT DAYS (Barnard, Bob & Friends)**
**Album:** Released Jan '83, on Swaggie Australia) Catalogue no: **S 1366**

## Barnard, Len

**LEN BARNARD'S FAMOUS JAZZ-BAND (The naked dance)**
**Album:** Released '88, on Swaggie (Australia) Catalogue no: **S 1287**

## Barnes, Alan

**AFFILIATION (Barnes, Alan Quartet)**
Tracks: / Fried bananas / Affiliation / You go to my head / Alice B / Easy does t / You don't know what love is / Pickles / Top flat / Straight life.
Note: With Dave Newton/Paul Morgan/Mark Taylor. Benny Green has written the sleeve notes for this album.
**Album:** Released Nov '87, on Miles Music by Miles Music Records. Catalogue no: **MM 002**

## Barnes, Emile

**EMILE BARNES & DOC PARLIN'S NEW (Barnes, Emile & Doc Parlin)**
**Album:** Released Jun '88, on Jazzology (USA) by Jazzology Records (USA). Catalogue no: **JCE 23**

**N.O.-THE LEGENDS LIVE (Barnes, Emile & His New Orleans Music)**
**Album:** Released Jun '86, on Jazzology (USA) by Jazzology Records (USA). Catalogue no: **JCE 34**

## Barnes, George

**GEORGE BARNES, 1946 (Barnes, George & His Octet)**
Tracks: / I can't give you anything but love / South side blues / Somebody loves me / Smoke gets in your eyes / Zebra's derby / September in the rain / Chicago / Undecided / Aren't you glad you're you / Starlight interlude / Kilroy was here / Priority on a moonbeam / Something to remember you by / At the jazz band ball / Imagination.
Note: Chicago jazz guitarist George Barnes, an early experimenter with the electric guitar, became a member of the staff orchestra at NBC and later at ABC in his hometown, surrounded on the job by classically orientated musicians. The eight-man chamber group he formed to play jazz at WENR in 1946 was heard regularly on network shows but never recorded commercially. This unique Hindsight album is derived from the octet's radio transcriptions. "Southside blues", "Zebra's derby", "Starlight interlude", "Kilroy is here" and "Priority on a moonbeam" are Barnes originals, and all arrangements are his. (Hindsight Catalogue - 1989)
**Album:** Released Mar '79, on Hindsight (UK) by Michele International Records. Catalogue no: **HSR 106**

**GUITARS, ANYONE? (Barnes, George / Carl Kress)**
**Album:** Released Aug '88, on Audiophile (USA) by Jazzology Records (USA). Catalogue no: **AP 87**

## Barnes, Johnny

**JAZZ MASTERS (Barnes, Johnny & Bruce Turner)**
**Album:** Released Feb '77, on Cadillac by Cadillac Music. Catalogue no: **SGC 1005**

## Barnes, Paul

**PAUL BARNES QUARTETS (Barnes, Paul Quartets)**
**Album:** Released '88, on Nola Catalogue no: **LP 17**
**Cass:** Released May '87, on Nola Catalogue no: **TC 017**

**PAUL "POLO" BARNES,**
**Album:** Released Jan '87, on CSA by CSA Records. Deleted '88. Catalogue no: **CLPS 1013**

**PORTRAIT OF A NOR CLARINET**
Note: Also featuring Louis Nelson, Joe Harris, Sing Miller.
**Album:** Released Jan '87, on CSA by CSA Records. Deleted '88. Catalogue no: **CLPS 1010**

**VIOLET & THE VINE, THE (Barnes, Paul & His Polo Players)**
**Album:** Released Feb '87, on Jazzology (USA) by Jazzology Records (USA). Catalogue no: **JCE 15**

## Barnes-Bocage Big Five

**BARNES-BOCAGE BIG FIVE**
**Album:** Released Apr '79, on Nola Catalogue no: **NOLA LP 9**

## Barnet, Charlie

**Biographical details:** Barnet, Charlie One of the most successful American bandleaders, Barnet was born in 1913 in New York City. He played saxophone, influenced by Coleman Hawkins on tenor and Johnny Hodges on alto; as a leader he was a blatent admirer of Duke Ellington and one of the most musical and faithful to jazz of white leaders in the Big Band Era. From a wealthy background he refused to become lawyer; he led a band on an ocean liner at 16, others from 1932, always including first-class lineups and arrangers; he was one of the white bandleaders brave enough to hire black musicians, as early as 1937. Nearly 30 big hits between 1936-46 included Ray Noble's *Cherokee*, which became a jazz standard and a favourite vehicle of bop musicians, and Barnet's own *Skyliner*. (Donald Clarke August 1988).

**...& HIS ORCHESTRA 1945/47**
**Album:** Released Jul '77, on First Heard by Submarine Records. Catalogue no: **FH 12**

**APRIL 1938 (Barnet, Charlie & His Orchestra)**
Tracks: / Make believe ballroom / Lullaby in rhythm / Stop, look & listen / In a jam / Prelude in C sharp minor / Chatterbox / Blue turning grey over you / Undecided / Harmony in Harlem / I let a song go out of my heart / You go to my head / Rock it for me / Prelude to a kiss / Ya got me / Jump jump's here.
**Album:** Released Apr '81, on Jazz Live (Italy) Catalogue no: **BLJ 8008**

**BIG BAND 1967**
Tracks: / Rabble rouser.
**CD:** Released '88, on Mobile Fidelity Sound Lab(USA) by Mobile Fidelity Records (USA). Catalogue no: **MFCD 841**

**CHARLIE BARNET (Barnet, Charlie Orchestra)**
**Album:** Released Apr '79, on Bright Orange Catalogue no: **BO 706**

**CHARLIE BARNET AND HIS ORCHESTRA (Barnet, Charlie and his Orchestra)**
**Album:** Released Aug '88, on Circle (USA) by Jazzology Records (USA). Catalogue no: **CLP 65**

**CHARLIE BARNET AND ORCHESTRA 1944-45 (Barnet, Charlie Orchestra)**
**Album:** Released '88, on Fanfare by Captain Billy's Music. Catalogue no: **LP 38-138**

**CHARLIE BARNET BIG BAND 1967 (Barnet, Charlie Big Band)**

**Album:** Released '87, on Creative World(USA) by GNP Crescendo Records (USA). Catalogue no: **ST 1056**

**CHARLIE BARNET & HIS ORCHESTRA (Barnet, Charlie & His Orchestra)**
**Album:** Released Apr '79, on First Heard by Submarine Records. Catalogue no: **FH 17**

**CHARLIE BARNET & HIS ORCHESTRA 1944-49 (Barnet, Charlie Orchestra)**
**Album:** Released Aug '89, on Golden Era by Delta Records. Catalogue no: **GELP 15015**

**CHARLIE BARNET ON THE AIR VOL 2 (Barnet, Charlie and his Orchestra)**
Tracks: / Smiles / Nobody knows the trouble I've seen / Everyday of my life / I can't get started / I like to riff / Keep the home fires burning / Cherokee / Until my baby comes back to me / Skyliner / Share croppin' blues / Blue skies / Washington whirligig / Cottontail.
**Album:** Released Feb '88, on Aircheck (USA) by Kiner Ents.(USA). Catalogue no: **AIRCHECK 30**
**Album:** Released Apr '79, on Aircheck (USA) by Kiner Ents.(USA). Catalogue no: **AIRCHECK 5**

**CHARLIE BARNET VOL.16 (1942/3)**
**Album:** Released Apr '79, on Ajax (USA) Catalogue no: **AJAX 140**

**CHARLIE BARNET VOL 17 (1944)**
**Album:** Released Apr '79, on Ajax (USA) Catalogue no: **AJAX 147**

**CHARLIE BARNET VOL 18**
**Album:** Released Apr '79, on Ajax (USA) Catalogue no: **AJAX 155**

**CLAP HANDS, HERE COMES CHARLIE (Barnet, Charlie & His Orchestra)**
Tracks: / Knockin' at the famous door / Girl from Joe's, The / Cherokee / Duke's idea, The / Right idea, The / Leapin' at the Lincoln / Afternoon of a moax / Flying home / Six lessons from Madame la Zonga / Rockin' in rhythm / Pompton turnpike / Wild Mab of the fishpond / Southern fried / Redskin Rhumba / You're my thrill / Charleston Alley / Murder at Peyton Hall / Count's idea, The / Between 18th and 19th on Chestnut Street / Clap hands here comes Charlie / Lumby.
**CD:** Released Jun '88, on Bluebird (2) by BMG Records (UK). Catalogue no: **ND 86273**

**DANCE BASH**
Tracks: / Jubilee jump / Charleston alley / Gal from Joe's, The / Deep purple / Blue Lou / Southern fried / Cherokee / Skyliner / Fur trappers boogie / Wosie posie / Let's blow the blues / Rhubarb / St. Louis blues / Swinging down the lane / Who's sorry now.
**Album:** Released May '82, on Verve Catalogue no: **2304 541**

**DANCE DATE (Barnet, Charlie & His Orchestra)**
**Album:** Released Apr '79, on Swing House by Submarine Records. Catalogue no: **SWH 6**

**DUKE'S IDEAS 1939/41 VOL 1**
**Album:** Released Nov '77, on Black & White by Black & White Records. Catalogue no: **PM 42041**

**FILM TRACKS OF..., THE**
**Album:** Released Jul '82, on Joyce Catalogue no: **JLP 3001**

**IN DISCO ORDER VOL 1**
**Album:** Released Jul '77, on Ajax (USA) Catalogue no: **AJAX 104**

**IN DISCO ORDER VOL 2**
**Album:** Released Jul '77, on Ajax (USA) Catalogue no: **AJAX 106**

**INDISPENSABLE CHARLIE BARNET VOLS 1/2**
Tracks: / Echoes of Harlem / Scotch and soda / Miss annabelle Lee / Lazy bug / Midweek function / I never knew / Ebony rhapsody / Lament for a lost love / Cherokee / All-night record man, The / Last jump, The / Duke's idea, The / Count's idea, The / Ogoun badagris . Oh what you siad / Wrong idea, The / Right idea, The / Night glow / Between 18th & 19th on Chestnut Street / Clap hands here come Charlie / Growlin' / Nagasaki / On a holiday/ / Always / I'm praying humble / Tin roof blues / Knocking at the famouis door / Gal from Joe's, The / Jump session / Swing street strut / Night song / Some like it hot / Only a rose.
**2 LP Set:** Released Sep '86, on Jazz Tribune by BMG Records (UK). Deleted May '89. Catalogue no: **NL 89743**
**Cass set:** Released Sep '86, on Jazz Tribune by BMG Records (UK). Deleted May '89. Catalogue no: **NK 89743**

**INDISPENSABLE CHARLIE BARNET VOLS 3/4 (1935-39)**
Tracks: / Comanche war dance / Tappin' at the Tappa / Southland shuffle / Lover's lullaby / Leapin' at the Lincoln / Wanderin' blues / Shake, rattle and roll / Lament for May / Flyin' home / No name jive, part 1&2 / Reverie of a moax,The (Oh Claire the goon) / It's the last time I'll fall in love / Rockin' in rhythm / Pompton turnpike / Ring dem bells / Sgt was shy, The / Wild Mab of the fishpond / Night and day / Redskin rhumba / Lumby / Phyllysee / Blue juice / Charleston alley / Little John ordinary / Haunted town / Merry-go-round / Birmingham breakdown / Ponce de leon / Little dip / Harlem speaks / I can't get started.
**2 LP Set:** Released Sep '86, on Jazz Tribune by BMG Records (UK). Deleted May '89. Catalogue no: **NL 89483**
**Cass set:** Released Sep '86, on Jazz Tribune by BMG Records (UK). Deleted May '89. Catalogue no: **NK 89483**

**LIVE AT BASIN ST. EAST**
**Album:** Released Jan '80, on Hep Jazz by Hep Records. Catalogue no: **HEP 2005**

**MAKE BELIEVE BALLROOM 1936-41 (Barnet, Charlie & His Orchestra)**
**Album:** Released Jun '88, on Bandstand Catalogue no: **BS 7123**

**ON STAGE WITH CHARLIE BARNET**
**Album:** Released Apr '79, on Bright Orange Catalogue no: **BO 719**

**ONE FOR MY BABY**
**Cass:** Released Jun '86, on Astar (USA) Catalogue no: **40180**

**REDSKIN RHUMBA**
**Album:** Released '88, on Fresh Sounds (Spain) by Fresh Sounds Records (Spain). Catalogue no: **FS 333**

**SHOWCASE**
**Album:** Released '84, on First Heard by Submarine Records. Catalogue no: **FH 44**

**SKYLINER (Big band bounce & boogie) (Barnet, Charlie & His Orchestra)**
Tracks: / Skyliner / Flat top flips his lid / Andy's boogie / Gulf coast blues / E-bob-o-lee-bob / Pow wow / Drop me off in Harlem / Xango / Washington whirligig / Moose / Sharecroppin' blues / Thing's ain't what they used to be / West End blues / Great lie, The / Strollin' / Just a sittin' and a rockin'.
**Album:** Released Sep '83, on Affinity by Charly Records. Catalogue no: **AFS 1012**

## Barr, Bert

**UPTOWN LOWDOWN JAZZBAND**
**Album:** Released Jun '88, on GHB by Jazzology Records (USA). Catalogue no: **GHB 149**

## Barrelhouse...

**BARRELHOUSE BLUES AND BOOGIE (Various artists)**
**Album:** Released Apr '89, on Blues Document Catalogue no: **BD 2033**

**BARRELHOUSE BLUES & STOMPS-VOL.4 (Various artists)**
**Album:** Released '79, on Euphonic Catalogue no: **ESR 1205**

**BARRELHOUSE BLUES & STOMPS-VOL.5 (Various artists)**
**Album:** Released '79, on Euphonic Catalogue no: **ESR 1204**

**DRIVING HOT JAZZ FROM THE 20'S (Barrelhouse Jazz Band)**
**Album:** Released Jun '86, on GHB by Jazzology Records (USA). Catalogue no: **GHB 49**

## Barrelhouse Piano...

**BARRELHOUSE PIANO (Various artists)**
**Album:** Released '88, on Jazz Piano Catalogue no: **JP 5007**

**BARRELHOUSE PIANO 1927-36 (Various artists)**
**Album:** Released Dec '88, on Yazoo (USA) by Shanachie Records (USA). Catalogue no: **L 1028**

## Barrett, Emma

**SWEET EMMA BARRETT & HER NEW ORLEANS MUSIC**
**Album:** Released Jun '88, on GHB by Jazzology Records (USA). Catalogue no: **GHB 141**

## Barrett Octet, Dan

**STRICTLY INSTRUMENTAL**
**Album:** Released Nov '87, on Concord Jazz by Concord Jazz Records (USA). Catalogue no: **CJ 331**
**Cass:** Released Nov '87, on Concord Jazz by Concord Jazz Records (USA). Catalogue no: **CJC 331**
**CD:** Released Dec '87, on Concord Jazz by Concord Jazz Records (USA). Catalogue no: **CCD 4331**

## Barron, Kenny

**1+1+1+1**
**Album:** Released Aug '86, on Black Hawk (USA) by Blackhawk Records (USA). Catalogue no: **BKH 50601**
**Cass:** Released Aug '86, on Black Hawk (USA) by Blackhawk Records (USA). Catalogue no: **BKHMC 50601**

**GOLDEN LOTUS**
**Album:** Released '82, on Muse by Black & Blue Records. Catalogue no: **MR 5220**

**IN TANDEM (Barron, Kenny & Ted Dunbar)**
**Album:** Released '75, on Muse by Black & Blue Records. Catalogue no: **MR 5140**

**LUCIFER**
Tracks: / Spirits / Firefly / Ethereally / Yours / Hellbound / Lucifer / Oleo.
**Album:** Released '81, on Muse by Black & Blue Records. Catalogue no: **MR 5070**

**SPIRAL**
**Album:** Released '85, on East Wind Catalogue no: **EWIND 709**

**SUNSET TO DAWN**
Tracks: / Sunset / Flower / Swamp demon / Al-Kifha / Delores St. S.F. / Dawn.
**Album:** Released '81, on Muse by Black & Blue Records. Catalogue no: **MR 5018**

**THE RED BARRON DUO (Barron, Kenny & Red Mitchell Trio)**
**CD:** Released Feb '90, on Storyville by Storyville Records AB. Catalogue no: **STCD 4137**
**Album:** Released Feb '90, on Storyville by Storyville Records AB. Catalogue no: **SLP 4137**

## Basie, Count

**Biographical details:** Born William Basie in New Jersey in 1904, Count Basie learned to play the piano from his mother and then studied informally with famous pianist Fats Waller. When turning professional, he began as a pianist on the vaudeville circuit, then joined the Blue Devils, many of whose members went on to play in Basie's own ensemble. When the Blue Devils broke up, a large proportion of their players joined a band under the leadership of Bennie Moten. With Moten passing away in 1935, the nucleus of his band became the first Basie outfit. It was when this ensemble began recording in '37 that Basie became an enormous star in the jazz field. His band gained international recognition for its hard-swinging style and freewheeling solo playing. Throughout the Forties & Fifties Count Basie consolidated on his reputation, always recruiting players of the highest musical calibre. Among his big band's most played numbers were "Swingin' At The Daisy Chain", "Every Tub", "One O'Clock Jump" and "Jumpin' At The Woodside". He was still able to hit the US Top 30 at the start of the rock'n'roll era, reaching No.28 in early 1956 with "April In Paris". In April 1960 he hit the UK albums Top 20 with Chairman Of The Board", though most of his greatest triumphs had occurred before the inception of the British charts.

**Count Basie**

William Allen Basie, born in 1904 in Redbank, New Jersey, was one of America's most popular bandleaders until he died in 1984 in Florida. He had tuition from Fats Waller on the cinema organ in Harlem; through primarily a pianist he often played organ in later years as well. He accompanied vaudeville acts on tour and was stranded in Kansas City; he joined Walter Page's Blue Devils (1928-9), which included blues singer Jimmy Rushing; that group folded and some of it joined Benny Moten's famous territory band; Moten died in 1935 and some of the best men joined Basie in a nine-piece group. Played in Kansas City's Reno Club, they were heard on the radio by John Hammond in Chicago, who told Benny Goodmen's booking agent Willard Alexander about them. Basie acquired his nickname during this period, a radio announcer deciding that as Goodman was the 'King of Swing', and there were already Duke Ellington and Earl Hines, a Count was needed. Basie hired more men and headed East; he had signed a bad contract with USA Decca, but in Chicago, Hammond produced four Smith-Jones small-group sides in 1936, using the names of drummer Jo Jones and trumpeter Carol 'Tatti' Smith; they remain joyous masterpieces, with two vocals by Rushing and Lester Young's first recorded solos.

In New York the band was unsuccessful at first; the men were not good readers and did not play in tune because they couldn't afford decent horns. But they opened at the Famous Door in 1937 and blew the town away, re-injecting basic values into big band jazz with a Kansas City blues-based style and a relentlessly rhythm section in a new, more modern style: Jones kept time with exquisite finesse on his top cymbal, bassist Page (aka 'Big 4) played four-to-the-bar instead of two, and Freddie Green was soon added, the greatest rhythm guitarist of the entire Swing Era. The band was profoundly influential on the modern jazz which was to come. Basie led it from the piano and was principally an editor; he could say more with a single note than other leaders with ten fingers, and by

running through an arrangement a couple of times, tailor it perfectly for the band. With Eddie Durham he created masterpieces like *One O' Clock Jump*; the band included Herschel Evans as well as Young on tenor; Buck Clayton, Harry 'Sweets' Edison, Ed Lewis and Shad Collins on trumpets; Dicky Wells and Benny Morton on trombones ; the girl singer was Helen Humes. (Billie Holiday sang with the band, but could not record with it; she is heard only on a couple of airchecks from the period).
Basie also recorded ten blues sides with just rhythm, rarely reissued. The first batch of USA Decca 78s from this era have been reissued on Hep in what looks like the first of a series, and these records are 20th century classics: the compilations on Affinity are also very good. The band switched to CBS labels in 1941 and Basie was guest on one fine record by the Goodman sextet ; then the band moved to Victor in 1947 for its biggest hit: but the no.1 smash *Open The Door, Richard!* was an R&B novelty (with many other hit versions) so untypical that it was not included in French RCA's complete compilations. By the late '40s the band included such greats as Emmett Berry on trumpet; Illinois Jacquet, Paul Govssalves and Buddy Tate on reeds, but the swing era was over: he disbanded and led a small group in 1950, but was persuaded to start all over again in 1952 on Norman Granz's Clef and Verve labels. The new band included many fine musicians, such as Joe Newman on trumpet, Marshall Royal, Ernie Wilkins, Lockjaw Davis and Paul Quinichette on reeds, but the accent was now on arrangements rather than on solos and so good was the band that it was one of the few to keep going through the post-war decades, such poor ones for jazz. Wilkins was an excellent arranger; 'The Two Franks' (Foster and Wess) were also contributors. The band's singer from 1954 was the wonderful Joe Williams; the album *Count Basie Swings/Joe Williams Sings* (1955) is a modern blues masterpiece that needs reissuing (Memphis Slim's *Every Day* was an R&B hit) although Williams is also a superb ballad singer. Basie switched to the new Roulette label and recorded an album of Neal Hefti arrangements called *The Atomic Mr Basie* in 1957: the stereo edition of this album is terrible, early and experimental, but PRT have reissued the state-of-the-art mono, which sounds wonderful. Benny Carter wrote his *Kansas City Suite* and another album for the Basie band during this period, among its last classics. By now the band was secure in the public's affection, and had been the first black band to play at top NYC hotels; it had also recorded with Billy Eckstine and Tony Bennett, and caried on with Ella Fitzgerald, Frank Sinatra and Sarah Vaughan; it remained internationally popular. In the late '60s it included such talent as arranger Sam Nestico, saxophonist Sal Nestico (cousins from NYC); but sometimes in the '70s it sounded like any well-drilled Las Vegas band: Basie's best late records are small-group sets on Granz's Pablo label. (Donald Clarke 23 August 1988).

**14 CLASSICS**
Tracks: / Hollywood jump / I never knew / Tickle toe / Let me see / Blow top / What's your number / Five o'clock whistle / Broadway / Stampede in G minor / Rockin' the blues / Wiggle woogie / Jitters / Tuesday at ten / I do mean you.
**Cass:** Released Jul '86, on CBS by CBS Records. Catalogue no: **40 21133**
**Album:** Released Jul '86, on CBS by CBS Records. Catalogue no: **CBS 21133**

**20 GOLDEN PIECES: COUNT BASIE**
Tracks: / One o'clock jump / Motem swing / Study in brown, A / Dinah / Good morning blues / Lady be good / Flat foot floogie / Every tub / Boogie woogie blues / Lullaby of Birdland / Summertime / These foolish things / One note samba / Makin' whoopee / April in Paris / Jumpin' at the woodside / Ain't misbehavin' / Shake, rattle and roll / I got it bad (and that ain't good) / Lester leaps in.
**Album:** Released Jul '82, on Bulldog Records by President Records. Catalogue no: **BDL 2020**
**Cass:** Released Jul '82, on Bulldog Records by President Records. Catalogue no: **BDC 2020**

**88 BASIE STREET (Basie, Count & His Orchestra)**
Tracks: / Bluesville / 88 Basie Street / Contractor's blues / Blues machine, The / Katy / Sunday at the Savoy.
**Album:** Released May '84, on Pablo Jazz (USA) by Pablo Records (USA). Catalogue no: **231 0901**
**Cass:** Released May '84, on Pablo Jazz (USA) by Pablo Records (USA). Catalogue no: **K10 901**

**1940 (Various artists)**
**Album:** Released '88, on Everybody's (USA) Catalogue no: **EV 3006**

**1944: COUNT BASIE**
**Album:** Released Jun '84, on Circle (USA) by Jazzology Records (USA). Catalogue no: **CLP 60**

**1946**
**Cass:** Released '84, on First Heard by Submarine Records. Catalogue no: **CFH 22**
**Album:** Released '84, on First Heard by Submarine Records. Catalogue no: **FH 22**

**1938-39**
**Album:** Released Jul '86, on Jazz Archives (USA) by Jazz Archives Inc.(USA). Catalogue no: **JA 41**

**AFRIQUE**
Tracks: / Step right up / Hobo flats / Gypsy queen / Love flower / Afrique / Kilimanjaro / African sunrise / Japan.
**Album:** Released Mar '85, on Doctor Jazz (USA) by CBS Records (USA). Catalogue no: **ASLP 809**
**Cass:** Released Mar '85, on Doctor Jazz (USA) by CBS Records (USA). Catalogue no: **ZCAS 809**

**AIN'T IT THE TRUTH (Basie, Count & His Orchestra)**
Tracks: / In case you didn't know / These foolish things / Peter Pan / Ain't it the truth / Ingin' the Ooh / Confessin'.
**Album:** Released Mar '81, on Black Lion Deleted '86. Catalogue no: **BLM 51009**

**AMERICANS IN SWEDEN 1954**
**2 LP Set:** Released Jan '88, on Jazz Society Catalogue no: **AA 526/527**

**AMERICANS IN SWEDEN VOL. 1 (Basie, Count & Orchestra)**
**CD:** Released Apr '88, on Tax Catalogue no: **TAXCD 3701-2**

**AMERICANS IN SWEDEN VOL. 2 (Basie, Count & Orchestra)**
**CD:** Released Apr '88, on Tax Catalogue no: **TAXCD 3702-2**

**APRIL IN PARIS**
**CD:** Released Jun '86, on Polygram by PolyGram UK Ltd. Catalogue no: **825 575-2**
**CD:** Released 10 Jul '89, on Vogue by Vogue Records. Catalogue no: **VGCD 670206**

**AT SAVOY BALLROOM 1937-44**
Tracks: / Moten swing / Shout and feel it / Me and you that used to be, The / Count steps in, The / I'll always be in love with you / When my dreamboat comes home / Swing brother swing / Down for double / Rockin' the blues / Wiggle woogie / Andy's blues / I've found a new baby / Basie boogie.
Note: Includes: Lester Young, Billie Holiday, Jimmy Rushing.
**Album:** Released '87, on Joker (USA) by Lifetime Records (USA). Catalogue no: **SM 3083**

**AT SOUTHLAND CAFE, BOSTON (Basie, Count / Chick Webb)**
**Album:** Released '88, on Collector's Classics Catalogue no: **CC 11**

**AT THE BLUENOTE (Basie, Count & His Orchestra)**
Tracks: / Fancy meeting you (Recorded at the Chicago Bluenote during August 1955) / Basie English (Recorded at the Chicago Bluenote during January 1956) / Everyday (Recorded at the Chicago Bluenote during January 1956) / Basses loaded (Recorded at the Chicago Bluenote during January 1956) / April in Paris (Recorded at the Chicago Bluenote during August 1955) / Peace pipe (Recorded at the Chicago Bluenote during August 1955) / Cherry point (Recorded at the Chicago Bluenote during August 1955) / Smack dab in the middle (Recorded at the Chicago Bluenote during January 1956) / Jumpin' at the woodside (Recorded at the Chicago Bluenote during January 1956) / Teach me tonight (Recorded at the Chicago Bluenote during August 1955) / How high the moon (Recorded at the Chicago Bluenote during August 1955).
Note: Personnel: Trumpets-Thad Jones,Joe Newman,Wendell Culley,Re-

unald Jones. Trombones-Henry Coker, Benny Powell, Bill Hughes. Saxes-Marshall Royal (cl,as), Frank Wess( fl,ts,as) ,Frank Foster & Bill Graham(ts),Charlie Fowlkes (bs). Rhythm: Freddie Green (guitar) ,Eddie Jones(bass), Sonnie Payne (drums) William 'Count' Basie (piano & leader). Vocals: Joe Williams
**Album:** Released Sep '86, on Magic (1) by Submarine Records. Catalogue no: **AWE 24**
**Cass:** Released Sep '86, on Magic (1) by Submarine Records. Catalogue no: **CAWE 24**

**AT THE MONTREUX JAZZ FESTIVAL, 1975**
Tracks: / Jam session / Billie's bounce / Festival blues / Lester leaps in.
**Album:** Released May '82, on Pablo Jazz (USA) by Pablo Records (USA). Catalogue no: **231 0750**
**Cass:** Released May '82, on Pablo Jazz (USA) by Pablo Records (USA). Catalogue no: **K10 750**

**ATOMIC MR. BASIE, THE (GIANTS OF JAZZ) (Basie, Count & His Orchestra)**
**CD:** Released Jan '89, on Giants of Jazz by Hasmick Promotions. Catalogue no: **CD 53043**

**ATOMIC MR. BASIE, THE (PRT) (Basie, Count & His Orchestra)**
**Cass:** Released Jul '84, on PRT by Castle Communications Records. Catalogue no: **ZCNFP 5503**
**Album:** Released Jul '84, on PRT by Castle Communications Records. Catalogue no: **NFP 5503**

**ATOMIC MR. BASIE, THE (ROULETTE) (Basie, Count & His Orchestra)**
Tracks: / Kid from Red Bank, The / Duet / After supper / Flights of the foo birds / Double -O / Teddy the toad / Whirly bird / Midnite blue / Splanky / Fantail / Lil' darlin'.
**CD:** Released Oct '89, on Roulette (EMI) by EMI Records. Catalogue no: **CZ 238**
**CD:** Released '89, on Roulette (EMI) by EMI Records. Catalogue no: **CDP 793 273 2**
**Album:** Released '89, on Roulette (EMI) by EMI Records. Catalogue no: **793 273 1**
**Album:** Released Oct '89, on Roulette (EMI) by EMI Records. Catalogue no: **ROU 1005**

**ATOMIC MR. BASIE, THE (VOGUE) (Basie, Count & His Orchestra)**
**Album:** Released May '84, on Vogue by Vogue Records. Catalogue no: **500 001**
**CD:** Released May '85, on Vogue by Vogue Records. Catalogue no: **VG 600 008**
**Cass:** Released May '84, on Vogue by Vogue Records. Catalogue no: **700 788**

**ATOMIC MR.CHAIRMAN, THE**
Tracks: / Kid from Red Bank, The / Duet / After supper / Flights of the foo birds / Double-O / Teddy the toad / Whirly-bird / Midnite blue / Splanky / Fantail / Li'l darlin' / Blues in Hoss's flat / H.R.H. / Segue in C / Kansas City shout / Speaking of sounds / T.V. time / Who, me? / Deacon, The / Half Moon Street / Mutt and Jeff.
**2 LP Set:** Released May '83, on Vogue Jazz (France) by Vogue Records. Catalogue no: **VJD 517**
**Cass set:** Released May '83, on Vogue Jazz (France) by Vogue Records. Catalogue no: **ZCVJD 517**

**ATOMIC PERIOD, THE (Basie, Count Orchestra)**
Tracks: / Shiny stockings / HRH / Bag of bones / Deacon, The / Whirly bird / In a mellow tone / Midgets, The / Basie boogie / Ol' man river / Sisteen men a'swinging.
**Album:** Released Apr '81, on Rarities Catalogue no: **RARITIES 52**

**AUTUMN IN PARIS (Basie, Count & His Orchestra)**
Tracks: / Whirlybird / Little pony / Corner pocket / Lovely baby / Blee blop blues / Nails / Kid from Redbank / Spring is here / Why not? / Well, alright, OK, you win / Roll 'em / Ol man river / Duet / Gee, baby ain't I good to you / One o'clock jump.
**Cass:** Released Jun '85, on Magic (1) by Submarine Records. Catalogue no: **CAWE 13**
**CD:** Released Aug '88, on Magic (1) by Submarine Records. Catalogue no: **DAWE 13**
**Album:** Released Jun '85, on Magic (1) by Submarine Records. Catalogue no: **AWE 13**

**AVENUE C (With Lester Young, 1944)**
**CD:** Released 21 Jul '89, on Jazz & Jazz Catalogue no: **CDJJ 604**
**Album:** Released Jun '89, on Jazz & Jazz Catalogue no: **JJ 604**

**BACK WITH BASIE**
**Album:** Released Oct '88, on Vogue by Vogue Records. Catalogue no: **500022**

**BASIC BASIE**
Tracks: / Idaho / Blues in my heart / I don't stand a ghost of a chance / Red roses for a blue lady / Moonglow / Ma he's making eyes at me / M-squad / Sweet Lorraine / Ain't misbehavin' / Don't worry 'bout me / As long as I live / I've got the world on a string.
Note: Count Basie, piano; M.F. Wanzo, Grover Mitchell, Bill Hughes, trombones; Gene Goe, Oscar Brashear, W. Reed, Sonny Cohn, trumpets; Charlie Fowlkes, baritone sax; Marshall Royal, Bobby Plater, alto saxes; Eric Dixon, Eddy Davis, tenor saxes; Eric Dixon, flute; Freddie Green, guitar; Norman Keenan bass; Harold Jones, drums. Recorded in Chicago, 1969.
**CD:** Released Nov '84, on Verve Deleted Mar '88. Catalogue no: **821 291-2**
**Album:** Released Sep '84, on MPS Jazz (Germany) Catalogue no: **821 291-1**

**BASIC BASIE, 1937-38 (Basie, Count & His Orchestra)**
**Album:** Released May '86, on Nostalgia by Mainline Records. Catalogue no: **NOST 7640**

**BASIE**
**2 LP Set:** Released Oct '88, on Vogue by Vogue Records. Catalogue no: **400614**

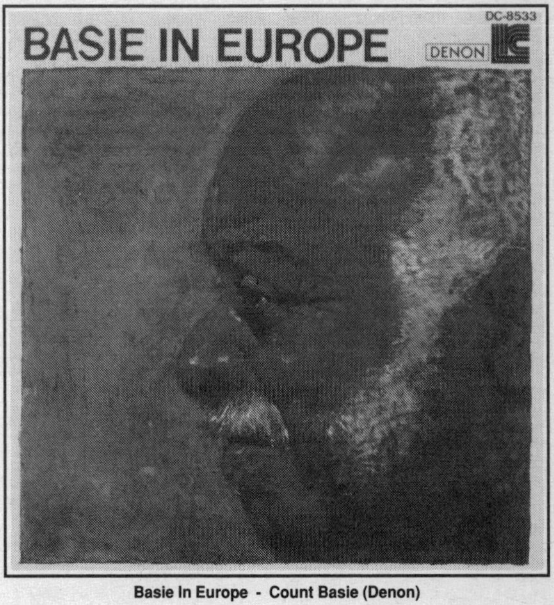


**Basie In Europe - Count Basie (Denon)**

**BASIE AT BIRDLAND**
**Album:** Released Oct '88, on Vogue by Vogue Records. Catalogue no: **500020**
**CD:** Released Oct '88, on Vogue by Vogue Records. Catalogue no: **VGCD 600 137**

**BASIE BIG BAND**
Tracks: / Front burner / Freckle face / Orange sherbert / Soft as velvet / Heat's on, The / Midnight freight / Give 'em time / Wind machine, The / Tall cotton.
**Album:** Released May '82, on Pablo Jazz (USA) by Pablo Records (USA). Catalogue no: **231 0756**
**CD:** Released Jan '89, on JVC/Fantasy Catalogue no: **VDJ 28004**
**Cass:** Released May '82, on Pablo Jazz (USA) by Pablo Records (USA). Catalogue no: **K10 756**

**BASIE BLUES**
**Album:** Released May '84, on MFP (France) by EMI Records. Catalogue no: **2M 056 64865**
**Cass:** Released May '84, on MFP (France) by EMI Records. Catalogue no: **2M 256 64865**

**BASIE BOOGIE (Basie, Count & His Orchestra)**
Tracks: / One o'clock jump / Basie boogie / Taps Miller / Red bank boogie / mad boogie / King / Hob nail boogie / Wild bill's boogie / Little pony / Hozit / Beaver junction / Nails / Squeeze me / Boone's blues / Jumping at the woodside.
**Album:** Released Mar '83, on CBS by CBS Records. Deleted '87. Catalogue no: **CBS 21063**
**Cass:** Released May '83, on CBS by CBS Records. Deleted Nov '87. Catalogue no: **40 21063**

**BASIE DOUBLE**
Tracks: / Rat race / Five o'clock in the morning / Easin' it / Blue on blue / Good time blues / Meetin' time / Counter block / Let's have a taste / Not now, I'll tell you when / Swingin' at the Waldorf / Vine Street rumble / Quince / Square at the round table / Brotherly shove / Blue five jive / Rare butterfly / Jackson County jubilee / Big walk, The.
**2 LP Set:** Released Jun '75, on Vogue by Vogue Records. Catalogue no: **VJD 509**

**BASIE IN EUROPE (see previous page).**
Tracks: / Hittin' twelve / Freckle face / Things ain't what they used to be / Whirly-bird / More I see you, The / Orange sherbet / Way out Basie / Basie jumpin' at the Woodside.
Note: Trombones - Mel Wanzo, Bill Hughes, Al Grey, Dennis Wilson. Trumpets - Sonny Cohn, Bobby Mitchell, Lyn Biviano, Waymon Reed, Clark Terry. Saxes - Jimmy Forrest, Eric Dixon, Bobby Plater, Charles Fowlkes, Danny Turner. Guitar - Freddie Green. Bass - John Duke. Drums - Butch Miles. Piano/leader - Count Basie.
The Count Basie story did not end with the loss of its leader, any more than the Ellington story terminated with the passing of the mantle from Duke to Mercer. Even if there were no Basie band today, it would be reasonable to state that he lives on vicariously through the innumerable bands and arrangers and solists who have found a source of inspiration in the unique Basie legend and legacy. It lives on also through the seemingly endless flow of discoveries
**CD:** Released Apr '89, on Denon Catalogue no: **MC 7481**
**CD:** Released Apr '89, on Denon Catalogue no: **DC 8533**

**BASIE IN SWEDEN**
**Album:** Released Oct '88, on Vogue by Vogue Records. Catalogue no: **500023**

**BASIE JAM**
Tracks: / Doubling blues / Hanging out / Red bank blues / One nighter / Freeport blues.
**CD:** Released '86, on Pablo Jazz (USA) by Pablo Records (USA). Catalogue no: **J33J 20017**
**CD:** Released Jan '89, on JVC/Fantasy Catalogue no: **VDJ 28005**

**BASIE JAM AT MONTREUX 1975**
Tracks: / Billie's bounce / Festival blues / Lester leaps in.
**CD:** on Pablo Jazz (USA) by Pablo Records (USA). Catalogue no: **J33J 20053**

**BASIE JAM NO.2**
Tracks: / Mama don't wear no drawers / Doggin' around / Kansas City line / Jjjjump.
**Cass:** Released May '82, on Pablo Jazz (USA) by Pablo Records (USA). Catalogue no: **K10 786**
**Album:** Released May '82, on Pablo Jazz (USA) by Pablo Records (USA). Catalogue no: **231 0786**
**Album:** Released Jan '77, on Pablo Jazz (USA) by Pablo Records (USA). Catalogue no: **2335 748**

**BASIE JAM NO.3**
Tracks: / Bye bye blues / Moten swing / I surrender, dear / Song of the islands.
**Cass:** Released May '82, on Pablo Jazz (USA) by Pablo Records (USA). Catalogue no: **K10 840**
**Album:** Released May '82, on Pablo Jazz (USA) by Pablo Records (USA). Catalogue no: **231 0840**

**BASIE ONE MORE TIME**
**Album:** Released Oct '88, on Vogue by Vogue Records. Catalogue no: **500006**

**BASIE PIANO**
**CD:** Released Oct '89, on Jazz Anthology by Musidisc Records (France). Catalogue no: **550 002**
**Album:** Released '88, on Ri-Disc Catalogue no: **RD 9**

**BASIE PLAYS HEFTI**
**Album:** Released Oct '88, on Vogue by Vogue Records. Catalogue no: **500002**

**BASIE RIDES AGAIN**
Note: 1952 recordings from Basie with both his big band and small unit. Oscar Peterson plays piano on Be My Guest and Blues for the Count and Oscar.
**Album:** Released Feb '82, on Polydor (Import) by Polydor Ltd. Catalogue no: **2304 410**

**BASIE SPECIAL, THE (Basie, Count Orchestra)**
**Album:** Released '88, on Everybody's (USA) Catalogue no: **EV 3004**

**BASIE & ZOOT (Basie, Count & Zoot Sims)**
Tracks: / I never knew / Its only a paper moon / Blues for Nat Cole / Captain Bligh / Honeysuckle rose / Hardav / Mean to me / Surrender dear.
**Cass:** Released '82, on Pablo Jazz (USA) by Pablo Records (USA). Catalogue no: **K10 745**
**Album:** Released '82, on Pablo Jazz (USA) by Pablo Records (USA). Catalogue no: **2310 745**
**CD:** Released Jul '86, on Pablo Jazz (USA) by Pablo Records (USA). Catalogue no: **J33J 20016**

**BASIE'S BASEMENT (Basie, Count & His Orchestra)**
Tracks: / Bill's mill / Swingin' the blues / Basie's basement / I never knew / Sugar / South / Seventh Avenue express / Your red wagon / Just a minute / Bye bye baby / Shoutin' blues / Rat race.
**Cass:** Released Jul '86, on RCA by BMG Records (UK). Deleted Jul '89. Catalogue no: **CK 89802**
**Album:** Released Jul '86, on RCA by BMG Records (UK). Deleted Jul '89. Catalogue no: **CL 89802**

**BEST OF BASIE VOL.1**
**CD:** Released Feb '89, on Vogue by Vogue Records. Catalogue no: **VGCD 600040**
**Album:** Released Oct '88, on Vogue by Vogue Records. Catalogue no: **500014**

**BEST OF BASIE VOL.2**
**Album:** Released Oct '88, on Vogue by Vogue Records. Catalogue no: **500015**
**CD:** Released Feb '89, on Vogue by Vogue Records. Catalogue no: **VGCD 600040**

**BEST OF COUNT BASIE**
Tracks: / Tree frog / Swee' pea / Ticker / Flirt / Blues for Alfy / Billie's bounce / Festival blues / Jumpin' at the Woodside / Blue & sentimental / Red bank boogie / Shorty George / Rockabye Basie / Every tub / Swingin' the blues / Sent for you yesterday / Boogie woogie / Broadway / Texas shuffle / Tickle toe / Doggin' around / Dickie's dream / Topsy / Lester leaps in / Out the window.
**CD:** Released '86, on Vogue by Vogue Records. Catalogue no: **VG 600 040**
**Album:** Released Oct '84, on Pablo Jazz (USA) by Pablo Records (USA). Catalogue no: **2310 852**
**Cass:** Released Oct '84, on Pablo Jazz (USA) by Pablo Records (USA). Catalogue no: **K10 852**

**BEST OF THE BASIE BIG BAND**
Tracks: / Blues for Alfy / Heat's on, The / C.B.Express / Swee'pea / Way out Basie / Featherweight / Katy / Prime time / Mr. Softie.
**Album:** Released 27 Jan '89, on Pablo

Jazz (USA) by Pablo Records (USA). Catalogue no: **PEM 002**
**CD:** Released 27 Jan '89, on Pablo Jazz (USA) by Pablo Records (USA). Catalogue no: **CDPEM 001**
**Cass:** Released 27 Jan '89, on Pablo Jazz (USA) by Pablo Records (USA). Catalogue no: **PEMC 002**

**BIG BASIE**
Tracks: / Avenue C / Tess torch song / Jumpin' at The Woodside / I'm gonna sit right down and write myself a letter / Rockabye Basie / Dance of the gremlins / When they ask about you / I've found a new baby / Slender, tender and tall / Do nothing till you hear from me / Basie boogie / Havard blues.
**Album:** Released Apr '81, on Queendisc (Italy) Catalogue no: **QU 025**

**BIRDLAND ERA VOL.1, THE (Basie, Count & His Orchestra)**
**Album:** Released Jun '86, on Duke by Melodisc Records. Catalogue no: **D 1013**

**BIRDLAND ERA VOL.2, THE (Basie, Count & His Orchestra)**
Tracks: / One o'clock jump / Why not? / Out of nowhere / How high the moon / Hobnail boogie / Jumpin' at The Woodside / Blee blop blues / Basie blues / Every tub / You're not the kind / Paradise squat / Lullaby of Birdland.
**Album:** Released Jun '86, on Duke by Melodisc Records. Catalogue no: **D 1018**

**BLUES BY BASIE**
Tracks: / Tootie / How long blues / Way back blues / Blues / Harvard blues / Bugle blues / Take me back baby / Golden bullet / Nobody knows / Royal garden blues / I'm gonna move to the outskirts of town / Bluebird blues.
**Album:** Released May '81, on CBS by CBS Records. Deleted '86. Catalogue no: **CBS 54304**

**BOARD OF DIRECTORS, THE (Basie, Count & Mills Brothers)**
Tracks: / Up a lazy river / I may be wrong but I think you're wonderful / Release me / I want to be happy / Down down down / Whiffenpoof song, The / I dig rock and roll music / Tiny bubbles / December / Let me dream / April in Paris.
**Album:** Released '86, on Memoir by Memoir Records. Catalogue no: **MOIR 201**
**CD:** Released Nov '89, on Memoir by Memoir Records. Catalogue no: **CMOIR 201**

**BOSSES, THE (Basie, Count & Joe Turner)**
Tracks: / Honeydripper / Honey hush / Cherry red / Night time is the right time / Blues around the clock / Since I fell for you / Flip flop and fly / Wee baby blues / Good morning blues / Roll 'em Pete.
**Album:** Released '82, on Pablo Jazz (USA) by Pablo Records (USA). Catalogue no: **231 0709**
**Cass:** Released '82, on Pablo Jazz (USA) by Pablo Records (USA). Catalogue no: **K10 709**

**BREAKFAST DANCE & BARBECUE**
**Album:** Released Oct '88, on Vogue by Vogue Records. Catalogue no: **500009**

**BROADCASTS 1944/45 (Basie, Count & His Orchestra)**
Tracks: / Basie blues / One o'clock jump / Basie boogie / I'm gonna sit right down & write myself.
**Album:** Released Mar '88, on Delta (1) by Delta Records. Catalogue no: **20 806**

**CAFE SOCIETY UPTOWN VOL. 1**
**Album:** Released '88, on Jazz Unlimited Catalogue no: **JU 4**

**CAFE SOCIETY UPTOWN VOL. 2**
**Album:** Released '88, on Jazz Unlimited Catalogue no: **JU 5**

**CARNEGIE HALL CONCERT**
**Album:** Released Oct '88, on Vogue (France) by Vogue Records. Catalogue no: **509168**

**CHAIRMAN OF THE BOARD**
**Album:** Released Apr '60, on Columbia by EMI Records. Deleted '65. Catalogue no: **33SX 1209**

**CHAIRMAN, THE**
**CD:** Released Oct '88, on Vogue by Vogue Records. Catalogue no: **VGCD 600 127**
**Album:** Released Oct '88, on Vogue by Vogue Records. Catalogue no: **500007**

**CHAPTER FIVE (Basie, Count Orchestra)**
Tracks: / Fiesta in blue / Tom Thumb / My old flame / Take me back, baby / Something new / Platterbrains / All of me / Feather merchant / Down for double / More than you know / Havard blues / Coming-out party / Blue shadows and white gardenias.
**Album:** Released Apr '81, on Queendisc (Italy) Catalogue no: **QU 034**

**CHAPTER FOUR (Basie, Count Orchestra)**
Tracks: / Nobody knows / How long blues / Blues (I still think of her) / Who am I? / I'll forget / Beau Brummel / Jump the blues away / Tuesday at ten / Undecided blues / Down, down, down / Tune town shuffle / One two three O'Leary / Diggin' for Dex.
**Album:** Released Apr '81, on Queendisc (Italy) Catalogue no: **QU 033**

**CHAPTER SIX**
**Album:** Released '88, on Queen Catalogue no: **QUEEN 035**
**Album:** Released Apr '81, on Queendisc (Italy) Catalogue no: **QU 035**

**CHAPTER THREE (Basie, Count Orchestra)**
Tracks: / Don't worry 'bout me / And the angels sing / If I didn't care / Lonesome Miss Pretty / You can count on me / You and your love / Apple jump, The / Volcano / Louisiana / You can't run around / World is mad, The / All or nothing at all / Moon fell in the river, The / Five o'clock whistle / My wandering man.
**Album:** Released '88, on Queen Catalogue no: **QUEEN 022**
**Album:** Released Apr '81, on Queendisc (Italy) Catalogue no: **QU 022**

**CLASS OF '54**
**Album:** Released 10 Jul '89, on Black Lion Catalogue no: **BLP 60924**
**Album:** Released 10 Jul '89, on Black Lion Catalogue no: **BLP7 60924**

**COUNT BASIE (Compact / Walkman Jazz)**
Tracks: / Shiny stockings / Down for the Count / Corner pocket / Blues backstage / April in Paris / One o'clock jump / I'm shouting again / Count 'Em / Nasty magnus / St. Louis Blues / All of me / Doodle oodle.
**Cass:** Released Jun '87, on Verve Catalogue no: **831 364 4**
**CD:** Released Jun '87, on Verve Catalogue no: **831 364 2**

**COUNT BASIE, 1940-44**
**Album:** Released '89, on Jazz Society Catalogue no: **AA 512**

**COUNT BASIE AND HIS ORCHESTRA (Basie, Count & His Orchestra)**
Tracks: / Moten swing / Bugle call rag / Lady be good / Darn that dream / Sent for you yesterday / I'm gonna sit right down and write myself a letter / Jumpin' at the woodside / 9.20 Special / Avenue C / Blue Lou / One o'clock jump.
**Album:** Released '87, on Joker (USA) by Lifetime Records (USA). Catalogue no: **SM 3109**

**COUNT BASIE AND HIS ORCHESTRA (Basie, Count & His Orchestra)**
**Album:** Released Jul '86, on Jazz Archives (USA) by Jazz Archives Inc.(USA). Catalogue no: **JA 16**

**COUNT BASIE AND HIS ORCHESTRA VOL. 3**
Tracks: / Little pony / Plymouth Rock / Backwater blues / Who me / April in Paris / Blues backstage / Good time blues / Peace pipe.
**Album:** Released Apr '82, on Jazz Reactivation Deleted Apr '87. Catalogue no: **JR 146**

**COUNT BASIE AND JOE WILLIAMS (Compact/Walkman jazz) (Basie, Count & Joe Williams)**
Tracks: / Every day (I have the blues) / Fine romance, A / Amazing love / Too close for comfort / Please send me someone to love / I'm beginning to see the light / In the evening (When the sun goes down) / Smack dab in the middle / I can't believe that you're in love... / Teach me tonight / Party blues / Come rain or come shine / Roll 'em Pete / Comeback, The / Thou swell / All right, okay, you win.
**CD:** Released Aug '88, on Verve Catalogue no: **835 329 2**
**Cass:** Released Aug '88, on Verve Catalogue no: **835 329 4**

**COUNT BASIE AND ORCHESTRA (Various artists)**
**Album:** Released '88, on Hindsight Catalogue no: **HSR 224**

**Album:** Released '89, on Echo Jazz Catalogue no: **EJLP 03**
**Album:** Released '88, on Joker (USA) by Lifetime Records (USA). Catalogue no: **SM 3970-2**
**CD:** Released '89, on Echo Jazz Catalogue no: **EJCD 03**
**Album:** Released Sep '87, on Giants of Jazz by Hasmick Promotions. Catalogue no: **LPJT 4**
**Cass:** Released '89, on Echo Jazz Catalogue no: **EJMC 03**
**Album:** Released Apr '81, on Queendisc (Italy) Catalogue no: **QU 008**

**COUNT BASIE BIG BAND**
Tracks: / Heat's on, The / Freckle face / Splanky / More I see you, The / Night in Tunisia / Hittin' twelve / Bag of dreams / Things ain't what they used to be / I needs to be'd with / Li'l darlin' / Jumpin' at the Woodside / One o'clock jump.
**Cass:** Released May '82, on Pablo Jazz (USA) by Pablo Records (USA). Catalogue no: **K 08 207**
**Album:** Released May '82, on Pablo Jazz (USA) by Pablo Records (USA). Catalogue no: **2308 207**

**COUNT BASIE COLLECTION**
**CD:** Released Oct '89, on Collection by K-Tel Records. Catalogue no: **OR 0076**
**Album:** Released Aug '85, on Deja Vu Catalogue no: **DVLP 2009**
**Cass:** Released Aug '85, on Deja Vu Catalogue no: **DVMC 2009**

**COUNT BASIE (featuring Tony Bennet)**
**CD:** Released '88, on Pickwick by Pickwick Records. Catalogue no: **PWK 032**

**COUNT BASIE & FREINDS (Basie, Count & Friends)**
**VHS:** Released Feb '90, on Verve Catalogue no: **CFV 10222**

**COUNT BASIE (IMPORT)**
Tracks: / Moten swing / Shout & feel it / Me and you that used to be, The / Count steps in, The / I'll always be in love with you / When my dreamboat comes home / Swing brother swing / Down for double / Rockin' the blues / Wiggle woogie / Andy's blues / I've found a new baby / Basie boogie / Fare thee honey, fare thee well / What's your number? / Draftin' blues / It's square but it rocks / You lied to me / Music makers / 9/20 special / Feedin' the Bean / H & J / Goin' to Chicago blues / You betcha my life / Down, down, down / King Joe.
Note: Recorded 1939, 1940, 1941.
**Album:** Released Apr '81, on Queendisc (Italy) Catalogue no: **QU 015**
**Album:** Released Oct '82, on Phoenix (2) by Audio Fidelity Enterprises. Catalogue no: **PHX 1010**

**COUNT BASIE JAM**
Tracks: / Bookie blues / She's funny that way / These foolish things / Kidney stew / Trio blues / I got it bad / Jumpin' at the Woodside.
**Cass:** Released May '82, on Pablo Jazz (USA) by Pablo Records (USA). Catalogue no: **K 08 209**
**Album:** Released May '82, on Pablo Jazz (USA) by Pablo Records (USA). Catalogue no: **2308 209**

**COUNT BASIE & JOE WILLIAMS (Basie, Count & Joe Williams)**
**2 LP Set:** Released May '83, on Vogue Jazz (France) by Vogue Records. Catalogue no: **VJD 553**

**COUNT BASIE SWINGS - TONY BENNETT SINGS (Basie, Count & Tony Bennett)**
Tracks: / Life is a song / With plenty of money and you / Jeepers creepers / Are you havin' any fun / Anything goes / Strike up the band / Chicago / I've grown accustomed to her face / Poor little rich girl / Growing pains / I guess I'll have to change my plans / After supper (CD only.).
**CD:** Released Feb '90, on Roulette (EMI) by EMI Records. Catalogue no: **CDROU 1009**
**CD:** Released Feb '90, on Roulette (EMI) by EMI Records. Catalogue no: **CDP 793 899 2**
**Album:** Released Feb '90, on Roulette (EMI) by EMI Records. Catalogue no: **ROU 1009**
**Album:** Released Feb '90, on Roulette (EMI) by EMI Records. Catalogue no: **793 899 1**

**COUNT BASIE & THE 16**
**Album:** Released '88, on Tax Catalogue no: **TAX 8029**

**COUNT BASIE & THE KANSAS CITY SEVEN (Basie, Count & The Kansas City Seven)**
Tracks: / Lady be good / Secrets / I want a little girl / Shoeshine boy / Count's place / Senator Whitehead / Tally-ho Mr. Basie / What'cha talkin'.
**Cass:** Released Jul '82, on Jasmine by Hasmick Promotions. Catalogue no: **JASC 3**
**CD:** Released '88, on Impulse by Impulse Records. Catalogue no: **MCAD 5656**
**Album:** Released Jul '82, on Jasmine by Hasmick Promotions. Catalogue no: **JAS 3**

**COUNT BASIE & VOICES**
**2 LP Set:** Released Oct '88, on Vogue by Vogue Records. Catalogue no: **400012**

**COUNT BASIE VOL.1**
Tracks: / Rat race / Five o'clock in the morning / Easin' it / Blue on blue / Peppermint pipes / Good time blues / Meetin' time / Counter block / Let's have a taste.
**Album:** Released Jul '82, on Jazz Reactivation Catalogue no: **JR 121**

**COUNT BASIE, VOL.2**
**CD:** Released Oct '89, on Hep Jazz by Hep Records. Catalogue no: **HEPCD 1027**
**Album:** Released May '83, on Jazz Reactivation Catalogue no: **JR 138**

**COUNT BASIE VOL.2 1937/8**
**Album:** Released Apr '79, on Ajax (USA) Catalogue no: **AJAX 129**

**COUNT BASIE VOL.3 1938**
**Album:** Released Apr '79, on Ajax (USA) Catalogue no: **AJAX 137**

**COUNT BASIE VOL 4 1938/9**
**Album:** Released Apr '79, on Ajax (USA) Catalogue no: **AJAX 143**

**COUNT BASIE VOL.5 1939**
**Album:** Released Apr '79, on Ajax (USA) Catalogue no: **AJAX 150**

**COUNT BASIE VOL.6 1939**
**Album:** Released Apr '79, on Ajax (USA) Catalogue no: **AJAX 157**

**COUNT BASIE VOL.7 1939**
**Album:** Released Apr '79, on Ajax (USA) Catalogue no: **AJAX 163**

**COUNT BASIE-VOL. I (Count & The President)**
Tracks: / Shoe shine boy / Evenin' / Boogie woogie / Oh lady be good / I ain't got nobody / Goin' to Chicago / Live and love tonight / Love me or leave me / What goes up must come down / Rockabye Basie / Baby don't you tell on me / If I could be with you / One house tonight / Taxi war dance / Don't worry 'bout me / Jump for me / And the angels sing / If I didn't care / Twelfth St. rag / Miss Thing (Part 1) / Miss Thing (Part 1) / Lonesome & pretty / Bolero at the Savoy / Nobody knows / Pound cake / You can count on me / You and your love / How long blues / Sub-deb blues.
**2 LP Set:** Released Jul '86, on CBS by CBS Records. Catalogue no: **CBS 88667**
**Cass:** Released Jul '86, on CBS by CBS Records. Catalogue no: **40 88667**

**COUNT BASIE-VOL.2 (Lester leaps in)**
Tracks: / Moonlight serenade / Song of the islands / I can't believe that you're in love with me / Clap hands here comes Charlie / Dickie's dream / Lester leaps in / Apple jump, The / I left my baby / Riff interlude / Volcano / Between the devil and the deep blue sea / Ham 'n' eggs / Hollywood jump / Someday, sweetheart / I never knew / Tickle toe / Let's make hay / Louisiana / Easy does it / Let me see / Blues (still think of her) / Somebody stole my gal / Blow top / Gone with "what" wind / Super chief / You can't run around / Evenin'.
**2 LP Set:** Released Jul '86, on CBS by CBS Records. Catalogue no: **CBS 88668**
**Cass:** Released Jul '86, on CBS by CBS Records. Catalogue no: **40 88668**

**COUNT BASIE-VOL.3 (Don for Prez)**
Tracks: / World is mad, The (part 1) / World is mad, The (part 2) / Moten swing / It's torture / I want a little girl / All or nothing at all / Moon fell in the river, The / What's your number / Draftin' blues / Five o'clock whistle / Love jumped out / My wandering man / Broadway / It's the same old south / Stampede in G minor / Who am I? / Rockin' the blues / It's square but it rocks / I'll forget / I'll forget-2 / You lied to me / Wiggle woogie / Beau Brummel / Music makers / Jump the blues away / Deep in the blues / Jitters / Tuesday at ten / Undecided blues / I do

mean you / 9.20 Special / H & J.
**2 LP Set:** Released Jul '86, on CBS by CBS Records. Catalogue no: **CBS 88672**
**Cass:** Released Jul '86, on CBS by CBS Records. Catalogue no: **40 88672**

**COUNT BASIE-VOL.4 (One o' clock jump)**
Tracks: / Goin' to Chicago blues / You betcha my life / Down down down / Tune town shuffle / I'm tired of waiting for you / One two three O'Leary / Basie boogie / Fancy meeting you / Diggin' for Dex / My old flame / Fiesta in blue / Tom Thumb / Take me back baby / King Joe (pt.I) / King Joe (pt.2) / Moon nocturne / Something new / I struck a match in the dark / In the dark / Platterbrains / All of me / Feather merchant / Down for double / More than you know / Havard blues / Coming out party / One o'clock jump / Blue shadows and white gardenias / Ay now / Basie blues.
**2 LP Set:** Released Jul '86, on CBS by CBS Records. Catalogue no: **CBS 88673**
**Cass:** Released Jul '86, on CBS by CBS Records. Catalogue no: **40 88673**

**COUNT BASIE-VOL. 5**
**Cass:** Released Sep '86, on CBS by CBS Records. Catalogue no: **40 88674**
**2 LP Set:** Released Sep '86, on CBS by CBS Records. Catalogue no: **CBS 88674**

**COUNT BASIE-VOL. 6**
**Cass:** Released Sep '86, on CBS by CBS Records. Catalogue no: **40 88675**
**2 LP Set:** Released Sep '86, on CBS by CBS Records. Catalogue no: **CBS 88675**

**COUNT ON THE COAST**
**Album:** Released '88, on Phontastic (Sweden) Catalogue no: **PHONT 7546**

**COUNT ON THE COAST, VOL. 1 1958 (Basie, Count & Joe Williams)**
**CD:** Released '88, on Phontastic (Sweden) Catalogue no: **PHONTCD 7555**
**Album:** Released Jan '85, on Phontastic (Sweden) Catalogue no: **PHONT 7555**

**COUNT ON THE COAST VOL. 3**
**Cass:** Released Oct '87, on Phontastic (Sweden) Catalogue no: **PHONT 8575**
**Album:** Released Jan '87, on Phontastic (Sweden) Catalogue no: **PHONT 7575**

**CUTE (Basie, Count Orchestra)**
Tracks: / Cute / Li'l darlin'.
**7" Single:** Released Feb '81, on Vogue by Vogue Records. Deleted Feb '84. Catalogue no: **7VJ 101**

**DANCE ALONG WITH BASIE**
**Album:** Released Oct '88, on Vogue by Vogue Records. Catalogue no: **500011**

**DECEMBER 1962 (Basie, Count & His Orchestra)**
Tracks: / Just before midnight / Comin' through the rye / Sometimes I feel like a motherless child / Evil weevil / Basically blue / Splash / Danny boy / Wash / Clementine Annie Laurie / Swing low sweet chariot.
**Album:** Released Oct '80, on Jazz Vault Catalogue no: **JV 102**

**DOCUMENT**
Tracks: / Moten swing / One o'clock jump / I can't get started / Study in brown, A / Rhythm in my nursery rhymes / John's idea / Good morning blues / Dinah / Every tub / Song of the wanderer / Flat foot floogie / Boogie woogie blues.
**Album:** Released May '82, on Nostalgia by Mainline Records. Catalogue no: **NOST 7640**

**DOWN FOR THE COUNT**
**CD:** Released Jan '90, on Jazz-Up Catalogue no: **JU 303**

**DOWN FOR TROUBLE**
Tracks: / Something new / I struck a match in the dark / Platterbrains / All of me / Feather merchant / Down for double / My old flame / Fiesta in blue / Tom Thumb.
**Cass:** Released Apr '86, on Castle Showcase by Castle Communications Records. Catalogue no: **SHTC 105**
**Album:** Released Apr '86, on Castle Showcase by Castle Communications Records. Catalogue no: **SHLP 105**

**EASIN' IT**
**Album:** Released Oct '88, on Vogue by Vogue Records. Catalogue no: **500019**

**ESSENTIAL COUNT BASIE VOL.1**
Tracks: / Lady be good / Goin' to Chicago Blues / Love tonight / Live and love tonight / Love me or leave me / Rockabye basie / Baby don't tell on me / If I could be with you one more hour tonight / Taxi war dance / Jump for me / Twelfth St. rag / Miss thing (part 1) / Miss thing (part 2) / Pound cake / How long blues.
**Album:** Released 27 Feb '88, on CBS (import) by CBS Records. Catalogue no: **4600611**
**Cass:** Released 27 Feb '88, on CBS (import) by CBS Records. Catalogue no: **4600614**

**ESSENTIAL COUNT BASIE VOL.2**
Tracks: / I can't believe that you're in love... / Clap hands, here comes Charlie / Dickie's dream / Lester leaps in / Apple jump, The / I left my baby / Volcano / Between the devil and the deep blue sea / I never knew / Tickle toe / Louisiana / Easy does it / Let me see / Blow top / Gone with "what" wind / Super chief.
**Album:** Released 14 Aug '88, on CBS by CBS Records. Catalogue no: **460828 1**
**Cass:** Released 14 Aug '88, on CBS by CBS Records. Catalogue no: **460828 4**

**ESSENTIAL COUNT BASIE VOL 3, THE**
Tracks: / World is mad, The (part 1) / Moten swing / What's your number / Broadway / Rockin' the blues / Jitters / Undecided blues / 9.20 special / World is mad, The (part 2) / I want a little girl / Love jumped out / Stampede in G minor / Jump the blues away / Tuesday at ten / I do mean you / Feedin' the bean.
**Album:** Released Apr '89, on CBS (import) by CBS Records. Catalogue no: **461 098 1**
**CD:** Released Apr '89, on CBS (import) by CBS Records. Catalogue no: **461 098 2**
**Cass:** Released Apr '89, on CBS (import) by CBS Records. Catalogue no: **461 098 4**

**EVERYDAY I HAVE THE BLUES**
**Album:** Released Oct '88, on Vogue by Vogue Records. Catalogue no: **500010**

**FANCY PANTS (Basie, Count & His Orchestra)**
Tracks: / Put it right there / By my side / Blue chip / Fancy pants / Hi five / Time stream / Samantha / Strike up the band.
**CD:** Released Apr '87, on Pablo Jazz (USA) by Pablo Records (USA). Catalogue no: **CD 231 0920**
**Album:** Released Dec '86, on Pablo Jazz (USA) by Pablo Records (USA). Catalogue no: **231 0920**
**Cass:** Released Dec '86, on Pablo Jazz (USA) by Pablo Records (USA). Catalogue no: **K10 920**

**FARMERS MARKET BARBEQUE**
Tracks: / Way out Basie / St. Louis blues / Beaver Junction / Lester leaps in / Blues for the barbeque / I don't know yet / Ain't that something / Jumpin' at the Woodside.
**CD:** Released Apr '86, on Pablo Jazz (USA) by Pablo Records (USA). Catalogue no: **J33J 20056**

**FIRST RECORDS HE EVER MADE, THE**
**Cass:** Released Aug '79, on Sandy Hook (USA) Catalogue no: **K10 833**
**Album:** Released Aug '79, on Sandy Hook (USA) Catalogue no: **SH 2017**

**FIRST TIME COUNT MEETS DUKE**
Tracks: / Battle royal / To you / Take the 'A' train / Until I met you / Wild man / Segue in C / B.D.B. / Jumpin' at the woodside.
**Cass:** Released 27 Feb '88, on CBS (import) by CBS Records. Catalogue no: **450 509 4**
**CD:** Released 27 Feb '88, on CBS (import) by CBS Records. Catalogue no: **450 509 2**
**Album:** Released 27 Feb '88, on CBS (import) by CBS Records. Catalogue no: **450 509 1**

**FIRST TIME WITH DUKE ELLINGTON**
**Album:** Released Jun '86, on CBS (import) by CBS Records. Catalogue no: **84417**
**Cass:** Released Jun '86, on CBS by CBS Records. Catalogue no: **40 84417**

**FOR THE FIRST TIME**
Tracks: / Baby Lawrence / Pres / I'll always be in love with you / Blues in the church / Lady be good / Lady be good (concept II) / Blues in the alley / As long as I live / Song of the islands / Royal Garden blues / Un-easy does it / O.P.
Note: Personnel: Count Basie- piano , organ/Ray Brown- bass/Louis Bellson- drums.
**CD:** Released Apr '86, on Pablo Jazz (USA) by Pablo Records (USA). Catalogue no: **J33J 20051**

**FOR THE SECOND TIME (Basie, Count /Kansas City 3)**
Tracks: / Sandman / If I could be with you one hour tonight / Draw / On the sunny side of the street / One I love belongs to somebody else, The / Blues for Eric / I surrender dear / Racehorse.
**Album:** Released Mar '83, on Pablo Jazz (USA) by Pablo Records (USA). Catalogue no: **2310 878**
**Cass:** Released Mar '83, on Pablo Jazz (USA) by Pablo Records (USA). Catalogue no: **K10 878**

**GET TOGETHER**
Tracks: / Ode to pres / Basies bag / Like it used to be / Swinging on the cusp / My main men / I can't get started / What will i tell my heart / Talk of the town / I can't give you anything but love / I'm confessin'.
**CD:** Released Apr '87, on Pablo Jazz (USA) by Pablo Records (USA). Catalogue no: **CD 231 0924**

**GIFTED ONES, THE (Basie, Count & Dizzy Gillespie)**
Tracks: / Back to the land / Constantinople / You got it / St. James Infirmary / Follow the leader / Ow.
**Album:** Released '82, on Pablo Jazz (USA) by Pablo Records (USA). Catalogue no: **231 0833**
**Cass:** Released '82, on Pablo Jazz (USA) by Pablo Records (USA). Catalogue no: **K10 833**

**GOLDEN YEARS, VOL.1, THE 1937**
Tracks: / Shout and feel it / You and me that used to be, The / Count steps in, The / They can;t take that away from me / I'll always be in love with you / When my dreamboat comes home / Swing, brother, swing / Bugle blues / I got rhythm / One o'clock jump / I can't get started / Study in brown, A / Rhythm in my nursery rhymes / John's idea / Good morning blues / Dinah.
**Album:** Released '88, on EPM by EPM Records. Catalogue no: **FDC 5502**

**GOLDEN YEARS, VOL.2, THE 1938**
Tracks: / Allez-oop / Blues with Helen / I ain't got nobody / Don't be that way / Song of the wanderer / Mortgage stomp / Every tub / Song of the wanderer / Flat foot floogie / Lady be good / Boogie woogie / One o'clock jump / I let a song go out of my heart / King Porter stomp / I haven't changed a thing.
**Album:** Released '88, on EPM by EPM Records. Catalogue no: **FDC 5510**

**GOLDEN YEARS, VOL.3, THE 1940/44**
Tracks: / One o'clock jump / Ebony rhapsody / Riff interlude / Darn that dream / Take it, pres / Baby, don't you tell on me / One hour / I got rhythm / Do nothing till you hear from me / Sent for you yesterday / Basie boogie / I've found a new baby / Rock-a-bye Basie / Swing shift / Red band boogie / Dinah / Baby, won't you please come home.
**Album:** Released '88, on EPM by EPM Records. Catalogue no: **FDC 5521**

**GOOD MORNIN' BLUES (Big band bounce & boogie) (Basie, Count / Jimmy Rushing)**
Tracks: / Good morning blues / Listen, my children / Exactly like you / London Bridge is falling down / Stop beatin' around the mulberry bush / Now, will you be good? / Boo hoo / Blues I like to hear, The / Blues in the dark / Pennies from Heaven / Boogie woogie / Evil blues / Don't you miss your baby? / Georgianna / I keep remembering / Do you wanna jump, children?.
**Album:** on Affinity by Charly Records. Catalogue no: **AFS 1002**

**GREAT CONCERT OF COUNT BASIE & HIS ORCHESTRA (Basie, Count & His Orchestra)**
Tracks: / All of me / Flight of the foo birds / Boone blues / Stormy Monday blues / Magic flea, The / Wee baby blues / In a mellow tone / Whirly bird / Night in Tunisia / Hittin' twelve / Cherokee / Midnight sun will never set, The / Blues for Eileen / Jumpin' at the woodside / April in Paris / I got rhythm / I needs to be'd with / Lil' darlin' / All heart / One o'clock jump.
**2 LP Set:** Released Apr '84, on Musidisc by Musidisc Records (France). Catalogue no: **ALB 231**

**HALL OF FAME: COUNT BASIE**
Tracks: / One o'clock jump / Study in brown / Rhythm in my nursery rhymes / Good morning blues / Shout and feel it / I'll always be in love with you / Count steps in, The / I got rhythm / When my dreamboat comes home / Bugle blues.
**Album:** Released Jan '77, on Black Lion Deleted '82. Catalogue no: **BLPS 20153**

**HAVE A NICE DAY**
Tracks: / Have a nice day / Plunger, The / Jamie / It's about time / This way / Scott's place / Doin' Basie's thing / Spirit is willing, The / Small talk / You'n'me / Feelin' free.
Note: Personnel: Paul Cohen / George 'Sonny' Cohn / George Minger / Waymond Reed / Al Grey / Bill Hughes / Grover Mitchell / Melvin Wanzo / John Watson Sr. / Bobby 'Jersey Bounce' Plater / Eric Dixon / Curtis Peagler / J.C. Williams / Eddie 'Lockjaw' Davis / Count William Basie / Freddie Green / Norman 'Dewey' Keenan / Harold Jones.
**CD:** Released Dec '85, on Verve (USA) by Polydor Ltd. Catalogue no: **824 867-2**

**HIGH VOLTAGE**
**CD:** Released '85, on Polydor by Polydor Ltd. Deleted Jul '88. Catalogue no: **825 194-2**
**CD:** Released Aug '85, on Polydor by Polydor Ltd. Deleted '88. Catalogue no: **781263 2**

**I GOT RHYTHM**
**Album:** Released Jan '81, on Affinity by Charly Records. Deleted May '88. Catalogue no: **AFF 48**

**I TOLD YOU SO**
Tracks: / Tree frog / Flirt / Blues for Alfy / Something to live for / Plain brown wrapper / Swee' pea / Too close for comfort / Told you so / Git, The.
**CD:** Released Jul '86, on Pablo Jazz (USA) by Pablo Records (USA). Catalogue no: **J33J 20020**

**IN DISCO ORDER VOL.1**
**Album:** Released Feb '78, on Ajax (USA) Catalogue no: **AJAX 126**

**IN EUROPE**
Tracks: / Hittin' twelve / Freckle face / Things ain't what they used to be / Whirlybird / More I see you, The / Orange sherbert / Way out Basie / Basie / Jumpin' at the woodside.
**CD:** Released '88, on Denon Catalogue no: **C38-7481**

**INDISPENSABLE COUNT BASIE, THE**
Tracks: / Bill's mill / Brand new wagon / One o'clock boogie / Futuile frustration / Swingin' the blues / St. Louis boogie / Basie's basement / Backstage at Stuff's / My buddy / Shine on harvest moon / Lopin' / I never knew / Sugar / Jungle king / I ain't mad at you / After you've gone / House rent boogie / South / Don't you want a man like me / Seventh Avenue express / Sophisticated swing / Guest in a nest / Your red wagon / Money is honey / Just a minute / Robbin's nest / Hey pretty baby / Bye bye baby / Just an old manuscript / She's a wine-o / Shoutin' blues / Wonderful thing / Mine too / Walking slow behind you / Normania / Rat race / Sweets.
**2 LP Set:** Released '83, on RCA (France) by BMG Records (France). Catalogue no: **PM 43688**

**JAZZ LEGENDS (Holiday, Billie & Count Basie)**
**Cass set:** Released '88, on Ditto by Pickwick Records. Catalogue no: **DTO 10256**

**JAZZ TIME VOL.18**
**Album:** Released '88, on Vogue (France) by Vogue Records. Catalogue no: **502718**

**JITTERS - 1939/41, THE**
**Album:** Released Mar '77, on Tax Catalogue no: **M 8027**

**JUBILEE 1904-1984**
**Album:** Released Jul '88, on Vanstory Catalogue no: **VS 3407**
**Cass:** Released Jul '88, on Vanstory Catalogue no: **VSK 3407**

**JUBILEE ALTERNATIVES (Basie, Count Orchestra)**
**CD:** Released Mar '90, on Hep Jazz by Hep Records. Catalogue no: **HEPCD 38**

**JUMPIN' WITH BASIE**
**Album:** Released '89, on Vogue by Vogue Records. Catalogue no: **VG JL 71**
**Album:** Released '88, on Vogue by Vogue Records. Catalogue no: **500071**

**JUST THE BLUES (Basie, Count & Joe Williams)**
**Album:** Released Oct '88, on Vogue by Vogue Records. Catalogue no: **500017**

**KANSAS CITY 5**
Tracks: / Jive at five / One o'clock jump / No special thing / Memories of you / Frog's blues / Rabbit / Perdido / Timekeeper / Mean to me / Blues for Joe Turner.
**Album:** Released May '82, on Pablo Jazz (USA) by Pablo Records (USA). Catalogue no: **231 2126**
**Cass:** Released May '82, on Pablo Jazz (USA) by Pablo Records (USA). Catalogue no: **K 12 126**

**KANSAS CITY 6**
Tracks: / Walking the blues / Blues for little jazz / Vegas drag / Wee baby / Scooter / St. Louis blues / Opus six.
**Album:** Released Sep '82, on Pablo Jazz (USA) by Pablo Records (USA). Catalogue no: **2310 871**
**Cass:** Released Sep '82, on Pablo Jazz (USA) by Pablo Records (USA). Catalogue no: **K10 871**

**KANSAS CITY 7**
Tracks: / Oh lady be good / Secrets / I want a little girl / Shoe shine boy / Count's place / Senator Whitehead / Tally ho Mr. Basie! / What'cha talkin'?.
**CD:** on Pablo Jazz (USA) by Pablo Records (USA). Catalogue no: **J33J 20007**
**Album:** Released Dec '84, on Pablo Jazz (USA) by Pablo Records (USA). Catalogue no: **231 0908**
**Cass:** Released Dec '84, on Pablo Jazz (USA) by Pablo Records (USA). Catalogue no: **K10 908**

**KANSAS CITY 8 (Get together)**
Tracks: / Ode to Pres / Basie's bag / Swinging on the cusp / Like it used to be / My main men / Pretty time / I can't get started / What will I tell my heart / Talk of the town / I can't give you anything but love / I'm confessin'.
**Cass:** Released Jan '87, on Pablo Jazz (USA) by Pablo Records (USA). Catalogue no: **K10 924**
**Album:** Released Jan '87, on Pablo Jazz (USA) by Pablo Records (USA). Catalogue no: **231 0924**

**KANSAS CITY SHOUT (Basie, Count, Joe Turner, Eddie Vinson)**
Tracks: / My jug & I / Cherry red / Apollo daze / Standing on the corner / Stormy Monday / Signifying / Just a dream on my mind / Blues for Joe Turner / Blues for Joel / Everyday I have the blues / Blues au four.
**Cass:** Released '82, on Pablo Jazz (USA) by Pablo Records (USA). Catalogue no: **K10 859**
**Album:** Released '82, on Pablo Jazz (USA) by Pablo Records (USA). Catalogue no: **D 2310 859**

**KANSAS CITY SOUL (Basie, Count/J Turner/ E Vinson)**
**CD:** Released '88, on Pablo Jazz (USA) by Pablo Records (USA). Catalogue no: **131 125 2**

**KANSAS CITY STYLE**
Tracks: / Aces and faces / Don't cry baby / Just an old manuscript / One o'clock jump (partial) / Mad boogie / One o'clock jump / You for me / Bubbles / You're not the kind / Jonesy / Two for the blues / Cleep, clop blues / Yesterdays / Perdido.
**Album:** Released Jun '86, on Giants of Jazz by Hasmick Promotions. Catalogue no: **GOJ 1004**
**Cass:** Released Jun '88, on Giants of Jazz by Hasmick Promotions. Catalogue no: **GOJC 1004**
**Album:** Released '88, on RCA by BMG Records (UK). Catalogue no: **AFM 1-5180**

**KANSAS CITY SUITE**
**CD:** Released '86, on Vogue by Vogue Records. Catalogue no: **VG 600 037**
**Album:** Released Oct '88, on Vogue by Vogue Records. Catalogue no: **500018**

**KING OF SWING**
**Album:** Released Apr '89, on Polydor by Polydor Ltd. Catalogue no: **837 433-1**
**Cass:** Released Apr '89, on Polydor by Polydor Ltd. Catalogue no: **837 433-4**

**LA CABARET CASINO BAHAMAS (Live stereo - 1969) (Basie, Count Band) (See panel below)**
Tracks: / All of me / Frankie & Johnny / Cute / Lonely Street / Cherokee / Does anyone ever win ? / Night in Tunisia, A / Little darlin' / Blues in Hosses flat.
Note: At the time of his death from cancer in April 1984, Count Basie had been leading a big band almost continuously since 1956. Although he didn't live to celebrate his fiftieth anniversary as a bandleader, celebrations in honour of Mister Basie will be going on, I believe, as long as civilization endures. His enormous popularity rivals that of the current demand for Duke Ellington material. Unlike Duke, Count didn't compose or arrange, nor was he among the great jazz instrumentalists. He was, however, a leader and a catalyst - a kind of presence that transcended his tangible contributions. In this program, captured live in Count's back-yard (he owned property in the Bahamas), his banter with the audience has been included to provide an insight into the Basie enigma for those listeners not privileged to have witnessed him in person. Count's impish humour and relaxed manner is evident as he spontaneously titles the fine instrumental track opening side two by asking the casino audience the rhetorical question: Does anyone ever win? Count liked to begin his club shows in later years with Billy Byers' arrangement of *All of me*, which spotlights the leader's distinctive piano stylings. The old standard 'Frankie and Johnny' is punctuated by the late Bobby Plater's broad-toned alto sax and the fine plunger work of Sonny Cohn, who incidentally still plays in the Basie band while doubling as road manager. The Basie standard 'Cut' fea-

**Count Basie - La Cabaret Casino Bahamas (Jazz Band)**

tures Rufus 'Speedy' Jones at the sticks and some tasty flute by Eric Dixon. Marshal played a number of alto sax features during those nineteen years, but none more beautifullly than Samy Nestico's *Lonely Street*. The celebrated 1939 Basie recording of *Cherokee* was a two sided 10-inch 78 that had Chu Berry and Lester Young together in the sax section. Thirty years later Eddie 'Lockjaw' Davis plays powerfully on this rarely performed arrangement of Ray Noble's classic tune. Perhaps the highlight of the first volume in this welcome series is the spectacular trumpet work of Oscar Brashear who also now resides in Los Angeles. Oscar is an under-recognized artist whose playing recalls the great Freddy Webster and we are lucky to have this fine example of his work that was recorded commercially. Neal Hefti's 1956 chart of *Lil darlin'* has been a crowd favourite over the years, contrasting as it does with the normal, more rhythmic Basie style. Notice Count's quote of solitude at the ending and more of Sonny Cohn in *A subdued mood*. While conducting the present day Basie band, Frank Foster plays his excellent tenor sax sparingly and finds even less time for composing or arranging - two of his great talents. On *Blues in hoss flat*, which dates from 1955, we hear the 1969 edition of the orchestra at its best. Part of the reason is the simple fact that the band was in residence for a few nights on Nassau and enjoying a respite from the rigors of the one-night trail. Also, the men always enjoyed tour stops like Reno, Las Vegas and, most especially. (Edgar Ward, San Diego, California, October, 1987)
**Album:** Released Jan '88, on Jazz Band by Flyright Records. Catalogue no: **EB 405**

**LAST DECADE, THE**
**2 LP Set:** Released Sep '86, on Artistry Catalogue no: **AR 2 107**

**LE DOUBLE DISQUE D'OR**
**2 LP Set:** Released Oct '88, on Vogue by Vogue Records. Catalogue no: **400525**

**LEGEND, THE**
**Album:** Released Oct '88, on Vogue by Vogue Records. Catalogue no: **500021**

**LEGEND, THE LEGACY, THE (Basie, Count Orchestra)**
Note: Directed by Frank Foster. Playing time 60:38.
**CD:** Released Nov '89, on Denon Catalogue no: **CY 73790**

**LESTER LEAPS IN VOL.2 (Basie, Count & His Orchestra)**
Tracks: / Dickie's dream / Lester leaps in / Song of the islands / Riff interlude / Volcano / Hollywood jump / Someday sweetheart / Tickle toe / Superchief.
**2 LP Set:** Released Sep '89, on CBS by CBS Records. Catalogue no: **88668**

**LESTER MEETS BASIE (Air Shots Birdland,Jan. 1953) (Basie, Count Orchestra)**
Tracks: / Theme & prevue / Jingle bells / Why not? / Hob nail boogie / Perdido / Fancy meeting you / Basie kicks / Jumpin' at the Woodside / Bread / Smooth sailing.
Note: Trumpets: W.Culley / R.Jones / P.Campbell / J.Newman/ Trombones: H.Coker / B.Powell / J.Wilkins / Alto sax: M.Royal / E.Wilkins / Tenor sax: P.Quinchette / Eddie'Lockjaw'Davis / Lester Young / Baritone sax: C.Fowlkes / Guitar: F.Greene / Bass: G.Ramsey / Piano: Count Basie / Drums: G.Johnson.
**Album:** Released Apr '81, on Unique Jazz by Spotlite Records. Catalogue no: **UJ 04**

**LESTER MEETS BASIE VOL.2 (Air Shots Birdland,Jan. 1953) (Basie, Count Orchestra)**
Tracks: / Basie English / Basie blues / Paradise squat / Every tub.
Note: Personnel: Trumpets: W.Culley,R.Jones,J.Newman,P.Campbell/Alto sax: H.Coker,B.Powell,J.Wilkins,M.Royal,E.Wilkins/ Tenor sax: P.Quinchette,Eddie 'Lockjaw'Davis,Lester Young/ Baritone sax: C.Fowlkes/ Guitar: F.Greene/ Bass: G.Ramsey/ Piano: Count Basie/ Drums: G.Johnson.
**Album:** Released Apr '81, on Unique Jazz by Spotlite Records. Catalogue no: **UJ 05**

**LESTER - AMADEUS 1936-38 (Basie, Count & Lester Young)**
**CD:** Released '88, on Phontastic (Sweden) Catalogue no: **PHONTCD 7639**

**LET'S JUMP - 1943/44 (Basie, Count & His Orchestra)**
**Album:** Released Jul '82, on Golden Era by Delta Records. Catalogue no: **GELP 15033**

**LIL' OL' GROOVEMASTER**
Tracks: / Pleasingly plump / Body rumble / Belly roll / Count 'em / Nasty Magnus / Dum dum / Lullaby for Jolie / Kansas City wrinkles / Li'l ol' groovemaker...Basie.
**CD:** Released Sep '86, on Verve Deleted Mar '88. Catalogue no: **821 799-2**

**LISTEN, YOU SHALL HEAR (Basie, Count & His Orchestra)**
**CD:** Released Feb '89, on Hep Jazz by Hep Records. Catalogue no: **HEPCD 1025**
**Album:** Released Jun '88, on Hep Jazz by Hep Records. Catalogue no: **HEP 1025**

**LIVE 1954 AT THE SAVOY BALLROOM, NEW YORK (Basie, Count & His Orchestra)**
**CD:** Released '88, on Delta (1) by Delta Records. Catalogue no: **11 089**

**LIVE AT MONTREUX: COUNT BASIE '77 (Basie Big Band)**
**CD:** on Pablo Jazz (USA) by Pablo Records (USA). Deleted '88. Catalogue no: **J33J 20019**

**LIVE AT THE SAVOY BALLROOM**
**Album:** Released Nov '84, on Astan (USA) Catalogue no: **20076**
**Cass:** Released Nov '84, on Astan (USA) Catalogue no: **40076**

**LIVE FROM BIRDLAND**
**Album:** Released May '80, on Vogue by Vogue Records. Catalogue no: **VJD 568**

**LIVE IN ANTIBES 1968**
Tracks: / Vine Street rumble / Pleasingly plump / Cherokee / Good times blues / Lonely Street / Night in Tunisia / Goin' to Chicago blues / I've got rhythm / In a mellow tone / Basie's / Lil' darlin' / Blues in Hoss's flat / Everyday I have the blues / Wee baby blues / Stormy Monday blues / Magic flute / Jumpin' at the woodside.
**Album:** Released Jun '88, on France's Concert Catalogue no: **FC 112**
**CD:** Released Jun '88, on France's Concert Catalogue no: **FCD 112**

**LIVE IN JAPAN '78**
Tracks: / Heat's on ,The / Freckle face / Ja da / Things ain't what they used to be / Bit of this & a bit of that, A / All of me / Shiny stockings / Left hand funk / John the III / Basie / Black velvet / Jumpin' at the Woodside.
Note: Personnel: Count Basie / Waymon Reed / Pete Minger / Sonny Cohns / Noran Smith Jr / Mel Wanzo / Bill Hughes / Dennis Wilson/Alonzo Wesley Jnr. / Bobby Plater / Danny Turner / Kenny Hing / Eric Dixon / Charlie Fowlkes / Freddie Greene / John Clayton / Butch Miles. A well balanced programme from the Basie book, with contributions from sise man Frank Foster-'Shiny stockings', Ernie Wilkins 'Basie' & Sam Nestico who wrote prolifically for the Basie Band. As well as these there are favourites like 'Jumpin' at the Woodside' & 'All of me' which was often used to spotlight singer Joe Williams.We expect good reviews for this previously unreleased album.
**Cass:** Released Sep '85, on Pablo Jazz (USA) by Pablo Records (USA). Catalogue no: **K 8246**
**Album:** Released Sep '85, on Pablo Jazz (USA) by Pablo Records (USA). Catalogue no: **230 8246**
**CD:** Released Jul '86, on Pablo Jazz (USA) by Pablo Records (USA). Catalogue no: **J33J 20042**

**LIVE IN NASSAU (Basie, Count Band)**
**Album:** Released Mar '90, on Jazz Band by Flyright Records. Catalogue no: **EB414**

**LIVE IN PERSON (Basie, Count Orchestra)**
**Album:** Released '79, on Natural Organic (USA) Catalogue no: **NAT:ORG:7002**

**LIVE IN STOCKHOLM (Feb, 1959) (Basie, Count Orchestra)**
**Album:** Released '88, on Magic (1) by Submarine Records. Catalogue no: **AWE 15**

**LONG LIVE THE CHIEF (Basie, Count & His Orchestra)**
Tracks: / You got it / April in Paris / Misunderstood blues / Autumn leaves / Foggy day, A / Hey, see you over there / Lil' darlin' / Bus dust / Corner pocket / Doctor Feelgood / Four five six / Shiny stockings.
**CD:** Released Jan '87, on Denon Catalogue no: **CY 1018**
**Cass:** Released Oct '88, on Denon Catalogue no: **CC 11**

**MASTERS OF JAZZ**
**Album:** Released '83, on RCA (Germany) Catalogue no: **CL.42113**

**ME AND YOU**
**CD:** Released May '86, on Pablo Jazz (USA) by Pablo Records (USA). Catalogue no: **CD 231 0891**

**MEMORIAL**
**Album:** Released '84, on First Heard by Submarine Records. Catalogue no: **FH 55**
**Cass:** Released Oct '84, on First Heard by Submarine Records. Catalogue no: **CFH 55**

**MEMORIES AD LIB**
**Album:** Released Oct '88, on Vogue by Vogue Records. Catalogue no: **500004**

**MONTREUX 77 (Basie, Count Big Band)**
**CD:** Released May '86, on Pablo Jazz (USA) by Pablo Records (USA). Catalogue no: **CD 20019**

**MOSTLY BLUES AND SOME OTHERS (Basie, Count Kansas City Seven)**
Tracks: / I'll always be in love with you / Snooky / Blues for Charlie Christian / Jaws / I'm confessin' / I want a little girl / Blues in C / Brio.
**Cass:** Released Jul '86, on Pablo Jazz (USA) by Pablo Records (USA). Catalogue no: **K10 919**
**Album:** Released Jul '86, on Pablo Jazz (USA) by Pablo Records (USA). Catalogue no: **231 0919**
**CD:** Released Feb '87, on Pablo Jazz (USA) by Pablo Records (USA). Catalogue no: **CD 231 0919**

**NIGHT RIDER (Basie, Count & Oscar Peterson)**
Tracks: / Night rider / Memories of you / 9.20 Special / Sweet Lorraine / It's a wonderful world / Blues for Pamela.
**Album:** Released '82, on Pablo Jazz (USA) by Pablo Records (USA). Catalogue no: **231 0843**
**Cass:** Released '82, on Pablo Jazz (USA) by Pablo Records (USA). Catalogue no: **K10 843**

**NOT NOW, I'LL TELL YOU WHEN**
**Album:** Released Oct '88, on Vogue by Vogue Records. Catalogue no: **500016**

**ON THE ROAD**
Tracks: / Wind machine, The / Blues for Stephanie / John the III / There'll never be another you / Bootie's blues / Splanky / Basie / Watch what happens / Work song / In a mellow tone.
**CD:** on Pablo Jazz (USA) by Pablo Records (USA). Catalogue no: **CD 231 2112**
**Album:** Released '82, on Pablo Jazz (USA) by Pablo Records (USA). Catalogue no: **231 2112**
**Cass:** Released '82, on Pablo Jazz (USA) by Pablo Records (USA). Catalogue no: **K 12 112**

**ON THE ROAD '79**
**CD:** Released May '86, on Pablo Jazz (USA) by Pablo Records (USA). Catalogue no: **CD 31121**

**ONE O'CLOCK JUMP**
Tracks: / One o'clock jump / When my dreamboat comes home / I got rhythm in my nursery rhymes / John's idea / Good morning blues / Dinah / Shout and fell about / I'll always be in love with you / Count steps in, The / I got rhythm / Study in brown, A / Bugle blues.
Note: Personnel: Buck Clayton/Eddie Durham/Earle warren/Lester Young/Freddie greene/Walter Page/Jo Jones. Recorded 1939.
**Cass:** Released Jun '86, on Astan (USA) Catalogue no: **40177**

**OUR SHINING HOUR (Basie, Count & Sammy Davis Jnr.)**
**Album:** Released Aug '89, on Verve Catalogue no: **837 446 1**

**PERDIDO (Basie, Count & Sarah Vaughan)**
**Album:** Released Oct '88, on Vogue by Vogue Records. Catalogue no: **500012**

**PLAYS BENNY CARTER'S KANSAS CITY SUITE**
Tracks: / Vine Street rumble / Katy-do / Miss Missouri / Jackson County Jubilee / Sunset glow / Wiggle walk / Meetin' time / Paseo promenade / Blue five jive / Rompin' at the Reno / Trot, The / Easy money / Amoroso / Goin' on / Swizzle / Legend, The / Who's blues / Turnabout.
**Cass:** Released May '83, on Vogue Jazz (France) by Vogue Records. Catalogue no: **ZCVJD 569**
**Album:** Released May '83, on Vogue Jazz (France) by Vogue Records. Catalogue no: **VJD 569**

**PLAYS QUINCY JONES & NEAL HEFTI**
**CD:** Released Dec '86, on Vogue by Vogue Records. Catalogue no: **VGCD 600108**

**PRIME TIME**
Tracks: / Prime time / Bundle o'funk / Sweet Georgia Brown / Featherweight / Reachin' out / Ja da / Great debate, The / Ya gotta try.
**CD:** Released Jul '86, on Pablo Jazz (USA) by Pablo Records (USA). Catalogue no: **J33J 20018**

**RHYTHM MEN**
**Cass:** Released '84, on Swing House by Submarine Records. Catalogue no: **CSWH 23**
**Album:** Released '84, on Swing House by Submarine Records. Catalogue no: **SWH 23**

**ROCK-A-BYE BASIE**
Tracks: / Jumping at the Woodside / Blue & sentimental / Red Bank boogie / Sent for you yesterday / Yesterday / Shorty George / Rockabye Basie / Every tub / Jive at five / Down for trouble / Boogie woogie / Taps Miller / Swinging the blues / Broadway / Texas shuffle / Tickle toe / Doggin' around / Dickie's dream / Topsy / Lester leaps in / Time out / 9.20 Special / Avenue C / Out the window.
**Album:** Released Jun '83, on Vogue Jazz (USA) by Vogue Records. Catalogue no: **VJD 503**
**Album:** Released '88, on Swing House by Submarine Records. Catalogue no: **SWH 41**

**SEND IN THE CLOWNS (Basie, Count & Sarah Vaughan)**
**Cass:** Released '82, on Pablo Jazz (USA) by Pablo Records (USA). Catalogue no: **K 12 130**
**Album:** Released '82, on Pablo Jazz (USA) by Pablo Records (USA). Catalogue no: **231 2130**

**SING ALONG WITH BASIE**
**Album:** Released Oct '88, on Vogue by Vogue Records. Catalogue no: **500003**
**CD:** Released Dec '86, on Vogue by Vogue Records. Catalogue no: **VG 600 094**

**SOUTHLAND CAFE (Basie, Count Orchestra & Chick Webb Orchestra)**
Tracks: / One o'clock jump / Ebony rhapsody / Riff interlude / Take it Prez / Baby don't you tell on me/ Breakin' 'em down / If I didn't care / Stars and stripes forever / My wild Irish rose/ Chew, chew, chew, chew (your bubble gum).
**Album:** Released Apr '81, on Joker (USA) by Lifetime Records (USA). Catalogue no: **SM 3084**

**SOUTHLAND CAFE 1940 (Basie, Count & Duke Ellington)**
**CD:** Released Oct '89, on Jazz Anthology by Musidisc Records (France). Catalogue no: **550 022**

**STANDING OVATION - THREE ERAS OF BASIE**
Tracks: / Down for trouble / Li'l darlin' / Broadway / Jive at five / Cherry Point / Jumpin' at the Woodside / One o'clock jump / Shiny stockings / Blue & sentimental / Every rub / Corner pocket / Kid from Red Bank, The.
**Album:** Released Jun '82, on Jasmine by Hasmick Promotions. Deleted Feb '88. Catalogue no: **JAS 30**

**Cass:** Released Jun '82, on Jasmine by Hasmick Promotions. Catalogue no: **JAS C30**

**STEREO SOUND OF COUNT BASIE, THE**
**Album:** Released Apr '79, on Bright Orange Catalogue no: **BO 702**

**STORMY MONDAY BLUES (Basie, Count & Billy Eckstine)**
**Album:** Released Oct '88, on Vogue by Vogue Records. Catalogue no: **500008**

**STRIKE UP THE BAND (Basie, Count & Tony Bennett)**
**Album:** Released Oct '88, on Vogue by Vogue Records. Catalogue no: **500005**

**STRING ALONG WITH BASIE**
**Album:** Released Oct '88, on Vogue by Vogue Records. Catalogue no: **500013**
**Album:** Released Mar '89, on Sonet by Sonet Records. Catalogue no: **SNTF 1005**

**SWINGIN' AT THE DAISY CHAIN**
Tracks: / Swingin' at the Daisy Chain / Glory of love / My heart belongs to daddy / Cherokee / How long how long blues / Dirty dozens / Honeysuckle rose / Thursday / One o'clock jump / Sing for your supper / Your red wagon / Smarty (you know it all) / Dark rapture / Dupree blues / When the sun goes down / Roseland shuffle.
**Album:** Released '86, on Affinity by Charly Records. Catalogue no: **AFS 1019**

**SWINGIN' THE BLUES (Big band bounce & boogie) (Basie, Count & His Orchestra)**
Tracks: / Swinging the blues / John's idea / Blue and sentimental / Texas shuffle / Panassie stomp / Sent for you yesterday / You can depend on me / Every tub / Jumpin' at the woodside / Time out / Jive at five / Oh lady be good / Shorty George / Out of the window / Topsy / Doggin' around.
**Cass:** Released '86, on Affinity by Charly Records. Catalogue no: **TCAFS 1010**
**Album:** Released Sep '83, on Affinity by Charly Records. Catalogue no: **AFS 1010**

**SWINGIN' THE BLUES (1937-1945) (Basie, Count & His Orchestra)**
**Album:** Released '88, on Joker (USA) by Lifetime Records (USA). Catalogue no: **SM 3968**
**Cass:** Released '88, on Joker (USA) by Lifetime Records (USA). Catalogue no: **MC 3968**

**THIS AND THAT (Very best of Count Basie, The)**
Tracks: / Basie boogie / Sent for you yesterday / Gotta be this or that / Old manuscript, An / Just sittin' & rockin' / I ain't mad about you / My silent love / Lady be good / Theme / Move / One o'clock jump / One golden bullet, Theme from / Andy's blues.
**Cass:** Released Jul '86, on Swing House by Submarine Records. Catalogue no: **CSWH 29**
**Album:** Released Jul '86, on Swing House by Submarine Records. Catalogue no: **SWH 29**

**TOPEKA, KANSAS '55**
**CD:** Released '88, on Jass Catalogue no: **JASSCD 17**

**TOPSY (1937-1945) (Basie, Count & His Orchestra)**
**Cass:** Released '88, on Joker (USA) by Lifetime Records (USA). Catalogue no: **MC 3969**
**Album:** Released '88, on Joker (USA) by Lifetime Records (USA). Catalogue no: **SM 3969**

**V-DISCS, VOL.1**
Tracks: / Basie strides again / Gee baby ain't I good to you / Circus in rhythm / Beaver junction / Kansas City stride / Aunt Hagar's country home / Taps miller / Old manuscript / Playhouse no 2 stomp / On the upbeat / Jimmy's blues / Take me back baby.
**Album:** Released '89, on Jazz Society Catalogue no: **AA 505**
**Album:** on Official by Official Records. Catalogue no: **OFF 3038**

**V DISCS VOL. 2**
Tracks: / Rhythm man / GI stomp / Dance of the gremlins / Yeah man / Harvard blues / San Jose / Jammin' o a v-disc / B glat blues / Sweet Lorraine / High tide / Jimmy's boogie woogie / Tippin' on the QT / Sent for you yesterday / Lady be good.
**Album:** Released '89, on Official by Official Records. Catalogue no: **OFF 3046**
**Album:** Released Mar '87, on Jazz Society Catalogue no: **AA 506**

**VOICES**
**CD:** Released Dec '86, on Vogue by Vogue Records. Catalogue no: **VGCD 600112**

**WARM BREEZE**
Tracks: / C.B. express / After the rain / Warm breeze / Cookie / Flight to Nassau / How sweet it is to be loved by you / Satin doll.
**CD:** Released May '86, on Pablo Jazz (USA) by Pablo Records (USA). Catalogue no: **CD 311240**
**Album:** Released '82, on Pablo Jazz (USA) by Pablo Records (USA). Catalogue no: **D 2312 131**
**Cass:** Released '82, on Pablo Jazz (USA) by Pablo Records (USA). Catalogue no: **K 12 131**

**YESSIR THAT'S MY BABY (Basie, Count & Oscar Peterson)**
Tracks: / Blues for roy / Teach me tonight / Joe turner / Blues for ct / Yes sir thats my baby / After youve gone / Tea for two / Poor butterfly.
Note: See also under Oscar Peterson.
**Album:** Released Mar '87, on Pablo Jazz (USA) by Pablo Records (USA). Catalogue no: **2310923**

## Baton Rouge Blues

**BATON ROUGE BLUES (Various artists)**
Tracks: / I'm a kingbee: *Anderson, Jimmy* / It's half past midnight: *Anderson, Jimmy* / Draft board blues: *Anderson, Jimmy* / Sittin' here wonderin': *Hogan, Silas* / Cigarettes: *Harpo, Slim* / G.I. blues: *Slim, Lightning* / Cold chills: *Grey, Henry* / I'm a lucky man: *Grey, Henry* / Hoodoo party: *Thomas, Tabby* / Bloodstains: *Lazy Lester* / Oh baby: *Dotson, Jimmy* / I need your love: *Dotson, Jimmy* / I don't know why: *Jack, Boogie.*
**Album:** Released Oct '86, on Flyright by Interstate Music. Catalogue no: **FLY 607**

## Baton Rouge Harmonicas

**BATON ROUGE HARMONICAS (Various artists)**
Tracks: / Tell me pretty baby: *Various artists* / Whoa now: *Various artists* / Sad city blues: *Various artists* / Courtroom blues: *Various artists* / One more day: *Various artists* / I'm getting tired: *Various artists* / My poor heart in pain: *Various artists* / Keep on naggin': *Various artists* / In the dark in the park Anderson: *Various artists* / Baby let's burn: *Various artists* / Looking for my baby: *Various artists* / Frankie and Johnnie: *Various artists* / Angel please: *Various artists* / I wanna boogie: *Various artists.*
Note: Featuring: Slim Harpo, Lazy Lester, Sylvester Buckley, Jimmy Dotson.
**Album:** Released '88, on Flyright by Interstate Music. Catalogue no: **FLY 614**

## Battle Of The Big Bands

**BATTLE OF THE BIG BANDS (Various artists)**
**Album:** Released Jun '81, on RCA by BMG Records (UK). Catalogue no: **RCALP 5015**
**Album:** Released Mar '82, on RCA by BMG Records (UK). Catalogue no: **RCALP 3067**
**Cass:** Released Mar '82, on RCA by BMG Records (UK). Catalogue no: **RCAK 3067**

**BATTLE OF THE BIG BANDS 1 (Various artists)**
**Album:** Released Apr '79, on Bright Orange Catalogue no: **BO 720**

**BATTLE OF THE BIG BANDS 2 (Various artists)**
**Album:** Released Apr '79, on Bright Orange Catalogue no: **BO 721**

## Battle Of The Blues

**BATTLE OF THE BLUES VOL. 3 (Various artists)**
Tracks: / Person to person: *Various artists* / I'm weak but willing: *Various artists* / Somebody done stole my cherry red: *Various artists* / Queen bee: *Various artists* / Featherbed mama: *Various artists* / I trusted you baby: *Various artists* / No good woman: *Various artists* / Ashes on my pillow: *Various artists* / JW: *Various artists* / Last mile, The: *Various artists* / 24 sad hours: *Various artists* / Blues in trouble: *Various artists* / Sad life: *Various*

*artists* / Don't tell me now: *Various artists* / Foolish prayer: *Various artists* / Highway to happiness: *Various artists* / I done told you: *Various artists.*
**Album:** Released '88, on Sing Catalogue no: **SING 634**

## Bauer, Billy

**ANTHOLOGY**
**Album:** Released Nov '88, on Interplay (USA) by Interplay Records (USA). Catalogue no: **IP 8603**

## Bayard, Eddie

**OWLS HOOT 1925-7, THE (Bayard, Eddie & Nor Classic Jazz Orch)**
**Album:** Released Apr '88, on Stomp Off (USA) Catalogue no: **SOS 1145**

## Beau, Heinie

**HEINIE BEAU & HIS HOLLYWOOD JAZZ QUARTET (Beau, Heinie & His Hollywood Jazz Quartet)**
**Album:** Released Jun '81, on Henri Catalogue no: **HRC 101**

## Be-Bop

**1945-53 (Various artists)**
**CD:** Released Mar '90, on Giants of Jazz by Hasmick Promotions. Catalogue no: **GOJCD53029**

**BE-BOP (Various artists)**
Note: Features Dizzy Gillespie, Max Roach and others.
**Album:** Released Oct '88, on Vogue (France) by Vogue Records. Catalogue no: **509170**
**Album:** Released '88, on New World (USA) by New World Records (USA). Catalogue no: **NW 271**

## Bebop Bebop

**BEBOP BEBOP (Various artists)**
Tracks: / Congo blues: *Norvo, Red & His Selected Sextet* / You're not the kind: *Vaughan, Sarah/Tadd Dameron's Orchestra* / Shaw 'nuff: *Gillespie, Dizzy All Star Quintet* / Parkers mood: *Parker, Charlie All Stars* / Things to come: *Gillespie, Dizzy & His Orchestra* / Relaxin' at Camarillo: *Parker, Charlie & His New Stars* / Embraceable you: *Parker, Charlie Quintet* / Koko: *Parker, Charlie Reboppers* / Lemon drop: *Herman, Woody & His Orchestra* / Un poco loco: *Powell, Bud Trio* / Jahbero: *Dameron, Tadd Septet* / Misterioso: *Monk, Thelonious Quartet* / What is this thing called love: *Roach, Max Quintet* / Stop time: *Silver, Horace Quintet.*
Note: Full archival information and a complete list of the performers of each selection may be found within the individual discussion of each work in the liner notes. Producer: Michael Brooks. Sound equalization: Doug Pomeroy, Researchers: Dan Morgenstern, Michael Brooks, Cover by Elaine Sherer Cox, Historical chart & bibliography compiled by Arthur E Scherr, Library of Congress Card no. 75-751058, P & C 1976 Recorded Anthology of American Music Inc.
**Album:** Released Sep '86, on New World (USA) by New World Records (USA). Catalogue no: **NW 271**

## Bebop Boys

**ANTHOLOGY - BEBOP BOYS (Various artists)**
Tracks: / Bebop in pastel: *Various artists* / Fool's fancy: *Various artists* / Bombay: *Various artists* / Ray's idea: *Various artists* / Serenade to a square: *Various artists* / Good kick: *Various artists* / Seven up: *Various artists* / Blues in bebop: *Various artists* / For heckler's only: *Various artists* / Smokey hollow jump: *Various artists* / Boppin' the blues: *Various artists* / Moody speaks: *Various artists* / Tropicana: *Various artists* / Blues to a debutante: *Various artists* / Scene changes, The: *Various artists* / Mean to me: *Various artists* / Baby I'm coming home: *Various artists* / Way you look tonight: *Various artists* / Ornithology: *Various artists* / Get out of that bed: *Various artists* / Body and soul: *Various artists* / Birdland story, The: *Various artists* / I got the blues: *Various artists* / Honeysuckle rose: *Various artists* / Wee dot: *Various artists* / Solitude: *Various artists* / Lion roars: *Various artists* / On the house: *Various artists* / Dinky: *Various artists* / Leo's bells: *Various artists* / Sweet talkin' Leo: *Various artists* / Swingin' for lowe: *Various artists.*
**2 LP Set:** Released '78, on Savoy Jazz (USA) by Malaco Records (USA). Catalogue no: **SJL 2225**

## Bebop Is Where It's At

**BEBOP IS WHERE IT'S AT VOL.1 (Various artists)**
**Album:** Released Oct '79, on Honeydew Catalogue no: **HD 6609**

**BEBOP IS WHERE IT'S AT VOL.2 (Various artists)**
**Album:** Released Oct '79, on Honeydew Catalogue no: **HD 6610**

## Be-Bop Keyboard

**BE-BOP KEYBOARD MASTERS (Featuring: George Wallington / Al Haig / Duke Jordan / Wade Leege) (Various artists)**
Tracks: / Fairyland: *Various artists* / Woody'n you: *Various artists* / Just one of those things: *Various artists* / Honeysuckle rose: *Various artists* / Star eyes: *Various artists* / N.Y.: *Various artists* / Day in Paris, A: *Various artists* / Yardbird suite: *Various artists* / Taboo: *Various artists* / Mighty like a rose: *Various artists* / 'S wonderful: *Various artists* / Just you and me: *Various artists* / Moon was yellow, The: *Various artists* / 'Round about midnight: *Various artists* / Embraceable you: *Various artists* / Scotch blues: *Various artists* / Confirmation: *Various artists* / Darn that dream: *Various artists* / They can't take that away from me: *Various artists* / Wait and see: *Various artists* / Perdido: *Various artists* / Dream a little dream of me: *Various artists* / Wade Legge's blues: *Various artists* / Swedish folk song, A: *Various artists* / Dance of the infidels: *Various artists* / Aren't you glad you're you: *Various artists* / These foolish things: *Various artists* / Why don't you believe me: *Various artists.*
**2 LP Set:** Released May '81, on Vogue by Vogue Records. Catalogue no: **VJD 574**

## Bebop Preservation...

**PIED PIPER OF HAMELIN SUITE (Bebop Preservation Society)**
Tracks: / Hamelin / Council cakewalk / Rats / Pied piper / Mayor's got the blues / Little boy lost / Town band birthday.
Note: Hank Shaw (trumpet)/Peter King(Alto sax)/Bill Le Sage(piano, Composer)/Spike Heatley (Bass)/Martin Drew (Drums)
**Album:** Released '83, on Spotlite by Spotlite Records. Catalogue no: **SPJ 500**

## Be-Bop Vocals

**BE-BOP VOCALS (Various artists)**
Tracks: / I don't want love: *Various artists* / Bye bye blackbird: *Various artists* / Sugar Ray: *Various artists* / Cool whalin': *Various artists* / But beautiful: *Various artists* / Gambler's blues: *Various artists* / Let there be love: *Various artists* / But beautiful (2): *Various artists* / Bless my soul: *Various artists* / Beautiful memories: *Various artists* / I'll remember April: *Various artists* / Gone with the wind: *Various artists* / Oop-pop-a-da: *Various artists* / Especially to you: *Various artists* / Nobody knows: *Various artists* / Searching blues: *Various artists* / Nightingale: *Various artists.*
Note: For lovers of vocal jazz this is a must.Featured here are:-Babs Gonzales, Joe Carroll, Kenny 'Pancho'Hagood,Eddie Jefferson, Earl Coleman and Frankie Passions
**Album:** Released '83, on Spotlite by Spotlite Records. Catalogue no: **SPJ 135**

## Bechet, Sidney

**Biographical details:** Bechet, Sidney The clarinettist and soprano saxophonist, with Louis Armstrong, Johnny Dodds, King Oliver and Jelly Roll Morton, is one of the greatest of the first generation of New Orleans jazz musicians. He was born there in 1897 and died in Paris 1959. In 1919 he went to Europe with Will Marion Cook's Southern Syncopated Orchestra; conductor Ernest Ansermet heard him and wrote one of the most famous of all early jazz commentaries: 'I wish to set down the name of this artist of genius; as for myself, I shall never forget it - it is Sidney Bechet.. who is glad one likes what he does, but who can say nothing of his art save that he follows his 'own way'..perhaps the highway the whole world will swing along tomorrow..' The clarinettist bought a straight model soprano sax in London, played in Paris till 1921 and made his first records with Clarence Williams back in the USA, and with Louis Armstrong in the Red Onion Jazz Babies in 1924, one of the best surviving exam-

Sidney Bechet

ples of what such musicians sounded like in the bars and dance halls of New Orleans. He played briefly with Duke Ellington in New York and had the same electrifying effect as Armstrong did with Fletcher Henderson: Ellington said, 'After that we forgot all about the sweet stuff'. He was the only jazzman until Steve Lacy and John Coltrane to concentrate on the soprano, but profoundly influenced the young Johnny Hodges, who played soprano (as well as alto) until 1940. Bechet co-led the New Orleans Feetwarmers with the legendary trumpeter Tommy Ladnier; they recorded for Victor, but times were so bad that they operated a tailor shop in 1933. He continued recording for Victor until 1941; he also recorded for the young Blue Note label beginning in 1939: *Blues For Tommy* was made a few days after Ladnier's death. Bechet went to France in 1949 and lived there for the rest of his life, an elder statesman of jazz more honoured in France than at home. His heavy vibrato was instantly recognisable; his uncompromising and intelligent New Orleans lyricism never became outdated, though sidemen on some of the later Victor records included bop drummer Kenny Clarke. His most famous compositions are *Petite Fleur* (a worldwide hit by Chris Barber in 1959, with clarinettist Monty Sunshine playing the Bechet part) and *Les Oignons*, made in France in 1949 with clarinettist Claude Luter, said to have sold a million copies by 1955. *Sidney Bechet Sessions* on Storyville include 1945-47 material. (Donald Clarke 23 August 1988).

**1939-44**
Note: Featuring Muggsy Spanier, Meade Lux Lewis, Henry Allen.
**Album:** Released Sep '87, on Giants of Jazz by Hasmick Promotions. Catalogue no: **LPJT 65**

**1953-55**
**CD:** Released 10 Jul '89, on Vogue by Vogue Records. Catalogue no: **VGCD 600207**

**AT EDDIE CONDON'S FLOOR SHOW**
**Album:** Released '88, on Queen Catalogue no: **QUEEN 029**

**BACK TO MEMPHIS (Bechet, Sidney & Sammy Prices Bluesicians)**
**Album:** Released Oct '88, on Vogue by Vogue Records. Catalogue no: **500053**

**BECHET**
**Album:** Released '88, on GNP Crescendo (USA) by GNP Crescendo Records (USA). Catalogue no: **GNPS 9012**

**BECHET VOLUME 5 (1941-43) (The Panassie session) (Bechet, Sidney, Mezzrow & T. Ladnier)**
Tracks: / Mood indigo (pt.1) / Mood indigo (pt.2) / Rose room / Lady be good / Lady be good (pt 2) / What is this thing called love? / After you've gone / Bugle call rag / Ole miss rag / St. Louis blues / Revolutionary blues / Comin' on with the come on (pt.1) / Comin' on with the come on (pt.2) / Careless love (swingin' for Mezz) / Careless love (swingin' for Mezz) (pt.2) / Royal Garden blues (part 1) / Royal Garden blues (part 2) / Everybody loves my baby (pt1) / Everybody loves my baby (pt2) / I ain't gonna give nobody none of my jelly roll (pt.1) / I ain't gonna give nobody none of my jelly roll (pt.2) / If you see me comin' (pt1) / If you see me comin' (pt2) / Gettin' together (pt.1) / Gettin' together (pt.2) / Rosetta / Minor jive / World is waiting for the sunrise, The / Who? / Blues my baby gave to me, The / Rompin'.
**Cass set:** Released Mar '86, on RCA by BMG Records (UK). Deleted Nov '88. Catalogue no: **NK 89751**
**2 LP Set:** Released Mar '86, on RCA by BMG Records (UK). Deleted Jul '89. Catalogue no: **NL 89751**

**BECHET-SPANIER BIG FOUR (Bechet, Sidney & Muggsy Spanier Big Four)**
Tracks: / Sweet Lorraine / Lazy river / China boy / Four or five times / That's plenty / If I could be with you / Squeeze me / Sweet Sue.
Note: With Carmen Maestren gt;Wellman Braud bs
**Album:** Released Apr '81, on Joker (USA) by Lifetime Records (USA). Catalogue no: **SM 3090**

**BIG FOUR WITH MUGGSY SPANIER**
**Album:** Released Jan '83, on Swaggie (Australia) Catalogue no: **S 1392**

**BLUEBIRD SESSIONS 1932-1943, THE**
Tracks: / Sweetie dear / I want you tonight / I've found a new baby / Lay your racket / Maple leaf rag / Shag / Ja da / Really the blues / When you and I were young / Maggie / Weary blues / Oh, didn't he ramble / High society / I thought I heard Buddy Bolden say / Winin' boy blues / Indian summer / One o'clock jump / Preachin' blues / Sidney's blues / Shake it and break it / Old man blues / Nobody knows the way I feel this morning / Wild man blues / Make me a pallet on the floor / St. Louis blues / Blues in thirds / Blue for you, Johnny / Ain't misbehavin' / Save it pretty mama / Stompy Jones / Muskrat ramble / Coal black shine / Egyptian fantasy / Baby won't you please come home / Slippin' and slidin' / Sheik of Araby, The / Blues of Bechet / Swing parade / I know that you know and you know that I know / When it's sleeptime down South / I ain't gonna give nobody none o' this jelly / I'm coming Virginia / Limehouse blues / Georgia cabin / Texas moaner blues / Strange fruit / You're the limit / Rip up the joint / Suey / Blues in the air / Mooche, The / Laughin' in rhythm / 12th Street rag / Mood indigo / Rose room / Oh lady be good / What is this thing called love / After you've gone / Bugle call rag / Old Miss Blues.
**LP Set:** Released Jul '89, on Bluebird (2) by BMG Records (UK). Catalogue no: **NL 90317**
**CD Set:** Released Jul '89, on Bluebird (2) by BMG Records (UK). Catalogue no: **ND 90317**

**BLUES IN PARIS**
**2 LP Set:** Released Oct '88, on Vogue

by Vogue Records. Catalogue no: **400672**

**BOSTON 1945 (Bechet/Bunk)**
**Album:** Released Jul '86, on Jazz Archives (USA) by Jazz Archives Inc.(USA). Catalogue no: **JA 48**

**BRUSSELS WORLD FAIR CONCERT 1958**
**Album:** Released Oct '88, on Vogue by Vogue Records. Catalogue no: **500203**

**BRUXELLES 1954**
**Album:** Released '88, on Vogue (France) by Vogue Records. Catalogue no: **502012**

**COMPLETE SIDNEY BECHET 1 & 2 1932-1941, THE(See panel below)**
Tracks: / One o'clock jump / Preachin' blues / Old man blues / Blues in thirds / Ain't misbehavin' / Save it pretty mama / Stomp Jones / Muskrat ramble / Coal black shine / Sweetie dear / Lay your racket / Maple leaf rag / Ja da / Really the blues / Weary blues / Indian summer / I want you tonight / I've found a new baby / When you and I were young Maggie / Maggie / Sidney's blues / Shake it and break it / Wild man blues / Nobody knows the way I feel this morning / Make a pallet on the floor / St. Louis blues / Blues for you / Johnny / Eygptian fantasy.
Note: 28 tracks including ones listed in tracks session
**Cass set:** Released Jul '86, on RCA by BMG Records (UK). Deleted Nov '88. Catalogue no: **NK 89760**
**2 LP Set:** Released '83, on RCA (France) by BMG Records (France). Catalogue no: **PM 42409**
**2 LP Set:** Released Jul '86, on RCA by BMG Records (UK). Deleted Jul '89. Catalogue no: **NL 89760**

**COMPLETE SIDNEY BECHET 3 & 4 1941**
Tracks: / I'm coming Virginia - 1 / I'm coming Virginia (2) / Limehouse blues / Geogia cabin (1) / Geogia cabin (2) / Texas moaner - 1 / Texas moaner - 2 / Strange fruit / You're the limit - 1 / You're the limit - 2 / Rip up the joint / Suey - 1 / Suey - 2 / Blues in the air - 1 / Blues in the air - 2 / Mooche, The / Mooche, The / Laughin' in rhythm / 12th Street rag - 1 / 12th Street rag - 2 / I know that you know - 3 / Egyptian fantasy / Baby won't you please come home? / Slippin' and slidin' / Sheik of Araby, The / Blues of Bechet / Swing parade - 1 / Swing parade - 2 / I know that you know - 1 / I know that you know - 2 / When it's sleepy time down South / I ain't gonna give nobody none of my jelly roll / I ain't gonna give nobody none of my jelly roll (pt.2).
**2 LP Set:** Released '83, on RCA (France) by BMG Records (France). Catalogue no: **PM 43262**
**Cass set:** Released Jan '87, on RCA by BMG Records (UK). Deleted May '89. Catalogue no: **NK 89759**
**2 LP Set:** Released Jan '87, on RCA by BMG Records (UK). Deleted Jul '89. Catalogue no: **NL 89759**

**CONCERT INEDITS VOL.2**
**Album:** Released Jan '85, on Vogue by Vogue Records. Catalogue no: **502 012**

**DEUX GEANTS DU JAZZ (Bechet, Sidney & Django Reinhardt)**
**CD:** Released '86, on Vogue by Vogue Records. Catalogue no: **VGCD 600103**

**FABULOUS SIDNEY BECHET, THE**
Tracks: / Original Dixieland one-step / Blues my naughty sweetie gives to me / That's a plenty / Ballin' the Jack / Avalon / Rose of the Rio Grande / Black and blue(What did I do to be so) / Sweet Georgia Brown / All of me / Ding dong daddy.
**Album:** Released Oct '84, on Blue Note by EMI Records. Catalogue no: **BLP 1207**

**GIANT OF JAZZ VOL.1**
**Cass:** Released Mar '84, on Blue Note (France) by EMI Records. Catalogue no: **BLC 12034**
**Album:** Released Sep '84, on Blue Note by EMI Records. Catalogue no: **BLP 1203**

**HIS WAY 1951**
**Album:** Released Apr '79, on Pumpkin Catalogue no: **PUMPKIN 102**

**HOLD TIGHT 1938-46**
**CD:** Released 21 Jul '89, on Jazz & Jazz Catalogue no: **CDJJ 603**
**Album:** Released Jun '89, on Jazz & Jazz Catalogue no: **JJ 603**

**IN PHILADELPHIA VOL.2**
**Album:** Released Oct '79, on Jazz Archives (USA) by Jazz Archives Inc.(USA). Catalogue no: **JA 37**

**INEDITS**
**2 LP Set:** Released Oct '88, on Vogue by Vogue Records. Catalogue no: **406503**
**Album:** Released '88, on Vogue (France) by Vogue Records. Catalogue no: **502001**

**INEDITS 1939-42**
**Album:** Released '88, on Vogue (France) by Vogue Records. Catalogue no: **502013**

**JAZZ AT STORYVILLE**
**Album:** Released Jun '88, on Black Lion Catalogue no: **BLP 60902**
**CD:** Released Jun '88, on Black Lion Catalogue no: **BLCD 760902**

**JAZZ CLASS**
Tracks: / Okey doke / Early every morn / Shag / Polka dot rag / Viper mad / Blackstick / Sweet patootie / I've found a new baby / Characteristic blues / Mandy make up your mind / Maple leaf rag / Ja da / Really the blues / When you and I were young Maggie / Weary blues / When the sun sets down south.
**Album:** Released Mar '89, on BBC by BBC Records & Tapes. Catalogue no: **REB 700**
**Cass:** Released Mar '89, on BBC by BBC Records & Tapes. Catalogue no: **ZCF 700**
**CD:** Released Mar '89, on BBC by BBC Records & Tapes. Catalogue no: **BBC CD 700**

**JAZZ CLASSICS VOL.1**
Tracks: / Blue horizon / Weary blues / Summer time / Blame it on the blues /

**Sidney Bechet - The Complete Sidney Bechet (RCA)**

Milenberg joys / Days beyond recall / Salty dog / Dear old southland / Weary way blues.
**Album:** Released Apr '83, on Blue Note by EMI Records. Deleted Jan '88. Catalogue no: **BLP 1201**

**JAZZ CLASSICS VOL.2**
Tracks: / St. Louis blues / Up in Sidney's flat / Lord let me in the lifeboat / Pounding heart blues / Changes made / High society / Jackass blues / Jazz me blues / Blues for Tommy Ladnier / Old stack o'lee blues.
**Album:** Released Apr '83, on Blue Note by EMI Records. Deleted Jan '88. Catalogue no: **BLP 1202**

**JAZZ NOCTURNE VOL.1**
**Album:** Released '88, on Vogue (France) by Vogue Records. Catalogue no: **502007**

**JAZZ TIME VOL.9**
**Album:** Released '88, on Vogue (France) by Vogue Records. Catalogue no: **502709**

**JAZZ TIME VOL.20 (Bechet, Sidney & Django Reinhardt)**
**Album:** Released '88, on Vogue (France) by Vogue Records. Catalogue no: **502720**

**LA GRANDE PARADE**
**2 LP Set:** Released Oct '88, on Vogue by Vogue Records. Catalogue no: **400001**

**LA MUSIQUE C'EST MA VIE**
**2 LP Set:** Released Oct '88, on Vogue by Vogue Records. Catalogue no: **430329**

**LE DISQUE D'OR**
**Album:** Released '88, on Vogue (France) by Vogue Records. Catalogue no: **509001**

**LE DOUBLE DISQUE D'OR VOL.1**
**2 LP Set:** Released Oct '88, on Vogue by Vogue Records. Catalogue no: **416001**

**LE DOUBLE DISQUE D'OR VOL.2**
**2 LP Set:** Released Oct '88, on Vogue by Vogue Records. Catalogue no: **416033**

**LE SOIR OU..L'ON CASA L'OLYMPIA**
**2 LP Set:** Released Oct '88, on Vogue by Vogue Records. Catalogue no: **400316**

**LEGENDARY SIDNEY BECHET, THE**
Tracks: / Maple leaf rag / I've found a new baby / Weary blues / Really the blues / High society / Indian summer / Sidney's blues / Shake it and break it / Wild man blues / Save it, pretty mama / Stompy Jones / Muskrat ramble / Baby, won't you please come home / Sheik of Araby, The / When it's sleepy time down South / I'm coming Virginia / Strange fruit / Blues in the air / Mooche, The / Twelfth St. rag / Mood indigo / What is this thing called love?.
**Album:** Released Apr '89, on Bluebird (2) by BMG Records (UK). Catalogue no: **NL 86590**
**CD:** Released Apr '89, on Bluebird (2) by BMG Records (UK). Catalogue no: **ND 86590**
**Cass:** Released Apr '89, on Bluebird (2) by BMG Records (UK). Catalogue no: **NK 86590**

Premier Bal - Sidney Bechet (Vogue)

**LEGENDARY SIDNEY BECHET, THE (2)**
**Album:** Released '88, on GNP Crescendo (USA) by GNP Crescendo Records (USA). Catalogue no: **GNPS 9037**

**LIVE IN NEW YORK**
**Cass:** Released Apr '84, on EMI (Europe) by EMI Records. Catalogue no: **2M 256 64846**
**Album:** Released Apr '84, on EMI (Europe) by EMI Records. Catalogue no: **2M 056 64846**

**MASTERS OF JAZZ VOL.4**
**Album:** Released May '86, on Storyville by Storyville Records AB. Catalogue no: **SLP 4104**

**MEMORIAL SET VOL.1**
Tracks: / House party / Perdido street stomp / Minor swoon / Sheik of Araby, The / Breathless blues / Really the blues(Parts 1 & 2) / Ole miss / Blowin' the blues / I'm gonna give nobody to my Jelly Roll / Perdido street stomp / Old school / Gone away blues / De luxe stomp / Out of the Gallion.
Note: With the Mezz Mezzrow Septet & Quintet
**Album:** Released Apr '81, on Joker (USA) by Lifetime Records (USA). Catalogue no: **SM 3078**

**MEMORIAL SET VOL.2**
Tracks: / Groovin' the minor / Where am I? / Tommy's blues / Revolutionary blues / I want some / I'm speaking my mind / Kaiser's last break / Funky butt / Delta mood / Blues of the roaring twenties.
Note: With the Mezz Mezzrow Septet & Quintet
**Album:** Released Apr '81, on Joker (USA) by Lifetime Records (USA). Catalogue no: **SM 3079**

**NEW ORLEANS DAYS (Bechet, Sidney & Louis Armstrong)**
**Album:** Released Nov '88, on Vogue by Vogue Records. Catalogue no: **500093**

**NEW ORLEANS, LOUISIANA**
**Album:** Released Oct '88, on Vogue (France) by Vogue Records. Catalogue no: **509071**

**NEW ORLEANS STYLE OLD AND NEW (Bechet, Sidney & Bob Wilber)**
Tracks: / Jelly roll blues / At a Georgia camp meeting / National emblem march / Hindustan / I'll take New Orleans music / Willie the weeper / Willie the weeper no.2 / Mabel's dream / Mabel's dream no.2 / Wild cat blues / Wild cat blues no.2 / Blues for fowler / Blues for fowler no.2.
**Album:** Released May '87, on Commodore Class Catalogue no: **6.25492**

**OLYMPIA 1954 (Bechet, Sidney & C.Luter)**
**CD:** Released Oct '88, on Vogue by Vogue Records. Catalogue no: **VGCD 600 159**

**OLYMPIA CONCERT**
Tracks: / At-tu Le Cafard / Sobbin' and Cryin' / Muskrat Ramble / Indicatif /

Buddy Bolden stomp / Monmartre boogie woogie / As-tu le cafard / Riverboat Shuffle Montmatre / Halle Hallelujah / Temperamental / Sobbin' and cryin' / On the sunnyside of the street / When the saints go marching in.
**CD:** Released Jun '84, on Vogue by Vogue Records. Catalogue no: **VG 600 023**

**PARISIAN ENCOUNTER (Bechet, Sidney & Teddy Buckner)**
Tracks: / Bravo / Aubergines / I can't get started / Souvenirs / Blue festival / Weary blues / Ain't misbehavin' / Sugar / Who's sorry now / All of me.
**CD:** Released Jun '86, on Vogue by Vogue Records. Catalogue no: **VG 600 018**
**Album:** Released Oct '88, on Vogue by Vogue Records. Catalogue no: **500113**

**PETITE FLEUR**
**CD:** Released 10 Jul '89, on Vogue by Vogue Records. Catalogue no: **VGCD 670204**

**PLATINUM FOR...**
Tracks: / Petite fleur / Promenade aux Champs D'Elysee / A-tu le cafard / Passport to paradise / Marchand de poissant / Si tu vois ma mere / Ce mossieu qui parle / Bechet creole blues / Madame Becassine / Blues in Paris / Moulin a cafe / Sobbin' & cryin' / Les oignons / Premier bal / Egyptian fantasy / Temperamental / Buddy Bolden story / Dans les rue's d'Antibes.
**CD:** Released '86, on Vogue by Vogue Records. Catalogue no: **VG 600 026**

**PLATINUM FOR SIDNEY BECHET**
**Album:** Released Jun '84, on Vogue by Vogue Records. Catalogue no: **522 008**
**Cass:** Released Jun '84, on Vogue by Vogue Records. Catalogue no: **722 008**

**PLEYEL CONCERTS 1952**
**CD:** Released Jun '86, on Vogue by Vogue Records. Catalogue no: **VGCD 600090**

**PREMIER BAL (See panel on previous page)**
Tracks: / Le marchand de poissons / Mon homme / Un ange comme ca / La canne - le fossoyeur / Ecoutez le trombone / Moi d'payer, A / Au clair de la lune / Brave Margot / J'ai deux amours / Ce n'est que votre main, Madame / La complainte des infideles / Bonjour Paris / Le loup: la biche et le chevalier / J'en al marre / Pleure pas, Nelly / Premier bal / La complainte de Mackie.
**CD:** Released Jun '88, on Vogue by Vogue Records. Catalogue no: **VG 670 039**

**RAREST OF ALL RARE PERFORMANCES**
**Album:** Released Jul '82, on Kings Of Jazz Catalogue no: **KLJ 20033**

**RECONTRES**
**CD:** Released Oct '88, on Vogue by Vogue Records. Catalogue no: **VGCD 600 186**

**REED ALBUM VOL. 1 (Bechet, Sidney)**
**Album:** Released '88, on Meritt (USA) Catalogue no: **MERITT 10**

**REFRESHING TRACKS -1958 VOL.1**
Tracks: / I only have eyes for you / Man I love, The / Exactly like you / These foolish things / Jeepers creepers / I never knew / All the things you are / All of me / Embraceable you / Wrap your troubles in dreams / Rose room / I don't mean a thing / Pennies from Heaven / Rosetta / Once in a while / Sweet Georgia Brown / St. Louis Blues / On the sunny side of the street / Sister Kate / I'm coming Virginia.
**2 LP Set:** Released Nov '77, on Vogue by Vogue Records. Catalogue no: **VJD 541**

**REFRESHING TRACKS VOL.2**
**2 LP Set:** Released '78, on Vogue by Vogue Records. Catalogue no: **VJD 552**

**SIDNEY BECHET**
**Cass:** Released '88, on Entertainers Catalogue no: **ENT MC 13027**
**Album:** Released Nov '87, on Entertainers Catalogue no: **ENT LP 13027**

**SIDNEY BECHET 1923/38**
Note: Featuring Clarence Williams, Louis Armstrong, Charlie Shavers.
**Album:** Released Sep '87, on Giants of Jazz by Hasmick Promotions. Catalogue no: **LPJT 52**

**SIDNEY BECHET: 1945-51**
**Cass:** Released Feb '89, on Giants of Jazz by Hasmick Promotions. Catalogue no: **MCJT 76**
**Album:** Released Feb '89, on Giants of Jazz by Hasmick Promotions. Catalogue no: **LPJT 76**

**SIDNEY BECHET AND FRIENDS (Bechet, Sidney & Friends)**
Tracks: / High society / On the sunny side of the street / Honeysuckle rose / I can't believe that you are in love with me / Wrap your troubles in dreams / It had to be you / Baby won't please come home / Please don't talk about me when I'm gone / Ooh boogie / After you've gone / I'm goin' way down home / Margie / Dutch swing college blues / King Porter stomp / Weary way blues / Panama / Tiger rag / Texas moaner blues / That's a plenty / Swanee river / Limehouse blues / Black stick / Les oignons.
**CD:** Released Jan '90, on Verve Catalogue no: **8406332**
**Cass:** Released Jan '90, on Verve Catalogue no: **8406334**

**SIDNEY BECHET COLLECTION (20 golden greats)**
Tracks: / Jelly roll blues / National emblem march / Hindustan / At a Georgia camp meeting / I'll take New Orleans music / Ain't misbehavin' / Sheik of Araby, The / Cindy blues / Wild cat blues / Blues for you, Johnny / I'm coming, Virginia / Coal black shine / Suey / You're the limit / Kansas City man blues / Summertime / Baby won't you please come home? / St. Louis blues / Polka dot stomp rag / I know that you know.
**Album:** Released Jul '86, on Deja Vu Catalogue no: **DVLP 2066**
**Cass:** Released Jul '86, on Deja Vu Catalogue no: **DVMC 2066**

**SIDNEY BECHET AND HIS AMERICAN**
**CD:** Released Oct '88, on Vogue by Vogue Records. Catalogue no: **VGCD 600 173**
**CD:** Released Dec '86, on Vogue by Vogue Records. Catalogue no: **VG 600 122**

**SIDNEY BECHET JUBLIEE AND C.LUTER**
**2 LP Set:** Released Oct '88, on Vogue by Vogue Records. Catalogue no: **400011**

**SIDNEY BECHET LEGACY**
**Album:** Released '88, on Vogue (France) by Vogue Records. Catalogue no: **502608**

**SIDNEY BECHET AND NEW ORLEANS JAZZ**
**Album:** Released '88, on Meritt (USA) Catalogue no: **MERITT 2**

**SIDNEY BECHET SESSIONS (With Mezzrow & Joe Sullivan) (Bechet, Sidney, Mezzrow & Joe Sullivan)**
**Album:** Released Sep '86, on Storyville by Storyville Records AB. Catalogue no: **SLP 4028**

**SIDNEY BECHET AND THE NEW ORLEANS FEET WARMERS VOL. 1 (Bechet, Sidney & New Orleans Feetwarmers)**
Tracks: / Sweetie dear / I want you tonight / I've found a new baby / Lay your racket / Maple leaf rag / Shag / Indian summer / One o'clock jump / Sidney blues / Shake it and break it / Old man blues / Wild man blues / Nobody knows the way I feel this morning / Make me a pallet on the floor / Blues in thirds.
**Album:** Released Apr '81, on Joker (USA) by Lifetime Records (USA). Catalogue no: **SM 3571**

**SIDNEY BECHET AND THE NEW ORLEANS FEET WARMERS VOL. 2 (Bechet, Sidney & New Orleans Feetwarmers)**
Tracks: / Blues for you, Johnny / Ain't misbehavin' 1 & 2 / Save it pretty mama / Coal black shine / Egyptian fantasy / Baby won't you please come home / Slippin' and slidin' / Sheik of Araby, The / Blues of Bechet / Swing parade / I know that you know / When it's sleepy time down south / I ain't give nobody none of this Jellyroll.
**Album:** Released Apr '81, on Joker (USA) by Lifetime Records (USA). Catalogue no: **SM 3572**

**SIDNEY BECHET AND THE NEW ORLEANS FEET WARMERS VOL. 3 (Bechet, Sidney & New Orleans Feetwarmers)**
Tracks: / I'm coming Virginia / Limhouse blues / Georgia cabin / Texas moaner / Strange fruit / You're the limit / Rip up the joint / Blues in the air / Mooche,

The/Laughin' in rhythm/Twelfth St. rag/Mood indigo/Rose room/Oh lady be good/What is this thing called love?
**Album:** Released Apr '81, on Joker (USA) by Lifetime Records (USA). Catalogue no: **SM 3573**

**SIDNEY BECHET VOL.1**
Tracks: / Petite fleur / Marchand de poissons / Temperamental / Promenade aux Champs-Elysses / A moi d'payer / Les oignons / Dans les rues d'Antibes / Premier bal / Si tu vois ma mere / Passport to Paradise / As-tu le cafard / Au secours.
**Album:** Released Jul '82, on Jazz Reactivation Catalogue no: **JR 145**

**SIDNEY BECHET WITH....**
Tracks: / Blues, The / Baby won't you please come home / Charleston / I know that you know / That's a plenty / Black & blue / You are some pretty doll / Farewell blues / Summertime / Sensation rag.
Note: Sidney Bechet with Mugsy Spanier, George Brunis, Albert Nicholas, Danny Parker, Pops Foster, Johnson, Baby Dodds
**Album:** Released Apr '81, on Kings Of Jazz Catalogue no: **KLJ 20004**
**Album:** Released Jul '86, on Jazz Archives (USA) by Jazz Archives Inc.(USA). Catalogue no: **JA 44**

**SIDNEY BECHET WITH EDDIE CONDON**
Tracks: / Buddy Bolden stomp / Black & blue / Summertime / Honeysuckle Rose / Argone stomp / High society / Blues in my heart / Sweet Georgia Brown / September song / Just one of those things / Blues / Ole Miss.
**Album:** Released Apr '81, on Queendisc (Italy) Catalogue no: **QU 029**

**SIDNEY'S BLUES**
Tracks: / Sweetie dear / Maple leaf rag / Shag / Ja da / Really the blues / Indian summer / Sidney's blues / Blues in thirds / Blues in the air / Suey / Mooche, The / Mood indigo.
**Cass:** Released Jul '86, on RCA by BMG Records (UK). Catalogue no: **CK 89800**
**Album:** Released Jul '86, on RCA by BMG Records (UK). Deleted Jul '89. Catalogue no: **CL 89800**

**SUMMERTIME**
Tracks: / Summertime / Muskrat ramble.
**7" Single:** Released Jun '79, on United Artists by EMI Records. Deleted '82. Catalogue no: **UP 36535**

**SUPERB SIDNEY**
**Cass:** Released Feb '85, on CBS (import) by CBS Records. Catalogue no: **40 54613**
**Album:** Released Feb '85, on CBS (import) by CBS Records. Catalogue no: **54613**

**THIRTIES, THE**
Tracks: / Black stick blues / Loveless love / Basement blues / Roll on, Mississippi, roll on / Viper mad / When the sun sets down south / Sweet patootie / Uncle Joe / Freight train blues / My daddy rocks me / You can't live in Harlem / T'ain't a fit night out for man or beast / Rhythm of Broadway moon / Polka dot rag.
**Album:** Released Jul '86, on Affinity by Charly Records. Catalogue no: **AFS 1025**

**TROPICAL MOOD, 1931-39**
**Album:** Released Sep '87, on Swingtime by Contact Records (Denmark). Catalogue no: **ST 1014**

**WHEN A SOPRANO MEETS A PIANO (Bechet, Sidney & Solal Martial)**
**Album:** Released Oct '88, on Vogue by Vogue Records. Catalogue no: **500087**

## Beckett, Harry

**BREMAN CONCERT (Beckett, Harry Quartet)**
**CD:** Released Oct '88, on West Wind Catalogue no: **WWCD 007**

**PICTURES OF YOU**
Tracks: / What's the secret / Pictures of you / One step ahead / In case you hadn't heard Mrs Smith is here / Chosen one, The.
**Album:** Released Apr '85, on Paladin Catalogue no: **PAL 2**

**Harry Beckett**

## Beiderbecke, Bix

**Biographical details:** Beiderbecke, Bix Leon Bix Beiderbecke was born in 1903 in Davenport, Iowa; he died in New York City in 1931. The cornettist also played the piano and wrote a few pieces influenced by contemporary 'classic' music. He began learning the piano at age 3; his brother brought home records by the Original Dixieland Jazz Band and Bix slowed down the turntable so that he could learn to play the correct solos. He first recorded with the Wolverines, a semi-pro band popular on college campuses, and soon became friends with songwriter Hoagy Carmichael; the records were badly made during the acoustic era and his tone was described as 'piercing a curtain of fudge.' His technique was unorthodox and he never read music well, but he had a faultless ear: his intonation was perfect and he experimented harmonically from the beginning. He was a lyrical, linear soloist; unlike Louis Armstrong he avoided bravura but like Louis he was a natural melodist, one of the first to be able to solo for 32 bars using logically compatible phrases, recomposing as he went along rather than improvising close to the melody. He and Louis admired each other and Louis allegedly once lent him his horn so Bix could sit in. Contemporaries said of Bix's unusually lovely tone that his notes sounded like they had been struck, as with a mallet on a bell. His best records were made with a small group led by saxophonist Frankie Trumbauer, often including guitarist Eddie Lang, Jimmie Dorsey on alto, Adrian Rollini on bass sax, the most famous tracks being *I'm Comin' Virginia* and *Singin' The Blues*. His compositions included *In a Mist*, which he recorded on solo piano. He became a distorted legend after his death from alcoholism, the famous book and film *Young Man With A Horn* being based loosely on his life.

**Bix Beiderbecke**

As a featured and highly paid sideman in the Paul Whiteman band he was at the top of his profession, but he never felt secure about his own talent: he sent copies of all his records home to his Midwestern German-Protestant family, but they didn't even open the parcels. (Donald Clarke 23 August 1988).

**1924: BIX BEIDERBECKE**
**Album:** Released Jan '83, on Swaggie (Australia) Catalogue no: **S 802**

**1924-30**
**Album:** Released Sep '87, on Giants of Jazz by Hasmick Promotions. Catalogue no: **LPJT 25**

**BEIDERBECKE FILE, THE**
Tracks: / Flock o' blues / I'm glad / Toddin' blues / Davenport blues / Three blind mice / Clarinet marmalade / Singin' the blues / Ostrich walk / Riverboat shuffle / I'm coming Virginia / Way down yonder in New Orleans / Lonely melody / San / At the jazz band ball / Jazz me blues / Goose pimples / Sorry / Somebody stole my gal / Margie / Deep down south.
**Album:** Released 10 Jul '89, on Saville by Conifer Records. Catalogue no: **SVL 201**
**Cass:** Released 10 Jul '89, on Saville by Conifer Records. Catalogue no: **CSVL 201**

**BIX AND HIS GANG (1927 - 28)**
**Album:** Released Jan '83, on Swaggie (Australia) Catalogue no: **S 1271**

**BIX AND TRAM (Beiderbecke, Bix & Frankie Trumbauer)**
**Album:** Released Dec '88, on Swaggie (Australia) Catalogue no: **S 1269**

**BIX AND TRAM (1927) (Beiderbecke, Bix & Frankie Trumbauer)**
**Album:** Released Jan '83, on Swaggie (Australia) Catalogue no: **S 1242**

**BIX AND TRAM (1928) (Beiderbecke, Bix & Frankie Trumbauer)**
**Album:** Released Apr '79, on BBMS Catalogue no: **UNKNOWN**

**BIX BEIDERBECKE COLLECTION (see panel on next page)**
**CD:** Released Oct '89, on Collection by K-Tel Records. Catalogue no: **OR 0072**
**Album:** Released Nov '85, on Deja Vu Catalogue no: **DVLP 2049**
**CD:** Released Dec '87, on Deja Vu Catalogue no: **DVCD 2049**
**Cass:** Released Nov '85, on Deja Vu Catalogue no: **DVMC 2049**

**BIX BEIDERBECKE JAZZ FESTIVAL, IOWA, 1972 (Various artists)**
**Album:** Released Apr '79, on BBMS Catalogue no: **BBMS 1**
**Album:** Released Apr '79, on BBMS Catalogue no: **BBMS 2**

**BIX BEIDERBECKE JAZZ FESTIVAL, IOWA, 1974 (Various artists)**
**Album:** Released Apr '79, on BBMS Catalogue no: **BBMS 3**
**Album:** Released Apr '79, on BBMS Catalogue no: **BBMS 4**

**BIX BEIDERBECKE JAZZ FESTIVAL, IOWA, 1975 (Various artists)**
**Album:** Released Apr '79, on BBMS Catalogue no: **BBMS 6**
**Album:** Released Apr '79, on BBMS Catalogue no: **BBMS 7**

**BIX BEIDERBECKE JAZZ FESTIVAL, IOWA, 1976 (Various artists)**
**Album:** Released Apr '79 on BBMS Catalogue no: **BBMS 9**
**Album:** Released Apr '79 on BBMS Catalogue no: **BBMS 10**

**BIX BEIDERBECKE STORY, THE**
Tracks: / Riverboat shuffle / Tiger rag / Davenport blues / I'm looking over a four leaf clover / Trumbology / Clarinet marmalade / Ostrich walk / Way down yonder in New Orleans / Three blind mice / Clementine / Royal Garden blues / Coquette / When / Lovable / Is it gonna be long? / Oh, you have no idea! / Felix, the cat / 'Tain't so, honey, 'tain't so / I'd rather cry over you / Louisiana / Futuristic rhythm / Raisin' the roof / Rockin' chair / Strut Miss Lizzie / Georgia on my mind.
Note: 3 LP set
**CD:** Released May '89, on Deja Vu Catalogue no: **DVRE CD 14**
**Cass:** Released May '89, on Deja Vu Catalogue no: **DVRE MC 14**
**Album:** Released Jun '86, on CBS (import) by CBS Records. Catalogue no: **66367**

**BIX BEIDERBECKE & THE CHICAGO CORNETS**
Tracks: / Fidgety feet / Jazz me blues / Oh baby / Copenhagen / Riverboat shuffle / Susie / Royal garden blues / Tiger rag / I need some pettin' / Sensation / Lazy daddy / Tia Juana / Big boy / I'm glad / Flovk o' blues / Toddlin' blues / Davenport blues / Prince of Wails / When my sugar walks down the street / Steady roll blues / Mobile blues / Really a pain / Chicago blues / Hot mittens / Buddy's habits.
**2 LP Set:** Released Oct '80, on Milestone by Ace Records. Deleted Jan '88. Catalogue no: **M 47019**

**BIX BEIDERBECKE & THE WOLVERINES (Beiderbecke, Bix & the Wolverines)**
**Album:** Released '88, on Jazz Treasury Catalogue no: **JT 1003**
**Album:** Released '88, on Olympic (1) by Olympic Records. Catalogue no: **OLYMPIC 7130**
**Album:** Released '88, on Fresh Sounds (Spain) by Fresh Sounds Records (Spain). Catalogue no: **FS 317**

**BIX BEIDERBECKE VOL 1 (Riverboat Shuffle)**
Tracks: / Jazz me blues / Fidgety feet / Oh babe / Copenhagen / Riverboat shuffle / Susie - A / Susie - B / I need some pettin' / Royal Garden blues / Tiger rag / Sensation / Lazy daddy - A / Lazy daddy - B / Tia Juana / Big boy.
**Album:** Released Apr '81, on Joker (USA) by Lifetime Records (USA). Catalogue no: **SM 3557**

**BIX BEIDERBECKE VOL 2 (Davenport Blues )**
Tracks: / Flock o' blues / I'm glad I didn't know / Toddling blues / Idolizing / Hush-a-bye / I'd rather be the girl in your arms / Sunday / Cover me up with sunshine /

**Bix Beiderbecke - Bix Beiderbecke Collection (Deja Vu)**

Just one more kiss.
**Album:** Released Apr '81, on Joker (USA) by Lifetime Records (USA). Catalogue no: **SM 3558**

**BIX BEIDERBECKE VOL 3 (My Pretty Girl)**
Tracks: / I'm proud of a baby like you / I'm looking over a four leaf clover / I'm gonna meet my sweetie now / Hoosier sweetheart / Look at the world and smile / My pretty girl / Sunny disposish / Lane in Spain, A.
**Album:** Released Apr '81, on Joker (USA) by Lifetime Records (USA). Catalogue no: **SM 3559**

**BIX BEIDERBECKE VOL 4 (Singin' The Blues)**
Tracks: / Trumbology / Clarinet marmalade / Singing the blues / Slow river / Ostrich walk / Riverboat shuffle / I'm coming Virginia / Way down yonder in New Orleans / For no reason at all in 'C' / In my merry oldsmobile / Three blind mice / Blue river / There's a cradle in Caroline.
**Album:** Released '88, on Big Band Era Catalogue no: **20179**
**Cass:** Released May '88, on Big Band Era Catalogue no: **40179**
**Album:** Released Apr '81, on Joker (USA) by Lifetime Records (USA). Catalogue no: **SM 3560**

**BIX BEIDERBECKE VOL 5 (In A Mist )**
Tracks: / In a mist / Blue river / Clementine / Wringin' and twistin' / Humpty dumpty / Krazy kat / Baltimore / There ain't no land like dixieland / There's a candle Caroline / Just an hour of love / I'm wondering who / At the jazz band ball / Royal Garden blues / Jazz me blues.
**Album:** Released Apr '81, on Joker (USA) by Lifetime Records (USA). Catalogue no: **SM 3561**

**BIX BEIDERBECKE VOL 6 (Good Man Is Hard To Find, A )**
Tracks: / Three blind mice / Clorinda / I'm more than satisfied / Goose pimples / Sorry / Crying all day / Good man is hard to find, A / Since my best gal turned me down.
**Album:** Released Apr '81, on Joker (USA) by Lifetime Records (USA). Catalogue no: **SM 3562**

**BIX BEIDERBECKE VOL 7 (Lonely Melody )**
Tracks: / Washboard blues / Changes / Mary (who are you waiting for) / Lonely melody / Smile / There'll come a time / Jubilee / Ol' man river / San 6 / San 7.
**Album:** Released Apr '81, on Joker (USA) by Lifetime Records (USA). Catalogue no: **SM 3563**

**BIX BEIDERBECKE VOL 8 (Mississippi Mud)**
Tracks: / Mississippi mud / Smile / Make believe / Dardanella / There ain't no sweet man that's worth the salt of my tears / Back in your own back yard / Love nest, The / From Monday to Mississippi mud / From Monday on.
**Album:** Released Apr '81, on Joker (USA) by Lifetime Records (USA). Catalogue no: **SM 3564**

**BIX BEIDERBECKE VOL 9 (Showboat)**
Tracks: / Why do I love you / Can't help lovin' dat man / You are my love / Make believes / Coquette / When / Metropolis / Lovable / Our bungalow of dreams / Lila.
**Album:** Released Apr '81, on Joker (USA) by Lifetime Records (USA). Catalogue no: **SM 3565**

**BIX BEIDERBECKE, VOL. 10**
**Album:** Released '88, on Joker (USA) by Lifetime Records (USA). Catalogue no: **SM 3566**

**BIX BEIDERBECKE VOL 11 (Ol' Man River)**
Tracks: / My melancholy baby / Is it gonna be long / Get out and get under the moon / Oh you have no idea / Felix the cat / T'aint so honey / I'd rather cry over you / That's my weakness now / Georgie porgie / Because my baby don't mean "Maybe" now / Out of town gal / Bless your sister / Dusty Stevedore / Ol' man river / Wa-da-da.
**Album:** Released Apr '81, on Joker (USA) by Lifetime Records (USA). Catalogue no: **SM 3567**

**BIX BEIDERBECKE VOL 12 (Rhythm King)**
Tracks: / Concerto in F (2nd movement pt 1) / Gipsy / Sweet Sue / Take your tomorrow / Love affairs / Rhythm king / Louisiana / Margie / Love nest, The / Japanese Sandman / High upon a hilltop / Sentimental baby.
**Album:** Released Apr '81, on Joker (USA) by Lifetime Records (USA). Catalogue no: **SM 3568**

**BIX BEIDERBECKE VOL 13 (Futuristic Rhythm )**
Tracks: / Futuristic rhythm / Raisin' the roof / Louise / Wait till you see ma cherie / Baby won't you please come home / No one can take your place / I like that / When my dreams come true / Reaching for someone (and not finding anyone there) / China boy / Oh miss Hannah / Waiting at the end of the road / When you're counting the stars alone.
**Album:** Released Apr '81, on Joker (USA) by Lifetime Records (USA). Catalogue no: **SM 3569**

**BIX BEIDERBECKE VOL 14 (Georgia On My Mind )**
Tracks: / Rockin' chair / Barnacle Bill the sailor / Loved one / Loved one B / Deep harlem / Strut Miss Lizzie / Deep south (takes 1&2) / I don't mind walking in the rain / I'll be a friend with pleasure (takes 2&3) / Georgia on my mind / One night in Havana / Bessie couldn't help it (takes 1&2).
**Album:** Released Apr '81, on Joker (USA) by Lifetime Records (USA). Catalogue no: **SM 3570**

**BIX LIVES (Various artists)**
Tracks: / Clementine: *Goldkette, Jchestra* / Proud (of a baby like you): *Goldkette, Jean & His Orchestra* / Changes: *Whiteman, Paul & His Orchestra* / What are you waiting for Mary: *Whiteman, Paul & His Orchestra* / Lonely melody: *Whiteman, Paul & His Orchestra* / San: *Whiteman, Paul & His Orchestra* / Smile:

*Whiteman, Paul & His Orchestra* / Back in your own backyard: *Whiteman, Paul & His Orchestra* / There ain't no sweetman that's worth the salt: *Whiteman, Paul & His Orchestra* / Dardanella: *Whiteman, Paul & His Orchestra* / Love nest, The: *Whiteman, Paul & His Orchestra* / From Monday on: *Whiteman, Paul & His Orchestra* / Sugar coquette: *Whiteman, Paul & His Orchestra* / When (take 2): *Whiteman, Paul & His Orchestra* / When (take 3): *Whiteman, Paul & His Orchestra* / Loveable: *Whiteman, Paul & His Orchestra* / My pet: *Whiteman, Paul & His Orchestra* / Forget me not: *Whiteman, Paul & His Orchestra* / Louisiana: *Whiteman, Paul & His Orchestra* / You took advantage of me: *Whiteman, Paul & His Orchestra* / Deep down South: *Beiderbecke, Bix & His Gang* / I'll be friend with pleasure: *Beiderbecke, Bix & His Gang.*

**CD:** Released Jul '89, on Bluebird (2) by BMG Records (UK). Catalogue no: **ND 86845**

**Cass:** Released Jul '89, on Bluebird (2) by BMG Records (UK). Catalogue no: **NK 86845**

**Album:** Released Jul '89, on Bluebird (2) by BMG Records (UK). Catalogue no: **NL 86845**

**BIX 'N' BING (Beiderbecke, Bix/Bing Crosby/Paul Whiteman Orchestra)**

Tracks: / Changes / (What are you waiting for?)! Mary / There ain't no sweet man that's worth the salt of my tears / Sunshine / Mississippi mud / High water / From Monday on / Loveable / My pet / Louisiana / Do I hear you saying "I love you"? / You took advantage of me / 'Tain't so, honey, 'tain't so / That's my weakness now / Because my baby don't mean maybe now / I'm in the seventh heaven / Reaching for someone (and not finding anyone there) / Oh, Miss Hannah / Your mother and mine / Waiting at the end of the road.

**CD:** on Living Era by Academy Sound & Vision Records. Catalogue no: **CD AJA 5005**

**Cass:** Released 1 Aug '81, on Living Era by Academy Sound & Vision Records. Catalogue no: **ZC AJA 5005**

**Album:** Released 1 Aug '81, on Living Era by Academy Sound & Vision Records. Catalogue no: **AJA 5005**

**BIXOLOGY**

Tracks: / Jazz me blues / At the Jazz Band Ball / Royal Garden blues / Sorry / Singing the blues / I'm comin', Virginia / Way down yonder in New Orleans / For no reason at all in C / Goose pimples / Trumbology / Ostrich walk / Riverboat shuffle / Davenport blues / Copenhagen / Fidgety feet / Tiger rag / In a mist / Clementine / Thou swell / Ol' man river / Wa-da-da / Louisiana / Margie / I'll be a friend with pleasure / Bessie couldn't help it.

**CD:** Released Jun '88, on Giants of Jazz by Hasmick Promotions. Catalogue no: **GOJCD 53017**

**FIDGETY FEET**

**Bix Beiderbecke - Golden Age of Bix Beiderbecke (EMI)**

Tracks: / Fidgety feet / Jazz me blues / Copenhagen / Riverboat shuffle / Oh baby / Susie / Sensation rag / Lazy daddy / Tiger rag / Big boy / Tia juana.

**Album:** Released Apr '81, on Joker (USA) by Lifetime Records (USA). Catalogue no: **SM 3087**

**Album:** Released Sep '85, on Saar Giants Of Jazz (Italy) Catalogue no: **LPJT 25**

**Cass:** Released Sep '85, on Saar Giants Of Jazz (Italy) Catalogue no: **MCJT 25**

**GOLDEN AGE OF BIX BEIDERBECKE (See panel above)**

Tracks: / Singing the blues / Riverboat shuffle / I'm coming Virginia / Way down yonder in New Orleans / There ain't no land like Dixieland to me / I'm wondering who / At the jazz band ball / Sorry / Crying all day / Since my best gal turned me down / Royal Garden blues / Humpty Dumpty / In a mist / Trumbology.

**Album:** Released Sep '83, on EMI by EMI Records. Deleted Jan '88. Catalogue no: **GX 2513**

**Cass:** Released May '88, on MFP by EMI Records. Catalogue no: **TC MFP 5828**

**CD:** Released Nov '88, on MFP by EMI Records. Catalogue no: **CD-MFP 6046**

**CD:** Released Nov '88, on MFP by EMI Records. Catalogue no: **CDB 791 439 2**

**Album:** Released May '88, on MFP by EMI Records. Catalogue no: **MFP 5828**

**INDISPENSABLE BIX BEIDERBECKE**

Tracks: / I didn't know / Idolizing / Sunday / I'm proud of a baby like you / I'm looking over a four leaf clover / I'm gonna meet my sweetie now / Hoosier sweetheart / My pretty girl / Slow river / In my merry Oldsmobile / Clementine (from New Orleans) / Washboard blues / Changes / Mary / Lonely melody / San / Back in your own back yard / There ain't no sweet man that's worth the salt of my tears / Dardanella / From Monday on / Mississippi Mud / Sugar / Coquette / When / Lovable / My pet / Forget me not / Louisiana / You took advantage of me / Rockin' chair / Barnacle Bill the sailor / Deep down south / I don't mind walking in the rain / I'll be a friend with pleasure / Georgia on my mind / Bessie couldn't help it.

**2 LP Set:** Released Sep '86, on Jazz Tribune by BMG Records (UK). Catalogue no: **NL 89572**

**Cass set:** Released Sep '86, on Jazz Tribune by BMG Records (UK). Catalogue no: **NK 89572**

**JAZZ CLASSICS IN DIGITAL STEREO**

Tracks: / Take your tomorrow / Goose Pimples / Wa-da-da / Rhythm King / Since my best gal turned me down / There'll come a time / Barnacle Bill the sailor / Deep Harlem / Rockin' chair / I like that / Jazz me blues / At the jazz band ball / Copenhagen / Royal garden blues / Mississippi mud / Sorry.

**CD:** Released Aug '86, on BBC by BBC Records & Tapes. Catalogue no: **BBC CD 601**

**Cass:** Released Aug '86, on BBC by BBC Records & Tapes. Catalogue no: **ZCF 601**

**LEGENDARY BIX BEIDERBECKE, THE**
**Cass:** Released May '88, on Classic Jazz Masters Catalogue no: **42020**
**Album:** Released May '88, on Classic Jazz Masters Catalogue no: **22020**
**Cass:** Released Mar '90, on Silva Screen by Silva Screen Records. Catalogue no: **MRT 40048**

**LOUISIANA (Bix Beiderbeck Vol.9)**
Tracks: / Borneo / My pet / Somebody stole my gal / Thou swell / My pet & I / It was the dawn of love / Forget me not / Louisiana / You took advantage of me.
**Album:** Released Apr '81, on Joker (USA) by Lifetime Records (USA). Catalogue no: **SM 4566**

**RARE BIX, 1927-29, THE**
**Album:** Released Jan '82, on Swaggie (Australia) Catalogue no: **S 1218**

**STUDIO BANDS-1927 , THE**
Tracks: / Trumbology / Clarinet marmalade / Singing the blues / Ostrich walk / Riverboat shuffle / I'm coming Virginia / Way down yonder in New Orleans / For no reason at all in C / Three blind mice / Blue river / There's a cradle in Caroline / In a mist / Wringin' and twistin' / Humpty Dumpty / Krazy Kat / Baltimore.
**Album:** Released Jul '81, on World by World Records. Deleted '86. Catalogue no: **SH 413**

**STUDIO BANDS LATE 1927 (VOL 2), THE**
Tracks: / There ain't no land like dixieland / There's a cradle in Caroline / Just an hour of love / I'm wondering who / At the jazz band ball / Royal Garden blues / Jazz me blues / I'm more than satisfied (Take 1) / I'm more than satisfied (Take 2) / Clorinda (Take 1) / Clorinda (Take 2) / Three blind mice (take 1) / Three blind mice (take 2) / Goose pimples / Sorry / Crying all day / Good man is hard to find, A / Since my best gal turned me down.
Note: The second volume from Bix Beiderbecke & His Gang and friends to follow up from last year's successful reissue of Volume 1,released to co-incide with 'The Beiderbecke Affair' TV series.Extensive sleeve notes by Brian Rust and detailed personnels make this an excellent purchase for the authentic enthusiast,while also containing the trad-jazz flavour so much in vogue today. A MONO recording
**Album:** Released Jul '81, on World by World Records. Deleted '86. Catalogue no: **SH 414**

**STUDIO BANDS 1928**
Tracks: / Sugar / Jubilee / Mississippi mud / Ol' man river / Lila / Borneo / My pet / Thou swell / Dusky stevedore / Take your tomorrow / Love affairs.
**Album:** Released Jul '81, on World by World Records. Deleted '86. Catalogue no: **SH 415**

**STUDIO BANDS 1928-38**
Tracks: / Rhythm king / Louisiana / Margie / Love nest / Japanese sandman / Futuristic rhythm / Louise / Baby won't you please come home / I like that / Loved one / Deep Harlem.
**Album:** Released Jul '81, on World by World Records. Deleted '86. Catalogue no: **SH 416**

**TRUMPET ALBUM Vol. 2 (Beiderbecke, Bix / Various Artists)**
**Album:** Released '88, on Meritt (USA) Catalogue no: **MERITT 9**

**UNHEARD BIX (Beiderbecke, Bix / Various Artists)**
**Album:** Released '79, on Broadway (USA) Catalogue no: **BWY 102**

**YOUNG MAN WITH A HORN**
Tracks: / Jazz me blues / Louisiana / Sorry / Thou swell / Ol' man river / Somebody stole my gal / Royal Garden blues / At the jazz band ball / Since my best gal turned me down / Wa-da-da (everybody's doin' it now) / Goose pimples / Rhythm King / Singing the blues / Clarinet marmalade / Way down yonder in New Orleans / Mississippi mud / For no reason at all in C / There'll come a time / I'm comin', Virginia / Ostrich walk / Good man is hard to find, A / Wringin' and twistin' / Crying all day / Riverboat shuffle.
**2 LP Set:** Released Mar '85, on CBS by CBS Records. Catalogue no: **CBS 22179**
**Cass:** Released Mar '85, on CBS by CBS Records. Catalogue no: **40 22179**

## Beirach, Richie

**COMMON HEART**
**CD:** Released Jul '88, on Owl (France) Catalogue no: **OWLLC 048**
**Album:** Released Jul '88, on Owl (France) Catalogue no: **OWLL 048**
**Cass:** Released Jul '88, on Owl (France) Catalogue no: **OWLL 748**

**DOUBLE EDGE (Beirach, Richie / Liebman, David)**
**Album:** Released Nov '86, on Storyville by Storyville Records AB. Catalogue no: **SLP 4091**
**CD:** Released Feb '89, on Storyville by Storyville Records AB. Catalogue no: **STCD 4091**

**ELEGY FOR BILL EVANS**
**CD:** Released Feb '90, on Storyville by Storyville Records AB. Catalogue no: **STCD 4151**

**LEAVING**
**CD:** Released Feb '90, on Storyville by Storyville Records AB. Catalogue no: **STCD 4149**

**OMERTA**
**CD:** Released Feb '90, on Storyville by Storyville Records AB. Catalogue no: **STCD 4154**

## Bell, Carey

**CAREY BELL'S BLUES HARP**
**Album:** Released Dec '88, on Delmark (USA) by Delmark Records (USA). Catalogue no: **DL 622**

**DYNASTY (Bell, Carey & Lurrie)**
**CD:** Released Feb '89, on JSP by JSP Records. Catalogue no: **JSPCD 222**

**GOIN' ON MAIN STREET (Bell Carey Blues Harp Band)**
Note: Also featuring Lurrie Bell.
**Album:** Released Dec '88, on L&R Catalogue no: **LR 42.051**

**HARPSLINGER**
**CD:** Released Apr '88, on JSP by JSP Records. Catalogue no: **JSP CD 211**

**SON OF A GUN (Bell, Carey & Lurrie)**
**Album:** Released Feb '84, on Rooster (USA) Catalogue no: **R 2617**

**STRAIGHT SHOOT (Bell, Carey & Lurrie & Junkyard Angels)**
**Album:** Released Feb '88, on Blues South West by Red Lightning Records Catalogue no: **BSW 001**

## Bell, Graeme

**Biographical details:** Bell, Graeme The first jazz revival began in the late '30s on the West Coast USA as white players adopted the original New Orleans style of 20 years earlier; this led to styles called Dixieland in the USA and Trad in Britain, often sneered at by critics but including many fine players, of whom the Australians are often overlooked. Graeme Bell is one of the best, a pianist and leader born in Melbourne in 1914. He began playing the New Orleans style in 1943, toured Europe in the late '40s, ran an art gallery in the late '50s, then formed a new band. Eight tracks made in London in 1948 and recently reissued on Esquire (eight tracks by Ken Colyer on the other side) include his brother Roger Bell on trumpet and vocalist/multi-instrumentalist Adrian 'Lazy' Ade Monsborough (born in 1917) who was offered a chair in Humphrey Lyttleton's band but turned it down. (Donald Clarke 23 August 1988).

**CZECHOSLOVAK JOURNEY**
**Album:** Released Jan '83, on Swaggie (Australia) Catalogue no: **S 1394**

**GRAEME BELL ALL STARS**
**Album:** Released Mar '84, on Jazzology (USA) by Jazzology Records (USA) Catalogue no: **J 75**

**GRAEME BELL & HIS AUSTRALIAN JAZZ BAND (1949-50)**
**Album:** Released Jan '83, on Swaggie (Australia) Catalogue no: **S 1224**

**GRAEME BELL & HIS AUSTRALIAN JAZZ BAND (London)**
**Album:** Released Jan '83, on Swaggie (Australia) Catalogue no: **S 1291**

**GRAEME BELL & HIS AUSTRALIAN JAZZ BAND (1949-52)**
**Album:** Released Jan '83, on Swaggie (Australia) Catalogue no: **S 1397**

**GRAEME BELL & HIS AUSTRALIAN JAZZ BAND (1949)**
**Album:** Released Jan '83, on Swaggie

(Australia) Catalogue no: **S 1268**

**GRAEME BELL & HIS AUSTRALIAN JAZZ BAND (1948-49)**
**Album:** Released Jan '83, on Swaggie (Australia) Catalogue no: **S 1396**

**GRAEME BELL & JAZZ BAND 1947-51**
Note: Featuring previously unissued 'See see rider" and "Way down yonder in New Orleans".
**Cass:** Released Jun '87, on Swaggie (Australia) Catalogue no: **S 1411**

**IN CZECHOSLOVAKIA (Bell, Graeme & His Dixieland Jazz Band)**
**Album:** Released Dec '86, on Dawn Club by Cadillac Music. Catalogue no: **DC 12002**

**PARIS (1948)**
**Album:** Released Jan '83, on Swaggie (Australia) Catalogue no: **S 1395**

## Bellson, Louis

**Biographical details:** Bellson, Louie Born Louis Paul Balassoni in 1924 in Rock Falls, Illinois, the drummer, bandleader and composer grew up in his father's music shop and won contests as an amateur, later worked for Benny Goodman, and Tommy Dorsey. He developed a unique style with two bass drums from 1946. He joined Duke Ellington 1951-53, married Pearl Bailey and has worked as her music director, with Norman Granz's Jazz At The Philharmonic, played with various bands and often formed his won, a powerful but always musical drummer with an unmistakeable personality. He led the band on a James Brown album *Soul on Top* in 1970. (Donald Clarke 23 August 1988).

**BIG BAND EXPLOSION LIVE**
Tracks: / Spacin' home / Intrigue / Groove blues / Spanish gipsy / I remember Duke / Time check.
**Album:** Released Apr '80, on Pye Deleted '85. Catalogue no: **N 127**

**BIG BAND JAZZ FROM THE SUMMIT**
**Album:** Released Feb '88, on Fresh Sounds (Spain) by Fresh Sounds Records (Spain). Catalogue no: **FS 83**

**COOL, COOL BLUE**
Tracks: / Tapooze don / If we were in love / Wanderlust / Boss / Cool cool blue / Long ago / Third 'I'.
**Album:** Released Oct '84, on Pablo Jazz (USA) by Pablo Records (USA). Catalogue no: **2310 899**

**EAST SIDE SUITE (Bellson, Louis & His Jazz Orchestra)**
Tracks: / Tenor time / What makes Moses run.
**Album:** Released '89, on Denon Catalogue no: **CIJD 40161W**
**CD:** Released '89, on Denon Catalogue no: **CIJD 60161X**

**ECUE (Bellson, Louis & Walfredo De Los Reyes)**
Tracks: / Javille / Sentifo en seis (six feeling) / Para buenos bailarines (for good dancers) / Salsa en cinco (salsa in five) / Ecue (folder sleeve).
**Cass:** Released '82, on Pablo Jazz (USA) by Pablo Records (USA). Catalogue no: **K10 807**
**Album:** Released '82, on Pablo Jazz (USA) by Pablo Records (USA). Catalogue no: **2310807**

**HOT (Bellson, Louis & His Jazz Orchestra)**
Tracks: / Caravan / Ode to a friend / Peaceful poet, The / Together we rise / Hot / Hookin' it / Waltzing at Denison / Walkin' with Buddy.
**CD:** Released '89, on Music Masters by Music Masters Records. Catalogue no: **CIJD 60160X**
**Album:** Released '89, on Music Masters by Music Masters Records. Catalogue no: **CIJD 460160ZY**
**CD:** Released Nov '89, on Limelight Catalogue no: **820 807-2**
**Cass:** Released '89, on Music Masters by Music Masters Records. Catalogue no: **CIJD 260160ZX**

**LIVE AT JAZZ SHOWCASE (Bellson, Louis Four)**
Tracks: / Sonny side / Duke's blues / 3 p.m. / I hear a rhapsody / Jam for your bread / Warm alley / Cherokee.
Note: With Don Menza on tenor and flute, pianist Larry Novak and bassist John Heard. CD version has one extra track.
**Cass:** Released Jul '88, on Concord Jazz by Concord Jazz Records (USA). Catalogue no: **CJC 350**
**CD:** Released Jul '88, on Concord Jazz by Concord Jazz Records (USA). Catalogue no: **CCD 4350**
**Album:** Released Jul '88, on Concord Jazz by Concord Jazz Records (USA). Catalogue no: **CJ 350**

**LONDON CONCERT, THE (see Peterson, Oscar) (Bellson, Louis / Oscar Peterson / John Heard)**
**Album:** Released '82, on Pablo Jazz (USA) by Pablo Records (USA). Catalogue no: **2620 111**

**LONDON GIG, THE (Bellson, Louis & Big Band)**
Tracks: / Sing a song of love / My mother / Drum squad / Blues for Fred / Jus fer us / We've come a long way together / Put it right here / Santos.
**Album:** Released May '83, on Pablo Jazz (USA) by Pablo Records (USA). Catalogue no: **2310 880**
**Cass:** Released May '83, on Pablo Jazz (USA) by Pablo Records (USA). Catalogue no: **K10 880**

**LONDON SCENE (Bellson, Louis & Big Band)**
**Album:** Released Nov '81, on Concord Jazz by Concord Jazz Records (USA). Catalogue no: **CJ 157**

**LOUIS BELLSON BIG BAND**
Tracks: / Intimacy of the bands / Quiet riots / Carnaby Street / Beyond category / Chameleon / Open your window / Movin' on / Groove blues / La banda grande.
**Album:** Released '82, on Pablo Jazz (USA) by Pablo Records (USA). Catalogue no: **2310 755**
**Cass:** Released '82, on Pablo Jazz (USA) by Pablo Records (USA). Catalogue no: **K10 755**

**LOUIS BELLSON & HIS JAZZ ORCHESTRA (Bellson, Louis & His Jazz Orchestra)**
Tracks: / It don't mean a thing / Fascinating rhythm / Latin affair, A.
**Cass:** Released Jan '89, on Music Masters by Music Masters Records. Catalogue no: **MMC 40120 Z**
**Album:** Released Jan '89, on Music Masters by Music Masters Records. Catalogue no: **MMD 20120 A**
**CD:** Released Jan '89, on Music Masters by Music Masters Records. Catalogue no: **MMD 60120 Y**

**LOUIS BELLSON JAM**
Tracks: / Melody for Thelma / Stein on vine / Shave tail / Gonga din / I wonder why / Ballad medley-All the way home / Time to ride a moonbeam / Bye bye to all the birds / Blue invasion / Gush of periwinkles, A.
**Album:** Released '82, on Pablo Jazz (USA) by Pablo Records (USA). Catalogue no: **2310 838**
**Cass:** Released '82, on Pablo Jazz (USA) by Pablo Records (USA). Catalogue no: **K10 838**

**MATTERHORN**
Tracks: / Matterhorn suite for drums, The (entrance) / Knuf brothers, The / Conversations / Then and now / War bird.
**Cass:** Released '82, on Pablo Jazz (USA) by Pablo Records (USA). Catalogue no: **K10 834**
**Album:** Released '82, on Pablo Jazz (USA) by Pablo Records (USA). Catalogue no: **2310 834**

**ORIGINALS (Bellson, Louis / Malach / Pizzapelli / Jones)**
**Album:** Released Apr '81, on Stash (USA) Catalogue no: **ST 205**

**SIDE TRACK**
**Album:** Released Apr '81, on Concord by Concord Jazz Records (USA). Catalogue no: **CJ 141**

**SUNSHINE ROCK (Bellson, Louis & The Explosion Orchestra)**
Tracks: / Sunshine swing / Mid-eastern spango / Night birds / Feels so good / Hawk talks, The / Rich outing / Niles blues / Numero uno.
**Album:** Released '82, on Pablo Jazz (USA) by Pablo Records (USA). Catalogue no: **2310 851**
**Cass:** Released '82, on Pablo Jazz (USA) by Pablo Records (USA). Catalogue no: **K10 851**

**THUNDERBIRD**
Tracks: / Thunderbird / Little pixie, The / Nails / Serenade in blues.
**Cass:** Released Aug '82, on Jasmine

by Hasmick Promotions. Catalogue no: **JAS C40**
**Album:** Released Aug '82, on Jasmine by Hasmick Promotions. Catalogue no: **JAS 40**

**WITH BELLS ON!**
Tracks: / Who's who / Cool / Amoroso / Prelude / Gumshoe / Blitzen / St. Louis / Moon is low / Doozy / Lou's blues / With bells on / Diplomat speaks, The / Mighty two, The / Paradiddle song / Rolls a la bossa nova / More flams / Swinging the rudiments / Que sticks / Two in one / Rhythmic excursion / Slides and hides.
**Album:** Released May '83, on Vogue Jazz (France) by Vogue Records. Catalogue no: **VJD 564**

## Beneke, Tex

**Biographical details:** Beneke, Tex The tenor saxist and vocalist was born in 1914 in Forth Worth, Texas. He was the biggest star in the classic Glenn Miller band of 1938-42, his likeable Texas drawl unmistakeable on *Chattanooga Choo Choo* (the first formally certified million-seller in history), many others; his competent tenor sax was often featured by Miller, most famously in the two-tenor 'chase' exchange with Al Klink on *String of Pearls* but also on ballads. After WWII he had hits for serveral years leading first the Glenn Miller Orchestra, then his own band. He was not even mentioned in the 1954 Glenn Miller Story which had the typically poor Hollywood script values of that period. (Donald Clarke 23 August 1988).

**BENEKE ON BROADWAY (Beneke, Tex & The Glenn Miller Sound)**
Tracks: / More I see you, The / Hello Dolly / I left my heart in San Francisco / My favourite things / Lemon tree / I wish you love / On a clear day / Walk right in / Stranger on the shore / I've grown accustomed to her face / Tonight.
**Cass:** Released Aug '82, on Bulldog Records by President Records. Catalogue no: **AJKL 1037**
**Album:** Released Apr '82, on Bulldog Records by President Records. Catalogue no: **BDL 1037**

**HI THERE TEX (Beneke, Tex & Miller Orchestra)**
**Album:** Released '88, on Swing World by Submarine Records. Catalogue no: **SWS 3**

**LOOSE LIKE (Beneke, Tex Orchestra)**
**Album:** Released '88, on Hep Jazz by Hep Records. Catalogue no: **HEP 29**

**MEMORIES**
Note: Mono
**Album:** Released Oct '84, on First Heard by Submarine Records. Catalogue no: **FH 33**
**Cass:** Released Oct '84, on First Heard by Submarine Records. Catalogue no: **CFH 33**

**RAMBLIN' AROUND**
Tracks: / Sleepy time gal / Put 'em in a box / Do you ever think of me / Don't blame me / Rainy afternoon / My romance / Ramblin' around.
**Cass:** Released 10 Jul '89, on Magic (1) by Submarine Records. Catalogue no: **CAWE 33**
**Album:** Released 10 Jul '89, on Magic (1) by Submarine Records. Catalogue no: **AWE 33**

**SALUTES GLENN MILLER (Beneke, Tex Orchestra)**
**Album:** Released Aug '89, on Golden Era by Delta Records. Catalogue no: **GELP 15093**

**SHOOTING STAR (1948) (Beneke, Tex & His Orchestra)**
Tracks: / Shooting star (Ted Beneke tenor sax solo.) / Now is the hour / Over the rainbow / Whistler, The / Dream lullaby (Deauville Medley with introduction by Ted Beneke) / 18th century drawing room / Thoughtless / Things ain't what they used to be / Rhapsody in blue / That feathery feeling (Tex Beneke) / Sabre dance / Pianissimo (Vocal Ronnie Deauville) / Saturday date (Tex Beneke vocal and tenor sax solo) / Body and soul / Cherokee canyon (Vocal Tex Beneke) / Dreamy lullaby / Beyond the sea / All the things you are.
Note: The music on this record comes from radio programmes recorded while the band played for dancing in locations such as New York, Iowa, New Jersey and Washington. Being 1948 items, they are of interest, as a studio ban operated that year. Several ex-Glenn Miller sidesmen were still in the orchestra, including trumpeters Bobby Nicholas and Whitey Thomas and trombonists Jimmy Priddy and Paul Tanner; Jack Sperling was on drums. Arrangements by Henry Mancini, Jerry Gray and Norman Leyden were still being used.
**Album:** Released Jun '83, on Magic (1) by Submarine Records. Catalogue no: **AWE 8**
**Cass:** Released Jun '83, on Magic (1) by Submarine Records. Catalogue no: **CAWE 8**

**TEX BENEKE AND ORCHESTRA, 1949 (Beneke, Tex Orchestra)**
**Album:** Released Aug '89, on Golden Era by Delta Records. Catalogue no: **GELP 15050**

**TEX BENEKE & THE GLENN MILLER ORCHESTRA (VIDEO) (Beneke, Tex & The Glenn Miller Sound)**
**VHS:** Released '88, on Kay Jazz (video) by Kay Jazz. Catalogue no: **KJ 046**

**UNDER THE RAINBOW**
**Cass:** Released Oct '84, on Artistic by Submarine Records. Catalogue no: **CART 004**
**Album:** Released '84, on Artistic by Submarine Records. Catalogue no: **ART 004**

**WITH NO STRINGS (Beneke, Tex Orchestra)**
Tracks: / What can you do / What's new / Begin the beguine / Devil and the deep blue sea / Blue moon / Cock a doodle / Way you look tonight / Java junction Look up / La Rosita / Castle rock / Horse / Dancer's delight / Hop scotch / Baby C / World on a string.
**Album:** Released Apr '81, on Hep Jaz by Hep Records. Catalogue no: **HEP 8**

## Bennett, Richard

**I GOT RHYTHM**
Tracks: / I got rhuthm / Swanee / No body but you / So it agin / I'll build a stairway to paradise / Three preludes Fascinating rhythm / Lady be good Promenade / Man I love / Somebody loves me / Jazzbo Brown blues / Tha certain feeling / Sweet and lowdown . Merry Andrew / Clap yo' hands / Do dc do / Impromptu in two keys / My one anc only / S'wonderful / Two waltzes in C . Strike up the band / Liza / Three quarter blues / Who cares.
**Album:** Released Sep '81, on H.M.V by EMI Records. Deleted Sep '86. Catalogue no: **EMD 5538**
**Cass:** Released Sep '87, on H.M.V. by EMI Records. Catalogue no: **ED 2913474**
**Album:** Released Sep '87, on H.M.V by EMI Records. Deleted Jul '89. Catalogue no: **ED 2913471**

## Bennett, Tony

**Biographical details:** Born Anthony Benedetto in New York in 1926, Bennett made his first public appearance in a church at the age of seven. After struggling for some years to make a name for himself, he won television and theatre contracts from Arthur Godfrey and Bob Hope. The early Fifties saw Tony Bennett become one of America's top singers with three massive No. 1 hits to his credit: *"Because Of You"*, *"Cold, Cold Heart"* (a song written by country legend Hank Williams) and *"Rags To Riches"*. A fourth smash *"Stranger In Paradise"* gave him his first and biggest British hit. It went to No. 1 in the UK in May '55, winning the race against no less than five other charted versions. it was his only British Top 10 single and indeed he was to have only one more in the States: after hitting No. 9 in the US with 1957's *"In The Middle Of An Island"*, Bennett turned to albums and cabaret. Strangely, Bennett's best known single was not a particularly big hit on either side of the Atlantic, *"I Left My Heart in San Francisco"* reached No. 19 in the US in 1962, winning the Grammy Award for record of the year. In the UK it had to wait untill the mid-Sixties before peaking at No. 25; it was followed shortly afterwards by the biggest of his six British chart albums - *"A String Of Tony's Hits"* reached No. 9. A permanent member of the top league of MoR entertainers, Bennett's theme song should more appropriately be called *"I Left My Heart in The Early Fifties"* - his style could hardly be described as progressive. A graphic summary of the singer's views on the rock 'n' roll and pop music that curtailed his career was contained in a late seventies interview with Britain's 'Radio Times':

America went through in the sixties what Germany went through in the Thirties. (Bob MacDonald)..

**16 GOLDEN CLASSICS**
Tracks: / There'll be some changes made / Blue moon / Lady is a tramp, The / Lover / Manhattan / Spring is here / I could write a book / Child is born, A / Make someone happy / Life is beautiful / Maybe september / Lonely girl / You don't know what love is / Thou swell / There's a small hotel / As time goes by.
Note: All tracks licensed from CBS Special Products: Design shoot that tiger!/(c) 1986/ Castle Communications Place, Units 7, 271 Merton Road, London SW18 5JS
**CD:** Released '86, on Unforgettable by Castle Communications Records. Catalogue no: **UNCD 19**
**Cass:** Released Oct '86, on Unforgettable by Castle Communications Records. Catalogue no: **UNMC 019**
**Album:** Released Dec '86, on Unforgettable by Castle Communications Records. Catalogue no: **UNLP 019**

**ALL TIME GREATEST HITS**
Tracks: / Something / Where do I begin / Maybe this time / Just in time / for once in my life / Firefly / Shadow of your smile / Put on a happy face / Love look away / Rags to riches.
**Album:** Released Aug '84, on CBS Cameo by CBS Records. Deleted '89. Catalogue no: **CAMEO 22176**

**ANYTHING GOES (Bennett, Tony & The Count Basie Big Band)(see panel below).**
Tracks: / I guess I'll have to change my plan / Chicago / With plenty of money and you / Anything goes / Live is a song / I've grown accustomed to her face / Jeepers creepers / Growing pains / Poor little rich girl / Are you having any fun?.
Note: In truth *Anything goes* when one of the most popular singers of the post-war years meets the swing'est big band of all time. Mind you, at one time the idea of using the Count Basie orchestra as a backing group for pop singers would have seemed out of place. It's always been regarded as a strictly instrumental band. But think of it for a while ... Basie has always had singers. Good ones too. The first Basie band, that came out of Kansas City fifty years ago, had the great Jimmy Rushing for fifteen years, then there was Helen Humes in the late thirties. And when the new Basie crew emerged in the fifties, the singing of Joe Williams was an integral part of its composition as were the scores of Ernie Wilkins and Neal Hefti. So the band's proficiency as an accompanying unit had been proved, somuch so that in later years it recorded with the likes of Nat King Cole, Sarah Vaughan and Sinatra. But these singers had all come up through the ranks, so to speak, paying their jazz dues along the way. Anthony Dominick Benedetto had no background in jazz or as a big band vocalist. When he made this album he had under his belt such million sellers as *Because of you* (1951), *Rags to riches* and *Stranger in paradise* (1953) and *In the middle of an island* (1957). All worthy songs which had helped a young singer building his career but hardly your basic jazz material.
But the collaboration paid off. The tight discipline which Count Basie habitually imposed on his band's performance rubbed off on Bennett's erst while erratic pitching and phrasing, and the result was a vindication of an artist who had always had the capability to be a good rhythm singer and who only needed the propulsive beat of the Basie band to realise his full potential. Certainly Tony Bennett responded with a display of his best singing to that time, allied to his impeccable choice of material, and that innate musicanship and good taste that has always separated him from the fly by night pop singers. Even now, he still refuses to compromise. If we want Tony Bennett in the eighties we take him on his own terms. This may well be Tony Bennett's best-ever album. It wasn't the last time he and this mighty band worked together on record or in person, and it shows why Basie and Bennett in tandem were the hardest of double acts to follow. (Arthur Jackson)
**Cass:** Released Oct '85, on Bulldog Records by President Records. Catalogue no: **BDC 1054**
**Album:** Released Oct '85, on Bulldog Records by President Records. Catalogue no: **BDL 1054**

Anything Goes - Tony Bennett (Bulldog)

**ART OF EXCELLENCE, THE**
Tracks: / Why do people fall in love / Moments like this / What are you afraid of? / When love was all we had / Everybody has the blues / How do you keep the music playing? / City of the angels / Forget the woman / I got lost in her arms / Day you leave me, The.
**Album:** Released Oct '86, on CBS by CBS Records. Deleted Jun '88. Catalogue no: **CBS 26990**
**CD:** Released Oct '86, on CBS by CBS Records. Deleted Jan '89. Catalogue no: **CD 26990**
**Cass:** Released Oct '86, on CBS by CBS Records. Deleted Jun '88. Catalogue no: **40 26990**

**ASTORIA - PORTRAIT OF THE ARTIST**
Tracks: / When do the bells ring for me / I was lost, I was drifting / Little street where old friends meet, A / Girl in love, The / It is like reaching for the moon / Speak low / Folks that live on the hill, The / Antonia / Waver of dreams / There will never be another you / Body and soul / Where do you go from love / Boulevard of broken dreams, The / Where did the magic go / We've come home again.
**Album:** Released Mar '90, on CBS by CBS Records. Catalogue no: **466005 1**
**Cass:** Released Mar '90, on CBS by CBS Records. Catalogue no: **466005 4**
**CD:** Released Mar '90, on CBS by CBS Records. Catalogue no: **466005 2**

**BENNETT & BASIE (Bennett, Tony & Count Basie)**
Tracks: / Strike up the band / I guess I'll have to change my plan / Chicago / With plenty of money and you / Life is a song / Anything goes / Are you havin' any fun

/ Jeepers creepers / Growing pains / Poor little rich girl / I've grown accustomed to her face.
**Album:** Released Jul '82, on Jazz Reactivation Catalogue no: **JR 149**

**BENNETT/BERLIN**
Tracks: / They say it's wonderful / Isn't this a lovely day / All of my life / Now it can be told / Song is ended, The / When I lost you / Cheek to cheek / Let yourself go / Let's face the music and dance / Shakin' the blues away / Russian lullaby / White Christmas.
Note: Produced by Danny Bennett; arranged by Tony Bennett; with the artistry of the Ralph Sharon Trio: Ralph Sharon, piano; Joe LaBarbera, drums; Paul Langosch, bass.With special guest artists (on certain tracks) George Benson, guitar; Dizzy Gillespie, trumpet; Dexter Gordon, sax. Recorded and mixed at Hillside studio, Englewood, New Jersey on Sony 3324 Digital multi-track recorder and Sony 1630 digital processor. Engineered by Paul Mufson and Daegel Bennett. Mastered at Masterdisk, New York City on the Neumann Direct to Metal System. Mastered by Bob Ludwig. Production co-ordinator: Tom Chiappa. Sleeve note: "God bless Irving Berlin; he's the heart & soul of american song" - Tony Bennett.
**Cass:** Released Feb '88, on CBS by CBS Records. Deleted Jan '90. Catalogue no: **460450 4**
**Album:** Released Feb '88, on CBS by CBS Records. Deleted 10 Jul '89. Catalogue no: **460 450-1**
**CD:** Released Feb '88, on CBS by CBS Records. Deleted Jan '90. Catalogue no: **460450 2**

**BEST OF TONY BENNETT**
**Cass:** Released Jul '84, on Creole (Everest-Europa) by Creole Records. Catalogue no: **16-19**

**CHICAGO (Bennett, Tony & Count Basie)**
**Album:** Released Nov '84, on Astan (USA) Catalogue no: **20029**
**Cass:** Released Nov '84, on Astan (USA) Catalogue no: **40029**
**CD:** Released Jun '86, on Dunhill Compact Classics (USA) Catalogue no: **DZS 004**

**CLOSE YOUR EYES**
Tracks: / Close your eyes.
**7" Single:** Released Sep '55, on Philips by Phonogram Ltd. Deleted '58. Catalogue no: **PB 445**

**COME NEXT SPRING**
Tracks: / Come next Spring.
**7" Single:** Released Apr '56, on Philips by Phonogram Ltd. Deleted '59. Catalogue no: **PB 537**

**FOR ONCE IN MY LIFE**
**Album:** Released Mar '68, on CBS by CBS Records. Deleted '73. Catalogue no: **SBPG 63166**

**GOOD LIFE, THE**
Tracks: / Good life.
**7" Single:** Released Jul '63, on CBS by CBS Records. Deleted '66. Catalogue no: **AAG 153**

**I LEFT MY HEART IN SAN FRANCISCO**
**Album:** Released May '65, on CBS by CBS Records. Deleted '70. Catalogue no: **BPG 62201**
**CD:** Released Mar '90, on Collector's Choice by CBS Records. Catalogue no: **902288-2**
**Album:** Released Mar '86, on CBS by CBS Records. Catalogue no: **CBS 32732**

**I LEFT MY HEART IN SAN FRANCISCO (OLD GOLD)**
Tracks: / I left my heart in San Francisco.
**7" Single:** Released Jul '82, on Old Gold by Old Gold Records. Catalogue no: **OG 9184**

**I LEFT MY HEART IN SAN FRANCISCO (SINGLE)**
**Cass:** Released Mar '86, on CBS by CBS Records. Deleted Aug '88. Catalogue no: **40 32732**
**7" Single:** Released May '65, on CBS by CBS Records. Deleted '68. Catalogue no: **CBS 201730**

**IF I RULED THE WORLD (SINGLE)**
Tracks: / If I ruled the world.
**7" Single:** Released May '65, on CBS by CBS Records. Deleted '68. Catalogue no: **CBS 201735**

**IN PERSON (Bennett, Tony & Count Basie) (See panel below)**
Tracks: / Just in time / When I fall in love / Taking a chance on love / Without a song / Fascinating rhythm / Solitude / Pennies from Heaven / Lost in the stars / Firefly / There will never be another you / Lullaby of Broadway / Ol' man river.
**Album:** Released Nov '83, on CBS Cameo by CBS Records. Catalogue no: **CBS 32373**

**JAZZ**
Tracks: / I can't believe that you're in love with me / Don't get around much anymore / Stella by starlight / On Green Dolphin Street / Let's face the music and dance / I'm through with love / Solitude / Lullaby of Broadway / Dancing in the dark / I let a song go out of my heart / When lights are low / Just one of those things / Crazy rhythm / Judy / Give me the simple life / Street of dreams / Love scene / While the music plays on / Close your eyes / Out of this world / Just friends / Have you met Miss Jones? / Danny boy / Sweet Lorraine.
**Cass:** Released '87, on CBS by CBS Records. Del '89. Catalogue no: **450 465-4**
**Album:** Released Jun '87, on CBS by CBS Records. Deleted Aug '88. Catalogue no: **450465 1**

**LIFE IS A SONG (Bennett, Tony & Count Basie)**
Tracks: / I've grown accustomed to her face / Jeepers creepers / Growing pains / Poor little rich girl / Are you having any fun / I guess I'll have to change my plans / Chicago / With plenty of money and you / Anything goes / Life is a song.
**Cass:** Released '86, on Topline by Charly Records. Catalogue no: **KTOP 115**
**Album:** Released '86, on Topline by Charly Records. Catalogue no: **TOP 115**

**MAGIC OF, THE**
Tracks: / What is this thing called love / Love for sale / I'm in love again / You'd

**Tony Bennett - In Person (CBS)**

be so nice to come home to / Easy to love / It's alright by me / Night and day / Dream dancing / I've got you under my skin / Get out of town / Experiment / One / This funny world / Lost in the stars / As time goes by / I used to be color blind / Mr. Magic.
**Cass:** Released Oct '89, on Horatio Nelson by Horatio Nelson Records & Tapes Ltd.. Catalogue no: **CYU 106**
**Album:** Released Oct '89, on Horatio Nelson by Horatio Nelson Records & Tapes Ltd.. Catalogue no: **YU 106**

### MY HEART SINGS
**Album:** Released Feb '88, on Fresh Sounds (Spain) by Fresh Sounds Records (Spain). Catalogue no: **FS 168**

### PORTRAIT OF A SONG STYLIST
Tracks: / Shadow of your smile, The / Who can I turn to / When Joanna loved me / Don't worry 'bout me / It had to be you / Where or when / Ain't misbehavin' / Dancing in the dark / Second time around / Old devil moon / My funny valentine / Autumn leaves / Taste of honey, A / I left my heart in San Francisco / Toot toot tootsie / September song / Moment of truth / I'll be around.
**Album:** Released Apr '89, on Masterpiece by Castle Communications Records. Catalogue no: **HARLP 105**
**CD:** Released Apr '89, on Masterpiece by Castle Communications Records. Catalogue no: **HARCD 105**
**Cass:** Released Apr '89, on Masterpiece by Castle Communications Records. Catalogue no: **HARMC 105**

### RODGERS AND HART COLLECTION
Tracks: / Thou swell / Most beautiful / Small hotel / I've got five dollars / You took advantage of me / I wish I were in love again / This funny world / My heart stood still / My romance / Mountain greenery / This can't be love / Blue moon / Lady is a tramp, The / Lover / Manhattan / Spring is here / Have you met Miss Jones / Isn't it romantic / Wait 'till you see her / I could write a book.
**CD:** Released Oct '89, on Horatio Nelson by Horatio Nelson Records & Tapes Ltd.. Catalogue no: **CDSIV 1119**
**Cass:** Released Oct '89, on Horatio Nelson by Horatio Nelson Records & Tapes Ltd.. Catalogue no: **CYU 108**
**Album:** Released Oct '89, on Horatio Nelson by Horatio Nelson Records & Tapes Ltd.. Catalogue no: **YU 108**

### RODGERS AND HART SONGBOOK
Tracks: / This can't be love (From The Boys From Syracuse) / Blue moon / Lady is a tramp, The (From Babes In Arms.) / Lover (From Love Me Tonight.) / Manhattan (From the first Garrick Gaieties.) / Spring is here (From I Married An Angel.) / Have you met Miss Jones? (From I'd Rather Be Right.) / Isn't it romantic (From Love Me Tonight.) / Wait 'till you see her (From By Jupiter.) / I could write a book (From Pal Joey.) / Thou swell (From A Connecticut Yankee.) / Most beautiful girl in the world, The (From Jumbo.) / There's a small hotel (From On Your Toes.) / I've got five dollars (From America's Sweetheat.) / You took advantage of me (From Present Arms.) / I wish I were in love again (From Babes In Arms.) / This funny world (From Betsy.) / My heart stood still (From One Damn Thing After Another.) / My romance (From Jumbo.) / Mountain greenery (From the second Garrick Gaieties.).
Note: Recorded at CBS Studios, New York City, September 28-30, 1973. Engineer: Frank Laico. Musicians: Ruby Braff, Cornet/George Barnes,Guitar/Wayne Wright,guitar/ John Giuffrida,Bass.
**2 LP Set:** Released Apr '88, on DRG (USA) by DRG Records (USA). Catalogue no: **DARC 2 2101**
**CD:** Released Apr '88, on DRG (USA) by DRG Records (USA). Catalogue no: **CDXP 2102**
**Cass set:** Released Apr '88, on DRG (USA) by DRG Records (USA). Catalogue no: **DARC 2C 2102**

### SAN FRANCISCO
Tracks: / I left my heart in San Francisco / Taking a chance on love / Have I told you lately that I love you / Candy kisses / I'm always chasing rainbows / MacArthur Park / Little green apples / Eleanor Rigby / My cherie amour / Look of love, The / Something.
**Cass:** Released Jan '83, on Ditto by Pickwick Records. Catalogue no: **DTO 10040**

### SNOWFALL
Tracks: / Snowfall / My favourite things / Christmas song, The / Santa Claus is coming to town / We wish you a merry Christmas / Silent night, holy night / O come all ye faithful / Jingle bells / Where is love / Christmasland / I love the winter weather / I've got my love to keep me warm / White Christmas / Winter wonderland / Have yourself a merry little Christmas.
**Album:** Released Dec '87, on CBS Cameo by CBS Records. Deleted 17 Apr '89. Catalogue no: **460468 1**
**Cass:** Released Dec '87, on CBS Cameo by CBS Records. Catalogue no: **460468 4**

### STRANGER IN PARADISE
Tracks: / Stranger in paradise.
**7" Single:** Released Apr '55, on Philips by Phonogram Ltd. Deleted '58. Catalogue no: **PB 420**

### STRING OF TONY'S HITS, A
**Album:** Released Feb '66, on CBS by CBS Records. Deleted '70. Catalogue no: **DP 66010**

### TILL
Tracks: / Till / Serenata.
**7" Single:** Released Jan '61, on Philips by Phonogram Ltd. Deleted '64. Catalogue no: **PB 1079**

### TO MY WONDERFUL ONE
Tracks: / Wonderful one / Till / September song / Suddenly / I'm a fool to want you / We mustn't say goodbye / Autumn leaves / Laura / April in Paris / Speak low / Tenderly / Just in time / When I fall in love / Taking a chance on love / Without a song / Fascinating rhythm / Solitude / Pennies from Heaven / Lost in the stars / Firefly / There will never be another you / Lullaby of Broadway / Ol' man river.
**Album:** Released Aug '85, on CBS by CBS Records. Catalogue no: **22184**
**Cass:** Released Jun '85, on CBS (Blue Diamond) by CBS Records. Deleted Aug '87. Catalogue no: **40 22184**

### TOGETHER AGAIN (Bennett, Tony & Bill Evans)
Tracks: / Child is born, A / Make someone happy / Bad & the beautiful / Lucky to be me / You're near me / Two lonely people / You don't know what love is / Maybe September / Lonely girl / You must believe in spring.
**CD:** Released Oct '89, on Horatio Nelson by Horatio Nelson Records & Tapes Ltd.. Catalogue no: **CDSIV 1122**
**Cass:** Released Oct '89, on Horatio Nelson by Horatio Nelson Records & Tapes Ltd.. Catalogue no: **CSIV 1122**
**Cass:** Released '88, on DRG (USA) by DRG Records (USA). Catalogue no: **MRSC 901**
**CD:** Released '88, on DRG (USA) by DRG Records (USA). Catalogue no: **CDMRS 901**
**Album:** Released '88, on DRG (USA) by DRG Records (USA). Catalogue no: **MRS 901**

### TONY BENNETT COLLECTION (20 golden greats)
Tracks: / Stranger in Paradise / Fascinating rhythm / I left my heart in San Francisco / Climb every mountain / April in Paris / Sunday / Ol' man river / Sometimes I'm happy / Always / Solitude / Just in time / All the things you are / Our love is here to stay / Lullaby of Broadway / Anything goes / Blue velvet / Love look away / My heart tells me / It amazes me / I'm just a lucky so and so.
**Album:** Released Nov '85, on Deja Vu Catalogue no: **DVLP 2026**
**Cass:** Released Nov '85, on Deja Vu Catalogue no: **DVMC 2026**

### TONY BENNETT & FRIENDS MAKE MAGNIFICENT MUSIC
**Album:** Released '88, on DRG (USA) by DRG Records (USA). Catalogue no: **MRS 910**
**Cass:** Released '88, on DRG (USA) by DRG Records (USA). Catalogue no: **MRSC 910**

### TONY BENNETT IN CONCERT
**VHS:** Released Nov '87, on Mastervision Catalogue no: **MV 051 A**

### TONY MAKES IT HAPPEN
**Album:** Released Sep '67, on CBS by CBS Records. Deleted '72. Catalogue no: **SBPG 63055**

### TONY'S GREATEST HITS
**Album:** Released Sep '67, on CBS by CBS Records. Deleted '72. Catalogue no: **SBPG 62821**

### VERY BEST OF TONY BENNETT (20 greatest hits)
**Album:** Released Feb '77, on Warwick

**George Benson**

by Warwick Records. Deleted '82. Catalogue no: **PA 5021**

### VERY THOUGHT OF YOU, THE

Tracks: / Very thought of you, The.
**7" Single:** Released Dec '65, on CBS by CBS Records. Deleted '68. Catalogue no: **CBS 20201**

## Benson, George

**Biographical details:** Born in Pennsylvania in 1943, George Benson began learning the guitar at the age of eight. Having moved to New York, he earned respect from fellow musicians during the Sixties and early Seventies with his jazz flavoured guitar work, culminating in 1973's much praised *"White Rabbit"* album. Under the name George 'Bad' Benson, he scored his first British hit single in the Autumn of '75 with *"Supership'*, which reached No. 30. George Benson's big break came in 1976 with the jazz-funk LP *"Breezin'"*. Suddenly it was apparent that this skilful guitarist was a strong singer too: *"This Masquerade"*, a remake of the Leon Russell song, became a US Top 10 from the US No. 1 album. 1977's *"In Flight"* continued the formula, giving Benson another US Top 10 album and his first UK chart album. *"Nature Boy"*, a remake of an early Sixties hit associated with Bobby Darin, was a Top 30 single in Britain. The Stevie Wonder-ish vocals of Benson were further pushed to the forefront on the next hit *"The Greatest Love Of All"*. This was the theme from the Muhammed Ali movie *"The Greatest"*. 1978's *"Weekend In L.A."* yielded a second American Top 10 single - indeed, *"On Broadway"* reached No. 7, two places higher than the Drifters had taken the song in 1963. The '79 single *"Love Ballad"* was one of the very best examples of dual talent, an excellent jazz/pop fusion showing off both vocals and guitar to best effect. The next turning point in his career came in 1980 when he teamed up with the famous producer Quincy Jones, who was fresh from his massive success with Michael Jackson's *"Off The Wall"* album. The combination of Benson and Jones made *"Give Me The Night"* a major commercial triumph - the producer's jazz-tinged, soul-inflected but ever commercial sound was just what the artist needed to complete his long-term move into the pop market. In the UK the LP reached No. 3 with 40 weeks on the chart, while the title track was Benson's first Top 10 single. In the US it was his biggest ever 45, reaching No. 4. *"Love X Love"* was a second UK Top Tenner from the album. *"Turn Your Love Around"* and *"Never Give Up On A Good Thing"* the two new hits on *"The George Benson Collection"*, conolidated on his success, with the former hitting No. 5 in the US and the latter reaching No. 14 in the UK. 1983's *"In Your Eyes"* album was once again well received and yielded several hit singles, but was the work of a stagnating artist, The title cut, a romantic ballad, gave Benson his biggest British single since *"Give Me The Night"*. He remains a major concert draw and has established a sufficiently broad following in the adult record-buying market to ensure continued high record sales. (Bob MacDonald).

He was born in 1943 in Pittsburgh Pennsylvania, began in R&B bands and became a fine jazz guitarists influenced by Wes Montgomery. Worked and recorded with organist Jack McDuff on Prestige; recorded for CBS; when Montgomery died, his producer Creed Taylor signed Benson to A&M, then to Taylor's own CTI label; during this period he began singing and soon became a huge star as a jazz-influenced soul balladeer he switched to Warner Brothers and *Breezin'* in 1976 became his first number one album in the USA, also winning Grammies. Taylor won a lawsuit against WB in 1988 claiming that they had helped to put him out of business by stealing Benson. Jazz fans were dismayed by Benson's funky crossover but Benson has a family to support and blames broadcasting and the music business: 'If kids can't hear it, I don't care how good it is, you can't sell it to them'. Others like Derek Jewell felt that he played his hits in concert 'with such panache, creation and re-creation..that he is in truth a great jazzman'. (Derek Jewell) (Donald Clarke 23 August 1988).

### 20/20

Tracks: / No one emotion / Please don't walk away / I just wanna hang around you / Nothing's gonna change my love for you / La mer / New day / You are the love of my life / Hold me / Stand up / 20/20 / Shark bite.
**CD:** Released Jan '85, on Warner Bros. by WEA Records. Catalogue no: **925178 2**
**Album:** Released Jan '85, on Warner Bros. by WEA Records. Catalogue no: **925178 1**
**Cass:** Released Jan '85, on Warner Bros. by WEA Records. Catalogue no: **925178 4**

### 20/20 (SINGLE)

Tracks: / 20/20 / Shark bite.
**12" Single:** Released Jan '85, on Warner Bros. by WEA Records. Catalogue no: **W 9120 T**
**7" Single:** Released Jan '85, on Warner Bros. by WEA Records. Catalogue no: **W 9120**

### BEST OF GEORGE BENSON

Tracks: / White rabbit / Somewhere in the east / Body talk / Take five / California dreamin' / Full compass.
**CD:** Released Sep '84, on CTI (1) by Polydor Ltd. Deleted '88. Catalogue no: **813 659-2**
**Album:** Released Mar '82, on A&M by A&M Records. Deleted '88. Catalogue no: **AMID 115**
**Cass:** Released Mar '82, on A&M by A&M Records. Deleted '88. Catalogue no: **CMID 115**

### BEYOND THE SEA (See panel on next page)

Tracks: / Beyond the sea / Breezin' / This masquerade (on 12" only).

**7" Single:** Released Apr '85, on Warner Bros. by WEA Records. Catalogue no: **W 9014**
**12" Single:** Released Apr '85, on Warner Bros. by WEA Records. Catalogue no: **WN 014 T**

**BLUE BENSON**
Tracks: / Billie's bounce / Low down and dirty / That lucky old sun / Thunder walk / Doobie, doobie blues / What's new / I remember Wes.
Note: This excellent album dates from 1976 and features an all star line-up with Herbie Hancock, Billy Cobham, Ron Carter, Garnett Brown and Clark Terry.
**Cass:** Released Jun '83, on Polydor (Italy) by Polydor Ltd. Catalogue no: **3186 098**
**Album:** Released Jun '83, on Polydor (Italy) by Polydor Ltd. Catalogue no: **2486 272**

**BODY TALK**
**CD:** Released Dec '86, on Musidisc by Musidisc Records (France). Catalogue no: **239206**
**Cass:** Released Feb '84, on CTI (Musidisc France) by Polydor Ltd. Catalogue no: **CTK 9503**

**BREEZIN'**
Tracks: / This masquerade / Six to four / Breezin' / So this is love / Lady / Affirmation.
**Album:** Released Jun '89, on Warner Bros. by WEA Records. Catalogue no: **K 56199**
**Cass:** Released Jun '89, on Warner Bros. by WEA Records. Catalogue no: **K4 56199**
**CD:** Released Jun '89, on Warner Bros. by WEA Records. Catalogue no: **K2 56199**

**COLLABORATION (Benson, George / Earl Klugh)**
Tracks: / Mt. Airy road / Mimosa / Brazilian stomp / Dreamin' / Since you're gone / Collaboration / Jamaica / Romeo and Juliet love theme.
**Cass:** Released Jul '87, on Warner Bros. by WEA Records. Catalogue no: **WX 91 C**
**Album:** Released Jul '87, on Warner Bros. by WEA Records. Deleted Jan '90. Catalogue no: **WX 91**
**CD:** Released Jul '87, on Warner Bros. by WEA Records. Catalogue no: **925580 2**

**COLLECTION: GEORGE BENSON**
Tracks: / Turn your love around / Love all the hurt away / Give me the night / Cast your fate to the wind / Love ballad / Nature boy / Last train to Clarksville / Livin' inside your love / Never give up on a good thing / On Broadway / White rabbit / This masquerade / Here comes the sun / Breezin' / Moody's mood / We got the love / Greatest love of all, The.
**CD:** Released Jul '88, on Warner Bros. by WEA Records. Catalogue no: **K2 66107**
**CD:** Released Nov '88, on Deja Vu Catalogue no: **DVCD 2076**
**Cass:** Released Nov '81, on Warner Bros. by WEA Records. Catalogue no: **K4 66107**
**Album:** Released Nov '88, on Deja Vu Catalogue no: **DVLP 2076**

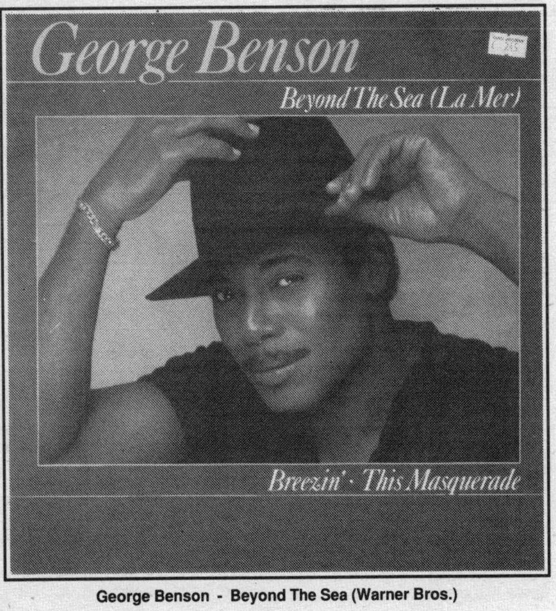


**George Benson - Beyond The Sea (Warner Bros.)**

**Cass:** Released Nov '88, on Deja Vu Catalogue no: **DVMC 2076**
**Album:** Released Nov '81, on Warner Bros. by WEA Records. Catalogue no: **K 66107**

**DETROIT'S GEORGE BENSON**
Note: With Reg Schwager, Archie Alleyne, Dave Young.
**Album:** Released Jul '88, on Parkwood Catalogue no: **PARKWOOD 107**

**EARLY YEARS**
Tracks: / White rabbit / Somewhere in the ast / Take five / California dreamin' / Body talk / Full compass.
**Album:** Released Jul '82, on CTI (1) by Polydor Ltd. Deleted Jul '87. Catalogue no: **CTI 2409219**
**Album:** Released Nov '83, on CTI (1) by Polydor Ltd. Catalogue no: **SPELP 53**
**CD:** Released Nov '83, on CTI (1) by Polydor Ltd. Deleted '88. Catalogue no: **8136 592**
**Cass:** Released Nov '83, on CTI (1) by Polydor Ltd. Catalogue no: **SPEMC 53**

**ELECTRIFYING GEORGE BENSON, THE (Benson, George Quartet)**
Tracks: / All the things you are / Love For Sale / Oleo / All Blues / Masquerade is over, The / Invitation / Li'l Darlin'.
Note: Really, there should be no need what so ever to make such an obvious statement of fact, but just in case there are any doubting Thomases: George Benson remains one of the greatest of all guitar-playing jazz musicians. Of this or any other era. A performer of consummate all-round artistry, whose combination of awesome technique, tonal beauty, rhythmic power, constant creativity and emotional projection has long since made him the Greatest Jazz Guitarist.
All of which must be obvious, not only to his fellow pickers, but to those who have followed his career since those first, sometimes tentative, days as a touring member of the dynamic Brother Jack McDuff combo, between the years 1962-1965. But for far too many jazz fans (even critics too) these days, Benson is either a has-been, jazz-wise, or might as well be non existent. True, the Pittsburgh-born George must shoulder a pile of the blame. For he is seldom (if ever) to be heard in any kind of public jazz situation, his proffessional career - from the beginning of the 1980s at least - being governed by his immense worldwide popularity as a warm sincere, essentially musical vocalist, encompassing both concert-going and record-buying publics alike.
True, he still uses his guitar, both inside the recording studios as well as on stage. But, sadly, the days when Benson would electrify even the hardest-to-please audiences with the kind of guitar playing artistry that isn't heard too often - long sets of dazzling, truly-exciting bebop 'n' blues solos that never let up for a second - seem to be - to all intents and purposes - over and done with at this time. (That the Benson guitar magic still

retains that devastating effect can be gauged from reports of his live performances. When on the odd occasion, - perhaps just once during a concert - he decides just to play. No vocal, except maybe for a passage of that highly-distinctive unison scat vocal-guitar technique he does so well).

Just how stunning a performer George Benson can be - especially in concert - can be easily ascertained by even casual reference to the contents of this constantly uplifting set, only recently made available in the UK for the first time. The listener will soon discover that this was no ordinary event - probably a one-off concert, with George taking time off from his already financially-rewarding career in pop singing. Accompanied for the occasion by three first-rate musicians - pianist Mickey Tucker, drummer Al Harewood, bassist George Duvivier. The venue: the Cassa Caribe, in Plainfield, New Jersey. The time: April 1973.

A special evening it turned out to be, because the vital chemistry that ignites a truly inspired performance is present throughout. Pickup band though this is, the rapport between the four is at optimum level at all times. Solo-wise, too, there is absolutely nothing at which to complain. An appreciative audience reacts to the quartet's splendid offerings in prescribed fashion.

Benson himself is in dazzling form. Take the opening *Love for sale*. Tucker opens proceedings by playing the verse, unaccompanied, out of tempo. Benson handles the refrain, fairly straight, punctuated by a pulsating Afro-Cuban background. Then, the guitarist fairly sails into his solo. He lays back on the beat and builds - intelligently, logically - to a natural, uncontrived climax. The performance affords the listener ample chance to assess his legendary technique. His well-nigh perfect articulation. The subtle manner on which, occasionally, he inserts deft little double-time ;runs. Then there is the unremitting drive; the essence of the blues that permeates so much of his playing ...

Li'l Darlin' finds Benson is superbly relaxed mood, both he and the other members of the quartet faithfully evoking both mood and essence of the classic Basie interpretation. The four achieve the same kind of 'authenticity' with Miles Davis' equally memorable *All blues*. Sonny Rollins' almost-as-famous *Oleo* finds the Benson Quartet coalescing beautiful at breakneck tempo, with Benson producing what is no less than a breathtaking, vituoso solo. His potent combination of exhilarating single-string playing - everything put together with marvellous spontaneity, yet each note clearly discernible and parallel octaves, plus a well-developed ability to build real excitement, together results in the kind of superior performance that for years had made him a legend almost the jazz-guitar playing fraternity. And for a single, yet as ever first class example of George Benson's singing then you need go no further than the relaxed warm version of *I'm afraid, the masquerade is over* to be found within this fascinating selection of truly 'live' performances by a genuine guitar great. Performances that are exceptional even by George's ace-high standards. *The electifying George Benson* is just about the most appropriate title this magnificent collection could possible have been accorded. Play it once - and you'll find it extremely difficult to remove from your CD player. (Stan Britt, Author, The Jazz Guitarists/Blandford Press, 184)

**Album:** Released Jan '87, on Masters (Holland) Catalogue no: **CL 001764**

**Cass:** Released Jan '87, on Masters (Holland) Catalogue no: **MCCL 091764**

**2 LP Set:** Released May '85, on Affinity by Charly Records. Catalogue no: **AFFD 140**

**CD:** Released Mar '86, on Charly by Charly Records. Catalogue no: **CDCHARLY 9**

**CD:** Released Jul '87, on Intertape Deleted '88. Catalogue no: **500 064**

## EXCLUSIVE BENSON

Tracks: / I am the walrus / You make me feel like a natural woman / Doobie doobie blues / Along comes Mary / Billie's bounce / Groovin' / Sunny / I remember Wes / Low down and dirty / Sack o' woe / Walk on by / Julie / What's new? / That lucky old sun / Giblet gravy / Windmills of your mind / People get ready / Thunder walk / Song for my father / Carnival joys.

**2 LP Set:** Released 1 Nov '87, on Connoisseur Collection by Connoisseur Collection Ltd.. Catalogue no: **VSOPLP 109**

**Cass:** Released 7 Nov '87, on Connoisseur Collection by Connoisseur Collection Ltd.. Catalogue no: **VSOPMC 109**

## FEEL LIKE MAKIN' LOVE

Tracks: / Feel like makin' love / Use me.

**12" Single:** Released Jul '83, on Warner Bros. by WEA Records. Deleted Jul '86. Catalogue no: **W 9551 T**

**7" Single:** Released Jul '83, on Warner Bros. by WEA Records. Deleted Jul '86. Catalogue no: **W 9551**

## GENIUS OF GEORGE BENSON

Tracks: / California dreamin' / Shell of a man / Summer knows, The / Summertime / Cast your fate to the wind / No sooner said than done / Changing world / Take five.

**Cass:** Released Nov '83, on Hallmark by Pickwick Records. Catalogue no: **HSC 3129**

**Album:** Released Nov '83, on Hallmark by Pickwick Records. Deleted '88. Catalogue no: **SHM 3129**

## GEORGE BENSON (Compact / Walkman jazz

Tracks: / Billie's bounce / What's new / Thunder walk / Low down and dirty / That lucky old sun / Song for my father / Sack o' woe / Doobie doobie blues / Tuxedo Junction / I remember Wes.

**CD:** Released Mar '88, on Verve Catalogue no: **833 292-2**

**Cass:** Released 27 Feb '88, on Verve Catalogue no: **833 292-4**

## GEORGE BENSON IN CONCERT

Tracks: / Love for sale / Witch craft / Love walked in / Dahlin's delight (* track on cassette only. End s1) / Masquerade is over, The / All the things you are / There will never be another you / All blues (* track on cassette only).

**Album:** Released May '85, on Premier by Premier Records. Deleted '88. Catalogue no: **CBR 1029**

**Cass:** Released May '85, on Premier by Premier Records. Catalogue no: **KCBR 1029**

## GEORGE BENSON AND JACK MCDUFF (Benson, George & Jack McDuff)

Tracks: / Shadow dancers, The / Sweet Alice blues, The / I don't know / Just another Sunday / Will you still be mine / Easy living / Rock a bye / Hot barbecue / Party's over, The / Briar patch / Hippy dip / 601 1/2 No. Poplar / Cry me a river / Three day thang, The.

**2 LP Set:** Released Jul '77, on Prestige Catalogue no: **PR 24072**

## GEORGE BENSON LIVE IN CONCERT

**Cass:** Released Apr '84, on Design by Breakaway Records. Deleted '87. Catalogue no: **CELD 309**

**Album:** Released Apr '84, on Design by Breakaway Records. Deleted '87. Catalogue no: **DELD 309**

## GIVE ME THE NIGHT

Tracks: / What's on your mind? / Dinorah Dinorah / Love dance / Star of the story / Midnight love affair / Turn out the lamplight / Love x love / Off Broadway / Moody's mood / Give me the night.

**Album:** Released Jul '80, on Warner Bros. by WEA Records. Catalogue no: **K 56823**

**CD:** Released '83, on Warner Bros. by WEA Records. Catalogue no: **K 256823**

**Cass:** Released Jul '80, on Warner Bros. by WEA Records. Catalogue no: **K4 56823**

## GIVE ME THE NIGHT (SINGLE)

Tracks: / Give me the night / Red lights.

**7" Single:** Released Aug '80, on Warner Bros. by WEA Records. Deleted '83. Catalogue no: **K 17673**

**7" Single:** Released Aug '80, on Warner Bros. by WEA Records. Catalogue no: **K 17673**

## GREATEST LOVE OF ALL

Tracks: / Greatest love of all, The.

**7" Single:** Released Nov '80, on Arista by BMG Records (UK). Catalogue no: **ARIST 133**

## GREATEST LOVE OF ALL (OLD GOLD)

Tracks: / Greatest love of all, The / Funkin' for Jamaica.

**7" Single:** Released Mar '90, on Old Gold by Old Gold Records. Catalogue no: **OG 9454**

## IN CONCERT - CARNEGIE HALL

**Album:** Released May '77, on CTI (1)

by Polydor Ltd. Catalogue no: **CTI 6072**

**IN FLIGHT**
Tracks: / Nature boy / Wind and I, The / World is a ghetto, The / Gonna love you more / Valdez in the country / Everything must change.
**CD:** Released '86, on Warner Bros. by WEA Records. Catalogue no: **256327**
**Album:** Released Jan '77, on Warner Bros. by WEA Records. Catalogue no: **K 56327**
**Cass:** Released Jan '77, on Warner Bros. by WEA Records. Catalogue no: **K4 56327**

**IN YOUR EYES**
Tracks: / Feel like making love / Inside love (so personal) / Lady love me (one more time) / Love will come again / In your eyes / Never too far to fall / Being with you / Use me / Late at night / In search of a dream.
**Album:** Released Jun '83, on Warner Bros. by WEA Records. Catalogue no: **923744 1**
**CD:** Released Jul '88, on Warner Bros. by WEA Records. Catalogue no: **923744 2**
**Cass:** Released Jun '83, on Warner Bros. by WEA Records. Catalogue no: **923744 4**

**IN YOUR EYES (SINGLE)**
Tracks: / In your eyes / Being with you.
**12" Single:** Released Sep '83, on Warner Bros. by WEA Records. Deleted Sep '86. Catalogue no: **W 9487T**
**7" Single:** Released Sep '83, on Warner Bros. by WEA Records. Catalogue no: **W 9487**

**INSIDE LOVE (SO PERSONAL)**
Tracks: / Inside love (so personal).
**7" Single:** Released Dec '83, on WEA (International) by WEA Records. Deleted '86. Catalogue no: **W 9427**

**IT'S UPTOWN / GEORGE BENSON COOKBOOK**
Tracks: / Clockwise / Summertime / Ain't that peculiar? / Jaguar / Willow weep for me / Foggy day, A / Hello birdie / Bullfight / Stormy weather / Eternally / Myna bird blues / Cooker, The / Benny's back / Bossa rocka / All of me / Big fat lady / Benson's rider / Ready and able / Borgia stick, The / Return of the prodigal son / Jumpin' with symphony Sid.
**Cass set:** Released Jun '85, on CBS (Blue Diamond) by CBS Records. Catalogue no: **40 22187**
**2 LP Set:** Released Jun '85, on CBS (Blue Diamond) by CBS Records. Catalogue no: **CBS 22187**

**KISSES IN THE MOONLIGHT**
Tracks: / Kisses in the moonlight / Open your eyes (instrumental).
**7" Single:** Released Jul '86, on Warner Bros. by WEA Records. Deleted Jun '87. Catalogue no: **W 8640**
**12" Single:** Released Jul '86, on Warner Bros. by WEA Records. Deleted Jun '87. Catalogue no: **W 8640 T**

**LADY LOVE ME (ONE MORE TIME)**
Tracks: / Lady love me (one more time) / In search of a dream.
**12" Single:** Released May '83, on Warner Bros. by WEA Records. Deleted '86. Catalogue no: **W 9614 T**
**7" Single:** Released May '83, on Warner Bros. by WEA Records. Deleted '86. Catalogue no: **W 9614**

**LATE AT NIGHT**
Tracks: / Late at night / Love will come again / Welcome into my world (On 12" only).
**12" Single:** Released Mar '84, on WEA by WEA Records. Catalogue no: **W 9325T**
**7" Single:** Released Mar '84, on WEA by WEA Records. Catalogue no: **W 9325**

**LET'S DO IT AGAIN**
Tracks: / Let's do it again / Let's go.
**12" Single:** Released Aug '88, on Warner Bros. by WEA Records. Catalogue no: **W 7780 T**
**7" Single:** Released 22 Aug '88, on Warner Bros. by WEA Records. Catalogue no: **W 7780**

**LIVIN' INSIDE YOUR LOVE**
Tracks: / Before you go / Welcome into my world / Love is a hurtin' thing / You're never too far from me / Love ballad / Change is gonna come, A / Prelude to fall / Soulful strut / Nassau day / Hey girl.
**2 LP Set:** Released Mar '79, on Warner Bros. by WEA Records. Catalogue no: **K 66085**
**Cass:** Released Mar '79, on Warner Bros. by WEA Records. Catalogue no: **K4 66085**
**CD:** Released Jun '89, on Warner Bros. by WEA Records. Catalogue no: **K 266085**

**LOVE ALL THE HURT AWAY**
Tracks: / Love all the hurt away / Whole lot of me / Hold on I'm coming.
**7" Single:** Released Aug '81, on Arista by BMG Records (UK). Deleted '86. Catalogue no: **ARIST 428**
**12" Single:** Released Aug '81, on Arista by BMG Records (UK). Deleted '86. Catalogue no: **ARIST 12 428**

**LOVE BALLAD**
Tracks: / Love ballad / You're too far from me.
**7" Single:** Released Mar '79, on Warner Bros. by WEA Records. Deleted '82. Catalogue no: **K 17333**

**LOVE FOR SALE**
**Album:** Released '88, on Masters (Holland) Catalogue no: **CL 91784**
**Cass:** Released '88, on Masters (Holland) Catalogue no: **CLMC 91784**

**LOVE SONGS: GEORGE BENSON**
Tracks: / Give me the night / Lady love me (one more time) / Love X love / New day / Feel like makin' love / 20/20 / Never give up on a good thing / Inside love (so personal) / No one emotion / In your eyes / Turn your love around / Greatest love of all, The.
**Album:** Released Oct '85, on K-Tel by K-Tel Records. Catalogue no: **NE 1308**
**Cass:** Released Oct '85, on K-Tel by K-Tel Records. Catalogue no: **CE 2308**

**LOVE WALKED IN**
**Cass:** Released Oct '85, on Platinum (W.Germany) Catalogue no: **PMC 36**
**Album:** Released Oct '85, on Platinum (W.Germany) Catalogue no: **PLP 36**

**LOVE X LOVE**
Tracks: / Love x love / Off Broadway.
**7" Single:** Released Sep '80, on Warner Bros. by WEA Records. Catalogue no: **K 17699**
**12" Single:** Released Sep '80, on Warner Bros. by WEA Records. Catalogue no: **LV 41**

**MASQUERADE**
Tracks: / Love for sale / Masquerade is over, The / There will never be another you / All blues.
**CD:** Released Oct '89, on Thunderbolt by Magnum Music Group. Catalogue no: **CDTB 072**
**Album:** Released Oct '89, on Thunderbolt by Magnum Music Group. Catalogue no: **THBL 072**

**NATURE BOY**
Tracks: / Nature boy.
**7" Single:** Released Jun '77, on Warner Bros. by WEA Records. Deleted '80. Catalogue no: **K 16921**

**NEVER GIVE UP ON A GOOD THING**
Tracks: / Never give up on a good thing / California p.m..
**7" Single:** Released Jan '82, on Warner Bros. by WEA Records. Catalogue no: **K 17902**
**12" Single:** Released Jan '82, on Warner Bros. by WEA Records. Catalogue no: **K 17902 T**

**NO ONE EMOTION (Benson, George / Roberta Flack)**
Tracks: / No one emotion / You are the love of my life.
**7" Single:** Released Oct '85, on Warner Bros. by WEA Records. Catalogue no: **W 8863**
**12" Single:** Released Oct '85, on Warner Bros. by WEA Records. Catalogue no: **W 8863T**

**ON BROADWAY**
Tracks: / On Broadway / Love will come again.
**12" Single:** Released Nov '83, on Warner Bros. by WEA Records. Catalogue no: **W 9427 T**
**7" Single:** Released Nov '83, on Warner Bros. by WEA Records. Catalogue no: **W 9427**

**REPLAY ON GEORGE BENSON**
**Album:** Released Aug '85, on Sierra by Sierra Records. Catalogue no: **FEDB 5019**
**Cass:** Released Aug '85, on Sierra by Sierra Records. Catalogue no: **CFEDB 5019**

**SHAPE OF THINGS TO COME**
Tracks: / Footin' it / Face it boy it's over / Shape of things that are and were / Chattanooga choo choo / Don't let me lose this dream / Last train to Clarksville.
**CD:** Released 28 Nov '88, on A&M by

A&M Records. Catalogue no: **CDA 0803**

**SHIVER**
Tracks: / Shiver / Love is here tonight.
**7" Single:** Released Nov '86, on Warner Bros. by WEA Records. Deleted Jan '88. Catalogue no: **W 8523**
**12" Single:** Released Nov '86, on Warner Bros. by WEA Records. Deleted Sep '87. Catalogue no: **W 8523T**

**SILVER COLLECTION, THE**
Tracks: / Billie's bounce / Low down and dirty / Thunder walk / Doobie doobie blues / What's new? / I remember Wes / Windmills of your mind / Song for my father / Carnival joys / Giblet gravy / Walk on by / Sack o' woe / Groovin'.
**CD:** Released Nov '85, on Verve Deleted Jan '89. Catalogue no: **823 450-2**

**SPACE**
Tracks: / Hold on I'm coming / Summertime / Son of sky dive / Gone / Octane.
**Album:** Released '79, on CTI (1) by Polydor Ltd. Deleted '85. Catalogue no: **CTI 7085**

**STAND UP**
**CD:** Released Dec '84, on WEA by WEA Records. Catalogue no: **925 178 2**

**STORMY WEATHER**
Tracks: / Clockwise / Big fat lady / Hammond's bossa nova / Stormy weather / Slow scene / Jumpin' with symphony Sid / Cooker, The / Push push / Bullfight / Ready 'n' able / Bossa rocka / Flamingo.
**Cass:** Released '84, on CBS by CBS Records. Catalogue no: **40 31689**
**Album:** Released '84, on CBS by CBS Records. Deleted '86. Catalogue no: **31689**

**SUMMERTIME**
**Album:** Released Sep '82, on Epic by CBS Records. Deleted '87. Catalogue no: **EPC 32191**
**Cass:** Released Sep '82, on Epic by CBS Records. Deleted '87. Catalogue no: **40 32191**

**SUPERSHIP**
Tracks: / Supership.
**7" Single:** Released Oct '75, on CTI (1) by Polydor Ltd. Deleted '78. Catalogue no: **CTSP 002**

**TEASER**
Tracks: / Did you hear the thunder / Teaser.
**7" Single:** Released Jan '87, on Warner Bros. by WEA Records. Deleted Jan '88. Catalogue no: **W 8437**
**12" Single:** Released Feb '87, on Warner Bros. by WEA Records. Deleted Jan '88. Catalogue no: **W 8437T**

**TENDERLY**
**Album:** Released Jul '89, on Warner Bros. by WEA Records. Catalogue no: **925 907 1**
**CD:** Released Jul '89, on Warner Bros. by WEA Records. Catalogue no: **925 907 2**
**Cass:** Released Jul '89, on Warner Bros. by WEA Records. Catalogue no: **WX 263 C**
**Album:** Released Jul '89, on Warner Bros. by WEA Records. Catalogue no: **WX 263**

**TURN YOUR LOVE AROUND**
Tracks: / Turn your love around / Nature boy.
**7" Single:** Released Nov '81, on Warner Bros. by WEA Records. Deleted '84. Catalogue no: **K 17877**

**TWICE THE LOVE**
Tracks: / Twice the love / Sarting all over / Good habit / Everybody does it / Living on borrowed love / Let's do it again / Stephanie / Tender love / You're still my baby / Until you believe.
**Cass:** Released 22 Aug '88, on Warner Bros. by WEA Records. Catalogue no: **WX 160 C**
**CD:** Released 22 Aug '88, on Warner Bros. by WEA Records. Catalogue no: **925705 2**
**Album:** Released 22 Aug '88, on Warner Bros. by WEA Records. Catalogue no: **WX 160**
**CD:** Released Nov '88, on Warner Bros. by WEA Records. Catalogue no: **WX 160 CD**

**TWICE THE LOVE (SINGLE)**
Tracks: / Twice the love (guitar love mix) / Love is here tonight.
**7" Single:** Released Nov '88, on Warner Bros. by WEA Records. Deleted Jan '90. Catalogue no: **W 7665**
**CD Single:** Released Nov '88, on Warner Bros. by WEA Records. Catalogue no: **W 7665 CD**
**12" Single:** Released Nov '88, on Warner Bros. by WEA Records. Deleted Jan '90. Catalogue no: **W 7665 T**

**UNCHAINED MELODY**
Tracks: / Unchained melody / Before you go.
**7" Single:** Released '79, on WEA by WEA Records. Deleted '82. Catalogue no: **K 17409**

**WEEKEND IN LA**
Tracks: / Greatest love of all, The / Down here on the ground / Ode to a Kudu / We as love / California PM / Lady blue / We all remember Wes / Windsong / On Broadway / It's all in the game / Weekend in LA.
**Cass:** Released Jan '78, on Warner Bros. by WEA Records. Catalogue no: **K4 66074**
**Album:** Released Jan '78, on Warner Bros. by WEA Records. Catalogue no: **K 66074**

**WHAT'S ON YOUR MIND?**
Tracks: / What's on your mind? / Turn out the lamplight.
**12" Single:** Released Feb '81, on Warner Bros. by WEA Records. Catalogue no: **K 17748 T**
**7" Single:** Released Feb '81, on Warner Bros. by WEA Records. Catalogue no: **K 17748**

**WHILE THE CITY SLEEPS**
Tracks: / Shiver / Love is here tonight / Teaser / Secrets in the night / Too many times / Did you hear the thunder / While the city sleeps / Kisses in the moonlight.
**Cass:** Released Sep '86, on Warner Bros. by WEA Records. Catalogue no: **WX 55 C**
**CD:** Released Sep '86, on Warner Bros. by WEA Records. Catalogue no: **925475 2**
**Album:** Released Sep '86, on Warner Bros. by WEA Records. Catalogue no: **WX 55**

**WONDERFUL YEARS, THE**
**Album:** Released Mar '84, on Proto by Proto Records. Catalogue no: **PENALP 2**

**YOU ARE THE LOVE OF MY LIFE**
Tracks: / You are the love of my life / I just wanna hang around you.
**12" Single:** Released Jul '85, on WDTC Deleted Jul '88. Catalogue no: **W 8985 T**
**7" Single:** Released Jul '85, on WDTC Deleted Jul '88. Catalogue no: **W 8985**

## Benson, Ivy

**IVY BENSON & HER ORCHESTRA (Benson, Ivy & Her Orchestra)**
**Album:** Released Jul '77, on SJB Records Deleted '80. Catalogue no: **LIB 3333**

## Benton, Brook

**Biographical details:** Born in South Carolina, Brook Benton scored his first major success as both songwriter and singer in 1959. The first of his hits which he co-wrote was *"It's Just A Matter Of Time"* a No. 3 hit on the US charts. it began a string of hits that lasted until the arrival of the Beatles. Benton was one of the artists who filled the American pop gap in the late Fifties and early Sixties, between the heyday of rock 'n' roll and the British Invasion. Backed with heavenly chorus and strings, Benton's smoky vocals provided the Top Ten hits *"So Many Ways"*, *"Kiddio"* and *"Hotel Happiness"* (an answer to Elvis' 1956 classic *"Heartbreak Hotel"*). his biggest American hit of all was 1961's novelty smash *"The Boll Weevil Song"* which reached No. 2. This was an adaptation of an old American ditty, telling of the plight of the cotton farmer battling against the Boll Weevil bugs, small insects that can ruin a cotton crop. He also chalked up two top 10 duet hits with Dinah Washington (who died in 1963): *"Baby (You've Got What It Takes)"* and *"A Rockin' Good Way (To Mess Around And Fall In Love)"*, the latter becoming a 1984 UK smash for Shakin' Stevens and Bonnie Tyler. Brook Benton never caught on in Britain, where the male vocalist market was already well catered for by such homegrown stars as Cliff Richard and Adam Faith. His first UK hit *"Endlessly"*, peaked at No. 28 and remained the biggest of his four chart records. From '64 onwards his American chart career floundered. His only bright spot since then has been his one-off 1970 return to the US Top 5 with his version of *"Rainy Night In Georgia"*. In Britain however, it was left to Randy Crawford to take the song into the charts eleven years later. (Bob MacDonald).

The soul singer was born in 1931 in Camden, South Carolina. Like so many in the genre he came from a gospel music background; he began writing songs as a teenager and made hundreds of demos for Nat Cole, Roy Hamilton, Clyde McPhatter, many others, with writing collaborator Clyde Otis. First signed as a solo artist to Epic, then Mercury, he had 21 million-sellers 1959-64, plus duet hits with Dinah Washington. He later recorded for RCA, Reprise and Cotillion; had a top five in 1970 with Tony Joe White's *Rainy Day In Georgia*, but no other hits: his ballad style appealed to almost everybody, yet he missed out on greater success during the golden age of soul in the late '60s, perhaps because he was too smooth. His albums are still selling and his live act is a top attraction. (Donald Clarke 23 August 1988).

## 16 GOLDEN CLASSICS

Tracks: / Kiddio / It's just a matter of time / My true confession / Frankie and Johnny / Think twice / Hotel happiness / Thank you pretty baby / Boll weevil song, The / Rainy night in Georgia / Lie to me / Revenge / So many ways / I got what I wanted / Ties that bind, The / Shadrack / For my baby.

**CD:** Released '88, on Unforgettable by Castle Communications Records. Catalogue no: **UNCD 010**

**Album:** Released Dec '86, on Unforgettable by Castle Communications Records. Catalogue no: **UNLP 010**

**Cass:** Released Dec '86, on Unforgettable by Castle Communications Records. Catalogue no: **UNMC 010**

## 20 GOLDEN PIECES: BROOK BENTON

Tracks: / Bayou baby / Sunshine / Endlessly / Old-fashioned strut / Soft / Trust me to do what you want me to do (and I'll do it) / Pulling me down / Makin' love is good for you / Love is best of all / Tribute to "Mamam" / Let the sun come out / We need what we need / Better times / Lover's question / Let me in your world / I love her / Lord, you know how men are / Till I can't take it anymore / I keep thinking to myself / There's still a little love left for me.

**Album:** Released Mar '84, on Bulldog Records by President Records. Catalogue no: **BDL 2039**

## 20 GREATEST HITS: BROOK BENTON

**CD:** Released '88, on Gusto (USA) by Gusto Records (USA). Catalogue no: **CD 1032**

**Cass:** Released '88, on Masters (Holland) Catalogue no: **MAMC 20983**

**Album:** Released '88, on Masters (Holland) Catalogue no: **MA 20983**

**CD:** Released Jan '90, on Phonogram by Phonogram Ltd. Catalogue no: **8367552**

## BEST OF BROOK BENTON

Tracks: / Fools rush in / Kiddio / Hotel happiness / Sill waters run deep / Shadrack / Think twice / Frankie and Johnny / Rockin' good way, A / Hit record / Boll weevil song, The / Revenge / Endlessly / Lie to me / So many ways / It's just a matter of time / Walk on the wild side / Baby (you've got what it takes).

**Cass:** Released Aug '84, on K-Tel Goldmasters by K-Tel Records. Catalogue no: **GM 0229**

**CD:** Released Jan '90, on Philips (Timeless) by PolyGram UK Ltd. Catalogue no: **8307722**

**Album:** Released Jul '84, on Philips (Timeless) by PolyGram UK Ltd. Catalogue no: **TIME 01**

**Cass:** Released Jul '84, on Philips (Timeless) by PolyGram UK Ltd. Catalogue no: **TIMEC 01**

## BEST OF BROOK BENTON 1931-1988

**CD:** Released '90, on K-Tel by K-Tel Records. Catalogue no: **NCD 3418**

## BEST OF BROOK BENTON, VOL 1

Tracks: / It's just a matter of time / Kiddio / Same one, The / It's just a house without you / My true confession / Fools rush in / Think twice / Hotel happiness / Thank you pretty baby / Boll weevil song, The.

**Album:** Released Oct '82, on Phoenix (2) by Audio Fidelity Enterprises. Catalogue no: **PHX 1019**

## BOLL WEEVIL SONG

Tracks: / Boll weevil song.

**7" Single:** Released Jul '61, on Mercury (EMI) Deleted '64. Catalogue no: **AMT 1148**

## BROOK BENTON

**Cass:** Released Oct '84, on Audio Fidelity(USA) by Audio Fidelity (USA). Catalogue no: **ZCGAS 722**

## BROOK BENTON SINGS THE STANDARDS

Tracks: / Hey there / That old feeling / Nightingale sang in Berkeley Square, A / Love is a many splendoured thing / Once in love with Amy / Try a little tenderness / Call me irresponsible / Blue moon / Second time around / Moon river / Hawaiian wedding song / More / There, I've said it again / I only have eyes for you / Unforgettable / There goes my heart.

**Cass:** Released '84, on RCA by BMG Records (UK). Deleted Jul '89. Catalogue no: **NK 89092**

**Album:** Released '84, on RCA by BMG Records (UK). Deleted Jul '89. Catalogue no: **NL 89092**

## DIAMOND SERIES: BROOK BENTON

Tracks: / That old feeling / Nightingale sang in Berkeley Square, A / Love is a many splendoured thing / Try a little tenderness / Hey there / Call me irresponsible / Peg o' my heart / Mother Nature, Father Time / I wanna be with you / More time to be with you / Cold cold heart / Funny how time slips away / He's got you / I really don't want to know / Hello walls / Gone.

**CD:** Released Apr '88, on Diamond Series by RCA Records. Catalogue no: **CD 90109**

## ENDLESSLY

Tracks: / It's just a matter of time / Boll weevil song, The / Baby you've got what it takes / Lie to me / So many ways / Hotel happiness / Kiddio / Endlessly / Revenge / Same one, The / Think twice / Rockin' good way, A.

**Cass:** Released Jan '87, on Topline by Charly Records. Catalogue no: **KTOP 158**

**Album:** Released Jan '87, on Topline by Charly Records. Catalogue no: **TOP 158**

**Cass:** Released Aug '84, on K-Tel Goldmasters by K-Tel Records. Catalogue no: **GM 0208**

## ENDLESSLY (SINGLE)

Tracks: / Endlessly.

**7" Single:** Released Aug '59, on Mercury (EMI) Deleted '62. Catalogue no: **AMT 1043**

## FOOLS RUSH IN

Tracks: / Fools rush in.

**7" Single:** Released Feb '61, on Mercury (EMI) Deleted '64. Catalogue no: **AMT 1121**

## HIS GREATEST HITS

**Album:** Released Aug '87, on Mercury (USA) by PolyGram Rec.Inc.(USA). Catalogue no: **822321 1**

**Cass:** Released Aug '87, on Mercury (USA) by PolyGram Rec.Inc.(USA). Catalogue no: **822321 4**

## HIS TOP HITS

**Cass:** Released Jul '86, on Timeless Treasures Catalogue no: **808**

## INCOMPARABLE BROOK BENTON, THE

Tracks: / It's just a matter of time / Kiddio / Same one, The / It's just a house without you / My true confession / Fools rush in / Think twice / Hotel happiness / Thank you pretty baby / Boll weevil song, The / Rainy night in Georgia / So close / Frankie and Johnny / Revenge / Lie to me / So many ways / I got what I wanted / Ties that bind, The / Shadrack / For my baby.

**Album:** Released Oct '82, on Audio Fidelity(USA) by Audio Fidelity (USA). Catalogue no: **AFEMP 1024**

## KIDDIO

Tracks: / Kiddio.

**7" Single:** Released Oct '60, on Mercury (EMI) Deleted '63. Catalogue no: **AMT 1109**

## MAGIC MOMENTS WITH BROOK BENTON

**Cass:** Released May '85, on RCA by BMG Records (UK). Catalogue no: **NK 89623**

## PORTRAIT OF A SONG STYLIST

**Cass:** Released Oct '89, on Masterpiece by Castle Communications Records. Catalogue no: **HARMC 109**

**CD:** Released Oct '89, on Masterpiece by Castle Communications Records. Catalogue no: **HARCD 109**

**RAINY NIGHT IN GEORGIA, A**
**Cass:** Released Jan '90, on Mainline (2) by Mainline Records. Catalogue no: **260 422 4**
**CD:** Released Jan '90, on Mainline (2) by Mainline Records. Catalogue no: **260 422 2**

**SONGS I LOVE TO SING**
Tracks: / Moonlight in Vermont / It's been a long long time / Lover come back to me / If you are but a dream / Why try to change me now / September song / Oh what it seemed to be / Baby won't you please come home / They can't take that away from me / I'll be around / I don't know enough about you / Fools rush in.
**Cass:** Released Dec '85, on Memoir by Memoir Records. Catalogue no: **CMOIR 112**
**Album:** Released Dec '85, on Memoir by Memoir Records. Catalogue no: **MOIR 112**
**CD 3":** Released '88, Catalogue no: **PWK 034**

**SPOTLIGHT ON BROOK BENTON**
**2 LP Set:** Released Jun '77, on Philips by Phonogram Ltd. Catalogue no: **6612 116**

**TWO OF US, THE (See Washington, Dinah) (Benton, Brook & Dinah Washington)**
**Cass set:** Released '78, on Mercury by Phonogram Ltd. Catalogue no: **7599 366**
**2 LP Set:** Released '78, on Mercury by Phonogram Ltd. Catalogue no: **6641 868**

## Bentzon, Adrian

**DANISH JAZZ, VOL 7**
**Album:** Released Jul '82, on Storyville by Storyville Records AB. Catalogue no: **SLP 416**

## Beresford, Steve

**DEADLY WEAPONS (Beresford, Steve / David Topp / John Zorn / Tonie Marshall)**
**Album:** Released Apr '87, on Nato Catalogue no: **950**

**ELEVEN SONGS FOR DORIS DAY**
Tracks: / I was there / Secret love / Let it ring / Serenade in blue / Sentimental journey / Black hills of Dakota, The / It's magic / Que sera sera / At last / I'm beginning to see the light / Back in Cincinnati.
Note: With Deb Bora, Tony Coe and Terry Day.
**Album:** Released Sep '86, on Chabada (France) Catalogue no: **CHABADA 07**

**TEA TIME**
**Album:** Released Nov '76, on Incus by Incus Records. Catalogue no: **INCUS 15**

## Berger, Karl

**ALL KINDS OF TIME (Berger, Karl & David Holland)**
Tracks: / Simplicity / Perfect love / Fragments / Beginning, The / Now is / D'Accord / All kinds of time / We are.
**Album:** Released Apr '81, on Sackville by Spotlite Records. Catalogue no: **3010**

**WITH SILENCE**
**Album:** Released Jan '82, on Enja (Germany) by Enja Records (West Germany). Catalogue no: **ENJA 2022**

## Bergeyk Van, Ton

**FAMOUS RAGTIME GUITAR SOLOS**
Tracks: / Buffalo rag / Atlanta rag / Felicity rag / Blake's breakdown / Grizzly bear / Ragtime nightmare / Silver swan, The / King Porter stomp / Pineapple rag / Smokey mokes / Powder rag / Original rags / Harlem rag / American beauty rag.
**Album:** on Kicking Mule by Sonet Records. Catalogue no: **SNKF 106**

**FROM SOUP TO NUTS**
Tracks: / Junk man rag / Mustard swing / Zither melodies / From soup to nuts / Kansas City stomp / Rondo caprice / Ragtime melody / Bantam step / Springtime rag / Wabash blues / Notoriety / If I had you / Moonlight serenade / Jazz me blues / Divertissment / Georgia grind / Coconut dance / Florida rag.
**Album:** Released '80, on Kicking Mule by Sonet Records. Catalogue no: **SNKF 114**

**I GOT RHYTHM**
Tracks: / I got rhythm / Sophisticated slide / Jubilee stomp / Take it easy / Somewhere over the rainbow / Sugar / Cat and the dog, The / Who's that knocking at my door? / Frog-I-more rag / Dirty dozens / Ain't misbehavin' / Stumbling / Ballin' the jack / These foolish things / Anno 1926 / Under the moon.
**Album:** Released '80, on Kicking Mule by Sonet Records. Catalogue no: **SNKF 125**

**LULU'S BACK IN TOWN (Hot Guitar Solos)**
Tracks: / Georgia on my mind / Black and tan fantasy / Nobody's sweetheart / Mexican bonito / Boogie dance, The / Rockin' chair / Between the lines / We're all alone / Fabulous Rosina, The / Blue monk / Cry me a river / Hombre mio / Lulu's back in town / Rosa De Castella / Lady Madonna / March of the hoodlums.
**Album:** Released Apr '81, on Kicking Mule by Sonet Records. Catalogue no: **SNKF 166**

## Bergman, Bill

**MIDNIGHT SAX**
**Cass:** Released '87, on Passport Jazz (USA) by Jem Records Inc.(USA). Catalogue no: **PJC 88022**
**Album:** Released '87, on Passport Jazz (USA) by Jem Records Inc.(USA). Catalogue no: **PJ 88022**
**CD:** on Passport Jazz (USA) by Jem Records Inc.(USA). Catalogue no: **PJCD 88022**

## Berigan, Bunny

**Biographical details:** Berigan, Bunny. Roland Bernard Berigan was born in 1908 in a tiny town in Wisconsin; he died in New York City in 1942. He was perhaps the best white trumpet player between Bix Beiderbecke and the bop era, winning a jazz poll in 1939 with five times as many votes as his nearest competitor. He joined Hal Kemp in 1930 and played with big name bands including Benny Goodman and Tommy Dorsey; his famous solos can be heard on Goodman's *King Porter Stomp* and Dorsey's *Marie* and *Song of India*, three of the biggest hits of the whole era. He led his own bands from 1936, but his capacity for alcohol was legendary and after 1940 it was killing him, as it killed Bix. His own biggest hit was *I can't get started*, which he recorded for Vocalion in 1936 and for Victor in 1938: the Victor was issued on both 12" and edited 10" 78s. Louis Armstrong refused to record the song, saying that it was Bunny's tune. Bunny's big band made some fine Victor records, but many were flawed by the fact that the band recorded so many second-rate tunes. (Donald Clarke 23 August 1988).

**1936 VOLUME 1**
Tracks: / It's been so long / I'd rather go blind / Let yourself go / Swing Mister Charlie / Melody from the sky, A / I can't get started / Rhythm saved the world / Little bit later on, A / If I had my own way / When I'm with you / Just to be in Carolina / It ain't nobody's biz'ness.
**Album:** Released May '86, on Jazz Information (Sweden) Catalogue no: **CAH 3000**

**BUNNY BERDIGAN 1931**
Tracks: / I can't get Mississippi off my mind / I apologise / Beggin' for love / Parkin' in the moonlight / In the merry month of maybe / How the time can fly / At your command / When Yuba plays the rumba on the tuba / Bubbling over with love / You're in my arms / Fiesta / Have you forgotten / Dancing with the daffodils / Love is like that / When the moon comes over the mountains / Nevertheless.
**Album:** Released '83, on Shoestring (1) Catalogue no: **SS 115**

**BUNNY BERIGAN**
Tracks: / Shanghai shuffle / Devils holiday / Sing you sinners / Sunday / 'Taint so honey, 'taint so / I'll always be in love with you / Frankie and Johnny / Flat foot floogie / Peg O' my heart / Mahogany hall stomp / Wearing of the green, The / Dardanella (blues).
**Cass:** Released Dec '86, on Atlantis by Charly Records. Catalogue no: **KATS 7**
**Album:** Released Dec '86, on Atlantis by Charly Records. Deleted '88. Catalogue no: **ATS 7**

**BUNNY BERIGAN 1937/40 VOL.2**
Tracks: / Tommy Dorsey theme / My ghost goes to town / Head over heels in love / Maria / Dark eyes / Fable of the rose, The / What can I say, after I say I'm sorry? / I can't get started with you / My melancholy baby / Deed I do / Savoy

jump / Sugar foot stomp / Linger awhile / Sunday / China boy.
**Album:** Released '81, on Shoestring (1) Catalogue no: **SS 101**

**BUNNY BERIGAN BAND 1938/9 (Berigan, Bunny & His Orchestra)**
Tracks: / I can't get started with you / Round my old deserted farm / Old straw hat, An / You took the words right out of my heart / Kiss me again / Moonshine over Kentucky / Heigh-ho / Prisoner's song / Shanghai shuffle / In a mist / Little gate's special / Livery stable blues.
**Album:** Released '81, on Shoestring (1) Catalogue no: **SS 100**

**BUNNY BERIGAN & HIS ORCHESTRA (Berigan, Bunny & His Orchestra)**
Tracks: / Theme / Intro / Started / Stompin' at the Savoy / Mr. Paganini / Sing me a sweet song / Copper coloured gal / There's a small hotel / Closing theme / St. Louis blues / Swing for sale / Pennies from Heaven / Skeleton in closet, The / Started / Organ grinders swing / You turned the tables on me.
**Album:** Released Jul '86, on Jazz Archives (USA) by Jazz Archives Inc.(USA). Catalogue no: **JA 11**

**BUNNY BERIGAN, LOUIS ARMSTRONG & THE MILLS BROTHERS (See under Armstrong, Louis (Berigan, Bunny/Louis Armstrong/Mills Brothers)**
**Album:** Released Apr '79, on Shoestring (1) Catalogue no: **SS 103**

**BUNNY BERIGAN WITH 1936 STUDIO BANDS**
Tracks: / Moonburn / My heart and I / It's been so long / Sing an old fashioned song / Whose big baby are you / Much too much / Garbo green / You hit the spot / Oh Susannah / Just because / Deep Elem blues / If I could be with you one hour tonight / Ja da / I can't get started with you / I can pull a rabbit out of a hat.
**Album:** Released '81, on Shoestring (1) Catalogue no: **SS 106**

**BUNNY BERIGAN WITH HAL KEMP & HIS ORCHESTRA 1930 VOL.1 (Berigan, Bunny & Hal Kemp)**
Tracks: / Give yourself a pat on the back (2 takes) / I remember you from somewhere / If I had a girl like you (2 take) / Washin' the blues from my soul (2 take) / Medley of Southern College songs / She loves me just the same (2 take) / Them there eyes.
**Album:** Released '81, on Shoestring (1) Catalogue no: **SS 110**

**COMPLETE BUNNY BERIGAN VOL 3, THE**
Tracks: / Ten easy lessons / When a prince of a fella meets Cinderella / Livery stable blues / Let this be a warning to you baby / Why doesn't somebody tell me these things / High society / Father dear father / Simple and sweet / Button, button / I won't tell a soul I love you / Rockin' rollers' jubilee / Sobbin' blues / I cried for you / Jelly roll blues / 'Deed I do / In a mist / Flashes / Davenport blues / Candlelights / In the dark / Walkin' the dog / Patty cake, patty cake / Jazz me blues / Ya had it comin' to ya / There'll be some changes made / Little Gate's special / Gangbuster's holiday / Peg o my heart / Night song / Ain't she sweet / Ay ay ay.
**CD Set:** Released Apr '90, on RCA by BMG Records (UK). Catalogue no: **ND 90349**
**Cass set:** Released Apr '90, on RCA by BMG Records (UK). Catalogue no: **NK 90349**
**2 LP Set:** Released Apr '90, on RCA by BMG Records (UK). Catalogue no: **NL 90349**

**INDISPENSABLE BUNNY BERIGAN (1937-39) (Berigan, Bunny & His Orchestra)**
Tracks: / Swanee river / Frankie and Johnnie / Study in brown, A / I can't get started / Prisoner's song / Black bottom / Azure / Russian lullaby / High society / Sobbin' blues / In a mist / Flashes / Candlelights / In the dark / Blue Lou / Jazz me blues / Night song / Honeysuckle rose / Blues / 'Cause my baby says so / All God's chillun got rhythm / Mahogany Hall stomp / Turn on that red hot heat / Wearing of the green, The / Livery stable blues / Rockin' rollers' jubilee / Jelly roll blues / Davenport blues / Walking the dog / Blues, The / There'll be some changes made / Little gates special / Ain't she sweet.
**Cass set:** Released Jul '86, on RCA by BMG Records (UK). Deleted Nov '88. Catalogue no: **NK 89744**
**2 LP Set:** Released Jul '86, on RCA by BMG Records (UK). Deleted Jul '89. Catalogue no: **NL 89744**

**INDISPENSABLE BUNNY BERIGAN, THE (1937-1939)**
Tracks: / Honeysuckle rose / Blues / 'Cause my baby says so / Swanee river / All God's chillun got rhythm / Frankie and Johnny / Mahogany hall stomp / Turn on that red hot heat / Study in brown, A / I can't get started / Prisoner's song / Mama, I wanna make rhythm / Black bottom / Russian lullaby / Azure / Wearing of the green, The / Livery stable boues / High society / Rockin' rollers jubilee / Sobbin' blues / Jelly roll blues / In a mist / Flashes / Davenport blues / Candlelights / In the dark / Walking the dog / Blue Lou / Be some changes made / Little gate's special / Peg o'my heart / Night song / Ain't she sweet.
**Album:** Released '83, on RCA (France) by BMG Records (France). Catalogue no: **PM 43689**

**LEADER AND SIDEMAN**
**Album:** Released Jan '87, on Meritt (USA) Catalogue no: **504**

**PORTRAIT OF BUNNY BERIGAN (See panel below)**
Tracks: / Me minus you / She reminds me of you / Troubled / Plantation moods / In a little Spanish town / Solo hop / Nothin' but the blues / Squareface / King Porter stomp / Buzzard, The / Tillie's downtown now / You took advantage of me / Chicken and waffles / I'm coming Virginia / Blues / Swing Mister Charlie / Blue Lou / Marie / Black bottom / Prisoner's song / I can't get started.
Note: Original recordings from 1932/6.
**CD:** Released 1 Apr '89, on Living Era

**Bunny Berigan - Portrait of BunnyBerigan (ASV)**

by Academy Sound & Vision Records. Catalogue no: **CD AJA 5060**
**Cass:** Released 1 Apr '89, on Living Era by Academy Sound & Vision Records. Catalogue no: **ZC AJA 5060**
**Album:** Released 1 Apr '89, on Living Era by Academy Sound & Vision Records. Catalogue no: **AJA 5060**

### SATURDAY NIGHT SWING CLUB 1936 (Berigan, Bunny & The Original Dixieland Jazz Band)
**Cass:** Released Mar '89, on Jasmine by Hasmick Promotions. Catalogue no: **JASMC 2524**
**Album:** Released Mar '89, on Jasmine by Hasmick Promotions. Catalogue no: **JASM 2524**

### UNKNOWN BAND 1939
**Album:** Released '88, on Phontastic (Sweden) Catalogue no: **NOST 7638**

### UNKNOWN BAND 1939
**Album:** Released '88, on Meritt (USA) Catalogue no: **MERITT 501**

## Berk, Dick

### BIG JAKE (Berk, Dick & The Jazz Adoption Agency)
Tracks: / Raving lunatic / Message, The / If I were a bell / Groovin' / Metamorphosis / Juxtaposition / Bewitched, bothered and bewildered / Big Jake / Force to hang.
**Album:** Released '84, on Discovery (USA) by Discovery Records (USA). Catalogue no: **DS 890**

### RARE ONE (Berk, Dick & The Jazz Adoption Agency)
Tracks: / Dizzy's business / Lament for Brad / I didn't know what time it was / Kadee Van Browne / Fun at sea / Rare one / Commissioner / Theme.
**Album:** Released '83, on Discovery (USA) by Discovery Records (USA). Catalogue no: **DS 877**

## Berkeley Blues Festival

### BERKELEY BLUES FESTIVAL (Various artists)
**Album:** Released '81, on Arhoolie (USA) by Arhoolie Records (USA). Catalogue no: **ARHOOLIE 1030**

## Berlin, Irving

**Biographical details:** Berlin, Irving. One of the greatest songwriters of the 20th century was born in 1888 in Russia, A printer's error on an early song changed his name from Israel Baline. With Cole Porter he was one of the few who wrote both words and music, and he was unique in adapting his style from the era of the coon shouter to the more sophisticated songwriting of the Golden Age of Broadway and musical films. His earliest songs still have a great period charm when performed in the right spirit, such as *When The Midnight Choo Choo Leaves For Alabam, I Want To Go Back To Michigan, Play A Simple Melody*, scores more; *Alexander's Ragtime Band* in 1911 had made him world famous as a ragtime composer, which he was not: he confessed that he didn't even know what it was. He never learned to read music fluently and used a special piano with a shift lever on it, because he could play in only one key; his songs, unlike those of Porter, George Gershwin or Rogers & Hart, rarely became favourite vehicles for jazzmen and he understood few trends in modern music, yet his knack for inventing songs that sounds as if they've always existed was unparalleled *God Bless America, Easter Parade, White Christmas*; he wrote for Fred Astaire films and his show 'Annie Get your Gun' in 1946 contained more hits than any other show ever written: *They Say It's Wonderful, I Got The Sun In The Morning, Doin' What Comes Naturally, The Girl That Imarry, There's No Business Like Show Business.* (Donald Clarke 23 August 1988).

### 100TH ANNIVERSARY COLLECTION (Irving Berlin)
Tracks: / Alexander's ragtime band / What'll I do / Puttin' on the Ritz / Cheek to cheek / I've got my love to keep me warm / All by myself / There's no business like show business / Anything you can do / Home again blues / Easter Parade / White Christmas / God bless America.
Note: The 100th anniversary if Irving Berlin's birth is currently being celebrated. This tribute album to one of America's most prolific adopted sons includes classics by Crosby/Jolson/Astaire / Ellington and Linda Rondstadt.
**CD:** Released Jul '88, on MCA by MCA Records. Catalogue no: **DMCL 1869**

### ALWAYS
**Cass:** Released '88, on Polydor by Polydor Ltd. Deleted Aug '89. Catalogue no: **835 450 4**

### CENTENARY- A CELEBRATION
Tracks: / Heatwave / Easter parade / Let's face the music and dance / Cheek to cheek.
**Album:** Released '88, on Pickwick by Pickwick Records. Catalogue no: **SHM 3233**
**Cass:** Released '88, on Pickwick by Pickwick Records. Catalogue no: **HSC 3233**
**CD:** Released Jun '88, on Pickwick by Pickwick Records. Catalogue no: **PWKS 501**

### FACE THE MUSIC (A century of Irving Berlin) (Various artists)
Tracks: / Always: *Various artists* / Russian lullaby: *Various artists* / Cheek to cheek: *Various artists.*
**Cass:** Released Jan '89, on Music Masters by Music Masters Records. Catalogue no: **MMD 20147 H**
**CD:** Released Jan '89, on Music Masters by Music Masters Records. Catalogue no: **MMD 60147 A**
**Album:** Released Jan '89, on Music Masters by Music Masters Records. Catalogue no: **MMC 40147 F**

### GOLDEN AGE OF IRVING BERLIN, THE
Tracks: / Me / Say it isn't so / How deep is the ocean / Maybe it's because I love you so much / Heatwave / Easter parade / Piccolino, The / Cheek to cheek / Isn't this a lovely day / Let yourself go / Let's face the music and dance / On the avenue - selection part 1 / Slumming on Park Avenue / You're laughing at me / He ain't got rhythm / On the avenue - selection part 2 / This year's kisses / I've got my love to keep me warm / Girl on the police gazette, The / Alexander's ragtime band / Now it can be told / Everybody's doing it now / I used to be colour blind / Change partners.
Note: The music of Irving Berlin, one of the worlds greatest composers. played by the best of the British Dance Bands during the 1930's. Artists included: The Orchestras of Ambrose, Henry Hall, Billy Cotton, Harry Roy, Lew Stone, Carroll Gibbons, Jack Hylton and Joe Loss. Features tracks: 'Say It Isn't So', 'How Deep Is The Ocean', 'Easter Parade', 'Cheek To Cheek', 'Isn't This A Lovely Day' and 'Alexander's Ragtime Band'.
**Album:** Released '84, on Golden Age by EMI Records. Catalogue no: **GX 41 2518-1**
**Cass:** Released '84, on Golden Age by EMI Records. Catalogue no: **GX 41 2518-4**

### IRVING BERLIN SONGBOOK, THE
**CD:** Released Jun '88, on Compact Selection Catalogue no: **TQ 143**

### MILESTONE OF MEMORY
**Album:** Released Jun '89, on Reid Catalogue no: **RD 3**

### SAY IT WITH MUSIC (1923-1933)
**2 LP Set:** Released '79, on Monmouth Evergreen Catalogue no: **MES 7084/5**

### SONG IS...IRVING BERLIN (Various artists)
Tracks: / Alexander's Ragtime Band: *Various artists* / All alone: *Various artists* / Because I love you: *Various artists* / Blue skies: *Various artists* / Cheek to cheek: *Various artists* / He ain't got rhythm: *Various artists* / Heat wave: *Various artists* / I never had a chance: *Various artists* / I'm putting all my eggs in one basket: *Various artists* / I've got my love to keep me warm: *Various artists* / Let me sing and I'm happy: *Various artists* / Let yourself go: *Various artists* / Let's face the music and dance: *Various artists* / Marie: *Various artists* / Piccolino, The: *Various artists* / Pretty girl is like a melody, A: *Various artists* / Slumming on Park Avenue: *Various artists* / This year's kisses: *Various artists* / Top hat, white tie and tails: *Various artists* / We saw the sea: *Various artists* / White Christmas: *Various artists* / You keep coming back like a song: *Various artists.*
Note: 64 minutes. Artists: Boswell Sisters, Al Bowlly, Sam Browne, Denny Dennis, Dorsey Brothers, Bob Farnon, Alice Faye, Roy Fox, Geraldo, Carroll Gibbons, Nat Gonella, Benny Goodman, Hildegarde, Dick James, Al Jolson, Teddy Joyce, George Melachrino, Jimmy Mesene, Ray Noble, Harry Roy, Artie Shaw, Lew Stone.
**CD:** Released 1 Dec '89, on Living Era

by Academy Sound & Vision Records. Catalogue no: **CD AJA 5068**
**Cass:** Released 1 Dec '89, on Living Era by Academy Sound & Vision Records. Catalogue no: **ZC AJA 5068**
**Album:** Released 1 Dec '89, on Living Era by Academy Sound & Vision Records. Catalogue no: **AJA 5068**

## Berman, Sonny

**Biographical details:** Berman, Sonny. The trumpeter was one of the brightest stars in early-modern jazz, doing his most famous work with the Woody Herman band before he died of a drug-related heart attack. He made only a few small-group recordings under his own name, most also featuring the Herman trombonist Bill Harris. (Donald Clarke 23 August 1988).

**JAZZ IMMORTAL 1946**
**Album:** Released Feb '88, on Fresh Sounds (Spain) by Fresh Sounds Records (Spain). Catalogue no: **FS 195**

## Bernard, Bob

**CLASS**
Tracks: / I cried for you / My foolish heart / Mamas gone goodbye / Linger awhile / My melancholy baby.
**Album:** Released Jun '88, on Calligraph Catalogue no: **CLGLP 017**

## Bernhardt, Clyde

**CLYDE BERNHARDT & THE HARLEM BLUES JAZZ BAND**
**Album:** Released '79, on Barron Deleted '88. Catalogue no: **VLP 7402**

**MORE BLUES & JAZZ FROM HARLEM**
**Album:** Released '79, on Baron Deleted '88. Catalogue no: **BARON 400**

## Berry, Bill

**SHORTCAKE**
Tracks: / Avalon / Betty / Bloose / I didn't know about you / Royal Garden blues / Moon song / I'm getting sentimental over you / I hadn't anyone till you....
**Album:** Released '79, on Concord by Concord Jazz Records (USA). Catalogue no: **CJ 75**

## Berry, Chuck

**Biographical details:** Charles Edward Berry was born on October 18th, 1926 in San Jose, California. Some years later his family moved to St.Louis, Missouri where he spent his formative years. He soon developed an interest in music and we know he played guitar at school gigs and sang in the local church choir. When he left school he started training as a hairdresser but during his free time he played in clubs with a small group. In 1955 he took some recordings he had made to blues musician Muddy Waters in Chicago who arranged for him to be signed to the famous R&B label Chess Records. Berry's first release "Maybelline" immediately topped the charts and was followed by a string of successes which from both a musical and a lyrical aspect had a very influential effect on the rock'n'roll scene. He was to inspire many musicians especially the British rock stars of the sixties. Following his musical success Berry also starred in a few films. In 1959 he was sent to prison on charges of immorality and did not resume his music career until 1964. Although he has had a few new hits, he has mainly concentrated on live performances in these years, running through his golden oldies.

**Chuck Berry**

Berry, Chuck. Born in 1926 in California, the guitarist, singer and songwriter was without doubt the greatest influence on rock 'n' roll until the Beatles. He grew up in St Louis, served time for armed robbery in 1944, became a hairdresser and began recording for Chess in 1955: his *Ida Red* was renamed *Maybelline* and became his first hit; thereafter his songs about cars, girls and high school flattened the fence between R&B and pop.
John Lennon said that if we needed another name for rock 'n' roll, we could call it Chuck Berry, while the Rolling Stones began as Berry imitators. His nine top 40 hits 1955-59 included *Roll Over Beethoven, Sweet Little Sixteen, Rock & Roll Music* and *Johnny B Goode*, while some of his best failed to cross over, such as the two-sided top ten R&B hit *Too Much Monkey Business/Brown Eyed Handsome Man*. He fell foul of an outmoded Federal law, transporting a minor across a state line 'for immoral purposes'; his first blatantly racist trial was thrown out, but the second sent him to prison again. His writing dried up and he handicapped his own career by refusing to tour with a band, often hiring second-rate local backing groups, but his legend and his influence were already complete. (Donald Clarke, 24 August 1988.)
As well as being one of the greats of the Fifties rock 'n' rollers, Chuck Berry stands among the most influential artists in the entire history of rock music. Depending on which source of information you believe, Berry was born either in San Jose or St Louis. He was definitely raised in St Louis, however and had a turbulent upbringing: three of his adolescent years were spent in a reform school for attempted robbery. During his first time at high school, he purchased his first second hand guitar and began listening to both 'race' music (the early name for rhythm and blues) and country and western. St Louis gave him ready access to both genres and it was this dual influence that was to prove vital in his future role as one of the architects of rock 'n' roll. Berry graduated in cosmotology and hairdressing, the later being his major career ambition. In 1952 he formed his own group and spent three years playing his local club circuit. 1955 saw him journey to Chicago, where he managed to impress his hero, the legendary bluesman Muddy Waters. At Waters' suggestion, he went to Chess Records with rough demos of a couple of his compositions and was able to impress the label's chief Leonard Chess sufficiently to get a debut single released. That first 45 was called *Maybellene* and was the first example of Berry's

fusion of country and R&B. It was given a heavy push by the powerful disc jockey Alan Freed (who is said to have invented the term rock'n'roll), who received a dubious co-writing credit. Such an arrangement did not raise as many eyebrows then as it undoubtedly would today and what mattered at the time was that it was a fine, fresh record that put Berry at the forefront of the new rock'n'rollers. *Maybellene* logged nine weeks atop the US rhythm & blues charts and hit No.5 on the pop list, in the late summer and early autumn on '55. The next two singles *Thirty days* and *No money down* were R&B successes but failed to repeat the pop success of the first disc. They were followed by *Roll over Beethoven*, a witty account of the advent of the new music, which managed to reach No. 29 on the American pop charts. Yet the next record, a double A side combining *Too much monkey business* and *Brown eyed handsome man*, again failed to consolidate and remained solely in the R&B charts. By now Elvis Presley was storming the world, being universally hailed as the biggest artist of the new rock'n'roll and one of the biggest show business sensations of the century. Bill Haley's early string of hits and Berry's success with *Maybellene* were now being dwarfed by the exciting and outrageous achievements of the new King. Berry longed for this kind of pop adulation, but his problem was that his early discs were failing to talk about the subjects that the new young audience wanted to hear about. Although still influenced by his heroes, Muddy Waters and Louis Jordan, he began to address himself to the fads, fashions and interests of the newly affluent youth of America. The first result of this new policy was *School day* which recounted a day in the life of a typical yankee youngster - but the important factor was that it emphasised what took place after schools closed in the afternoon. By stressing the teenage themes of jukeboxes, dancing and romance, while retaining and improving his musical originality and excellence, Berry suddenly appealed to the mass youth market. *School day* reached No. 3 on the US pop charts in the early summer of 1957; it also gave him his first UK hit, peaking at No. 24. By the end of the year he was returning to the US Top 10 with another anthem, simply called *Rock'n'roll music*. It was followed in 1958 by two further smashes, *Sweet little sixteen* - No. 2 in the States and No. 16 in Britain (his second UK hit), and *Johnny B Goode*. One of the most important features of these instant rock'n'roll classics was that the lyrics were articulated clearly; because Berry ensured that every word could be understood. The full impact of his witty tales of teenage life reached the target audience. In addition he was becoming a major live attraction, with his concert performers; and along with many of his contempories, he was appearing in the spate of rock films that were being made in the late fifties. In 1959 things started to tail off. Rock music was mellowing and his new hits like *Almost grown* and *Back in the USA* were each receiving a lower US chart position than the single before.

Then, later in the year, he appeared in an American court on a charge of transporting an under-age girl across State lines for sexual purposes. Berry consistently professed his innocence and claimed that the real reason for the trial was an attempt to punish a black man; for becoming successful and famous. Reports of the whole episode vary, but it seems that the first trial was indeed terminated on the grounds of racial bias, the final outcome however, was that the black superstar began a two year jail sentence in the early Sixties.

During this period of enforced inactivity, music was moving on, and in his absense he was being left behind. Yet upon his release he suddenly found that he was a new hero in a country that had not previously given him much recognition: the Beatles, and the Rolling Stones were rapidly becoming the new pop sensations and both were acknowledging Chuck Berry as a key influence. Berry had only had two relatively small hits in the UK during the Fifties and his other singles had failed to chart at all. So when the Stones sang and played numerous Berry songs in their stage act and scored their first hit single with his song *Come on* and when the Beatles recorded *Roll over Beethoven* as an album track they were introducing a man's work to a whole new audience. Meanwhile the United States' big new group, the Beach Boys, were hitting with *Surfin' USA*; this was an adaptation of *Sweet little sixteen*, with new surfing lyrics substituted. All of a sudden Berry was being hailed by the world's new superstars. What's more the song *Memphis Tennessee* (also commonly known as simply *Memphis*) was enjoying success in the form of two cover versions: Lonnie Mack reached No. 5 in the US with an instrumental rendition and a singer called Dave Berry (no relation) peaked at No. 19 on the British charts. Chuck Berry's own version of *Memphis* (coupled with *Let it rock*) then raced into the British charts and gave him a long overdue Top 10 debut in the UK in late '63. Simultaneously, he was making his first big impression on the British album charts - having first entered them in May of that year with a self-titled set, reaching No. 6 towards the end of '63. Encouraged by his new acclaim, the freed Berry returned to the recording studio and came up with three brand new hits, all reaching the Top 30 on both sides of the Atlantic during 1964: the biggest of these was *No particular place to go* which featured the same melody as *School day* but with new words, thus proving that his style had not changed at all in the intervening years. It was nevertheless a great record as there were two other singles *Nadine (is it you)* and *You never can tell*, the latter including some of his wittiest ever lyrics. After this glorious period of renewed success, his career floundered. No good new material surfaced for the rest of the Sixties. It is one of pop history's strangest ironies that this legendary rock'n'roll star, who had such a great influence on the music of the Fifties and Sixties, should suddenly have the biggest hit of his career in the early Seventies with a record totally out of keeping with the style that had made his name; but that is what happened. An old song called *My ding a ling* had been in Berry's live set for many years under a different title.

But in 1972, a new naughty live version recorded at a British arts festival went No. 1 on both sides of the Atlantic; it was his first chart topper in both the USA and UK. Despite the protestations of moral campaigner Mary Whitehouse in the latter nation, it was a runaway novelty favourite. Towards the middle of the decade Elvis Presley recorded Berry's *Promised land*; it hit the Top 20 in both Britain and America. Subsequently Chuck had recieved mixed fortunes. On the bright side, the Steve Gibbons Band took his song *Tulane* into the UK Top 20 and Berry played at the White House by personal invitation of US President Jimmy Carter. On the black side, he was given another prison sentence, this time for tax evasion. Chuck Berry has had his ups and downs but there is one permanent up that can not be changed. He is recognised all over the world as one of rock music's pioneers. Not only was he one of the greatest stars of the rock'n'roll heyday itself, but he also had a vital and direct influence on the emergence of rock's next great era - where would the Beatles and Stones have been without his legendary guitar work, songwriting and showmanship. (Bob MacDonald).

## 20 GOLDEN GREATS: CHUCK BERRY

**Album:** Released Dec '79, on Hammer Deleted '84. Catalogue no: **HMR 9003**

## 20 GREATEST HITS: CHUCK BERRY

**Album:** Released '88, on Masters (Holland) Catalogue no: **MA 16983**

**Cass:** Released Dec '88, on Masters (Holland) Catalogue no: **MAMC 91683**

**CD:** Released Dec '88, on Spectrum (CD) by M.S.D.. Catalogue no: **SPEC 85004**

**Cass:** Released Dec '88, on Fun by Balaclava Records. Catalogue no: **FUNC 9012**

**Album:** Released '88, on Fun by Balaclava Records. Catalogue no: **FUN 9012**

## 20 SUPER HITS: CHUCK BERRY

**Album:** Released Dec '85, on Chess (PRT) Deleted '88. Catalogue no: **6 24372**

**Cass:** Released Dec '85, on Chess (PRT) Deleted '88. Catalogue no: **4 24372**

## 21 GREATEST HITS

**CD:** Released Jan '90, on Zeta Catalogue no: **ZET 520**

## 21 GREATEST HITS,THE

Tracks: / Maybellene / Sweet little six-

een / School days / Rock and roll music / Johnny B. Goode / Carol / Reelin' and rockin' / Memphis Tennessee / Bring another drink / Good lovin' woman / Roll over Beethoven / Back in the USA / Sweet little rock 'n' roller / Oh baby doll / C.C. rider / Thirty days / Goodnight, well it's time to go / Back to Memphis / Check me out / My heart will always belong to you / I really do love you.
**CD:** Released May '87, on Bescol Catalogue no: **CD 30**

## 100 MINUTES OF CHUCK BERRY
**Cass:** Released '82, on PRT (100 Minute Series) Catalogue no: **ZCTON 114**

## AFTER SCHOOL SESSION
**Album:** Released Oct '88, on Vogue (France) by Vogue Records. Catalogue no: **515030**

## BACK IN THE U.S.A.
**LP Pic:** Released Dec '85, on Astan (USA) Catalogue no: **PD 50009**

## BERRY IS ON TOP
Tracks: / Almost grown / Carol / Maybelline / Sweet little rock & roller / Anthony boy / Johnny B Goode / Little Queenie / Jo Jo gun / Roll over Beethoven / Around and around / Hey Pedro / Blues for Hawaiians.
**Cass:** Released Oct '87, on Chess by Vogue Records. Catalogue no: **GCHK 78043**
**Album:** Released Oct '87, on Chess by Vogue Records. Catalogue no: **GCH 8043**

## BEST OF CHUCK BERRY
**CD:** Released '88, on K-Tel by K-Tel Records. Catalogue no: **ONCD 5155**
**Cass:** Released '84, on Creole (Everest-Europa) by Creole Records. Catalogue no: **16-2**
**CD:** Released Dec '86, on Vogue by Vogue Records. Catalogue no: **VG 600 033**

## BIO
Tracks: / Bio / Hello little girl / Goodbye / Woodpecker / Rain eyes / Aimlessly driftin' / Got it and gone / Talkin' about my buddy.
**Cass:** Released May '88, on Chess by Vogue Records. Catalogue no: **GCHK 78046**
**Album:** Released May '88, on Chess by Vogue Records. Catalogue no: **GCH 8046**

## CHESS BOX
**CD:** Released Mar '90, on MCA by MCA Records. Catalogue no: **CHD 38**

## CHESS MASTERS
Tracks: / Maybellene / Wee wee hours / You can't catch me / Downbound train / No money down / Brown eyed handsome man / Roll over Beethoven / Too much monkey business / Havana moon / School days / La Juanda / Rock and roll music / Oh baby doll / Sweet little sixteen / Johnny B. Goode / Round and round / Carol / Jo Jo Gunne / Beautiful Delilah / House of blue lights / Memphis / Sweet little rock 'n' roller / Johnny B. Goode / Nadine / Hail, hail rock'n'roll / My ding a ling.
**Album:** Released '83, on Chess (PRT) Deleted '88. Catalogue no: **CXMD 4016**

## CHESS MASTERS : CHUCK BERRY
Tracks: / No particular place to go / Maybellene / You can't catch me / School days / Roll over Beethoven / Sweet little sixteen / Round and round / Sweet little rock 'n' roller / Nadine / Rock and roll music / Old baby doll / Johnny B. Goode / Reelin' and rockin' / Memphis Tennessee / Carol / Come on.
**Album:** Released 19 Mar '88, on Stylus by Stylus Music Records. Catalogue no: **SMR 848**
**CD:** Released '88, on Stylus by Stylus Music Records. Catalogue no: **SMD 848**
**Cass:** Released 19 Mar '88, on Stylus by Stylus Music Records. Catalogue no: **SMC 848**

## CHICAGO GOLDEN YEARS (Golden decade Vol.3)
**2 LP Set:** Released Oct '88, on Vogue by Vogue Records. Catalogue no: **427010**
**2 LP Set:** Released Oct '88, on Vogue by Vogue Records. Catalogue no: **427009**
**2 LP Set:** Released Oct '88, on Vogue by Vogue Records. Catalogue no: **427008**

## CHUCK BERRY
**CD:** Released May '89, on Object Enterprises Catalogue no: **ONN 31**
**Album:** Released Apr '83, on Chess by Vogue Records. Deleted Jan '88. Catalogue no: **CXMP 2011**
**LP Pic:** Released Dec '85, on Astan (USA) Catalogue no: **AR 30013**
**Album:** Released '88, on Joker (USA) by Lifetime Records (USA). Catalogue no: **SM 3989-2**
**Album:** Released May '63, on Pye International Deleted '68. Catalogue no: **NPL 28024**
**Cass:** Released '84, on Audio Fidelity(USA) by Audio Fidelity (USA). Catalogue no: **ZCGAS 726**

## CHUCK BERRY BOX SET
**Cass set:** Released Nov '89, on Charly by Charly Records. Catalogue no: **TCBOX 256**
**LP Set:** Released Sep '89, on MCA by MCA Records. Catalogue no: **CH 68001**
**CD Set:** Released Nov '89, on Charly by Charly Records. Catalogue no: **CDBOX 256**
**Cass set:** Released Sep '89, on MCA by MCA Records. Catalogue no: **CHC 68001**
**LP Set:** Released Nov '89, on Charly by Charly Records. Catalogue no: **BOX 256**
**CD Set:** Released Sep '89, on MCA by MCA Records. Catalogue no: **CD 8001**

## CHUCK BERRY ON STAGE
**Album:** Released Oct '63, on Pye International Deleted '68. Catalogue no: **NPL 28027**

## CHUCK BERRY'S ROCK 'N' ROLL PARTY
Note: Live in Hamburg, 1977. With the Flying Saucers.
**Album:** Released Jul '88, on Driving Wheel Catalogue no: **C 7788**

## COLLECTION: CHUCK BERRY (20 rock 'n' roll greats)
Tracks: / Maybellene / Carol / Johnny B. Goode / Roll over Beethoven / Hoochie coochie man / Brown eyed handsome man / Oh baby doll / Around and around / Hail, hail rock'n'roll / Thirty days / Sweet litle sixteen / Memphis / Reelin' and rockin' / Too much monkey business / You can't catch me / In the wee wee hours / Rock and roll music / Havana moon / No particular place to go / Little Queenie.
**Album:** Released Jul '86, on Deja Vu Catalogue no: **DVLP 2068**
**Cass:** Released Jul '86, on Deja Vu Catalogue no: **DVMC 2068**
**CD:** Released Sep '87, on Deja Vu Catalogue no: **DVCD 2068**

## COLLECTION: CHUCK BERRY (2)
Tracks: / Sweet little sixteen / Johnny B. Goode / Back in the USA / Maybellene / Too much monkey business / Rock and roll music / Reelin' and rockin' / No particular place to go / Roll over Beethoven / You never can tell / Nadine / Carol / School days / My ding a ling / Almost grown / Let it rock / Little Queenie / Promised land / Memphis / Sweet little rock 'n' roller / Thirty days / Brown eyed handsome man / Run Rudolph run / Merry Christmas baby.
**CD:** Released Jun '88, on Castle Collector Series by Castle Communications Records. Catalogue no: **CCSCD 194**
**2 LP Set:** Released Jun '88, on Castle Collector Series by Castle Communications Records. Catalogue no: **CCSLP 194**
**Cass:** Released Jun '88, on Castle Collector Series by Castle Communications Records. Catalogue no: **CCSMC 194**

## DECADE '55-'65
Tracks: / School days / Maybellene / Sweet little sixteen / Roll over Beethoven / Too much monkey business / Memphis / Let it rock / Little Queenie / Carol / Almost grown / Nadine / Johnny B. Goode / No particular place to go / Promised land / Back in the USA / Rock and roll music.
**CD:** Released Apr '88, on Platinum Music by Prism Leisure. Catalogue no: **PLATCD 24**
**Album:** Released Apr '88, on Platinum Music by Prism Leisure. Catalogue no: **PLAT 24**
**Cass:** Released Apr '88, on Platinum Music by Prism Leisure. Catalogue no: **PLAC 24**

## DUCK WALK
**Album:** Released Jul '88, on Entertainers Catalogue no: **ENT LP 13046**
**Cass:** Released Jul '88, on Entertainers Catalogue no: **ENT MC 13046**
**CD:** Released Jul '88, on Entertainers Catalogue no: **ENTCD 263**

## DUCKWALKING
Tracks: / School days / No particular

place to go / Promised land / Reelin' and rockin' / Sweet little sixteen / Memphis Tennessee / Nadine / You never can tell.
**Cass:** Released '83, on Chess (PRT) Deleted '88. Catalogue no: **ZCDOW 14**
**Album:** Released '83, on Chess (PRT) Deleted '88. Catalogue no: **DOW 14**

**GO GO GO**
Tracks: / Go go go.
**7" Single:** Released Jul '63, on Pye International Deleted '66. Catalogue no: **7N 25209**

**GREATEST HITS: CHUCK BERRY**
**Album:** Released May '88, on Black Tulip Catalogue no: **2636801**
**Album:** Released Apr '86, on Castle Showcase by Castle Communications Records. Catalogue no: **SHLP 136**
**Cass:** Released May '88, on Black Tulip Catalogue no: **2636804**
**Cass:** Released Apr '86, on Castle Showcase by Castle Communications Records. Catalogue no: **SHTC 136**
**CD:** Released May '88, on Black Tulip Catalogue no: **2636802**

**GREATEST HITS: CHUCK BERRY (CD)**
Tracks: / Brown eyed handsome man / Maybellene / Johnny B. Goode / Sweet little rock 'n' roller / School days.
Note: Original Chess Recordings. Licensed from Sugarhill Records Inc.
**CD:** Released Jul '86, on Greenline by Charly Records. Deleted '88. Catalogue no: **CD CHESS 21**

**GREATEST HITS LIVE: CHUCK BERRY**
Tracks: / Johnny B. Goode / Sweet little sixteen / In the wee wee hours / Rock and roll music / Maybellene / Too much monkey business / Hail, hail rock'n'roll / My ding a ling.
**Cass:** Released '83, on Spot by Pickwick Records. Catalogue no: **SPC 8512**
**Album:** Released '83, on Spot by Pickwick Records. Catalogue no: **SPR 8512**

**HAIL HAIL ROCK 'N' ROLL (VIDEO)**
Note: "Racism, ripoffs and rock 'n' roll are the key ingredients in the video biography of the man from St Louis - Chuck Berry. Apart from performing his greatest hits in concert, this 116 minute rock 'n' roll documentary features musical contributions by Eric Clapton, Julian Lennon, Linda Ronstadt and Etta James. It also offers interviews with Little Richard, Bo Diddley, Jerry Lee Lewis and Bruce Springsteen, among others. The films musical director and behind the scenes force was Keith Richards. Cert: U." (August 1988)
**VHS:** Released Oct '88, on CIC Video Catalogue no: **VHR 1317**

**HAIL, HAIL, ROCK & ROLL**
Tracks: / Maybelline / Thirty days / No money down / Roll over Beethoven / Brown eyed handsome man / Too much monkey business / You can't catch me / School day (ring ring goes the bell) / Rock and roll music / Sweet little sixteen / Reelin' and rockin' / Johnny B Goode / Around and around / Beautiful Delilah / Carol / Sweet little rock and roller / Almost grown / Little Queenie / Back in the U.S.A. / Memphis Tennesse / Too pooped to pop / Let it rock / Bye bye Johnny / I'm talking about you / Come on / Nadine (is it you) / No particular place to go / You never can tell / Little Marie / Promised land / Tulane / My ding-a-ling.
**CD:** Released '89, on Chess by Vogue Records. Catalogue no: **CDCHESS 1003**
**2 LP Set:** Released '87, on Chess by Vogue Records. Catalogue no: **DETD 207**

**HAIL, HAIL, ROCK 'N' ROLL (Original soundtrack)**
Tracks: / Maybellene / Around and around / Sweet little sixteen / Brown eyed handsome man / Memphis, Tenessee / Too much monkey business / Back in the USA / Wee wee hours / Johnny B. Goode / Little Queenie / Rock and roll music / Roll over Beethoven / I'm through with love.
**CD:** Released 20 Feb '88, on MCA by MCA Records. Catalogue no: **DMCF 3411**
**Album:** Released Feb '88, on MCA by MCA Records. Catalogue no: **MCF 3411**
**Cass:** Released Feb '88, on MCA by MCA Records. Catalogue no: **MCFC 3411**

**HIS LATEST AND GREATEST**
**Album:** Released May '64, on Pye International Deleted '69. Catalogue no: **NPL 28037**

**LEGENDARY CHUCK BERRY, THE**
**VHS:** Released Nov '87, on Channel 5 by Channel 5 Video. Catalogue no: **CFV 02372**

**LET IT ROCK**
**Album:** Released Oct '87, on Checkmate Catalogue no: **CHECKMATE 1955**

**LET IT ROCK (SINGLE)**
Tracks: / Let it rock / Memphis Tennessee.
**7" Single:** Released Oct '63, on Pye International Deleted '66. Catalogue no: **7N 25218**

**LIVE: CHUCK BERRY**
Tracks: / No particular place to go / Hail, hail rock'n'roll / In the wee wee hours / Johnny B. Goode / Promised land / Hoochie coochie man / Sweet little sixteen / Memphis tennessee / My ding a ling.
Note: Previously released on the Everest label.
**Album:** Released '84, on Premier by Premier Records. Catalogue no: **CBR 1007**
**Cass:** Released '84, on Premier by Premier Records. Catalogue no: **KCBR 1007**

**LONDON CHUCK BERRY SESSIONS, THE**
**Album:** Released '84, on Chess (France) by Vogue Records. Catalogue no: **515 035**

**LONG LIVE ROCK 'N' ROLL (Berry, Chuck & Little Richard)**
**Cass set:** Released Jun '88, on Spectrum (1) Catalogue no: **M 10154**

**MAYBELLENE VOL. 2**
**Album:** Released '88, on Joker (USA) by Lifetime Records (USA). Catalogue no: **SM 3984**

**MEMPHIS TENNESSEE**
Tracks: / Memphis Tennessee / No particular place to go.
**7" Single:** Released '83, on Old Gold by Old Gold Records. Deleted Jul '88. Catalogue no: **OG 9296**

**MORE CHUCK BERRY**
**Album:** Released Dec '63, on Pye International Deleted '68. Catalogue no: **NPL 28028**

**MOTIVE SERIES**
Tracks: / Louis to Frisco / Sweet little rock 'n' roller / Roll over Beethoven / Back to Memphis / Wee baby blues / Johnny B. Goode / Club nitty gritty / Sweet little sixteen / School days / Feelin' it / Let it rock / Carol.
**Cass:** Released '82, on Mercury by Phonogram Ltd. Catalogue no: **7145 129**
**Album:** Released '82, on Mercury by Phonogram Ltd. Catalogue no: **6463 129**

**MOTORVATIN' (Greatest hits live)**
Tracks: / Maybelline / Carol / Johnny B. Goode / Roll over Beethoven / Hoochie coochie man / Brown eyed handsome man / Oh baby doll / Around and around / Hail, hail rock'n'roll / Thirty days / Sweet little sixteen / Memphis Tennessee / Reelin' and rockin' / Too much monkey business / You can't catch me / In the wee wee hours / Rock and roll music / Havana moon / No particular place to go / Little queenie.
**Album:** Released Dec '87, on Starburst by Magnum Music Group. Catalogue no: **SMT 009**
**Album:** Released Feb '77, on Chess by Vogue Records. Catalogue no: **9288 690**

**MR ROCK 'N' ROLL**
**Album:** Released Oct '88, on Vogue (France) by Vogue Records. Catalogue no: **509075**

**MY DING-A-LING**
Tracks: / My ding a ling / School days / No particular place to go / Johnny B. Goode.
**7" Single:** Released '84, on SMP (2) Catalogue no: **SKM 04**
**7" Single:** Released Jun '88, on Chess by Vogue Records. Catalogue no: **GCHN 01**
**12" Single:** Released Jun '88, on Chess by Vogue Records. Catalogue no: **GCHX 101**

**MY DING-A-LING (OLD GOLD)**
Tracks: / My ding a ling.
**7" Single:** Released Jan '89, on Old Gold by Old Gold Records. Catalogue no: **OG 9845**

## NADINE (IS IT YOU)
Tracks: / Nadine.
**7" Single:** Released Feb '64, on Pye International Deleted '67. Catalogue no: **7N 25236**

## NEW JUKE BOX HITS
Tracks: / I'm talking about you / Diploma for two / Thirteen question method / Away from you / Don't you lie to me / The way it was before / Little star / Route 66 / Sweet sixteen / Run around / Stop and listen / Rip it up.
**Cass:** Released Aug '86, on Chess by Vogue Records. Catalogue no: **GCHK 78008**
**Album:** Released Oct '88, on Vogue (France) by Vogue Records. Catalogue no: **515032**
**Album:** Released Aug '86, on Chess by Vogue Records. Catalogue no: **GCH 8008**

## NO PARTICULAR PLACE TO GO
Tracks: / No particular place to go / Johnny B. Goode / You never can tell / Memphis Tennessee.
**CD Single:** Released Feb '89, on Charly by Charly Records. Catalogue no: **CDS 6**
**7" Single:** Released May '64, on Pye International Deleted '67. Catalogue no: **7N 25242**
**7" Single:** Released '83, on Flashback by Mainline Records. Catalogue no: **FBS 18**

## NO PARTICULAR PLACE TO GO (OLD GOLD)
Tracks: / No particular place to go.
**7" Single:** Released Jan '89, on Old Gold by Old Gold Records. Catalogue no: **OG 9843**

## ONE DOZEN BERRYS
**Album:** Released Oct '88, on Vogue (France) by Vogue Records. Catalogue no: **515031**

## PROFILE: CHUCK BERRY
**Album:** Released '81, on Teldec (1) by ASV (Academy Sound & Vision). Catalogue no: **6.24472**
**Cass:** Released '81, on Teldec (1) by ASV (Academy Sound & Vision). Catalogue no: **CL4 24472**

## PROMISED LAND
Tracks: / Promised land.
**7" Single:** Released Jan '65, on Pye International Deleted '68. Catalogue no: **7N 25285**

## REELIN' AND ROCKIN' (COLLECTION)
Tracks: / Johnny B. Goode / Carol / Hoochie coochie man / Maybellene / Memphis Tennessee / My ding a ling / Nadine / No particular place to go / Reelin' and rockin' / Rock and roll music / Sweet little sixteen / Too much monkey business / In the wee wee hours.
**CD:** Released Aug '87, on The Collection by Object Enterprises. Catalogue no: **OR 0016**

## REELIN' AND ROCKIN' (LIVE)
Tracks: / Reelin' and rockin' / School days / My ding a ling / Too much monkey business / Memphis / Maybellene / Nadine.
Note: Some of Chuck Berry's greatest hits recorded live at the Toronto Rock and Roll festival including a seventeen minute version of "My ding-a-ling".
**Album:** Released '84, on Magnum Force by Magnum Music Group. Catalogue no: **MFM 017**

## REELIN' AND ROCKIN' (SINGLE)
Tracks: / Reelin' and rockin'.
**7" Single:** Released Feb '73, on Chess by Vogue Records. Deleted '76. Catalogue no: **CHESS 6145 020**

## REELIN' AND ROCKIN' (TOPLINE)
Tracks: / Bonsoir cherie / Carol / Hail, hail rock'n'roll / Hoochie coochie man / In the wee wee hours / Johnny B. Goode / Johnny B. Goode (encore) / Maybellene / Sweet little sixteen / Too much monkey business.
**Album:** Released '85, on Topline by Charly Records. Catalogue no: **TOP 117**
**Cass:** Released Jan '85, on Topline by Charly Records. Catalogue no: **KTOP 117**

## REELING, ROLLING & ROCKING
Tracks: / Memphis Tennessee / Too much monkey business / My ding a ling / Reelin' & rockin' / Johnny B. Goode / Maybellene / Nadine / Hail, hail rock'n'roll / Sweet little sixteen.
**Album:** Released Nov '83, on Bulldog Records by President Records. Catalogue no: **BDL 1051**

## ROCK AND ROLL MUSIC
Tracks: / Maybelline / School days / Rock and roll music / Sweet little sixteen / Johnny B. Goode / Memphis Tennessee / Come on / Let it rock / Reelin' and rockin' / Nadine / No particular place to go / You never can tell / Promised land / My ding a ling.
**CD:** Released Jul '89, on Instant (2) by Charly Records. Catalogue no: **CDINS 5002**
**Album:** Released Jul '89, on Instant (2) by Charly Records. Catalogue no: **INS 5002**
**Cass:** Released Jul '89, on Instant (2) by Charly Records. Catalogue no: **TCINS 5002**

## ROCK AND ROLL MUSIC (ROOTS)
**CD:** Released Mar '90, on Roots Catalogue no: **RTS 33008**

## ROCK IT
Tracks: / Move it / Oh what a thrill / I need you baby / If I were / House lights / I never thought / Havana moon / Pass away.
**Album:** Released Dec '79, on Atlantic by WEA Records. Deleted '84. Catalogue no: **K 50648**
**CD:** Released Nov '88, on Magnum Force by Magnum Music Group. Catalogue no: **CDMF 065**
**Album:** Released Nov '88, on Magnum Force by Magnum Music Group. Catalogue no: **MFLP 065**

## ROCKIN' AT THE HOPS
Tracks: / Bye,bye,Johnny / Worried life blues / Down the road a piece / Confessin' the blues / To pooped to pop / Mad lad / I got to find my baby / Betty Jean / Childhood sweetheart / Broken arrow / Driftin' blues / Let it rock.
**Cass:** Released Oct '87, on Chess by Vogue Records. Catalogue no: **GCHK 78041**
**Album:** Released Oct '88, on Vogue (France) by Vogue Records. Catalogue no: **515033**
**Album:** Released Aug '87, on Chess by Vogue Records. Catalogue no: **GCH 8041**
**Album:** Released '84, on Chess (France) by Vogue Records. Catalogue no: **515 033**

## ROCKING WITH CHUCK BERRY
**Cass:** Released '81, on Mercury by Phonogram Ltd. Catalogue no: **7259 140**
**Album:** Released '81, on Mercury by Phonogram Ltd. Catalogue no: **9279 140**

## ROCK 'N' ROLL HITS
Tracks: / Johnny B. Goode / Rock and roll music / School days / Maybellene / Back in the USA / Sweet little sixteen / Memphis / Roll over Beethoven / Forty days / Carol / Club nitty gritty.
Note: 3 UK singles hit plus 8 other classics
**Cass:** Released '83, on Mercury (USA) by PolyGram Rec.Inc.(USA). Catalogue no: **7259 138**
**Album:** Released '83, on Mercury (USA) by PolyGram Rec.Inc.(USA). Catalogue no: **9279 138**

## ROCK 'N' ROLL RARITIES (CHESS)
Tracks: / Rock & roll music (demo) / Rock & roll music / Sweet little sixteen (demo) / Sweet little sixteen / Reelin' and rockin' / Johhny B Goode / Beautiful Delilah / Oh yeah / House of blue lights / Time was / Sweet little rock'n'roller / Run Rudolph run / Little Queenie / Betty Jean / County line / Bye bye Johnny / I got to find my baby / Down the road a piece / Route 66 / I'm talking about you / Come on / Go go go / Brown eyed handsome man / Nadine (is that you) / You never can tell / Promised land / No particular place to go / I want to be your driver / Little Marie / My Mustang Ford / Ain't that just like a woman / It wasn't me.
**CD:** Released '89, on Chess by Vogue Records. Catalogue no: **CHESS 1005**
**2 LP Set:** Released Oct '88, on Vogue by Vogue Records. Catalogue no: **427018**
**2 LP Set:** Released Aug '87, on Chess by Vogue Records. Catalogue no: **DETD 206**
**Cass set:** Released Aug '87, on Chess by Vogue Records. Catalogue no: **DETDK 7206**
**CD:** Released Dec '86, on Vogue by Vogue Records. Catalogue no: **VG 600 120**

## ROCK 'N' ROLL RARITIES (MCA)
Tracks: / No particular place to go / Rock 'n' roll music / It wasn't me / Reelin' & rockin' / Come on / Johnny B. Goode / Bye bye Johnny / Little Marie / Time was / Promised land / Little Queenie / You

never can tell / Sweet little 16 / Country line / Run rudolph run / Nadine / Betty Jean / I want to be your driver / Beautiful Delilah / Oh yeah.
**CD:** Released Feb '90, on MCA by MCA Records. Catalogue no: **CHD 92521**

**ROLL OVER BEETHOVEN**
**Album:** Released Jun '89, on Ocean (2) Catalogue no: **OCN 2033WL**
**Album:** Released '88, on Joker (USA) by Lifetime Records (USA). Catalogue no: **SM 3983**
**Cass:** Released Jun '89, on Ocean (2) Catalogue no: **OCN 2033WK**
**CD:** Released Jun '89, on Ocean (2) Catalogue no: **OCN 2033WD**

**ROLL OVER BEETHOVEN (OLD GOLD)**
Tracks: / Roll over Beethoven / Johnny B. Goode / Rock and roll music.
**CD Single:** Released 30 May '89, on Old Gold by Old Gold Records. Catalogue no: **OG 6143**
**7" Single:** Released Jan '89, on Old Gold by Old Gold Records. Catalogue no: **OG 9847**

**RUN RUDOLPH RUN**
Tracks: / Run Rudolph run.
**7" Single:** Released Dec '63, on Pye International Deleted '66. Catalogue no: **7N 25228**

**SCHOOL DAY**
Tracks: / School days.
**7" Single:** Released Jul '57, on Columbia by EMI Records. Deleted '60. Catalogue no: **DB 3951**

**SPOTLIGHT ON CHUCK BERRY**
Tracks: / School days / Sweet little sixteen / Carol / Route 66 / Back in the USA / Rock and roll music / Promised land / Let it rock / Brown eyed handsome man / Maybellene / Round and round / Run Rudolph run / No particular place to go / You never can tell / Nadine / Roll over Beethoven / Too much monkey business / Go go go / Reelin and rockin / Memphis / Johnny B. Goode / Tulane / Come on / My ding a ling.
**Album:** Released '80, on PRT by Castle Communications Records. Catalogue no: **SPOT 1003**
**Cass:** Released '80, on PRT by Castle Communications Records. Catalogue no: **ZCSPT 1003**

**ST LOUIS**
**CD:** Released Jun '88, on MCA (USA) by MCA Records (USA). Catalogue no: **31261**

**ST LOUIS TO FRISCO TO MEMPHIS (Berry, Chuck & Steve Miller band)**
**Album:** Released '82, on Karussell (Germany) Catalogue no: **2872 103**
**Cass:** Released '82, on Karussell (Germany) Catalogue no: **3472 103**

**ST. LOUIS TO LIVERPOOL**
Tracks: / Little Marie / Our little rendezvous / No particular place to go / You two / Promised land / You never can tell / Go bobby soxer / Thing's I used to do / Liverpool drive / Night beat / Merry christmas baby / Brenda Lee.
**Album:** Released Oct '88, on Vogue (France) by Vogue Records. Catalogue no: **515034**
**Album:** Released Aug '86, on Chess by Vogue Records. Catalogue no: **GCH 8007**
**Cass:** Released Aug '86, on Chess by Vogue Records. Catalogue no: **GCHK 78007**

**SWEET LITTLE ROCK 'N' ROLLER**
**Cass:** Released '84, on Mercury (Holland) Catalogue no: **758 1340**
**Album:** Released '84, on Mercury (Holland) Catalogue no: **661 9039**

**SWEET LITTLE SIXTEEN**
Tracks: / Sweet little sixteen.
**7" Single:** Released '84, on SMP (2) Catalogue no: **SKM 05**
**7" Single:** Released Apr '58, on London-American Deleted '61. Catalogue no: **HLM 8585**
**7" Single:** Released '85, on Chess (PRT) Deleted '88. Catalogue no: **CHES 4000**

**SWEET LITTLE SIXTEEN (OLD GOLD)**
Tracks: / Sweet little sixteen.
**7" Single:** Released Jan '89, on Old Gold by Old Gold Records. Catalogue no: **OG 9849**

**TWO DOZEN BERRYS**
**CD:** Released '86, on Vogue by Vogue Records. Catalogue no: **VG 600 085**

**TWO GREAT GUITARS (Diddley Bo / Chuck Berry)**
Note: See under **Diddley, Bo** for full details.
**Album:** Released Oct '88, on Vogue (France) by Vogue Records. Catalogue no: **515023**

**WHAT A THRILL**
Tracks: / What a thrill / California.
**7" Single:** Released Aug '79, on Atlantic by WEA Records. Deleted '82. Catalogue no: **K 11354**

**YOU NEVER CAN TELL**
**Album:** Released Oct '64, on Pye International Deleted '69. Catalogue no: **NPL 29039**

**YOU NEVER CAN TELL (SINGLE)**
Tracks: / You never can tell.
**7" Single:** Released Aug '64, on Pye International Deleted '67. Catalogue no: **7N 25257**

## Berry, Leon Chu

**CALLOWAY YEARS, THE 1937**
**Album:** Released '88, on Meritt (USA) Catalogue no: **MERITT 21-2**

**DENTISTRY IN RHYTHM (VOL. 3) (Fillin' the Chu gaps) (Berry, Leon Chu with Cab Calloway)**
**Album:** Released Jan '88, on Two Flat Discs Catalogue no: **TFD 5.009**

**DENTISTRY IN RHYTHM (VOL. 4) (Fillin' the Chu gaps)**
Note: with Cab Calloway & Mildred Bailey.
**Album:** Released Jan '88, on Two Flat Discs Catalogue no: **TFD 5.011**

**GIANT OF THE TENOR SAX, A (with Little Jazz Ensemble 1938 & 1941)**
Tracks: / Blowin' up a breeze (2) / On the sunny side of the street / On the sunny side of the street (2) / Monday at Minton's / Monday at Minton's (2) / Gee baby ain't I good to you / Gee baby ain't I good to you (2) / Sittin' in (2 takes) / Stardust / Body and soul / Forty six west fifty two / Forty six west fifty two (2) / Blowin' up a breeze.
**Album:** Released Nov '86, on Commodore Class Catalogue no: **AG6 24293**
**CD:** Released May '87, on Commodore Class Catalogue no: **824 291**

**INDISPENSABLE, THE**
**Album:** Released '85, on RCA (France) by BMG Records (France). Catalogue no: **NL 89481**

**LEON CHU BERRY**
**Album:** Released '88, on Meritt (USA) Catalogue no: **MERITT 12**

**RAREST...,THE 1037/40**
**Album:** Released '82, on Everybody's (Sweden) Catalogue no: **E 1002**

## Berry, Steve

**TRIO (Berry, Steve Trio)**
Note: Debut album from British bass player Steve Berry & His Trio- Mark Lockheart (saxaphone) and Peter Fairclough (drums). Both Steve & Mark are members of the collective British big band Loose Tubes.
**Album:** Released Oct '88, on Loose Tubes by Loose Tubes Records. Catalogue no: **LTLP 007**
**CD:** Released Oct '88, on Loose Tubes by Loose Tubes Records. Catalogue no: **LTCD 007**

## Bert, Eddie

**KALEIDOSCOPE**
**Album:** Released Jun '88, on Savoy Jazz (USA) by Malaco Records (USA). Catalogue no: **SJL 1186**

**LET'S DIG BERT**
**Album:** Released Feb '88, on Fresh Sounds (Spain) by Fresh Sounds Records (Spain). Catalogue no: **FS 189**

## Best Of...

**BEST OF A SWINGING ERA (Various artists)**
**Cass:** Released Jul '83, on RCA (Germany) Catalogue no: **PK 42381**
**Album:** Released Jul '83, on RCA (Germany) Catalogue no: **PL 42381**

**BEST OF ACAPPELLA, VOLUME 7 (Various artists)**
**Album:** Released Aug '87, on Relic (USA) Catalogue no: **RELIC 109**

**BEST OF BATON R & B (Various artists)**
Note: with Marie Knight, Ann Cole etc.
**Album:** Released Feb '87, on Flyright by Interstate Music. Catalogue no: **FLY 552**

**BEST OF BIG BANDS (Various ar-**

**tists)**
**Album:** Released May '88, on Music Power Catalogue no: **33013**
**Cass:** Released May '88, on Music Power Catalogue no: **63013**

**BEST OF BLUES AND SOUL (Various artists)**
**CD:** Released Apr '87, on Malaco by Malaco Records (UK). Catalogue no: **MALCD 341**

**BEST OF DIXIELAND (Various artists)**
**Album:** Released Apr '83, on RCA (Australia) Catalogue no: **26.21745**
**Cass:** Released Aug '85, on RCA by BMG Records (UK). Catalogue no: **NK 81431**
**Album:** Released Aug '85, on RCA by BMG Records (UK). Deleted Jul '89. Catalogue no: **NL 81431**

**BEST OF FRANCES CONCERT (Various artists)**
**CD:** Released '89, on France's Concert Catalogue no: **FCD 130**
**Album:** Released '89, on France's Concert Catalogue no: **FC 130**

**BEST OF I LOVE JAZZ (Various artists)**
**Cass:** Released Aug '84, on CBS (import) by CBS Records. Catalogue no: **40 21120**
**Album:** Released Aug '84, on CBS (import) by CBS Records. Catalogue no: **CBS 21120**

**BEST OF MUSIC AND RHYTHM (Various artists)**
**CD:** on PVC (USA) by Jem Records Inc.(USA). Catalogue no: **PVCD 6902**
**Album:** Released '87, on PVC (USA) by Jem Records Inc.(USA). Catalogue no: **PVC 6902**
**Cass:** Released '87, on PVC (USA) by Jem Records Inc.(USA). Catalogue no: **PVCC 6902**

**BEST OF NEWHOUSE (Various artists)**
**2 LP Set:** Released '88, on Blu-Disc (USA) Catalogue no: **T 5001/2**

**BEST OF THE AMERICAN FOLK BLUES (Various artists)**
Note: Includes Howlin' Wolf, Lightning Hopkins etc.
**Album:** Released Aug '87, on L&R Catalogue no: **LR 42.066**

**BEST OF THE BLUES (Various artists)**
Note: With Big Joe Williams / Memphis Slim / Broonzy etc.
**Album:** Released May '86, on Storyville by Storyville Records AB. Catalogue no: **SLP 4023**

**BEST OF THE CAJUN HITS (Various artists)**
**Album:** on Swallow (USA) by Flat Town Music Co.(USA). Catalogue no: **6001**
**Cass:** Released '88, on Swallow (USA) by Flat Town Music Co.(USA). Catalogue no: **6001TC**

**BEST OF THE CLASSIC YEARS, THE (20 tracks from The Classic Years in digital stereo) (Various artists)**
Note: Best of:- Bing Crosby, Al Bowlly, Dance Bands USA, Love Songs, Silly Songs, Opera, Movie Musicals, Swing-Big Bands, Fred Astaire, Swing-Small Groups.
**CD:** Released '88, on BBC by BBC Records & Tapes. Catalogue no: **BBC CD 667**

## Best Of Blue Note

**BEST OF BLUE NOTE VOL 1 (Various artists)**
Tracks: / Un poco loco: *Powell, Bud* / Tin tin deo: *Moody, James* / Criss cross: *Monk, Thelonious* / Bag's Groove: *Various artists* / Cherokee: *Brown, Clifford* / Tempus fugit: *Davis, Miles* / Blue train: *Coltrane, John* / Maiden voyage: *Hancock, Herbie* / Cristo redentor: *Byrd, Donald* / Moanin': *Blakey, Art* / Blues walk: *Donaldson, Lou* / Song for my father: *Silver, Horace* / Back to the chicken shack: *Smith, Jimmy (USA)* / Chitlins con carne: *Burrell, Kenny* / Sidewinder, The: *Morgan, Lee.*
**Cass:** Released Mar '86, on Blue Note by EMI Records. Catalogue no: **TCBST 844291**
**2 LP Set:** Released Jul '89, on Blue Note by EMI Records. Catalogue no: **BST2 84429**

**BEST OF BLUE NOTE VOL 2 (Various artists)**
Tracks: / Blue Harlem: *Quebec, Ike* / Our delight: *Dameron, Tadd* / Round midnight: *Monk, Thelonious* / Gears, The: *Melle, Gil* / Collard greens and black-eyed peas: *Powell, Bud* / Senor blues: *Silver, Horace* / Brownie speaks: *Brown, Clifford* / Three o'clock in the morning: *Gordon, Dexter* / Lou's blues: *Donaldson, Lou* / Blues march: *Blakey, Art* / Wadin': *Parlan, Horace* / Rumproller, The: *Morgan, Lee* / Something else: *Adderley, Julian Cannonball & Nat Adderley* / Blues bossa: *Henderson, Joe* / Watermelon man: *Hancock, Herbie* / Decision: *Rollins, Sonny.*
Note: The first collection of the Best of Blue Note,which commemorated the initial year of Blue Note's reactivation,met with surprising success.Our second year brings a second collection from the rich & vast Blue Note vaults,bringing together more of the labels most popular and significant recordings.
**Cass:** Released Mar '86, on Blue Note by EMI Records. Catalogue no: **TCBST 844292**
**2 LP Set:** Released Jul '89, on Blue Note by EMI Records. Catalogue no: **BST2 84433**

## Best Of Blues Singers

**BEST OF BLUES SINGERS (Various artists)**
Tracks: / Georgia on my mind: *Charles, Ray* / Kansas City: *Waters, Muddy Blues Band* / Luther's blues: *Waters, Muddy Blues Band* / I've got my Mojo working: *Waters, Muddy Blues Band* / Come Baby: Goin' to Chicago: *Williams, Joe* / Early in the morning: *Williams, Joe* / Outside man, The: *Parker, Little Junior* / Flip flop and fly: *Turner, Big Joe* / Summertime: *Turner, Big Joe.*
**CD:** Released Jan '89, on Denon Catalogue no: **DC 8530**

## Best Of British...

**BEST OF BRITISH BARBERSHOP (Various artists)**
Tracks: / I'd give a million tomorrows: *Various artists* / Darkness on the delta: *Various artists* / Berkeley Square: *Various artists* / Let the rest of the world go by: *Various artists* / Muskrat ramble: *Various artists* / Carolina in the morning: *Various artists* / Sam, the old accordion man: *Various artists* / What a wonderful world: *Various artists* / Don't bring Lulu: *Various artists* / Sweet and lovely: *Various artists* / Over the rainbow: *Various artists* / Do you remember: *Various artists* / Born free: *Various artists* / I believe: *Various artists* / 76 trombones: *Various artists* / Wonderful guy: *Various artists* / Oh Susannah: *Various artists* / Swing low sweet chariot: *Various artists* / Daddy sang bass: *Various artists* / Pollution: *Various artists.*
**Album:** Released Jun '82, on MWM Catalogue no: **MWM 1010**

**BEST OF BRITISH DANCE BANDS (Various artists)**
Tracks: / Happy days are here again: *Ambrose & His Orchestra* (Recorded: 29/1/30) / After the sun's kissed the world goodbye: *Elizalde, Fred Rhythmicians* (Recorded: 4/12/29) / It's the girl: *Cotton, Billy & His Band* (Recorded:10/10/31) / By the river Sainte Marie: *Bowlly, Al* (Recorded:16/6/31) / My baby just cares for me: *Payne, Jack & His BBC Dance Orchestra* (Recorded:15/10/31) / Crazy rhythm: *Starita, Ray & His Ambassadors* (Recorded:29/9/28) / How can you say no: *Hall, Henry & His BBC Dance Orchestra* (Recorded:4/11/32) / My silent love: *Gibbons, Carroll & The Hotel Orpheans* (Recorded:19/9/32) / I'm in the market for you: *Ambrose & His Orchestra* (Recorded:24/4/30) / Too many tears: *Cotton, Billy & His Band* (Recorded:3/6/32) / Good little, bad little you: *New Mayfair Dance Orchestra* (Recorded:19/2/29) / Any times the time to fall in love: *New Mayfair Dance Orchestra* (Recorded:20/6/30) / Honeymoon Hotel: *Hylton, Jack & His Orchestra* (Recorded:27/2/33) / Wind's in the west, The: *Fox, Roy & His Band* (Recorded:31/10/33) / Baby face: *Savoy Orpheans* (Recorded:13/10/26) / Like taking candy from a baby: *Roy, Harry* (Recorded: / 7/34) / Say it: *Roy, Harry* (Recorded: / 9/34) / Play to me gypsy: *Costa, Sam* (Recorded:16/1/34) / Kiss me dear: *Jackson, Jack & His Orchestra* (Recorded:1/9/34) / For all we know: *Gibbons, Carroll & The Hotel Orpheans* (Recorded:23/10/34).
**Album:** Released Jul '86, on Saville by Conifer Records. Catalogue no: **SVL 177**
**CD:** Released Jul '86, on Saville by Conifer Records. Catalogue no: **CDSVL 177**

**Cass:** Released Jul '86, on Saville by Conifer Records. Catalogue no: **CSVL 177**

**BEST OF BRITISH JAZZ (Various artists)**
Tracks: / Moanin' at Minden: *Various artists* / Strutting with some barbeque: *Various artists* / Mean to me: *Various artists* / Sonny boy: *Various artists* / Exactly like you: *Various artists* / Pretty girl is like a melody: *Various artists* / Maybe it's because I'm a Londoner: *Various artists* / It don't mean a thing: *Various artists.*
**Album:** Released Jul '81, on ASV (Academy Sound & Vision). Deleted '86. Catalogue no: **ALM 4001**

**BEST OF BRITISH TRADITIONAL JAZZ (Various artists)**
Tracks: / St. George's rag: *Barber, Chris Jazz & Blues Band* / Lazy river: *Barber, Chris Jazz & Blues Band* / Stevedore stomp: *Barber, Chris Jazz & Blues Band* / Phil's late: *Barber, Chris Jazz & Blues Band* / Tuxedo rag: *Sunshine's, Monty Jazz Band* / Creole love call: *Sunshine's, Monty Jazz Band* / 1919 rag: *Sunshine's, Monty Jazz Band* / Oh Monah: *Gonella, Nat/his Jazz Band* / Wild man blues: *Gonella, Nat/his Jazz Band* / Nagasaki: *Gonella, Nat/his Jazz Band* / Dardanella: *Welsh, Alex & His Jazz Band* / Monmartre: *Welsh, Alex & His Jazz Band* / Hindustan: *Welsh, Alex & His Jazz Band* / Creole jazz: *Bilk, Acker & His Paramount Jazz Band* / Perdido street blues: *Bilk, Acker & His Paramount Jazz Band* / Papa dip: *Bilk, Acker & His Paramount Jazz Band* / South: *Colyer, Ken Jazzmen* / Mabel's dream: *Colyer, Ken Jazzmen* / Sweet Sue: *Colyer, Ken Jazzmen.*
**CD:** Released Jul '84, on Polydor by Polydor Ltd. Deleted Jan '89. Catalogue no: **818 651 2**

**VERY BEST OF BRITISH JAZZ, THE (Various artists)**
Tracks: / Hi ya: *Various artists* / Watch what happens: *Various artists* / Time's a wastin': *Various artists* / Sweet Sue: *Various artists* / Stompin' at the Savoy: *Various artists* / Misty: *Various artists* / Preacher, The: *Various artists* / Honeysuckle Rose: *Various artists* / Rosetta: *Various artists.*
Note: The Best Of British Jazz includes:- Betty Smith, Kenny Baker, Don Lusher, Tony Lee, Tony Archer, Jack Parnell.
**Album:** Released Mar '84, on Polyphonic by Polyphonic Reproductions. Catalogue no: **PRJ 501**
**Cass:** Released '88, on Polyphonic by Polyphonic Reproductions. Catalogue no: **CPRJ 501**

## Best Of Chicago Blues

**BEST OF CHICAGO BLUES (Various artists)**
Tracks: / Love me or leave me: *Various artists* / Next time you see me: *Various artists* / Rocket 88: *Various artists* / Vietcong blues: *Various artists* / When my baby left me: *Various artists* / Spaan's stomp: *Various artists* / Twisted snake: *Various artists* / One room country shack: *Various artists* / Sweet little angel: *Various artists* / I had a dream last night: *Various artists* / Somebody been talkin': *Various artists* / Mule kicking in my stall: *Various artists* / Blues is a botheration: *Various artists* / S.P. blues someday: *Various artists* / Blues keep falling, The: *Various artists* / Rockin' my boogie: *Various artists* / Five long years: *Various artists* / Checking on my baby: *Various artists* / Tobacco road: *Various artists* / Money (that's all I want): *Various artists* / Stealin' back: *Various artists.*
**Album:** Released '83, on Vanguard (USA) by CBS Records. Catalogue no: **VSD 1**

## Best Of Dance Band

**BEST OF DANCE BAND DAYS VOL. 1 (Various artists)**
Tracks: / Moonlight serenade: *Various artists* / Clarinade: *Various artists* / Jumpin' at the woodside: *Various artists* / Sweet Georgia Brown: *Various artists* / Stars fell on Alabama: *Various artists* / Angry: *Various artists* / Stardust: *Various artists* / Song of India: *Various artists* / Caldonia: *Various artists* / Airmail stomp: *Various artists* / Rockin' in rhythm: *Various artists* / Bei mir bist du schon: *Various artists* / Little brown jug: *Various artists* / Don't be that way: *Various artists* / Tweet tweet: *Various artists* / Button up your overcoat: *Various artists* / Some people: *Various artists* / 'S wonderful: *Various artists* / Opus one: *Various artists* / At the woodchoppers ball: *Various artists* / Blue moon: *Various artists* / I got a girl named Netty: *Various artists.*
**CD:** Released Oct '87, on Dance Band Days by Prism Leisure. Catalogue no: **DBCD 20**
**Cass:** Released Jun '88, on Dance Band Days by Prism Leisure. Catalogue no: **DBDC 20**
**Album:** Released Jun '88, on Dance Band Days by Prism Leisure. Catalogue no: **DBD 20**

**BEST OF DANCE BAND DAYS VOL. 2 (Various artists)**
Tracks: / Symphony: *Various artists* / King Porter stomp: *Various artists* / Rockin' in rhythm: *Various artists* / I'll be seeing you: *Various artists* / Down the road apiece: *Various artists* / Man with a horn: *Various artists* / Begin the beguine: *Various artists* / Cheek to cheek: *Various artists* / There, I've said it again: *Various artists* / Everybody eats when they come to my house: *Various artists* / Newport up: *Various artists* / Lullaby of Broadway: *Various artists* / Seven-o-five: *Various artists* / All the cats join in: *Various artists* / King size blues: *Various artists* / Fare thee well to Harlem: *Various artists* / Bedford drive: *Various artists* / Blue skies: *Various artists* / Goosey gander: *Various artists* / Cruisin' with cab: *Various artists* / St. Louis blues: *Various artists* / Rum and coca cola: *Various artists.*
**CD:** Released Oct '87, on Dance Band Days by Prism Leisure. Catalogue no: **DBCD 21**
**Album:** Released Jun '88, on Dance Band Days by Prism Leisure. Catalogue no: **DBD 21**
**Cass:** Released Jun '88, on Dance Band Days by Prism Leisure. Catalogue no: **DBDC 21**

## Best Of Dixie Records

**BEST OF DIXIE RECORDS, VOL 3 (Various artists)**
Tracks: / Three little wishes: *Lee, Jimmie* / Dizzy: *Peters, Pete* / Rockin' in my sweet baby's arms: *Peters, Pete* / Red Rover: *Bragg, Doug* / Pretty little thing: *Bragg, Doug* / Lovin' on my mind: *Bragg, Doug* / Gotta keep it swinging: *Skelton, Eddie* / Curly: *Skelton, Eddie* / Love you too much: *Skelton, Eddie* / Rebel's retreat: *Skelton, Eddie* / Handful of love: *Keefer, Lyle* / Blues hanging around: *Kelley, C..*
**Album:** Released Jul '84, on Million (Holland) Catalogue no: **MILLION 3**

**BEST OF DIXIE RECORDS, VOL 4 (Various artists)**
Tracks: / Feel so good: *Carroll, Bill* / Who shot Sam?: *Jones, George Thumper* / This little girl of mine: *Half Brothers* / Way you want it, The: *Meers, Arvil* / Little things you do, The: *Lee, Jimmie* / Never again: *Clayton, Johnny* / Don't tease me: *Pat & Dee* / Little dog blues: *Price, Mel* / Lonesome tavern blues: *Benson, Eddy.*
**Album:** Released Jul '84, on Million (Holland) Catalogue no: **MILLION 4**

**BEST OF DIXIE RECORDS, VOL 5 (Various artists)**
Tracks: / I like to go: *McDaniel, Floyd* / Meanest blues: *Thomas, Jake* / Poor boy blues: *Thomas, Jake* / Concussion: *Holidays* / Big, big man: *Brockman, Danny* / Easy does it: *Couch, Orville* / She told a lie: *Mishoe, Watson* / Teen lover: *Reynolds, Eddy* / What's gonna do now?: *Williams Brothers* / My baby don't want me no more: *Ridings, Jim* / You're gonna pay: *Ridings, Jim* / Ali Baba: *Williams Brothers.*
**Album:** Released Jul '84, on Million (Holland) Catalogue no: **MILLION 5**

**BEST OF DIXIE RECORDS, VOL 6 (Various artists)**
Tracks: / Queen from Bowling Green: *Buchanan, Art* / Wonder why: *Buchanan, Art* / It must be me: *Ontario, Art* / Just look, don't touch, she's mine: *Johnson, Dee* / Crazy legs: *Gallegher, Jay* / Steady: *Gallegher, Jay* / Piano polka: *Bailey, M. & D.* / Blue guitar stomp: *Hammock, Ken* / Rock and roll: *White, J.R.* / Weekend boogie: *Croock, Tom* / I'm your guy: *Johnson, Dee* / Brady and Dunky: *Hanna, Jack.*
**Album:** Released Jul '84, on Million (Holland) Catalogue no: **MILLION 6**

**BEST OF DIXIE RECORDS VOL 7 (Various artists)**
**Album:** Released '88, on Million (Holland) Catalogue no: **MILLION 7**

## Best Of Jazz...

**BEST OF JAZZ**

**CD:** Released May '89, on Object Enterprises Catalogue no: **ONN 28**

**BEST OF JAZZ CLASSICS, THE (20 tracks from jazz classics in digital stereo series) (Various artists)**
Note: Best of:- New Orleans, Chicago, New York, Louis Armstrong, Fats Waller, Bix Beiderbecke, Bessie Smith, Johnny Dodds, Jelly Roll Morton, Duke Ellington, Joe Venuti/Eddie Lang.
**CD:** Released '88, on BBC by BBC Records & Tapes. Catalogue no: **BBC CD 662**

## Best Of New Orleans ...

**BEST OF NEW ORLEANS RHYTHM AND BLUES (Various artists)**
Tracks: / Loud mouth Annie: *Various artists* / Rhythmatic rhythum: *Various artists* / Jockomo: *Various artists* / Mardi gras: *Various artists* / Country boy: *Various artists* / Flat foot Sam: *Various artists* / Ding dong darling: *Various artists* / Lawdy mama: *Various artists* / What can I do: *Various artists* / Joke, The: *Various artists* / Walk that walk: *Various artists* / I cried all the way home: *Various artists* / Foolish woman: *Various artists* / Oh oh: *Various artists* / This should go on forever: *Various artists* / Needing your love: *Various artists* / Baby please: *Various artists*.
**Album:** Released Oct '84, on Chess (PRT) Deleted '88. Catalogue no: **CXMP 2055**

## Best Of The Jazz ...

**BEST OF THE JAZZ GUITARS (Various artists)**
Tracks: / Apex: *Benson, George* / Flavors: *Benson, George* / Chim chim cheree: *Byrd, Charlie* / Satin doll: *Various artists* / Blues bag: *Burrell, Kenny* / Blues in Green: *Green, Grant* / Cantaloupe woman: *Green, Grant* / Seven minds: *Ponder, Jimmy* / Visions: *Ponder, Jimmy*.
**CD:** Released Jan '89, on Denon Catalogue no: **DC 8531**

**BEST OF THE JAZZ SAXOPHONE VOL. 2 (Various artists)**
Tracks: / Soft winds: *Jacquet, Illinois* / Somebody loves me: *Sims, John Haley 'Zoot'* / On Green Dolphin Street: *Davis, Eddie 'Lockjaw'* / OC-DC: *Barieri, Gato* / Duty free: *Stitt, Sonny* / Blue Lou: *Carter, Benny* / Out of nowhere: *Woods, Phil* / Taurus moon: *Mulligan, Gerry*.
**Album:** Released Jan '89, on Denon. Catalogue no: **DC 8529**

**BEST OF THE JAZZ VIOLINS**
Tracks: / Sweet Georgia Brown: *Venuti, Joe* / Tea for two: *Venuti, Joe* / Almost like being in love: *Venuti, Joe* / Hot canary, The: *Venuti, Joe* / Deed I do: *Grappelli, Stephane* / After you've gone: *Grappelli, Stephane* / Parisian thoroughfare: *Grappelli, Stephane* / Sysmo: *Grappelli, Stephane*.
**Album:** Released Jan '89, on Denon. Catalogue no: **DC 8532**

## Best Of Sun Rockabilly

**BEST OF SUN ROCKABILLY VOL 1 (Various artists)**
Tracks: / Ten cats down: *Various artists* / Jump right out of this jukebox: *Various artists* / Gonna romp and stomp: *Various artists* / Domino: *Orbison, Roy* (Record 3 of 12. Ooby dooby.) / Rakin' and scrapin': *Various artists* / Slow down: *Various artists* / Red cadillac and a black moustache: *Various artists* / Break up: *Various artists* / Greenback dollar: *Various artists* / Red headed woman: *Various artists* / Flyin' saucers rock 'n' roll: *Various artists* / Crawdad hole: *Earls, Jack* / Love my baby: *Various artists* / Red hot: *Various artists* / We wanna boogie: *Various artists* / Come on little mama: *Various artists* / Right behind you baby: *Various artists* / Ubangi stomp: *Various artists* / Let's bop: *Various artists* / Rabbit action: *Various artists* / Put your cat clothes on: *Various artists* / Rocking with my baby: *Various artists*.
**Album:** on Charly by Charly Records. Catalogue no: **CR 30123**
**CD:** Released Apr '86, on Charly by Charly Records. Catalogue no: **CDCHARLY 16**

**BEST OF SUN ROCKABILLY VOL 2 (Various artists)**
Tracks: / Got love if you want it: *Smith, Warren* / That don't move me: *Perkins, Carl* / Itchy: *Burgess, Sonny* / Drinkin' wine: *Simmons, Gene* / How come you do me: *Thompson, Junior* / Gimme some lovin': *Jenkins, Harold* / Johnny Valentine: *Anderson, Andy* / Baby please don't go: *Riley, Billy Lee* / Sentimental fool: *Pittman, Barbara* / Rebound: *Rich, Charlie* / Miss Froggie: *Smith, Warren* / Rock around the town: *Beard, Dean* / Wild one: *Lewis, Jerry Lee* / My baby don't rock: *McDaniel, Luke* / Find my baby for me: *Burgess, Sonny* / My gal Mary Ann: *Earls, Jack* / Me and my rhythm guitar: *Powers, Johnny* / All night rock: *Honeycutt, Glenn* / Your loving man: *Taylor, Vernon* / Mad man 1: *Wages, Jimmy* / Fairlane rock: *Thompson, Hayden* / I need your loving kiss: *Jenkins, Harold* / Perkins wiggle: *Perkins, Carl* / Ain't got a thing: *Burgess, Sonny*.
Note: Original Sun recordings. Licensed from Charly Records International APS.
**Album:** on Charly by Charly Records. Catalogue no: **CR 30124**
**CD:** Released Nov '86, on Charly by Charly Records. Catalogue no: **CDCHARLY 36**

## Best Of The Sweet Bands

**BEST OF THE SWEET BANDS (Various artists)**
**Album:** Released Apr '86, on Hindsight (UK) by Michele International Records. Catalogue no: **HUK 312**

## Betts, Harry

**JAZZ SOUL OF DR. KILDARE.... (Betts, Harry & His Orchestra)**
**CD:** on Mobile Fidelity Sound Lab(USA) by Mobile Fidelity Records (USA). Catalogue no: **MFCD 839**

## Bickert, Ed

**BORDER CROSSING**
Tracks: / For all we know / Man I love, The / Goodnight my love / My funny valentine.
**Album:** Released Jun '83, on Concord Jazz by Concord Jazz Records (USA). Catalogue no: **CJ 216**

**BYE BYE BABY**
Tracks: / You're in love with someone / Bye bye baby / Barbados / It's time / Nobody else but me / Things are getting better / Flower is a lovesome thing / Pensativa / Keeping myself for you.
**Album:** Released '84, on IMS by Polydor Ltd. Deleted '89. Catalogue no: **CJ 232**

**DANCE TO THE LADY (Bickert, Ed & Don Thompson)**
Tracks: / Bluesette / Ruby my dear / Solar / Dance to the lady / Take five / Blue monk.
**Album:** Released Apr '83, on Sackville by Spotlite Records. Catalogue no: **4010**

**FROM CANADA WITH LOVE**
**Album:** Released Oct '79, on PM Catalogue no: **PM 011**

**I WISHED ON THE MOON (Bickert, Ed Quartet)**
Tracks: / CTA / Easy street / Somewhere along the way / Blues for Tommy / Blues my naughty sweetie gives to me

/ Handful of stars, A / I wished on the moon / I'll never stop loving you.
Note: This lyrical Canadian guitarist is joined by three fellow alumni from Rob McConnell's Boss Brass,to present some of the loveliest,yet rarely heard, standards. Personnel: Ed Bickert - guitar / Terry Clarke - drums / Steve Wallace - bass / Rick Wilkins - tenor sax.
**Album:** Released Dec '85, on Concord Jazz by Concord Jazz Records (USA). Catalogue no: **CJ 284**
**CD:** Released Nov '86, on Concord Jazz by Concord Jazz Records (USA). Catalogue no: **CCD 4284**

**IN CONCERT AT THE GARDEN PARTY (Bickert, Ed & Don Thompson)**
Tracks: / Alone together / Face like yours, A / You are too beautiful / What is this thing called love? / Who can I turn to? / Walkin' my baby back home / Please be kind.
Note: Recorded on 22 January 1978.
**Album:** Released Apr '81, on Sackville by Spotlite Records. Catalogue no: **4005**

**THIRD FLOOR RICHARD (Bickert, Ed Trio)**
Tracks: / Band call / Together / Louisiana / I know why and so do you / One moment worth years / Tonite I shall sleep / I got a right to sing the blues / Circus / Third floor Richard / I surrender dear / This can't be love.
**Cass:** Released Jul '89, on Concord Jazz by Concord Jazz Records (USA). Catalogue no: **CJ 380 C**
**CD:** Released Jul '89, on Concord Jazz by Concord Jazz Records (USA). Catalogue no: **CCD 4380**
**Album:** Released Jul '89, on Concord Jazz by Concord Jazz Records (USA). Catalogue no: **CJ 380**

## Big Band Beat

**BIG BAND BEAT (Various artists)**
Tracks: / Hawk talks, The: *Parnell, Jack & his Orchestra* / Fanfare boogie: *Parnell, Jack & his Orchestra* / Skin deep: *Parnell, Jack & his Orchestra* / Trip to Mars: *Parnell, Jack & his Orchestra* / Sky blue shirt and a rainbow tie: *Parnell, Jack & his Orchestra* / Champ, The: *Parnell, Jack & his Orchestra* / Bedtime for drums: *Ainsworth, Alyn Orchestra* / If I had you: *Ainsworth, Alyn Orchestra* / Cobblers song, The: *Ainsworth, Alyn Orchestra* / Buckingham brownies: *Ainsworth, Alyn Orchestra* / Hells bells: *Ainsworth, Alyn/Rock-A-Fellas* / 18th century rock: *Ainsworth, Alyn/Rock-A-Fellas* / Moon was yellow, The: *Watt, Tommy & Orchestra* / Five foot two, eyes of blue: *Watt, Tommy & Orchestra* / Poor little rich girl: *Watt, Tommy & Orchestra* / Won't you come ome Bill Bailey: *Watt, Tommy & Orchestra* / I'll string along with you: *Watt, Tommy & Orchestra* / Creep, The: *Mackintosh, Ken & His Orchestra* / Monster, The: *Mackintosh, Ken & His Orchestra* / Air express: *Mackintosh, Ken & His Orchestra* / Glow worm, The (idyll): *Mackintosh, Ken & His Orchestra* / Berkeley hunt, The: *Mackintosh, Ken & His Orchestra* / Creeping Tom: *Mackintosh, Ken & His Orchestra* / Policeman's holiday, The: *Mackintosh, Ken & His Orchestra.*
**2 LP Set:** Released Oct '89, on MFP by EMI Records. Catalogue no: **DL 1161**
**Cass:** Released Oct '89, on MFP by EMI Records. Catalogue no: **TCDL 1161**

## Big Band Boogie

**BIG BAND BOOGIE, 1938 - 42 (Various artists)**
**Album:** Released Jun '88, on Bandstand Catalogue no: **BS 7107**
**Cass:** Released Jun '88, on Bandstand Catalogue no: **BS 7107C**

## Big Band Classics

**BIG BAND CLASSICS (Various artists)**
Tracks: / In the mood: *Miller, Glenn* / Little brown jug: *Miller, Glenn* / American patrol: *Miller, Glenn* / Moonlight serenade: *Miller, Glenn* / Tuxedo junction: *Miller, Glenn* / Pennsylvania 6-5000: *Miller, Glenn* / String of pearls: *Miller, Glenn* / Take the 'A' train: *Ellington, Duke* / Perdido: *Ellington, Duke* / Creole love call: *Ellington, Duke* / Black and tan fantasy: *Ellington, Duke* / Mood indigo: *Ellington, Duke* / Caravan: *Ellington, Duke* / Solitude: *Ellington, Duke* / Stompin' at the Savoy: *Goodman, Benny* / Avalon: *Goodman, Benny* / King Porter stomp: *Goodman, Benny* / Moonglow: *Goodman, Benny* / One o' clock jump: *Goodman, Benny* / And the angels sing: *Goodman, Benny* / Sing sing sing: *Goodman, Benny* / Pinetop boogie: *Dorsey, Tommy* / Night and day: *Dorsey, Tommy* / After you've gone: *Dorsey, Tommy* / Song of India: *Dorsey, Tommy* / Blue skies: *Dorsey, Tommy* / I'm getting sentimental over you: *Dorsey, Tommy* / Marie: *Dorsey, Tommy.*
**2 LP Set:** Released Nov '89, on Kaz by Kaz Records. Catalogue no: **KAZLP 106**
**Album:** Released Nov '84, on Telstar by Telstar Records (UK). Catalogue no: **STAR 2004**
**CD:** Released Nov '89, on Kaz by Kaz Records. Catalogue no: **KAZCD 106**
**Cass:** Released Nov '84, on Telstar by Telstar Records (UK). Catalogue no: **STAC 2004**
**Cass:** Released Nov '89, on Kaz by Kaz Records. Catalogue no: **KAZMC 106**

**BIG BAND CLASSICS 1957-58 (Various artists)**
Note: Featuring: Harry Arnold, Quincy Jones & Benny Bailey
**2 LP Set:** Released Feb '88, on Dragon by Dragon Records. Catalogue no: **DRLP 139/40**

## Big Band Collection

**BIG BAND COLLECTION, THE (Various artists)**
**CD:** Released Dec '87, on In-Market Catalogue no: **DRIVE 3011**

## Big Band Jazz...

**BIG BAND JAZZ (Various artists)**
Note: Charlie Johnson, Troy Harmonists, Charlie Skeete, Blanche Calloway.
**Album:** Released Jan '88, on Gaps Catalogue no: **GAPS 160**

**BIG BAND JAZZ VOL.1 (Various artists)**
Tracks: / How deep is your love: *Various artists* / Eubie's boogie: *Various artists* / All stops: *Various artists* / Lovely day: *Various artists* / Easy living: *Various artists* / How's this for choosers: *Various artists.*
**Album:** Released Apr '80, on Manhattan Records by President Records. Deleted '85. Catalogue no: **MAN 5011**

**LIVE AT FITZGERALDS (Jazz Members Big Band)**
**Album:** Released Nov '88, on Sea Breeze Catalogue no: **SB 2028**

## Big Band Treasures

**BIG BAND TREASURES (Various artists)**
**CD:** Released Dec '86, on Dunhill Compact Classics (USA) Catalogue no: **DZS 023**

## Big Bands

**50TH ANNIVERSARY OF THE BIG (Various artists)**
**7" Single:** Released May '89, on Garland Catalogue no: **GRZ 008**

**BEST OF BIG BANDS (Various artists)**
Tracks: / Let's dance: *Various artists* / King Porter stomp: *Various artists* / Don't be that way: *Various artists* / Jumpin' at the Woodside: *Various artists* / Way out Basie: *Various artists* / Whirly bird: *Various artists* / Three day sucker: *Various artists* / At the woodchoppers ball: *Various artists* / Northwest Passage: *Various artists* / Flyin' home: *Various artists* / Take the 'A' train: *Various artists* / Rockin' in rhythm: *Various artists* / Hawk talks, The: *Various artists* / Killer Joe: *Various artists.*
Note: Tracks by: Benny Goodman, Count Basie, Buddy Rich, Woody Herman, Harry James, Duke Ellington, Lionel Hampton.p
**CD:** Released '88, on Denon Catalogue no: **DC-8518**
**Cass:** Released '88, on Denon Catalogue no: **MC 8518**

**BEST OF BIG BANDS VOL. II (Various artists)**
Tracks: / Take the 'A' train: *Ellington, Duke* / C-Jam blues: *Ellington, Duke* / West Indian pancake: *Ellington, Duke* / Things ain't what they used to be: *Basie, Count* / Basie: *Basie, Count* / Freckle face: *Basie, Count* / Stealin' apples: *Goodman, Benny* / Bugle call rag: *Goodman, Benny* / Sing, sing, sing: *Goodman, Benny* / Shiny stockings: *James, Harry Orchestra* / Sophisticated lady: *James, Harry Orchestra* / Green onions: *James, Harry Orchestra* / Jazz connoisseur: *James, Harry Orchestra.*
Note: Tracks by Count Basie, Duke Ellington, Benny Goodman, Harry James.
**CD:** Released Jan '89, on Denon Cata-

logue no: **DC 8528**

**BEST OF THE BIG BANDS (Various artists)**
Tracks: / Swing that music: *Various artists* / Woodchoppers ball: *Herman, Woody & His Orchestra* / I'm getting sentimental over you: *Dorsey, Tommy* / One o'clock jump: *Basie, Count* / Dorsey dervish: *Dorsey, Jimmy* / I get a kick out of you: *Shaw, Artie* / East St. Louis toodle-oo: *Ellington, Duke* / Black and tan fantasy: *Ellington, Duke* / Stompin' at the Savoy: *Goodman, Benny (duplicate)* / Flying home: *Hampton, Lionel* / Moonlight Bay: *Miller, Glenn* / Fidgety feet: *Henderson, Fletcher* / Rosetta: *Hines, Earl* / Blues in the night: *Lunceford, Jimmie* / Tisket a tasket, A: *Webb, Chick* / Undecided: *Webb, Chick.*
**Cass:** Released Oct '87, on MCA by MCA Records. Deleted Apr '88. Catalogue no: **MCLC 1861**
**Album:** Released Oct '87, on MCA by MCA Records. Deleted Apr '88. Catalogue no: **MCL 1861**

**BIG BAND BONANZA (Various artists)**
**Cass set:** Released '88, on Ditto by Pickwick Records. Catalogue no: **DTO 10221**

**BIG BAND CLASSICS 1940s-60s (Various artists)**
Note: Benny Goodman; Artie Shaw, Duke Ellington, Harry James, Stan Kenton.
**Album:** Released Nov '89, on Memoir by Memoir Records. Catalogue no: **MOIR 508**
**Cass:** Released Nov '89, on Memoir by Memoir Records. Catalogue no: **CMOIR 508**

**BIG BAND JAZZ VOL.2 (Various artists)**
Tracks: / Uskadara: *Various artists* / Easy: *Various artists* / Procrastination: *Various artists* / Just the way you are: *Various artists* / All stops: *Various artists* / Glad Hamp: *Various artists.*
**Album:** Released Aug '80, on Manhattan Records by President Records. Deleted '85. Catalogue no: **MAN 5024**

**BIG BANDS ARE BACK VOL.1 (Various artists)**
Tracks: / In the mood: *Miller, Glenn* / Cherolee: *Barnet, Charlie* / Seven come eleven: *Goodman* / Jumpin' at the woodside: *Basie Big Band* / Trumpet blues: *James, Harry.*
**Cass:** Released Aug '89, on One For The Road by One For The Road. Catalogue no: **CONE 6**

**BIG BANDS ARE BACK VOL.2 (Various artists)**
Tracks: / American patrol: *Miller, Glenn* / Kid from red band: *Basie Big Band* / East of the sun: *Teagarden, Jack* / Song of India: *Dorsey* / Tuning up: *Krupa, Gene* / Deep Purple: *Ellington, Duke.*
**Cass:** Released Aug '89, on One For The Road by One For The Road. Catalogue no: **CONE 7**

**BIG BANDS COLLECTOR'S SERIES (Various artists)**
**CD:** Released May '89, on PRT by Castle Communications Records. Catalogue no: **GHCD 10**
**Cass:** Released May '89, on PRT by Castle Communications Records. Catalogue no: **G 9010**

**BIG BANDS FROM THE SWING ERA (Various artists)**
Tracks: / Pigeon talk: *Beneke, Tex Orchestra* / Carioca: *Beneke, Tex Orchestra* / Lover's leap: *Beneke, Tex Orchestra* / By heck: *Webb, Chick* / I've got a right to sing the blues: *Teagarden, Jack Orchestra* / Pagan love call: *Crosby, Bob & His Bobcats* / Blue moon: *Crosby, Bob Orchestra* / Loveless love: *Hopkins, Claude Orchestra* / Old Kentucky home: *Rhythm Makers* / In the bottom: *Rhythm Makers* / Stompin' at The Savoy: *Brooks, Randy & His Orchestra* / Moonglow: *Brooks, Randy & His Orchestra* / Jimmy Cricket: *Savitte, Jan Orchestra* / Margie: *Savitte, Jan Orchestra.*
**Album:** Released Apr '81, on Jazz Live (Italy) Catalogue no: **BLJ 8009**

**BIG BANDS OF THE 40'S (Various artists)**
**Album:** Released Jul '84, on Decca by Decca International. Deleted '87. Catalogue no: **RFLD 42**

**BIG BANDS OF THE SWINGING YEARS (Various artists)**
**CD:** Released '88, on Bescol Catalogue no: **CD 41**

**BIG BANDS ON THE AIR, 1938-46 (Various artists)**
Tracks: / There'll be some changes made: *Goodman, Benny* / Gotta be this or that: *Gray, Glen* / Together: *Dorsey, Jimmy* / Cotton pickers' congregation: *Morgan, Russ* / Tiger rag: *Miller, Glenn* / In an 18th century drawing room: *Rey, Alvino* / Kickapoo joy juice jolt: *Rey, Alvino* / Stompin' at the Savoy: *Henderson, Fletcher* / You're a lucky guy: *Kemp, Hal* / Just an angel in disguise: *Ayres, Mitchell* / Boogie woogie lullaby: *Fio Rito, Ted.*
**Album:** Released Apr '81, on Solid Sender Catalogue no: **SOL 505**

**BIG BANDS, VOL.3 (Various artists)**
**Album:** Released Oct '82, on Fonitcetra Deleted Oct '87. Catalogue no: **VLD 1011**

**DIGITAL BIG BANDS (Various artists)**
**CD:** Released 17 Oct '88, on GRP by GRP Records (USA). Catalogue no: **D 5002**

**GOLDEN AGE, THE**
**Cass:** Released Jul '84, on Creole (Everest-Europa) by Creole Records. Catalogue no: **16-17**

**HARLEM ROOTS VOL 1 (Various artists)**
**VHS:** Released Feb '90, on Storyville by Storyville Records AB. Catalogue no: **SV 6000**

**LIVE: BIG BANDS (Various artists)**
**Album:** Released '88, on Fanfare by Captain Billy's Music. Catalogue no: **LP 45-145**

**LIVE: BIG BANDS AT THE WALDORF 1938-40 (Various artists)**
**Album:** Released '88, on Fanfare by Captain Billy's Music. Catalogue no: **LP 41-141**

**SOUNDIES VOL 2 (VIDEO) (Various artists)**
**VHS:** Released Feb '90, on Storyville by Storyville Records AB. Catalogue no: **SV6012**

**SWEET AND LOW BLUES (Various artists)**
Tracks: / Static strut: *Tate, Erskine Vendome Orchestra* / Symphonic raps: *Dickerson, Carroll & His Orchestra* / Boy in the boat,The: *Johnson, Charlie & His Paradise Orchestra* / That's how I feel today: *Chocolate Dandies* / Sweet and low blues: *Smith, Jabbo & His Rhythm Aces* / Till times get better: *Smith, Jabbo & His Rhythm Aces* / Willow tree: *Louisiana Sugar Babes* / What is this thing called love: *Reisman, Leo Orch.* / Starvation blues: *Stone, Jess Blue Serenaders* / Blue devil blues: *Page, Walter Blue Devils* / There's a squabblin': *Page, Walter Blue Devils* / Dreamland blues: *Floyd, Troy & His Plaza Hotel Orchestra* / Dreamland blues II: *Floyd, Troy & His Plaza Hotel Orchestra* / Ruff scuffling: *Lee, George E & His Kansas Orchestra* / Black and blue rhapsody: *Trent, Alphonso & His Orchestra* / After you've gone: *Trent, Alphonso & His Orchestra* / I've found a new baby: *Trent, Alphonso & His Orchestra.*
Note: Mono recording. Full black strip should read: Big Bands & Territory Bands of the 20's.
**Album:** Released Sep '86, on New World (USA) by New World Records (USA). Catalogue no: **NW 256**

**SWINGING BIG BANDS (Various artists)**
**LP Set:** Released '88, on Joker (USA) by Lifetime Records (USA). Catalogue no: **C 68/4 BOX 4**

## Big Boy Teddy Edwards

**1930-36**
**Album:** Released Sep '87, on Document Catalogue no: **LE 300.002**

## Big Maceo

**BIG MACEO**
Note: Doubleplay cassette contains albums: King Of Chicago Blues Piano Vol. 1 - BC 28;Vol. 2 - BC 29.
**Cass:** Released '88, on Arhoolie (USA) by Arhoolie Records (USA). Catalogue no: **C 210**

**KING OF CHICAGO BLUES PIANO, VOL. 1**
**Album:** Released May '84, on Blues Classics(USA) by Arhoolie Records (USA). Catalogue no: **BC 28**

**KING OF CHICAGO BLUES PIANO,VOL. 2**
**Album:** Released May '84, on Blues Classics(USA) by Arhoolie Records (USA). Catalogue no: **BC 29**

## Big Maybelle

**Biographical details:** Big Maybelle. Born Mabel Louise Smith in 1924 in Tennessee, the R&B singer died in 1972. A big person with a voice to match, she toured with the all-female Sweethearts of Rhythm from 1936 into the '40s, with Tiny Bradshaw '47-50; as a solo she reached the top 30 of the USA R&B chart six times between 1953-67 and appeared in the 1958 Newport Jazz Festival film 'Jazz on a Summer's Day'. Donald Clarke, 24 August 1988..

**OKEH SESSIONS, THE**
Tracks: / Just want your love / So good to my baby / Gabbin blues / My country man / Rain down rain / Way back home / Stay away from my Sam / Jinny Mule / Maybelle's blues / I've got a feeling / You'll never know / No more trouble out of me / My big mistake / Ain't no use / I'm getting 'long alright / You'll be sorry / Hairdressin' women / One monkey don't stop no show / Don't leave poor me / Ain't to be played with / New kind of mambo / Whole lotta shakin' goin' on.
**Cass:** Released Sep '88, on Charly by Charly Records. Catalogue no: **TCCDX 27**
**2 LP Set:** Released Sep '88, on Charly by Charly Records. Catalogue no: **CDX 27**
**CD:** Released '88, on Charly by Charly Records. Catalogue no: **CDCHARLY 108**

**ROOTS OF ROCK & ROLL AND EARLY SOUL**
**Album:** Released Mar '85, on Savoy Jazz (USA) by Malaco Records (USA). Catalogue no: **SJL 1143**

## Big Walter

**BOOGIES FROM COAST TO COAST**
Tracks: / I don't know / Walking across Texas / It had to be / Bloodstains on the wall / Long way to go / I won't lie to you anymore / Clock on the motel wall / I want to be your chauffeur / Darkest hour is just before dawn, The / I thought I heard my baby cry / Someone who don't understand / Walter's boogie.
**Album:** Released 30 Aug '88, on Ace by Ace Records. Catalogue no: **CHD 246**

## Bigard, Barney

**Biographical details:** Bigard, Barney. The New Orleans clarinettist and tenor saxist (1906-80) played with King Oliver, Luis Russell, then contributed beautiful clarinet filigree to many of Duke Ellington's best records from 1928 until 1940, as well as co-writing *Mood Indigo.* He played with Louis Armstrong's All Stars 1946-55 and later as a guest; he also freelanced widely, recording well into the 70's. Donald Clarke, 24 August 1988..

**BARNEY BIGARD 37-40 (Goin' easy)**
**Album:** Released '88, on Tax Catalogue no: **TAX 8026**

**BARNEY BIGARD & THE PELICAN TRIO (Bigard,Barney & The Pelican Trio)**
**Album:** Released Apr '79, on Crescent Jazz Prods. Catalogue no: **CJP 5**

**BUCKET'S GOT A HOLE IN IT**
Tracks: / I'll be back.
**Album:** on Delmark (USA) by Delmark Records (USA). Catalogue no: **DS 211**

## Bilk, Acker

**Biographical details:** Bilk, Acker. Bernard Stanley Bilk was born in 1929 in Somerset; he took up the clarinet to pass the time while in the guardhouse in Egypt in 1947, formed a band in 1958 and as Mr Acker Bilk became one of the most popular leaders during the trad. boom. A total of 11 singles and nine albums charted 1960-78, including many top tens; his own composition *Stranger On The Shore* (with strings) was no. 2 in the uK in 1961, no. 1 in the USA the next year. 'Acker' was rural English for 'mate' or 'chum'. Donald Clarke, 24 August 1988.
Born Bernard Bilk in Somerset, England in 1929, this accomplished clarinettist formed his Paramount Jazz Band in 1958. Having played in their local Bristol area and then in Dusseldorg, they scored their first British hit in early 1960. The gentle bluesy number *Summer set* entered the charts in January, strangely enough, and peaked at No. 5. It was quickly followed by a debut chart album *Seven ages of Acker*, which reached No. 6. Mr Acker Bilk (as he was known) and his Paramount Jazz Band then scored several more chart singles, including two futher top tenners, *Buona sera* and *That's my home*. Bilk became one of the most successful artists of the early sixties trad jazz boom, helped by a skilful marketing campaign and image which included two clothing trademarks - the bowler hat and the striped waistcoat. In late 1961 came the biggest success of his career. His self-penned tune *Stranger on the shore*, used at the time as the theme to a BBC Children's TV series, entered the UK chart in November of that year and stayed on the list for 55 consecutive weeks; this was a new longevity record that has only been subsequently bettered once. It peaked No. 2 but went all the way to No. 1 in the States, thus becoming Bilk's only US Top 40 hit. This classic single was credited to Mr Acker Bilk with the Leon Young String Chorale. His success on the album charts in Britain was continuing apace. In addition to his own discs he hit the Top 10 twice with *Best of Barber and Bilk* Volumues One and Two. In October 1962 *Best of Ball, Barber and Bilk* hit No. 1. These LPs were collaborations with fellow ace jazzmen Chris Barber and Kenny Ball. In 1963 the Beatles revolution torpedoed the traditional jazz merchants out of the charts. Like many of his peers, Bilk moved into cabaret and TV variety shows and in 1976, *Aria* reached No. 5 on the UK charts. The following year he scored his highest placed LP, when *Sheer magic* climbed to No.5 on the album chart. (Bob MacDonald).

**16 GOLDEN MEMORIES**
**CD:** Released Dec '88, on Spectrum (CD) by M.S.D.. Catalogue no: **SPEC 85022**

**100 MINUTES OF ACKER BILK**
**Cass:** Released Jun '82, on PRT (100 Minute Series) Catalogue no: **ZCTON 107**

**ACKER**
**Album:** Released Mar '61, on Columbia by EMI Records. Deleted '66. Catalogue no: **33SX 1248**

**ACKER BILK IN HOLLAND**
Tracks: / I can't believe that you're in love with me / Clarinet marmalade / Mood indigo / Them there eyes / Take the 'A' train / World is waiting for the sunshine, The / Just a closer walk with thee / Jeepers creepers / Lover man / Watermelon man / I don't want to set the world on fire / St. Thomas / Georgia / Senora Signora / Blues walks / Stranger on the shore / Nobody's sweetheart / Once in a while / Old music master, The.
**CD Set:** Released Nov '86, on Timeless by Timeless Records. Catalogue no: **CDTTD 506/7**
**2 LP Set:** Released Aug '85, on Timeless by Timeless Records. Catalogue no: **TTD 506**
**Cass set:** Released Aug '85, on Timeless by Timeless Records. Catalogue no: **TTD 5506**

**ACKER BILK & PARAMOUNT JAZZ BAND (Bilk, Acker & His Paramount Jazz Band)**
Tracks: / St. Philip breakdown / All the girls / Gladiolus rag / East coast trot / Bei mi bist du schoen / Bye and bye / St. Louis blues / Breeze / Old rugged cross.
**Album:** Released Dec '79, on Boulevard by Boulevard Records. Deleted '84. Catalogue no: **BD 3006**
**Album:** Released '88, on Timeless by Timeless Records. Catalogue no: **TTD 543-4**

**ACKER BILK PLAYS LENNON & MCCARTNEY**
**Album:** Released '88, on GNP Crescendo (USA) by GNP Crescendo Records (USA). Catalogue no: **GNPS 2191**
**CD:** Released '88, on GNP Crescendo (USA) by GNP Crescendo Records (USA). Catalogue no: **GNPD 2191**
**Cass:** Released '88, on GNP Crescendo (USA) by GNP Crescendo Records (USA). Catalogue no: **GNP5 2191**

**ACKER BILK SAGA, THE**
Tracks: / Perdido street blues / Papa dip / South / Summerset / Snag it / Should I / Acker's personal jungle / Royal Garden blues / Blues for this year / Blues for last year / Acker raga / La paloma / Soho blues / Bustamento / Adios mi chaparita / Too-ra-loo-ra-loo-ra / Petite fleur /

Honeysuckle rose / Basin Street blues / Georgia on my mind / Creole love call / Dinah / Stranger on the shore.
**Cass:** on Polydor by Polydor Ltd. Deleted '87. Catalogue no: **3577 348**
**2 LP Set:** Released Jul '79, on Polydor by Polydor Ltd. Catalogue no: **2668 020**

**ACKER BILK'S OMNIBUS**
**Album:** Released Apr '60, on Pye Deleted '65. Catalogue no: **NJL 22**

**ACKER'S CHOICE**
**Album:** Released Jan '85, on Teldec (1) by ASV (Academy Sound & Vision). Catalogue no: **DP6 28490**

**ACKER'S LULLABY**
Tracks: / Acker's lullaby / One more time.
**7" Single:** Released Jun '84, on PRT by Castle Communications Records. Catalogue no: **7P 313**

**ARANJUEZ**
Tracks: / Aranjuez / Summer never came.
**7" Single:** Released Jan '79, on Pye Deleted '82. Catalogue no: **7N 46145**

**ARIA**
**7" Single:** Released Jun '76, on PRT by Castle Communications Records. Catalogue no: **7N 45607**

**BEST OF ACKER BILK, HIS CLARINET AND STRINGS**
Tracks: / Aria / Canio's tune / Pachelbel canon / You are the sunshine of my life / Miss you nights / First of spring, The / Evergreen / Aranjuez mon amour / Stranger on the shore / Chi mai / Spanish Harlem / Up in the world / Cavatina / Without you / Chariots of fire / Don't cry for me Argentina.
**Album:** Released Jan '88, on PRT by Castle Communications Records. Catalogue no: **PYL 6030**
**Cass:** Released Jan '88, on PRT by Castle Communications Records. Catalogue no: **PYM 6030**
**Cass:** Released '88, on GNP Crescendo (USA) by GNP Crescendo Records (USA). Catalogue no: **GNP5 2116**
**Album:** Released '88, on GNP Crescendo (USA) by GNP Crescendo Records (USA). Catalogue no: **GNPS 2116**
**Cass:** Released Aug '89, on PRT by Castle Communications Records. Catalogue no: **PYC 6030**

**BEST OF ACKER BILK VOLUME 2**
Tracks: / Aria / Sugar / Windmills of your mind / Swan Lake Theme / Dancing in the dark / Clair / When / Honeysuckle Rose / Canio's tune / Hundred years from today / Shepherds song / Wolverine blues / Sailing / Missing you / Fire and rain / Snow Goose Themes / Feeling / Rose of the Rio Grande / Homecoming.
**Album:** Released '88, on GNP Crescendo (USA) by GNP Crescendo Records (USA). Catalogue no: **GNPS 2171**
**Cass:** Released '88, on GNP Crescendo (USA) by GNP Crescendo Records (USA). Catalogue no: **GNP5 2171**
**Album:** Released Mar '79, on Golden Hour Catalogue no: **GH 667**

**BLAZE AWAY (Bilk, Acker & His Paramount Jazz Band)**
Tracks: / Riverboat shuffle / I'm gonna sit right down... / Black and tan fantasy / Spain / Blaze away / Wabush blues / Way down yonder in New Orleans / Aria / Keepin' out of mischief now / Jazz me blues / Memphis blues / Exactly like you / Is you is or is you ain't my baby / Singin' the blues / Please don't talk to me... / Stranger on the shore.
**CD:** Released Mar '90, on Timeless by Timeless Records. Catalogue no: **CDTTD 543**

**BUONA SERA**
Tracks: / Buona sera.
**7" Single:** Released Dec '60, on Columbia by EMI Records. Deleted '63. Catalogue no: **DB 4544**

**COLLECTION: ACKER BILK**
**CD:** Released Jan '89, on Castle Collector Series by Castle Communications Records. Catalogue no: **CCSCD 209**
**2 LP Set:** Released Jan '89, on Castle Collector Series by Castle Communications Records. Catalogue no: **CCSLP 209**
**Special:** Released Sep '78, on PRT by Castle Communications Records. Catalogue no: **11PP 605**
**Cass:** Released Jan '89, on Castle Collector Series by Castle Communications Records. Catalogue no: **CCSMC 209**

**DREAMING IN THE SUN (Bilk, Acker & Norman Candler)**
**Album:** Released Dec '86, on Intersound Catalogue no: **ISST 130**

**EVERGREEN**
**Album:** Released Nov '78, on Warwick by Warwick Records. Deleted '83. Catalogue no: **PW 5045**

**EXTREMELY LIVE IN STUDIO 1**
**Cass:** Released Jul '78, on PRT by Castle Communications Records. Catalogue no: **ZCP 18569**

**FIND A WAY**
Tracks: / Find a way / Moment I'm with you.
**7" Single:** Released Sep '81, on PRT by Castle Communications Records. Deleted '84. Catalogue no: **7 P 221**

**FINEST MOMENTS**
Tracks: / Stranger on the shore / Send in the clowns / Night that made me forget,The / Red haired girl / August evening / Fond memories / Just for you / Birchtree road / Aria / Fool on the hill / Autumn evening / Goodbye / You won't see a tear / Western farm / Dusk / Windharp.
**Album:** Released Apr '86, on Castle Showcase by Castle Communications Records. Catalogue no: **SHLP 138**
**Cass:** Released Apr '86, on Castle Showcase by Castle Communications Records. Catalogue no: **SHTC 138**

**FRANKIE AND JOHNNY**
Tracks: / Frankie and Johnny.
**7" Single:** Released Mar '62, on Columbia by EMI Records. Deleted '65. Catalogue no: **DB 4795**

**FREE**
**Cass:** Released Feb '78, on PRT by Castle Communications Records. Catalogue no: **ZCP 41056**

**GOLDEN HOUR OF THE BEST OF ACKER BILK**
**Cass:** Released Nov '76, on Golden Hour Catalogue no: **ZCGH 624**

**GOLDEN TREASURY OF BILK**
**Album:** Released Apr '61, on Columbia by EMI Records. Deleted '66. Catalogue no: **33SX 1304**

**GOODNIGHT SWEET PRINCE**
Tracks: / Goodnight sweet prince.
**7" Single:** Released Jun '60, on Melodisc Deleted '63. Catalogue no: **MEL 1547**

**GOTTA SEE MY BABY TONIGHT**
Tracks: / Gotta see my baby tonight.
**7" Single:** Released Jul '62, on Columbia by EMI Records. Deleted '65. Catalogue no: **SCD 2176**

**HIS CLARINET & STRINGS LOVE SONGS**
Tracks: / Evergreen / Miss you nights / (They long to be) close to you.
**CD:** Released Sep '88, on Pickwick by Pickwick Records. Catalogue no: **PWKS 508**
**Cass:** Released Sep '88, on Hallmark by Pickwick Records. Catalogue no: **HSC 3239**
**Album:** Released Sep '88, on Hallmark by Pickwick Records. Catalogue no: **SHM 3239**

**HITS, BLUES & CLASSICS (Bilk, Acker & His Paramount Jazz Band)**
Tracks: / Louisian-i-ay / Black and tan fantasy / My baby just cares for me / Papa dip / That's my home / Sempre fidelis / Basin St.Blues / White cliffs of Dover, The / Blaze away / Nairobi / Sleepytime down South / Savoy blues / Just a closer walk with thee / South / Mood indigo / Buona sera / Ain't misbehavin' / Aria / Beale Street blues / Stranger on the shore.
**2 LP Set:** Released Aug '88, on Kaz by Kaz Records. Catalogue no: **KAZ LP 10**
**Cass set:** Released Aug '88, on Kaz by Kaz Records. Catalogue no: **KAZ MC 10**
**CD:** Released Aug '88, on Kaz by Kaz Records. Catalogue no: **KAZ CD 10**

**I'M IN THE MOOD FOR LOVE**
Tracks: / Stranger on the shore / Frenesi / I'm in the mood for love / La paloma / Petite fleur / Scarlet ribbons / Georgia on my mind / Taste of honey, A / Greensleeves / Non dimenticar / Nature boy / Perhaps, perhaps perhaps / Meravigliose labbra / Moon river.
**Album:** Released Aug '83, on Philips (Italy) by PolyGram UK Ltd. Catalogue no: **9279 608**
**Cass:** Released Aug '83, on Philips (Italy) by PolyGram UK Ltd. Catalogue no: **7259 608**

**IMAGES: ACKER BILK**
Tracks: / Petite fleur / Scarlet ribbons / La mer / Greensleeves / Moon river /

Nature boy / Stranger on the shore.
**CD:** Released Aug '89, on Knight by Knight Records Ltd.. Catalogue no: **KNCD 16002**
**Cass:** Released Aug '89, on Knight by Knight Records Ltd.. Catalogue no: **KNMC 16002**

**INVITATION**
**Cass:** Released Feb '77, on PRT by Castle Communications Records. Catalogue no: **ZCP 41054**

**IT LOOKS (Bilk, Acker & Ken Colyers Jazzmen)**
**Album:** Released '88, on Stomp Off (USA) Catalogue no: **SOS 1119**

**JOHN HENRY**
Tracks: / John Henry.
**7" Single:** Released Jul '83, on PRT by Castle Communications Records. Catalogue no: **7P 278**

**JOHN, PAUL AND ACKER (Bilk, Acker, His Clarinet & Strings)**
Tracks: / Norwegian wood / With a little luck / Imagine / Michelle / World without love / Mull of Kintyre / Fool on the hill / Ebony and ivory / Nowhere man / Yesterday / She's leaving home / Here, there and everywhere / Pipes of peace.
**Album:** Released '87, on PRT by Castle Communications Records. Catalogue no: **PYL 2**
**CD:** Released Nov '86, on PRT by Castle Communications Records. Deleted '89. Catalogue no: **CDN 6561**
**Album:** Released Nov '86, on PRT by Castle Communications Records. Deleted Jan '90. Catalogue no: **N 6561**
**Cass:** Released Nov '86, on PRT by Castle Communications Records. Catalogue no: **ZCN 6561**
**Cass:** Released '87, on PRT by Castle Communications Records. Catalogue no: **PYM 2**
**CD:** Released '87, on PRT by Castle Communications Records. Catalogue no: **PYC 2**

**LONELY**
Tracks: / Lonely.
**7" Single:** Released Sep '62, on Columbia by EMI Records. Deleted '65. Catalogue no: **DB 4897**

**LOVE ALBUM, THE**
Tracks: / When I fall in love / Groovy kind of love, A / Silvery nights / Could've been / My love / He ain't heavy he's my brother / Good times / One moment in time / Till I loved you / Candle in the wind / Tune for melody / Take my breath away / Love changes everything / Sweet crystal / Lady in red / Every time we say goodbye.
**Album:** Released Oct '89, on Pickwick by Pickwick Records. Catalogue no: **SHM 3282**
**Cass:** Released Oct '89, on Pickwick by Pickwick Records. Catalogue no: **HSC 3282**
**CD:** Released Oct '89, on Pickwick by Pickwick Records. Catalogue no: **PWKS 534**

**LOVE SONGS: ACKER BILK (BRIDGE)**
Tracks: / Strangers on the shore / We've only just begun / Morning has broken / Ramblin' Rose / My way.
**CD:** Released Feb '86, on Bridge (MCS Bridge) Catalogue no: **100 002**

**LOVE SONGS: ACKER BILK (PRT)**
**CD:** Released Nov '85, on PRT by Castle Communications Records. Deleted '88. Catalogue no: **CDNP 7774**

**LOVE SONGS MY WAY**
Tracks: / Let it be me / First time ever I saw your face, The / Rose, The / My way / Hey Jude / Never my love / Ramblin' rose / We've only just begun / Morning has broken / I can't stop loving you / Stranger on the shore / (Eres Tu) touch the wind.
**Cass:** Released Jan '87, on Topline by Charly Records. Catalogue no: **KTOP 160**
**Album:** Released Jan '87, on Topline by Charly Records. Catalogue no: **TOP 160**

**MADE IN HUNGARY**
Tracks: / Victors theme / New summer / Needing someone / Berolina / From night to night / Mama please / Love is different / Summer song / Miracle / Heartbreak / Fly high / Fancy / How many evenings / Those were beautiful.
**Album:** Released Jan '80, on PRT by Castle Communications Records. Deleted Dec '86. Catalogue no: **N 124**
**Cass:** Released May '80, on PRT by Castle Communications Records. Catalogue no: **ZCN 124**

**MAGIC CLARINET OF ACKER BILK**
**CD:** Released Nov '86, on K-Tel by K-Tel Records. Catalogue no: **ONCD 3280**

**MAMA TOLD ME SO (Bilk, Acker & His Paramount Jazz Band)**
Tracks: / Mama told me so / Chips are down, The / Gee baby ain't I good to you / Time's a wastin' / Bloodshot eyes / Um / Liza / Someday you'll be sorry / Gospel truth.
**Cass:** Released Nov '85, on PRT by Castle Communications Records. Catalogue no: **ZCN 128**
**Album:** Released Nov '85, on Flashback by Mainline Records. Catalogue no: **FBLP 8092**
**Cass:** Released Nov '85, on Flashback by Mainline Records. Catalogue no: **ZCFBL 8092**
**Album:** Released Jul '80, on Pye Deleted Jul '85. Catalogue no: **N 128**

**MOMENT I'M WITH YOU, THE**
Tracks: / Norwegian wood / Colours of my life, The / Bilitis / Little green apples / How does it feel / Imagine / Chi mai / Spanish harlem / First of spring, The / Moment I'm with you, The / Chariots of fire / Pechel canon / Missing you ain't easy / Love letters / For the good times / Soap.
**Album:** Released Oct '81, on PRT by Castle Communications Records. Catalogue no: **N 141**
**Album:** Released Nov '81, on PRT by Castle Communications Records. Deleted '86. Catalogue no: **PRT N141**
**Cass:** Released Oct '81, on PRT by Castle Communications Records. Catalogue no: **ZCN 141**

**MR. ACKER BILK COLLECTION**
**Album:** Released '88, on Masters (Holland) Catalogue no: **MA 3686**
**Cass:** Released '88, on Masters (Holland) Catalogue no: **MAMC 93686**

**NATURE BOY**
**CD:** Released Oct '85, on PRT by Castle Communications Records. Deleted '88. Catalogue no: **CDNSP 7774**

**ON STAGE**
Tracks: / Aria / Canio's tune / Pachelbel canon / You are the sunshine of my life / Miss you nights / First of spring, the / Evergreens / Aranjuel mon amour / Stranger on the shore / Chi mai / Spanish harlem / Up in the world / Cavatina / Without you / Chariots of fire / Don't cry for me Argentina.
**Cass:** Released Mar '88, on Start by Start Records Ltd.. Catalogue no: **STOC 101**
**Album:** Released Mar '88, on Start by Start Records Ltd.. Catalogue no: **STOL 101**
**CD:** Released Mar '88, on Start by Start Records Ltd.. Catalogue no: **STOCD 101**

**ONE FOR ME, THE**
**Album:** Released Oct '76, on Pye Deleted '81. Catalogue no: **NSPX 41052**
**Cass:** Released Jul '86, on PRT by Castle Communications Records. Catalogue no: **ZCP 41052**

**RELAXIN**
Tracks: / Verde / One more time / Minuetto / Stay / Cavatina / I'm happy when I'm dancing with you / Volveras / On Sunday / Incredible Hulk, Theme from / Piccolino / Back to you / Summer never came / Aranjuez mon amour / Best out of me, The.
**Album:** Released Feb '81, on Piccadilly Catalogue no: **N 138**
**Cass:** Released Feb '81, on Piccadilly Catalogue no: **ZCN 138**

**SEVEN AGES OF ACKER**
**Album:** Released Mar '60, on Columbia by EMI Records. Deleted '65. Catalogue no: **33SX 1304**

**SHEER MAGIC**
**Album:** Released Jun '77, on Warwick by Warwick Records. Deleted '82. Catalogue no: **WW 5028**

**SMILE SAM SMILE**
Tracks: / Smile Sam smile / Smile Sam smile (Instrumental).
**7" Single:** Released Jun '86, on PRT by Castle Communications Records. Catalogue no: **7P 357**

**SOME OF MY FAVOURITE THINGS**
Tracks: / Stranger on the shore / What are you doing the rest of your life / Folks who live on the hill, The / Makin' Whoppee / Misty / Close to you / Raindrops keep falling on my head / This guy's in

love with you / Sugar / What a wonderful world / Hundred years from today / Going home / Summer knows, The.
**CD:** on PRT by Castle Communications Records. Catalogue no: **CDNSPL 4102**
**Album:** Released '73, on PRT by Castle Communications Records. Catalogue no: **NSPL 41022**
**Cass:** Released '73, on PRT by Castle Communications Records. Catalogue no: **CDNSPL 4102**

**SONG FOR GUY**
Tracks: / Song for Guy / Just the way you are.
**7" Single:** Released Mar '80, on Piccadilly Deleted '83. Catalogue no: **7P 169**

**SPOTLIGHT ON ACKER BILK**
Tracks: / Verde / Universe / Incontro / Volveras / Canio's tune / Swan Lake, Theme from / Stranger on the shore / Bridge over troubled water / Fool on the hill / Close to you / Clair / Way we were, The / Aria sailing / Amazing grace / We're all alone / Fire and rain / Aranjuez mon amour / Cavatina / Where do I begin / Miss you nights / Don't cry for me Argentina / Song I wrote to you, The / I don't want to talk about it.
**2 LP Set:** Released '80, on PRT by Castle Communications Records. Catalogue no: **SPOT 1005**
**Cass:** Released '80, on PRT by Castle Communications Records. Catalogue no: **ZCSPT 1005**

**SPOTLIGHT ON ACKER BILK VOL. 2**
**Album:** Released Oct '82, on PRT Spotlight Catalogue no: **SPOT 1024**
**Cass:** Released Oct '82, on PRT Spotlight Catalogue no: **ZCSPT 1024**

**STARS AND STRIPES FOREVER**
Tracks: / Stars and stripes forever / Creole jazz.
**7" Single:** Released Nov '61, on Columbia by EMI Records. Deleted '64. Catalogue no: **SCD 2155**

**STRANGER ON THE SHORE**
Tracks: / When I need you / Amazing grace / Down in nempnett thrumbwell / If / Together we are beautiful / Stranger on the shore / Fool on the hill / Up in the world / First of spring, The / Norwegian wood / You are the sunshine of my life / On Sunday.
**CD:** Released May '88, on Polydor by Polydor Ltd. Catalogue no: **830 799-2**
**Album:** Released Nov '80, on Polydor by Polydor Ltd. Catalogue no: **2482 489**
**Cass:** Released Nov '80, on Polydor by Polydor Ltd. Catalogue no: **3192 615**
**Album:** Released May '62, on Columbia by EMI Records. Deleted '67. Catalogue no: **33SX 1407**
**Cass:** Released Jul '86, on PRT Flashback Catalogue no: **ZCFBL 8099**
**Album:** Released Jul '86, on PRT Flashback Catalogue no: **FBLP 8099**

**STRANGER ON THE SHORE (OLD GOLD)**
Tracks: / Stranger on the shore / Summer set.
**7" Single:** Released Jul '82, on Old Gold by Old Gold Records. Catalogue no: **OG 9151**

**STRANGER ON THE SHORE (SINGLE)**
Tracks: / Stranger on the shore.
**7" Single:** Released Nov '61, on Columbia by EMI Records. Deleted '64. Catalogue no: **DB 4750**

**SUMMER SET**
Tracks: / Summer set.
**7" Single:** Released Jan '60, on Columbia by EMI Records. Deleted '63. Catalogue no: **DB 4382**

**TASTE OF HONEY, A**
**Album:** Released May '63, on Columbia by EMI Records. Deleted '68. Catalogue no: **33SX 1493**

**TASTE OF HONEY, A (SINGLE)**
Tracks: / Taste of honey, A.
**7" Single:** Released Jan '63, on Columbia by EMI Records. Deleted '66. Catalogue no: **DB 4949**

**THAT'S MY HOME (Bilk, Acker & His Paramount Jazz Band)**
Tracks: / China boy / Nagasaki / Maryland march / Creole jazz / Jazz me blues / Savoy blues / New Orleans stomp / Buona sera / South / Lazy river / Milenberg joys / Original Dixieland one-step / That's my home / Black label blues.
**CD:** Released Mar '88, on ECM Catalogue no: **830 778 2**

**THAT'S MY HOME (SINGLE)**
Tracks: / That's my home.
**7" Single:** Released Jul '61, on Columbia by EMI Records. Deleted '64. Catalogue no: **DB 4673**

**TRAD DAYS 1959/60**
**CD:** Released Jan '90, on Polydor by Polydor Ltd. Catalogue no: **8307862**

**TWOGETHER (Bilk, Acker & Max Bygraves)**
Tracks: / You say something nice about everybody / Who wants to be a millionaire / I like beer / Harmonize / Wait till the sun shines Nellie / Down by the old mill stream / Goodnight ladies / Civilisation / Hometown / Movies / Crazy / Stranger on the shore / Guilty / Prisoner / Dreaming my dreams / Tonight you belong to me.
**Cass:** Released Oct '80, on Piccadilly Catalogue no: **ZCN 133**
**Album:** Released Oct '80, on Piccadilly Catalogue no: **N 133**

**UNISSUED ACKER**
Tracks: / Dauphine street blues / Corina Corina / Gloryland / Trouble in mind / Travelling blues / Salutation march / Monday date / King Joe / Lou-easy-an-i-a / Darkness on the delta / Careless love / Deep bayou blues.
**Album:** Released Mar '85, on Harlequin by Interstate Music. Catalogue no: **HQ 3004**

**UNIVERSE**
Tracks: / Universe / Anytime around.
**7" Single:** Released Jan '78, on Pye Deleted '81. Catalogue no: **7N 46032**

**VERDE**
Tracks: / Verde / When we were young.
**7" Single:** Released Jun '80, on Piccadilly Deleted Jun '83. Catalogue no: **7P 182**

**VERY BEST OF ACKER BILK**
**Album:** Released May '85, on Pickwick by Pickwick Records. Catalogue no: **HMA 262**
**Cass:** Released May '85, on Hallmark by Pickwick Records. Catalogue no: **HSC 262**

**WERELDSUCCESSEN**
Tracks: / Stranger on the shore / Petite fleur / Summer set / White cliffs of Dover, The.
**2 LP Set:** Released Jul '82, on Philips (Germany) by PolyGram UK Ltd. Catalogue no: **6641 954**
**Cass:** Released Jul '82, on Philips (Germany) by PolyGram UK Ltd. Catalogue no: **7599 449**

**WHITE CLIFFS OF DOVER**
Tracks: / White cliffs of Dover, The.
**7" Single:** Released Aug '60, on Columbia by EMI Records. Deleted '63. Catalogue no: **DB 4492**

## Bilk, Barber, Brown

**THREE B'S, THE**
Note: Artists are: Acker Bilk, Chris Barber and Sandy Brown.
**Album:** Released Dec '87, on Esquire by Titan Int. Prod.. Catalogue no: **ESQ 333**

## Birdland All Stars...

**BIRDLAND ALL STARS AT THE CARNEGIE HALL (Various artists)**
**CD:** Released Oct '88, on Vogue by Vogue Records. Catalogue no: **VGCD 670 202**
**CD:** Released Dec '86, on Vogue by Vogue Records. Catalogue no: **VG 600 089**

## Black Ace

**BLACK ACE & HIS STEEL GUITAR**
**Album:** Released May '81, on Arhoolie (USA) by Arhoolie Records (USA). Catalogue no: **ARHOOLIE 1003**

## Black Bands

**ON FILM 1928-1935**
**Album:** Released May '86, on Harlequin by Interstate Music. Catalogue no: **HQ 2038**

## Black Bottom Stompers

**BLACK BOTTOM STOMPERS**
Tracks: / Weatherbird rag / Shout 'em Aunt Tillie / Wild man blues / Cornet chop suey / Sidewalk blues / Garittin' with some barbeque / Hiawatha rag / Blue blood blues / Mahogany hall stomp / Where did you stay last night / Potato head blues / Alligator hop.
Note: Recorded 4/12/71. Tracks include: Weatherbird/Shout 'em Aunt Tillie/Blue blood blues/Where did you stay last night, etc. Cassette only.
**Cass:** Released Apr '86, on VJM (Vintage Jazz Music) by Vintage Jazz Music

Society(VJM). Catalogue no: **VC 10**
**Album:** Released Jun '86, on Stomp Off (USA) Catalogue no: **SOS 1045**

**FOUR O'CLOCK BLUES**
**Album:** Released Nov '87, on Stomp Off (USA) Catalogue no: **SOS 1130**

## Black Eagle Jazz Band

**AT SYMPHONY HALL**
**Album:** Released '88, on Philo (USA) by Rounder Records (USA). Catalogue no: **PH 1086**
**Cass:** Released '88, on Philo (USA) by Rounder Records (USA). Catalogue no: **PH 1086C**

**BLACK EAGLE JAZZ BAND (1981 with Rudi Ballieu & Butch Thompson) (Black Eagle Jazz Band / B.Thompson)**
**Album:** Released Jan '84, on Stomp Off (USA) Catalogue no: **SOS 1048**

**DON'T MONKEY WITH IT**
**Album:** Released May '89, on Stomp Off (USA) Catalogue no: **SOS 1147**

**MOUNT GRETNA WEEKEND**
**Album:** Released '88, on Stomp Off (USA) Catalogue no: **SOS 1092**

**TIGHT LIKE THIS (Black Eagle Jazz Band / B.Thompson)**
**Album:** Released Jan '84, on Stomp Off (USA) Catalogue no: **SOS 1054**

## Black Gospel

**BLACK GOSPEL (Various artists)**
Note: Doubleplay cassette contains albums: A Capella Gospel Singing - 9045; The Golden Age Of Gospel - 9046.
**Cass:** Released '88, on Arhoolie (USA) by Arhoolie Records (USA). Catalogue no: **C 223**
**Cass:** Released May '85, on MCA by MCA Records. Catalogue no: **MCLDC 614**
**Album:** Released May '85, on MCA by MCA Records. Catalogue no: **MCLD 614**

## Black Swing Tradition

**BLACK SWING TRADITION (Various artists)**
**Album:** Released Mar '85, on Savoy Jazz (USA) by Malaco Records (USA). Catalogue no: **SJL 2246**

## Blackwell, Ed

**Biographical details:** Blackwell, Ed. An avant-garde jazz drummer whose combination of roots and technique have kept him in the first class for decades. He was born in 1927 in New Orleans, played rhythm & blues including with Huey 'Piano' Smith and Ray Charles; he replaced Billy Higgins in the Ornette Coleman Quartet in 1960, and also played in the legendary Eric Dolphy band that recorded *Live At The Five Spot* on Prestige. He also recorded with Don Cherry, Archie Shepp, John Coltrane etc. and in the Coleman alumni group Old and New Dreams on ECM. Donald Clarke, 24 August 1988..

**EL CORAZON (Blackwell, Ed and Don Cherry)**
**CD:** Released Oct '86, on ECM Catalogue no: **829 199-2**

**OLD AND NEW DREAMS (Blackwell, Ed, Don Cherry & Redman)**
**Album:** Released Jul '78, on Black Saint (Italy) Deleted '83. Catalogue no: **BSR 0013**
**CD:** on Black Saint (Italy) Catalogue no: **BSR 0013**

## Blackwell, Scrapper

**BLUES**
**Album:** Released Dec '88, on Agram Catalogue no: **AB 2008**

**SCRAPPER'S BLUES**
Tracks: / Goin' where the moon crosses.... / 'A' blues / Geaorge Street blues / Little boy blue / Penal farm blues / Nobody knows you (when you're down and out) / Little girl blue / Blues before sunrise / Shady lane.
**Album:** Released Oct '88, on Ace by Ace Records. Catalogue no: **CH 255**

**VIRTUOSO GUITAR OF SCRAPPER BLACKWELL**
**Album:** Released Dec '88, on Yazoo (USA) by Shanachie Records (USA). Catalogue no: **L 1019**

## Blake, Eubie

**Biographical details:** Blake, Eubie. The pianist, bandleader and songwriter James Herbert Blake was born in 1883 in Baltimore, Maryland; he lived long enough to celebrate his 100th birthday. He began playing in Baltimore cafes in 1899, teamed with Noble Sissle in 1915; they wrote one of the first hit black Broadway shows 'Shufflin' Along' in 1921: *Love Will Find A Way* and *I'm Just Wild About Harry*. They were successful in the UK; *You Were Meant For Me* was introduced by Noel Coward and Gertrude Lawrence in a 1923 London revue. Blake teamed with Spencer Williams on *Chocolate Dandies* in 1924, with Andy Razaf (Fats Waller's favourite lyricist) on *Blackbirds Of 1930* (smash hit: *Memories Of You*), much else. In old age he had a whole new career, playing piano and reminiscing; he said that if he'd known he was going to live that long he'd have taken better care of himself. Donald Clarke, 24 August 1988..

**EIGHTY SIX YEARS, THE**
**Album:** Released '88, on CBS (import) by CBS Records. Catalogue no: **CBS 22223**

**LIVE CONCERT**
**Album:** Released Nov '87, on Stash (USA) Catalogue no: **ST 130**

**RAGS TO RICHES**
**Album:** Released Aug '88, on Stash (USA) Catalogue no: **ST 128**

## Blake, Ran

**Biographical details:** Blake, Ran. The unique jazz pianist and composer was born in 1935 in Springfield, Massachusetts. He teamed with singer Jeanne Lee in 1957, experimenting with vocal/piano duo improvisations; since then albums such as *The Blue Potato And Other Outrages* in 1969 have had a cult following, but have brought less fame than he deserves. Some of his albums have guests such as saxophonists Ricky Ford, Anthony Braxton, Houston Person, vocalist Chris Connor on various tracks, but they are mostly solo. Donald Clarke, 24 August 1988..

**BREAKTHRU (Solo piano)**
**Album:** Released Jan '88, on Improvising Artists Catalogue no: **IAI 373842**

**DUKE DREAMS, THE LEGACY OF STRAYHORN - ELLINGTON**
**Album:** Released Jul '82, on Soul Note Catalogue no: **SN 1027**

## Blakey, Art

**Biographical details:** Blakey, Art. The drummer/bandleader, born in Pittsburgh in 1919, is one of the best loved jazz musicians in the world. He used the name Messengers for a 17-piece band, then an octet called the Jazz Messengers in 1947; he led a quintet in 1954 with pianist Horace Silver, who set up a Blue Note recording date, so the first Jazz Messengers date was not made under Silver's name, but under Blakey, one of the all-time great talent scouts, it has graduated more first-class musicians than any other in history: its 'hard bop' combined modern harmonies with the blues and a gospel feeling, becoming a mainstay of the Blue Note label and remains influential today. Just a few of the more famous Blakey sidemen have been Benny Golson, Freddie Hubbard, Wayne Shorter, Bobby Watson and Wynton Marsalis; in the early '80s the band included Terence Blanchard abd Donald Harrison, now co-leading their own successful combo; Jean Toussaint, now gigging and teaching in England; and new piano star Mulgrew Miller, who described Blakey as drummer/leader: 'a master of tension and release'. Blakey also toured with the Giants of Jazz in the early '70s; a Thelonious Monk trio session with Blakey and bassist Al McKibbon was made in London in '71, produced by Alan Bates on his Black Lion label. (Donald Clarke, 24 August 1988.).

**AIN'T LIFE GRAND? (Blakey, Art Big Band & Quintet)**
Tracks: / Midriff / Ain't life grand? / Tippin' pristine / El toro valiente / Kiss of no return / Late date / Outer world.
Note: Ain't life grand? was recorded in 1957 during a rare return to big band music by Art Blakey. Although drummer Blakey led the Jazz Messengers -- along the line introducing such talents as Clifford Brown, Donald Byrd, Denny Dorham, Freddie Hubbard, Horace Silver, Benny Jolsen, Lee Morgan, Wayne Shorter, Wynton Marsalis and countless others stars -- he had started, back in the early 40's, as a big band drummer. A fascinating line-up on this record includes tenor saxman John Coltrane, in 1957 at the peak of his first period of tenor revolution. Blakey and Coltrane

rarely worked together: the only other famous recording was the Monk's Music session for Riverside.
**Album:** Released Nov '83, on Affinity by Charly Records. Catalogue no: **AFF 106**

**ALBUM OF THE YEAR**
Tracks: / Cheryl / Ms. BC / In case you missed it / Little man / Witch hunt / Soulful Mister Timmons.
Note: This album, recorded in Paris in April 1981, received the highest-possible ratings by both Downbeat and Swing Journal.
**CD:** Released Oct '86, on Timeless by Timeless Records. Catalogue no: **CDSJP 155**
**Album:** Released Aug '85, on Timeless by Timeless Records. Catalogue no: **SJP 155**

**ALL STAR JAZZ MESSENGER, THE**
**Album:** Released '83, on RCA (France) by BMG Records (France). Catalogue no: **PL 45365**

**ART BLAKEY**
**CD:** Released Jul '89, on Cleo Catalogue no: **CLCD 5001**

**ART BLAKEY IN SWEDEN 1959**
**Album:** Released Jul '87, on Dragon by Dragon Records. Catalogue no: **DRLP 137**

**ART BLAKEY AND THE JAZZ MESSENGERS (Blakey, Art\Jazz Messengers)**
Tracks: / A la mode / Invitation / Circus / You don't know what love is / I hear a rhapsody / Gee baby ain't I good to you.
**Album:** Released Mar '83, on Jasmine by Hasmick Promotions. Deleted Feb '88. Catalogue no: **JAS 72**

**ART BLAKEY AND THE JAZZ MESSENGERS (Blakey, Art\Jazz Messengers)**
Note: Recorded in New York City, April 1960.
**CD:** Released Jan '86, on RCA Jazz (Japan) Catalogue no: **886 001**
**Album:** Released '81, on Kings Of Jazz Catalogue no: **KLJ 20023**
**Album:** Released Aug '83, on RCA (Germany) Catalogue no: **CL 42789**
**CD:** Released '85, on Roulette by Vogue Records. Catalogue no: **PRT 600030**
**Cass:** Released '88, on Star Jazz (USA) by Charly Records. Catalogue no: **S JAZZ C9**
**Album:** Released '88, on Star Jazz (USA) by Charly Records. Catalogue no: **SJAZZ 9**

**ART BLAKEY AND THE JAZZ MESSENGERS (VIDEO) (Blakey, Art/Jazz Messengers)**
**VHS:** Released '88, on Kay Jazz (video) by Kay Jazz. Catalogue no: **KJ 061**

**ART'S BREAK (Blakey, Art\Jazz Messengers)**
**Album:** Released Sep '86, on Lotus Catalogue no: **LPPS 111 13**
**Album:** Released Sep '87, on Lotus Catalogue no: **LOP 14 071**

**AT RONNIE SCOTT'S**
**CD:** Released Dec '87, on Hendring Deleted '88. Catalogue no: **HEN 6019 Y**

**AT RONNIE SCOTTS (VIDEO)**
Note: Running time: 58 mins.
**VHS:** Released '88, on Castle Hendring Video by Castle Communications Records. Catalogue no: **HEN 2019 G**

**AT THE CAFE BOHEMIA VOL.1 (Blakey, Art\Jazz Messengers)**
Tracks: / Soft winds / Theme / Minors holiday / Alone together / Prince Albert.
**Cass:** Released May '87, on Blue Note by EMI Records. Deleted Jan '88. Catalogue no: **4BN 81507**
**CD:** Released Jul '87, on Blue Note by EMI Records. Catalogue no: **BNZ 51**
**Album:** Released Nov '85, on Blue Note by EMI Records. Catalogue no: **BST 81507**
**CD:** Released Jul '87, on Blue Note by EMI Records. Catalogue no: **CDP 746 521 2**

**AT THE CAFE BOHEMIA VOL.2 (Blakey, Art\Jazz Messengers)**
Tracks: / Like someone in love (8.43) / Yesterdays (4.20) / Avila & Tequila (12.11) / Sportin'crowd (6.22) / I waited for you (9.16) / Just one of those things* (9.23 *Extra track on CD) / Hanks symphony (Extra track on CD) / Gone with the wind / Soft winds / Theme / Minor's holiday / Alone together / Prince Albert.
Note: This historic group(Art Blakely,Horace Silver,Hank Mobley,Denny Dorham and Doug Watkins) almost single-handedly develop modern hard bop and blue note sound.On this second album of their historic appearance at New York's Cafe Bohemia in 1955,they explore a variety of material from the cookin'Latin rythms to 'Avila And Tequila'to the bop classic 'Sportin' Crowd'to the standard ballards such as 'Yesterdays'.This live session sounds as fresh and vital as it did 30 years ago,when it set the trend for a new jazz sound that is still in force today.Produced by Alfred Lion.
**CD:** Released May '87, on Blue Note by EMI Records. Catalogue no: **BNZ 52**
**CD:** Released May '87, on Blue Note by EMI Records. Catalogue no: **CDP 746 522 2**
**Album:** Released Jul '89, on Blue Note by EMI Records. Catalogue no: **BST 81508**

**BACKGAMMON (Blakey, Art\Jazz Messengers)**
Tracks: / Uranus / Whisper not / Backgammon / Blues march / Georgia on my mind / Third world express / Namefully / I can't get started.
**Album:** Released Jan '83, on Carosello Catalogue no: **RLP 1007**

**BEST OF ART BLAKEY (Blakey, Art/Jazz Messengers)**
Tracks: / Moanin' / Blues march / Lestger's left town / Night in Tunisia, A / Dat dere / Mosaic (CD only.) / Free for all (CD only.).
**Album:** Released Feb '90, on Blue Note by EMI Records. Catalogue no: **793 205 1**
**CD:** Released Feb '90, on Blue Note by EMI Records. Catalogue no: **CDP 793 205 2**
**Album:** Released Feb '90, on Blue Note by EMI Records. Catalogue no: **B1 93205**
**CD:** Released Feb '90, on Blue Note by EMI Records. Catalogue no: **BNZ 232**

**BIG BEAT**
Tracks: / It's only a paper moon / Chess players / Sakeena's vision / Politely / Dat dere / Lester left town / It's only a paper moon (alternate take).
**Album:** Released Jul '89, on Blue Note by EMI Records. Catalogue no: **BST 84029**
**Cass:** Released Apr '85, on Blue Note by EMI Records. Deleted Jun '88. Catalogue no: **4BN 84029**
**CD:** Released Jun '87, on Blue Note by EMI Records. Catalogue no: **BNZ 2**
**CD:** Released Jun '87, on Blue Note by EMI Records. Catalogue no: **CDP 746 400 2**

**BIRDLAND 21ST FEB 1954. (Blakey, Art & Clifford Brown)**
**CD:** Released Mar '90, on Giants of Jazz by Hasmick Promotions. Catalogue no: **GOJCD53031**

**BLUE NIGHT (Blakey, Art\Jazz Messengers)**
Tracks: / Two of a kind / Blue minor / Blue night / Body and soul / Mr. Combinated.
Note: Latest offering from legendary drummer Art Blakey and his young Jazz Messengers.Featuring Terrence Blanchard on trumpet(some believe him to be better than Wynton Marsalis) and Donald Harrison on alto,this is the same group that appeared at Ronnie Scott's & jazz festivals here last year. Personnel: Art Blakey - drums / Terrence Blanchard - trumpet / Donald Harrison-alto sax / Julgrew Miller - piano / Lonnie Plaxico - bass.
**Album:** Released Feb '86, on Timeless by Timeless Records. Catalogue no: **SJP 217**

**BLUES BAG (Blakey, Art/Buddy de Franco)**
Tracks: / Blues bag / Rain dance / Straight no chaser / Cousin Mary / Blues connotation / Kush / Twelve tone blues.
**Cass:** Released Dec '86, on Atlantis by Charly Records. Catalogue no: **KATS 4**
**Album:** Released Dec '86, on Atlantis by Charly Records. Deleted '88. Catalogue no: **ATS 4**
**Album:** Released Jan '81, on Affinity by Charly Records. Deleted '88. Catalogue no: **AFF 55**
**Cass:** Released '86, on Atlantis by Charly Records. Catalogue no: **TCATS 4**

**BLUES MARCH (Blakey, Art\Jazz Messengers)**

Tracks: / Blues march / Uranus / Whisper not / Backgammon / Georgia on my mind / Third world express / Nam fulay / I can't get started.
**Album:** Released Oct '88, on Vogue (France) by Vogue Records. Catalogue no: **520235**
**CD:** Released 10 Jul '89, on Vogue by Vogue Records. Catalogue no: **VG 670 209**
**CD:** Released May '85, on Vogue (France) by Vogue Records. Catalogue no: **VG 600 030**

**BUHAINA (The continuing message) (Blakey, Art\Jazz Messengers)**
Tracks: / For minors only / Right down front / Leo-x / Sweet sakeena / For miles & miles / Krafty / Late spring.
**Album:** on Affinity by Charly Records. Catalogue no: **AFF 113**

**BUTTERCORN LADY (Blakey, Art\Jazz Messengers)**
Tracks: / Buttercorn lady / Recuerdo / Theme / Between races / My romance / Secret love.
**CD:** Released Apr '85, on Emarcy Catalogue no: **822 471-2**

**CARAVAN (Blakey, Art\Jazz Messengers)**
**Album:** Released Jun '84, on RCA (France) by BMG Records (France). Catalogue no: **NL 70244**
**CD:** Released Jan '89, on JVC/Fantasy Catalogue no: **VDJ 1623**

**CARAVAN (SINGLE) (Blakey, Art \ Jazz Messengers)**
Tracks: / Caravan.
**CD 3":** Released '88, on Delos (USA) Catalogue no: **D/PC 2104**

**CHICAGO GOLDEN YEARS (Blakey, Art/Max Roach)**
**2 LP Set:** Released Oct '88, on Vogue by Vogue Records. Catalogue no: **427002**

**CHILD'S DANCE (Blakey, Art\Jazz Messengers)**
Tracks: / C.C. / Child's Dance / Song for a lonely woman / I can't get started.
**Cass:** Released Mar '88, on Prestige Deleted Jan '90. Catalogue no: **PRC 10047**
**Album:** Released Mar '88, on Prestige Catalogue no: **PR 10047**

**COMPLETE DEBUT SESSION '53 (Blakey, Art/Mingus, Charles/Bley, Paul)**
**Album:** Released Feb '89, on Raretone Catalogue no: **FC 5014**

**DAY WITH ART BLAKEY, A - VOLUME 1**
**CD:** Released Jan '86, on East Wind Catalogue no: **CDWIND 707**

**DAY WITH ART BLAKEY, A - VOLUME 2**
Tracks: / Night in Tunisia / Nelly Bly / Dat Dere / Round about midnight / Night in Tunisia.
**Album:** Released Apr '85, on East Wind Catalogue no: **EWIND 708**
**CD:** Released Jan '86, on East Wind Catalogue no: **CDWIND 708**

**DES FEMMES DISPARAISSENT / LES TRICHEURS (1958 soundtracks)**
**CD:** Released Jan '89, on Polygram (France) by PolyGram UK Ltd. Catalogue no: **834 752-2**

**DRUM NIGHT AT BIRDLAND**
Note: With Art Blakey, Philly Joe Jones, Charlie Persip & Elvin Jones.
**CD:** Released '86, on Vogue by Vogue Records. Catalogue no: **VG 600 107**

**DRUM SOUNDS (Blakey, Art\Jazz Messengers)**
Tracks: / New world / Angel eyes / Slide No.2 / Theme.
**Album:** Released Apr '86, on Star Jazz (USA) by Charly Records. Catalogue no: **SJAZZ 9**
**Cass:** Released Apr '86, on Star Jazz (USA) by Charly Records. Catalogue no: **SJAZZC 9**

**DRUM SUITE**
Tracks: / Sacrifice / Cubano chant / Oscalypso / Nica's tempo / D's dilemma / Just for Marty.
**Album:** Released May '83, on CBS by CBS Records. Deleted '86. Catalogue no: **CBS 21067**
**Cass:** Released May '83, on CBS by CBS Records. Catalogue no: **40 21067**

**FEEL THE WIND (Blakey, Art/Freddie Hubbard)**
Note: Personnel: Freddie Hubbard (tpt), Javon Jackson (tenor sax), Benny Green (piano), Leon Dorsey (bass), Art Blakey (drums), Mulgrew Miller (piano), Lonnie Plaxico (bass).
**Album:** Released Jun '89, on Timeless by Timeless Records. Catalogue no: **SJP 307**
**CD:** Released Jun '89, on Timeless by Timeless Records. Catalogue no: **CDSJP 307**

**FEELING GOOD**
**CD:** Released Mar '90, on delos Catalogue no: **JJCD4**
**CD:** Released '88, on Delos (USA) Catalogue no: **DCD 4007**

**FOR MINORS ONLY (Blakey, Art \ Jazz Messengers)**
Tracks: / Right down front / Deo X / For minors only / Sweet Sakeena / For miles and miles / Krafty / Late spring / Tippin' / Pristine.
**CD:** Released '86, on Charly by Charly Records. Catalogue no: **CDCHARLY 23**

**FREE FOR ALL (Blakey, Art\Jazz Messengers)**
Tracks: / Free for all / Hammer head / Core, The / Pensativa.
**CD:** Released Apr '88, on Blue Note by EMI Records. Catalogue no: **BNZ 5**
**Album:** Released Oct '84, on Blue Note by EMI Records. Deleted '87. Catalogue no: **BST 84170**
**CD:** Released Apr '88, on Blue Note by EMI Records. Catalogue no: **CDP 784 170 2**
**Cass:** Released Nov '84, on Blue Note by EMI Records. Deleted Jun '88. Catalogue no: **TC-BST 84170**

**GYPSY FOLK TALES**
**Album:** Released Oct '88, on Vogue (France) by Vogue Records. Catalogue no: **520292**

**HARD BOP**
Tracks: / Cranky spanky / Stella by starlight / My heart stood still / Little Melonae / Stanley's stiff chickens.
**Album:** Released May '81, on CBS by CBS Records. Deleted '86. Catalogue no: **CBS 54302**

**HARD CHAMPION**
**CD:** Released Sep '88, on Electric Bird Catalogue no: **K32Y 6209**
**Album:** Released Sep '88, on Electric Bird Catalogue no: **K 28P 6472**

**IN MY PRIME VOL. 1 (Blakey, Art\Jazz Messengers)**
**Album:** Released Apr '81, on Timeless by Timeless Records. Catalogue no: **SJP 114**

**IN MY PRIME VOL.2 (Blakey, Art\Jazz Messengers)**
Tracks: / Hawkman / People who laugh / Time will tell / Ronnie's a dynamite lady.
**Album:** Released Sep '86, on Timeless by Timeless Records. Catalogue no: **SJP 118**

**IN SWEDEN (Blakey, Art\Jazz Messengers)**
Tracks: / Webb city / How deep is the ocean / Skylark / Gypsy folk tales.
**Album:** Released Jul '82, on Amigo Catalogue no: **AMLP 839**

**INDESTRUCTIBLE (Blakey, Art \ Jazz Messengers)**
Tracks: / Egyptian, The / Sortie / Calling Miss Khadija / When love is new / Mr. Jin.
Note: This is the only album of Blakey's classic sextet band of the early 60's on which Lee Morgan returns to the Jazz Messengers to replace Freddie Hubbard. Wayne Shorter, Curtis Fuller, Cedar Walton and Reggie Wormans complete the band. Walton's tender When Love Is New is a lyrical showcase for Morgan's trumpet. The Egyptian is pure-charging Messengers music.
**Cass:** Released Sep '87, on Blue Note by EMI Records. Catalogue no: **4BN 84193**
**CD:** Released Aug '87, on Blue Note by EMI Records. Deleted Feb '90. Catalogue no: **CDP 746 429 2**
**CD:** Released Aug '87, on Blue Note by EMI Records. Catalogue no: **BNZ 3**
**Album:** Released Jul '89, on Blue Note by EMI Records. Catalogue no: **BST 84193**

**JAZZ AT THE SMITHSONIAN VOL.2 (Blakey, Art/Jazz Messengers)**
Note: This concert introduces the brilliant trumpet playing of Wynton Marsalis, and his brother Branford on alto sax, to the Messengers. Humour, virtosity and a sense of fresh discovery run through his trumpet lines like adrenalin through a genius. The concert accents the rhythm section, as befits a drummer-led band, as Blakey keeps everyone in line.

Complete with an intermissin interview, this concert makes essential viewing for all jazz following. Running time: 55 mins.
**VHS:** Released Sep '89, on Parkfield Publishing Catalogue no: **MKJ 0004**

**JAZZ MESSAGE**
Tracks: / Cafe / Just knock on my door / Summertime / Blues back / Sunday / Song is you, The.
**Album:** Released Feb '84, on Jasmine by Hasmick Promotions. Deleted Feb '88. Catalogue no: **JAS 76**
**CD:** Released Jul '87, on MCA by MCA Records. Deleted Dec '89. Catalogue no: **MCAD 5648**

**JAZZ MESSENGERS (That's jazz) (Blakey, Art/Thelonious Monk)**
Tracks: / Evidence / In walked bud / Blue Monk / I mean you / Rhythm a ning / Purple shades.
**CD:** Released May '89, on MCA (Import) by MCA Records. Catalogue no: **MCAD 5886**
**CD:** Released '88, on Atlantic Jazz by WEA Records. Catalogue no: **K 7813322**
**Album:** Released '88, on Atlantic by WEA Records. Catalogue no: **K 50248**
**Album:** Released Jun '89, on MCA (Import) by MCA Records. Catalogue no: **MCA 5886**

**JAZZ MESSENGERS (CBS) (Blakey, Art Percussion Ensemble)**
Tracks: / Sacrifice / Cubano chant / Oscalypso / Nica's tempo / D's dilemma / Just for Marty.
**Album:** Released '84, on CBS by CBS Records. Catalogue no: **21067**
**Cass:** Released '84, on CBS by CBS Records. Catalogue no: **40 21067**

**JAZZ TIME VOL.19**
**Album:** Released '88, on Vogue (France) by Vogue Records. Catalogue no: **502719**

**KEYSTONE 3 (Blakey, Art/Jazz Messengers)**
Tracks: / When it's sleepy time down south / When my sugar walks down the street / When i fall in love / As long as I live / America, the beautiful / Louisiana / High society / I'll be with you in apple blossom time / I ain't got nobody / This is all I ask.
**CD:** Released Mar '90, on Concord by Concord Jazz Records (USA). Catalogue no: **CCD 4196**

**KILLER JOE (Blakey, Art/George Kawaguchi)**
**Album:** Released Jun '86, on Storyville by Storyville Records AB. Catalogue no: **SLP 4100**

**LES LIAISONS DANGEREUSES 1960 (Blakey, Art \ Jazz Messengers)**
Tracks: / No problem (Music from the film directed by Roger Vadim) / No hay problems (Music from the film directed by Roger Vadim) / Prelude in blue (Music from the film directed by Roger Vadim) / Valmontana (Music from the film directed by Roger Vadim) / Miguel's party (Music from the film directed by Roger Vadim) / Weehawken mad pad (Music from the film directed by Roger Vadim).
**Album:** Released Aug '83, on Phonogram (France) Catalogue no: **8120 171**
**Cass:** Released Aug '83, on Phonogram (France) Catalogue no: **8120 174**
**CD:** Released Jan '89, on Polygram (France) by PolyGram UK Ltd. Catalogue no: **812 017-2**

**LIKE SOMEONE IN LOVE (Blakey, Art/Jazz Messengers)**
Tracks: / Like someone in love / Johnny's blue / Noise in the attic / Sleeping dancer sleep on / Giants / Sleeping dancer sleep on (alt. take) (CD only.).
**Album:** Released Apr '89, on Blue Note by EMI Records. Catalogue no: **B1 84245**
**CD:** Released Apr '89, on Blue Note by EMI Records. Catalogue no: **BNZ 156**
**CD:** Released Apr '89, on Blue Note by EMI Records. Catalogue no: **CDP 784 245 2**

**LIVE: ART BLAKEY (Blakey, Art \ Jazz Messengers)**
**Album:** Released Apr '84, on Carrere (France) Catalogue no: **64513**

**LIVE AT BUBBA'S (Blakey, Art / Jazz Messengers)**
Tracks: / Moanin' / My funny valentine / Soulful Mister Timmons / Au privave / Free for all.
**Cass:** Released '89, on Kingdom Jazz by Kingdom Records. Catalogue no: **CGATE 7003**
**Album:** Released Sep '83, on Kingdom Jazz by Kingdom Records. Catalogue no: **GATE 7003**

**LIVE AT KIMBALL'S (Blakey, Art \ Jazz Messengers)**
Tracks: / Second thoughts / I Love You / Jody / Old Folks / You and the Night and the Music / Polka Dots and Moonbeams / Doctor Jekyll.
**Album:** Released Dec '86, on Concord Jazz by Concord Jazz Records (USA). Catalogue no: **CJ 307**
**Cass:** Released Dec '86, on Concord Jazz by Concord Jazz Records (USA). Catalogue no: **CJC 307**

**LIVE AT MONTREUX & NORTH-SEA (Blakey, Art \ Jazz Messengers)**
Tracks: / Minor thesis / Wheel within a wheel, A / Bit a bittadose / Stairway to the stars / Linwood.
**Album:** Released '81, on Timeless (Import) by Timeless Records. Catalogue no: **SJP 150**

**LIVE AT RONNIE SCOTTS**
Tracks: / On the Ginza / Dr.Jeckyll / Two of a kind / I want to talk about you.
**Cass:** Released Feb '90, on Essential by Castle Communications Records. Catalogue no: **ESMMC 014**
**CD:** Released May '87, on Hendring Deleted '88. Catalogue no: **WHCD 001**
**CD:** Released Feb '90, on Essential by Castle Communications Records. Catalogue no: **ESMCD 014**

**LIVE AT SWEET BASIL (Blakey, Art\Jazz Messengers)**
Tracks: / Jodi / Blues march / Mr. Babe / Moanin'.
Note: Album recorded in March 1985,Blakey's current Messengers,as featured on this album,need no introduction.They have been frequent visitors to the UK over the past three years,packing them in down at Ronnie Scotts.Straight ahead be-bop featuring two of Blakey's most popular vehicles'Blues March'&'Moanin''.
**Cass:** Released '88, on GNP Crescendo (USA) by GNP Crescendo Records (USA). Catalogue no: **GNP5 2182**
**Album:** Released Jul '86, on King (Japan) Catalogue no: **K 28P 6357**
**Album:** Released '88, on GNP Crescendo (USA) by GNP Crescendo Records (USA). Catalogue no: **GNPS 2182**

**LIVE IN BERLIN 1959 & 1962 (Blakey, Art/Jazz Messengers)**
**CD:** Released Mar '90, on Jazz-Up Catalogue no: **JU 321**

**MESSAGES (Blakey, Art/John Handy III)**
**2 LP Set:** Released Oct '88, on Vogue by Vogue Records. Catalogue no: **421004**
**Album:** Released Feb '79, on Vogue Jazz (France) by Vogue Records. Catalogue no: **VJD 557**

**MOANIN'**
Tracks: / Moanin' / Moanin' (alt. take) / Are you real / Along came Betty / Drum thunder suite, The / Blues march / Come rain or come shine.
Note: Produced by Alfred Lion. Produced for release by Michael Cuscana.
**Album:** Released Jul '89, on Blue Note by EMI Records. Catalogue no: **BLJ 84003**
**Album:** Released Sep '84, on Blue Note by EMI Records. Deleted '87. Catalogue no: **BST 84003**
**CD:** Released Jan '88, on Blue Note by EMI Records. Catalogue no: **CDP 746 516 2**
**CD:** Released Jan '88, on Blue Note by EMI Records. Catalogue no: **BNZ 4**
**Album:** Released '79, on Blue Note by EMI Records. Deleted '84. Catalogue no: **BNS 40012**

**MOSAIC (Blakey, Art\Jazz Messengers)**
Tracks: / Mosaic / Down under / Children of the night / Arabia / Crisis.
**CD:** Released May '87, on Blue Note by EMI Records. Catalogue no: **CDP 746 523 2**
**Album:** Released Dec '84, on Blue Note by EMI Records. Catalogue no: **BST 84090**
**CD:** Released May '87, on Blue Note by EMI Records. Catalogue no: **BNZ 7**

**NEW YEAR'S EVE AT SWEET BASIL (Blakey, Art\Jazz Messengers)**
Tracks: / Hide and seek / Little man / New York / I want to talk about you.

Note: Recorded 1985/6.
**Album:** Released Apr '87, on King (Japan) Catalogue no: **K 28P 6426**
**CD:** Released Oct '87, on King (Japan) Catalogue no: **K32Y 6079**

### NEW YORK SCENE
Tracks: / Oh by the way / It's easy to remember / Who cares / Controversy / Tenderly / Falafel.
Note: Includes the following medley's :Ballad medley which contains the following tracks Oh by the way/It's easy to remember/My one and only love/who cares/tenderly/falafel
**Cass:** Released Nov '84, on Concord Jazz by Concord Jazz Records (USA). Catalogue no: **CJC 256**
**Album:** Released Nov '84, on Concord Jazz by Concord Jazz Records (USA). Catalogue no: **CJ 256**
**CD:** Released Sep '86, on Concord Jazz by Concord Jazz Records (USA). Catalogue no: **CCD 4256**

### NIGHT AT BIRDLAND, VOL 1 (Blakey, Art Quintet)
Tracks: / Split kick / Once in a while / Quicksilver / Wee-dot / Blues / Night in Tunisia / Mayreh.
**CD:** Released May '87, on Blue Note by EMI Records. Catalogue no: **BNZ 8**
**Album:** Released Apr '85, on Blue Note by EMI Records. Deleted Jun '88. Catalogue no: **BST 81521**
**CD:** Released May '87, on Blue Note by EMI Records. Catalogue no: **CDP 746 519 2**
**Cass:** Released Apr '85, on Blue Note by EMI Records. Deleted Nov '88. Catalogue no: **4BN 81521**
**Album:** Released '79, on Blue Note by EMI Records. Deleted '84. Catalogue no: **BNS 40007**
**Album:** Released Sep '84, on Blue Note by EMI Records. Deleted '87. Catalogue no: **BLP 1521**

### NIGHT AT BIRDLAND, VOL 2 (Blakey, Art Quintet)
Tracks: / Wee dot / If I had you / Quicksilver / Now's the time / Blues / Confirmation.
**Album:** Released Aug '82. on Blue Note by EMI Records. Deleted Jan '88. Catalogue no: **BLP 1522**
**Album:** Released Jul '89, on Blue Note by EMI Records. Catalogue no: **BST 81522**
**CD:** Released Aug '88, on Blue Note by EMI Records. Catalogue no: **CDP 746 520 2**
**Album:** Released '79, on Blue Note by EMI Records. Deleted '84. Catalogue no: **BNS 40008**
**Cass:** Released Aug '85, on Blue Note by EMI Records. Deleted Nov '88. Catalogue no: **4BN 81522**
**CD:** Released Aug '88, on Blue Note by EMI Records. Catalogue no: **BNZ 9**

### NIGHT IN TUNISIA, A (Blakey, Art/Jazz Messengers)
Tracks: / Night in Tunisia / Sincerely Diana / So tired / Yama / Kozo's waltz.
**Album:** Released Aug '89, on Blue Note by EMI Records. Catalogue no: **B1 84049**
**CD:** Released May '87, on Blue Note by EMI Records. Catalogue no: **BNZ 6**
**Cass:** Released Mar '84, on Blue Note by EMI Records. Catalogue no: **BSC 840494**
**Album:** Released Sep '84, on Blue Note by EMI Records. Deleted '87. Catalogue no: **BST 84049**
**CD:** Released '88, on Kingdom Jazz by Kingdom Records. Catalogue no: **800 064 2**
**CD:** Released May '87, on Blue Note by EMI Records. Deleted Aug '89. Catalogue no: **CDP 746 532 2**

### NOTES FROM JAZZ (VIDEO)
**VHS:** Released '88, on Kay Jazz (video) by Kay Jazz. Catalogue no: **KJ 001**

### OH BY THE WAY (Blakey, Art\Jazz Messengers)
Tracks: / Oh by the way / Duck soup / Tropical breeze / One by one / Sudan blue / My funny valentine / Alicia.
**Album:** Released Aug '82, on Timeless by Timeless Records. Catalogue no: **SJP 165**

### ONE BY ONE (Blakey, Art\Jazz Messengers)
Tracks: / One by one / Rhapsody in blue / Summertime / It ain't necessarily so / Someone to watch over me / Man I love, The / Song is you, The / Moanin'.
**Album:** Released '81, on Palcoscenico (Italy) Catalogue no: **PAL 15005**

### ORGY IN RHYTHM, VOL 1
**Album:** Released Sep '84, on Blue Note by EMI Records. Deleted '87. Catalogue no: **BST 81554**

### PARIS JAM SESSION (Blakey, Art\Jazz Messengers)
Tracks: / Dance of the infidels / Bouncing with Bud / Midget, The / Night in Tunisia.
Note: Recorded Paris 1959. Special guest Bud Powell. Art Blakey/Barney Wilen/Wayne Shorter/Lee morgan/Jimmy Meritt/Walter Davis Junior.
**Cass:** Released Mar '88, on Fontana Import Catalogue no: **8326924**
**Album:** Released Mar '88, on Fontana Import Catalogue no: **8326921**
**CD:** Released Mar '88, on Fontana Import Catalogue no: **8326922**

### PERCUSSION DISCUSSION (Blakey, Art/Max Roach)
Tracks: / Scotch blues / Flight to Jordan / Transfiguration / Exhibit A / Gershwin medley / Crackle hut / Speculate / That ole devil called love / Audio blues / CM / Four - X.
Note: Third album in the Chess Masters series, featuring two of the all-time greatest jazz drummers.
**2 LP Set:** Released Jul '88, on Chess by Vogue Records. Catalogue no: **GCH 2-6028**
**2 LP Set:** Released Oct '84, on Chess (PRT) Deleted '88. Catalogue no: **CXJD 6703**
**Cass set:** Released Oct '84, on Chess (PRT) Deleted '88. Catalogue no: **ZCCJD 6703**
**CD:** Released Feb '89, on Vogue by Vogue Records. Catalogue no: **VGCD 600091**

### REFLECTIONS IN BLUE (Blakey, Art\Jazz Messengers)
Tracks: / Reflections in blue / E.T.A. / Say, Dr J / Mishima / My foolish heart / My one and only love / Chelsea Bridge / In a sentimental mood / Stretching.
**Album:** Released Apr '81, on Timeless by Timeless Records. Catalogue no: **SJP 128**

### RITUAL
Tracks: / Little T.A. / Exhibit A / Scotch blues / Once upon a groove / Sam's tune / Touche / Wake up / Art Blakey's comments on Ritual / Ritual.
**CD:** Released Nov '88, on Blue Note by EMI Records. Catalogue no: **BNZ 118**
**CD:** Released Nov '88, on Blue Note by EMI Records. Catalogue no: **CDP 746 858 2**

### STANDARDS
**CD:** Released Nov '89, on King Catalogue no: **292E6026**

### STRAIGHT AHEAD
**Album:** Released Dec '81, on Concord by Concord Jazz Records (USA). Catalogue no: **CJ 168**

### THEORY OF ART (Blakey, Art\Jazz Messengers)
Tracks: / Night in Tunisia / Off the wall / Couldn't it be you? / Theory of Art / Evans / Night at Tony's, A / Social call.
**CD:** Released Apr '88, on Bluebird (2) by BMG Records (UK). Catalogue no: **ND 86286**

### UGETSU
Tracks: / One by one / Ugetsu / Time off / Ping pong / I didn't know what time it was / On the ginza.
**Album:** Released Jun '84, on Prestige (USA) by Fantasy Inc (USA). Catalogue no: **OJC 090**

## Blanchard, Terence

**Biographical details:** Blanchard, Terence. This young trumpet player, born in 1962 in New Orleans, was one of the stars of Art Blakey's Jazz Messengers on records from 1982, and began recording in '84 co-leading a similar band with ex-Blakey alto and soprano saxophonist Donald Harrison (also born in New Orleans, in 1960), at first on Concord Jazz, then on CBS. They are also both composers; from the same generation and provenance as Wynton Marsalis, they do not let their egos get in the way of their music. It's true that they are revivalists, in the modern, imprecise meaning that they are not yet innovators, but they have long careers ahead of them and in the mean time the music is gorgeous. Donald Clarke, 24 August 1988..

### DISCERNMENT (Blanchard, Terence & Donald Harrison)
Tracks: / Worth the pain / When the saints go marching in / When I Fall in Love / Directions / Discernment / Are you sleeping? / Akira / Dorchester House.

**Album:** Released Apr '86, on George Wein Collection(USA) by Concord Jazz Records (USA). Catalogue no: **GW 3008**
**CD:** Released Jan '86, on Concord Jazz by Concord Jazz Records (USA). Catalogue no: **CCD 43008**
**Cass:** Released Apr '86, on George Wein Collection(USA) by Concord Jazz Records (USA). Catalogue no: **GWC 3008**

### NEW YORK SECOND LINE (Blanchard, Terence & Donald Harrison)
Tracks: / New York second line (Donald Harrison plays reeds.) / Oliver Twist (Donald Harrison plays reeds.) / I can't get started (Donald Harrison plays reeds.) / Duck steps (Donald Harrison plays reeds.) / Doctor Drums (Donald Harrison plays reeds.) / Isn't it so? (Donald Harrison plays reeds.) / Subterfuge (Donald Harrison plays reeds.).
Note: Terence Blanchard, trumpet; Donald Harrison, reeds; Mulgrew Miller, piano; Lonnie Plaxico, bass; Marvin "Smitty" Smith, drums.
**CD:** Released '88, on Concord by Concord Jazz Records (USA). Catalogue no: **CCD 430 02**
**Album:** Released Apr '84, on George Wein Collection(USA) by Concord Jazz Records (USA). Catalogue no: **GW 3002**

## Bland, Bobby

**Biographical details:** Bland, Bobby 'Blue'. The soul/blues singer was born Robert Clavin Bland in 1930 in Rosemark, Tennessee; he is a smooth pop balladeer using a palette of blues feeling and vocal effects. His influence has been huge; he began recording in 1954; he had 37 hits in the Billboard R&B chart 1960-70, with 17 top tens; double-sided hit *That's The Way Love Is/Call On Me* made the pop chart as well. Always true to himself, his work is classic stuff from the early part of Soul's golden era. *Members Only* in 1986 on Malaco was said to be his best since the early classic days. Donald Clarke, 24 August 1988.

Bobby Bland

### AFTER ALL
**Album:** Released Dec '86, on Malaco by Malaco Records (UK). Catalogue no: **MALP 009**

### AIN'T NOTHING YOU CAN DO
**Album:** Released '77, on Duke by Melodisc Records. Catalogue no: **DL 78**

### ANGELS IN HOUSTON: LEGENDARY DUKE BLUES (Bland, Bobby /Various)
**Cass:** Released '88, on Rounder (USA) by Rounder Records (USA). Catalogue no: **ROUNDER 2031C**
**Album:** Released '88, on Rounder (USA) by Rounder Records (USA). Catalogue no: **ROUNDER 2031**

### BAREFOOT ROCK (Bland, Bobby & Junior Parker)
**Album:** Released '77, on Duke by Melodisc Records. Catalogue no: **DL 72**

### BEST OF BOBBY BLAND
Tracks: / Cry cry cry / I pity the fool / Turn on your lovelight / Stormy Monday blues / That's the way love is / Ain't nothing you can do / Too far gone / Good time Charlie / That did it / Rockin' in the same old boat / Chains of love / Do what you set out to do / This time I'm gone for good / It's not the spotlight / Ain't no love in the heart of the city / Yolanda / Love to see you smile / Soon as the weather breaks.
**Cass:** Released Apr '82, on ABC Records by MCA Records. Catalogue no: **MCLC 1673**
**Album:** Released Apr '82, on ABC Records by MCA Records. Catalogue no: **MCL 1673**
**CD:** Released Jun '88, on MCA (USA) by MCA Records (USA). Catalogue no: **31219**

### BLUES IN THE NIGHT
Tracks: / Blue moon / If I hadn't called you back / Ask me 'bout nothing but the blues / Jelly jelly jelly / When you put me down / Blind man / Chains of love / Fever / Blues in the night / Loneliness hurts / Feeling is gone, The / I'm too far gone / Black night / Share your love with me.
**Album:** Released May '85, on Ace by Ace Records. Catalogue no: **CH 132**
**Cass:** Released May '85, on Ace by Ace Records. Deleted Jun '88. Catalogue no: **CHC 132**

### BLUES YOU CAN USE
**CD:** Released '88, on Malaco by Malaco Records (UK). Catalogue no: **MAL CD 7444**
**Album:** Released Oct '88, on Malaco by Malaco Records (UK). Catalogue no: **MAL 7444**

### CALIFORNIA ALBUM
Tracks: / This time I'm gone for good / Up and down world / It's not the spotlight / (If loving you is wrong) I don't wanna be right / Goin' down slow / Right place at the right time, The / Help me through the day / Where baby went / Friday the 13th child / I've got to use my imagination.
**CD:** Released Jan '90, on Beat Goes On by Andy's Records. Catalogue no: **BGOCD 64**
**Album:** Released Jan '89, on Beat Goes On by Andy's Records. Catalogue no: **BGOLP 64**

### CALL ON ME
**Album:** Released '77, on Duke by Melodisc Records. Catalogue no: **DL 77**

### COME FLY WITH ME
**Album:** Released Jun '78, on ABC Records by MCA Records. Catalogue no: **ABCL 5249**

### DREAMER
**CD:** Released 2 Oct '89, on Beat Goes On by Andy's Records. Catalogue no: **BGOCD 63**
**Album:** Released 2 Oct '89, on Beat Goes On by Andy's Records. Catalogue no: **BGOLP 63**

### FIRST CLASS BLUES
**CD:** Released '88, on Malaco by Malaco Records (UK). Catalogue no: **MALCD 5000**

### FOOLIN' WITH THE BLUES
Tracks: / You got me (where you want me) / Loan me a helping hand / I pity the fool / Who will the next fool be? / Two steps from the blues / Reconsider, baby / Bobby's blues / Cry cry cry / Touch of the blues, A / You're worth it all / Don't

cry no more / I'm not ashamed / I'll take care of you / 36-22-36 / Ain't no telling / Yield not to temptation.
**Album:** Released '83, on Charly R&B by Charly Records. Catalogue no: **CRB 1049**

**HERE'S THE MAN**
**Album:** Released '77, on Duke by Melodisc Records. Catalogue no: **DL 75**

**INSTRUMENTAL ALBUM**
**Album:** Released Oct '85, on Rockhouse by Rockhouse Records (Holland). Catalogue no: **LP 8502**

**INTROSPECTIVE OF THE EARLY YEARS**
**Album:** Released '77, on Duke by Melodisc Records. Catalogue no: **DL 92**

**LIKE 'ER RED HOT**
**Album:** Released '77, on Duke by Melodisc Records. Catalogue no: **DL 73**

**MEMBERS ONLY**
Tracks: / Members only / In the ghetto / I've just got to know / Straight / From the shoulder / Sweet woman's love / Can we make love tonight / Sweet surrender / I need your love so bad / Heart open up again.
**Album:** Released '88, on Malaco by Malaco Records (UK). Catalogue no: **MALP 004**
**Album:** Released Nov '85, on Malaco by Malaco Records (UK). Catalogue no: **MAL 7429**
**Cass:** Released Mar '89, on Malaco by Malaco Records (UK). Catalogue no: **MALC 7429**

**MEMBERS ONLY (SINGLE)**
Tracks: / Members only / Straight from the shoulder / Sweet surrender.
**12" Single:** Released Mar '86, on Malaco by Malaco Records (UK). Deleted '88. Catalogue no: **MAL 12 031**

**REFLECTIONS IN BLUE**
**Album:** Released May '77, on ABC Records by MCA Records. Catalogue no: **ABCL 5196**

**SHOES**
Tracks: / Shoes / Call me / Getting used to the blues / Good time Charlie.
**7" Single:** Released Jun '85, on Kent by Ace Records. Catalogue no: **TOWN 108**

**SOUL OF THE MAN, THE**
**Album:** Released '77, on Duke by Melodisc Records. Catalogue no: **DL 79**

**SOUL WITH A FLAVOUR**
Tracks: / Wishing well / St. James' infirmary / Ain't that lovin' you / Turn on your lovelight / You're the one (that I adore) / Stormy Monday blues / Your friends / Honky tonk / That's the way love is / These hands (small, but mighty) / Poverty / Driftin' blues / Sad feeling / Rockin' in the same old boat / Gotta get to know you / Soon as the weather breaks / You'd be a millionaire / Soul with a flavour / Real woman is what it takes, A / Try me I'm real / Recess in heaven / You're about to win / Is this the blues / Just because I love you / Looking back.
**2 LP Set:** Released Nov '88, on Charly by Charly Records. Catalogue no: **CDX 30**
**Cass Set:** Released Nov '88, on Charly by Charly Records. Catalogue no: **TCCDX 30**

**SOULFUL SIDE OF BOBBY BLAND, THE**
Tracks: / Getting used to the blues / Yum yum tree / These hands (small, but mighty) / Back in the same old bag again / Keep on loving me / Honey child / Wouldn't you rather have me / Call on me / Dear Bobby / How does a cheating woman feel / I ain't myself anymore / That did it / Ain't doing too bad(pt.1) / Love with a reputation / Good time Charlie / Ain't nothing you can do.
**Album:** Released Oct '86, on Kent by Ace Records. Deleted Jan '90. Catalogue no: **KENT 044**

**SPOTLIGHTING THE MAN B.B.**
**Album:** Released '77, on Duke by Melodisc Records. Catalogue no: **DL 89**

**TELL MR. BLAND**
**Album:** Released Oct '83, on MCA by MCA Records. Deleted Oct '88. Catalogue no: **MCF 3181**

**TOGETHER AGAIN - LIVE (Bland, Bobby & B.B. King)**
Tracks: / Let the good times roll / Strange things happen / Feel so bad / Mother in law blues / Mean old world / Everyday (I have the blues) / Thrill is gone, The / I ain't gonna be the first to cry.
**Album:** Released Oct '87, on MCA by MCA Records. Catalogue no: **IMCA 27012**
**Album:** Released Jul '76, on Impulse by Impulse Records. Catalogue no: **IMPL 8027**

**TOUCH OF THE BLUES**
**Album:** Released '77, on Duke by Melodisc Records. Catalogue no: **DL 88**

**TWO STEPS FROM THE BLUES (Bland, Bobby & B.B. King)**
Tracks: / Cry, cry, cry / I pity the fool / I'll take care of you.
**CD:** Released Jan '90, on MCA by MCA Records. Catalogue no: **MCAD 4160**
**CD:** Released Sep '89, on MCA (Import) by MCA Records. Catalogue no: **MCAD 27036**
**Album:** Released Sep '89, on MCA (Import) by MCA Records. Catalogue no: **MCA 27036**
**Album:** Released Jan '90, on MCA by MCA Records. Catalogue no: **MCA 4160**
**Album:** Released '77, on Duke by Melodisc Records. Catalogue no: **DL 74**

**WOKE UP SCREAMING**
Tracks: / No blow, no show / Wise man blues / Army blues / Lost lover blues / It's my life baby / Honey bee / Time out / Little boy blue / Woke up screaming / You've got bad intentions / I can't put you down baby / I smell trouble / Don't believe / I learned my lesson / Farther up the road.
**Album:** Released Oct '81, on Ace by Ace Records. Deleted Jan '90. Catalogue no: **CH 41**

## Bless My Bones

**BLESS MY BONES (Memphis Gospel Radio)**
**Album:** Released '88, on Rounder (USA) by Rounder Records (USA). Catalogue no: **ROUNDER 2063**
**Cass:** Released '88, on Rounder (USA) by Rounder Records (USA). Catalogue no: **ROUNDER 2063C**
**CD:** Released '88, on Rounder (USA) by Rounder Records (USA). Catalogue no: **CD 2063**

## Bley, Carla

**Biographical details:** Bley, Carla. The pianist, composer abd bandleader began in a New York City club selling cigarettes. She was married to pianist Paul Bley for more than ten years, contributing much of his repertoire during those years; with second husband Michael Mantler she co-founded the Jazz Composers Orchestra Association and the Watt abd XtraWatt record labels. She wrote *A Genuine Tong Funeral* for Gary Burton and she has played with Charlie Haden's Liberation Music Orchestra; she contributed to the A&M tribute albums produced by Hal Willner: *The Way I Feel Now* (the music of Thelonious Monk) and the title track of *Lost In The Stars* (Kurt Weill); she played organ on Steve Swallow's album *Afterglow*, while her *Carla* is effectively her sextet playing Swallow's music. She has recorded with groups of various sizes including big bands; her witty and distinctive tunes have been recorded by other leaders including George Russell, Steve Lacey and Art Farmer; her mid-'80s output has tended to an MOR-ish vein. Donald Clarke, 24 August 1988..

**CARLA BLEY BAND, THE (Bley, Carla Band)**
**Cass:** Released Oct '88, on ECM Catalogue no: **815 730-4**

**DINNER MUSIC**
**Cass:** Released Jul '85, on ECM Catalogue no: **7200191**

**DUETS (Bley, Carla & Steve Swallow)**
Tracks: / Baby baby / Walking batteriewoman / Utviklingssang / Ladies in Mercedes / Romantic notions / Remember / Ups and downs / Reactionary tango parts 1/2/3 / Soon I will be done with the troubles of this world (CD only.).
Note: Carla Bley joins forces with longtime musical associate, Steve Swallow, in an album of superb duo performances. On this album Carla returns to the acoustic piano and once more shows her strong affinity with the style of Thelonius Monk. The repertoire consists of older Carla Bley standards and some new compositions by Carla and Steve.
**Album:** Released Nov '88, on ECM Catalogue no: **WATT 20**
**CD:** Released Nov '88, on ECM Catalogue no: **837 345-2**

**ESCALATOR OVER THE HILL**
Note: A significant and vivid portrait of American jazz and musical life of the late

60s. The 2-CD set is packaged in the original boxed set with a 36 page LP size booklet containing libretto and session photos. music by Carla Bley, Words by Paul hains. The jazz Composer's Orchestra.
**CD Set:** Released Jan '90, on ECM Catalogue no: **839 310 2**
**LP Set:** Released Jan '90, on ECM Catalogue no: **JCOA EOTH**
**LP Set:** Released Dec '81, on ECM Deleted '86. Catalogue no: **264 180-2**

**EUROPEAN TOUR 1977**
**CD:** Released Jul '87, on ECM Catalogue no: **8318302**

**FLEUR CARNIVORE**
**CD:** Released Nov '89, on Watt (ECM) Catalogue no: **839 662 2**
**Album:** Released Nov '89, on Watt (ECM) Catalogue no: **WATT 21**

**HEAVY HEART**
Tracks: / Light or dark / Talking hearts / Joyful noise / Ending it / Starting again / Heavy heart.
**Album:** Released Mar '84, on Watts Catalogue no: **WATT 14**
**Cass:** Released Jul '85, on Watts Catalogue no: **818 862 4**

**I HATE TO SING**
**Album:** Released Jan '85, on ECM Catalogue no: **WATT 1212**

**LIVE: CARLA BLEY**
Tracks: / Blunt object / Lord is listenin' to ya,hallelujah, The / Time & us / Still in the room / Real life hits / Song sung long.
**CD:** Released Feb '86, on ECM Catalogue no: **815 730 2**
**Cass:** Released Jun '84, on ECM Catalogue no: **3103 112**

**MORTELLE RANDONNEE**
Tracks: / Musique mecanique / Whistling palomino / Morning / Death rolls / Los Palominos / Sad paloma / Paloma, La / Some dirge / Teenage Paloma / Grown up Paloma / Blunt object.
**Album:** Released Jun '83, on Phonogram by Phonogram Ltd. Catalogue no: **812 097- 1**
**Cass:** Released Jun '83, on Phonogram by Phonogram Ltd. Catalogue no: **812 097-4**

**MUSIQUE MECANIQUE**
**CD:** Released 1 Sep '89, on ECM Catalogue no: **839 313 2**
**Album:** Released 1 Sep '89, on ECM Catalogue no: **WATT 9**
**Cass:** Released Jul '85, on ECM Catalogue no: **7200151**

**NIGHT-GLO**
Tracks: / Pretend you're in love / Night-glo / Rut / Crazy with you / Wildlife (Horn-paws with out claws - sex with birds).
Note: With her new album 'Night-Glo' Carla Bley moves clearly into the direction already indicated on 'Heavy Heart'. With a slightly reduced line up of excelent musicians she sticks closely to fixed musical structures, rather than leaving spacefor extended improvisations. The album is built around the bass of Steve Swallow. Her instruction for the album shows her intentions; 'Slip into something comfortable, make yourself a cool drink, turn down the lights and and put on 'Night-Glo". With its perfect mixture of melancholy and subtle humour this new albumis another example of Carla Bley's musical flexibility. Personnel: Carla Bley -organ, synthesizers / Steve Swallow-bass / Larry Willis-piano, electric piano / Hiram Bullock-guitar / Victor Lewis-drums / Manolo Badrena-percussion.
**Album:** Released Dec '85, on ECM Catalogue no: **WATT 16**
**CD:** Released Dec '85, on ECM Catalogue no: **827 640-2**

**SEXTET**
Tracks: / More Brahms / Houses and people / Girl who cried champagne, The / Brooklyn bridge / Lawns / Healing power.
Note: With 'Sextet' Carla Bley continues along the musical road she set out on with "Heavy Heart" and "Night-Glo" (WATT 14 & 16). Putting aside the avantgarde, shehas developed a style that is accessible to a large audience.
**Album:** Released Apr '87, on ECM Catalogue no: **WATT 17**
**CD:** Released Apr '87, on ECM Catalogue no: **8316972**

**SOCIAL STUDIES**
**CD:** Released Jul '87, on ECM Catalogue no: **8318312**
**Album:** Released Jun '81, on ECM Catalogue no: **WATT 11**

## Bley, Paul

**Biographical details:** Bley, Paul. The pianist, composer and bandleader was born in 1932 in Montreal, where he led his own quartet in a hotel in 1945. Since then he has made a long steady rise to become one of the most highly regarded of small-group leaders and composers, compensating us somewhat for the death of Bill Evans. His debut album in 1953 was a trio album with Charles Mingus ad Art Blakey; while married to Carla Bley he was a founder member of the Jazz Artists Guild in the mid-'60s, which failed but led to the more successful Jazz Composers Association formed by Carla and Mike Mantler. He has had a particular empathy with great bassists, recording with Mingus, Charlie Haden, Scott La Faro, Gary Peacock, Dave Holland; his trio often included drummer Barry Altschul in the '60s. He teamed with singer Annette Peacock in the '70s and they experimented with synthesisers. *Fragments* in 1986 with drummer Paul Motian, saxist John Surman and guitarist Bill Frissell emphasised the comparison with Evans: the low-key beauty of this kind of music has influenced New Age music, but like Evans, Bley has too much talent and integrity to disappear into that gormless genre. (Donald Clarke, 24 August 1988.).

**ALONE AGAIN**
**Album:** Released Jul '78, on Improvising Artists Catalogue no: **IAI 37 3840**

**BALLADS (Bley, Paul, Altschul & Peacock)**
**Album:** Released Jul '87, on ECM Catalogue no: **ECM 1010**

**FRAGMENTS**
**Album:** Released Sep '86, on ECM Catalogue no: **ECM 1320**
**CD:** Released Sep '86, on ECM Catalogue no: **829 280-2**

**JAPAN SUITE**
**Album:** Released Jul '78, on Improvising Artists Catalogue no: **IAI 373849**

**LIVE AGAIN**
**CD:** Released Jul '88, on Steeplechase (USA) Catalogue no: **SCCD 31230**
**Album:** Released Jul '88, on Steeplechase (USA) Catalogue no: **SCS 1230**

**OPEN TO LOVE**
Tracks: / Closer / Ida Lupino / Open to love / Started / Harlem / Seven / Nothing ever was anyway.
**CD:** Released May '87, on ECM Catalogue no: **827 751-2**

**PAUL BLEY, CHARLES MINGUS & ART BLAKEY 1953**
**Album:** Released '88, on Raretone Catalogue no: **RARETONE 5014**

**PAUL BLEY QUARTET (Bley, Paul Quartet)**
Note: "In July 1986 four musicians came together in an Oslo studio for a spontaneous recording based on compositions provided by all four. Some of them had played together before, some were meeting for the first time. They result, Fragments (ECM 1320), with Bley, John Surman, Bill Frisell and Paul Motian, showed some of the most intense interplay. Since then the group has widely toured Europe -- the formation was actually initiated by the proposed recording contract -- and has turned into a working unit. After a recent tour they recorded this album, which developed out of spontaneous ideas. Paul Bley, piano; John Surman, soprano sax, bass clarinet; Bill Frisell, guitar; Paul Motian, drums." (IMS Records, May 1988.)
**CD:** Released May '88, on ECM Catalogue no: **835 240-2**
**Album:** Released May '88, on ECM Catalogue no: **ECM 1365**

**QUIET SONG (Bley, Paul, Connors & Guiffre)**
**Album:** Released Jul '78, on Improvising Artists Catalogue no: **IAI 373839**

**RAMBLING**
**Album:** Released Jan '80, on Affinity by Charly Records. Deleted '88. Catalogue no: **AFF 37**

**SOLEMN MEDITATION**
**Album:** Released '88, on GNP Crescendo (USA) by GNP Crescendo Records (USA). Catalogue no: **GNPS 31**

**SONOR**
Tracks: / Little bell / Landscape / Speed / Recollection / Joined / Sonor / Waltz /

Set / Darkness / Tightrope.
**Album:** Released May '85, on Soul Note Catalogue no: **SN 1085**

**TURNING POINT (Bley, Paul & various artists)**
**Album:** Released '78, on Improvising Artists Catalogue no: **IAI 373841**

**VIRTUISI (Bley, Paul, Altschul & Peacock)**
**Album:** Released Jul '78, on Improvising Artists Catalogue no: **IAI 373844**

## Blind Blake

**Biographical details:** The guitarist and blues singer's real name was probably Arthur Phelps; even his dates (1890-1933) are approximate, but his records have long been prized by collectors. (Donald Clarke, 24 August 1988.).

**1926-29: THE REMAINING TITLES**
**Album:** Released May '85, on Matchbox by Flyright Records. Catalogue no: **MSE 1003**

**ACCOMPIANIST, THE 1926-31**
**Album:** Released '88, on Wolf Catalogue no: **WSE 133**

**BLIND BLAKE**
**2 LP Set:** Released Oct '88, on Yazoo (USA) by Shanachie Records (USA). Catalogue no: **YAZOO 1068**

**BLIND BLAKE & PAPA CHARLIE (Blind Blake / Papa Charlie Jackson)**
**Album:** Released '88, on Collector's Classics Catalogue no: **CC 6**

**BOOTLEG RUM DUM BLUES**
Tracks: / Come on Boys / Let's do that messin' around / Skeedle loo doo blues / Bucktown Blues / Black dog blues / Bad feeling blues / That will never happen no more / Brownskin man / Hey hey daddy blues / Low down loving girl / Bootleg rum dum blues / Paying policy blues / Righteous blues.
**Album:** Released Feb '88, on Blue Moon (1) by Magnum Music Group. Catalogue no: **BMLP 1044**

**RAGTIME GUITAR'S FOREMOST**
**2 LP Set:** Released Feb '85, on Yazoo (USA) by Shanachie Records (USA). Catalogue no: **L 1068**

## Blood, Sweat & Tears

**Biographical details:** Blood Sweat & Tears. This was a jazz-rock group formed by former Bob Dylan sessioneer Al Kooper on keyboards and vocals after leaving the Blues Project. A rock quartet with Steve Katz on guitar, Jim Fielder on bass and Bobby Colomby on drums was augmented by a four-man horn section including Randy Brecker; they made a huge splash at the time on CBS, their first album *Child Is Father To The Man* in 1968 mixing brash blues-rock with Maynard Ferguson-inspired horn arrangements on songs by Carole King, Randy Newman, others; their second (eponymous) album and biggest hit included Laura Nyro's *Spinning Wheel*: Kooper had left, replaced by Englishman (naturalised Canadian) David Clayton Thomas; since then there have been many albums and personnel changes: ten albums slowly sank in their billboard USA chart placings through 1976 as they became less fashionable. Donald Clarke, 24 August 1988..

**BLOOD, SWEAT AND TEARS**
**Album:** Released Dec '88, on Beat Goes On by Andy's Records. Catalogue no: **BGOLP 28**
**Album:** Released Apr '69, on CBS by CBS Records. Deleted '74. Catalogue no: **63504**
**CD:** Released '88, on CBS by CBS Records. Deleted Jan '89. Catalogue no: **CD 63504**
**CD:** Released '88, on CBS by CBS Records. Catalogue no: **30DP 304**

**BLOOD, SWEAT AND TEARS 3**
**Album:** Released Aug '70, on CBS by CBS Records. Deleted '75. Catalogue no: **64024**

**CHALLENGE, THE**
**Album:** Released Nov '84, on Astan (USA) Catalogue no: **20140**
**Cass:** Released Nov '84, on Astan (USA) Catalogue no: **40140**

**CHILD IS FATHER TO THE MAN**
**CD:** Released '88, on CBS by CBS Records. Catalogue no: **30DP 303**
**Album:** Released Jul '68, on CBS by CBS Records. Deleted '73. Catalogue no: **63296**

**CLASSIC BLOOD SWEAT AND TEARS**
Tracks: / You've made me so very happy / I can't quit her / Go down gamblin' / Hi de ho / Sometimes in the winter / Without her / When I die / Spinning wheel / Lisa / Listen to me / Smiling phases / I love you more than you'll ever know / Lucretia MacEvil / God bless the child.
**Album:** Released Jun '80, on CBS by CBS Records. Deleted '85. Catalogue no: **CBS 31824**

**GREATEST HITS: BLOOD, SWEAT AND TEARS**
Tracks: / Spinning wheel / I can quit her / Go down gamblin' / God bless the child / Hi-de-ho.
**Album:** Released Jul '83, on CBS by CBS Records. Deleted '85. Catalogue no: **CBS 32159**
**CD:** Released Nov '87, on CBS by CBS Records. Catalogue no: **CD 64803**

**LATIN FIRE**
**Cass:** Released Oct '85, on Platinum (W.Germany) Catalogue no: **PMC 25**
**Album:** Released Oct '85, on Platinum (W.Germany) Catalogue no: **PLP 25**

**MIDNIGHT CONCERT**
**Album:** Released '88, on Masters (Holland) Catalogue no: **MA 25884**
**Cass:** Released Dec '88, on Masters (Holland) Catalogue no: **MAMC 925884**

**NUCLEAR BLUES**
Tracks: / Agitato / Nuclear blues / Manic depression / I'll drown in my own tears / Fantasy stage / Spanish wine / Latin fire / Challenge, The / Duel, The / Amor.
**Album:** Released Sep '89, on Big Time by Mainline Records. Catalogue no **2215235**
**Album:** Released Apr '80, on MCA by MCA Records. Deleted '85. Catalogue no: **MCF 3061**
**Cass:** Released Sep '89, on Big Time by Mainline Records. Catalogue no: **211 523 5**

**NUCLEAR BLUES (SINGLE)**
Tracks: / Nuclear blues / Agitato / Drowning in my own tears (Only on 12" single.).
**7" Single:** Released Mar '80, on MCA by MCA Records. Deleted '83. Catalogue no: **MCA 569**
**12" Single:** Released Mar '80, on MCA by MCA Records. Deleted '83. Catalogue no: **MCAT 569**

**YOU'VE MADE ME SO VERY HAPPY**
Tracks: / You've made me so very happy.
**7" Single:** Released Jul '84, on CBS by CBS Records. Deleted Jul '87. Catalogue no: **A 4576**
**7" Single:** Released Apr '69, on CBS by CBS Records. Deleted '72. Catalogue no: **CBS 4116**

## Blount, Chris

**CHRIS BLOUNT'S NEW ORLEANS JAZZ BAND (Blount, Chris New Orleans Jazz Band)**
**Album:** Released 8 Apr '89, on GHB by Jazzology Records (USA). Catalogue no: **GHB 234**

**LIVE AT THE KENDAL JAZZ FESTIVAL**
Tracks: / Hindustan / Wabash blues / Lily of the valley / Just a closer walk with thee / Collegiate / My old kentucky home / Take my hand / Precious Lord / Old grey bonnet / In the upper garden / I can't escape from you / Red wing.
Note: With Sonny Morris, Colin Bowden.
**Cass:** Released Apr '88, on Lake by Lake Records. Catalogue no: **LA 5009C**
**Album:** Released Apr '88, on Lake by Lake Records. Catalogue no: **LA 5009**

**MAYBE ANOTHER DAY (Blount, Chris New Orleans Jazz Band) (See panel on next page)**
Tracks: / Bugle boy march / Honey swat blues / My life will be sweeter / Eyes of Texas, The / Does Jesus care / It's a sin to tell a lie / I ain't gonna give nobody none of... / Plaisir d'amour / Yaaka hula hickey dula / Franklin St blues / If I had my life to live over / Ole miss rag.
Note: Bill Dickens (trumpet), Jeff Milner (trombone), Chris Blount (clarinet), Dave Brennan (banjo), Harry Slater (bass), Mike Ellis (drums).
Back in the 1940's when George Lewis and the Bunk Johnson band were making jazz history at the Stuyvesant Casino in New York and revivalist New Orleans Jazz, via Bill Russell's famous American Music '78's, was spreading the news around the world, eventually, as far away as Derby in the Midlands the receptive ears of a fifteen year old Chris

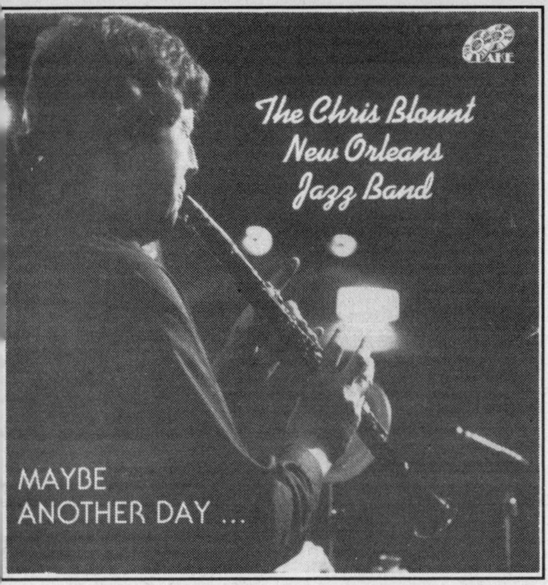


Chris Blount - Maybe Another Day (Lake)

Blount were absorbing the message of this music. I had already experienced the very special sound of the American Music sessions a few years before and wrote down my impressions in a letter to Dorothy Tate, George Lewis's manager.
The emergence of George Avakian's reviews of the first Bunks with George Lewis on clarinet excited us here in Britain. When the records finally arrived - some smashed during the journey - the recording technique was rough and the balance questionable after the clarity and expert handling of the 1929 Mortons and Olivers. But we were particularly thrilled by the purity of the clarinet playing, and the smearing foundation of Jim Robinson's trombone ... and we learned, perhaps for the first time, that true native New Orleans jazz had laws all of its own. The impact of the American Music session's opened a whole new chapter in jazz appreciation which, in a few short years, spread all over the world, particularly in Britain, where the Guv'nor, Ken Colyer, headed a musical revival which still goes on, especially in Derby where the Chris Blount New Orleans Jazz Band have kept alive the revivalist style for a quarter of a century and this album is a sincere and delightful tribute to a beautiful style of jazz. Chris Blount has led a band for around 25 years, working throughout that period as a professional chef. He also plays as a member of Dave Brennan's band and regularly as a part of the Heritage New Orleans Parade Band.
Bill Dickens began playing trumpet in the late 1950's and owes his introduction to the music - as do so many of his contemporaries - to the early influence of Ken Colyer and has been to New Orleans on two occasions. His passion for the Bill Russell American Music records and the work of such Crescent City veterans as Kid Ory, Bunk and Lewis brought him into contact with Chris Blount back in 1976. He became the band's regular trumpet player in the 'eighties. A carpenter by trade he professes more than a passing interest in motor racing, photography and architecture. Trombonist Jeff Milner also discovered New Orleans music in the fifties and fronted his own band for 20 years. He has paid several visits to the Crescent City marched in the Olympia Brass Band, blew on a number of sessions with Ernie Cagnollatti and, most significantly, with his idol, Jim Robinson. Working as a carpenter he loves roaming the hills and dales of Yorkshire and recently was a member of a mountain rescue team. Dave Brennan is the band's banjo player, a founder member of the Heritage New Orleans Parade Band and leader of his own band. Apart from his many musical commitments he works as an engineering manager and broadcasts weekly on BBC Radio Sheffield with his own *Now you has jazz* programme.
Harry Slater, like Dave Brennan found his way into jazz by playing in various local skiffle groups in the fifties. He joined the Blount band in 1976 and remains as devoted to the music as the rest of this fine band - he has also made the pilgrimage to New Orleans. He drives Heavy Goods Vehicles for a living and somehow manages to brew his own wine, fish, breed cage birds and tramp the Derbyshire dales in what spare time he can find. Mike Ellis is the drummer and professes a wider experience. After playing in the station R.A.F. band during National Service he worked in London in a variety of gigs, including theatre pit orchestra, coffee bars, package tours plus a long stint on a Cunard liner as a bonus. He has now worked with the Blound band for 18 years and does not wish to play any other form of music. His favourite drummers are Joe Watkins, Cie Frazier and our own Barry 'Kid' Martyn. He now owns and runs a nursing home and spends most of his spare time on the golf links. This record is a further milestone in the story of this remarkable New Orleans group from the Midlands. Their first album was recorded in 1981 and was No.5 in the Melody Maker monthly top ten jazz record releases and recieved an award from the Music Trades Association for the most outstanding jazz recording of 1981. It is now scheduled to be released in the States on George Buck's GHB label. This is honest music from a group of musicians who give a collective contribution to a form of music to which they have unswerving loyalty, love and commitment. (James Asman, London 1986
**Album:** Released Nov '86, on Lake by Lake Records. Catalogue no: **LA 5005**
**Cass:** Released Sep '87, on Lake by Lake Records. Catalogue no: **LA 5005C**

**TELL ME YOUR DREAMS (Blount, Chris New Orleans Jazz Band)**
**Album:** Released Oct '86, on Rainbow Sound Catalogue no: **RSL 142**

## Blue Bop

**BLUE BOP (Various artists)**
Tracks: / Dem tambourines: *Wilkerson, Don* / True blue: *Brooks, Tina* / Jeannie: *Byrd, Donald* / So tired: *Blakey, Art* / Nica's dream: *Silver, Horace* / Happy Johnny: *Wilkerson, Don.*
Note: Artists include: Don Wilkerson, Tina Brooks, Donald Byrd, Art Blakey, Horace Silver.
**Album:** Released Oct '86, on Blue Note by EMI Records. Deleted Jun '89. Catalogue no: **BNSLP 2**
**Cass:** Released Oct '86, on Blue Note by EMI Records. Deleted Nov '88. Catalogue no: **TC BNSLP 2**

## Blue Bossa

**BLUE BOSSA (Latin for beginners) (Various artists)**
Tracks: / Congalegre: *Parlan, Horace* / Latona: *Patton, Big John* / Back down to the tropics: *Rouse, Charlie* / Sandalia dela: *Pearson, Duke* / Afrodisia: *Dorham, Kenny* (MONO track) / Mambo Inn: *Green, Grant* / Cape Verdean blues, The: *Silver, Horace* / You're everything: *McRae, Carmen.*
Note: Transfer engineer: Ron McMaster All tracks are stereo except 'Afrodisia' which is presented in its original form.

**Cass:** Released Jun '86, on Blue Note by EMI Records. Deleted Jun '88. Catalogue no: **TC BNSLP 1**
**Album:** Released Jun '86, on Blue Note by EMI Records. Catalogue no: **BNSLP 1**

**BLUE BOSSA II (Various artists)**
Tracks: / Recado bossa nova: *Mobley, Hank* / Samba de Orfeu: *Rouse, Charlie* / Mira: *Hill, Andrew* / Stormy: *Pearson, Duke* / South of the border: *Donaldson, Lou* / Brazil: *Green, Grant* / Ghana: *Byrd, Donald* / Old devil moon: *Johnson, J J.*
**Cass:** Released Aug '87, on Blue Note by EMI Records. Deleted Nov '88. Catalogue no: **TC-BNSLP 4**
**Album:** Released Sep '87, on Blue Note by EMI Records. Deleted Jun '89. Catalogue no: **BNSLP 4**

## Blue Note...

**BLUE NOTE 50TH ANNIVERSARY SET (Various artists)**
Note: Box set containing:- Vol. 1-From Boogie To Bop 1939-1956/Vol. 2-The Jazz Message 1956-1965/Vol. 3-Funk & Blues 1956-1967/Vol. 4-Outside In 1964-1989/Vol. 5-Lighting The Fuse 1970-1989.
**CD Set:** Released Jul '89, on Blue Note by EMI Records. Catalogue no: **CDB1 92547**
**CD Set:** Released Jul '89, on Blue Note by EMI Records. Catalogue no: **CDS 792 547 2**
**LP Set:** Released Jul '89, on Blue Note by EMI Records. Catalogue no: **B1 92547**

**BLUE NOTE '86 (Various artists)**
**Album:** Released Aug '86, on Blue Note by EMI Records. Deleted Jun '88. Catalogue no: **BQ 85127**

**BLUE NOTE SAMPLER VOL.2 (Various artists)**
Tracks: / Better days: *Reeves, Dianne* / Timothee: *Lagrene, Bireli* / Ally the wallygator: *Smith, Tommy* / Eleanor Rigby: *Jordan, Stanley* / Thinkin' about your body: *McFerrin, Bobby* / Two's and fews: *Ammons, Albert & Meade Lux Lewis* / Donna: *Davis, Miles* / Glass enclosure: *Powell, Bud* / Alligator bogaloo: *Donaldson, Lou* / Song for my father: *Silver, Horace.*
**Cass:** Released Jul '89, on Blue Note by EMI Records. Catalogue no: **TCBNX 2**
**CD:** Released Jul '89, on Blue Note by EMI Records. Catalogue no: **CDBNX 2**
**Album:** Released Jul '89, on Blue Note by EMI Records. Catalogue no: **BNX 2**
**CD:** Released Jul '89, on Blue Note by EMI Records. Catalogue no: **CDP 792 812 2**

**BLUE NOTE SAMPLER VOL.3 (Various artists)**
**Album:** Released Jun '80, on Blue Note by EMI Records. Deleted '85. Catalogue no: **UALP 21**

**ONE NIGHT WITH BLUE NOTE VOL. 1 (Various artists)**
Note: Running time: 59 mins. First part of a celebratory concert held on behalf of the Blue Note Jazz label in New York, by many of its artists.
**VHS:** Released Aug '85, on PMI by EMI Records. Catalogue no: **MVP 99 1090 2**
**Beta:** Released Aug '85, on PMI by EMI Records. Deleted '88. Catalogue no: **MXP 99 1090 4**
**VHS:** Released Mar '90, on PMI by EMI Records. Catalogue no: **MVA 007**

**ONE NIGHT WITH BLUE NOTE VOL. 2 (Various artists)**
Note: Running time: 55 mins. Second part of a celebratory concert held on behalf of the Blue Note Jazz label in New York, by many of its artists.
**VHS:** Released May '86, on PMI by EMI Records. Catalogue no: **MVP 99 1091 2**

## Blue Note Jazzband

**BLUE NOTE JAZZBAND**
**Album:** Released Jul '88, on Saydisc by Amon Ra Records. Catalogue no: **SDL 288**

## Bluebird Sampler

**BLUEBIRD SAMPLER (Various artists)**
Tracks: / Sweetheart of Sigmund Freud: *Rogers, Shorty & His Orchestra & Giants* / Just a mood: *Norvo, Red* / Salt peanuts: *Powell, Bud* / Evans: *Blakey, Art\Jazz Messengers* / Tijuana gift shop: *Mingus, Charles* / Ill wind: *Desmond, Paul* / Bridge, The: *Rollins, Sonny* / Swingin' 'til the girls come home: *Lambert, Hendricks...* / Runnin' wild: *Goodman, Benny Quartet* / As you make your bed: *Sextet of Orchestra USA* / Stratusphunk: *Johnson, Jay Jay* / Song after sundown, A: *Getz, Stan* / Figurine: *Hodges, Johnny* / Blood count: *Ellington, Duke* / Sunset bell: *Burton, Gary.*
**CD:** Released Apr '88, on Bluebird (2) by BMG Records (UK). Deleted Jul '89. Catalogue no: **ND 86389**

**BLUEBIRD SAMPLER 88 (Various artists)**
Tracks: / Pearls, The: *Morton, Jelly Roll* / Down south camp meeting: *Goodman, Benny & His Orchestra* / Where or when: *Goodman, Benny Trio* / (When you) squeeze me: *Waller, Fats* / When lights are low: *Hampton, Lionel* / Body and soul: *Hawkins, Coleman* / Relaxin' at the Touro: *Spanier, Muggsy* / Concerto for cootie: *Ellington, Duke* / Little jazz: *Shaw, Artie & his Orchestra* / Rockin' chair: *Armstrong, Louis* / Somebody loves me: *Cohn, Al & Zoot Sims* / Concerto for Billy the Kid: *Russell, George* / Every night: *Williams, Joe* / Cottage for sale: *Hines, Earl* / Joy spring: *Evans, Gil* / Early autumn: *Herman, Woody* / Marnie: *Barbieri, Gato* / King Porter stomp: *Air.*
**CD:** Released Nov '88, on Bluebird (2) by BMG Records (UK). Catalogue no: **ND 88337**

## Blues...

**Biographical details:** Blues A genre created by Americans of African descent, one of the few new art forms of modern times, also (paradoxically) true folk music, its development com pleted shortly after 1900. Jazz include a greater European element, while blue remained relatively unsophisticated, a cessible to untrained players and si gers, whose art was in subtle but dire communication. Ex-slaves sang as the worked; the inexorable rhythm of wo songs, with lyrics full of irony and earth imagery became a commentary on dai life and love, and a relief of tension. Th classic blues is a 12- bar form, thre lines of four bars each; the lyric is couplet with the first line repeated onc each line of lyric takes about 2.5 bar the rest of each 4-bar segment bein improvised fill, sometimes vocal, usual instrumental on the singer's own guit or piano. The form has been further de veloped by many artists: 13-bar blue are not uncommon; it used to be sai that songs such as W.C. Handy's *Louis Blues* were not really blues, bu such distinctions now seem unneces ary. Blues are contrary to European mu sical practice, was therefore frowne upon by educated blacks (who were als taught that polyphonic music was in vented in Renaissance Europe, whil Africans had practised it for centuries Blues are played not in major or mino but in a 'blue mode'; the off-pitch 'blu notes' cannot be played on the pian and are now thought to be more or les direct from African music. The first pub lished blues appeared in 1912 (*Dalla Blues* and Handy's *Memphis Blues*), bu Bill Broonzy claimed that some of hi blues dated to 1890; the first blues rec ord was Mamie Smith's version of Perr Bradford's *Crazy Blues* in 1920, a su prise hit that discovered a new marke Great female blues singers included th Smiths, not related: Mamie, Clara, Trixi and Bessie, the greatest of all: Victori Spivey, Ida Cox, Ma Rainey, man more, accompanied on piano by Jame P.Johnson, Fats Waller, Fletcher Her derson, many others; Louis Armstron and other jazz greats were sidemen o records. A pattern of fractured family lif resulting from slavery followed by institu tionalised racism meant that male blue singers were itinerant, accompanyin themselves on guitar and often recorde in the field by talent scouts and re searchers; they led hard lives and ofte died young, such as Robert Johnso (perhaps the greatest of all), Charlie Pa ton and Blind Lemon Jefferson. So House and Bukka White also came fron the Mississippi Delta; Tommy Johnson Peetie Wheatstraw and many more ha a profound effect on post-war pop musi decades after they died, thanks to rec ords. Blind Boy Fuller, Sonny Terry Brownie McGhee and Gary Davis repre sented the more delicate Piedmont tradi tion of the Southeast USA. Instrumenta blues piano enjoyed a vogue in the '40s called boogie-woogie; Memphis Slim (Peter Chatman) and Roosevelt Sykes played piano and wrote and sang classic songs, with guitarists John Lee Hooke and Lightnin' Hopkins becoming leg ends in their own lifetimes. Musicians like Patton, Snooks Eaglin, Mance Lipsome and Mississippi John Hurt were all round entertainers, influenced as much by ragtime and other styles as by blues. Leroy Carr played piano and sang a smoother, urban style in the 1930s, influencing later black styles. The emergence of the Count Basie Band and others from Kansas City in the late 1930s gave a powerful reinjection of blues into the big-band jazz of the Swing Era; partly for this reason, post-war bop had a strong blues element for all its technical sophistication; in '50s-60s small-group 'blowing sessions' from labels like Prestige and Blue Note always included a blues: the blues is not jazz but the best jazz had blues in it. Rhythm & Blues began in the 1940s, influenced equally by the Swing Era and the blues: this black pop/party music was imitated by '50s rock 'n' rollers. Muddy Waters went to Chicago in '43; urban blues emerged as performers adopted microphones and electric guitars in order to be heard in noisy taverns: a Chicago scene of great power developed with Waters, Willie Dixon, Walter Horton, Little Walter, James Coton, Otis Rush, Howlin' Wolf, Otis Spann, J.B. Hutto, Magic Sam, Johnny Shines and many others; inspired by country blues artists of '20s-30s mentioned above, their own post-war work in Chicago was imitated in the '60s by a new generation of rock bands and singers: tours and imported records inspired a London scene that threw up Alexis Korner, John Mayall, then the Rolling Stones, thus having a profound impact on pop music of the last 20 years. Beginning in the late '50s whites in USA like Paul Butterfield, John Koerner, John Hammond and Dave Van Ronk worked hard at playing authentic blues styles: at the Newport Folk Festival in1965 folkies booed Bob Dylan, appearing with Butterfield's electric band, but accepted the band separately because they had never heard electric blues before; despite a foolishly insulting introduction from Alan Lomax, Michael Bloomfield's guitar did not fail to impress: Lomax thought he was an expert on the blues but had apparently never heard a southside Chicago tavern band. From the 1960s younger black Chicagoans like Junior Wells, Buddy Guy Jimmy Dawkins and Houndog Taylor held down the scene; B.B.King began at a Memphis radio station in the late 1940s, worked the 'chitlin circuit' for years and emerged as the most highly regarded living bluesman (Albert King and Freddie King were also highly rated; may or may not have been related). As the blues were worked to death by rock 'n' rollers (leading to heavy metal, whose lack of subtlety is a vulgar antithesis), Texans Albert Collins and Johnny Copeland and in the '80s Robert Cray (born in Georgia, raised in Washington state) have emerged as new keepers of the flame. White guitarists such as Roy Buchanan and Johnny Winter have never strayed far from the blues; in the mid-'80s Otis Rush was recording again, Earl King was backed on an album by the white band Roomful of Blues; white bands like the Fabulous Thunderbirds and Kingsnake carried on with love for the music, and new black talents like Cray and Walter 'Wolfman' Washington seem to transcend the category, while Koko Taylor and Big Twist are going strong, and Lil' Ed and the Blues Imperials (two of whom are Hutto's nephews) are the latest blues sensation. (Donald Clarke 23 August 1988).

## 24 GEANTS DU BLUES (Various artists)

**2 LP Set:** Released Oct '88, on Vogue by Vogue Records. Catalogue no: **400037**

## 100 MINUTES OF BLUES

**Cass:** Released Jun '82, on PRT (100 Minute Series) Catalogue no: **ZCTON 117**

## BEST OF THE BLUES AND JAZZ (Various artists)

Tracks: / On the sunny side...: *Various artists* / Oh lady be good: *Basie, Count* / I smell trouble: *Bland, Bobby* / Mood indigo: *Ellington, Duke* / Tisket a tasket, A: *Fitzgerald, Ella* / How high the moon: *Hampton, Lionel* / Quintessence: *Jones, Quincy* / Blue room: *Rollins, Sonny* / Sweet little angel: *King, B.B.* / My home is on the delta: *Spann, Otis* / Cherry red: *Turner, Joe* / I wonder why: *Hooker, John Lee* / Poor man: *McGhee,Brownie/Sonny Terry* / Stormy Monday: *Walker, T-Bone* / I don't know why: *Witherspoon, Jimmy* / I ain't from Chicago: *Reed, Jimmy* / Sent for you yesterday: *Rushing, Jimmy.*

**Album:** Released Oct '87, on MCA by MCA Records. Catalogue no: **MCL 1862**

**Cass:** Released Oct '87, on MCA by MCA Records. Catalogue no: **MCLC 1862**

## BIG BAND VOL.1

**Album:** Released Apr '82, on Fonitcetra Deleted Apr '87. Catalogue no: **VDL 1001**

## BIG BAND VOL.2

**Album:** Released Apr '82, on Fonitcetra Deleted Apr '87. Catalogue no: **VDL 1002**

## BIG BAND VOL. 5

**Album:** Released '88, on Joker (USA) by Lifetime Records (USA). Catalogue no: **SM 3951**

## BLUES (Various artists)

**CD:** Released Dec '87, on In-Market Catalogue no: **DRIVE 3015**

## BLUES - 1923 TO 1933, THE (Jazz classics in digital stereo) (Various artists)

Tracks: / Give me a break blues: *Cox, Ida (with Jesse Crump)* / Nothin' but the blues: *Gibson, Cleo (with her Hot Three)* / Barrel house blues: *Henderson, Scott* / Midnight mama: *Hereford, Frances (with the Levee Serenaders)* / Kansas City blues: *Memphis Jug Band* / Prove it on me blues: *Rainey, Ma (with her Tub Jug Washboard Band)* / Be on your merry way: *Ringgold, Issie* / Blue yodel no. 9: *Rodgers, Jimmie (with Louis and Lil armstrong)* / Nobody knows you (when you're down and out): *Smith, Bessie* / Jenny's ball: *Smith, Mamie* / Moaning the blues: *Spivey, Victoria* / I've got what it takes: *Webster, Margaret (with clarence William's Washboard Band)* / That thing's done been put on me: *Whitmire, Margaret (with Arnold Wiley)* / He used to be your man: *Wilson, Lena (with the Nubian Five).*

**Cass:** Released Jul '88, on BBC by BBC Records & Tapes. Catalogue no: **ZCF 683**

**CD:** Released Jul '88, on BBC by BBC Records & Tapes. Catalogue no: **BBC CD 683**

**Album:** Released Jul '88, on BBC by BBC Records & Tapes. Catalogue no: **REB 683**

## BLUES - A REAL SUMMIT MEETING, THE (Various artists)

Tracks: / Little red rooster: *Thornton, Big Mama* / Ball & chain: *Thornton, Big Mama* / Clean head blues: *Vinson, Eddie "Cleanhead"* / Back door blues: *Vinson, Eddie "Cleanhead"* / Kidney stew: *Vinson, Eddie "Cleanhead"* / That's alright mama: *Crudup, Arthur 'Big Boy'* / Honkey tonk train blues: *Glen, Lloyd* / After hours: *Glen, Lloyd* / Pinetop's boogie woogie: *Glen, Lloyd* / Long distance call: *Waters, Muddy* / Wheres my woman been: *Waters, Muddy* / Got my mojo working: *Waters, Muddy* / Drifter, The: *Brown, Clarence* / Please Mr. Nixon: *Brown, Clarence* / Outside help: *King, B.B.* / Smooth sailing: *McShann, Jay* / Confeein' the blues: *McShann, Jay.*

**Cass:** Released '88, on Charly by Charly Records. Catalogue no: **TCCDX 34**

**2 LP Set:** Released '88, on Charly by Charly Records. Catalogue no: **CDX 34**

**CD:** Released Oct '88, on Charly by Charly Records. Catalogue no: **CDCHARLY 135**

## BLUES ALBUM VOL.1 (Various artists)

Tracks: / Don't Start Me To Talkin': *Various artists* / First time I met the blues: *Various artists* / Worried Life Blues: *Various artists* / My Babe: *Various artists* / Walkin' The Boogie: *Various artists* / Hoochie coochie man: *Various artists* / Reconsider Baby: *Various artists* / Smokestack lightning: *Various artists* / Juke: *Various artists* / When The Lights Go Out: *Various artists* / Just make love to me: *Various artists* / Spoonful: *Various artists.*

**CD:** Released May '88, on Arcade Deleted Dec '88. Catalogue no: **01125061**

## BLUES ALBUM VOL.2 (Various artists)

**CD:** Released May '88, on Arcade Deleted Dec '88. Catalogue no: **01225061**

## BLUES AND THE ABSTRACT TRUTH (Various artists)

Tracks: / Stolen moments: *Various artists* / Hoe down: *Various artists* / Cas-

cades: *Various artists* / Yearnin': *Various artists* / Butch butch: *Various artists* / Teenie's blues: *Various artists.*
Note: Featuring : Bill Evans, Roy Hanes, Oliver Nelson, Eric Dolphy, Paul Chambers and Freddie Hubbard.
**Album:** Released Jun '82, on Jasmine by Hasmick Promotions. Deleted Feb '88. Catalogue no: **JAS 20**
**Cass:** Released Jun '82, on Jasmine by Hasmick Promotions. Catalogue no: **JAS C20**

**BLUES AS BIG AS TEXAS, VOL 1 (Various artists)**
Note: With, among others, Johnny Copeland, Jimmy "T99" Nelson.
**Album:** Released Jul '88, on Home Cooking (USA) by Flat Town Music Co.(USA). Catalogue no: **HCS 106**
**Cass:** Released Jul '88, on Home Cooking (USA) by Flat Town Music Co.(USA). Catalogue no: **HCS 106 TC**

**BLUES EP, THE (Various artists)**
Tracks: / Help me: *Various artists* / I just wanna make love to you: *Various artists* / My babe: *Various artists* / Smokestack lightning: *Various artists.*
**7" Single:** Released Jul '85, on Chess (PRT) Deleted '88. Catalogue no: **CHES 4008**

**BLUES FROM GEORGIA (Various artists)**
**Album:** Released Oct '88, on Roots (Germany) Catalogue no: **RL 309**

**BLUES GIRLS FROM THE '40'S (Various artists)**
**Album:** Released Apr '85, on Pathe Marconi (France) Catalogue no: **PM 1561421**

**BLUES IN THE BOTTLE (Various artists)**
Tracks: / Blues in the bottle: *Holy Modal Rounders* / Baby Please Don't Go: *Rush* / Pretty boy Floyd: *Elliott* / Sometimes I feel like a motherless child: *Van Ronk, Dave* / He Was a Friend of Mine: *Schmidt (composer)* / House of Carpenter, The: *Van Ronk, Dave* / Junco Partner: *Holy Modal Rounders* / Duncan Brady: *Rush* / Candy Man: *Nelson, Tracy* / Death Letter Blues: *Van Ronk, Dave* / Barbry Allen: *Rush* / So Long It's Been Good To Know: *Elliott* / Long John: *Van Ronk, Dave* / Down On Me: *Schmidt (composer)* / Alabama Bound: *Rush* / Cuckoo, The: *Elliott* / Good gin blues: *Muldair.*
**CD:** Released 25 Apr '88, on Big Beat by Ace Records. Catalogue no: **CDWIK 71**
**Album:** Released 25 Apr '88, on Big Beat by Ace Records. Catalogue no: **WIK 71**

**BLUES VOL 1, THE (Various artists)**
Tracks: / Don't start me to talkin': *Williamson, Sonny Boy* / First time I met the blues: *Guy, Buddy* / Worried life blues: *Berry, Chuck* / My baby: *Little Walter* / Juke: *Little Walter* / Walkin' the boogie: *Hooker, John Lee* / Hoochie coochie man: *Waters, Muddy* / Just make love to me: *Waters, Muddy* / Reconsider baby: *Fulson, Lowell* / Smokestack: *Howlin' Wolf* / Spoonful: *Howlin' Wolf* / When the lights go out: *Witherspoon, Jimmy.*
**Album:** Released Apr '87, on Chess by Vogue Records. Catalogue no: **GCH 8027**
**CD:** Released Jun '88, on MCA (USA) by MCA Records (USA). Catalogue no: **31262**
**Cass:** Released Apr '87, on Chess by Vogue Records. Catalogue no: **GCHK 78027**

**BLUES VOL 2, THE (Various artists)**
Tracks: / Thirty days: *Berry, Chuck* / Wee wee hours: *Berry, Chuck* / Sugar mama: *Hooker, John Lee* / Evil: *Howlin' Wolf* / Got my mojo working: *Waters, Muddy* / I'm a man: *Diddley, Bo* / Blues with a key to the highway: *Little Walter* / Key to the highway: *Little Walter* / It's ain't no secret: *Witherspoon, Jimmy* / Ten years ago: *Guy, Buddy* / So many roads: *Rush, Otis.*
**Album:** Released Oct '87, on Chess by Vogue Records. Catalogue no: **GCH 8035**
**Cass:** Released Oct '87, on Chess by Vogue Records. Catalogue no: **GCHK 78035**
**CD:** Released Jun '88, on MCA (USA) by MCA Records (USA). Catalogue no: **31263**

**BLUES VOL 3, THE (Various artists)**
**Album:** Released '82, on Big Bear by Big Bear Records. Deleted '88. Catalogue no: **BDUB 1**

**BLUES VOL 4, THE (Various artists)**
Tracks: / I've been down so long: *Various artists* / Every jug stands on its own bottom: *Various artists* / I wish you would: *Various artists* / Fool is what you wanted, A: *Various artists* / Chicken head: *Various artists* / Seems like a million years: *Various artists* / Gamblin' man: *Various artists* / Make your bed up mamma: *Various artists* / I'm a root man: *Various artists* / I can't lose with the stuff I use: *Various artists* / Letter dressed in red, A: *Various artists* / Leavin' Kansas City: *Various artists* / New York, New York: *Various artists* / Hazel: *Various artists* / Dangerous woman: *Various artists* / I feel so fine: *Various artists* / Blue midnight: *Various artists* / Sloppy drunk: *Various artists* / You're never too old to boogie: *Various artists* / Crossroads: *Various artists* / Hard luck blues: *Various artists* / Bury me back in the USA: *Various artists* / After hours: *Various artists* / Sassy: *Various artists.*
**Album:** Released '82, on Big Bear by Big Bear Records. Deleted '88. Catalogue no: **BDUB 2**

**BLUES WITH A DIFFERENCE (Various artists)**
**CD:** Released '88, on Rounder (USA) by Rounder Records (USA). Catalogue no: **CDS 4**

**BLUES-THE BRITISH CONNECTION (Various artists)**
**Cass:** Released Apr '86, on Decca by Decca International. Catalogue no: **KTBC 88**
**Album:** Released Apr '86, on Decca by Decca International. Catalogue no: **TAB 88**

**CENTRAL MISSISSIPPI BLUES (Various artists)**
**Album:** Released '88, on Wolf Catalogue no: **WSE 130**

**EAGLE OF THE USA, THE (San Francisco Blues Serenaders)**
**Album:** Released '88, on Merry Makers Catalogue no: **MMRC 107**

**FROM NEW ORLEANS TO CHICAGO VOL. 3**
**Album:** Released '88, on Joker (USA) by Lifetime Records (USA). Catalogue no: **SM 3949**

**GREAT VOCALISTS VOL. 6**
**Album:** Released '88, on Joker (USA) by Lifetime Records (USA). Catalogue no: **SM 3952**

**HOUSTON GHETTO BLUES (Various artists)**
**Album:** on Flyright by Interstate Music. Catalogue no: **FLY 527**

**LOW BLOWS (An anthology of Chicago harmonica blues) (Various artists)**
**Album:** Released Oct '88, on Rooster (USA) Catalogue no: **R 7610**

**NATIONAL DOWNHOME BLUES FESTIVAL VOL.1 (Various artists)**
Note: with Sunnyland Slim/T. Burt/F. Edwards etc.
**Album:** Released Mar '87, on Southland by Delta Records. Catalogue no: **SLP 21**

**NATIONAL DOWNHOME BLUES FESTIVAL VOL.2 (Various artists)**
**Album:** Released Mar '87, on Southland by Delta Records. Catalogue no: **SLP 22**

**NATIONAL DOWNHOME BLUES FESTIVAL VOL.3 (Various artists)**
**Album:** Released Mar '87, on Southland by Delta Records. Catalogue no: **SLP 23**

**NATIONAL DOWNHOME BLUES FESTIVAL VOL.4 (Various artists)**
**Album:** Released Mar '87, on Southland by Delta Records. Catalogue no: **SLP 24**

**REAL BLUES, THE (Various artists)**
**Album:** Released '88, on Excello (USA) Catalogue no: **LP 8011**

**RIOT IN BLUES, A (Various artists)**
**CD:** on Mobile Fidelity Sound Lab(USA) by Mobile Fidelity Records (USA). Catalogue no: **MFCD 874**

**SOUL OF TEXAS BLUES WOMEN (Various artists)**
**Cass:** Released '88, on Home Cooking (USA) by Flat Town Music Co.(USA). Catalogue no: **HCS 108 TC**
**Album:** Released '88, on Home Cooking (USA) by Flat Town Music Co.(USA). Catalogue no: **HM 108**

**VINTAGE BLUES (Various artists)**
Tracks: / Kid man blues: *Various artists*

/ Cheating and lying blues: *Various artists* / Who's been fooling you: *Various artists* / War is over: *Various artists* / Whisky headed buddies: *Various artists* / Some day baby: *Various artists* / My love is down: *Various artists* / Sober: *Various artists* / My story blues: *Various artists* / My heart belongs to you: *Various artists* / Farewell little girl: *Various artists* / Broke and hungry: *Various artists* / Bobby sox blues: *Various artists* / Her little machine: *Various artists* / Give me mine now: *Various artists* / Better leave my man alone: *Various artists* / Drop down blues: *Various artists* / Wanita: *Various artists* / We got to win: *Various artists* / Sonny boys jump: *Various artists*.
**Album:** Released Jan '82, on RCA by BMG Records (UK). Deleted Jan '87. Catalogue no: **INTS 5099**
**Cass:** Released '84, on RCA International by BMG Records (UK). Catalogue no: **NK 89418**
**Album:** Released '84, on RCA International by BMG Records (UK). Deleted Nov '88. Catalogue no: **NL 89418**

## Blues Alive

### BLUES ALIVE (VIDEO) (Various artists)
Note: A reunion concert by John Mayall and former members of his Bluesbreakers like John McVie and Mick Taylor plus guest bluesmen Albert King, Buddy Guy and Junior Wells filmed in 1982. Running time: 58 mins.
**VHS:** Released Oct '84, on RCA by BMG Records (UK). Catalogue no: **RVT 10377**

## Blues Anthology

### BLUES ANTHOLOGY, VOL. 1 (Memphis Blues) (Various artists)
**Album:** Released '88, on Echo by Echo Records. Catalogue no: **ECB 801**

### BLUES ANTHOLOGY, VOL. 2 (More Memphis Blues) (Various artists)
**Album:** Released '88, on Echo by Echo Records. Catalogue no: **ECB 802**

### BLUES ANTHOLOGY, VOL. 3 (Real Chicago Blues) (Various artists)
**Album:** Released '88, on Echo by Echo Records. Catalogue no: **ECB 803**

### BLUES ANTHOLOGY, VOL. 4 (More From Chicago) (Various artists)
**Album:** Released '88, on Echo by Echo Records. Catalogue no: **ECB 804**

### BLUES ANTHOLOGY, VOL. 5 (blues From St. Louis) (Various artists)
**Album:** Released '88, on Echo by Echo Records. Catalogue no: **ECB 805**

## Blues Brothers

### BEST OF THE BLUES BROTHERS
Tracks: / Expressway / Everybody needs somebody to love / I don't know / She caught the Katy / Soul man / Rubber biscuit / Goin' back to Miami / Gimme some lovin' / B movie / Box car blues / Flip flop fly.
**CD:** Released Jun '89, on Atlantic by WEA Records. Catalogue no: **781 586-2**
**Album:** Released Jan '82, on Atlantic by WEA Records. Catalogue no: **K 50858**
**Cass:** Released Jun '89, on Atlantic by WEA Records. Catalogue no: **K 250858**

### BLUES BROTHERS (film soundtrack) (Various artists)
**VHS:** Released Feb '90, on CIC Video Catalogue no: **VHR 1382**
**Cass:** Released Oct '80, on Atlantic by WEA Records. Catalogue no: **K4 50715**
**Album:** Released Oct '80, on Atlantic by WEA Records. Catalogue no: **K 50715**
**CD:** Released Feb '87, on Atlantic by WEA Records. Catalogue no: **250 715**

### BRIEFCASE FULL OF BLUES
Tracks: / I can't turn you loose / Hey bartender / Messin' with the kid / I got everything I need almost / Shot gun blues / Rubber biscuit / Groove me / Soul man / Flip flop and fly / B movie box car blues.
**CD:** Released Mar '87, on Atlantic by WEA Records. Catalogue no: **250 556**
**Album:** Released '87, on Atlantic by WEA Records. Catalogue no: **K 50556**
**Cass:** Released '87, on Atlantic by WEA Records. Catalogue no: **K 450556**

### EVERYBODY NEEDS SOMEBODY TO LOVE
Tracks: / Everybody needs somebody to love / Think / Shotgun blues (Available on 12" format only.).
**12" Single:** Released Mar '90, on Atlantic by WEA Records. Catalogue no: **A 7951T**
**7" Single:** Released Oct '80, on Atlantic by WEA Records. Deleted Oct '83. Catalogue no: **K 11625**
**CD Single:** Released Mar '90, on Atlantic by WEA Records. Catalogue no: **A 7951CD**
**7" Single:** Released Mar '90, on Atlantic by WEA Records. Catalogue no: **A 7951**
**Cassingle:** Released Mar '90, on Atlantic by WEA Records. Catalogue no: **A 7951C**

### GIMME SOME LOVIN'
Tracks: / Gimme some lovin' / She caught me Katie.
**7" Single:** Released Jul '80, on Atlantic by WEA Records. Deleted '82. Catalogue no: **K 11499**

### MADE IN AMERICA
Tracks: / Soul finger / Funky Broadway / Who's making love / Do you love me / Guilty / Perry Mason (theme from) / Riot in cell block 9 / Green onions / I ain't got you / From the bottom / Going to Miami.
**CD:** Released Jun '89, on Atlantic by WEA Records. Catalogue no: **781 478-2**
**Cass:** Released Feb '81, on Atlantic by WEA Records. Catalogue no: **K4 50768**
**Album:** Released Feb '81, on Atlantic by WEA Records. Catalogue no: **K 50768**

### SOUL MAN
Tracks: / Soul man / Excusez moi mon cherie.
**7" Single:** Released Feb '79, on Atlantic by WEA Records. Deleted '82. Catalogue no: **K 11244**

## Blues Burglars

### BREAKIN' IN
Tracks: / Feels so good / Up and down the avenue / Sugar Mama / Shake your moneymaker / Built for comfort / Hoochie coochie man / Trouble no more / Don't start me to talking / Mojo working / Spaced out / Evening / Walkin' / Whoppin.
**Album:** Released Nov '86, on Red Lightnin' by Red Lightning Records. Deleted Jun '89. Catalogue no: **RL 070**

## Blues Came Down...

### BLUES CAME DOWN FROM MEMPHIS (Various artists)
Tracks: / Boogie disease, The: *Doctor Ross* / Juke box boogie: *Doctor Ross* / Come back baby: *Doctor Ross* / Chicago breakdown: *Doctor Ross* / Cotton crop blues: *Cotton, James* / Baker shop boogie: *Nix, Willie* / Seems like a million years: *Nix, Willie* / Bear cat: *Thomas, Rufus* / Tiger man: *Thomas, Rufus* / Take a little chance: *Deberry, Jimmy* / Time has made a change: *Deberry, Jimmy* / I feel so worried: *Lewis, Sammy & Willie Johnson* / So long baby goodbye: *Lewis, Sammy & Willie Johnson.*
**Album:** Released '77, on Charly by Charly Records. Catalogue no: **CR 30125**

### BLUES CAME DOWN FROM MEMPHIS (CD)(Various artists)
Tracks: / We all gotta go sometime: *Louis, Joe Hill* (Composer: Louis.) / She may be yours but she comes to see me somet: *Louis, Joe Hill* / Keep your arms around me: *Louis, Joe Hill* (Composer: Louis.) / Tiger man: *Thomas, Rufus* (Composer: Louis.) / Come back baby: *Doctor Ross* (Composer: Ross.) / That ain't right: *Doctor Ross* (Composers: Hill/Rose.) / Take a little chance: *Deberry, Jimmy* (Composers: DeBerry/Burns.) / Wolf call boogie: *Deberry, Jimmy* (Composer: Love.) / Easy: *Jimmy And Walter* (Composer: W. Horton.) / West winds are blowing: *Horton, Walter "Shakey"* (Composer: W. Horton.) / Walter's instrumental swing: *Horton, Walter "Shakey"* (Composer: W. Horton.) / Seems like a million years: *Nix, Willie* (Composers: Nix/Phillips.) / Baker shop boogie: *Nix, Willie* / Take a little walk with me: *Nix, Willie* (Composer: Nix.) / Bear cat: *Thomas, Rufus* (Composer: Phillips.) / Cotton crop blues: *Cotton, James* (Composer: Cotton.) / Feelin' good: *Little Junior's Blue Flames* (Composer: Parker.) / Mystery train: *Little Junior's Blue Flames* (Composer: Parker/Phillips.) / Love my baby: *Little Junior's Blue Flames* (Composer: Parker.) / Carry my business on: *Boines, Houston* (Composer: Boines.) / I feel so worried: *Lewis, Sammy* (Composer: Johnson.) / So long baby goodbye: *Johnson, Willie* / Hot shot love: *Deberry,*

*Jimmy.*
**CD:** Released Apr '87, on Charly by Charly Records. Catalogue no: **CDCHARLY 67**

## Blues Caravan

### BLUES CARAVAN
**Cass:** Released '88, on GNP Crescendo (USA) by GNP Crescendo Records (USA). Catalogue no: **GNP5 2178**
**Album:** Released '88, on GNP Crescendo (USA) by GNP Crescendo Records (USA). Catalogue no: **GNPS 2178**

## Blues Deluxe

### BLUES DELUXE (Various artists)
Tracks: / Clouds in my heart: *Blues Deluxe* / Hey bartender: *Taylor, Koko* / Wang dang doodle: *Dixon, Willie* / Sweet home Chicago: *Brooks, Lonnie* / Don't throw your love on me so strong: *Seals, Son* / You too might need a friend: *Young, Mighty Joe.*
Note: 'Blues Deluxe' was recorded live at the 1980 Chicagofest and featuring the best of Chicago blues, including Muddy Waters, Willie Dixon, Koko Taylor, Lonnie Brooks, Mighty Joe Young and Son Seals. Lonnie delivers a great performance of 'Sweet Home Chicago', Koko roars through 'Hey Bartender', Muddy sends shivers up your spine with 'Clouds of Joy' and Willie caps it all off with 'Wang Dang Doodle'. (Alligator catalogue 7/88)
**Album:** Released Jan '81, on Alligator (Sonet) by Alligator Records (USA). Catalogue no: **SNTF 859**

## Blues For Coltrane

### BLUES FOR COLTRANE (A Tribute) (Various artists)
**Album:** Released May '89, on MCA (Import) by MCA Records. Catalogue no: **MCA 42122**
**CD:** Released May '89, on MCA (Import) by MCA Records. Catalogue no: **MCAD 42122**

## Blues For You

### BLUES FOR YOU (Various artists)
Tracks: / Blues for you: *Various artists.*
**CD Single:** Released Jul '89, Catalogue no: **ALSCD 7958**

## Blues From...

### BLUES FROM BIG BILL'S COPACABANA (Various artists)
**Album:** Released Oct '85, on Vogue (France) by Vogue Records. Catalogue no: **515041**

### BLUES FROM SOUTH CAROLINA & GEORGIA 1924/32 (Various artists)
Tracks: / Boogie lovin': *Various artists* / Thirty days in jail: *Various artists* / Ding dong ring: *Various artists* / Pick and shovel captain: *Various artists* / Six months ain't no sentence: *Various artists* / Hard times hard times: *Various artists* / Trouble ain't nothin' but: *Various artists* / Down in the chain gang: *Various artists* / Prison bound blues: *Various artists* / Georgia chain gang: *Various artists* / Gonna leave from Georgia: *Various artists* / Black woman: *Various artists* / Shootin' craps and gamblin': *Various artists* / Nobody knows my name: *Various artists* / Been pickin' and shovellin': *Various artists.*
**Album:** Released May '84, on Heritage (USA) by Heritage Records (USA). Catalogue no: **HT 304**

### BLUES FROM THE WESTERN STATES (Various artists)
**Album:** Released Dec '88, on Yazoo (USA) by Shanachie Records (USA). Catalogue no: **L 1032**

## Blues From The Fields...

### BLUES FROM THE FIELDS TO THE TOWNS 1 (Various artists)
Tracks: / John Henry: *McGhee, Brownie & Sonny Terry* / Take this hammer: *McGhee, Brownie & Sonny Terry* / Snake: *Johnson, Luther* / Chicken shack: *Johnson, Luther* / Hobo blues: *Hooker, John Lee* / C.C. Rider: *Hooker, John Lee* / Everyday I have the blues: *Davis Blind John* / Bertha May: *Various artists* / Diggin' my potatoes: *Various artists* / Watch dog: *Various artists.*
**Cass:** Released Feb '83, on Fontana Import Catalogue no: **MF 990099**
**Album:** Released Feb '83, on Fontana Import Catalogue no: **F 90099**

### BLUES FROM THE FIELDS TO THE TOWNS 2 (Various artists)
Tracks: / Noted rider: *Leadbelly* / I brought you a brand new home: *Hooker, John Lee* / I believe I'll lose my mind: *Hooker, John Lee* / Worried life blues: *McGhee, Brownie & Sonny Terry* / Going down slow: *McGhee, Brownie & Sonny Terry* / C.C. rider: *Davis, Blind John* / Love 'n' trouble: *Johnson, Luther* / Love without jealousy: *Johnson, Luther* / This is a good time to write a song: *Various artists* / Three women blues: *Various artists* / Excuse me baby: *Various artists* / Mud in your ear: *Various artists.*
**Album:** Released May '83, on Fontana Import Catalogue no: **F 90134**
**Cass:** Released May '83, on Fontana Import Catalogue no: **MF 990134**

### BLUES FROM THE FIELDS TO THE TOWNS 3 (Various artists)
Tracks: / Dekalb woman: *Leadbelly* / Teasin' me: *Hooker, John Lee* / Time is marching: *Hooker, John Lee* / Right now: *McGhee, Brownie & Sonny Terry* / That good old Jelly Roll: *McGhee, Brownie & Sonny Terry* / How long blues: *Davis, Blind John* / I'm so glad: *Johnson, Luther* / Evil: *Johnson, Luther* / El Capitan: *Various artists* / Two of a kind: *Various artists* / Long distance call: *Various artists* / Sting it: *Various artists.*
**Album:** Released Jun '84, on Happy Bird (Germany) Catalogue no: **F 90142**
**Cass:** Released Jun '84, on Happy Bird (Germany) Catalogue no: **MF 90142**

## Blues Giants

### MASTERS OF JAZZ
**Album:** Released '83, on RCA (Germany) Catalogue no: **CL 42858**

## Blues Guitar

### BLUES GUITAR ALBUM (SET) (Various artists)
**2 LP Set:** Released Oct '88, on Vogue by Vogue Records. Catalogue no: **400027**

### BLUES GUITAR ALBUM (Various artists)
Tracks: / Girl you're nice and clean: *Guy buddy* / I'm a stranger: *Kirkland, Eddie* / Garbage man blues: *Guy, Phil* / Blues stomp: *Hound dog Taylor* / One room country shack: *Left hand Frank* / Honk Tonk: *Left hand Frank* / Lonsome blues: *Granderson, John Lee* / I was wrong: *Davis, Bobbay Trio*
**Album:** Released Feb '83, on JSP by JSP Records. Catalogue no: **JSP 1055**
**Album:** Released Mar '82, on JSP by JSP Records. Catalogue no: **JSP 1016**

### BLUES GUITAR BLASTERS (Various artists)
Tracks: / After hours: *Nolan, Jimmy* / Killing floor: *King, Albert* / You threw your love on me too strong: *King, Albert* / Talkin' woman: *Fulson, Lowell* / Everytime it rains: *Fulson, Lowell* / Early in the morning: *King, B.B.* / Talkin' the blues: *King, B.B.* / Dust my blues: *James, Elmore* / Elmo's shuffle: *James, Elmore* / Hawaiian boogie: *James, Elmore* / Jumpin' in the heart of town: *Thomas, Lafayette* / Certainly all: *Guitar Slim* / Things that I used to do, The: *Guitar Slim* / Twistin' the strings: *Turner, Ike* / 3 hours past midnight: *Watson, Johnny 'Guitar'* / Twinky: *Crayton, Pee Wee* / Mistreated so bad: *Crayton, Pee Wee* / Hey hey baby: *Walker, T-Bone* / I had a good girl: *Hooker, John Lee.*
**CD:** Released 30 Jan '88, on Ace by Ace Records. Catalogue no: **CDCH 232**
**Album:** Released Feb '88, on Ace by Ace Records. Catalogue no: **CHA 232**

## Blues Guitar Workshop

### BLUES GUITAR WORKSHOP (Various artists)
Tracks: / Black monk: *Various artists* / Cat's squirrel: *Various artists* / How come you do me like you do: *Various artists* / Buck dance: *Various artists* / Turnaround: *Various artists* / I just want to make love to you: *Various artists* / Always: *Various artists* / Panic room blues: *Various artists* / Morning star blues: *Various artists* / Forty ton parachute: *Various artists* / When I've been drinking: *Various artists* / Stroll: *Various artists* / Blake's rag: *Various artists* / Keep a bootin': *Various artists* / Clown: *Various artists.*
**Album:** Released Mar '89, on Kicking Mule by Sonet Records. Catalogue no: **KM 141**
**Album:** Released Jan '80, on Kicking Mule by Sonet Records. Deleted '88. Catalogue no: **SNKF 159**

## Blues In D Natural

### BLUES IN D NATURAL - ANTHOLOGY (Various artists)
Tracks: / Crying won't help you: *Night-*

hawk, *Robert* / Moon is rising, The: *Nighthawk, Robert* / Hawaiian boogie: *James, Elmore* / Early in the morning: *James, Elmore* / Hidden charms: *Clarke, Charles* / Row your boat: *Clarke, Charles* / Woman I love, The: *Homesick James* / Blues in D natural: *Hooker, Earl* / Tanya: *Hooker, Earl* / She likes to boogie real low: *Sims, Frankie Lee* / Southern woman: *Brown, Tommy* / Remember me: *Brown, Tommy* / I believe in a woman: *Williams, Sly* / Boot Hill: *Williams, Sly.*
**Album:** Released Apr '79, on Red Lightnin' by Red Lightning Records. Deleted Jun '89. Catalogue no: **RL 005**

## Blues In The Night

**BLUES IN THE NIGHT (Original London Cast) (Various artists)**
**CD:** Released Sep '87, on First Night by First Night Records. Catalogue no: **SCENE CD9**
**Album:** Released Sep '87, on First Night by First Night Records. Catalogue no: **SCENE 9**
**Cass:** Released Sep '87, on First Night by First Night Records. Catalogue no: **SCENE C 9**

## Blues Is Alright

**BLUES IS ALRIGHT 1 (Various artists)**
Tracks: / Down home blues: *Hill, Z.Z.* / Blues is alright, The: *Little Milton* / Your husband is cheatin' on us: *Lasalle, Denise* / End of the rainbow, The: *Mitchell, McKinley* / Misty blue: *Moore, Dorothy* / Lady, my whole world is you: *Lasalle, Denise* / Down home blues (x-rated): *Lasalle, Denise* / Two steps from the blues: *Bland, Bobby* / I'm a bluesman: *Hill, Z.Z.* / Bad risk: *Latimore.*
**Album:** Released Feb '86, on Malaco by Malaco Records (UK). Catalogue no: **MAL 7430**

**BLUES IS ALRIGHT 2 (Various artists)**
**Album:** Released Dec '86, on Malaco by Malaco Records (UK). Catalogue no: **MALP 010**

## Blues Is Killing

**BLUES IS KILLING (Various artists)**
**Album:** Released Apr '79, on Juke Joint Catalogue no: **JUKE JOINT 1501**

## Blues Jam In Chicago

**BLUES JAM IN CHICAGO (Various artists)**
Tracks: / Watch out: *Various artists* / Ooh baby: *Various artists* / South Indiana: *Various artists* / Last night: *Various artists* / Red hot jam: *Various artists* / I'm worried: *Various artists* / I held my baby last night: *Various artists* / Madison blues: *Various artists* / I can't hold out: *Various artists* / I need your love: *Various artists* / I got the blues: *Various artists* / World's in a tangle, The: *Various artists* / Talk with you: *Various artists* / Like it this way: *Various artists* / Someday soon baby: *Various artists* / Hungry country girl: *Various artists* / Black Jack blues: *Various artists* / Rockin' boogie: *Various artists* / Sugar mama: *Various artists* / Home work: *Various artists.*
**2 LP Set:** Released Feb '83, on Epic by CBS Records. Catalogue no: **EPC 88591**

## Blues Jubilee

**BLUES JUBILEE (Various artists)**
**CD:** Released Oct '88, on Vogue by Vogue Records. Catalogue no: **VGCD 600 171**

## Blues Legend

**BLUES LEGEND (Various artists)**
**Album:** Released '88, on Joker (USA) by Lifetime Records (USA). Catalogue no: **SM 3947**
**Cass:** Released '88, on Joker (USA) by Lifetime Records (USA). Catalogue no: **MC 3947**

**BLUES LEGEND, VOL 1 (Various artists)**
Tracks: / Little wheel: *Hooker, John Lee* / I'm in the mood: *Hooker, John Lee* / Hobo blues: *Hooker, John Lee* / Crawling king snake: *Hooker, John Lee* / Blues before sunrise: *Hooker, John Lee* / Want ad blues: *Hooker, John Lee* / My first wife left me: *Hooker, John Lee* / Wednesday evening blues: *Hooker, John Lee* / Maudie: *Hooker, John Lee* / Time is marching: *Hooker, John Lee* / Short-haired woman: *Hopkins, Lightnin'* / Bottle it up and go: *Hopkins, Lightnin'* / Long time: *Hopkins, Lightnin'* / Foot race is on, The: *Hopkins, Lightnin'* / Prison blues come down on me: *Hopkins, Lightnin'* / Bunion stew: *Hopkins, Lightnin'* / Mama and Papa Hopkins: *Hopkins, Lightnin'* / Get off my toe: *Hopkins, Lightnin'* / Trouble in mind: *Hopkins, Lightnin'* / Gonna pull a party: *Hopkins, Lightnin'* / Till the rain runs out: *Hopkins, Lightnin'* / When the saints go marching in: *Hopkins, Lightnin'* / Bourgeois blues: *Leadbelly* / Looky looky yonder: *Leadbelly* / Black Betty: *Leadbelly* / Yellow woman's doorbells: *Leadbelly* / Poor Howard: *Leadbelly* / Green corn: *Leadbelly* / Gallis pole, The: *Leadbelly* / Dekalb woman: *Leadbelly* / Noted rider: *Leadbelly* / Big fat woman: *Leadbelly* / Burrow Love & Co: *Leadbelly* / Bring a little water Sylvie: *Leadbelly* / Julie Ann: *Leadbelly* / Line 'em: *Leadbelly* / Whoe black buck: *Leadbelly* / John Hardy: *Leadbelly* / El capitan: *Various artists* / This is a good time to write a song: *Various artists* / I'm so alone: *Various artists* / Two of a kind: *Various artists* / Big city girl: *Various artists* / Three and one boogie: *Various artists* / Bertha May: *Various artists* / Celeste boogie No 2: *Various artists.*
**LP Set:** Released Aug '83, on Happy Bird (Germany) Catalogue no: **F4 50031**

**BLUES LEGEND, VOL 2 (Various artists)**
Tracks: / I bought you a brand new home: *Hooker, John Lee* / I believe I'll lose my mind: *Hooker, John Lee* / Teasin' me: *Hooker, John Lee* / My cryin' days are over: *Hooker, John Lee* / Sittin' here thinkin': *Hooker, John Lee* / Mean mistreatin': *Hooker, John Lee* / How long? how many more years?: *Hooker, John Lee* / C.C. rider: *Hooker, John Lee* / Sad and lonesome: *Hooker, John Lee* / Can't you see what you're doing to me?: *Hooker, John Lee* / My own boogie: *Davis, Blind John* / Everyday I have the blues: *Davis, Blind John* / Texas Tony: *Davis, Blind John* / Trouble in mind: *Davis, Blind John* / If I had a listen: *Davis, Blind John* / St. Louis blues: *Davis, Blind John* / After hours: *Davis, Blind John* / How long blues: *Davis, Blind John* / Everybody's boogie: *Davis, Blind John* / Memphis blues: *Davis, Blind John* / Rockin' chair boogie: *Davis, Blind John* / House of blue lights: *Davis, Blind John* / Run away boogie: *Davis, Blind John* / Pinetop: *Davis, Blind John* / You hear me talkin': *Terry, Sonny & Brownie McGhee* / Going down slow: *Terry, Sonny & Brownie McGhee* / Raise a ruckus tonight: *Terry, Sonny & Brownie McGhee* / Right now: *Terry, Sonny & Brownie McGhee* / Worried life blues: *Terry, Sonny & Brownie McGhee* / John Henry: *Terry, Sonny & Brownie McGhee* / Crawdad hole: *Terry, Sonny & Brownie McGhee* / Down by the riverside: *Terry, Sonny & Brownie McGhee* / Take this hammer: *Terry, Sonny & Brownie McGhee* / That good old jelly roll: *Terry, Sonny & Brownie McGhee* / Diggin' my potatoes: *Waters, Muddy* / Watchdog: *Waters, Muddy* / Sting it: *Waters, Muddy* / Why d'you do me?: *Waters, Muddy* / Natural wig: *Waters, Muddy* / Mud in your ear: *Waters, Muddy* / Excuse me baby: *Waters, Muddy* / Sad day uptown: *Waters, Muddy* / Top of the boogaloo: *Waters, Muddy* / Long distance call: *Waters, Muddy* / Cindy Cindy: *Terry, Sonny & Brownie McGhee.*
**LP Set:** Released Aug '83, on Happy Bird (Germany) Catalogue no: **F4 90098**

**BLUES LEGEND, VOL 3 (Various artists)**
Tracks: / Bourgeois blues: *Leadbelly* / Whoe black buck: *Leadbelly* / John Henry: *Terry, Sonny & Brownie McGhee* / Take this summer: *Terry, Sonny & Brownie McGhee* / Hobo blues: *Hooker, John Lee* / C.C. rider: *Hooker, John Lee* / Everyday I have the blues: *Davis, Blind John* / Bertha May: *Various artists* / Diggin' my potatoes: *Waters, Muddy* / Mini dress: *Johnson, Luther with the Muddy Waters Blues Band* / Remember me: *Johnson, Luther with the Muddy Waters Blues Band* / Snake: *Johnson, Luther with the Muddy Waters Blues Band* / Comin' home baby: *Johnson, Luther with the Muddy Waters Blues Band* / Blues for hippies: *Johnson, Luther with the Muddy Waters Blues Band* / Chicken shack: *Johnson, Luther with the Muddy Waters Blues Band* / Love 'n' trouble: *Johnson, Luther with the Muddy Waters Blues Band* / I'm so glad: *Johnson, Luther with the Muddy Waters Blues Band* / Love without jealousy: *Johnson, Luther with the Muddy Waters Blues Band* / Evil: *Johnson, Luther with the Muddy Waters Blues Band* / Easy riding

gal: *Charles, Ray* / Ray's blues: *Charles, Ray* / Here I am: *Charles, Ray* / Blow my baby back home: *Charles, Ray* / Blues is my middle name: *Charles, Ray* / I'm just a lonely boy: *Charles, Ray* / Going down slow: *Charles, Ray* / St. Pete blues: *Charles, Ray* / Late in the evening: *Charles, Ray* / Mercy on me: *Dupree, Champion Jack* / Sleeping in the street: *Dupree, Champion Jack* / I'm a gamblin' man: *Dupree, Champion Jack* / I hate to be alone: *Dupree, Champion Jack* / Door-to-door blues: *Dupree, Champion Jack* / When I've been drinking: *Dupree, Champion Jack* / Cold ground is my bed, The: *Dupree, Champion Jack* / Lonesome bedroom blues: *Dupree, Champion Jack* / Good woman is hard to find, A: *Dupree, Champion Jack* / I'm growing older every day: *Dupree, Champion Jack*.
**LP Set:** Released Aug '83, on Happy Bird (Germany) Catalogue no: **F4 90111**

## Blues Project

**BLUES PROJECT (Various artists)**
Tracks: / Fiin' to die: *Ray, David* / Blow whistle blow: *Schmidt Von Eric* / My little woman: *Koerner, John* / Ginger man: *Muldaur, Geoff* / Bad dream blues: *Van Ronk, Dave* / Winding boy: *Buchanan Ian* / I'm troubled: *Kalb Danny* / France blues: *Spoelstra Mark* / Don't leave me here: *Van Ronk, Dave* / Devil got my woman: *Muldaur, Geoff* / Southbound train: *Koerner, John* / Slappin' on my black cat Bone: *Ray, David* / She's gone: *Spoelstra Mark* / Hello baby blues: *Kalb Danny*.
**Album:** Released Dec '87, on Edsel by Demon Records. Catalogue no: **ED 248**
**Album:** Released Aug '86, on Polydor by Polydor Ltd. Deleted Jan '88. Catalogue no: **SPELP 104**
**Cass:** Released Aug '86, on Polydor by Polydor Ltd. Deleted Jan '88. Catalogue no: **SPEMC 104**

## Blues Rarities

**BLUES RARITIES (Various artists)**
Tracks: / Recession blues: *King, B.B.* / Don't keep me waiting: *King, B.B.* / Tickle britches: *King, B.B.* / Don't break your promise: *King, B.B.* / You can't put me out: *Howlin' Wolf* / Gettin' late: *Howlin' Wolf* / Rockin' daddy: *Howlin' Wolf* / I better go now: *Howlin' Wolf* / New crawlin' king snake: *Howlin' Wolf* / My mind is ramblin': *Howlin' Wolf* / Tail dragger: *Howlin' Wolf* / Poor wind that never change: *Howlin' Wolf* / Stick around: *Guy, Buddy* / Gully hully: *Guy, Buddy* / That's it: *Guy, Buddy* / American banstand: *Guy, Buddy* / Untitled instumental: *Guy, Buddy* / My love is real: *Guy, Buddy* / Moanin': *Guy, Buddy* / Down home special: *Taylor, Hound Dog* / Watch out: *Taylor, Hound Dog* / Scrappin': *Taylor, Hound Dog* / Sittin' here alone: *Taylor, Hound Dog* / Hound dog: *Taylor, Hound Dog* / Little village: *Williamson, Sonny Boy* / Unseen eye: *Williamson, Sonny Boy*.
**Album:** Released '89, on Chess by Vogue Records. Catalogue no: **GCH 2-6035**
**Album:** Released Mar '85, on Chess (PRT) Deleted '88. Catalogue no: **CXMD 4055**

## Blues Roots

**BLUES ROOTS (Various artists)**
**CD:** Released Mar '90, on Tomato (USA) by Tomato Music Co. (USA). Catalogue no: **JJCD48**
**Album:** Released Mar '79, on Tomato (USA) by Tomato Music Co. (USA). Catalogue no: **TOM 2-7006**
**CD:** Released Feb '89, on UNKNOWN Catalogue no: **269604 2**

**BLUES ROOTS VOL 1 (Mississippi blues) (Various artists)**
Note: Artists include : Big Joe Williams, Johnny Young.
**Album:** Released Jun '86, on Storyville by Storyville Records AB. Catalogue no: **SLP 4035**

**BLUES ROOTS VOL 2 (Blues all around my bed) (Various artists)**
Note: Artists include: Leroy Dalls, Carl Hodges etc.
**Album:** Released Jun '86, on Storyville by Storyville Records AB. Catalogue no: **SLP 4036**

**BLUES ROOTS VOL 3 (I ain't gonna pick no more cotton) (Various artists)**
**Album:** Released Jun '86, on Storyville by Storyville Records AB. Catalogue no: **SLP 4037**

**BLUES ROOTS VOL 4 Dirty dozen, The (Speckled Red)**
Note: Artists: Speckled Red
**Album:** Released Jun '86, on Storyville by Storyville Records AB. Catalogue no: **SLP 4038**

**BLUES ROOTS VOL 5 (Ramblin' & wanderin' blues) (Williams, Big Joe)**
Note: Artists: Big Joe Williams
**Album:** Released Jun '86, on Storyville by Storyville Records AB. Catalogue no: **SLP 4039**

**BLUES ROOTS VOL 6 (I'm growing older everyday) (Various artists)**
Note: Artists: Champion Jack Dupree
**Album:** Released Jun '86, on Storyville by Storyville Records AB. Catalogue no: **SLP 4040**

**BLUES ROOTS VOL 7 Good morning Mr. Blues (Spann, Otis)**
Note: Artists: Otis Spann
**Album:** Released Jun '86, on Storyville by Storyville Records AB. Catalogue no: **SLP 4041**

**BLUES ROOTS VOL 8 (Swingin' with Lonnie) (Various artists)**
Note: Artist: Lonnie Johnson.
**Album:** Released Jun '86, on Storyville by Storyville Records AB. Catalogue no: **SLP 4042**

**BLUES ROOTS VOL 9 (Sad & lonesome blues) (Various artists)**
Note: Artist: Sunnyland Slim
**Album:** Released Jun '86, on Storyville by Storyville Records AB. Catalogue no: **SLP 4043**

**BLUES ROOTS VOL 10 (I'm so alone) (Various artists)**
Note: Artist: Memphis Slim
**Album:** Released Jun '86, on Storyville by Storyville Records AB. Catalogue no: **SLP 4044**

## Blues Round Midnight

**BLUES ROUND MIDNIGHT (Various artists)**
Tracks: / Three o'clock blues: *Davis, Larry* / Old man blues: *Copeland, Johnny* / Something about you: *Davis, Larry* / Blues around midnight: *Fulson, Lowell* / Love will lead you right: *Walker, T-Bone* / You're breaking my heart: *King, B.B.* / Down now: *King, B.B.* / Shattered dreams: *Fulson, Lowell* / T-99 Blues: *Nelson, Jimmy* (Available on CD and cassette only) / I'm wonderin' & wonderin': *Charles, Ray* (Available on CD and cassette only) / Secondhand fool: *Nelson, Jimmy* / Quit hanging around: *King, Saunders* / Dragnet blues: *Ervin, Frankie* / Crazy with the blues: *Jones Marti* / Love is here to stay: *Holden, Lorenzo* / I need somebody: *Witherspoon, Jimmy* / Gee baby ain't I good to you: *Witherspoon, Jimmy* / Picture of you: *Green, Vivianne* / Playing the numbers: *Ervin, Frankie* / It just wasn't true: *Jones Marl*.
**Cass:** Released Apr '88, on Ace by Ace Records. Catalogue no: **CHC 235**
**Album:** Released Apr '88, on Ace by Ace Records. Catalogue no: **CH 235**
**CD:** Released Apr '88, on Ace by Ace Records. Catalogue no: **CDCH 235**

## Blues Singers Of The...

**BLUES SINGERS OF THE 20'S SERIES (Various artists)**
Note: MONO Recording Artists include: Edna Hicks,Rosa Henderson etc.
**Cass:** Released Jul '86, on Emporium Cassettes Catalogue no: **047**

## Blues & Soul Power

**BLUES & SOUL POWER (Various artists)**
Note: Selection of tracks from original U.S Kent and Modern Record labels:Include;Johnny Otis - 'Signifying Monkey', Lowell Fulson - 'Tramp', Ikettes - 'Peaches and Cream', Ike and Tina Turner - 'Chicken Shack' etc.
**Album:** Released Jun '87, on Kent by Ace Records. Deleted Jan '90. Catalogue no: **KENT 068**

## Blues Southside Chicago

**BLUES SOUTHSIDE CHICAGO (Various artists)**
Tracks: / Can't help myself: *Horton, Shakey* / One more time: *Young, Johnny* / Every time I get to drinking: *Sunnyland Slim* / I won't be happy: *Poor Bob* / Where you belong: *Boyd, Eddie* / Merry Christmas: *Nighthawk, Robert* / Crutch and cane: *Homesick James* / Little girl: *Young, Johnny* / Sun is rising, The: *Poor Bob* / Got to move: *Homesick James* / I got to get to my baby: *Sunnyland Slim* / J.F. Kennedy's reservation: *Mitchell, Ronda & Mrs.Lovell* / Lula Mae: *Nighthawk, Robert* / Losing hand: *Boyd, Eddie*.
**Album:** Released Jul '87, on Flyright by Interstate Music. Catalogue no: **FLY 521**
**Album:** Released Feb '83, on Rock Echoes by Decca Records. Catalogue no: **TAB 63**

## Blues Story

**BLUES STORY, THE (Various artists)**
**Cass:** Released '88, on Masters (Holland) Catalogue no: **MAMC 95686**
**CD:** Released Dec '88, on Spectrum (CD) by M.S.D.. Catalogue no: **SPEC 85023**
**Album:** Released '88, on Masters (Holland) Catalogue no: **MA 5686**

## Blues Summit...

**BLUES SUMMIT LIVE AT NEWPORT (Various artists)**
**CD Set:** Released Oct '86, on Mobile Fidelity Sound Lab(USA) by Mobile Fidelity Records (USA). Catalogue no: **MFCD 2-813**

## Blues Upside Your Head

**BLUES UPSIDE YOUR HEAD (Various artists)**
Tracks: / I'm goin' upside your head: *Various artists* (Composer: J M Duncan.) / I'm gonna love you: *Various artists* (Composer: Eddie Taylor.) / Two steps from the blues: *Various artists* (Composers: Malone/Brown) / House rent boogie: *Various artists* (Composer: J L Hooker) / Strange angels: *Various artists* (Composer: James) / Those lonely, lonely feelings: *Various artists* (Composers: Earl King/Johnny Vincent) / Have you ever loved a woman: *Various artists* (Composer: Billy Myles) / Southern country boy: *Various artists* (Composer: Duke Coleman) / I ain't got you: *Various artists* (Composer: Carter) / Messin' around: *Various artists* (Composer: F Hunt) / Reconsider Baby: *Various artists* (Composer: L Fulson) / Stroll out west: *Various artists* / Gangster of love: *Various artists* (Composer: John Watson) / Booze in the bottle: *Various artists* (Composer: Duke Coleman) / Jelly roll king: *Various artists* (Composer: Frost) / I wish you would: *Various artists* (Composer: Arnold) / You've got to love her with a feeling: *Various artists* (Composers: Freddie King/Sonny Thompson) / Steppin' out: *Various artists* (Composer: Bracken) / Mama, you've got a daughter: *Various artists* (Composer: J B Lenoir) / Put it all in there: *Various artists* (Composer: Ann Ducontee) / Look on yonder wall: *Various artists* (Composers: Sehorn/James) / When you're doing alright (don't say nothing): *Various artists* (Composer: J M Dunson).
Note: Tracks 1,2,4,9,10,12,16,18,19,22: Original Vee-Jay recordings. Licensed from Charly Records International APS. Tracks 6,7,13,17: Original King recordings. Licensed from Gusto Records Inc. Tracks 8,14,20: Original Jewel recordings. Licensed from Charly Records International APS. Tracks 3,11: Original Duke recordings. Licensed from MCA Records Ltd. Tracks 5,21: Original Fury recordings via Sansu Enterprises. Licensed from Charly Records International APS. Track 15: Original Sun recording. Licensed from Charly Records International APS.
**CD:** Released Oct '87, on Charly by Charly Records. Catalogue no: **CDCHARLY 26**

## Blues Women

**BLUES WOMEN (Various artists)**
**Album:** Released Apr '85, on Krazy Kat by Interstate Music. Catalogue no: **KK 793**

## Bluesman Songsters

**BLUESMAN SONGSTERS 1929-33 (Various artists)**
**Album:** Released Dec '88, on Earl Archives Catalogue no: **BD 2016**

## Blues'n'Trouble

**BLUES 'N' TROUBLE 1 (Various artists)**
**Album:** Released '81, on Arhoolie (USA) by Arhoolie Records (USA). Catalogue no: **ARHOOLIE 1006**

**BLUES 'N' TROUBLE 2 (Various artists)**
**Album:** Released '81, on Arhoolie (USA) by Arhoolie Records (USA). Catalogue no: **ARHOOLIE 1012**

## Blues'n'Trouble (Group)

**BLUES 'N' TROUBLE**
**Album:** Released Aug '88, on Ammunition Communications by Ammunition Communications. Catalogue no: **BNTLP 1**

**CADILLAC**
Tracks: / Cadillac / Natural born lover.
**7" Single:** Released Sep '85, on Ammunition Communications by Ammunition Communications. Catalogue no: **BNT 3**

**FINE,FINE,FINE**
Tracks: / Fine, fine, fine / Free to ride / Red hot.
**7" Single:** Released Feb '86, on Ammunition Communications by Ammunition Communications. Catalogue no: **BNT 4**

**HAT TRICK**
Tracks: / I got your number / Why / Cherry peaches / Travelling light / When the lights go down / Comin' home / What's the matter / Be mine tonight / Rockin' with you Jimmy / T.N.T / See my baby shake it / Don't need no doctor.
**Album:** Released Aug '87, on Blue Horizon by Ace Records. Catalogue no: **BLUH 001**
**CD:** Released Nov '87, on Line by Line Records (W.Germany). Catalogue no: **INCD 900397**

**LIVE**
Tracks: / Clock on the wall / Cherry peaches / BNT blues / Why? / Honey pot / See my baby shake it / Lying on the kitchen floor / Born in Chicago / Sugar coated love / What's the matter? / Travelling light / Driftin' blues / Madison blues.
**Album:** Released 21 May '88, on Cacophony Catalogue no: **SKITE 002**
**Cass:** Released 21 May '88, on Cacophony Catalogue no: **SKITEC 002**
**CD:** Released May '88, on Line by Line Records (W.Germany). Catalogue no: **INCD900572**

**MYSTERY TRAIN**
Tracks: / Mystery train / C.T..
**7" Single:** Released Aug '84, on Plus One Catalogue no: **BNT 2**

**NO MINOR KEYS**
**Cass:** Released May '86, on Ammunition Communications by Ammunition Communications. Catalogue no: **BNTC 2**
**Album:** Released May '86, on Ammunition Communications by Ammunition Communications. Catalogue no: **BNTLP 2**

**OLD TIME BOOGIE**
Tracks: / Old time boogie.
**7" Single:** Released Oct '83, on Castle Rock Catalogue no: **BNT 1**

**THANK YOU AND GOODNIGHT**
**Album:** Released Jul '87, on Ammunition Communications by Ammunition Communications. Catalogue no: **BNTLP 3**

**WITH FRIENDS LIKE THESE**
**Album:** Released Dec '89, on Unamerican Activities by American Activities. Catalogue no: **BRAVE 11**

## Blues/Rock Avalanche

**BLUES/ROCK AVALANCHE (Various artists)**
Tracks: / I hear you knocking: *McDaniel, Elias* / You can't judge a book by the cover: *Dixon, Willie* / Diddley daddy: *McDaniel, Elias* / Early in the morning: *Morganfield, McKinley* / Baby what you want me to do?: *Reed, Jimmy* / Wang dang doodle: *Dixon, Willie* / I got what it takes: *Dixon, Willie* / Wrinkles: *Leake, Lafayette* / Swiss boogie: *Leake, Lafayette* / County jail: *Morganfield, McKinley* / Trouble no more: *Morganfield, McKinley* / Got my mojo working: *Morganfield, McKinley* / Stormy Monday: *Walker, Aaron T-Bone* / She says she loves me: *Walker, Aaron T-Bone & Jane Jarest*.

**Album:** Released Mar '85, on Chess (PRT) Deleted '88. Catalogue no: **CXMD 4056**
**2 LP Set:** on Chess by Vogue Records. Catalogue no: **GCH 2-6033**

## Bluesville

### BLUESVILLE (Various artists)
**Album:** Released Feb '79, on Goldband by Charly Records. Catalogue no: **GRLP 7774**

### BLUESVILLE VOL.1 (Various artists)
Tracks: / Judge Boushay blues: *Lewis, Furry* / Country girl blues: *B, Memphis Willie* / Big road blues: *Douglas, K.C.* / Levee camp blues: *Williams, Big Joe* / Catfish: *Smith, Robert Curtis* / San Quentin blues: *Maiden, Sidney* / Big fat mama: *Walton, Wade* / Grievin' me: *Franklin, Pete* / Dyin' crapshooters blues, The: *McTell, Blind Willie* / Fine booze and heavy dues: *Johnson, Lonnie* / Blues before sunrise: *Blackwell, Scrapper* / You got to move: *Davis, Rev. Gary* / Brown skinned woman: *Eaglin, Snooks* / Pawn shop: *McGhee, Brownie & Sonny Terry* / T-model blues: *Lightnin' Hopkins* / You is one black rat: *Quattlebaum, Doug* / Highway 61: *B, Memphis Willie* (Available on CD and cassette only) / Shake 'em on down: *Lewis, Furry* (Available on CD and cassette only) / Hand-me-down baby: *Maiden, Sidney* (Available on CD and cassette only) / Alberta: *Eaglin, Snooks* (Available on CD and cassette only) / See what you have done: *Tate, Baby* (Available on CD and cassette only) / Goin' where the moon crosses the yellow dog: *Blackwell, Scrapper* (Available on CD and cassette only).
**CD:** Released Jun '88, on Ace by Ace Records. Catalogue no: **CDCH 247**
**Album:** Released Jun '88, on Ace by Ace Records. Catalogue no: **CH 247**
**Cass:** Released Jun '88, on Ace by Ace Records. Catalogue no: **CHC 247**

### BLUESVILLE VOL.2 (Various artists)
Tracks: / Train done gone: *Kirkland, Eddie* / Down on my knees: *Kirkland, Eddie* / Homesick's blues: *James, Homesick* / Stones in my passway: *James, Homesick* / Rack 'em back Jack: *Memphis Slim* / Happy blues for John Glenn: *Lightnin' Hopkins* / Devil jumped the black man: *Lightnin' Hopkins* / My baby done gone: *Terry, Sonny* / School time: *Arnold, Billy Boy* / Big leg woman: *Johnson, Lonnie* / I have to worry: *King Curtis* / Calcutta: *Sykes, Roosevelt* / Show down: *Lucas, Buddy* / How long how long blues: *Witherspoon, Jimmy* / You better cut that out: *Arnold, Billy Boy* (Available on CD and cassette only) / Driving wheel: *Sykes, Roosevelt* (Available on CD and cassette only) / It's a lonesome old world: *Witherspoon, Jimmy* (Available on CD and cassette only) / Jelly roll baker: *Johnson, Lonnie* (Available on CD and cassette only).
**CD:** Released Oct '88, on Ace by Ace Records. Catalogue no: **CDCH 250**
**Cass:** Released Oct '88, on Ace by Ace Records. Catalogue no: **CHC 250**
**Album:** Released Sep '88, on Ace by Ace Records. Catalogue no: **CH 250**

## Bluiett, Hamiet

**Biographical details:** Bluiett, Hamiet. A baritone saxophonist who also plays flute and clarinet, born in 1940 in Lovejoy, Illinois. He played on Julius Hemphill's wonderful *Coon Bid'ness* album in 1975, also recorded with Lester Bowie, Dollar Brand, etc. as well as his own albums as leader on India Navigation, Black Saint and Soul Note. He also plays in the World Saxophone Quartet and leads the Clarinet Family, with seven clarinets incl. Buddy Collette, plus rhythm: *Live In Berlin With The Clarinet Family* came out in 1984 on Black Saint. (Donald Clarke, 24 August 1988.).

### EBU
**CD:** Released Jan '86, on Soul Note Catalogue no: **SN 1088**

## Blythe, Arthur

**Biographical details:** Blythe, Arthur. Born in 1940 in Los Angeles, this alto/soprano saxophonist and composer, aka Black Arthur, has not reached the status his talent deserves. He worked and recorded with Stanley Crouch in 1967-73, Julius Hemphill in 1975, also Jack DeJohnette's Special Edition, Gil Evans etc. His own albums began with two sextet sets made on the same day for India Navigation and a trio set on Adelphi, all in 1977; then with CBS: *Lennox Avenue Breakdown* was praised in 1978 but sales were never spectacular. Eight CBS albums included a stab at synth-funk with Stanley Clarke on *Put Sunshine In It*; *Da-da* was better; acoustic *Basic Blythe* in '87 (with a string quartet) was probably better still. Also, tours with The Leaders, with Chico Freeman, etc. (album *Mudfoot* on Blackhawk). (Donald Clarke, 24 August 1988.).

### BASIC BLYTHE
Tracks: / Autumn in New york / Lenox Avenue breakdown / Heart to heart / As of yet / Ruby my dear / Faceless woman.
**Album:** Released 22 Aug '88, on CBS (import) by CBS Records. Catalogue no: **4606771**
**Cass:** Released 22 Aug '88, on CBS (import) by CBS Records. Catalogue no: **4606774**

### BLYTHE SPIRIT
Tracks: / Contemplation / Faceless woman / Reverence / Stike up the band / Misty / Spirits in the field / Just a closer walk with thee.
**Album:** Released Jan '82, on CBS by CBS Records. Deleted Jan '87. Catalogue no: **CBS 85194**

### BUSH BABY
**Album:** Released '88, on Echo by Echo Records. Deleted Jun '89. Catalogue no: **ECJ 404**

### DA-DA
Tracks: / Odessa / Spain thang / Esquinas / Crescent / Break tune / After Paris.
**Cass:** Released Jun '86, on CBS by CBS Records. Deleted Aug '87. Catalogue no: **40 26888**
**Album:** Released Jun '86, on CBS by CBS Records. Deleted Aug '87. Catalogue no: **CBS 26888**

### ELABORATION
Tracks: / Elaboration / Metamorphosis / Sister Daisy / One mint julep / Shadows / Lower Nile.
**Album:** Released '83, on CBS by CBS Records. Deleted '88. Catalogue no: **CBS 85980**

### GRIP, THE
**Album:** Released May '78, on India Navigation Catalogue no: **IN 1029**

### IN THE TRADITION
Tracks: / Jitterbug waltz / In a sentimental mood / Breaktune / Caravan / hip dripper / Naima.
**Album:** Released Jul '80, on CBS by CBS Records. Deleted Jul '85. Catalogue no: **CBS 84152**

### LENNOX AVENUE BREAKDOWN
Tracks: / Down San Diego way / Slidin' through / Lennox Avenue breakdown / Odessa.
**Album:** Released '79, on CBS by CBS Records. Deleted '84. Catalogue no: **CBS 83350**

### LIGHT BLUE
Tracks: / We see / Light blue / Off minor / Epistrophy / Coming on the hudson / Nutty / Tumalumah / Put sunshine in it / Uptown strut / Silhouette / 15 / Sentimental walk.
**Cass:** Released Jun '83, on CBS by CBS Records. Catalogue no: **40 25397**
**Album:** Released Jun '83, on CBS by CBS Records. Catalogue no: **CBS 25397**

### PUT SUNSHINE IN IT
Tracks: / Tumalumah / Put sunshine in it / Uptown strut / Silhouette / 15 / Sentimental walk.
**Cass:** Released Mar '85, on CBS by CBS Records. Deleted '87. Catalogue no: **40 26098**
**Album:** Released Mar '85, on CBS by CBS Records. Deleted '87. Catalogue no: **CBS 26098**

## Blythe, Jimmy

### STOMP YOUR STUFF (1927-31)
**Album:** Released Jan '83, on Swaggie (Australia) Catalogue no: **S 1324**

## Bocage, Peter

### AT SAN JACINTO HALL (Bocage, Peter with George Lewis/Louis Nelson)
Note: With George Lewis/Louis Nelson. MONO recording.
**Album:** Released '88, on Jazzology (USA) by Jazzology Records (USA). Catalogue no: **JCE 29**

### NEW ORLEANS- THE LEGENDS LIVE (Bocage, Peter & His Creole Serenaders)
**Album:** Released Jun '86, on Jazzology (USA) by Jazzology Records (USA). Catalogue no: **JCE 33**

## Bogan, Lucille

**BESSIE JACKSON 1923-35**
**Album:** Released Aug '89, on Blues Document Catalogue no: **BD 2046**

**LUCILLE BOGAN & WALTER ROLAND (Bogan, Lucille & Walter Roland)**
**Album:** Released Dec '88, on Yazoo (USA) by Shanachie Records (USA). Catalogue no: **L 1017**
**Album:** Released Oct '88, on Roots (Germany) Catalogue no: **RL 317**

**WOMAN WON'T NEED NO MAN**
**Album:** Released Dec '88, on Agram Catalogue no: **AB 2005**

## Boland, Francy

**OPEN DOOR**
Tracks: / New box / A Rose Negra / Duas rosas / Milkshake / Open door / Dia blues / Total blues.
**Album:** Released Apr '81, on Muse by Black & Blue Records. Catalogue no: **MR 5056**

## Bolling, Claude

**CLAUDE BOLLING**
Tracks: / California suite / Suite for flute & jazz piano.
**Album:** Released May '81, on RCA by BMG Records (UK). Deleted '86. Catalogue no: **RL 25348**

**CONCERTO FOR CLASSIC GUITAR AND JAZZ PIANO**
**Album:** Released Jun '80, on H.M.V. by EMI Records. Deleted '85. Catalogue no: **EMD 5535**
**Album:** Released Aug '82, on CBS by CBS Records. Deleted Jan '88. Catalogue no: **CBS 73651**

**JAZZ A LA FRANCAIS (Bolling, Claude Trio)**
Tracks: / A La Francaise / Garnerama / Bach to swing / Not this time / Etude in blue / Blue kiss from Brazil / Fiancees en folie.
**CD:** Released Aug '86, on CBS by CBS Records. Catalogue no: **MK 39244**
**Album:** Released Mar '85, on CBS by CBS Records. Catalogue no: **FM 39244**
**Cass:** Released Mar '85, on CBS by CBS Records. Catalogue no: **FMT 39244**

**LIVE AT THE MERIDIEN (Bolling Claude, Big Band)**
**Album:** Released Oct '85, on CBS (import) by CBS Records. Catalogue no: **FM 39245**

**NUANCES (Bolling, Claude & his French All-stars)**
**Album:** Released '88, on DRG (USA) by DRG Records (USA). Catalogue no: **SL 5201**

**PLAYS ELLINGTON VOL 1**
Tracks: / Stomp, look and listen / Blue serge / Koko / Echoes of Harlem / Sepia panorama / Cottontall / Sophisticated lady / It don't mean a thing / Magenta haze / In a mellow tone
**Cass:** Released 5 Feb '88, on CBS (import) by CBS Records. Catalogue no: **FMT 42474**
**Album:** Released 5 Feb '88, on CBS (import) by CBS Records. Catalogue no: **FM 42474**

**RAGTIME BOOGIE-WOOGIE**
Tracks: / 3-4 6-8 boogie / Mississippi rag / Death ray boogie / On the Mississippi / Louisiana glide / Maple leaf rag / Tiger rag / Man that got away, The / Yesterdays / Begin the beguine / Tea for two / Dardanella / Honky tonk train blues / Harlem strut / Pinetop's boogie woogie / Entertainer's rag, The / Waiting for the Robert E. Lee / Perfect rag.
**CD:** on Phonogram by Phonogram Ltd. Catalogue no: **822 506-2**

## Bonano, Sharkey

**SHARKEY BONANO AND HIS NEW ORLEANS BOYS AND SHARKS OF RHYTHM**
**Cass:** Released Jun '86, on Holmia Cassettes Catalogue no: **HM 09**

**SHARKEY & HIS KINGS OF DIXIELAND (Sharkey & His Kings of Dixieland)**
**Album:** Released Jun '86, on GHB by Jazzology Records (USA). Catalogue no: **GHB 122**

## Bond, Graham

**Biographical details:** British instrumentalist Bond started his career as an alto saxophonist but soon switched to keyboards. He replaced Cyril Davies in Alexis Korner's acclaimed Blues Incorporated in 1962. His interest in the electric organ led him to quit the following year and he formed his own trio with Jack Bruce and Ginger Baker. They began by playing jazz but then switched to rhythm-and-blues. The Graham Bond Organisation, as the outfit was called, were popular on the club circuit but failed to sell records. Bond was hailed by critics as a quiet but vital influence on Britain's healthy R & B scene. In common with fellow bluesmen Alexis Korner and John Mayall, Bond's role proved to be that of catalyst rather than star. In 1965 Baker and Bruce left, later joining Eric Clapton to form the legendary trio Cream. Bond then spent 18 months in the United States. In 1970 he scored his only UK chart success: the album *Solid Bond* reached No 40 on the LP chart. This solitary, paltry chart performance is a gross understatement of his influence. The next few years saw him embark on a variety of short-lived projects, including membership of Ginger Baker's abortive combo Airforce. Graham Bond met a sad death in May 1974, when he fell under a train at London's Finsbury Park Station. (Bob MacDonald, 1984.)

Graham Bond (1937-74) was born in Romford. He played saxophone on a Don Rendell quintet, but forsook jazz for R&B, joining Alexis Korner's Blues Incorporated in 1962 and soon switching to organ. He formed a trio with Jack Bruce and Ginger Baker which became a quartet with John McLaughlin on guitar (later Neil Hubbard, with Dick Heckstall-Smith on sax); Baker was later replaced by Jon Hiseman. The name of the group became the Graham Bond Organisation. He was an innovator, credited with being the first to use the Hammond organ and Leslie speaker combination in R&B context, first to split the keyboard for portability, first to build an electronic keyboard and first to use a Mellotron. He made several albums in the UK between 1965 and 1972 and briefly played in Baker's Airforce; he suffered from a nervous breakdown and died under a London tube train. He was one of the founders of UK R&B, but had little commercial success in his lifetime. ( Donald Clarke, 24 August 1988.).

**BEGINNING OF JAZZ-ROCK**
Tracks: / Wade in the water / Big boss man / Early in the morning / Person to person blues / Spanish blues / First time I met the blues / Stormy Monday / Train time / What'd I say?.
**Album:** Released Jan '77, on Charly by Charly Records. Catalogue no: **CR 30198**

**HOLY MAGIC**
**Album:** Released '89, on Beat Goes On by Andy's Records. Catalogue no: **BGOLP 35**

**LIVE AT KLOOKS KLEEK**
Tracks: / Wade in the water / Big boss man / Early in the morning / Person to person blues / Spanish blues / Introduction by Dick Jordan / First time I met the blues, The / Stormy Monday / Train time / What's I say.
**Album:** Released Sep '88, on Decal by Charly Records. Catalogue no: **LIK 47**

**SOLID BOND**
**Album:** Released Jun '70, on Warner Bros. by WEA Records. Deleted '75. Catalogue no: **WS 3001**

**SOUND OF '65/THERE'S A BOND (Bond, Graham Organisation)**
Tracks: / Hoochie coochie / Baby make love to me / Neighbour neighbour / Early in the morning / Spanish blues / Oh baby / Little girl / I want you / Wade in the water / Got my mojo working / Train time / Baby be good to me / Half a man / Tammy / Who's afraid of Virginia Woolfe / Hear me calling your name / Night time is the right time / Walking in the park / Last night / Baby can it be true / What'd I say / Dick's instrumental / Don't let go / Keep-a drivin' / Have you ever loved a woman / Camels and elephants.
**2 LP Set:** Released 19 Mar '88, on Edsel by Demon Records. Catalogue no: **DED 254**

**WE PUT OUR MAGIC ON YOU**
**Album:** Released '89, on Beat Goes On by Andy's Records. Catalogue no: **BGOLP 73**

## Bonestructure

**BONESTRUCTURE (Various artists)**
Tracks: / Dolphin Street: *Various artists* / Vatican roulette: *Various artists* / Modal t: *Various artists* / Lush life: *Various ar-*

*tists* / Doodlin': *Various artists* / Bone idle rich, The: *Various artists*.
**Album:** Released Jul '89, on Calligraph Catalogue no: **CLGLP 020**
**CD:** Released Jul '89, on Calligraph Catalogue no: **CLGCD 020**

## Bonfa, Luiz

### JAZZ SAMBA ENCORE (see Getz, Stan) (Bonfa, Luiz/Stan Getz)
Note: Classic Verve re-issue featuring the compositions of Luiz Bonfa & Antonio Carlos Jobim. Latin jazz at it's best. Stan Getz - tenor sax / Luiz Bonfa - guitar / Antonio Carlos Jobim - guitar, piano / george Duvivier - bass / Tommy Williams- bass / Paulo ferreira - drums / Jose Carlos - drums / Don Payne - bass / dave Bailey - drums.
**Album:** Released May '84, on Verve (USA) by Polydor Ltd. Catalogue no: **V 68523**

## Bonnel, Jean

### JEAN FRANCOIS BONNEL AND LYTTELTON AND COHEN
**Album:** Released '88, on Stomp Off (USA) Catalogue no: **SOS 1104**

### WHAT A DREAM
**Album:** Released Nov '87, on Stomp Off (USA) Catalogue no: **SOS 1131**

## Bonner, Juke Boy

**Biographical details:** Bonner, Juke Boy. Weldon H Philip Bonner (1932-78) was a Texas blues singer and guitarist who also played drums and harmonica, and sometimes worked as a one-man band. His style was influenced by Lightning Hopkins, but with a more driving rhythm; he was also influenced by country music on electric and acoustic guitars including 12-string; he also wrote poetry and his lyrics were often more interesting than traditional blues lines. Dobald Clarke, 24 August 1988..

### GOING BACK TO THE COUNTRY
**Album:** Released May '81, on Arhoolie (USA) by Arhoolie Records (USA). Catalogue no: **ARHOOLIE 1036**

### LEGACY OF THE BLUES-5
Tracks: / I'm a bluesman / Problems all round / Trying to get ahead / If you don't want to get mistreated / Lonesome ride back home / Funny money / I'm lonely too / Real good money / Come to me / Yammin' the blues / Better place to go / Tired of the greyhound blues.
**Album:** Released '87, on Sonet by Sonet Records. Catalogue no: **SNTF 634**
**CD:** Released '87, on Sonet by Sonet Records. Catalogue no: **SNTCD 634**
**Album:** Released May '89, on GNP Crescendo (USA) by GNP Crescendo Records (USA). Catalogue no: **GNPS 10015**

### ONE MAN TRIO, THE
**Album:** Released Oct '79, on Flyright by Interstate Music. Catalogue no: **FLY 548**

### STRUGGLE, THE
**Album:** Released May '81, on Arhoolie (USA) by Arhoolie Records (USA). Catalogue no: **ARHOOLIE 1045**

### THEY CALL ME JUKE BOY
Tracks: / Best way to lose the blues, The / Distant feel, A / Nowhere to run / Don't ever get down / It don't take too much / Shame, shame, shame / Boone's farm / What the blues has done to me / Texas zydeco / Nothing but a child / European tour / Live my troubles on down / Loving arms / Gettin' low down.
Note: This is real down home stuff from Weldon 'Juke Boy' Bonner, cut in Texas in about 1967-69. Born in 1932, he started playing as a professional musician in the late forties in Houston. For the first 15 years was almost totally confined to the Juke Joints, where he frequently appeared as the 'human juke box', playing the blues hits of the days for nickels and dimes. After recovering from an illness in the early '60's, his career finally took off largely because of the British blues fraternity, who financed a record and arranged a European tour. He cut several more albums during this period and it is during this time that the material on this album was recorded. It is mostly previously unissued material and really catches a man at the height of his career. (Ace Records, July 1989)
**Album:** Released 31 Jul '89, on Ace by Ace Records. Catalogue no: **CHD 269**

## Boogie Blues

### BOOGIE BLUES (Women Sing And Play The Boogie Woogie) (Various artists)
**Album:** Released Mar '84, on Rosetta (USA) Catalogue no: **RR 1309**

## Boogie Woogie

**Biographical details:** Boogie Woogie. The original blues piano style, combined with the influence of ragtime 'sixteens' and the habenera (New Orleans 'Spanish tinge'). Whereas jazz pianists in the eastern USA in the 1920s often had formal training and played 'stride' piano, elsewhere they taught themselves what they wanted to play and left it at that, like itinerant blues guitarists: boogie woogie, like the blues itself, was a limited genre which depended for its subtlety on the native skill of the player. It began in lumber camps in Texas and Louisiana, where the only entertainment was a barroom piano (the 'bar' was planks laid over barrels, hence 'barrelhouse'); the style used repeated figures in the left hand, often 8 notes to the bar, with blues improvisation in right hand: the player could keep the beat going while he grabbed a drink or a bite. It did not provide a good living: Jimmy Yancey was a grounds keeper in a Chicago baseball park; Meade Lux Lewis and Albert Ammons were taxi drivers in Chicago; other players were Pete Johnson, Cow Cow Davenport, Pine Top Smith, Roosevelt Sykes, Little Brother Montgomery and Little Willie Littlefield. Memphis Slim (Peter Chatman) played, sang and wrote good songs for decades. Ammons and Lewis played at John Hammond's Carnegie Hall 'Spirituals to Swing' concert in 1938; formalised and played too fast, the style became a fad during the Big Band Era: Pinetop Smith had been accidentally killed in a bar-room shootout, but his *Boogie Woogie* was arranged for Tommy Dorsey's band in 1938 and became one of the biggest hits of the era; Will Bradley had a fluke smash hit with *Beat Me Daddy,Eight To The Bar* in 1940, then a rash of sequels;Bradley's piano player Freddie Slack had the first million-seller on the new Capitol label with *Cow Cow Boogie* (vocal by Ella Mae Morse). Adolescents all over the country pounded out boogie-woogie on parlour pianos (it is superficially easy to play, like the adolescent blues guitar style which became rock). The boogie-woogie influence was heard in R&B shuffle rhythms played by Louis Jordan's extremely popular jump band, and in early rock 'n' roll through the piano styles of Fats Domino, Huey 'Piano' Smith, Little Richard and Jerry Lee Lewis, and in countless song titles. (Donald Clarke 23 August 1988.)

### BIG BANDS MEET BOOGIE WOOGIE
**Album:** Released '88, on Joker (USA) by Lifetime Records (USA). Catalogue no: **SM 4086**

### BOOGIE WOOGIE (Various artists)
Note: MONO production. With Meade Lux Lewis,Pete Johnson,Albert Ammons.
**Album:** Released May '86, on Storyville by Storyville Records AB. Catalogue no: **SLP 4006**

### BOOGIE WOOGIE A LA PARISIENNE (Various artists)
**Album:** Released Sep '84, on Pathe Marconi (France) Catalogue no: **PM 1552601**

### BOOGIE WOOGIE BOYS VOL.1 (Various artists)
**Album:** Released Feb '90, on Storyville by Storyville Records AB. Catalogue no: **SLP 4094**

### BOOGIE WOOGIE REVIVAL
**Album:** Released '88, on Joker (USA) by Lifetime Records (USA). Catalogue no: **SM 4083**

### BOOGIE WOOGIE, THE (Various artists)
Tracks: / In the mood: *Various artists* / Red bank boogie: *Various artists* / Beulah's sister's boogie: *Various artists* / Honky tonk train blues: *Various artists* / Yancey special: *Various artists* / Jammin' the boogie: *Various artists* / Hamp's boogie woogie No. 1: *Various artists* / Pinetop's boogie woogie: *Various artists* / Jimmy's boogie woogie: *Various artists* / Boogie woogie on St. Louis blues: *Various artists* / Hamp's walkin' boogie: *Various artists* / Chip's boogie woogie: *Various artists* / Calloway boogie: *Various artists* / Boo woo: *Various artists* / Central Avenue breakdown: *Various artists* / Roll 'em: *Various artists* / Cow cow blues: *Various artists* / Tatum-pole boogie: *Various artists* / Oscar's boogie: *Various artists* / Just jazz boogie: *Vari-*

*ous artists.*
**CD:** Released Feb '88, on Entertainers Catalogue no: **ENTCD 208**
**CD:** Released '88, on Giants of Jazz by Hasmick Promotions. Catalogue no: **GOJCD 0208**

**BOOGIE WOOGIE (VIDEO) (Various artists)**
**VHS:** Released Feb '90, on Storyville by Storyville Records AB. Catalogue no: **SV6013**

**BOOGIE WOOGIE VOL. 1 (Various artists)**
**Album:** Released '88, on Joker (USA) by Lifetime Records (USA). Catalogue no: **SM 3903**
**Cass:** Released '88, on Joker (USA) by Lifetime Records (USA). Catalogue no: **MC 3903**

**BOOGIE WOOGIE VOL. 2 (Various artists)**
**Album:** Released '88, on Joker (USA) by Lifetime Records (USA). Catalogue no: **SM 3904**
**Cass:** Released '88, on Joker (USA) by Lifetime Records (USA). Catalogue no: **MC 3904**

**GREAT PIANISTS MEET BOOGIE WOOGIE VOL. 1, THE**
**Album:** Released '88, on Joker (USA) by Lifetime Records (USA). Catalogue no: **SM 4084**

**GREAT VOCALISTS MEET BOOGIE WOOGIE VOL. 2, THE**
**Album:** Released '88, on Joker (USA) by Lifetime Records (USA). Catalogue no: **SM 4085**

**GREATEST HITS: BOOGIE WOOGIE (Various artists)**
**Album:** Released Feb '82, on Boogie Woogie (USA) Catalogue no: **BW 1000**

**I WANT TO BOOGIE WOOGIE (Various artists)**
**Album:** Released Sep '87, on Esoldun Catalogue no: **RR 2021**

**PIONEERS OF BOOGIE WOOGIE**
**Album:** Released '88, on Joker (USA) by Lifetime Records (USA). Catalogue no: **SM 4081**

## Boogie Woogie Fever

**BOOGIE WOOGIE FEVER (Various artists)**
Tracks: / Barracuda: *Stone, Cliffie* / Catfish boogie: *Ford, Tennessee Ernie* / Jukebox boogie: *Dolan, Ramblin' Jimmie* / Louisiana boogie: *Travis, Merle* / I'm a do right daddy: *Chappel, Leon* / Blackberry boogie: *Ford, Tennessee Ernie* / Cash on the barrelhead: *Louvin Brothers* / Downtown boogie: *Milo Twins* / Boogie woogie fever: *O'Quin, Gene* / Shotgun boogie: *Ford, Tennessee Ernie* / Hot rod race: *Dolan, Ramblin' Jimmie* / Texas boogie: *O'Quin, Gene* / Honky tonkin' all the time: *Willard, Jess* / Baby buggy boogie: *Milo Twins* / Slow down sweet mama: *Chappel, Leon* / Jump rope boogie: *Stone, Cliffie.*
**Album:** Released May '82, on Charly by Charly Records. Catalogue no: **CR 30215**

## Boogie Woogie Hits

**BOOGIE WOOGIE HITS (Various artists)**
Tracks: / Yancey stomp: *Yancey, Jimmy* / Roll 'em: *Goodman, Benny* / Boogie woogie man: *Various artists* / Barrel-house boogie: *Ammons, Albert & Pete Johnson* / Boogie woogie: *Dorsey, Tommy* / Boogie woogie on St. Louis blues: *Hines, Earl* / Whisky and gin blues: *Slim, Memphis* / One o'clock boogie: *Basie, Count* / Chicago breakdown: *Maceo, Big* / Rooming house boogie: *Calloway, Cab* / Hey ba ba re bop: *Hampton, Lionel* / Hamps boogie woogie: *Hampton, Lionel.*
**Cass:** Released Jul '86, on RCA by BMG Records (UK). Catalogue no: **CK 89803**
**Album:** Released Jul '86, on RCA by BMG Records (UK). Catalogue no: **CL 89803**

## Boogie Woogie Kings

**BOOGIE WOOGIE KINGS (Various artists)**
**Album:** Released Apr '79, on Euphonic Catalogue no: **ESR 1209**
**Album:** Released Apr '79, on Euphonic Catalogue no: **ESR 1208**

## Boogie Woogie Masters

**BOOGIE WOOGIE MASTERS (Big Band Bounce & Boogie) (Various artists)**
Tracks: / Cow cow blues / State street jive / Pinetop's blues: *Smith, Pine Top* / Pinetop's boogie woogie: *Smith, Pine Top* / Jump steady blues: *Smith, Pine Top* / Detroit rocks: *Taylor, Montana* / Dirty dozen, The: *Perryman, Rufus* / Right string baby but the wrong yoyo: *Perryman, Rufus* / Honky tonk train blues: *Lewis, Meade Lux* / Yancey special: *Lewis, Meade Lux* / Celeste blues: *Lewis, Meade Lux* / Boogie woogie stomp: *Ammons, Albert* / Mr. Freddie blues: *Williams, Mary Lou* / Boogie woogie: *Basie, Count* / Basement boogie: *Johnson, Pete* / Death ray boogie: *Johnson, Pete.*
**CD:** on Official by Official Records. Catalogue no: **OFF 83031**
**Cass:** Released Aug '86, on Affinity by Charly Records. Catalogue no: **TCAFS 1005**
**Album:** on Official by Official Records. Catalogue no: **OFF 3031**
**Album:** Released Aug '86, on Affinity by Charly Records. Catalogue no: **AFS 1005**

## Booker, James

**BOOGIE WOOGIE AND RAGTIME PIANO**
**Album:** Released Apr '79, on Gold by Gold Records. Catalogue no: **GOLD 11055**

**CLASSIFIED**
Tracks: / All around the world / One for the highway / King of the road / Bald head Tipitina / Baby face / Swedish rhapsody / Classified / Lawdy Miss Clawdy / Angel eyes / Hound dog / If you're lonely / Three keys.
**Album:** Released Apr '88, on Rounder (USA) by Rounder Records (USA). Catalogue no: **ROUNDER 2036**
**Cass:** Released '88, on Rounder (USA) by Rounder Records (USA). Catalogue no: **ROUNDER 2036C**
**Album:** Released Jul '83, on Demon by Demon Records. Catalogue no: **FIEND 7**

**JUNCO PARTNER**
**Album:** Released Jan '77, on Island by Island Records. Deleted '80. Catalogue no: **HELP 26**

**KING OF THE NEW ORLEANS KEYBOARD**
Tracks: / How do you feel / Going down slow / Classified / One hell of a nerve / Blues rhapsody / Rockin' pneumonia / Please send me someone to love / All by myself / Ain't nobody's business / Something you got / Harlem in Hamburg.
**Album:** Released Dec '84, on JSP by JSP Records. Catalogue no: **JSP 1083**
**Album:** Released Mar '85, on JSP by JSP Records. Catalogue no: **JSP 1086**

**MR MYSTERY**
**Album:** Released Feb '85, on Sundown by Magnum Music Group. Catalogue no: **CG 709-09**

**NEW ORLEANS PIANO WIZARD: LIVE**
**Album:** Released '88, on Rounder (USA) by Rounder Records (USA). Catalogue no: **ROUNDER 2027**
**Cass:** Released '88, on Rounder (USA) by Rounder Records (USA). Catalogue no: **ROUNDER 2027C**

## Boots & His Buddies

**SAN ANTONIO JAZZ 1935-36**
**Album:** Released Aug '87, on Tax Catalogue no: **M 8002**

## Booty, Charlie

**BOOGIE WOOGIE 8-TO-THE-BAR**
Note: With Ben Conroy
**Album:** Released Feb '87, on Jazzology (USA) by Jazzology Records (USA). Catalogue no: **JCE 88**

## Bop

**Biographical details:** A jazz genre developed by black musicians in the early 1940s, the beginning of the modern era in jazz. Its name came from re-bop or be-bop, onomatopoeiac in origin from the music itself , or possibly from scat-singing. Rhythm section playing had become smoother and the technical fluency of soloists higher than ever; influenced by Lester Young, Charlie Christian, Jo Jones, Art Tatum and others, younger musicians such as Charlie Parker, Dizzy Gillespie, Kenny Clarke, Thelonius Monk, Miles Davis, Fats Navarro, Max Roach and many others jammed in Harlem clubs, improvising on the chords instead of the melody and inventing new tunes from chord structures of standards: they used altered chords and higher intervals, and insisted on using a wider range of notes (a process that has been going on in classical music for centuries). Tempi were often furiously fast or very slow (but even when the tempo was slow the soloist often played fast, using machine-gun runs of sixteenth notes).

Syncopation finally disappeared; new accents within measures, together with phrases of unusual lengths, changed even the rhythmic nature of jazz; in addition, the drum kit emerged as a musical instrumental in its own right, and the bass player often played often played on top of the beat, taking over some of the drummer's timekeeping function, whereas earlier he had more often played behind the beat, taking over some of the drummer's timekeeping function, whereas earlier he had more often played behind the beat. An intense music was created, technically brilliant, full of pride, sardonic wit and fierce joy. The scene was accompanied by attitudes and language incomprehensible to outsiders (some of this had been pioneered by Young; the zany wit of Gillespie was also important). The chromatic style of Coleman Hawkins had been influencial; he encouraged boppers, hiring them for record dates. The first bop records were made in 1944-45 by small groups on independent labels, mainly Savoy. Bop big bands were led by Gillespie and Billy Eckstine; the white bands of Boyd Raeburn and Woody Herman were heavily influenced by bop, but the developement of these big bands (and of bop itself) was poorly documented on disc because of USA musicians' union strikes, which also meant that bop emerged very suddenly in the late '40s upon an unsuspecting public. There were white boppers in black combos (e.g. Reg Rodney, Joe Albany, Al Haig), but pressure on black leaders to practise Crow Jim sent them into obsurity later; many made comebacks as bop became repertory music in the '70s. Boppers often flattened the fifth note of a chord, inventing short routes between keys: Eddie Condon said, 'We don't flatten our fifths, we drink 'em' (but Igor Stravinsky had used flattened fifths in 1910). Alot of people hated it; Cab Calloway called it 'Chinese music'. Bop was not a revolution, but a further flowering of an art-form already decades old; the orthodoxy is that bop was not commercially successful because it wasn't dance music, but bop was fun, and Gillespie regarded it as dance music. He formed the Dee-Gee label and went broke, but reissues (now on Savoy) hold up much better than the pop of the period. Bop was also very obviously black music, long before the Civil Rights era, and in any case the music business tends to mishandle anything it doesn't understand, as it did rock'n'roll a decade later. The Max Roach Quintet of 1954-55, with Cifford Brown and Harold Land (replaced by Sonny Rollins) was probably the peak of bop's perfection; modern jazz was already developed in several direction: sheer beauty came from Miles Davis's quintet of 1956, and as composers and arrangers such as Tadd Dameron, Mal Waldon, George Russell, Gil Evans and Benny Golson applied their talent to the new harmonic ideas. Independent USA labels (Prestige, Riverside and especially Blue Note) developed the blowing session, where the tenor saxophone was king, leading to further developed of the music by Sonny Rollins, John Coltrane and many others. The 'hard top' school of Art Blakey's Jazz Messengers, playing a less frenetic mucic with modern harmonies and a strong backbeat, graduated scores of fine young musicians, Milt Jackson, Horace Silver, Bobby Timmons, Lee Morgan and Herbie Hancock played modern jazz with soul, which came to be called funk, and led directly to the cliches of today's jazz-funk, but also to a renewal of interest in the roots of today's pop music..

## Bop (Group)

**TOO YOUNG TO KNOW**
Tracks: / Too young to know / World's collide.
**12" Single:** Released Feb '84, on EMI by EMI Records. Deleted '87. Catalogue no: **12PAGE 1**
**7" Single:** Released Feb '84, on EMI by EMI Records. Catalogue no: **PAGE 1**

## Bop City

**BOP CITY: EVIDENCE (Various artists)**
**Album:** Released Sep '85, on Boplicity by Ace Records. Deleted '88. Catalogue no: **BOPM 12**

**BOP CITY: MIDNIGHT (Various artists)**
**Album:** Released Sep '85, on Boplicity by Ace Records. Deleted '88. Catalogue no: **BOPM 9**

**BOP CITY: STRAIGHT AHEAD (Various artists)**
**Album:** Released Sep '85, on Boplicity by Ace Records. Deleted '88. Catalogue no: **BOPM 10**

**BOP CITY: THINGS ARE GETTING BETTER (Various artists)**
**Album:** Released Sep '85, on Boplicity by Ace Records. Deleted '88. Catalogue no: **BOPM 11**

## Bop Fathers In Paris

**BOP FATHERS IN PARIS (Various artists)**
Note: Featuring Gillespie, Stitt, Winding, Blakey, Monk, McKibbon.
**Album:** Released Sep '87, on Lotus Catalogue no: **LOP 14 072**

## Bop Session

**BOP SESSION, THE**
**CD:** Released '88, on Vogue by Vogue Records. Catalogue no: **VG 651 6000 39**

## Bostic, Earl

**Biographical details:** Bostic, Earl. The USA alto saxophonist and bandleader was born in 1913 in Tulsa, Oklahoma, and died in 1965. He played in big bands during the Swing era and led his own small groups from 1945, on the King label from 1949 to 1963, and very successfully: in the early '50s nearly every juke box in a black neighbourhood had Bostic records on it, and many a white box as well. *Flamingo* was a no. 1 R&B hit in 1951 and there were many other hits; sidemen passing through included guitarists Al Casey and Mickey Baker, drummer Earl Palmer, John Coltrane, Stanley Turrentine, Benny Golson and Bill Doggett. Bostic probably sacrificed tone for technique as a saxophonist, but he was an acknowledged master of the instrument: Art Blakey said that if Coltrane worked for Bostic, he must have learned a lot. (Donald Clarke, 24 August 1988.).

**14 ORIGINAL GREATEST HITS: EARL BOSTIC**
**Album:** Released Mar '88, on King (USA) Catalogue no: **K 5010**

**16 SWEET TUNES OF THE 50'S**
**Cass:** Released Apr '87, on Starday (USA) by Gusto Records (USA). Catalogue no: **GT 53022**
**Album:** Released Apr '87, on Starday (USA) by Gusto Records (USA). Catalogue no: **SLP 3022**

**ALTO MAGIC IN HI-FI**
Tracks: / Twilight time / Stairway to the stars / Rockin' with Richard / Be my love / Pinkie / Goodnight sweetheart / Over the waves rock / Jer-on-imo / C jam blues / Wee-gee board / Wrecking rock, The / Home sweet home rock.
**Album:** Released Jun '88, on Sing Catalogue no: **SING 597**
**CD:** Released Mar '90, on King Catalogue no: **KCD 597**

**BEST OF BOSTIC**
Tracks: / Flamingo / Always / Deep purple / Smoke rings / What no pearls / Jungle drums / Serenade / I can't give you anything but love / Seven steps / I'm gettin' sentimental over you / Don't you do it / Steamwhistle jump.
**Album:** Released Aug '88, on Sing Catalogue no: **SING 500**
**CD:** Released Mar '90, on King Catalogue no: **KCD 500**

**BLOWS A FUSE**
Tracks: / Night train / 8.45 stomp / That's the groovy thing / Special delivery stomp / Moonglow / Mambostic / Earl blows a fuse / Harlem nocturne / Who snuck the wine in the gravy / Don't you do it / Disc jockey's nightmare / Flamingo / Steam whistle jump / What, no pearls / Tuxedo Junction.
**Album:** Released Jul '85, on Charly R&B by Charly Records. Catalogue no: **CRB 1091**
**Cass:** Released Jul '85, on Charly R&B by Charly Records. Catalogue no: **TCCRB 1091**

**BOSTIC FOR YOU**
Tracks: / Sleep / Moonglow / Velvet sunset / For you / Very thought of you, The / Linger awhile / Cherokee / Smoke gets in your eyes / Memories / Embraceable you / Wrap your troubles in dreams / Night and day.

**CD:** Released Mar '90, on King Catalogue no: **KCD 503**
**Album:** Released '88, on Sing Catalogue no: **SING 503**

**BOSTIC ROCKS**
**Album:** Released 7 Nov '87, on Swingtime by Contact Records (Denmark). Catalogue no: **ST 1022**
**Album:** Released Dec '88, on Syndicate Chapter Catalogue no: **SC 1022**

**DANCE MUSIC FROM THE BOSTIC WORKSHOP**
Tracks: / Third man theme / Key, The / Does your heart beat for me / El choclo cha cha / Gondola / Sweet pea / Ducky / Sentimental journey / Barcarolle / Who cares / Rose Marie / Up there in orbit.
**Album:** Released '88, on Sing Catalogue no: **SING 613**
**CD:** Released Mar '90, on King Catalogue no: **KCD 613**

**DANCE TIME**
Tracks: / Harlem nocturne / Where or when / Sweet Lorraine / Poems / You go to my head / Off shore / Moon is low, The / Ain't misbehavin' / Sheik of Araby, The / I hear a rhapsody / Roses of picardy / Melancholy serenade.
**Album:** Released '88, on Sing Catalogue no: **SING 525**

**EARL BOSTIC**
**Album:** Released Jul '88, on Bellaphon Catalogue no: **BID 8010**

**LET'S DANCE**
Tracks: / Lover come back to me / Merry widow waltz, The / Cracked ice / Song of the islands / Danube waves / Wrap it up / Blue skies / Ubangi stomp / Cherry bean / Earl's imagination / My heart at thy sweet voice / Lieberstraum.
**CD:** Released Oct '88, on King Catalogue no: **KCD 529**
**Album:** Released Dec '87, on Sing Catalogue no: **SING 529**

**SAX 'O' BOOGIE**
**Album:** Released May '84, on Oldie Blues Catalogue no: **OL 8007**

**THAT'S EARL BROTHER**
**Album:** Released '88, on Spotlite by Spotlite Records. Catalogue no: **SPJ 152**

**TRADING LICKS (Bostic, Earl & Bill Doggett)**
Tracks: / Honky tonk Part 1 & 2 / Big Boy / Buttered Popcorn / Backwoods / Slow Walk / Quaker City / Night Train / Rambunk-shush / Peacock Alley / Hold It / Rainbow Riot Pt 1 & 2 / Flamingo / Steam Whistle Jump / What, No Pearls / Don't you do it / Moonglow / Special Delivery Stomp / Harlem Nocturne / Mambostic.
**CD:** Released Feb '87, on Charly by Charly Records. Catalogue no: **CDCHARLY 51**

## Boswell, Connie

**BOSWELL, CONNIE: ON THE AIR (Boswell, Connie & Boswell Sisters)**
Tracks: / Object of my affection, The / Dinah / If love came wrapped in cellophane / Don't forget / I can't give you anything but love / When I'm with you / These foolish things / Until the real thing comes along / Silver threads among the gold / Manhattan / I hear a rhapsody / Amapola / Gay ranchero, A / Time was / Maria Elena.
**Album:** Released Jun '79, on Totem Catalogue no: **TOTEM 1025**

**ON THE AIR 1939**
Tracks: / Heaven can wait / Little skipper / And the Angels sing / Lullaby in rhythm / Wishing will make it so / Snug as a bug in a rug / Masquerade is over, The / Sing a song of sunbeams / Sunrise serenade / Lady's in love with you, The / Begin the beguine / Guess I'll go back home / Ain'tcha comin' out.
**Album:** Released '87, on Totem Catalogue no: **TOTEM 1043**

**SAND IN MY SHOES**
Tracks: / Top hat, white tie and tails / Cheek to cheek / I'm gonna sit right down and write me a letter / Music goes round and around, The / Let yourself go / I'm putting all my eggs in one basket / Between 18th and 19th on Chestnut Street / Yes indeed / Trust in me / Mama don't allow / Martha ah so pure / Fare thee, honey, fare thee well / Sand in my shoes / I hear a rhapsody / I let a song go out of my heart / That old feeling / Mr. Freddie blues / Sunrise serenade / Home on the range / Blueberry Hill.
**Cass:** Released Jun '82, on MCA by MCA Records. Deleted Jan '88. Catalogue no: **MCLC 1689**
**Album:** Released Jun '82, on MCA by MCA Records. Deleted Jan '88. Catalogue no: **MCL 1689**

**SINGING THE BLUES**
Tracks: / Singin' the blues / You need some lovin' / I'm gonna sit right down / Heebie jeebie blues / I gotta right to sing the blues / Right kind of man, The / Someday, sweetheart / Baby, won't you please come home / My little nest of heavenly blues / If I give my heart to you / How important can it be? / Begin the beguine / Believe it beloved / Fill my heart with happiness / I compare you / Main street on Saturday night.
**Album:** Released '88, on Official by Official Records. Catalogue no: **OFF 12004**

**SWING ME A LULLABY**
Tracks: / Panic is on, The / I let a song go out of my heart / Is it love or infatuation? / Heart and soul / Loveliness of you, The / There's something about an old love / I'm glad for your sake (but I'm sorry for mine / I hadn't anyone till you / Life is a song / If it rains, who cares? / On the beach at Bali-Bali / I can't give you anything but love, baby / I'm away from it all / Whispers in the dark / Outside of Paradise / Where are you? / Am I in love? / Chasin' shadows / Blossoms on Broadway / Swing me a lullaby.
**Album:** Released Jun '88, on Conifer Happy Days by Conifer Records. Catalogue no: **CHD 159**
**Cass:** Released Jun '88, on Conifer Happy Days by Conifer Records. Catalogue no: **MCHD 159**

## Boswell Sisters

**Biographical details:** Boswell Sisters. Connie (1907-76; aka Connee), Martha and Helvetia ('Vet') were a vocal trio from New Orleans, the first girl group, paving the way for the Andrew Sisters and many more. They had a middle-class upbringing, but grew up listening to blues, spirituals and opera (Connie, who was a victim of polio and worked in a wheelchair, gave Caruso credit for inspiring her breath control). They also played several instruments. Connie did the arrangements; they were successful on radio and in films, recorded with Bing Crosby and had 20 hit records in the '30s, including a top ten called *Rock and Roll* in 1934 (from a film called 'Transatlantic Merry-Go-Round'), proving that there's nothing new under the sun, and a number one hit in 1935 with *The Object Of My Affection.* Connie recorded solo from 1932 and had over 30 hits of her own through 1954, several with Crosby; both the trio and especially Connie as a solo were highly regarded by jazzmen: the girls recorded with Tommy and Jimmy Dorsey, Bunny Berigan and others; Connie's hits in 1952-53 were accompanied by Artie Shaw's Gramercy Five and the Lawson-Haggart Jazz Band (alumni of the Bob Crosby band of Swing era fame). (Donald Clarke, 24 August 1988.).

**BOSWELL SISTERS, THE**
**LP Set:** Released Aug '87, on Murray Hill Catalogue no: **59892**

**IT'S THE GIRLS (Boswell Sisters & Connie Boswell)**
Tracks: / It's the girls / That's what I like about you / Heebie jeebies / Concentratin' on you / Wha'd ja do to me? / I'm all dressed up with a broken heart / When I take my sugar to tea / Don't tell him what happened to me / Roll on, Mississippi, roll on / I'm gonna cry (cryin' blues) / This is the missus / That's love / Life is just a bowl of cherries / My future just passed / What is it? / Shine on, harvest moon / Gee, but I'd like to make you happy / We're on the highway to Heaven / Time on my hands / Nights when I'm lonely / Shout, sister, shout! / It's you!.
**Cass:** Released Jun '82, on Living Era by Academy Sound & Vision Records. Catalogue no: **ZC AJA 5014**
**Album:** Released Jun '82, on Living Era by Academy Sound & Vision Records. Catalogue no: **AJA 5014**

**MUSIC GOES ROUND AND ROUND, THE**
**Album:** Released Aug '88, on Halcyon (USA) by Submarine Records. Catalogue no: **HDL 118**
**Cass:** Released Aug '88, on Halcyon (USA) by Submarine Records. Catalogue no: **CHDL 118**

**OKAY AMERICA!**
Note: Includes rarities, alternate takes with Mills Brothers, Dorseys and Eddie Lang. 1931-35
**Album:** Released Jun '88, on Jass Catalogue no: **JASS 1**

**THREE SYNCOPATIN' BOSWELL**
Tracks: / I've lost you / Sharing / Poor little Cinderella Brown / If my friends find you they'll steal you from / Abscence makes the heart grow fonder for someo / Livin' in the sunlight, Lovin' in the moonligh / Crazy people / Nothing is sweeter than you / Cheek to cheek / Top hat / I'm gonna sit right down and write myself a le / Way back home / I'll never say "never again" again / Dinah.
**Album:** Released '87, on Totem Catalogue no: **TOTEM 1042**

**YOU OUGHTA BE IN PICTURES**
Tracks: / Alexander's ragtime band (Recorded 23/5/35 (New York)) / You oughta be in pictures (Recorded 23/5/35 (New York)) / Doggone I've done it (Recorded 17/6/32 (New York)) / I hate myself (Recorded 23/3/34 (New York)) / Going home (Recorded 27/4/34 (New York)) / Louisiana hayride (Recorded 27/11/32 (New York)) / If I had a million dollars (Recorded 4/10/34 (Los Angeles)) / Object of my affection, The (Recorded 10/12/34 (Los Angeles)) / Old Yazoo (Recorded 29/6/32 (New York)) / Sentimental gentleman from Georgia (Recorded 13/9/32 (New York)) / It don't mean a thing (Recorded 22/11/32 (New York)) / Rock & roll (Recorded 4/10/34 (Los Angeles)) / Minnie the moocher's wedding day (Recorded 22/11/32 (New York)) / If it ain't love (Recorded 9/4/32 (New York)) / Lonesome road (Recorded 27/4/34(New York)) / There'll be some changes made (Recorded 21/3/32(New York)) / Stop the Sun, stop the Moon (Recorded 24/2/32(New York)) / Mood indigo (Recorded 9/1/33(New York)).
Note: MONO recording.
**Cass:** Released Sep '86, on Conifer Happy Days by Conifer Records. Catalogue no: **MCHD 136**
**Album:** Released Sep '86, on Conifer Happy Days by Conifer Records. Catalogue no: **CHD 136**

## Boustedt, Christer

**PLAYS THELONIOUS MONK**
Tracks: / Trinkle tinkle / Pannonica / Straight, no chaser / Reflections / Gallop's gallop / Ruby my dear / Well you needn't.
**Album:** Released Jun '83, on Dragon by Dragon Records. Catalogue no: **DRLP 38**

## Boutte, Lillian

**BIRTHDAY PARTY (Boutte, Lillian & Her Music Friends)**
**Album:** Released Feb '89, on Music Mecca by Ambia Music ApS. Catalogue no: **ML 123**

**FINE ROMANCE, A (Boutte, Lillian & Thomas l'Etienne)**
Note: with Jeanette Kimball / Frank Fields / Stanley Stephens
**Album:** Released Dec '87, on GHB by Jazzology Records (USA). Catalogue no: **GHB 206**

**I SING BECAUSE I'M HAPPY**
**Album:** Released '88, on Timeless by Timeless Records. Catalogue no: **JC 11003**
**CD:** Released 16 Jan '88, on Timeless by Timeless Records. Catalogue no: **CDJC 11003**

**LET THEM TALK (Boutte, Lillian & Thomas l'Etienne)**
Tracks: / Tennessee waltz / Let them talk / I still get jealous / He's funny that way / Bugle call rag / Love / I surrender dear / Who rolled the stone away / Nobody knows the trouble I've seen / Traveller's tune.
**Album:** Released '88, on Storyville by Storyville Records AB. Catalogue no: **SLP 439**

**LILLIAN**
**Cass:** Released Sep '88, on Calligraph Catalogue no: **ZCLG 018**

**LILLIAN BOUTTE WITH HUMPHREY LYTTLETON (Boutte, Lillian / Humphrey Lyttleton & His Band)**
Tracks: / Back in your own back yard / Miss Otis regrets / Squiggles / I double dare you / Lillian.
**CD:** Released Oct '88, on Calligraph Catalogue no: **CLGCD 018**
**Cass:** Released Oct '88, on Calligraph Catalogue no: **ZCLG 018**
**Album:** Released Oct '88, on Calligraph Catalogue no: **CLGLP 018**

**MUSIC IS MY LIFE (Boutte, Lillian & Her Music Friends)**
**Album:** Released Oct '86, on Timeless by Timeless Records. Catalogue no: **JC 11002**

## Bowie, Lester

**Biographical details:** Bowie, Lester. The trumpet player, composer and bandleader was born in 1941 in Maryland. He began with R&B bands and was music director for soul singer Fontella Bass, who became his wife (his brothers Joseph and Byron, trombonist and saxist respectively, succeeded him as Bass's MD). Lester, whose humour, smears and growls have caused him to be described as 'the Cootie Williams of the avant-garde', described himself as a 'research trumpet player'. He was a founder member of AACM (the Chicago black music collective formed in 1967) and if the Art Ensember of Chicago; the album *Nos. 1 & 2* on Nessa was effectively the first Art Ensemble album. On a Roscoe Mitchell album *Congliptious* on Nessa, he answered the question 'Is jazz as we know it dead yet?' (asked by a journalist from 'Jism' magazine) with a 7-minute solo called *Jazz Death?* followed by the remark, 'Well, I guess that all depends, uh, on what you know'. Apart from albums with the Art Ensemble, he made a duet set with the excellent Phillip Watson (who might have been the Art Ensemble's drummer, but went with Paul Butterfield to make some money); Joseph plays on *Rope_A_Dope*. Lester's albums on ECM are affectionate pastiches; his large group Brass Fantasy is now a popular concert attraction. (Donald Clarke, 24 August 1988.).

**ALL THE MAGIC**
**Album:** Released Apr '83, on ECM Catalogue no: **ECM 1246**

**AVANT POP (Bowie, Lester, Brass Fantasy)**
**Album:** Released Sep '86, on ECM Catalogue no: **ECM 1326**
**CD:** Released Sep '86, on ECM Catalogue no: **829 563-2**

**DUET (Bowie, Lester & Philip Wilson)**
**Album:** Released Jul '78, on Improvising Artists Catalogue no: **IAI 373854**
**Album:** Released Feb '87, on King (Japan) Catalogue no: **K 28P 6367**

**FAST LAST**
**Album:** Released Apr '81, on Muse by Black & Blue Records. Catalogue no: **MR 5055**

**FIFTH POWER, THE (Bowie, Lester with Various artists)**
**Album:** Released Jul '78, on Black Saint (Italy) Catalogue no: **BSR 0020**

**GREAT PRETENDER**
**Album:** Released Mar '82, on ECM Catalogue no: **ECM 1209**

**I ONLY HAVE EYES FOR YOU**
**Album:** Released Nov '85, on ECM Catalogue no: **ECM 1296**

**NOS. 1 & 2**
**Album:** Released Mar '79, on Nessa Deleted '83. Catalogue no: **N 1**

**ROPE-A-DOPE**
**Album:** Released Apr '81, on Muse by Black & Blue Records. Catalogue no: **MR 5081**

**TWILIGHT DREAMS (Bowie, Lester, Brass Fantasy)**
Tracks: / I am with you / Personality / Duke's fantasy / Thriller / Night Time (Is The Right Time) / Vibe Waltz / Twilight dreams.
**Album:** Released Jul '87, on Venture (2) by Virgin Records. Catalogue no: **VE 2**
**CD:** Released Jun '88, on Venture (2) by Virgin Records. Catalogue no: **CDVE 2**
**Cass:** Released Jul '87, on Venture (2) by Virgin Records. Catalogue no: **TCVE 2**

**WORKS: LESTER BOWIE**
Tracks: / Charlie M / Rose drop / B funk / When the spirit returns / Let the good times roll.
**CD:** Released Jun '89, on ECM Catalogue no: **837 274-2**
**Album:** Released Jun '89, on ECM Catalogue no: **837 274-1**

## Bowlly, Al

**Biographical details:** Bowlly, Al. Born in 1898 in what is now Maputo, Mozambique, of a Greek father and a Lebanese mother, Al Bowlly is still one of the all-time most popular British vocalists. He grew up in Johannesburg, became a barber (like Perry Como) and learned to play the ukelele; he toured Africa and India as a banjo/guitarist and was a resident at Raffles in Singapore; he made his first records in Berlin in 1927, then freelanced in London, making 678 sides in 1930-34, mainly with the Roy Fox and Ray Noble bands. His best-known records are Noble compositions: *The Very Thought Of You* and others also did well in the USA; Noble took Bowlly with him to NYC in 1934, where Glenn Miller was Noble's arranger; Bowlly sang an early lyric to a Miller tune that later became *Moonlight Serenade*. He was successful in the USA but returned to London in 1937; he toured with his own Radio City Rhythm Makers and teamed with Maltese singer Jimmy Messini in Radio Stars With Two Guitars. He worked with West Indian bandleader Ken 'Snakehips' Johnson in 1940-41. A famous bomb hit the Cafe de Paris, killing Johnson and many others in March 1941; Bowlly was killed by another in April. He made the UK top 10 album chart in 1978 as the featured singer in the 'Pennies From Heaven' soundtrack. (Donald Clarke, 24 August 1988).

**20 GOLDEN PIECES OF AL BOWLLY**
**Album:** Released '88, on Old Bean by Submarine Records. Catalogue no: **OLM 2**
**Cass:** Released '86, on Old Bean by Submarine Records. Catalogue no: **COLM 2**

**1931 SESSIONS**
**Cass:** Released Jan '86, on Saville by Conifer Records. Catalogue no: **CSVL 150**

**AL BOWLLY AND PHYLLIS ROBINS (Bowlly, Al/Phyllis Robins)**
Tracks: / What do your know about love / Hey gypsy, play gypsy / South of the border / Dark eyes / Moon love / Au revoir but not goodbye / Man and his dream / Ridin' home / That's what I like about you / What are you thinkin' about baby? / It's a hap-hap-happy day / Over the rainbow / Scatterbrain / Oh, Johnny / Chatterbox / Sing for your supper.
**Album:** Released Jan '79, on World Records by EMI Records. Deleted Jan '84. Catalogue no: **SH 307**

**AL BOWLLY CIRCLE, THE**
Tracks: / Cuddle up close - You'll never understand / Torn sails / Moon / Gone forever / If you were only mine / Call it a day / Sweepin' the clouds away / Who'll buy an old ring / Foolish facts / Eleven more months and ten more days / Minnie the moocher's wedding day / Roy Fox's commentary on the wedding reception / Lazy Louisiana moon / Moonlight on the Colorado (Duet with Les Allen.) / Dark clouds / Save the last dance for me.
**Album:** Released Feb '84, on Joy by President Records. Catalogue no: **JOYD 281**

**AL BOWLLY IN NEW YORK**
Tracks: / Say When (Copyright Control.) / When love comes singing along (Copyright Control.) / Be still my heart / My melancholy baby / St. Louis blues / Way back home / If I had a million dollars / You and the night and the music / You were there / Little white gardenia, A / Piccolino, The / Everything's been done before / Little gypsy tearoom, A / Red sails in the sunset / Dinner for one please James.
**Album:** Released Jan '87, on Joy by President Records. Catalogue no: **JOY 288**

**AMBASSADOR OF SONG**
Tracks: / Fancy our meeting / My canary has circles under his eyes / Judy / I'm through with love / Be still, my heart / Roll on, Mississippi, roll on / Heartaches / Maria, my own / If I had a million dollars / Miss Elizabeth Brown / If anything happened to you / Got a date with an angel / There's rain in my eyes / Night and day / Brother, can you spare a dime.
**Album:** Released '66, on Ace Of Clubs by Decca Records. Deleted '88. Catalogue no: **ACL 1204**

**AU REVOIR (BUT NOT GOODBYE) (Bowlly, Al & Jim Mesene)**
Tracks: / Make love with a guitar / When I dream of home / Over the rainbow / Careless / Make believe island / Woodpecker song, The / What do you know about love / Old pal of mine / Only forever / It was a lover and his lass / Dreaming / I'm stepping out with a memory tonight / I haven't time to be a millionaire / Turn your money in your pocket / I'll never smile again / We'll go smiling along / Walkin' thru Mockin' Bird Lane / Let the curtain come down / When you wear your Sunday blue / Ferry boat serenade, The / Moon love / Nicky the Greek (has gone) / Au revoir (but not goodbye) / You made me care / When that man is dead and gone.
**Cass:** Released Apr '90, on C5 by C5 Records. Catalogue no: **C5K-542**
**Album:** Released '89, on C5 by C5 Records. Catalogue no: **C5-542**

**CLASSIC YEARS (Bowlly, Al & Ray Noble)**
Tracks: / Brighter than the sun / Pied piper / Makin' wickey wackey down in waikiki / Hold My Hand / Lady of Spain / Shout for happiness / My Hat's On The Side of My Head / Got A Date With An Angel / Time On My Hands / I'll Do My Best To Make You Happy / Love Is The Sweetest Thing / What More Can I Ask / Very Thought of You, The / On The Other Side of Lover's Lane / Love Locked Out / It's Time To Say Goodnight.
**Cass:** Released Oct '87, on BBC by BBC Records & Tapes. Catalogue no: **ZCF 649**
**CD:** Released Oct '87, on BBC by BBC Records & Tapes. Catalogue no: **BBC CD 649**
**Album:** Released Oct '87, on BBC by BBC Records & Tapes. Catalogue no: **REB 649**

**DANCE BAND DAYS, THE**
Tracks: / Time on my hands / Can't get Mississippi off my mind / Tell me (you love me) / Moon / Linda / I'm glad I waited / Heartaches / Goodnight sweetheart / Waltz you saved for me, The / Life is meant for love / We've got the Moon and sixpence / Longer that you linger in Virginia, The / Roll on, Mississippi, roll on / Lady play your mandolin / Time alone will tell / Can't we be friends / Girl in the upstairs flat, The / Trusting my luck / I'm saving the last waltz for you / Somebody's thinking of you tonight / Louisiana hayride / It's a long way to your heart / There's a goldmine in the sky / Proud of you / Souvenir of love / Waves of the ocean are whisp'ring goodnight / Little lady make believe / Fare thee well / Sweet Genevieve / Because it's love / In my little red book / In a shelter from a shower / I won't tell a soul / Riding on a haycart home / Say goodnight to your old fashioned mother.
**Album:** Released Nov '84, on Recollections (Decca) by Decca Records. Catalogue no: **RFLD 46**

**FLOWERS FOR MADAME 1935-37**
Tracks: / I can dream, can't I / Basin Street blues / Carelessly / My melancholy baby / Flowers for madame / Sweet is the word for you / You opened my eyes / In a blue and pensive mood / Half moon on the Hudson / On a little dream ranch / I wished on the moon / Blue Hawaii / Why the stars come out at night / Where am I? / Blazin' the trail / Why dream.
**Album:** Released Jul '88, on Harlequin by Interstate Music. Catalogue no: **HQ 3024**

**GERALDO & AL BOWLLY (Bowlly, Al & Geraldo)**
**Cass:** Released Aug '87, on Halcyon (USA) by Submarine Records. Catalogue no: **CHAL 12**

**GOLDEN AGE OF AL BOWLLY, THE**
Tracks: / Love is the sweetest thing / Bei mir bist du schon (Means that you're grand) / Marie / In my little red book / Something to sing about / Walkin' thru Mockin' Bird Lane / My melancholy baby / Blow, thou winter wind / It was a lover and his lass / Have you ever been lonely? / You're a sweetheart / I'll string along with you / Only forever / Goodnight sweetheart.
Note: Al Bowlly represented the sound that won the hearts of the public during the 30's and would have gone onto greater things had his life not been brought to a sudden end in 1943.
**Cass:** Released Jul '83, on Golden Age by EMI Records. Catalogue no: **TC-GX 2512**
**Album:** Released Jul '83, on Golden Age by EMI Records. Catalogue no: **GX 2512**

**GOODNIGHT SWEETHEART 1931**
Tracks: / I'm telling the world she's mine / Goodnight sweetheart / Lazy day / Hang out the stars in Indiana / There's a ring around the Moon / Goodnight Vienna / I'll do my best to make you happy / Love is the sweetest thing / Wanderer / Maybe I love you too much / Shadow waltz / I've got to sing a torch song / Close your eyes / Unless / Who walks in when I walk out? / Very thought of you, The / I'll string along with you / Grinzing

/ Dreaming a dream / Sing as we go / Don't say goodbye / I'm glad I waited.
Note: A 20-track compilation of great songs from the incomparable Al Bowlly, including all-time classics such as Love is the Sweetest Thing, The Very Thought of You and, of course, Goodnight Sweetheart. On most titles Al Bowlly is accompanied by Ray Noble & His Orchestra, the combination which produced the best Bowlly material of all.
**Album:** Released Mar '86, on Retrospect by EMI Records. Catalogue no: **SH 502**
**Cass:** Released Mar '86, on Retrospect by EMI Records. Deleted Jun '89. Catalogue no: **TCSH 502**

## GOODNIGHT SWEETHEART (2)

Tracks: / Time on my hands / What are you thinking about, baby? / Guilty / Take it from me (I'm taking to you) / Oh Rosalita / Time alone will tell / Thank your father / Would you like to take a walk / I'll keep you in my heart always / That's what I like about you / Bubbling over with love / Just one more chance / Dance Hall doll / By the river Sainte Marie / You didn't have to tell me / By my side / Song of happiness / Lady, play your mandoline / Smile, darn ya, smile / Goodnight, sweetheart.
**Cass:** Released '88, on Saville by Conifer Records. Catalogue no: **CSVL 150**
**CD:** Released '88, on Saville by Conifer Records. Catalogue no: **CDSVL 150**
**Album:** Released Jun '82, on Saville by Conifer Records. Catalogue no: **SVL 150**

## LEGENDARY, THE

**Cass:** Released Mar '90, on Silva Screen by Silva Screen Records. Catalogue no: **MRT 40042**

## LONDON SESSIONS, THE 1928-30

Tracks: / Just imagine / Wherever you are / If I had you / Misery farm / I'm sorry Sally / When the lilac blooms again / Up in the clouds / After the sun's kissed the world goodbye / If anything happened to you / Happy days are here again / On the sunny side of the street / Sweepin' the clouds away / Dancing with tears in my eyes / Adeline / Beware of love / Frankie and Johnnie / By the old oak tree / Never swat a fly / Sunny days / Roamin' through the roses.
**Cass:** Released '86, on Saville by Conifer Records. Catalogue no: **CSVL 148**
**Album:** Released '86, on Saville by Conifer Records. Catalogue no: **SVL 148**

## MILLION DREAMS, A

Tracks: / Moonstruck / Maria my own / Love locked out / There's a cabin in the pines / Night and day / Learn to croon / I'm getting sentimental over you / I'll follow you / Million dreams, A / My romance / Keep your last goodnight for me / Goodnight but not goodbye / Wherever you are / I'll do my best to make you happy / So ashamed / Glorious Devon / That's all that matters to me / You must believe me / Fancing our meeting / Lover come back to me.
**Album:** Released Mar '84, on Saville by Conifer Records. Catalogue no: **SVL 163**
**Cass:** Released '88, on Saville by Conifer Records. Catalogue no: **CSVL 163**

## MY SONG GOES ROUND THE WORLD (Bowlly, Al & Ray Noble)

Tracks: / Wanderer / Just an echo in the valley / Can't we meet again / When you've fallen in love / Let me give my happiness to you / Hustling and bustling for my baby / Waltzing in a dream / It's within your power / Hiawatha's lullaby / Couple of fools in love, A / On the other side of lover's lane / It's bad for me / Dinner at eight / Experiment / Weep no more / Thanks / Oceans of time / On a steamer coming over / Did you ever see a dream walking / My song goes round the world.
**Cass:** Released Mar '87, on Halcyon (USA) by Submarine Records. Catalogue no: **CHAL 18**
**Album:** Released Oct '86, on Halcyon (USA) by Submarine Records. Catalogue no: **HAL 18**

## ON THE SENTIMENTAL SIDE (SET) (Bowlly, Al & Geraldo)

Tracks: / My heart is taking lessons / On the sentimental side / In a little toy sailboat / Small fry / Never break a promise / When Mother Nature sings her lullaby / Penny serenade / Heart and soul / Two sleepy people / Is that the way to treat a sweetheart / Colorado sunset / While a cigarette was burning / Any broken hearts to mend? / Summers end / My own / You're as pretty as a picture / They say / If ever a heart was in the right place / One day when we were young / I'm in love with Vienna.
**2 LP Set:** Released '78, on Decca by Decca International. Deleted '88. Catalogue no: **DDV 5009/10**

## ON THE SENTIMENTAL SIDE (Bowlly, Al & Geraldo)

**Album:** Released May '88, on Retrospect by EMI Records. Deleted Oct '89. Catalogue no: **SH 516**
**Cass:** Released May '88, on Retrospect by EMI Records. Catalogue no: **TC SH 516**
**Cass:** Released May '88, on Retrospect by EMI Records. Catalogue no: **EG 2604624**
**Album:** Released May '88, on Retrospect by EMI Records. Deleted Oct '89. Catalogue no: **EG 2604621**

## ONE & ONLY

Tracks: / I've had my moments / I'm so used to you now / I'm for you a hundred per cent / Whispering / Dark clouds / You didn't know the music / When we're alone / It was so beautiful / Ending with a kiss / Melody in Spring / Faded Summer love / Tell me you are from Georgia / Beat o' my heart / What a perfect night for love / Rose Mia / You are my heart's delight / Dinah / Leave the rest to nature.
**Album:** Released Nov '80, on Decca by Decca International. Deleted Nov '85. Catalogue no: **RFL 1**

## PROUD OF YOU

Tracks: / Marie / Sweet someone / Colorado sunset / Is that the way to treat a sweetheart? / When Mother Nature sings her lullaby / Two sleepy people / Sweet as a song / Goodnight angel / Any broken hearts to mend? / Al Bowlly remembers (medley) / Very thought of you, The / You're as pretty as a picture / Proud of you / True / Summer's end / There's rain in my eyes / Bei mir bist du schon / When the organ played 'O promise me' / While the cigarette was burning / Penny serenade.
Note: 67 minutes. Medley (Al Bowlly remembers) includes Lover come back to me; Dancing in the dark; I'm gonna sit right down and write myself a letter; Auf Wiedersehn, my dear.
**CD:** Released 1 Sep '89, on Living Era by Academy Sound & Vision Records. Catalogue no: **CD AJA 5064**
**Cass:** Released 1 Sep '89, on Living Era by Academy Sound & Vision Records. Catalogue no: **ZC AJA 5064**
**Album:** Released 1 Sep '89, on Living Era by Academy Sound & Vision Records. Catalogue no: **AJA 5064**

## SENTIMENTALLY YOURS

Tracks: / Madonna mine / I'm getting sentimental over you / Judy / Everything I have is yours / Glorious Devon / Isle of Capri / Lover come back to me / There's a cabin in the pines / If I had a million dollars / True / It's all forgotten now / That's me without you / Fancy our meeting / Learn to croon / Night & day / Love locked out / Be still my heart.
Note: MONO recording.
**Cass:** Released Jan '86, on Conifer Happy Days by Conifer Records. Catalogue no: **MCHD 127**
**Album:** Released Jan '86, on Conifer Happy Days Catalogue no: **CHD 127**

## SOMETHING TO SING ABOUT

Tracks: / Home town / Grandma said / Deep in a dream / You're a sweet little headache / I'm madly in love with you / Same old story / Could be / Between a kiss and a sigh / To mother with love / Thanks for everything / I miss you in the morning / Small town / What do you know about love / Moon love / Au revoir but not goodbye / Vieni, vieni / Le touquet / Smile when you say goodbye / Something to sing about / In my little red book.
Note: Produced, compiled and transferred by Chris Ellis
**Cass:** Released Jun '87, on Retrospect by EMI Records. Deleted Jun '89. Catalogue no: **TCSH 501**
**Album:** Released Jun '87, on Retrospect by EMI Records. Catalogue no: **SH 501**

## SWEET AS A SONG

Tracks: / Carelessly / On a little dream ranch / Blue Hawaii / Sweet is the word for you / Bei mir bist du schon / Marie / You're a sweetheart / Pretty little patchwork quilt, The / Sweet as a song / Sweet someone / Goodnight angel / When the

organ played 'O promise me (intro 'I love you truly) / Romany / Lonely / I miss you in the morning / Violin in Vienna / What do you know about love / Hey gypsy, play gypsy / South of the border / Dark eyes.
Note: A brand new compilation of titles sung by the legendary Al Bowlly. These tracks from between 1937 and 1939, were recorded as solos for Browlly, most accompanied by Ronnie Munro and his Orchestra. The original 78 rpm issuse of these tracks have long been highly treasured and highly priced collectors pieces, and on this rcecord appear in LP form for the first time. Bowlly is accompanied on piano on two tracks on this album by Violet Carson - Coronation Street's Ena Sharples.
**Cass:** Released Jun '85, on Retrospect by EMI Records. Deleted Jul '87. Catalogue no: **EG 2604574**
**Album:** Released Jun '85, on Retrospect by EMI Records. Deleted Jul '87. Catalogue no: **EG 2604571**

**TIME ON MY HANDS**
**Cass:** Released '88, on Saville by Conifer Records. Catalogue no: **CSVLD 003**
**2 LP Set:** Released Sep '87, on Saville by Conifer Records. Catalogue no: **SVLD 003**

**VERY THOUGHT OF YOU, THE**
**Cass set:** Released '88, on Ditto by Pickwick Records. Catalogue no: **DTO 10219**
**CD:** Released Sep '88, on Burlington (nostalgia) by Counterpoint Distribution. Catalogue no: **2 BUR 003**
**Album:** Released Jun '88, on Burlington (nostalgia) by Counterpoint Distribution. Catalogue no: **BUR 003**

**VERY THOUGHT OF YOU, THE (EMI)**
Tracks: / Time on my hands / Goodnight sweetheart / Sweet and lovely / Pied piper of Hamelin, The / By the fireside / Love is the sweetest thing / How could we be wrong? / Weep no more my baby / Love locked out / You ought to see Sally on Sunday / One morning in May / Very thought of you, The / Isle of Capri / Blue Hawaii / In my litt red book / Penny serenade / They say / South of the border / Over the rainbow / Somewhere in France with you / When you wish upon a star / Who's taking you home tonight / Blow, blow, thou winter wind / It was lover and his lass.
**Album:** Released May '90, on EMI by EMI Records. Catalogue no: **794 341 1**
**Cass:** Released May '90, on EMI by EMI Records. Catalogue no: **794 341 4**
**Album:** Released May '90, on EMI by EMI Records. Catalogue no: **SH 518**
**Cass:** Released May '90, on EMI by EMI Records. Catalogue no: **TCSH 518**
**CD:** Released May '90, on EMI by EMI Records. Catalogue no: **CDP 794 341 2**
**CD:** Released May '90, on EMI by EMI Records. Catalogue no: **CZ 306**

## Brace, Brent

**VALLEY GIRL JAZZ**
**Album:** Released '88, on Progressive Catalogue no: **PRO 7071**

## Brackeen, Joanne

**Biographical details:** Brackeen, Joanne. This marvellous jazz pianist and composer was born Joanne Grogan in 1938 in Ventura, California, and was subsequently married to saxophonist Charles Brackeen. She is mostly self-taught, having started by copying her parents' Frankie Carle records, then solos of Charlie Parker and Bud Powell, later John Coltrane, developing her own rhythmic complexity and an experimental approach to harmony. She played with Art Blakey in 1970-72, joining during a Blakey club date (the pianist got lost and Brackeen took over). Most of her albums are trio sets, but she has also recorded duo (with bassist Eddie Gomez on *Prism* on the Choice label) and solo (*Mythical Magic* on MPS). She usually plays her own music, but *Havin' Fun* is a delightful album of mostly classic standards, plus George Michael's *Everything She Wants*, with drummer Al Foster, bassist Cecil McBee. (Donald Clarke, 24 August 1988.).

**AFT**
Tracks: / Haiti B / Charlotte's dream / Dreamers / Aft / Winter is here / Green voices of play air.
**Album:** Released Sep '86, on Timeless by Timeless Records. Catalogue no: **SJP 115**

**FI-FI GOES TO HEAVEN**
Tracks: / Estilo magnifico / Stardust / Fi-Fi goes to heaven / Zingaro / I hear a rhapsody / Cosmonaut / Doctor Chang.
Note: Personnel: Joanne Brackeen - piano / Terance Blanchard - trumpet / Branford Marsalis - alto & soprano sax / Cecil McBee - bass / Al Foster - drums.
**Cass:** Released Jul '87, on Concord Jazz by Concord Jazz Records (USA). Catalogue no: **CJC 316**
**CD:** Released Jul '87, on Concord Jazz by Concord Jazz Records (USA). Catalogue no: **CCD 4316**
**Album:** Released Jul '87, on Concord Jazz by Concord Jazz Records (USA). Catalogue no: **CJ 316**

**HAVIN' FUN (Brackeen, Joanne Trio)**
Tracks: / Thinking of you / I've got the world on a string / Emily / Just one of those things / This is always / Everything she wants / Manha de carnaval / Day by day.
**CD:** Released Jan '87, on Concord Jazz by Concord Jazz Records (USA). Catalogue no: **CCD 4280**
**Album:** Released Dec '85, on Concord Jazz by Concord Jazz Records (USA). Catalogue no: **CJ 280**

**INVITATION**
**Album:** Released '78, on Freedom Catalogue no: **FLP 41044**

**LIVE AT MAYBECK RECITAL HALL**
Tracks: / Thou swell / Dr Chu Chow / Yesterdays / Curved space / My foolish heart / Calling Carl / I'm old fashioned / Strike up the band / Most beautiful girl in the world, The (Available on CD only) / It could happen to you (Available on CD only) / African Aztec (CD only).
**CD:** Released '90, on Concord by Concord Jazz Records (USA). Catalogue no: **CCD 4409**
**Cass:** Released Mar '90, on Concord by Concord Jazz Records (USA). Catalogue no: **CJ 409C**

**NEW TRUE ILLUSION (Brackeen, Joanne & Clint Houston)**
Tracks: / Steps what was / Search for peace / New true illusion / My romance / Freedent / Solar.
**Album:** Released Apr '81, on Timeless by Timeless Records. Catalogue no: **SJP 103**

**SPECIAL IDENTITY**
**Album:** Released Jun '82, Catalogue no: **AN 1001**

**TRINKETS & THINGS (Brackeen, Joanne & Ryo Kawaski)**
Tracks: / Trinkets & things / Showbrook air / Winnie & Woodstock / Fair weather / Whim within / Spring of things / Haiti B.
**Album:** Released Apr '81, on Timeless by Timeless Records. Catalogue no: **SJP 123**

## Bradley, Will

**Biographical details:** Bradley, Will was born in 1912 in New Jersey; he played trombone in swing bands, formed a band co-led by drummer Ray McKinley, changed his name because Wilbur Schwichtenberg wouldn't fit on a marquee. It was a good white jazz-orientated dance band whose big hit *Beat Me Daddy, Eight To The Bar* fueled the boogie-woogie fad; *Celery Stalks At Midnight* was one of the 78s smashed by yobs in the 1955 movie 'Blackboard Jungle', which also introduced Bill Haley. (Donald Clarke, 24 August 1988.).

**1941 (Featuring Ray McKinley) (Bradley, Will & Orchestra)**
**Album:** Released Jun '88, on Circle (USA) by Jazzology Records (USA). Catalogue no: **CLP 88**

**BASIN STREET BOOGIE 1941 - 42 (Bradley, Will & His Orchestra)**
**Album:** Released Jun '88, on Bandstand Catalogue no: **BS 7110**

**FIVE O'CLOCK WHISTLE 1939 - 41 (Bradley, Will & His Orchestra)**
**Album:** Released Jun '88, on Bandstand Catalogue no: **BS 7101**

**IN DISCO ORDER VOL. 1**
**Album:** Released Jul '77, on Ajax (USA) Catalogue no: **AJAX 112**

**IN DISCO ORDER VOL. 2**
**Album:** Released Dec '77, on Ajax (USA) Catalogue no: **AJAX 115**

**IN DISCO ORDER VOL. 3**
**Album:** Released Dec '77, on Ajax (USA) Catalogue no: **AJAX 119**

**ROCK-A-BYE THE BOOGIE 1940-41 (Bradley, Will & His Orchestra)**
**Album:** Released Jun '88, on Bandstand Catalogue no: **BS 7112**
**Cass:** Released Jun '88, on Bandstand Catalogue no: **BS 7112C**

**WILL BRADLEY & RAY MCKINLEY, 1940-41 (Bradley, Will & Ray McKinley)**
Tracks: / Fatal fascination / Cherry / I guess I'll have to dream the rest / Just a little bit south of North Caralina / I went out of my way / Be I bi / Song of the islands / Booglie wooglie piggy, The / This little icky went to town / Flying home / All the things you are / Wham / King Calypso / 'S wonderful / It's a wonderful world / Starlight hour, The / Hallelujah.
**Album:** Released Apr '79, on Aircheck (USA) by Kiner Ents.(USA). Catalogue no: **AIRCHECK 15**

**WILL BRADLEY - VOL 4, 1940**
**Album:** Released Apr '79, on Ajax (USA) Catalogue no: **AJAX 131**

**WILL BRADLEY - VOL 5, 1940-41**
**Album:** Released Apr '79, on Ajax (USA) Catalogue no: **AJAX 136**

**WILL BRADLEY - VOL 6, 1941**
**Album:** Released Apr '79, on Ajax (USA) Catalogue no: **AJAX 142**

**WILL BRADLEY - VOL 7, 1941**
**Album:** Released Apr '79, on Ajax (USA) Catalogue no: **AJAX 150**

**WILL BRADLEY - VOL 8, 1941-46**
**Album:** Released Apr '79, on Ajax (USA) Catalogue no: **AJAX 158**

**WILL BRADLEY & WINGY MANONE (Bradley, Will & Wingy Manone)**
**Album:** on Harlequin by Interstate Music. Catalogue no: **HQ 2037**

## Bradshaw, Tiny

**Biographical details:** Bradshaw, Tiny. Myron Bradshaw (1905-58) was a singer, drummer, pianist and bandleader who formed his own band in 1934 and switched from big band to R&B combo style in the mid-'40s: his was said to be Buddy Holly's favourite band, it's R&B hits in the late '40s and early '50s usually featuring raunchy sax solos by Sil Austin or Red Prysock, both of whom went off and started similar successful combos of their own. (Donald Clarke, 24 August 1988.).

**BREAKING UP THE HOUSE**
Tracks: / Breaking up the house / Walk that mess / Train kept a rollin' / T 99 / Bradshaw boogie / Walking the chalk line / Mailman's sack / Snaggle tooth Ruth / Rippin' and runnin' / Blues came pouring down, The / Two dry bones on the pantry shelf / Brad's blues / Boodie green / Well oh well / Newspaper boy blues / One,two,three, kick blues.
**Cass:** Released Jul '85, on Charly R&B by Charly Records. Catalogue no: **TCCRB 1092**
**Album:** Released Jul '85, on Charly R&B by Charly Records. Catalogue no: **CRB 1092**
**CD:** Released '85, on Charly by Charly Records. Catalogue no: **CDCHARLY 43**

**GREAT COMPOSER, THE**
**CD:** Released Oct '88, on King 1 Catalogue no: **KLP 653**

**I'M A HIGH BALLIN' DADDY**
Tracks: / I've been around / Straighten up and fly again / Salt Lake City bounce / School day blues / After you've gone / Bradshaw bounce / These things are love / Butterfly / I'm a high ballin' daddy / Pompton turnpike / Lay it on the line / If I had a million dollars / Spider web / If you don't love me tell me so / Overflow / Strange.
**Album:** Released Jan '88, on Jukebox Lil (Sweden) Catalogue no: **JB 621**

**STOMPING ROOM ONLY**
Tracks: / Walk that mess / Bradshaw boogie / T 99 / Breaking up the house / Well oh well / Train kept a rollin' / Cat fruit / Stomping room only / Gravy train / Newspaper boy blues / I'm gonna have myself a ball / Long time baby / Mailman's sack / Blues came pouring down, The / Heavy juice / Cat nap.
**Album:** Released Jan '84, on Krazy Kat by Interstate Music. Catalogue no: **KK 419**

**TINY BRADSHAW 1934 / TEDDY HILL (Bradshaw, Tiny/Hill, Teddy)**
Tracks: / Shout Sister Shout / Mister will you serenade / Darktown strutters ball / Sheik of Araby / Ol' man river / I ain't got nobody / I'm a ding dong daddy from Dumas / She'll be coming round the mountain / Lookie lookie lookie here comes Cookie / Got me doin' things / When the robin sings his song again / When love knocks at your heart / Uptown rhapsody / At the rug cutter's ball / Blue rhythm fantasy / Passionette.
**Album:** Released Jan '87, on Harlequin by Interstate Music. Catalogue no: **HQ 2053**

**TRIBUTE TO THE LATE TINY**
Tracks: / Soft / Off and on / Heavy juice / Well oh well / Free for all / Choice / Bushes / Stack of dollars / Later / Powder stuff / South of the Orient / Train kept a-rollin', The / Light / Ping pong / Come on / Cat fruit.
**Album:** Released Dec '87, on Sing Catalogue no: **SING 653**

## Braff, Ruby

**Biographical details:** Braff, Ruby. Born in Boston, Massachusetts in 1927, Braff played trumpet, then switched to cornet in 1967. He was always highly rated by critics for swing, tone, ideas and technique, but played a mainstream style in the heyday of 'modern' or 'progressive' jazz: he had a playing and acting role in Rodgers and Hammerstein's musical 'Pipe Dream' in 1955-6, then was mostly out of work for years, though making the occasional record on Bethlehem (now on Affinity), on Vanguard with Buck Clayton, etc. Since all jazz in the '80s is repertory music, however, the barriers are down between genres, revivalists and older and younger players, and Braff is making more records than ever, as well as making frequent visits to the UK. He has recorded with the highly rated Canadian guitarist Ed Bickert, the Chicago guitarist George Barnes and veteran pianists Dave McKenna and Dick Hyman (who recorded ragtime in the '50s as Knuckles O'Toole, and plays organ on *Amercia The Beautiful*) as well as the young tenor saxist Scott Hamilton. (Donald Clarke, 24 August 1988.).

**AMERICA THE BEAUTIFUL (Braff, Ruby & Dick Hyman)**
Tracks: / When it's sleepy time down South / When my sugar walks down the street / When I fall in love / As long as I live / America the beautiful / Louisiana / High society / I'll be with you in apple blossom time / I ain't got nobody / This is all I ask.
**Album:** Released Jul '84, on George Wein Collection(USA) by Concord Jazz Records (USA). Catalogue no: **GW 3003**

**BEST I'VE HEARD**
Tracks: / Our love is here to stay / On the sunny side of the street / It don't mean a thing / It don't mean a thing / You're a lucky guy / Struttin' with some barbecue / Rockin' in rhythm / Body and soul / Sugar.
**Cass:** Released Jan '83, on Vogue Jazz (France) by Vogue Records. Catalogue no: **ZC VJD 519**
**Album:** Released Jan '83, on Vogue Jazz (France) by Vogue Records. Catalogue no: **VJD 519**

**BRAFF PLAYS BING**
**Cass:** Released Nov '79, on Pizza Express by Pizza Express Records. Catalogue no: **PIZZA C5501**
**Album:** Released Oct '79, on Pizza Express by Pizza Express Records. Catalogue no: **PIZZA 5501**

**EASY NOW**
Tracks: / My walking stick / Willow weep for me / When my sugar walks down the street / Song is ended, The / Give my regards to broadway / This is my lucky day / Someday you'll be sorry / Yesterdays / For now / I just couldn't take it baby / Little man, you've had a busy day / Swinging on a star / Old folks / Did you ever see a dream walking / Pocketful of dreams / Moonlight becomes you / Pennies from Heaven / Go fly a kite / Please / All alone / You're sensational / Too-ra-loo-ra-loo-ra / White Christmas.
**Album:** Released '83, on RCA (France) by BMG Records (France). Catalogue no: **PL 45140**

**FINE MATCH, A (Braff, Ruby & Scott Hamilton)**
Tracks: / Romance in the dark / When a woman loves a man / Rockin' chair / Dinah / All my life / Shine / If you were mine (Part of medley) / I wished on the moon (Part of medley) / Bugle blues (Part of medley).
Note: This is the first time that Scott Hamilton's group and Ruby Braff have been heard together on record, although Scott & Ruby have appeared together several times since 1979.

**Album:** Released Dec '85, on Concord Jazz by Concord Jazz Records (USA). Catalogue no: **CJ 274**

**CD:** Released Jan '89, on Concord by Concord Jazz Records (USA). Catalogue no: **CCD 4274**

## HEAR ME TALKIN'

Tracks: / You've changed / Hear me talkin' to ya / Don't blame me / No one else but you / Nobody knows you (when you're down and out) / Buddy Bolden's blues / Mean to me / Where's Freddy?.

**Album:** Released Jan '85, on Black Lion Catalogue no: **BLP 30110**

## HUSTLIN' & BUSTLIN'

Tracks: / Hustlin' & bustlin' / There's a small hotel / What's the reason / 'S wonderful / When it's sleepy time down South / Flaky / Fine and mellow / Ad lib blues.

**Album:** Released 16 Sep '88, on Black Lion Catalogue no: **BLP 60908**

**CD:** Released 16 Sep '88, on Black Lion Catalogue no: **BLCD 760908**

## ME, MYSELF AND I (Braff, Ruby Trio)

Tracks: / Muskrat ramble / You've changed / Honey / Me, myself and I / When I fall in love / That's my home / Let me sing and I'm happy / You're a lucky guy / No one else but you / When you're smiling / Swan lake / Jubilee.

**Cass:** Released Jul '89, on Concord by Concord Jazz Records (USA). Catalogue no: **CJ 381C**

**Album:** Released Jul '89, on Concord by Concord Jazz Records (USA). Catalogue no: **CJ 381**

**CD:** Released Jul '89, on Concord by Concord Jazz Records (USA). Catalogue no: **CCD 4381**

## MIGHTY BRAFF, THE

Tracks: / When you're smiling / Easy living / Pullin' through / You're a lucky guy / Blue room / I can't get started / This can't be love / Flowers for a lady / Foolin' myself / I'll be around / It's easy to blame the weather / Struttin' with some barbeque / Mean to me / Ellie / You're a sweetheart / Blue and sentimental.

Note: When Ruby Braff graviated from Boston to New York jazz scene in the mid-50's, he was quickly espoused by influential writers and by record producers, including particularly John Hammond. Because he didn't sign an exclusive contract with any one company, he was courted by many and became one of the prolific performers of the first LP boom. After early contributions to *Jazz at Storyville* record dates and the Vic Dickenson Septet, his discography comprises at least 19 albums during 1954 and 1955, nine of them under his own name. At least some of these found a release in the U.K. (not so much on the Continent, where at that time they preferred their American musicians to be black) and leading reviewers here readily assumed that Braff was as busy in the nightclubs as he was in the studios. Soon the reviewers were in receipt of letters from Braff explaining that the two things did not go together, that often he did not know where his next gig was coming from (frequently it came from his Boston booster George Wein) and that a tour of England would be most welcome of the reviewers could wield the necessary influence - which they finally did in the mid-1960's.

The appeal of Braff's music was very real- and has continued to be so - but must have seemed especially strong to the would be tastemakers of the time. For a start, it did not fall into the rigid categories of traditional modern jazz, which were believed to be mutually exclusive and hostile schools, endlessly recycling themselves and undergoing no further development. Which was not true of either camp, as it turned out. Nor was it true that the Vic Dickensons or the Buck Claytons or the other Vanguard recordings or the similar material on Clef / Verve could be classified as 'trad' or 'mod', but the term 'mainstream' had yet to be coined and, as usual, most critics relied on categories rather than ears. For a second thing, the Vic Dickensons, Vanguards, Clefs and Claytons were being performed almost exclusively by players in their 40s who had made their initial impact during the swing era. Braff, on the other hand, only became a professional musician as the swing era came to an end and was replaced by the era of trad-versus modern warfare. So it was particularly significant that a younger player was able to stand aside musically from this internecine strife; able even (on some engagements) to adopt the 'traditional' repertoire without falling into the hallowed cliches; able to allow some more contemporary influences (e.g. from Dizzy Gillespie or Miles Davis) to touch his playing without sounding like a second generation bebopper or West Coaster. In short unlike the revivalists who prided themselves on the supposed accuracy of their copying, Braff was what I prefer to call an 'extensionist' of the swing soloists' feeling and musical philosophy.

The music on the enclosed CD comes from three Bethlehem 10 inch Lps, all recorded within the space of six months in the middle of the 1950s (absolutely literally, in one case). And they portray Braff in three suitably contrasting settings which bring out different strengths in his playing. The quartet session naturally finds him as the only horn and, in the way that he still does to this day, he uses such an intimate situation to vary the dynamic level of his contributions, switching for instance to the harmon mute for the middle chorus of Blue Room and coutering that with his rocking, open-toned lead in the final chorus. Note too how Ruby capitalises on the possibility of varied textures, even in such a small group, including the bowed bass on *I can't get started* and *Blue and sentimental* by the great Walter page (who was, of course, on the original Basie version of the latter piece). The varied styles of pianist Johnny Guarnieri also assist the textural variety, from single note lines to a relaxed modified stride pattern to the punchy block chords in unison with Braff on *Struttin' with some barbeque*, its melody sufficiently altered to qualify as a new composition.

The fact that two songs from this set are associated with Billie Holiday, *Started* and *Mean to me*, is perhaps what gave Ruby the idea for the March 1955 sessions which appeared as the album *Holiday in Braff*. Supervised by Bethlehem's then jazz producer Creed Taylor (later famous for his own CTI label, specialising in a vastly different kind of fusion), this presented an instrumental translation of six Billie-linked songs, one original arranged as a homage and one tune *I'll be around* which was, according to Ruby, 'A song she should have sung'. (Was it as a homage to Braff's sentiments that, three years later, she did finally get around to recording it on the album *Lady in satin*. As well as retaining the rhythm team of Walter Page and drummer Bobby Donaldson and adding the mellow piano of Ellis Larkins, these eight tunes are unlike anything else Ruby ever recorded, thanks to the work of his contemporary and fellow Piscean, saxist, arranger Bob Wilber. Seeming at the time to be the only other younger musician into swing, Bob wrote for a four piece saxophone section (Al Klink and Boomie Richman alternate on second tenor, I believe) in a way that was idiomatic enough for ex-Goodman altoist Hymie Schertzer to play the lead and more importantly, for Braff to have both a cushion and a catalyst. Replying to an observation that he was never a big band sideman in his youth (except briefly with Goodman later in 1955), Ruby once commented to me, 'It would have been a privilege and a thrill to be in one of those great bands'. This session shows exactly how well it would have suited Braff, especially when the saxes use the last chorus of *When you're smiling* to harmonise the Lester Young solo from Billie and Teddy Wilson's famous record, with Ruby joining in (a la Buck Clayton) for the last eight bars.

A considerable change of pace is afforded by the New Year's Eve session from the rare (and never previously reissued) *Ball at Bethlehem*. Taped by engineer Tom Dowd (who, after working with such as Ray Charles and Aretha Franklin, became a fully fledged producer in the 1970s), this has only head arrangements with a slightly Dixieland feel augmented by riffs concocted on the spot by Braff. According to Dowd's original liner-notes, the informality of the occasion led to the musicians talking with non playing guests during each other's solos, and happily ignoring the fact that the piano tuner arrived to late to perform any useful function. Yet the relaxed celebration clearly aided the music no end, as did Ruby's familiarity with the equally young Eddie Hubble (also a former colleague of Bob Wilber's) and the slightly senior Sam Margolis who appeared on several of the same sessions as Braff at this period. The vantage point of the

decade's dead-centre found Ruby jazzing up *Auld lang syne* for the music biz crowd (as it found the six months older John Coltrane doing *Nancy with the laughing face* at a black dance in Philadelphia) and it would have taken a genius to predict how their respective careers would develop. Happily, Braff is still with us, playing in basically the same way, only more so. But this early work stands up extremely well in hindsight, and deserves to be preserved for its own sake. (Brian Priestley, Author, Jazz on record: A history, Elm Tree Books)
**Album:** Released May '83, on Affinity by Charly Records. Deleted '88. Catalogue no: **AFF 98**
**CD:** Released Nov '89, on Affinity by Charly Records. Catalogue no: **CDAFF 757**

**MR. BRAFF TO YOU (Braff, Ruby Quintet)**
Note: Featuring: Scott Hamilton & John Bunch.
**CD:** Released Apr '88, on Phontastic (Sweden) Catalogue no: **PHONT CD 7568**

**MUSIC FROM MY FAIR LADY (Braff, Ruby & Dick Hyman)**
Tracks: / Wouldn't it be loverly / With a little bit of luck / I'm an ordinary man / Rain in Spain, The / I could have danced all night / Ascot gavotte / On the street where you live / Show me / Get me to the church on time / Without you / I've grown accustomed to her face.
**Cass:** Released '89, on Concord by Concord Jazz Records (USA). Catalogue no: **CJ 393C**
**CD:** Released '89, on Concord by Concord Jazz Records (USA). Catalogue no: **CCD 4393**

**ON SUNNIE'S SIDE OF THE STREET (Braff, Ruby & Ralph Sutton)**
**Album:** Released Apr '79, on BAJC Catalogue no: **BAJC 501**

**PIPE ORGAN RECITAL PLUS ONE (Braff, Ruby & Dick Hyman)**
**CD:** Released Mar '90, on Concord by Concord Jazz Records (USA). Catalogue no: **CCD 43003**

**PLAY GERSHWIN (Braff, Ruby & George Barnes)**
**CD:** Released Jul '88, on Concord Jazz by Concord Jazz Records (USA). Catalogue no: **CCD 6005**

**PRETTIES**
Tracks: / Nancy with the laughing face / Love me or leave me / Tangerine / S'posin'.
**Album:** Released Jun '79, on Sonet by Sonet Records. Catalogue no: **SNTF 777**

**RODGERS & HART (Braff, Ruby & George Barnes)**
**CD:** Released Jul '88, on Concord Jazz by Concord Jazz Records (USA). Catalogue no: **CCD 6007**

**RUBY BRAFF, FEATURING DAVE MCKENNA**
Tracks: / Dancing in the dark / Blue prelude / Why was I born / Blue / If I could be you / I'm crazy about my baby / Louisiana / It's wonderful / Almost like being In love / Love come back to me / I must have that man.
**Album:** Released Jun '84, on Jasmine by Hasmick Promotions. Deleted Feb '88. Catalogue no: **JASM 1043**

**RUBY BRAFF & SCOTT HAMILTON (Braff, Ruby & Scott Hamilton)**
**Album:** Released Nov '86, on Phontastic (Sweden) Catalogue no: **PHONT 7568**

**RUBY BRAFF WITH THE ED BICKERT TRIO (Braff, Ruby & the Ed Bickert Trio)**
Tracks: / True love / I've got a feeling I'm falling / This year's kisses / World is waiting for the sunrise, The / Very thought of you, The / After a while / What is there to say / My funny valentine / Song is ended, (The) / When I fall in love.
**Album:** Released Apr '81, on Sackville by Spotlite Records. Catalogue no: **3022**

**RUBY BRAFF / MARSHALL BROWN SEXTET (Braff, Ruby / Marshall Brown Sextet)**
**Album:** Released Feb '88, on Fresh Sounds (Spain) by Fresh Sounds Records (Spain). Catalogue no: **FS 142**

**RUBY GOT RHYTHM**
**Album:** Released '78, on Black Lion Catalogue no: **BLP 30188**

**SAILBOAT IN THE MOONLIGHT (Braff, Ruby & Scott Hamilton)**
Tracks: / Lover come back to me / Where are you? / Deed I do / When lights are low / Jeepers creepers / Milkman's matinee, The / Sweethearts on parade / Sailboat in the moonlight.
**Cass:** Released Apr '86, on Concord Jazz by Concord Jazz Records (USA). Catalogue no: **CJC 296**
**Album:** Released Apr '86, on Concord Jazz by Concord Jazz Records (USA). Catalogue no: **CJ 296**
**CD:** Released Nov '86, on Concord Jazz by Concord Jazz Records (USA). Catalogue no: **CCD 4296**

**SWING THAT MUSIC (Braff, Ruby & Red Norvo)**
**2 LP Set:** Released Feb '80, on Affinity by Charly Records. Deleted '88. Catalogue no: **AFFD 45**

**THEM THERE EYES**
Tracks: / Swinging on a star / Same old South / Yesterdays / Medley: I'm pulling through / It's the little things that mean so much / Them there eyes / I've grown accustomed to her face / Why was I born / Dream dancing / Love lies / Tea for two.
Note: with J. Rowles, Vic Dickenson, B. Pizzarelli.
**Album:** Released Mar '87, on Sonet by Sonet Records. Catalogue no: **SNTF 713**

## Bran, Mike

**MIKE BRAN SEXTET (Bran, Mike Sextet)**
**Album:** Released '88, on Storyville by Storyville Records AB. Catalogue no: **SLP 234**

## Brand, Dollar

**Biographical details:** Brand, Dollar. This South African jazz pianist is now know as Abdullah Ibrahim; see there for biographical information, although many of his records are still available under his original name. Donald Clarke, 24 August 1988.

**AFRICA - TEARS AND LAUGHTER (Brand, Dollar Quartet)**
**Album:** Released Jan '82, on Enja (Germany) by Enja Records (West Germany). Catalogue no: **ENJA 3039**

**AFRICAN DAWN**
**CD:** Released '88, on MCA (Import) by MCA Records. Catalogue no: **3112 10**
**Album:** Released Sep '84, on Enja (Germany) by Enja Records (West Germany). Catalogue no: **ENJA 4030**

**AFRICAN PIANO**
Tracks: / Bra Joe from Kilimanjaro / Selby that the eternal spirit / Is the only reality / Moon, The / Xaba / Sunset in the blue / Kippy / Jabulani-easter joy / Tintinyana.
**CD:** Released Sep '88, on ECM Catalogue no: **835 020-2**
**Album:** Released Apr '84, on ECM Catalogue no: **JAPO 60002**

**AFRICAN PORTRAITS**
Tracks: / Cherry / Bra Joe from Kilimanjaro / Blues for Hughie / Kipoie gafsa / Life is for the living / Death is for us all / Gwangwa / Little boy / Easter joy / Jabulani / Xaba.
**Album:** Released Apr '81, on Sackville by Spotlite Records. Catalogue no: **3009**

**AFRICAN SKETCH BOOK**
**Album:** Released Jan '82, on Enja (Germany) by Enja Records (West Germany). Catalogue no: **ENJA 2026**

**AFRICAN SPACE PROGRAMME**
**Album:** Released Jan '82, on Enja (Germany) by Enja Records (West Germany). Catalogue no: **ENJA 2032**

**AFRICAN SUN**
Tracks: / African sun / Bra Joe from Kilimanjaro / Rollin' / Memories of you / Sathima / African herbs / Nobody knows the trouble I've seen / Blues for B / Gwidza / Kamalie.
**2 LP Set:** Released Jul '88, on Kaz by Kaz Records. Catalogue no: **KAZ LP 102**
**CD:** Released Jul '88, on Kaz by Kaz Records. Catalogue no: **KAZ CD 102**
**Cass set:** Released Jul '88, on Kaz by Kaz Records. Catalogue no: **KAZ MC 102**

**ANCIENT AFRICA**
Tracks: / Bra Joe from Kilimanjaro / Mamma / Tokai / Ilanga / Cherry / African sun / Tintinyana / Xaba / Peace-Salaam air.
**Album:** Released Apr '84, on ECM Catalogue no: **JAPO 60005**

**ANTHEM FOR THE NEW NATION**
Tracks: / Anthem of the New Nations /

Biral / Liberation dance / Trial, The / Cape town / Wedding suite, The / Wedding, The / Lovers / I surrender dear / One day when we were young / Thaba nchu.
**Album:** Released Mar '82, on Denon Deleted '88. Catalogue no: **YX 7537**
**CD:** on Denon Catalogue no: **C38-7261**

**BLACK LIGHTNING**
**CD:** Released Aug '87, on Bellaphon Catalogue no: **CDBID 155502**

**BLUES FOR A HIP KING**
Tracks: / Ornette's cornet / All day & all night long / Sweet Basil blues / Blue monk / Tsakwe here comes the postman / Blues for a hip king / Blues for B / Mysterioso / Just you just me / Eclipse at dawn / King Kong / Khumbula Jane / Boulevarde east (not on CD).
**Cass set:** Released Oct '88, on Kaz by Kaz Records. Catalogue no: **KAZ MC 104**
**CD:** Released Oct '88, on Kaz by Kaz Records. Catalogue no: **KAZ CD 104**
**2 LP Set:** Released Oct '88, on Kaz by Kaz Records. Catalogue no: **KAZ LP 104**

**BROTHER WITH PERFECT TIMING, A**
**VHS:** Released 6 Feb '89, on Island Visual Arts by Island Records. Catalogue no: **IVA 010**

**CHILDREN OF AFRICA**
**Album:** Released Jan '82, on Enja (Germany) by Enja Records (West Germany). Catalogue no: **ENJA 2070**

**DUKES' MEMORIES**
**CD:** Released '86, on Black & Blue (1) by Black & Blue Records. Catalogue no: **233 853**

**ECHOES FROM AFRICA**
**Album:** Released Jan '82, on Enja (Germany) by Enja Records (West Germany). Catalogue no: **ENJA 3047**

**EKAYA (Brand, Dollar (Abdullah Ibrahim))**
Tracks: / Ekaya / Sotho blue / Ntyilo, Ntyilo / Bra timing from Phomolong / Ek se ou windhoek toe nou / Cape Town.
**Album:** Released Jul '84, on Ekapa (USA) Deleted '88. Catalogue no: **EKAPA 005**

**GOOD NEWS FROM AFRICA (Brand, Dollar Duo)**
**Album:** Released Jan '82, on Enja (Germany) by Enja Records (West Germany). Catalogue no: **ENJA 2048**

**LIVE AT MONTREUX: DOLLAR BRAND**
**Album:** Released Sep '84, on Enja (Germany) by Enja Records (West Germany). Catalogue no: **ENJA 3079**
**CD:** Released '88, on Enja (Germany) by Enja Records (West Germany). Catalogue no: **ENJA 307 902**

**LIVE AT SWEET BASIL (Brand, Dollar & Carlos Ward)**
Tracks: / Dream, The / And find me a shelter in the storm / Mummy / For Coltrane II / New York City / Anthem for the new nations / Gwangwa / King Kong, Theme from / Black lightning / Gwidza / Strides, The / Soweto.
**Album:** Released Feb '85, on Ekapa (USA) Deleted '88. Catalogue no: **EKAPA 004**

**MATSIDISO**
**CD:** Released '86, on Plane (Germany) Catalogue no: **PCD 88448**

**MINDIF**
**Album:** Released Jul '88, on Enja (Germany) by Enja Records (West Germany). Catalogue no: **ENJA 5073**
**CD:** Released Jul '88, on Enja (Germany) by Enja Records (West Germany). Catalogue no: **ENJA 5073-50**
**Cass:** Released Jul '88, on Enja (Germany) by Enja Records (West Germany). Catalogue no: **ENJA 45073**

**ODE TO DUKE ELLINGTON**
Tracks: / Impressions on a caravan / Ode to Duke / What really happened in the cornfield / Rose got it bad in Harlem / Solitude / In a sentimental mood / Two spirituals.
**Album:** Released Jan '89, on Bellaphon Catalogue no: **WW 020**
**CD:** Released Jan '89, on Bellaphon Catalogue no: **WWCD 2020**

**ROUND MIDNIGHT AT MONTMARTRE**
**Album:** Released Feb '89, on Black Lion Catalogue no: **BLP 60111**

**SANGOMA (VOLUME 1)**
**Album:** Released Jul '86, on Sackville by Spotlite Records. Catalogue no: **3006**

**SOUTH AFRICAN SUNSHINE**
**CD:** Released '86, on Plane (Germany) Catalogue no: **PCD 88449**

**SOWETO**
**CD:** Released Aug '87, on Bellaphon Catalogue no: **CDBID 155501**

**THIS IS DOLLAR BRAND**
Tracks: / Little Niles / Resolution / Which way? / On the banks of Allen Waters / Knight's night / Pye R squared / Mood indigo / Don't get around much anymore / Take the 'A' train.
**Album:** Released Apr '85, on Black Lion Catalogue no: **BLP 30139**

**TINTINYANA**
Tracks: / Soweto is where it's at / Tintinyana / Little boy / Cherry / Bra Joe from Kilimanjaro / Shrimp boats / Salaam / Just a song.
**CD:** Released Oct '88, on Kaz by Kaz Records. Catalogue no: **KAZ CD 103**
**Album:** Released Oct '88, on Kaz by Kaz Records. Catalogue no: **KAZ LP 103**
**Cass:** Released Oct '88, on Kaz by Kaz Records. Catalogue no: **KAZ MC 103**

**VOICE OF AFRICA**
Tracks: / Black lightning / Little boy / Black and brown cherries / Ntyilo, Ntyilo / Mannenberg / Pilgrim, The.
**2 LP Set:** Released Jun '88, on Kaz by Kaz Records. Catalogue no: **KAZ LP 101**
**Cass:** Released Feb '89, on Kaz by Kaz Records. Catalogue no: **KAZ MC 101**

**WATER FROM AN ANCIENT WELL (Brand, Dollar & Ekaya)**
Tracks: / Mandela / Song for Sathima / Manenberg revisited / Tuang Guru / Water from an ancient well / Wedding, The / Mountain, The / Sameeda.
**CD:** Released Mar '87, on Black Hawk (USA) by Blackhawk Records (USA). Catalogue no: **CDBKH 50207**

**ZIMBABWE**
**CD:** Released '88, on Enja (Germany) by Enja Records (West Germany). Catalogue no: **311 224**
**Album:** Released Sep '84, on Enja (Germany) by Enja Records (West Germany). Catalogue no: **ENJA 4056**

## Branscombe, Alan

**SWINGIN' ON THE SOUND STAGE (Branscombe, Alan and Friends)**
Tracks: / On Green Dolphin Street / Rose room / Blues for Alan, The / Out of nowhere / For Pete's sake / On the Alamo / Tangerine / Close your eyes.
Note: A tribute to Alan Branscombe with Kenny Wheeler, Bob Efford, Duncan Lamont, Eddie Blair and Stan Roderick.
**Album:** Released Jul '87, on Esquire by Titan Int. Prod.. Catalogue no: **ESQ 332**

**SWINGING ON THE SOUND STAGE, VOL. 2**
**Album:** Released Dec '87, on Esquire by Titan Int. Prod.. Catalogue no: **ESQ 342**

## Brass Bands

**MUSIC OF NEW ORLEANS (The Brass Bands) (various artists)**
**Album:** Released May '89, on Jazzology (USA) by Jazzology Records (USA). Catalogue no: **JCE 35**

## Braxton, Anthony

**Biographical details:** Braxton, Anthony. Born in 1945 in Chicago, this saxophonist and composer began studying music at age 17, influenced by Roscoe Mitchell; he joined the AACM (Chicago's black music collective) and taught harmony. He formed the Creative Construction Company and went to Europe in '69, playing and recording there with the group, drummer Steve McCall, Muhal Richard Abrams and the Art Ensemble of Chicago; back in New York he formed Circle in 1970 with Chick Corea, Dave Holland and Barry Altschul. Initially interested in the scientific (mathematical) aspects of music, many of his compositions had diagrammatic titles, but he has somewhat softened that approach; he plays standards, ragtime, compositions of Warne Marsh and Charles Mingus, etc. but his own music is ambitious and unclassifiable. with Mitchell he is one of the most impressive figures in black music in the 1980s. His first LP as leader was *Three Compositions Of New Jazz* on Delmark in 1968, a trio with Leo Smith and Leroy Jenkins playing about 20 instruments; he has also recorded solo and in almost every conceivable format. His 1976 RCA album *Creative Orchestra Music*, recently reissued on CD, has Holland, Abrams, Mitchell and Smith onit, plus Kenny Wheeler, John Faddis and many more, playing six selections. Donald Clarke, 24 August 1988..

**3 COMPOSITIONS OF NEW JAZZ**
**Album:** on Delmark (USA) by Delmark Records (USA). Catalogue no: **DS 415**

**ANTHONY BRAXTON**
**Album:** Released '78, on Affinity by Charly Records. Deleted '88. Catalogue no: **AFF 15**

**ANTHONY BRAXTON - LONDON NOV. 1986 (Braxton, Anthony Quartet)**
**2 LP Set:** Released Oct '88, on Leo by Leo Records. Catalogue no: **LR 414/15**

**BELGIUM CONCERT (Various artists)**
**CD:** Released Oct '88, on West Wind Catalogue no: **WWCD 013**

**COMPOSITION 96 FOR ORCHESTRA**
**Album:** Released Jun '89, on Leo by Leo Records. Catalogue no: **LR 169**

**COVENTRY CONCERT, THE**
**Album:** Released Jul '88, on West Wind Catalogue no: **WW 001**
**CD:** Released Jul '88, on West Wind Catalogue no: **WWCD 001**

**CREATIVE CONSTRUCTION COMPANY**
**Album:** Released Apr '81, on Muse by Black & Blue Records. Catalogue no: **MR 5071**

**CREATIVE CONSTRUCTION COMPANY VOL. 2**
**Album:** Released Apr '81, on Muse by Black & Blue Records. Catalogue no: **MR 5097**

**CREATIVE MUSIC ORCHESTRA**
**LP Set:** Released Jul '78, on Ring Deleted '85. Catalogue no: **RING 01024/5/6**

**CREATIVE ORCHESTRA 1987 Pieces Nos. 1-6**
**CD:** Released Jun '88, on Bluebird (2) by BMG Records (UK). Catalogue no: **ND 86579**

**DUETS 1976**
**Album:** Released Jan '77, on Arista by BMG Records (UK). Deleted '80. Catalogue no: **AL 4101**

**FOUR COMPOSITIONS (1973)**
**Album:** Released Mar '82, on Denon Deleted '88. Catalogue no: **YX 7506**

**IF MY MEMORY SERVES ME RIGHT (Braxton, Anthony Quartet)**
**CD:** Released Oct '88, on West Wind Catalogue no: **WWCD 004**

**IN THE TRADITON VOL.2**
**Album:** Released Jul '88, on Steeplechase (USA) Catalogue no: **SCS 1045**
**CD:** Released Jul '88, on Steeplechase (USA) Catalogue no: **SCCD 31045**

**LIVE - MOERS FESTIVAL 74**
**2 LP Set:** Released Jul '78, on Ring Catalogue no: **RING 01010/11**

**MAX ROACH & ANTHONY BRAXTON (Braxton, Anthony & Max Roach)**
Tracks: / Birth / Magic and music / Tropical forest / Dance riot / Spirit possession / Soft show / Rebirth.
Note: Anthony Braxton-saxaphone and clarinet. Max Roach-drums
**Album:** Released Apr '79, on Black Saint (Italy) Catalogue no: **BSR 0024**

**ROYAL VOL 1 (Braxton, Anthony & Derek Bailey)**
**Album:** Released '84, on Incus by Incus Records. Catalogue no: **INCUS 43**

**SIX COMPOSITIONS (QUARTET) 1984**
**CD:** Released Jan '86, on Black Saint (Italy) Catalogue no: **BSR 0086**

**SIX MONK COMPETITIONS**
**CD:** Released Aug '88, on Black Saint (Italy) Catalogue no: **120116-2**

**SOLO - LIVE AT MOERS FESTIVAL, 74**
**Album:** Released Jul '78, on Ring Catalogue no: **RING 01002**

**THIS TIME**
**Album:** Released Jan '80, on Affinity by Charly Records. Deleted '88. Catalogue no: **AFF 25**

**TOGETHER ALONE (Braxton, Anthony & J. Jarman)**
**Album:** Released Jul '75, on Delmark (USA) by Delmark Records (USA). Catalogue no: **DS 428**

**TRIO & DUET**
Note: Artists include: D.Holland/Leo Smith/R.Teitelbaum
**Album:** Released Jul '86, on Sackville by Spotlite Records. Catalogue no: **3007**

## Brecker, Michael

**DON'T TRY THIS AT HOME**
**Cass:** Released May '89, on MCA (Import) by MCA Records. Catalogue no: **MCAC 42229**
**Album:** Released May '89, on MCA (Import) by MCA Records. Catalogue no: **MCA 42229**
**CD:** Released May '89, on MCA (Import) by MCA Records. Catalogue no: **MCAD 42229**

**MICHAEL BRECKER Z**
Tracks: / Sea glass / Syzygy / Choices / Nothing personal / Cost of living / Original rays.
**Album:** Released Jun '87, on MCA by MCA Records. Catalogue no: **IMCA 5980**
**CD:** Released Nov '89, on MCA by MCA Records. Catalogue no: **MCAD 5980**
**Cass:** Released Nov '89, on MCA by MCA Records. Catalogue no: **MCAC 5980**
**Album:** Released Nov '89, on MCA by MCA Records. Catalogue no: **MCA 5980**
**Cass:** Released Jun '87, on MCA by MCA Records. Catalogue no: **IMCAC 5980**

## Brecker, Randy

**Biographical details:** Brecker, Randy and Michael. Trumpeter Randy (born 1945) and saxophonist Michael (born 1949) are from Philadelphia, both fine technicians and all-round sidemen of the fusion era, recording with just about everyone in jazz and pop and as the Brecker Brothers in the late '70s. They did little solo recording until recently. Randy is married to keyboardist Eliane Elias (from Sau Paulo); Michael made his solo debut on the revived Impulse label playing an electronic wind instrument plugged into a synthesiser, adding octaves, sampling etc. but still a wind driven sound of human origin. (Donald Clarke, 24 August 1988.).

**AMANDA (Brecker, Randy & Eliane Elias)**
Tracks: / Splash / Para nada / Pandamandium / Samba de bamba / Amandamada / Guaruja.
**CD:** on Passport Jazz (USA) by Jem Records Inc.(USA). Catalogue no: **PJCD 88013**
**Album:** Released '87, on Passport Jazz (USA) by Jem Records Inc.(USA). Catalogue no: **PJ 88013**
**Cass:** Released '87, on Passport Jazz (USA) by Jem Records Inc.(USA). Catalogue no: **PJC 88013**
**Album:** Released Jul '86, on Sonet by Sonet Records. Catalogue no: **SNTF 958**

**IN THE IDIOM**
Tracks: / No scratch / Hit and miss / Forever young / Sang / You're in my heart / There's a Mingus a Monks us / Moontide / Little Miss P.
Note: Brecker's reputation as a trumpet/flugelhorn soloist has long been established but his gift as composer / arranger- all eight titles are his creation - have never before been as amply displayed as on this release. *In the idiom*, an impressive, unadulterated jazz celebration, is probably his finest work upto date (Denon 10/88).Other musicians on this recording are: Joe Henderson (Tenor sax), David Kikoski (Piano), Ron Carter (Bass), Al Foster (Drums).)
**Cass:** Released Oct '88, on Denon Catalogue no: **CC 15**
**CD:** Released Oct '88, on Denon Catalogue no: **CY 1483**

**LIVE AT SWEET BASIL**
**Album:** Released Mar '89, on Sonet by Sonet Records. Catalogue no: **SNTF 1011**
**CD:** Released Mar '89, on Sonet by Sonet Records. Catalogue no: **SNCD 1011**

## Brennan, Dave

**AMAZING GRACE**
**Album:** on VJM (Vintage Jazz Music) by Vintage Jazz Music Society(VJM). Catalogue no: **LC 12**

**BOUNCING AROUND**
**Album:** on VJM (Vintage Jazz Music) by Vintage Jazz Music Society(VJM). Catalogue no: **LC 20S**

## Britain's Greatest Jazz Band

**BRITAIN'S GREATEST JAZZ BAND (Various)**
**Album:** Released '88, on Nor Jazz Catalogue no: **IS RT 105**

## British Dance Bands...

**BRITISH DANCE BANDS OF THE FORTIES (Various artists)**
Tracks: / If I had my way / More & more / Cookhouse serenade / Better not roll those blue blue eyes / Hour never passes, An / I threw a kiss in the ocean / Shrine of St Cecilia / My wubba dolly / Coming in on a wing and a prayer / It's a blue world: *Stone, Lew & His Band* / In a little rocky valley: *Stone, Lew & His Band* / There's nothing new to tell you: *Stone, Lew & His Band* / Sing a round up song: *Stone, Lew & His Band* / Too romantic: *Stone, Lew & His Band* / Hut sut song, The: *Stone, Lew & His Band* / Mother's prayer at twilight, A: *Stone, Lew & His Band* / And so do I: *Stone, Lew & His Band* / We'll meet again: *Stone, Lew & His Band* / Keep an eye on your heart: *Royal Airforce Dance Orchestra* / Blue champagne: *Royal Airforce Dance Orchestra* / It's foolish but it's fun: *Royal Airforce Dance Orchestra* / Out of nowhere: *Royal Airforce Dance Orchestra* / There I go: *Royal Airforce Dance Orchestra* / Whistler's mother-in-law, The: *Royal Airforce Dance Orchestra* / Lover's lullaby: *Royal Airforce Dance Orchestra* / All our tomorrows: *Royal Airforce Dance Orchestra* / You started something: *Royal Airforce Dance Orchestra* / Apple for teacher, An: *Rabin, Oscar & His Band* / You're mine: *Rabin, Oscar & His Band* / When the night is thru': *Rabin, Oscar & His Band* / Sometimes: *Rabin, Oscar & His Band* / Man and his dream, A: *Rabin, Oscar & His Band* / Moonlight avenue: *Rabin, Oscar & His Band* / When the rose of Tralee met Danny boy: *Rabin, Oscar & His Band* / Basin Street ball: *Rabin, Oscar & His Band* / Sing,everybody,sing: *Rabin, Oscar & His Band.*
Note: Setting the style for the future double album multi-artists format:each act having one complete side of the release.This thirty six track value-for-money package features four of Britain's top dance bands of the 1940's,with an impressive line-up of vocalists interpreting many big hits of the decade. Featured vocalists with Ambrose & His Orchestra: Ann Shelton/Leslie Douglas/George Melachrino/Doroty Carless/Denny Dennis/Evelyn Dall. Featured vocalists with Lew Stone & His Band:Sam Browne/Rita Carr/Wendy Claire / Carl Barriteau. Featured vocalists with The Royal Airforce Dance Orchestra: Sid Collin / Jimmy Miller / Dorothy Carles. Featured vocalists with Oscar Rabin & His Band: Beryl Davis / Garry Gowan / Diane / Bob Dale / Terry Devon / Benny Lee.
**2 LP Set:** Released Sep '86, on Recollections (Decca) by Decca Records. Deleted Feb '89. Catalogue no: **RECDL 2**
**Cass set:** Released Sep '86, on Recollections (Decca) by Decca Records. Deleted Feb '89. Catalogue no: **RECDC 2**

## British Jazz Awards

**BRITISH JAZZ AWARDS 1987 (Various artists)**
Note: Features: Humphrey Lyttelton, Ray Williams, Pete King, Dick Morrissey, Johnny Barnes, Dave Green & Allan Ganley.
**Album:** Released Feb '88, on Big Bear by Big Bear Records. Catalogue no: **BEAR 27**
**Cass:** Released Feb '88, on Big Bear by Big Bear Records. Catalogue no: **BEAR MC 27**

## Broadway Syncopaters

**BROADWAY SYNCOPATERS AND FOSDICKS HOOSIERS**
**Album:** Released '88, on Fountain by Retrieval Records. Catalogue no: **FG 406**

## Brookmeyer, Bob

**AT THE VILLAGE VANGUARD (Brookmeyer, Bob with Mel Lewis & The Jazz Orchestra)**
Tracks: / Ding dong ding / First love song / Hello and goodbye / Skylark / El co / Fan club.
**Album:** Released Apr '81, on Rhapsody by President Records. Catalogue no: **RHAP 11**

**BACK AGAIN**
**Album:** Released Jul '88, on Sonet by Sonet Records. Catalogue no: **SNTF 778**

**BLUES HOT & COLD (Brookmeyer, Bob Quartet)**
Tracks: / Languid blues / On the sunny side of the street / Stompin' at the Savoy / I got rhythm / Smoke gets in your eyes / Hot and cold blues.
**Album:** Released Oct '84, on Verve (USA) by Polydor Ltd. Catalogue no: **821 550-1**

**BOB BROOKMEYER WITH STOCKHOLM JAZZ ORCHESTRA (Brookmeyer, Bob & Stokholm Jazz Orchestra)**
Tracks: / Cats / Lies / Tick tock / Dreams / Missing work / Ceremony.
**Album:** Released Sep '89, on Dragon by Dragon Records. Catalogue no: **DRCD 169**

**BOBBY BROOKMEYER AND HIS ORCHESTRA (Brookmeyer, Bobby & His Orchestra)**
Tracks: / Oh Jane snavely / Nature boy / Just you, just me / I'm old fashioned / Gone latin / Zing went the strings of my heart / Big city life / Confussion blues / Open country.
**Album:** Released Jan '83, on RCA (France) by BMG Records (France). Catalogue no: **PL 43550**

**KANSAS CITY REVISITED (Brookmeyer, Bob KC Seven)**
**Album:** Released Feb '88, on Fresh Sounds (Spain) by Fresh Sounds Records (Spain). Catalogue no: **FS 33**

**OSLO (Brookmeyer, Bob Quartet)**
Tracks: / With the wind and the rain in your hair / Oslo / Later blues / Detour ahead / Tootsie samba / Alone together / Who could care / Caravan.
Note: Personnel: Bob Brookmeyer - valve trombone / Alan Broadbent - piano and synthesizer / Eric von Essen - bass / Michael Stephans - drums
**CD:** Released Jul '87, on Concord Jazz by Concord Jazz Records (USA). Catalogue no: **CCD 4312**
**Album:** Released Feb '87, on Concord Jazz by Concord Jazz Records (USA). Deleted Jun '88. Catalogue no: **CJ 312**

**TRADITIONALISM REVISITED**
Tracks: / Louisiana / Santa Claus blues / Truckin' / Some sweet day / Sweet like this / Jada / Don't be that way / Honeysuckle rose.
**Album:** Released Nov '84, on Affinity by Charly Records. Catalogue no: **AFF 127**

## Brooks, John Benson

**FOLK JAZZ USA**
Tracks: / New saints, The / Venezuela / Black is the colour / Betsy / Randall my son / Turtle dove / Shenandoah / Joe's old folks / Sara Jane / Scarlet Town / Wayfaring stranger / Darling Corey.
**Album:** Released Jan '83, on RCA (France) by BMG Records (France). Catalogue no: **PM 43767**

## Brooks, Lonnie

**BAYOU LIGHTNING**
Tracks: / Voodoo daddy / Figure head / Watch dog / Breakfast in bed / Worked up woman / Alimony / Watch what you got / I ain't superstitious / You know what my body needs / In the dark.
Note: Lonnie Brooks' session on the 'Living Chicago Blues' series triggered rave reviews and led to his debut album for the label, produced by Lonnie with Bruce Iglauer. 'He blisters sering licks with pungent lines behind strong vocals and pulsating band work...sizzling deep, funky groove...one of the most undeservedly overlooked talents in Chicago. ("Downbeat", Alligator catalogue 7/88)
**Album:** Released Sep '79, on Sonet by Sonet Records. Catalogue no: **SNTF 798**
**CD:** Released '88, on Sonet by Sonet Records. Catalogue no: **SNTCD 798**

**BROKE AN' HUNGRY**
Tracks: / Wee, wee hours / Things they used to do / Go to the Mardi Gras / Texas

flood / Tom cat blues / Rooster blues / Train and the horse, The / Broke and hungry / When there's no way out / Don't touch me,baby / Red bug blues.
**Album:** Released Apr '84, on Crosscut by Topic Records. Catalogue no: **CCR 1006**

**CRAWL, THE**
Tracks: / Crawl / Family rules / I got it made / Tell me baby / Love me love me Mary Ann / Now you know / Pick me up on your way down / Roll roll roll / Broken hearted rollin teats / Oo wee baby / Knocks me out fine fine fine.
**Album:** Released Apr '84, on Charly R&B by Charly Records. Catalogue no: **CRB 1068**

**HOT SHOT**
Tracks: / Don't take advantage of me / Wrong number / Mesed up again / Family rules / Back trail / I want all my money back / Mr. hot shot / One more shot.
Note: "Lonnie Brooks' toughest album yet - unadorned raw energy, cut in the studio but as hot as his great live sets. Sparked by his new band, Lonnie tears into five new originals plus remakes of his classics 'Family Rules' and 'Mr Hot Shot'. 'A sound that's unique in modern blues...His blues packs enough power, drive and funky undertone to bust outta the narrow confines of the R&B market and grab a whole new audience." - Echoes (Alligator catalogue 7/88)
**CD:** Released Jun '88, on Sonet by Sonet Records. Catalogue no: **SNTCD 903**
**Album:** Released Oct '83, on Alligator (Sonet) by Alligator Records (USA). Catalogue no: **SNTF 903**

**LIVE AT PEPPERS**
**Album:** Released Feb '85, on Black Magic by Topic Records. Catalogue no: **BM 9008**

**LIVE FROM CHICAGO**
Tracks: / Two headed man / Trading post / In the dark / Got me by the tail / One more shot / Born with the blues / Eyeballin' / Cold lonely nights / Hideaway.
**Album:** Released Jun '88, on Alligator (Sonet) by Alligator Records (USA). Catalogue no: **AL 4759**
**CD:** Released 30 Apr '88, on Alligator (Sonet) by Alligator Records (USA). Catalogue no: **ALCD 4759**

**TURN ON THE NIGHT**
Tracks: / Eyeballin' / Inflation / Teenage boogie man / Heavy traffic / I'll take care of you / T.V. mama / Mother nature / Don't go to sleep on me / Something you got / Zydeco.
**Album:** Released Jul '88, on Sonet by Sonet Records. Catalogue no: **SNTF 858**

**WORKED UP WOMAN**
Tracks: / Worked up woman / Breakfast in bed.
**7" Single:** Released Jun '80, on Sonet by Sonet Records. Deleted '83. Catalogue no: **SON 2209**

**WOUND UP TIGHT**
Tracks: / Got lucky last night / Jealous man / Belly rubbin' music / Bewitched / End of the rope / Wound up tight / Boomerang / Musta' been dreaming / Skid Row / Hush mouth money.
**CD:** Released Jun '88, on Sonet by Sonet Records. Catalogue no: **SNTCD 974**
**Album:** Released Jan '87, on Alligator (Sonet) by Alligator Records (USA). Catalogue no: **SNTF 974**

## Brooks, Randy

**Biographical details:** Brooks, Randy. A trumpet-playing USA bandleader (1917-67) who formed his own outfit in 1945; Stan Getz joined in '46. Best records were bop-tinged; many were ballads with sweet solos and vocals. He had a stroke in 1950 which ended his career. (Donald Clarke, 24 August 1988.).

**1945-1947 (Brooks, Randy & His Orchestra)**
**Album:** Released Jun '86, on Circle (USA) by Jazzology Records (USA). Catalogue no: **CLP 35**

**RADIO DISCS OF ....1945, THE**
**Album:** Released Jul '82, on Joyce Catalogue no: **JLP 2003**

## Broonzy, Big Bill

**Biographical details:** Broonzy, Big Bill. William Lee Conley Broonzy (1893-1958) recorded regularly from 1926 as a singer, guitarist and accompaniest on other people's records and was said to be the best-selling black male artist in the late '30s. He performed in John Hammond's Spirituals To Swing concerts in 1938-39; he ran a tavern in Chicago in the '50s; he first visited Europe in 1951 and was famous there; his mother was born a slave and died in 1957 at age 102. When he was asked if he sang folk songs he gave a famous reply: 'I never heard no horse sing 'em.' (Donald Clarke, 24 August 1988.)

**1955 LONDON SESSIONS, THE**
**CD:** Released Apr '90, on Sequel by Sequel Records. Catalogue no: **NEXCD 119**

**1927-32**
**Album:** Released Sep '85, on Matchbox by Flyright Records. Catalogue no: **MSE 1004**

**1934-47 VOL.1**
**Album:** Released Jul '87, on Document Catalogue no: **DOC 510**

**BIG BILL BROONZY**
**Album:** Released '88, on Joker (USA) by Lifetime Records (USA). Catalogue no: **SM 3608**
**Cass:** Released '88, on Joker (USA) by Lifetime Records (USA). Catalogue no: **MC 3608**

**BIG BILL BROONZY 1935-39 (Broonzy, Big Bill / Blind John Davis)**
**Album:** Released Dec '88, on Earl Archives Catalogue no: **BD 2012**

**BIG BILL BROONZY 1935-41**
**Album:** on Best Of Blues (USA) by Blue Island Records (USA). Catalogue no: **BOB 2**

**BIG BILL BROONZY, VOL. 1 1934-47 (Broonzy, Big Bill / Memphis Slim)**
**Album:** Released '88, on Document Catalogue no: **DLP 510**

**BIG BILL BROONZY, VOL. 2 1935-49**
**Album:** Released Dec '88, on Document Catalogue no: **DLP 539**

**BIG BILL BROONZY & WASHBOARD SAM (Broonzy, Big Bill / Washboard Sam)**
Tracks: / Little city woman / Lonesome / Jacqueline / Romance without finance / By Myself / Shirt tail / Diggin' my potatoes / Bright Eyes / Minding my own business / Never never / Horse shoe over my door / I'm a lonely man.
**Cass:** Released Apr '87, on Chess by Vogue Records. Catalogue no: **GCHK 78025**
**Album:** Released Apr '87, on Chess by Vogue Records. Catalogue no: **GCH 8025**

**BIG BILL'S BLUES**
**CD:** Released '86, on Vogue by Vogue Records. Catalogue no: **VG 600 041**
**Cass:** Released May '85, on CBS (import) by CBS Records. Deleted Aug '87. Catalogue no: **40-21122**
**Album:** Released May '85, on CBS (import) by CBS Records. Catalogue no: **21122**

**BLACK, BROWN & WHITE**
**Album:** Released Jun '86, on Storyville by Storyville Records AB. Catalogue no: **SLP 4052**

**DO THAT GUITAR RAG 1928-35**
**Album:** Released Dec '88, on Yazoo (USA) by Shanachie Records (USA). Catalogue no: **L 1035**

**FEELIN' LOW DOWN**
**Album:** Released May '89, on GNP Crescendo (USA) by GNP Crescendo Records (USA). Catalogue no: **GNPS 10004**
**Album:** Released Oct '88, on Vogue (France) by Vogue Records. Catalogue no: **512510**

**HOLLERIN' & CRYIN' THE BLUES VOL.3**
**Album:** Released Oct '88, on Vogue (France) by Vogue Records. Catalogue no: **512511**

**LAST SESSION VOL 1**
**Album:** Released Oct '82, on Verve (Import) Catalogue no: **2304 559**

**LAST SESSION VOL 2**
Tracks: / This train / Hush hush / Backwater blues / Blues / It hurts me too / Kansas city blues / When the sun goes down / Worried life blues / Trouble in mind / Take this hammer / Glory of love / Louise blues.
**Album:** Released Oct '83, on Polydor (France) by Polydor Ltd. Catalogue no: **813 367-1**

**LONESOME ROAD BLUES**
**Album:** Released May '89, on GNP Crescendo (USA) by GNP Crescendo Records (USA). Catalogue no: **GNPS 10009**

**MIDNIGHT STEPPERS**
**Album:** Released Aug '86, on Bluetime (Denmark) by Contact Records (Denmark). Catalogue no: **BT 2001**

**MY GAL IS GONE**
**Album:** Released Mar '87, on EMI-Manhattan by EMI Records. Catalogue no: **MAN 502**

**STORY VOL. 3**
Tracks: / Willie Mae Blues / Alberta / Old folks at home / Crawdad song / John Henry / Just a dream / Frankie and Johnny / Bill Bailey won't you please come home / Slow blues.
**Album:** Released Apr '84, on Verve (France) Catalogue no: **8177 791**

**TROUBLE IN MIND**
Tracks: / Trouble in mind / This train / Willie Mae blues / In the evenin' / Glory of love / Midnight special / Ananias / Keep your hands off her / Nobody's business / Labour man blues / I'm gonna sit down at the feastin' table / Swing low sweet chariot / Make me a pallet on the floor / House rent stomp / Bill bailey / I've been waitin' for you / Goodnight Irene.
**Album:** Released '83, on Spotlite by Spotlite Records. Catalogue no: **SPJ 900**

**YOUNG BIG BILL BROONZY 1928-35 (Broonzy, Bill)**
**Album:** Released Dec '88, on Yazoo (USA) by Shanachie Records (USA). Catalogue no: **L 1011**

## Brown, Andrew

**BIG BROWN'S CHICAGO BLUES**
**Album:** Released Oct '82, on Black Magic by Topic Records. Catalogue no: **BM 9001**

**ON THE CASE**
**Album:** Released Dec '88, on Double Trouble by Topic Records. Catalogue no: **DT 3010**

## Brown, Clarence

**Biographical details:** Brown, Clarence 'Gatemouth'. A black vocalist, bandleader, guitarist and fiddler, born in 1924 in Luoisiana, who wears a Stetson and switches from blues to bluegrass. Raised in Texas, his 20-year contract with the Peacock label prevented him from exercising all his talents; he is in fact a great example of the country/R&B cross-influence that led to the golden age of soul music in the '60s. His eclectic big-band album *One More Mile* was made for MCA in 1978. One of the great all-round entertainers, Brown has worked both jazz and country festivals, made commercials for Lone Star beer, and was once a deputy sheriff in New Mexico. (Donald Clarke, 24 August 1988.)

**ALRIGHT AGAIN (Brown, Clarence 'Gatemouth')**
Tracks: / Frosty / Strollin' with bones / Give me time to explain / Baby take it easy / Sometimes I slip / I feel alright again / Alligator bogaloo / Dollar got the blues / Honey in the bobo / Gate walks to the board.
**Album:** Released '88, on Rounder (USA) by Rounder Records (USA). Catalogue no: **ROUNDER 2028**
**Cass:** Released '88, on Rounder (USA) by Rounder Records (USA). Catalogue no: **ROUNDER 2028C**
**Album:** Released May '82, on Demon by Demon Records. Catalogue no: **FIEND 2**

**ATOMIC ENERGY**
**Album:** Released Mar '84, on Blues Boy (Sweden) Catalogue no: **BB 305**

**GATE'S ON HEAT VOL.3**
**Album:** Released Nov '79, on Barclay (France) by Decca Records. Catalogue no: **80603**

**MORE STUFF**
**Album:** Released Jan '85, on Black & Blue (1) by Black & Blue Records. Catalogue no: **BB 33561**

**NASHVILLE SESSION 1965**
Tracks: / Cross my heart / Don't start me talkin' / Gate's salty blues / My time is expensive / Ninety nine / Goin' down slow / Long way home / Tippin' in / For now so long / May the bird of paradise fly up your nose.
**Album:** Released Feb '89, on Chess by Vogue Records. Catalogue no: **LPM 7003**

**ONE MORE MILE (Brown, Clarence 'Gatemouth')**
Tracks: / Information blues / Song for Renee / Stranded / Sunrise cajun style / Big yard / Ain't that dandy / One more mile / I wonder / Flippin' out / Neat baku.
**Album:** Released '88, on Rounder (USA) by Rounder Records (USA). Catalogue no: **ROUNDER 2034**
**Album:** Released Jul '83, on Demon by Demon Records. Catalogue no: **FIEND 6**
**Cass:** Released '88, on Rounder (USA) by Rounder Records (USA). Catalogue no: **ROUNDER 2034C**

**ORIGINAL PEACOCK RECORDINGS (Brown, Clarence 'Gatemouth')**
**Cass:** Released '88, on Rounder (USA) by Rounder Records (USA). Catalogue no: **ROUNDER 2039C**
**Album:** Released '88, on Rounder (USA) by Rounder Records (USA). Catalogue no: **ROUNDER 2039**

**PRESSURE COOKER**
**Album:** Released Nov '87, on Alligator (Sonet) by Alligator Records (USA). Catalogue no: **SL 4745**

**REAL LIFE**
Tracks: / Real Life / Okie Dokie Stomp / Frankie And Johnny / Next time you see me / Take the 'A' train / Please Send Me Someone To Love / Catfish / St. Louis Blues / What a shame what a shame.
**Album:** Released '88, on Rounder (USA) by Rounder Records (USA). Catalogue no: **ROUNDER 2054**
**CD:** Released '88, on Rounder (USA) by Rounder Records (USA). Catalogue no: **CD 2054**
**Cass:** Released '88, on Rounder (USA) by Rounder Records (USA). Catalogue no: **ROUNDER 2054C**
**Album:** Released Apr '87, on Rounder Europa (USA) Catalogue no: **REU 1015**

**SAN ANTONIO BALLBUSTER**
Tracks: / Gate's salty blues / It never can be that way / I've been mistreated / She winked her eye / Win with me baby / She walked right in / Boogie uproar / Baby take it easy / Just got lucky / Didn't reach my goal / You got money / Okie dokie stomp / Just before dawn / Dirty work at the crossroads / Sad hours / Rock my blues away.
**Album:** on Charly by Charly Records. Catalogue no: **CR 30169**
**Album:** Released Sep '82, on Red Lightnin' by Red Lightning Records. Deleted Jun '89. Catalogue no: **RL 010**

**TEXAS GUITARMAN (Duke-Peacock Story Vol.1)**
Tracks: / Boogie rambler / Justice blues / Atomic energy / Two o'clock in the morning / Mary is fine / Didn't reach my goal / I live the life / My time is expensive / She walked right in / I've been mistreated / Win with me baby / Just got lucky / Mercy on me / Too late baby / Taking my chances / It can never be that way.
**Album:** Released Jan '86, on Ace by Ace Records. Deleted Dec '89. Catalogue no: **CHD 161**

**TEXAS SWING (Brown, Clarence 'Gatemouth')**
**CD:** Released '88, on Rounder (USA) by Rounder Records (USA). Catalogue no: **CD 11527**

## Brown, Cleo

**BOOGIE WOOGIE**
Tracks: / When Hollywood goes black and tan / When / You're my fever / Breakin' in a pair of shoes / Latch on / Love in the first degree / My gal Mezzanine / Here comes cookie / Boogie woogie / You're a heavenly thing / I'll take the south / Stuff is here and it's mellow, The / Never too tired for love / Give a broken heart a break / Mama don't want no peas an' rice / Me and my wonderful one.
**Album:** Released '88, on Official by Official Records. Catalogue no: **OFF 3010**

**LIVING IN THE AFTERGLOW (Brown, Cleo & Marian McPartland)**
**2 LP Set:** Released Oct '88, on Audiophile (USA) by Jazzology Records (USA). Catalogue no: **AP 216**

## Brown, Clifford

**Biographical details:** Brown, Clifford. One of the all-time great modern jazz trumpet players, whose name is always involved when critics need superlatives, Brownie was born in 1930 and killed in a car crash in 1956. He played in various small groups, recording for Blue Note and Pacific Jazz; he joined the Max Roach Quintet in 1954, with Ritchie Powell (Bud's brother) on piano, and Harold Land, who was replaced by Sonny Rollins in late '55; the group and Brown were becoming the hottest attractions in jazz when he and Powell were killed. *With Strings* was arranged by Quincy Jones in 1955; *At Basin Street* and the *Study In Brown* albums are the quintet classics; the *A Night At Birdland* albums by Art Blakey feature Brown; *Pure Genius* on Elektra Musician is from the collection of Mrs. Brown. (Donald Clarke, 24 August 1988.)

**ALTERNATE TAKES**
Tracks: / Bellarosa / Carvin' the clock / Cookin' / Get happy / Wail bait / Brownie eyes / Cherokee / Hymn of the orient.
**Album:** Released Apr '85, on Blue Note by EMI Records. Deleted Nov '88. Catalogue no: **BST 84428**

**ARR: BY QUINCY JONES (Brown, Clifford Big Band)**
**CD:** Released '84, on Vogue by Vogue Records. Catalogue no: **VG 600 025**

**AT BASIN STREET (Brown, Clifford & Max Roach)**
Tracks: / What is this thing called love? / Love is a many splendoured thing / I'll remember April / Powell's prences / Time / Scene is clean, The / Gertrude's bounce.
**CD:** Released Dec '83, on Emarcy Catalogue no: **814 648 2**
**Album:** Released Dec '83, on Emarcy Catalogue no: **6336 707**

**BIRDLAND 21ST FEBRUARY 1954 (Brown, Clifford & Art Blakey)**
**CD:** Released Mar '90, on Giants of Jazz by Hasmick Promotions. Catalogue no: **GOJCD 53033**

**BLACK & WHITE SERIES 1 - TRUMPET GENIUSES 1950's (Brown, Clifford & Chet Baker)**
**Album:** Released Oct '88, on Philology Catalogue no: **214W 13**

**CHEROKEE 1954-55**
**Album:** Released Feb '89, on Giants of Jazz by Hasmick Promotions. Catalogue no: **LPJT 74**

**CLIFFORD BROWN BIG BAND**
**CD:** Released Feb '89, on Vogue by Vogue Records. Catalogue no: **VGCD 600025**

**CLIFFORD BROWN (JAZZ IMMORTAL)**
Tracks: / Daahoud / Minders keepers / Joy spring / Gone with the wind / Bones for Jones / Blueberry Hill / Tiny capers / Tiny capers (alternate take).
**CD:** Released Jul '88, on Pacific Jazz by EMI Records. Catalogue no: **CDP 746 850 2**
**Album:** Released Nov '84, on Affinity by Charly Records. Catalogue no: **AFF 129**
**CD:** Released Aug '88, on EMI by EMI Records. Catalogue no: **CZ 47**

**CLIFFORD BROWN MEMORIAL (Various artists)**
**CD:** Released Jan '89, on JVC/Fantasy Catalogue no: **VDJ 1609**
**Album:** Released '88, on QJC Catalogue no: **QJC 7055**

**CLIFFORD BROWN QUARTET (Brown, Clifford Quartet)**
**CD:** Released Dec '86, on Vogue by Vogue Records. Catalogue no: **VG 600 020**

**CLIFFORD BROWN VOL.1**
Tracks: / Jordu / I can't get started / I get a kick out of you / Parisian thoroughfare / All God's chillun got rhythm / Tenderly / Sunset eyes / Clifford's axe.
**Album:** Released Jan '82, on Jazz Reactivation Catalogue no: **JR 118**

**CLIFFORD BROWN VOL.2**
Tracks: / Brown skins / Deltitnu / Keeping up with the Jonesey / Conception / All the things you are / I cover the waterfront.
**Album:** Released May '83, on Jazz Reactivation Catalogue no: **JR 136**

**CLIFFORD BROWN VOL.3**
Tracks: / Goofin' with me / Minority / Salute to the Bandbox / Strictly romantic / Baby / Quick step / Bum's rush / No start no end / Venez donc chez moi.
**Album:** Released May '83, on Jazz Reactivation Catalogue no: **JR 140**

**CLIFFORD BROWN VOL.4**
Tracks: / Hello / All weird / Blue and brown / I can dream, can't I / Song is you / Come rain or come shine / It might as well be spring / You're a lucky guy.
**Album:** Released May '83, on Jazz Reactivation Catalogue no: **JR 142**

**COMPLETE PARIS COLLECTION VOL 4**
**Album:** Released Nov '88, on Vogue by Vogue Records. Catalogue no: **500109**

**DEAUX GEANTS**
**2 LP Set:** Released Oct '88, on Vogue by Vogue Records. Catalogue no: **416008**

**IN CONCERT (Brown, Clifford & Max Roach)**
**Album:** Released '88, on GNP Crescendo (USA) by GNP Crescendo Records (USA). Catalogue no: **GNPS 18**
**CD:** Released '88, on GNP Crescendo (USA) by GNP Crescendo Records (USA). Catalogue no: **GNPD 18**
**Cass:** Released '88, on GNP Crescendo (USA) by GNP Crescendo Records (USA). Catalogue no: **GNP5 18**
**Album:** Released Oct '88, on Vogue by Vogue Records. Catalogue no: **500 751**

**LIVE AT BASIN STREET-1956 (Brown, Clifford & Max Roach)**
Tracks: / Valse hot / I feel a song coming on / Sweet Georgia Brown / What's new? / Daahoud - drum conversation.
**Album:** Released Apr '81, on Ingo Catalogue no: **INGO 2**

**MEMORIAL ALBUM**
Tracks: / Hymn of the Orient / Easy living / Minor mood / Cherokee (Indian love song) / Wail bait / Brownie speaks / De-dah / Cookin' you go to my head / Carvin' the rock.
**CD:** Released Aug '85, on Blue Note by EMI Records. Catalogue no: **BNZ 202**
**Album:** Released Aug '85, on Blue Note by EMI Records. Catalogue no: **BST 81526**
**Cass:** Released Aug '85, on Blue Note by EMI Records. Deleted Jun '88. Catalogue no: **4BN 81526**

**MORE STUDY IN BROWN**
Tracks: / I'll remember April / Junior's arrival / Flossie Lou / Mildama / Jordu / These foolish things / Land's end / Blues walk.
**CD:** on Emarcy Catalogue no: **814 637 2**

**PURE GENIUS (Brown, Clifford & Max Roach)**
**Album:** Released Jun '82, on Elektra (Musician) by Elektra Records (USA). Catalogue no: **K 52388**

**STUDY IN BROWN (Brown, Clifford & Max Roach)**
Tracks: / Cherokee / Jacqui / Land's end / George's dilemma / Sandu / Gherkin for Perkin / If I love again / Take the 'A' train.
**CD:** Released Dec '83, on Emarcy Catalogue no: **814 646 2**
**Album:** Released Dec '83, on Emarcy Catalogue no: **6336 708**

**TRUMPET MASTERS (Brown, Clifford & D.Gillispie)**
Tracks: / Trumpet masters.
**2 LP Set:** Released Mar '75, on Vogue by Vogue Records. Catalogue no: **VJD 507**

**WITH STRINGS**
Tracks: / Yesterdays / Laura / What's new? / Blue moon / Can't help lovin' dat man / Embraceable you / Willow weep for me / Smoke gets in your eyes / Portrait of Jennie / Where or when / Stardust.
**CD:** Released Dec '83, on Emarcy Catalogue no: **814 642 2**
**Album:** Released Dec '83, on Emarcy Catalogue no: **6336 711**

## Brown, Lawrence

**Biographical details:** Brown, Lawrence. Duke Ellington's greatest trombone star was born in Lawrence, Kansas in 1905. Among his many big hits and famous solos with Duke was *Rose Of The Rio Grande* with Ivy Anderson's vocal in 1938. He also recorded freelance with Johnny Hodges and many others. (Donald Clarke, 24 August 1988.).

**INSPIRED ABANDON (Brown, Lawrence All-Stars & Johnny Hodges)**
Tracks: / Stompy Jones / Mood indigo / Good Queen Bess / Little brother / Jeep's blues / Do nothing till you hear from me / Ruint / Sassy cue.
**Album:** Released Apr '83, on Jasmine by Hasmick Promotions. Deleted Feb '88. Catalogue no: **JAS 66**

## Brown, Les

**Biographical details:** Brown, Les. Arranger, bandleader and reed player Les Brown was born in 1912 in Pennsylvania; he formed a band at Duke University in the early '30s, started over in 1938 and 'Les Brown and his Band of Renown' was the most popular white dance band in the USA in the '40s and early '50s. Doris Day was his vocalist; biggest hits included *My Dreams Are Getting Better All The Time* and *Sentimental Journey* (both with Day, both no. one in Billboard in 1945), plus instrumentals *I've Got My Love To Keep Me Warm* (no. one in 1948, the last big instrumental hit of the Swing era), *Bizet Has His Day*, *Leap Frog*, etc. He had quit in 1946, but had forgot a March '47 ballroom gig; he couldn't get out of it, formed a bew band, eventually did radio and TV work and remained one of the most popular leaders on the West Coast. Albums made in the '80s included long-time Brown vocalist Jo Ann Greer, sideman Butch Stone on baritone sax and vocals (top 10 hit *Doctor, Lawyer, Indian Chief* 1946), guests Rosemary Clooney, Georgie Auld, Buddy DeFranco. *Digital Swing* on Fantasy celebrated over 50 years as a bandleader in 1986. (Donald Clarke, 24 August 1988.)

**20 GOLDEN PIECES: LES BROWN (Brown, Les & His Band of Renown)**
Tracks: / Strictly instrumental / You made me love you / Blue flame / So rare / Lazy river / How high the moon / Baby elephant walk / Gentle on my mind / Sentimental journey / Pink panther (theme from) / Let's dance / Jersey bounce / Moonglow / At the woodchopper's ball / On the sunny side of the street / Ballin' the jack / Pretty girl is like a melody, A / Softly as in a morning sunrise / I want to hold your hand / Walk on by.
**Cass:** Released Feb '82, on Bulldog Records by President Records. Catalogue no: **BDC 2024**
**Album:** Released Nov '81, on Bulldog Records by President Records. Catalogue no: **BDL 2024**

**1943 BAND, THE**
Tracks: / OK for baby / I heard you cried last night / Canteen bounce, The / Baby knock me a kiss / Taking a chance on love / Later tonight / What's the good word Mr. Bluebird / Things ain't what they used to be.
Note: With Randy Brooks, Hal Derwin, Town Criers.
**Album:** Released Jun '79, on Fanfare by Captain Billy's Music. Catalogue no: **FANFARE 30-130**

**1946 (Brown, Les & His Orchestra)**
Note: With Doris Day, Butch Stone, Jack Haskell. Mono.
**Album:** Released Dec '86, on Circle (USA) by Jazzology Records (USA). Catalogue no: **CLP 90**

**1949, VOL 1 (Brown, Les & His Orchestra)**
Tracks: / Sometimes I'm happy / Three little words / On the Alamo / Something cool / Honeysuckle rose / Negra consentida / Where are you / April showers / Song is ended / Just squeeze me / Pell mell / Stardust / Them there eyes / Lip / Black coffee / Bopple sauce.
**Album:** Released Oct '79, on London Records by London Records Ltd. Deleted '84. Catalogue no: **HMP 5054**

**1949, VOL 2 (Brown, Les & His Orchestra)**
Tracks: / Squawkin' 'bout my walkin' / All the things you are / Thank you Count / Baby I need you / September song / Tenderly / Don't do something to someone else / Moten swing / Teaset toe / Shadow time / Ah boo ah boo / Pretty baby / Boptized / Dreamers holiday / Just a gigolo / Leap frog.
**Album:** Released Oct '79, on London Records by London Records Ltd. Deleted '84. Catalogue no: **HMP 5059**

**ALL WEATHER MUSIC (Brown, Les & His Band of Renown)**
Tracks: / Clouds / Ill wind / Rain / Lost in a fog / Let it snow, let it snow, let it snow / Stormy weather / Over the rainbow / Blue skies / Azure / Heatwave / Moon was yellow (and the night was young), The / You are my sunshine.
**Album:** Released Jun '83, on Jasmine by Hasmick Promotions. Deleted Feb '88. Catalogue no: **JASM 1019**

**AT THE HOLLYWOOD PALLADIUM**
**Cass:** Released Jan '88, on Starline (Jazz) Catalogue no: **SLC 61015**

**COMPLETE LES BROWN - VOL.2, THE**
**Album:** Released Apr '84, on Ajaz (USA) Catalogue no: **AJAZ 415**

**CONCERT AT THE HOLLYWOOD PALLADIUM, VOL.1 (Brown, Les & His Band of Renown)**
Tracks: / Opening announcement (Leap frog) / Moontoona clipper / Caravan / Strange / Baby / Speak low (when you speak of love) / Rain / Street of dreams / Brown's little jug / I let a song go out of my heart / Back in your own back yard / Invitation / You're the cream in my coffee.
**Album:** Released Feb '83, on Jasmine by Hasmick Promotions. Catalogue no: **JASM 1001**

**CONCERT AT THE HOLLYWOOD PALLADIUM, VOL.2 (Brown, Les & His Band of Renown)**
Tracks: / Midnight sun / Begin the Beguine / Happy hooligan / I would do anything for you / Laura / Jersey bounce / From this moment on / Crazy legs / Flying home / One o' clock jump / Cherokee / Sentimental journey.
**Album:** Released Feb '83, on Jasmine by Hasmick Promotions. Catalogue no: **JASM 1002**

**DANCE TO SOUTH PACIFIC (Brown, Les & His Band of Renown)**
Tracks: / Honey bun / Happy talk / Some enchanted evening / Loneliness of evening / Wonderful guy / Bloody Mary / Bali ha'i / Dites-moi / Younger than Springtime / This nearly was mine / There is nothin' like a dame / I'm gonna wash that man right out of my hair.
Note: A highly dance-able album from Les Brown and his Band of Renown. Arrangements designed for dancing of popular titles from the South Pacific such as 'Bali Ha'i','I'm gonna wash that man right out of my hair','Some enchanted evening' and more.
**Cass:** Released Apr '85, on Capitol by EMI Records. Deleted Jul '87. Catalogue no: **ED 2604134**
**Album:** Released Apr '85, on Capitol by EMI Records. Deleted Nov '88. Catalogue no: **ED 2604131**

**DOUBLE DATE (Brown, Les / Sam Donahue)**
**Album:** Released Dec '77, on Hep Jazz by Hep Records. Catalogue no: **HEP 14**

**DUKE BLUE DEVILS, THE**
**Album:** Released Jul '82, on Golden Era by Delta Records. Catalogue no: **GELP 15045**

**FROM THE CAFE ROUGE**
**Album:** Released Oct '84, on Giants of Jazz by Hasmick Promotions. Catalogue no: **GOJ 1027**

**JAZZ SONG BOOK, THE**
Tracks: / King Phillip stomp / Willow weep for me / Don't get around much anymore / Wonderful / Apple honey / I remember you / Claw / Let's get away from it all / Pizza boy & love is here to stay / I only have eyes for you / Chelsea bridge.
**Album:** Released Apr '84, on Jasmine by Hasmick Promotions. Deleted Feb '88. Catalogue no: **JASM 1506**

**LES BROWN AND HIS ORCHESTRA 1944/46 (Brown, Les & His Orchestra)**
Tracks: / Leap frog / Invitation to the blues / Just a gigolo / Man with a horn / I can't help it / Flip lid / Lou's blues / Lover's leap / Sentimental journey / Ready to go steady / 12.55 express / Kiss to remember / I can't believe that you're in love with me / I'm making believe / I've got my love to keep me warm / Paper moon.
**Album:** Released Feb '79, on London Records by London Records Ltd. Deleted '84. Catalogue no: **HMP 5039**

**LES BROWN & HIS ORCHESTRA 1946/50 (Brown, Les & His Orchestra)**
**Album:** Released Oct '79, on First Heard by Submarine Records. Catalogue no: **FH 18**

**LES BROWN, VOL. 1, 1944-45**
Tracks: / Leap frog / Invitation to the blues / Just a gigolo / Man with a horn / Flip your lid / Lou's blues / Lover's leap / Sentimental journey / Ready to go steady / 12:55 express / Kiss to remember, A / I can't believe that you're in love with me / I'm making believe / I've got my love to keep me warm / Paper moon.
Note: Doris Day's arrival was the harb-

inger of success for Les Brown and his Band of Renown, the leader reveals to music authority Dave Dexter, Jr. in the liner notes for this album. Ms. Day offers corroboration in five distinctive performances - her famed "Sentimental journey" and four other tunes never before on record by her and the band. Trumpeter Jimmy Zito plays the title role in "Man with a horn". Ted Nash, Abe Most, Geoff Clarkson, Dick Shanahan and Kenny Meisel are featured throughout. Ben Homer, Bob Higgins, Frank Comstock, Skip Martin and Brown wrote the arrangements.
**Album:** Released Apr '89, on Hindsight Catalogue no: **HSR 103**

**LES BROWN, VOL. 2, 1949**
Tracks: / Sometimes I'm happy / Three little words / On the Alamo / Something cool / Honeysuckle rose / Negra consentida / Where are you / April showers / Song is ended, The / Just squeeze me / Pell mell / Stardust / Them there eyes / Lips / Black coffee / Bopple sauce.
Note: These transcriptions, complete with announcements by Jimmy Wallington, are the source of Volume 2 of the Band of Renown. The personnel is an exercise in big-name dropping - Abe Most, Dave Pell, Ronnie Lang, Butch Stone, Eddie Sherr in the reed section; Ray Simms, Ralph Piffner, Stumpy Brown, Ray Klein or Frank Comstock, trombones; Wes Hensel, Frank Beach, Bob Fowler, Bob Higgins, trumpets; Geoff Clarkeson, piano; Tony Rizzi or Bobby Gibbons, guitar; Ray Leatherwood, bass, and Dick Shanahan, Irv Cottler or Jack Sperling, drums. George T. Simon conferred with Hensel in compiling the liner notes. (Hindsight Catalogue - 1989)
**Album:** Released '88, on Hindsight Catalogue no: **HSR 131**

**LES BROWN, VOL. 3, 1949**
Tracks: / Squawkin' 'bout my walkin' / All the things you are / Thank you, Count / September song / Baby, I need you / Tenderly / Don't do something to someone else / Moten stomp / Teasey toe / Shadow time / Ah-boo ah-boo / Pretty baby / Boptized / Dreamers holiday / Just a gigolo / Leap frog.
Note: Brown's Band of Renown was a band of inspired soloists. Volume 3 offers nearly equal time to former Stan Kenton trumpeter Frank Beach and tenor saxophonist Dave Pell on "Squawkin' 'bout my walkin'", "Moten stomp" and "Teasey toe" plus more BEach on "All the things you are", "Boptized" and "Ah-boo ah-boo" and Pell on "Thank you, Count". There are generous individual tastes of Geoff Clarkeson's piano, Ray Sims' and Ray Klein's trombones and Tony Rizzi's guitar. Lucy Ann Polk, an original Town Crier with Les and an alumna of the bands of Tommy Dorsey, Kay Kyser and Bobby Sherwood, sings four numbers. (Hindsight Catalogue - 1989)
**Album:** Released '88, on Hindsight Catalogue no: **HSR 132**

Les Brown - The One and Only (Intercord(Germany))

**LES BROWN, VOL. 4 1956-57**
**Album:** Released '88, on Hindsight Catalogue no: **HSR 199**

**LES BROWN'S IN TOWN**
Tracks: / Just you, just me / Harlem nocturne / Checkin' in / Moonlight in Vermont / Continental, The / Spanich monster / Meanwhile back on the bus / Ridin' high / Nina never knew / On a little street in Singapore / Piccolino, The.
**Album:** Released Apr '84, on Capitol (import) Catalogue no: **2C 068 86543**

**ONE AND ONLY, THE (See panel above)**
Tracks: / On a sunny day / One more blues / Holiday in big band land / Say what? / Turn around / Perky / Bruised bones / Summer talk / LB special / Boogie train blues / Goldfish / Swing flow.
Note: This is a new recording and features 3 original Les Brown compositions.The album also has the benefit of Direct Metal Mastering. Born in the year 1912, Les Brown started his musical career in 1935 at Duke University leading the 'Duke Blue Devils' dance band. In 1937 he was writing arrangements for Ruby Newman, Isham Jones, Jimmy Dorsey, Larry Clinton and Red Nichols and a year later formed the big band which became known as 'Les Brown & His Band Of Renown'. A clean-cut, hard swinging band playing outstanding arrangements which quickly established an international reputation, performing at the 'New York World's Fair' in 1939 and recording the million sales record hit *Sentimental journey* sung by Doris Day in 1944. 1947 saw the beginning of the band's long association with Bob Hope, which continued into the '80's, on radio and TV shows and overseas tours. During this period Les Brown recorded regularly and in 1948 had an another international record hit *I've got my love to keep me warm.* He was and still is, musical director of innumerable TV shows, guest conductor of the Los Angeles Symphony; Denver Symphony; Burbank Symphony; North Carolina Symphony; Inglewood Symphony and the Duke University Concert Band.
Les Brown is writer, or co-writer of several successful songs and instrumentals which have become world-wide record hits, recording with stars such as Bing Crosby; Bob and Dolores Hope; Johnny Mercer; Nancy Wilson; Dick Haymes; The Ames Brothers and a host of others. 'Les Brown & His Band Of Renown' appeared in films such as *Will Cowan Shorts* (Universal), *Seven days leave* (RKO), *The nutty professor*(Paramount) and played at the inauguration balls for President Nixon (1973) and President Reagan (1981 and 1985) and is one of the very few great big bands still an active part of the American Show Business scene even after all these years. (Intersound)
**Album:** Released Aug '86, on Intercord (Germany) Catalogue no: **ISST 170**

**ONE NIGHT STAND (Brown, Les / Krupa/Osborne)**
**Album:** Released Apr '84, on Joyce (USA) Catalogue no: **JOYCE 1119**

**RHAPSODY IN BLUE (Brown, Les**

/ Day, Doris)
**Cass:** Released Sep '89, on Big Band Era Catalogue no: **40134**
**Album:** Released May '85, on Astan (USA) Catalogue no: **F 20134**

**SENTIMENTAL JOURNEY**
**CD:** Released '88, on Polydor by Polydor Ltd. Catalogue no: **825 493-2**

**SENTIMENTAL THING**
**Cass:** Released Oct '84, on First Heard by Submarine Records. Catalogue no: **CFH 31**
**Album:** Released Nov '79, on First Heard by Submarine Records. Catalogue no: **FH 31**

**SWEETEST SOUNDS (Brown, Les & Rosemary Clooney)**
Tracks: / Sweetest sounds, The / How am I to know / My funny valentine / Why shouldn't I? / My romance / I get along without you very well / Angry / Some people / Man with a horn / Show me / Have you met Miss Jones? / Little Brown jug / Sleepy time girl / I didn't know what time it was.
**Cass:** Released '84, on Artistic by Submarine Records. Catalogue no: **CART 003**
**Album:** Released '84, on Artistic by Submarine Records. Catalogue no: **ART 003**

**SWING GOES ON VOL 5**
Tracks: / Ridin' high / Just you, just me / Swingin' down the lane / Checkin' in / Stardust / My melancholy baby / Piccolino, The / I've got my love to keep me warm / Sentimental journey / Happy talk / Continental, The / Sophisticated swing / Josephine / Leap frog.
**Album:** Released '83, on EMI (Germany) by EMI Records. Catalogue no: **IC 054 52714**

**SWING SONG BOOK (Brown, Les & His Band of Renown)**
Tracks: / Swing book blues / How high the moon / Early Autumn / King Porter stomp / Lullaby of Birdland / Moten swing / Just in time / I want to be happy / Take the 'A' train / I'm beginning to see the light / Pick yourself up / Lean baby.
**Album:** Released '83, on Jasmine by Hasmick Promotions. Deleted Feb '88. Catalogue no: **JASM 1503**

**THAT SOUND OF RENOWN**
Tracks: / I've got your love to keep me warm / New Mexican hat dance / I'm forever blowing bubbles / Bernie's tune / Highlights of 'an American in Paris / It's all right with me / Something's gotta give / Gal from Joe's, The / Lullaby in rhythm / Nutcracker suite op 71.
**Album:** Released Feb '83, on Jasmine by Hasmick Promotions. Deleted Feb '88. Catalogue no: **JASM 1012**

**TODAY (Brown, Les & His Band of Renown)**
Tracks: / On a clear day you can see forever / My kind of girl / Song sung blue / Sentimental journey / Thands for the memory / Airport 1975 / Bad bad Leroy Brown / Good man is hard to find / Sing / Juicy fruit / Everybody loves somebody.

**Marion Brown**

**Album:** Released Nov '81, on Harmonia Mundi (France) by Harmonia Mundi (UK). Deleted '86. Catalogue no: **MPS 68 118**

## Brown, Marion

**Biographical details:** Brown, Marion. Born in Atlanta, Georgia in 1935, Marion Brown plays alto sax and composes; like many others in contemporary black music he is perhaps better appreciated overseas than at home. He has worked with the most important names in modern black music, including Archie Shepp, Bill Dixon, the Jazz Composers Orchestra, Sun Ra, Anthony Braxton, Leo Smith; his academic work included a study of black fife-and-drum corps in Southern States. *La Placita* has a quartet with guitar, bass and drums. Many of his other records are on German and Japanese labels. Donald Clarke, 24 August 1988..

**LA PLACITA (LIVE IN WILLISAU) (Brown, Marion Quartet)**
**Album:** Released Sep '86, on Timeless by Timeless Records. Catalogue no: **SJP 108**

**MARION BROWN QUARTET (Brown, Marion Quartet)**
**Album:** Released '88, on ESP Base Catalogue no: **ESP 1022**

## Brown, Nappy

**Biographical details:** Brown, Nappy. An R&B singer from Charlotte, North Carolina who made 25 singles for Savoy 1955-61, including several top ten R&B hits and crossovers to the Billboard's Hot 100 pop chart. (Donald Clarke, 24 August 1988.).

**BLACK TOP BLUES-A-RAMA, LIVE AT TIPITINA'S VOL. 2 (Various artists)**
**Album:** Released '88, on Black Top (USA) by Rounder Records (USA). Catalogue no: **BT 1045**
**Cass:** Released '88, on Black Top (USA) by Rounder Records (USA). Catalogue no: **BT 1045C**
**CD:** Released '88, on Black Top (USA) by Rounder Records (USA). Catalogue no: **CD 1045**

**DON'T BE ANGRY**
**Album:** Released Mar '85, on Savoy Jazz (USA) by Malaco Records (USA). Catalogue no: **SJL 1149**

**I NONE GOT OVER (Brown, Nappy / The Roosters)**
**Album:** Released Jun '85, on Stockholm (Sweden) Catalogue no: **RJ 205**

**JUST FOR ME**
Note: With Big Jay McNeely.
**CD:** Released Jul '88, on JSP by JSP Records. Catalogue no: **JSP CD 218**

**SOMETHING GONNA JUMP OUT THE BUSHES**
**CD:** Released '88, on Black Top (USA) by Rounder Records (USA). Catalogue no: **BT 1039CD**
**Album:** Released '88, on Black Top (USA) by Rounder Records (USA). Catalogue no: **BT 1039**
**Cass:** Released '88, on Black Top (USA). Catalogue no: **BT 1039C**

**THAT MAN**

Tracks: / That man / Is it true is it true / Open up that door / Bye bye baby / Right time, the / Down in the alley / Baby cry cry cry baby / Coal miner / Didn't you know / I wonder / Two faced woman / Little by little / My baby / Long time / Baby I got news for you / What's come over you baby / I've had my fun.
**Album:** Released Aug '87, on Mr.R&B (Sweden) Catalogue no: **RB 100**

**TORE UP (Brown, Nappy with The Heartfixers)**
Tracks: / Tore up.
**Album:** Released Jun '86, on Nightflite by Nightflite Communications. Catalogue no: **NTFL 2002**

## Brown, Ray

**Biographical details:** Brown, Ray The great USA jazz bassist was born in Pittsburgh in 1926; he played with Dizzy Gillespie in the late 1940s; he was married to Ella Fitzgerald and accompanied her 1948-52; he was a memebr of the Oscar Peterson trio 1951-66 and has played on an uncountable number of albums on Norman Granz's Verve and Pablo labels, as a sideman with Duke Ellington, Milt Jackson and many others (*This One's For Blanton* with Duke recreated the 1940 Ducal duets with Jimmy Blanton) and leading his own small group sets. More recently he has recorded for Concord Jazz, including nine albums on that label with the L A Four: guitarist Laurinado Almeida, Bud Shank on reeds, Shelley Manne or Jeff Hamilton on drums. He has also managed other artists (such as Quincy Jones), published instruction books, produced Hollywood Bowl concerts, etc. He is one of the busiest and most highly regarded musicians in the business. (Donald Clarke, 24 August 1988.).

**BAM BAM BAM (Brown, Ray Trio)**
Note: There isn't a trio around that swings harder nor generates more excitement than the Ray Brown Trio. Captured live in concert at the Fujitsu Concord Jazz Festival in Tokyo, Japan 1988, Ray Brown and Jeff Hamilton lay down a rock solid rhythmic foundation, while Gene Harris' ten fingers pull an entire big band out of his piano. An electrifying set of jazz classics and well crafted Ray Brown originals. 'Bam bam bam' is a testimony to how exciting live jazz can be. Personnel: Ray Brown (bass), Gene Harris (piano), Jeff Hamilton (drums).
**Cass:** Released May '89, on Concord Jazz by Concord Jazz Records (USA). Catalogue no: **CJ 375 C**
**Album:** Released May '89, on Concord Jazz by Concord Jazz Records (USA). Catalogue no: **CJ 375**
**CD:** Released May '89, on Concord Jazz by Concord Jazz Records (USA). Catalogue no: **CCD 4375**

**BYE BYE BLACKBIRD**
Tracks: / Everything happens to me / Mean to me / Things ain't what they used to be / The rev. / I remember / I should care.
Note: Eight popular and jazz standards tastefully performed by the excellent Ray Brown Trio & featuring two of Japan's best musicians, Ichiro Mauda on vibraphone & Emi Nakajima on vocals.
**Album:** Released Jul '86, on King (Japan) Catalogue no: **K 28P 6303**

**DON'T FORGET THE BLUES (Brown, Ray All Stars)**
Tracks: / Blues'd Out / Jim / Night Train / If I Could Be With You (One Hour Tonight) / Rocks in my bed / You Don't Know Me / Jumpin' the blues / Don't forget the blues.
Note: Personnel: Ray Brown-Bass/Ron Eschete-Guitar / Al Grey-Trombone / Gene Harris-piano and fender Rhodes / Grady Tate-Drums.
**Album:** Released Feb '86, on Concord Jazz by Concord Jazz Records (USA). Catalogue no: **CJ 293**
**CD:** Released Jan '87, on Concord Jazz by Concord Jazz Records (USA). Catalogue no: **CCD 4293**
**Cass:** Released Feb '86, on Concord Jazz by Concord Jazz Records (USA). Catalogue no: **CJC 293**

**I FEEL THAT YOUNG MAN'S RHYTHM**
Tracks: / Deep sea diver / Bye bye bye / Lollipop mama / Woman's a wonderful thing / Miss Fanny Brown / Rockin' at midnight / Please don't go / Riding high / I feel that young man's rhythm / Gamblin' man / Crazy crazy women / Don't let it rain / Big town / Cryin' and singin' the blue / Rockabye baby / It's a crying shame.
**Album:** Released Apr '85, on Route 66 (Sweden) Catalogue no: **KIX 26**

**LIVE AT THE CONCORD JAZZ FESTIVAL - 1979 (Brown, Ray Trio)**
Tracks: / Blue bossa / Bossa nova do marilla / Manha de carnaval / St Louis blues / Fly me to the moon / Georgia on my mind / Here's that rainy day / Please send me someone to love / Honeysuckle rose.
**CD:** Released Mar '90, on Concord by Concord Jazz Records (USA). Catalogue no: **CCD 4102**

**ONE O'CLOCK JUMP 1953 (Brown, Ray, Ben Webster & Oscar Peterson)**
**Album:** Released Apr '84, on Verve Catalogue no: **LP VRV 1**
**Cass:** Released Apr '84, on Verve Deleted '85. Catalogue no: **MC VRVC 1**

**RAY BROWN THREE, A (Brown, Ray, Monty Alexander & Sam Most)**
Tracks: / I wish you love / I can't stop loving you / Jamento / Blue monk / Candy man The / Too late now / You're my everything / There is no greater love.
Note: Sam Most has appeared on many Contemporary albums and has recently been involved with Bobby Hutcherson's group. Artists include Ray Brown Bass Monty Alexander piano Sam Most flute
**Album:** Released May '83, on Concord Jazz by Concord Jazz Records (USA). Catalogue no: **CJ 213**
**Cass:** Released May '83, on Concord Jazz by Concord Jazz Records (USA). Catalogue no: **CJC 213**

**RED HOT RAY BROWN TRIO, THE**
Tracks: / Have you met Miss Jones? / Meditation / Street of dreams / Lady be good / That's all / Love me tender / How could you do a thing like this to me? / Captain Bill.
Note: Recorded live at the Blue Note, New York. Personnel : Ray Brown - bass / Gene Harris - piano / Mickey Roker - drums.
**Cass:** Released Jul '87, on Concord Jazz by Concord Jazz Records (USA). Catalogue no: **CJC 315**
**Album:** Released Jul '87, on Concord Jazz by Concord Jazz Records (USA). Catalogue no: **CJ 315**

**SOLAR ENERGY**
Tracks: / Exactly like you / Cry me a river / Teach me tonight / Take the 'A' train / Mistreated but undefeated blues / That's all / Easy does it / Sweet Georgia Brown.
**Cass:** Released Jul '85, on Concord Jazz by Concord Jazz Records (USA). Catalogue no: **CJC 268**
**CD:** on Concord Jazz by Concord Jazz Records (USA). Catalogue no: **CCD 4268**
**Album:** Released Jul '85, on Concord Jazz by Concord Jazz Records (USA). Catalogue no: **CJ 268**

**SOMETHING FOR LESTER**
Note: With Cedar Walton and Elvin Jones.
**CD:** Released Jan '86, on JVC/Fantasy Catalogue no: **VDJ 1555**

## Brown, Roy

**Biographical details:** Brown, Roy An R&B singer from New Orleans (1925-81). He recorded his own *Good Rockin' Tonight* for De Luxe in 1948, covered by Wynonie Harris on King, later by Elvis Presley on Sun; *Boogie At Midnight* was a no. 3 R&B hit in 1949, then *Hard Luck Blues* was no. 1 in 1950, followed by more hits. He switched to King in 1952 and had less luck, though always a popular act; then to Imperial in 1956, teaming with Dave Bartholemew for a cover of Buddy Knox's *Party Doll* which was a no. 14 R&B hit in 1957, and reached the pop Hot 100; *Let The Four Winds Blow* was a pop top 40 the same year; he later joined the Johnny Otis review and reformed his own band in the late '70s. (Donald Clarke, 24 August 1988.)

**BATTLE OF THE BLUES VOL. 2 (Brown, Roy & Wynonie Harris)**
Tracks: / RB / Hard luck blues / Dreaming blues / 'Long about sundown / Double crossin' woman / Sweet peach / Wrong woman blues / Brown angel / WH / Man, have I got troubles / I'll never give up / Here comes the night / Luscious woman / Drinking blues / Nearer my love to thee / Tremblin'.
**CD:** Released Mar '90, on King Catalogue no: **KCD 627**
Album: Rerleased Dec'87. on King Catalogue no: **KLP 627**

**BLUESWAY SESSIONS, THE**
Tracks: / Hard times / Higher and higher / New Orleans woman / Driving me mad / Till the end of never / Soul lover / Man in trouble blues / Standing on broadway (watching the girls) / Woman trouble blues / Cryin' with the blues / Deep down in my soul.
**Album:** Released Oct '88, on Charly R&B by Charly Records. Catalogue no: **CRB 1199**

**BOOGIE AT MIDNIGHT**
Tracks: / Mighty mighty man / Boogie at midnight / Cadillac baby / Hard luck blues / Love don't love nobody / Too much lovin' ain't no good / Big town / Rockabye baby / Answer to big town / Ain't no rockin' no more / My gal from kokomo / Fannie Brown got married / Black diamond / Shake em up baby / Adorable one / Good looking and foxy too.
Note: In some respects Roy Brown's jumping R & B style was similar to that of Tiny Bradshaw, Wyonie Harris and others, i.e he was another of the hot R & B acts that immediately preceeded and help to shape the rock 'n' roll boom of the mid fifties. However, unlike Bradshaw and Harris, Brown was a quality cry style singer rather than an R & B shouter he had a lot of gospel inflections in his voicethat would surface more noticeably still in the next generation of early soul singers. This difference is evident in the untempo ravers such as Mighty Mighty Man Love don't Love nobody My gal from Kokomo Black diamond and many more but it's particularly blatent in the dramatic Hard luck blues (1950) and a 1959 ballad "Adorable one" on the latter Brown sounds astonishingly like Jackie Wilson, whomof course he influenced. Essential stuff from a key figure in the development of R & B.
**Album:** Released Jul '85, on Charly R&B by Charly Records. Catalogue no: **CRB 1093**
**Cass:** Released Jul '85, on Charly R&B by Charly Records. Catalogue no: **TCCRB 1093**

**CHEAPEST PRICE IN TOWN**
**Album:** Released Feb '79, on Faith Catalogue no: **91020**

**GOOD ROCKIN' TONIGHT**
Tracks: / Travellin blues / Let the four winds blow / Love for sale / Boogie woogie blues / Good rockin' tonight / Boogie at midnight / Love don't love nobody / Losing hand / Tin pan alley.
**Album:** Released Jun '84, on Magnum Force by Magnum Music Group. Catalogue no: **MFLP 1025**

**GOOD ROCKING TONIGHT**
Tracks: / Good rockin' tonight / Long about midnight / Whose what is that / Fore day in the morning / Dreaming blues / Butcher Pete part 2 / Good man blues / Miss Fanny Brown returns / Brown angel / Grandpa stole my baby / Teenage jamboree / Black diamond / This is my last goodbye / Mighty, mighty man.
**Album:** Released Jun '80, on Route 66 (Sweden) Catalogue no: **KIX 6**

**HARD LUCK BLUES**
**Cass set:** Released Mar '88, on Gusto (USA) by Gusto Records (USA). Catalogue no: **GD 5036**
**Album:** Released Jul '88, on Bellaphon Catalogue no: **BID 8025**

**I'M LOOKING SICK**
Tracks: / I'm looking sick / Gossamer.
**7" Single:** Released Jan '82, on Really Rude by Neat Records. Catalogue no: **FU 2**

**LAUGHING BUT CRYING**
Tracks: / Roy Brown boogie / Special lesson No.1 / Rainy weather blues / End of my journey / Fool in love, A / Butcher Pete part 1 / New Rebecca / Double crossing woman / Letter from home / Hurry hurry baby / Up jumped the devil / School bell rock / Money can't buy love / Lonesome lover / Laughing but crying.
**Album:** Released Jun '80, on Route 66 (Sweden) Catalogue no: **KIX 2**

**SATURDAY NITE**
Tracks: / Mr. Hound dog's in town / Caldonia's wedding day / Everyday / Saturday nite / I'm sticking with you / I love you I need you / I'm ready to play / Good looking and foxy too / Midnight lover man / Bootleggin' baby / Tick of the clock, The / We're goin' rockin' tonight / Ain't gonna do it / Slow down little Eva / Rinky dinky doo / Let the four winds blow.
**Album:** Released Aug '87, on Mr.R&B (Sweden) Catalogue no: **RB 104**

## Brown, Ruth

**Biographical details:** Brown, Ruth. Born in 1928 in Virginia, this vocalist was one of the first big artists on the new Atlantic label; her huge hits from 1949 had enormous influence just before the rock 'n' roll explosion: one of the most important artists of the period along with LaVerne Baker and Big Joe Turner, who were also on Atlantic. *Rockin' With Ruth* includes her best tracks from that period. Donald Clarke, 24 August 1988..

**BLACK IS BROWN AND BROWN IS BEAUTIFUL (RHAPSODY)**
Tracks: / Yesterday / Please send me someone to love / Looking back / Try me and see / Miss Browns blues / My prayer / Since I fell for you / This bitter earth.
**Album:** Released May '81, on Rhapsody by President Records. Catalogue no: **RHAP 10**

**BLACK IS BROWN AND BROWN IS BEAUTIFUL (S.D.E.G.)**
Tracks: / I want to sleep with you / What color is blue? / Brown sugar / Lot's more of me leaving (less of me coming) / Ain't no piece of cake / Stop knocking / Old fashioned good time loving you / Sugar babe / My ol' bed / I love my man.
**CD:** Released Mar '90, on S.D.E.G. Catalogue no: **SDECD 4020**
**Album:** Released Mar '90, on S.D.E.G. Catalogue no: **SDE 4023**
**Cass:** Released Mar '90, on S.D.E.G. Catalogue no: **SDEMC 4020**

**BROWN SUGAR**
Tracks: / Sugar baby / Stop knocking / Old fashioned good time / I love my man / My old bed / Brown sugar / I want to sleep with you / What colour is blue / Lot more of me leaving / Life ain't no piece of cake.
**Cass:** Released May '86, on Topline by Charly Records. Catalogue no: **KTOP 136**
**Album:** Released May '86, on Topline by Charly Records. Catalogue no: **TOP 136**

**HITS, THE**
Tracks: / 5-10-15 hours / Teardrops from my eyes / (Mama) he treats your daughter mean / Oh what a dream / Mambo baby / I'll wait for you / Daddy daddy / Wild wild young men / I wanna do more / So long / As long as I'm moving / It's love baby / I don't know / Lucky lips / I know / Mend your ways.
**CD:** on Official by Official Records. Catalogue no: **OFF 86053**
**Album:** on Official by Official Records. Catalogue no: **OFF 6053**

**I WANT TO SLEEP WITH YOU**
**Album:** Released Mar '90, on S.D.E.G. Catalogue no: **SDE 4023**
**CD:** Released Mar '90, on S.D.E.G. Catalogue no: **SDE 4023CD**
**Cass:** Released Mar '90, on S.D.E.G. Catalogue no: **SDE 4023MC**

**I'LL WAIT FOR YOU**
Tracks: / I'll wait for you / Standing on the corner / I gotta have you / Love has joined us together / I still love you / Mam oh mam / I want to be loved / New love, A / Look me up / I'll step aside / Mama, he treats your daughter mean / What I wouldn't give / I burned your letter / Honey boy / Sure 'nuff / Here he comes.
**Album:** Released '88, on Official by Official Records. Catalogue no: **OFF 6004**

**ROCKIN' WITH RUTH**
Tracks: / Teardrops from my eyes / Five, ten, fifteen hours / Daddy, daddy / Mama, he treats your daughter mean / Wild, wild young men / Love contest / Hello, little boy / Oh what a dream / Somebody touched me / Bye bye young men / I can see everybody's baby / As long as I'm moving / This little girl's gone rockin' / I can't hear a word you say / Papa daddy / Don't deceive me.
Note: Ruth "Miss Rhythm" Brown was Atlantic Records' first real star signing, the most popular and successful female R'n'B star of the fifties. This compilation covers the years from her first R'n'B no. 1 (Teardrops, October 1950) to her last Atlantic hit (Don't decieve me, April

**Sandy Brown - In The Evening (Hep Jazz)**

1960) including most of her significant recordings in between. However, certain hits are omitted (i.e her first pop hit Lucky lips).
**Cass:** Released Mar '84, on Charly R&B by Charly Records. Deleted '88. Catalogue no: **TCCRB 1069**
**Album:** Released Mar '84, on Charly R&B by Charly Records. Deleted '88. Catalogue no: **CRB 1069**

### SUGAR BABE
Tracks: / Sugar babe / Stock knocking / Old fashioned good time / I love my man / Old bed / Brown sugar / I want to sleep with you / What colour is blue / You're gonna see a lot more of me / Leaving / Life ain't no piece of cake.
**Album:** Released Jan '77, on President by President Records. Catalogue no: **PTLS 1067**

### SWEET BABY OF MINE
Tracks: / Love my baby / I'll come someday / It's all in the mind / Mend your ways / Ever since my baby's been gone / I want to do more / Am I making the same mistakes / Tears keep tumbling down, the / It's raining / R.B. blues / Without love / Rain is a bringdown / Sweet baby of mine / My heart is breaking for you / I would if I could.
**Album:** Released Aug '87, on Route 66 (Sweden) Catalogue no: **KIX 16**

### TAKING CARE OF BUSINESS
Tracks: / Takin' care of business / 5-10-15 hours / I can see everybody's baby / On my way / God holds the power / Oh what a dream / Teardrops from my eyes / So long / Seven days.
**Album:** Released Mar '84, on Stockholm (Sweden) Catalogue no: **RJ 202**

## Brown, Sandy

### CLARINET OPENING
**Album:** Released '88, on CSA by CSA Records. Catalogue no: **CLPS 1009**

### IN THE EVENING (Brown, Sandy / Brian Lemon Trio) (See panel above)
Tracks: / Ole Miss / Oxford Brown / In the evening / Ebun / Eight / Legal Pete / Badger, The / True love's heart / Lucky Schiz and the big dealer / Minstrel song / Louis.
Note: Sandy Brown (clarinet and vocal), Brian Lemon (piano), Tony Archer (bass), Bobby Orr (drums). Recorded at Trident Studios, London - May 16th 1971.
'The average age, the average life span, for a jazz musician is fourty four years. I put this through the computer. I'm fourty four. So I'm living on borrowed time'. The speaker, Sandy Brown on a television programme devoted to his work as both architect and clarinettist in 1974. Prophetically the borrowed time ran out next year and Sandy died on Saturday, 15th March, 1975, watching Scotland lose to England in the Calcutta Cup, his hand around a glass of Scotch. He was 46. Sandy was one of the most unforgettable characters I have ever known and today, in the greyness of November, 1983, I miss him as much as I did when my good friend Jackie Docherty broke the terrible news to me over the telephone in March 1975. I first met Sandy shortly after he came down to London a the end of 1954, to put the architects an the jazzers right; I last saw him fiv weeks before he died, at a concert I wa involved with staging in the Gulbenkia Theatre at the University of Kent in Can terbury. He clearly was not in the best c health at Canterbury and admitted tha he had not played for some weeks ye he performed like an angel with Bruc Turner and the John Burch Trio. Th concert was designed to show off a range of styles of reed players includin Evan Parker. Acting as MC I introduce Evan who elected to play an unaccom panied solo on soprano. As Evan too middle and leg I retreated stage-righ and hastened to the bar, only to fin Sandy there first, a glass of Scotch ir one hand and a glass of water in the other. Over the PA came some off the instrument harmonics. Sandy sippe from both glasses in turn and remarked 'while I respect the courage and deter mination of young men to push the boun daries of music further out, I reserve the right not to f**king well listen.'
In fact he was one of the least prejudice people I know and spent quite some time over lunch one day convincing me tha the then current Tamla Motown sounc was valid, earthy and exciting. Take a look at his discography and you will finc he recorded works by Woody Herman Charlie Mingus and Johnny Mandel as well as Leroy Carr, Spencer Williams and Louis Armstrong. Let us not forge the splendour and richness of his owr writing for he took the instrumentation o the traditional jazz band and used to produce music which was entirely new and different. He jokingly referred to his 'High life' music as coming from British West Hampstead but the fact remains that works such as *Go Ghana* are unique and very personal. The enclosed record has nine pieces which are wholly his and two which have benefited from sligh modification. I always regret that I did no take up his invitation to attend the date which occurred on a Sunday, when I was already committed to some long standing family duties. The session took place in a studio he had designed himself, no doubt complete with his patented low-frequency modular absorber boxes on the walls and his magnetic seals to all the door openings, for Sandy was arguably the first man to bring science and a practical building approach to the study of acoustics. We worked together on the design and construction of the London Weekend Television studios in Waterloo, a period when I first got to know Sandy's brilliant and likeable partner, David Binns. The music generally speaks for itself. It is, in fact, the last LP he made under his own name and appeared all too briefly on Doug Dobell's 'Seventy seven' label. Sandy sent me a copy when it appeared and with it a short note: 'Dear Alun, this album is free. If you want a pint as well, write a few words on it for something or other. Adverse criticism will reduce the offer to half a pint. See you soon'. I earned a few pints by

extolling its obvious virtues on a BBC guest review spot and in my regular weekly column in the 'Evening Post'. The blues runs like an unbroken thread throughout the course of this marvellous LP and on tracks such as *Eight* and *In the evening* Sandy is at the peak of his inventive powers.
Just a few other points. On the strength of this LP alone you may wonder why the record shop racks are not groaning under the weight of dozens of Brian Lemon albums. The fact remains that Brian, along with men such as Fred Hunt, is an unsung hero of Britain's jazz scene. Sandy loved him and just appreciated him. One day, perhaps, Brian will get just some of the recognition he so richly deserves as an always on form accompianist and soloist. Much the same may be said for Tony Archer and Bobby Orr, often to be found in Sandy's company, either in public or at one of those marvellous parties which Sandy used to organise. And Legal Pete? This refers to solicitor Pete Nixon who descended on London and made an impression. Sandy, like Lester Young, had names for friends and aquaintances. Ray Bolden, erstwhile assistant at Dobell's record shop, was 'The pieman' and I was sometimes 'Jazzbo'. Playing this record through again, just to refresh my memory, has been an experience both pleasureable and painful. The pleasure is there for all to enjoy. The pain lies in the sense of loss I still feel at Sandy's passing, greater than the loss I felt when Bird, Pres, even Wardell were taken from us. Jim Godbolt says he cried for a week after hearing the news. I know how it felt. Men like Sandy Brown occur in your lifetime very, very infrequently and I'm just grateful he came into mine. (Alun Morgan, 1983)
**Album:** Released Mar '84, on Hep Jazz by Hep Records. Catalogue no: **HEP 2017**

### MCJAZZ (Brown, Sandy Jazz Band)
**Album:** Released May '86, on Dormouse Catalogue no: **DM 6**

### SPLANKY
Tracks: / Splanky / In the evening / Roll em Pete / I got it bad / Royal Garden blues.
**Album:** Released May '83, on Spotlite by Spotlite Records. Catalogue no: **SPJ 901**

## Brown, Ted

### IN GOOD COMPANY (Brown, Ted Quintet)
**Album:** Released '88, on Criss Cross Catalogue no: **CRISS 1020**

## Brown, Walter

**Biographical details:** Brown, Walter A Kansas City blues singer (1917-56) who was born in Dallas and died in Oklahoma. He sang with Jay McShann's band in the early '40s, when Charlie Parker was in it; his first record with the band in 1941 was *Confessin' The Blues*, a big hit and a classic: Chuck Berry sang it in high school, B B King covered it in 1969 on one of his best albums. He also recorded for Queen/King, with the Tiny Grimes Sextet on Bob Thiele's Signature label in 1947 (one of many covers of *Open The Door Richard*), with a McShann quartet on Mercury, etc. The Affinity compilations including McShann's contain the vintage tracks. (Donald Clarke, 24 August 1988.).

### CONFESSIN' THE BLUES
**Album:** Released Sep '81, on Affinity by Charly Records. Deleted May '88. Catalogue no: **AFF 66**

## Browne, Tom

**Biographical details:** This American jazzy rhythm and blues vocalist and trumpeter released his debut album in 1979. The critical acclaim received by the *Browne Sugar* set paved the way for the success of his second LP, 1980's *Love Approach*. It was boosted by the single *Funkin' For Jamaica (N.Y.)*, a slice of hard, meaty funk. It was a smash No. 1 on the US soul charts, but became one of the few black music chart toppers to fail to cross over to the American pop charts - it was unable to crack even the lower reaches of the Billboard Hot 100. Pop radio in the States was unwilling to give airplay to such an uncompromisingly funky track. No such problems existed, however, in Britain. The single went to No. 10 on the UK chart. Next came the album *Magic*, which yielded a minor British hit entitled *Thighs High (Grip Your Hips And Move)*. At the end of 1981 he issued the *Yours Truly* album. Once again their was a small UK hit single, the ludicrous title being *Fungi Mama (bebopafunkadiscocalypso)*. The electicism suggested by this single's sub-title was the feature of Browne's work that made him a consistently interesting artist. 1983's *Rockin' Radio* album continued the formula, as did the 1984 LP *Tommy Gun*. He was now associated with Maurice Starr, the writer and producer who had been responsible for recent records by New Edition and the Jonzun Crew. Several tracks on the latter LP were highly derivative, 'borrowing' from a number of familiar hit records. Browne was attempting to attract a more mainstream audience, while still keeping the specialist R&B and jazz enthusiasts happy. (Bob MacDonald)..

### BROWNE SUGAR
**CD:** Released Sep '88, on GRP by GRP Records (USA). Catalogue no: **GRD 9517**

### BYE GONES
Tracks: / Bye gones.
**12" Single:** Released '82, on Arista by BMG Records (UK). Deleted '87. Catalogue no: **ARIST 12462**
**7" Single:** Released '82, on Arista by BMG Records (UK). Deleted '87. Catalogue no: **ARIST 462**

### FUNGI MAMA
Tracks: / Fungi mama / Funkin' for Jamaica / Come for a ride.
**12" Single:** Released Jan '82, on Arista by BMG Records (UK). Deleted '86. Catalogue no: **ARIST 12450**
**7" Single:** Released Jan '82, on Arista by BMG Records (UK). Deleted '85. Catalogue no: **ARIST 450**
: by BMG Records (UK).

### FUNKIN' FOR JAMAICA
Tracks: / Funkin' for Jamaica / Her silent smile.
**7" Single:** Released '82, on Arista by BMG Records (UK). Deleted '87. Catalogue no: **ARIST 357**
**12" Single:** Released '82, on Arista by BMG Records (UK). Deleted '87. Catalogue no: **ARIST 12857**

### FUNKIN' FOR JAMAICA (OLD GOLD)
Tracks: / Funkin' for Jamaica / Rockin' radio.
**12" Single:** Released Jan '88, on Old Gold by Old Gold Records. Catalogue no: **OG 4042**

### LOVE APPROACH
Tracks: / Funkin' for Jamaica / Her silent smile / Forever more / Dreams of lovin' you / Nocturne / Martha / Moon rise / Weak in the knees.
**Album:** Released Jul '80, on Arista by BMG Records (UK). Catalogue no: **GRP 5008**

### MAGIC
Tracks: / Magic / Midnight interlude.
**12" Single:** Released Jan '81, on Arista by BMG Records (UK). Catalogue no: **ARIST 12 387**
**7" Single:** Released Jan '81, on Arista by BMG Records (UK). Catalogue no: **ARIST 387**

### MAGIC (ALBUM)
Tracks: / Let's dance / Magic / I know / Midnight interlude / God bless the child / Night wind / Thighs high (grip your hips and move) / Making plans.
**Album:** Released '82, on Arista by BMG Records (UK). Deleted '87. Catalogue no: **GRP 5503**

### ROCKIN' RADIO
Tracks: / Rockin' radio / Never my love / Feel like making love / Cruisin' / Turn it up (come on y'all) / Angeline / Brighter tomorrow / Mr. Business.
Note: Tracks include the above.
**Cass:** Released Oct '83, on Arista by BMG Records (UK). Catalogue no: **405 151**
**Album:** Released Oct '83, on Arista by BMG Records (UK). Catalogue no: **205.151**

### THIGHS HIGH (GRIP YOUR HIPS AND
Tracks: / Thighs high (grip your hips and move).
**7" Single:** Released Oct '80, on Arista by BMG Records (UK). Deleted '83. Catalogue no: **ARIST 367**
**12" Single:** Released Oct '80, on Arista by BMG Records (UK). Deleted '83. Catalogue no: **ARIST 12367**

### TOMMY GUN
**Cass:** Released Oct '84, on Arista by

BMG Records (UK). Catalogue no: **406 495**
**Album:** Released Oct '84, on Arista by BMG Records (UK). Catalogue no: **206.495**

### YOURS TRULY
Tracks: / Fungii mama / Bygonnes / Charisma / Can't can't give it away / Lazy bird / Naima / Come for a ride / My latin sky / Message, A: pride and pity.
Note: *Yours Truly* is Tom Browne's fourth Arista / GRP album and follows Browne Sugar, "*Love Approach*" and "*Magic*". On his new album Browne and his band pay homage to their jazz influences, while also continuing their funk explosion and getting farther into dance rhythms. *Yours Truly* conains two compositions by the immortal John Coltrane (Lazy bird and Naima) one by Lonnie Smith (My latin sky and some Tom Browne originals.
**Album:** Released Dec '81, on GRP by GRP Records (USA). Catalogue no: **GRP 5507**

## Brubeck, Dave
**Biographical details:** Born in Califonia in 1920, this American pianist (real name David Warren) made his name as a top concert attraction in the late Forties and early Fifties, first on college campuses and later in the United States at large. The Dave Brubeck Quartet, an instrumental jazz combo, comprised Brubeck, alto saxophone player Paul Desmond, drummer Joe Morello and bassist Eugene Wright. Of the many albums and singles released by the group, the one that they are best known for is the Desmond-penned 1961 *Take Five*. This 45 reached No. 25 in the US and No. 6 in the UK. It was their only American Top 40 hit, but they managed two follow-ups in Britain: *It's A Raggy Waltz* (No. 36) and *Unsquare Dance*, a Brubeck composition which reached No. 14. Their two big-selling LPs of the period were *Time out* and *Time Further Out*. Brubeck's distinctive and original style continued to win him much respect amongst the jazz fraternity for many years. A British tribute was paid in 1981, when one of his tracks *Blue Rondo A La Turk* became the name of a marginally successful but highly fashionable London jazz-influenced pop group. (Bob MacDonald)..

### 25TH ANNIVERSARY REUNION CONCERT
Tracks: / St. Louis blues / Three to get ready / African times suite / 1st movement - African theme / 2nd movement - African breeze / 3rd movement - African dance / Salute to Stephen Foster / Take five / Don't worry 'bout me.
**CD:** Released 28 Nov '88, on A&M by A&M Records. Catalogue no: **CDA 0806**
**Album:** Released Mar '77, on Horizon by A&M Records. Catalogue no: **AMLJ 714**

### 1975 THE DUETS (Brubeck, Dave/Paul Desmond)
**Album:** Released Jan '76, on Ode Catalogue no: **AMLJ 703**

### 1954-1972
**Album:** Released Jan '87, on CBS by CBS Records. Catalogue no: **CBS 54490**

Dave Brubeck

### ALL TOGETHER AGAIN
**CD:** Released Jul '87, on Atlantic Jazz by WEA Records. Catalogue no: **781 390-2**

### BLUE RONDO (Brubeck, Dave Quartet)
Tracks: / How does your garden grow? / Festival hall / Easy as you go / Blue Rondo a la turk / Dizzy's dream / I see, Satie / Swing bells / Strange meadowlark / Elana Joy.
Note: Personnel: Dave Brubeck - piano / Bill Smith - clarinet / Chris Brubeck - electric bass & bass trombone / Randy Jones - drums.
**CD:** Released Jul '87, on Concord Jazz by Concord Jazz Records (USA). Catalogue no: **CCD 4317**
**Album:** Released Jul '87, on Concord Jazz by Concord Jazz Records (USA). Catalogue no: **CJ 317**
**Cass:** Released Jul '87, on Concord Jazz by Concord Jazz Records (USA). Catalogue no: **CJC 317**

### COLLECTION: DAVE BRUBECK
Tracks: / Take five / It's a raggy waltz / Castillian drums / St. Louis blues / Blue rondo a la turk / Tea for two / Blue moon / Let's fall in love / Some day my prince will come / Forty days / Summer song / For all we know.
**CD:** Released Aug '85, on Deja Vu Catalogue no: **DVCD 2036**
**Cass:** Released Aug '85, on Deja Vu Catalogue no: **DVMC 2036**

### CONCORD ON A SUMMER NIGHT (Brubeck, Dave Quartet)
Tracks: / Benjamin / Koto Song / Black And Blue / Take five / Softly, William, Softly.
**CD:** Released Nov '86, on Concord Jazz by Concord Jazz Records (USA). Catalogue no: **CCD 4198**

### DAVE BRUBECK (Featuring Paul Desmond in concert)
Tracks: / Take five / Blue rondo a la turk / Mr. Broadway / Three to get ready / Unsquare dance / Its a raggy waltz / Rotterdam blues.
**Album:** Released Jul '88, on Atlantic by WEA Records. Catalogue no: **K 20092**
**Cass:** Released Jul '88, on Atlantic by WEA Records. Catalogue no: **K4 20092**

### DAVE BRUBECK COLLECTION
**CD:** Released Oct '89, on Collection by K-Tel Records. Catalogue no: **OR 0064**

### DAVE BRUBECK IN CONCERT (Brubeck, Dave Quartet)
**CD:** Released Apr '87, on London Records by London Records Ltd. Catalogue no: **FCD 60013**

### DAVE BRUBECK OCTET, THE (Brubeck, Dave Octet)
**Album:** Released Aug '84, on Riverside (USA) by Fantasy Inc (USA). Catalogue no: **OJC 101**

### DAVE BRUBECK & PAUL DESMOND (Brubeck, Dave/Paul Desmond)

**Album:** Released Sep '87, on Giants of Jazz by Hasmick Promotions. Catalogue no: **LPJT 3**

**DAVE BRUBECK QUARTET (With Paul Desmond) (Brubeck, Dave Quartet)**
Tracks: / Maria / I feel pretty / Somewhere / Tonight / Quiet girl / Dialogues for jazz combo and orchestra.
**CD:** Released Jan '89, on JVC/Fantasy Catalogue no: **VDJ 1595**
**Album:** Released Dec '80, on CBS by CBS Records. Deleted Dec '85. Catalogue no: **61995**
**CD:** Released Aug '88, on Giants of Jazz by Hasmick Promotions. Catalogue no: **CD 53031**

**DAVE BRUBECK / PAUL DESMOND**
Tracks: / Jeepers creepers / On a little street in Singapore / Trolley song (rehearsal) / Trolley song / I may be wrong / Blue moon / My heart stood still / Let's fall in love / You go to my head / Crazy girl / Give a little whistle / Over the rainbow / Crazy Chris / Lady be good / Tea for two / This can't be love.
Note: 2 LP set
**2 LP Set:** Released May '84, on Prestige (USA) by Fantasy Inc (USA). Catalogue no: **OJCD 501**

**DAVE BRUBECK'S QUARTET IN CONCERT (Brubeck, Dave Quartet)**
**CD:** Released '88, on Crusader Catalogue no: **985 72**

**DAVE DIGS DISNEY (Brubeck, Dave Quartet)**
Tracks: / Alice in Wonderland / Give a little whistle / Heigh-ho / When you wish upon a star / Some day my prince will come / One song.
**Album:** Released Jul '83, on CBS by CBS Records. Deleted Jul '88. Catalogue no: **CBS 21060**

**FOR IOLA (Brubeck, Dave Quartet)**
Tracks: / Polly / I hear a rhapsody / Thank you / Big bad Basie / For Iola / Summer song / Pange lingua march.
Note: Dave Brubeck, piano; Bill Smith, clarinet; Chris Brubeck, bass, trombone; Randy Jones, drums.
**Album:** Released Feb '85, on Concord Jazz by Concord Jazz Records (USA). Catalogue no: **CJ 259**
**CD:** Released Jul '88, on Concord Jazz by Concord Jazz Records (USA). Catalogue no: **CCD 4259**
**Cass:** Released Feb '85, on Concord Jazz by Concord Jazz Records (USA). Catalogue no: **CJC 259**

**GONE WITH THE WIND**
Tracks: / Swanee river / Lonesome road / Georgia on my mind / Camptown races / Sort'nin' bread / Basin Street blues / Ol' man river / Gone with the wind.
**Album:** Released 27 Feb '88, on CBS (import) by CBS Records. Catalogue no: **4509841**
**Cass:** Released 27 Feb '88, on CBS (import) by CBS Records. Catalogue no: **4509844**

**GREAT CONCERTS, THE**
Tracks: / Pennies from Heaven / Blue rondo a la turk / Take the 'A' train / Wonderful Copenhagen / Tangerine / For all we know / Take five / Real ambassador, The / Like someone in love.
**CD:** Released Jun '89, on CBS (import) by CBS Records. Catalogue no: **462 403 2**
**Cass:** Released Apr '89, on CBS (import) by CBS Records. Catalogue no: **462 403 4**
**Album:** Released Apr '89, on CBS (import) by CBS Records. Catalogue no: **462 203 1**

**GREATEST HITS: DAVE BRUBECK**
Tracks: / Take five / I'm in a dancing mood / In your own sweet way / Camptown races / Duke, The / It's a raggy waltz / Bossa nova USA / Trolley song, The / Unsquare dance / Blue rondo a la turk / Mr. Broadway, Theme from.
**Album:** Released Jun '81, on CBS by CBS Records. Catalogue no: **CBS 32046**
**Cass:** Released Jun '81, on CBS by CBS Records. Catalogue no: **40 32046**
**CD:** Released Jun '89, on CBS by CBS Records. Catalogue no: **CD 32046**

**IT'S A RAGGY WALTZ (Brubeck, Dave Quartet)**
Tracks: / It's a raggy waltz.
**7" Single:** Released Feb '62, on Fontana by Phonogram Ltd. Deleted '65. Catalogue no: **H 352**

**JAZZ AT COLLEGE OF PACIFIC (Brubeck, Dave Quartet)**
**CD:** Released '88, on Crusader Catalogue no: **985 70**

**JAZZ AT OBERLIN (Brubeck, Dave Quartet)**
Tracks: / These foolish things remind me of you / Perdido / Stardust / Way you look tonight, The / How high the moon.
**CD:** Released Sep '89, on Riverside (USA) by Fantasy Inc (USA). Catalogue no: **CDRIVM 007**
**CD:** Released Jan '89, on JVC/Fantasy Catalogue no: **VDJ 1597**
**CD:** Released '88, on Crusader Catalogue no: **985 69**

**JAZZ AT STORYVILLE (Brubeck, Dave Trio & Quartet)**
**CD:** Released Jan '89, on JVC/Fantasy Catalogue no: **VDJ 1596**

**LA FIESTA DE LA POSADA**
**Album:** Released Jan '80, on CBS by CBS Records. Deleted Jan '85. Catalogue no: **CBS 73903**

**LAST SET AT NEWPORT**
**CD:** Released Jul '87, on Atlantic Jazz by WEA Records. Catalogue no: **781 382-2**

**LIVE AT MONTREUX: DAVE BRUBECK**
Tracks: / It's a raggy waltz / Brandenburg gate / In your own sweet way / It could happen to you / God's love (made invisible) / Summer love.
**Album:** Released Jan '89, on Affinity by Charly Records. Catalogue no: **AFF 201**

**LIVE FROM BASIN STREET (Brubeck, Dave Quartet)**
**Album:** Released Sep '87, on Flyright by Interstate Music. Catalogue no: **EB 402**

**MOSCOW NIGHT**
Note: Recorded in Russia, 1987, with Chris Brubeck, Randy Jones and Bill Smith.
**Album:** Released Oct '88, on Concord Jazz by Concord Jazz Records (USA). Catalogue no: **CJ 353**
**CD:** Released Jul '88, on Concord Jazz by Concord Jazz Records (USA). Catalogue no: **CCD 4353**
**Cass:** Released Jul '88, on Concord Jazz by Concord Jazz Records (USA). Catalogue no: **CJ 353 C**

**MUSIC FROM WEST SIDE STORY..... (Brubeck, Dave with New York Philharmonic)**
Tracks: / Maria / I feel pretty / Somewhere / Quiet girl, A / Tonight / Allegro I / Andante-ballad II / Adagio-ballad III / Allegro-blues IV.
Note: Full title: Dave Brubeck with the New York Philharmonic(Bernstein)- Music from 'West Side Story" Wonderful Town'& Dialogues for Jazz Combo & Orchestra.
**Album:** Released Mar '86, on CBS by CBS Records. Deleted Aug '87. Catalogue no: **CBS 32734**
**Cass:** Released Mar '86, on CBS by CBS Records. Deleted Aug '87. Catalogue no: **40 32734**

**MUSICAL PORTRAIT (VIDEO)**
**VHS:** Released '88, on BBC Video by BBC Video. Catalogue no: **BBCV/B 3014**

**NEAR-MYTH**
**Album:** Released Apr '86, on Original Jazz Classics (USA) by Fantasy Inc (USA). Catalogue no: **OJC 236**

**NEW QUARTET AT MONTREUX**
**CD:** Released Mar '90, on Tomato (USA) by Tomato Music Co. (USA). Catalogue no: **JJCD6**

**NEWPORT ('58 Brubeck plays Ellington)**
Tracks: / Things ain't what they used to be / Jump for joy / Perdido / Liberian suite dance No. 3 / Duke, The / Flamingo / C Jam blues.
**Album:** Released Jul '87, on CBS by CBS Records. Deleted Jan '89. Catalogue no: **450317 1**
**Cass:** Released Jul '87, on CBS by CBS Records. Catalogue no: **450317 4**

**PAPER MOON**
Tracks: / Music maestro please / I hear a rhapsody / Symphony / I thought about you / It's only a paper moon / Long ago and far away / St. Louis blues.
**Album:** Released Apr '82, on Concord Jazz by Concord Jazz Records (USA). Catalogue no: **CJ 178**
**Cass:** Released Apr '82, on Concord Jazz by Concord Jazz Records (USA). Catalogue no: **CJC 178**

**PLACE IN TIME, A (Brubeck, Dave Quartet)**
Tracks: / Audrey / Jeepers creepers /

Pennies from Heaven / Why do I love you / Stompin' for Milli / Keepin' out of mischief now / Fine romance, A / Brother can you spare a dime.
Note: Featuring Paul Desmind -sax/Bob Bates-bass/Joe Dodge-drums.
**Album:** Released Aug '86, on Avan-Guard Catalogue no: **BVL 012**
**Album:** Released Jul '80, on CBS by CBS Records. Deleted Jul '85. Catalogue no: **CBS 61900**

**PLAYS WEST SIDE STORY / PLAYS MY FAIR LADY (Dave Brubeck / Andre Previn) (Brubeck, Dave / Andre Previn)**
Tracks: / Maria / I feel pretty / Somewhere / Tonight / On the street where you live / With a little bit of luck / Wouldn't it be lovely / Get me to the church on time.
**Album:** Released May '83, on CBS by CBS Records. Deleted '86. Catalogue no: **CBS 21065**
**Cass:** Released May '83, on CBS by CBS Records. Deleted Nov '87. Catalogue no: **40 21065**

**QUARTET, THE**
Tracks: / Castillian drums / Three to get ready / St. Louis Blues / Forty days / Summer song / Some day my prince will come / Brandenburg Gate / In your own sweet way.
Note: Personnel; Dave Brubeck (Piano), Paul Desmond (Alto sax), Gene Wright (Bass), Joe Morello (Drums).
**CD:** Released '88, on Denon Catalogue no: **C38-7681**
**Cass:** Released '88, on Denon Catalogue no: **MC 7681**

**REFLECTIONS (Brubeck, Dave Quartet)**
Tracks: / Reflections of you / Misty morning, A / I'd walk a country mile / My one bad habit / Blues for Newport / We will remember Paul / Michael,my second son / Blue Lake Tahoe.
Note: Dave Brubeck, piano; Bill Smith, clarinet; Chris Brubeck, bass, trombone; Randy Jones, drums.
**CD:** Released Jul '88, on Concord Jazz by Concord Jazz Records (USA). Catalogue no: **CCD 4299**
**Cass:** Released Jun '86, on Concord Jazz by Concord Jazz Records (USA). Catalogue no: **CJC 299**
**Album:** Released Jun '86, on Concord Jazz by Concord Jazz Records (USA). Catalogue no: **CJ 299**

**SEE HOW IT FEELS (Brubeck, Dave Quartet)**
**Album:** Released Aug '86, on Black Hawk (USA) by Blackhawk Records (USA). Catalogue no: **BKH 51401**

**SHISH KEBAB**
Tracks: / Shish kebab / Fairy day / Don't worry 'bout me / Lover come back to me / Royal Garden blues / Love walked in / How high the moon.
**Album:** Released Apr '81, on Joker (USA) by Lifetime Records (USA). Catalogue no: **SM 3804**

**SOUTHERN SCENE (Brubeck, Dave with Quartet/Trio/Duo)**
**Album:** Released Apr '79, on Japanese Import Catalogue no: **20 AP 1433**

**'SUPERB' CANADIAN CONCERT OF.., THE (Brubeck, Dave/Paul Desmond)**
**Album:** Released Nov '87, on Can-Am (USA) Catalogue no: **CA 1500**

**TAKE FIVE**
Tracks: / Take five / Bossa nova USA / Unsquare dance / Some day my prince will come / I'm in a dancing mood / It's a raggy waltz / Blue rondo a la turk / Kathy's waltz / My favourite things / Castillian drums / Duke, The / Trolley song, The.
**Album:** Released Dec '79, on CBS by CBS Records. Deleted '84. Catalogue no: **CBS 31769**
**Cass:** Released Nov '81, on CBS by CBS Records. Catalogue no: **40 32084**
**Album:** Released Nov '81, on CBS by CBS Records. Catalogue no: **CBS 32084**

**TAKE FIVE (DOUBLE CASSETTE)**
**Cass set:** Released '88, on Ditto by Pickwick Records. Catalogue no: **DTO 10205**

**TAKE FIVE (OLD GOLD)**
Tracks: / Take five / Unsquare dance.
**7" Single:** Released Apr '83, on Old Gold by Old Gold Records. Deleted Apr '88. Catalogue no: **OG 9300**

**TAKE FIVE (SINGLE)**
**7" Single:** Released Oct '61, on Fontana by Phonogram Ltd. Deleted '64. Catalogue no: **H 339**

**TIME FURTHER OUT (Brubeck, Dave Quartet)**
**Album:** Released Apr '62, on Fontana by Phonogram Ltd. Deleted '67. Catalogue no: **TFL 5161**

**TIME OUT**
Tracks: / Blue rondo a la turk / Strange meadowlark / Take five / Three to get ready / Kathy's waltz / Everybody's jumpin' / Pick up sticks / It's a raggy waltz / Bluesette / Charles Matthew halleluya / Far more blue / Far more drums / Maori blues / Unsquare dance / Bru's boogie woogie / Blue shadows in the street.
**CD:** Released May '87, on CBS by CBS Records. Catalogue no: **CD 62068**
**Album:** Released Apr '88, on CBS (import) by CBS Records. Catalogue no: **4606111**
**Album:** Released Jun '60, on Fontana by Phonogram Ltd. Deleted '65. Catalogue no: **TFL 5085**
**Cass:** Released Apr '88, on CBS (import) by CBS Records. Catalogue no: **4606114**

**TIME OUT / TIME FURTHER OUT**
Tracks: / Blue rondo a la turk / Strange meadow lark / Take five / Three to get ready / Kathy's waltz / Everybody's jumpin' / Pick up sticks / It's a raggy waltz / Bluette / Charles Matthew hallelujah / Far more blue / Far more drums / Maori blues / Unsquare dance / Bru's boogie woogie / Blue shadows in the street.
**Cass set:** Released May '82, on CBS by CBS Records. Deleted Jun '88. Catalogue no: **40 22120**
**2 LP Set:** Released May '82, on CBS by CBS Records. Deleted Jan '89. Catalogue no: **CBS 22120**

**UNSQUARE DANCE (Brubeck, Dave Quartet)**
Tracks: / Unsquare dance.
**7" Single:** Released May '62, on CBS by CBS Records. Deleted '65. Catalogue no: **AAG 102**

**WE'RE ALL TOGETHER AGAIN FOR THE FIRST TIME (Brubeck, Dave & Friends)**
Tracks: / Truth / Unfinished woman / Koto song / Take five / Rotterdam blues / Sweet Georgia Brown.
**Album:** on Atlantic by WEA Records. Catalogue no: **K 40489**

**WEST SIDE STORY**
**CD:** Released 27 Feb '88, on CBS (import) by CBS Records. Deleted 17 Apr '89. Catalogue no: **450410 2**
**Album:** Released 27 Feb '88, on CBS (import) by CBS Records. Catalogue no: **450410 1**
**Cass:** Released 27 Feb '88, on CBS (import) by CBS Records. Catalogue no: **450410 4**

## Brunies, Albert

**NEW ORLEANS SHUFFLE 1925-28 (Brunies, Albert & Halfway House Orchestra)**
**Album:** Released Jun '87, on VJM (Vintage Jazz Music) by Vintage Jazz Music Society(VJM). Catalogue no: **VLP 62**

## Brunious, Wendell

**IN THE TRADITION**
Note; with J. Kimball, Louis Nelson, S. Rimington, Frank Fields, Barry Martyn.
**Album:** Released Feb '87, on GHB by Jazzology Records (USA). Catalogue no: **GHB 194**

## Brunis, George

**KING OF TAILGATE TROMBONE**
**Album:** Released '87, on Commodore Class Catalogue no: **6.25896**

**TIN ROOF BLUES (Commodore classics) (Brunis, George & Wild Bill Davison)**
Tracks: / Royal Garden blues / Royal Garden blues (part 2) (Alternate choice-previously un-issued) / Ugly child (Based on'You're some pretty doll'.) / Ugly child (2) (Based on'You're some pretty doll'.) / Tin roof blues / Tin roof blues(2) (Alternate choice previously un-issued) / That da da strain / That da da strain (2) (Alternate choice previously un-issued) / High society / High society (2) (Alternate choice previously un-issued) / Wrap your troubles in dreams / Wrap your troubles in dreams (2) (Alternate choice previously un-issued) / I'm coming Virginia / I'm coming Virginia(2)

(Alternate choice previously un-issued) / Wabash blues / Wabash blues(2) (Alternate choice previously un-issued).
**Album:** Released Mar '83, on Commodore Class Catalogue no: **AG6 24094**

## Brunis, Merritt

### MERRITT BRUNIS & HIS ORCH. (Brunis, Merritt & His Friars Inn Orchestra)
**Album:** Released Sep '86, on Fountain by Retrieval Records. Catalogue no: **FJ 124**

## Brunskill, Bill

### 30 YEARS ON (Brunskill, Bill Jazzmen)
Tracks: / Marie / Kitchen man / Ampola / Coney Island / Washboard / Down in Honky Tonk Town / If you're a viper / Mama's gone goodbye.
Note: Artists include: Mike Pointon, Hugh Crozier, Bill Stagg, Jim Bray, Les Allen, Dave Jenkins. A celebration of 30 years in jazz.
**Album:** Released Jul '82, on VLP Catalogue no: **LC 34**

## Bryant, Ray

### ALL BLUES (Bryant, Ray Trio)
Tracks: / All blues / C-jam blues / Please send me someone to love / Jumpin' with symphony Sid / Blues changes / Billie's bounce / Stick with it.
**Album:** Released '82, on Pablo Jazz (USA) by Pablo Records (USA). Catalogue no: **231 0820**
**Cass:** Released '82, on Pablo Jazz (USA) by Pablo Records (USA). Catalogue no: **K10 820**

### ALONE WITH THE BLUES
Tracks: / Blues no 3 / Joy / Lover man / Me and the blues / Rocking chair / Stocking feet.
**Album:** Released Jan '87, on Original Jazz Classics (USA) by Fantasy Inc (USA). Catalogue no: **OJC 249**

### BEST OF RAY BRYANT
Tracks: / Stick with it / Girl talk / In de back room / Please send me someone to love / Li'l darlin' / All blues / Moanin' / Good morning heartache.
**Album:** Released '82, on Pablo Jazz (USA) by Pablo Records (USA). Catalogue no: **231 0846**
**Cass:** Released '82, on Pablo Jazz (USA) by Pablo Records (USA). Catalogue no: **K10 846**

### CON ALMA
Tracks: / Con alma / Milestones / 'Round midnight / Django / Nuts and bolts / Cubano chant / Ill wind / Autumn leaves / C jam blues.
**Cass:** Released '88, on CBS by CBS Records. Catalogue no: **461 097 4**
**CD:** Released '88, on CBS by CBS Records. Catalogue no: **461 097 2**
**Album:** Released '88, on CBS by CBS Records. Catalogue no: **461 097 1**

### HERE'S RAY BRYANT
Tracks: / Girl talk / Good morning heartache / Manteca / When sunny gets blue / Hold back mon / Li'l darlin' / Cold turkey / Prayer song.
**Cass:** Released '82, on Pablo Jazz (USA) by Pablo Records (USA). Catalogue no: **K10 764**
**CD:** Released Jan '89, on JVC/Fantasy Catalogue no: **VDJ 28014**
**Album:** Released '82, on Pablo Jazz (USA) by Pablo Records (USA). Catalogue no: **231 0764**

### IT'S MADISON TIME (Bryant, Ray Combo)
Tracks: / It's Madison time / Mama didn't lie / Foot stompin' (Available on 12" only.).
**12" Single:** Released Jul '88, on MCA by MCA Records. Catalogue no: **MCAT 1258**
**7" Single:** Released Jul '88, on MCA by MCA Records. Catalogue no: **MCA 1258**

### PLAYS BASIE & ELLINGTON
Tracks: / Jive at five / Swingin' the blues / 9.20 special / Teddy the toad / Blues for Basie / I let a song go out of my heart / It don't mean a thing / Things ain't what they used to be.
Note: Medley: Sophisticated Lady - Prfelude to A Kiss - Mood Indigo.
**CD:** Released Mar '88, on ECM Catalogue no: **8322352**

### POTPOURRI (Bryant, Ray Trio)
Tracks: / D.B. blues / One o'clock jump / Milestones / Undecided / In walked Bud / In a mellow tone / My one and only love / Night in Tunisia.
**Cass:** Released '82, on Pablo Jazz (USA) by Pablo Records (USA). Catalogue no: **K10 860**
**Album:** Released '82, on Pablo Jazz (USA) by Pablo Records (USA). Catalogue no: **231 0860**

### RAY BRYANT
Tracks: / Take the 'A' train / Georgia on my mind / Jungletown jubilee / If I could just make it to heaven / Django / Blues No. 6 / Satin doll / Sometimes I feel like a motherless child / St. Louis blues / Things ain't what they used to be.
**Album:** Released '82, on Pablo Jazz (USA) by Pablo Records (USA). Catalogue no: **2308 201**
**Cass:** Released '82, on Pablo Jazz (USA) by Pablo Records (USA). Catalogue no: **K 08 201**

### RAY BRYANT PLAYS (Bryant, Ray Trio)
**Album:** Released Feb '88, on Fresh Sounds (Spain) by Fresh Sounds Records (Spain). Catalogue no: **FS 183**

### RAY BRYANT TRIO (Bryant, Ray Trio)
**CD:** Released Apr '87, on JVC/Fantasy Catalogue no: **VDJ 1543**

### SOLO FLIGHT
Tracks: / In de back room / What are you doing the rest of your life / Monkey business / Blues in de big brass bed / Moanin' / St. Louis blues / Take the 'A' train / Lullaby.
**Cass:** Released '82, on Pablo Jazz (USA) by Pablo Records (USA). Catalogue no: **K10 798**
**Album:** Released '82, on Pablo Jazz (USA) by Pablo Records (USA). Catalogue no: **231 0798**

### TRIO
**CD:** Released Apr '87, on Carrere (France) Catalogue no: **98438**

## Bubbles, John W.

### BACK ON BROADWAY
Tracks: / It ain't necessarily so / Belitting me / Somebody's gonna make you fall / Why was I born / Sweet mama / On the sunny side of the street / Bubbles blue / Wrap your troubles in dreams / Lady be good / Nobody knows / My mother's eyes / Somebody loves me.
**Album:** Released Nov '86, on Uptown (USA) Catalogue no: **UP 27 03**

## Buckner, Milt

**Biographical details:** Buckner, Milt A pianist and organist (1915-77) who was an innovator, pioneering the 'locked hands' piano style, both hands playing parallel chords, as early as 1934; it was not his fault that it became a cliche. He wrote *Hamp's Boogie Woogie*, many more while working with Lionel Hampton; he led a band and then a trio from '52. He pioneered the electric organ in jazz but was eclipsed by others such as Jimmy Smith. *Rockin' Hammond* was made in 1956. He was the best known of several musical Buckners, including distant relative J E 'Teddy' Buckner, a Louis Armstrong-inspired trumpeter. Donald Clarke, 24 August 1988.

### EARLY YEARS, THE 1947-53
Tracks: / Fatstuff boogie / Buck's bop / Milt's boogie / Oo-be-doop / M.B. blues / Who shot John / Buck-a-boo / Yesterdays / By the river St Marie / Russian lullaby / Trapped / Boo it / Taking a chance on love / Flying home / There'll never be another you / Hawk talk, The.
**Album:** on Official by Official Records. Catalogue no: **OFF 3033**

### PLAY MILT, PLAY
Tracks: / Perdido / I don't stand a ghost of a chance / Swinging in Toulouse / Hey ba ba re bop / Play, fiddle, play / Cute / Caravan / Buckner's boogie woogie / Mighty low / Flying home / Stardust.
**CD:** Released Jan '88, on Esoldun Catalogue no: **FCD 103**
**Album:** Released Jan '88, on Esoldun Catalogue no: **FC 103**

### ROCKIN HAMMOND
Tracks: / Count's basement / Mighty low / We'll be together again / Jumpin' at the woodside / One o'clock jump / Wild scene / Blue and sentimental / Deep purple / Jumpin' at the Zanzibar / When you wish upon a star / Late late show, The.
**Album:** Released '83, on Capitol (import) Catalogue no: **2C 068 85194**

### UNFORGETTABLE
Tracks: / Hamp's boogie woogie / Honeysuckle rose / Pick yourself up / I de Clare / Willie's blues / Glady's dance / If I could be with you one hour tonight / Jitterbug waltz / God knows / Robbins

nest.
**Album:** Released '79, on MPS Jazz Deleted '84. Catalogue no: **5C 064 61178**

## Buckner, Teddy

**JAZZ FESTIVAL**
**Album:** Released Oct '88, on Vogue by Vogue Records. Catalogue no: **500052**

**JAZZ TIME VOL.11**
**Album:** Released '88, on Vogue (France) by Vogue Records. Catalogue no: **502711**

**LA GRAND PARADE DE LA NOUVELLE**
**2 LP Set:** Released Oct '88, on Vogue by Vogue Records. Catalogue no: **400022**

**MARTINIQUE**
**CD:** Released 10 Jul '89, on Vogue by Vogue Records. Catalogue no: **VG 670218**

**TEDDY BUCKNER 1955: VOLUME 1**
Tracks: / Mahogany hall stomp / I want to linger / Dippermouth blues / Bluin' the blues / Tiger rag / Dear old southland / Big butter and egg man / Twelfth St. rag / Ain't misbehavin' / Memphis blues / Royal Garden blues.
**Album:** Released Apr '79, on Aircheck (USA) by Kiner Ents.(USA). Catalogue no: **AIRCHECK 10**

**TEDDY BUCKNER AT THE CRESCENDO**
**Album:** Released '88, on Dixieland Jubilee (USA) by GNP Crescendo Records (USA). Catalogue no: **DJA 516**

**TEDDY BUCKNER & HIS DIXIELAND BAND (Buckner, Teddy & His Dixieland Band)**
**Album:** Released '88, on Dixieland Jubilee (USA) by GNP Crescendo Records (USA). Catalogue no: **DJA 504**

**TEDDY BUCKNER IN CONCERT**
**Album:** Released '88, on Dixieland Jubilee (USA) by GNP Crescendo Records (USA). Catalogue no: **DJA 503**

**TEDDY BUCKNER & THE ALL STARS (Buckner, Teddy & The All Stars)**
**Album:** Released '88, on Dixieland Jubilee (USA) by GNP Crescendo Records (USA). Catalogue no: **DJA 507**

## Bucks, George

**JAZZOLOGY ALLSTARS**
**Album:** Released Jun '88, on Jazzology (USA) by Jazzology Records (USA). Catalogue no: **J 48**

## Bucktown Five

**BUCKTOWN FIVE, STOMP SIX, JUNGLE KINGS ETC, THE (Bucktown Five & Others)**
**Album:** Released Apr '79, on Fountain by Retrieval Records. Catalogue no: **FJ 108**

## Budd, Ray

**HAVE A JAZZY CHRISTMAS (Budd, Ray Trio)**
**Cass:** Released Nov '89, on Master Mix Catalogue no: **CHEMC 9**
**Album:** Released Nov '89, on Master Mix Catalogue no: **CHELP 9**
**CD:** Released Nov '89, on Master Mix Catalogue no: **CHECD 9**

## Bue, Papa

**ALL THAT MEAT & NO POTATOES (Bue, Papa Viking Jazz Band / Wild Bill Davison)**
Note: with Gustav Winckler
**Album:** Released Jan '88, on Storyville by Storyville Records AB. Catalogue no: **SLP 280**

**ANNIVERSARY ALBUM 1956-1966 (Bue, Papa & His Viking Jazzband)**
**Album:** Released Feb '90, on Storyville by Storyville Records AB. Catalogue no: **SLP 191**

**DANISH JAZZ VOL.8 1957-77**
**Album:** Released Jul '82, on Storyville by Storyville Records AB. Catalogue no: **SLP 417**

**DANSK (Liller & Papa Bue's Viking Jazzband)**
**Album:** Released Feb '90, on Storyville by Storyville Records AB. Catalogue no: **SLP 848**

**DE GO'E GAMIE MED LILLER (Liller & Papa Bue's Viking Jazzband)**
**Album:** Released Feb '90, on Storyville by Storyville Records AB. Catalogue no: **SLP 847**

**DIXIELAND (Bue, Papa Viking Jazz Band)**
**Album:** Released '88, on Storyville by Storyville Records AB. Catalogue no: **SLP 833**

**GREATEST HITS: PAPA BUE'S VIKING JAZZ BAND (Bue, Papa Viking Jazz Band)**
**Album:** Released '88, on Storyville by Storyville Records AB. Catalogue no: **SLP 836**

**IN THE MOOD (Bue, Papa & His Viking Jazzband)**
Tracks: / In the mood / Just a little while / Stardust / Burgundy Street blues / Song is ended, The / Coffee grinder / Lil' Liza Jane / 1919 march / Walking with the king / You'll never walk alone / Beautiful dreamer.
**Album:** Released May '89, on Timeless by Timeless Records. Catalogue no: **TTD 539**
**Album:** Released Feb '89, on Nathan Catalogue no: **MLP 101**

**JAZZ PARTY (Bue, Papa Viking Jazz Band)**
**Album:** Released '88, on Storyville by Storyville Records AB. Catalogue no: **SLP 420**

**LIVE IN TIVOLI (Bue, Papa Viking Jazz Band)**
**Album:** Released '88, on Storyville by Storyville Records AB. Catalogue no: **SLP 418**

**NEW ORLEANS (Bue, Papa Viking Jazz Band)**
**Album:** Released Jun '86, on Storyville by Storyville Records AB. Catalogue no: **SLP 832**

**ON STAGE (Bue, Papa Viking Jazz Band)**
**CD:** Released Jan '86, on Timeless by Timeless Records. Catalogue no: **CDTTD 511**
**Album:** Released Sep '86, on Timeless by Timeless Records. Catalogue no: **TTD 511**

**PAPA BUE CLASSICS (Bue, Papa & His Viking Jazzband)**
**Album:** Released Feb '90, on Storyville by Storyville Records AB. Catalogue no: **SLP 197**

**PAPA BUE'S VIKING JAZZ BAND (Bue, Papa Viking Jazz Band)**
Note: Jazzband with friends, George Lewis/Art Hodes
**Album:** Released Jun '86, on Storyville by Storyville Records AB. Catalogue no: **SLP 405**

**PAPA BUE'S VIKING JAZZ BAND WITH WINGY MANONE (Bue, Papa Viking Jazz Band & Wingy Manone)**
Note: MONO production
**Album:** Released Jun '86, on Storyville by Storyville Records AB. Catalogue no: **SLP 210**

**TRIBUTE TO LOUIS (Liller & Papa Bue's Viking Jazzband)**
**Album:** Released Feb '90, on Storyville by Storyville Records AB. Catalogue no: **SLP 845**

**WITH FRIENDS (Bue, Papa Viking Jazz Band)**
Note: Friends include: George Lewis / Edmond Hall / Wingy Manone / Art Hodes / Albert Nicholas / Wild Bill / Jack Dupree etc.
**Album:** Released Jun '86, on Storyville by Storyville Records AB. Catalogue no: **SLP 425**

## Bull City Blues

**BULL CITY BLUES (Various artists)**
**Album:** Released Sep '87, on Magpie by Interstate Music. Deleted '88. Catalogue no: **PY 1812**

## Bull City Red

**BULL CITY RED 1935-39**
**Album:** Released Apr '89, on Blues Document Catalogue no: **BD 2030**

## Bull, Geoff

**Biographical details:** See under - John Handy..

**IN NEW ORLEANS**
**Album:** Released Jul '87, on GHB by Jazzology Records (USA). Catalogue no: **GHB 203**

## Bullock, Chick

**Biographical details:** Bullock, Chick USA vocalist (1908-81), one of the most prolifically recorded of all time, with a deep, virile voice; he made hundreds of records 1930-42; sides with Duke Ellington, Adrian Rollini etc. but mainly studio lineups with a different name each time; many really were all-star bands, with sidemen such as Tommy & Jimmy Dorsey, Bunny Berigan, Benny Goodman, Jack Teagarden, many others. Bullock quit mid-'40s, always shunned publicity. Donald Clarke, 24 August 1988..

**CHICK BULLOCK & HIS LEVEE LOUNGERS (Bullock, Chick & His Levee Loungers)**
**Album:** Released Jul '82, on Everybody's (Sweden) Catalogue no: **E 1001**

## Bunn, Teddy

**SPIRITS OF RHYTHM**
**CD:** Released Apr '89, on JSP by JSP Records. Catalogue no: **JSPCD 307**

**TEDDY BUNN 1930-39**
**Album:** Released '89, on Blues Document Catalogue no: **BD 2069**

## Burbank, Albert

**CREOLE CLARINET**
**Album:** Released Apr '79, on Smokey Mary Deleted '84. Catalogue no: **SMOKEY MARY 1969**

## Burgess, Sally

**SALLY BURGESS SINGS JAZZ**
**Album:** Released Dec '89, on T. E. R. by That's Entertainment Records. Catalogue no: **VIR 8308**
**CD:** Released Dec '89, on T. E. R. by That's Entertainment Records. Catalogue no: **CDVIR 8308**
**Cass:** Released Dec '89, on T. E. R. by That's Entertainment Records. Catalogue no: **ZCVIR 8308**

## Burke, Chris

**CHRIS BURKE & HIS NEW ORLEANS MUSIC (Burke, Chris & His New Orleans Music)**
**Album:** Released '85, on GHB by Jazzology Records (USA). Catalogue no: **GHB 175**

## Burke, Ray

**RAY BURKE SPEAKEASY BOYS (Burke, Ray Speakeasy Boys)**
**Album:** Released Sep '86, on New Orleans Catalogue no: **NOR 7202**

## Burke, Vinnie All Stars

**VINNIE BURKE ALL STARS**
**Album:** Released 7 Nov '87, on Fresh Sounds (Spain) by Fresh Sounds Records (Spain). Catalogue no: **FS 264**

## Burns, Eddie

**DETROIT BLACK BOTTOM (Burns, Eddie 'guitar')**
**Album:** Released Apr '79, on Big Bear by Big Bear Records. Deleted '88. Catalogue no: **BEAR 7**

**TREAT ME LIKE I TREAT YOU**
**Album:** Released Dec '85, on Moonshine Catalogue no: **BLP 106**

## Burns, Ralph

**BIJOU (Burns, Ralph Quartet)**
**Album:** Released Feb '88, on Fresh Sounds (Spain) by Fresh Sounds Records (Spain). Catalogue no: **FS 250**

**RALPH BURNS CONDUCTS 1951-54**
**Album:** Released '88, on Raretone Catalogue no: **RARETONE 5017**

## Burrage, Harold

**SHE KNOCKS ME OUT 1956-58**
**Album:** Released Jun '81, on Flyright by Interstate Music. Catalogue no: **FLY 579**

## Burrell, Dave

**Biographical details:** Burrell, Dave Born in 1940 in Ohio, a pianist, composer and academic who made albums with Archie Shepp, Pharoah Sanders and Marion Brown on several labels; the septet set *Echo* was made in Paris in 1969 with Shepp, Grachan Moncur III and Sonny Murray. *Lush Life* and *Round Midnight* from 1978 are solos with bass accompaniment on some tracks. Other albums on European and Japanese labels; not one listed in USA catalogues. (Donald Clarke, 24 August 1988.)

**DAVE BURRELL PLAYS ELLINGTON & MONK**
Tracks: / In a sentimental mood / Lush life / Come Sunday / Straight, no chaser / Sophisticated lady / Flower is a lovesome thing.
**CD:** Released Jun '89, on Denon Catalogue no: **DC 8550**

**ECHO**
**Album:** Released Sep '79, on Affinity by Charly Records. Deleted '88. Catalogue no: **AFF 36**

**LUSH LIFE**
Tracks: / In a sentimental mood / Lush life / Come Sunday / Flower is a lovesome thing, A / Mexico city / Trade winds / Crucificade / Budapest conclusion.
**Album:** Released Mar '82, on Denon Deleted '88. Catalogue no: **YX 7533**

**ROUND MIDNIGHT**
Tracks: / Straight no chaser / Round midnight / Blue monk / Black roberts / No games / New York.
**Album:** Released Mar '82, on Denon Deleted '88. Catalogue no: **YX 7541**

## Burrell, Kenny

**Biographical details:** Burrell, Kenny A guitarist born in Detroit in 1931. He played with Dizzy Gillespie, the Oscar Peterson Trio, '55, Benny Goodman; also his own combos since 1951. Internationally popluar, in demand for club, concert and studio work as well as college seminars, festivals, etc. He recorded on Verve with Astrid Gilberto, Gil Evans, Stan Getz and others including *Guitar Forms* in 1964, arranged by Evans. He has made about 40 albums. (Donald Clarke, 24 August 1988.).

**A LA CARTE**
Tracks: / I've been in love before / Dreamy / Our love / St. Thomas / Tenderly / I thought about you / A la carte.
Note: Produced by: Helen Keane./Recorded by: Malcom Addey./recorded live at Village West-NYC August 23rd. 1983. Kenny Burrell-guitar/Rufus Reid-bass
**Album:** Released Jan '86, on Muse by Black & Blue Records. Catalogue no: **MR 5317**

**AT THE FIVE SPOT CAFE VOL 1**
Tracks: / Birk's works / Lady be good / Lover man / Swingin' / Hallelujah / Beef stew blues / If you could see me now / 36-23-36.
Note: Guitar master Kenny Burrell was a 1956 Blue Note discovery who is back on the label in 1986! This live session at New York's legendary Five Spot took place in 1959 with a swinging cast that included Art Blakey, saxophonist Tina Brooks and alternating pianists Roland Hanna & Bobby Timmons. The tone is definitely straight ahead jazz with rousing versions of 'Lady Be Good' & 'Birk's Work' as well as funky originals such as 'Hallelujah' & '36-23-36'.
**CD:** Released Apr '87, on Blue Note by EMI Records. Catalogue no: **CDP 746 538 2**
**CD:** Released Apr '87, on Blue Note by EMI Records. Catalogue no: **BNZ 11**
**Album:** Released May '86, on Blue Note by EMI Records. Catalogue no: **BST 84021**

**BLUE LIGHTS, VOL.1**
Tracks: / Phinupi / Yes baby / Scotch blues / Man I love, The / I never knew.
**CD:** Released Aug '89, on Blue Note by EMI Records. Catalogue no: **BNZ 223**
**CD:** Released Aug '89, on Blue Note by EMI Records. Catalogue no: **CDP 781 596 2**

**BLUE LIGHTS, VOL.2**
Tracks: / Caravan / Chuckin' / Rock salt / Autumn in New York.
**CD:** Released Aug '89, on Blue Note by EMI Records. Catalogue no: **CDP 781 597 2**
**CD:** Released Aug '89, on Blue Note by EMI Records. Catalogue no: **BNZ 224**

**BLUESIN' AROUND**
**Album:** Released Jan '84, on CBS (import) by CBS Records. Catalogue no: **25514**

**CHICAGO GOLDEN YEARS**
**Album:** Released Oct '88, on Vogue (France) by Vogue Records. Catalogue no: **515001**

**FOR CHARLIE CHRISTIAN & BENNY GOODMAN**
Note: Performance dedicated to the memory of Charlie Christian & the Benny Goodman small groups. Recorded between December 1966 & March 1967. This CD has 3 additional tracks which were not on the original album.
**CD:** Released May '87, on Verve Catalogue no: **831 087-2**

**GENERATIONS**
Tracks: / Mark 1 / Fungii mama / Generation / Hi-fly / Jumpin' the blues / Lover man / Dolphin dance / Naima / Star crossed / Just friends / So little time.

Note: Kenny Burrell, fresh from Detroit, made his very first album for Blue Note in 1956. He has recorded as a leader for the label many times since then in many settings. One of his loveliest efforts was the exciting live album "At The Five Spot" from 1959. On his latest album, he is heard with a very different band live at the Village Vanguard. The electricity of the live event is evident throughout. This album is called "Generation" because it features this great guitarist with two fine guitarists of the next generation Bobby Broom and Rodney Jones. Backed only by bass and drums, the three guitarists weave arrangements that are intricate and almost orchestral, but they swing! The album features a blend of new compositions with jazz standards such as Jay McShann's "Jumpin' The Blues" as well as the pop standard "Lover Man", which coincidentally also appears on "At The Five Spot". (EMI, May 1987)
**CD:** Released Jun '87, on Blue Note by EMI Records. Catalogue no: **BNZ 12**
**Album:** Released May '87, on Blue Note by EMI Records. Catalogue no: **BT 85137**
**CD:** Released Jun '87, on Blue Note by EMI Records. Catalogue no: **CDP 746 756 2**

**GROOVIN' HIGH**
Tracks: / Peace / Someone to light up my life / Lament / If I Love Again / Spring can really hang you up the most / Secret love / Groovin' high.
**Album:** Released Feb '87, on Muse by Black & Blue Records. Catalogue no: **MR 5281**

**GUITAR FORMS (Burrell, Kenny & Gil Evans)**
Tracks: / Geensleeves / Last night when we were young / Breadwinner / Downstairs / Lotus land / Prelude No.2 / Moon and sand / Loie / Terrace theme.
Note: Kenny Burrell one of today's finest jazz guitarists,teamed with Gil Evans for this 1965 recording.
**CD:** Released Aug '81, on Verve Catalogue no: **825 576-2**
**Album:** Released Aug '81, on Verve Catalogue no: **2304 158**

**HANDCRAFTED**
Tracks: / You and the night and the music / So little time / I'm glad there is you / All blues / It could happen to you.
**Album:** Released Apr '81, on Muse by Black & Blue Records. Catalogue no: **MR 5144**

**KENNY BURRELL**
**Album:** Released Jul '82, on Jazz Reactivation Catalogue no: **JR 152**

**KENNY BURRELL IN NEW YORK**
Tracks: / Pent up house / But beautiful / Begs groove / Makin' whoopee / Come rain or come shine / Love your magic spell is everywhere.
Note: Artists: Larry Gales, Sherman (Recorded at The Villiage Vanguard, New York City)
**Album:** Released '81, on Muse by Black & Blue Records. Catalogue no: **MR 5241**

**KENNY BURRELL & JOHN COLTRANE (Burrell, Kenny & John Coltrane)**
**CD:** Released Nov '86, on JVC/Fantasy Deleted '88. Catalogue no: **VDJ 1533**

**LISTEN TO THE DAWN**
Tracks: / Yours is my heart / Alone / My one and only love / You're my everything / Listen to the dawn / Isabella / It amazes me / Never let me go / Papa Joe.
Note: Artists: Kenny Burrell/Rufus Reid/Ben Rilet. Recorded December 9th & 10th 1980
**Album:** Released Feb '83, on Muse by Black & Blue Records. Catalogue no: **MR 5264**

**LIVE AT THE VANGUARD (Burrell, Kenny Trio)**
Tracks: / All night long / Will you still be mine / I'm a fool to want you / Trio / Broadway / Soft winds / Just a sittin' and a rockin'.
**CD:** Released May '87, on Greenline by Charly Records. Catalogue no: **CD CHESS 76**

**LIVE AT THE VILLAGE VANGUARD (Burrell, Kenny Trio)**
Tracks: / All night long / Will you still be in my mind / I'm a fool to want you / Trio / Broadway / Soft winds / Just a sittin' and a rockin' / Well you needn't / Second balcony jump / Willow weep for me / Work song / Woodyn' you / In the still of the night / Don't you know I care / Love you madly / It's getting dark.
**Album:** Released Apr '81, on Muse by Black & Blue Records. Catalogue no: **MR 5216**
**Album:** Released May '86, on Arco by Charly Records. Deleted May '88. Catalogue no: **ARC 500**

**MIDNIGHT BLUE**
Tracks: / Chitlins con carne / Mule / Soul lament / Midnight blue / Wavy gravy / Gee baby ain't I good to you / Saturday night blues.
Note: This soulful, after hours album couples Stanley Turrentine and Kenny Burrell with a pianoless rhythm section.The performances range from the sensitive guitarsolo 'Soul Lament' to the full blown, hard cooking 'Chitlins Con Carne' with thewhole band.Another highlight in there reading of Don Redman's 'Gee baby ain't I good to you'
**Album:** Released Nov '85, on Blue Note by EMI Records. Catalogue no: **BST 84123**
**CD:** Released Jun '87, on Blue Note by EMI Records. Catalogue no: **BNZ 10**
**Cass:** Released Sep '87, on Blue Note by EMI Records. Deleted Nov '88. Catalogue no: **4BN 84123**
**CD:** Released Jun '87, on Blue Note by EMI Records. Catalogue no: **CDP 746 399 2**

**MIDNIGHT BLUES**
**Album:** Released '79, on Blue Note by EMI Records. Deleted '84. Catalogue no: **BNS 40015**

**NIGHT SONG**
Tracks: / Night song / Blues for lues / Namely you / Love you madly / Just a sittin' and a rockin' / Shadow of your smile / Brother where are you / Night hawk / Teach me tonight.
**Album:** Released May '82, on Verve Catalogue no: **2304 539**

**PIECES OF BLUE AND THE BLUES (Burrell, Kenny & The Jazz Guitar Band)**
Tracks: / Confessin' the blues / Raincheck / Blue days, blue dreams / Salty papa (A.K.A. blues chantez) / Jedannine / Round midnight / No hype blues.
**Album:** Released Jun '89, on Blue Note by EMI Records. Deleted Jan '90. Catalogue no: **B1 90260**
**CD:** Released Jun '89, on Blue Note by EMI Records. Catalogue no: **CDP 790 260 2**

**RECAPITULATION**
Tracks: / Mother in law / Hot bossa / Isabella / People / Tender gender,The / I'm a fool to want you / Broadway / Afternoon in Paris / Tricotism / Just a settin' and a rockin' / Well you need'nt / Suite for guitar and orchestra / So little time / Growing / Round and round we go / Recapitulation / I want my baby back / Blues fuse / Wild man / My state, my Kansas, my home / Pine cones and holly berries / My favourite things / Suzy / Wild is the wind.
**Album:** Released '89, on Chess by Vogue Records. Catalogue no: **GCH26034**

**TOGETHERING (Burrell, Kenny & Grover Washington Jr.)**
Tracks: / Soulero / Sails of your soul / Daydream / Beautiful friendship, A / Togethering / Romance dance / Asphalt canyon blues / What am I here for.
Note: 'Togethering' is a distinctly straight-ahead album, teaming two of Jazz's most distinguished and popular instrumentalists and designed to be accessible to all fans of contemporary instrumental music.The pairing of Washington & Burrell was the brainchild of Bruce Lundvall, the renowned record executive vehind the relaunch of the Blue Note label and founder of the Electra Musician label, for which this album was originally recorded.Backed by Ron Carter, Jack De Johnette and Ralph MacDonald, this is the first jazz record that Grover Wahington has made for quite some time.
**CD:** Released Jul '89, on Blue Note by EMI Records. Catalogue no: **BNZ 179**
**CD:** Released Jul '89, on Blue Note by EMI Records. Catalogue no: **CDP 746 093 2**
**Album:** Released Jul '89, on Blue Note by EMI Records. Catalogue no: **BT 85106**

**TWO GUITARS (Burrell, Kenny & Jimmy Rainey)**
**Album:** Released Apr '86, on Original Jazz Classics (USA) by Fantasy Inc (USA). Catalogue no: **OJC 216**

## Burrough, Roslyn

### LOVE IS HERE

Tracks: / Devil may care / Love is here(lonely tears) / Song for Jean-Gene / If I were a bell / Never let me go / Did he ever love me / All the things you are / So much in love / I want to make you smile / Young folks.
Note: Personnel:Kevin Ewbanks - elec, & accoustic guitars / Eddie Gladden-drums / Jerry Gladden - percussions & trumpet / Onaje Allan Cumbs - piano & synthesiser / Kirk Lightsey-piano / Rufus Reid-acoustic bass / Warren Smith-vibraphone / Akira Tana-drums.
**Album:** Released Jan '86, on Sunnyside Jazz(USA) Catalogue no: **SSC 1009**

## Burton, Gary

**Biographical details:** Burton, Gary The vibist, composer and leader was born in Indiana in 1953; he studied piano but is self-taught on vibes, generating unusually rich harmony with four mallets. He joined George Shearing in 1963 and Shearing made an album of his tunes; leading his own small groups he made 12 LPs on RCA in the '60s, seven on Atlantic 1967-71; 12 on ECM 1972-82. Carla Bley wrote *A Genuine Tong Funeral* for him. He has helped many other artists, from Larry Coryell in the early years to (most recently) Scottish saxophonist Tommy Smith. (Donald Clarke, 24 August 1988.).

### ARTIST'S CHOICE

Tracks: / Careful / Chega de saudade / Norwegian wood / I want you / Faded love / Ballet / General Mojo's well laid plan / I'm you're pal / June 15th 1967 / Fanfare (mother of the dead man)( / Interlude "lament intermission music / Blue comedy / Sunset bell / And on the third day / True or false / Country roads.
**CD:** Released Jul '88, on Blue Bird (1) by Blue Sun Records (USA). Catalogue no: **ND 86280**

### COUNTRY ROADS AND OTHER PLACES (Burton, Gary Quartet)

Tracks: / Country roads / Green mountains, The / True or false / Gone, but forgotten / Ravel prelude / And on the third day / Singing song, The / Whichita breakdown / My foolish heart / Family joy, A.
**Album:** Released Jan '83, on RCA (France) by BMG Records (France). Catalogue no: **PL 45139**

### CRYSTAL SILENCE (Burton, Gary & Chick Corea)

Tracks: / Senor Mouse / Arise, her eyes / I'm your pal / Desert air / Crystal silence / Falling grace / Feelings and things / Childrens song / What game shall we play today.
**CD:** Released Mar '88, on ECM Catalogue no: **8313312**

### DREAMS SO REAL (Music of Carla Bley)

Note: With Mick Goodrick, Pat Metheny, Steve Swallow, Bob Moses.
**Album:** Released '88, on ECM Catalogue no: **ECM 1072**
**CD:** Released Jul '88, on ECM Catalogue no: **833 329-2**

### DUET: GARY BURTON & CHICK COREA (Burton, Gary & Chick Corea)

Note: Duo performances with pianist Chick Corea.
**CD:** Released Oct '88, on ECM Catalogue no: **829 941-2**
**Album:** Released Oct '88, on ECM Catalogue no: **ECM 1140**

### EASY AS PIE (Burton, Gary Quartet)

**Album:** Released Jun '81, on ECM Catalogue no: **ECM 1184**

### GARY BURTON & THE BERKLEE ALL STARS (Burton, Gary & The Berklee All Stars)

Note: Digital recording of a concert by vibes virtuoso Burton and the All Stars, students from the Berklee Jazz School. CD version has one extra track.
**Cass:** Released Jul '88, on JVC Catalogue no: **JC 3301**
**Album:** Released Feb '89, on JVC Catalogue no: **JLP 3301**
**CD:** Released Jul '88, on JVC Catalogue no: **JD 3301**

### NEW QUARTET, THE

Note: With Michael Goodrick (guitar); Abraham Laboriel (bass); Harry Blazer (drums).
**CD:** Released Sep '88, on ECM Catalogue no: **835 002-2**

### PASSENGERS (Burton, Gary & Eberhard Weber)

Note: All-star quartet featuring Pat Metheney, Steve Swallow & Dan Gottlieb, plus special guest Eberhard Weber.
**CD:** Released Oct '88, on ECM Catalogue no: **835 016-2**
**Album:** Released Apr '77, on ECM Catalogue no: **EMC 1092**

### PICTURE THIS (Burton, Gary Quartet)

Note: Gary Burton (vibraharp), Jim Odgren (alto sax), Steve Swallow (bass), Mike Hyman(drums) playing pieces by, among others, Carla Bley, Chick Corea, Mike Gibbs.
**Album:** Released Mar '83, on ECM Catalogue no: **ECM 1226**

### REAL LIFE HITS

Tracks: / Syndrome / Beatle, The / Fleurette Africaine (the African flower) / Ladies in Mercedes / Real life hits / I need you here / Ivanushka Durachok.
Note: 'Real Life Hits' is probably Gary Burton's most coherent and vital record in a long time.In his quartet, Burton introduces the young talented Japanese piano player Makoto Ozone who with this recording,proves a unique and adequate partner for Burton.'Real Life Hits' comprises compositions by Carla Bley,Duke Ellington, John Scofield,Makoto Ozone and the Quartet's bassist Steve Swallow.He in particular contributes to the group's overall sound.
**CD:** on ECM Catalogue no: **825 235-2**

### REUNION

**CD:** Released Mar '90, on GRP by GRP Records (USA). Catalogue no: **JJCD8**
**Album:** Released Jan '90, on GRP by GRP Records (USA). Catalogue no:

Gary Burton

**GRP 95981**
**Cass:** Released Jan '90, on GRP by GRP Records (USA). Catalogue no: **GRP 95984**
**CD:** Released Jan '90, on GRP by GRP Records (USA). Catalogue no: **GRP 95982**

**SING**
**CD:** Released Oct '86, on ECM Catalogue no: **829 191-2**

**SOMETHING'S COMING**
**Album:** Released Nov '84, on RCA (France) by BMG Records (France). Catalogue no: **NL 89377**

**TENNESSEE FIREBIRD (Burton, Gary & Friends)**
Tracks: / Gone / Tennessee firebird / Just like a woman / Black is the colour of my true love's hair / Faded love / Panhandle rag / I can't help it / I want you / Alone and forsaken / Walter L. / Born to lose / Beauty contest / Epilogue.
**CD:** Released 1 Jun '89, on Bear Family by Bear Family Records (Germany). Catalogue no: **BCD 15458**

**THAT'S JAZZ (Burton, Gary & Keith Jarrett)**
Tracks: / Grow your own / Moonchild / In your quiet place / Como en Vietnam / Fortune smiles / Raven speaks, The.
**Album:** Released Jul '76, on Atlantic by WEA Records. Deleted '83. Catalogue no: **K 50242**

**TIMES LIKE THESE**
Note: For his GRP debut, vibraphonist Gary Burton has gathered together an all-star ensemble of international soloists. These include guitarist John Scofield, Marc Johnson on bass, Peter Erskine on drums and the incomparable Michael Brecker ontenor saxophone. The CD contains an extra track.
**CD:** Released Sep '88, on GRP by GRP Records (USA). Catalogue no: **GRD 9569**
**Album:** Released Sep '88, on GRP by GRP Records (USA). Catalogue no: **GR 9569**
**Cass:** Released Sep '88, on GRP by GRP Records (USA). Catalogue no: **GRC 9569**

**WHIZ KIDS (Burton, Gary Quartet)**
Tracks: / Last clown, The / Yellow fever / Soulful Bill / La divetta / Cool train / Loop, The.
Note: Gary Burton back again with a great line-up of tremendous new talent.British tenor sax player Tommy Smith has already caused quite a stir along with American drummer Martin Richards,Japanese pianist Makoto Ozone has already recorded with Burton on "Real Life Hits" in 1984.Steve Swallow on bass needs no introduction as their musical partnership goes back to the very beginning of Burton's recording career. Personnel: Gary Burton - vibraphone / Makoto Ozone - piano / Tommy Smith - saxaphone / Steve Swallow - bass / Martin Richards - drums.
**Album:** Released Feb '87, on ECM Catalogue no: **ECM 1329**
**CD:** Released Mar '87, on ECM Catalogue no: **831 110 2**

**WORKS: GARY BURTON**
Tracks: / Olhos de gato / Desert air / Tunnel of love / Vox humana / Three / Brotherhood / Chelsea Bells / Coral / Domino biscuit.
Note: Personnel: Gary Burton, Chick Corea, Pat Metheny, Eberhard Weber, Ralph Towner, Steve Swallow.
**CD:** Released Jun '89, on ECM Catalogue no: **823 267-2**
**Album:** Released Jun '89, on ECM Catalogue no: **823 267-1**

## Burton, Tommy

**IT AIN'T EXACTLY BACKGROUND MUSIC**
Note: Good time Jazz. Tracks include: Dinah / Happy feet / Darktown strutters ball / Down among the sheltering palms / Your feets too big, etc.
**Album:** Released May '85, on Unit Catalogue no: **TRALP 2002**

**TOMMY BURTON'S SPORTINGHOUSE (Burton, Tommy Quartet)**
**Album:** Released Jul '87, on Lost Catalogue no: **TRAC 2002**

**TONIGHT'S MY... (Burton's, Tommy Sporting House Quartet)**
**Album:** Released '88, on Lost Catalogue no: **LRCLP 2003**

## Burton, W.E. 'Buddy'

**SOUTHSIDE CHICAGO JAZZ & BLUES**
**Album:** Released Mar '89, on Wolf Catalogue no: **WJS 1006**

## Bush, Lou

**Biographical details:** Busch, Lou The USA piainist (1910-79) worked on the A&R staff at Capitol in the early '50s and recorded ragtimey piano as Joe 'Fingers' Carr; under his own name his instrumental *Zambesi* was a UK no. 2 in 1956. (Donald Clarke, 24 August 1988.)

**ZAMBESI**
Tracks: / Zambesi.
**7" Single:** Released Jan '56, on Capitol by EMI Records. Deleted '59. Catalogue no: **CL 14504**

**ZAMBESI (OLD GOLD)**
Tracks: / Zambesi / Sixteen tons.
**7" Single:** Released Apr '87, on Old Gold by Old Gold Records. Deleted Sep '89. Catalogue no: **OG 9719**

## Buskin, Joe

**WORLD IS WAITING 1942-46 (see Powell, Mel) (Buskin, Joe & Mel Powell)**
Tracks: / When did you leave heaven / World is waiting for the sunrise / Blue skies / Mood at twilight / Lover man / Avalon / Pickin' at the pic / Fade out / Oh lady be good / Georgia.
**Album:** Released Sep '82, on Commodore Class Catalogue no: **AG6 24063**

## Busse, Henry

**Biographical details:** Busse, Henry A trumpeter born in Germany in 1894; Busse died in 1955. He came to the USA in 1916 and played with Paul Whiteman 1918-28, then formed his own dance band with a characteristic shuffle beat and his muted 'sweet jazz' horn. He co-wrote *Wang Bang Blues* and *Hot Lips*; issued back-to-back in 1920 for a big hit with Whiteman, the same pairing with his own band in 1935 stayed in print for many years. (Donald Clarke, 24 August 1988.)

**1935 (Busse, Henry & His Orchestra)**
Tracks: / Hot lips / Rose room / Clouds / Continental / Honeysuckle rose / Haunting blues / Here comes Cookie / idewalks of Cuba / When day is done / Ja da / Solitude / What's the reason / Haunting me / Darktown strutters ball / Love is just around the corner.
**Album:** Released Oct '79, on London Records by London Records Ltd. Deleted '84. Catalogue no: **HMP 5051**

**1949 (Busse, Henry & His Orchestra)**
Note: Mono.
**Album:** Released Jan '87, on Circle (USA) by Jazzology Records (USA). Catalogue no: **CLP 76**

**1941/44 VOL. 2 (Busse, Henry & His Shuttle Rhythm Orchestra)**
**Album:** Released Mar '84, on Hindsight Catalogue no: **HSR 193**

**HENRY BUSSE, 1935**
Tracks: / Rose room / Clouds / Continental, The / Honeysuckle rose / Haunting clues / Here comes cookie / Sidewalks of Cuba / When day is done / Ja da / Solitude / What's the reason (I'm not pleasing you) / Hot lips / Haunting me / Darktown strutters' ball / Love is just around the corner.
Note: Trumpeter Henry Busse and his hit song "Hot lips" were at the crest of their nationwide popularity when the Busse orchestra cut the radio air-checks reproduced on this album. These are two complete radio broadcasts with "Hot lips" the opening theme and "When day is done" the closing theme and they were recorded in Hollywood during a triumphant six-week spring engagement at the Coconut Grove of the Ambassador Hotel, following thirteen months at Chicago's Chez Paree. The announcer is the then-unknown Ken Carpenter. The only exsisting recording of Busse's speaking voice introduces the full arrangement of "Hot lips" on Side 2. Vocals are by Marion Holmes. (Hindsight Catalogue - 1989)
**Album:** Released '88, on Hindsight Catalogue no: **HSR 122**

## Butterbeans & Susie

**PAPA'S GOT THE MOJO**
**Album:** Released Feb '89, on Bluetime (Denmark) by Contact Records (Denmark). Catalogue no: **BT 2009**

## Butterfield, Billy

### BILLY BUTTERFIELD & BENNY SIMKINS' BAND (Butterfield, Billy & Benny Simkin's Band)
**Album:** Released Jun '88, on Jazzology (USA) by Jazzology Records (USA). Catalogue no: **J 93**

### RAPPORT (Butterfield, Billy & Dick Wellstood)
**Album:** Released Sep '79, on 77 by 77 Records. Catalogue no: **77 S 54**

### WATCH WHAT HAPPENS
**Album:** Released Aug '79, on Flyright by Interstate Music. Catalogue no: **FLY 205**

## Butterfield, Erskine

### 1944 & 1956, PIANO SOLOS
**Album:** Released Sep '86, on Harlequin by Interstate Music. Catalogue no: **HQ 2050**

### TUESDAY AT TEN
**Album:** Released Aug '88, on Circle (USA) by Jazzology Records (USA). Catalogue no: **CLP 62**

## Butterfield, Paul

**Biographical details:** Butterfield, Paul A white singer and harmonica player (born in Chicago in 1942; died in 1987 in Los Angeles) who ventured to Chicago's south side to jam with blues legends Muddy Waters, Howlin' Wolf, etc.; he formed a band in 1963 with ex-Wolf bassist Jerome Arnold and drummer Sam Lay, adding Mike Bloomfield (1944-81) and Elvin Bishop (born 1942) on guitars, Mark Naftalin on keyboards; the first LP *Paul Butterfield Blues Band* on Elektra in 1965 was followed by their Newport Folk Festival appearance with Billy Davenport replacing Lay on drums, after their set backing Bob Dylan in his controversial first electric performance. *East-West* stretched out from traditional blues: the 13-minute title track had solos by Bloomfield and Bishop that helped establish the modern role of rock guitarists. Bloomfield left; later albums had Phillip Wilson on drums, added horns including David Sanborn. *An Offer You Can't Refuse* on Red Lightnin' label UK is a radio broadcast with Butterfield and Walter Horton; he also played on Muddy Water's *Fathers And Sons* in 1969, formed Better Days (Amos Garrett and Geoff Muldaur on guitars); still later toured with Levon Helm, then Rick Danko. (Donald Clarke, 24 August 1988.)

### AN OFFER YOU CAN'T REFUSE (Butterfield, Paul & Walter Horton)
Tracks: / Easy / Have a good time / Mean mistreater / In the mood / West side blues / Louise / Tin pan alley / Walters boogie / Everything's gonna be alright / Poor boy / Got my mojo working / Last night / Loaded / One room country shack.
**Album:** Released Sep '82, on Red Lightnin' by Red Lightning Records. Deleted Jun '89. Catalogue no: **RL 008**

### EAST WEST (Butterfield Blues Band)
Tracks: / Walkin' blues / Get out of my life woman / I got a mind to give up living / All these blues / Work song / Mary mary / Two trains running / Never say no / East West / East West.
**Album:** Released Feb '87, on Edsel by Demon Records. Catalogue no: **ED 212**
**CD:** Released '89, on WEA by WEA Records. Catalogue no: **960 751 2**

### PAUL BUTTERFIELD BLUES BAND (Butterfield Blues Band)
Tracks: / Born in Chicago / Shake your moneymaker / Blues with a feeling / Thank you Mr. Poobah / I got my mojo working / Mellow down easy / Screamin' / Our love is drifting / Mystery train / Last night / Look over yonders wall.
**CD:** Released '89, on WEA by WEA Records. Catalogue no: **960 647 2**
**Album:** Released Mar '85, on Edsel by Demon Records. Catalogue no: **ED 150**

### RESURRECTION OF THE PIGBOY CRABSHAW (Butterfield Blues Band)
Tracks: / One more heartache / Driftin' and driftin' / Pity the fool / Born under a bad sign / Run out of time / Double trouble / Drivin' wheel / Droppin' out / Tollin' bells.
**Album:** on Elektra by Elektra Records (UK). Catalogue no: **K 42017**
**Album:** Released '88, on Edsel by Demon Records. Catalogue no: **ED 301**

## Byard, Jaki

**Biographical details:** Byard, Jaki This USA pianist and composer was born in Worcester, Massachusetts in 1922; he was a mainstay in the Boston jazz scene from the late '40s, also working with Maynard Ferguson in 1959-62, then Charles Mingus in 1963-70. He also taught at Berklee and other places. He said that Mingus hired him for Town Hall Concert because he needed somebody who could play 'old fashioned': he plays the blues from the inside to a degree unusual in an East Coast musician, also first class stride piano, but also 'modern' as anybody. (Donald Clarke, 24 August 1988.)

### BLUES FOR SMOKE
**CD:** Released May '89, on Candid Catalogue no: **CCD 9018**
**Album:** Released May '89, on Candid Catalogue no: **CS 9018**

### FAMILY MAN
Tracks: / Just rolling along / Mood indigo / Chelsea bridge / L.H gatewalk rag / Ballad to Louise / Family suite.
**Album:** Released Apr '81, on Muse by Black & Blue Records. Catalogue no: **MR 5173**

### IMPROVISATIONS (Byard, Jaki & Ran Blake)
**Album:** Released Jul '82, on Soul Note Catalogue no: **SN 1022**

### LIVE AT THE ROYAL FESTIVAL HALL (Byard, Jaki & Howard Riley)
**Album:** Released 1 Mar '88, on Leo by Leo Records. Catalogue no: **LR 133**

### PHANTASIES (Byard, Jaki & The Apollo Stompers)
**CD:** Released Dec '86, on Soul Note Catalogue no: **SN 1075**

### THERE'LL BE SOME CHANGES MADE
Tracks: / There'll be some changes made / Lonely town / Blues au gratin / Excerpts from songs of proverbs / Besame mucho / Spanish tinge / Journey night of departure / To Bob Vatel of Paris-Blues for Jennie / Some other spring-Every year / Tribute to Jimmy Slide.
**Album:** Released Apr '81, on Muse by Black & Blue Records. Catalogue no: **MR 5007**

## Byas, Don

**Biographical details:** Byas, Don A tenor saxist (1912-72) who was born in Oklahoma, went to Europe in 1946 with a Don Redman Band and stayed, settling in Amsterdam. He was one of the Coleman Hawkin's school, but a more modern stylist in rhythmic and harmonic conception; he could be described as a link between the swing era and bop, but he was too good a musician for a label. *Savoy Jam Party* has 22 tracks from 1944-6 by five different small groups; *Meets The Girls* has '53-5 sessions with piano trios; *Danish Brew* '59 has expatriate tenor sax Brew Moore (1924-73). Donald Clarke, 24 August 1988.

### ALL THE THINGS YOU ARE
**CD:** Released May '88, on Jazz Life Catalogue no: **2673732**
**Album:** Released May '88, on Jazz Life Catalogue no: **2673731**
**Cass:** Released May '88, on Jazz Life Catalogue no: **2673734**

### AMBIENCES ET SLOWS
**Album:** Released Nov '79, on Barclay (France) by Decca Records. Catalogue no: **80970/1**

### ANTHROPOLOGY
Tracks: / Anthropology / Moonlight in Vermont / Billie's bounce / Night in Tunisia / Don't blame me.
**Album:** Released Apr '85, on Black Lion Catalogue no: **BLP 30126**

### DON BYAS
**Album:** Released '88, on GNP Crescendo (USA) by GNP Crescendo Records (USA). Catalogue no: **GNPS 9027**

### DON BYAS AND FRIENDS
**Album:** Released '89, on Jazz Society Catalogue no: **AA 500**

### DON BYAS MEETS THE GIRLS
**Album:** Released Sep '79, on Jazz Legacy by Vogue Records. Catalogue no: **JL 95**

### DON BYAS ON BLUE STAR
Tracks: / Please don't talk about me when I'm gone / Mad monk / Billie's bounce / I surrender dear / Red cross / Cynamo A / Summertime / Stardust / Ol' man river / Night and day / Man I love, The / Georgia on my mind / Easy to love

/ Over the rainbow / Where or when / En ce temps-la / Somebody loves me / Riviera blues (blues a la Don) / Laura / Smoke gets in your eyes / Old folks at home / Don't blame me / I cover the waterfront.
Note: Rare tracks recorded in Paris between 1947 and 1952.
**CD:** Released Mar '88, on ECM Catalogue no: **8334052**

**JAZZ TIME VOL.1**
**Album:** Released '88, on Vogue (France) by Vogue Records. Catalogue no: **502701**

**MEMORIAL**
**2 LP Set:** Released Oct '88, on Vogue by Vogue Records. Catalogue no: **400015**

**SAVOY JAM PARTY**
Tracks: / Riffin' and jivin' / Free and easy / Free and easy (2) / Worried and blue / Don's idea (1) / Don's idea (2) / Savoy jam party (2) / Savoy jam party (1) / 1944 stomp / What do you want with my heart / Bass C jam / Sweet and lovely / White rose kick / My deep blue dream / Byas'd opinion / Candy / How high the moon / Donby / Byas a drink / I don't know why / Danny boy / Old folks / Cherokee / September in the rain / Living my life / To each his own / They say it's wonderful / Cynthia's in love / September song / St. Louis blues / I've found a new baby / Marie.
**2 LP Set:** Released Mar '85, on Arista by BMG Records (UK). Catalogue no: **SJL 2213**
**2 LP Set:** Released '88, on Savoy (France) Deleted May '89. Catalogue no: **WL 70512**

**TENDERLY (Byas, Don Trios & Quartet)**
**CD:** Released Dec '86, on Vogue by Vogue Records. Catalogue no: **VG 600 088**

**THOSE BARCELONA DAYS**
**Album:** Released Feb '88, on Fresh Sounds (Spain) by Fresh Sounds Records (Spain). Catalogue no: **FS 135**

**TWO KINGS OF THE TENOR SAX 44-45 (Byas, Don & Ben Webster)**
**Album:** Released May '87, on Commodore Class Catalogue no: **6.24058**
**Album:** Released Sep '82, on Commodore Class Catalogue no: **AG6 24058**

## Byers, Billy

**JAZZ WORKSHOP**
**Album:** Released Dec '87, on Fresh Sounds (Spain) by Fresh Sounds Records (Spain). Catalogue no: **FS 301**

## Byrd, Charlie

**Biographical details:** Byrd, Charlie Plays Spanish guitar; born in 1925 in Suffolk, Virginia, prolific recording - about 40 LPs under his own name - places him in the 'easy listening' category, but apart from first class technique he is one of the most versatile on the instrument, playing jazz, classical, South American music in same concerts. For *Jazz Samba* in 1962 with Stan Getz, he suggested tunes by Antonio Carlos Jobim, helping to spark off much pretty music in the bossa nova fad; that was a number one pop album in the USA, listed under both Byrd's and Getz's names. (Donald Clarke, 24 August 1988 )
Born in Virginia, USA in 1925, this guitarist plays both classical music and modern jazz. He began learning the instrument at the age of nine, being taught by his father, eventually playing in various school, college and US Army bands. After the end of the Second World War, Byrd spent fifteen years building a strong reputation in both the jazz and classical fields. In 1961 he embarked upon a US-Government-sponsored tour of South America, during which he discovered and liked the bossa nova sound. Literally meaning 'new style', this Brazilian variation of jazz plus its accompanying dance became a fashionable new craze in both the US and the UK in the early Sixties, largely due to the exposure Byrd gave the style on his return to the States.
In 1962 he teamed with well-known saxaphone player Stan Getz and released a bossa nova instrumental single called *Desafinado*. It reached the Top 20 on both sides of the Atlantic, as did the duo's album *Jazz Samba*.
Charlie Byrd was never a chart star again, but he continued to be very active in the music business. He had his own club, the Byrd Cage in Washington DC, which saw him remaining loyal to both wings of his musical self. (Bob MacDonald)..

**BRAZILVILLE (Byrd, Charlie & Bud Shank)**
Tracks: / Zingaro / Brazilville / Saquarema / Speak low / Yesterdays / Charlotte's fancy / What are you doing the rest of your life?.
**Cass:** Released Mar '82, on Concord Jazz by Concord Jazz Records (USA). Catalogue no: **CJPC 173**
**CD:** Released Jul '88, on Concord Jazz by Concord Jazz Records (USA). Catalogue no: **CCD 4173**
**Album:** Released Mar '82, on Concord Jazz by Concord Jazz Records (USA). Catalogue no: **CJP 173**

**BYRD AT THE GATE**
Tracks: / Shiny stockings / More / Blues for night people / Big butter and egg man / Ela mi deixon / Broadway / I left my heart in san fransisco / Some other spring / Where are the hebrew children.
**Album:** Released Jan '87, on Original Jazz Classics (USA) by Fantasy Inc (USA). Catalogue no: **OJC 262**

**BYRD & BRASS (Byrd, Charlie Trio/Annapolis Brass Quintet)**
Tracks: / Strike up the band / Byrd & brass / Thou swell / En memoria de chano pozo / Solitude / Franz und Johann / I'm getting sentimental over you / It don't mean a thing.
Note: This recording by Charlie Byrd & The Annapolis Brass Quintet is an extraordinary first.From the different worlds of jazz and chamber music emerge a stunning blend of fresh, beautiful sounds. The programme consists of six standards arranged by Tommy Newsom."En Memoria De Chano Pozo" was composed by David Amram, & "Byrd & Brass" written by Warren Kellerhouse: Personnel: Charlie Byrd - guitar / Joe Byrd - bass / Chuck Redd - drums / David Cran-trumpet, flugelhorn & cornet / Robert Suggs - trumpet / Arthur Brooks - french horn / Wayne Wells -trombone / Robert Posten - bass, trombone & tuba.
**Album:** Released Sep '86, on Concord Jazz by Concord Jazz Records (USA). Catalogue no: **CJ 304**
**Cass:** Released Sep '86, on Concord Jazz by Concord Jazz Records (USA). Catalogue no: **CJC 304**

**CHRISTMAS ALBUM**
Tracks: / O come all ye faithful / Deck the halls / Hark the herald angels sing / Christmas song, The / In the bleak mid winter / God rest ye merry gentlemen / Holly and the ivy, The.
**Album:** Released Nov '82, on Concord Classics Catalogue no: **CC 2004**
**CD:** Released '89, on GRP by GRP Records (USA). Catalogue no: **CCD 42004**

**DESAFINADO (Byrd, Charlie & Stan Getz)**
Tracks: / Samba deese day's / O pata / Samba triste / Samba de una nota so / E luxo so / Baia / Desafinado.
**CD:** Released '83, on Verve Catalogue no: **810 161-2**
**Album:** Released '84, on Verve (France) Catalogue no: **2615 054**

**DIRECT TO DISC**
Tracks: / Moliendo cafe / Old hymn / At seventeen / Swing 39 / It's all clear to me now / Something / Moonlight serenade / This can't be love / Mama, I'll be home someday.
**CD:** Released Nov '87, on Teldec (Germany) by ASV (Academy Sound & Vision). Catalogue no: **8.26516**

**GREAT GUITARS (Byrd, Charlie/ Barney Kessel/ Herb Ellis)**
**CD:** Released Jul '88, on Concord Jazz by Concord Jazz Records (USA). Catalogue no: **CCD 6004**

**HOLLYWOOD BIRD**
Tracks: / Time for love, A / Georgy girl / Alfie / Wishing doll, The / Wish me a rainbow / Born free / In the arms of love / Any Wednesday / Moment to moment / I'll be back.
**Cass:** Released Aug '84, on CBS by CBS Records. Catalogue no: **40 32507**
**Album:** Released Sep '84, on CBS by CBS Records. Deleted Sep '89. Catalogue no: **CBS 32507**

**IN GREENWICH VILLAGE**
Tracks: / Just squeeze me / Why was I born? / You stepped out of a dream / Fantasia on / Which side are you on? / Shiny stockings / More / Blues for night people / Butter and egg man / Ela me

Deixou / Broadway / I left my heart in San Francisco / Some other Spring / Where are the Hebrew children?.
**2 LP Set:** Released '79, on Prestige Deleted '84. Catalogue no: **M 47049**

**ISN'T IT ROMANTIC (Byrd, Charlie Trio)**
Tracks: / Isn't it romantic / I could write a book / Cheek to cheek / Very thought of you, The / Thou swell / One morning in May / I didn't know what time it was / There's a small hotel / Someone to watch over me / Thought about me.
Note: A superb set of love songs, skillfully interpreted by the Charlie Byrd Trio. Collection of romantic ballads from the pens of Roger & Hart, Hoagy Carmichael Johnny Mercer & Jimmy van heusen, Cole Porter, George Gershwin, and Irvin BerlinPersonnel; Charlie Byrd - Guitar/Joe Byrd - Bass/Chuck riggs-Drums.
**Album:** Released Nov '84, on Concord Jazz by Concord Jazz Records (USA). Catalogue no: **CJ 252**

**IT'S A WONDERFUL WORLD (Featuring Scott Hamilton) (Byrd, Charlie Trio)**
Note: Charlie Byrd's latin flavoured acoustic guitar and Scott Hamilton's warm breathy tenor saxophone combine to create a programme of lightly swinging and melodic jazz. Personnel: Charlie Byrd (guitar), John Goldsby (bass), Chuck Redd (drums), Special guest Scott Hamilton (ten sax).
**CD:** Released May '89, on Concord Jazz by Concord Jazz Records (USA). Catalogue no: **CCD 4374**
**Album:** Released May '89, on Concord Jazz by Concord Jazz Records (USA). Catalogue no: **CJ 374**
**Cass:** Released May '89, on Concord Jazz by Concord Jazz Records (USA). Catalogue no: **CJ 374 C**

**LATIN BYRD**
Tracks: / Mediticao / Samba de una nota so / Yvone voce e eu / Coisa mais linda / O barquinho / Desafinado / Sambra triste / Carnaval / Ho ba la la / Ela me deixou / O passaro / Otra vez / Presente de natal / Insensatez / Three note samba / Samba da minha terra / Limehouse blues / Saudade de Bahia / Anna / Socegadamente / Chega de saudade / Cancao de nimar par Carol.
**2 LP Set:** Released Nov '80, on Milestone by Ace Records. Catalogue no: **M 47005**

**LATIN ODYSSEY (Byrd, Charlie & Laurindo Almeida)**
Tracks: / Memory / Zum and resurrection del angel / El nino / Gitanerias / Adios / El Vacilan / Estrllita / Turbihao de beijos / Intermizzo malinconico.
**Album:** Released May '83, on Concord Jazz by Concord Jazz Records (USA). Catalogue no: **CJP 211**
**Cass:** Released May '83, on Concord Jazz by Concord Jazz Records (USA). Catalogue no: **CJPC 211**

**MEDITATION**
**Album:** Released Aug '84, on Riverside (USA) by Fantasy Inc (USA). Catalogue no: **OJC 107**

**SUGARLOAF SUITE**
**CD:** Released Jul '88, on Concord Jazz by Concord Jazz Records (USA). Catalogue no: **CCD 4114**

**TAMBU (Byrd, Charlie & Cal Tjader)**
Note: For full information see: Tjader, Cal & Charlie Byrd.
**CD:** Released Jun '87, on Fantasy (import) by Fantasy Inc (USA). Catalogue no: **FCD 6169453**

## Byrd, Donald

**Biographical details:** Byrd, Donald Born in 1932 in Detroit, the trumpeter came to fame with Art Blakey's Jazz Messengers in 1955; he made a lot of very popular albums. *A New Perspective* in 1963 included *Christo Rendentor*, a hymn written and arranged by Duke Pearson, personnel including a choir: it marked Byrd's moving away from hard bop. Finally obtained a doctorate, studied law and became an ethnomusicologist, helped launch students in a funk group called Blackbyrds. He was of course accused of selling out; he has recently started recording again. (Donald Clarke, 24 August 1988.)

This American jazz trumpeter first came to the attention of jazz fans in the Fifties and has remained a active and respected figure ever since. by the Seventies he had become director of jazz studies at Washington's Howard University. It was while in this capacity that he took a group of his students in 1973 and formed a group called the Blackbyrds. Their aim was to experiment with Byrd's musical ideas, as a way of complementing and enhancing their studies. They suddenly broke big in 1975 with their catchy single *Walking In Rhythm*. One of the first jazz-funk fusion hits, it was perfect for the new disco era and reached No. 6 on the American pop charts. It also climbed to No. 23 in Britain. The following year they scored a second US Top 20 hit, peaking at No. 19 with *Happy Music*. When they went on tour, their itinerary included university and college lectures and demonstrations, in addition to conventional concerts. Subsequent record releases became less interesting and less successful, however.
In 1981 Donald Byrd returned to the lower reaches of the UK pop charts as a solo artist. His double A sided single *Love Has Come Around/Loving You* reached No. 41, while his album *Love Byrd* peaked at No. 70. He remains active in the jazz field, often incorporating the soul and R&B tinges that gave him major success in the mid-Seventies. (Bob MacDonald)..

**AND 125TH STREET N Y C**
Tracks: / Pretty baby / Gold the moon, white the sun / Giving it up / Marilyn / People supposed to be free / Veronica / Morning, I love you.
**Album:** Released '88, on Elektra by Elektra Records (UK). Catalogue no: **K 52199**

**AT THE HALF NOTE CAFE VOL. 1**
Tracks: / My girl Shirl / Soulful kiddy / Portrait of Jennie / Cecile / Pure D funk (theme) / Child's play / Chant.
Note: After graduating from the Jazz Messengers and before pioneering a variety of jazz-fusion successes,Donald Byrd & Pepper Adams co-led a beautifully relaxed and lyrical quintet that often included another Blue Note artist Duke Pearson as pianist and musical director.Their live Half Note recordings are generally considered to be their finest.A secret to their success was the quality and appeal of their material as"My Girl Shirl""Soulful Kiddy" and "A Portrait Of Jenny" amply prove here. P 1986 Manhattan Records, a division of Capitol Records Inc.
**Album:** Released Jul '89, on Blue Note by EMI Records. Catalogue no: **BST 84060**
**CD:** Released Jun '87, on Blue Note by EMI Records. Catalogue no: **CDP 746 539 2**
**CD:** Released Jun '87, on Blue Note by EMI Records. Catalogue no: **BNZ 14**

**AT THE HALF NOTE CAFE VOL. 2**
Tracks: / Jeannine / Pure D funk / Between the devil and the deep blue sea / Mr. Lucky / Kimyas / When sunny gets blue.
**CD:** Released Jan '88, on Blue Note by EMI Records. Catalogue no: **CDP 746 540 2**
**CD:** Released Jan '88, on Blue Note by EMI Records. Catalogue no: **BNZ 15**
**Album:** Released Jul '89, on Blue Note by EMI Records. Catalogue no: **BLJ 84061**

**BLUE NOTE COLLECTION**
Tracks: / Lansana's priestess / Sister love / Flight time / Stepping into tomorrow / Where are we going / Think twice / Wild life / Love's so far away / Design a nation / Change / Places and spaces / Onward 'til morning / Wind parade / Just my imagination / Dominos.
**Album:** Released Jul '83, on Liberty by EMI Records. Deleted Jul '88. Catalogue no: **LCSP 1867013**

**BYRD IN HAND**
Tracks: / Witchcraft / Here I am / Devil whip / Bronze dance / Clarion calls / Injuns, The.
Note: With a sextet that includes his long time partner Pepper Adams as well as Charlie Rouse and Walter Davis, the trumpeter presents a straight ahead program of sixpieces with great varity. The breakneck paced "Devil Whip" Witchcraft and two Walter Davis compositions (Bronze dance and clarion calls) stand out.
**CD:** Released May '89, on Blue Note by EMI Records. Catalogue no: **BNZ 165**
**Album:** Released Jul '89, on Blue Note by EMI Records. Catalogue no: **BST 84019**
**CD:** Released May '89, on Blue Note by EMI Records. Catalogue no: **CDP 784 019 2**

**BYRD IN PARIS VOL.1**
Tracks: / Dear old stockholm / Paul's pals / Flute blues / Ray's idea / Blues walk, The.
**Album:** Released Nov '87, on Polygram (France) by PolyGram UK Ltd. Catalogue no: **833 394-1**
**CD:** Released Jan '89, on Polygram (France) by PolyGram UK Ltd. Catalogue no: **833 394-2**

**BYRD IN PARIS VOL.2**
**CD:** Released Jan '89, on Polygram (France) by PolyGram UK Ltd. Catalogue no: **833 395-2**
**Album:** Released Nov '87, on Polygram (France) by PolyGram UK Ltd. Catalogue no: **833 395-1**

**CAT WALK, THE**
Tracks: / Say you're mine / Duke's mixture / Each time I think of you / Cat walk, The / Cute / Hello bright sunflower.
**Album:** Released Nov '84, on Blue Note by EMI Records. Deleted Jun '88. Catalogue no: **BST 84075**

**DOMINOES**
Tracks: / Dominoes / Change (makes you want to hustle).
**12" Single:** Released Oct '88, on Domino by Domino Records. Catalogue no: **DOM T5**
**12" Single:** Released Apr '80, on United Artists by EMI Records. Deleted '82. Catalogue no: **12UP 622**

**DOMINOES(LIVE)**
Tracks: / Dominoes(live) / Wind parade.
Note: DJ limited edition
**12" Single:** Released Mar '86, on Streetwave Catalogue no: **SWAVE 7**

**DONALD BYRD**
**Album:** Released '88, on Black Lion Catalogue no: **BLP 60134**
**CD:** Released '88, on Black Lion Catalogue no: **BLCD7 60134**

**FREE FORM**
Tracks: / Pentecostal feelin' (Take 23) / Night flower (Take 15.) / Nai nai (Take 2) / French spice (Take 9) / Free form (Take 24) / Three wishes (CD only.).
Note: With Wayne Shorter,Herbie Hancock,Dutch Warren and Billy Higging,Donald Byrd introduced a variety of excellent material on the forward looking 1962 date. Highlights include the adventurous title tune,Hancock's lovely ballad'Night Flower',the gospel-like'Pentecostal Feelin''and the funky'Nai Nai'.
**CD:** Released Jun '89, on Blue Note by EMI Records. Catalogue no: **BNZ 193**
**Album:** Released Jul '89, on Blue Note by EMI Records. Catalogue no: **BST 84118**
**CD:** Released Jun '89, on Blue Note by EMI Records. Catalogue no: **CDP 784 118 2**

**FUEGO**
Tracks: / Fuego / Bup a loup / Funky mama / Lament / Amen.
Note: P 1987 Manhattan Records,a division of Capitol records Inc.
**CD:** Released May '87, on EMI-Manhattan by EMI Records. Catalogue no: **BNZ 13**
**CD:** Released May '87, on EMI-Manhattan by EMI Records. Catalogue no: **CDP 746 534 2**

**GETTING DOWN TO BUSINESS (Byrd, Donald Sextet)**
Tracks: / Theme for Malcolm / That's all there is to love / Pomponio / I got it bad and that ain't good (Available on CD only) / Certain attitude, A / Lonliest, The / Around the corner.
**CD:** Released Mar '90, on Landmark (USA) by Fantasy Inc (USA). Catalogue no: **LCD 15232**
**Album:** Released Mar '90, on Landmark (USA) by Fantasy Inc (USA). Catalogue no: **LLP 1523**

**HARLEM BLUES**
Tracks: / Harlem blues / Fly, little Byrd / Voyage a deux / Blue Monk / Alter ego / Sir Master Kool Guy.
Note: "Brand-new album from jazz trumpet star Donald Byrd. A prolific recording artist, he has made over 60 albums for Blue Note, Savoy and Prestige, sharing sessions with Thelonious Monk, John Coltrane, Sonny Rollins and Phil Woods, to name but a few. Probably best know today for his 70's recordings with the Blackbyrds, one of the best jazz/funk fusion groups of the period. Harlem Blues is a quintet album with Donald Byrd leading an all-star group. With Kenny Garrett, Mulgrew Miller, Rufus Reid, Marvin 'Smitty' Smith." (IMS Records, May 1988.)
**Album:** Released May '88, on Landmark (USA) by Fantasy Inc (USA). Catalogue no: **LLP 1516**
**CD:** Released Jul '88, on Landmark (USA) by Fantasy Inc (USA). Catalogue no: **LCD 15162**

**HOUSE OF BYRD**
Tracks: / Round midnight / Dig / Third, The / Contour / When your lover has gone / Dewey Square / Dupeltook / Once more / House of Chan / In walked George / Lover man (oh where can you be).
**Album:** Released '79, on Prestige Deleted '84. Catalogue no: **PR 24066**

**I'LL ALWAYS LOVE YOU**
Tracks: / I'll always love you / Falling.
**7" Single:** Released Jan '82, on Elektra by Elektra Records (UK). Catalogue no: **K 12580**

**I'M TRYIN' TO GET HOME**
Tracks: / Brother Isaac / Noah / I'm tryin' to get home / I've longed and searched for my mother / March children / Pearly gates.
**CD:** Released Aug '89, on Blue Note by EMI Records. Catalogue no: **BNZ 227**
**CD:** Released Aug '89, on Blue Note by EMI Records. Catalogue no: **CDP 784 188 2**
**Album:** Released Jul '89, on Blue Note by EMI Records. Catalogue no: **BST 84188**

**LOVE BYRD**
Tracks: / Love has come around / Butterfly / I feel like loving you today / I love your love / I'll always love you / Love for sale / Falling.
**Album:** Released '88, on Elektra by Elektra Records (UK). Catalogue no: **K 52301**
**Cass:** Released '88, on Elektra by Elektra Records (UK). Catalogue no: **K4 52301**

**LOVE FOR SALE**
Tracks: / Love for sale / I love your love.
**7" Single:** Released Apr '82, on Elektra by Elektra Records (UK). Catalogue no: **K 13172**

**LOVE HAS COME AROUND**
Tracks: / Love has come around / Loving you.
**7" Single:** Released Sep '81, on Elektra by Elektra Records (UK). Deleted '84. Catalogue no: **K 12559**
**12" Single:** Released Sep '81, on Elektra by Elektra Records (UK). Deleted '84. Catalogue no: **K 12559T**

**NEW FORMULAS FROM THE JAZZ LAB (Byrd, Donald & Gigi Gryce)**
**Album:** Released Jan '83, on RCA (France) by BMG Records (France). Catalogue no: **PL 43698**

**NEW PERSPECTIVE , A**
Tracks: / Elijah / Beast of burden / Cristo redentor / Black discipline, The / Chant.
**Album:** Released Apr '85, on Blue Note by EMI Records. Deleted Jun '88. Catalogue no: **BST 84124**

**SEPTEMBER AFTERNOON (Byrd, Donald & Clare Fischer & Strings)**
Tracks: / Stardust / Indian summer / I'm a fool to want you / Some day my prince will come / Moon mist / I get along without you very well / Touch of your lips, The / Lazy afternoon / Varmeland / Love is the sweetest thing / September afternoon / Dearly beloved.
**Album:** Released Jun '83, on Discovery (USA) by Discovery Records (USA). Catalogue no: **DS 869**

**STAR TRIPPIN**
Tracks: / Star trippin'.
**12" Single:** Released Nov '82, on Elektra by Elektra Records (UK). Catalogue no: **9679620 T**

**THANK YOU...FOR F.U.M.L.**
Tracks: / Thank you...for F.M.U.L. / Sunning in your loveshine / Your life is ecstasy / Loving you / Have you heard the news / In love with love / Cristo Redentor / Close your eyes and look within.
**Album:** Released Jan '79, on Elektra by Elektra Records (UK). Deleted Jan '84. Catalogue no: **K 52097**

**WORDS, SOUNDS, COLOURS & SHAPES**
Tracks: / Sexy dancer / Midnight / So much in love / High energy / Star trippin' / I'm coming home / Forbidden love / Everyday.
**Album:** Released Nov '82, on Elektra by Elektra Records (UK). Deleted '86. Catalogue no: **K 52427**

# C

The following information was taken from the Music Master database on 14th April, 1990.

## Caceres, Emilio

**ERNIE AND EMILIO CACERES (Caceres, Emilio & Ernie)**
**Album:** Released Aug '88, on Audiophile (USA) by Jazzology Records (USA). Catalogue no: **AP 101**

## Cain, Jackie

**WE'VE GOT IT - THE MUSIC OF CY COLEMAN (Cain, Jackie & Roy Kral)**
Tracks: / We've got it / Best is yet to come, The / When in Rome / Why try to change me now / I've got your number / You're a loveable lunatic / My city / Our private world / Doop do de oop / I love my wife / Witchcraft / It's a nice face / Riviera, The.
**Cass:** Released '88, on Discovery (USA) by Discovery Records (USA). Catalogue no: **DSC 907**
**Album:** Released Nov '84, on Discovery (USA) by Discovery Records (USA). Catalogue no: **DS 907**

## Cairns, Forrie

**GOLDEN CLARINET, THE**
Tracks: / Wooden heart / May of Argyle / Petite fleur / Aloha / Paper roses / Precious Lord / Mona Lisa / Amazing Grace / Beautiful dreamer / Clarinette lullaby / Rowan tree / Poor butterfly / Brahms' lullaby / Lonesome / Enjoy yourself / Auf wiedersehen.
**Album:** Released Sep '84, on Country House by BGS Productions Ltd. Catalogue no: **BGC 353**

## California Ramblers

**1920'S FLAPPER PARTY**
Tracks: / Ev'rything is hotsy totsy now / Sweet Georgia Brown / I'm gonna charleston back to Charleston / Show me the way to go home / No foolin' / Girlfriend / Ya gotta know how to love / Stockholm stomp / We love the college girls / Yes she do - no she don't / Vo-do-do-de-o blues / Nothin' does-does like it used to do-do-do / Make my cot where the cot-cot-cotton grows / Mine - all mine / Singapore sorrows / Pay-off, The.
**Cass:** Released May '87, on Halcyon (USA) by Submarine Records. Catalogue no: **CHAL 8**

**CALIFORNIA RAMBLERS (California Ramblers, Rollini, Red Nichols, T.& J.Dorsey)**
**Album:** Released Dec '86, on Jazz Supreme Catalogue no: **JS 101**

## Calloway, Cab

**Biographical details:** The singer and bandleader (born in 1907) was the scat singing, zoot-suited Highness of He-de-ho, leading the most commercially successful of black bands in the 1930's-40's; he was an underrated ballad singer as well. He fronted the Missourians, took it over and followed Duke Ellington into the Cotton Club and became famous through broadcasts in 1931-32. Of many film appearances, the best known is the all-black musical *Stormy weather* in 1943. More than 40 hits 1930-45 included *Minnie the moocher, Kicking the gong around* and *Blues in the night*. The band included at various times tenor saxists Ben Webster and Chu Berry, trumpeter Shad Collins, bassist Milt Hinton and Dizzy Gillespie in 1939-41 (sacked in famous spitball incident). George Gershwin allegedly wrote the part of Sportin' life in *Porgy & Bess)* with Calloway in mind; he later played it in several revivals. He also appeared opposite Pearl Bailey in the hit all-black version of *Hello Dolly* in 1967, in the film *The Blues Brothers* in 1980, in the show *Bubbling brown sugar* and in the UK TV film *The Cotton Club comes to the Ritz* at the London hotel, broadcast in 1985. (Donald Clarke, April 1989).

**1938-1947 (Calloway, Cab & His Orchestra)**
**Cass:** Released '88, on Joker (USA) by Lifetime Records (USA). Catalogue no: **MC 4047**
**Album:** Released '88, on Joker (USA) by Lifetime Records (USA). Catalogue no: **SM 4047**

**BOOG-IT**
**Album:** Released 21 Jul '89, on Jazz & Jazz Catalogue no: **JJ 607**

**CAB CALLOWAY**
**Album:** Released Jul '88, on Glendale (USA) by Glendale Records (USA). Catalogue no: **GLS 9007**

**CAB CALLOWAY 1937-8**
**Album:** Released '88, on Jazz Document Catalogue no: **VA 7998**

**CAB CALLOWAY COLLECTION**
**CD:** Released Oct '89, on Collection by K-Tel Records. Catalogue no: **OR 0079**
**Cass:** Released May '86, on Deja Vu Catalogue no: **DVMC 2056**
**Album:** Released May '86, on Deja Vu Catalogue no: **DVLP 2056**

**CAB CALLOWAY STORY, THE**
Tracks: / Nagasaki / Hoy hoy / Jumpin' jive / Give baby give / I want to rock / Minnie the moocher / Honeydripper / Hi de ho / Jungle king / Calloway boogie / Two blocks down town to the left / Chicken ain't nothin' but a bird, A / I can't give you anything but love / Stormy weather / You got it / Everybody eats when they come to my house / Afternoon moon / This is always / Duck trot / That old black magic / How big can you get / Hey now hey now / Birth of the blues / We the cats shall help you / Foo a little bally hoo.
**Cass:** Released May '89, on Deja Vu Catalogue no: **DVREMC 22**
**CD:** Released May '89, on Deja Vu Catalogue no: **DVRECD 22**

**CAB & CO.**
Tracks: / Evenin' / Harlem hospitality / Lady with the fan, The / Harlem camp meeting / Zaz zuh zaz / Father's got his glasses on / Minnie the moocher (takes 1 & 2) / Scat song, The (takes 1 & 20 / Kickin' the gong around / There's a cabin in the cotton / I learned about love from her (takes 3 & 4) / Little town gal / Long about midnight / Moon glow / Jitterbug (takes 1 & 2) / Hotcha razz-ma-tazz / Margie / Emaline / Ol' Joe Louis / Your voice / Rooming house boogie / I beeped when I shoulda bopped / I need lovin' / Just a crazy song / It looks like Susie / Growlin' Dan / Concentratin' on you / Last dollar / Oh you sweet thing.
**2 LP Set:** Released Oct '85, on RCA by BMG Records (UK). Catalogue no: **NL 89560**
**Cass set:** Released Oct '85, on RCA by BMG Records (UK). Deleted May '89. Catalogue no: **NK 89560**

**CAB, ELLA & CHICK 1936 - 40 (Calloway, Cab/ Ella Fitzgerald/ Chick Webb)**
**Album:** Released Jun '88, on Bandstand Catalogue no: **BS 7125**

**CLUB ZANZIBAR BROADCASTS**
Tracks: / For a little rally / Russian lullaby / I was here when you left me / St. Louis blues / Frantic in the Atlantic / 9/20 special / Great lie, The / I can't give you anything but love / Rose Marie / I'm not ashamed of my tears / One o'clock jump.
**Album:** Released Apr '81, on Unique Jazz by Spotlite Records. Catalogue no: **UJ 06**

**CLUB ZANZIBAR BROADCASTS 1945**
**Album:** Released Mar '90, on Jazz & Jazz Catalogue no: **JJ006**

**COTTON CLUB REVUE 1958**
Tracks: / Born to be happy / Tzotskele / Sinful / Beginnin' of sinnin' / Sweeter than sweet / Never had it so good / Minnie the moocher / Copper colored gal / Got the world on a string / She's tall, she's tan, she's terrific / Don't worry 'bout me / St James Infirmary.
**Album:** Released '88, on Official by Official Records. Catalogue no: **OFF 3000**
**Album:** Released Aug '85, Catalogue no: **AFA 5031**

**FRANTIC IN THE ATLANTIC**
Tracks: / I got a girl named Netty / this is always.
**Album:** Released Oct '87, on Dance Band Days by Prism Leisure. Catalogue no: **DBD 10**
**Cass:** Released Oct '87, on Dance Band Days by Prism Leisure. Catalogue no: **DBDC 10**
**CD:** Released Dec '88, on Dance Band Days by Prism Leisure. Catalogue no: **DBCD 10**

**GET WITH IT**
**Album:** Released '84, on Swing House by Submarine Records. Catalogue no: **SWH 38**
**Cass:** Released '84, on Swing House by Submarine Records. Catalogue no: **CSWH 38**

**HI-DE-HO MAN, THE**
Tracks: / Jumping jive, The / Minnie the moocher / It ain't necessarily so / St. James infirmary / I see a million people / Hi de ho man, The / Summertime / Kickin' the gong around / Stormy weather / You rascal you.
**Album:** Released '83, on RCA (France) by BMG Records (France). Catalogue no: **PL 45163**

**JAZZ OF THE AIR (VOL 4)**
Tracks: / We the cats shall help you / Dawn time / Minnie the moocher / Rhythm cocktail / Very thought of you, The / Foo a little bally hoo / Is you is or is you ain't my baby / Frantic in the Atlantic / Blue skies / Cruisin' with Cab / Body and soul / Minnie the moocher / Kabla / Lammar's boogie / Coastin' with JC.
Note: Another band that not all could make. Featuring Ike Quebec, Jonah Jones, Ilinois Jacquet and Benny Carter.
**Album:** Released '83, on Spotlite by Spotlite Records. Catalogue no: **SPJ 148**

**JUMPIN' STUFF**
**Album:** on Golden Era by Delta Records. Catalogue no: **GELP 15013**

**JUMPING JIVE**
**Cass:** Released Aug '84, on CBS by CBS Records. Catalogue no: **40 21115**
**Album:** Released Aug '84, on CBS by CBS Records. Catalogue no: **CBS 21115**
**Album:** Released '84, on Swing House by Submarine Records. Catalogue no: **SWH 15**
**Cass:** Released '84, on Swing House by Submarine Records. Catalogue no: **CSWH 15**

**JUMPING & JIVING 1930-37**
**Album:** Released Jan '86, on Swingtime by Contact Records (Denmark). Deleted Jun '89. Catalogue no: **ST 1001**

**KICKING THE GONG AROUND**
Tracks: / Minnie the moocher / Without rhythm / Aw, you dog! / Bugle call rag / Downhearted blues / Nightmare, The / Black rhythm / Yaller / Between the Devil and the deep blue sea / Nobody's sweetheart / Trickeration / St. Louis blues / Mood indigo / Farewell blues / You rascal you / My honey's lovin' arms / Some of these days / Six or seven times / Somebody stole my gal / Kicking the gong around.
**Cass:** Released 1 May '82, on Living Era by Academy Sound & Vision Records. Catalogue no: **ZC AJA 5013**
**Album:** Released 1 May '82, on Living Era by Academy Sound & Vision Records. Catalogue no: **AJA 5013**

**LEGENDARY CAB CALLOWAY 1933/34, THE**
Tracks: / Harlem camp meeting / Father got his glasses on / Kicking the gong around / Scat song, The / Moonglow / Jitterbug / Harlem hospitality / Margie / Long about midnight / Minnie the moocher.
**Cass:** Released Sep '89, on Nostalgia by Mainline Records. Catalogue no: **MRT 40054**

**MAN FROM HARLEM, THE 1930-32**
**Album:** Released '88, on Sweet Folk & Country Catalogue no: **ET 5**
**Album:** on Swing Classics Catalogue no: **ET 4**

**MINNIE THE MOOCHER (Calloway, Cab & His Orchestra)**
Tracks: / Harlem hospitality / Lady with a fan / Harlem camp meeting / Zah zu sah / Father's got his glasses on / Little town gal / There's a cabin in the cotton / Scat song / Minnie the moocher / Kickin' the gong around / Long about midnight / Moonglow / Margie / Jitterbug / Hotcha razz-ma-tazz.
**Album:** Released Jul '82, on RCA International by BMG Records (UK). Deleted Jul '87. Catalogue no: **INTS 5121**
**Album:** Released Jun '86, on Big Band Era Catalogue no: **20185**
**Album:** Released Jun '88, on Bandstand Catalogue no: **BS 7124**
**Album:** Released '84, on RCA by BMG Records (UK). Catalogue no: **NL 89338**
**Album:** Released Sep '86, on President by President Records. Catalogue no: **PLE 524**
**Cass:** Released '84, on RCA by BMG Records (UK). Catalogue no: **NK 89338**
**Cass:** Released Jun '88, on Bandstand Catalogue no: **BS 7124C**
**Cass:** Released Jun '86, on Big Band Era Catalogue no: **40185**

**MISSOURIANS**
Tracks: / Market street stomp / Ozark mountain blues / You'll cry for me but I'll be gone / Missouri moan / I've got someone / 400 hop / Vine street drag / Scotty blues / Two hundred squabble / Swingin' dem cats / Stoppin' the traffic / Prohibition blues / Gotta darn good reason now / St. Louis blues / Sweet Jenny Lee / Happy feet / Yaller / Viper's drag / Is that religion? / Some of these days.
Note: Recorded: 1929 - 1930 in mono.
**Album:** Released Jul '86, on VJM (Vintage Jazz Music) by Vintage Jazz Music Society(VJM). Catalogue no: **VLP 58**

**MOST IMPORTANT RECORDINGS OF CAB CALLOWAY, THE**
Tracks: / Some of these days / Saint James Infirmary / Minnie the moocher / Six or seven times / Sweet Georgia Brown / Bugle call rag / Somebody stole my gal / Corinne, Corrina / Scat song, The / Minnie the moocher's wedding day / How come you do me like you do / Reefer man / Man from Harlem, The / Doin' the new low down / Lady with the fan, The / Zaz, zuh, zaz / Margie / Keep that hi-de-hi in your soul / Nagasaki / Wedding of Mr and Mrs Swing / Swing, swing, swing / Savage rhythm / At the clam-bake carnival / Jive / Ratamacue / Jumpin' jive / Ghost of a chance, A / Calling all bars / Jonah joins the cab / Hey, Doc / Hi de ho man / I beeped when I should'a bopped.
**LP Set:** on Official by Official Records. Catalogue no: **OFF 3041-2**

**ON FILM**
Tracks: / Minnie the moocher / Rail rhythm / Zaz zuh zaz / Lady with the fan, The / Got a right to sing the blues / Hi de ho man, The / Frisco Flo / Some of these days / Skunk song / Virginia, Georgia and Caroline / Blues in the night / Jumpin' jive / Sunday in Savannah / Geechie Joe / Calloway boogie.
**Album:** Released Jan '84, on Harlequin by Interstate Music. Catalogue no: **HQ 2005**

**SINGIN' AND SWINGIN'**
**Cass:** Released Jun '88, on Giants of Jazz by Hasmick Promotions. Catalogue no: **GOJC 1012**
**Album:** Released Apr '79, on Giants of Jazz by Hasmick Promotions. Catalogue no: **GOJ 1012**

## Cambridge City

**CAMBRIDGE BLUES**
Note: "Jassband" is correct spelling.
**Album:** Released Nov '81, on Plant Life Jazz by Plant Life Records. Catalogue no: **PLJ 004**

## Campbell, Gene

**TEXAS BLUES PIONEER**
**Album:** Released '88, on Wolf Catalogue no: **WSE 112**

## Canal Street Jazz Band

**NEW ORLEANS STOMP**
**Album:** Released Sep '86, on Stomp Off (USA) Catalogue no: **SOS 1005**

## Candoli, Conte

**Biographical details:** Brothers secondo 'Conte' Candoli (born 1927) and

Walter Joseph 'Pete' Candoli (both 1923) are trumpeters; both played with big bands, Conte playing with Woody Herman while he was still in high school: he is the more aggressive soloist, Pete a talented arranger. They worked together on the film *Bell, book and candle* in 1958 and had a hit album *Bell, book and candoli.* Conte recorded with Thelonious Monk, *Pete with Stravinsky*; between them they've played on hundreds of albums. Conte's *Fine and Dandy* combines tracks from two mid-'50's albums with rhythm section, Bill Holman on tenor sax on some tracks. (Donald Clarke, April 1989)e.

**FINE AND DANDY**
Tracks: / Fine and dandy / I'm getting sentimental over you / Night flight / I can't get started / On the Alamo / Groovin' higher / Tune for Tex / My funny Valentine / They can't take that away from me / Everything happens to me / Toot suite / I'll remember April.
Note: A Bethlehem recording. Licenced from International Jazz Emporium Inc.
**Album:** Released Jan '87, on Affinity by Charly Records. Catalogue no: **AFF 173**

**GROOVIN' HIGHER (Candoli, Conte Quintet)**
Tracks: / Toot suite / Jazz city blues / My old flame / Full count / I'm getting sentimental over you / Four / Groovin higher.
**Album:** Released May '82, on Affinity by Charly Records. Deleted '88. Catalogue no: **AFF 92**

**WEST COASTING (Candoli, Conte & Stan Levy)**
**Album:** Released Feb '88, on Fresh Sounds (Spain) by Fresh Sounds Records (Spain). Catalogue no: **FS 152**

## Cannon, Gus

**GUS CANNON 1963**
**Album:** Released '88, on Collectable Issues Catalogue no: **C 5523**

## Cannon's Jug Stompers

**CANNON'S JUG STOMPERS**
**Album:** Released Oct '88, on Roots (Germany) Catalogue no: **RL 336**

## Capitol Jazzmen

**JAZZMEN 1943-47**
**Album:** Released '88, on Swaggie (Australia) Catalogue no: **S 1406**

## Capp-Pierce Juggernaut

**Biographical details:** A big band in the swing era mould, led by drummer Frankie Capp, a veteran L.A. studio/session player, and Nat Pierce, an excellent arranger and pianist who worked for Woody Herman and Count Basie, and could sound as much like Basie as Basie. This band was called 'a juggernaut in Basin Street' in 1976 and the name stuck. Though everybody says big bands are dead, uneconomic and so forth, Concord Jazz sells the records anyway. The albums have vocals by Ernie Andrews, while *Live at Century Plaza* has vocals by Joe Williams and *Live at the Alley* in 1987 featured Ernestine Anderson. (Donald Clarke, April 1989).

**CAPP-PIERCE JUGGERNAUT**
**Album:** Released '79, on Concord by Concord Jazz Records (USA). Catalogue no: **CJ 72**

**JUGGERNAUT STRIKES AGAIN**
Tracks: / One for Marshall / I remember Clifford / New York shuffle / Chops, fingers & sticks / You are so beautiful / Parker's mood / Word from Bird / Charade / Things ain't what they used to be / Little Pony.
**Album:** Released '82, on Concord by Concord Jazz Records (USA). Catalogue no: **CJ 183**

**LIVE AT THE ALLEY CAT**
**CD:** Released Dec '87, on Concord Jazz by Concord Jazz Records (USA). Catalogue no: **CCD 4336**
**Cass:** Released Nov '87, on Concord Jazz by Concord Jazz Records (USA). Catalogue no: **CJC 336**
**Album:** Released Nov '87, on Concord Jazz by Concord Jazz Records (USA). Catalogue no: **CJ 336**

## Carle, Frankie

**Biographical details:** Francis Nunzio Carlone was a pianist, bandleader and composer who led a sweet dance band in the USA. He clung to the melody line with integrity and lack of pretension. He hit big in 1944 and had about 20 big hits in five years. He wrote *sunrise serenade*, a very pretty tune which had already been a big hit by Glenn Miller; he used it as his theme, and his own number one hits were *Oh! What it seemed to be* and *Rumours are flying*, both with vocals by his daughter, Marjorie Hughes. Today's excellent jazz composer and pianist Joanne Brackeen says that she began by copying Carle's solos from records. (Donald Clarke, April 1989).

**1944-1946 (Carle, Frankie & His Orchestra)**
**Album:** Released Jun '86, on Circle (USA) by Jazzology Records (USA). Catalogue no: **CLP 43**

**GOLDEN TOUCH, THE**
**Album:** Released Apr '89, on Circle Catalogue no: **CLP 138**

## Carlisle, Una Mae

**Biographical details:** The singer, pianist and songwriter (1918-56) had American Indian and Afro American ancestry. She was a protege of Fats Waller, with whom she recorded *I can't give you anything but love* in 1939, singing straight to his wisecracks; she recorded solo on Bluebird with all-star casts, backed by Lester Young, Benny Carter and Slam Stewart on her own *Walking by the river*, a hit in 1941. See also Savannah Churchill. (Donald Clarke, April 1989) .

**UNA MAE CARLISLE Savannah Churchill 1944**
Tracks: / 'Tain't yours / Without you baby / I'm a good good woman / Ain't nothin' much / I like it 'cause I love it / You gotta take your time / He's the best little Yankee to me / I speak so much about you / Teasin' me / You and your heart of stone / You're gonna change your mind / Rest of my life / He's commander in chief of my heart / Two faced man / Tell me your blues / Fat meat is good meat.
**Album:** Released '82, on Harlequin by Interstate Music. Catalogue no: **HQ 2002**

## Carmichael, Hoagy

**Biographical details:** Howard Hoagland Carmichael (1899-1981) was a singer, pianist, bandleader and actor, but mainly perhaps the most quintessentially American songwriter. As a college boy he studied law but became friends with Bix Beiderbecke; after the cornettist died Carmichael carried his mouthpiece in his pocket for the rest of his life. *Stardust* and *Skyliner* were both perhaps from Bix solos; the former is the most recorded song of the century after *Silent night.* He sang in a rumpled down-home style, occasionally wrote his own lyrics but usually collaborated with top people. He recorded for RCA in the late 1920's-30's and for ARA, the USA Decca (now MCA) in the '40's. His *Ole buttermilk sky* was a big hit in 1946; the film song *In the cool cool cool of the evening* (with Johnny Mercer) won an Oscar in 1951. (Donald Clarke, April 1989) .

**16 CLASSIC TRACKS: HOAGY CARMICHAEL**
Tracks: / I may be wrong, but, I think you're wonderful / Talking is a woman / Shh the old man's sleepin' / Don't forget to say no baby / Casanova cricket / Man could be a wondeful thing, A / Put yourself in my place baby / Tune for humming, A / That's a plenty / Gonnna get a girl / For every man there's a woman / Ten to one it's Tennessee / Coney Island washboard / Some days there just ain't no fish / Monkey song, The / Rogue river valley.
**Album:** Released Jun '82, on MCA by MCA Records. Deleted Jan '88. Catalogue no: **MCL 1692**
**Cass:** Released Jun '82, on MCA by MCA Records. Deleted Jan '88. Catalogue no: **MCLC 1692**

**BALLADS FOR DANCING**
Tracks: / I walked with music / Sky lark / I get along without you very well / Two sleepy people / Lamplighter's serenade, The / Heart and soul / Nearness of you, The / Ivy / One morning in May / How little we know / Blue orchids / Star dust.
Note: A strong addition to MCA's terrific nostalgia releases, "Ballads for Dancing" features many of the great Hoagy Carmichael's best works.
**Album:** Released May '86, on MCA by MCA Records. Deleted Jan '88. Catalogue no: **MCL 1819**

**CARMICHAEL, HOAGY 1944-45**
Tracks: / Baltimore oriole / Hong Kong blues / Stardust / No more toujours l'amour / Billy-A-dick / Memphis in June / Sleepy time gal / Ginger and spice / Am I blue? / Everybody's seen him but his

daddy / Rogue river valley / Riverboat shuffle / Two sleepy people / Doctor, lawyer, Indian, chief / Old spinning wheel / Huggin' and chalkin'.
**Album:** Released Feb '88, on Totem Catalogue no: **TOTEM 1039**

**HOAGY**
Tracks: / Rockin' chair / Georgia on my mind / Sing it way down low / Lazybones / March of the hoodlums / Snowball / Walking the dog / Pap's gone goodbye / Bessie couldn't help it / One morning in May / Washboard blues / Moon country / Cosmics / Sittin' and whittlin' / Stardust / Lazy river / Judy / Barnacle Bill the sailor.
**Album:** Released '82, on RCA by BMG Records (UK). Deleted '84. Catalogue no: **INTS 5181**
**Cass:** Released '82, on RCA by BMG Records (UK). Deleted '84. Catalogue no: **INTK 5181**
**Album:** Released '84, on RCA by BMG Records (UK). Deleted Jul '89. Catalogue no: **NL 89096**
**Cass:** Released '84, on RCA by BMG Records (UK). Deleted Jul '89. Catalogue no: **NK 89096**

**HOAGY CARMICHAEL 1951**
Note: Piano solos with whistling and singing. Not all the old warhorses. Recorded privately in 1951.
**Album:** Released Jul '82, on Harlequin by Interstate Music. Catalogue no: **HQ 2000**

**HOAGY CARMICHAEL COLLECTION**
**CD:** Released Oct '89, on Collection by K-Tel Records. Catalogue no: **OR 0081**

**HOAGY CARMICHAEL SINGS HOAGY**
Tracks: / Old music master, The / Hong Kong blues / Memphis in June / Ode buttermilk sky / My resistance is low / Rockin' chair / Riverboat shuffle / Georgia on my mind / Lazy river / Judy / Stardust / In the cool cool cool of the evening (From the film "Here comes the groom".) / Moon country / Baltimore oriole / Little old lady / Washboard blues.
**Cass:** Released Aug '81, on MCA by MCA Records. Catalogue no: **MCLC 1620**
**Album:** Released Aug '81, on MCA by MCA Records. Catalogue no: **MCL 1620**

**HOAGY CARMICHAEL SONGBOOK**
Tracks: / Stardust / Washboard blues / Rockin' chair / Little old lady / Lamplighters serenade / Lazybones / Georgia on my mind / Skylark / Old music master / Nearness of you, The / Old buttermilk sky / I should have known you years ago / One morning in May / Blue orchids / I get along without you very well / In the cool cool cool of the evening / Doctor lawyer indian chief / Judy / My resistance is low / When love goes wrong / Memphis in June / Ivy / How little we know / Stardust.
**CD:** Released Oct '88, on Connoisseur Collection by Connoisseur Collection Ltd.. Catalogue no: **VSOPCD 123**
**2 LP Set:** Released Oct '88, on Connoisseur Collection by Connoisseur Collection Ltd.. Catalogue no: **VSOPLP 123**
**Cass:** Released Oct '88, on Connoisseur Collection by Connoisseur Collection Ltd.. Catalogue no: **VSOPMC 123**

**HOAGY SINGS CARMICHAEL**
Tracks: / Georgia on my mind / Winter moon / New Orleans / Memphis in June / Skylark / Two sleepy people / Baltimore oriole / Rockin' chair / Ballad in blue / Lazy river / Georgia on my mind (instrumental).
Note: Art Pepper - alto sax.
**CD:** Released Jan '89, on Pacific Jazz by EMI Records. Catalogue no: **CDP 746 862 2**
**Album:** Released Oct '84, on Retrospect by EMI Records. Deleted Nov '88. Catalogue no: **EG 2602951**
**CD:** Released Jan '89, on Pacific Jazz by EMI Records. Catalogue no: **CZ 66**
**Cass:** Released Oct '84, on Retrospect by EMI Records. Catalogue no: **EG 2602954**

**INDIANA SUMMER (1923-28) (See also under Curtis Hitch)**
**Cass:** Released Sep '87, on Fountain by Retrieval Records. Catalogue no: **CFJ 109**

**STARDUST**
Tracks: / In the cool cool cool of the evening / Heart and soul / Honky Kong blues / Old music master / Who killed 'er / Stardust / Ole buttermilk sky / Doctor, lawyer, indian chief.
**CD:** Released Nov '89, on Bluebird (2) by BMG Records (UK). Catalogue no: **ND 88333**
**Album:** Released May '82, on MFP by EMI Records. Deleted May '87. Catalogue no: **MFP 50558**
**Cass:** Released Nov '89, on Bluebird (2) by BMG Records (UK). Catalogue no: **NK 88333**
**Album:** Released Nov '89, on Bluebird (2) by BMG Records (UK). Catalogue no: **NL 88333**

## Carmichael, Judy

**JAZZ PIANO**
**Album:** Released Nov '87, on Statiras (USA) by Statiras(USA) Records. Catalogue no: **SLP 8074**

**PEARLS**
Note: With Warren Vache Jr./Red Callender/H. Alden.
**Album:** Released May '86, on Statiras (USA) by Statiras(USA) Records. Catalogue no: **SLP 8078**

**TWO HANDED STRIDE**
Tracks: / Christopher Columbus / Viper's drag / Ja da / Honeysuckle Rose / Ain't misbehavin' / Handful of keys / I ain't got nobody / (I would do) anything for you.
Note: Recorded 4/4/1980 & 29/4/1980. Judy Carmichael/Marshall Royal/Freddie Greene/Red Callender/Harold Jones.
**Album:** Released Nov '82, on Progressive (USA) by Jazzology Records (USA). Catalogue no: **PRO 7065**
**Album:** Released Nov '87, on Statiras (USA) by Statiras(USA) Records. Catalogue no: **SLP 8072**

## Carolina Blues

**CAROLINA BLUES GUITAR (1936-1951) (Various artists)**
**Album:** Released Dec '88, on HK Catalogue no: **HK 4006**
**Album:** Released Dec '88, on Old Tramp Catalogue no: **OT 1211**

## Carolina Slim

**CAROLINA BLUES AND BOOGIE (1950-1952)**
Tracks: / Money blues / Mama's boogie / Black chariot / Worrying blues / One more drink / Carolina boogie / I'll get by somehow / Rag mama / Sugarfree / Blues go away from me / Blues knockin' at my door / Worry you off my mind / Wine head baby / Slo freight blues.
**Album:** Released Mar '85, on Travelin' Man by Interstate Music. Catalogue no: **TM 805**

## Carr, Ian

**Biographical details:** Born in 1933 in Dumfries, the trumpeter, flugelhornist, composer and teacher worked with Don Rendell, Joe Harriot, John McLaughlin, Don Byas and others; he formed the influential fusion group Nucleus in 1969 and also played on five albums with the United Jazz & Rock Ensemble. He is also a first-class writer, including a critical biography of Miles Davis. (Donald Clarke, April 1989).

**DIRECT HIT (Carr, Ian Nucleus)**
**Album:** Released Mar '76, on Vertigo by Phonogram Ltd. Catalogue no: **9286 019**

**IN FLAGRANTE DELICTO (Carr, Ian Nucleus)**
Tracks: / Gestalt / Mysteries / Heyday / In flagrante delicto.
**Album:** Released Jul '78, on Capitol by EMI Records. Catalogue no: **EST 11771**

**OLD HEARTLAND**
Tracks: / Open country / Interiors / Disjunctive boogie / Spirit of place / Full fathom five / Old heartland / Things past.
**CD:** Released Oct '88, on MMC by MMC Records. Catalogue no: **CDP 791 071 2**
**Cass:** Released Oct '88, on MMC by MMC Records. Catalogue no: **TCMMC 1016**
**Album:** Released Oct '88, on MMC by MMC Records. Catalogue no: **MMC 1016**
**CD:** Released Nov '88, on MMC by MMC Records. Catalogue no: **CDMMC 1016**

**OUT OF THE LONG DARK (Carr, Ian Nucleus)**
Tracks: / Gone with the weed / Lady bountiful / Solar wind / Selina / Out of the long dark / Sassy (American girl) / Simply this (The human condition) / Black ballad / For Liam.
**Album:** Released Feb '79, on Capitol

Ian Carr

by EMI Records. Catalogue no: **EST 11916**

## Carr, Joe 'Fingers'

**BEST PIANO OF JOE CARR, THE**
**Cass:** Released Dec '88, on Capitol (Specials) Catalogue no: **4XL 9293**

**PORTUGUESE WASHERWOMAN**
Tracks: / Portuguese washerwoman.
**7" Single:** Released Jun '56, on Capitol by EMI Records. Deleted Jun '59. Catalogue no: **CL 14587**

## Carr, Larry

**FIT AS A FIDDLE**
**Album:** Released Jul '87, on Audiophile (USA) by Jazzology Records (USA). Catalogue no: **AP 223**

**LARRY CARR SINGS VERSE AND CHORUS**
**Album:** Released Aug '88, on Audiophile (USA) by Jazzology Records (USA). Catalogue no: **AP 13**

## Carr, Leroy

**Biographical details:** This pianist and blues singer (1905-35) started from Indianpolis, Indiana to become popular in black communities all over the USA; he wrote and sang a smoother style that was to be enormously influential in rhythm & blues: his songs include the classics *How long blues* and *In the evening when the sun goes down*, the latter recorded by Count Basie and Joe Williams in 1955. Carr was teamed with guitarist and singer Scrapper Blackwell on his classic records; he died of alcoholism. (Donald Clarke, April 1989).

**BLUES BEFORE SUNRISE**
Tracks: / Barrelhouse woman / I believe I'll make a change / Midnight hour blues / Talk a walk around the corner / Southbound blues / Mean mistreater mama / Big four blues / It's too short / My woman's gone wrong / Hustler's blues / Bobo stomp / Shady lane blues / Corn Likker blues / Hurry down sunshine.
**Album:** Released '88, on Official by Official Records. Catalogue no: **OFF 6023**

**GREAT PIANO, GUITAR DUETS, 1929-35 (Carr, Leroy & Scrapper Blackwell)**
**Album:** Released Aug '87, on Old Tramp Catalogue no: **OT 1204**

**LEROY CARR (1928)**
Tracks: / My own lonesome blues / How long how long blues / Broken spoke blues / Tennessee blues / Truthful blues / Mean old train blues / You got to reap what you sow / Low down dirty blues / How long how long blues no.2 and part 3 / Tired of your low down ways / I'm going away and leave my baby / Prison bound blues / You don't mean me no good.
**Album:** Released May '83, on Matchbox (Bluesmaster) by Saydisc Records. Catalogue no: **MSE 210**

**LEROY CARR: 1929-34 (Carr, Leroy & Scrapper Blackwell)**
**Album:** Released Feb '89, on Document Catalogue no: **DLP 543**

**LEROY CARR & SCRAPPER BLACKWELL, 1929-35 (Carr, Leroy & Scrapper Blackwell)**
**Album:** Released '89, on Best Of Blues (USA) by Blue Island Records (USA). Catalogue no: **BOB 13**

**LEROY CARR, VOL. 2**
**Album:** Released '88, on Collector's Classics Catalogue no: **CC 50**

**NAPTOWN BLUES (Carr, Leroy & Scrapper Blackwell)**
**Album:** Released Dec '88, on Yazoo (USA) by Shanachie Records (USA). Catalogue no: **L 1036**

## Carr, Mike

**Biographical details:** Born in 1937 in Durham, the pianist and composer formed the Emcee Five with his brother Ian Carr: popular in Newcastle and recently re-issued, the early '60's tracks show that superb modern jazz was happening in England outside London. He took up organ with bass pedals in 1966 and was highly praised by Oscar Peterson as an exciting, swinging player; his trio recorded at Ronnie Scott's (with Jim Mullen on guitar, Hal Smith on drums) sounds bigger than it is. He formed the jazz-funk recording group Cargo in 1980; see listings from Emcee Five and Cargo. (Donald Clark, April 1989) .

**LIVE AT RONNIE SCOTT'S (Carr, Mike Trio)**
Tracks: / Claremont Avenue / Teach me tonight / Shaw 'nuff / It's impossible / Footloose.
**Album:** Released '83, on Spotlite by Spotlite Records. Catalogue no: **SPJ 517**

## Carr, Richard

**AFTERNOON IN NEW YORK**
**Album:** Released Aug '88, on Audiophile (USA) by Jazzology Records (USA). Catalogue no: **AP 194**

## Carroll, Barbara

**AT THE PIANO**
Tracks: / Emily / Soon it's gonna rain / Child is born, A / Dream dancing / Gal in calico, A.
**Album:** Released '88, on Discovery (USA) by Discovery Records (USA). Catalogue no: **DS 847**

**JULY 24TH, 1959 (Carroll, Barbara Trio)**
**Album:** Released Oct '80, on From The Jazz Vault by Damont Audio Ltd.. Catalogue no: **JV 114**

## Carson, Ernie

**ERNIE CARSON & HIS CAPITOL CITY JAZZ BAND (Carson, Ernie & His Capitol City Jazz Band)**
**Album:** Released Jun '86, on Jazzology (USA) by Jazzology Records (USA). Catalogue no: **J 54**

**ERNIE CARSON & RHYTHM**
**Album:** Released Jun '88, on Jazzology (USA) by Jazzology Records (USA). Catalogue no: **J 89**

**JAZZ GOES COUNTRY (with Marilyn Stafford) (Carson, Ernie and the Wrecking Crew)**

**Album:** Released Aug '88, on Circle (USA) by Jazzology Records (USA). Catalogue no: **CLP 66**

**SOUTHERN COMFORT (Carson, Ernie & His Capitol City Jazz Band)**
**Album:** Released '88, on GHB by Jazzology Records (USA). Catalogue no: **GHB 162**

## Carson, Tee

**BASICALLY COUNT (Carson, Tee & The Basie Bandsmen)**
**Album:** Released Jan '84, on Palo Alto Catalogue no: **PA 8005**

## Carter, Benny

**Biographical details:** Born in New York City in 1907, this composer, arranger and bandleader is one of the giants of jazz. As an alto saxist there was no greater influence in the '30 and '40's except Johnny Hodges; as an arranger Carter has always been in a class by himself. He worked for Fletcher Henderson and Chick Webb, and was leader of McKinney's Cotton Pickers after Don Redman left; he also organised the all-star band for the famous New York Spike Hughes record dates in 1933, the same year he formed his own first band. He was in Europe from 1935-38, working for Henry Hall at the BBC and recording with Django Reinhardt in 1937; that summer he led an interracial band at a Dutch seaside resort. He subsequently said that the reason there were so many good Scottish musicians is because 'Where ever they are, there's happiness'. Back in the USA leading his own band again in 1938, he also contributed to Lionel Hampton's small-group sessions on Victor, including a classic version of his own *When lights are low* in 1939. He also occasionally played clarinet, and played trumpet and trombone on Capitol records by Julia Lee, having settled on the West Coast in the early '40's as a freelance studio writer-arranger. Later he recorded for Norman Granz, with Hodges, Charlie Parker, Art Tatum and others. Among the many albums he's written over the years are *Kansas City suite* and *The legend* for Count Basie circa 1960-61, and his own *Further definitions* in 1961 on *Impulse*, duplicating the instrumentation and some of the tunes of the 1937 Paris session: with four reeds including Coleman Hawkins Hawk and a rhythm section, Carter's writing is so richly beautiful that the group sounds bigger. He's still at it: his American Jazz Orchestra recorded *Central City Sketches* in 1987. (Donald Clarke, April 1989).

**ADDITIONS TO FURTHER DEFINITIONS**
Tracks: / Fantastic that's you / Come on back / We were in love / If dreams come true / Prohibido / Doozy / Rock bottom / Titmouse.
**Album:** Released Sep '82, on Jasmine by Hasmick Promotions. Catalogue no: **JAS 57**
**Cass:** Released Sep '82, on Jasmine by Hasmick Promotions. Catalogue no: **JAS C57**

**ALONE TOGETHER (Carter, Benny & Oscar Peterson)**
Tracks: / Isn't it romantic? / Long ago and far away / Alone together / Bewitched.
**Album:** Released Dec '81, on Verve Catalogue no: **2304 512**

**BENNY CARTER 1945: METRONOME ALL STARS**
Tracks: / Who's sorry now? / Co-ed / Prelude to a kiss / Back bay boogie / I got it bad and that ain't good / Patience and fortitude / I surrender, dear / Stompin' at The Savoy / King Porter stomp / Royal flush / Dear old Southland / I got rhythm / Sweet Lorraine / Nat meets June, takes 1 & 2.
Note: The great sax star featured with the Benny Carter Orchestra, the Benny Carter Jubilee All-Stars, the Metronome All-Stars.
**Album:** Released Apr '81, on Queen-disc (Italy) Catalogue no: **QU 009**

**BENNY CARTER, 1928-1952**
Tracks: / Charleston is the best dance, after all / Old fashioned love / Apologies / Sendin' the vipers / Thirty fifth and Calumet / I'm in the mood for swing / Push out / I just got a letter / When lights are low / Walkin' by the river / All of me / Very thought of you, The / Cocktails for two / Takin' my time / Cuddle up, huddle up / Babalu / There, I've said it again / Midnight / My favourite blues / Lullaby to a dream / What a difference a day made / Sunday / Ill wind / Back bay boogie / Tree of hope / Lullaby in blue / Cruisin' / I wanna go home / You belong to me / Love is Cynthia / Sunday afternoon / Georgia on my mind.
**2 LP Set:** Released '83, on RCA (France) by BMG Records (France). Catalogue no: **PM 42406**

**BENNY CARTER ALL STARS (Featuring Nat Adderley and Red Norvo)**
Tracks: / Easy money / Memories of you / Here's that rainy day / Blues for lucky lovers / Work song / When lights are low.
Note: Produced by Rune Ofwerman.
**CD:** Released Sep '86, on Sonet by Sonet Records. Deleted Mar '89. Catalogue no: **SNTCD 947**
**Album:** Released Sep '86, on Sonet by Sonet Records. Catalogue no: **SNTF 947**

**BENNY CARTER AND ORCHESTRA 1944 (Carter, Benny & His Orchestra)**
**Album:** Released '88, on Hindsight Catalogue no: **HSR 218**

**BENNY CARTER COLLECTION (16 golden greats)**
Tracks: / Charleston is the best dance, after all / Once upon a time / Lonesome nights / Waltzing the blues / Out of nowhere / My buddy / Sunday / Rockin' chair / Stardust / Riffamarole / Jump call / Off dah / Cruisin' / 9:20 special / Blue Lou / Rose room.
**Cass:** Released Dec '87, on Deja Vu Catalogue no: **DVMC 2112**
**Album:** Released Dec '87, on Deja Vu Catalogue no: **DVLP 2112**

**BENNY CARTER FOUR**
Tracks: / Three little words / In a mellow tone / Wave / Undecided / Body and soul / On Green Dolphin Street / Here's that rainy day.
**Cass:** Released '82, on Pablo Jazz (USA) by Pablo Records (USA). Catalogue no: **K 08 204**
**Album:** Released '82, on Pablo Jazz (USA) by Pablo Records (USA). Catalogue no: **2308 204**

**BENNY CARTER IN HOLLYWOOD**
**Album:** Released '89, on Jazz Society Catalogue no: **AA 502**

**BEST OF BENNY CARTER**
Tracks: / Three little words / In a mellow tone / Wave / Squattyroo / It don't mean a thing.
**Album:** Released '82, on Pablo Jazz (USA) by Pablo Records (USA). Catalogue no: **231 0853**
**Cass:** Released '82, on Pablo Jazz (USA) by Pablo Records (USA). Catalogue no: **K10 853**

**CARTER, GILLESPIE INC (Carter, Benny & Dizzy Gillespie)**
Tracks: / Sweet and lovely / Broadway / Courtship, The / Constantinople / Nobody knows the trouble I've seen / Night in tunisia / Three little words / In a mellow tone / Waves / Undecided / Body and soul / On Green Dolphin Street / Here's that rainy day.
**Cass:** Released '82, on Pablo Jazz (USA) by Pablo Records (USA). Catalogue no: **K10 781**
**Album:** Released '82, on Pablo Jazz (USA) by Pablo Records (USA). Catalogue no: **2310 781**

**CENTRAL CITY SKETCHES (Carter, Benny & The American Jazz Orchestra)**
Tracks: / Lonesome nights / Easy money.
**CD:** Released Jan '89, on Music Masters by Music Masters Records. Catalogue no: **CIJD 60126 X**
**LP Set:** Released Jan '89, on Music Masters by Music Masters Records. Catalogue no: **CIJD20126Z/27X**
**Cass:** Released Jan '89, on Music Masters by Music Masters Records. Catalogue no: **CIJD40126Y/27W**

**DELUXE RECORDINGS VOL 1**
**Album:** Released 7 Nov '87, on Swingtime by Contact Records (Denmark). Catalogue no: **ST 1013**

**EARLY FORTIES**
Tracks: / By the watermelon vine / Lindy Lou / Last kiss you gave me, The / Boogie woogie sugar blues / I've been in love before / Poinciana / Just a baby's prayer at twilight / Hurry, hurry / Love for sale / I can't escape from you / I'm lost / I can't get started / I surrender dear / Malibu / Forever blues / Prelude to a kiss / Just you, just me.
**Album:** Released Dec '88, on Official

by Official Records. Catalogue no: **OFF 3019**

**FURTHER DEFINITIONS**
Tracks: / Honeysuckle rose / Midnight sun will never set, The / Crazy rhythm / Blue star / Cottontail / Body and soul / Cherry / Doozy.
**Album:** Released Jul '82, on Jasmine by Hasmick Promotions. Catalogue no: **JAS 14**
**Cass:** Released Jul '82, on Jasmine by Hasmick Promotions. Catalogue no: **JASC 14**
**CD:** Released Jul '87, on MCA by MCA Records. Deleted Dec '89. Catalogue no: **MCAD 5651**

**GENTLEMAN AND HIS MUSIC, A**
Tracks: / Sometimes I'm happy / Blues for George / Things ain't what they used to be / Lover man / Idaho / Kiss from you, A.
**CD:** Released Jan '87, on Concord Jazz by Concord Jazz Records (USA). Catalogue no: **CCD 4285**
**Album:** Released Dec '85, on Concord Jazz by Concord Jazz Records (USA). Catalogue no: **CJ 285**

**GENTLEMAN OF JAZZ**
**Album:** Released '88, on Meritt (USA) Catalogue no: **MERITT 17**

**IN PARIS 1935-1946 (Carter, Benny & Coleman Hawkins)**
**CD:** Released '88, on DRG (USA) by DRG Records (USA). Catalogue no: **CDSW 8403**
**Cass:** Released '88, on DRG (USA) by DRG Records (USA). Catalogue no: **SWC 8403**
**Album:** Released '88, on DRG (USA) by DRG Records (USA). Catalogue no: **SW 8403**

**IN THE MOOD FOR SWING**
Tracks: / I'm in the mood for swing / Another time, another place / Courtship, The / Rock me to sleep / Janel / Romp, The / Summer serenade / Not so blue / You, only you / Blue moonlight / South side samba.
**Album:** Released Jan '89, on Music Masters by Music Masters Records. Catalogue no: **CIJD 40144 W**
**CD:** Released Jan '89, on Music Masters by Music Masters Records. Catalogue no: **CIJD 60144 T**
**Cass:** Released Jan '89, on Music Masters by Music Masters Records. Catalogue no: **CIJD 20144 X**
**CD:** Released Nov '89, on Limelight Catalogue no: **820 806-2**

**JAZZ GIANT**
Tracks: / Old fashioned love / I'm coming Virginia / Walkin' thing / Blue Lou / Ain't she sweet / How can you lose / Blues my naughty sweetie gives to me.
**Album:** Released Aug '87, on Boplicity by Ace Records. Deleted '88. Catalogue no: **COP 015**

**JAZZ OFF THE AIR, VOL 3 (Carter, Benny & His Orchestra)**
Tracks: / Rose room / Boy meets horn / Stardust / Tea for two / Roll 'em / Jump call / My gal Sal / Just you, just me / Untitled.
Note: Featuring Rex Stewart, Barney Bigard, Miles Davis, Lucky Thompson, Dexter Gordon, Al Grey.
**Album:** Released '83, on Spotlite by Spotlite Records. Catalogue no: **SPJ 147**

**KING, THE**
Tracks: / Walkin' thing, A / My kind of trouble is you / Easy money / Blue star / I still love him so / Green wine / Malibu / Blues in D flat.
**Album:** Released '82, on Pablo Jazz (USA) by Pablo Records (USA). Catalogue no: **231 0768**
**Cass:** Released '82, on Pablo Jazz (USA) by Pablo Records (USA). Catalogue no: **K10 768**

**LATE FORTIES, THE**
Tracks: / Melodrama in a v-disc record room / Prelude to a kiss / Sweet Georgia Brown / Out of my way / What'll be / Cadillac Slim / Baby you're mine for keeps / You'll never break my heart again / Chilpancingo / An old love story / Reina / Let us drink a toast together / Cotton tail / Time out for blues / Surf board / You are too beautiful.
**Album:** Released Aug '88, on Official by Official Records. Catalogue no: **OFF 3006**

**LIVE & WELL IN JAPAN**
Tracks: / Squattyroo / Tribute to Louis Armstrong / When it's sleepy time down South / I'm confessin' / When you're smiling / Them there eyes / It don't mean a thing.
**Cass:** Released '82, on Pablo Jazz (USA) by Pablo Records (USA). Catalogue no: **K 08 216**
**Album:** Released '82, on Pablo Jazz (USA) by Pablo Records (USA). Catalogue no: **2308 216**
**CD:** Released Jan '89, on JVC/Fantasy Catalogue no: **VDJ 28010**
**CD:** Released May '86, on Pablo Jazz (USA) by Pablo Records (USA). Catalogue no: **CD 20039**

**MELANCHOLY BENNY**
**Album:** Released '88, on Tax Catalogue no: **M 8004**

**SOMEBODY LOVES ME (Carter, Benny & His Orchestra)**
**Cass:** Released Jul '87, on Magic (1) by Submarine Records. Catalogue no: **CAWE 28**
**Album:** Released Jul '87, on Magic (1) by Submarine Records. Catalogue no: **AWE 28**

**SUMMER SERENADE (Carter, Benny Quartet)**
Note: Mono production.
**Album:** Released Jun '86, on Storyville by Storyville Records AB. Catalogue no: **SLP 4047**

**SWINGIN' AT MAIDA VALE (Carter, Benny & His Orchestra)**
Tracks: / Swingin' at Maida Vale / Nightfall / I've got two lips / There'll be some changes made / If only I could read your mind / Gin and jive / Accent on swing / Just a mood / Royal Garden blues / When lights are low / Waltzing the blues / When day is done.
**Album:** Released Feb '83, on Jasmine by Hasmick Promotions. Deleted Jun '87. Catalogue no: **JASM 2010**

**SWINGIN' THE 20'S**
**Album:** Released Jul '81, on Contemporary (Import) Catalogue no: **1007 561**

**WHEN LIGHTS ARE LOW (Carter, Benny & His Orchestra)**
Tracks: / When lights are low swingin' at Maida Vale / Nightfall / Big Ben blues / These foolish things / When day is done / I've got two lips / Just a mood / Swingin' the blues / Gin and jive / If I could only read your mind / I gotta go / When lights are love / Poor butterfly / Drop in next time you're passing / Man I love, The / That's how the first song was born.
**Cass:** Released Dec '87, on Conifer Happy Days by Conifer Records. Catalogue no: **MCHD 131**
**Album:** Released Dec '87, on Conifer Happy Days Catalogue no: **CHD 131**

## Carter, Betty

**Biographical details:** Born in 1930 in Flint, Michigan, Betty 'Be bop' Carter toured with Lionel Hampton in the early '50's and is one of the most highly regarded jazz singers in the business, so neglected for many years that she issued albums on her own Bet-Car label. The reissue of her 1960 album with Ray Charles was a critics choice in the USA in 1988; her first album on a major label in many years, *Look what I got* was on Billboard's top ten jazz albums in early 1989. (Donald Clarke, April 1989).

**AUDIENCE WITH BETTY CARTER**
Tracks: / Sounds (movin' on) / I think I got it now / Caribbean sun / Trolley song, The / Everything I have is yours / I'll buy you a star / I could write a book / Can't we talk it over? / Either it's love or it isn't / Deep night / Spring can really hang you up the most / Tight / Fake / So / My favourite things / Open the door.
**2 LP Set:** Released Jul '82, on Bet-Car (Import) Catalogue no: **MK 1003**

**BEBOP GIRL, THE**
Tracks: / Moonlight in Vermont / Thou swell / I could write a book / Gone with the wind / Way you look tonight, The / Can't we be friends / Tell him I said hello / Social call / Runaway / Frenesi / Let's fall in love.
**Album:** on Official by Official Records. Catalogue no: **OFF 3023**
**CD:** on Official by Official Records. Catalogue no: **OFF 83023**

**BETTY CARTER VOL 1**
Tracks: / By the bend of the river / Ego / Body and soul / Heart and soul / Surrey with the fringe on top / Girl talk / I didn't know what time it was / All the things you are / I could write a book / Sun dies, The / Please do something.
**Album:** Released Jul '82, on Bet-Car (Import) Catalogue no: **MK 1001**

**BETTY CARTER VOL 2**
Tracks: / You're a sweetheart / I can't help it / What is it? / On our way up / We

tried / Happy / Sunday, Monday or always / Tight / Children learn what they live / Sounds.
**Album:** Released Jul '82, on Bet-Car (Import) Catalogue no: **MK 1002**

**INSIDE BETTY CARTER**
Tracks: / This is always / Look no further / Beware my heart - this time / Something big (from Kwamina) / My favourite things / Some other time / Open the door / Spring can really hang you up the most.
**Album:** Released Mar '88, on Bet-Car (Import) Catalogue no: **MK 1000**

**LOOK WHAT I GOT**
**Album:** Released '88, on Verve Deleted Dec '89. Catalogue no: **835 661 1**
**Cass:** Released '88, on Verve Deleted Dec '89. Catalogue no: **835 661 4**
**CD:** Released '88, on Verve Deleted Dec '89. Catalogue no: **835 661 2**

**OUT THERE**
**Album:** Released Feb '88, on Fresh Sounds (Spain) by Fresh Sounds Records (Spain). Catalogue no: **FS 172**

**ROUND MIDNIGHT**
**CD:** Released 10 Jul '89, on Vogue by Vogue Records. Catalogue no: **VGCD 600210**

**WHATEVER HAPPENED TO LOVE?**
Tracks: / What a little moonlight can do / New blues / I cry alone / Abre la Puerta / Every time we say goodbye / Cocktails for two / Social call / Goodbye / With no words.
**Album:** Released Mar '83, on Bet-Car (Import) Catalogue no: **MK 1004**

## Carter, Joe

**CHESTNUT (Carter, Joe & Lee Konitz)**
**Album:** Released May '84, on Empathy (USA) Catalogue no: **E 1002**

**ORIGINAL CHICAGO BLUES (Carter, Joe & Kansas City Red)**
Tracks: / Mama talk to your daughter / You're the one / Rock me / Open your heart / Crawling king snake / Sweet black angel / Rollin' and tumblin' / Standing around cryin' / Moon is rising, The.**Album:** Released Aug '82, on JSP by JSP Records. Catalogue no: **JSP 1038**

**TOO MARVELLOUS FOR WORDS (Carter, Joe & Rufus Reid)**
**Album:** Released May '84, on Empathy (USA) Catalogue no: **E 1001**

## Carter, Ron

**Biographical details:** Born in 1937 in Michigan, Ron Carter practically single-handedly kept the acoustic bass (and cello) alive at a time when the former at least was in danger of being swamped by the electric instrument. His work on Eric Dolphy and Mal Waldron albums on Prestige in the early '60's was revelatory, and since then his contributions to jazz (and pop) albums have been too numerous to keep track of (including Hot House Flowers, by Wynton Marsalis) but any album with his name on it is worth a listen. (Donald Clarke, April 1989).

**ALL BLUES**
**Album:** Released Feb '84, on CTI (Musidisc France) by Polydor Ltd. Catalogue no: **CTI 9017**

**BLUES FARM**
**CD:** Released '88, on CBS by CBS Records. Deleted 17 Apr '89. Catalogue no: **450556 2**

**ETUDES**
Tracks: / Last resort, The / Bottoms up / Arboretum / Rufus / Echoes / Doctors' row.
**Album:** Released Feb '83, on Elektra (Musician) by Elektra Records (USA). Catalogue no: **E 0214**

**HEART AND SOUL (Carter, Ron & Cedar Walton)**
**Album:** Released '88, on Timeless by Timeless Records. Catalogue no: **SJP 158**

**LIVE AT VILLAGE WEST (Carter, Ron & Jim Hall)**
Tracks: / Bag's groove / All the things you are / Blue Monk / New waltz / St. Thomas / Embraceable you / Laverne walk / Baubles, bangles and beads.
**Album:** Released Jul '84, on Concord Jazz by Concord Jazz Records (USA). Catalogue no: **CJ 245**

**MAN WITH THE BASS, THE**
**CD:** Released May '87, on JVC/Fantasy Deleted '88. Catalogue no: **VDJ 1026**

**NEW YORK SLICK**
Tracks: / Slight smile / Tierra Espanola / Aromatic / Alternate route.
**Album:** on Milestone by Ace Records. Catalogue no: **M 9096**

**PARADE**
Tracks: / Parade / Theme in 3/4 / Sometimes I feel like a motherless child / Tinderbox / Gipsy / G.J.T..
**Album:** Released Feb '80, on Milestone by Ace Records. Deleted '85. Catalogue no: **M 9088**

**PASTELS**
**CD:** Released Nov '86, on JVC/Fantasy Catalogue no: **VDJ 1034**

**PATRAO**
Tracks: / Ah, Rio / Nearly / Tail feathers / Yours truly / Third plane.
**Album:** Released Aug '81, on Milestone by Ace Records. Deleted Aug '86. Catalogue no: **M 9099**

**PICK 'EM**
**Album:** Released Jun '80, on Milestone by Ace Records. Catalogue no: **M 9092**

**RON CARTER PLAYS BACH**
**CD:** Released Mar '88, on ECM Catalogue no: **8308902**

**RON CARTER PRESENTS DADO MORNI**
**CD:** Released Feb '90, on Emarcy Catalogue no: **834 027 2**

**SONG FOR YOU**
Tracks: / Song for you / El ojo de dios / Quiet place / Good time / Someday my prince will come / N.O. blues.
**Album:** Released '79, on Milestone by Ace Records. Deleted '84. Catalogue no: **M 9086**

**TELEPHONE (Carter, Ron & Jim Hall)**
Tracks: / Telephone / Indian summer / Candlelight / Chorale and dance / Alone together / Stardust / Two's blues.
**Album:** Released Jul '85, on Concord Jazz by Concord Jazz Records (USA). Catalogue no: **CJ 270**
**CD:** Released Sep '86, on Concord Jazz by Concord Jazz Records (USA). Catalogue no: **CCD 4270**
**Cass:** Released Jul '85, on Concord Jazz by Concord Jazz Records (USA). Catalogue no: **CJC 270**

**THIRD PLANE (Carter, Ron, Tony Williams & Herbie Hancock)**
Note: For full details see under Herbie Hancock.
**CD:** Released '88, on Carrere (France) Catalogue no: **98134**

## Cary, Ted

**TED CARY WITH TED EASTON'S JAZZ BAND (Cary, Ted & Ted Easton's Jazzband)**
**Album:** Released Aug '88, on Jazzology (USA) by Jazzology Records (USA). Catalogue no: **SLP 18**

## Casa Loma Orchestra

**Biographical details:** USA Dance band, formed in 1929 and fronted by reedman Glen Gray. Before the Swing Era properly began in 1935 it was the best-known (with Ben Pollock's) of the white dance bands which allowed a strong jazz influence, with guitarist/arranger Gene Gifford, clarinettist Clarence Hutchenrider and trumpeter Sonny Dunham as founder members, and other well-known sidemen passing through. Kenny Sergeant sang romantic ballads like *For you* and *It's the talk of the town*, but hot arrangements such as such as *Black jazz, white jazz, Casa Loma stomp* etc. (many written by Gifford, as was their theme *Smoke rings*) made the band a legend among the college-age audience of the time. (Donald Clarke, April 1989) .

**CASA LOMA STOMP**
**Album:** Released Aug '86, on Hep Jazz by Hep Records. Catalogue no: **HEP 1010**

**WHITE JAZZ 1931-34**
**Album:** Released '88, on Old Bean by Submarine Records. Catalogue no: **OLD 5**

## Case, Russ

**RUSS CASE AND ORCHESTRA 1950 (Case, Russ & Orchestra)**
**Album:** Released Dec '88, on Circle (USA) by Jazzology Records (USA). Catalogue no: **CLP 119**

## Cash, Bernie

**CONTRA BACH**

**Album:** Released Apr '79, on Wave by Wave Records. Catalogue no: **WAVE LP 20**

## Castle, Lee

**Biographical details:** Born in New York in 1915, Lee Castaldo was a fine Swing Era trumpeter, playing with Artie Shaw, Tommy Dorsey, Glenn Miller, Benny Goodman and others; he once subbed for Buck Clayton at a Basie small group date produced by John Hammond and fitted right in. He changed his name and led his own bands; he led Jimmy Dorsey's band during Dorsey's final illness, then let and partly owned the Dorsey ghost band. He also transcribed Louis Armstrong solos for publication. (Donald Clarke, April 1989).

### DIXIELAND HEAVEN

Tracks: / Stars and stripes forever / Alabama blues / Save it pretty Mama / Birmingham special / Trombone jitters / Feeling sentimental / My wild Irish rose / Fair Jennie's lament / Dixieland mambo / On the banks of the Wabash / Mood in blue / When the saints go marching in.
**Album:** Released Jan '84, on Harlequin by Interstate Music. Catalogue no: **HQ 2003**

## Catfish Hodge Band

### EYE WITNESS BLUES

**Album:** Released May '81, on Adelphi (1) Catalogue no: **AD 4113**

## Celebration Of Duke

### CELEBRATION OF DUKE (Various artists)

Tracks: / Caravan: *Quadrant* / Happy-go-lucky local: *Terry, Clark* / Tonight I shall sleep: *Sims, John Haley 'Zoot'* / I ain't got nothin' but the blues: *Vaughan, Sarah* / Come Sunday: *Terry, Clark* / Everything but you: *Vaughan, Sarah* / Take the 'A' train: *Quadrant* / Rockin' in rhythm: *Sims, John Haley 'Zoot'* / Echoes of Harlem: *Terry, Clark* / Main stem: *Quadrant.*
**Cass:** Released '82, on Pablo Jazz (USA) by Pablo Records (USA). Catalogue no: **K 12 119**
**Album:** Released '82, on Pablo Jazz (USA) by Pablo Records (USA). Catalogue no: **2312 119**

## Celestin, Papa

**Biographical details:** The trumpeter, vocalist and leader (1884-1954) was a New Orleans legend, leading his own band at Tuxedo Hall in 1910-13, and staying at it until his was one of the last traditional bands of its type. He was featured in the film Cinerama Holiday in 1953 and played for President Eisenhower that year. (Donald Clarke, April 1989).

### CELESTIN'S ORIGINAL TUXEDO JAZZ ORCHESTRA (1926-28) (Celestin's Original Tuxedo Orchestra)

**Album:** Released Oct '88, on VJM (Vintage Jazz Music) by Vintage Jazz Music Society(VJM). Catalogue no: **VLP 33**

### PAPA CELESTIN & HIS NEW ORLEANS (Celestin, Papa, & His New Orleans Jazz Band)

**Album:** Released Dec '86, on Folklyric (USA) by Arhoolie Records (USA). Catalogue no: **FL 9030**

### PAPA CELESTIN & HIS NEW ORLEANS (Celestin, Papa, & His New Orleans Ragtime Band)

Note: With Alphonse Picou. Recorded in mono.
**Album:** Released Jun '86, on Jazzology (USA) by Jazzology Records (USA). Catalogue no: **JCE 28**

## Challis, Bill

### BILL CHALLIS AND HIS ORCHESTRA (Challis, Bill and His Orchestra)

**Album:** Released Aug '88, on Circle (USA) by Jazzology Records (USA). Catalogue no: **CLP 71**

### GOLDKETTLE PROJECT, THE

**Album:** Released '89, on Circle Catalogue no: **CLP 118**
**Cass:** Released '89, on Circle Catalogue no: **CLMC 118**
**CD:** Released '89, on Circle Catalogue no: **CLCD 118**

### MORE 1936 (Challis, Bill and His Orchestra)

**Album:** Released Aug '88, on Circle (USA) by Jazzology Records (USA). Catalogue no: **CLP 72**

## Chaloff, Serge

**Biographical details:** Baritone saxophonist (1923-57). His mother was a music teacher and father played in the Boston Symphony Orchestra. He studied piano and clarinet but was self taught on baritone; he played with Boyd Raeburn, Georgie Auld, Jimmy Dorsey; he joined Woody Herman's Second Herd in 1947 and became a star, the anchor in the famous 'Four Brothers' reed section and featured on the uptemp *Man, don't be ridiculous.* As the first major bop player on the instrument he dispaced Harry Carney in Down Beat polls three years in a row. He was a heroin addict but later cleaned up but was too ill with spinal paralysis. The superb albums made for Capitol and now on Affinity are his best legacy. (Donald Clarke, April 1989).

### BLUE SERGE

Tracks: / Handful of stars, A / Goof and I, The / Thanks for the memory / All the things you are / I've got the world on a string / Susie's blues / Stairway to the stars.
**Album:** Released '86, on Affinity by Charly Records. Catalogue no: **AFF 146**

### BOSTON BLOW UP (Chaloff, Serge Sextet)

Tracks: / Bob, the robin / Yesterday's gardenias / Sergical / What's new / J.R. / Body and soul / Kip / Diana's melody / Unison.
**Album:** Released Apr '81, on Affinity by Charly Records. Catalogue no: **AFF 63**

## Chamber Jazz Sextet

### PLAYS PAL JOEY

Tracks: / I could write a book / My funny valentine / I didn't know what time it was / Zip / Lady is a tramp.
**CD:** Released Jun '88, on Candid Catalogue no: **CCD 9030**
**Album:** Released Jul '87, on Candid Catalogue no: **CS 9030**

## Chambers, Paul

**Biographical details:** One of the most influential bassists of the post-war years (1935-69). With Miles Davis 1955-60 he was part of one of the most influential rhythm sections of all time, so that it was listed as Art Pepper and The Rhythm Section on a Pepper album. He played in a trio with Wynton Kelly and Jimmy Cobb; he had already began making small group albums as a leader in 1955 and also recorded with Sonny Rollins, John Coltrane, Johnny Griffin, Bill Evans and others. (Donald Clarke, April 1989).

### BASS ON TOP

Tracks: / Yesterdays / You'd be so nice to come home to / Chasin' the bird / Dear old Stockholm / Theme / Confessin' / Chamber mates.
**CD:** Released May '87, on Blue Note by EMI Records. Catalogue no: **CDP 746 533 2**
**CD:** Released May '87, on Blue Note by EMI Records. Catalogue no: **BNZ 16**

### EASE IT (Chambers, Paul & Cannonball Adderly)

Tracks: / Ease it / Just friends / I got rhythm / Julie Ann / Awful mean / There is no greater love.
Note: This original Vee Jay Album presents a fascinating combination of top flight jazz stars from the early sixties. In the front line we have Cannonball Adderly, the number one soul jazz alto player of the era, teamed with a young Freddie Hubbard, who just started to make his mark in the jazz world at the time this album was recorded. The rhythm section was at the time propelling the famous Miles Davis Quintet. This album has been long unavailable in the world and solid sales are to be expected, since the upturn in interest in hardbop music is definitely here.
**Album:** Released Mar '84, on Affinity by Charly Records. Catalogue no: **AFF 115**

### WE THREE (Chambers, Paul, Roy Haynes & Phineas Newborn)

**CD:** Released Nov '86, on JVC/Fantasy Catalogue no: **VDJ 1542**

## Changing Face Of Harlem

### CHANGING FACE OF HARLEM

Tracks: / I got what it takes / Good for stompin' / I'll always love you just the same / Romance without finance / Bye bye / My lucky day / Groovin' the blues / Smack that mess / Dee Dee's dance / Little Benny / Shoot the arrow to me cupid.
**Album:** Released '82, on Arista by BMG Records (UK). Deleted '87. Cata-

logue no: **SJL 2208**
**Album:** Released Mar '85, on Savoy Jazz (USA) by Malaco Records (USA). Catalogue no: **SJL 1149**

**CHANGING FACE OF HARLEM VOL.2 (Various artists)**
**Album:** Released '78, on Savoy Jazz (USA) by Malaco Records (USA). Catalogue no: **SJL 2224**

## Charles, Ray

**Biographical details:** This American singer, pianist, arranger and songwriter is one of the most important artists in the post-war history of black music. Born Ray Charles Robinson in Georgia in 1932, he was blinded at the age of six and rendered an orphan while in his early teens. After moving to Seattle, Washington, he spent the early 50's playing in a trio which based its style heavily on that of Nat King Cole. It was about this time that he dropped his surname, in order to avoid confusion with star boxer Sugar Ray Robinson. During the mid to late 50's Charles developed his own highly distinctive style, fusing rhythm and blues, gospel and jazz, and helping to create soul music, a genre that exploded into fashion in the 60's. Charles' first American Top Forty hit was 1957's Swanee River Rock, which reached No 34. His big breakthrough was 1959's self-penned *What'd I Say?*, a frantic, frenetic call-and-response single which was an enormously exciting listening experience appealing to fans of rock 'n' roll, blues, gospel and jazz. It reached No 6 on the US chart and its instant classic status was confirmed by the fact that, within five years, it had become a US Top Thirty hit for Jerry Lee Lewis, Bobby Darin and Elvis Presley. Charles' next milestone record was a 1960 rendition of a 1930 Hoagy Carmichael number: *Georgia On My Mind*, a tribute to Ray's own birthplace, gave him his first US No 1 and his first UK hit of any kind. A second American chart-topper came in '61 with another classic, the highly catchy *Hit The Road, Jack*, a No 6 hit in Britain. All these achievements, though, were dwarfed by the red-hot Ray Charles' 1962 exploits. *I Can't Stop Loving You*, a country ballad written by fellow hitmaker Don Gibson, was reworked by Charles and became his biggest-ever single on both sides of the Atlantic and his only single to go to No 1 in both America and Britain. It was featured on his seminal, highly influential LP *Modern Sounds In Country And Western Music*, which further enhanced his status as a bridge between white country music and the black R & B style. Its success inspired a Volume 2 follow-up the following year. By the mid-60's he had chalked up two more Trans-Atlantic Top Ten singles -- *You Don't Know Me* and *Take These Chains From My Heart* -- plus another three US Top Tenners with *You Are My Sunshine, Busted* and *Cryin' Time*. By this time he had lost the raw edge that had been so much a part of his earlier work and was concentrating on ballads. His late 70's and early 80's recordings did not break new ground but were nonetheless competent restatements of his eclectic approach that, 20 years earlier, had opened up new possibilities for countless future stars. (Bob MacDonald, 1985.)

**Ray Charles**

Ray Charles Robinson was born in 1930 or 1932 in Albany, Georgia; blinded at age six, he became the most successful soul artist of all time. He went to Florida school for the blind, then to Seattle to get as far from the South as possible. He began heavily influenced by Nat 'King' Cole, like Cole leading a trio, and was the first black in the Northwest to have a TV show, with hits in the R&B chart, but soon developed his own style: his soulful arrangement of *Things that I used to do* for Guitar Slim was a number one R&B hit in 1954; meanwhile he had signed with Atlantic and his string of originals began in 1953: *Losing hand, It should've been me, Mess around, I got a woman* (covered by Elvis Presley), *Hallelujah, I love here so* and others were all R&B hits, sometimes fitting new words to gospel tunes: *Talkin' 'bout Jesus* became *Talkin' 'bout you*; Clara Ward's *This little light of mine* became *This little girl of mine*; *How Jesus died* became *Lonely Avenue*. Big Bill Broonzy said 'He's mixing the blues with the spirituals. I know what's wrong ... he should be singing in a church.' But the mixture of gospel emotion, secular subject matter and smooth but honest delivery led to comic Bill Cosby's routine about Columbus going to America so he could discover Ray Charles. He used a female quartet, The Raelets; on the soulful *What kind of man are you* carried the vocal on their own. His first LP *The great Ray Charles* in 1957 was a jazz set, with laid back instrumentals such as Horace Silver's *Doodlin'* and his own *Sweet sixteen bars*; his first top 40 pop hit was *Swanee river rock* the same year. Another jazz-oriented album, with Basie and Ellington sidemen and arrangements by Ralph Burns, Quincy Jones and others dubbed him 'The Genius'. His extended arrangement with the Raelets *What'd I say* was a hard-driving gospel style rock'n'roll hit in 1959 and he was already a legend; he switched to ABC in 1960 with an astonishing contract for a black artist then, allowing him to retain ownership of his own recordings at the end of the association; he soon had a smash number one hit with a down-home vocal on the Hoagy Carmichael evergreen *Georgia on my mind*, used in film soundtracks of *In the heat of the night* in 1969 and *George's friends* in 1982. The impulse album *Genius plus soul equals jazz* was arranged by Jones; women got the upperhand as the Raelets told him to *Hit the road Jack*, his second number one single in 1961 charted, followed by the number one hit album *Modern sounds in country and western music* in 1962: his version of Don Gibson's *I can't stop loving you* hit the top of the pop, black and country charts. A sequel was a number two album the same year; he could do no wrong. His eclectic material predictably upset some critics, but he was voted best male singer five years in a row from 1961 by international jazz critics in Down Beat magazine, and won his first Grammy in 1961. He formed his own company, Tangerine in 1962, recording Louis Jordan and others, leasing the records to ABC. He packed a huge sports stadium in Paris several nights at the height of the Algerian crisis; he walked out of an Atlanta gig because the audience was segretated and played the first integrated concert in the Memphis municipal auditorium.The hits continued to alternate between straight soul numbers and others with slushy strings setting off blues-flecked vocals and piano: there were more country songs in the top ten singles chart, including the humorous *Busted* (written by Harlan Howard); *Crying time* in 1966 won two Grammies. He had 32 top 40 pop hits altogether (1957-71) and more than 50 in the R&B chart (1951-71), and is still pleasing crowds at jazz festivals today. (Donald Clarke, April 1989).

**14 ORIGINAL GREATEST HITS:RAY CHARLES**
**Album:** Released Mar '88, on King (USA) Catalogue no: **K 5011**

**16 GREATEST HITS**
**CD:** Released Jan '90, on Mainline (2) by Mainline Records. Catalogue no: **264823 2**
**Cass:** Released Jan '90, on Mainline (2) by Mainline Records. Catalogue no: **264823 4**

**16 ORIGINAL HITS: RAY CHARLES**
**Cass:** Released Sep '87, on Timeless Treasures Catalogue no: **MC 1631**

**20 GOLDEN PIECES: RAY CHARLES**
Tracks: / Alone in the city / Can anyone ask for more? / Rockin' chair blues / Let's have a ball / How long how long blues / Sentimental blues, A / You always miss the water (when the well runs dry) / I've had my fun / Sitting on top of the world / Ain't that fine? / Don't put all your dreams in one basket / Ray Charles blues / Honey honey / She's on the ball / Baby won't you please come home? / If I give you my love / This love of mine / Can't you see me, darling? / Someday.
**Album:** Released Jul '82, on Bulldog Records by President Records. Catalogue no: **BDL 2012**

**20 GREATEST HITS: RAY CHARLES**
**Cass:** Released Jan '87, on Masters (Holland) Catalogue no: **MB 990108**
**Album:** Released Jan '87, on Masters (Holland) Catalogue no: **B 90108**

**25TH ANNIVERSARY IN SHOW BUSINESS**
**Album:** Released '87, on Atlantic by WEA Records. Catalogue no: **K 60014**

**1950**
**Album:** on Vogue by Vogue Records. Catalogue no: **522 011**

**AIN'T IT SO**
Tracks: / Some enchanted evening / Blues in the night / Just because / What'll I do / One of these days / Love me or set me free / Drift away / Love me tonight.
**Album:** Released '79, on London Records by London Records Ltd. Deleted '84. Catalogue no: **SHL 8537**

**BLUES IS MY MIDDLE NAME**
**CD:** Released May '89, on Object Enterprises Catalogue no: **ONN 37**

**BROTHER RAY**
Tracks: / Compared to what / Anyway you want to / Don't you love me anymore / Poor man's song / Now that we've found each other / Ophelia / I can't change it / Questions.
**Album:** Released Jan '81, on London Records by London Records Ltd. Deleted Jan '86. Catalogue no: **SH 8546**

**BUSTED**
Tracks: / Busted.
**7" Single:** Released Oct '63, on H.M.V. by EMI Records. Deleted Oct '66. Catalogue no: **POP 1221**

**CAN'T STOP LOVING YOU**
**Cass:** Released Oct '85, on Platinum (W.Germany) Catalogue no: **PMC 22**
**Album:** Released Oct '85, on Platinum (W.Germany) Catalogue no: **PLP 22**

**C.C. RIDER**
Tracks: / C.C. rider / I wonder who's kissing her now / Going down slow / Lovin' the girls / Kiss me baby / All alone again / Sitting on top of the world / Tell me baby / Baby let me hold your hand / Hey now / All to myself alone / Walkin' and talkin'.
**Album:** Released Jun '85, on Premier by Premier Records. Catalogue no: **CBR 1018**
**Cass:** Released Jun '85, on Premier by Premier Records. Catalogue no: **KCBR 1018**

**COLLECTABLES, THE**
**CD:** Released '89, on K-Tel by K-Tel Records. Catalogue no: **NCD 5149**

**COLLECTION: RAY CHARLES**
**Album:** Released Apr '86, on Star Jazz (USA) by Charly Records. Catalogue no: **SJAZZ 1**
**Cass:** Released Apr '86, on Star Jazz (USA) by Charly Records. Catalogue no: **SJAZZC 1**

**COLLECTION: RAY CHARLES (2)**
**CD:** Released Mar '90, on Arcade Catalogue no: **RCLD 101**
**Album:** Released Mar '90, on Arcade Catalogue no: **RCLP 101**
**Cass:** Released Mar '90, on Arcade Catalogue no: **RCLC 101**

**COLLECTION: RAY CHARLES (20 GOLDEN GREATS)**
Tracks: / Georgia on my mind / What'd I say / Sitting on top of the world / Ain't that fine / Can't you see darling / Sentimental blues, A / If I give you my love / She's on the ball / Ray Charles blues / How long / Come rain or come shine / Alone in the city / Someday / This love of mine / I'm going down to the river / You always miss the water (when the well runs dry) / Baby won't you please come home / Don't put all your dreams in one basket / I've had my fun / Let's have a ball.
**Cass:** Released Aug '85, on Deja Vu Catalogue no: **DVMC 2005**
**Album:** Released Aug '85, on Deja Vu Catalogue no: **DVLP 2005**
**CD:** Released Sep '87, on Deja Vu Catalogue no: **DVCD 2005**

**COLLECTION: RAY CHARLES (THE LOVE SONGS)**
Tracks: / I wonder who's kissing her now / Here am I / Oh baby / I used to be so happy / Honey honey / Ego song, The / Hey now / Late in the evening blues / I live only for you / St. Pete's blues / I'm glad for your sake / I'm just a lonely boy / All night long / See see rider / All to myself alone / Blues is my middle name.
**Cass:** Released Jun '88, on Deja Vu Catalogue no: **DVMC 2123**
**CD:** Released Jul '88, on Deja Vu Catalogue no: **DVCD 2123**
**Album:** Released Jun '88, on Deja Vu Catalogue no: **DVLP 2123**

**COLLECTION, THE**
**2 LP Set:** Released 19 Mar '90, on Castle Collector Series by Castle Communications Records. Catalogue no: **CCSLP 241**
**Cass set:** Released 19 Mar '90, on Castle Collector Series by Castle Communications Records. Catalogue no: **CCSMC 241**
**CD:** Released 19 Mar '90, on Castle Collector Series by Castle Communications Records. Catalogue no: **CCSCD 241**

**COME LIVE WITH ME**
**Album:** Released '74, on London Records by London Records Ltd. Catalogue no: **SHU 8467**

**COMPARED TO WHAT**
Tracks: / Compared to what / Now that found each other.
**7" Single:** Released Feb '81, on London by London Records Ltd. Deleted Feb '84. Catalogue no: **HL 10579**

**COUNTRY SIDE OF RAY CHARLES**
**Album:** Released Apr '86, on Arcade Music Gala Catalogue no: **ADAH 447**
**Cass:** Released Apr '86, on Arcade Music Gala Catalogue no: **ADAHC 447**

**CRYIN' TIME**
Tracks: / Crying time.
**7" Single:** Released Feb '66, on H.M.V. by EMI Records. Deleted Feb '69. Catalogue no: **POP 1502**

**DO I EVER CROSS YOUR MIND?**
Tracks: / I had it all / Do I ever cross your mind / Woman sensuous woman / Then I'll be over you / Lay around & love on you / Love of my life / They call it love / If I were you / Workin' man's woman / I was on Georgia time.
**Cass:** Released Jul '84, on CBS by CBS Records. Deleted '87. Catalogue no: **40 25764**
**Album:** Released Jul '84, on CBS by CBS Records. Deleted '87. Catalogue no: **CBS 25764**

**DON'T SET ME FREE**
Tracks: / Don't set me free.
**7" Single:** Released Mar '63, on H.M.V. by EMI Records. Deleted Mar '66. Catalogue no: **POP 1133**

**EARLY YEARS**
**Album:** Released '88, on Zeta Catalogue no: **ZET 707**

**ELEANOR RIGBY**
Tracks: / Eleanor Rigby.
**7" Single:** Released Jul '68, on Stateside by EMI Records. Deleted Jul '71. Catalogue no: **SS 2120**

**EVERYTHING**
Tracks: / Kiss me baby / Sitting on top of the world / I'm gonna drown myself / All alone again / Lovin' the girls / I will not let you go / I'm glad for your sake / Walkin' and talkin'.
**Album:** Released Sep '80, on Manhattan Records by President Records. Catalogue no: **MAN 5029**

**FANTASTIC RAY CHARLES, THE**
Tracks: / Going down slow / Blues is my middle name / If I give you my love / Can't you see, darling? / Going away blues / Sitting on top of the world / Late in the evening blues / Here am I / Ray's blues / I'm just a lonely boy / St. Pete blues / Easy-ridin' gal / See see rider / I wonder who's kissing her now / I'm going down to the river / I'm glad for your sake / Ego song, The / I used to be so happy / Hey now / What have I done? / All night long / All to myself alone / Oh baby / I live only for you.
Note: Recorded between 1949 and 1952 with, among others, Teddy Buckner, Marshall Royaland Rudy Pitts.
**2 LP Set:** Released Mar '85, on Musidisc by Musidisc Records (France). Catalogue no: **ALB 103**

**FRIENDSHIP**
Tracks: / Two old cats like us / This old heart of mine / We didn't see a thing / Who cares / Rock and roll shoes / Friendship / It ain't gonna worry my mind / Little hotel room / Crazy old soldier / Seven Spanish angels.
**Album:** Released Oct '84, on CBS by CBS Records. Deleted '87. Catalogue no: **CBS 26060**
**Cass:** Released Oct '84, on CBS by CBS Records. Deleted Aug '87. Catalogue no: **40 26060**

**FROM THE PAGES OF MY MIND**
Tracks: / Pages of my mind, The / Slip away / Anybody with the blues / Class reunion / Caught a touch of your love / Little bit of heaven, A / Dixie moon / Over and over (again) / Beaucoup love / Love is worth the pain.
**Cass:** Released Aug '86, on CBS by CBS Records. Catalogue no: **40 26856**
**Album:** Released Aug '86, on CBS by CBS Records. Catalogue no: **CBS 26856**

**GENIUS - 20 GREATEST HITS, THE**
**CD:** Released '88, on Import (label unknown) Catalogue no: **CD 74002**

**GENIUS + SOUL = JAZZ**
**Cass:** Released 7 Aug '89, on Essential by Castle Communications Records. Catalogue no: **ESSMC 009**
**CD:** Released 7 Aug '89, on Essential by Castle Communications Records. Catalogue no: **ESSCD 009**
**Album:** Released 7 Aug '89, on Essential by Castle Communications Records. Catalogue no: **ESSLP 009**

**GENIUS, THE**
Tracks: / Sitting on top of the world / Kiss my baby / I'm gonna drown myself / All alone again / I had my fun / Snow is falling / Blues is my middle name / Oh baby / C.C. rider / Hey now / Tell me baby / Going down slowly / Walkin' and talkin' / I'm glad for your sake / Baby let me hold your hand / All to myself alone.
**Cass:** Released Mar '88, on Exel Catalogue no: **XELMC 106**
**CD:** Released Mar '88, on Exel Catalogue no: **XELCD 106**
**Album:** Released Mar '88, on Exel Catalogue no: **XELLP 106**

**GEORGIA ON MY MIND**
**Album:** Released '88, on Joker (USA) by Lifetime Records (USA). Catalogue no: **SM 3926**

**GEORGIA ON MY MIND (SINGLE)**
Tracks: / Georgia on my mind.
**7" Single:** Released Dec '60, on H.M.V. by EMI Records. Deleted Dec '63. Catalogue no: **POP 792**

**GOIN' DOWN SLOW**
Tracks: / Going down slow / Alone in the city / Now she's gone / Rockin' chair blues / Can anyone ask for more / Let's have a ball / This love of mine / Can't see you darling? / If I give you my love.
**Album:** Released Jun '84, on Meteor by Magnum Music Group. Catalogue no: **MTM 002**

**GREAT HITS**
Tracks: / Going down slow / All night long / I'm givin' up / Guitar blues / Talkin' 'bout you / I found my baby there / I'm wonderin' & wonderin' / By myself / Snowfall.
**Album:** Released '82, on Phoenix (2) by Audio Fidelity Enterprises. Catalogue no: **PHX 1013**

**GREATEST COUNTRY & WESTERN HITS**
Tracks: / Your cheating heart / Hey good lookin' / Take these chains from my heart / Don't tell me your troubles / I can't stop loving you / Just a little lovin' / It makes no difference now / You don't know me / You are my sunshine / Someday (you'll want me to want you) / I love you so much it hurts / Careless love / Oh, lonesome me / Midnight / No letter today / Crying time / Together again / Don't let her know / I'll never stand in your way (Only on CD.) / Hang your head in shame (Only on CD.).
**Album:** Released Dec '89, on Castle Collector Series by Castle Communications Records. Catalogue no: **NEXLP 100**
**Cass:** Released Dec '89, on Castle Collector Series by Castle Communications Records. Catalogue no: **NEXMC 100**
**CD:** Released Dec '89, on Castle Collector Series by Castle Communications Records. Catalogue no: **NEXCD 100**

**GREATEST HITS: RAY CHARLES**
**Album:** Released Jul '63, on H.M.V. by EMI Records. Deleted Jul '68. Catalogue no: **CLP 1626**

**GREATEST HITS: RAY CHARLES, VOL. 2**
**Album:** Released Oct '68, on Stateside by EMI Records. Deleted Oct '73. Catalogue no: **SSL 10241**

**HEART TO HEART - 20 HOT HITS**
**Album:** Released Jul '80, on London Records by London Records Ltd. Deleted Jul '85. Catalogue no: **RAY TV 1**

**HERE AM I**
Tracks: / Easy riding gal / Tapeworld / Ray's blues / Here am I / Blow my baby back home / Blues is my middle name.
**Album:** Released Apr '83, on Barclay (France) by Decca Records. Catalogue no: **B 10106**
**Cass:** Released Apr '83, on Barclay (France) by Decca Records. Catalogue no: **MB9 10106**

**HERE WE GO AGAIN**
Tracks: / Here we go again.
**7" Single:** Released Jul '67, on H.M.V. by EMI Records. Deleted Jul '70. Catalogue no: **POP 1595**

**HIT THE ROAD JACK**
**Album:** Released Oct '85, on Platinum (W.Germany) Catalogue no: **PLP 21**
**Cass:** Released Oct '85, on Platinum (W.Germany) Catalogue no: **PMC 21**

**HIT THE ROAD JACK (SINGLE)**
Tracks: / Hit the road Jack.
**7" Single:** Released Oct '61, on H.M.V. by EMI Records. Deleted Oct '64. Catalogue no: **POP 935**

**HITS OF A GENIUS**
**Album:** Released May '88, on Commander Catalogue no: **39009**
**CD:** Released May '88, on Commander Catalogue no: **99009**
**Cass:** Released May '88, on Commander Catalogue no: **69009**

**I CAN SEE CLEARLY NOW**
Tracks: / I can see clearly now / Let it be.
**7" Single:** Released Aug '80, on London by London Records Ltd. Deleted '83. Catalogue no: **HL 10554**

**I CAN'T STOP LOVING YOU**
Tracks: / Hit the road Jack / Hallelujah I love her so / Mess around / Let's go get stoned / Don't let the sun catch you cryin' / What'd I say / Georgia on my mind / I got a woman / Drown in my own tears / Night time is the right time / Eleanor Rigby / I can't stop loving you.
**Album:** Released '88, on Coldrado Catalogue no: **24004**
**Album:** Released Sep '80, on Pickwick

by Pickwick Records. Catalogue no: **SSP 3075**

**I CAN'T STOP LOVING YOU (SINGLE)**
Tracks: / I can't stop loving you.
**7" Single:** Released Jun '62, on H.M.V. by EMI Records. Deleted Jun '65. Catalogue no: **POP 1034**

**I WISH YOU WERE HERE TONIGHT**
Tracks: / I wish you were here tonight / You feel good all over.
**7" Single:** Released May '83, on CBS by CBS Records. Catalogue no: **A 3407**

**I WONDER WHO'S KISSING HER NOW?**
Tracks: / I wonder who's kissing her now / She's on the ball / Baby won't you please come home.
**7" Single:** Released '87, on Charly by Charly Records. Catalogue no: **CYZ 7 119**
**12" Single:** Released Feb '87, on Charly by Charly Records. Catalogue no: **CYZ 119**

**IF I GIVE YOU MY LOVE**
**LP Pic:** Released May '88, on Picture Disc Catalogue no: **PD 50014**
**Cass:** Released Oct '82, on IMS by Polydor Ltd. Catalogue no: **MF 950014**
**Album:** Released Oct '82, on IMS by Polydor Ltd. Catalogue no: **F 50014**

**JAMMIN' THE BLUES**
**Cass:** Released Nov '84, on Astan (USA) Catalogue no: **40078**
**Album:** Released Nov '84, on Astan (USA) Catalogue no: **20078**

**JUST BETWEEN US**
Tracks: / Nothing like a hundred miles / I wish I'd never loved you at all / Too hard to love you / Now I don't believe that anymore / Let's call the whole thing off / Stranger in my own hometown / Over the top / I'd walk a little more for you / If that's what'cha want / Save the bones for Henry Jones.
**Album:** Released Sep '88, on CBS by CBS Records. Catalogue no: **461183 1**
**CD:** Released Sep '88, on CBS by CBS Records. Catalogue no: **461183 2**
**Cass:** Released Sep '88, on CBS by CBS Records. Catalogue no: **461183 4**

**KING OF THE BLUES**
**Cass:** Released Sep '81, on Ampro Catalogue no: **AMP 011**

**LEGEND LIVES**
**CD:** Released May '88, on Arcade Deleted Dec '88. Catalogue no: **ADEHCD 780**

**LIVE : RAY CHARLES**
**2 LP Set:** Released Nov '87, on Atlantic by WEA Records. Catalogue no: **2-503**

**LOVE SONGS, THE**
Tracks: / I wonder who's kissing her now / Oh baby / Honey honey / Hey now / I live only for you / I'm glad for your sake / All night long / Blues is my middle name / Here am I / I used to be so happy / Ego song, The / Late in the evening blues / St. Pete's blues / I'm just a lonely boy / See see rider.

**Album:** Released 24 Jun '88, on Deja Vu Catalogue no: **DVLP 2121**
**Cass:** Released 24 Jun '88, on Deja Vu Catalogue no: **DVMC 2121**

**MAKIN' WHOOPEE**
Tracks: / Makin' whoopee.
**7" Single:** Released Jan '65, on H.M.V. by EMI Records. Deleted Jan '68. Catalogue no: **POP 1383**

**MODERN SOUNDS IN COUNTRY AND WESTERN MUSIC, VOL. 2**
**Album:** Released Jul '62, on H.M.V. by EMI Records. Deleted Jul '67. Catalogue no: **CLP 1580**
**Album:** Released Feb '63, on H.M.V. by EMI Records. Deleted Feb '68. Catalogue no: **CLP 1613**

**NO ONE**
Tracks: / No one.
**7" Single:** Released Sep '63, on H.M.V. by EMI Records. Deleted Sep '66. Catalogue no: **POP 1202**

**NO ONE TO CRY TO**
Tracks: / No one to cry to.
**7" Single:** Released Sep '64, on H.M.V. by EMI Records. Deleted Sep '67. Catalogue no: **POP 1333**

**RAY CHARLES**
**CD:** Released Sep '87, on Entertainers Catalogue no: **ENT CD 203**
**Album:** Released Sep '87, on Entertainers Catalogue no: **ENT 13005**
**Album:** Released Jul '88, on Bellaphon Catalogue no: **BID 8011**
**Cass:** Released Oct '84, on Audio Fidelity(USA) by Audio Fidelity (USA). Catalogue no: **ZCGAS 729**
**Album:** Released '88, on Entertainers Catalogue no: **ENT LP 13005**
**Cass:** Released Sep '80, on Pickwick by Pickwick Records. Catalogue no: **SSC 3075**
**Cass:** Released '88, on Entertainers Catalogue no: **ENT MC 13005**

**RAY CHARLES AND BETTY CARTER (Charles, Ray & Betty Carter)**
Tracks: / Every time we say goodbye / You and I / Goodbye, we'll be together again / People will say we're in love / Cocktails for two / Side by side / Baby it's cold outside / Together / For all we know / It takes two to tango / Alone together / Just you and me / But on the other hand baby / I never see Maggie alone / I like to hear it sometimes.
**Album:** Released Nov '89, on Essential by Castle Communications Records. Catalogue no: **ESSLP 012**
**CD:** Released Dec '89, on Essential by Castle Communications Records. Catalogue no: **ESSCD 012**
**Cass:** Released Nov '89, on Essential by Castle Communications Records. Catalogue no: **ESSMC 012**

**RAY CHARLES BLUES**
**Cass:** Released Nov '84, on Astan (USA) Catalogue no: **40079**
**Album:** Released Nov '84, on Astan (USA) Catalogue no: **20079**

**RAY CHARLES (DOUBLE CASSETTE)**
**Cass set:** Released '88, on Ditto by Pickwick Records. Catalogue no: **DTO 10202**

**RAY CHARLES (JOKER (USA))**
**Album:** Released '88, on Joker (USA) by Lifetime Records (USA). Catalogue no: **SM 3712**

**RAY CHARLES STORY, THE**
Tracks: / Baby won't you please come home / Ego song, The / You always miss the water (when the well runs dry) / St. Pete's blues / I live only for you / What have I done / C.C. rider / I've had my fun / Honey honey / Here am I / I wonder who's kissing her now / Ray Charles blues / She's on the ball / If I give you my love / I'm going down to the river / Let's have a ball / Hey now / Sitting on top of the world / Sentimental blues, A / I used to be so happy / Ain't that fine / All to myself alone / Georgia on my mind / What'd I say / Come rain or come shine.
**Cass:** Released May '89, on Deja Vu Catalogue no: **DVREMC 02**
**CD:** Released May '89, on Deja Vu Catalogue no: **DVRECD 02**

**RAY CHARLES VOL.2**
Tracks: / Alone in the city / Can anyone ask for more / Rockin' chair blues / Let's have a ball / If I give you my love / Can't see you darling? / This love of mine / Sentimental blues, A / Now she's gone / Going down slow.
**Album:** Released Apr '81, on Joker (USA) by Lifetime Records (USA). Catalogue no: **SM 3729**

**RAY OF HOPE**
Tracks: / See see rider / I wonder who's kissing her now / Hey now / Tell me baby / Kiss me baby / I'm gonna drown myself / Winter scene / Lovin' the girls.
**Album:** Released Aug '80, on Manhattan Records by President Records. Catalogue no: **MAN 5020**

**RIGHT TIME, THE**
Tracks: / Leave my woman alone / My Bonnie / That's enough / Drown in my own tears / Fool for you, A / Hallelujah I love her so / This little girl of mine / Mary Ann / I got a woman / Yes indeed / Swanee river rock / Lonely avenue / I had a dream / Early in the morning / Right time, The / I'm movin' on / What kind of man are you (Extra track on CD only) / I want to know (Extra track on CD only) / What'd I say part 1 (Extra track on the CD only) / What'd I say (part 2) (Extra track on the CD only) / Jumpin' in the mornin'.
**Cass:** Released Jul '87, on Atlantic by WEA Records. Catalogue no: **241 119-4**
**Album:** Released Jul '87, on Atlantic by WEA Records. Catalogue no: **241 119-1**
**CD:** Released Jul '87, on Atlantic by WEA Records. Catalogue no: **241 119-2**

**ROCKIN' WITH RAY**
**Album:** Released '88, on Joker (USA) by Lifetime Records (USA). Catalogue no: **SM 3871**

**SEVEN SPANISH ANGELS**
Tracks: / Seven Spanish angels / Who cares.

**7" Single:** Released May '85, on CBS by CBS Records. Deleted May '88. Catalogue no: **A 4991**

### SHAKE YOUR TAIL FEATHER
Tracks: / Shake your tail feather / Minnie the moocher.
**7" Single:** Released Oct '80, on Atlantic by WEA Records. Deleted Oct '83. Catalogue no: **K 11615**

### SIMPLY RAY
Tracks: / All to myself alone / Going down slow / Baby let me hold your hand / I won't let you go / Sitting on top of the world / By myself / Winter scene / Lovin' the girls.
**Album:** Released May '80, on Manhattan Records by President Records. Catalogue no: **MAN 5019**

### SOUL MEETING (Charles, Ray & Milt Jackson)
Tracks: / Hallelujah I love her so / Blue genius / X-ray blues / Soul meeting / Love on my mind / Bags of blues.
**Album:** Released Jul '76, on Atlantic by WEA Records. Catalogue no: **K 50234**

### SPIRIT OF CHRISTMAS, THE
Tracks: / What child is this / Little drummer boy / Santa Claus is coming to town / This time of the year / Rudolph the red nosed reindeer / That spirit of Christmas / All I want for Christmas / Christmas in my heart / Winter wonderland / Christmas time.
**Album:** Released Dec '85, on CBS by CBS Records. Deleted '87. Catalogue no: **CBS 26562**
**Cass:** Released Dec '85, on CBS by CBS Records. Deleted Aug '87. Catalogue no: **40 26562**

### STAR COLLECTION
Tracks: / I got a woman / Let the good times roll / Ray, The / Loosing hand / Mess around / Mary Ann / This little girl of mine / Talkin' bout you / Undecided / Alexanders Rag Time Band / Don't let the sun catch you crying.
**Album:** Released '88, on Atlantic by WEA Records. Catalogue no: **K 20015**
**Cass:** Released '88, on Atlantic by WEA Records. Catalogue no: **K4 20015**

### TAKE THESE CHAINS FROM MY HEART
Tracks: / Take these chains from my heart.
**7" Single:** Released May '63, on H.M.V. by EMI Records. Deleted May '66. Catalogue no: **POP 1161**

### TELL THE TRUTH
Tracks: / Mess around / It should've been me / Losing hand / Greenbacks / I got a woman / This little girl of mine / Hallelujah / I love her so / Drown in my own tears / Leave my woman alone / Lonely Avenue / That's enough / Talkin' 'bout you / You be my baby / Right time, The / Tell the truth / What'd I say?.
**Cass:** Released Mar '84, on Charly R&B by Charly Records. Deleted '88. Catalogue no: **TCCRB 1071**
**Album:** Released Mar '84, on Charly R&B by Charly Records. Deleted '88. Catalogue no: **CRB 1071**

### THIS LOVE OF MINE
Tracks: / Kiss me baby / Baby let me hold your hand / C.C. rider / I wonder who's kissing her now / I'm going down to the river / They're crazy about me / Going down slow / Sentimental blues, A / Can anyone ask for more / Rockin' chair blues / If I give you my love / This love of mine.
**Cass:** Released '86, on Topline by Charly Records. Catalogue no: **KTOP 126**
**Album:** Released '86, on Topline by Charly Records. Catalogue no: **TOP 126**
**CD:** Released Apr '87, on Topline by Charly Records. Catalogue no: **TOP CD 512**

### TOGETHER AGAIN
Tracks: / Together again.
**7" Single:** Released Apr '66, on H.M.V. by EMI Records. Deleted Apr '69. Catalogue no: **POP 1519**

### TRUE TO LIFE
**Album:** Released Jan '78, on London Records by London Records Ltd. Catalogue no: **SHU 8509**

### WHAT IS LIFE?
Tracks: / Going to the river / Steppin' out baby / Dear heart / Glow worm / Take some and leave some / All alone / I'll do anything but work / My mama told me / I'm yours for the asking / Blow my baby back home / Too late to change / What is life?.
Note: Recorded, 1949.
**Cass:** Released Apr '83, on Barclay (France) by Decca Records. Catalogue no: **MB9 90112**
**Album:** Released Apr '83, on Barclay (France) by Decca Records. Catalogue no: **B 90112**

### WISH YOU WERE HERE TONIGHT
Tracks: / 3/4 times / I wish you were here tonight / Ain't your memory got no pride at all / Born to love me / I don't want no stranger sleepin' in my bed / Let your love flow / You feel good all over / String bean / You've got the longest leaving act in town / Shakin' your head.
**CD:** Released Mar '90, on Collector's Choice by CBS Records. Catalogue no: **9022892**

### YESTERDAY
Tracks: / Yesterday.
**7" Single:** Released Dec '67, on Stateside by EMI Records. Deleted Dec '70. Catalogue no: **SS 2071**

### YOU DON'T KNOW ME
Tracks: / You don't know me.
**7" Single:** Released Sep '62, on H.M.V. by EMI Records. Deleted Sep '65. Catalogue no: **POP 1064**

### YOUR CHEATIN' HEART
Tracks: / Your cheatin' heart.
**7" Single:** Released Dec '62, on H.M.V. by EMI Records. Deleted Dec '65. Catalogue no: **POP 1099**

## Charles, Teddy

### ON CAMPUS (Charles, Teddy & Zoot Sims)
**Album:** Released Feb '88, on Fresh Sounds (Spain) by Fresh Sounds Records (Spain). Catalogue no: **FS 237**

### SALUTE TO HAMP
**Album:** Released Feb '88, on Fresh Sounds (Spain) by Fresh Sounds Records (Spain). Catalogue no: **FS 151**

## Charleston Chasers

### CHARLESTON CHASERS 1925/28
**Album:** Released Apr '79, on VJM (Vintage Jazz Music) by Vintage Jazz Music Society(VJM). Catalogue no: **VLP 26**

### CHARLESTON CHASERS 1929/31
**Album:** Released Apr '79, on VJM (Vintage Jazz Music) by Vintage Jazz Music Society(VJM). Catalogue no: **VLP 44**

## Charlesworth, Dick

### BILLY BOY
Tracks: / Billy boy.
**7" Single:** Released May '61, on Top Rank (1) Deleted May '64. Catalogue no: **JAR 558**

## Charquet & Co

### CHARQUET & CO.-VOLUME 3
**Album:** Released Jun '86, on Stomp Off (USA) Catalogue no: **SOS 1053**

### CHARQUET & CO.-VOLUME 4
**Album:** Released Jun '86, on Stomp Off (USA) Catalogue no: **SOS 1076**

### DANS LES JUNGLES DU POITOU
**Album:** Released Aug '77, on Pragmaphone Deleted '83. Catalogue no: **PRG LP 16**

### LIVE AT THE JOSEPH LAM JAZZ CLUB
**Album:** Released Jan '84, on Stomp Off (USA) Catalogue no: **SOS 1039**

### YOU'LL LONG FOR ME
**Album:** Released '89, on Stomp Off (USA) Catalogue no: **SOS 1195**

## Chase, Tommy

### DRIVE
Tracks: / Drive / Close your eyes / Love for sale / Sunset eyes / Bogata George / Honest John / Whisper not / Straight edge / Tin tin red / Ray's idea.
**Album:** Released May '85, on Paladin Deleted Aug '87. Catalogue no: **PAL 5**

### GROOVE MERCHANT
Note: Hard-driving bop drummer with exciting combo, including brilliant young keyboards man Mark Edwards.
**Cass:** Released Jun '87, on Stiff by Stiff Records. Catalogue no: **ZSEEZ 66**
**CD:** Released Jun '87, on Stiff by Stiff Records. Catalogue no: **CDSEEZ 66**
**Album:** Released Jun '87, on Stiff by Stiff Records. Catalogue no: **SEEZ 66**

### HARD (Chase, Tommy Quartet)
Tracks: / Minority / Blue sunset / Message, The / Del Sasser / No problem / Ladybirds.
**Album:** Released 3 Feb '84, on Boplicity by Ace Records. Deleted '88. Catalogue no: **BOP 5**

### KILLER JOE (RIGHT CROSS)
Tracks: / Killer Joe / Double street.
**7" Single:** Released Feb '87, on Stiff by

Stiff Records. Catalogue no: **BUY 256**
**12" Single:** Released Feb '87, on Stiff by Stiff Records. Catalogue no: **BUYIT 256**

**ONE WAY (Chase, Tommy & Ray Warleigh)**
Tracks: / I remember you / Stars fell on Alabama / Speak low / Like someone in love / Chasin' the Bimpt / What's new?.
Note: With Jon Eardley.
**Album:** Released '83, on Spotlite by Spotlite Records. Catalogue no: **SPJ 510**

## Cheatham, Doc

**Biographical details:** Adolphus Anthony Cheatham, born in 1905 in Nashville, Tennessee, has been a first-class lead trumpet player and soloist for more than 50 years. He also played reeds as a young man, recording with Ma Rainey on soprano sax in the 1920's; he worked for Sam Wooding in Europe in the late '20's and for many others, but his most famous tour of duty was with Cab Calloway intermittently from 1933. Unusually for a brass prayer, he just gets better as he gets older. Sammy Price (on the Sackville duet album) was house pianist at Decca Records USA for many years, recording with Rosetta Tharp, Trixie Smith and others, as well as his own Texas Bluesicians in the early '40's, including Lester Young. (Donald Clarke, April 1989).

**BLACK BEAUTY**
Tracks: / Travellin' all alone / Some of these days / Love will find a way / After you've gone / Someday you'll be sorry / Old fashioned love / I'm coming Virginia / Squeeze me / Memphis blues / I've got a feeling I'm falling / Louisiana.
**Album:** Released Nov '83, on Sackville by Spotlite Records. Catalogue no: **3029**

**DOC & SAMMY (Cheatham, Doc & Sammy Price)**
Tracks: / Honeysuckle rose / Sam & Doc's blues / Summertime / Tishomingo blues / Sheik of Araby, The / I can't give you anything but love / You can depend on me / Ain't misbehavin' / Dear old Southland.
**Album:** Released Jul '86, on Sackville by Spotlite Records. Catalogue no: **3013**

**ECHOES OF HARLEM (Cheatham, Doc & George Kelly)**
**Album:** Released Jan '88, on Stash (USA) Catalogue no: **ST 265**

**FABULOUS DOC CHEATHAM, THE**
Note: With Dick Wellstood, Bill Pemberton, Jackie Williams.
**Album:** Released Jul '88, on Parkwood Catalogue no: **PARKWOOD 104**

**FESSOR'S NIGHTHAWKS (Cheatham, Doc/John Williams/Herb Hall)**
**Album:** Released Jun '81, on Metronome (Denmark) Catalogue no: **MELP 627**
**Album:** Released Jan '88, on Storyville by Storyville Records AB. Catalogue no: **SLP 430**

**IT'S A GOOD LIFE (Cheatham, Doc & His New York Quartet)**
**Album:** Released Jul '88, on Parkwood Catalogue no: **PARKWOOD 101**

**I'VE GOT A CRUSH ON YOU, VOL.2**
Tracks: / I've got a crush on you / I'd do most anything for you / It's been a long time / Squeeze me / Upstairs with the judge / It's that great Basie band.
**Album:** Released 8 Apr '89, on New York Catalogue no: **J 003**

**TOO MARVELLOUS FOR WORDS, VOL.1**
Tracks: / It's been so long / East St Louis toodle-oo / Let's do it / Procurement, Smith here / Too marvellous for words / Blues in the night / It's that great Basie Band.
**Album:** Released 8 Apr '89, on New York Catalogue no: **J 002**

**TRIBUTE TO BILLIE HOLIDAY (Cheatham, Doc & Swedish All Stars)**
Note: with Henri Chaix.
**Album:** Released Jan '88, on Kenneth Catalogue no: **KS 2061**

## Cheatham, Jeannie

**BACK TO THE NEIGHBORHOOD (Cheatham, Jeannie & Jimmy)**
**Cass:** Released 12 Apr '89, on Concord by Concord Jazz Records (USA). Catalogue no: **CJ 373C**
**CD:** Released 12 Apr '89, on Concord by Concord Jazz Records (USA). Catalogue no: **CCD 4373**
**Album:** Released 12 Apr '89, on Concord by Concord Jazz Records (USA). Catalogue no: **CJ 373**

**HOMEWARD BOUND (Cheatham, Jeannie & Jimmy)**
Tracks: / Permanent solution / Going down slow / Daddy o / Trouble in mind / You don't have to go / Hello, little boy / Detour ahead / Sometimes it be that way.
Note: Personnel: Jeannie Cheatham - piano & vocals / Jimmy Cheatham - bass trombone / Red Callender - bass/ John 'Ironman' Harris - drums / Dinky Morris - Tenor & Baritone sax / Jimmie Noone - tenor saxophone & clarinet / Curtis Peagler - alto & tenor saxophone / Snooky Young - trumpet / Eddie "Cleanhead" Vinson - also sax &vocal (special guest).
**CD:** Released Jul '87, on Concord Jazz by Concord Jazz Records (USA). Catalogue no: **CCD 4321**
**Album:** Released Jul '87, on Concord Jazz by Concord Jazz Records (USA). Catalogue no: **CJ 321**
**Cass:** Released Jul '87, on Concord Jazz by Concord Jazz Records (USA). Catalogue no: **CJC 321**

**MIDNIGHT MAMA (Cheatham, Jeannie & Jimmy)**
Tracks: / Wrong direction blues / C.C. rider / Worried life blues / Big fat daddy blues / Midnight mama / Piney Brown / Finanace company / How long blues / Reel ya' deel ya dee dee dee..
Note: This lively set of blues from singer/pianist Jeanie Cheatham and trombonist/arranger Jimmy Cheatham follows their overwhelmingly successful debut release 'Sweet baby blues'(CJ 258).
Personnel: Jeannie Cheatham - piano & vocals/Jimmy Cheatham - bass trombone/Red Callender - bass/John'Ironman'Harris - drums/Dinky Morris - tenor, soprano & baritone sax/Jimmie Noone - tenor sax & clarinet/Curtis Peagler - alto sax/Snooky Young - trumpet. Special guest - Eddie 'Lockjaw' Davis - tenor sax.
**Cass:** Released Apr '86, on Concord Jazz by Concord Jazz Records (USA). Catalogue no: **CJC 297**
**Album:** Released Apr '86, on Concord Jazz by Concord Jazz Records (USA). Catalogue no: **CJ 297**

**SWEET BABY BLUES (Cheatham, Jeannie & Jimmy)**
Tracks: / Brand new blues blues / Roll 'em Pete / Sweet baby blues / I got a mind to ramble / Ain't nobody's business if i do / Muddy water blues / Cherry red / Meet me with your black drawers on.
**Album:** Released Feb '85, on Concord Jazz by Concord Jazz Records (USA). Catalogue no: **CJ 258**
**CD:** Released Nov '89, on Concord by Concord Jazz Records (USA). Catalogue no: **CCD 4258**

## Cherry, Don

**Biographical details:** Trumpeter, cornettist and composer Don Cherry (born in 1936 in Oklahoma City) also plays flutes, bells, gamelon, etc. He came to prominence in Ornette Coleman's 'free jazz' quartet, playing a small 'pocket' trumpet; he also recorded with John Coltrane in 1960, played with Steve Lacy and Sonny Rollins, and was a cofounder of the New York Contempory Five in 1963-4 with Archie Shepp and John Tchicai. Most recently he has been a member of Old and New Dreams, modeled after Coleman's original group. (Donald Clarke, April 1989).

**ART DECO**
Tracks: / Art deco / Body and soul / Maffy / Blessing, The / I've grown accustomed to her face / When will the blues leave / Bemsha swing / Folk medley / Passing / Compute.
**Album:** Released 24 Jul '89, on A&M by A&M Records. Catalogue no: **395 258-1**
**Cass:** Released 24 Jul '89, on A&M by A&M Records. Catalogue no: **395 258-4**
**CD:** Released 24 Jul '89, on A&M by A&M Records. Catalogue no: **395 258-2**

**AVANTE-GARDE (Cherry, Don & John Coltrane)**
Tracks: / Cherryco / Focus on sanity / Blessing, The / Invisible, The / Bemsha swing.
**Album:** Released Jan '79, on Atlantic by WEA Records. Catalogue no: **K 50523**

**BAND OF GOLD**
Tracks: / Band of gold.

**7" Single:** Released Feb '56, on Philips by Phonogram Ltd. Deleted Feb '59. Catalogue no: **PB 549**

**BROWN RICE**
Tracks: / Brown rice / Malkauns / Chenrezig / Degi-degi.
**CD:** Released 28 Nov '88, on A&M by A&M Records. Catalogue no: **CDA 0809**

**COMPLETE COMMUNION**
Tracks: / Complete communion / And now / Golden heard / Remeberance / Elephantasy / Our feelings / Bishmallah / Wind sand & stars.
**Album:** Released Sep '84, on Blue Note by EMI Records. Deleted '87. Catalogue no: **BST 84226**

**DON CHERRY**
**Album:** on A&M by A&M Records. Deleted '88. Catalogue no: **AMLJ 717**

**EL CORAZON (Cherry, Don & Ed Blackwell)**
**Album:** Released Oct '82, on ECM Catalogue no: **ECM 1230**

**ETERNAL NOW, THE**
Tracks: / Gamla Stan / Old town by night, The / Love train / Piano piece for two pianos and three piano players / Moving pictures for the ear.
**Album:** on Sonet by Sonet Records. Deleted '74. Catalogue no: **SNTF 653**

**ETERNAL RHYTHM**
**Album:** Released Dec '74, on Polygram by PolyGram UK Ltd. Catalogue no: **21-20680**

**HOME BOY, SISTER OUT**
Tracks: / Butterfly friend / I walk / Rappin' recipe / Reggae to the high tower / Art deco / Call me / Treat your lady right / Alphabet city / Bamako love.
Note: Don Cherry first became known while playing his "pocket trumpet" with Ornette Coleman Quartet in the late fifties. He has been described as the "Universal World Musician". This new album on Barclay takes Cherry away from the the avante-garde. The theme here is contemporary black music and features the sounds of reggae, funk and rappin'.Cherry also sings as well as playing trumpet, piano and synthesizer. Personnel: Don Cherry/Ramuntoho Matta/Jannick Top/Claude Salmieri/Negrito Trasante/Elli Medieros/Abdoulaye Prosper Niang/Jean-Pierre Coco/Fil Mong.
**Cass:** Released Dec '85, on Barclay (France) by Decca Records. Catalogue no: **827 488 4**
**CD:** Released Dec '85, on Barclay (France) by Decca Records. Catalogue no: **827 488 2**
**Album:** Released Dec '85, on Barclay (France) by Decca Records. Catalogue no: **827 488 1**

**IN ANKARA**
Tracks: / Gandalf's travels / Ornette's concert / Ornette's tune / St. John and the dragon / Efeler / Anadolu havasi / Discovery of Bhupala / Water boy / Yaz geldi / Tamzara / Kara Deniz / Kocekce / Man on the moon / Creator has a master plan, The / Two flutes.
**Album:** Released Aug '78, on Sonet by Sonet Records. Catalogue no: **SNTF 669**

**MU-FIRST PART**
Tracks: / Brilliant action / Amejelo / Total vibration (part 1) / Total vibration (part 2) / Sun of the East / Terrestrial beings.
**Album:** on Affinity by Charly Records. Deleted '88. Catalogue no: **AFF 8**

**MU-SECOND PART**
**Album:** Released '78, on Affinity by Charly Records. Deleted '88. Catalogue no: **AFF 17**

**OLD AND NEW DREAMS (Cherry, Don/Dewey Redman/Charlie Haden/Eddie Blackwell)**
**CD:** Released Jan '86, on Black Saint (Italy) Catalogue no: **BSR 0013**

**ORIENT**
Tracks: / Eagle eyes / Si ta ra ma / Togetherness.
**2 LP Set:** Released Mar '83, on Affinity by Charly Records. Deleted '88. Catalogue no: **AFFD 82**

## Chess (label)

**BEST OF CHESS BLUES, THE (Various artists)**
Tracks: / Rollin' stone: *Waters, Muddy* / Black angel blues: *Nighthawk, Robert* / 24 hours: *Boyd, Eddie* / Seventh son: *Mabon, Willie* / Reconsider baby: *Fulson, Lowell* / Hoochie coochie man (I'm your): *Waters, Muddy* / Smokestack lightnin': *Howlin' Wolf* / Juke: *Little Walter* / Eisenhower blues: *Lenoir, J.B.* / Walking by myself: *Rogers, Jimmy* / Back door man: *Howlin' Wolf* / Madison blues: *James, Elmore* / Your funeral my trial: *Williamson, Sonny Boy* / So many roads,so many trains: *Rush, Otis* / My time after a while: *Guy, Buddy* / Bring it on home: *Williamson, Sonny Boy* / One bourbon one scotch one beer: *Hooker, John Lee* / Baby what you want me to do: *James, Etta* / Stormy monday: *Little Milton* / Wang dang doodle: *Taylor, Koko.*
**CD:** Released Oct '88, on Vogue by Vogue Records. Catalogue no: **VGCD 670 080**
**CD:** Released Feb '90, on MCA by MCA Records. Catalogue no: **CHD 31315**
**Cass:** Released Dec '87, on Chess by Vogue Records. Catalogue no: **GCHK 2-6023**
**2 LP Set:** Released Dec '87, on Chess by Vogue Records. Catalogue no: **GCH 2-6023**

**BEST OF CHESS, CHECKER, CADET (Various artists)**
**Album:** Released Apr '81, on Checker (USA) Catalogue no: **CXMP 2003**

**CHESS BLUES RARITIES (Various artists)**
Tracks: / Recession blues: *King, B.B.* / Don't keep me waiting: *King, B.B.* / Tickle britches: *King, B.B.* / Don't break your promise: *Burnett, Chester* / You can't put me out: *Burnett, Chester* / Gettin' late: *Burnett, Chester* / Rockin daddy: *Burnett, Chester* / I didn't know: *Burnett, Chester* / I better go now: *Burnett, Chester* / New crawlin' king snakes: *Burnett, Chester* / My mind is ramblin': *Burnett, Chester* / Tail dragger: *Burnett, Chester* / Poor wind that never changes: *Burnett, Chester* / Stick around: *Guy, Buddy* / Gully hully: *Guy, Buddy* / That's it: *Guy, Buddy* / American bandstand: *Guy, Buddy* / Untitled instrumental: *Guy, Buddy* / My love is real: *Guy, Buddy* / Moanin': *Timmons, Bobby* / Down home special: *Taylor, Hound Dog* / Watch out: *Taylor, Hound Dog* / Scrappin': *Taylor, Hound Dog* / Sittin' here alone: *Taylor, Hound Dog* / Hound dog: *Taylor, Hound Dog* / Little village: *Williamson, Sonny Boy* / Unseen eye: *Williamson, Sonny Boy.*
Note: Five great blues artists on one double album - BB King, Howlin' Wolf, Buddy Guy, Hound Dog Taylor and Sonny Boy Williamson perform some of their rarest sides. A must for blues fans.
**Album:** Released May '85, on Chess (PRT) Deleted '88. Catalogue no: **CMXD 4055**

**CHESS, CHECKER, CADET (Various artists)**
Note: Includes Mel Robbins 'Save It', Dale Hawkins 'Suzy Q', etc.
**Album:** Released Apr '78, on Chess (PRT) Deleted '88. Catalogue no: **9124213**

**CHESS CHICAGO BLUES (Various artists)**
**Album:** Released May '83, on Chess (USA) Catalogue no: **CXMD 4013**

**CHESS DOO WOP (Various artists)**
Tracks: / White cliffs of Dover: *Blue Jays* / Darling I know: *El Rays* / Shoo doo be doo: *Moonlighters* / Newly weds: *Orchids* / Show me the way: *Five Notes* / Give me (a simple prayer): *Ravens* / Nadine: *Coronets* / Ding dong: *Quintones* / 4 o'clock in the morning: *Tornados* / I want to love: *Sentimentals* / Teardrops: *Andrews, Lee & The Hearts* / Soft shadows: *Monotones* / I'm so young: *Students* / So far away: *Pastels* / This broken heart: *Sonics* / False alarm: *Ravels.*
**Album:** Released '89, on Chess by Vogue Records. Catalogue no: **DET 200**
**Album:** Released '89, on Chess by Vogue Records. Catalogue no: **GCH 8101**
**Cass:** Released '89, on Chess by Vogue Records. Catalogue no: **GCHK78101**

**CHESS MASTERS (Various artists)**
**Album:** Released Apr '82, on Chess (USA) Catalogue no: **CXMD 4010**

**CHESS NEW ORLEANS R&B (Various artists)**
**Album:** Released 7 Nov '87, on Chess by Vogue Records. Catalogue no: **DET 205**

**CHESS SAMPLER (Various artists)**
Tracks: / My babe: *Little Walter* / Help me: *Williamson, Sonny Boy* / Smokestack lightning: *Howlin' Wolf* / Mannish

boy: *Waters, Muddy* / Sugar mama: *Hooker, John Lee* / Dust my broom: *James, Elmore* / Walking by myself: *Rodgers, Jimmie (1)* / Road runner: *Diddley, Bo* / Brown eyed handsome man: *Berry, Chuck* / Wang dang doodle: *Taylor, Koko* / We're gonna make it: *Little Milton* / High heel sneakers: *Little Tommy Tucker* / Soulful dress: *Sugar Pie Desanto* / Security: *James, Etta*.
**Cass:** Released Oct '84, on Chess (PRT) Deleted '88. Catalogue no: **ZCCXSP 7250**
**Album:** Released Oct '84, on Chess (PRT) Deleted '88. Catalogue no: **CXSP 7250**

**CHESS SISTERS OF SOUL (Various artists)**
Tracks: / Wang dang doodle: *Taylor, Koko* / Selfish one: *Ross, Jackie* / Mama didn't lie: *Bradley, Jan* / Two sides (to every story): *James, Etta* / Take me for a little while: *Ross, Jackie* / Rescue me: *Bass, Fontella* / Sally go round the roses: *Jaynettes* / Only time will tell: *James, Etta* / I had a talk with my man: *Collier, Mitty* / Lovin' you more every day: *James, Etta* / Yield not to temptation: *Franklin, Aretha*.
Note: Some of the greatest soul records of all time on one album. All performed by girls. A great package which is a must for all 60's soul freaks.
**Cass:** Released Jun '84, on Chess (PRT) Deleted '88. Catalogue no: **ZCCXMP 2052**
**Album:** Released Jun '84, on Chess (PRT) Deleted '88. Catalogue no: **CXMP 2052**

**CHESS SOUL CLASSICS (Various artists)**
**CD:** Released '88, on Greenline by Charly Records. Catalogue no: **CD CHESS 100**

**CHESS THE RHYTHM AND THE BLUES (Various artists)**
**CD:** Released Jul '88, on Chess by Vogue Records. Catalogue no: **CDSAM 500**
**Cass:** Released Jul '88, on Chess by Vogue Records. Catalogue no: **TCSAM 500**
**Album:** Released Jul '88, on Chess by Vogue Records. Catalogue no: **SAM 500**

## Chess Story

**CHESS STORY 1954-1969 (Various artists)**
Tracks: / Bye bye Johnny: *Berry, Chuck* / Suzie Q: *Hawkins, Dale* / Rinky dink: *Cortez, Dave 'Baby'* / In the mood: *Hooker, John Lee* / Madison blues: *James, Elmore* / Ain't got no home: *Henry, Clarence 'Frogman'* / Sincerely: *Moonglows* / Sneakin' around: *Little Milton* / Rescue me: *Fontella Bass* / Stop around: *Guy, Buddy* / Bring it to Jerome: *Diddley, Bo* / High heel sneakers: *Tucker, Tommy* / Mannish boy: *Waters, Muddy* / Smokestack lightning: *Howlin' Wolf* / In crowd, The: *Lewis, Ramsey Trio* / Peanut butter: *Marathons* / Only time will tell: *James, Etta* / Get closer together: *Tex, Joe* / Selfish one: *Ross, Jackie*.
**2 LP Set:** Released Apr '89, on Connoisseur Collection by Connoisseur Collection Ltd.. Catalogue no: **VSOPLP 130**
**CD:** Released Apr '89, on Connoisseur Collection by Connoisseur Collection Ltd.. Catalogue no: **VSOPCD 130**
**Cass:** Released Apr '89, on Connoisseur Collection by Connoisseur Collection Ltd.. Catalogue no: **VSOPMC 130**

## Chevallier, Christian

**FORMIDABLE**
**Album:** Released Feb '88, on Fresh Sounds (Spain) by Fresh Sounds Records (Spain). Catalogue no: **FS 186**

**SIX PLUS SIX**
**Album:** Released Feb '88, on Fresh Sounds (Spain) by Fresh Sounds Records (Spain). Catalogue no: **FS 185**

## Chicago Blues

**BEST OF CHICAGO BLUES, THE**
**CD:** Released May '89, on Start by Start Records Ltd.. Catalogue no: **VNP 7312**
**Cass:** Released May '89, on Start by Start Records Ltd.. Catalogue no: **VNP 6312**
**Album:** Released May '89, on Start by Start Records Ltd.. Catalogue no: **VNP 5312**

**CHICAGO BLUES (Various artists)**
Tracks: / Tough times: *Brim, John* / Be careful: *Brim, John* / Anna Lee: *Nighthawk, Robert* / Jackson town gal: *Nighthawk, Robert* / So glad I found you: *Shines, Johnny* / Having fun: *Slim, Memphis* / Goin' away baby: *Rogers, Jimmy* / Chicago bound: *Rogers, Jimmy* / Dark road: *Jones, Floyd* / You can't live long: *Jones, Floyd* / Dust my broom: *James, Elmore* / I see my baby: *James, Elmore* / Eisenhower blues: *Lenoir, J.B.* / Korea blues: *Lenoir, J.B.* / By myself: *Broonzy, Big Bill/Washboard Sam* / Murmur low: *Spires, Big Boy* / I can't stop: *Rush, Otis* / You know my love: *Rush, Otis* / Third degree: *Boyd, Eddie* / Ten years ago: *Guy, Buddy* / My time after a while: *Guy, Buddy*.
**Cass:** Released Feb '86, on RCA by BMG Records (UK). Deleted Jul '89. Catalogue no: **NK 89588**
**Album:** Released Feb '86, on RCA by BMG Records (UK). Deleted Jul '89. Catalogue no: **NL 89588**

**CHICAGO BLUES (Various artists)**
**CD:** Released Aug '87, on Greenline by Charly Records. Catalogue no: **CDCHESS 1001**

**CHICAGO BLUES 1937-41 (Various artists)**
**Album:** Released '89, on HK Catalogue no: **HK 4007**

**CHICAGO BLUES ANTHOLOGY (Various artists)**
Tracks: / Tough times: *Brim, John* / Anna Lee: *Nighthawk, Robert* / So glad I found you: *Shines, Johnny* / Having fun: *Various artists* / Goin' away baby: *Rodgers, Jimmie (1)* / I don't know: *Mabon, Willie* / Dark road: *Jones, Floyd* / Dust my broom: *James, Elmore* / Eisenhower blues: *Lenoir, J.B.* / By myself: *Broonzy, Big Bill* / Murmur low / Rattlesnake: *Brim, John* / I see my baby: *James, Elmore* / Korea blues: *Lenoir, J.B.* / You can't live long: *Jones, Floyd* / I can't stop: *Rush, Otis* / Third degree: *Boyd, Eddie* / Ten years ago: *Guy, Buddy* / Be careful: *Brim, John* / Jackson Town gal: *Nighthawk, Robert* / World's in a tangle, The: *Rodgers, Jimmie (1)* / You know my love: *Rush, Otis* / My time after awhile: *Guy, Buddy* / Chicago bound: *Guy, Buddy*.
**Album:** Released Jul '84, on Chess (PRT) Deleted '88. Catalogue no: **CXMD 4053**

**CHICAGO BLUES AT HOME (Various artists)**
**Album:** Released Apr '79, on Advent by Advent Records. Catalogue no: **ADVENT 2806**

**CHICAGO BLUES -EARLY 50'S**
**Album:** Released '88, on Blues Classics(USA) by Arhoolie Records (USA). Catalogue no: **BC 8**

**CHICAGO BLUES HARMONICAS (Various artists)**
**CD:** Released 10 Jul '89, on Flyright by Interstate Music. Catalogue no: **FLYCD 11**

**CHICAGO BLUES LIVE (Various artists)**
Note: Homesick james, Detroit Junior, Small Blues Charlie, J. Bhutto, Brewer Phillips.etc.
**Album:** Released Jan '88, on Wolf Catalogue no: **WOLF 120.287**

**CHICAGO BLUES (RED LIGHTNIN') (Various artists)**
Tracks: / We're ready: *Guy, Buddy & Junior Wells* / First time I met the blues: *Guy, Buddy & Junior Wells* / Country girl: *Guy, Buddy & Junior Wells* / Hoodoo man: *Guy, Buddy & Junior Wells* / In my younger days: *Guy, Buddy & Junior Wells* / Driving wheel: *Young, Johnny* / Walking groundhog: *Young, Johnny* / She's 19 years old: *Waters, Muddy* / Hoochie coochie man: *Waters, Muddy* / I got my mojo working: *Waters, Muddy* / Why you want to hurt me: *Young, Mighty Joe* / Wang dang doodle: *Taylor, Koko* / Speak my mind: *Hutto, J.B.* / Come on back home: *Hutto, J.B.* / You're gonna miss me: *Lewis, Johnny* / Uncle Sam: *Lewis, Johnny* / Hobo blues: *Lewis, Johnny*.
**CD:** Released '89, on Red Lightnin' by Red Lightning Records. Catalogue no: **RLCD 0080**
**2 LP Set:** Released Jun '85, on Red Lightnin' by Red Lightning Records. Deleted Jun '89. Catalogue no: **RL 055**
**Album:** Released Jun '85, on Red Lightnin' by Red Lightning Records. Catalogue no: **RL 0055**

**CHICAGO BLUES SESSION 2 (Various artists)**
Album: Released '88, on Wolf Catalogue no: **WOLF 120 848**

**CHICAGO BLUES SESSION 3 (Various artists)**
Note: Magic Slim & Teardrops etc.
**Album:** Released '88, on Wolf Catalogue no: **WOLF 120 249**

**CHICAGO BLUES SESSION 8 (Various artists)**
Note: Artists include Honey Boy Edwards.
**Album:** Released Jul '88, on Wolf Catalogue no: **WOLF 120 854**

**CHICAGO BLUES (VIDEO) (Various artists)**
**VHS:** Released '88, on Kay Jazz (video) by Kay Jazz. Catalogue no: **KJ 004**

## Chicago Blues Meeting

**SNAKE IN MY BEDROOM**
Tracks: / For my love / I can't stop / When the cat is gone / Take a walk with me / You can't lose what you ain't never had / Snake in my bedroom / 'Bout the break of day / Doing the dishes / Blues for an unhappy girl / You got to notify your lover / Fine body / Tribute to Walter Horton / Bad boy / Going down slow.
Note: Stereo. C-Red Lightnin' Ltd. 1988. P-Red Lightnin' Ltd. 1988. Made in England.
**Album:** Released Aug '88, on Red Lightnin' by Red Lightning Records. Catalogue no: **RL 0073**

## Chicago Bluesmasters

**CHICAGO BLUESMASTERS, VOL.1 (Various artists)**
Tracks: / Combination boogie: *Various artists* / Now she's gone: *Various artists* / Pet cream man: *Various artists* / Dim lights: *Various artists* / Loving you: *Various artists* / Price of love, The: *Various artists* / Things are so slow: *Various artists* / Judgement day: *Various artists* / Someone to love me: *Various artists* / You tried to ruin me: *Various artists* / Nervous wreck: *Various artists* / No more love: *Various artists* / Just can't stay: *Various artists* / All by myself: *Various artists.*
**Album:** Released Mar '83, on Charly R&B by Charly Records. Catalogue no: **CRB 1042**

**CHICAGO BLUESMASTERS, VOL.2 (Ain't times hard) (Various artists)**
Tracks: / Schooldays on my mind: *Various artists* / Floyd's blues: *Various artists* / Any old lonesome day: *Various artists* / Delta Joe: *Various artists* / 4 o'clock blues: *Various artists* / I cried: *Various artists* / Johnnie Mae: *Various artists* / Lonesome ole train: *Various artists* / Whisky headed woman: *Various artists* / Williamson boogie: *Various artists* / I had a dream: *Various artists* / My baby's gone: *Various artists* / Can't eat, can't sleep: *Various artists* / Hesitatin blues: *Various artists.*
**Album:** Released Jul '88, on Charly R&B by Charly Records. Catalogue no: **CRB 1047**

**CHICAGO BLUESMASTERS, VOL.3 (Goin' back home) (Various artists)**
Tracks: / Goin' back home: *Various artists* / My baby left me: *Various artists* / Kings Highway: *Various artists* / Eula Mae: *Various artists* / About to lose my mind: *Various artists* / Which one do I love: *Various artists* / Silver haired woman: *Various artists* / Fat mouth: *Various artists* / That's alright: *Various artists* / Just keep loving her: *Various artists* / Talkin' boogie: *Various artists* / Miss Lorraine: *Various artists* / I love to boogie: *Various artists* / Graveyard blues: *Various artists* / 609 boogie: *Various artists* / Road trouble: *Various artists.*
**Album:** Released Feb '84, on Charly R&B by Charly Records. Catalogue no: **CRB 1067**

**CHICAGO BLUESMASTERS, VOL.4 (Chills & fever) (Various artists)**
Note: 15 tracks from Vee Jay Records: featuring: L.C.McKinley/Jimmy Eager (Tampa Red)/Birmingham Jones/Hubert Sumlin/Willie Cobbs. The fourth and final volume of this series, which, like CRB's 1042,1047 & 1067,presents some of the rarest, most collectable blues masters from the vaults of VJ Records. This volume contrasts differing styles of blues: Side One: Features downhome blues, with harmonica and guitar in rural style. Side Two: offers more sophisticated city guitars stylings. As with the three volumes the principal market for this release will of course be among hardcore blues collectors but the reputation of this series created by the previous volumes should ensure fairly broad interest and sales.
**Album:** Released Apr '85, on Charly R&B by Charly Records. Catalogue no: **CRB 1080**

## Chicago Gospel Pioneers

**CHICAGO GOSPEL PIONEERS (Various artists)**
Note: With Robert Anderson, Lucy Smith, Delois Barrett Campbell and others.
**Album:** Released Jun '88, on Spirit Feel by Shanachie Records (USA). Catalogue no: **SF 1004**

## Chicago Hot Six

**STOMPING AT THE GOOD TIME**
**Album:** Released Jun '86, on GHB by Jazzology Records (USA). Catalogue no: **GHB 176**

## Chicago Jazz

**CHICAGO (Various artists)**
**Album:** Released '83, on RCA (France) by BMG Records (France). Catalogue no: **PM 43267**

**CHICAGO AND ALL THAT JAZZ (Various artists)**
Note: Telecast, 26 November, 1961. A musical journey into the history of Chicago jazz hosted by Gary Moore and featuring such musicians as Jack Teagarden, Eddie Condon, Gene Krupa, Kid Ory, Red Allen and Johnny Guarnieri.
**Album:** Released Apr '88, on Sounds Great Catalogue no: **SG 8007**

**CHICAGO JAZZ 1928-33 (Various artists)**
Tracks: / There'll be some changes made: *Chicago Rhythm Kings* / I've found a new baby: *Chicago Rhythm Kings* / Baby won't you please come home?: *Chicago Rhythm Kings* / Jazz me blues: *Various artists* / Trying to stop me crying: *Manone, Joe 'Wingy' & Club Royal Orchestra* / Isn't there a little love?: *Manone, Joe 'Wingy' & Club Royal Orchestra* / Eel, The: *Condon, Eddie & His Orchestra* / Copenhagen: *Schoebel, Elmer & Friars Society Orchestra* / Prince of wails: *Schoebel, Elmer & Friars Society Orchestra* / Milenberg joys: *O'Hare, Husk & Wolverines* / My daddy rocks me: *O'Hare, Husk & Wolverines* / Wailing blues takes A & B: *Cellar Boys* / Barrel house stomp ABC: *Cellar Boys.*
**Album:** Released Jan '83, on Swaggie (Australia) Catalogue no: **S 809**

**CHICAGO JAZZ VOL.2 Russell's Hot Six (Various artists)**
Note: Richard M. Jones/Omer Simeon etc.
**Album:** Released Jul '81, on Classic Jazz Masters Catalogue no: **CJM 40**

## Chicago Jump

**CHICAGO JUMP (Various artists)**
**Album:** Released Jan '82, on JSP by JSP Records. Catalogue no: **JSP 1004**

## Chicago Rhythm

**CAUTION BLUES**
**Album:** Released Jun '88, on Jazzology (USA) by Jazzology Records (USA). Catalogue no: **J 157**

**MADE IN CHICAGO (Various artists)**
**Album:** Released Nov '88, on Stomp Off (USA) Catalogue no: **SOS 1164**

**REMEMBERS HERITAGE OF '20S & '30S**
**Album:** Released '88, on Stomp Off (USA) Catalogue no: **SOS 1026**

**ROUND EVENING**
**Album:** Released Jun '86, on Jazzology (USA) by Jazzology Records (USA). Catalogue no: **J 127**

## Chicago Slickers

**CHICAGO SLICKERS 1948-53 VOL 1 (Various artists)**
**Album:** Released Apr '79, on Nighthawk by Nighthawk Records (USA). Catalogue no: **NH 102**

**CHICAGO SLICKERS 1948-55 VOL 2 (Various artists)**
Note: This album is released in mono. Featuring: Little Walter, Floyd Jones, John Brim, Robert Nighthawk etc.
**Album:** Released Jan '87, on Nighthawk by Nighthawk Records (USA). Catalogue no: **NH 107**

## Chief John

**BYE & BYE (Chief John & His Mahogany Hall Stompers)**

**Album:** Released Sep '87, on Five O Four Records Catalogue no: **504 LP 13**
**Cass:** Released Sep '87, on Five O Four Records Catalogue no: **504 TC 13**

## Chisholm, George

### CHISHOLM TRAIL (Chisholm, George All Stars)
**Album:** Released Jul '88, on 77 by 77 Records. Catalogue no: **77 SEU 12/43**

### GEORGE CHISHOLM/KEITH SMITH/HEFTY JAZZ (Chisholm, George/Keith Smith/Hefty Jazz)
**Album:** Released Jul '82, on Flutegrove Catalogue no: **HJ 107**

### SWINGING MR.C
Tracks: / Swinging Mr.C / Tin roof blues / Sophisticated lady / One for monk / Flip flop / You've changed / Don't worry 'bout me / Old feeling, The / Dear bix / I'm beginning to see the light.
**Album:** Released Oct '86, on Zodiac by Delta Records. Catalogue no: **ZR 1026**

### THAT'S A PLENTY (Chisholm, George Jazz Giants)
Note: With Kenny Baker, Tommy Whittle, Henry McKenzie, Brian Lemon.
**Album:** Released Jul '88, on Zodiac by Delta Records. Catalogue no: **ZR 1025**

### WITH MAXINE DANIELS & JOHN PETTERS BAND (Chisholm, George/Maxine Daniels & John Petters)
**CD:** Released Mar '90, on CMJ Catalogue no: **CMJ CD 011**
**Cass:** Released Mar '90, on CMJ Catalogue no: **CMJ MC 011**

## Chittison, Herman

### AT THE PIANO
**Cass:** Released Jun '86, on Holmia Cassettes Catalogue no: **HM 05**

### COCKTAIL PIANO FAVOURITES (Chittison Trio, Herman)
Tracks: / Memories of you / Dancing in the ceiling / September in the rain / Can't we be friends / My blue heaven / I've had my moments / Continental, The / Should I / Let's fall in love / Isn't it romantic / They can't take that away from me / On the sunny side of the street / Just a memory / On the Alamo / Ain't misbehavin'.
**Cass:** Released Jul '89, on CBS (import) by CBS Records. Catalogue no: **461 078 4**

### ELEGANT PIANO STYLING OF...
Note: Full title:- Elegant piano styling of Herman Chittison Jazz Piano Solos.
**Album:** Released Jan '88, on 88-UR Catalogue no: **88-UR 006**

### MASTER OF STRIDE PIANO
**Album:** Released '88, on Meritt (USA) Catalogue no: **MERITT 20**

### PIANO GENIUS
Tracks: / Song has ended, The / How high the moon / Poor butterfly / I should care / These foolish things / I had the craziest dream / Where or when.
**Album:** Released '88, on Musicraft (USA) by Discovery Records (USA). Catalogue no: **MVS 506**

## Chocolate Dandies

### CHOCOLATE DANDIES (1928-1933)
**Album:** Released Jan '83, on Swaggie (Australia) Catalogue no: **S 1249**

### JAZZ BANDS 1926/30
**Album:** on Historical (USA) by Biograph Records (USA). Catalogue no: **HLP 16**

## Christian, Charlie

**Biographical details:** A pioneer of the electric guitar and a jazz giant before his early death from TB (1916-42). Born in Texas, he was the first to understand that the amplified instrument made possible sustained notes as well as greater volume, inventing a style which influenced bop and every subsequent guitarist in jazz. He made nearly all his recordings with the Benny Goodman Sextet, but also played acoustic guitar with an Edmond Hall Quartet on Blue Note, and some informal jam session recordings at Minton's Playhouse in Harlem. (Donald Clarke, April 1989).

### 1941 HISTORICAL PERFORMANCES
**CD:** Released Oct '88, on Vogue by Vogue Records. Catalogue no: **VGCD 600 135**

### 1941 LIVE SESSIONS
**Album:** Released Oct '88, on Vogue by Vogue Records. Catalogue no: **500114**

### CHARLIE CHRISTIAN
Note: Featuring Benny Goodman, Lester Young, Count Basie, Fletcher Henderson, etc.
**Album:** Released Sep '87, on Giants of Jazz by Hasmick Promotions. Catalogue no: **LPJT 13**

### CHARLIE CHRISTIAN & BENNY GOODMAN SEXTET (Christian, Charlie/Benny Goodman Sextet & Orch.)
**Album:** Released '88, on Jazz Catalogue no: **JA 23**

### CHARLIE CHRISTIAN WITH BENNY GOODMAN SEXTET (Christian, Charlie/Benny Goodman Sextet & Orch.)
**Album:** on Realm Catalogue no: **525 38**

### GENIUS OF THE ELECTRIC GUITAR
Tracks: / Rose room / Seven Come Eleven / Till Tom Special / Gone with "what" wind / Grand slam / Six appeal / Wholly cats / Royal Garden blues / As Long As I Live / Benny's bugle / Breakfast Feud / I Found A New Baby / Solo Flight / Blue in B / Waiting for Benny / Air Mail Special.
**Album:** Released Apr '88, on CBS (import) by CBS Records. Catalogue no: **4606121**
**Cass:** Released Apr '88, on CBS (import) by CBS Records. Catalogue no: **4606124**
**CD:** Released Mar '90, on Giants of Jazz by Hasmick Promotions. Catalogue no: **GOJCD53049**

### HARLEM JAZZ SCENE 1941
**Album:** Released Feb '88, on Fresh Sounds (Spain) by Fresh Sounds Records (Spain). Catalogue no: **FS 278**

### LIVE AT MINTON'S 1941
**CD:** Released Oct '89, on Jazz Anthology by Musidisc Records (France). Catalogue no: **550012**

## Christian, Emile

### EMILE CHRISTIAN & HIS NEW ORLEANS JAZZ BAND (Christian, Emile & His New Orleans jazz band)
**Album:** Released Mar '87, on Southland by Delta Records. Catalogue no: **SLP 223**

## Christie, Keith

### HOMAGE TO THE DUKE (See also under Johnny Dankworth/Ray Nance/Johnny Hodges)
**Album:** Released Dec '87, on Esquire by Titan Int. Prod.. Catalogue no: **ESQ 336**

## Christmas New Orleans

### CHRISTMAS NEW ORLEANS STYLE (Various artists)
**Album:** Released May '79, on Dawn Club by Cadillac Music. Catalogue no: **DC 12020**

## Christy, June

**Biographical details:** A popular and influential jazz singer who replaced Anita O'Day in the Stan Kenton band in 1945; she sounded like O Day but developed a more personal style. hits with Kenton included *Tampico*, she won polls and made an album for CBS with Nat Cole and other poll winners called *Nat meets June with the Metronome Allstars.* She married Kenton's tenor solist Bob Cooper in 1946 and when solo when he dibanded in 1946, but continued recording with him later; her solo albums on Capitol were bestsellers in the '50's and have recently been digitally remastered with excellent results. (Donald Clarke, April 1989).

### BEST OF JUNE CHRISTY
Tracks: / Just a-sittin' and a-rockin' / Midnight sun / They can't take that away from me / Bewitched / How high the moon / My heart belongs to only you / Willow weep for me / Across the alley from the Alamo / Nobody's heart / Sing something simple / Something cool.
**Album:** Released Apr '84, on Capitol by EMI Records. Catalogue no: **CAPS 2600091**

### BEST THING FOR YOU
Tracks: / When lights are low / My one and only love / How high the moon / Easy street / Kissin' bug / My heart belongs to only you / Something cool / Midnight sun / I'll take romance / This time the dream's on me / Dearly beloved / Until the real thing comes along / This year's kisses / When sunny gets blue / Best thing for

you, The / Give me the simple life.
**Album:** Released '86, on Affinity by Charly Records. Catalogue no: **AFF 145**

**CAPITOL YEARS, THE:JUNE CHRISTY (Best of)**
Tracks: / Give me the simple life / Imagination / It's a most unusual day / When sunny gets blue / I want to be happy / I'm thrilled / They can't take that away from me / Something cool / It don't mean a thing / I should care / When lights are low / My ship / Give a little whistle / Do nothing till you hear from me / Just a sittin' and a rockin' / How high the moon.
**CD:** Released Jul '89, on Capitol by EMI Records. Catalogue no: **CDEMS 1336**
**CD:** Released Jul '89, on Capitol by EMI Records. Catalogue no: **CDP 792 588 2**
**Cass:** Released Jul '89, on Capitol by EMI Records. Catalogue no: **792 588 4**
**Album:** Released Jul '89, on Capitol by EMI Records. Catalogue no: **EMS 1336**
**Cass:** Released Jul '89, on Capitol by EMI Records. Catalogue no: **TCEMS 1336**
**CD:** Released Jul '89, on Capitol by EMI Records. Catalogue no: **CZ 198**
**Album:** Released Jul '89, on Capitol by EMI Records. Catalogue no: **792 588 1**

**HOLLYWOOD BOWL PT.1 (Christy, June & Stan Kenton)**
**Album:** Released '84, on First Heard by Submarine Records. Catalogue no: **FH 52**
**Cass:** Released '84, on First Heard by Submarine Records. Catalogue no: **CFH 52**

**IMPROMPTU (Christy, June & Lou Levy Sextet)**
Tracks: / Everything must change / I'll remember April / Angel eyes / Willow weep for me / My shining hour.
**Album:** Released Sep '79, on Interplay (USA) by Interplay Records (USA). Deleted Sep '84. Catalogue no: **IP 7710**
**Album:** Released '88, on Discovery (USA) by Discovery Records (USA). Catalogue no: **DS 836**
**CD:** Released '88, on Discovery (USA) by Discovery Records (USA). Catalogue no: **DSCD 826**

**INTERLUDE**
Tracks: / It's so peaceful in the country / When the sun comes out / It's most unusual day / Interlude / Love turns winter to spring / When you awake / Lazy after-noon / When the world was young / Gone for the day / Lost in a summer night / Give me the simple life / Love's got me in a lazy mood.
**Album:** Released Apr '85, on Discovery (USA) by Discovery Records (USA). Catalogue no: **DS 911**
**Cass:** Released '88, on Discovery (USA) by Discovery Records (USA). Catalogue no: **DSC 911**

**JUNE CHRISTY 1977**
**CD:** Released Feb '90, on Storyville by Storyville Records AB. Catalogue no: **STCD 4168**

**JUNE CHRISTY AND THE KEY-TONES 1946**
**Album:** Released '88, on Hindsight Catalogue no: **HSR 219**

**JUNE TIME (Christy, June & Friends)**
Tracks: / How high the moon / What's new / Wrap your troubles in dreams / Can't help lovin' dat man / I'm thrilled / Stompin' at the Savoy.
**Cass:** Released Jun '85, on Swing House by Submarine Records. Catalogue no: **CSWH 20**
**Album:** Released Jun '85, on Swing House by Submarine Records. Catalogue no: **SWH 20**

**JUNE'S GOT RHYTHM**
**Album:** Released Feb '88, on Fresh Sounds (Spain) by Fresh Sounds Records (Spain). Catalogue no: **FS 12**

**LOVELY WAY TO SPEND AN EVENING,**
Tracks: / Lovely way to spend an evening / From this moment on / Let there be love / I'll take romance / Midnight sun / How high the moon / Rock me to sleep / It's a most unusual day / Willow weep for me / It don't mean a thing / Lullaby in rhythm / That's all.
**Cass:** Released Sep '89, on Jasmine by Hasmick Promotions. Catalogue no: **JASMC 2528**
**Album:** Released Jan '88, on Sounds Great Catalogue no: **SG 5009**
**Album:** Released Sep '89, on Jasmine by Hasmick Promotions. Catalogue no: **JASM 2528**

**MISTY MISS CHRISTY**
Tracks: / That's all / I didn't know about you / Daydream / Sing something simple / Maybe you'll be there / Dearly beloved / Round midnight / Lovely way to spend an evening, A / Wind, The / This years' kisses / For all we know / There's no you.
Note: Quite a rare album of late, this record was a best seller when it was first released in the 50's. This is one of Miss Cristy's most successful albums of late night listening also featuring the great writing talents of Berlin, Kern and Ellington.
**Cass:** Released Jan '86, on Capitol by EMI Records. Deleted Jan '88. Catalogue no: **TCEMS 1132**
**Album:** Released Jan '86, on Capitol by EMI Records. Deleted Jun '89. Catalogue no: **EMS 1132**

**MISTY MISS CHRISTY (IMPORT)**
Tracks: / That's all / I didn't know what time it was / Daydream / Sing something simple / For all we know / There's no you / Maybe you'll be there / Dearly beloved / Round midnight / Lovely way to spend an evening, A / This year's kisses.
Note: Orchestra arranged and conducted by Pete Rugolo.
**Album:** Released '88, on Discovery (USA) by Discovery Records (USA). Catalogue no: **DS 919**
**Cass:** Released '88, on Discovery (USA) by Discovery Records (USA). Catalogue no: **DSC 919**

**RECALL THOSE KENTON DAYS**
Tracks: / Just a sittin' and a rockin' / Hundred years from today / Lonesome road / He's funny that way / It's a pity to say goodnight / Willow weep for me / Easy street / Across the valley from the Alamo / Come rain or come shine / How high the moon.
**Cass:** Released Mar '88, on Capitol by EMI Records. Deleted Nov '88. Catalogue no: **TCEMS 1286**
**Album:** Released Mar '88, on Capitol by EMI Records. Deleted Nov '88. Catalogue no: **EMS 1286**

**THIS IS JUNE CHRISTY**
Tracks: / My heart belongs to only you / Whee baby / You took advantage of me / Get happy / Look out up there / Great scot / Kicks / Why do you have to go home / Bei mir bist du schon / Until the real thing comes along / I'll remember April / I never wanna look in those eyes again.
**Album:** Released Apr '84, on Capitol by EMI Records. Deleted Nov '88. Catalogue no: **CAPS 2600511**
**Cass:** Released Apr '84, on Capitol by EMI Records. Deleted Jan '88. Catalogue no: **TC CAPS 2600514**

**WAY TO THE WEST (Christy, June/Parker, Johnny/Ferguson, Maynard)**
**Album:** Released Feb '88, on Fresh Sounds (Spain) by Fresh Sounds Records (Spain). Catalogue no: **FS 28**

## Chrysanthemum

**BRINGIN' EM BACK**
**Album:** Released '88, on Stomp Off (USA) Catalogue no: **SOS 1047**

**CHRYSANTHEMUM RAGTIME BAND (Chrysanthemum Ragtime Band)**
**Album:** Released Jun '86, on Stomp Off (USA) Catalogue no: **SOS 1079**

**DANCING ON THE EDGE**
**Album:** Released '88, on Stomp Off (USA) Catalogue no: **SOS 1168**

**PRESERVES (Chrysanthemum Ragtime Band)**
**Album:** Released Mar '87, on Stomp Off (USA) Catalogue no: **SOS 1123**

## Churchill, Savannah

**Biographical details:** A top R&B and jazz singer (c.1924-74) who worked with Benny Carter. She had several hits between 1947-53, some with all-star jazzmen backing. See also under Una Mae Carlisle. (Donald Clarke, April 1989).

**TIME OUT FOR TEARS**
**Album:** Released Jun '85, on Jukebox Lil (Sweden) Catalogue no: **JB 1101**

## Cincinnati Blues

**CINCINNATI BLUES 1928-36 (Various artists)**
**Album:** Released Dec '88, on Earl Archives Catalogue no: **BD 2021**

## Clarinet...

**CLARINET JAZZ GIANTS Golden hour (Various artists)**
**Album:** Released '78, on Golden Hour Catalogue no: **GH 649**

**CLARINET JAZZ GIANTS (SET) (Various artists)**
**Cass set:** Released '88, on Ditto by Pickwick Records. Catalogue no: **DTO 10227**

**CLARINET PLAYING LEADERS (Various artists)**
**Album:** Released '79, on Golden Era by Delta Records. Catalogue no: **GELP 15078**

**YOU BETTER FLY AWAY (Various artists)**
**Album:** Released '81, on MPS Jazz Catalogue no: **MPS 68 251**

## Clark, Buddy

**Biographical details:** Born in 1912, Buddy Clarke was a superior singer with big bands whose real name was Samuel Goldberg. He attended law school but turned to music in 1932; he sang on the radio and on a great many records without even getting label credit, but finally began getting personal recognition on hits with Xavier Cugat and Ray Noble (the delightful *Linda* was a USA number one hit in 1947), duets with Doris Day and Dinah Shore, and even under his own name: he had six hits in 1949 and was killed in a plane crash in October. His easy phrasing and fresh, young voice means that his work still hasn't dated. (Donald Clarke, April 1988).

**BUDDY CLARK**
Tracks: / Come rain or come shine / I get a kick out of you / Way down yonder in New Orleans / Let's face the music and dance / If I had my life to live over / But not for me / One more time / There's a great day coming, Manana / So in love / You'll never walk alone / It ain't necessarily so (with Dinah Shore) / Five foot two, eyes of blue / Just look at me / Baby, it's cold outside (with Doris Day).
Note: Taken from 1949 broadcasts
**Album:** Released '87, on Ajaz (USA) Catalogue no: **AJAZ 516**

**BUDDY CLARK COLLECTION, THE (The Columbia years 1942-49)**
Tracks: / It's a big wide, wonderful world / Here I'll stay / I'll get by / Just one more chance / Linda / I'll dance at your wedding / You're too dangerous, cherie / Dreamer's holiday, A / I'll see you in my dreams / Apple blossom wedding, An / How are things in Glocca Morra? / That old gang of mine / My darling, my darling (with Doris Day) / Peg o' my heart / South America, take it away / Ballerina / Girl of my dreams / If this isn't love / You'd be so nice to come home to / When day is done.
**2 LP Set:** Released Aug '87, on Murray Hill Catalogue no: **P2-18848**

## Clark, Sonny

**Biographical details:** Jazz pianist (1931-63) who was already influential when he died much too young of a heart attack. He attracted attention touring with clarinettist Buddy De Franco in the mid '50's; most of his records as a leader were about ten albums for Blue Note beginning in 1957, often with all star casts. *Sonny's crib* includes John Coltrane; *Cool struttin'* has Jackie McLean and Art Farmer; both these plus the trio album have the wonderful Miles Davis sideman Paul Chambers on bass. (Donald Clarke, April 1989).

Kenny Clark - At Her Majesty's Pleasure (Polydor)

**COOL STRUTTIN'**
Tracks: / Cool struttin' / Blue minor / Sippin' at bells / Deep night / Royal flush / Lover.
**Album:** Released Feb '88, on Blue Note by EMI Records. Catalogue no: **BLJ 81588**
**CD:** Released Aug '88, on Blue Note by EMI Records. Catalogue no: **BNZ 19**
**CD:** Released Aug '88, on Blue Note by EMI Records. Catalogue no: **CDP 746 513 2**

**LEAPIN' AND LOPIN'**
Tracks: / Something special / Deep in a dream / Melody for C / Melody for C (alternate take) / Eric walks / Voodoo / Midnight mambo / Zellmar's delight.
**CD:** Released Apr '88, on Blue Note by EMI Records. Catalogue no: **BNZ 17**
**CD:** Released Apr '88, on Blue Note by EMI Records. Catalogue no: **CDP 784 091 2**
**Album:** Released Oct '84, on Blue Note by EMI Records. Deleted '87. Catalogue no: **BST 84091**

**SONNY CLARK TRIO (Clark, Sonny Trio)**
Tracks: / I didn't know what time it was (alternate take) / I didn't know what time it was / Two bass hit (alternate take) / Be-bop / Tadd's delight (alternate take) / Tadd's delight / Softly as in a morning sunrise / I'll remember April.
**CD:** Released Sep '87, on Blue Note by EMI Records. Catalogue no: **CDP 746 547 2**
**CD:** Released Sep '87, on Blue Note by EMI Records. Catalogue no: **BNZ 20**

**SONNY'S CRIB**
Tracks: / With a song in my heart / With a song in my heart (alternate take) / Speak low (From the musical production "One Touch of Venus") / Speak low (Alternate take) / Come rain or come shine / Sonny's crib / Sonny's crib (alternate take) / News for Lulu.
**CD:** Released Aug '87, on Blue Note by EMI Records. Catalogue no: **CDP 746 819 2**
**CD:** Released Aug '87, on Blue Note by EMI Records. Catalogue no: **BNZ 18**

## Clark, Spencer

**PLAY SWEET & HOT (Clark, Spencer & His Bass Sax)**
**Album:** Released Jun '86, on Audiophile (USA) by Jazzology Records (USA). Catalogue no: **AP 131**

## Clarke, Kenny

**Biographical details:** Along with Charlie Parker and Dizzy Gillespie, the famous bop drummer (1914-85) was one of the most important innovators in post-war jazz. He played on the original recording of *In the mood* in 1938 (by Edgar Hayes, copied within a year by Glenn Miller), then worked for Teddy Hill, who gave him his nickname 'Klook', complaining about his 'klook-mop' sound; but Hill later became the bandleader at Minton's in Harlem, where he allowed the young boppers to do their thing. Clarke was among the liberators of the drum kit; he began to play music rather than merely keep time, and was famous for dropping 'bombs' (bass drum accents) wherever he liked rather than on every beat. He later complained that his foot had got tired, but that sounds like the response of a man who had got tired of a dumb question. He played in the Gillespie and Billy Eckstine big bands and was a founder member of the Modern Jazz Quartet in 1952-55, and moved to France in 1956. He played with pianist Bud Powell and bassist Pierre Michelot from 1959 in the Three Bosses, the ace Paris rhythm section, e.g. on Dexter Gordon's *Our man in Paris* in 1963. He was co-leader with the Belgian pianist/arranger Francy Boland of the Clarke-Boland Big band albums of the post war era; but the albums were not well distributed and the band never even toured the USA. (Donald Clarke, April 1989).

**ALL BLUES**
**Album:** Released may '81, on MPS Jazz Catalogue no: **MPS 68 227**

**AT HER MAJESTY'S PLEASURE (Code O)(Clarke, Kenny & Francy Boland Big Band)**
**Album:** Released '75 on Code O Catalogue no: **2460 131**

**AT HER MAJESTY'S PLEASURE(Black Lion) (Clarke, Kenny & Francy Boland Big Band)**
Tracks: / Pentonville / Wormwood Scrubs: dawn / Doing time / Broadmoor / Holloway / Reprieve / Going straight.
**Album:** Released Jan '85 on Black Lion Catalogue no: **BLP 30109**

**KENNY CLARKE MEETS THE DETROIT JAZZMEN**
**Album:** Released Feb '85 on Savoy (France) Deleted May '89. Catalogue no: **WL 70515**

**LIVE IN PARIS**
**Cass:** Released Mar '84, on EMI (France) by EMI Records. Catalogue no: **2M 256 64848**
**Album:** Released Mar '84, on EMI (France) by EMI Records. Catalogue no: **2M 056 64848**

**PARIS/COLOGNE 1957 AND 1960**
**Album:** Released Oct '86, on Ace by Ace Records. Catalogue no: **SW 8411**

**PLAYS ANDRE HODEIR (Clarke, Kenny Sextet)**
**Album:** Released Jan '89, on Polygram (France) by PolyGram UK Ltd. Catalogue no: **834 542-1**

## Clarke, Stanley

**Biographical details:** This American bass guitarist, vocalist and producer, born in Philadelphia in June 1951, is at the forefront of jazz funk music. Clarke, who is a classically trained musician, began his move up the jazz ladder when he moved to New York in 1970. He spent the first half of the seventies in various bands, most notably with Chick Corea in group called Return To Forever, and also played with such well known names as Aretha Franklin and Carlos Santana. His debut eponymous album was issued in '74, and was followed by a further four solo LPs by the end of the seventies. 1980 brought Clarke his first British chart LP when *"Rocks, pebbles and sand"* reached no.42. The following year he teamed with fellow jazz funk fusionist George Duke for an album that was logically titled *"The Clarke/Duke project"*; this LP yielded the US top 20 single *"Sweet baby"*, Clarke's only taste of singles success. Typically for an artist of his genre, he puts musicianship before commercial dictates, and is content to serve his specialist market without moving over to the potentially big record sales of the broader pop audience. He is an innovative bassist, successfully projecting this instrument from an upfront position in preference to its conventional background role. (Bob Macdonald 1985) Born in Philadelphia in 1951, the bassist and composer is one of those who can use both acoustic and electric bass, knowing the difference. Early rock experience in the late '60's was followed by gigs with Horace Silver, Joe Henderson, Pharoah Sanders and Stan Getz, then with Chick Corea's fusion group *Return to forever*.He also played some violin and cello. His own albums have charted in the USA and he is also part of the Clarke/Duke Project with pianist/composer George Duke. Influential in both jazz and rock, he also played with Jeff Beck, the New Barbarians (a Rolling Stones spin-off), and made a funk cover of Bruce Springsteen's *Born in the USA*). (Donald Clarke, April 1989).

**BORN IN THE U.S.A.**
Tracks: / Born in the U.S.A. / Campo Americano.
**12" Single:** Released Jul '85, on Epic by CBS Records. Deleted Jul '88. Catalogue no: **TA 6372**
**7" Single:** Released Jul '85, on Epic by CBS Records. Deleted Jul '88. Catalogue no: **A 6372**

**CLARKE/DUKE PROJECT II (Clarke, Stanley & George Duke)**
Tracks: / Put it on the line / Heroes / Try me, baby / Every reason to smile / Great danes / Good times, The / You're gonna love it / Trip you in love / Atlanta.
**Album:** Released Dec '83, on Epic by CBS Records. Catalogue no: **EPC 25685**
**Cass:** Released Dec '83, on Epic by CBS Records. Deleted '85. Catalogue no: **40 25685**

**FIND OUT (Clarke, Stanley Band)**
Tracks: / Find out / What if I should fall in love? / Born in the USA / Sky's the limit, The / Don't turn the lights out / Campo Americano / Stero typica / Psychedelic / My life.
**Cass:** Released Jul '85, on Epic by CBS Records. Deleted Aug '87. Catalogue no: **40 26521**
**CD:** Released May '87, on CBS by CBS Records. Deleted Jan '89. Catalogue no: **CD 26521**
**Album:** Released Jul '85, on Epic by CBS Records. Catalogue no: **EPC 26521**

**FUSE ONE (Clarke, Stanley/Larry Coryell/John McLaughlin)**
**Album:** Released Mar '81, on IMS by Polydor Ltd. Catalogue no: **1063**

**HEAVEN SENT YOU**
Tracks: / Heaven sent you / Speedball.
**7" Single:** Released Jun '84, on Epic by CBS Records. Catalogue no: **A 4493**

**HEROES (Clarke, Stanley & George Duke)**
Tracks: / Heroes / Atlanta.
**12" Single:** Released Nov '83, on Epic by CBS Records. Deleted '86. Catalogue no: **TA 3860**
**7" Single:** Released Nov '83, on Epic by CBS Records. Deleted '86. Catalogue no: **A 3860**

**HIDEAWAY**
Tracks: / Overjoyed / My love, her inspiration / Where do we go / Boys of Johnson street / Old friends / When it's cold outside / Listen to the beat of your heart / Basketball / I'm here to stay.
**Cass:** Released Nov '86, on Epic by CBS Records. Catalogue no: **40 26964**
**CD:** Released '87, on Epic by CBS Records. Catalogue no: **CD 26964**

**I WANNA PLAY FOR YOU**
Tracks: / Rock'n'roll jelly / All about / Jamaican boy / Christopher Ivanhoe / My greatest hits / Strange weather / I wanna play for you / Just a feeling / Streets of Philadelphia / School days / Quiet afternoon / Together again / Blues for Mingus / Off the planet / Hot fun.
**Cass set:** Released Aug '79, on Epic by CBS Records. Catalogue no: **40 88331**
**2 LP Set:** Released May '82, on Epic by CBS Records. Catalogue no: **EPC 22133**

**IF THIS BASS COULD ONLY TALK**
Tracks: / If this bass could talk / I wanna play for you / Funny how time flies / Bassically taps / Working man / Come take my hand / Stories to tell / Tradition.
**Cass:** Released Aug '88, on Epic by CBS Records. Catalogue no: **460883 4**
**CD:** Released Aug '88, on Epic by CBS Records. Catalogue no: **460883 2**
**Album:** Released Aug '88, on Epic by CBS Records. Catalogue no: **460883 1**

**JOURNEY TO LOVE**
Tracks: / Silly putty / Journey to love / Hello Jeff / Song to John (part 1) / Song to John (part 2) / Concerto for jazz-rock orchestra.
**Album:** Released '79, on Nemperor (USA) Catalogue no: **K 50187**

**Cass:** Released Nov '81, on Epic by CBS Records. Catalogue no: **40 32093**
**Album:** Released Nov '81, on Epic by CBS Records. Deleted '86. Catalogue no: **EPC 32093**

### LET ME KNOW YOU
Tracks: / Straight to the top / Let me know you / You are the one for me / I just want to be your brother / Force of love / Play the bass / Secret to my heart / New York City.
**Album:** Released Sep '82, on Epic by CBS Records. Deleted Sep '87. Catalogue no: **EPC 85846**

### MODERN MAN
Tracks: / Opening (statement) / He lives on / More hot fun / Slow dance / Interlude / Serious occasion / Got to find my own place / Dayride / It's what she didn't say / Modern man / Relaxed occasion / Rock 'n' roll jelly / Closing (statement).
**Cass:** Released Feb '84, on CBS by CBS Records. Catalogue no: **40 32108**
**CD:** Released May '87, on CBS by CBS Records. Deleted Jan '89. Catalogue no: **CD 82674**
**Album:** Released Feb '84, on CBS by CBS Records. Deleted '86. Catalogue no: **CBS 32108**

### PROJECT (Clarke, Stanley & George Duke)
Tracks: / Wild dog / Louie Louie / Sweet baby / I just want to love you / Never judge a cover by it's book / Let's get started / Winners / Touch and go / Finding my way.
**Album:** Released May '81, on Epic by CBS Records. Deleted '86. Catalogue no: **EPC 84848**

### ROCKS, PEBBLES & SAND
Tracks: / Danger Street / All hell broke loose / Rocks, pebbles & sand / You / Me together / Underestimation / We supply / Story of a man and a woman / She thought I was Stanley Clarke / Fool again, A / I nearly went crazy (until I realised what had occurred).
**Cass:** Released Mar '83, on Epic by CBS Records. Catalogue no: **40 32300**
**Album:** Released Mar '83, on Epic by CBS Records. Deleted '86. Catalogue no: **EPC 32300**
**Album:** Released Jul '80, on Epic by CBS Records. Deleted Jul '85. Catalogue no: **EPC 84342**

### SCHOOL DAYS
Tracks: / School days / Quiet afternoon / Danger / Desert song, The / Hot fun / Life is just a game / Dancer.
**Album:** on Atlantic by WEA Records. Catalogue no: **K 50296**
**Cass:** Released Mar '82, on Epic by CBS Records. Deleted '87. Catalogue no: **40 32094**
**Album:** Released Mar '82, on Epic by CBS Records. Deleted '87. Catalogue no: **EPC 32094**
**CD:** Released May '87, on Epic by CBS Records. Deleted 17 Apr '89. Catalogue no: **450402 2**

### SHIELDSTONE (Clarke, Stanley & Bill Shields)
**CD:** Released Oct '87, on Optimism (Germany) Catalogue no: **RSVCD 9001**
**Album:** Released Oct '87, on Optimism (Germany) Catalogue no: **RSVP 9001**

### STANLEY CLARKE
Tracks: / Vulcan princess / Yesterday Princess / Lopsy lu / Power / Spanish phases for strings and bass / Life suite (part 1) / Life suite (part 2) / Life suite (part 3) / Life suite (part 4).
**Album:** Released Jul '81, on Epic by CBS Records. Deleted '86. Catalogue no: **EPC 32042**
**Album:** Released '81, on Nemperor (USA) Deleted '82. Catalogue no: **K 50101**

### STRAIGHT TO THE TOP
Tracks: / Straight to the top / Forces of love.
**7" Single:** Released Aug '82, on Epic by CBS Records. Deleted Aug '85. Catalogue no: **EPCA 2697**

### SWEET BABY (Clarke, Stanley & George Duke)
Tracks: / Sweet baby / Never judge a cover by it's book.
**7" Single:** Released Apr '81, on Epic by CBS Records. Deleted Apr '86. Catalogue no: **EPC A 1123**

### TIME EXPOSURE
Tracks: / Play the bass 103 / Are you ready / Speedball / heaven sent you / Time exposure / Future shock / Future / Spacerunner / I know just how you feel.
**Album:** Released May '84, on Epic by CBS Records. Catalogue no: **EPC 25486**
**Cass:** Released May '84, on Epic by CBS Records. Deleted '86. Catalogue no: **40 25486**

### YOU/ME TOGETHER
Tracks: / You/me together / Rocks, pebbles and sand.
**7" Single:** Released Aug '80, on Epic by CBS Records. Deleted '82. Catalogue no: **EPC 8945**

## Classic Hoagy Carmichael

### CLASSIC HOAGY CARMICHAEL (Various artists)
Tracks: / Stardust: *Various artists* / Georgia on my mind: *Various artists* / Lazy river: *Various artists* / Nearness of you, The: *Various artists* / Skylark: *Various artists* / Lazybones: *Various artists* / Rockin' chair: *Various artists.*
Note: Definitive tribute albums in conjunction with major Radio 2 series about the music of Hoagy Carmichael. Features major artists including Bing Crosby, Ella Fitzgerald, Louis Armstrong, Billie Holiday, Benny Goodman, Mills Brothers, Bob Hope, Sarah Vaughan, Paul Whiteman, Coleman Hawkins and Art Pepper. 55 recordings of the greatest Carmichael songs. Includes classic versions and previously unreleased rare material. (BBC, Nov 1988)
**CD Set:** Released Oct '88, on BBC by BBC Records & Tapes. Catalogue no: **BBC CD 4000**
**LP Set:** Released Oct '88, on BBC by BBC Records & Tapes. Catalogue no: **BBC 4000**
**Cass set:** Released Oct '88, on BBC by BBC Records & Tapes. Catalogue no: **ZCJ 4000**

## Classic Jazz Piano

### CLASSIC JAZZ PIANO (1927-1957) (Various artists)
Tracks: / Mr. Jelly Lord: *Morton, Jelly Roll* / Glad rag doll: *Hines, Earl* / State street special: *Yancey, Jimmy* / Honky tonk train blues: *Lewis, Meade Lux* / Thou swell: *Johnson, James P.* / Rompin': *Johnson, James P.* / Smashing thirds: *Waller, Fats* / Contrary motion: *Smith, Willie The Lion* / Out of nowhere: *Tatum, Art* / Where or when: *Wilson, Teddy* / Daybreak serenade: *Stacy, Jess* / Rosetta: *Hines, Earl* / Honeysuckle rose: *Waller, Fats* / Solitude: *Ellington, Duke* / Tonk: *Ellington, Duke/Billy Strayhorn* / Shine on, harvest moon: *Basie, Count* / All God's chillun got rhythm: *Williams, Mary Lou* / Erroll's bounce: *Garner, Erroll* / Poor butterfly: *Peterson, Oscar* / I don't stand a ghost of a chance with you: *Tristano, Lennie* / Shaw 'nuff: *Powell, Bud* / Concerto for Billy the Kid: *Evans, Bill.*
**Cass:** Released Apr '89, on Bluebird (2) by BMG Records (UK). Catalogue no: **NK 86754**
**CD:** Released Apr '89, on Bluebird (2) by BMG Records (UK). Catalogue no: **ND 86754**
**Album:** Released Apr '89, on Bluebird (2) by BMG Records (UK). Catalogue no: **NL 86754**

## Classic Jazz To Swing To

### CLASSIC JAZZ TO SWING TO - GREAT TRUMPETS (Various artists)
Tracks: / That's my home: *Armstrong, Louis* / West end blues: *Oliver, King* / Snag it: *Johnson, Bunk* / Everybody loves my baby: *Ladnier, Tommy* / Tip easy blues: *Collins, Lee* / Feeling drowsy: *Allen, Henry 'Red'* / Nobody knows the way I feel this morning: *De Paris, Sidney* / 'Sippi: *Smith, Jabbo* / Lonely melody: *Beiderbecke, Bix* / Davenport blues: *Nichols, Red* / Blues: *Berigan, Bunny* / (What did I do to be so) black and blue: *Spanier, Muggsy* / Jumpy nerves: *Manone, Wingy* / Shimme-shawabble: *Kaminsky, Max* / Peckin': *James, Harry* / Bublitchki: *Elman, Ziggy* / Concerto for Cootie: *Williams, Cootie* / Subtle slough: *Stewart, Rex* / Little jazz: *Eldridge, Roy* / Skull duggery: *Page, Hot Lips* / Blues my baby gave to me, The: *Newton, Frankie* / Buckin' the blues: *Clayton, Buck* / Mahogany hall stomp: *Armstrong, Louis.*
**CD:** Released Apr '89, on Bluebird (2) by BMG Records (UK). Catalogue no: **ND 86753**
**Cass:** Released Apr '89, on Bluebird (2) by BMG Records (UK). Catalogue no: **NK 86753**
**Album:** Released Apr '89, on Bluebird (2) by BMG Records (UK). Catalogue no: **NL 86753**

## Classic Jazz Ensemble

### CLASSIC BLUES
**Album:** Released '89, on Delmark (USA) by Delmark Records (USA). Catalogue no: **DS 221**

## Classic Jazz Quartet

### CLASSIC JAZZ QUARTET
Note: with Marty Grosz/Dick Sudhalter/Dick Wellstood.
**Album:** Released Jun '86, on Jazzology (USA) by Jazzology Records (USA). Catalogue no: **J 139**
**Album:** Released Mar '87, on Stomp Off (USA) Catalogue no: **SOS 1125**

## Classic Veji

### VANCOUVER ENSEMBLE OF JAZZ
**Album:** Released Nov '87, on From Bebop To Now(Canada) by From Bebop To Now Records (Canada). Catalogue no: **BBN 1003**

## Clay, Sonny

### SONNY CLAY 1922-1960
Tracks: / Mama likes to do it / What a wonderful time / Lou / Yama yama man / Weary blues / Front room blues / I found a new baby / Chimes blues / Tack head blues / Gang o'blues / Punishing the piano / Sister Kate / If I could be with you / Honeysuckle rose / After you've gone / Ain't misbehavin'.
**Album:** Released Nov '85, on Harlequin by Interstate Music. Catalogue no: **HQ 2007**

## Clayborn, Rev. Edward

### GUITAR EVANGELIST - 1926-1929, THE
Note: Released in mono.
**Album:** Released Jan '87, on Earl Archives Catalogue no: **BD 614**

## Clayton, Buck

**Biographical details:** The trumpeter and arranger, born in Parsons, Kansas in 1911, was playing in Shanghai with pianist Teddy Weatherford in 1935; the following year he replaced Hot Lips Page in Count Basie's band and has been one of the best loved stalwarts in mainstream jazz ever since. The series of excellent *Jam session* studio albums he made for CBS in the mid '50's is overdue for re-issue. (Donald Clarke, April 1989)..

### 1966: BUCK CLAYTON & HUMPHREY (Clayton, Buck & Humphrey Lyttleton)
**Album:** Released Jan '85, on Harlequin by Interstate Music. Catalogue no: **HQ 3002**

### A LA BUCK
**Album:** Released Nov '88, on Vogue by Vogue Records. Catalogue no: **500106**

### ALL THE CATS JOIN IN
**Album:** Released Feb '88, on Fresh Sounds (Spain) by Fresh Sounds Records (Spain). Catalogue no: **FS 272**

### ART FORD'S JAZZ PARTY (July 1958)
Tracks: / Foolin' myself / Perdido / It don't mean a thing / I surrender dear / I found a new baby / Easy to remember.
Note: With Tyree Glenn/Georgie Auld/Hank D'amico/Marty Napoleon/Vinnie Burke/Osie Johnson/Mal Waldron/Billie Holiday/Jackie Cooper/Mary Osborne.
**Album:** Released Oct '87, on Jazz Connoisseur by Spotlite Records. Catalogue no: **AFJP 1**

### CAT MEETS CHICK (Clayton, Buck/Ada Moore/Jimmy Rushing)
**Album:** Released Feb '88, on Fresh Sounds (Spain) by Fresh Sounds Records (Spain). Catalogue no: **FS 269**

### FEEL SO FINE (Clayton, Buck & Joe Turner)
Tracks: / Honeysuckle rose / I'm in a world of trouble / I can't get started / Feel so fine / Perdido / I want a little girl / Too late too late.
Note: With the Zagreb Jazz Quartet. 1965.
**Album:** Released Jul '87, on Black Lion Catalogue no: **BLP 30145**

### HUCKLE-BUCK AND ROBIN'S NEST 1953, THE
**Album:** Released May '79, on Japanese Import Catalogue no: **20 AP 1427**

### JAM SESSION FEATURING WOODY HERMAN
**Album:** Released Feb '88, on Fresh Sounds (Spain) by Fresh Sounds Records (Spain). Catalogue no: **FS 268**

### JAM SESSIONS FROM THE VAULT
**Album:** Released May '89, on CBS (import) by CBS Records. Catalogue no: **463 336 1**
**Cass:** Released May '89, on CBS (import) by CBS Records. Catalogue no: **463 336 4**
**CD:** Released May '89, on CBS (import) by CBS Records. Catalogue no: **463 336 2**

### JAMMIN' AT EDDIE CONDON'S, VOL.1 (Clayton, Buck & His Band)
Tracks: / Lulu's back in town / Basin Street blues / Fidgety feet / Medley / Big noise from Winnetka / At the Jazz Band Ball / Wolverine blues.
Note: Recorded in a live session.
**CD:** Released Nov '89, on Jazz-Up Catalogue no: **JU 311**

### JAMMIN' AT EDDIE CONDON'S, VOL.2 (Clayton, Buck & His Band)
Tracks: / When the saints go marching in / Ballin' the Jack / Medley / Ja da / Indiana / Bye bye blackbird / At the Jazz Band Ball / Basin Street blues / Original dixieland one step.
Note: Recorded in a live session.
**CD:** Released Nov '89, on Jazz-Up Catalogue no: **JU 312**

### JAZZ FESTIVAL JAZZ (Clayton, Buck & Duke Ellington)
Tracks: / Perdido / Finger-bustin' / Squeeze me / Tea for two / Diminuendo and crescendo in blue (Featuring tenor saxist Paul Gonsalves' famous 37 choruses) / Blues jam / Mood indigo.
**Album:** Released Apr '81, on Queendisc (Italy) Catalogue no: **QU 044**

### LIVE IN PARIS (Clayton, Buck & Jimmy Witherspoon)
Tracks: / Swingin' at the Camarillo / Polka dots and moonbeams / Outerdrive / Robin's nest / Moonglow / Swingin' the blues / I'll always be in love with you / Gee baby ain't I good to you / See see rider / I make a lot of money / Blowin' the blues / T'aint nobody's business if I do / Roll 'em Pete / Everything you do is wrong.
**2 LP Set:** Released Jan '77, on Vogue by Vogue Records. Catalogue no: **VJD 527**

### OLYMPIA CONCERT 1961
**CD:** Released Oct '87, on Vogue by Vogue Records. Catalogue no: **VGCD 600160**
**Album:** Released Oct '88, on Vogue by Vogue Records. Catalogue no: **500054**

### RARITIES VOL 1
Note: With Trummy Young and Slam Stewart.
**Album:** Released Jun '88, on Swingtime by Contact Records (Denmark). Catalogue no: **ST 1024**

### TRUMPET SUMMIT (Clayton, Buck & Roy Eldridge)
**Album:** Released Jun '78, on Pumpkin Catalogue no: **PUMPKIN 101**

### VERY SPECIAL BUCK CLAYTON, THE
**Album:** Released 21 Jul '89, on Jazz & Jazz Catalogue no: **JJ 608**

## Clayton, Doctor

### GOTTA FIND MY BABY
**Album:** Released Oct '87, on Bluetime (Denmark) by Contact Records (Denmark). Catalogue no: **BT 2005**

## Clayton, John

### TRIBUTE TO JOHN CLAYTON BIG BAND (Clayton, John Big Band)
**Album:** Released '88, on Timeless by Timeless Records. Catalogue no: **JC 11005**

## Clayton, Kid

### EXIT STARES, THE (Clayton's, Kid Happy Pals)
**Album:** Released '88, on Jazzology (USA) by Jazzology Records (USA). Catalogue no: **JCE 22**

### FIRST SESSION 1952, THE
**Album:** Released Mar '84, on Folkways (USA) by Folkways Records (USA). Catalogue no: **FJ 2859**

## Cleveland Gospel

### CLEVELAND GOSPEL (Various artists)

Tracks: / Need Jesus on my journey: *Friendly Brothers* / You can't thumb a ride: *Friendly Brothers* / You can't win: *Friendly Brothers* / Ten commandments: *Friendly Brothers* / I thank you Jesus: *Shield Brothers* / Saviour don't pass me: *Shield Brothers* / Won't you hear me pray: *Shield Brothers* / Pray every step: *Elite Jewels* / Going to move: *L & N Gospel Singers* / You been so good: *L & N Gospel Singers* / Ride on King Jesus: *Elite Jewels* / Standing on the rock: *Elite Jewels* / I'm going through: *Angels Of Harmony* / Now Lord: *Angels Of Harmony* / Do not pass me by: *Kings Of Harmony* / Jesus is everything: *Kings Of Harmony*.
**Album:** Released 22 Apr '88, on Heritage by Interstate Music. Catalogue no: **HT 316**

## Cleveland, Jimmy

**TROMBONE SCENE (Cleveland, Jimmy/Green, Urbie/Rehack, Frank)**
**Album:** Released Feb '88, on Fresh Sounds (Spain) by Fresh Sounds Records (Spain). Catalogue no: **FS 30**

## Clinton, Larry

**Biographical details:** The trumpeter and arranger (1909-85) worked for Isham Jones, the Casa Loma Band and Tommy Dorsey, for whom he wrote many hits; he later used the Dorsey hit *The dipsy doodle* as his theme and had hits with his own dance band, making over 200 sides for RCA in less than 4 years, more than 30 of them big hits, mostly sweet stuff like *My reverie* and *Deep purple* in 1938-39. In the late '40's he recorded for USA Decca and had a few more hits. (Donald Clarke, April 1989).

**1941 & 1949 (Clinton, Larry & His Orchestra)**
**Album:** Released Jun '84, on Circle (USA) by Jazzology Records (USA). Catalogue no: **CLP 58**

**DIPSY DOODLE 1938 - 39 (Clinton, Larry & His Orchestra)**
Tracks: / Dipsy doodle theme / East of the sun / Chopsticks / Sunday / Wishing / In a mist / Lonesome road / One rose, The / S'good enough for me / There's that faraway look in your eye / Midnight in the madhouse / Chant of the jungle / Chew, chew, chew, chew (your bubble gum) / Study in blue / Limehouse blues.
Note: With Bea Wain, Ford Leary, Dick Todd.
**Album:** Released Jun '88, on Bandstand Catalogue no: **BS 7133**

**FROM THE GLEN ISLAND CASINO 1938/9 (Clinton, Larry & His Orchestra)**
**Album:** Released Jan '87, on Kaydee Catalogue no: **KAYDEE 3**

**IN A PERSIAN MARKET 1939 - 41 (Clinton, Larry & His Orchestra)**
**Album:** Released Jun '88, on Bandstand Catalogue no: **BS 7102**

**LARRY CLINTON AND HIS ORCHESTRA 1937-38 (Clinton, Larry & His Orchestra)**
Tracks: / Dipsy doodle / Glen island hop / Whistle while you work / Let 'er go / Hollywood pastime / Where in the world / Chris and his gang / Zig zag / Feeling like a dream / Saving myself for you / Remember / I double dare you / Martha / Sugarfoot stomp.
**Album:** Released Feb '79, on London Records by London Records Ltd. Deleted Feb '84. Catalogue no: **HMP 5045**

**LARRY CLINTON & HIS ORCHESTRA 1937-38 (Clinton, Larry & His Orchestra)**
Tracks: / Dipsy doodle / Glen island hop / Whistle while you work / Let her go / Hollywood pastime / Where in the world (Vocal by Bea Wain) / Chris and his gang / Zig zag / Feeling like a dream / Saving myself for you / Remember / I double dare you / Martha / Sugarfoot stomp / You go to my head / I want to rock.
Note: Larry Clinton became a full-time bandleader because of his excellence as a composer and arranger. Originally, Victor encouraged him to form a recording band but the public soon demanded to see and hear the band in person--about the same time the radio transcriptions on this album were made. Clinton never had the opportunity to record commercially his most successful composition. "Dipsy Doodle", because Tommy Dorsey made it a hit first on Victor. Clinton chose the tune for his bands theme, and Bea Wain sings it here, along with others which have never before been released by the Clinton band. Annotator Irving Townsend interviewed Clinton for the notes. (Hindsight Catalogue - 1989)
**Album:** Released '87, on Hindsight Catalogue no: **HSR 109**

**MY REVERIE 1937-38 (Clinton, Larry & His Orchestra)**
**Album:** Released Jun '88, on Bandstand Catalogue no: **BS 7109**
**Cass:** Released Jun '88, on Bandstand Catalogue no: **BS 7109C**

**SHE'S WANTED IN THREE STATES**
Tracks: / She's wanted in three states.
**7" Single:** Released Sep '79, on Grapevine (Northern Soul) by BMG Records (UK). Deleted '80. Catalogue no: **GRP 120**

## Clooney, Rosemary

**Biographical details:** This American singer, born in Kentucky, began her career in duet with her sister Betty. In 1949 Rosemary was discovered by Mitch Miller of Columbia Records, who launched her as a major solo artist. The early Fifties were golden years for both Clooney and Miller. She had a string of hits, with him as producer. Working not only with Clooney but also with other top singers such as Frankie Laine, Guy Mitchell and Johnnie Ray, Miller became America's king of middle-of-the-road music; he represented the old school of popular music that the rock 'n' roll revolution was soon to rebel against.
The record that gave Clooney major stardom was 1951's *Come on-a my*

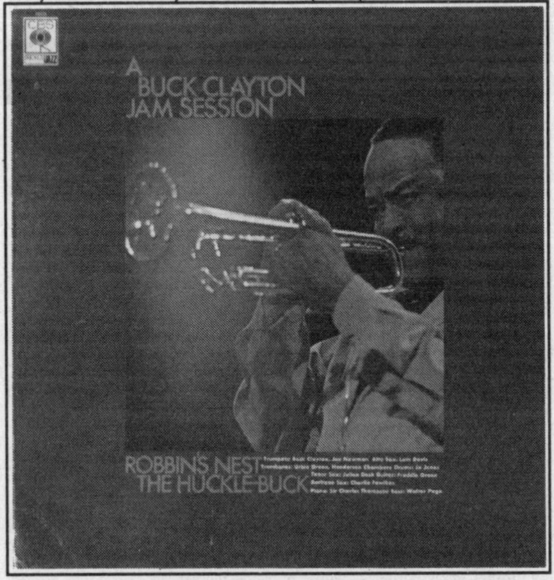


**Buck Clayton - Jam Session (CBS)**

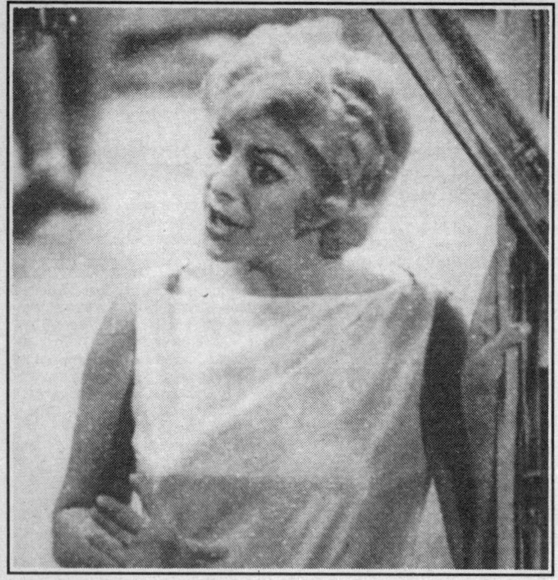

Rosemary Clooney

*house*, a huge-selling US No. 1. The following year brought further hits with *Tenderly*, *Botch-a-me* and *Half as much*. The singer's early successes predated the British record charts, but *Half as much* had the honour of being listed on the first ever UK chart, published by the New Musical Express in 14th November 1952: it was at No. 6 that week and eventually peaked at No. 3. Clooney's success continued into the mid-Fifties with the US No. 1 *Hey there!* (No. 4 in the UK), the UK No. 1 *Mambo Italiano* (No. 10 in the US) and *This ole house*. The latter topped the charts on both sides of the Atlantic and was an uptempo, jolly interpretaion of a song originally written as an epitaph for a dead mountain hunter. The song achieved a second UK No. 1 placing in 1981, courtesy of Shakin' Stevens.

Married to film star Jose Ferrer, Clooney also enjoyed movie stardom in the Fifties: amongst others, she appeared with Bing Crosby in "White Christmas" and with Bob Hope in "Here come the girls". After her final big hit record - 1957's *Mangos* - Clooney's star gradually faded. (Bob MacDonald).

One of the biggest pop stars of the early '50's, with a warm, always clear and musical voice, Rosie began as a duo with sister Betty in the Tony Pastor band, went solo, signed with Columbia (CBS-USA) and had 24 hits in four years. *Come on a my house* was a number one for six weeks in 1951: written some years earlier for a Broadway play by Ross Bagdasarian, who later became David Seville and discovered Chipmunks, its bouncy arrangement featured an amplified harpsichord played by pianist Stan Freeman, as did several other CBS hits of the period, including *Too old to cut the mustard*, a duet by Rosie and Marlene Dietrich. Other Clooney hits included *Sisters*, a duet with Betty; *You're just in love* was a duet with Guy Mitchell, and her other number ones were *Hey there* (from *Pajama Game*, *This ole house* and the Hank Williams song *Half as much*. She also recorded with Duke Ellington and the vocal group the Hi-Lo's, and switched labels to record with Bing Crosby, Les Brown and others. She's made a splendid comeback on Concord Jazz in the 80's, backed by first rate jazzmen including Scott Hamilton and Woody Herman. (Donald Clarke, April 1989).

**BEST OF ROSEMARY CLOONEY**

**Cass:** Released Jul '84, on Creole (Everest-Europa) by Creole Records. Catalogue no: **16-20**

**BLUE ROSE (Clooney, Rosemary & Duke Ellington)**

**CD:** Released '88, on Mobile Fidelity Sound Lab(USA) by Mobile Fidelity Records (USA). Catalogue no: **MFCD 850**

**CLAP HANDS**

Tracks: / Clap hands, here comes Rosie / Everything's coming up roses / Give me the simple life / Bye bye blackbird / Aren't you glad you're you / You got / Too marvellous for words / Something's gotta give / Hooray for love / Mean to me / Oh what a beautiful morning / It could happen to you / Makin' whoopee.

**Cass:** Released Oct '84, on RCA by BMG Records (UK). Deleted '87. Catalogue no: **NK 89461**

**Album:** Released Oct '84, on RCA by BMG Records (UK). Deleted '87. Catalogue no: **NL 89461**

**EVERYTHING'S COMING UP ROSIE (Clooney, Rosemary/Nat Pierce Quintet)**

Tracks: / I cried for you / I can't get started / Do you know what it means to miss New Orleans? / I've got such a crush on you / As time goes by / More than you know / Foggy day, A / Hey there.

Note: Personnel: Rosemary Clooney (vocals), Nat Pierce (piano), Bill Berry (trumpet) Scott Hamilton (tenor sax), Monty Budwig (bass), Jake Hanna (drums).

**CD:** Released Jun '89, on Concord Jazz by Concord Jazz Records (USA). Catalogue no: **CCD 4047**

**FANCY MEETING YOU HERE (Clooney, Rosemary & Bing Crosby)**

Tracks: / Fancy meeting you here / On a slow boat to China / I can't get started / Hindustan / It happened in Monterey / You came a long way / From St. Louis / You can take the boy out of the country / Love won't let you get away / How about you / Brazil / Here we are (face to face again) / Isle of Capri / Say si si / Calcutta.

**Cass:** Released Jul '82, on RCA International by BMG Records (UK). Catalogue no: **INTK 5217**

**Album:** Released Jul '82, on RCA International by BMG Records (UK). Catalogue no: **INTS 5217**

**Cass:** Released Jul '82, on RCA International by BMG Records (UK). Deleted May '89. Catalogue no: **NK 89315**

**Album:** Released Jul '82, on RCA International by BMG Records (UK). Deleted May '89. Catalogue no: **NL 89315**

**GREATEST HITS: ROSEMARY CLOONEY**

Tracks: / This old house / Hey there / Tenderly / Half as much / Mambo Italiano / You're just in love / Come on-a my house / Botch-a-me / Mangos / Blues in the night / Too old to cut the mustard / Beautiful brown eyes / Where will the baby's dimple be? / Be my life's companion / If teardrops were pennies / I could have danced all night.

**Album:** Released Mar '83, on CBS Cameo by CBS Records. Catalogue no: **CBS 32263**

**Cass:** Released Mar '83, on CBS Cameo by CBS Records. Deleted Nov '87. Catalogue no: **40-32263**

**HALF AS MUCH**

Tracks: / Half as much.

**7" Single:** Released Nov '52, on Columbia by EMI Records. Deleted Nov '55. Catalogue no: **DB 3129**

**HERE'S TO MY LADY**
**2 LP Set:** Released Mar '79, on Concord by Concord Jazz Records (USA). Catalogue no: **CJ 81**

**HEY THERE**
Tracks: / Hey there.
**7" Single:** Released Sep '55, on Philips by Phonogram Ltd. Deleted Sep '58. Catalogue no: **PB 494**

**MAMBO ITALIANO**
Tracks: / Mambo Italiano.
**7" Single:** Released Dec '54, on Philips by Phonogram Ltd. Deleted Dec '57. Catalogue no: **PB 382**

**MAN**
Tracks: / Man.
**7" Single:** Released Feb '54, on Philips by Phonogram Ltd. Deleted Feb '57. Catalogue no: **PB 220**

**MANGOS**
Tracks: / Mangos.
**7" Single:** Released Apr '57, on Philips by Phonogram Ltd. Deleted Apr '60. Catalogue no: **PB 671**

**MIXED EMOTIONS**
Tracks: / Bless this house / Beautiful brown eyes / Lady is a tramp, The / Be my life's companion / Why don't you haul off and love me / Too young / While we're young / I laughed until I cried / Close your eyes (Brahms' Lullaby) / Mixed emotions.
**Album:** Released Mar '86, on CBS by CBS Records. Deleted Aug '87. Catalogue no: **CBS 32708**

**MY BUDDY (Clooney, Rosemary & Woody Herman Big Band)**
Tracks: / I believe in love / Summer knows, The / Glory of love / You're gonna hear from me / Don't let me be lonely / Tonight / I'm beginning to see the light / My buddy / You've made me so very happy.
**Album:** Released Nov '83, on Concord Jazz by Concord Jazz Records (USA). Catalogue no: **CJ 226**

**OUR FAVOURITE THINGS (Clooney, Rosemary with Les Brown & His Band)**
Tracks: / Sweetest sounds, The / How am I to know / My funny valentine / Why shouldn't I? / My romance / I get along without you very well / Angry / Some people / Man with a horn / Show me / Have you seen Miss Jones? / Little brown jug / Sleepy time gal / I didn't know what time it was / One o'clock jump.
**Cass:** Released Jun '86, on Dance Band Days by Prism Leisure. Catalogue no: **DBDC 06**
**Album:** Released Jun '86, on Dance Band Days by Prism Leisure. Catalogue no: **DBD 06**

**RING AROUND ROSIE (Clooney, Rosemary & The Hi-Lo's)**
Tracks: / Doncha go 'way mad / Moonlight becomes you / Love letters / I could write a book / I'm in the mood for love / Coquette / Together / Everything happens to me / What is there to say / I'm glad there is you / How about you.
**Album:** Released Dec '85, on Memoir by Memoir Records. Catalogue no: **MOIR 114**
**Cass:** Released Dec '85, on Memoir by Memoir Records. Catalogue no: **CMOIR 114**

**ROSEMARY CLOONEY**
**Album:** Released Sep '87, on Hindsight Catalogue no: **HSR 234**

**ROSEMARY CLOONEY SINGS COLE PORTER**
**Album:** Released Apr '82, on Concord Jazz by Concord Jazz Records (USA). Catalogue no: **CJ 185**
**Cass:** Released Apr '82, on Concord Jazz by Concord Jazz Records (USA). Catalogue no: **CJC 185**
**CD:** Released Jan '89, on Concord by Concord Jazz Records (USA). Catalogue no: **CCD 4185**

**ROSEMARY CLOONEY SINGS HAROLD ARLEN**
Tracks: / Hooray for love / Happiness is a thing called love / One for my baby / Get happy / Ding dong the witch is dead / Out of this world / My shining hour / Let's take the long way home / Stormy weather.
**Album:** Released Apr '83, on Concord Jazz by Concord Jazz Records (USA). Catalogue no: **CJ 210**
**Cass:** Released Apr '83, on Concord Jazz by Concord Jazz Records (USA). Catalogue no: **CJC 210**

**ROSEMARY CLOONEY SONGBOOK, THE**
Note: 2 LP set.
**Cass set:** Released Jun '84, on CBS (import) by CBS Records. Catalogue no: **4088598**
**2 LP Set:** Released Jun '84, on CBS (import) by CBS Records. Catalogue no: **88598**

**ROSIE SOLVES THE SWINGIN' RIDDLE**
Tracks: / Get me to the church on time / Angry / I get along without you very well / How am I to know / You took advantage of me / April in Paris / I ain't got nobody / Some of these days / By myself / Shine on harvest moon / Cabin in the sky / Limehouse blues.
**Cass:** Released Nov '80, on RCA by BMG Records (UK). Catalogue no: **INTK 5057**
**Album:** Released Nov '80, on RCA by BMG Records (UK). Catalogue no: **INTS 5057**

**SHOW TUNES**
Tracks: / I wish I were in love again / I stayed too long at the fair / How are things in Glocca Morra / When do you start / I'll see you again / Guys and dolls / Manhattan / Everything I've got / Come back to me / Taking a chance on love / All the things you are.
**CD:** Released Jan '89, on Concord by Concord Jazz Records (USA). Catalogue no: **CCD 346**
**Album:** Released Jan '89, on Concord by Concord Jazz Records (USA). Catalogue no: **CJ 346**
**Cass:** Released Jan '89, on Concord by Concord Jazz Records (USA). Catalogue no: **CJ 346C**

**SINGS BALLADS**
**Album:** Released Nov '85, on Concord Jazz by Concord Jazz Records (USA). Catalogue no: **CJ 282**
**Cass:** Released Nov '85, on Concord Jazz by Concord Jazz Records (USA). Catalogue no: **CJC 282**

**SINGS RODGERS, HART & HAMMERSTEIN**
Tracks: / Oh, what a beautiful morning / People will say we're in love / Love, look away / Gentleman is a dope, The / It might as well be spring / Sweetest sounds, The / I could write a book / You took advantage of me / Lady is a tramp, The / Little girl blue / My romance / Yours sincerely (CD only.).
**Cass:** Released Mar '90, on Concord by Concord Jazz Records (USA). Catalogue no: **CJ 405 C**
**CD:** Released Mar '90, on Concord by Concord Jazz Records (USA). Catalogue no: **CCD 4405**

**SINGS THE LYRICS OF IRA GERSHWIN**
Tracks: / But not for me / Nice work if you can get it / How long has this been going on / Fascinating rhythm / Love is here to stay / Strike up the band / Long ago and far away / They all laughed / Man that got away, The / They can't that away from me.
**CD:** Released Mar '90, on Concord by Concord Jazz Records (USA). Catalogue no: **CCD 4112**

**SINGS THE LYRICS OF JOHNNY MERCER**
**CD:** Released Dec '87, on Concord Jazz by Concord Jazz Records (USA). Catalogue no: **CCD 4333**
**Cass:** Released Nov '87, on Concord Jazz by Concord Jazz Records (USA). Catalogue no: **CJC 333**
**Album:** Released Nov '87, on Concord Jazz by Concord Jazz Records (USA). Catalogue no: **CJ 333**

**SINGS THE MUSIC OF IRVING BERLIN**
Tracks: / It's a lovely day today / Be careful, it's my heart / Cheek to cheek / How about me / Best thing for you would be me, The / I got lost in his arms / There's no business like show business / Better luck next time / What'll I do / Let's face the music and dance.
Note: Rosemary Clooney is magnificent as she (backed by her all-star band) plays tribute to the Dean of American song writers, Irving Berlin. The repertoire is first rate and Rosemary's treatment is superb. A must for those who love great melody and artful interpretation. Rosemary Clooney - Vocals. Ed Bickert - Guitar. Phil Flanigan - Bass. Chris Flory - Guitar.
**Cass:** Released Nov '84, on Concord Jazz by Concord Jazz Records (USA). Catalogue no: **CJC 255**
**Album:** Released Nov '84, on Concord

Jazz by Concord Jazz Records (USA). Catalogue no: **CJ 255**

**SINGS THE MUSIC OF JIMMY VAN HEUSEN**
Tracks: / Love won't let you get away / I thought about you / My heart is a hobo / Second time around / It could happen to you / Imagination / Like someone in love / Call me irresponsible / Walking happy / Last dance.
Note: Rosemary Clooney is backed by her usual stellar group of All Stars led by saxophonist Scott Hamilton and cornetist Warren Vache. Liner notes by Sammy Cahn. Personnel: Rosemary Clooney-vocals/Ed Bickert-guitar/Joe Cocuzzo-drums/Scott Hamilton-tenor saxophone/Michael Moore-bass/John Oddo-piano/Emily Remier- guitar/Warren Vache-cornet.
**Cass:** Released Jan '87, on Concord Jazz by Concord Jazz Records (USA). Catalogue no: **CJC 308**
**CD:** Released Mar '87, on Concord Jazz by Concord Jazz Records (USA). Catalogue no: **CCD 4308**
**Album:** Released Jan '87, on Concord Jazz by Concord Jazz Records (USA). Catalogue no: **CJ 308**

**SWING AROUND ROSIE (Clooney, Rosemary & The Buddy Cole Trio)**
Tracks: / Deed I do / You took advantage of me / Blue moon / Sing you sinners / Touch of the blues, A / Goody, goody / Too close for comfort / Do nothing till you hear from me / Moonlight Mississippi / I wish I were in love again / Sunday in Savannah / This can't be love.
**Album:** Released '83, on Jasmine by Hasmick Promotions. Deleted Feb '88. Catalogue no: **JASM 1502**

**THIS OLE HOUSE**
Tracks: / This ole house.
**7" Single:** Released Oct '54, on Philips by Phonogram Ltd. Deleted Oct '57. Catalogue no: **PB 336**

**WHERE WILL THE BABY'S DIMPLE BE?**
Tracks: / Where will the baby's dimple be.
**7" Single:** Released May '55, on Philips by Phonogram Ltd. Deleted May '58. Catalogue no: **PB 428**

**WITH LOVE**
Tracks: / Just the way you are / Way we were, The / Alone at last / Come in from the rain / Meditation / Hello young lovers / Just in time / Tenderly / Will you still be mine?.
Note: Consisting of 9 beautiful standards from such writers as Billy Joel, Neil Sedaka and Richard Rogers. Personnel: Scott Hamilton - tenor sax, Warren Vache - cornet and flugelhorn, Cal Collins - guitar, Nat Pierce - piano, Cal Tjader - vibes, Bob Maize - bass.
**Album:** Released May '81, on Concord by Concord Jazz Records (USA). Catalogue no: **CJ 144**
**CD:** Released Sep '84, on Capitol (import) Catalogue no: **CDCP 353048**
**CD:** Released '88, on Capitol (import) Catalogue no: **CDCP 035 304**
**CD:** Released '89, on Concord Jazz by Concord Jazz Records (USA). Catalogue no: **CCD 4144**

## Clyde Valley Stompers

**Biographical details:** This all-male British band had been in existence for over a decade before they achieved their one-off hit single in 1962. In the years following the end of the Second World War, British jazz enthusiasts had benefited from the increased availability of American jazz discs and, discovering previously unheard styles of their favourite music, had formed bands up and down the UK. This trend eventually led to the 'trad jazz' boom of the early Sixties, a phenomenon that filled an otherwise lacklustre period in British popular music prior to the arrival of the Beatles. One such band was the Clyde Valley Stompers - they reached No. 25 on the UK chart in the late summer of '62 with *Peter & The Wolf*. They were unable to follow up this instrumental hit and soon returned to their tried and trusted live circuit. Many years after breaking up, the Stompers recorded a reunion LP in 1981. (Bob MacDonald)..

**FIDGETY FEET**
Tracks: / At the jazz band ball / Isle of Capri / When my dreamboat comes home / Fidgety feet / Salty dog / Creole love call / Tiger rag / My mother's eyes / Hiawatha rag / Goodnight, my sweet prince / When the saints go marching in / I can't stop loving you.
**Cass:** Released Jul '85, on Country House by BGS Productions Ltd. Catalogue no: **KBGC 351**
**Album:** Released Jul '85, on Country House by BGS Productions Ltd. Catalogue no: **BGC 351**

**PETER AND THE WOLF**
Tracks: / Peter and the wolf.
**7" Single:** Released Aug '62, on Parlophone by EMI Records. Deleted Aug '65. Catalogue no: **R 4928**

**REUNION '81**
Tracks: / Hindustan / Old rugged cross / Sister Kate / High Society / Bourbon Street parade / Old tyme religion / Savoy blues / Bill Bailey.
**Album:** Released Dec '81, on Country House by BGS Productions Ltd. Catalogue no: **BGC 300**
**Cass:** Released Dec '81, on Country House by BGS Productions Ltd. Catalogue no: **KBGC 300**

## Cobb, Arnett

**Biographical details:** (1918-89) One of the many fine tenor saxists from Texas. He replaced Illinois Jacquet in the Lionel Hampton band in 1942, formed his own band in 1947 and has mostly been a leader ever since. Like Jacquet he can honk to please the crowd and also play lovely ballads; as Brian Priestley put it, the Texas players demonstrate 'the strong links between jazz balladry and R&B bawdy.' (Donald Clarke, April 1989).

**AND HIS MOB (Cobb, Arnett & Dinah Washington)**
Tracks: / Jumpin' the blues / Cocktails for two / Smooth sailing / Someone to watch over me / Shy one, The / Go red go / When I grow too old to dream / Make believe dreams / Journey's end / It's magic / I got it bad and that ain't good.
**Album:** Released Apr '81, on Phoenix (USA) by All Star Talent Inc.(USA). Catalogue no: **LP 18**

**ARNETT COBB IS BACK**
Tracks: / Flying home / Big red's groove / Cherry / Sweet Georgia Brown / Blues for Shirley / Take the 'A' train / I don't stand a ghost of a chance / Funky butt.
**Album:** Released Apr '81, on Progressive (USA) by Jazzology Records (USA). Catalogue no: **PRO 7037**

**BLOW ARNETT, BLOW**
Tracks: / When I grow too old to dream / Go power / Dutch kitchen bounce / Go red go / Eely one, The / Fluke, The.
**Album:** Released Mar '88, on Prestige Catalogue no: **PR 7151**
**Cass:** Released Mar '88, on Prestige Deleted Jan '90. Catalogue no: **PRC 7151**

**COMPLETE APOLLO SESSIONS**
**Album:** Released Mar '84, on Vogue by Vogue Records. Catalogue no: **500116**

**FUNKY BUTT**
Tracks: / Radium springs swings / Jumpin' at the woodside / Satin doll / Georgia on my mind / I got rhythm / September in the rain / Isfahan.
**Album:** Released '81, on Progressive (USA) by Jazzology Records (USA). Catalogue no: **PRO 7054**

**LIVE AT SANDY'S (Cobb, Arnett & The Muse All Stars)**
Tracks: / Just a closer walk with thee / Blue & sentimental / On the sunny side of the street / September song / Broadway / Blues for Lester / Go red go / Smooth sailing / Flying home.
**Album:** Released Apr '81, on Muse by Black & Blue Records. Catalogue no: **MR 5191**
**Album:** Released May '83, on Muse by Black & Blue Records. Catalogue no: **MR 5236**

**LIVE IN PARIS, 1974 (Cobb, Arnett & Tiny Grimes)**
**Album:** Released '89, on France's Concert Catalogue no: **FC 133**
**CD:** Released '89, on France's Concert Catalogue no: **FCD 133**

**PARTY TIME**
**Album:** Released Apr '86, on Original Jazz Classics (USA) by Fantasy Inc (USA). Catalogue no: **OJC 219**

## Cobb, Junie C.

**JUNIE C.COBB 1926-9 South side Chicago jazz**
**Album:** Released Apr '88, on Swaggie (Australia) Catalogue no: **S 852**

## Cobham, Billy

**Biographical details:** Born in Panama

in 1944, the drummer and composer has been a leader in the fusion movement. After military service he played with Horace Silver and others; he played in Isaac Hayes' *Shaft* soundtrack. He formed a fusion band called Dreams 1969-70, recorded with Miles Davis, then John McLaughlin and his Mahavishnu Orchestra. His own bands included Airto and David Sancious. He recorded for Elektra with a quartet called Billy Cobham's Glass Menagerie in the early '80's. He has had a big impact on jazz/rock. (Donald Clarke, April 1989) .

**B.C.**
Tracks: / Mendocino / Dana / What is your fantasy / Little travelin' music / Lonely bull / I don't want to be without you / Bring up the house lights / Vlastar an encounter.
**Album:** Released Dec '79, on CBS by CBS Records. Deleted '84. Catalogue no: **CBS 83641**

**BEST OF BILLY COBHAM**
Tracks: / On a magic carpet ride / Bolinas / Pocket change / Puffinstuff / What is your fantasy / Anteres the star / Indigo / Mendocino.
**Album:** Released Jun '80, on CBS by CBS Records. Deleted '85. Catalogue no: **CBS 84235**

**BEST OF BILLY COBHAM, THE**
Tracks: / Quadrant 4 / Snoopy's search / Red baron / Spanish moss - "A sound portrait" / Moon germs / Stratus / Pleasant pheasant, The / Solo panhandler / Do what cha wanna.
**Cass:** Released '88, on Atlantic by WEA Records. Catalogue no: **K4 50620**
**CD:** Released '88, on Atlantic Jazz by WEA Records. Catalogue no: **K 781 558 2**
**Album:** Released '88, on Atlantic by WEA Records. Catalogue no: **K 50620**

**BILLY'S BEST HITS**
Note: A 'Best of..' collection that highlights the awesome power & musicianship of the world's number one drummer. Personnel includes Grover Washington, Ron Carter, Gerry Etkins, Victor Bailey & Onaje Allan Gumbs. CD version contains 3 bonus tracks.
**CD:** Released Oct '88, on GRP by GRP Records (USA). Catalogue no: **GRPD 9575-2**
**Cass:** Released Oct '88, on GRP by GRP Records (USA). Catalogue no: **GRPM 9575-4**
**Album:** Released Oct '88, on GRP by GRP Records (USA). Catalogue no: **GRPA 9575-1**

**CROSSWINDS**
Tracks: / Spanish moss - "A sound portrait" / Spanish moss / Savannah the serene / Storm / Flash flood / Pleasant pheasant, The / Heather / Crosswinds.
**Album:** Released '88, on Atlantic by WEA Records. Catalogue no: **K 50037**

**FLIGHT TIME**
**CD:** Released '88, on Inak Catalogue no: **INAK 8616**
**Album:** Released Apr '81, on Sandra Catalogue no: **SMP 2112**

**FUNKY THIDE OF SINGS, A**
Tracks: / Panhandler / Sorcery / Funky thide of sings, A / Thinking of you / Some skunk funk / Light at the end of the tunnel / Funky kind of thing, A / Moody modes.
**Album:** on Atlantic by WEA Records. Catalogue no: **K 50189**

**LIFE AND TIMES**
**Album:** Released Mar '76, on Atlantic by WEA Records. Catalogue no: **K 50253**

**LIVE ON TOUR IN EUROPE (Cobham, Billy, George Duke Band)**
Tracks: / Hip pockets / Ivory tattoo / Space lady / Almustafa the beloved / Do what cha wanna / Frankenstein goes to the disco / Sweet wine / Juicy.
**Cass:** Released '88, on Atlantic by WEA Records. Catalogue no: **K4 50316**
**Album:** Released '88, on Atlantic by WEA Records. Catalogue no: **K 50316**

**PICTURE THIS**
Tracks: / Two for Juan / Same ole love / Taurian matador / You within me within you / This one's for Armando / Sign of the times / Juggler, The / Danse for noh masque.
**CD:** Released Oct '87, on GRP by GRP Records (USA). Catalogue no: **GRD 9551**
**Cass:** Released Sep '87, on GRP by GRP Records (USA). Catalogue no: **GRPM 91040**
**Album:** Released Sep '87, on GRP by GRP Records (USA). Catalogue no: **GRP 91040**

**POWER PLAY**
Tracks: / Times of my life / Zanzibar breeze / Radioactive / Light shines in your eyes, A / Summit Afrique / Foundation, The - Isisekelo Zulu / Dance of the blue men / Nomads, The / Debate, The (Indaba) / Little one / Dessicated coconuts / Tinsel Town.
Note: Following on from the successful album 'Warning' (GRP 91020), Billy's debut recording for GRP, 'Power Play' is a dazzling display of the legendary drummer' total mastery of his power, style and technique. Cobham uses his skills as a writer to project a wide range of moods, rhythms and melodic ideas.
**Album:** Released Jun '86, on GRP by GRP Records (USA). Catalogue no: **GRP 91027**
**Cass:** Released Jun '86, on GRP by GRP Records (USA). Catalogue no: **GRPM 91027**
**CD:** Released Jun '86, on GRP by GRP Records (USA). Catalogue no: **GRD 9536**

**SAME OLE LOVE**
Tracks: / Same ole love / Juggler, The / Mozaik *.
Note: * Extra track on 12" format.
**12" Single:** Released Oct '87, on GRP by GRP Records (USA). Catalogue no: **GRPMS 91040**
**7" Single:** Released Oct '87, on GRP by GRP Records (USA). Catalogue no: **GRPS 91040**

**SHABAZZ**
Tracks: / Shabazz / Taurian matador / Red baron / Tenth pinn.
**Album:** on Atlantic by WEA Records. Catalogue no: **K 50147**

**SMOKIN'**
Tracks: / Some other kind / Chiquita Linda / Looks bad, feel good / Red baron / Situation comedy.
**Album:** Released Jun '83, on Elektra (Musician) by Elektra Records (USA). Catalogue no: **960 233-1**

**SPECTRUM**
Tracks: / Quadrant 4 / Searching for the right door / Spectrum / Anxiety / Taurian matador / Stratus / To the women in my life / Le lis / Snoopy's search / Red baron.
**Album:** Released '88, on Atlantic by WEA Records. Catalogue no: **K 40506**

**STRATUS**
Note: Recording made in London with Cobham's Galss Menagerie.,
**CD:** Released '88, on Inak Catalogue no: **INAK 813 CD**

**TOTAL ECLIPSE**
Tracks: / Solarization / Second phase / Crescent sun / Voyage / Solarization - recapitulation / Lunarputians / Total eclipse / Bandits / Moon germs / Moon ain't made of green cheese, The / Sea of Tranquility / Last frontier, The.
**Album:** Released Nov '74, on Atlantic by WEA Records. Catalogue no: **K 50098**

**WARNING**
Tracks: / Moziak / Red and yellow cabriolet / Slow body poppin' / Unknown Jeromes / Dancer / Stratus / Come join me / Go for it.
**CD:** Released Sep '85, on GRP by GRP Records (USA). Catalogue no: **GRD 9528**
**Cass:** Released Sep '85, on GRP by GRP Records (USA). Catalogue no: **GRPM 91020**
**Album:** Released Sep '85, on GRP by GRP Records (USA). Catalogue no: **GRP 91020**

## Coe, Tony

**Biographical details:** A first class British reedman, session player and composer, born in 1934. He played with Humphrey Lyttelton on alto in 1957, formed a highly rated quintet in 1960, joined Count Basie in 1965 and was a regular member of the Kenny Clarke-Francy Boland Big Band in the late '60's. A quintet called Coe, Wheeler and Co. included Kenny Wheeler; there were other small groups called Martrix and Axel; he took over Plas Johnson's role playing Henry Mancini's *Pink Panther theme*, among other film work *Le Chat se Retourne* has duos, trios with clarinettist Alan Hacker and others. Coe's works have been played by several European bands; he teaches, writes articles and sessions with Paul McCartney, Louden Wainright, etc. (Donald Clarke, April 1989).

**CANTERBURY SONG**
Tracks: / Canterbury song / How beautiful is the night / Light blue / Sometime

Tony Coe

ago / Re: person I knew / I guess I'll hang my tears out to dry / Lagos / Blue in green.
Note: Recorded November 1988, in London. Personnel: Tony Coe (tenor & soprano sax, clt), Benny Baily (tpt), Horace Parlan (piano), Jimmy Woode (bass), Idris Muhammad (drums).
**Cass:** Released Jun '89, on Hot House by Hot House Records. Catalogue no: **HHMC 1005**
**CD:** Released Jun '89, on Hot House by Hot House Records. Catalogue no: **HHCD 1005**
**Album:** Released Jun '89, on Hot House by Hot House Records. Catalogue no: **HH 1005**

**COE-EXISTENCE**
**Album:** Released May '80, on Lee Lambert by Lee Lambert Records. Catalogue no: **LAM 100**

**LE CHAT SE RETOURNE**
Tracks: / Marche funebre d'une marionnette - gounod / Paul / Petite suite en Avion I / Three for thee / Petite suite en Avion II / Les yeux prasins (I) / Les yeux prasins (II) / An-og mhadainn.
**Album:** Released Sep '86, on Nato Catalogue no: **NATO 257**

**MAINLY MANCINI**
Tracks: / Pink panther / Crazy world / Hank neuf / Mister lucky / Mancinissimo / Days of wine and roses / Charade.
Note: With Tony Hymas and Chris Laurence.
**Album:** Released Sep '86, on Chabada (France) Catalogue no: **CHABADA 08**

**TONY COE**
**Album:** on Hep Jazz by Hep Records. Catalogue no: **HEP 2038**

**TOURNEE DU CHAT**
Tracks: / Jolly corner, The / Makoko / Vive la chantenay / Iberiana / Debussy.
**Album:** Released Jun '99, on Nato Catalogue no: **NATO 19**

## Cohn, Al

**Biographical details:** The tenor saxist and arranger (1925-88) also played other reeds; he was an exhuberant, highly-rated bop-influenced player, originally influenced by Lester Young but developing his own individuality. He sessioned widely and his studio work was always first-rate. He often worked with Ernie Wilkins or Zoot Sims. (Donald Clarke 1989) .

**AL COHN MEETS THE JAZZ SEVEN**
Tracks: / Bilbo Baggins / Mood indigo / Casa 50 comp / Keeper of the flame / High on you / Feel more like I do now.
**Album:** Released '89, on Frog by Frog Records. Catalogue no: **FRG 717**

**AL & ZOOT (Cohn, Al Quintet feat. Zoot Sims)**
Tracks: / It's a wonderful world / Brandy and beer / Two funky people / Chasing the blues / Halley's comet / You're a lucky guy / Wailing boat, The / Just you, just me.
**Album:** Released Jun '83, on Jasmine by Hasmick Promotions. Deleted Feb '88. Catalogue no: **JASM 1014**

**AMERICA (Various)**
**Album:** Released '88, on Xanadu Catalogue no: **XAN 138**

**BODY AND SOUL (Cohn, Al & Zoot Sims)**
**Album:** Released Jun '77, on Muse by Black & Blue Records. Catalogue no: **MR 5016**

**BROTHERS, THE (Cohn, Al/Bill Perkins/Richie Kamuca)**
Tracks: / Blixed / Kim's kaper / Rolling stone / Sioux zan / Walrus, The / Blue skies / Gay blade / Three of a kind / Hags / Pro-ex / Strange again / Cap snapper.
**Album:** Released '83, on RCA (France) by BMG Records (France). Catalogue no: **PL 43240**

**DATE IN NEW YORK VOL 2 (Cohn, Al & Jay Jay Johnson)**
**Album:** Released Nov '88, on Vogue by Vogue Records. Catalogue no: **500096**

**EITHER WAY (Cohn, Al & Zoot Sims)**
Tracks: / P-Town / I like it like that / Sweet Lorraine / Autumn leaves / Thing, The / I'm tellin' ya / Nagasaki / Morning fun.
**Album:** Released Apr '81, on Zim (USA) Catalogue no: **ZMS 2002**

**FOUR BRASS, ONE TENOR**
Tracks: / Rosetta / Song is ended, The / Linger awhile / Every time / Haroosh / Just plain Sam / I'm coming, Virginia / Cohn, not Cohen / Little song / Foggy water / Sugar Cohn / Alone together.
**Album:** Released '83, on RCA (France) by BMG Records (France). Catalogue no: **PM 45164**

**FROM A TO Z (Cohn, Al & Zoot Sims Sextet)**
Tracks: / Mediolistic / Crimea river / New moan, A / Moment's notice, A / My blues / Sandy's swing / Somebody loves me.
**Album:** Released Feb '79, on RCA by BMG Records (UK). Catalogue no: **PM 42303**
**Album:** Released Oct '85, on RCA (France) by BMG Records (France). Catalogue no: **NL 89644**

**FROM A-Z & BEYOND (Cohn, Al & Zoot Sims)**
Tracks: / Mediolistic / Crimea river / New moan, A / Moment's notice, A / My blues / Sandy's swing / Somebody loves me / More bread / Sherm's terms / From A to Z / East of the sun (and west of the moon) / Tenor for two please, Jack / My blues (alt. take) / More bread(alt. take) / Tenor for two please, Jack (alternate take) / Somebody loves me (alternate take).
**CD:** Released Jun '88, on Bluebird (2) by BMG Records (UK). Catalogue no: **ND 86469**

**MOTORING ALONG (Cohn, Al & Zoot Sims)**
Tracks: / Stockholm - LA / My funny Valentine / Yardbird suite / Motoring along / Falling / What the world needs now is love.
**Album:** Released '76, on Sonet by Sonet Records. Catalogue no: **SNTF 684**

**MPS JAZZ TIME,VOLUME 10 (Cohn, Al & James Moody)**
**Album:** Released Jun '79, on MPS Jazz (France) Catalogue no: **5C 064 61173**

Al Cohn

**NATURAL SEVEN, THE**
**Album:** Released Aug '84, on RCA (France) by BMG Records (France). Catalogue no: **NL 89278**

**NIGHT FLIGHT TO DAKAR (Cohn,Al/Billy Mitchell/D. Coker)**
Tracks: / Night flight to Dakar / Don't let the sun catch you cryin' / Blues up and down / Sweet Senegelese Brown / King, The.
**Album:** Released Jan '83, on Xanadu Catalogue no: **XAN 185**

**NON PAREIL**
**Album:** Released Aug '81, on Concord by Concord Jazz Records (USA). Catalogue no: **CJ 155**

**OVERTONES**
Tracks: / P-Town / Woody's lament / High on you / I love you / Vignette / Pensive / I don't want anybody at all / Let's be buddies.
**Album:** Released Nov '82, on Concord Jazz by Concord Jazz Records (USA). Catalogue no: **CJ 194**

**PROGRESSIVE AL COHN, THE**
Note: Artists include: Al Cohn/tenor sax, George Wallington/piano, Tommy Potter/bass, Tony Kahn/drums - Recorded New York 1950. Nick Travis/trumpet, Al Cohn/tenor sax, Horace Silver/piano, Curley Russell / bassMax Roach/drums - Recorded New York 1953. Produced by Gus Statiras (then called Gus Grant after film star Cary) for his progressive label, Gus sold these masters to Savoy Records when his own financial mess became untenable, and so, here we are, thirty years later, with a fine album.
**Album:** Released Dec '85, on Savoy (France) Deleted May '89. Catalogue no: **WL 70508**

**RIFFTIDE**
Tracks: / Speak low / Hot house / Blue monk / Thing, The / We'll be together again / Rifftide.
**Album:** Released Jan '88, on Timeless by Timeless Records. Catalogue no: **SJP 259**

**STANDARDS OF EXCELLENCE**
Tracks: / Russian lullaby / When your lover has gone / O grande amor / You say you care / I want to be happy / Embraceable you / Remember you / When day is done.
**Album:** Released Jun '84, on Concord Jazz by Concord Jazz Records (USA). Catalogue no: **CJ 241**
**Cass:** Released Jun '84, on Concord Jazz by Concord Jazz Records (USA). Catalogue no: **CJC 241**

**TOUR DE FORCE (Cohn, Al/Scott Hamilton)**
Tracks: / Blues up and down / Tickle toe / Let's get away from it all / Soft winds / Stella by starlight / Broadway / Do nothing till you hear from me / Jumpin' at the woodside / Bernie's tune / Rifftide / If.
**2 LP Set:** Released Mar '82, on Concord Jazz by Concord Jazz Records (USA). Catalogue no: **CJ 172**

## Coker, Dolo

**ALL ALONE**
**Album:** Released '88, on Xanadu Catalogue no: **XAN 178**

## Coker, Jerry

**MODERN MUSIC FROM INDIANA UNIVERSITY**
**Album:** on Fantasy Inc (USA) by Fantasy Inc (USA). Catalogue no: **1902116**

## Cola, Kid Sheik

**IN ENGLAND**
Note: With S.Rimmington, Jack Wedell, B.Martin etc.
**Album:** Released Jan '87, on GHB by Jazzology Records (USA). Catalogue no: **GHB-187**

**KID SHEIK COLA (Cola, Kid Sheik/Sadie Goodson)**
**Album:** Released Sep '86, on 504 Catalogue no: **LPS 12**

**KID SHEIK & JOHN HANDY**
**Cass:** Released Mar '87, on Nola Catalogue no: **TC 001**

**N.O. - THE LEGENDS LIVE (Cola, Kid Sheik - Sheik's Swingers)**
Note: Recorded in mono.
**Album:** Released Jun '86, on Jazzology (USA) by Jazzology Records (USA). Catalogue no: **JCE 31**

**SHEIK OF ARABY, THE (Sheik, Kid Storyville Ramblers)**
**Cass:** Released Sep '86, on 504 Catalogue no: **TCS 1**
**Album:** Released Sep '86, on 504 Catalogue no: **LPS 1**

## Cole, Cozy

**Biographical details:** The prominent Swing Era drummer (1909-81) recorded with everybody from Jelly Roll Morton to Benny Goodman and played in Louis Armstrong's All Stars in the early '50s. In the mid-'50s he operated a drum school with Gene Krupa; in 1958 he had a fluke number one novelty hit in the USA with *Topsy*, an old Count Basie tune written by Edgar 'Puddinghead' Battle and Eddie Durham. He toured with Jonah Jones, the ex-Cab Calloway trumpeter, another Swing Era veteran who had unexpected popular success in the '50s. (Donald Clarke 1989).

**ALL STAR SWING GROUPS (Cole, Cozy/Pete Johnson)**
Tracks: / Jericho / Talk to me / Concerto for Cozy / Body and soul / Nice and cozy / Ol' man river / Wrap your troubles in dreams / Ridin' the riff / Flat rock / Jersey jump off / Stompin' at the Savoy / On the sunny side of the street / Jump a while / Pete's lonesome blues / Mr. Drum meets Mr. Piano / Mutiny in the doghouse / Mr. Clarinet knocks twice / Ben rides out / Ben rides out (master) / Page Mr. Trumpet / Page Mr. Trumpet (master) / J.C. from K.C. / Pete's house warming blues / Atomic boogie / Backroom blues / Twelve eighty (1280) stomp / I may be wonderful / Man wanted.
**2 LP Set:** Released Mar '85, on Savoy Jazz (USA) by Malaco Records (USA). Catalogue no: **SJL 2218**

**COZY COLE**
**CD:** Released Jul '89, on Cleo Catalogue no: **CLCD 5024**

### TOPSY

Tracks: / Topsy.
**7" Single:** Released Dec '58, on London Records by London Records Ltd. Deleted Dec '61. Catalogue no: **HL 8750**

## Cole, Freddy

### COLE NOBODY KNOWS, THE

**Album:** Released Aug '88, on Audiophile (USA) by Jazzology Records (USA). Catalogue no: **AP 123**

### RIGHT FROM THE HEART

Tracks: / Right from the start / She believes in me / Girl from the piano bar / I loved you for a minute / Summer love / Somewhere down the line / Teach me tonight / This song's for you / To be with you / Day that my heart caught fire.
**Album:** Released Feb '80, on Sonet by Sonet Records. Deleted '85. Catalogue no: **SKL 5321**

## Cole, Nat "King"

**Biographical details:** This American singer and pianist, born Nathaniel Cole in Montgomery, Alabama in 1917, began playing piano while still a small child and was highly accomplished at this instrument by the time he left school. during the mid to late Thirties, he toured parts of the States with a band in a revue, made his recording debut and formed his own trio. It was not until this period that Cole began to sing - an extraordinarily late start in view of his later acclaim as a vocalist. Legend has it that his singing career commenced unintentionally in a Hollywood night club, when asked to give an impromptu vocal performance of a particular song by a member of the audience. By the late Forties, Cole had perfected his relaxed but polished singing style to such an extent that a fully fledged career in that capacity was launched and the public began to view him as a singer who also played piano. By this time Nat Cole had inserted the 'king' nickname, in recognition of the popularity that his trio had gained on the West Coast jazz scene. The threesome went their separate ways in 1948 when Cole achieved his first vocal smash hit as a solo performer.
That record was *Nature Boy*, a monster Stateside hit that ushered in a lengthy career of jazz-tinged middle-of-the-road successes. (*Nature Boy* has subsequently been a British hit for Bobby Darin, George Benson and Central Line.) Accompanied by smooth, lush orchestral movements, Cole's sound appealed to a mass audience; together with Louis Armstrong, a figure whom he much admired, Cole was one of the first black superstars. His string of hits continued throughout the Fifties and into the early Sixties, but his colour brought its occasional problems: in 1956, he was attacked on stage by a gang of racists in Birmingham, Alabama; the following year, a national American TV series failed due to alleged discrimination by advertising agencies.
Cole, from the Fifties onwards never obtained a No. 1 record in either the US or the UK - his biggest American hits were 1955's *A Blossom Fell* and 1962's *Ramblin' Rose*; his greatest British successes were 1953's *Pretend*, 1954's *Smile* and 1957's *When I Fall In Love*. All these songs peaked at No. 2 in the respective nations. In 1962 he achieved a hit album in duet with blind British jazzman George Shearing.
Cole died of cancer in Santa Monica on 15th February 1965, at the age of 45. The world was without a man who, for a period during the Fifties, had clocked up estimated global disc sales totalling 7 million copies per year. In 1978 a TV advertised *20 Golden Greats* collection reached No. 1 on the UK album charts. By this time, his daughter Natalie Cole had carved a substantial career for herself on the American pop and soul charts. (Bob MacDonald).
Nathaniel Adams Cole (1917-65) was born in Alabama, grew up in Chicago and became an influential jazz pianist, leading an innovative trio with guitar and bass but no drums (because the drummer didn't show up for their first gig). Influenced by Earl Hines, along with Billy Kyle (who later secured a comfortable slot with Louis Armstrong's All Stars) he influenced the next generation, including Bud Powell, Horace Silver, Oscar Peterson and Bill Evans. He also recorded with other jazzmen, as on *Meets The Master Saxes*, and he began to sing occasionally, as on *Straighten Up And Fly Right* and *When I Take My Sugar To Tea*, and finally became one of the best-loved vocalists in the history of popular music. He was not a jazz singer but a balladeer; his first number one was *Nature Boy* in 1948, a strange song by a writer called Eben Ahbez, but his mature style was reached with *Mona Lisa*, number one in 1950 and in the charts for 27 weeks. His jazz background was revived on the album *After Midnight*, which featured the trio with guest soloists Willie Smith, Harry Edison, Stuff Smith and Juan Tizol; and a bumper box of original trio tracks is planned by the American Mosaic label. All the classic Capitol albums have been reissued by EMI. *Love Is The Thing* is one of his best; an EP from it made the USA pop chart in 1957 because of *Stardust*. Nat's version revived the introduction, which hadn't been widely heard since hit records by Artie Shaw and Glenn Miller in 1940 dispensed with it. The album also includes *When I Fall In Love*, a UK hit recently after Rick Astley's ludicrously bad version even imitated Gordon Jenkins' original arrangement. This was followed in 1958 by *The Very Thought Of You*, also with Jenkins, its title track reviving the beautiful Ray Noble song originally recorded by Al Bowlley. Nat also made albums with Nelson Riddle, Billy May and Capitol producer Dave Cavanaugh (*Welcome To The Club* has Cavanaugh conducting what amounts to the Count Basie band). (Donald Clarke 1989).

### 16 GOLDEN CLASSICS

Tracks: / Don't cry, cry baby / Last but not least / On the sunny side of the street / Yes sir that's my baby / Frim fram sauce / If you can't smile and say yes / Satchel mouth baby / Sweet Lorraine / Trouble with me is you / Old piano plays the blues / It's only a paper moon / Greatest invention, The / Bugle call rag / I'm lost / Nat meets June / Tea for two.
**CD:** Released '86, on Unforgettable by Castle Communications Records. Catalogue no: **UNCD 02**
**Album:** Released Dec '86, on Unforgettable by Castle Communications Records. Catalogue no: **UNLP 002**
**Cass:** Released Dec '86, on Unforgettable by Castle Communications Records. Catalogue no: **UNMC 002**

### 16 ORIGINAL HITS: NAT KING COLE

**Cass:** Released Sep '87, on Timeless Treasures Catalogue no: **MC 1628**

### 20 GOLDEN GREATS: NAT KING COLE

Tracks: / Sweet Lorraine / Straighten up and fly right / Nature boy / Dance ballerina dance / Mona Lisa / Too young / Love letters / Smile / Around the world / For all we know / When I fall in love / Very thought of you, The / On the street where you live / Unforgettable / It's all in the game / Ramblin' rose / Portrait of Jennie / Let there be love / Somewhere along the way / Those lazy, hazy, crazy days of summer.
**Album:** Released Mar '78, on Capitol by EMI Records. Catalogue no: **EMTV 9**
**CD:** Released Dec '87, on Capitol by EMI Records. Catalogue no: **CDEMTV 9**
**Cass:** Released Mar '78, on Capitol by EMI Records. Catalogue no: **TC EMTV 9**
**CD:** Released Sep '87, on Deja Vu Catalogue no: **DVCD 2012**
**CD:** Released Dec '87, on Capitol by EMI Records. Catalogue no: **CDP 746 737 2**

### 20 GREAT TRACKS (Live)

**CD:** on Magic (1) by Submarine Records. Catalogue no: **DATOM 1**

### 20 GREATEST LOVE SONGS

Tracks: / Stardust / Answer me / Autumn leaves / Walkin' my baby back home / These foolish things / There goes my heart / Nightingale sang in Berkeley Square, A / You made me love you / Blossom fell, A / More / Love letters / Oh, how I miss you tonight / Brazilian love song / You're my everything / Love is a many splendoured thing / You'll never know / He'll have to go / Stay as sweet as you are / More I see you, The / Party's over, The.
**Cass:** Released Nov '82, on EMI by EMI Records. Catalogue no: **TC EMTV 35**
**CD:** Released Dec '87, on EMI by EMI Records. Catalogue no: **CDP 748 614 2**
**CD:** Released Dec '87, on EMI by EMI Records. Catalogue no: **CDEMTV 35**
**Album:** Released Nov '82, on EMI by

:MI Records. Catalogue no: **EMTV 35**

**943-49 VOCAL SIDES, THE (Cole, lat King Trio)**
**:D:** Released Jun '86, on Delta (1) by )elta Records. Catalogue no: **11 044**

**942-1949 (VIDEO) (Cole, Nat King The Mills Brothers)**
**'HS:** Released Feb '90, on Verve Catalogue no: **CFV10232**

**AFTER MIDNIGHT**
racks: / Just you, just me / Sweet Loraine / Sometimes I'm happy / Caravan It's only a paper moon / You're lookin' t me / What is there to say / I was a little oo lonely / Two loves have I / Lonely ne, The / Don't let it go to your head / I now that you know / Blame it on my outh / When I grow too old to dream / Route 66 - get your kicks on / You can lepend on me / Candy.
Note: This excellent album heralds the econd phase in the digitally re-mastered Nat King Cole re-issues. Contains previously unreleased tracks from the riginal sessions, added to the 12-track ersion. Original sleeve design, plus ew, informative sleeve note from roadcaster Alan Dell. This, Nat's last najor piano album, will be enjoyed by Capitol and King Cole fans, but appeal will be broader still by the inclusion of a strong jazz flavour.
**Album:** Released Feb '86, on Capitol by EMI Records. Catalogue no: **EMS 1103**
**CD:** Released Feb '88, on Capitol by EMI Records. Catalogue no: **CDP 748 328 2**
**CD:** Released Feb '88, on Capitol by EMI Records. Catalogue no: **CDEMS 1103**
**Cass:** Released Feb '86, on Capitol by EMI Records. Catalogue no: **TCEMS 1103**

**ANATOMY OF A JAM SESSION**
Tracks: / Black market stuff / Laguna eap / I'll never be the same / Swingin' on central / Kicks.
Note: With Buddy Rich, Charlie Shavers, he Sunset Allstars.
**Album:** Released Jan '85, on Black Lion Catalogue no: **BLP 30104**

**ANY OLD TIME (Cole, Nat King Trio)**
**Album:** Released Oct '86, on Giants of Jazz by Hasmick Promotions. Catalogue no: **GOJ 1031**
**Cass:** Released Oct '86, on Giants of Jazz by Hasmick Promotions. Catalogue no: **GOJC 1031**

**AT HIS RAREST OF ALL RARE PERFORMANCES VOL 1**
**Album:** Released Jul '82, on Kings Of Jazz Catalogue no: **KLJ 20029**

**BALLADS OF THE DAY**
Tracks: / Blossom fell, A / Unbelievable / Blue gardenia / Angel eyes / It happens to be me / Smile / Darling, je vous aime beaucoup / Alone too long / My one sin (in life) / Return to paradise / If love is good to me / Sand and the sea, The.
Note: This album was originally released as a compilation album as a sequel to the 1955 album 'Unforgettable'. Arranged by Nelson Riddle, the songs contained on this album are stamped through with Nat's magical style and comprised of hit singles from between 1953 and 1954.
**Cass:** Released Nov '85, on Capitol by EMI Records. Catalogue no: **TC EMS 1102**
**Album:** Released Nov '85, on Capitol by EMI Records. Catalogue no: **EMS 1102**

**BECAUSE YOU'RE MINE**
Tracks: / Because you're mine.
**7" Single:** Released Dec '52, on Capitol by EMI Records. Deleted Dec '55. Catalogue no: **CL 13811**

**BEST OF NAT KING COLE**
Tracks: / Unforgettable / Nature boy / When I fall in love / Ramblin' Rose / Let there be love / Too young / Mona Lisa.
**CD:** Released Jun '86, on Card/Grand Prix Catalogue no: **CD 860704**
**Cass:** Released '83, on EMI (Holland) by EMI Records. Catalogue no: **1A 222 58069**
**Album:** Released '83, on EMI (Holland) by EMI Records. Catalogue no: **1A 022 58069**

**BEST OF NAT KING COLE, VOL 1**
**Album:** Released Dec '68, on Capitol by EMI Records. Deleted Dec '73. Catalogue no: **ST 21139**

**BEST OF NAT KING COLE, VOL.2**
**Album:** Released '70, on Capitol by EMI Records. Deleted '85. Catalogue no: **ST 21687**

**BEST OF NAT KING COLE VOL.3**
**Album:** on Capitol by EMI Records. Catalogue no: **ST 21874**

**BLOSSOM FELL, A**
Tracks: / Blossom fell, A.
**7" Single:** Released Feb '55, on Capitol by EMI Records. Deleted Feb '58. Catalogue no: **CL 14235**

**BODY AND SOUL**
Tracks: / It's only a paper moon / Don't cry, cry baby / Cole's bop blues / Frim fram sauce / If you can't smile and say yes / On the sunny side of the street / Miss thing / Sweet Lorraine / Satchel mouth baby / Body and soul / Trouble with me is you / Sweet Georgia Brown / Yes sir, that's my baby / Last but not least.
Note: Licensed from Charly International APS. This CD (P) 1987 Charly Holdings Ltd. (C) Charly Records Ltd
**Album:** Released Nov '84, on Topline by Charly Records. Catalogue no: **TOP 112**
**CD:** Released Apr '87, on Topline by Charly Records. Catalogue no: **TOP CD 508**

**BRAZILIAN LOVE SONG**
Tracks: / Brazilian love song.
**7" Single:** Released Mar '62, on Capitol by EMI Records. Deleted Mar '65. Catalogue no: **CL 15241**

**CAN'T I?**
Tracks: / Can't I?.
**7" Single:** Released Aug '53, on Capitol by EMI Records. Deleted Aug '56. Catalogue no: **CL 13937**

**CAPITOL COLLECTORS SERIES**
Tracks: / Straighten up and fly right / Get your kicks on route 66 / I love you for sentimental reasons / Christmas song (Merry Christmas to you) / Nature boy / Too young / Walkin' my baby back home / Pretend / Answer me, my love / Darling, je vous aime beaucoup / Blossom fell, A / Send for me / Non dimenticar (Don't forget) / Ramblin' rose / Dear lonely hearts / All over the world / Those lazy-hazy-crazy days of summer / L-O-V-E / Mona Lisa.
**CD:** Released Apr '90, on Capitol by EMI Records. Catalogue no: **CZ 303**
**CD:** Released Apr '90, on Capitol by EMI Records. Catalogue no: **CDP 793 590 2**

**CAPITOL YEARS, THE: NAT KING COLE**
Tracks: / Unforgettable / Sings for two in love / Ballads of the day / After midnight / Love is the thing / Just one of those things / Very thought of you, The / Welcome to the club / To whom it may concern / Tell me all about yourself / At the sands / Touch of your lips, The / Let's face the music / Nat King Cole sings / George Shearing plays / Where did everyone go? / Ramblin' rose / Those lazy hazy crazy days of summer / L.O.V.E. / Piano style of Nat King Cole, The.
**LP Set:** Released Oct '87, on Capitol by EMI Records. Catalogue no: **NKC 20**

**CHRISTMAS SONG, THE**
Tracks: / Christmas song, The / Deck the hall / Adeste fideles / Tannenbaum / O little town of Bethlehem / I saw three ships / O holy night / Hark the herald angels sing / Cradle in Bethlehem, A / Away in a manger / Joy to the world / First Noel, The / Caroling, caroling / Silent night.
**Album:** Released Nov '84, on Capitol by EMI Records. Deleted Jun '89. Catalogue no: **EG 2603221**
**Album:** Released Dec '82, on MFP by EMI Records. Deleted '86. Catalogue no: **MFP 50313**
**Cass:** Released Nov '84, on Capitol by EMI Records. Catalogue no: **EG 2603224**

**CHRISTMAS WITH NAT KING COLE**
Tracks: / Little boy that Santa Claus forgot, The / I saw three ships / Deck the hall / O come all ye faithful / Nature boy / Joy to the world / Cradle in Bethlehem, A / Away in a manger / Hark the herald angels sing / Caroling caroling / First Noel, The.
**Album:** Released Nov '88, on Stylus by Stylus Music Records. Catalogue no: **SMR 868**
**CD:** Released Nov '88, on Stylus by Stylus Music Records. Catalogue no: **SMD 868**

Nat 'King' Cole

**Cass set:** Released Nov '88, on Stylus by Stylus Music Records. Catalogue no: **SMC 868**

**CLASSICS**
**2 LP Set:** Released Jan '85, on Pathe Marconi (France) Catalogue no: **PM 155 1863**

**COLE ESPANOL**
**Album:** Released Aug '84, on EMI (Holland) by EMI Records. Catalogue no: **1A 038 80402**

**COLE ESPANOL AND MORE VOL.1**
Tracks: / Cachito / Maria Elena / Quizas quizas quizas / Las mananitas / Acercate Mas (come close to me) / Bodeguero, El / Noche de Ronda / Te quiero dijiste / Adelita (with Mariachis) / Ay, Cosita Linda / Aguellos ojus verdes / Saus Maos / Capullito de aleli / Fantastico / Nadie me ama.
**CD:** Released Mar '87, on Capitol by EMI Records. Deleted Feb '90. Catalogue no: **CDP 746 469 2**

**COLE ESPANOL AND MORE VOL. 2**
Tracks: / La feria de las flores / Tres Palabras / Las chiapanecas (while there's music there's romance) / Adios Mariquita Linda (adios and farewell my lover) / Vaya con Dios / La golondrina/ Solamente una verez (you belong to my heart) / Piel Canela / Yo vendo unos ojos negros / Perfidia / El Choclo / Ansiedad / No tenho lagrimas.
**CD:** Released Mar '87, on Capitol by EMI Records. Catalogue no: **CDP 746 482 2**

**COLLECTION: NAT 'KING' COLE**
Tracks: / Don't cry, cry baby / Last but not least / On the sunny side of the street / Sweet Georgia Brown / Yes sir that's my baby / Body and soul / Cole's bop blues / Frim fram Sauce / If you can't smile and say yes / Miss thing / Satchel mouth baby / Sweet Lorraine / Trouble with me is you / Old piano plays the blues / It's only a paper moon / Greatest invention, The / Bugle call rag / Blues / I'm lost / Nat meets June / Rosetta / Tea for two / Man on the little white keys, The.
Note: Contains early recordings which can reveal quality limitations of the tape source.
**2 LP Set:** Released Jul '86, on Castle Collector Series by Castle Communications Records. Catalogue no: **CCSLP 144**
**Cass:** Released Jul '86, on Castle Collector Series by Castle Communications Records. Catalogue no: **CCSMC 144**

**COMPLETE AFTER MIDNIGHT SESSIONS**
**CD:** Released Feb '88, on Capitol by EMI Records. Catalogue no: **CDP 748 328 2**

**COOL COLE, THE**
**Album:** Released Feb '89, on Sounds Rare Catalogue no: **SR 5003**

**DEAR LONELY HEARTS**
Tracks: / Dear lonely hearts.
**7" Single:** Released Dec '62, on Capitol by EMI Records. Deleted Dec '65. Catalogue no: **CL 15280**

**DISQUE D'OR(COLLECTION)**
Tracks: / Love / Those lazy, hazy, crazy days of summer / Stardust / St. Louis blues / Blue gardenia / Girl from Ipanema / Unforgettable / Brazilian love song / Ramblin' rose / Three little words / Darling, je vous aime beaucoup / All over the world / Miss you / Les feuilles mortes.
**Album:** Released '83, on EMI (France) by EMI Records. Catalogue no: **2C 070 81267**

**DREAMS CAN TELL A LIE**
Tracks: / Dreams can tell a lie.
**7" Single:** Released Jan '56, on Capitol by EMI Records. Deleted Jan '59. Catalogue no: **CL 14513**

**EMBRACEABLE YOU**
**Cass:** Released Jul '88, on Vanstory Catalogue no: **VSK 3408**
**Album:** Released Jul '88, on Vanstory Catalogue no: **VS 3408**

**FAITH CAN MOVE MOUNTAINS**
Tracks: / Faith can move mountains.
**78 RPM:** Released Jan '53, on Capitol by EMI Records. Deleted Jan '56. Catalogue no: **CL 13811**

**FASCINATION**
**Album:** Released '88, on Entertainers Catalogue no: **ENT LP 13042**
**Cass:** Released '88, on Entertainers Catalogue no: **ENT MC 13042**

**FAVOURITE BALLADS BY NAT**
**Cass:** Released Dec '88, on Capitol (Specials) Catalogue no: **4XL 8318**

**FOR THOSE IN LOVE**
Tracks: / When I fall in love / Love is here to stay / Almost like being in love / This can't be love / Love is the thing / L-O-V-E / Love letters.
**Cass:** Released Dec '88, on Capitol (Specials) Catalogue no: **4XL 8316**

**FOREVER NAT**
**Cass:** Released Jun '89, on Spectrum (CD) by M.S.D.. Catalogue no: **U3013-2**
**CD:** Released Jun '89, on Spectrum (CD) by M.S.D.. Catalogue no: **K3013-2**

**FORGOTTEN YEARS (Cole, Nat King Trio)**
Tracks: / On the sunny side of the street / Man on the little white keys, The / Frim fram sauce / If you can't smile and say yes / Trouble with me is you / Sweet Georgia Brown / Satchel mouth baby / Miss thing / Sweet Lorraine / Paper moon.
**Album:** Released Jan '85, on Giants of Jazz by Hasmick Promotions. Catalogue no: **GOJ 1013**

**FROM THE VERY BEGINNING**
Tracks: / Honeysuckle rose / Sweet Lorraine / This side up / Gone with the draft / Stompin' at the Panama / Early morning blues / Babs / Slow down / Honey hush / I like to riff / This will make you laugh / Hit the ramp / Stop, the red light's on / (Bedtime) sleep, baby, sleep / Call the police / That ain't right / Are you fer it? / Hit that jive Jack / Thunder.
**Album:** Released Apr '82, on Coral by MCA Records. Deleted Apr '88. Catalogue no: **MCL 1671**
**Cass:** Released Apr '82, on Coral by

MCA Records. Catalogue no: **MCLC 1671**

## GREAT CAPITOL MASTERS

Tracks: / I'm an errand boy for rhythm / Kee mo ky mo / I used to love you / These foolish things / Dream a little dream of me / Love nest, The / But all I've got is me / I've got a way with women / When I take my sugar to tea / I miss you so / You're the cream in my coffee / But she's my buddy's chick / Naughty Angeline / Best man, The / I think you get what I mean / That's what.

Note: A new compilation of the Nat Cole Trio's earlier recordings for Capitol Records.This swinging collection of well known tracks combined with Nat's inimitable voice which provides a good blend of jazz and nostalgia.

**Cass:** Released Dec '85, on Capitol by EMI Records. Deleted Nov '88. Catalogue no: **TCEMS 1142**

**Album:** Released Dec '85, on Capitol by EMI Records. Deleted Nov '88. Catalogue no: **EMS 1142**

## GREAT FILMS AND SHOWS, THE

Tracks: / Around the world / Smile / When I fall in love / Love letters / Ain't misbehavin' / At last / Stay as sweet as you are / More I see you, The / You're my everything / More / Am I blue / Spring is here / It's all in the game / But beautiful / Paradise / Very thought of you, The / Because you're mine / Again / An affair to remember / Mood indigo / Only forever / I remember you / Don't get around much anymore / I should care / Just one of those things / Party's over, The / Song is ended (but the melody lingers on), The / Bidin' my time / Ebony rhapsody / Let's face the music and dance / Cold cold heart / Lover come back to me / Who's sorry now / Almost like being in love / This can't be love / You stepped out of a dream / Best thing for you, The / For you / How little we know / Like someone in love / Beale Street blues / St. Louis blues / Ballad of Cat Ballou / In the good old summertime / With a little bit of luck / I could have danced all night / Rain in Spain, The / On the street where you live / I'm an ordinary man / Get me to the church on time / Show me / I've grown accustomed to her face / You did it / Wouldn't it be luverly / Hymn to him / I got it bad and that ain't good / Pick yourself up / September song / All by myself / They can't make her cry / Three little words / You'll never know / I am in love / Your cheatin' heart / Mona Lisa / Love is here to stay / Let's fall in love / There will never be another you / Blue gardenia / China gate / Hajji baba / Never let me go / Return to paradise / Night of the quarter moon / To whom it may concern / Nightingale sang in Berkeley Square, A / Magic moment / People / Love is a many splendoured thing / Sometimes I'm happy / Caravan / Just you, just me / It's only a paper moon / When I grow too old to dream / Get your kicks on Route 66 / When I fall in love / More I see you, The / Just one of those things / Love is here to stay / On the street where you live / Very thought of you, The / September song / St. Louis blues / Let's fall in love / Lover come back to me / Mona Lisa / It's only a paper moon / Nightingale sang in Berkeley Square, A / People / I should care / Smile / More / In the good old summertime.

Note: Album & CD box set containing 4 records + 1 free cassette. Mail order only.

**CD Set:** Released Aug '89, on Capitol by EMI Records. Catalogue no: **CDNKC 1**

**CD Set:** Released Aug '89, on Capitol by EMI Records. Catalogue no: **793 207 2**

**LP Set:** Released Aug '89, on Capitol by EMI Records. Catalogue no: **NKC 1**

**LP Set:** Released Aug '89, on Capitol by EMI Records. Catalogue no: **793 207 1**

## GREAT NAT KING COLE 1940 - 1956

**CD:** Released '88, on Delta (1) by Delta Records. Catalogue no: **11 086**

## GREATEST HITS:NAT 'KING' COLE

Tracks: / Nature boy / Mona Lisa / Too young / When I fall in love / Quizas quizas quizas / Unforgettable / Fly me to the moon / Let there be love / Love / Darling, je vous aime beaucoup / Ramblin' rose / Those lazy hazy crazy days of summer / Lost April / Answer me my love / Sweet Lorraine / I don't want to hurt anymore / Route 66 / Dear lonely hearts / Ay cosita Linda / Perfidia / Blue gardenia / It's only a paper moon / Acerta te mast / Smile / Blossom fell, A / Stardust / Love is the thing.

**Album:** Released '83, on Capitol (import) Catalogue no: **5C 180 82269/70**

## HAVIN' FUN WITH NAT KING COLE

Tracks: / Open up the doghouse / Long, long ago / If I may / My personal possession / That's all there is to that / My baby just cares for me / For you my love / Can I come in for a second / Get out and get under the moon / Hey, not now / Save the bones for Henry Jones / Harmony.

**Album:** Released '88, on Official by Official Records. Catalogue no: **OFF 12003**

**CD:** Released '88, on Official by Official Records. Catalogue no: **OFF 812003**

**Cass:** Released '88, on Official by Official Records. Catalogue no: **OFF 412003**

## HIS GREATEST SUCCESS

Tracks: / Darling, je vous aime beaucoup / Crazy but I'm in love / Sand and the sea, The / Stompin' down Broadway / Somebody loves me / I've grown accustomed to her face / Tea for two / Unforgettable / This can't be love / Beautiful friendship, A / Mona Lisa / Thou swell / Two different worlds / It's only a paper moon / Early American / Till the end of the years / Sweet Sue / I'm shooting high / Autumn leaves / Just one of those things / Little girl / When you're smiling / Night lights / Take me back to Toyland / Just in time / House with love in it, A / Mr. Santa Claus / You stepped out of a dream / Pick yourself up / Jingle bells / Christmas song, The / Cuba.

**2 LP Set:** Released Oct '83, on Musidisc by Musidisc Records (France). Catalogue no: **ALB 223**

## IF I GIVE MY HEART TO YOU

Tracks: / If I give my heart to you / Walkin' my baby back home / Somewhere along the way / Funny (not much) / More I see you, The / Ballerina / It's all in the game / Laughing on the outside (crying on the inside) / Teach me tonight.

**Cass:** Released Dec '88, on Capitol (Specials) Catalogue no: **4XL 9050**

## IN THE COOL OF THE EVENING (Cole, Nat King Trio)

Tracks: / Jumpin' at Capitol / Is it better to be yourself / Everyone is sayin' hello again / To a wild rose / Oh, but I do / You should have told me / In the cool of the evening / That's the beginning of the end / I want to thank you folks / Come in out of the rain / You don't learn that in school / Can you look me in the eyes / Meet me at no special place / I can't be bothered / There I've sold it again / Trouble with me is you, The.

**Album:** on Official by Official Records. Catalogue no: **OFF 3026**

**CD:** on Official by Official Records. Catalogue no: **OFF 83026**

## INCOMPARABLE

Tracks: / You're the cream in my coffee / Embraceable you / Prelude in 'C' sharp / Nature boy / For all we know / Gee baby ain't I good to you / Love is a many splendoured thing / Route 66 / You stepped out of a dream / Stardust / Don't get around much anymore / Coquette.

**Album:** Released Sep '85, on Meteor by Magnum Music Group. Catalogue no: **MTM 008**

## IT'S ALMOST LIKE BEING IN LOVE (Cole, Nat King Trio)

**Album:** Released Jun '88, on Dance Band Days by Prism Leisure. Catalogue no: **DBD 15**

**CD:** Released Jul '89, on Dance Band Days by Prism Leisure. Catalogue no: **DBCD 15**

**Cass:** Released Jun '88, on Dance Band Days by Prism Leisure. Catalogue no: **DBDC 15**

## JUST AS MUCH AS EVER

Tracks: / Just as much as ever.

**7" Single:** Released Nov '60, on Capitol by EMI Records. Deleted Nov '63. Catalogue no: **CL 15163**

## JUST ONE OF THOSE THINGS

Tracks: / When your lover has gone / Cottage for sale / Who's sorry now / Once in a while / These foolish things / Just for the fun of it / Don't get around much anymore / I understand / I understand / Just one of those things / Song is ended, The / I should care / Party's over, The / Day in, day out / I'm gonna sit right down (and write myself a letter) / Something makes me want to dance with you.

Note: A full 12-track stereo, digitally remastered album containing songs of ended romance and unrequited love, by one of the great love song singers of all time. Billy May heads the orchestra, adding his own musical ideas, while Nat

croons the message of the song in his intimate style, showing their compatible view of each number. Includes late night listening such as *Don't get around much anymore*, *A cottage for sale* and *These foolish things*, as well as more uptempo easy listening in *Who's sorry now* and the title track *Just one of those things*.
**Cass:** Released Feb '86, on Capitol by EMI Records. Catalogue no: **TCEMS 1105**
**Album:** Released Feb '86, on Capitol by EMI Records. Catalogue no: **EMS 1105**
**CD:** Released Mar '88, on Capitol by EMI Records. Catalogue no: **BU 10**
**CD:** Released Mar '88, on Capitol by EMI Records. Catalogue no: **CDP 746 649 2**

### KING COLE TRIO, THE
**Album:** Released Sep '87, on Giants of Jazz by Hasmick Promotions. Catalogue no: **LPJT 14**

### LEGENDARY NAT KING COLE, THE
Tracks: / Just can't see for looking / Hit the jive Jack / Swinging the blues / I'm in the mood for love / On the sunny side of the street / Sweet Georgia Brown / Baby won't you please come home / Too marvellous for words.
**Cass:** Released Sep '89, on Nostalgia by Mainline Records. Catalogue no: **MRT 40052**

### LET THERE BE LOVE (Cole, Nat King & George Shearing)
Tracks: / September song / Pick yourself up / I got it bad & that ain't good / Let there be love / Azure - te / Lost April / Beautiful friendship, A / Fly me to the moon / Serenata / I'm lost / There's a lull in my life / Don't go.
**Cass:** Released Apr '83, on MFP by EMI Records. Deleted '87. Catalogue no: **TCMFP 5612**
**Album:** Released Apr '83, on MFP by EMI Records. Deleted '87. Catalogue no: **MFP 5612**

### LET THERE BE LOVE (SINGLE) (Cole, Nat King & George Shearing)
Tracks: / Let there be love.
**7" Single:** Released Jul '62, on Capitol by EMI Records. Deleted Jul '65. Catalogue no: **CL 15257**

### LET TRUE LOVE BEGIN
Tracks: / Let true love begin.
**7" Single:** Released Nov '61, on Capitol by EMI Records. Deleted Nov '64. Catalogue no: **CL 15224**

### LET'S FACE THE MUSIC
Tracks: / Ebony Rhapsody / Too little, too late / Let's face the music and dance / Day in, day out / Bidin' my time / When my sugar walks down the street / Warm and willing / I'm gonna sit right down and write myself a letter / Cold, cold heart / Something makes me want to dance with you / Moon love / Rules of the road, The.
**Cass:** Released Aug '86, on Capitol by EMI Records. Catalogue no: **TCEMS 1112**
**Album:** Released Aug '86, on Capitol by EMI Records. Catalogue no: **EMS 1112**

### LIVE - KONGRESSHAUS, ZURICH (Oct. 19th 1950) (Cole, Nat King Trio)
**Album:** Released Jul '87, on Duke by Melodisc Records. Catalogue no: **D 1014**

### L.O.V.E.
Tracks: / L.O.V.E. / Girl from Ipanema / Three little words / There's love / My kind of girl / Thanks to you / Your love / More / Coquette / How I'd love to love you / Swiss retreat.
Note: Music conducted by Ralph Carmichael. Trumpet solos by Bobby Bryant.
**Album:** Released Sep '86, on Capitol by EMI Records. Catalogue no: **EMS 1117**
**Cass:** Released Sep '86, on Capitol by EMI Records. Catalogue no: **TCEMS 1117**

### LOVE IS THE THING
Tracks: / When I fall in love / End of a love affair, The / Stardust / Stay as sweet as you are / Where can I go without you / Maybe it's because I love you too much / Love letters / Ain't misbehavin' / I thought about Marie / At last / It's all in the game / When Sunny gets blue / Love is the thing.
Note: A romantic collection of favourite love songs including *When I fall in love*, *Stay as sweet as you* are and *It's all in the game*, delivered in Nat Cole's unmistakable warm style. This predominantly stereo, digitally re-mastered album is the full 12-track original version. Until now, the only available album was the abridged 10-track U.S. release. Contains one of Nat's most popular songs, *Stardust*, as well as a string of popular classics from the great composers of the day, with orchestra conducted by Gordon Jenkins.
**Cass:** Released Feb '86, on Capitol by EMI Records. Catalogue no: **TCEMS 1104**
**CD:** Released Mar '88, on Capitol by EMI Records. Catalogue no: **BU 11**
**Album:** Released Feb '86, on Capitol by EMI Records. Catalogue no: **EMS 1104**
**CD:** Released Mar '88, on Capitol by EMI Records. Catalogue no: **CDP 746 648 2**

### LOVE ME AS THOUGH THERE WERE NO TOMORROW
Tracks: / Love me as though there were no tomorrow.
**7" Single:** Released Sep '56, on Capitol by EMI Records. Deleted Sep '59. Catalogue no: **CL 14621**

### LOVE SONGS: NAT KING COLE
**Cass:** Released Dec '88, on Capitol (Specials) Catalogue no: **4XL 8355**

### MAGIC OF NAT KING COLE, THE
**CD:** Released Jun '88, on Spectrum (1) Catalogue no: **U 4035**

### MAKE HER MINE
Tracks: / Make her mine.
**7" Single:** Released Oct '54, on Capitol by EMI Records. Deleted Oct '57. Catalogue no: **CL 14149**

### MEETS THE MASTER SAXES
Tracks: / Heads / Pro-sky / It had to be you / I can't give you anything but love / Indiana / I can't get started / Tea for two / Body and soul / I found a new baby / Rosetta / Sweet Lorraine / I blowed and gone.
**Album:** Released '83, on Spotlite by Spotlite Records. Catalogue no: **SPJ 136**

### MIDNIGHT FLYER
Tracks: / Midnight flyer.
**7" Single:** Released Sep '59, on Capitol by EMI Records. Deleted Sep '62. Catalogue no: **CL 15056**

### MONA LISA
Tracks: / Mona Lisa / Kings Cross-follow Anderson.
**7" Single:** Released Aug '86, on Capitol by EMI Records. Deleted Oct '87. Catalogue no: **CL 414**

### MORE COLE ESPANOL
**Album:** Released Jan '85, on EMI (Holland) by EMI Records. Catalogue no: **5C 038 80483**

### MOTHER NATURE AND FATHER TIME
Tracks: / Mother nature and father time.
**7" Single:** Released Sep '53, on Capitol by EMI Records. Deleted Sep '56. Catalogue no: **CL 13912**

### MY KIND OF GIRL
Tracks: / Ramblin' rose / Goodnight Irene / My kind of girl / Portrait of Jennie / Ballerina / Miss Otis regrets / Here's to my lady / Adelita / Sweet Lorraine / On a bicycle built for two / Girl from Ipanema / I thought about Marie / Marnie / Mona Lisa / Maria Elena / Annabelle.
**Album:** on Capitol by EMI Records. Catalogue no: **ST 21873**

### MY ONE SIN
Tracks: / My one sin.
**7" Single:** Released Aug '55, on Capitol by EMI Records. Deleted Aug '58. Catalogue no: **CL 14327**

### MY PERSONAL POSSESSION
Tracks: / My personal possession.
**7" Single:** Released Oct '57, on Capitol by EMI Records. Deleted Oct '60. Catalogue no: **CL 14765**

### NAT KING COLE
Note: Featuring Lester Young, Charlie Parker, Coleman Hawkins, Stuff Smith, Buddy Rich.
**Cass:** Released '88, on Entertainers Catalogue no: **ENT MC 13003**
**LP Set:** Released Dec '81, on World Records by EMI Records. Catalogue no: **ALBUM 46**
**Album:** Released Sep '87, on Giants of Jazz by Hasmick Promotions. Catalogue no: **LPJT 62**
**Cass:** Released '88, on EMI (Italy) by EMI Records. Catalogue no: **1868204**
**Album:** Released '88, on Entertainers Catalogue no: **ENT LP 13003**

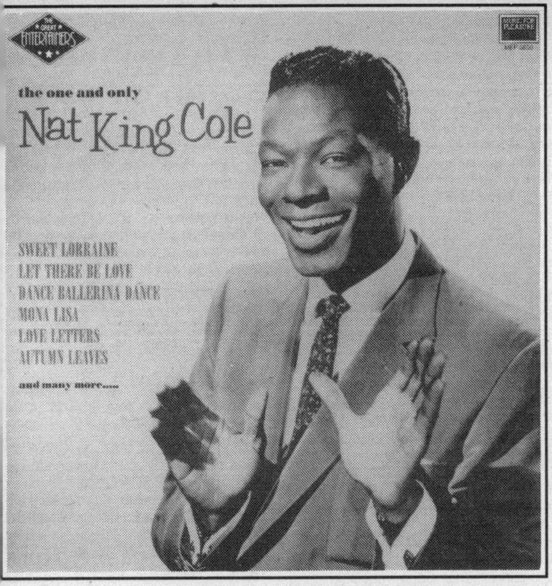


**Nat King Cole - The One and Only (MFP)**

**CD:** Released Jul '87, on Intertape Deleted '88. Catalogue no: **500 057**
**Cass set:** Released Dec '81, on World Records by EMI Records. Catalogue no: **CASSETTE 46**
**Album:** Released Apr '87, on Capitol by EMI Records. Catalogue no: **1868201**
**Album:** Released Sep '87, on Entertainers Catalogue no: **ENT 13003**
**Album:** Released '88, on EMI (Italy) by EMI Records. Catalogue no: **1868201**

**NAT KING COLE AT THE SANDS**
Tracks: / Ballerina / Funny - not much / Continental, The / I wish you love / You leave me breathless / Thou swell / My kind of love / Surrey with the fringe on top / Where or when / Miss Otis regrets (she's unable to lunch today) / Joe Turner blues.
Note: A collection of popular classics recorded live at The Sands club in January 1960, but not released until after his death in 1966. This unique album - Nat's only official on-stage recording is being re-issued in its original gatefold packaging as part of our Nat King Cole re-issue programme. In keeping with this series, an informative sleeve note is provided by renowned broadcaster, Alan Dell.
**Cass:** Released May '86, on Capitol by EMI Records. Catalogue no: **TCEMS 1110**
**Album:** Released May '86, on Capitol by EMI Records. Catalogue no: **EMS 1110**

**NAT KING COLE COLLECTION**
**CD:** Released Oct '89, on Collection by K-Tel Records. Catalogue no: **OR 0075**
**CD:** Released Jul '87, on Deja Vu Catalogue no: **DVCD 2012**
**Album:** Released Aug '85, on Deja Vu Catalogue no: **DVLP 2012**
**Cass:** Released Aug '85, on Deja Vu Catalogue no: **DVMC 2012**

**NAT KING COLE LIVE (Cole, Nat King/Nelson Riddle Orchestra)**
Tracks: / Two different worlds / Thou swell / Mona Lisa / Night lights / Too young / That's my girl / But not for me / Repeat after me / True love / Little girl / Love letters / Just in timeA / Unforgettable / Love me tender / My foolish heart / Sweet Sue / Somewhere along the way / This can't be love / I'm sitting on top of the world / You are my first love / It's just a little street / Toyland.
Note: With Nelson Riddle Orchestra and Gordon Jenkins Orchestra.
**Album:** Released Apr '88, on A Touch Of Magic by Submarine Records. Catalogue no: **ATOM 1**
**Cass:** Released Apr '88, on A Touch Of Magic by Submarine Records. Catalogue no: **CATOM 1**
**CD:** Released Apr '88, on A Touch Of Magic by Submarine Records. Catalogue no: **DATOM 1**

**NAT KING COLE SINGS AND PLAYS**
Tracks: / Sweet Lorraine / Honeysuckle rose / Gone with the draft / This side up / Babs / Scotchin' with soda / Early morning blues / This will make you laugh / I like to riff / Call the police / Are you fer it? / That ain't right.
**Album:** Released Apr '81, on Joker (USA) by Lifetime Records (USA). Catalogue no: **SM 3611**

**NAT KING COLE SINGS THE GEORGE SHEARING QUINTET**
Tracks: / September song / Pick yourself up / I got it bad and that ain't good / Let there be love / Azure te / Lost April / Everything happens to me / Beautiful friendship, A / Fly me to the moon / Serenata / I'm lost / There's a lull in my life / Don't go / Guess I'll go back home.
**CD:** Released Feb '88, on Capitol by EMI Records. Catalogue no: **CDP 748 332 2**
**Cass:** Released Aug '86, on Capitol by EMI Records. Catalogue no: **TCEMS 1113**
**CD:** Released Feb '88, on Capitol by EMI Records. Catalogue no: **CDEMS 1113**
**Album:** Released Oct '62, on Capitol by EMI Records. Deleted Oct '67. Catalogue no: **W 1675**
**Album:** Released Aug '86, on Capitol by EMI Records. Catalogue no: **EMS 1113**

**NAT KING COLE TRIO (Cole, Nat King Trio)**
**CD:** Released '89, on Echo Jazz Catalogue no: **EJCD 08**
**Album:** Released '89, on Echo Jazz Catalogue no: **EJLP 08**
**Cass:** Released '89, on Echo Jazz Catalogue no: **EJMC 08**

**NAT KING COLE TRIO 1943/49 (The vocal sides) (Cole, Nat King Trio)**
Tracks: / Embraceable you / You're the cream in my coffee / When I take my sugar to tea.
**Album:** Released Mar '88, on Delta (1) by Delta Records. Catalogue no: **20 808**

**NAT KING COLE TRIO (AND GUESTS) (Cole, Nat King Trio)**
Tracks: / Sweet Lorraine / I know that you know / Don't let it go to your head / Caravan / You're looking at me / Route 66 / Just you, just me / Lonely one, The / It's only a paper moon / When I grow too old to dream / Bop kick / Peaches / For sentimental reasons / This way out / Straighten up and fly right / Rhumba Azul / I like to riff / What is this thing called love? / Riffamarole / But all I've got is me / I've found a new baby / Honeysuckle rose / Exactly like you.
**CD:** Released '88, on Giants of Jazz by Hasmick Promotions. Catalogue no: **GOJCD 0231**

**NAT KING COLE TRIO COLLECTION (20 golden greats) (Cole, Nat King Trio)**
Tracks: / Man I love, The / This way out / Sweet Georgia Brown / Embraceable you / Is you is or is you ain't my baby / Get your kicks on Route 66 / What is this thing called love? / Boogie a la king / I'm in the mood for love / For sentimental reasons / Honeysuckle rose / Baby won't you please come home? / Sweet Lorraine / It's only a paper moon / Somebody loves you / Swingin' the blues / Easy-listening blues / Straighten up and fly right / Rhumba Azul / Just can't

see for looking.
**Cass:** Released Nov '85, on Deja Vu Catalogue no: **DVMC 2048**
**Album:** Released Nov '85, on Deja Vu Catalogue no: **DVLP 2048**

## NAT KING COLE (VIDEO)
**VHS:** Released '88, on Missing In Action Catalogue no: **V 9996**

## NAT KING COLE WITH GEORGE SHEARING (Cole, Nat King & George Shearing)
**Cass:** Released May '78, on Capitol by EMI Records. Deleted '87. Catalogue no: **TC CAPS 1020**

## NATURE BOY VOL.4
**Album:** Released '88, on Joker (USA) by Lifetime Records (USA). Catalogue no: **SM 4053**
**Album:** Released Nov '84, on Astan (USA) Catalogue no: **20108**

## ONE AND ONLY, THE
Tracks: / Sweet Lorraine / Love is here to stay / Autumn leaves / Dance ballerina dance / September song / Beautiful friendship, A / Fly me to the moon / Let there be love / Mona Lisa / Pick yourself up / More I see you, The / Just one of those things / Let's fall in love / Love is the thing / Stay as sweet as you are / Love letters / Azure-te (CD only) / Serenata (CD only) / Party's over, The (CD only).
**CD:** Released Mar '90, on MFP by EMI Records. Catalogue no: **CDMFP 6082**
**Cass:** Released Mar '89, on MFP by EMI Records. Catalogue no: **TCMFP 5850**
**CD:** Released Mar '90, on MFP by EMI Records. Catalogue no: **CDB 793 747 2**
**Album:** Released Mar '89, on MFP by EMI Records. Catalogue no: **MFP 5850**

## PIANO STYLE OF NAT KING COLE, THE
Tracks: / Love walked in / My heart stood still / Imagination / I never knew / Stella by starlight / What can I say after I say I'm sorry / I didn't know what time it was / Taking a chance on love / April in Paris / I want to be happy / I see your face before me / Just one of those things / I get a kick out of you / If I could be with you one hour tonight / I hear music / Tea for two.
**Album:** Released Sep '88, on Capitol by EMI Records. Catalogue no: **EMS 1271**
**Cass:** Released Sep '88, on Capitol by EMI Records. Catalogue no: **TCEMS 1271**

## PIECES OF COLE
**Album:** Released Oct '84, on Swing House by Submarine Records. Catalogue no: **SWH 12**
**Cass:** Released Oct '84, on Swing House by Submarine Records. Catalogue no: **CSWH 12**

## PRETEND
Tracks: / Pretend.
**7" Single:** Released Apr '53, on Capitol by EMI Records. Deleted Apr '56. Catalogue no: **CL 13878**

## RAMBLIN' ROSE
Tracks: / Ramblin' Rose / Wolverton mountain / Twilight on the trail / I don't want it that way / He'll have to go / When you're smiling / Dear lonely hearts (Extra track on CD only) / All over the world (Extra track on CD only) / All by myself (Extra track on CD only) / Goodnight, Irene, goodnight / Your cheatin' heart / One has my name the other has my heart / Skip to my Lou / Good times, The / Sing another song (and we'll all go home).
Note: Orchestra and chorus conducted by Balford Hendricks.
**CD:** Released Mar '88, on Capitol by EMI Records. Catalogue no: **CDP 746 651 2**
**Cass:** Released Sep '86, on Capitol by EMI Records. Catalogue no: **TCEMS 1115**
**Album:** Released Sep '86, on Capitol by EMI Records. Catalogue no: **EMS 1115**
**CD:** Released Mar '88, on Capitol by EMI Records. Catalogue no: **BU 13**

## RAMBLIN' ROSE (SINGLE)
Tracks: / Ramblin' rose.
**7" Single:** Released Sep '62, on Capitol by EMI Records. Deleted Sep '65. Catalogue no: **CL 15270**
**7" Single:** Released Mar '78, on Capitol by EMI Records. Deleted '88. Catalogue no: **CL 15975**

## REPLAY ON NAT KING COLE
**Album:** Released Feb '85, on Sierra by Sierra Records. Catalogue no: **FEDB 5002**
**Cass:** Released Feb '85, on Sierra by Sierra Records. Catalogue no: **CFEDB 5002**

## RIGHT THING TO SAY, THE
Tracks: / Right thing to say, The.
**7" Single:** Released May '62, on Capitol by EMI Records. Deleted May '65. Catalogue no: **CL 15250**

## ROMANTIC WORLD OF, THE
**CD:** Released Sep '87, on Entertainers Deleted '88. Catalogue no: **ENT CD 214**

## SINGS AND PLAYS
**Cass:** Released '88, on Joker (USA) by Lifetime Records (USA). Catalogue no: **MC 3611**
**Album:** Released '88, on Joker (USA) by Lifetime Records (USA). Catalogue no: **SM 3611**

## SINGS FOR TWO IN LOVE
Tracks: / Love is here to stay / Handful of stars, A / This can't be love / Little street where old friends meet, A / Autumn leaves / Let's fall in love / There goes my heart / Dinner for one please James / Almost like being in love / Tenderly / You stepped out of a dream / Too much / Thousand thoughts of you, A / If you said no.
Note: On this album, Nat emerges as one of the world's most sensitive and artistic ballad singers. Originally an 8 song 10" album, the project was extended by 4 tracks to a 12" LP format.
**Album:** Released Nov '85, on Capitol by EMI Records. Catalogue no: **EMS 1101**
**CD:** Released Mar '88, on Capitol by EMI Records. Catalogue no: **BU 12**
**CD:** Released Mar '88, on Capitol by EMI Records. Catalogue no: **CDP 746 650 2**
**Cass:** Released Nov '85, on Capitol by EMI Records. Catalogue no: **TC EMS 1101**

## SMILE
Tracks: / Smile.
**7" Single:** Released Sep '54, on Capitol by EMI Records. Deleted Sep '57. Catalogue no: **CL 14149**

## SNADER TELESCRIPTIONS (VIDEO)
**VHS:** Released Feb '90, on Storyville by Storyville Records AB. Catalogue no: **SV6010**

## SOMETIMES
**LP Pic:** Released Aug '86, on Lotus Catalogue no: **PD 30033**

## SOMEWHERE ALONG THE WAY
Tracks: / Darling je vous aime beaucoup / It's crazy but I'm in love / Sand and the sea, The / Unforgettable / Love letters / Mona Lisa / Too young / My foolish heart.
**Cass:** Released Aug '89, on One For The Road by One For The Road. Catalogue no: **CONE 3**

## SOMEWHERE ALONG THE WAY (SINGLE)
Tracks: / Somewhere along the way.
**7" Single:** Released Nov '52, on Capitol by EMI Records. Deleted Nov '55. Catalogue no: **CL 13774**

## SONGS FOR LOVERS (2)
**Album:** Released May '88, on Coldrado Catalogue no: **22013**
**Cass:** Released May '88, on Coldrado Catalogue no: **42013**

## SPECIAL YEARS
Tracks: / Sweet Georgia Brown / Body and soul / Sweet lorraine / Miss thing / Cole's bop blues / It's only a paper moon / On the sunny side of the street / Bugle call rag / I'm lost, I'm lost / Let's spring one / My lips remember your kisses / Got a penny / Let's pretend / Satchel mouth baby / Pitchin up a boogie / Fine, sweet and tasty / It ain't necessarily so / Let's pretend again / This is my night to dream / Smooth sailing.
**Album:** Released Feb '87, on Arena Catalogue no: **ARA 1005**
**Cass:** Released Feb '87, on Arena Catalogue no: **ARAC 1005**

## STARDUST
Tracks: / Stardust.
**7" Single:** Released Oct '57, on Capitol by EMI Records. Deleted Oct '60. Catalogue no: **CL 14787**

## STARDUST (RE-RELEASE)
Tracks: / Stardust / When I fall in love.
**7" Single:** Released Oct '82, on Capitol by EMI Records. Deleted '85. Catalogue no: **CL 267**

## STRING ALONG WITH NAT KING COLE
**Album:** Released Aug '61, on Encore

by EMI Records. Deleted Aug '66. Catalogue no: **ENC 102**

## SWEET HOUR OF PRAYER

**Cass:** Released Dec '88, on Capitol (Specials) Catalogue no: **4XL 9375**

## SWEET LORRAINE VOL.2

**Album:** Released '88, on Joker (USA) by Lifetime Records (USA). Catalogue no: **SM 4051**

## TELL ME ALL ABOUT YOURSELF

Tracks: / Tell me all about yourself / Until the real thing comes along / Best thing for you, The / When you walked by / Crazy she calls me / You've got the Indian sign on me / For you / Dedicated to you / You are my love / This is always / My life / I would do - anything for you.

Note: This album, heralding the next batch of Nat King Cole re-issues in our ongoing series, was one of 7 recorded in 1958 - the busiest year of his career. Contains some colourful additions to his usual repertoire and is backed by the conventional brass and reed big band conducted by Dave Cavanaugh - a change from his usual string background. Tracks comprise of a good mixture of familiar standards plus the new songs of the day.

**Cass:** Released May '86, on Capitol by EMI Records. Deleted Aug '89. Catalogue no: **TCEMS 1109**

**Album:** Released May '86, on Capitol by EMI Records. Catalogue no: **EMS 1109**

## TENDERLY

Tracks: / Tenderly.

**7" Single:** Released Apr '54, on Capitol by EMI Records. Deleted Apr '57. Catalogue no: **CL 14061**

## THAT'S YOU

Tracks: / That's you.

**7" Single:** Released May '60, on Capitol by EMI Records. Deleted May '63. Catalogue no: **CL 15129**

## THIS IS NAT 'KING' COLE

Tracks: / Dreams can tell a lie / I just found out about love / Too young to go steady / Forgive my heart / Annabelle / Nothing ever changes my love for you / To the ends of the earth / I'm gonna laugh you out of my life / Someone you love / Love me as though there were no tomorrow / That's all / Never let me go.

**Album:** Released Jul '85, on Capitol by EMI Records. Deleted Nov '88. Catalogue no: **EG 2606041**

**Album:** Released Oct '84, on Pathe Marconi (France) Catalogue no: **PM 1552931**

**Cass:** Released Jul '85, on Capitol by EMI Records. Deleted Jun '89. Catalogue no: **EG 2606044**

**Cass:** Released Oct '84, on Pathe Marconi (France) Catalogue no: **PM 1552934**

## THOSE LAZY-HAZY-CRAZY DAYS OF SUMMER

Tracks: / Get out and get under the moon / There is a tavern in the town / On a bicycle built for two / That Sunday, that summer / On the sidewalks of New York / Our old home team / After the ball is over / You tell me your dream (Adapted by Nat King Cole) / That's what they meant by the good old summertime / Don't forget / In the good old summertime / Those lazy hazy crazy days of summer.

**Album:** Released Sep '86, on Capitol by EMI Records. Catalogue no: **EMS 1116**

**Cass:** Released Sep '86, on Capitol by EMI Records. Deleted Jan '90. Catalogue no: **TCEMS 1116**

## TIME AND THE RIVER

Tracks: / Time and the river.

**7" Single:** Released Feb '60, on Capitol by EMI Records. Deleted Feb '63. Catalogue no: **CL 15111**

## TO WHOM IT MAY CONCERN

Tracks: / Thousand thoughts of you, A / You're bringing out the dreamer in me / My heart's treasure / If you said no / Can't help it / Lovesville / Unfair / This morning it was summer / To whom it may concern / Love-wise / Too much / In the heart of Jane Doe.

Note: In this collection of tracks, Nat is once again joined by the late, great Nelson Riddle and his Orchestra - one of the most successful partnerships in Nat's career. As always in this series, this genuine stereo album is both digitally remastered and direct metal mastered to bring you the best sound quality ever of this original recording.

**Cass:** Released '88, on Pathe Marconi (France) Catalogue no: **PM 1552934**

**Cass:** Released Apr '86, on Capitol by EMI Records. Catalogue no: **TCEMS 1108**

**Album:** Released '88, on Pathe Marconi (France) Catalogue no: **PM 1552931**

**Album:** Released Apr '86, on Capitol by EMI Records. Catalogue no: **EMS 1108**

## TOO YOUNG VOL.5

**Album:** Released '88, on Joker (USA) by Lifetime Records (USA). Catalogue no: **SM 4054**

## TOO YOUNG TO GO STEADY

Tracks: / Too young to go steady.

**7" Single:** Released May '56, on Capitol by EMI Records. Deleted May '59. Catalogue no: **CL 14573**

## TOP POPS

Tracks: / Somewhere along the way / If I give my heart to you / Faith can move mountains.

Note: Originally released in 1956 and a welcome re-issue 30 years later.

**Album:** Released Dec '85, on Capitol T (USA) Catalogue no: **T 9110**

## TOUCH OF YOUR LIPS, THE

Tracks: / Touch of your lips, The / I remember you / Illusion / You're mine you / Funny / Poinciana / Sunday, Monday or always / Not so long ago / Nightingale sang in Berkley Square, A / Only forever / My need for you / Lights out.

Note: A new conductor joins Nat on his album - Ralph Carmichael - a man of great versatility and ability who made a highly successful harmonious companion for the voice of Nat King Cole. As the title suggests, the tracks contained are easy listening material with a fair degree of smooch!

**Cass:** Released Dec '88, on Capitol (Specials) Catalogue no: **4XL 9166**

**Album:** Released May '86, on Capitol by EMI Records. Catalogue no: **EMS 1111**

**Cass:** Released May '86, on Capitol by EMI Records. Deleted Aug '89. Catalogue no: **TCEMS 1111**

## TRIO DAYS (Big band bounce & boogie) (Cole, Nat Trio)

Tracks: / Honeysuckle rose / Sweet Lorraine / This side up / Gone with the draft / Call the Police / That ain't right / Are you fer it? / Hit that jive Jack / Early morning blues / Babs / Scotchin' with soda / Slow Down / I like to Riff / This will make you laugh / Hit the Ramp / Stop, the red light's on.

**Cass:** Released Nov '84, on Affinity by Charly Records. Catalogue no: **TCAFS 1001**

**Album:** Released Nov '84, on Affinity by Charly Records. Catalogue no: **AFS 1001**

## UNFORGETTABLE

**Album:** Released Sep '83, on Capitol (import). Deleted '88. Catalogue no: **2C 068 54571**

**Album:** Released Mar '65, on Capitol by EMI Records. Deleted Mar '70. Catalogue no: **W 20664**

**Album:** Released May '86, on Spot by Pickwick Records. Catalogue no: **SPR 8587**

**Album:** Released Mar '84, on Capitol (import). Catalogue no: **2C 068 54579**

**Album:** Released Nov '85, on Capitol by EMI Records. Catalogue no: **EMS 1100**

**Cass:** Released Dec '85, on Capitol by EMI Records. Deleted Jul '88. Catalogue no: **TCSW 20664**

**Cass:** Released May '86, on Spot by Pickwick Records. Catalogue no: **SPC 8587**

**Cass:** Released Nov '85, on Capitol by EMI Records. Catalogue no: **TCEMS 1100**

**Cass:** Released Dec '88, on Capitol (Specials). Catalogue no: **4XL 9110**

## UNFORGETTABLE (IMPORT)

Tracks: / Too young / Party's over, The / More I see you, The / Love is here to stay / Quizas, quizas, quizas / Angel eyes / Portrait of Jennie / Teach me tonight / Ballerina / Very thought of you, The / She's funny that way / I wish I knew the way to your heart / You made me love you / Ramblin' rose / Love letters / Fascination / Unforgettable / Piel Canela / These foolish things / Around the world.

**Cass:** Released Sep '86, on EMI (Italy) by EMI Records. Catalogue no: **186826 5**

**Album:** Released Sep '86, on EMI (Italy) by EMI Records. Catalogue no: **186826 3**

## UNFORGETTABLE (SINGLE)

Tracks: / Unforgettable / Because of rain

/ Silent night / For a moment of your love (12" only).
**7" Single:** Released Nov '88, on Capitol by EMI Records. Deleted Oct '89. Catalogue no: **CL 518**
**12" Single:** Released Nov '88, on Capitol by EMI Records. Deleted Aug '89. Catalogue no: **12CL 518**
**CD Single:** Released Nov '88, on Capitol by EMI Records. Deleted Aug '89. Catalogue no: **CDCL 518**

**UNFORGETTABLE, THE (VIDEO)**
Tracks: / Unforgettable / These foolish things / Tonight you belong to me / Breezy and the bass / (Get your kicks on) Route 66 / Sweet Lorraine / Christmas song, The / Straighten up and fly right / It's only a paper moon / Too young / Dance, ballerina dance / Yes we have no bananas / I've grown accustomed to her face / With all my heart / Nature boy / Here's that rainy day / Very thought of you, The / Smile / Autumn leaves / Lush life / Mona Lisa / Love is the thing / When I fall in love / In the evening may I come and sing to you? / Foggy day, A / How high the moon / Bewitched, bothered and bewildered / What's wrong with me / It's all right with me / Darling, je vous aime beaucoup / Pick yourself up / Let there be love / Stardust.
Note: The only existing documentary on Cole, made possible by the co-operation of his widow, Maria. Features rare archive footage and photographs, along with revealing home movies which have never been shown before. Traces the life of the legendary Nat 'King' Cole through the early years of his career up to his untimely death in February 1965. This documentary shows the calibre of talent of this man, whose popularity has never waned. His songs even now are still capable of top chart success, as in the recent case of the top 5 hit *When I fall in love.* (EMI Records October, 1988).
**VHS:** Released Oct '88, on PMI by EMI Records. Catalogue no: **MVNNAT 1**
**VHS:** Released Oct '88, on PMI by EMI Records. Catalogue no: **MVN 991 169 3**

**UNRELEASED, THE**
Tracks: / How little we know / When I'm alone / Who's who / For a moment of your love / Should I / I'm shooting high / How did I change / Like someone in love / I heard you cried last night / Come to the Mardi Gras.
**Album:** Released Sep '88, on Capitol by EMI Records. Catalogue no: **EMS 1279**
**Cass:** Released Sep '88, on Capitol by EMI Records. Catalogue no: **TCEMS 1279**

**VERY BEST OF NAT 'KING' COLE**
Tracks: / Those lazy, hazy, crazy days of summer / When my sugar walks down the street / You're my everything / Unforgettable / Love letters / Ramblin' rose / Route 66 / Autumn leaves / Affair to remember, An / I found a million dollar baby / Your cheatin' heart / Dance, ballerina, dance / On the street where you live / There's a goldmine in the sky / Nightingale sang in Berkeley Square, A / Stardust.
**Cass:** Released Jul '74, on Capitol by EMI Records. Catalogue no: **TCEST 23165**
**Album:** Released Dec '73, on Capitol by EMI Records. Deleted Jun '89. Catalogue no: **EST 23165**

**VERY THOUGHT OF YOU, THE**
Tracks: / Very thought of you, The / But beautiful / Impossible / I wish I knew the way to your heart / I found a million dollar baby / Magnificent obsession / My heart tells me - should I believe my heart / Paradise / This is all I ask / Cherie, I love you / Making believe you're here / Cherchez la femme / For all we know / More I see you, The / I wish I knew.
Note: This album has as its title track on of Nat's all time favourite classics. Recorded in 1958 at Capitol's Hollywood studios with Gordon Jenkins, these tracks contain the rich string arrangements so evident in the previous reissue of *Love is the thing* which featured the same acclaimed vocalist/conductor collaboration.
**CD:** Released Feb '88, on Capitol by EMI Records. Catalogue no: **CDP 748 331 2**
**Cass:** Released Apr '86, on Capitol by EMI Records. Catalogue no: **TCEMS 1106**
**Album:** Released Apr '86, on Capitol by EMI Records. Catalogue no: **EMS 1106**
**CD:** Released Feb '88, on Capitol by EMI Records. Catalogue no: **CDEMS 1106**

**WELCOME TO THE CLUB**
Tracks: / Welcome to the club / Anytime, anyday, anywhere / Blues don't care, The / Mood indigo / Baby won't you please come home? / Late late show, The / Avalon / She's funny that way / I want a little girl / Wee baby blues / Look out for love.
Note: This album will please both Nat Cole's 50's fans and those who followed the Nat King Cole Trio in earlier days. Accompanied by Dave Cavanaugh and orchestra, this collection of tracks have a decidedly jazz-orientated flavour so typical of the 'Trio' days while still retaining the Nat Cole style of the late 50's. The orchestra used on this recording was usually headed by Count Basie (who himself was signed to another company) - another, like Nat, whose roots were in jazz.
**Album:** Released Mar '84, on Pathe Marconi (France) Catalogue no: **PM 154 769 1**
**Album:** Released Apr '86, on Capitol by EMI Records. Catalogue no: **EMS 1107**
**Cass:** Released Mar '84, on Pathe Marconi (France) Catalogue no: **PM 154 769 4**
**Cass:** Released Apr '86, on Capitol by EMI Records. Deleted Aug '89. Catalogue no: **TCEMS 1107**

**WHEN I FALL IN LOVE**
Tracks: / When I fall in love / Mona Lisa / Ramblin' rose / Christmas song, The / Love letters (extended version).
**7" Single:** Released Apr '57, on Capitol by EMI Records. Deleted Apr '60. Catalogue no: **CL 14709**
**12" Single:** Released Dec '87, on Capitol by EMI Records. Deleted Nov '88. Catalogue no: **12CL 15975**
**7" Single:** Released Dec '87, on Capitol by EMI Records. Catalogue no: **CLS 15975**
**CD Single:** Released Dec '87, on Capitol by EMI Records. Deleted Jul '88. Catalogue no: **CDCL 15975**

**WHEN ROCK 'N' ROLL CAME TO TRINIDAD**
Tracks: / When rock 'n' roll came to Trinidad.
**7" Single:** Released Jul '57, on Capitol by EMI Records. Deleted Jul '60. Catalogue no: **CL 14733**

**WHERE DID EVERYONE GO**
Tracks: / Where did everyone go? / Say it isn't so / If love ain't there / Ah, the apple trees - when the world was young / Am I blue / Someone to tell it to / End of a love affair, The / I keep going back to Joe's / Laughing on the outside - crying on the inside / No, I don't want her / Spring is here / That's all there is there isn't any more.
**Album:** Released Aug '86, on Capitol by EMI Records. Catalogue no: **EMS 1114**
**Cass:** Released Aug '86, on Capitol by EMI Records. Deleted Aug '89. Catalogue no: **TCEMS 1114**

**WHITE CHRISTMAS (Cole, Nat King & Dean Martin)**
**Album:** Released Dec '82, on MFP by EMI Records. Deleted '87. Catalogue no: **MFP 5224**

**WORLD IN MY ARMS, THE**
Tracks: / World in my arms, The.
**7" Single:** Released Feb '61, on Capitol by EMI Records. Deleted Feb '64. Catalogue no: **CL 15178**

**YOU MADE ME LOVE YOU**
Tracks: / You made me love you.
**7" Single:** Released May '59, on Capitol by EMI Records. Deleted May '62. Catalogue no: **CL 15017**

## Cole, Richie

**ALTO ANNIE'S THEME**
**Album:** Released Jun '84, on Palo Alto Catalogue no: **PA 8036**

**ALTO MADNESS**
Tracks: / Price is right, The / Common touch, The / Last tango in Paris / Island breeze / Big Bo's paradise / Remember your day off... / Moody's mood.
Note: Cole - alto; Eddie Gladden - drums; Harold Mabern - piano; Rick Laird bass; Steve Gilmore - bass; Vic Juris - guitar; Ray Mantilla - percussion; Eddie Jefferson - vocal on *The common touch* and *Moody's mood.*
**Album:** Released Apr '81, on Muse by Black & Blue Records. Catalogue no: **MR 5155**

**HOLLYWOOD MADNESS**
Tracks: / Hooray for Hollywood / Hi-fly / Tokyo rose sing the Hollywood blues / Relaxin' at Camarillo / Malibu breeze / I

love Lucy / Waiting for Waits / Hooray for Hollywood (reprise).
Note: Cole - alto sax; Bruce Forman - guitar; Dick Hindman - piano; Marshall Rawkins - bass; Michael Spiro - percussion; Les DeMerle - drums; Bob Magnusson - bass; Eddie Jefferson - vocals on 3 tracks; Manhattan Transfer vocals on 4 tracks.
**CD:** Released Feb '86, on Muse (USA) by Muse Records (USA). Catalogue no: **MCD 5207**
**Album:** Released Apr '81, on Muse by Black & Blue Records. Catalogue no: **MR 5207**

**KEEPER OF THE FLAME**
Tracks: / Harold's house of jazz / New York afternoon / As time goes by / I can't get started / Keeper of the flame / Holiday for strings / Strange groove.
Note: Personnel: Cole - alto sax; Harold Mabern - piano; Vic Juris - guitar; Rick Laird - bass; Eddie Gladden - drums; Eddie Jefferson - vocal on first 2 titles.
**Album:** Released Apr '81, on Muse by Black & Blue Records. Catalogue no: **MR 5192**

**LIVE AT THE VILLAGE VANGUARD**
**Album:** Released Jul '82, on Muse by Black & Blue Records. Catalogue no: **MR 5270**

**NEW YORK AFTERNOON**
Tracks: / Dorothy's den / Waltz for a rainy be-bop evening / Alto madness / New York afternoon / It's the same thing everywhere / Stormy weather (Trenton style) / You'll always be my friend.
Note: Personnel: Richie - alto sax; Eddie Jefferson - vocal; Rick Laird - bass; Vic Juris - guitar; Mickey Tucker - piano; Eddie Gladden - drums; Ray Mantilla percussion.
**Album:** Released Apr '81, on Muse by Black & Blue Records. Catalogue no: **MR 5119**

**POP BOP**
Tracks: / Overjoyed / Eddie Jefferson / On a misty night / L dorado kaddy / La Bamba / When you wish upon a star / Spanish Harlem / Star Trek 1 / Sonomascope / Saxophobia.
**Album:** Released Feb '88, on Milestone by Ace Records. Catalogue no: **MX 9152**

**PURE IMAGINATION**
Tracks: / White cliffs of Dover, The / Dreamy / Come fly with me / Concord blues / Tin Palace shuffle / Flying down to Rio / Pure imagination / Blue room / Starburst.
Note: Personnel: Richie Cole - alto sax; Vic Jurusz - guitar; Ed Howard - bass; Victor "Yahya" Jones - drums; Ray Mantilla - percussion.
**Album:** Released Jul '87, on Concord Jazz by Concord Jazz Records (USA). Catalogue no: **CJ 314**
**Cass:** Released Jul '87, on Concord Jazz by Concord Jazz Records (USA). Catalogue no: **CJC 314**

**RETURN TO ALTO ACRES**
**Cass:** Released Jul '86, on Palo Alto Catalogue no: **PAC 8023**
**Album:** Released Jan '84, on Palo Alto Catalogue no: **PA 8023**

**RICHIE COLE QUINTET (VIDEO) (Cole, Richie Quintet)**
**VHS:** Released '88, on Kay Jazz (video) by Kay Jazz. Catalogue no: **KJ 059**

**SIDE BY SIDE**
Tracks: / Save your love for me / Naughayde reality (Live spiral) / Scrapple from the apple / Donna Lee / Polka dots and moonbeams (Richie Cole alto sax solo) / Eddie's mood / Side by side.
Note: Recorded live at The Historic Paramount Theatre, Denver.
**Album:** Released Sep '86, on Muse by Black & Blue Records. Catalogue no: **MR 5237**

**STILL ON THE PLANET (Cole, Richie & E. Jefferson)**
**Album:** Released Jun '77, on Muse by Black & Blue Records. Catalogue no: **MR 5063**

**YAKETY MADNESS! (Cole, Richie & Boots Randolph)**
**Cass:** Released Jan '84, on Palo Alto Catalogue no: **PAC 8041**
**Album:** Released Jan '84, on Palo Alto Catalogue no: **PA 8041**

## Coleman, Bill

**Biographical details:** A fine jazz trumpeter (1904-81) who played in Paris, Bombay and Egypt, and settled in France in 1948. His best-known records were made with Luis Russell in 1929 and at a Paris session with trombonist Dicky Wells in 1937. He continued touring, including Africa; he was less well known in the end than he deserved, perhap because he left the USA. (Donald Clarke 1989).

**1935-37**
**Album:** Released Sep '84, on Pathe Marconi (France) Catalogue no: **PM 1552571**

**GREAT PARISIAN SESSION, THE**
Note: This superb album was recorded by Polydor during January 1960. The specially assembled personnel for this date was taken from the ranks of the Quincy Jones Orchestra which was touring Europe with the Free and Easy revue. This orchestra was probably the most impressive assembly of stars in the history of jazz.
Personnel: Bill Coleman - trumpet; Quentin Jackson - trombone; Budd Johnson - tenor sax; Patti Brown - piano; Buddy Cattlet - bass; Joe Harris - drums; Les Spann - guitar.
**CD:** Released Feb '89, on Polygram (France) by PolyGram UK Ltd. Catalogue no: **837 235-2**

**...IN PARIS VOL.1 (1935-38)**
**Album:** Released Jan '83, on Swaggie (Australia) Catalogue no: **S 1307**
**Album:** Released Jan '83, on Swaggie (Australia) Catalogue no: **S 1308**

**IN PARIS 1936-1938**
**Album:** Released '88, on DRG (USA) by DRG Records (USA). Catalogue no: **SW 8402**
**Cass:** Released '88, on DRG (USA) by DRG Records (USA). Catalogue no: **SWC 8402**

**MAINSTREAM AT MONTREUX (Coleman, Bill & George Lafitte)**
Tracks: / Blue Lou / Idaho / Sur les quais du vieux Paris / L and L blues / Tour de force / Montreux jump.
**Album:** Released Jul '87, on Black Lion Catalogue no: **BLP 30150**

**SWINGIN' IN LONDON (Coleman, Bill & Ben Webster)**
Tracks: / Bill Coleman / But not for me / Pound horn / Sunday / For all we know / Satin doll / For Max.
**Album:** Released Apr '85, on Black Lion Catalogue no: **BLP 30127**

**TALE OF TWO CITIES, A**
**Album:** Released Jan '88, on Two Flat Discs Catalogue no: **TFD 5.010**

**TOWN HALL CONCERT 1945 (Coleman, Bill, G Krupa, C Ventura, T Wilson, S Smith, R Norvo)**
**Album:** Released '87, on Commodore Class Catalogue no: **6.26169**
**CD:** Released '87, on Commodore Class Catalogue no: **8.26169**
**Album:** Released '87, on Commodore Class Catalogue no: **6.26168**

## Coleman, Cy

**Biographical details:** Born in 1929 in New York City, the singer, pianist and composer was playing supper clubs in Manhattan at the age 17. He wrote several musical shows, including *Sweet Charity* with lyricist Dorothy Fields (including *Big spender*), and *Barnum* with Michael Stewart. (Donald Clarke 1989).

**BARNUM (Coleman, Cy Trio)**
Tracks: / One brick at a time / Black and white / Love makes such fools of us all / Bigger isn't better / Colours of my life, The / Join the circus / I like your style / There is a sucker born ev'ry minute / At least I tried / Thank God I'm old / Come follow the band.
**Album:** Released Aug '81, on Rhapsody by President Records. Catalogue no: **RHAP 12**

**COMIN' HOME**
Tracks: / But not for me / Time after time / Fly me to the moon.
**CD:** Released '88, on DRG (USA) by DRG Records (USA). Catalogue no: **CDSL 5205**
**Album:** Released '88, on DRG (USA) by DRG Records (USA). Catalogue no: **SL 5205**

## Coleman, George

**Biographical details:** Born in 1935, this tenor saxist and composer is one of the best of his generation, but his generation was overshadowed by John Coltrane. He played with Max Roach in the late '50s, with Miles Davis in the mid-'60s and worked with his wife, bassist/vocalist/organist Gloria Bell Coleman. He writes for groups of all sizes and plays many gigs at colleges. He leads his own quartet and octet; the octet on *Big George* includes Dannie Moore on trumpet and flugelhorn, Mario Rivera on baritone, Harold Mabern on piano; Frank Strozier on alto, Junior Cook on second tenor, Idris Muhammad on drums and Lisle Atkinson on bass; a similar group played at the Camden Jazz Festival in 1981. *Meditation* is a duo with pianist Tete Montoliu, and *Amsterdam after dark* has a quartet with Hilton Ruiz on piano, Sam Jones on bass and Billy Higgins on drums. (Donald Clarke 1989).

### AMSTERDAM AFTER DARK

Tracks: / Amsterdam after dark / New arrival / Lo-Joe / Autumn in New York / Apache dance / Blondie's waltz.

**Album:** Released Apr '81, on Timeless by Timeless Records. Catalogue no: **SJP 129**

### AT YOSHI'S

Tracks: / They say it's wonderful / Good morning heartache / Laig gobblin' blues / Ten / Up jumped spring / Father / Soul eyes.

Note: Post-bop tenor player George Coleman and quartet caught live at Yoshi's jazz club in San Francisco. Programme includes compositions by Irving Berlin, Mal Waldron, Freddie Hubbard and George Coleman. A fine selection of popular standards and jazz originals. Over 66 minutes of music.

Personnel: George Coleman - tenor; Harold Mabern - piano; Ray Drummond - bass; Alvin Queen - drums.

**Album:** Released Nov '89, on Theresa (USA) by Theresa Records (USA). Catalogue no: **TR 126**

**CD:** Released Nov '89, on Theresa (USA) by Theresa Records (USA). Catalogue no: **TRCD 126**

### BIG GEORGE (Coleman, George Octet)

Tracks: / On Green Dolphin street / Frank's tune / Big George / Joggin' / Body and soul / Revival.

Note: Recorded at Blank Studios, New York City, November, 1977. Featuring George Coleman - tenor sax; Frank Strozier - alto sax; Junior Cook - tenor sax; Mario Rivera - baritone sax; Danny Moore - trumpet, flugelhorn; Harold Mabern - piano; Lisle Atkinson - bass; Idris Muhammed - drums; Azzedin Weston - percussion on *Joggin'*.

'Everybody in this band is a bitch' bass player Lisle Atkinson told Zan Stewart of Jazz Radio KBCA. 'A lot of times you record and you can tell they're out to make money with a certain kind of material. George didn't let that happen. We played some music, instead'. Atkinson is a man with wide experience (a graduate from the Manhattan School of Music who has worked with the bands of Clark Terry, Dizzy Gillespie and Howard McGhee and the trios of Betty Carter and Billy Taylor) and his opinion is valuable. It is certainly born out by the music for this one of the most invigorating jazz CD's I have heard for some time. Its release in Britain should help to increase the following for George Coleman, surely one of the most underrated saxophonists, composers and arrangers of the 'sixties and seventies'.

George was born in Memphis, Tennessee, on March 8, 1935; Memphis is also the place of birth of Frank Strozier (in 1937) and Harold Mabern (1936). Other Memphis-born jazzmen of importance include Phineas Newborn, trumpeters Booker Little and Louis Smith, saxophonists Sonny Criss and John Williams, clarinettist Buster Bailey and drummer Jimmy Crawford. In fact, Coleman, Strozier, Mabern and Little were school friends. George's first touring job was with the band of blues man B.B. King in the early '50s. (B.B.'s band in those days also contained men such as Phineas Newborn, Hank Crawford and Ike Turner on piano; George recorded with King for the Houston based RPM label). He gigged around in Chicago for a time then gravitated to New-York. At the beginning of 1958 he became part of the Max Roach Quintet (which also had Booker Little on trumpet) then he spent a couple of years with trombonist Slide Hampton's octet. Then, early in 1963, George became a member of the Miles Davis Quintet, the first permanent tenor saxist since the departure of John Coltrane. (Sonny Stitt and Hank Mobley had been with Miles for short periods in 1961 and 1962). Almost immediately Coleman played on the record dates which produced the fine *Seven steps to heaven* album under Miles' name and, for a tour of the west coast, Frank Strozier and Harold Mabern joined the trumpeters group, proving yet again that the Young Men from Memphis have a habit of sticking together. George left Miles in the summer of 1964 and spent some time with the bands of Lionel Hampton, Lee Morgan and Shirley Scott. He made a couple of European tours with Elvin Jones and also worked with Cedar Walton's *Eastern rebellion* in 1975.

The first idea for the octet came in 1973 and the group worked its first job, in New-York, the following year. George did most of the writing (and in fact, despite some scores by Strozier and Frank Foster, Coleman is still the main contributor to the library); at the time of recording this present CD there were about 40 scores in the book and the octet had already done a short European tour. At the time of writing (June 1980) the group in due in Europe again with much the same personnel heard here although Sal Nistico takes Junior Cook's place.

The success of the unite lies in its careful balance between written ensemble passages and improvised solos. Few soloists are capable of maintaining genuine interest for chorus after chorus and Coleman's intelligent and almost architectural designing of the the arrangements ensures that the listener's attention is captured and maintained throughout. Take a song such as *Body and soul*, both a challenge and an inspiration for any tenor saxophonist. George has cast this in a series of different tempos, illustrating his mastery of all moods with a solo of truly giant stature. After Harold Mabern's solo the band returns, cleverly voiced to recall the inimitable sound of the 'Four Brothers'.

The opening *Green Dolphin Street* is the longest performance and a good introduction to everyone in the band. The opening two choruses by George are guaranteed to bring the listener to the edge of his seat, then the percussion passage acts as a prelude to Mabern's slow rhapsodic solo leading into a tempo more usually associated with the tune. The next soloist is Junior Cook, one-time saxophonist with Horace Silver then it is the turn of Mario Rivera, a baritone saxist of considerable personality who has been buried deep in the reed section of Machito's orchestra for some time. Danny Moore (flugelhorn), Frank Strozier, piano, bass and drums all solo before Coleman has his second solo outing. Frank's tune is a Strozier composition and arrangement previously recorded by Shelly Manne (on his Atlantic Boss Sounds' album) in 1966 when Strozier was one of Manne's men. Frank and George are the front-line soloists and the voicing of the ensemble by the composer is noteworthy. Strozier is a woefully underrated soloist who has worked with the MJT Plus Three as well as drummer leaders Shelly Manne and Roy Haynes. Two days after his octet LP was made Strozier acted as leader on his *What's goin' on* album for Steeplechase which also featured Danny Moore and Harold Mabern.

The title tune *Big George* was written by organist Shirley Scott and is based on the same intriguing exciting harmonic base as those used for Coltrane's *Giant steps* and Miles Davis' *Tune up*. This has what is probably Coleman's most inspired solo in terms of playing with time values and the relationships of notes to bar lines. *Joggin'* is, according to George 'our rock'n'roll tune but it has some merits'. Coleman is being modest for this is considerably more than that. The tempo is perfect and pianist Randy Weston's son, Azzedin Niles Weston, helps out in the percussion department to assist Coleman and Mabern in their solos. The same two men solo on the closing *Revival* which George wrote originally when he was a member of Dedar Walton's band. Danny Moore, who plays the tricky trumpet passages in the ensemble so well, will be best known for his work with the big bands of both Quincy Jones and Thad Jones-Mel Lewis. As a soloist he can produce happy, tripping solos which bring to mind the work of the late lamented Clifford Brown as witness Danny's solo on *Green Dolphin Street.* Here then is the brilliant, enjoyable music of the invigorating George Coleman Octet, a little band with a big sound which is bound is bring joy to its listeners. The perceptive Mike Hennessey put it all in a nutshell when he wrote that Coleman 'plays, as it were, from a great height and with such massive assurance, such vigorous fluency and techni-

**Ornette Coleman**

cal resource that you find yourself swept along on a powerful current of sound.' (Alun Morgan)
**Album:** Released Nov '87, on Affinity by Charly Records. Catalogue no: **AFF 178**
**CD:** Released Oct '87, on Charly by Charly Records. Catalogue no: **CDCHARLY 83**

**BONGO JOE**
**Album:** Released May '81, on Arhoolie (USA) by Arhoolie Records (USA). Catalogue no: **ARHOOLIE 1040**

**GEORGE COLEMAN LIVE**
Tracks: / Blues inside out / Walking / Stella by starlight.
**Album:** Released Dec '79, on Pye Deleted '84. Catalogue no: **N 121**

**GEORGE COLEMAN OCTET**
**Album:** Released Jan '81, on Affinity by Charly Records. Deleted '88. Catalogue no: **AFF 52**

**MAMA ROOTS (Coleman, George & Charlie Earland)**
Tracks: / Undecided / Dozens, The / Red, green and black blues / Mama roots / Old folks / Bluesette.
**Album:** Released Apr '81, on Muse by Black & Blue Records. Catalogue no: **MR 5156**

**MEDITATION (Coleman, George & Tete Montoliu)**
Tracks: / Lisa / Dynamic duo / First time down / Waltzing at Rosa's place / Meditation / Sophisticated lady.
**Album:** Released Apr '81, on Timeless by Timeless Records. Catalogue no: **SJP 110**

**PLAYING CHANGES**
Tracks: / Laura / Siorra / Moment's notice.
Note: American tenor sax player George Coleman recorded this album live at Ronnie Scott's Club in April 1979. Another regular visitor to the Club and the European circuit, the one time Miles Davis sideman has a reputation as an extrovert honest musician who plays full-blown contemporary jazz with no concessions.
**Album:** Released Nov '88, on Jazz House Catalogue no: **JHR 002**
**Cass:** Released Jan '89, on Jazz House Catalogue no: **JHC 002**

## Coleman, Ornette

**Biographical details:** Born March 1930 Fort Worth, Texas. Coleman turned the jazz world on its ear in the late fifties and early sixties with his plastic alto saxophone and his radically simple idea that jazz improvisation did not require any fixed harmonic or rhythmic patterns at all. On *Of human feelings* recorded digitally in 1979, Coleman and his fiery young band Prime Time affect a seamless blend of harmolodics and funk. In the middle and late seventies Coleman began developing the electrified brand of free jazz that is heard on *Of human feelings*. At the same time however, his public performances became increasingly infrequent. In 1979 he stopped performing altogether. Today, under the aegis of managers Sid and Stan Bernstein and Antilles Records, Coleman is back on the scene with a vengeance. In addition to performing with Prime Time, he is actively composing, his most recent project being the score for the Joseph Bogdanovitch film "Boxoffice". And he is working to achieve two life long ambitions. The first is the creation of an orchestra with members from all 50 states. The second is the establishment of a school to teach young, underprivileged musicians their craft. A building in New York has already been chosen as the site. (Island Records 84)
Born in Fort Worth Texas, this alto saxist and composer also plays tenor, trumpet and violin. He was as Enfant Terrible in 1959 and 30 years later is the godfather of today's avant-gardists, who mostly don't have his roots. Coleman played in R&B bands, went to L.A. and studied music while working as a lift operator; his first album was *Something else!!!*, bravely recorded early in 1958 by Lester Koenig at Contemporary: Coleman was playing a plastic alto because he liked the sound, and Don Cherry played a 'pocket trumpet' (these looked like toys, giving critics something else to complain about), and the quintet also included Billy Higgins on drums, Walter Norris on piano and an early synthesiser, Don Payne on bass, blazed trail for free jazz with original 'atonal' compositions. His second Contemporary album the same year, *Tomorrow is the question!*, had Cherry with Shelly Manne and bassist Red Mitchell. A gig at NYC's Five Spot in November, together with titles of Atlantic LPs *The shape of jazz to come* and *Change the century* (with Coleman, Cherry, Charlie Haden and Higgins) put the fat in the fire: Coleman's 'atonal' free jazz had the support of critics Nat Hentoff and Martin Williams, as well as jazz academic and third stream composer Gunther Schuller; John Lewis said that 'Coleman is doing the only really new thing in jazz since the (bop) innovations of the mid-40s; while Charles Mingus was initially uncertain whether Coleman could play at all. A few years later, and especially for anyone who had listened to contemporary classical music, it is hard to see what all the fuss was about. Composer George Russell knew immediately what Coleman was doing: 'Ornette seems to depend mostly on the over-all tonality of the song as a point of departure for melody. By this I don't mean the key the music might be in...This approach liberates the improviser to sing his own song, really, without having to meet the deadline of any particular chord.' And many of Ornette's songs were beautiful. Soon he priced himself out of the market, foolishly expecting to be paid as much as Dave Brubeck; his recording career has been peripatetic. *The empty foxhole* in 1966, a trio album on Blue Note, had his son Ornette Denardo Coleman on drums, then 9-years-old. He also wrote music for large ensembles, sometimes recorded but scandalously soon out of print, for example *Skies of America* in 1972 on CBS: a quartet with Dewey

Redman, Charlie Haden and Ed Blackwell with the London Symphony Orchestra, which gave Coleman a standing ovation for his work at rehearsals and recording. To describe this piece he invented the word 'harmelodic', perhaps best defined (by Gary Giddins) as improvised coloration. The 'new thing' had combined a revival of collective improvisation with harmonic freedom ('If I'm going to follow a preset chord sequence I may as well write out my solo') - the freedom that Coleman Hawkins had found 30 years earlier improvising on chords instead of the melody was extended by improvising on harmony itself. *Dancing in your head* was made in Morocco by a sextet with two guitars plus local musicians. It is arguable that Coleman's avant-gardism arose directly from his early R&B experience, a genre despised as tavern/sex music by some (just like early jazz); at any rate, harmelodics began to allow echoes of funk and rock, the crossover appeal creating coalitions among listeners and musicians. He formed Prime Time, an electric group which made albums in the late '70s, and his latest project has been a label called Caravan Of Dreams: *Opening the caravan of dreams* and *Prime design/Time design* were followed by the two-disc *In all languages* in 1987, one disc a reunion with Higgins, Haden and Cherry, the other by Prime Time. *Song X* in 1986 on Geffen was co-led by Coleman and guitarist Pat Metheny, demanding music played by a quintet with Haden, Denardo and Jack DeJohnette. Prime Time sidemen Charlie Ellerbee, Jamaaladeen Takuma, drummer Ronald Shannon Jackson are now up-and-comers; Jackson plays in *Last exit* with Bill Laswell and with his own Decoding Society, while Tacuma's *Music world* on Gramavision is heavily electronic. (Donald Clarke 1989).

**AT THE GOLDEN CIRCLE VOL 1**
Tracks: / Announcement / Faces and places / European echoes / Dee dee / Dawn.
**CD:** Released Jul '89, on Blue Note by EMI Records. Catalogue no: **CDP 784 224 2**
**CD:** Released Jul '89, on Blue Note by EMI Records. Catalogue no: **BNZ 180**
**Album:** Released Sep '84, on Blue Note by EMI Records. Deleted '87. Catalogue no: **BST 84224**

**AT THE GOLDEN CIRCLE VOL 2**
Tracks: / Snowflakes and sunshine, The / Morning song / Riddle, The / Antiques.
**CD:** Released Aug '89, on Blue Note by EMI Records. Catalogue no: **CDP 784 225 2**
**Album:** Released Sep '84, on Blue Note by EMI Records. Deleted '87. Catalogue no: **BST 84225**
**CD:** Released Aug '89, on Blue Note by EMI Records. Catalogue no: **BNZ 181**

**BEAUTY PORTRAIT**
**Album:** Released Aug '88, on Virgin by Virgin Records. Catalogue no: **PRT 461 1193 1**

**BODY META**
**Album:** Released May '81, on Artists House Catalogue no: **AH 1**

**DANCING IN YOUR HEAD**
Tracks: / Theme from a symphony (variation one) / Theme from a symphony (variation two) / Midnight sunrise.
**Album:** Released Aug '77, on Horizon by A&M Records. Catalogue no: **AMLJ 722**
**CD:** Released 28 Nov '88, on A&M by A&M Records. Catalogue no: **CDA 0807**

**EUROPEAN CONCERT (Coleman, Ornette Quartet)**
Tracks: / Street woman / Song for Che / Whom do you work for? / Rock the clock / Written word.
**Album:** Released Nov '86, on Unique Jazz by Spotlite Records. Catalogue no: **UJ 13**

**EVENING WITH ORNETTE COLEMAN VOL.1**
Tracks: / Sounds and forms for wind quintet / Sadness / Clergyman's dream.
**Album:** Released Jul '88, on Black Lion Catalogue no: **BLM 51503**

**EVENING WITH ORNETTE COLEMAN VOL.2**
Tracks: / Falling stars / Silence / Happy fool / Ballad / Doughnuts.
**Album:** Released Jul '88, on Black Lion Catalogue no: **BLM 51504**

**FORMS AND SOUNDS**
Tracks: / Forms and sounds / Saints and soldiers / Space flight (with the Philadelphia woodwind quintet and the Chamber Symp).
**CD:** Released Jun '88, on Bluebird (2) by BMG Records (UK). Catalogue no: **ND 86561**

**FREE JAZZ - THAT'S JAZZ**
Tracks: / Free jazz (part 1) / Free jazz (part 2).
**Album:** Released '88, on Atlantic by WEA Records. Catalogue no: **K 50240**

**IN ALL LANGUAGES**
Tracks: / Peace warriors / Feet music / Africa is the mirror of all colors / Word for bird / Space church / Latin genetics / In all mercury / Sound manual / Mothers of the veil / Cloning / Music news / Art of love is happiness, The / Today, yesterday and tomorrow / Listen up / Feet up / Biosphere / Story tellers.
**CD:** Released Jul '87, on Caravan Of Dreams (USA) Catalogue no: **DREAM 009**
**Cass:** Released Jul '87, on Caravan Of Dreams (USA) Catalogue no: **CDPT 85008**
**Album:** Released Jul '87, on Caravan Of Dreams (USA) Catalogue no: **CDP 85008**

**LIVE IN MILANO, 1968 (Coleman, Ornette Quartet)**
Note: A rare delicacy for lovers of free jazz and of its main apostle, Ornette Coleman. Recorded at the Teatro Lirico in Milan, 1968.
Personnel: Ornette Coleman - alto sax; Charlie Haden - bass; David Izenzon - bass; Ed Blackwell - drums.
**CD:** Released Nov '89, on Jazz-Up Catalogue no: **JU 310**

**LOVE CALL**
Tracks: / Airborne / Check out time / Check out time (alt) / Open to the public / Love call / Love call (alt.) / Just for you.
**CD:** Released Apr '90, on Blue Note by EMI Records. Catalogue no: **CDP 784 356 2**
**CD:** Released Apr '90, on Blue Note by EMI Records. Catalogue no: **BNZ 243**

**NEW YORK IS NOW**
Tracks: / Garden of souls, The / Toy dance / Broad Way blues / Broad Way blue (alt) / Round trip / We now interrupt for a commercial (Contains narration.).
**CD:** Released Apr '90, on Blue Note by EMI Records. Catalogue no: **BNZ 242**
**CD:** Released Apr '90, on Blue Note by EMI Records. Catalogue no: **CDP 784 287 2**

**OF HUMAN FEELINGS**
**CD:** Released Jan '86, on Polystar (Japan) Catalogue no: **J33D 20002**
**Album:** Released Apr '82, on Antilles/New Directions by Island Records. Catalogue no: **AN 2001**

**OPENING THE CARAVAN OF DREAMS (Coleman, Ornette & Prime Time)**
Note: Personnel: Bern Nix, Charles Ellerbee, Jamaaladeen Tacuma, Albert MacDowell, DenardoColeman, Sabir Kamal.
**Album:** Released Apr '87, on Caravan Of Dreams (USA) Catalogue no: **CDP 85001**

**ORNETTE LIVE AT PRINCE STREET**
Tracks: / Friends and neighbours / Long time no see / Let's play / Forgotten songs / Tomorrow.
**Album:** Released '83, on RCA (France) by BMG Records (France). Catalogue no: **PL 43548**

**SHAPE OF JAZZ TO COME, THE**
**CD:** Released Jul '87, on Atlantic Jazz by WEA Records. Catalogue no: **781 339-2**

**SOAPSUDS SOAPSUDS (Coleman, Ornette & Charlie Haden)**
**Album:** Released May '81, on Artists House Catalogue no: **AH 6**

**SOMETHING ELSE**
**Album:** Released May '89, on Contemporary by Ace Records. Catalogue no: **COP 024**

**SONG X (Coleman, Ornette/Pat Metheny)**
Tracks: / Song X / Mob job / Endangered species / Video games / Kathelin Gray / Trigonometry / Song X duo / Long time no see.
**Album:** Released '86, on Geffen by Geffen Records (USA). Catalogue no: **924096 1**
**CD:** Released '86, on Geffen by Geffen Records (USA). Catalogue no: **924096 2**
**Cass:** Released '86, on Geffen by Gef-

fen Records (USA). Catalogue no: **924096 4**

**THAT'S JAZZ SERIES**
**Album:** Released Jul '76, on Atlantic by WEA Records. Catalogue no: **ATL 50240**

**TOMORROW IS THE QUESTION**
Tracks: / Tomorrow is the question / Tears inside / Mind and time / Compassion / Giggin' / Rejoicing / Lorraine / Turnaround / Endless.
**Album:** Released Feb '89, on Contemporary by Ace Records. Catalogue no: **COP 002**
**CD:** Released Jan '89, on JVC/Fantasy Catalogue no: **VDJ 1634**

**UNPRECEDENTED MUSIC OF ORNETTE COLEMAN, THE**
Tracks: / Lonely woman / Monsieur Le Prince / Forgotten children / Buddah blues.
Note: Live recording, previously unissued.
**Album:** Released Apr '81, on Lotus Catalogue no: **LPPS 111 16**
**Album:** Released '88, on Lotus Catalogue no: **LOP 14074**

**VIRGIN BEAUTY**
Tracks: / Three wishes / Bourgeois boogie / Happy hour / Virgin beauty / Healing the feeling / Singing in the shower / Desert players / Honeymooners / Chanting / Spelling the alphabet / Unknown artist.
**Cass:** Released Jun '88, on Portrait by CBS Records. Deleted Jan '90. Catalogue no: **461193 4**
**CD:** Released Jun '88, on Portrait by CBS Records. Catalogue no: **461193 2**
**Album:** Released Jun '88, on Portrait by CBS Records. Deleted Jan '90. Catalogue no: **461193 1**

**WHO'S CRAZY?**
Tracks: / January / Sortie le coquard / Dans la neige / Changes, The / Better get yourself another self / Duel, The / Two psychic lovers and eating time / Mis-used blues, The / Poet, The / Wedding day and fuzz / Fuzz / Feast / Breakout / European echoes / Alone and the arrest.
**2 LP Set:** Released '83, on Affinity by Charly Records. Deleted May '88. Catalogue no: **AFFD 102**

**WHO'S CRAZY? PART 1**
**Album:** Released '87, on Atmospheric Deleted Jun '89. Catalogue no: **IRI 5006**

**WHO'S CRAZY? PART 2**
**Album:** Released '87, on Atmospheric Deleted Jun '89. Catalogue no: **IRI 5006**

## Colianni, John

**BLUES O MATIC (Colianni, John Trio)**
Note: John Colianni's second release on the Concord label. His three year stint as Lionel Hampton's pianist gave him the opportunity to play with a wide variety of veteran players. Downbeat magazine says 'His nimble fingers move with the grace of Tatum and speed of Peterson'. This trio boasts jazz giants drummer Mel Lewis and bassist Lynn Seaton, with a very special guest. Lew Tabackin on four selections.
**CD:** Released Feb '89, on Concord by Concord Jazz Records (USA). Catalogue no: **CCD 4367**
**Cass:** Released Feb '89, on Concord by Concord Jazz Records (USA). Catalogue no: **CJ 367 C**
**Album:** Released Feb '89, on Concord by Concord Jazz Records (USA). Catalogue no: **CJ 367**

**JOHN COLIANNI**
Tracks: / Raincheck / Soft shoe / Pick yourself up / Home grown / Slow blues / I am in love / Get happy / All of you / Jitterbug waltz / Long ago and far away.
Note: Twenty-three year old pianist John Colianni's debut performance for Concord. A former pianist for Lionel Hampton, his style hints of Art Tatum and Oscar Peterson. John is featured here in solo, trio, quartet and quintet settings.
Personnel: John Colianni - piano; Bob Field - bass; Connie Kay - drums; Emily Remier - guitar; Joe Wilder - trumpet.
**Album:** Released Jan '87, on Concord Jazz by Concord Jazz Records (USA). Catalogue no: **CJ 309**
**Cass:** Released Jan '87, on Concord Jazz by Concord Jazz Records (USA). Catalogue no: **CJC 309**

## Collectors Jackpot

**COLLECTORS JACKPOT (Various artists)**
Note: Recorded in mono.
**Album:** Released Jul '86, on Jazz Archives (USA) by Jazz Archives Inc.(USA). Catalogue no: **JA 21**

**COLLECTORS JACKPOT 2 (Various artists)**
Note: Recorded in mono.
**Album:** Released Jul '86, on Jazz Archives (USA) by Jazz Archives Inc.(USA). Catalogue no: **JA 40**

## Collie, Max

**20 YEARS JUBILEE (Collie, Max & his Rhythm Aces)**
**Album:** Released Sep '86, Catalogue no: **TTD 519**

**AT THE BEIDERBECKE FESTIVAL 1975**
**Album:** Released Apr '79, on BBMS Catalogue no: **BBMS 5**

**BACK-LINE VOLUME 2 (Collie, Max & his Rhythm Aces)**
**Album:** Released Nov '85, on Timeless (Import) by Timeless Records. Catalogue no: **TTD 508**

**BATTLE OF TRAFALGAR (Collie, Max & his Rhythm Aces)**
**2 LP Set:** Released Mar '87, on Reality (USA) by Fantasy Inc (USA). Catalogue no: **R 106**

**BY POPULAR DEMAND (Collie, Max & His Rhythm Aces)**
Tracks: / When you're smiling / Passport to Paradise / Doctor Jazz / Summertime / Begin the beguine / Just a gigolo / Onions / Willie the weeper / As time goes by / Maryland / Margie / Tres moutarde.
**Album:** Released Mar '79, on Black Lion Catalogue no: **BLP 12181**

**FRONT-LINE VOLUME 1 (Collie, Max & His Rhythm Aces)**
**Album:** Released Nov '85, on Timeless by Timeless Records. Catalogue no: **TTD 504**

**GOSPEL TRAIN**
Tracks: / Gospel train / Over the rainbow / Nobody knows you (when you're down and out) / Woodworm stomp / My blue Heaven / Lullaby / After you've gone / Clarinet marmalade.
**Album:** Released Nov '77, on Black Lion Catalogue no: **BLP 12147**

**JAZZ ROOLS OK**
**Album:** Released Jun '78, on Black Lion Catalogue no: **BLP 12168**

**LIVE IN SWEDEN (Collie, Max & His Rhythm Aces)**
Tracks: / Light from the lighthouse / Original Dixieland one-step / Summertime / Black cat on a fence / World is waiting for the sunrise, The / Travelling blues / Mad dog / East Coast trot / Wabash blues / Pretty baby / Cheek to cheek / Snag it / Martinique, The / Ostrich walk / Short-dress gal / Entertainer, The.
**2 LP Set:** Released May '81, on Sweet Folk All by Sweet Folk All Records. Catalogue no: **SFAX 108**

**LIVE: MAX COLLIE (Collie, Max & His Rhythm Aces)**
Tracks: / Runnin' wild / At a Georgia camp meeting / Shimme-sha-wabble / Blue bells goodbye / Tiger rag / Yellow dog blues / Ice cream.
**Cass:** Released Jul '83, on Happy Bird (Germany) Catalogue no: **MB 90029**
**Album:** Released Jul '83, on Happy Bird (Germany) Catalogue no: **B 90029**

**MAX COLLIE'S RHYTHM ACES VOL.1 (Collie, Max & His Rhythm Aces)**
**Album:** Released May '87, on Wam Catalogue no: **WAM/O No.1**

**MAX COLLIE'S RHYTHM ACES VOL.2 (Collie, Max & His Rhythm Aces)**
**Album:** Released May '87, on Wam Catalogue no: **WAM/O No.2**

**SENSATION**
**CD:** Released 16 Jan '88, on Timeless (Import) by Timeless Records. Catalogue no: **CDTTD 530**

**TEN YEARS TOGETHER (Collie, Max & His Rhythm Aces)**
Tracks: / Georgia grind / Give me your telephone number / I guess I'll have to change my plans / Dippermouth blues / Everybody loves my baby / I'm gonna sit right down and write myself a letter / Girl in clover / Beautiful dreamer / Hindustan / Ace in the hole / Dallas blues / Buddy's habits / Kneedrops / Jumping Jack sax / Rainbow round my shoulder / Cielito Lindo / Wolverine blues / Hi lili hi lo.
**2 LP Set:** Released May '81, on Sweet Folk All by Sweet Folk All Records. Catalogue no: **SFAX 118**

**THRILL OF JAZZ, THE (Collie, Max & His Rhythm Aces)**
**CD:** Released Mar '90, on Reality Catalogue no: **RCD 111**
**Cass:** Released Mar '90, on Reality Catalogue no: **R 111C**

**WORLD CHAMPIONS OF JAZZ (Collie, Max & His Rhythm Aces)**
Tracks: / Too bad / Sweet like this / Salutation march / 'S wonderful / I'm crazy 'bout my baby / Didn't he ramble / Ragtime dance / Dans les rues D'Antibes / Fidgety fingers.
**2 LP Set:** Released Aug '76, on Black Lion Catalogue no: **BLPX 12137/8**

## Collier, Graham

**Biographical details:** A British jazz composer, born in 1937 in Tynemouth. He studied trumpet from age 11 and was a band boy in the army at 16; he took up bass and composition, entered a 'Down Beat' competition while stationed in Hong Kong and won part of his tuition to the Berklee School of Music in Boston. He formed his own septet in 1964 and did a lot of educational and studio work. He was the first jazz composer to get funds from the Arts Council, in 1967. Many of his works have been recorded but are out of print, including *Mosaics* in 1970 on Philips with the septet; he formed his own Mosaic label and issued 11 albums 1974-78. *Day of the dead* has 13 pieces plus a narrator; it was for the Ilkey Literature Festival in 1977, with words from the Malcom Lowry novel "Under The Volcano"; this led to a BBC commission for a TV version. He has also made educational recordings for Cambridge University Press. He gave up the bass and low-paid live work for full-time composition. (Donald Clarke 1989).

**DARIUS (Collier, Graham & Various artists)**
**Album:** Released Jan '77, on Mosaic by Mosaic Records (UK). Catalogue no: **GCM 741**

**DAY OF THE DEAD**
**2 LP Set:** Released Jun '78, on Mosaic by Mosaic Records (UK). Catalogue no: **GCMD 783/4**

**MIDNIGHT BLUE**
**Album:** Released Jan '77, on Mosaic by Mosaic Records (UK). Catalogue no: **GCM 751**

**NEW CONDITIONS**
**Album:** Released Jan '77, on Mosaic by Mosaic Records (UK). Catalogue no: **GCM 761**

**SYMPHONY OF SCORPIONS**
**Album:** Released Aug '77, on Mosaic by Mosaic Records (UK). Catalogue no: **GCM 773**

## Collier, Mitty

**SHADES OF GENIUS**
Tracks: / Come back baby / I had a talk with my man last night / Would you have listened / I gotta get away from it all / My babe / Hallelujah (I love him so) / Drown in my own tears / No faith, no love / Together / Let them talk / Little miss loneliness / Ain't that love.
**Cass:** Released Jun '88, on Chess by Vogue Records. Catalogue no: **GCHK 78049**
**Album:** Released Jun '88, on Chess by Vogue Records. Catalogue no: **GCH 8049**

## Collier, Sheila

**CHANGE IS GONNA COME, A**
Tracks: / Change is gonna come, A / On my way / I've had it / Why don't you do right? / What a day for a daydream / Blues, get off my shoulder / Do your duty / Harmony alone / Sweet man / On revival day / Am I blue?.
**Album:** Released Nov '81, on Plant Life Jazz by Plant Life Records. Catalogue no: **PLJ 005**

**TRIBUTE TO BESSIE SMITH**
**Album:** Released '88, on Hayfield Catalogue no: **SR 3785**

## Collins, Cal

**CAL COLLINS**
**Album:** Released Apr '79, on Concord by Concord Jazz Records (USA). Catalogue no: **CJ 71**

**CROSS COUNTRY**
Tracks: / Corina Corina / My gal Sal / On the Atchison, Topeka and Santa Fe.
**Album:** Released Dec '81, on Concord by Concord Jazz Records (USA). Catalogue no: **CJ 166**

**OHIO BOSS GUITAR**
**Album:** Released Aug '79, on Famous Door (USA) by Famous Door Records (USA). Catalogue no: **HL 123**

## Collins, Lee

**IN THE 30'S**
**Album:** Released Jul '86, on Collectors Items Catalogue no: **CI 009**

**NIGHT AT THE VICTORY CLUB, A**
**Album:** Released Apr '79, on New Orleans Catalogue no: **NOR 7203**

**RALPH SUTTON'S JAZZOLA SIX-VOL.1**
Tracks: / Do you know what it means / Down in jungle town / Panama / After you've gone / Little Rock getaway / West End blues / Indiana / St. James infirmary / Honeysuckle rose / Johnson rag / Sunny side of the street / Hindustan.
**Album:** Released Apr '81, on Rarities Catalogue no: **RARITIES 31**

**RALPH SUTTON'S JAZZOLA SIX-VOL.2**
Tracks: / Do you know what it means / I've found a new baby / Buddy Bolden's blues / Muskrat ramble / Our Monday date / Clarinet marmalade / Do you know what it means (2) / Fidgety feet / Chinatown, my Chinatown / Viper's drag / Basin Street blues / Big butter and egg man.
**Album:** Released Apr '81, on Rarities Catalogue no: **RARITIES 32**

## Colosseum

**Biographical details:** This British band comprised at the time of their greatest success, Dave Greenslade, Dick Heckstall-Smith, Jon Hiseman, James Litherland and Tony Reeves.
Colosseum were formed in 1968 by Heckstall-Smith and Hiseman, as vehicle for fusing blues, jazz and rock music. They built a strong cult following but their highly artistic and ambitious eclecticism never gained the commercial acceptance of the blues rock of Fleetwood Mac or the jazz rock of Chicago, two other groups who were taking off at about the same time. Nevertheless they managed to reach No.15 on the UK album chart with both of their first two albums, both 1969 releases: *Those who are about to die salute you* and *Valentyne suite*. On the published charts, the former LP was listed simply as *Colosseum*, its real title being considered unsuitable for printing! For the third LP, 1970's *Daughter of time*, Litherland and Reeves were replaced by Dave Clempson and Mark Clarke. Chris Farlowe, famous for his 1966 No.1 *Out of time*, performed vocals on this album and also on 1971's live set, which was Colosseum's final LP.
After the group's break-up, Greenslade was reunited with Reeves in a group simply called Greenslade, Heckstall-Smith pursued a disjointed career as solo artist, session player and leader of his own short lived band, Litherland was already following a similarly unsettled path, Clempson joined Humble Pie, Hiseman and Clarke formed the short lived Tempest. After this Clarke had a spell in Rainbow; and Hiseman assembled a fresh band of musicians under the banner Colossum II, a mid-seventies outfit that failed to win the acclaim of the original group.(Bob Macdonald 1/2/85)
A jazz-rock group formed in 1968 by drummer Jon Hiseman. Other founder members were Dick Heckstall-Smith on reeds, Dave Greenslade on keyboards; Tony Reeves on bass and guitarist James Litherland. Hiseman and Heckstall-Smith had worked with pioneers Graham Bond and John Mayall, Greenslade with Chris Farlowe. Litherland left after two top 20 albums, replaced by Dave 'Clem' Clempson; this lineup produced their third album and Reeves left, replaced by Mark Clarke, and Farlowe was enlisted to take over vocals. This final lineup lasted another year, including *Live* in 1971 (which stayed longer in the UK top 20 than any of the others) and *Collectors Colosseum*, both in 1971. Clempson joined Humble Pie, replacing Peter Frampton; Farlowe joined Atomic Rooster and Greenslade formed his own eponymous band. Hiseman formed Tempest for two albums, then formed Colosseum II with an entirely new lineup: *Strange new flesh* came out in 1976. Hiseman and his wife, saxophonist/composer Barbara Thompson, were founder members of the United Rock & Jazz Ensemble in 1975 and he has worked in her fusion group Paraphernalia since 1979. (Donald Clarke 1989).

John Coltrane

### DAUGHTER OF TIME

**Album:** Released Dec '70, on Vertigo by Phonogram Ltd. Deleted Dec '75. Catalogue no: **6360 017**

### EPITAPH

Tracks: / Walking in the park / Bring out your dead / Those about to die / Beware the Ides of March / Daughter of time / Valentine suite.

**CD:** Released Apr '86, on Raw Power by Castle Communications Records. Catalogue no: **RAWCD 014**

**Cass:** Released Apr '86, on Raw Power by Castle Communications Records. Catalogue no: **RAWTC 014**

**Album:** Released Apr '86, on Raw Power by Castle Communications Records. Catalogue no: **RAWLP 014**

### VALENTYNE SUITE

**Album:** Released Nov '69, on Vertigo by Phonogram Ltd. Deleted Nov '84. Catalogue no: **VO 1**

## Coltrane, Alice

### ETERNITY

Tracks: / Spiritual eternal / Wisdom eye / Los caballos / Om supreme / Morning worship / Spring rounds / From rite of spring.

**Album:** on Warner Bros. by WEA Records. Catalogue no: **K 56198**

## Coltrane, John

**Biographical details:** John William Coltrane was born in Hamlet, North Carolina in 1926. Around 1944 he emerged professionally on the jazz scene. Initially he was influenced by Johnny Hodges and played alto sax in dance clubs, switching to tenor after a period of military service in Hawaii. In 1948 he worked in Philadelphia and there got to know Charlie Parker. In 1949 he played alto in Dizzie Gillespie's Orchestra - until 1953 when he joined the Johnny Hodges Orchestra and played tenor. In 1955 he joined up with Miles Davis and other members of his quintet - Red Garland, Philly Joe Jones and Paul Chambers - achieving a forceful original sound which was to be a determining factor in his musical development. Two years later he signed with Thelonius Monk and was able to express further his personal musical sensitivity. In 1958 Coltrane was back with Miles Davis but they were both musically too strong to play side by side for long and in 1959 he broke away, confident of the direction he wanted to take. From then on he led his own groups and recorded some very fine material. John Coltrane has had compelling influence on the development of jazz. He was an unprepossessing, introspective person who was totally dedicated to his music which was always a reflection of his spiritual evolution. We can trace this progress from his early lyrical interpretations to his mature, mystical style. He died in New York on July 17th 1967.

Tenor and soprano saxist John Coltrane (1926-67) was the most popular and influential jazz musician of the 1960s, and after Louis Armstrong and Charlie Parker one the most influential of all time. He turned pro in his native Philidelphia with a cocktail band, played in the U.S. Navy, toured with an Eddie Vinson R&B band a.d played and recorded with Dizzy Gillespie (on alto as well as tenor) all before 1950. He worked for Earl Bostic in 1952, who knew as much about the saxophone as anyone alive, and for Johnny Hodges in 1953-54, fired him for nodding out (he was a heroin addict). He made many albums in the '50s, as a sideman and as a leader, all of them holding out very well today: he was obviously going to be a giant. From 1955 he played with the legendary Miles Davis Quintet on Prestige and then through the early '60s on CBS, his stlye balancing the economy of Davis; some critics did not like Coltrane (or Philly Joe Jones on drums) but the group was described as the Louis Armstrong Hot Five of modern jazz. In the spring of 1957 Coltrane quit drugs and alcohol for good; he spent most of that year with Thelonious Monk, including the album *Monk's Music*. He searched for the means to harmonic richness, using strings of notes as though to play every note in a chord, a technique later dubbed 'sheets of sound' by Ira Gitler; he now learned more harmonic background from Monk's complex music. He recorded with a Davis sextet including Cannonball Adderly on alto, and an Adderly album in early 1959 on Mercury without Davis as the *Cannonball Adderly Quintet In Chicago*; then Davis's sextet album *Kind Of Blue* in a 'modal' style, one of the most influential albums of the decade. His own albums *Giant Steps* and *Coltrane Jazz* were breakthroughs on Atlantic in 1959. Coltrane played high on tenor as though on alto, superimposing chords and exploring overtones: a music teacher had recomended soprano sax some years earlier; Coltrane picked up a soprano and began practising on it. He formed his own quartet in 1960, which soon included McCoy Tyner on piano, Elvin Jones on drums and Jimmy Garrison on bass: several more albums on Atlantic included *The Avant Garde* with Ornette Coleman sidemen and *My Favourite Things*, the first of several recordings of the title tune on soprano, turning a song from *Sound Of Music* (of all places) into something almost hypnotic. *My Favourite Things* soon sold 50,000 copies, compared to 5,000 for most jazz albums. He recorded with Davis again but in 1961 began the association with Impulse (then ABC, now MCA) which lasted the rest of his life. He was produced on Impulse at first by Creed Taylor, then by Bob Thiele. The quartet was often augmented, using such musicians as Pharoah Sanders and Eric Dolphy; he also recorded with vocalist Johnny Hartman and with Duke Ellington, Duke and Coltrane playing together with each others' rhythm sections. He had been introduced to Islamic literature and philosophy in the early '50s by Yusef Lateef, and probably also influenced by Sun Ra; his religious nature came to the fore: *A Love Supreme* in 1964 was a four-part composition central to his canon and one of his best sellers. He was probably reaching out towards complete harmonic freedom, influenced by the 'free jazz' of Ornette Coleman and others, when he died of liver cancer. Some of his posthumous releases were controversially overdubbed by his second wife, harpist Alice Coltrane. With its transparant integrity, his music fulfilled the 'love and peace' era of the 1960s better than that of the flower-power brigade by addressing the hearts of listeners rather than the media; as with Armstrong and Parker before him, the challenge for subsequent jazzmen has been how to break free of his stylistic and tonal domination. (Donald Clarke 1989).

**1951-65**
**Album:** Released '88, on Rare LPs Catalogue no: **RARE 11**

**AFRICA (Coltrane, John & Wilbur Harden)**
Tracks: / Dial Africa / Tanganyika strut / Gold Coast / Oomba / B.J. / Anedac / Once in a while.
**CD:** Released Nov '86, on MCA by MCA Records. Deleted Dec '89. Catalogue no: **2546 382**
**CD:** Released Nov '86, on RCA by BMG Records (UK). Deleted Nov '89. Catalogue no: **ZD 70818**

**AFRICA AND INDIA**
**Album:** Released Jun '86, on Crusader Jazz Masterworks Catalogue no: **CJZ LP 3**

**AFRICA BRASS (Coltrane,John Quartet)**
Tracks: / Greensleeves / Africa / Blues minor.
**Album:** Released Jun '82, on Jasmine by Hasmick Promotions. Deleted Feb '88. Catalogue no: **JAS 8**
**Cass:** Released Jun '82, on Jasmine by Hasmick Promotions. Catalogue no: **JAS C8**

**AFRICA BRASS SESSIONS 1 & 2**
Tracks: / Africa / Blues minor / Greensleeves (version) / Greensleeves / Song of the underground railraod / Africa (version).
Note: Recorded 1961. Personnel include John Coltrane (tenor sax), McCoy Tyner (piano), Paul Chambers (bass) Elvin Jones (drums), Freddie Hubbard (tpt), Eric Dolphy (alto sax). Two sessions on one CD (only), including previously unissued alternate takes.
**CD:** Released Jun '89, on MCA (Impulse Jazz) Catalogue no: **MCAD 42001**

**AFRICA BRASS SESSIONS VOL 2**
**Album:** Released May '89, on MCA (Import) by MCA Records. Catalogue no: **MCA 42232**

**AFRICA BRASS VOL.2**
Tracks: / Song of underground railroad / Africa.
**Cass:** Released Sep '82, on Jasmine by Hasmick Promotions. Catalogue no: **JAS C59**
**Album:** Released Sep '82, on Jasmine by Hasmick Promotions. Deleted Feb '88. Catalogue no: **JAS 59**

**AFRO BLUE IMPRESSIONS**
Tracks: / Lonnie's lament / Naima / Chasin' the trane / My favourite things / Afro blue / Cousin Mary / I want to talk about you / Spiritual / Impressions.
**Cass set:** Released May '82, on Pablo Jazz (USA) by Pablo Records (USA). Catalogue no: **K 20 101**
**2 LP Set:** Released May '82, on Pablo Jazz (USA) by Pablo Records (USA). Catalogue no: **262 0101**

**AND THE JAZZ GIANTS**
**CD:** Released Apr '87, on London Records by London Records Ltd. Catalogue no: **FCD 60014**

**ART OF JOHN COLTRANE**
Tracks: / Sveeda's song flute / Aisha / Countdown / Mr. Knight / My shining hour / Blues to Bechet / Invisible, The / My favourite things / Giant steps / Central Park West / Like Sonny / Body and soul.
**Album:** Released '87, on Atlantic by WEA Records. Catalogue no: **K 60052**

**ARTISTRY IN JAZZ Greatest hits**
**CD:** Released May '87, on JVC/Fantasy Deleted '88. Catalogue no: **VDJ 1587**

**ASCENSION (Coltrane, John Orchestra)**
Tracks: / Ascension, parts 1 & 2.
**Album:** Released Aug '82, on Jasmine by Hasmick Promotions. Catalogue no: **JAS 45**
**Cass:** Released Aug '82, on Jasmine by Hasmick Promotions. Catalogue no: **JAS C45**

**BAGS AND TRANE (Coltrane, John & Milt Jackson)**
Tracks: / Bags and trane / Three little words / Night we called it a day, The / Be-bop / Late late blues, The.
**Album:** Released '88, on Atlantic by WEA Records. Catalogue no: **K 30016**

**BALLADS (Coltrane,John Quartet)**
Tracks: / Say it (over and over again) / You don't know what love is / Too young to go steady / All or nothing at all.
**Album:** Released Aug '82, on Jasmine by Hasmick Promotions. Catalogue no: **JAS 37**
**Cass:** Released Aug '82, on Jasmine by Hasmick Promotions. Catalogue no: **JAS C37**

**BEST OF JOHN COLTRANE (LIVE)**
**CD:** Released May '86, on Pablo Jazz (USA) by Pablo Records (USA). Catalogue no: **CD 2310 886**

**BLACK PEARLS**
Tracks: / Black pearls / Lover come back to me / Sweeet aspphire blues / Believer / Nakatini serenade / Do I love you because your beautiful.
**Album:** Released Jul '80, on Prestige Deleted Jul '85. Catalogue no: **PR 24037**

**BLUE TRAIN**
Tracks: / Blue train / Moments notice / Locomotion, The / I'm old fashioned / Lazy bird.
**Cass:** Released Mar '86, on Blue Note by EMI Records. Catalogue no: **TC BST 81577**
**CD:** Released Jul '87, on Blue Note by EMI Records. Catalogue no: **CDP 746 095 2**
**Album:** Released Apr '85, on Blue Note by EMI Records. Catalogue no: **BST 81577**
**CD:** Released Jul '87, on Blue Note by EMI Records. Catalogue no: **BNZ 21**

**BRAZILIA (Coltrane,John Quartet)**
**Album:** Released Jan '80, on Blue Parrot Catalogue no: **AR 705**

**BYE BYE BLACKBIRD**
Tracks: / Bye bye blackbird / Traneing in.
**Album:** Released Oct '84, on Pablo Jazz (USA) by Pablo Records (USA). Catalogue no: **230 8227**
**CD:** Released Apr '87, on Pablo Jazz (USA) by Pablo Records (USA). Catalogue no: **CD 230 8227**
**Album:** Released Nov '85, on Crusader Catalogue no: **CJZ LP 4**

**COLETRANE QUARTET AND QUINTET**
**Album:** Released Apr '79, on Jazz Connoisseur by Spotlite Records. Catalogue no: **JC 112**

**COLLECTION: JOHN COLTRANE**
Tracks: / Love supreme, A (part 1) (Acknowledgement) / Love supreme, A (part 2) (Resolution) / Love supreme, A (part 3) (Pursuance) / Love supreme, A (part 4) (Psalm) / Traneing in / Bye bye blackbird.
**CD:** Released Sep '87, on Deja Vu Catalogue no: **DVCD 2037**
**Cass:** Released Aug '85, on Deja Vu Catalogue no: **DVMC 2037**

**COLTRANE (Coltrane,John Quartet)**
Tracks: / Out of this world / Soul eyes / Inch woman / Tunji / Miles made.
**Album:** Released Jun '82, on Jasmine by Hasmick Promotions. Catalogue no: **JAS 10**
**CD:** Released May '89, on MCA (Import) by MCA Records. Catalogue no: **MCAD 5883**
**CD:** Released Jun '82, on MCA by MCA Records. Deleted Dec '89. Catalogue no: **2546 092**
**Cass:** Released Jun '82, on Jasmine by Hasmick Promotions. Catalogue no: **JAS C10**
**CD:** Released '88, on Fantasy (import) by Fantasy Inc (USA). Catalogue no: **FCD 6357105**

**COLTRANE LEGACY, THE**
Tracks: / 26 - 2 / To her Ladyship / Untitled original / Centerpiece / Stairway to the stars / Blues legacy.
**Album:** Released May '81, on Atlantic by WEA Records. Deleted '86. Catalogue no: **K 40120**

**COLTRANE TIME**
**Album:** Released Sep '83, on Boplicity by Ace Records. Deleted '88. Catalogue no: **BOP 001**

**COLTRANOLOGY VOLUME 1**
**Album:** Released May '78, on Affinity by Charly Records. Catalogue no: **AFF 14**

**COLTRANOLOGY VOL. 2**
Note: Featuring McCoy Tyner, Jimmy Garrison, Elvin Jones.
**Album:** Released '78, on Affinity by Charly Records. Catalogue no: **AFF 16**

**COPENHAGEN CONCERTS, THE (Coltrane, John Quartet)**
Tracks: / Chasin' the trane / Every time we say goodbye / I want to talk about you / Mr. P.C..
**Album:** Released May '81, on Ingo Catalogue no: **INGO 4**

**COUNTDOWN (Coltrane, John & Wilbur Harden)**
Tracks: / Wells Fargo - take 1 / Wells Fargo - take 2 / E.F.F.P.H. / Countdown - take 1 / Countdown - take 2 / Rhodomagnetics 1 / Rhodomagnetics 2 / Snuffy / West 42nd street.
**2 LP Set:** Released Mar '86, on RCA by BMG Records (UK). Deleted May '89. Catalogue no: **WL 70529**
**Cass set:** Released Mar '86, on RCA by BMG Records (UK). Catalogue no: **WK 70529**
**CD:** Released Mar '86, on RCA by BMG Records (UK). Deleted Nov '89. Catalogue no: **ZD 70529**

**COUNTDOWN: THE SAVOY SESSIONS (Coltrane, John & Wilbur Harden)**
Tracks: / Wells Fargo take 1 / Wells fargo take 2 / E.F.F.P.H. / Countdown 1 / Countdown 2 / Rhodomagnetics 1 / Rhodomagnetics 2 / Snuffy / West 42nd street.
**2 LP Set:** Released Mar '85, on Savoy Jazz (USA) by Malaco Records (USA). Catalogue no: **SJL 2203**

**CREATION (Coltrane,John Quartet)**
**Album:** Released Feb '77, on Blue Parrot Catalogue no: **AR 700**

**CRESCENT (Coltrane,John Quartet)**
Tracks: / Crescent / Wise one / Bessie's blues / Lonnie's lament / Drum thing, The.
**CD:** Released May '89, on MCA (Import) by MCA Records. Catalogue no: **MCAD 5889**
**CD:** Released Aug '82, on MCA by MCA Records. Deleted Dec '89. Catalogue no: **2546 082**
**Album:** Released '82, on Jasmine by Hasmick Promotions. Catalogue no: **JAS 41**
**Cass:** Released '82, on Jasmine by Hasmick Promotions. Catalogue no: **JAS C41**

**DAKAR**
Tracks: / Dakar / Mary's blues / Route 4 / Velvet scene / Witches' pet / Cat walk / C.T.A. / Interplay / Anatomy / Light blue / Soul eyes.
**2 LP Set:** Released Mar '82, on Prestige Deleted May '89. Catalogue no: **P 24104**

**EUROPEAN TOUR, THE**
Tracks: / Promise, The / I want to talk about you / Naima / Mr. P.C..
**Cass:** Released May '82, on Pablo Jazz (USA) by Pablo Records (USA). Catalogue no: **K 08 222**
**Album:** Released May '82, on Pablo Jazz (USA) by Pablo Records (USA). Catalogue no: **2308 222**

**EXOTIC**
**CD:** Released Jan '86, on Dunhill Compact Classics (USA) Catalogue no: **DZS 012**

**EXOTICA - ONE AND FOUR (Coltrane, John & Lee Morgan)**
**Album:** Released Oct '88, on Vogue by Vogue Records. Catalogue no: **500 889**

**EXPRESSIONS**
Tracks: / Ogunde / To be / Offering / Expression.
**Album:** Released Feb '84, on Jasmine by Hasmick Promotions. Catalogue no: **JAS 73**

**FIRST STEPS 1951 - 54 - 56**
Tracks: / Birk's works / Good bait / Night in Tunisia / Sideways / Don't blame me / In a mellow tone / Tune up / Walkin'.
Note: Recorded in mono.
**Album:** Released Oct '86, on Jazz Live (Italy) Catalogue no: **BLJ 8039**

**GIANT STEPS**
Tracks: / Giant steps / Cousin Mary / Countdown / Spiral / Syeeda's song flute / Naima / Mr. P.C..
**CD:** Released '87, on Atlantic by WEA Records. Catalogue no: **781 337-2**
**Album:** Released Apr '87, on Atlantic by WEA Records. Deleted Jan '90. Catalogue no: **K 50239**

**GOLD COAST**
Tracks: / Tanganyika strut / Dial Africa / Gold coast / B.J..
**Album:** Released Oct '85, on Savoy (France) Deleted Aug '89. Catalogue no: **WL 70518**
**Cass:** Released Oct '85, on RCA by BMG Records (UK). Deleted Nov '88. Catalogue no: **WK 70518**

**IMPRESSIONS**
Tracks: / India / Up against the wall / Impressions / After the rain.
**Album:** Released '86, on Crusader Jazz Masterworks Catalogue no: **CJZ LP 2**
**Cass:** Released Aug '82, on Jasmine by Hasmick Promotions. Catalogue no: **JAS C39**
**Cass:** Released Jun '86, on MCA by MCA Records. Deleted Dec '89. Catalogue no: **ASC 42**
**Album:** Released Jul '82, on Jasmine by Hasmick Promotions, Deleted Feb '88. Catalogue no: **JAS 39**
**CD:** Released Jun '86, on MCA by MCA Records. Deleted Dec '89. Catalogue no: **MCAD 5887**

**IMPRESSIONS OF EUROPE**
Tracks: / Impressions / I want to talk about you / Inch worm, The.
**Album:** Released Nov '82, on Ingo Catalogue no: **INGO 7**

**IMPULSE (Coltrane, John & John Hartman)**
Tracks: / They say it's wonderful / Dedicated to you / My one and only love / Lush life / You are too beautiful / Autumn serenade.
**CD:** Released Apr '87, on MCA by MCA Records. Deleted Dec '89. Catalogue no: **MCAD 5661**

**JOHN COLTRANE**
Tracks: / Slow dance / Bass blues / You leave me breathless / Soft lights and sweet music / Good bait / I want to talk about you / You say you care / Theme for Ernie / Russian lullaby.
**2 LP Set:** Released '79, on RCA by BMG Records (UK). Deleted '82. Catalogue no: **PR 24003**

**JOHN COLTRANE LIVE AT THE VILLAGE VANGUARD**
Tracks: / Spiritual / Softly as in a morning sunrise / Chasin' the 'Trane.
**Cass:** Released Jun '82, on Jasmine by Hasmick Promotions. Catalogue no: **JAS C9**
**Album:** Released Jun '82, on Jasmine by Hasmick Promotions. Deleted Feb '88. Catalogue no: **JAS 9**

**JOHN COLTRANE QUARTET (Coltrane,John Quartet)**
**Album:** Released '88, on Unique Jazz by Spotlite Records. Catalogue no: **UJ 32**

**JOHN COLTRANE QUARTET LIVE WITH RAY DRAPER**
**CD:** Released Feb '89, on Vogue by Vogue Records. Catalogue no: **VGCD 600133**

**JOHN COLTRANE QUARTET PLAYS (Coltrane,John Quartet)**
Tracks: / Chim chim cheree / Brazilia / Nature boy / Song of praise.
**CD:** Released Jan '90, on MCA (Impulse Jazz) Catalogue no: **MCAD 33110**

**JOHN COLTRANE AND RAY DRAPER (Coltrane, John & Ray Draper)**
Tracks: / Essie's dance / Doxy / I talk to the trees / Yesterdays / Oleo / Angel eyes.
**Album:** Released Jul '82, on Jazz Reactivation Catalogue no: **JR 147**

**KULU SE' MAMA**
**Album:** Released Sep '82, on Jasmine by Hasmick Promotions. Catalogue no: **JAS 51**
**Cass:** Released Sep '82, on Jasmine by Hasmick Promotions. Catalogue no: **JAS C51**

**LEGENDARY MASTERS, THE (Unissued or rare 1951-65)**
Note: 5 Box set contains tracks as album and compact disc Cat. No.'s 11/12/13/14/15.
**LP Set:** Released Apr '88, on Recording Arts Ref. Edition Catalogue no: **RARELP 11/15**
**CD Set:** Released Apr '88, on Recording Arts Ref. Edition Catalogue no: **RARECD 11/15**

**LEGENDARY MASTERS, THE (1951-58) (Unissued or rare)**
Tracks: / Good bait / Birk's works / Thru for the night / Castle rock / Don't blame me / I've got a mind to ramble blues / Don't cry baby blues / In a mellow tone / Globetrotter / Tune up / Walkin' / Four.
**Album:** Released '88, on Recording

Arts Ref. Edition Catalogue no: **RARELP 11**
**CD:** Released '88, on Recording Arts Ref. Edition Catalogue no: **RARECD 11**

**LEGENDARY MASTERS, THE (1961-62) (Unissued or rare)**
Tracks: / Chim chim cheree / Naima / Bye bye blackbird / I want to talk about you.
**CD:** Released '88, on Recording Arts Ref. Edition Catalogue no: **RARECD 13**
**Album:** Released '88, on Recording Arts Ref. Edition Catalogue no: **RARELP 13**

**LEGENDARY MASTERS, THE (1961-65) (unissued or rare)**
Tracks: / Love supreme, A (part 1) / Resolution - part III / Pursuance - part IV / Psalm / Good bait / Thru for the night / Don't blame me / Don't cry baby blues / Globetrotter / Walkin' / Chim chim cheree / Bye bye blackbird / Roy / Impressions / Mr. P.C. / Cousin Mary / Lonnie's lament / Birk's works / Castle rock / I've got a mind to ramble blues / In a mellow tone / Tune up / Four / Acknowledgement - part I / Pursuance - Part IV / Spiritual / Naima / I want to talk about you / Chasin' the trane / Afro-blue / My favourite things / Miles mode / Body and soul.
**Album:** Released '88, on Recording Arts Ref. Edition Catalogue no: **RARELP 12**
**CD:** Released '88, on Recording Arts Ref. Edition Catalogue no: **RARECD 12**

**LEGENDARY MASTERS, THE (1962-63) (Unissued or rare)**
Tracks: / Roy / Chasin' the trane / Impressions / Afro-blue / Mr. P.C..
**Album:** Released '88, on Recording Arts Ref. Edition Catalogue no: **RARELP 14**
**CD:** Released '88, on Recording Arts Ref. Edition Catalogue no: **RARECD 14**
**Album:** Released '88, on Recording Arts Ref. Edition Catalogue no: **RARELP 15**
**CD:** Released '88, on Recording Arts Ref. Edition Catalogue no: **RARECD 15**

**LIKE SONNY**
Tracks: / One and four (aka Mr. Day) / Exotica (alternate take) / Exotica / Like Sonny (aka simple like) / Essii's dance / Doxy / Oleo / I talk to the trees (CD only.) / Yesterdays (CD only.) / Angel eyes (CD only.).
**Album:** Released Feb '90, on Roulette (EMI) by EMI Records. Catalogue no: **793 901 1**
**CD:** Released Feb '90, on Roulette (EMI) by EMI Records. Catalogue no: **CDROU 1012**
**CD:** Released Feb '90, on Roulette (EMI) by EMI Records. Catalogue no: **CDP 793 901 2**
**Album:** Released Feb '90, on Roulette (EMI) by EMI Records. Catalogue no: **ROU 1012**

**LIVE 1962**
Tracks: / My favourite things / Improvisation / Miles' mode / Inch worm, The / Every time we say goodbye / Impressions.
**2 LP Set:** Released Aug '83, on Musidisc by Musidisc Records (France). Catalogue no: **ALB 378**

**LIVE AT BIRDLAND (Coltrane, John Quartet)**
Tracks: / Afro blue / I want to talk about you / Promise, The / Alabama / Your lady.
Note: Featuring Eric Dolphy. A Vee Jay recording. An Affinity release from Charly Records International APS.
**CD:** Released Jan '90, on MCA (Impulse Jazz) Catalogue no: **MCAD 33109**
**Album:** Released Jun '82, on Jasmine by Hasmick Promotions. Catalogue no: **JAS 11**
**Cass:** Released Jun '82, on Jasmine by Hasmick Promotions. Catalogue no: **JAS C11**

**LIVE AT BIRDLAND (2)**
Tracks: / Mr. P.C. / Miles mode / My favourite things / Body and soul.
**CD:** Released Jun '87, on Charly by Charly Records. Catalogue no: **CDCHARLY 68**
**Album:** Released Feb '82, on Affinity by Charly Records. Catalogue no: **AFF 79**

**LIVE AT THE VILLAGE VANGUARD**
Tracks: / Naima / My favourite things.
**Album:** Released Jun '82, on Jasmine by Hasmick Promotions. Catalogue no: **JAS 16**
**Cass:** Released Jun '82, on Jasmine by Hasmick Promotions. Catalogue no: **JAS C16**

**LIVE IN ANTIBES 1965 / LIVE IN PARIS 1965**
**Album:** Released Oct '88, on France's Concert Catalogue no: **FC 119**
**CD:** Released Oct '88, on France's Concert Catalogue no: **FCD 119**

**LIVE IN DENMARK, 1962 (Coltrane, John Quartet)**
Tracks: / Chasin' the train / Every time we say goodbye / I want to talk about you / Mr. P.C. / Inch worm, The.
Note: Coltrane's historic quartet recorded in concert at the Falkonercentret in Copenhagen during November 1962. John Coltrane - tenor and soprano sax; McCoy Tyner - piano; Elvin Jones - drums. 51:56 minutes playing time.
**CD:** Released Nov '89, on Jazz-Up Catalogue no: **JU 316**

**LIVE IN PARIS**
Tracks: / Naima / Impressions / Blue valse / Afro blue / Impressions (2nd version).
**2 LP Set:** on Affinity by Charly Records. Catalogue no: **AFFD 24**
**CD:** Released Oct '87, on Charly by Charly Records. Catalogue no: **CDCHARLY 87**

**LIVE IN STOCKHOLM - 1961**
Tracks: / My favourite things / Blue train / Naima / Impressions.
**CD:** Released May '88, on Charly by Charly Records. Catalogue no: **CDCHARLY 117**

**LIVE IN STOCKHOLM - 1963**
Tracks: / Mr. P.C. / Traneing in / Spiritual / I want to talk about you.
**CD:** Released Dec '86, on Charly by Charly Records. Catalogue no: **CDCHARLY 33**

**LOVE SUPREME, A (CRUSADER)**
**Album:** Released Jun '86, on Crusader Jazz Masterworks Catalogue no: **CJZ LP 1**

**LOVE SUPREME, A (ESOLDUN)**
**CD:** Released Jan '88, on Esoldun Catalogue no: **FCD 106**
**Album:** Released Jan '88, on Esoldun Catalogue no: **FC 106**

**LOVE SUPREME, A (INGO)**
**Album:** Released Jul '82, on Ingo Catalogue no: **INGO 11**

**LOVE SUPREME, A (IMPULSE)**
**Cass:** Released Feb '82, on Impulse by Impulse Records. Catalogue no: **MCLC 1648**
**Album:** Released Feb '82, on Impulse by Impulse Records. Deleted Apr '88. Catalogue no: **MCL 1648**
**Cass:** Released Feb '87, on Impulse by Impulse Records. Deleted Dec '89. Catalogue no: **ASC 54**
**CD:** Released Feb '87, on Impulse by Impulse Records. Deleted Dec '89. Catalogue no: **MCAD 5660**
**Album:** Released Oct '85, on Impulse by Impulse Records. Catalogue no: **AS 42**

**LOVE SUPREME, A (MCA)**
**CD:** Released Jan '90, on MCA by MCA Records. Catalogue no: **DMCL 1S05**
**CD:** Released Jan '90, on MCA by MCA Records. Catalogue no: **DMCL 1648**

**LUSH LIFE**
Tracks: / Like someone in love / I love you / Tranes's slow blues / Lush life / I hear a rhapsody.
**Cass:** Released Mar '88, on Prestige Deleted Jan '90. Catalogue no: **PRC 7188**
**CD:** Released Apr '87, on Carrere (France) Catalogue no: **98442**
**Album:** Released Mar '88, on Prestige Catalogue nó: **PR 7188**
**CD:** Released Nov '86, on JVC/Fantasy Catalogue no: **VDJ 1544**

**MEDITATIONS**
Tracks: / Love / Consequences / Serenity / Father, Son and Holy Ghost.
**Album:** Released Jan '85, on Jasmine by Hasmick Promotions. Catalogue no: **JAS 80**

**MORE LASTING THAN BRONZE**
Tracks: / Lush life / I hear a rhapsody / Like someone in love / I love you / 'Tranes's slow blues / Bakai / Violets for your furs / Time was / Straight Street / While my lady sleeps / Chronic blues.
**Album:** Released May '84, on Prestige (USA) by Fantasy Inc (USA). Catalogue no: **OJCD 502**
**2 LP Set:** Released Feb '81, on Prestige Catalogue no: **PR 24014**

**MY FAVOURITE THINGS**
Note: N.J.F. 1963 and Europe 1962.
**Album:** Released Jun '86, on Crusader Jazz Masterworks Catalogue no: **CJZ LP 5**
**CD:** Released Jul '87, on Atlantic Jazz by WEA Records. Catalogue no: **K 781 246 2**

**John Coltrane - Soultrane (Prestige)**

**NEW THING AT NEWPORT (Coltrane, John & Archie Shepp)**
Tracks: / Le matin des noire / Scag / Call me by my rightful name / Introduction / One down, one up / Rufus.
**Cass:** Released Jun '82, on Jasmine by Hasmick Promotions. Catalogue no: **JAS C22**
**Album:** Released Jun '82, on Jasmine by Hasmick Promotions. Catalogue no: **JAS 22**

**NEWPORT FESTIVAL 1961**
**Album:** Released May '88, on Musica Jazz Catalogue no: **2MJP 1051**

**OM**
Note: Recorded 1965. Personnel: John Coltrane (tenor sax), McCoy Tyner (piano), Jimmy Garrison (bass), Donald Garrett (bass), Elvin Jones (drums), Joe Brazil (flute).
**CD:** Released Jun '89, on MCA (Impulse Jazz) Catalogue no: **MCAD 39118**
**Album:** Released Jun '89, on MCA (Impulse Jazz) Catalogue no: **MCA 39118**

**ON A MISTY NIGHT**
Tracks: / How deep is the ocean / Just you, just me / Bob's boys / Tenor conclave / On a misty night / Romas / Super jet / Mating call / Gnid / Soultrain.
**2 LP Set:** Released '79, on Prestige Deleted Jun '84. Catalogue no: **PR 24084**

**PARIS CONCERT, THE**
Tracks: / Mr. P.C. / Inch worm, The / Every time we say goodbye.
**Album:** Released May '82, on Pablo Jazz (USA) by Pablo Records (USA). Catalogue no: **2308 217**
**Cass:** Released May '82, on Pablo Jazz (USA) by Pablo Records (USA). Catalogue no: **K 08 217**

**PRESTIGE 7105**
**CD:** Released Jan '89, on JVC/Fantasy Catalogue no: **VDJ 1511**

**RARE JOHN COLTRANE QUARTET (Coltrane,John Quartet)**
Tracks: / Impressions / Inch worm, The / My favourite things.
Note: Recorded at Konserthuset, Stockholm, Sweden, on 19 November 1962: first time on record.
**Album:** Released Oct '82, on Duke by Melodisc Records. Catalogue no: **D 1016**

**REFLECTIONS**
Tracks: / Untitled original / Impressions / Chim chim cheree.
**Album:** Released Oct '82, on Audio Fidelity(USA) by Audio Fidelity (USA). Catalogue no: **AFEMP 1041**

**SETTIN' THE PACE**
Tracks: / I see your face before me / If there's someone lovelier than you / Little Melonae / Rise and shine.
**Album:** Released Feb '84, on Prestige (USA) by Fantasy Inc (USA). Catalogue no: **OJC 078**

**SOULTRANE (See panel above)**
Tracks: / Good bait / I want to talk about you / You say you care / Theme for Ernie / Russian lullaby.
Note: John Coltrane - tenor sax, Red Garland - piano, Paul Chambers - bass, Art Taylor - drums. Recorded in New York City, February 7, 1958.
When reading The New Yorker, usually, I am most amused by an S.J. Perelman gem, the cartoons or something in The Talk of the Town. In May 17th, 1958, issue, however, it was the jazz department that gave me my biggest guffaw when Whitney Balliett, in the course of reviewing a Miles Davis album, wrote, "Coltrane, a student of Sonny Rollins..."
It is true that when Coltrane joined Miles Davis' quintet in late 1955, Sonny (the Rollins of that time and slightly before) was exerting a peripheral influence over him. Even this proved to be transient. The influences of Dexter Gordon (vintage 1946), Sonny Stitt, Stan Getz (certain facets of sound) and a general essence of Charlie Parker were more evident, even then. Since that time, Trane has developed along personal lines to become quite an influence himself. He and Sonny are parallel figures now, each contributing new ideas to jazz in his own way.
*Soultrane* is a ballad, written by Tadd Damerson, which appears on *Mating call* (an album which features Coltrane and Damerson). This album, called *Soultrane*, does not include that tune but Prestige thought the name an apt one for an entire collection of Coltrane because it plays on its name in a truly descriptive way.
Trane is very serious about his playing; playing jazz is what he is most concerned with. There is a constant effort, on his part, to keep improvising. He is self-critical and helpfully, because of clear insight, self-analytical. Practice is not foreign to him.
As in his last album, Trane has the support of Red Garland, Paul Chambers and Arthur Taylor. These four have done much playing together. In this case, familiarity breeds rapport.
Another admirable facet is duplicated from the last album. That is the playing of seldom-done tunes. *John Coltrane* had *Soft lights and sweet music, You leave me breathless* and Alonzo Levister's *Slow dance*. In *Soultrane*, none of the selections have been overdone and three are entirely new to jazz interpretation.
The opening selection is an exploration, at length, of *Good bait*, a Tadd Dameron/Count Basie collaboration, first recorded by Dizzy Gillespie in the forties. The way Trane plays the little turns in the melody gives it a slight minuet flavour. The excitement he builds in his choruses is done by degrees. The solos by Garland and Chambers (pizzicato) are in the same firm, solid groove that the rhythm section sets down for the entire performance. Before the theme is re-stated. Trane and Arthur Taylor have a most intelligent, foul bar-styled conversation. *I want to talk about you* is a ballad, written and originally recorded by Billy Eckstine when B was leading his band in the mid-forties. To my knowledge, this extremely pretty song had not been done since until now. This is how to play

a ballad with jazz feeling. Trane is emotional but never baroque. Garland's languid, blue piano and other excellent picked solo by Chambers enhance the romantic mood. Side two opens with a Joe Stein/Leo Robin tune, *You say you care*, which I have never heard before in a jazz context. Trane makes the most of the interesting chord changes in a swinging, medium-up setting. Garland's fluid single-line and Chambers' flying fingers are also featured before the final theme statement.

*Theme for Ernie* is a dedicatory piece by Philadelphian Freddie Lacey to Ernie Henry, the ex-Gillespie alto saxophonist who died suddenly in December of 1957 at the age of thirty-one. Trane plays the lament without much deviation from the air of reminiscence and melancholy. Red and Trane divide the last chorus.

Red begins *Russian lullaby* with an out-of-tempo introduction before Trane comes ripping in.

Taking this and *Soft lights and sweet music* as evidence, it would seem that the boys like to play their Irving Berlin at high velocity. I'm sure this lullaby would keep Nikita awake and swinging all night. Trane's "sheets of sound", which he has since put to wider use, are demonstrated in the beginning of the tag. (Ira Gitler)

**CD:** Released Apr '86, on JVC/Fantasy Catalogue no: **VDJ 1502**

**CD:** Released Apr '87, on Carrere (France) Deleted '88. Catalogue no: **98373**

**CD:** Released Sep '89, on Riverside (USA) by Fantasy Inc (USA). Catalogue no: **CDRIVM 003**

**STANDARD COLTRANE**

**Album:** Released Jan '87, on Original Jazz Classics (USA) by Fantasy Inc (USA). Catalogue no: **OJC 246**

**STARDUST SESSION, THE**

Tracks: / Spring is here / Invitation / I'm a dreamer aren't we all / Love thy neighbour / Don't take your love from me / My ideal / Stardust / I'll get by.

**2 LP Set:** Released '79, on Prestige Deleted '84. Catalogue no: **PR 24056**

**TRANE'S BLUES**

**CD:** Released Mar '90, on Giants of Jazz by Hasmick Promotions. Catalogue no: **GOJCD53058**

**Album:** Released Feb '89, on Giants of Jazz by Hasmick Promotions. Catalogue no: **LPJT 72**

**UNISSUED CONCERT IN GERMANY 1963 (Coltrane, John Quartet)**

**Cass:** Released Sep '81, on Jazz Galore Catalogue no: **1001**

**WHEELIN'**

Tracks: / Wheelin' (take 1) / Wheelin' (take 2) / Dealin' (take 1) / Dealin' (take 2) / Things ain't what they used to be / Robbin's nest cha cha / Blue calypso / Falling in love with love.

**Album:** Released '79, on Prestige Deleted '84. Catalogue no: **PR 24069**

## Columbo, Russ

**Biographical details:** A singer and songwriter (1908-34) who was Bing Crosby's only real competition in the early 1930s. He led his own band in 1931 and soon became a sensation with his silky ballad style; he co-wrote his theme *You Call It Madness* as well as *Let's Pretend There's A Moon* and others including *Prisoner Of Love*, also recorded by Crosby, The Ink Spots and others, and a number one for Perry Como in 1946. Columbo was killed in a bizarre accident: a friend, using an ancient pair of duelling pistols as paperweights, struck a match on one which turned out to be loaded: Columbo was hit in the head by a ricochet. (Donald Clarke 1989).

**ON THE AIR 1933-4**

Tracks: / More than you know / Time on my hands / Easy come, easy go / With my eyes wide open, I'm dreaming / Stardust / True / Rolling in love / I've had my moments / I'm dreaming.

**Album:** Released Jan '89, on Silva Screen by Silva Screen Records. Catalogue no: **SH 2038**

**Album:** Released May '79, on Totem Catalogue no: **TOTEM 1031**

**RARE RADIO PERFOMANCES**

**Cass:** Released Jan '89, on Silva Screen by Silva Screen Records. Catalogue no: **CSH 2006**

**Album:** Released Jan '89, on Silva Screen by Silva Screen Records. Catalogue no: **SH 2006**

**RUSS COLUMBO 1931 AND 1934**

**Album:** Released Apr '79, on Sandy Hook (USA) Catalogue no: **SH 1006**

## Colyer, Ken

**Biographical details:** A trad jazz trumpeter, guitarist and leader (1928-88) born in Great Yarmouth. He first formed his own band in 1949. *The Great Revival* on *Esquire* has vintage tracks by Colyer on one side, by Australian Graham Bell (with Ade Monsborough) on the other. (Donald Clarke 1989).

**1957 - A VERY GOOD YEAR (Colyer, Ken Jazzmen & George Lewis)**

Tracks: / Happy wanderer / Gatemouth / Workingman blues / One sweet letter from you / Dusty rag / Joplins sensation / Over the waves / Walking with the king / Corina Corina / Ice cream / Running wild. Note: I have just been listening to these recordings after thirty years. I have never listened to my own records for pleasure, I am too self critical and can only hear what is wrong, and what could be improved on, so it was a pleasant surprise to hear so many good moments captured and preserved, that were also in safe hands. Mike Slatter was the man responsible. He was an ardent fan and was more aware than I that as much of this music as possible must be preserved. Tape machines weren't readily available in those days, and a few people owned one in our circle. Mike would rent machines at every opportunity and record what he could, wherever we were playing. I now realize his endeavours paid huge dividends. He has captured more great moments than are on any studio session. Some of this music will come as a tremendous surprise to you as it did to me, and fill the air with a joyous sound. One evening as we were setting up at Eel Pie Island Hotel and all was quiet I said to the boys, "This is as close as you will get to New Orleans in England, the atmosphere and feel is here, I have never experienced it so strongly anywhere else". The hotel had run to seed, its heyday long gone, when it was a famous and favorite place for people to go in the summer, to relax by the Thames and enjoy themselves and partake of the eel pies which gave the island its name. It took on a new lease of life for a few years when a jazz club was established there, and people flocked to hear the good music. It was dark and dingy, nobody bothered much to take their glasses back to the bar, but a fellow used to go round once the crowd were in, with a large whicker basket and a torch picking them up and taking them back to the bar. This is the only place I have ever seen this happen. I have said before that playing hot New Orleans music is like walking a tight-rope, you daren't slip, but the odd slips are bound to happen, they are worth taking the risks for though, and it is far more rewarding than playing the cardboard music that passes for jazz. Jazz is a small club music, and always will be. Though a band may play well in concert it will rarely build the atmosphere that it can achieve in a club that is conducive to the music. It doesn't matter with cardboard music but is vitally important to the creation of good music. This band is considered by many to be the best I ever had. This is possibly true but I have always striven to get the best out of the men around me and produce a good unit sound. The boys I have here (two unfortunately dead now, Johnny Bastable and Mac Duncan) were together for quite a long spell. This is important, for sometimes seems casual is the result of working and developing together. The short but beautiful session with George Lewis is another story.

We drove straight from the 51 Club, Great Newport Street, London, W1 after finishing the session, to Manchester Airport as George was coming in on an early morning plane and we wanted to be there to greet him before commencing the now famous tour. This was his first time in England. The arrival time kept getting delayed but when the airport manager discovered what all the people were waiting for - there were also musicians and fans from Manchester and elsewhere - he was very co-operative. When the plane's arrival was definite, he allowed us to set up by a hanger. He must have radioed the pilot as the plane stopped by the hanger and George and his manager were allowed to disembark, the plane then taxied off to its usual

**Ken Colyer - Decca Skiffle Sessions 1954-57 (Lake)**

stopping place. Though it was a dismal morning, drizzling with rain, we brightened it up with a couple of rousing numbers and George was delighted. The only opportunity for a quick rehearsal was that afternoon so we got to the hotel and grabbed a couple of hours sleep. I found a pub that would allow us to use their small upstairs room for a couple of hours. I can't remember who suggested that it would be a good idea to tape the rehearsal soley as a memento but I sent Ian Wheeler off to try and find somewhere where he could hire a machine for the two hours. We started playing and it went from the word go, everybody was enjoying themselves. After a couple of numbers George said "We don't need no rehearsal we're musicianers". I knew that, but also knew that that was the only chance we had of a quiet get together. Poor Ian had a terrible time trying to locate a machine. He had finally succeeded but there was only half an hour left and we had to vacate the room. As I said, I have not heard these four numbers for so long I had forgotten how good they were. I would go as far to say, never has the New Orleans sound and all that goes to make, been captured so well by six white Europeans and one New Orleanean who was one of the finest clarinettists who ever lived.Listen and the music speaks for itself, coming straight from the heart. It could get pretty hectic at Eel Pie Island but the crown noise is surprisingly quiet and hardly interferes with the music. There are none there that seem to think they are at a football match, constantly shouting catcalls, whistling or talking louder and louder as if it is more important that they be heard rather than the band. They have ruined many a potentially good session. As I said before, I am intensely critical of my own bands as I have always tried to raise the standard of the music so that even on an off night it will still sound pretty good. So I will not spoil your enjoyment with comments on the finer points of the music. There is too much that is good here. I always varied the program to try and play a balanced selection of tunes that portray the various aspects of the music and always tried to bear in mind Jelly Roll's dictum.

On hearing *Ice Cream*, one of my first thoughts was of how this tune has been debased by crass, ignorant musicians. Here it is a vehicle for creative musicians to find endless variations, to quote Peter Clayton: "Gives one a sense of space and wayward poetry". On my way to a recording session, I once jokingly said to a musician, "Come and hear history being made". Here it is true but fortunately we weren't conscience of the fact. What makes William Russell's *American Music* recordings so good is that the men are playing unself-consciously. Complete relaxation and the music flows and sometimes an hour seems like five minutes. George was not a highly literate man but was very aware and was very happy. As I timed the numbers I was continually surprised that they were shorter than I expected. I have found this with Duke Ellington's early records. The man packs so much music into a short space of time. Ian Wheeler finally got a chance to play on our last number *Corrine Corrine*. The harmonies move beautifully and cross in the way that gives New Orleans music its distinctive sound. Today, instead of having a field of musicians who are expert in this, it has become almost a lost art. *Over The Waves* was one of Georges specialities and he often played it solo but here he was quite happy for the band to come in on the ensemble, he had no ego in the bad sense and had to come up in the old school that demanded that the good of the band as a whole came first, and he played to the lead. *Walking With The King* drifts in quietly (Jelly Roll Morton: "if you start with half a glass of water you can add to it".) then builds to an eventual exciting climax. I hope you enjoy this music, with the happy knowledge that there is more to come. Also, there is every danger that this timeless music in a few years time will be gone forever, except on record. Ken Colyer.

**Album:** Released Dec '87, on Ken Colyer Catalogue no: **KC 1**

## CONCERT VOL.1

**Album:** Released May '87, on Wam Catalogue no: **WAM/O No.3**

## DARKNESS ON THE DELTA

Tracks: / Lord, Lord you've sure been good to me / Darkness on the delta / Yaaka hula hickey dula / Gettysburg march / Deep Bayou blues / Shine / Auf wiedersehen.

**Album:** Released Jan '80, on Black Lion Deleted Jan '85. Catalogue no: **BLP 12136**

## DECCA SKIFFLE SESSIONS 1954-57

Tracks: / Midnight Special / Casey Jones / K.C. Moan / Take this hammer / Down by the riverside / Go down, old Hannah / Streamline Train / Old Riley / Down bound tain / Stack o lee blues / Muleskinner blues / Grey goose / Sporting life / House rent stomp / I can't sleep / This train / Midnight Hour Blues / Go down sunshine / Ella Speed.

Note: Featuring Alexis Korner. What a curious hybrid 'Skiffle' of the 1950's turned out to be. Of course, like so many other things it was a typically British concoction. It embraced elements of Country Blues, Urban Blues, American Folk Music, Jugband Music, Old Timey, Bluegrass, Country, Gospel, Spirituals, Vaudeville, the social comment of the songs of Woody Guthrie, and, at its most commercial, Music Hall and specially written novelty numbers. Its origins lay with the New Orleans style jazz bands in Britain in the late 1940's although the term Skiffle had been applied to spasm bands of the 1920's and early 1930's. One such British style band was the Crane River Band of which Ken Colyer was a founder member. Like any enthusiasts the Cranes took their music very seriously and were not above 'educating' their audiences. This led to a 'band within' a band' formation performing what we call Skiffle, although at the time, it was simply part of their perfor-

**Ken Colyer - Decca Years (1955-59) (Lake)**

mance illustrating some of the influences on the Jazz. When Ken Colyer returned from his now famous visit to New Orleans in 1953 his new band had one Tony Donegan on banjo. Again, the band featured the 'band within' a band' performing the Skiffle type music. When the band broke up leaving Ken on his own the others went on to form Chris Barber's Jazzband. It was as a member of this band, which continued to have a Skiffle feature, that 'Lonnie Donegan' as he was now known, recorded *Rock Island line* for Decca which was to become Skiffle's first hit record. Donegan was to take Skiffle on to commercial acceptance and is still the man popularly associated with it. In 1954 Ken found himself without a band and although an interim band formed for a while it was not until 1955 that the line-up settled down to start the long run of regular Ken Colyer Jazzmen. Skiffle was beginning to become accepted as a music form in its own right and Skiffle clubs began to emerge. In the summer of 1954 Ken recorded the first Skiffle sessions under his own name (they pre date the Donegan *Rock Island Line* session by just over two weeks). They are the first ones included on this album. The line-up included the late Alexis Korner, who was to go on to become a respected figure in Blues and Rock music circles. Just before his untimely death Alexis recalled meeting the Colyer brothers in 1951 and having singing sessions with them and the American painter Ralston Crawford. Alexis also cited as an influence Ken Lindsay who used to give lectures on Blues and Folk music in the mid to late forties. Billy Colyer has been described by Lonnie Donegan as 'the originator' of Skiffle, a little fanciful perhaps, but his name did crop up a lot in those early days.

Ken had bought a guitar during a trip to Canada as a merchant seaman in 1947 and the acquisition of a collection of Leadbelly '78' in New York gave him his early influences. As in other aspects of his music, Ken's approach to his Skiffle sessions was to eschew commercial acclaim and let the music stand or fall on its own merits. His was not the brash, aggressive approach of those groups courting the 'Hit Parade' as it was called then. He pursued a much more narrow repertoire than all the encompassing one outlined above it: it sticks quite rigidly to Negro Country Blues, Worksongs, Freedom Songs, Spirituals with the odd foray into American Folksong. Despite a seeming contradiction, the result is on one hand a sincere, loving recreation and on the other - despite the accent - unnervingly 'authentic'. As with his Jazz this music feels as though it belongs with Ken Colyer; it has a natural, lived in quality as though he has submerged himself in it, absorbed it and honed it until it rests comfortably with him. His singing is like his trumpet playing: often understated, subtle shifts of the rhythm and a superb sense of timing. On one level it is simple, direct music, but never trite or quaint. Time gives this music a lot in the scheme of things: it started off with British New Orleans style Jazzmen trying to illustrate some roots of their music and in turn it became the roots music for so many of the Blues and Rock musicians of the Sixties and Seventies. Listening back to them you sometimes wish that the musicians would let their hair down a bit; there are times when it lacks sparkle, but the music is handled lovingly and I find it strangely compelling. This record contains all the tracks recorded by Ken Colyer for the Decca Record Comapany during the period 1953-58. (Paul Adams, 1987)

**Cass:** Released Dec '87, on Lake by Lake Records. Catalogue no: **LA 5007C**
**Album:** Released Dec '87, on Lake by Lake Records. Catalogue no: **LA 5007**

### DECCA YEARS 1955-59

Tracks: / Dippermouth blues. / Heliotrope bouquet / Beale street blues / Fig leaf rag / Gravier St. blues / Canal street blues / World is waiting for the sunrise, The / Girls go crazy, The / Entertainer, The / If ever I cease to love / Sensation / Perdido St. blues / Kinklets / Maryland, my Maryland.
**Album:** Released '85, on Lake by Lake Records. Catalogue no: **LA 5001**

### DECCA YEARS VOL.3, THE (Club Session with Colyer) (Colyer, Ken Jazzmen)

Tracks: / Uptown rumps / Blame it on the blues / Creole song / Chysanthemum rag / Snag it / Thriller rag / Black cat / Old rugged cross, The / Walking with the King / Home sweet home / Auf wiedersehen.
Note: Personnel: Ken Colyer (Trumpet, Vocals), Mac Duncan (Trombone), Ian Wheeler (Clarinet), John Bastable (Banjo), Ron Ward (Bass), Colin Bowden (Drums).
When I first embarked on this series of reissues from the Decca Archives of the Ken Colyer Jazzmen, I received a letter from Ken which read *Club Session with Colyer* is much sought after and would be worth thinking about if you have success with the first issue'. When we were able to talk briefly following a concert in Workington, Ken said that he is often asked for that particular album. Our mail also revealed it to be popular because we keep being asked if we are going to reissue it. Well, here it is. It has some significance for me in that it was the first of Ken's LP's I ever bought - second hand (guaranteed is rubber stamped on it) from James Asman in 1965. Little did I know then that some twenty years later Jimmy would give me such encouragement to pursue *Lake Records.* The reason why I waited until nine years after it was recorded to purchase a copy was that I was only eight years old in 1956.
I asked Ken if he had any memories of the session and he wrote 'the idea was mine to record with an invited audience from the '51 Club. There was a violent storm on one of the nights which interfered with the electricity and some of the numbers couldn't be used'. The line-up by now had settled down after a bit of shuffling and (with the later addition of Ray Foxley on piano) was to stay together for the next three or four years

Ken Colyer - Decca Years (Volume 3) (Lake)

and become almost the classic Ken Colyer Jazzmen. Much as I have enjoyed the record over the years I was surprised to learn that it was still so sought after. John Reddihough in his *National Jazz Federation* booklet on Ken said that the session was not helped 'by particularly bad recording'. I certainly know what he means because there is some very wayward sound balance in places, but I think he is a little too hard on it. Most of it is down to 'knob twiddling': a good band is well balanced internally and all you really need to do is get a good balance using as few microphones as possible and let it roll leaving well alone. The somewhat wayward balance in places surprises me, because it was the Decca engineers who made those superb live recordings of Ken (see *Lake* LA 5004) Chris Barber, Alex Walsh, etc. at the Royal Festival Hall in 1954 and 55. To me, though, the oddities of the recording are part of its charm. One of my friends once said that it was like being in a clubroom and as you moved about the balance changed. A little fanciful perhaps, but there's an element of truth in it.

There's a lot of 'live' spirit been captured here; a certain rumbustiousness in the ensemble playing. Whilst writing these notes I'm checking the master tapes by playing them at high volume over the studio monitors and I am very conscious of the 'sheer drive' on some of the numbers.

Ken himself plays in a more forthright manner than is typical of him (I always associate his playing with a sort of quiet intensity). When I bumped into Ian Wheeler a few months ago I asked him why he thought this was such a popular album: 'Perhaps, it's the tunes: there were some good tunes on it,' he replied. He's right of course. Ken doesn't give much away, but I have a sneaky feeling that out of the many albums he's made over the years he has a soft spot for this one, himself. (Paul Adams, 1987)

**Cass:** Released Dec '87, on Lake by Lake Records. Catalogue no: **LA 5006C**

**Album:** Released Aug '87, on Lake by Lake Records. Catalogue no: **LA 5006**

**GREAT REVIVAL, THE**

Tracks: / South / Yama yama blues / Shim me sha wabble / Big chief battle axe / Won't you come over to my house baby / Come back sweet papa / I'll walk through the streets of the city / Nobody knows you when you're ai / Bucket got a hole in it / Cielito Lindo.

**Album:** Released Jun '81, on Esquire by Titan Int. Prod.. Catalogue no: **ESQ 312**

**GUV'NOR 1959-1961, THE**

**CD:** Released 5 Jun '89, on Polydor by Polydor Ltd. Catalogue no: **830 782 2**

**HISTORIC RECORDINGS VOL 2 (Guvnor, The) (Colyer, Ken Skiffle Group & Jazzmen)**

Tracks: / How long blues / Streamline train / Poor Howard / Highway blues / This train / Sporting life / House rent stomp / Heebie jeebies / Tin roof blues / Red wing / Aunt Hager's blues / Maryland.

**Album:** Released Jun '88, on Ken Colyer Catalogue no: **KC 2**

**IN NEW ORLEANS 1953**

**Album:** Released May '79, on Dawn Club by Cadillac Music. Catalogue no: **DC 12025**

**KEN COLYER AND WHITE EAGLE NEW ORLEANS BAND (Colyer, Ken & White Eagle New Orleans Band)**

**Album:** on Wam Deleted May '87. Catalogue no: **WAM/O No.9**

**KEN COYLER AT THE THAMES HOTEL (Colyer, Ken Jazzmen)**

Tracks: / Milneburg joys / Lowlands blues / Trombonium / Short dress gal / Blue skies / Glory of love / Hindustan / Hiawatha rag.

**Album:** on Joy by President Records. Catalogue no: **JOY 170**

**LIVE 1953-54 (Dixie Gold) (Colyer, Ken Jazzmen)**

**Album:** Released Jan '90, on Limelight Catalogue no: **8208791**

**CD:** Released Jan '90, on Limelight Catalogue no: **8208792**

**LIVE AT THE 100 CLUB (Colyer, Ken Jazzmen)**

Note: Recorded in mono.

**Album:** Released Jun '86, on GHB by Jazzology Records (USA). Catalogue no: **GHB 161**

**Cass:** Released Oct '87, on VJM (Vintage Jazz Music) by Vintage Jazz Music Society(VJM). Catalogue no: **CC 17**

**LIVE AT THE DANCING SLIPPER (1969) (Colyer, Ken Jazzmen)**

Tracks: / Drop me off in Harlem / Teasin' rag / Sweet fields / High society / Barefoot boy / Get out of here / Harlem rag / Salutation march / Shoe shine boy / Peanut vendor / Birth of the blues / Home sweet home / Auf wiedersehen.

Note: Previously unissued material, now in LP form by special arrangement with Ken Colyer, Tony Pyke, Geoff Cole, Johnny Bastable, Malc Murphy, Bill Cole. Recorded at the Dancing Slipper Ballroom, Nottingham, in 1969.

In its heyday I used to enjoy Nottingham. It was a good jazz town and was more pleasant than Manchester or Liverpool. At one time there seemed to be more good clarinettists there than any other town and many's the night I've blown for hours with them after a session. Ken Allsop ran the Trent Bridge Hotel sessions. They had the worst beer I've ever tasted. Bill Kinnel ran "The dancing slipper". Bill and Ken were genuine promoters and kept going for many years. We played much fine music in both clubs. In the boom period of the later fifties and early sixties, clubs sprouted up everywhere and were continuously splitting the crowds. Now competition is a good thing, but when you have got a limited market it can be detrimental to the common good. Of course, the cowboys are never worried about this or whether they end up wrecking the scene, instead of building something of lasting worth and value. They, along with commercialisation, did a successful job of ruining what was my original and still is my intent: to have good, viable clubs to play in, and to nurture musicians and the music and improve the standard of jazz musicianship. The times I am told how much people love the music, yet they don't seem to put much effort into it. As Milton Mesirow said, you have to humble yourself and go cap-in-hand to the music. As Art Hodes did, you have to do more than woodshed - go and read his story.

You have to learn how to listen to and appreciate the music. Classical music lovers take the score with them to appreciate the interpretation and any variations. I have always said, on average, we will play a certain tune exceptionally well one time in six; sometimes the odds are longer, but one must always be aware of how well a tune can be played. A German musician recently said to me that he hated *St Louis Blues*. "Think of the Bunk Johnson version on 'American music'", I said, "and it will get better". Many things can get in the way of a good performance, often things out of the hands of the performers. The music is volatile and must be kept that way. It is full of paradoxes. No wonder a fellow called his record label "Paradox". The takes he issued of a session with Wooden Joe and Raymond Burke, seem to me to be worse than the other takes Raymond played me. Bill Kinnell was the first man to book the "Crane River Jazz Band", which I created and led, on our first out of town job. The band started working out of Cranford sooner than I really wanted but maybe it was just as well that it did. It changed the jazz scene, or one facet of it, and opened up another avenue of the music. Many musicians have joined me, for many reasons, other than the essential ones. I have never made a secret of my musical intentions throughout my life and have always accepted that they were common knowledge, this should have attracted the right men but not always so. Alan Gilmore used to handle the amplification at the Slipper and also taped many sessions. These tapes were forgotten until recently.

Except for the bandits who wax fat, it is a hazardous business investing money in an LP issue. The jazz lovers don't rush out and buy it. And you have no guarantee that it will sell enough to merit the issue. In the age of the cassette, copying and pirating have become intolerable. The cassette machine is a boon in some ways and a menace in others. This band was together for quite a long period and was a well-drilled professional group, with some degree of what I want in musicians. I consider my own playing satisfactory, in spite of the fact that my health was bad at the time, and I was receiving intensive radiotherapy after a malignancy. If you survived this, for years you felt that it would have been better to be dead. Here is a cross section of the tunes in the band's repertoire. Duke Ellington's music is difficult for a small band to play, and we come to the purist argument. I accept the confines of the idiom, but a band of high calibre should be able to stretch a little, and the Duke wrote so much beautiful music, and he had New Orleans' musicians in the orchestra. Any band has to have its sparking plugs. I know how *Drop me off at Harlem* should be played and this gets a little near it. Ballads need a slightly different approach that seems beyond some rhythm sections, as do the various ways of playing the blues. We really should have had a New Orleans school. I once said that that was our great disadvantage. When we started out we had to learn by trial and error. It is all there on the records but is not always easily grasped. The Bob Wilbur WildCats were coached by top men, Sidney Bechet, Pops Foster and others. But with talent and intense concentration, one can learn. Some people seem to think that I went to New Orleans in 1952 and by some magical process learnt the music in a couple of months. I did learn, and my playing and contribution to the music has been compared, by Emile Barnes, Willie Humphrey and George Lewis, to that of the legendary Chris Kelly and Buddy Petit. *The barefoot boy* - there are claims that it was composed by Bolden or Buddy Petit - shows a degree of complexity that belies the word primitive when it is used scathingly. Benny Green once said I was a primitive and I like to think he said it complementarily. Humph said I played "As if to the manner born". I like savage, primitive music, but I also like delicate beauty. New Orleans music encompasses it all and this is one of its great attractions. Ragtime needs a different approach and presents difficulties to free-wheeling musicians. The mental strain and the self-discipline can be painful. Many pianists and so-called ragtime orchestras fail dismally to grasp the essential elements of ragtime. They should go back and listen to the *London* LP AL3515 and start all over again. The Swingle Singers and their ragtime interpretations were like a breath of fresh air. This was an interesting period of the British jazz era. I can see no signs of any true revival, and the vultures would make sure it didn't do any good for the music anyway. So sit back and listen and get a whiff of the recent past. (Ken Colyer)

**Album:** Released Dec '84, on VJM (Vintage Jazz Music) by Vintage Jazz Music Society(VJM). Catalogue no: **LC 35**

## LONESOME ROAD (Decca years Vol. 5) (Colyer, Ken Jazzmen) (See panel on next page)

Tracks: / Beautiful doll / Over the rainbow / All of me / Pretty baby / Swanee river / Underneath the bamboo tree / Lonesome road / Bluebells / Goodbye Dinah / Curse of an aching heart, The.

Note: Recorded 19th June, 1958 at the Railway Hotel, Hampstead, England, except *Curse of an Aching Heart* which was recorded on 5th August, 1958 at the Decca Studios, London. These sides ought to be called *The original Colyer plays standards*. The story behind these tapes is quite fascinating even though in the end it is slightly disappointing to only have oné unissued 'tune'. But here I am jumping ahead. Since John Reddihough's brief biography of Ken in the 1960s there has been speculation as to unissued tracks from the session which produced *Colyer Plays Standards* (*Decca* LK 4294). Discographers Gerard Bielderman and Walter Bruyninck even found matrix numbers for some titles. It seems logical that there might be other material given that the session was a live one. *Decca* denied all knowledge of any unissued material. I also had doubts because I had always felt that *Colyer Plays Standards* was not a live session: the applause was obviously added on later. Having accepted from *Decca* that they did not have any unissued tracks I thought no more of it until I received a telephone call from John Griffith, banjoist and seasoned Colyer-watcher. He asked me if I had a copy of a budget LP, put out by *Decca* called *Sounds Trad* (MOR 12). It has three K.C. tracks on it from the *Standards LP*. The tracks have been 'enhanced' (a misnomer if ever there was one) into artificial stereo. Did this mean that *Decca* had stereo versions of the whole of the *Standards* set? If so why had they not used them all on the *Sounds Trad* LP instead of just one? These questions have still not been answered.

Futher investigation created a little more excitement because on listening to *Beautiful Doll* closely it was clear that it was not quite the same tak as on the *Standards* LP. Pushing the mono button revealed a different sound and the applause sounded as though it belonged. I concluded that this was a different session altogether. I put this to Decca and after a while I got a message that they had discovered a tape box marked Ken Colyer's Jazzmen Stereo. They sent me a cassette and I was surprised to find it contained all the Standards tunes minus *Curse of an Aching Heart* and plus *Lonesome Road*. It was clearly a different session, clearly live and the plot had thickened. Two recording sessions with Ken playing the same tunes is very un-Colyer like. When Ken went ot the South of France in 1987 due to illness, we kept up quite a prolific correspondence so I sent him a copy of the cassette and asked him for his thoughts and any light throwing he could do. He was unable to help and was also mystified. He felt the music was excellent. 'The material is worthy of issue, wonderful natural sound, best New Orleans band in the world. But I can't remember where or when they might have been done', he wrote. Ken was something of a Luddite regarding stereo although I suspect it has more to do with it coinciding with the Trad boom and Ken fighting recording engineers generally and I suspected that he might have rejected the session. I was still no further forward except that I had Ken's approval. Colin Bowden could not find the appropriate diary which

**Ken Colyer - Lonesome Road (Lake)**

was still no further forward except that I had Ken's approval. Colin Bowden could not find the appropriate diary which might have helped and Ian Wheeler could not remember.
In the meantime I had made contact with Ray Foxley and it was he who solved it all. 'The original session was done with a live audience at the Railway Hotel, West Hampstead' (as was *Club Session with Colyer* LA 5006). As far as Ray understood it was rejected by Decca engineers and not by Ken. 'My personal vague recollection was that it was a frenetic session anyway. The band had been there all afternoon and was a bit high by the evening and the audience got even higher and did a noisy singa-long'. From his diary, Ray established that this was 19th June, 1958. When he had heard these stereo tapes, Ray commented that they were much better than he expected. 'I can only imagine that the noisier bits were rejected - we did after all play a full evening so obviously we must have done a lot more numbers. I can't see why Decca didn't issue these'. They returned to Decca studios on 5th August, 1958 and re-cut the sides without an audience. Whether the full session exists somewhere in Decca's vaults remains a matter of conjecture. So what about these tapes? The most obvious thing is the beautiful stereo. It was early days for stereo in the U.K. and Decca made a superb job of these. (I would stick my neck out and say that no-one made as good stereo recordings of Ken's bands for almost another ten years.) There's a degree more tension and slight edginess in these sides compared with the studio versions. Here, though, is the greatest Colyer band, at its peak, free wheeling and well recoreded in live setting. Lovely stuff - play it loud.
My dilemma is what to do about the tapes which appeared as *Colyer Plays Standards* as far as this reissue project is concerned. As the quantities sold are small it would have been financial suicide to issue two LPs with the same tracks on them. As there was obviously a lot more interest value in these sides I have decided to do these only. *Curse of an Aching Heart* has been included from the studio set so that I have reissued the complete set of tunes (plus the bonus of *Lonesome Road*). You can also compare the sound between the two. This record is my tribute to Ken who died in March, 1988. For those of us who have had Ken around for all of our 'musical' lives we thought he was immortal. When the news broke my telephone never stopped ringing. People wanted to talk about Ken, to encourage me to continue to reissue the records and to gain information. Invariably they ended the conversation with 'I'm just going to open a bottle and put the records on'. A fitting tribute. The obituaries rolled in; all the major newspapers carried one and there was even a mention in Hansard. BBC Radio turned in a dreadful tribute on one programme which was redressed by a more intelligent one elsewhere on BBC Radio by Humphrey Lyttelton. Humph displayed much more understanding and obvious respect - musically they have both had to stand up for what they believed in. I got a little weary of comments in the press which said that 'Ken was not a great trumpet player'. How do they define great? From a technical point of view it is probably true, but we all know that music is more than mere technicalities.
The ability to play exciting music, the ability to rarely put a foot wrong in the ensemble, the ability to transform even mediocre bands, the ability to generate a loyal and devoted group of followers for forty years worldwide, the ability to totally absorb your chosen musical style and make it uniquely your own, the ability to gain the respect of fellow musicians even if they did not subscribe to your own style - these are the things greatness is made of. He was certainly not an easy person to deal with and sometimes his musical furrow was a true 'lonesome road', but I for one am grateful he ploughed it.
Since starting this project, I have become even closer to his music. I am sure, that he was one of the greatest jazz musicians of any style, any colour. As one other respected Englishman put it 'we shall not see his like again', but his music lives on in the legacy of records and the memories he left - this is just one classic example. (Paul Adams, 1988)
**Cass:** Released Nov '88, on Lake by Lake Records. Catalogue no: **LA 5010 C**
**Album:** Released Nov '88, on Lake by Lake Records. Catalogue no: **LA 5010**

## ONE FOR MY BABY (Colyer, Ken Jazzmen)

Tracks: / Royal Garden blues / High society / Drop me off in Harlem / Bogalousa strut / One for my baby / Stardust / Tiger rag.
**Album:** Released May '74, on Joy by President Records. Catalogue no: **JOY 140**

## OUT OF NOWHERE (Colyer, Ken Jazzmen)

Tracks: / Melancholy blues / Lady is a tramp, The / Indiana / Eccentric rag / There's yes yes in your eyes / Lily of the valley / Out of nowhere / Ole' miss rag / Darktown strutters ball.
Note: Originally issued 22 years ago. With Sam Rimington, Geoff Cole, John Bastable, Bryan Hetherington, Bill Cole, Richard Simmons.
**Album:** Released Jul '87, on Ken Colyer Catalogue no: **GNO 101**

## RAGTIME REVISITED (Colyer, Ken Jazzmen)

Tracks: / Cataract rag / Grace and beauty / Minstrel man / Pineapple rag / Chrysanthemum / Tuxedo rag / Joplin's sensation / Harlem rag / Heliotrope bouquet / Ragtime oriole / Fig leaf rag / Kinklets / Thriller rag.
**Album:** Released May '82, on Joy by President Records. Catalogue no: **JOY 194**

**RAREST KEN COYLER, THE**
**Album:** Released Apr '79, on Nola Catalogue no: **NOLA LP 15**

**SENSATION (Colyer, Ken Jazzmen)**
Tracks: / Dippermouth blues / Heliotrope bouquet / Beale Street blues / Fig leaf rag / Gravier Street blues / Canal St. Blues / World is waiting for the sunrise, The / Girls go crazy, The / Entertainer, The / If ever I cease to love / Sensation / Perdido street blues / Kinklets / Maryland my Maryland.
Note: There seems to be two ways of pursuing your chosen art form: either continually diversify and innovate or you stick doggedly to one aspect of it, perfecting, honing and moulding. Ken Colyer chose New Orleans Jazz, took the latter course and his progress has been well documented on the back of many LP sleeves. For devoted Colyer-Watchers there have been four significant front lines - the first with Chris Barber and Monty Sunshine; the third one with Mac Duncan and Ian Wheeler; the 1960's one with Geoff Cole and Sammy Rimmington; and the late 1960's-early 70's one of Geoff Cole and Tony Pyke. The tracks here selected from the *Decca* archives, feature the second of the above mentioned. By the time the last tracks here were recorded it had evolved into one of the best units Ken has ever fronted. Such comments are very subjective and coloured a little by nostalgia, but the evidence is in the plastic and this line up did produce the EP. *They All Played Ragtime* (*Decca* DFE 6466) widely regarded as one of Ken's most significant records and now very much a collector's item. None of these tracks has been issued together in this form before. They were originally a colection of singles and EP'S. The earliest recording here, dating from 19th April, 1955, were originally issued as a single and show the band still in the process of evolving following the split with Barber, Sunshine *et al.* This was the third line-up in two years, *The Entertainer* is a fairly straight foward reading of the tune (Ken was to record it nine years later on 77 LEU 12/10). This, and its partner, *If ever I cease to love,* was originally issued as a single and suffers from having been recorded in a rather 'boomy' acoustic. The original master of *The Entertainer* is also beginning to demonstrate its age, and the quality is not all that it should be, but it does not detract from the music. Incidentally, this season also produced two EP's entitled *And Back to New Orleans* (1 and 2) (*Decca* DFE 6268, DFE 6299). a year later they were back in the studio and Stan Greig had been replaced by the imitable Colin Bowden and the personnel was virtually settled. They were treated to a much better recording quality and produced four up tempo numbers, *Dippermouth Blues* and *The Girls Go Crazy*, come over extremely well with the former providing a real *tour de force* to open this album. Of the other two tracks from this session, *The World Is Waiting For The Sunrise* moves along very nicely, but *Maryland* is rather frentic and provides a somewhat 'abandoned' close to the album! (Ken recorded this tune again some eight years later, *Columbia* DB 4676).
Two albums *Ken Colyer Plays Standards* (*Decca* LK 4294) and the 10" *Ken Colyer In Hamburg* (*Decca* LF 16092), followed before the final tracks here appeared as an E.P, *Walking The Blues.* They are a rather dignified set of 'Street' blues from a band which, by now, had lost a lot of its earlier harshness and had a fine internal balance to it. Within a year Ken was to change record companies and his front line. In the interest of providing a balanced programme I have not presented the tracks in chronological order. They were recorded in the days when record companies wanted a playing time of 3+ minutes, so jazz bands felt themselves very restricted and it severely limited the possibilities of developing a theme. I have indulged in a little re-equalisation of the original recordings to make them compatible with each other. I think that these are significant recordings in the history of one man's music and the development of one band. As they have not been readily available in recent years it is a pleasure to be able to reissue them. I would like to extend my grateful thanks to the staff at *Decca* for their co-operation and assistance in bringing this project to fruition and to Ken himself for giving it his blessing. (Paul Adams 1985)
**Album:** Released May '85, on Lake by Lake Records. Catalogue no: **LA 5001**
**Cass:** Released Dec '87, on Lake by Lake Records. Catalogue no: **LA 5001C**

**SPIRITUALS VOL. 1 (Colyer, Ken Jazzmen)**
Tracks: / We shall walk through the streets of the city / Darkness on the Delta / It's nobody's fault but mine / My life will be sweeter someday / Were you there when they satisfied my soul / Sometimes my burden is so hard to bear / Old rugged cross, The.
**Album:** Released May '74, on Joy by President Records. Catalogue no: **JOY S 235**

**SPIRITUALS VOL. 2 (Colyer, Ken Jazzmen)**
Tracks: / Ghost soldier / Precious Lord / In the sweet bye and bye / Ain't you glad / Sing on / Just a closer walk with thee / Lead me saviour.
**Album:** Released May '74, on Joy by President Records. Catalogue no: **JOY S 236**

**SWINGING AND SINGING**
Tracks: / Darktown strutters' ball / Tishomingo blues / Shine / Going home to New Orleans / Celito lindo / Louisana I.A. / K.C. moon / Doctor Jazz / St. James infirmary.
Note: Ken Colyer - trumpet and vocals / John Wurr - clarinet / Len Baldwin - trombone / Ray Smith - piano / Annie Hawkins - bass / Bill Strotesbury - banjo / Paul Rosenberg - drums. Recorded November, 1975.
**Cass:** Released Jul '83, on Happy Bird (Germany) Catalogue no: **MB 90016**
**Album:** Released Jul '83, on Happy Bird (Germany) Catalogue no: **B 90016**

**TOO BUSY (1985 at Harlow)**
Tracks: / Tunes too busy / My old Kentucky home / Tishamingo blues / Down home rag / Old rugged cross, The / One sweet letter from you / Bogalusa strut / Snag it / Nobody's fault but mine / Home sweet home.
**Cass:** Released 10 Jul '89, on CMJ Catalogue no: **CMJMC 008**
**CD:** Released 10 Jul '89, on CMJ Catalogue no: **CMJCD 008**

**TUXEDO RAG (Colyer, Ken Jazzmen)**
Tracks: / Perdido street blues / Dippermouth Blues / Heliotrope bouquet / Beale Street blues / Fig leaf rag / Gravier Street blues / Canal street blues / World is waiting for the sunrise, The / Girls go crazy, The / Entertainer, The / If I ever cease to love / Sensation / Kinklets / Maryland, my Maryland.
**Album:** Released Dec '86, on Lake by Lake Records. Catalogue no: **LA 5004**
**Cass:** Released Dec '87, on Lake by Lake Records. Catalogue no: **LA 5004C**

**WATCH THAT DIRTY TONE OF YOURS (There are Ladies Present) (Colyer, Ken Jazzmen)**
Tracks: / Till then / One sweet letter from you / Arkansas blues / Poor butterfly / Bugle boy march / If you're a viper / Runnin' wild / My gal Sal / Black and blue / Swipsey cake walk.
**Album:** Released May '74, on Joy by President Records. Catalogue no: **JOY 164**

## Compact Jazz

**COMPACT JAZZ (Various artists)**
Note: Box set of 4 CD's featuring Art Blakey, Chet Baker, Anita O'Day, Memphis Slim.
**LP Set:** Released Jul '87, on IMS by Polydor Ltd. Catalogue no: **CD BOX 15**

## Compact Sound of Jazz

**COMPACT SOUND OF JAZZ (Various artists)**
Tracks: / Koko: *Various artists* / King Porter stomp: *Teagarden, Jack* / I hear music: *Connor, Chris* / Doggin' around: *Sims, John Haley 'Zoot'* / Just friends: *Adderley, Cannonball* / Lulu's back in town: *Torme, Mel* / Number four: *Gordon, Dexter* / Little girl blue: *Simone, Nina* / My one and only love / In a sentimental mood: *Webster, Ben* / Autumn leaves: *Evans, Bill* / For minors only: *Blakey, Art\Jazz Messengers* / Girl next door, The: *Montgomery, Wes* / Triple threat: *Kirk, Roland* / Powder keg: *Various artists* / Body and soul: *Coltrane, John* / Sophisticated lady: *Shepp, Archie.*
**CD:** Released Sep '87, on Charly by Charly Records. Catalogue no: **CDSAM 102**

## Company

**COMPANY VOL.1 (Various artists)**
**Album:** Released Nov '76, on Incus by Incus Records. Catalogue no: **INCUS 21**

**COMPANY VOL.2 (Various artists)**
**Album:** Released Nov '76, on Incus by Incus Records. Catalogue no: **INCUS 23**

**COMPANY VOL.5 (Various artists)**
**Album:** Released '78, on Incus by Incus Records. Catalogue no: **INCUS 28**

**COMPANY VOL.6 (Various artists)**
Note: Featuring: Lol Coxhill, Derek Bailey, Steve Beresford, M. Mengelberg, Evan Parker, Steve Lacey, Leo Smith.
**Album:** Released Oct '86, on Incus by Incus Records. Catalogue no: **INCUS 29**

**COMPANY VOL.7 (Various artists)**
Note: Featuring: Lol Coxhill, Tristan Honsinger, Martin V.R. Altena, Han Bennink.
**Album:** Released Oct '86, on Incus by Incus Records. Catalogue no: **INCUS 30**

**FICTIONS**
Note: Featuring: Lol Coxhill, Derek Bailey, Steve Beresford, M. Mengelberg.
**Album:** Released Oct '86, on Incus by Incus Records. Catalogue no: **INCUS 38**

## Concert Arban

**RAGTIME FROM SCOTT JOPLIN TO CLAUDE BOLLING**
**Album:** Released '85, on Arion by Arion Records (France). Catalogue no: **ARN 33786**
**Cass:** Released '85, on Arion by Arion Records (France). Catalogue no: **ARN 40.33786**

## Concert at Carnegie Hall

**CONCERT AT CARNEGIE HALL (Various artists)**
Tracks: / Lullaby of Birdland: *Ellington, Duke* / Hawk talks, The: *Ellington, Duke* / Tattooed bride, The: *Ellington, Duke* / Medley: *Ellington, Duke* / I'm beginning to see the light: *Ellington, Duke* / Night in Tunisia: *Ellington, Duke* / Strike up the band: *Getz, Stan* / Just friends: *Parker, Charlie* (With Charlie Parker.) / Easy to love: *Parker, Charlie* / Repetition: *Parker, Charlie* / Sentimental mood, A: *Ellington, Duke*.
**2 LP Set:** Released Dec '86, on Atlantis by Charly Records. Deleted '88. Catalogue no: **ATSD 2**
**Cass set:** Released Dec '86, on Atlantis by Charly Records. Catalogue no: **TCATSD 02**
**Cass:** Released Dec '86, on Atlantis by Charly Records. Catalogue no: **KATSD 2**

## Concord All Stars

**OW!**
Tracks: / Ow! / Fungi mama / My shining hour / I'll close my eyes / Why did I choose you / Blue hodge / I love being here with you / All blues / Down home blues.
Note: Musicians include Dan Barrett (trombone), Scott Hamilton (tenor sax), Red Holloway (alto sax), Warren Vache (cornet), Dave McKenna (piano), Ed Bickert (guitar), with singer Ernestine Anderson on three numbers. Recorded at the Concord Jazz Festival in Japan, 1987. Sleeve notes by Leonard Feather. (CD version has one extra track).
**CD:** Released Jul '88, on Concord Jazz by Concord Jazz Records (USA). Catalogue no: **CCD 348**
**Album:** Released Jul '88, on Concord Jazz by Concord Jazz Records (USA). Catalogue no: **CJ 348**
**Cass:** Released Jul '88, on Concord Jazz by Concord Jazz Records (USA). Catalogue no: **CJ 348 C**

**TAKE EIGHT**
Note: Musicians include Dan Barrett (trombone), Scott Hamilton (tenor sax), Red Holloway (alto sax), Warren Vache (cornet), Dave McKenna (piano), Ed Bickert (guitar). Recorded at the Concord Jazz Festival in Japan, 1987. Sleeve notes by Leonard Feather. (CD version has one extra track).
**Album:** Released Jul '88, on Concord Jazz by Concord Jazz Records (USA). Catalogue no: **CJ 347**
**CD:** Released Jul '88, on Concord Jazz by Concord Jazz Records (USA). Catalogue no: **CCD 4347**
**Cass:** Released Jul '88, on Concord Jazz by Concord Jazz Records (USA). Catalogue no: **CJ 347 C**

## Concord Jazz Guitar...

**CONCORD JAZZ GUITAR COLLECTION (Various artists)**
Tracks: / La petite mambo: *Various artists* / Isn't this a lovely place: *Various artists* / Dolphin dance: *Various artists* / Zigeuner: *Various artists* / Prelude to a kiss: *Various artists* / I'm on my way: *Various artists* / I can't get started: *Various artists* / Side track: *Various artists* / Georgia on my mind: *Various artists* / You don't know what love is: *Various artists* / Claire de Lune samba: *Various artists* / Seven come eleven: *Various artists* / When sunny gets blue: *Various artists* / Orange, brown and green: *Various artists* / Don't cry for me Argentina: *Various artists*.
**Album:** Released '81, on Concord Jazz by Concord Jazz Records (USA). Catalogue no: **CJ 160**
**CD:** Released Mar '90, on Concord Jazz by Concord Jazz Records (USA). Catalogue no: **CCD 4160**

## Concord Jazz All Stars

**CONCORD JAZZ ALL STARS (At the Northsea Festival, Vol. 2)**
Tracks: / Vignette / Emily / That's your red wagon / Sweet Lorraine / Can't we be friends? / Out of nowhere / Once in a while / In a mellow tone.
**Album:** Released '82, on Concord by Concord Jazz Records (USA). Catalogue no: **CJ 182**
**Album:** Released '83, on Concord Jazz by Concord Jazz Records (USA). Catalogue no: **CJ 205**
**Cass:** Released '83, on Concord Jazz by Concord Jazz Records (USA). Catalogue no: **CJC 205**

## Concord Sound

**CONCORD SOUND, THE (Various artists)**
**Album:** Released Nov '85, on Concord Jazz by Concord Jazz Records (USA). Catalogue no: **CJ 278**

## Concord Super Band

**CONCORD SUPER BAND IN TOKYO**
**Album:** Released '79, on Concord by Concord Jazz Records (USA). Catalogue no: **CJ 80**

## Condon, Eddie

**Biographical details:** A rhythm guitarist (1905-73), his name synonymous with tavern dixieland for tired businessmen, but also more than that: a tireless spark plug, organiser and proselytiser for jazz. He became famous along with the young white Chicagoans who invented a style in imitation of their black heroes in the late 1920s, was later a bandleader and often recorded for *Commodore*, the first independant jazz label, and was a club owner in New York. His *CBS* recordings from the '50s deserve re-issue. He was also the author of an autobiography, *We Call It Jazz*, in which he told the famous story of getting Fats Waller out of bed for a classic 1929 recording session; and the author of celebrated wisecracks: when French critic Hugues Panassie came to NYC to produce records, Condon said 'Do I tell him how to jump on a grape?' On the subject of Bop he said, 'We don't flatten our fifths, we drink 'em'. (Donald Clarke 1989) .

**1938 (Condon, Eddie & His Windy City Seven)**
Tracks: / Love is just around the corner / Beat to the shocks / Carnegie drag / Carnegie jump / Ja da / Embraceable you / Meet me tonight in dreamland / Diana / Serenade to a Shylock.
**Album:** Released Aug '82, on Commodore Class Catalogue no: **AG6 24054**

**AT THE JAZZ BAND BALL**
Tracks: / At the jazz band ball / Aunt Hagar's blues / There'll be some changes made / Somebody loves me / Improvisation for march of time / We called it music / She's funny that way / Impromptu ensemble no.1 / Nobody's sweetheart / Farewell blues / Down among the sheltering palms / Stars fell on Alabama / Nobody knows / Grace and beauty / Sheik of Araby, The / Friars point shuffle.
Note: Licensed from MCA Records. This compilation (P) 1986 Charly Records Ltd. (C) 1986 Charly Records Ltd.
**Album:** Released May '86, on Affinity by Charly Records. Deleted May '88. Catalogue no: **AFS 1021**

**CHICAGO STYLE**
Tracks: / Sugar / China boy / Nobody's sweetheart / Liza / There'll be some changes made / I've found a new baby / My baby came home / From Monday on

/ One step to heaven / Shimme-sha-wabble / Oh baby / Indiana / I'm sorry I made you cry / Makin' friends / I'm gonna stomp, Mr. Henry Lee / That's a serious thing / Tennessee twilight / Madame Dynamite / Eel, The / Home cooking.
Note: Mono. 1927 to 133 recordings.
**Album:** Released '85, on VJM (Vintage Jazz Music) by Vintage Jazz Music Society(VJM). Catalogue no: **VLP 55**

**CHICAGO STYLE RHYTHMAKERS**
**Album:** Released '74, on Jazz Archives (USA) by Jazz Archives Inc.(USA). Catalogue no: **JA 1**

**CHICAGO STYLED**
**Album:** Released '83, on Swaggie (Australia) Catalogue no: **S 1358**

**COMMODORE CLASSICS (Condon, Eddie & Fats Waller)**
**Album:** Released '83, on Commodore Class Catalogue no: **AG6 24095**

**CONDON CONCERT (Condon, Eddie & His All Stars)**
Note: All Stars include: Wild Bill/Cutty Cuttshall/Bob Wilber/Leonard Gaskin/George Wettling etc.
**Album:** Released Jun '86, on Jazzology (USA) by Jazzology Records (USA). Catalogue no: **J 10**

**EDDIE CONDON**
Tracks: / I must have that man / Time on my hands / Balling the jack / Sheik of Araby, The / Zaza / I've found a new baby / Jazz me blues.
Note: Artists: Max Kaminsky, Bobby Hackett, Hot Lips Page, Rex Stewart, Miff Mole, PeeWee Russell, Earnie Caceres, Gene Schroeder, Condon, John Kirby, Sonny Greer, Impromptu Ensemble, Kaminsky, Hackett Benny Morton, Joe Grauso, Willie the Lion Smith.
**Album:** Released '81, on Kings Of Jazz Catalogue no: **KLJ 20018**

**EDDIE CONDON BAND (1945) (Condon, Eddie Band)**
Tracks: / Sunday / How come you do me like you do / Every night / Keep smiling at trouble / That's a plenty / Sugar / Carnegie leap / September in the rain / Body and soul / Rose room / Monday date / How long has this been going on / Jazz band ball.
Note: Personnel: Featuring Earl Hines, George Wettling, Max Kaminsky, Ernie Caceres, Sid Weiss, Billy Butterfield, Tommy Dorsey, Lee Wiley, Muggsy Spanier. Recorded 6th January, 1945 and 13th January, 1945.
**Album:** Released '81, on Rarities Catalogue no: **RARITIES 37**

**EDDIE CONDON AND HIS JAZZ CONCERT ORCHESTRA (Condon, Eddie & His Orchestra)**
**Cass:** Released '82, on Jazz Bird Catalogue no: **ZCJAZ 2012**
**Album:** Released '82, on Jazz Bird Catalogue no: **JAZ 2012**

**EDDIE CONDON - VOLUME ONE (1938)**
Note: Condon's Windy Seven and jam sessions.
**Album:** Released May '87, on Commodore Class Catalogue no: **6.24054**
**CD:** Released May '87, on Commodore Class Catalogue no: **824 054**

**FLOORSHOW, VOL. 1**
Tracks: / Blues / Riverboat shuffle / Ja da / In a little Spanish town / Everything happens to me / Hotter than that / Look at me now / Fascinating rhythm / I got a crush on you / 'S wonderful / They can't take that away from me / Man I love, The / Embraceable you / I got rhythm / At the Jazz Band Ball / As time goes by / Running wild / I'm gonna sit right down and write myself a letter / My funny valentine.
**Album:** Released '88, on Queen Catalogue no: **QUEEN 030**
**Album:** Released '81, on Queendisc (Italy) Catalogue no: **QU 030**

**FLOORSHOW, VOL. 2**
Tracks: / Sheik of Araby, The / I've got a feeling I'm falling / Keepin' out of mischief now / Handful of keys / Squeeze me / Joint is jumpin', The / Stars fell on Alabama / Limehouse blues / Ain't misbehavin' / Seems like an old time / Ballin' the jack / Relaxin' at the Touro / But not for me / Muskrat ramble / Birth of the blues / Louisiana / New Orleans / High society / My old flame / Dixieland band.
**Album:** Released '88, on Queen Catalogue no: **QUEEN 031**
**Album:** Released Apr '81, on Queendisc (Italy) Catalogue no: **QU 031**

**GOOD BAND IS HARD TO FIND, A**
**Album:** Released May '87, on Commodore Class Catalogue no: **6.25526**

**GOOD YEARS OF JAZZ VOL. 4 (VIDEO)**
**VHS:** Released Feb '90, on Storyville by Storyville Records AB. Catalogue no: **SV3004**

**INTOXICATING DIXIELAND (1944-45) (Condon, Eddie & The Dorsey Brothers)**
Tracks: / My blue Heaven / Through a veil of indifference / After you've gone / Pee Wee original / Riverside blues / Wherever there's love / Impromptu ensemble / Honeysuckle rose / Baby won't you please come home? / China boy / Body and soul / I can't believe that you're in love with me / Royal Garden blues / Any old time.
Note: Musicians include Pee Wee Russell, Billy Butterfield, George Wettling, Lee Wiley, Sidney Bechet, Lou McGarity, Jess Stacy.
**Album:** Released Apr '81, on Rarities Catalogue no: **RARITIES 44**

**JAM SESSION (Condon, Eddie & Bobby Hackett)**
Tracks: / Oh baby / Wrap your troubles in dreams / Struttin' with some barbecue / On the sunny side of the street / My honey's loving arms / Fidgety feet.
**Album:** Released Oct '86, on Aircheck (USA) by Kiner Ents.(USA). Catalogue no: **AIRCHECK 28**

**JAZZ ON THE AIR - EDDIE CONDON (Various artists)**
Tracks: / Them there eyes: *Various artists* / Blues in my heart: *Various artists* / Riverboat shuffle: *Various artists.*
**CD:** Released Mar '88, on Delta (1) by Delta Records. Catalogue no: **20 803**

**LIEDERKRANZ SESSIONS, THE (Condon, Eddie & His Band)**
**Album:** Released May '87, on Commodore Class Catalogue no: **6.24295**

**SPIRIT OF CONDON,THE**
**Album:** Released Aug '79, on Jazzology (USA) by Jazzology Records (USA). Catalogue no: **J 73**

**TOWN HALL BROADCASTS (VOL. 1) (Condon, Eddie & His All Stars)**
Note: Recorded in mono.
**Album:** Released Jun '86, on Rhapsody by President Records. Catalogue no: **RHA 6028**

**TOWN HALL BROADCASTS VOL. 2**
Note: Rcorded in mono.
**Album:** Released Jun '86, on Rhapsody by President Records. Catalogue no: **RHA 6029**

**TOWN HALL CONCERTS (Condon, Eddie & Various artists)**
**2 LP Set:** Released Nov '88, on Jazzology (USA) by Jazzology Records (USA). Catalogue no: **JCE 1005/6**

**TOWNHALL CONCERTS VOL 2**
Note: With Bobby Hackett, James P Johnson and Gene Krupa.
**CD Set:** on Jazzology (USA) by Jazzology Records (USA). Catalogue no: **JCECD 1003/1004**
**2 LP Set:** Released Jun '88, on Jazzology (USA) by Jazzology Records (USA). Catalogue no: **JCE 1003/1004**

## Conners, Gene

**COPENHAGEN STEW (Conners, Gene 'Mighty Flea" (with Fessors Session Boys)**
**Album:** Released Jun '86, on Storyville by Storyville Records AB. Catalogue no: **SLP 436**

## Connick, Harry Jr

**20**
Tracks: / Avalon / Blue skies / Imagination / Do you know what it means to miss New Orleans / Basin Street blues / Lazy river / Please don't talk about me when I'm gone / Stars fell on Alabama / 'S wonderful / If I only had a brain / Do nothing till you hear from me.
**CD:** Released 20 Mar '89, on CBS by CBS Records. Catalogue no: **462996 2**
**Album:** Released 20 Mar '89, on CBS by CBS Records. Catalogue no: **462996 1**
**Cass:** Released 20 Mar '89, on CBS by CBS Records. Catalogue no: **462996 4**

**IT HAD TO BE YOU**
Tracks: / It had to be you / Love is here to stay / Imagination / If I only had a brain / Let's call the whole thing off / Do nothing 'til you hear from me / S'wonderful.
**12" Single:** Released Mar '90, on CBS by CBS Records. Catalogue no: **655 314 6**

**7" Single:** Released Mar '90, on CBS by CBS Records. Catalogue no: **655 314 7**
**CD Single:** Released Mar '90, on CBS by CBS Records. Catalogue no: **655 314 5**

**WHEN HARRY MEETS SALLY**
**Album:** Released Nov '89, on CBS by CBS Records. Catalogue no: **465 753 1**
**CD:** Released Nov '89, on CBS by CBS Records. Catalogue no: **465 753 2**
**Cass:** Released Nov '89, on CBS by CBS Records. Catalogue no: **465 753 4**

## Connor, Bob

**BOB CONNOR'S NEW YANKEE RHYTHM**
**Album:** Released '88, on Stomp Off (USA) Catalogue no: **SOS 1050**

**BOB CONNORS NEW YANKEE RHYTHM (Connor, Bob & Jimmy Mazzy)**
**Album:** Released '88, on Stomp Off (USA) Catalogue no: **SOS 1067**
**Album:** Released Mar '87, on Stomp Off (USA) Catalogue no: **SOS 1015**

## Connor, Chris

**Biographical details:** Jazz singer born in Kansas City in 1927. She sang with Claude Thornhill's vocal group the Snowflakes, went solo and joined Stan Kenton, establishing a reputation in the line of Kenton singers Anita O'Day and June Christy as a stylist in the cool school. She signed with *Bethlehem* in 1953, some albums including one with Carmen McRae now on *Affinity*. She recorded for *Atlantic* from the late '50s, then *ABC-Paramount* from '65; came back on *Progressive* in 1978 and has also recorded for *Stash* and *Contemporary*: her voice is as good as ever, interpretations maybe even better. (Donald Clarke 1989) .

**COOL CHRIS**
Tracks: / I hear music / Lullaby of Birdland / What is there to say / Come back to Sorrento / Why shouldn't I? / All about Ronnie / Try a little tenderness / Out of this world / Lush life / Cottage for sale / How long has this been going on / Stella by starlight / Gone with the wind / He's coming home / Goodbye.
**CD:** Released Jun '88, on Charly by Charly Records. Catalogue no: **CDCHARLY 115**

**I HEAR MUSIC (Connor, Chris & Carmen McRae)**
Tracks: / You made me care / Last time for love / Too much in love to care / Misery / Easy to love / If I'm lucky / Old devil moon / Tip toe gently / What is there to say? / Try a little tenderness / Lullaby of Birdland / Spring is here / Stella by starlight / Gone with the wind / Blame it on my youth / It's all right with me / Thrill is gone, The / I concentrate on you.
**Album:** Released '83, on Affinity by Charly Records. Catalogue no: **AFF 97**

**OUT OF THIS WORLD**
Tracks: / I hear music / All about Ronnie / Why shouldn't I / Come back to Sorrento / Out of this world / Cottage for sale / How long has this been going on / Goodbye / Lush life / He's coming home / Riding high / All dressed up with a broken heart / Trouble is a man / All this and heaven too / Someone to watch over me / In other words (fly me to the moon) / From this moment on.
**Album:** Released Jun '84, on Affinity by Charly Records. Catalogue no: **AFF 122**

**SWEET AND SWINGING**
Tracks: / Things are swinging / Any place I hang my hat is home / Just in time / Here's that rainy day / Out of this world / Sweetest sounds, The / Where flamingos fly / I've got you under my skin / I wish you love / I feel a song coming on / When Sunny gets blue.
**Album:** Released Aug '88, on Audiophile (USA) by Jazzology Records (USA). Catalogue no: **AP 208**
**Album:** Released Apr '81, on Progressive (USA) by Jazzology Records (USA). Catalogue no: **PRO 7028**

## Connors, Gene

**SANCTIFIED**
Tracks: / Marco's tune / Sanctified / Disconnected / Maha's tune / Good rockin' tonight / Goobers / Blueberry hill / Tunk for monk / It was a dream / Biscuits.
**Album:** Released Dec '81, on JSP by JSP Records. Catalogue no: **JSP 1031**

## Conti, Robert

**JAZZ QUINTET**
Note: All music composed by Robert Conti. Featuring Mike Wofford (piano), Herman Riley (saxes), John B.Williams (bass), Jim Plank (percussion), Llew Matthews (co-arranger).
**Album:** Released '88, on Discovery (USA) by Discovery Records (USA). Catalogue no: **DS 834**

**LATIN LOVE AFFAIR (Conti, Robert Jazz Quintet)**
Tracks: / Latin love affair / Midnight in Monte Carlo / Last time, The / Sunrise in Rio / Acapulco strut / Evening in Portugal.
**Album:** Released Jun '83, on Verydisc (Import) Catalogue no: **VDS 100**

**LAURA**
Tracks: / Softly as I leave you / You are the sunshine of my life / People / My favourite things / Like someone in love / Laura / His eyes, her eyes / Tenderly / When we met again / Hello young lovers / Stella by starlight / Little girl blue / Nuages / My romance.

Note: Includes the following medleys :I love you / Easy to love
**Album:** Released '88, on Trend (USA) by Trend Records (USA). Catalogue no: **TR 540**
**CD:** Released Sep '86, on Trend (USA) by Trend Records (USA). Catalogue no: **TRCD 540**
**Cass:** Released '88, on Trend (USA) by Trend Records (USA). Catalogue no: **TRC 540**

**SOLO GUITAR**
Tracks: / Time for love, A / My funny Valentine / Yesterday / Man and a woman, A / Feelings / I've grown accustomed to your world.
**Album:** Released '88, on Trend (USA) by Trend Records (USA). Catalogue no: **TR 519**

## Cook, Junior

**GOOD COOKIN'**
Tracks: / I'm getting sentimental over you / Play together again / Waltz for Junior / I waited for you / Mood.
**Album:** Released '81, on Muse by Black & Blue Records. Catalogue no: **MR 5159**

**PRESSURE COOKER**
**Album:** Released '81, on Affinity by Charly Records. Deleted '88. Catalogue no: **AFF 53**

**SOMETHIN'S COOKIN'**
**Album:** Released '82, on Muse by Black & Blue Records. Catalogue no: **MR 5218**

## Cool Heat

**COOL HEAT (Various artists)**
Tracks: / Garden party: *Mezzoforte* / Space princess: *Liston Smith, Lonnie* / Brazilian love affair: *Duke, George* / Jazz carnival: *Azymuth* / Funkin' for Jamaica: *Brown, Tom* / Invitations: *Shakatak* / Let's stay together: *M, Bobby* / I thought it was you: *Hancock, Herbie* / Stuff like that: *Jones, Quincy* / Birdland: *Weather Report* / Morning dance: *Spyro Gyra* / Sign of the times: *James, Bob* / Groove: *Franklin, Rodney* / Together again: *Clarke, Stanley* / Chinese way, The: *Level 42* / Stomp: *Brothers Johnson* / What's going on?: *Mason, Harvey* / Rockall: *Mezzoforte*.
**Cass:** Released '83, on K-Tel by K-Tel Records. Catalogue no: **CE 2231**
**Album:** Released '83, on K-Tel by K-Tel Records. Catalogue no: **NE 1231**

## Coon, Jackie

**JAZZIN' AROUND**
**Album:** Released Nov '88, on Sea Breeze Catalogue no: **SB 1009**

## Cooper, Al

**JUMP STEADY (Big Band Bounce & Boogie (Cooper, Al & His Savoy Sultans)**
Tracks: / Jump steady / Thing, The / Looney / Rhythm doctor man / Gettin' in the groove / Jeep's blues / Stitches / Jumpin' at the Savoy / We'd rather jump than swing / Draggin' my heart around / Little Sally Water / Jumpin' the blues / Frenzy / Sophisticated jump / Norfolk ferry / Second balcony jump.
**Album:** Released Sep '83, on Affinity by Charly Records. Catalogue no: **AFS 1009**

## Cooper, Bob

**Biographical details:** Jazz reedman (especially tenor sax) born in 1925 in Pittsburgh. He played with Stan Kenton

1945-51, married Kenton's vocalist June Christy; he played and recorded with Howard Rumsey's Lighthouse All-Stars, Kenton, Christy and many others well in to the sixties, including albums as a leader.
Like many other West Coast Jazzmen of that era he disappeared into studio work during lean years for jazz, especially valued for his oboe playing. He has recently re-emerged, playing as well as ever. His *Affinity* albums were originally made for Capitol in 1954-55.
(Donald Clarke 1989).

**GROUP ACTIVITY (Cooper, Bob Sextet & Bill Holman Octet)**
**Album:** Released Jul '81, on Affinity by Charly Records. Deleted '88. Catalogue no: **AFF 65**

**MUSIC OF MICHEL LEGRAND, THE (Cooper, Bob Quartet)**
**CD:** Released Jul '88, on Discovery (USA) by Discovery Records (USA). Catalogue no: **DSCD 935**

**PLAYS THE MUSIC OF MICHEL LEGRAND (Cooper, Bob & The Mike Wofford Trio)**
Tracks: / Watch what happens / What are you doing the rest of my life / His eyes / Discovery me / Where's the love.
**Album:** Released '88, on Discovery (USA) by Discovery Records (USA). Catalogue no: **DS 822**

**SHIFTING WINDS**
**Album:** Released Apr '81, on Affinity by Charly Records. Deleted '88. Catalogue no: **AFF 59**

**TENOR SAX JAZZ IMPRESSIONS**
Tracks: / We'll be together again / I've got the world on a string.

Note: Bob Cooper (tenor sax), Carl Schroeder (piano), Bob Magnusson (bass), Jimmie Smith (drums).

**Album:** Released '88, on Trend (USA) by Trend Records (USA). Catalogue no: **TR 518**
**CD:** Released Oct '87, on Trend (USA) by Trend Records (USA). Catalogue no: **TRCD 543**

## Cooper, Mike

**CONTINUOUS PREACHING BLUES, THE (Cooper, Mike & Ian Anderson)**
**Album:** Released Jul '85, on Appaloosa Catalogue no: **AP 037**

## Cooper, Thelma

**THELMA COOPER AND DAISY MAE AMD HER HEP CATS (Cooper, Thelma & Daisy Mae & Her Hep Cats)**
Tracks: / I need a man / Let's try again / Ooh daddy / Cute poppa / Talk to my baby / Down by the woodshed / Fanny Duncan (2 takes) / Lonesome playgirl / Want me a man / Stuff you got to watch / Woman trouble / Hop scotch / Frosty's groove.
**Album:** Released Jan '88, on Krazy Kat by Interstate Music. Catalogue no: **KK 822**

## Copeland, Johnny

**Biographical details:** Blues singer and guitarist born in 1937 in Louisiana.
He led local bands in Texas backing visiting stars, went to NYC in 1975 and became a local hero in Harlem.
Copeland Special was his debut album in 1977 (featuring 'Black Arthur' Blythe). He is an heir to the blues chair of T-Bone Walker and Freddy King. *Showdown!* with Robert Cray and Albert Collins made the Billboard charts in 1986.
(Donald Clarke 1989).

**AIN'T NOTHIN' BUT A PARTY (Live in Houston, Texas)**
**Album:** Released '88, on Rounder (USA) by Rounder Records (USA). Catalogue no: **ROUNDER 2055**
**Cass:** Released '88, on Rounder (USA) by Rounder Records (USA). Catalogue no: **ROUNDER 2055C**
**CD:** Released '88, on Rounder (USA) by Rounder Records (USA). Catalogue no: **CD 2055**

**BRINGIN' IT ALL BACK HOME**
Tracks: / Kasavubu / Jungle / Ngote / Djeli, djeli blues / Abidjan / Bozalimalamu / Same thing / Conakry.
**Cass:** Released '88, on Rounder (USA) by Rounder Records (USA). Catalogue no: **ROUNDER 2050C**
**Album:** Released '88, on Rounder (USA) by Rounder Records (USA). Catalogue no: **ROUNDER 2050**
**Album:** Released Feb '86, on Demon by Demon Records. Catalogue no: **FIEND 47**

**COPELAND COLLECTION, VOL. 1**
**Cass:** Released Jul '88, on Home Cooking (USA) by Flat Town Music Co.(USA). Catalogue no: **HCS 107 TC**
**Album:** Released Jul '88, on Home Cooking (USA) by Flat Town Music Co.(USA). Catalogue no: **HCS 107**

**COPELAND SPECIAL**
Tracks: / Claim jumper / I wish I was single / Everybody wants a piece of me / Copeland special / It's my own tears / Third party / Big time / Down on bended knee / Done got over it / St. Louis blues.
**Album:** Released May '82, on Demon by Demon Records. Catalogue no: **FIEND 3**
**Cass:** Released '88, on Rounder (USA) by Rounder Records (USA). Catalogue no: **ROUNDER 2025C**
**Album:** Released '88, on Rounder (USA) by Rounder Records (USA). Catalogue no: **ROUNDER 2025**

**DEDICATED TO THE GREATEST**
Tracks: / It's me / Love attack / I waited too long / Stealing / Mother Nature / Invitation / Wizard of art / Old man blues / Dear mother / Johnny Ace medley / No puppy love / Oh how I miss you.
**Album:** Released Apr '87, on Kent by Ace Records. Catalogue no: **KENT 067**

**DOWN ON BENDING KNEES**
Tracks: / Down on bended knees / There's a blessing / May the best man win / I got to go home / Coming to see about you / It's my own tears that's being wasted / I wish I was single / It's me / I'm going to make my home where........ / If love is your friend / You're gonna reap what you sow / Suffering city / Hurt hurt hurt / Old man blues / Love prayer.
**Album:** Released Feb '85, on Mr.R&B (Sweden) Catalogue no: **RB 1002**

**HOUSTON ROOTS**
Tracks: / Rock me baby take 1 / Late hours / I wish I was single / Hear what I said / Please let me know / Baby please don't go / I don't want nobody / Night time is the right time (part 1) / Night time is the right time (part 2) / I need you now / Heebie jeebies / All these things / Rock me baby take 2.
**Album:** Released Mar '88, on Ace by Ace Records. Catalogue no: **CHD 238**

**I'LL BE AROUND**
Tracks: / Rock & roll Lilly / Year round blues / It don't bother you / Mama told me / Heebie jeebies / Just one more time / Working man's blues / Funny feeling / I'll be around / Ain't nobody's business (but mine) / That's alright mama / Trying to reach my goal / Hear what I said / Ghetto child / Do better somewhere else / You must believe in yourself.
**Album:** Released Oct '84, on Mr.R&B (Sweden) Catalogue no: **RB 1001**

**MAKE MY HOME WHERE I HANG MY HAT**
Tracks: / Natural born believer / Make my home where I hang my hat / Devil's hand / Cold outside / Love Utopia / Boogie woogie nighthawk / Honky tonkin' / Well well baby-la / Old man blues / Rock 'n' roll Lilly.
**Cass:** Released '88, on Rounder (USA) by Rounder Records (USA). Catalogue no: **ROUNDER 2030C**
**Album:** Released Jan '87, on Rounder (USA) by Rounder Records (USA). Catalogue no: **ROUNDER 2030**
**Album:** Released Nov '82, on Demon by Demon Records. Catalogue no: **FIEND 4**

**TEXAS TWISTER**
Tracks: / Midnight fantasy / North Caroline / Don't stop by the creek son / Excuses / Jessanne / Hounston / When the rain starts fallin' / I de go now / Early in the morning / Twister / Idiom / Easy to love / Media / Morning coffee / Jelly roll / Where or when.
**Cass:** Released '88, on Rounder (USA) by Rounder Records (USA). Catalogue no: **ROUNDER 2040C**
**CD:** Released '88, on Rounder (USA) by Rounder Records (USA). Catalogue no: **CD 11504**
**Album:** Released '84, on Demon by Demon Records. Catalogue no: **FIEND 15**
**Album:** Released '88, on Rounder (USA) by Rounder Records (USA). Catalogue no: **ROUNDER 2040**

**WHEN THE RAIN STARTS FALLIN'**
**CD:** Released '88, on Rounder (USA) by Rounder Records (USA). Catalogue no: **CD 11515**

## Coppieters, Francis

**COLOURS IN JAZZ**
**Album:** Released Dec '87, on Intersound Catalogue no: **ISST 184**

## Copulatin' Blues

**COPULATIN' BLUES CD, THE (Various artists)**
**CD:** Released '88, on Jass Catalogue no: **JASSCD 1**

**COPULATIN' BLUES VOL. 1 (Various artists)**
Tracks: / Preachin' blues / Stavin' chain / Do your duty / New rubbin' on the darned old thing / Press my button (ring my bell) / Don't make me high / You stole my cherry / I need a little sugar in my bowl / Get off with me / My daddy rocks me / Keep your hands of my mojo / Winnin' boy / Shave 'em dry / Barbeque Bess / I'll keep sittin' on it if I can't sell it.
**Album:** Released Apr '81, on Stash (USA) Catalogue no: **ST 101**

**COPULATIN' BLUES VOL. 2 (Various artists)**
**Album:** Released May '84, on Stash (USA) Catalogue no: **ST 122**

## Copulatin' Rhythm

**COPULATIN' RHYTHM (Various artists)**
Note: 16 jazz and blues rarities. Lil Johnson, Memphis Minnie, Bo Carter, Ora Alexander.
**Album:** Released Jun '88, on Jass Catalogue no: **JASS 3**

**COPULATIN' RHYTHM VOL.2 (Various artists)**
Note: Includes Georgia White, Hokum Boys, Blind Boy Fuller, Roosevelt Sykes. More jazz and blues rarities
**Album:** Released Jun '88, on Jass Catalogue no: **JASS 5**

## Corea, Chick

**Biographical details:** A jazz-rock fusion keyboardist and composer. He recorded as a sideman in the '60s with Herbie Mann, Hubert Laws, Blue Mitchell, Mongo Santamaria and others; he joined Miles Davis in 1968, playing electric and accoustic piano on *In A Silent Way* and *Bitches Brew* and other albums, then formed Circle with Dave Holland and Barry Altschul, later another group called *Return To Forever* which had six albums reach the Billboard pop album chart in the '70s, three in the top 40. He has also recorded Mozart's Concerto for two pianos and orchestra and his own piano concerto was premiered in 1986. His latest group in 1986 was a trio called the Elektric Band with bassist John Patitucci, drummer Dave Weckl and an assortment of Yamaha and Synclavier electronics. He has also accompanied his wife, vocalist Gayle Moran. (Donald Clarke 1989).

**AGAIN AND AGAIN (The Jo'burg Session)**
Tracks: / No.3 / Waltz / Again & again / 1 - 2 - 1234 / Diddle diddle / Twang.
**CD:** Released Jun '84, on Elektra by Elektra Records (UK). Catalogue no: **960 167-2**
**Album:** Released Feb '83, on Elektra (Musician) by Elektra Records (USA). Catalogue no: **E 0167**

**AKOUSTIC BAND, THE**
Tracks: / Autumn leaves / So in love / Morning sprite / Circles / Spain.
Note: From out of the highly successful Chick Corea Elektric Band comes the Akoustic Band. A cohesive tightly knit ensemble with enough open space to give Corea, Patitucci and Weckl the freewheeling room to be on their own.
**Album:** Released Feb '89, on GRP by GRP Records (USA). Catalogue no: **GRP 95821**
**Cass:** Released Feb '89, on GRP by GRP Records (USA). Catalogue no: **GRP 95824**
**CD:** Released Feb '89, on GRP by GRP Records (USA). Catalogue no: **GRP 95822**

**A.R.C. (Corea, Chick & Holland & Altschul)**
Tracks: / Nefertitti / Ballad for Tillie / A.R.C. / Vedana / Thanatos / Games.
**CD:** Released Mar '88, on ECM Catalogue no: **833 678 2**
**Album:** Released Jul '87, on ECM Catalogue no: **ECM 1009**

**BLISS**
Tracks: / Turkish woman at the baths / Dancing girls / Love planet / Marjoun / Bliss / Sin street / And so.
**Album:** Released '88, on Masters (Holland) Catalogue no: **MA 99058**
**Album:** Released Apr '81, on Muse by Black & Blue Records. Catalogue no: **MR 5011**

**CHICK COREA (Compact Walkman Jazz)**
Tracks: / Captain Marvel / Captain Senor Mouse / Armando's Rhumba / 500 Miles High / Love Castle / Vulcan worlds / No Mystery / Spain.
**Cass:** Released Jun '86, on Polydor by Polydor Ltd. Catalogue no: **831 365 4**
**CD:** Released Jun '86, on Polydor by Polydor Ltd. Catalogue no: **831 365 2**

**CHICK COREA IN CONCERT (Corea, Chick & Gary Burton)**
Tracks: / Senor Mouse / Bud Powell / Crystal silence / Tweak / Falling grace / Mirror mirror / Song to Gayle / Endless trouble, endless pleasure.
**CD:** Released '84, on ECM Catalogue no: **821 415-2**

**CHILDREN'S SONGS**
**Album:** Released Apr '84, on ECM Catalogue no: **ECM 1267**
**CD:** Released Apr '84, on ECM Catalogue no: **815 680 2**

**COREA, HANCOCK AND JARRET (Corea, Chick/Herbie Hancock/Keith Jarret)**
**CD:** Released '88, on Atlantic Jazz by WEA Records. Catalogue no: **K78 140 22**

**DELPHI, VOL. 1**
Tracks: / Delphi 1-8 / Children's song No. 20 / Stride time 1-7.
**Album:** Released '79, on Polydor by Polydor Ltd. Deleted '84. Catalogue no: **2490150**

**EARLY DAYS**
Tracks: / Brain, The / Converge / Waltz for Bill Evans / Sundance / Dave / Vamp, The / Jamala.
Note: Personnel: Chick Corea (piano), Woody Shaw (trumpet), Hubert Laws (flute / Piccolo), Bennie Maupin (tenor sax), Dave Holland (bass), Horace Arnold (drums), Jack De Johnette (drums).
**Cass:** Released Apr '89, on Denon Catalogue no: **MC 7969**
**CD:** Released Apr '89, on Denon Catalogue no: **DC 8541**
**CD:** Released '88, on Denon Catalogue no: **C38-7969**

**ELEKTRIC BAND, THE**
Tracks: / Rumble / Side walk / Cool weasel boogie / Got a match / Elektrik city / No zone / King cockroach / India town.
**Cass:** Released 1 Mar '86, on GRP by GRP Records (USA). Catalogue no: **GRPM 91026**
**Album:** Released Apr '86, on GRP by GRP Records (USA). Catalogue no: **GRP 91026**
**CD:** Released Apr '86, on GRP by GRP Records (USA). Catalogue no: **GRD 9535**
**CD:** Released '88, on GRP by GRP Records (USA). Catalogue no: **GRPD 9535**

**EYE OF THE BEHOLDER (Corea, Chick Elektric Band)**
Tracks: / Home Universe / Eternal child / Passage / Beauty / Cascade Part 1 & 2 / Trance dance / Eye of the beholder.
**CD:** Released Jul '88, on GRP by GRP Records (USA). Catalogue no: **GRD 91053**
**Cass:** Released Jul '88, on GRP by GRP Records (USA). Catalogue no: **GRPM 91053**
**CD:** Released Nov '88, on GRP by GRP Records (USA). Catalogue no: **GRD 9564**
**Album:** Released Jul '88, on GRP by GRP Records (USA). Catalogue no: **GRP 91053**

**FEMME FATALE (Corea, Chick & Garbor Szabo)**
Tracks: / Femme fatale / Xingaro / Sarena / Thousand times / Out of the night.
**Album:** Released Aug '82, on Hungaroton (Hungary) Deleted Jan '88. Catalogue no: **SLPR 707**

**FIESTA**
Tracks: / Sea journey / Moment's notice / Fiesta / I ain't mad at you / Come rain or come shine.
**Album:** Released Oct '82, on IMS by Polydor Ltd. Catalogue no: **B 90061**

**INNER SPACE**
Tracks: / Straight up and down / This is new / Tones for Joan's bones / Litha / Inner space / Windows / Guijira / Trio for flute, bassoon and piano.
**Album:** Released Sep '74, on Atlantic

by WEA Records. Catalogue no: **K 60081**

**INSIDE OUT (Corea, Chick Elektric Band)**
Tracks: / Inside out / Make a wish (part 1) / Make a wish (part 2) / Stretch it (part 1) / Stretch it (part 2) / Kicker / Childs play / Tale of daring (chapter 1) / Tale of daring (chapter 2) / Tale of daring (chapter 3) / Tale of daring (chapter 4).
**Album:** Released Feb '90, on GRP by GRP Records (USA). Catalogue no: **GRP 96011**
**CD:** Released Feb '90, on GRP by GRP Records (USA). Catalogue no: **GRP 96012**
**Cass:** Released Feb '90, on GRP by GRP Records (USA). Catalogue no: **GRP 96014**

**LIGHT AS A FEATHER**
Tracks: / You're everything / Light as a feather / Captain Marvel / 500 miles high / Children's song / Spain.
**CD:** on ECM Catalogue no: **827 148-2**
**Album:** Released Sep '81, on Polydor by Polydor Ltd. Deleted Sep '86. Catalogue no: **MID 1006**
**Album:** Released Jul '81, on Polydor by Polydor Ltd. Deleted '86. Catalogue no: **2482497**

**LIGHT YEARS**
**DAT:** Released Jul '88, on GRP by GRP Records (USA). Catalogue no: **GRT 9546**
**CD:** Released May '87, on GRP by GRP Records (USA). Catalogue no: **GRD 9546**
**Cass:** Released May '87, on GRP by GRP Records (USA). Catalogue no: **GRPM 91036**
**Album:** Released May '87, on GRP by GRP Records (USA). Catalogue no: **GRP 91036**

**LIVE AT MIDEM, 1978 (Corea, Chick & Lionel Hampton)**
Tracks: / Sea breeze / Moment's notice / Come rain or come shine / Fiesta piano solo / I ain't mad at you.
**Album:** Released Sep '83, on Kingdom Jazz by Kingdom Records. Catalogue no: **GATE 7005**
**Cass:** Released '89, on Kingdom Jazz by Kingdom Records. Catalogue no: **CGATE 7005**

**LIVE IN MADRID**
Note: Running time: 54 mins.
**VHS:** Released '87, on Channel 5 by Channel 5 Video. Catalogue no: **CFV 06922**

**LYRIC SUITE FOR SEXTET (Corea, Chick & Gary Burton)**
Tracks: / Overture / Waltz / Sketch / Rollercoaster / Brasilia / Dream / Finale.
**Album:** Released Oct '83, on ECM Catalogue no: **ECM 1260**

**MIRROR MIRROR (Corea, Chick and Joe Henderson)**
**Album:** Released May '81, on MPS Jazz Catalogue no: **MPS 68 255**

**MY SPANISH HEART**
Tracks: / Love castle / Gardens, The / Day danse / My Spanish heart / Night streets / Hilltop, The / Sky, The - parts 1 & 2 / Wind danse / Armando's rhumba / Prelude to El Bozo - parts 1-3 / Spanish fantasy (parts 1-4).
**Album:** Released Feb '77, on Polydor by Polydor Ltd. Catalogue no: **2672 031**
**CD:** Released Feb '77, on Polydor by Polydor Ltd. Deleted Mar '88. Catalogue no: **825 657-2**

**NO MYSTERY**
**CD:** on Polydor by Polydor Ltd. Deleted Mar '88. Catalogue no: **827 149-2**

**NOW HE SINGS, NOW HE SOBS**
Tracks: / Matrix / My one and only love (CD only.) / Now he beats the drum now he stops / Bossa (CD only.) / Now he sings, now he sobs / Steps - what was / Fragments (CD only.) / Windows (CD only.) / Pannonica (CD only.) / Samba yantra (CD only.) / I don't know (CD only.) / Law of falling and catching up, The / Gemini (CD only.).
**CD:** Released Nov '88, on Blue Note by EMI Records. Catalogue no: **BNZ 107**
**CD:** Released Nov '88, on Blue Note by EMI Records. Catalogue no: **CDP 790 055 2**
**Album:** Released Aug '89, on Blue Note by EMI Records. Catalogue no: **B1 90055**

**PIANO IMPROVISATIONS**
Tracks: / Noon Song / Song for Sally / Ballad for Anna / Song of the wind / Sometime ago / Where are you now?.
**CD:** on ECM Catalogue no: **811 979-2**

**PIANO IMPROVISATION VOL. 2**
**CD:** on ECM Catalogue no: **829 190-2**

**RETURN TO FOREVER**
Tracks: / Return to forever / Crystal silence / What game shall we play today / Sometime ago - la fiesta.
Note: Recorded 1972.
**CD:** Released Mar '88, on ECM Catalogue no: **8119782**
**Cass:** Released Jun '84, on ECM Catalogue no: **310 1022**

**SEA JOURNEY**
**Album:** Released Oct '85, on Platinum (W.Germany) Catalogue no: **PLP 31**
**Cass:** Released Oct '85, on Platinum (W.Germany) Catalogue no: **PMC 31**

**SECRET AGENT**
Tracks: / Golden dawn / Slinky / Mirage / Drifting / Glebe Street blues / Fickle funk / Bagatelle No.4 / Hot news blues / Central Park.
**Album:** Released Jan '79, on Polydor by Polydor Ltd. Catalogue no: **2391 381**

**SEPTET**
Tracks: / 1st movement / 2nd movement / 3rd movement / 4th movement / 5th Movement / Temple of Isfahan, The.
**CD:** on ECM Catalogue no: **827 258-2**
**Album:** Released Dec '85, on ECM Catalogue no: **ECM 1297**

**SONG OF SINGING**
Tracks: / Toy room / Ballad I. / Rhymes / Flesh / Ballad III / Nefertiti.
**CD:** Released Jul '89, on Blue Note by EMI Records. Deleted Jun '89. Catalogue no: **BNZ 22**
**CD:** Released Jul '89, on Blue Note by EMI Records. Deleted Jun '89. Catalogue no: **CDP 746 401 2**
**Album:** Released Apr '85, on Blue Note by EMI Records. Deleted Jan '88. Catalogue no: **BST 84353**

**TAP STEP**
Tracks: / Samba L.A. / Embrace, The / Tap step / Magic carpet / Slide, The / Grandpa blues / Flamenco.
**Album:** on Warner Bros. by WEA Records. Catalogue no: **K 56801**

**THREE QUARTETS**
Tracks: / Quartet No.1 / Quartet No.2 / Quartet No.3.
**Album:** on Warner Bros. by WEA Records. Catalogue no: **K 56908**

**TONES FOR JOAN'S BONES**
Tracks: / Litha / This is new / Tones for Joan's Bones / Straight up and down.
**Album:** Released '88, on Atlantic by WEA Records. Catalogue no: **K 50302**

**TRIO MUSIC**
Tracks: / Trio improvisations 1,2,3 / Duet improvisation 1,2,4,5 / Slippery when wet / Rhythm-a-ning / Round midnight / Eronel / Think of one / Little Rootie Tootie. / Reflections / Hackensack / Music of Thelonious Monk.
**CD Set:** Released May '87, on ECM Catalogue no: **827 702-2**
**2 LP Set:** Released Oct '82, on ECM Catalogue no: **ECM 1232/33**

**TRIO MUSIC LIVE IN EUROPE**
Tracks: / Loop / I hear a rhapsody / Night and day / Summer night / Prelude no 2 / Mock up / Hittin it / Microvisions.
Note: Recorded during their 1984 European tour. The compact disc contains an extra track which is a bass solo by Miroslav Vitous. Recorded in September, 1984. Personnel: Chick Corea (piano), Miroslav Vitous (bass), Roy Haynes (drums).
**CD:** Released Dec '86, on ECM Catalogue no: **827 769-2**
**Album:** Released Dec '86, on ECM Catalogue no: **ECM 1310**

**VOYAGE**
Tracks: / Mallorca / Diversions / Star Island / Free fall / Hong Kong.
Note: Voyage is the first duet recording of pianist Corea and flautist Steve Kujala.
**CD:** on ECM Catalogue no: **823 468-2**
**Album:** Released Mar '85, on ECM Catalogue no: **ECM 1282**

**WHERE HAVE I KNOWN YOU BEFORE?**
Tracks: / Beyond the seventh galaxy / Earth juice / Shadow of Lo, The / Song to the pharoah kings / Vulcan worlds / Where have I danced with you before / Where have I known you before / Where have I loved you before.
**Album:** Released Sep '81, on Polydor by Polydor Ltd. Deleted Sep '86. Catalogue no: **MID 1005**
**CD:** Released Jun '81, on Polydor by Polydor Ltd. Deleted Mar '88. Catalogue no: **825 206-2**

**Album:** Released Jun '81, on Polydor by Polydor Ltd. Deleted '86. Catalogue no: **2482 502**

**WORKS: CHICK COREA**
Tracks: / Where are you now / Noon song / Children's song / Brasilia / Slippery when wet / Duet improvisation / New place, A / La Fiesta / Return to forever / Song of the wind / Round midnight / Rhythm-a-ning / Senor mouse / Sometime ago / Addendum.

Note: Personnel: Chick Corea, Gary Burton, Miroslav Vitous, Roy Haynes, Joe Farrell, Stanley Clarke, Airto Moreira, Flora Purim.
**Album:** Released Jun '89, on ECM Catalogue no: **825 426-1**
**CD:** Released Jun '89, on ECM Catalogue no: **825 426-2**
**Cass:** Released Nov '83, on ECM Catalogue no: **3100 392**

**ZURICH CONCERT (Corea, Chick & Gary Burton)**
**2 LP Set:** Released Nov '80, on ECM Catalogue no: **ECM 1182**

## Corvini, Alberti

**FIREWORKS (Corvini, Alberti Jazz Big Band)**
**Album:** Released Jun '89, on Fonitcetra Catalogue no: **IJC 004**

## Coryell, Larry

**Biographical details:** Jazz-fusion guitarist, born in 1943 in Texas, described in the 1960s in *Down Beat* as 'perhaps the most original guitarist around'.
He grew up in Washington state and went to NYC in 1965.
He worked with Chico Hamilton, in the fusion band Free Spirits, toured and recorded with Gary Burton 1967-8 and began recording on *Vanguard* as a leader (on *PRT* in UK). His guitar duet records include *Together* with Emily Remler, who soon made her own debut as a leader. He has also recorded transcriptions of classical pieces for guitar. (Donald Clarke 1989).

**ASPECTS**
Tracks: / Kowloon jag / Titus / Pyramids / Rodrigo reflections / Yin-yang / Woman of truth and future.
**Album:** Released Jul '76, on Arista by BMG Records (UK). Catalogue no: **ARTY 133**

**AT VILLAGE GATE**
**Album:** Released '77, on Vanguard by Start Records Ltd.. Catalogue no: **VSD 6573**

**BACK TOGETHER (Coryell, Larry & A. Mouzon)**
Tracks: / Beneath the earth / Express / Back together again / Phonse, The / Transvested express / Crystallization / Rock 'n' roll lovers / Get on up / Reconciliation / Mr. C / High love.
**Album:** Released Aug '77, on Warner Bros. by WEA Records. Catalogue no: **K 50382**

**BAREFOOT BOY**

Larry Coryell

**Album:** Released Dec '84, on RCA (Germany) Catalogue no: **CL 13961**

**BOLERO (Coryell, Larry & Brian Keane)**
**CD:** on Black & Blue (1) by Black & Blue Records. Catalogue no: **233 850**

**BOLERO AND SCHEHERAZADE**
**CD:** on Philips by Phonogram Ltd. Catalogue no: **810 024-2**

**COMING HOME**
Tracks: / Good citizen swallow / Glorielle / Twelve and twelve / Confirmation / It never entered my mind.
**CD:** on Muse by Black & Blue Records. Catalogue no: **MCD 5303**
**Album:** Released Jan '86, on Muse by Black & Blue Records. Catalogue no: **MR 5303**

**EQUIPOISE**
Tracks: / Unemployed Floyd / Tender tears / Equipoise / Christina / Joy Spring / First Things First.
**CD:** Released Feb '87, on Muse by Black & Blue Records. Catalogue no: **MCD 5319**
**Album:** Released Feb '87, on Muse by Black & Blue Records. Catalogue no: **MR 5319**

**FIREBIRD AND PETROUCHKA**
**Album:** Released '84, on Philips (Holland) by PolyGram UK Ltd. Catalogue no: **8128 641**
**CD:** Released '84, on Philips (Holland) by PolyGram UK Ltd. Catalogue no: **812 864 2**

**INTRODUCING 11TH HOUSE**
**Album:** Released Jun '74, on Vanguard by Start Records Ltd.. Catalogue no: **VSD 79342**

**JUST LIKE BEING BORN (Coryell, Larry & Brian Keane)**
**Album:** Released Mar '89, on Flying Fish (USA) by Flying Fish Records (USA). Catalogue no: **FF 337**

**LE SACRE DU PRINTEMPS**
**CD:** on Philips by Phonogram Ltd. Catalogue no: **814 750 2**

**LEVEL ONE**
Tracks: / Other side, The / Level one / Diedra / Some greasy stuff / Nyctaphobia / Suite.
**Album:** Released '76, on Arista by BMG Records (UK). Catalogue no: **ARTY 113**

**L' OISEAU DE FEU**
**CD:** on Philips by Phonogram Ltd. Catalogue no: **812 864-2**

**PLANET END**
**Album:** Released '76, on Vanguard by Start Records Ltd.. Catalogue no: **VSD 79367**

**QUIET DAY IN SPRING, A (Coryell, Larry and Urbaniak, M)**
**CD:** Released '88, on Steeplechase (USA) Catalogue no: **SCCD 311 87**

**RESTFUL MIND, THE**
Tracks: / Improvisation on Robert De Visee's Minuet II / Ann Arbor / Pavane for a dead princess / Improvisation on Robert De Visee's Sarabande / Song for Jim Webb / Julie La Belle / Restful mind, The.
**Album:** Released '75, on Vanguard by Start Records Ltd.. Catalogue no: **VSD**

79353

**RETURN**
Tracks: / Cisco at the disco / Rue Gregoire du Tour / Three mile island / Return / Sweet shuffle / Mediterranean sundance / Entre dos Aguas.
**Album:** Released Jan '80, on Vanguard by Start Records Ltd.. Deleted Jan '85. Catalogue no: **VSD 79426**

**SPACES**
Tracks: / Spaces / Rene's theme / Gloria's step / Wrong is right / Chris / New year's day in Los Angeles-1968.
**Album:** Released Aug '89, on Start by Start Records Ltd.. Catalogue no: **VMLP 5305**
**Album:** Released '74, on Vanguard by Start Records Ltd.. Catalogue no: **VSD 79345**
**Cass:** Released Aug '89, on Start by Start Records Ltd.. Catalogue no: **VMTC 6305**
**CD:** Released Aug '89, on Start by Start Records Ltd.. Catalogue no: **VMCD 7305**

**SPLENDID (Coryell, Larry & Philip Catherine)**
Tracks: / One plus two blues / Snowshadows / Transvested express / Deus Xango / My serenade / No more booze / Father Christmas / Quiet day in Spring, A / Train and the river, The.
**Album:** Released '78, on Elektra by Elektra Records (UK). Catalogue no: **K 52086**

**STANDING OVATION**
**Album:** Released May '81, on Arista by BMG Records (UK). Deleted '86. Catalogue no: **AN 3024**

**TOGETHER (Coryell, Larry & Emily Remler)**
Tracks: / Arabian nights / Joy spring / Ill wind / How my heart sings / Six beats, six strings / Gerri's blues / First things first.
**CD:** Released Nov '86, on Concord Jazz by Concord Jazz Records (USA). Catalogue no: **CCD 4289**

**TRIBUTARIES**
Tracks: / File, The / Mother's day / Little B's poem / Zimbabwe / Solo on Wednesday / Thurman Munson / Equinox / Alster fields.
**Album:** Released Apr '90, on RCA by BMG Records (UK). Catalogue no: **NL 83072**
**Cass:** Released Apr '90, on RCA by BMG Records (UK). Catalogue no: **NK 83072**
**CD:** Released Apr '90, on RCA by BMG Records (UK). Catalogue no: **ND 83072**

## Costa, Don

**NEVER ON SUNDAY**
Tracks: / Never on Sunday.
**7" Single:** Released Oct '60, on London-American Deleted Oct '63. Catalogue no: **HLT 9195**

## Costa, Eddie

**EDDIE COSTA-VINNIE BURKE TRIO (Costa, Eddie & Vinnie Burke)**
**Album:** Released Feb '88, on Fresh Sounds (Spain) by Fresh Sounds Records (Spain). Catalogue no: **FS 129**

## Cotton, Billy

**Biographical details:** Cotton, Billy This British bandleader and singer, born in 1899, got his first big break in showbusiness when he played at the Regent, Brighton in 1924. His career blossomed in the late Twenties; during and after the 1939-45 war, he cemented his position as one of Britain's best known and best loved musical personalities, and became a radio and television regular. His signature tune was *Somebody Stole My Gal* and this remained his band's most famous number. Because the British record charts did not begin until 1952, Cotton's disc sales are not fairly reflected by his chart track record. His first charted disc on the newly inaugurated listings was *In A Golden Coach* which was timed to celebrate the Queen's coronation in the summer of '53, and reached No.3. *I Saw Mommy Kissing Santa Claus* took him to No.11 that Christmas and, the following year, he hit No.3 with *Friends and Neighbours*.
Accompanied by his famous band and a variety of vocalists, Cotton remained a national institution until his death in 1968 at the age of 69. His son Bill Cotton kept the family name in the public eye by enjoying a high flying career as a top BBC executive, most notably for his period in charge of light entertainment on television. (Bob Macdonald 4/2/85)

**BILLY COTTON (Cotton, Billy & His Band)**
Tracks: / New tiger rag / Why did she fall for the leader of the band? / Dancing with my shadow / Bessie couldn't help it / Tattooed lady, The / St. Louis blues / What a difference a day made / Avalon / Nobody loves a fairy when she's forty / Hyde Park Corner / Truckin' / They all start whistling Mary / After you've gone / She was only somebody's daughter / I'll never say "never again" again.
**Album:** Released '71, on Retrospect by EMI Records. Catalogue no: **SH 141**

**CRAZY WEATHER (Cotton, Billy & His Band)**
Tracks: / Crazy weather / Isle of Capri / Why am I blue? / Margie / Lazybones / Annie doesn't live here any more / St. Louis blues / Two cigarettes in the dark / Judy / Hold me / I was in the mood / Man from Harlem, The / Ole faithful / Oh mother, mother (please speak to Willie) / Third tiger, The (tiger rag no.3) / Hand in hand (we go together) / Down a long, long road / Who made little boy blue?.
**Album:** Released Jan '86, on Conifer Happy Days Catalogue no: **CHD 125**
**Cass:** Released Jul '86, on Conifer Happy Days by Conifer Records. Catalogue no: **MCHD 125**

**FRIENDS AND NEIGHBOURS (Cotton, Billy & His Band)**
Tracks: / Friends and neighbours.
**7" Single:** Released Apr '54, on Decca by Decca International. Deleted Apr '57. Catalogue no: **F 10299**

**GOLDEN AGE OF BILLY COTTON, THE**
Tracks: / New tiger rag / Why did she fall for the leader of the band / Dancing with my shadow / Bessie couldn't help it / Tattooed lady, The / St. Louis blues / What a difference a day made / Avalon / Nobody loves a fairy when shes forty / Hyde Park Corner / Truckin' / Shine / They all start whistling Mary / She was only somebody's daughter / I'll never say "never again" again.
**Cass:** Released Jul '84, on Golden Age by EMI Records. Catalogue no: **GX 412521-4**
**Album:** Released Jul '84, on Golden Age by EMI Records. Catalogue no: **GX 412521-1**

**I SAW MOMMY KISSING SANTA CLAUS (Cotton, Billy & His Band)**
Tracks: / I saw mommy kissing Santa Claus.
**7" Single:** Released Dec '53, on Decca by Decca International. Deleted Dec '55. Catalogue no: **F 10206**

**IN A GOLDEN COACH (Cotton, Billy & His Band)**
Tracks: / In a golden coach.
**7" Single:** Released May '53, on Decca by Decca International. Deleted May '58. Catalogue no: **F 10058**

**LET'S ALL JOIN IN (Cotton, Billy & His Orchestra)**
Tracks: / When you're smiling / Put your arms around me honey / Side by side / Tea for two / I can't give you anything but love / Ain't she sweet? / Dream / Are you lonesome tonight? / Oh what a beautiful morning / Daisy bell / Ma (he's making eyes at me) / Woody Woodpecker / Jeepers creepers / Beer barrel polka / Alexander's ragtime band / Me and my shadow / My blue Heaven / Who's sorry now? / Just one more chance / You were meant for me / Black bottom / Deep in the heart of Texas / Around the world in 80 days / True love / Ballin' the jack / After the ball / Goodnight sweetheart / Last mile home.
**Album:** Released Nov '83, on Bulldog Records by President Records. Catalogue no: **BDL 1050**

**MELODY MAKER (Cotton, Billy & His Band)**

Tracks: / Melody maker / You and i / Bring out the little brown jug / You'll be happy little sweetheart in the sprin / Turn your money in your pocket / Yeah man / Don't worry 'bout me / Over and done with / Somebody stole my gal / Ten little men with feathers / When you know you're not forgotten / Hold tight / Do I love you / Hut sut song / Wishing / Somebody cares about you / I know why / Something to remember you by.
**Album:** Released Mar '83, on Decca by Decca International. Deleted Mar '88. Catalogue no: **RFL 27**

**NOBODY'S SWEETHEART (Cotton, Billy & His Orchestra)**
**Cass set:** Released '88, on Saville by Conifer Records. Catalogue no: **CSVLD 006**
**2 LP Set:** Released Sep '87, on Saville by Conifer Records. Catalogue no: **SVLD 006**

**ROCK YOUR CARES AWAY (Cotton, Billy & His Band)**
Tracks: / Somebody loves you / Clouds will soon roll by, The / Thompson's old grey mule / Say it isn't so / We just couldn't say goodbye / There's another trumpet playing in the sky / Georgia on my mind / Just another dream of you / Rock your cares away / Nightfall / Wrap your arms around me / Now that you're gone / Listen to the German band / Leave the pretty girls alone / Goodnight Vienna / Let's all sing like the birdies sing.
**Album:** Released Aug '83, on Joy by President Records. Catalogue no: **JOY 279**

**SING A NEW SONG (Cotton, Billy & His Band)**
Tracks: / Sing a new song / Day by day / I'm crazy 'bout my baby / Give me your affection honey / Nina Rosa / They all start whistling Mary / Let's get friendly / Smile darn ya smile / Sunshine and roses / Whistle and blow your blues away / Ooh that kiss / I heard / What'd ja do to me / Bungalow, a piccolo and you / Too many tears / We're a couple of soliders / How'm I doin' / That's where the South begins / Roll on, Mississippi, roll on / I'm just wild about Harry.
**Album:** Released Jul '83, on Saville by Conifer Records. Catalogue no: **SVL 160**

**SOMEBODY STOLE MY GAL (Cotton, Billy & His Band)**
Tracks: / Diggin' my potatoes / Ying yang / 23 hours too long / No more doggin' / No cuttin' loose / Ain't doing too bad / Sunny road / Superharp / Easy loving / high compression.
**Album:** Released Jul '86, on Old Bean by Submarine Records. Catalogue no: **OLD 7**

**THAT RHYTHM MAN (Cotton, Billy & His Band)**
Tracks: / Sing a new song / We just couldn't say goodbye / Leave the pretty girls alone / Look what I've got / Margie / Georgia on my mind / Somebody loves you / You rascal you / Day by day / Bessie couldn't help it / I wanna be loved by you / That rhythm man / Auf wiedersehen my dear / Goodnight Vienna / Just another dream of you / Clouds will soon roll by, The / In the park in Paree / Now that you're gone.
Note: Featuring Nat Gonella on trumpet and vocal 20 tracks including Bessie couldn't help it, New tiger rag, That rhythm man, Nobody's sweetheart, You brought a new kind of love to me, Yes-yes.
**Album:** Released Jun '88, on Burlington (nostalgia) by Counterpoint Distribution. Catalogue no: **BUR 007**
**CD:** Released Sep '88, on Burlington (nostalgia) by Counterpoint Distribution. Catalogue no: **2 BUR 007**
**Cass:** Released Jul '88, on Burlington (nostalgia) by Counterpoint Distribution. Catalogue no: **4 BUR 007**

**THAT RHYTHM MAN (1928-31) (Cotton, Billy & His Orchestra)**
Tracks: / From Monday on / My southern home / Puttin' on the Ritz / That rhythm man / You brought a new kind of love to me / New tiger rag, The / Bessie couldn't help it / You're lucky to me / Memories of you / That Lindy hop / It looks like love / Were you sincere? / Why shouldn't I? / You wouldn't / Parkin' in the moonlight / It's the girl / You call it madness (but I call it love) / Yes-yes (my baby said Yes-yes) / Nobody's sweetheart / Sleepy time down south.
**Cass:** Released '86, on Saville by Conifer Records. Catalogue no: **CSVL 149**
**Album:** Released Jun '82, on Saville by Conifer Records. Catalogue no: **SVL 149**

**WAKEY WAKEY (LIVING ERA) (Cotton, Billy & His Band)**
Tracks: / Somebody stole my gal / Bugle call rag / I'm just wild about Harry / Third tiger, The (tiger rag no.3) / Mood indigo / Fancy our meeting / So green / It's only a paper moon / Rhapsody in blue / Skirts / Sweep / Mrs. Bartholomew / You don't understand / Why has a cow only got four legs? / Best wishes / St. Louis blues / She was only somebody's daughter / Night owl / Young and healthy / You're getting to be a habit with me / Shuffle off to buffalo / Forty-second Street / Smile darn ya, smile.
Note: The Band could and did play everything from knockabout comedy to hot jazz via standard sentiment and romantic balladry (Brian Rust).
**Cass:** Released 1 Nov '85, on Living Era by Academy Sound & Vision Records. Catalogue no: **ZC AJA 5037**
**Album:** Released 1 Nov '85, on Living Era by Academy Sound & Vision Records. Catalogue no: **AJA 5037**

**WAKEY WAKEY (C5)**
Tracks: / Somebody stole my gal / Sing, sing, sing / Exodus Song / And the great.. / Let's face the music and dance / She's Funny That Way / Sing-Song / Oh by jingo, oh by gee / Let the rest of the world go by / Ring down the curtain / Angelo / What will they do / Sing-Song.
**Cass:** Released Jun '88, on C5 by C5 Records. Catalogue no: **C5K-513**
**Album:** Released Apr '88, on C5 by C5 Records. Catalogue no: **C5-513**

## Cotton Club

**Biographical details:** The famous Harlem night-spot was built in 1918 as the Douglas Casino, with a theatre on the ground floor and a dance hall upstairs; boxer Jack Johnson turned it into the Club Deluxe, then bootlegger Owney Madden into an outlet for his beer, with entertainment for white downtowners. Duke Ellington's residency in 1927-31 helped make both Ellington and the club nationally famous with broadcasts; Ellington was followed by Cab Calloway. Revues were written by Dorothy Fields and Jimmy McHugh, Harold Arlen and others. The club moved downtown in 1936; by then the Harlem Renaissance was over, based as it had been on a shaky foundation of white patronage fuelled by Prohibition (which ended in 1933). The film made in 1984 had a good soundtrack in part, recreation of some of the period music overseen by Bob Wilber. (Donald Clarke 1989) .

**COTTON CLUB (Film Soundtrack) (Various artists)**
Tracks: / Mooche, The: *Various artists* / Cotton Club stomp No 2: *Various artists* / Drop me off in Harlem: *Various artists* / Creole love call: *Various artists* / Ring dem bells: *Various artists* / East St. Louis toodle-oo: *Various artists* / Truckin': *Various artists* / Ill wind: *Various artists* / Cotton Club stomp No 1: *Various artists* / Mood indigo: *Various artists* / Minnie the moocher: *Various artists* / Copper coloured gal: *Various artists* / Dixie kidnaps Vera: *Various artists* / Depression hits, The: *Various artists* / Best beats sandman: *Various artists* / Daybreak Express medley: *Various artists*.
**CD:** Released Aug '88, on Giants of Jazz by Hasmick Promotions. Catalogue no: **CD 53022**
**Album:** Released Sep '87, on Lotus Catalogue no: **LOP 14 105**
**Cass:** Released May '85, on Geffen by Geffen Records (USA). Deleted '87. Catalogue no: **40 70260**
**CD:** Released '88, on CBS by CBS Records. Catalogue no: **CD CBS 702 96**
**Album:** Released May '85, on Geffen by Geffen Records (USA). Deleted '87. Catalogue no: **GEF 70260**

**COTTON CLUB LEGEND (Various artists)**
**Album:** Released May '85, on RCA by BMG Records (UK). Deleted Jul '89. Catalogue no: **NL 89506**
**Cass:** Released May '85, on RCA by BMG Records (UK). Deleted Jul '89. Catalogue no: **NK 89506**

**COTTON CLUB, THE (Various artists)**
Tracks: / Cotton Club stomp: *Ellington, Duke/his Cotton Club Orchestra* / Just a crazy song: *Robinson, Bill 'Bojangles'* / Am I blue?: *Waters, Ethel* / Heebie jeebies: *Webb, Chick/his orchestra* / I

must have that man: *Hall, Adelaide* / Stormy weather: *Arlen, Harold* / When you're smiling: *Armstrong, Louis/his orchestra* / Lazybones: *Williams, Midge* / Old yazoo: *Calloway, Cab & His Orchestra* / Honey just for you: *Kirk, Andy/his Twelve Clouds of Joy* / Between the Devil and the deep blue sea: *Armstrong, Louis/his orchestra* / Sweet rhythm: *Lunceford, Jimmie/his Chickasaw Syncopators* / Blues I love to sing, The: *Hall, Adelaide* / Kicking the gong around: *Calloway, Cab & His Orchestra* / Serenade to a wealthy widow: *Foresythe, Reginald* / Jubilee stomp: *Ellington, Duke/his Cotton Club Orchestra* / I can't give you anything but love: *Waters, Ethel* / Doin' the new low down: *Mills, Irving.*
**CD:** Released Oct '88, on Living Era by Academy Sound & Vision Records. Catalogue no: **CD AJA 5031**
**Album:** Released 1 Oct '84, on Living Era by Academy Sound & Vision Records. Catalogue no: **AJA 5031**
**Cass:** Released 1 Oct '84, on Living Era by Academy Sound & Vision Records. Catalogue no: **ZC AJA 5031**

**COTTON CLUB, THE (VIDEO) (Various artists)**
**VHS:** Released Oct '89, on Spectrum (1) Catalogue no: **SPC 00282**

**RARE PERFORMANCES (Various artists)**
Tracks: / Swingin' at the Cotton Club: *Three Peppers* / I found a new baby: *Preer, Andy & The Cotton Club Orchestra* / Cotton Club stomp: *Ellington, Duke/his Cotton Club Orchestra* / Misty morning: *Ellington, Duke/his Cotton Club Orchestra* / Freeze and melt: *Ellington, Duke/his Cotton Club Orchestra* / Ozark Mountain blues: *Missourians* / Ain't misbehavin': *Robinson, Bill 'Bojangles'* / Happy feet: *Calloway, Cab & His Orchestra* / Go Harlem: *Johnson, Jimmy & His Orchestra* / Baby: *Hall, Adelaide with Duke Ellington & His Orchestra* / King Porter stomp: *Calloway, Cab & His Orchestra* / Minnie the moocher's wedding day: *Banks, Billy & His Blue Rhythm Boys* / Stormy weather: *Ellington, Duke/his Cotton Club Orchestra* / Happy as the day is long: *Arlen, Harold* / Minor mania: *Hopkins, Claude & His Orchestra* / Breakfast in Harlem: *Buck & Bubbles* / It must be love: *Three Peppers* / Edgar steps out: *Hayes, Edgar & His Orchestra* / I'll get along somehow: *Waters, Ethel* / Jammin' for the jackpot: *Millinder, Lucky & The Mills Blue Rhythm Band* / Wrap your cares in rhythm and dance: *Nicholas Brothers* / They say he ought to dance: *Nicholas Brothers* / Say it with a kiss: *Sullivan, Maxine* / Moon ray: *Fitzgerald, Ella/her Famous Orchestra* / Give, baby, give: *Calloway, Cab & His Orchestra* / Liza: *Long, Avon* / Ain't gonna study war no more: *Dandridge Sisters with Jimmy Lunceford & His Orchestra* / How long has this been going on?: *Horne, Lena with The Phil Moore Four* / Hip hip hooray: *Kirk, Andy/his Twelve Clouds of Joy* / Rock Daniel: *Millinder, Lucky & His Orchestra with Sister Rosetta Tharpe* / Song is ended, The: *Armstrong, Louis/Mills Brothers.*
**Album:** Released Apr '85, on SPI Milan (France) Catalogue no: **A 252**
**Cass:** Released Apr '85, on SPI Milan (France) Catalogue no: **LC 8126**

## Cotton Club Stars

**COTTON CLUB STARS (Various artists)**
**CD:** Released Mar '90, on Rare'n'Darin Catalogue no: **RNDCD1302**

## Cotton, Mike

**SWING THAT HAMMER (Cotton, Mike Jazzmen)**
Tracks: / Swing that hammer.
**7" Single:** Released Jun '63, on Columbia by EMI Records. Deleted Jun '66. Catalogue no: **DB 7029**

## Cottrell, Louis

**CLARINET LEGENDS**
**Album:** Released Mar '84, on GHB by Jazzology Records (USA). Catalogue no: **GHB 156**

## Counce, Curtis

**Biographical details:** Bassist and leader (1926-63) born in Kansas City and prominent in West Coast jazz, which seemed to be dominated by whites in the 1950s beacuase Counce and others did not get enough attention. His excellent albums feature Harold Land on tenor, Carl Butler on drums, Jack Sheldon and Rolf Erickson on trumpet and the wonderful pianist Carl Perkins, who was also cheated by the lottery of life, except for *Exploring The Future*, which has the different but equally wonderful Elmo Hope. (Donald Clarke 1989).

**CARL'S BLUES**
Tracks: / Pink lady / I can't get started / Nica's dream / Love walked in / Larue / Butler did it, The / Carl's blues.
Note: 1960 release recorded shortly before the death of pianist Carl Perkins.
**Album:** Released May '87, on Contemporary (USA) Catalogue no: **COP 040**

**COUNCELTATION**
**Album:** Released Dec '81, on Contemporary (Import) Catalogue no: **1007 539**

**CURTIS BLUES**
Tracks: / Pink lady / I can't get started / Nica's dream / Love walked in / Larue / Butler did it, The / Carl's blues.
**Album:** Released May '83, on Contemporary (Import) Catalogue no: **1007 574**

**EXPLORING THE FUTURE (Counce, Curtis Quintet)**
Tracks: / So nice / Angel eyes / Into the orbit / Move / Race for space / Someone to watch over me / Countdown, The.
**Album:** Released Jul '84, on Boplicity by Ace Records. Deleted '88. Catalogue no: **BOP 007**

## Country Negro Jam...

**COUNTRY NEGRO JAM SESSIONS (Various artists)**
**Album:** Released May '81, on Arhoolie (USA) by Arhoolie Records (USA). Catalogue no: **ARHOOLIE 2018**

## Country All Stars

**JAZZ FROM THE HILLS**
Tracks: / Stompin' at the Savoy / Tennessee rag / Do something / Indiana march / Sweet Georgia Brown / Midnight train / In a little spanish town / My little girl / Lady in red / Marie / It goes like this / What's the reason (I'm not pleasing you) / When it's darkness on the delta / Vacation train, The / Fiddle patch / Fiddle sticks.
**Album:** Released 1 Jun '89, on Bear Family by Bear Family Records (Germany). Catalogue no: **BFX 15350**

## Country Blues...

**COUNTRY BLUES BOTTLENECK GUITAR (Various artists)**
**Album:** Released Dec '88, on Yazoo (USA) by Shanachie Records (USA). Catalogue no: **L 1026**

**COUNTRY BLUES VOL. 1 (Various artists)**
**Album:** Released '88, on Blues Classics(USA) by Arhoolie Records (USA). Catalogue no: **BC 5**

**COUNTRY BLUES VOL. 2 (Various artists)**
**Album:** Released '88, on Blues Classics(USA) by Arhoolie Records (USA). Catalogue no: **BC 6**

**COUNTRY BLUES VOL. 3 (Various artists)**
**Album:** Released '88, on Blues Classics(USA) by Arhoolie Records (USA). Catalogue no: **BC 7**

**COUNTRY BLUES VOL. 4 (Various artists)**
**Album:** Released '88, on Blues Classics(USA) by Arhoolie Records (USA). Catalogue no: **BC 14**

**COUNTRY BLUES COLLECTOR ITEMS (Various artists)**
**Album:** Released Aug '89, on Blues Document Catalogue no: **BD 2042**

**COUNTRY BLUES COLLECTOR ITEMS, (Various artists)**
**Album:** Released '89, on Blues Document Catalogue no: **BD 2057**

**COUNTRY BLUES, LIVE (Various artists)**
Note: With Mississippi John Hurt, John Jackson, Sleepy John Estes.
**Album:** Released Jul '88, on Document Catalogue no: **DLP 525**

**COUNTRY BLUES OBSCURITIES VOL. 1 (Various artists)**
**Album:** Released Oct '88, on Roots (Germany) Catalogue no: **RL 334**
**Album:** Released Oct '88, on Roots (Germany) Catalogue no: **RL 340**

**COUNTRY BLUES - THE FIRST GENERATION (1927) (Various artists)**
Tracks: / Gang of brown skin women: *Papa Harvey Hull & Long Cleve Reed* / France blues: *Various artists* / Two little tommie blues: *Papa Harvey Hull & Long Cleve Reed* / Don't you leave me here: *Papa Harvey Hull & Long Cleve Reed* /

Mama you don't know how: *Long Cleve Reed & The Down Home Boys* / Original stack o' lee blues: *Long Cleve Reed & The Down Home Boys* / James Alley blues: *Richard 'Rabbit' Brown* / Never let the same bee sting you twice: *Richard 'Rabbit' Brown* / I'm not jealous: *Richard 'Rabbit' Brown* / Mystery of the dunbar's child: *Richard 'Rabbit' Brown* / Sinking of the Titanic: *Richard 'Rabbit' Brown.*
**Album:** Released Nov '82, on Matchbox (Bluesmaster) by Saydisc Records. Catalogue no: **MSE 201**

### FAVOURITE COUNTRY BLUES (Piano guitar duets 1929-35) (Various artists)
**Album:** Released Dec '88, on Yazoo (USA) by Shanachie Records (USA). Catalogue no: **L 1015**

### GIANTS OF COUNTRY BLUES GUITAR (1966-82) (Various artists)
**Album:** Released Sep '87, on Wolf Catalogue no: **120.911**

### GIANTS OF COUNTRY BLUES PIANO (Various artists)
Note: Featuring Whistlin' Alex Moore, Robert Shaw, Lavada Durst etc.
**Album:** Released Aug '87, on Wolf Catalogue no: **120.910**

### GIANTS OF COUNTRY BLUES VOL. 1 (1927-32) (Various artists)
Note: Bobby Grant, Rube Lacy, Willie Brown, Son House etc.
**Album:** Released Jan '88, on Wolf Catalogue no: **WSE 116**

### KINGS OF COUNTRY BLUES (Various artists)
**Album:** Released Dec '88, on Arhoolie (USA) by Arhoolie Records (USA). Catalogue no: **ARHOOLIE 1084**

### KINGS OF COUNTRY BLUES VOL. 2 (Various artists)
**Album:** Released Dec '88, on Arhoolie (USA) by Arhoolie Records (USA). Catalogue no: **ARHOOLIE 1085**

### WORRIED ALL THE TIME (Country blues 1929-36) (Various artists)
**Album:** Released Apr '78, on Whoopee by Whoopee Records. Catalogue no: **WP 104**

## Country Spirituals

### COUNTRY SPIRITUALS (Various artists)
**Album:** Released Jan '88, on Storyville by Storyville Records AB. Catalogue no: **SLP 135**

## Cousin Joe

### GOSPEL-WAILING-JAZZ-PLAYING
Tracks: / When a woman loves a man / Checkin' out / Touch me / I got news for you / Too late to turn back now / Lipstick trails / Railroad avenue / You talk too much / Barefoot boy / How come my dog don't bark / Night life.
**Album:** Released '82, on Big Bear by Big Bear Records. Deleted '88. Catalogue no: **BEAR 3**

### IN HIS PRIME (Cousin Joe from New Orleans)
**Album:** Released Dec '84, on Oldie Blues Catalogue no: **OL 8008**

### RELAXING IN NEW ORLEANS
**Album:** Released '87, on Great Southern (USA) by Flat Town Music Co.(USA). Catalogue no: **11011**
**Cass:** Released '87, on Great Southern (USA) by Flat Town Music Co.(USA). Catalogue no: **11011 TC**

## Cowell, Stanley

### BACK TO THE BEAUTIFUL
Tracks: / Theme for Ernie / Wall / It don't mean a thing / But beautiful / Sylvia's place / Come Sunday (on CD only) / Carnegie six / St. Croix / Prayer for peach (on CD only) / Nightingale sang in Berkeley Square, A.
Note: This is pianist Stanley Cowell's debut album for Concord Jazz. Stanley Cowell (piano), Steve Coleman (alto & soprano sax), Joe Chambers (drums) and Santi W. Debriano (bass).
**Cass:** Released Nov '89, on Concord Jazz by Concord Jazz Records (USA). Catalogue no: **CJ 398C**
**CD:** Released Nov '89, on Concord Jazz by Concord Jazz Records (USA). Catalogue no: **CCD 4398**

### BLUES FOR THE VIET CONG
**Album:** Released May '79, on Freedom Catalogue no: **FLP 41032**

### LIVE AT CAFE DES COPAINS
**Album:** Released '88, on Unisson (Canada) Catalogue no: **DDA 1004**

### NEW WORLD
Tracks: / Come Sunday / Ask him / Island of Haitoo / I'm tryin' to find a way / El space-o / Sienna / Welcome to this new world.
**Album:** Released Sep '81, on Galaxy (1) by President Records. Catalogue no: **GXY 5131**

### TALKIN' 'BOUT LOVE
**Album:** Released '79, on Galaxy (1) by President Records. Deleted '84. Catalogue no: **GXY 5111**

### WAITING FOR THE MOMENT
**Album:** Released '79, on Galaxy (1) by President Records. Deleted '84. Catalogue no: **GXY 5104**

## Cox, Ida

**Biographical details:** A blues singer (c.1896-1967). She toured with minstrel shows, worked with Jelly Roll Morton and King Oliver amd recorded for *Paramount* from 1923.
She toured with her own revues from 1929 into the '40s, said to have been the best such shows on the road, her style influenced by vaudeville as well as rural blues.
She recorded with Hot Lips Page and Fletcher Henderson and appeared in John Hammond's *Spirituals To Swing* concert in 1939; she suffered a stroke in 1944 but recorded with Coleman Hawkins on Riverside in 1961. (Donald Clarke 1989).

### IDA COX 1923 VOL. 1
**Album:** Released Apr '79, on Fountain by Retrieval Records. Catalogue no: **FB 301**

### IDA COX 1923-4 VOL. 2
**Album:** Released Apr '79, on Fountain by Retrieval Records. Catalogue no: **FB 304**

### IDA COX & BERTHA CHIPPIE HILL (Cox, Ida & Bertha Chippie Hill)
Tracks: / Off my mind / Last mile blues / I can't quit that man / How long blues / Careless love / Darktown strutters' ball / Lonesome road / Don't leave me daddy / Baby won't you please come home / Some of these days / Blues, The.

Note: Musicians on the various tracks include Hot Lips Page, Red Allen (trumpet), Wild Bill Davison (cornet), Jimmy Archey (trombone), J.C. Higginbotham, Ed Hall, Albert Nicholas (clarinet), J.P. Johnson, Fletcher Henderson, Ralph Sutton (piano), Charlie Christian, Danny Parker (guitar), Pops Foster (bass), Cliff Jackson, Lionel Hampton, Johnny Blowers, Baby Dodds (drums).
**Album:** Released Apr '81, on Queendisc (Italy) Catalogue no: **QU 048**

## Coxhill, Lol

**Biographical details:** Born in 1932 in Portsmouth, Coxhill plays reeds, especially soprano sax, and is also and actor. He is an eclectic and has a unique musical personality. He worked with R&B groups like Alexis Korner, such visiting Americans as Otis Spann; with pianist Steve Miller's Delivery blues band in the late '60s and Chris McGregor's Brotherhood of Breath in the mid-'70s, and rock groups like the avant-garde Henry's Cow. He was the subject of a British Arts Council documentary film *Frog Dance*, the embellished soundtrack on Impetus in 1987 including solo sax, bagpipes, birds, seals, etc. (Donald Clarke 1989).

### 10:02 (Coxhill, Lol & Daniel Deshays)
Tracks: / On golden flaque / Fromage a varese incl. Regardez Edgar / Solitudinette / Ceux qu ils aiment / Cleito (Including Tape Dancing.) / Un homme au plafond / Amies Americaines / Choral a tchang / Sgt. De Ville tres occupe / Tea for two.
**Album:** Released Sep '86, on Nato Catalogue no: **NATO 439**

Lol Coxhill

**COUSCOUS**
Tracks: / West lawn dirge / Hotlavaband extensions / Variations pour violoncelle, Contrebasse, Sopranino et piano / And lo, the chapel walls trembled at the voice of the M.C.
Note: With Buck Funk, Reverend Anthony W. Reeves, Alan Tomlinson, Phil Minton, Steve Beresford, Jac Berrocal, Sylvia Hallett, Georgie Born, Susan Ferrar, Mike Cooper, Peter Bennink, Fred Van Hove, Joelle Leandre, Roger Turner, Veryan Weston.
**Album:** Released Sep '86, on Nato Catalogue no: **NATO 157**

**DIVERSE**
**Album:** Released Oct '86, on Ogun by Cadillac Music. Catalogue no: **OG 510**

**DUNOIS SOLOS, THE**
Tracks: / Dunois solos, The / Distorted reminiscences / Further developments.
**Album:** Released Sep '86, on Nato Catalogue no: **NATO 95**

**FLEAS IN CUSTARD**
**Album:** Released Feb '76, on Caroline Catalogue no: **C 1515**

**FRENCH GIGS (Coxhill, Lol and Fred Frith)**
Tracks: / French gigs.
**Album:** Released Oct '86, on AAA (France) Catalogue no: **AAA AO2**

**INIMITABLE, THE**
Tracks: / Moon was yellow, The / Spring is here / Folks who live on the hill, The / It never entered my mind / Little froggies / Certain smile, A / Time after time / Change partners / Requiem major / Cocktails for two / Two sleepy people.
**Album:** Released Sep '86, on Chabada (France) Catalogue no: **CHABADA 09**

**INSTANT REPLAY**
Tracks: / Le bagad de kemperle / La Chantenay / Sienne A1-A2-A3-B1-B2 / Embraceable you -B3-C1 / Potpourri / Caravan - C2-C3-D1-D2.
**Album:** Released Sep '86, on Nato Catalogue no: **NATO 25/32**

**JOY OF PARANOIA, THE**
**Album:** Released '78, on Ogun by Cadillac Music. Catalogue no: **OG 525**

**STORY SO FAR - OH REALLY (Coxhill, Lol & Steve Miller)**
**Album:** Released Oct '74, on Caroline Catalogue no: **C 1507**

## Crafton, Harry

**HARRY CRAFTON**
Tracks: / Get off mama / Let me tell you baby / Roly poly mama / I don't want your money honey / Guitar boogie / It's been along time baby / Bring my cadillac back / It's been a long time baby / Rust dusty / In the middle of the night / She got a mule kick / Big fat hot dog / So long baby / Saturday night boogie.
**Album:** Released Nov '87, on Krazy Kat by Interstate Music. Catalogue no: **KK 818**

## Craig, Lorraine

**SHADES OF BLUE AND GREEN (Craig, Lorraine & National Jazz Youth Orchestra)**
Tracks: / Another always / Deflated bounce, the / As if I cared / Insignificant song / I thought I was through with love / Where is the music / With you in mind / Shades of blue & green / I have been here before / But me no buts.
**Album:** Released Oct '88, on BBC by BBC Records & Tapes. Catalogue no: **REN 702**
**Cass:** Released Oct '88, on BBC by BBC Records & Tapes. Catalogue no: **ZCN 702**
**CD:** Released Oct '88, on BBC by BBC Records & Tapes. Catalogue no: **BBC CD 702**

**WHERE IS THE MUSIC? (Craig, Lorraine & National Jazz Youth Orchestra)**
Tracks: / Where is the music / Much too much.
**7" Single:** Released Oct '88, on BBC by BBC Records & Tapes. Catalogue no: **RESL 228**

## Crane River Jazz Band

**CRANE RIVER JAZZ BAND (1950-53)**
Note: Featuring Ken Colyer, Monty Sunshine.
**Album:** Released Apr '88, on Dormouse Catalogue no: **DM 18**

**LEGENDARY CRANE RIVER JAZZ BAND**
**Album:** Released May '79, on Dawn Club by Cadillac Music. Catalogue no: **DC 12026**

## Crawford, Hank

**Biographical details:** Saxist, pianist, leader and composer born in 1934 in Memphis. He joined the Ray Charles band on baritone in 1958, switched to alto in '59 and became its music director, leaving in 1963 to start his own small group. His blues-drenched small-band soul music anticipated the jazz-funk of the '70s and continues to be successful to this day. (Donald Clarke 1989) .

**CAJUN SUNRISE**
Tracks: / What a difference you've made in my life / I don't want no happy songs / New York's one soulful city / Take this job and shove it / Just the way you are / Daytime friends / Evergreen / Cajun sunrise.
**Album:** Released '79, on Polydor by Polydor Ltd. Deleted '84. Catalogue no: **KU 39**

**HANK CRAWFORD'S BACK**
Tracks: / Funky pigeon / I can't stop loving you / You'll never find another love like mine / Canadian sunset / Midnight over Memphis.
**Album:** Released Apr '77, on Kudu Catalogue no: **KU 33**

**INDIGO BLUE**
**CD:** Released Nov '86, on Fantasy (import) by Fantasy Inc (USA). Catalogue no: **FCD 6219119**

**ROADHOUSE SYMPHONY (Crawford, Hank & Doctor John)**
Tracks: / Roadhouse symphony / Track magick / Jubilee / Say it isn't so / Time is on our side / Precious Lord / Sugar ditch.

Note: Some fine blues playing here from alto sax player Hank Crawford who first came to prominence as a key soloist with the Ray Charles orchestra during the late fifties and early sixties. Since those early years he has made countless albums, mainly in the jazz funk mould, for *Atlantic* and more recently CTI's *Kuda* label.
Throughout the album, Doctor John plays keyboards and sings on the track *Tragick Magick*. Recommended tracks: *Tragick Magick*, *Precious Lord* and *Sugar Ditch*. Personnel: Hank Crawford (alto sax), Doctor John (piano, organ, vocals), Melvin Spark (guitar), Wilbur Bascombe,Jnr (bass), Bernard Purdie (drums), Randy Brecker, Alan Rubin (trumpets), Howard Johnson (baritone sax), Houston Person (tenor sax), David Fathead Newman (tenor and alto sax).
**Album:** Released Feb '86, on Milestone by Ace Records. Catalogue no: **M 9140**

**SOUL BROTHERS (See also under McGriff, Jimmy) (Crawford, Hank & Jimmy McGriff)**
**Album:** Released 2 May '89, on Milestone by Ace Records. Catalogue no: **MX 9171**

**TICO RICO**
Tracks: / Tico Rico / Teach me tonight / Lady Soul / Lullaby of love / I've just seen a face / Lament / Funky rooster.
**Album:** Released Sep '77, on Kudu Catalogue no: **KU 35**

**WILDFLOWER**
**CD:** Released '88, on CBS by CBS Records. Deleted Jan '89. Catalogue no: **450566-2**

## Crawford, Sugar Boy

**CHICAGO YEARS**
**2 LP Set:** Released Oct '88, on Vogue by Vogue Records. Catalogue no: **427017**

**SUGAR BOY CRAWFORD**
**Album:** Released Apr '85, on Pathe Marconi (France) Catalogue no: **PM 156 1351**

## Crawley, Wilton

**CRAWLEY CLARINET MOAN (1927-28)**
**Album:** Released Sep '85, on Harlequin by Interstate Music. Catalogue no: **HQ 2035**

## Crayton, Pee Wee

**AFTER HOURS BOOGIE**
**Album:** Released Feb '89, on Blues Boy (Sweden) Catalogue no: **BB 307**

**BLUES AFTER DARK**
Tracks: / I got news for you / Baby, won't you please come home / Piney Brown blues / Call it stormy Monday / Good rockin' tonight / Blues after dark / How long how long blues / Tie it down / Fiddle de dee / Frosty night, A / Telephone is ringing, The / Blues after hours / I found my peace of mind / I love her still.
**Album:** Released Aug '88, on Charly R&B by Charly Records. Catalogue no: **CRB 1186**

**BLUES AFTER HOURS**
Tracks: / Blues after hours / My baby's on the line / Lucille / Need your love so bad / In the evening / Texas hop / Don't forget to close the door / If I ever get lucky / Blues in the ghetto / Louella Brown.
**Album:** Released 22 Aug '88, on Blue Moon (1) by Magnum Music Group. Catalogue no: **BMLP 1060**

**BLUES GUITAR GENIUS**
Tracks: / Poppa stoppa / Good little woman / Guitar boogie / Cool evening / Dedicating the blues / Brand new woman / Telephone call from my baby / Bop hop / Huckle boogie / Rosa Lee.
**Album:** Released Dec '80, on Ace by Ace Records. Deleted Dec '85. Catalogue no: **10 CH 23**

**EARLY HOURS**
**Album:** Released Sep '87, on Murray Brothers (USA) by Topic Records. Catalogue no: **MB 1007**

**EVERY DAY I HAVE THE BLUES (Crayton, Pee Wee, Sonny Stitt and Joe Turner)**
Tracks: / Stormy Monday / Piney Brown blues / Martin Luther King southside / Everyday / Shake rattle and roll / Lucille.
**Album:** Released May '82, on Pablo Jazz (USA) by Pablo Records (USA). Catalogue no: **231 0818**
**Cass:** Released May '82, on Pablo Jazz (USA) by Pablo Records (USA). Catalogue no: **K10 818**
**Album:** Released Dec '88, on Masters (Holland) Catalogue no: **CL 918983**

**MAKE ROOM FOR PEE WEE**
**Album:** Released Sep '87, on Murray Brothers (USA) by Topic Records. Catalogue no: **MB 1005**

**MEMORIAL ALBUM**
Tracks: / Texas hop / Miserable old feeling / Blues for my baby / Californian women / Walkin' with Crayton / Old fashioned baby / Bop hop / Money is all we need / Mistreated so bad / All or nothing at all / Twinky / Blue night / Mojo blues / Need your love so bad.
**Album:** Released May '86, on Ace by Ace Records. Catalogue no: **CHD 177**

**PEACE OF MIND**
Tracks: / Tie it down / Fiddle de dee / Frosty night, A / Telephone is ringing, The / Blues after hours / I don't care / Is this the price I pay / Second hand love / I love her still.
**Album:** Released May '82, on Charly by Charly Records. Deleted '88. Catalogue no: **CFM 601**

**ROCKING DOWN ON CENTRAL AVENUE**
Tracks: / Austin boogie / Tired of travelin' / Crayton's blues / Change your way of loving / Answer to blues after hour / T for Texas (mistreated blues) / Rockin the blues / Huckle boogie / Central Avenue blues / Long after hours / Louella Brown / When a man has the blues / Please come back / Pee Wee's wild.
**Album:** Released Nov '82, on Ace by Ace Records. Deleted Jun '88. Catalogue no: **CHA 61**

## Creole Jazzband

**DELVING BACK TO HUMPH**
**Album:** Released '88, on Stomp Off (USA) Catalogue no: **SOS 1051**

## Criss, Sonny

**Biographical details:** A jazz saxophonist (1927-77) who spent 1962-65 in Europe. Back home he did a lot of work on community music projects in 1970-4, especially with young people, and continued to visit Europe regularly. (Donald Clarke, April 1989).

**AT THE CROSSROADS**
**Album:** Released Feb '88, on Fresh Sounds (Spain) by Fresh Sounds Records (Spain). Catalogue no: **FS 173**

**CINCH, THE (Criss, Sonny & Buddy Rich Quintet)**
**Album:** Released Jan '80, on Spotlite by Spotlite Records. Catalogue no: **SPJ 125**

**CRISSCRAFT**
Tracks: / Isle of Celia, The / Blues in my heart / This is for Ben / All night long / Crisscraft.
**Album:** Released Apr '81, on Muse by Black & Blue Records. Catalogue no: **MR 5068**

**I'LL CATCH THE SUN**
Tracks: / Don't rain on my parade / I thought about you / Cry me a river / Blue sunset / California screamin' / I'll catch the sun.
**Album:** Released May '88, on Prestige Catalogue no: **PR 7628**
**Cass:** Released May '88, on Prestige Deleted Jan '90. Catalogue no: **PRC 7628**

**LIVE IN ITALY**
**Album:** Released Feb '88, on Fresh Sounds (Spain) by Fresh Sounds Records (Spain). Catalogue no: **FS 310**

**OUT OF NOWHERE**
Tracks: / All the things you are / Dreamer, The / El tiante / My ideal / Out of nowhere / Brother can you spare a dime / First one, The.
**Album:** Released Apr '81, on Muse by Black & Blue Records. Catalogue no: **MR 5089**

**SATURDAY MORNING**
**CD:** Released '88, on Xanadu Catalogue no: **FDC 5163**

**SONNY CRISS IN PARIS (Mr. Blues Poor Flirter)**
**LP Set:** Released Feb '88, on Fresh Sounds (Spain) by Fresh Sounds Records (Spain). Catalogue no: **FSBOX 2**

## Crombie, Tony

**Biographical details:** This British drummer, leader of the Rockets, has a unique and honoured place in British pop history - he is credited with having the UK's first rock'n'roll band. Crombie had been a jazz drummer since the Forties, and switched to rock in th mid-Fifties. He made this move because he wanted his music to keep up to date, rather than because of any huge love for

the new music. Nevertheless, it showed a far-sighted approach at a time when Britain was only just waking up to the revolution and, even then, was buying solely American rock records. Rockets' leader modelled himself on the first ever rock'n'roll giant, Bill Haley.
Unfortunately Crombie's chart life was brief in the extreme: his only UK chart record was October 1956's double A sided disc *Teach you to rock / Shortnin' bread*, which peaked at No.25. The latter track preceded the Viscounts' Top 20 version by four years. Tony Crombie and his Rockets recorded this single under the guidance of *Columbia Records'* A & R executive Norrie Paramor, who was one of Britain's leading record producers. Although not yet converted to rock, this represented Paramor's first period of flirtation with the new music, the possibilities of which he did not begin to explore fully for another two years. Crombie, on the other hand, was always ready to latch onto the latest style and, convinced of the viability of the Donegan led skiffle movement, announced his intention to move into that area. His name rapidly faded from public memory. (Bob MacDonald, 8th Feb 1985).

### ATMOSPHERE (Crombie, Tony and His Rockets)

Tracks: / Beryl's bounce / Ninth man / St James Infirmary / Invitation / Stompin' at the Savoy / Duke's joke / Panic stations / I'll close my eyes / Small talk / Perpetual lover / Shapes / Copy cats.
Note: This recording, made in 1958 in stereo, is a fine example of the best that British jazz had to offer in the '50s. Indeed the line-up of Tony Crombie, Tubby Hayes, Ronnie Scott, Tommy Whittle, Lennie Bush etc. reads today like a *Who's Who* of British jazz. The tunes are a mixture of standards and originals by Crombie, who also did all the arrangements. Interestingly, Crombie and the late great Tubby Hayes, can also be heard to great effect on their other instruments, on the three small group tracks. Tubby provides an excellent vibes' solo on *Invitation*, while Tony moves to piano for *Stompin' at the Savoy* and his own tune *Perpetual Lover*, on which he solos with great sensitivity. The eight-piece band plays with a vitality which is as invigorating today as when the album was originally released. Listen, for example, to *I'll Close My Eyes*, a *tour de force* for Tubby Hayes on baritone sax. This is matched a couple of tracks later by Ronnie Scott, on the twelve bar blues theme *Shapes*; and don't overlook the exciting alternate lead trumpet work of Stan Roderick and Jimmy Watson. The marvellous attack and verve of the group's playing is well illustrated by the track *Small Talk*. The remaining soloists comprise Les Condon (trumpet), Bob Burns (alto sax), Tommy Whittle, (alternating with Ronnie Scott on tenor sax), and Norman Stenfalt (piano). The great Lennie Bush plays bass on most tracks; his talent, then as now, is the kind guaranteed to improve the sound of almost any rhythm section. (Renaissance)
**Cass:** Released Jul '89, on Renaissance Catalogue no: **ZCREN 002**
**CD:** Released Jul '89, on Renaissance Catalogue no: **CDREN 002**
**Album:** Released Jul '89, on Renaissance Catalogue no: **REN 002**

### RELAUNCH (Crombie, Tony and his Rockets)

Tracks: / We're gonna rock tonight / Big beat, The / Rock, rock, rock / Let's you and I rock / Sham rock / Brighton rock / London rocker / Teach you to rock / Short'nin' bread rock / Rock shuffle boogie / Forgive me, baby / Dumplin's / Town special / Ungang / Pickukauugoung / Rock cha cha / Lonesome train (on a lonesome track) / Red for danger / Sticks and stones / Stop it (I like it) / Rock 'n' roller coaster / Rex rocks.
**Album:** Released Dec '86, on See For Miles by See For Miles Records. Catalogue no: **CM 115**

### SWEET, WILD AND BLUE

Tracks: / Cocktails for two / Wrap your troubles in dreams / So near, so far / I've got the world on a string / Embraceable you / Tulip or turnip / To each his own / Love is the tender trap / Hold my hand / All the way / It's magic / High and mighty, The / So rare / Percussion staccato / I should care / For you alone / Summertime / You are my lucky star.
Note: Recorded in 1960, this album is being re-issued to coincide with the 40th Anniversary of Tony Crombie's first studio sessions. The band was culted extensively from the Ted Heath band of the time, which included some of the greatest names in British jazz, and features the great and sadly missed Victor Feldman, who died so suddenly in 1988. The selections merge jazz and popular styles in swinging big band arrangements by some of the best names in the business, including Stan Tracey, Harry South, Jimmy Deuchar, Kenny Napper, Victor Feldman and Crombie himself. Today, these are still exciting and unusual arrangements which bristle with original ideas. Just listen to the humour of *Tulip or Turnip* and *I've Got the World on a String*, or the simple beauty of *Summertime* and *So Near so Far*, one of Crombie's own favourite compositions. The superb vibes playing of Victor Feldman, particularly on *You are My Lucky Star*, is just one of the many high spots of the album. To the original album we have added six tracks from a jazz-slanted film themes set Crombie recorded in 1961. Although a commercial release not aimed at the jazz market, the titles we have chosen make for a well rounded selection. It is obvious the band were having a great time that day. We hope listening will be just as much fun for you too. (Renaissance, 1989).
**CD:** Released '89, on Renaissance Catalogue no: **CDREN 003**

### TEACH YOU TO ROCK (Crombie, Tony and His Rockets)

Tracks: / Teach you to rock / Short'nin' bread.
**7" Single:** Released Oct '56, on Columbia by EMI Records. Deleted Oct '59. Catalogue no: **DB 3822**

### TONY CROMBIE AND FRIENDS

Tracks: / Tango '89 / Sophisticated lady / Moonglow / 12 note samba / Raising the temperature / Fallen bird / I don't stand a ghost of a chance with you / Serenade in blue / Allson adamant / Autumn rustle / Prelude to a kiss / So near, so far / Rabbit pie / Child of fancy / Raising the temperature / Viva Rodriguez.
Note: It is more than thirty years now since I first discovered the music of Tony Crombie, half a lifetime ago, yet the depth of my commitment to his cause has never changed. We were fellow members of Ronnie Scott's band of 1953, and it fell to me to assist him in copying the scores of the orchestrations he was writing for the band. That was my first surprise, I had assumed him to be merely a gifted drummer, yet here he was, arranging. Sometimes he would break off from his chores and play a succession of brooding harmonic combinations which told of his abiding love of Duke Ellington's music. He had played the drums for Duke in 1948, and clearly that experience had marked him for life, in the most benign sense. Further revelations came to me when among the pieces he scored for the band were compositions of his own. I can recall being startled by them, astonished at their depth of emotion, their mature poise, their calm originality. Where does such inspiration come from? I had no idea, nor do I have now, all these years later. I soon learned something else about Crombie, a tendency to a sort of playfulness which would show itself in unexpected ways. Having been conditioned by the sombre beauty of the piano playing to expect Ellingtonian balladry, I was non-plussed when he played me a sort of miniature suite so redolent of the old Wild West that you could almost sniff the sagebrush. I am happy to find from the evidence of this album that he has not lost this habit of expressing affection for odd little corners of musical life, with pieces whose perfect aptness to the genre in hand may well baffle those who still think of Tony as a drummer. Intimations of *Come Dancing* may be found in *Tango '89*, but only by the undiscerning, who will miss the point that behind the rhythmic measures lie harmonies finely attuned to the demands of the improviser; the matching of violin and accordion might look like a joke, but when the accordion solo starts the originality of the whole business becomes apparent. It is the same with the other exercises in Latin rhythms which features in this album, everyone of which is distinguished from the conventional Palais fodder by its harmonic daring.
In a separate category are the piano solos by Tony, six of them, some with rhythm backing, some without, all of them brief to the brink of reticence, yet

deeply moving, and all belonging to that common stockpot of standard song we usually define as the past. Two of the six tracks reflect the Ellington presence, and three belong to the golden age of popular song when Tony was growing up. The sixth is an exception I will return to in a moment. The various instrumental tracks feature playing as brilliant as any I remember hearing by any band outside America. What is especially striking is the blend of youth and experience, paricularly the juxtaposition of Ronnie Scott and Nigel Hitchcock, which struck me as an uplifting business. And then there is the wonderful virtuosity of Peter King, who, everytime he plays, shows his world class. But the real point of this album is that except for the piano features and *Tango '89*, a collaboration with Alan Clare, every note of every composition is Tony Crombie's work. How long it took him, I can only guess, but I do remember how quickly ideas would come to him in the past. That is why, once I knew the album was on the way to me, I looked forward to the discovery of some new piece which would move me as in the old days. I found it in *Child of Fancy*, a composition which features John Van Derrick on violin. The effect of this tune upon me was comically predictable. After hearing it twice, I began, despite myself, to write a lyric. This has always been the effect of Tony's music upon me, to aspire to express in words the mood evoked by the music. I never even came close to it, and once I had completed the lyric of *Child of Fancy* I tore it up in deference to the charm of the original, consoling myself with thoughts of the time when the sixth of Tony's piano solos first became known to me. We had been writing songs together for a while - this would be around 1955 - with no commercial success. Naturally, when I interrupted his supper one evening, he told me he would be free in fifteen minutes and why didn't I while away the time by looking at a new song on the piano. As he often did, Tony had appended a title to the new song *So Near, so Far*, and I saw from its constitution that merely by filling in the title and concocting a matching phrase with rhymes for near and far, the first eight bars would be finished. Intrigued by the exercise I moved on to the next eight bars and decided to work from the same plan - at which point I ran into the brick wall of bars 13-16, where the whole piece suddenly veered off into a new tonality. Fortunately for me, in spite of the originality of this switch, the metre remained the same, so I was able to proceed. The middle section, again composed of long notes, required only a single rhymed couplet, followed by a return to the beginning, which I was able to complete just as Tony emerged from the kitchen. Nothing ever happened to the song, but is some comfort to me to hear not only that the tune has survived but that somewhere along the way my lyrics have melted away. Thirty years is a long time to follow a muse, but I have always regarded Crombie as a special case, a man with genuine creative gifts, unlike so many of the cuckoos of the music business who thrive as composers without possessing one hundredth part of his talent. It is a terrible indicement of the music industry that so richly endowed a musician should have suffered such long neglect. Then again, as somebody once observed long before either Tony or myself was born, when it comes to music, the public never did know chalk from cheese. (Benny Green, 1989)

**Cass:** Released Jul '89, on Renaissance Catalogue no: **ZCREN 001**

**Album:** Released Jul '89, on Renaissance Catalogue no: **REN 001**

**CD:** Released Jul '89, on Renaissance Catalogue no: **CDREN 001**

## Crosby, Bing

**Biographical details:** This American singer, born Harry Lillis Crosby in Tacoma, Washington in 1904, gained his nickname Bing while a child; it was inspired by Bingo, the name of one of the characters from *The Bingville Bugle*, his favourite comic book. It became one of the most famous nicknames in history, because Bing Crosby rose to become a worldwide entertainment legend. His original intended career was law, and it was that subject that he was studying at university when he decided to quit his learning and enter showbusiness. Starting at the bottom of the ladder, his first big break came three years later when he was invited to join Paul Whiteman's ensemble, one of America's foremost bands. After three years with Whiteman, Crosby began to build up a reputation in Los Angeles as a solo singer.

His string of hit records began in the early Thirties, and his first million-seller *Sweet Leilani* was issued in 1937. Its success encapsulated all of Crosby's talents - his superb light baritone voice, his personable on-screen presence and, in particular, his successful marriage of the two: the song came from Crosby's movie *Waikiki Wedding*, and it won the Oscar for the best film song of the year. Of Crosby's many movie appearances, the best was probably 1956's star studded *High Society*. During the Forties he was a huge success on US radio, often with showbiz friends, Bob Hope and Frank Sinatra. The most important day of Crosby's career was 29 May, 1942. In a Los Angeles studio on that summer's day, he recorded *White Christmas*, a song by Irving Berlin. Although written for the film *Holiday Inn*, the song quickly broke out of its movie context to become the United States favourite Yuletide song. After its original 1942 success, the record entered the American charts for a further eighteen Christmases and inspired so many cover versions that it became a whole industry in itself. But for all the numerous remakes by an extraordinary array of artists, it was Crosby's original waxing that remained the definitive version. By the late Sixties, a quarter of a century after being recorded, it had sold 30 million copies thus becoming the world's best-selling disc of all time. Bing's *White Christmas* maintained this honour for some fifteen years, until being overtaken in 1984 by Michael Jackson's LP *Thriller*.

Crosby's performance on this single was, like the song itself brilliant in its sheer straightforward. To many people, *White Christmas* is their first thought when Bing's name is mentioned. But casual Crosby observers should not overlook three other Yuletide smashed that were recorded in the wake of the success of *White Christmas*: his versions of *Silent Night, Oh Come all ye Faithful* and *Jingle Bells* were multi million sellers. Indeed he recorded approximately 100 Christmas songs in his 50-year showbusiness career, ending in fine style with 1977's *Peace on Earth-little drummer boy*, an unlikely duet with David Bowie; that medley was recorded for a TV show in the final weeks of Crosby's life and became a British Top 3 hit five years later. Joseph Murrells' tome *The Records That Sold a Million* lists over twenty Crosby million-sellers, mostly recorded during the Forties. He had the honour of being listed on the very first British record chart, published on 14 November 1952 - Crosby was No.4 that week with *Isle of Innisfree*.

Bing Crosby died in October 1977 at the age of 73; he suffered a heart attack in Madrid, Spain, minutes after indulging in one of his favourite occupations, golf.

This final scene of contentment was a fitting end for a man who reportedly once told a journalist, 'I really have accomplished just about everything I wanted to do'. One of the biggest showbusiness phenomenons of the 20th century, Crosby was the king of the crooners who dominated popular music in the pre-rock 'n' roll era. (Bob MacDonald, 9th Feb 1985)

The all time great crooner, Harry Lillis Crosby (1904-77), was nicknamed as a child after a comic-strip character called Bingo who had big ears. He was the biggest selling recording artist of the first 70 years of recorded sound, and by a very wide margin. With Al Rinker (Mildred Bailey's brother) and Harry Barris, he formed a successful vaudeville act; they were hired by bandleader Paul Whiteman, (the second best-selling recording artist in the entire pre-rock period), as The Rhythm Boys. Crosby's first solo was probably *I've Got the Girl* in 1926, with Whiteman. They left Whiteman and were booked at the Coconut Grove in Los Angeles, with the Gus Arnheim band; among the records they sang on was Duke Ellington's *Three Little Words*, a number one hit in 1930. Crosby's solo *I Surrender Dear* with Arnheim helped land his first radio show in 1931; he commissioned his theme *Where the Blue of the Night (meets the gold of the day)* and took a co-writing credit. He had well over 300 hit singles; German soldiers during the Second World War called him 'Der Bingle'.

Bing Crosby - One of the all-time greats in the history of music

He began steeped in minstrelsy, influenced in terms of projection and pleasing an audience by Al Jolson, and was then influenced stylistically by jazz musicians Louis Armstrong, Bix Beiderbecke and Ethel Waters. (The first great jazz guitarist Eddie Land, was his personal accompanist). He added his own technique and virtually invented pop singing, with his natural insoucience, cannily informal phrasing and husky voice as opposed to the wimpish style of the period. Notes on his vocal chords produced the effect of 'singing into a rain barrel'; he called himself 'The Groaner'. In fact he was one of the first to understand the microphone, then a recent invention, and the first to sing to it as though to an individual listener. Rudy Vallee (who sang through a megaphone) said that as soon as he heard Crosby he knew that his style was outdated; the only real rival Crosby had in the early '30's was Russ Columbo, who was killed in an accident; in the '40's Frank Sinatra, Dick Haymes and Perry Como followed in Crosby's footsteps. He broadcast for 20 years; about 2,600 singles and 120 albums sold an estimated 400 million by 1975. He made over 60 films, many with first class original songs written by Johnny Burke and Jimmy Van Heusen, Nacio Herb Brown, Rodgers & Hart and others; *Holiday Inn* in 1942 had an Irving Berlin score including *White Christmas*, still one of the all time best sellers. There was also the series of comedy musical *Road* films between 1940 and 1962 with his close friend Bob Hope (they maintained a friendly feud until the end). He recorded for *Brunswick*, then switched to the new American *Decca* label (but the records continued to appear on Brunswick in this country). His million sellers began with *Sweet Leilani* in 1937, an Oscar winner (the gold record gimmick was only invented a few years later by *RCA Victor*, to honour a Glenn Miller hit); another was Bob Will's *San Antonio Rose* in 1940 (with brother Bob Crosby's band). He recorded many other excellent country songs and was the first pop singer to cover them. *Swingin' on a Star* in 1944 was an Oscar winner by Burke and Van Heusen from *Going My Way*. Andy Williams sang in the backing group and the song was included in a songbook for school children.

He recorded with the Andrews Sisters, Al Jolson, Les Paul, Jane Wyman (Ronald Reagan's first wife), the Ink Spots, Johnny Mercer and many others, including his son Gary and Gary's mother, Dixie Lee; and later with Rosemary Clooney and Grace Kelly (*True Love* with Kelly from *High Society*, was his last chart single in 1956). His earliest records have a remarkable clarity and an obvious difference from earlier pop singing, to say nothing of good songs, many now forgotten; his many hits of the 1940s are even more relaxed, and simply do not date, not even the treacly ones, because he sounded as if he meant them. (Donald Clarke, April 1989).

**10TH ANNIVERSARY COLLECTION, THE**

**Cass:** Released Sep '87, on Warwick by Warwick Records. Catalogue no: **WW 4 1005**

**CD:** Released Oct '87, on Warwick by Warwick Records. Catalogue no: **U 1005**

**Album:** Released Sep '87, on Warwick by Warwick Records. Catalogue no: **WW 1005**

**16 GOLDEN CLASSICS**

Tracks: / As time goes by / Way we were, The / Hey Jude / Little green apples / Both sides now / It's all in the game / Those were the days / Carolina in the morning / Way down yonder in New Orleans / Georgia on my mind / Besame mucho / Spanish eyes / If you should ever need me / Swanee / Night is young and you're so beautiful, The / Breeze and I, The.

**Album:** Released Dec '86, on Unforgettable by Castle Communications Records. Catalogue no: **UNLP 016**

**Cass:** Released Dec '86, on Unforgettable by Castle Communications Records. Catalogue no: **UNMC 016**

**20 GOLDEN GREATS: BING CROSBY**

Tracks: / Swinging on a star / Gone fishin' / White Christmas / You are my sunshine / Moonlight bay / Pennies from heaven / MacNamara's band.

**Album:** Released Dec '79, on MCA by MCA Records. Deleted '84. Catalogue no: **MCTV 3**

**CD:** Released Nov '89, on MCA by MCA Records. Catalogue no: **DMCTV 3**

**20 GOLDEN GREATS: BING CROSBY**

**Cass:** Released Dec '85, on Nostalgia (USA) by Sonic Arts Corporation (USA). Catalogue no: **42015**

**ALL THE WAY**

Tracks: / What is there to say? / Ford gives more convertable value / Now if you want a wagon / All the way / Everybody's eyeing a Ford / You're ahead in a Ford / Forever and ever / Witchcraft / Catch a falling star / Gigi / Chances are.

**Album:** Released Oct '86, on Blue & Gold (USA) by Kiner Ents.(USA). Catalogue no: **B&G 1**

**AROUND THE WORLD**

Tracks: / Around the world.

**7" Single:** Released May '57, on Brunswick by Decca Records. Deleted May '60. Catalogue no: **05674**

**BEST OF BING**

Tracks: / Where the blue of the night / Swinging on a star / You are my sunshine / It's been a long long time / MacNamara's band / Sweet Leilani / I'm an old cowhand / Pennies from Heaven / White Christmas / Mexicali rose / Whiffenpoof song, The / I can't begin to tell you / Play a simple melody / Sam's song / Now is the hour / Dear hearts and gentle people / Galway Bay / In the cool cool cool of the evening / Too-ra-loo-ra-loo-ra.

**CD:** Released Nov '88, on MCA by MCA Records. Catalogue no: **DMCL 1607**

**Cass:** Released Aug '81, on MCA by

MCA Records. Catalogue no: **MCLC 1607**
**Album:** Released Nov '77, on MCA by MCA Records. Deleted Nov '82. Catalogue no: **MCF 2540**
**Album:** Released Aug '81, on MCA by MCA Records. Catalogue no: **MCL 1607**

**BEST OF BING CROSBY**
Tracks: / Where the blue of the night / Pennies from Heaven / Swinging on a star / MacNarmara's band / Don't fence me in / Whiffenpoof song, The / Sam's song / Dear hearts and gentle people / In the cool cool cool of the evening / Mr. Gallagher and Mr. Shean / Waiter, the porter & the upstairs maid, The / Accentuate the positive / In the good old summertime / When Irish eyes are smiling / Chattanooga shoe shine boy / Danny boy.
**Album:** Released 5 Oct '87, on MFP by EMI Records. Deleted Apr '90. Catalogue no: **MFP 5814**
**Cass:** Released 5 Oct '87, on MFP by EMI Records. Catalogue no: **TC MFP 5814**

**BING AND AL VOL. 1 (Crosby, Bing & Al Jolson)**
Tracks: / Running around in circles / What am I gonna do about you? / Let me sing and I'm happy / Rockabye your baby with a Dixie melody / Who paid the rent for Mrs Rip Van Winkle? / Back in your own back yard / You made me love you / Waiting for the Robert E. Lee / Anniversary song / There'll be a hot time in the old town tonight / Nobody / Oh Susannah / Goin' to heaven on a mule / Hear dem bells / In the evening by the moonlight / Beautiful dreamer / On the banks of the Wabash / My mammy / Alabamy bound.
**Album:** Released Jun '79, on Totem Catalogue no: **TOTEM 1003**

**BING AND AL VOL. 2 (Crosby, Bing & Al Jolson)**
Tracks: / I've got a lovely bunch of coconuts / Sorry / Swanee / When the red, red robin comes bob, bob, bobbin' along / I only have eyes for you / Waiting for the Robert E. Lee / I can dream, can't I / Dear hearts and gentle people / Bye bye baby / Is it true what they say about Dixie? / Carolina in the morning / My blue Heaven / Alabamy bound / One I love belongs to somebody else, The / All by myself.
**Album:** Released Jun '79, on Totem Catalogue no: **TOTEM 1007**

**BING AND AL VOL. 3 (Crosby, Bing & Al Jolson)**
Tracks: / New Ashmolean, The / Happy times / California, here I come / Yaaka hula hickey dula / Whispering / Bye, bye baby / Waiting for the Robert E. Lee / You're wonderful / I've got a lovely bunch of coconuts / Toot, toot, tootsie / Back in your own back yard / Baby face / That lucky old sun.
**Album:** Released Jun '79, on Totem Catalogue no: **TOTEM 1013**

**BING AND AL VOL. 4 (Crosby, Bing & Al Jolson)**
Tracks: / Pass that peace pipe / Kate / Ma blushin' Rosie / Sunbonnet Sue / Pretty girl is like a melody, A / Best things in life are free, The / Country style / Linda / Oh! How I hate to get up in the morning / Lazy / All by myself / Alexander's ragtime band / Easter parade.
**Album:** Released Jun '79, on Totem Catalogue no: **TOTEM 1015**

**BING AND AL VOL. 5 (Crosby, Bing & Al Jolson)**
Tracks: / Horse told me, The / I hadn't anyone till you / Stay with the happy people / Give my regards to Broadway / Ma blushin' Rosie / Avalon / Lullaby of Broadway / My old Kentucky home / Rainy night in Rio, A / Anniversary song / April showers / Ma blushin' Rosie / Swanee / Philco singing commercial, The / One I love belongs to somebody else, The.
**Album:** Released Jun '79, on Totem Catalogue no: **TOTEM 1016**

**BING AND AL VOL. 6 (Crosby, Bing & Al Jolson)**
Tracks: / April showers / For me and my gal / Whiffenpoof song, The / George Gershwin medley / Toot, toot, tootsie / Malaguena / Waiting for the Robert E. Lee / Sleepy time gal / Carolina in the morning / But beautiful / Beautiful dreamer.
**Album:** Released Jun '79, on Totem Catalogue no: **TOTEM 1017**

**BING AND BOB HOPE (Crosby, Bing & Bob Hope)**
Tracks: / Swinging on a star / Take it easy / One I love belongs to somebody else, The / Speak to me of love / It's love, love, love / Amor / Bless 'em all / Milkman, keep those bottles quiet / Day after forever, The / Together / Put it there, pal / I'll be seeing you.
**Album:** Released Feb '88, on Spokane (USA) by Kiner Ents.(USA). Catalogue no: **SPOKANE 22**

**BING AND CONNIE BOSWELL (Crosby, Bing and Connie Boswell)**
Tracks: / Manhattan / You ain't kidding / Hut sut song, The / Everything happens to me / Number ten lullaby lane / Rose O'Day / Basin street blues / Look at me now / Yes, indeed! / East street / Between 18th and 19th on Chestnut Street.
**Album:** Released Feb '88, on Spokane (USA) by Kiner Ents.(USA). Catalogue no: **SPOKANE 18**

**BING AND DINAH SHORE (Crosby, Bing & Dinah Shore)**
Tracks: / My old Kentucky home / Bing and Dinah medley 1 / Tipperary / It ain't necessarily so / Bing and Dinah medley 2 / Easter parade / Summertime / Over there / Mr. Crosby and Mr. Carpenter / Basin street blues / Mr. C and Miss Dinah / How deep is the ocean / San Antonio rose / Bing, Dinah and Ukie medley / Bing and Dinah medley 3 / Oh what a beautiful morning.
**Album:** Released Feb '88, on Spokane (USA) by Kiner Ents.(USA). Catalogue no: **SPOKANE 31**

**BING AND THE MUSIC MAIDS**
Tracks: / I've got a lot of dreaming to do / Honolulu / In a bungalow where the red roses grow / You're the only star in my blue heaven / Stop It's wonderful / El Rancho Grande / Scatterbrain / You're a lucky guy / Looking at the world through rose coloured glasses / Holy smoke can't you take a joke / Little red fox, The / Confucius say / Sunday / Sweet potato piper / I've got my eyes on you / Woodpecker song, The / Ma, he's making eyes at me / Down by the O-H-I-O / If I had my way / Friendly tavern, The.
**Album:** Released Feb '88, on Spokane (USA) by Kiner Ents.(USA). Catalogue no: **SPOKANE 21**

**BING, BOB AND JUDY (Crosby, Bing, Bob Hope & Judy Garland)**
Tracks: / Sam's song / Get happy / I cross my fingers / Mona Lisa / Goodnight Irene / Tzena, Tzena, Tzena / All my love / Friendly star / Third man, Theme from / High on the list.
**Album:** Released Feb '88, on Totem Catalogue no: **TOTEM 1009**

**BING CROSBY**
**CD:** Released Jul '87, on Intertape Deleted Jan '89. Catalogue no: **500 027**
**Album:** Released '88, on Joker (USA) by Lifetime Records (USA). Catalogue no: **SM 4011**
**Album:** Released Sep '87, on Entertainers Catalogue no: **ENT LP 13021**
**Cass:** Released '88, on Entertainers Catalogue no: **ENT MC 13021**

**BING CROSBY (1927 TO 1934) (Classic Years Vol. 1)**
Tracks: / Someday, sweetheart / Mary / So the bluebirds and the blackbirds got together / I surrender, dear / Where the blue of the night / Please / Thanks / Last round-up, The / St. Louis blues / Black moonlight / Beautiful girl / We'll make hay while the sun shines / Temptation / Did you ever see a dream walking? / She reminds me of you / Love in bloom.
**CD:** Released Oct '87, on BBC by BBC Records & Tapes. Catalogue no: **BBC CD 648**
**Cass:** Released Oct '87, on BBC by BBC Records & Tapes. Catalogue no: **ZCF 648**
**Album:** Released Oct '87, on BBC by BBC Records & Tapes. Catalogue no: **REB 648**

**BING CROSBY CHRISTMAS COLLECTION (Bing's Christmas Greats)**
Tracks: / White Christmas / Silent night / Adeste fideles / Christmas song, The / Too-ra-loo-ra-loo-ra / Silver bells / God rest ye merry gentlemen / Rudolph the red nosed reindeer / Deck the halls with boughs of holly (medley) / MacNamara's band / Baby, it's cold outside / Hark the herald angels sing.
Note: Deck the Halls medley: Deck the Halls with Boughs of Holly/ Away in a Manger/ O Little Town of Bethlehem/ The First Noel.
**Cass:** Released Aug '86, on Deja Vu Catalogue no: **DVMC 2078**

**CD:** Released Dec '87, on Deja Vu Catalogue no: **DVCD 2078**
**Album:** Released Aug '86, on Deja Vu Catalogue no: **DVLP 2078**

**BING CROSBY COLLECTION**
**CD:** Released Oct '89, on Collection by K-Tel Records. Catalogue no: **OR 0084**
**Album:** Released Dec '85, on Deja Vu Catalogue no: **DVLP 2027**
**Cass:** Released Dec '85, on Deja Vu Catalogue no: **DVMC 2027**

**BING CROSBY COLLECTION 1 (14 sides never released on LPs)**
**Cass:** Released '84, on CBS by CBS Records. Deleted '85. Catalogue no: **40 31618**
**Album:** Released '84, on CBS by CBS Records. Catalogue no: **31618**

**BING CROSBY COLLECTION 2 (14 sides never released on LPs)**
Tracks: / I'll follow you / Try a little tenderness / You're getting to be a habit with me / Young and healthy / You're beautiful tonight my dear / What do I care its home / You're crying again / I've got to pass you house to get my house / Shadow waltz / I've got to sing a torch song / Little dutch mill / Shadows of love / Ridin' around in the rain / Give me a heart to sing to.
**Cass:** Released '84, on CBS by CBS Records. Catalogue no: **40 31656**
**Album:** Released '84, on CBS by CBS Records. Catalogue no: **31656**

**BING CROSBY COLLECTION 3 (14 sides never released on LPs)**
Tracks: / My angeline / Orange blossom time / I'm sorry dear / Can't we talk it over / Waltzing in a dream / Let's try again / Someday we'll meet again / It's within power / I'm playing with fire / Here is my heart / My love / I would if I could but I can't / Home on the range / Lets spend an evening at home.
**Album:** Released '84, on CBS by CBS Records. Catalogue no: **31751**
**Cass:** Released '84, on CBS by CBS Records. Catalogue no: **40 31751**

**BING CROSBY AND FRIENDS 1**
Tracks: / Dearie / Lazybones / Wedding samba, The / Lonesome in the saddle / Just the way you are / Yessir that's my baby / Yakka hula hicky dula / Enjoy yourself / Have I told you lately that I love you / Play a simple melody / Let's take an old fashioned walk / Blueberry Hill / To prove that I'm in love.
Note: Medley: Hello my baby/In my merry oldsmobile / Call me up some rainy afternoon / Walking by baby back home, (with Judy Garland). Medley: Lily of Laguna / Goodbyee, (with Beatrice Lillie and Alec Templeton).
**Cass:** Released Apr '85, on Magic (1) by Submarine Records. Catalogue no: **CAWE 3**
**CD:** Released Oct '89, on Magic (1) by Submarine Records. Catalogue no: **DAWE 3**
**Album:** Released Apr '85, on Magic (1) by Submarine Records. Catalogue no: **AWE 3**

**BING CROSBY AND FRIENDS 2**
**Cass:** Released '84, on Magic (1) by Submarine Records. Catalogue no: **CAWE 10**
**Album:** Released '84, on Magic (1) by Submarine Records. Catalogue no: **AWE 10**

**BING CROSBY, JUDY GARLAND AND THE ANDREWS SISTERS**
Tracks: / Ol buttermilk sky / I've got to get me somebody to love / I've got you under my skin / Liza / Wait till the sun shines Nellie / All by myself / You gotta get me somebody to love / Very thought of you, The / South America take it away / You don't have to know the language / So would I.
**Album:** Released Oct '82, on Black Lion Catalogue no: **BLM 52003**

**BING CROSBY ON THE AIR**
**Album:** Released Jan '79, on Sandy Hook (USA) Catalogue no: **SH 2002**

**BING CROSBY ON THE AIR VOL 1**
Tracks: / I'm hummin', I'm singin' / Heebie jeebies / I kiss your hand madame / Just a-wearyin' for you / Why don't you practise what you preach? / Love in bloom / On the sentimental side / I simply adore you / Smiles / Remember me / Guilty / Kissable baby / I cried for you / As time goes by.
**Album:** Released Feb '88, on Spokane (USA) by Kiner Ents.(USA). Catalogue no: **SPOKANE 1**

**BING CROSBY (SET)**
**Cass set:** Released Jul '86, on RCA by BMG Records (UK). Deleted Nov '88. Catalogue no: **NK 89535**
**2 LP Set:** Released Jul '86, on RCA by BMG Records (UK). Deleted Nov '88. Catalogue no: **NL 89535**

**BING CROSBY SINGS MORE GREAT SONGS**
Tracks: / There's no business like show business / Secret love / Stranger in paradise / Accentuate the positive / I'll be seeing you / I love Paris / People will say we're in love / They can't take that away from me / You must have been a beautiful baby / Nightingale sang in Berkeley Square, A / You made me love you / Red sails in the sunset / Wrap your troubles in dreams / Georgia on my mind / Autumn leaves.
**Album:** Released Feb '89, on Pickwick by Pickwick Records. Catalogue no: **SHM 3259**
**Cass:** Released Feb '89, on Pickwick by Pickwick Records. Catalogue no: **HSC 3259**
**CD:** Released Feb '89, on Pickwick by Pickwick Records. Catalogue no: **PWK 088**

**BING CROSBY STORY, THE**
Tracks: / Where blue of the night meets gold of the day / Someday, sweetheart / I'm an old cowhand / Pennies from Heaven / Marie / Folks who live on the hill, The / When you wore a tulip / I still love to kiss you goodnight / I don't want to get well / Once in a while / Mexicali rose / Thousand violins, A / Christmas song, The / Silent night / White Christmas / Silver bells / Adeste fideles / Down yonder / Glow worm / Mr. Moon / Maybe it's because / Pittsburgh Pennsylvania / Please Mr. Sun / Blues my naughty sweetie gives to me / Whispering.
**Cass:** Released May '89, on Deja Vu Catalogue no: **DVRE MC 16**
**CD:** Released May '89, on Deja Vu Catalogue no: **DVRE CD 16**

**BING CROSBY WITH AL JOLSON (Crosby, Bing & Al Jolson)**
Tracks: / There'll be a hot time in the old town tonight / Nobody / Oh Susannah / Going to the Heavens / In the evening by the moonlight (medley) / Mammy / Alabama bound / Getting nowhere / What am I gonna do about you? / Let me sing and I'm happy / Rockabye your baby with a Dixie melody / You made me love you (medley).
Note: In the evening by the moonlight medley: In the evening by the moonlight/ Beautiful dreamer/ On the banks of the Wabash. You made me love you medley: You made me love you/ Waitin' for the Robert E. Lee.
**Album:** Released Jan '87, on Black Lion Catalogue no: **BLM 52023**

**BING CROSBY WITH MAURICE CHEVALIER AND FRANKIE LAINE**
Tracks: / Smile right back at the sun / I want to thank your folks / You brought a new kind of love to me / My love parade / Hello beautiful / My ideal / Learn to croon / Louise / Mimi / I'll close my eyes / Old chaperon, The / That's my desire / Two loves have I.
**Album:** Released Jul '84, on Black Lion Catalogue no: **BLM 52043**

**BING CROSBY WITH PEGGY LEE, JACK BENNY AND GARY COOPER**
Tracks: / I do do like you / I love you for sentimental reasons / What am I gonna do about you? / Lover / Love in bloom / Margie / Anniversary song / My heart is a hobo / It takes a long, long train / Mam'selle (medley) / Home on the range / El Rancho Grande / You do.
Note: Mam'selle medley: Mam'selle/ Chi ba ba/ Peg o' my heart.
**Album:** Released Jul '88, on Black Lion Catalogue no: **BLM 52033**

**BING CROSBY WITH SPIKE JONES AND JIMMY DURANTE**
Tracks: / My heart goes crazy / Hawaiian war chant / Love in bloom / Fascinating rhythm / Little surplus me / All by myself / Blue skies.
**Album:** Released Jan '87, on Black Lion Catalogue no: **BLM 52013**

**BING CROSBY'S CHRISTMAS CLASSICS**
Tracks: / Winter wonderland / Have yourself a merry little Christmas / What a child is this? / Holly and the ivy, The / Little drummer boy / O holy night / Littlest angel, The / Let it snow, let it snow, let it snow / Hark the herald angels sing / It came upon a midnight clear / Frosty the snowman / I wish you a merry Christmas.

**Cass:** Released Nov '85, on Capitol by EMI Records. Deleted Jun '89. Catalogue no: **ED 2607214**
**Album:** Released Nov '85, on Capitol by EMI Records. Deleted Jun '89. Catalogue no: **ED 2607211**

### BING IN THE THIRTIES VOL. 1
Tracks: / Someone else may be there while I'm gone / At long last love / I'm just wild about Harry / Have you forgotten? / I'm building a sailboat of dreams / That sly old gentleman / Ciribiribin / After all / Blame it on my youth / Japanese sandman / Things might have been different / Easy to remember / Alexander's ragtime band / Old faithful / Lullaby of broadway.
**Album:** Released Feb '88, on Spokane (USA) by Kiner Ents.(USA). Catalogue no: **SPOKANE 12**

### BING IN THE THIRTIES VOL. 2
**Album:** Released May '79, on Spokane (USA) by Kiner Ents.(USA). Catalogue no: **SPOKANE 14**
Album: Released Jan '85, on JSP by JSP Records. Catalogue no: **JSP 1084**

### BING IN THE THIRTIES VOL. 3 (On the Air From Kraft Music Hall)
Tracks: / Where or on / Can I forget you / Smarty / Remember me / Smile / On the beach at Waikiki / Let's call a heart a heart / So do I / 1,2, button your shoe / With all my heart / Here lies love / Please.
**Album:** Released Jun '84, on Spokane (USA) by Kiner Ents.(USA). Catalogue no: **SPOKANE 24**

### BING IN THE THIRTIES VOL. 4 (On the Air From Kraft Music Hall)
Tracks: / Dipsy doodle, The / On the sentimental side / On moonlight bay / I see your face before me / Moon of manakoora / Gypsy love song / Thanks for the memory / Gypsy in my soul / You're a sweetheart / My heart stood still / Side by side / Old flame never dies, An / Sympathy / My heart is taking lessons / Down where the trade wind blows / Whistle while you work / Let's waltz for old times sake / I'd love to live in loveland / I simply adore you.
**Album:** Released Jun '84, on Spokane (USA) by Kiner Ents.(USA). Catalogue no: **SPOKANE 25**

### BING IN THE THIRTIES VOL. 5 (On the Air From Kraft Music Hall)
Tracks: / Ti-pi-ti-pi-tin / On the sentimental side / Mexicali rose/Sweet as a song / Where the blue of the night / My heart is taking lessons / I can dream, can't I / Don't be that way / Home town / Call me up some rainy afternoon / Love walked right in / One song / Cuddle up a little closer / Little lady make believe / You're an education / Hello Hawaii, how are you? / Flat foot floogie / Lovelight in the starlight / Silver on the Sage / Someone else may be there while I'm gone / Naturally.

**Album:** Released Jun '84, on Spokane (USA) by Kiner Ents.(USA). Catalogue no: **SPOKANE 26**

### BING IN THE THIRTIES VOL. 6
Tracks: / Small fry / Now it can be told / Ride, Tenderfoot, ride / Sleep Kentucky baby / Garden of the moon / You must have been a beautiful baby / Ya got me / Red wing / My reverie / Dipsy doodle / Who blew out the flame / Don't be that way / Lullaby in rhythm / Hurry home / When you're a long, long way from home / Funny old hills, The / I cried for you / I have eyes / Old folks / Lonesome road.
**Album:** Released Feb '88, on Spokane (USA) by Kiner Ents.(USA). Catalogue no: **SPOKANE 27**

### BING IN THE THIRTIES VOL. 7
Tracks: / Between a kiss and a sigh / Thanks for everything / Deep in a dream / Together / Missouri waltz / Could be / Teacher teacher / Umbrella man / Penny serenade / Yaaka hula hickey dula / I dream of Jeannie with the light brown hair / S'posin' / Little Sir Echo / Sing a song of sunbeams / East side of heaven / Honolulu / I get along without you very well / Sweet Genevieve / You're the only star in my blue heaven.
**Album:** Released Feb '88, on Spokane (USA) by Kiner Ents.(USA). Catalogue no: **SPOKANE 28**

### BING IN THE THIRTIES VOL. 8
Tracks: / Hang your heart on a hickory limb / I want a girl / Little Sir Echo / I'm building a sailboat of dreams / Class will tell / We've come a long way together / Mickey / Our love / Tuck me to sleep in my old Kentucky home / Delightful delirium / Wishing will make it so / Snug as a bug in a rug / Oh by jingo, oh by gee / Go fly a kite / Apple for teacher, An / Are you having any fun / If I knew then / Scatterbrain / I can't believe that you're in love with me.
**Album:** Released Feb '88, on Spokane (USA) by Kiner Ents.(USA). Catalogue no: **SPOKANE 29**

### BING IS BACK (Philco Radio Time Programme)
Tracks: / I got the sun in the morning / Moonlight bay / Put it there, pal / Love on a greyhound bus / Cynthia / Connecticut / A-huggin' and a-chalkin' / I've got you under my skin / Tearbucket Jim / And so to sleep.
**Album:** Released Jun '79, on Totem Catalogue no: **TOTEM 1002**

### BING AND LOUIS LIVE (Crosby, Bing & Armstrong, Louis)
**CD:** Released Jun '88, on Spectrum (1) Catalogue no: **U 4016**

### BING 'N' BASIE (Crosby, Bing & Count Basie)
Tracks: / Gentle on my mind / Everything is beautiful / Gonna build a mountain / Sunrise, sunset / Hangin' loose / All his children / Put your hand in the hand / Snowbird / Little green apples / Sugar don't you know / Have a nice day.
**CD:** on Verve Deleted '88. Catalogue no: **824 705-2**

### BING SINGS BROADWAY
**Album:** Released '82, on MCA by MCA Records. Deleted '87. Catalogue no: **MCL 1730**
**Cass:** Released '82, on MCA by MCA Records. Deleted '87. Catalogue no: **MCLC 1730**

### BING SINGS THE GREAT SONGS
Tracks: / Begin the beguine / Fine romance, A / Ol' man river.
**Album:** on Pickwick by Pickwick Records. Catalogue no: **SHM 3235**
**CD:** on Pickwick by Pickwick Records. Catalogue no: **PWK 065**
**Cass:** on Pickwick by Pickwick Records. Catalogue no: **HSC 3235**

### BING - THE FINAL CHAPTER
Tracks: / Introduction / Feels good feels right / Bing and Alan Dell / Nevertheless / Only way to go, The / Summer wind / Variety bandbox / Night is young, The / Final chapter / There's nothing that I haven't sung about / As time goes by / Once in a while.
**Album:** Released Nov '80, on BBC by BBC Records & Tapes. Deleted '88. Catalogue no: **REB 398**
**Cass:** Released Nov '80, on BBC by BBC Records & Tapes. Deleted '88. Catalogue no: **ZCF 398**

### BING AND TRUDY ON THE AIR (Crosby, Bing & Trudy Erwin)
Tracks: / Constantly / Hit the road to dreamland / My heart stood still / You'll never know / You took advantage of me / Wait for me Mary / People will say we're in love / Right kind of love, The / One alone / Stormy weather / My ideal / My shining hour / Oh! What a beautiful morning / Way you look tonight.
**Album:** Released Oct '86, on Spokane (USA) by Kiner Ents.(USA). Catalogue no: **SPOKANE 23**

### BING'S MAGIC
**Album:** Released '84, on Magic (1) by Submarine Records. Catalogue no: **AWE 1**
**Cass:** Released Aug '85, on Magic (1) by Submarine Records. Catalogue no: **CAWE 1**

### BING'S MUSIC HALL HIGHLIGHTS
Tracks: / It's only a paper moon / You brought a new kind of love to me / Candle light and wine / Easter parade / Nevada / Put your arms around me honey / As time goes by / My ideal / After you've gone / After a while / I'm making believe / Cuddle up a little closer / Moonlight bay / Side by side.
**Album:** Released Oct '86, on Spokane (USA) by Kiner Ents.(USA). Catalogue no: **SPOKANE 16**

### BING'S PARTY
Tracks: / Love is so terrific / But beautiful / Ballerino / Lady be good / Someone to watch over me / Gershwin medley / I got rhythm / Third piano prelude / Saturday date / Some sunny day / Civilization / Wonderful / To see you is to love you / When the blue of the night / Down by the river.
**Cass:** Released Oct '84, on Artistic by Submarine Records. Catalogue no: **CART 001**

**Album:** Released Nov '79, on Artistic by Submarine Records. Catalogue no: **ART 001**

**BIRTH OF THE BLUES JANUARY 23, 1951**
Tracks: / Birth of the blues / Cake walk, The / Basin street blues / Thats what I like about the south / Ida, sweet as apple cider / That's a plenty / Cuddle up a little closer / Memphis blues / Wait till the sun shines Nellie / Dixieland band / My melancholy baby / Way down yonder in New Orleans / Waiter, the porter & the upstairs maid, The / St Louis blues / Ballin' the Jack.
**Album:** Released Feb '88, on Spokane (USA) by Kiner Ents.(USA). Catalogue no: **SPOKANE 9**

**BLACK MOONLIGHT**
Tracks: / Once in a blue moon / Snuggled on your shoulder / If you should ever need me / Home on the range / Where the blue of the night / Black moonlight / Just one more chance / How deep is the ocean / Song of the islands / Our big love scene / May I / Out of nowhere / Brother can you spare a dime / Lazy day / Goodnight sweetheart / Star dust / Try a little tenderness / Sweet Georgia Brown.
**Cass:** Released Apr '87, on Joy by President Records. Catalogue no: **TC-JOYD 290**
**Album:** Released May '87, on Joy by President Records. Catalogue no: **JOY 290**

**BOTH SIDES OF...**
**Album:** Released '88, on Curtain Calls (USA) by Music & Arts Programs of America(USA). Catalogue no: **CC 100/2**

**CBS YEARS, THE**
**CD:** Released Nov '89, on CBS by CBS Records. Catalogue no: **465 569 2**
**Cass:** Released Nov '89, on CBS by CBS Records. Catalogue no: **465 569 4**
**Album:** Released Nov '89, on CBS by CBS Records. Catalogue no: **465 569 1**

**CHANGING PARTNERS**
Tracks: / Changing partners.
**7" Single:** Released Mar '54, on Brunswick by Decca Records. Deleted Mar '57. Catalogue no: **05244**

**CHRISTMAS ALBUM (Crosby, Bing & Rosemary Clooney)**
Tracks: / White christmas / Adeste fideles / Rudolph the red nosed reindeer / Away in a manger / O little town of Bethlehem / Silent night / Christmas song, The / It came upon a midnight clear / Have yourself a merry little Christmas / Little drummer boy / Jingle bells.
**Cass:** Released Nov '86, on Meteor by Magnum Music Group. Catalogue no: **MTC 024**
**Cass:** Released '87, on Meteor by Magnum Music Group. Catalogue no: **MTMC 004**
**Album:** Released Nov '86, on Meteor by Magnum Music Group. Catalogue no: **MTM 024**

**CHRISTMAS WITH BING CROSBY**
Tracks: / Christmas is a comin' / Rudolph the red nosed reindeer / Sleigh ride / Deck the halls / That Christmas feeling / Looks like a cold cold winter / I heard the bells on Christmas day / Silent night, holy night / First snowfall / Marshmallow world, A / Snow / Sleigh bell serenade / Is Christmas only a tree / Little Jack Frost get lost / Snowman, The / Happy holiday.
**Cass:** Released Dec '89, on Pickwick by Pickwick Records. Catalogue no: **HSC 3292**
**Album:** Released Dec '89, on Pickwick by Pickwick Records. Catalogue no: **SHM 3292**
**CD:** Released Dec '89, on Pickwick by Pickwick Records. Catalogue no: **PWKS 561**

**CHRONOLOGICAL BING CROSBY 1**
**Album:** Released Jun '85, on Jonzo Catalogue no: **JZ 1**

**CHRONOLOGICAL BING CROSBY 2**
**Album:** Released Jun '85, on Jonzo Catalogue no: **JZ 2**

**CHRONOLOGICAL BING CROSBY 3 (1928)**
**Album:** Released Dec '86, on Jonzo Catalogue no: **JZ 3**

**CHRONOLOGICAL BING CROSBY 4 (1928)**
**Album:** Released Dec '86, on Jonzo Catalogue no: **JZ 4**

**CHRONOLOGICAL BING CROSBY 5**
**Album:** Released Dec '86, on Jonzo Catalogue no: **JZ 5**

**CHRONOLOGICAL BING CROSBY 6**
**Album:** Released Jun '86, on Jonzo Catalogue no: **JZ 6**

**CHRONOLOGICAL BING CROSBY 7**
**Album:** Released Oct '86, on Jonzo Catalogue no: **JZ 7**

**CHRONOLOGICAL BING CROSBY 8**
**Album:** Released Jul '87, on Jonzo Catalogue no: **JZ 8**

**CHRONOLOGICAL BING CROSBY 9**
**Album:** Released Nov '87, on Jonzo Catalogue no: **JZ 9**

**CHRONOLOGICAL BING CROSBY 10**
**Album:** Released '89, on Jonzo Catalogue no: **JZ 10**

**CHRONOLOGICAL BING CROSBY 11**
**Album:** Released '89, on Jonzo Catalogue no: **JZ 11**

**CHRONOLOGICAL BING CROSBY 12**
**Album:** Released '89, on Jonzo Catalogue no: **JZ 12**

**CLASSIC YEARS**
**Album:** Released Mar '90, on BBC by BBC Records & Tapes. Catalogue no: **REB 766**
**Cass:** Released 5 Mar '90, on BBC by BBC Records & Tapes. Catalogue no: **ZCF 766**
**CD:** Released 5 Mar '90, on BBC by BBC Records & Tapes. Catalogue no: **BBCCD 766**

**COME RAIN OR COME SHINE**
**Album:** Released May '80, on Philips by Phonogram Ltd. Catalogue no: **6359.013**

**COME SHARE THE WINE**
**Album:** Released Apr '80, on United Artists by EMI Records. Catalogue no: **UAG 30294**

**COUNT YOUR BLESSINGS**
Tracks: / Count your blessings.
**7" Single:** Released Jan '55, on Brunswick by Decca Records. Deleted Jan '58. Catalogue no: **05339**

**CROSBYANA VOL. 6 (From Bings' Personal Collection)**
**Album:** Released Oct '87, on Broadway (USA) Catalogue no: **BR 136**

**DANCING IN THE DARK**
**Album:** Released Jun '88, on Dance Band Days by Prism Leisure. Catalogue no: **DBD 14**
**Cass:** Released Jun '88, on Dance Band Days by Prism Leisure. Catalogue no: **DBDC 14**

**DARK MOON**
Tracks: / Maybe it's because / Blacksmith blues / Come what pay / Pittsburgh Pennsylvania / Please Mr. Sun / Everything I have is yours / Thousand violins, A / Dark moon / Blues my naughty sweetie gives to me / Down yonder / Feet up / Glow worm / Cock-eyed optimist / Now that I need you / Chi chi o chi / Blame it on my youth / Lady play your mandolin.
Note: Mono recording.
**Cass:** Released Jul '86, on Magic (1) by Submarine Records. Catalogue no: **CAWE 7**
**Album:** Released Jul '86, on Magic (1) by Submarine Records. Catalogue no: **AWE 7**

**DER BINGLE: VOL. 1**
Tracks: / White cliffs of Dover, The / Army air corps song, The / Yankee doodle dandy / I don't want to walk without you / Song of freedom / You'd be so nice to come home to / What do you do in the infantary / Coming in on a wing and a prayer / Wait for me Mary / Brother Bill / Stardust / It's always you / Basin street blues.
**Album:** Released Feb '88, on Spokane (USA) by Kiner Ents.(USA). Catalogue no: **SPOKANE 5**

**DER BINGLE: VOL. 2**
Tracks: / Riding herd on a cloud tonight / Get on the road to victory / What do you do in the infantary / Sunday, Monday or always / Victory polka / It's all over now / As time goes by / I'll be seeing you / Shoo shoo baby / There'll be a hot time in the town of Berlin / Song of the bombadiers / Long ago and far away / I'll get by / Is you is or is you ain't my baby /

Saturday night.
**Album:** Released Feb '88, on Spokane (USA) by Kiner Ents.(USA). Catalogue no: **SPOKANE 10**

**DER BINGLE: VOL. 3**
Tracks: / Swinging on a star / You belong to my heart / Too-ra-loo-ra-loo-ra / Ida, sweet as apple cider / Bless 'em all / Is you is or is you ain't my baby / Fifth marines, The / Amphibians battle hymn, The / Sunday, Monday or always / Riding herd on a cloud tonight / Bombadiers song, The / Coming in on a wing and a prayer / Shoo shoo baby.
**Album:** Released Feb '88, on Spokane (USA) by Kiner Ents.(USA). Catalogue no: **SPOKANE 20**

**DER BINGLE: VOL. 4**
Tracks: / Where the blue of the night / White Christmas / Easter parade / Shoo shoo baby / You are my sunshine / San Fernando valley / If I had my way / There's no place like home / You're a grand old flag / Darling Nellie Gray / De Camptown races / Home on the range / Friend of ours, A / When you were sweet sixteen / And the band played on / God bless America.
**Album:** Released Feb '88, on Spokane (USA) by Kiner Ents.(USA). Catalogue no: **SPOKANE 30**

**DER BINGLE: VOL. 5**
Tracks: / My darling Clementine / Stardust / You are my sunshine / Abraham / Miss you / Great day / As time goes by / It can't be wrong / I never mention your name / Sunday, Monday or always / On moonlight bay / Swinging on a star / Long ago and far away / You must have been a beautiful baby.
**Album:** Released Feb '88, on Spokane (USA) by Kiner Ents.(USA). Catalogue no: **SPOKANE 32**

**EARLY YEARS, THE (Volume 5, 1934)**
**Cass:** Released Nov '87, on Neovox by Neovox Records. Catalogue no: **NEO 922**

**EASY TO REMEMBER 1931-36**
Tracks: / Out of nowhere / Now that you're gone / Love you funny thing / You're still in my heart / Let's try again / I'm playing with fire / What do I care it's home / I've got to pass your house to get to my house / I would if I could but I can't / Let's spend an evening at home / I'm hummin'-I'm whistlin'-I'm singin' / Someday, sweetheart / Two cigarettes in the dark / It's easy to remember / My heart and I / Moonburn / Lovely lady / Let's call a heart a heart / South sea island magic / I never realised.
Note: Songs from films, shows, showbiz.
**Album:** Released Jan '88, on Saville by Conifer Records. Catalogue no: **SVL 190**
**Cass:** Released Jan '88, on Saville by Conifer Records. Catalogue no: **CSVL 190**

**FEELS GOOD, FEELS RIGHT**
Tracks: / Feels good, feels right / Once in a while / As time goes by / Old fashioned love / Time on my hands / Way we were, The / There's nothing that I haven't sung about / Night is young and you're so beautiful, The / Nevertheless (I'm in love with you) / Rose in her hair, The / What's new? / When I leave the world behind / That old black magic / I'm getting sentimental over you / At last.
**CD:** Released Jun '88, on London Records by London Records Ltd. Catalogue no: **820 586-2**

**FOREVER (30 Evergreens)**
Tracks: / Whispering / Some sunny day / Exactly like you / Mack the knife / Them there eyes / It's a good day / Mary / Muddy water / Loveable / Brazil / Ol' man river / How about you / Isle of Capri / High water / Just a gigolo / I'm through with love / Just one more chance / Mama loves papa.
**2 LP Set:** Released May '83, on RCA (Germany) Catalogue no: **NL 43860**
**2 LP Set:** Released Aug '86, on RCA by BMG Records (UK). Deleted Nov '88. Catalogue no: **NL 89535**
**Cass set:** Released Aug '86, on RCA by BMG Records (UK). Deleted Nov '88. Catalogue no: **NK 89535**
**Cass set:** Released May '83, on RCA (Germany) Catalogue no: **TC-NL 43860**

**GIVE ME THE SIMPLE LIFE**
Tracks: / Give me the simple life / Any town in Paris when you're young / Dance ballerina dance / Kiss in your eyes, The / Pretty baby / Marrying for love / Watermelon weather / Love thy neighbour / Sunshine cake / When the world was young / But beautiful / I love Paris / It's more fun than a picnic / Some enchanted evening / When you're in love / Laroo, laroo Lilli Bolero.
**Cass:** Released May '87, on MCA by MCA Records. Deleted Apr '88. Catalogue no: **MCLC 1848**
**Album:** Released May '87, on MCA by MCA Records. Deleted Apr '88. Catalogue no: **MCL 1848**

**GOLDEN AGE OF AMERICAN RADIO**
Tracks: / Where the blue of the night / Lady of Spain / Hello, hello / For me and my gal / Young at heart / Lazy river / Paper doll / Where is your heart Lullaby of Broadway / It might as well be Spring / It's only a paper moon / That's a plenty / You go to my head / Zip-a-dee-doo-dah / Tell me why / I can dream, can't I / Takes two to Tango / Mona Lisa / I'd have baked a cake (If I knew you were comin') / On a slow boat to China / You brought a new kind of love to me / My love parade / Louise / Mimi / You gotta start off each day / You belong to me / Wish you were here / May the Good Lord bless and keep you.
Note: Includes duets with Judy Garland, Maurice Chevalier, The Mills Brothers and Bob Hope.
**Album:** Released '78, on United Artists by EMI Records. Catalogue no: **UAK 30115**

**GOLDEN GREATS 1: BING CROSBY**
**Cass:** Released May '88, on Coldrado Catalogue no: **42014**
**Album:** Released May '88, on Coldrado Catalogue no: **22014**

**GOLDEN GREATS 2: BING CROSBY**
**Cass:** Released May '88, on Coldrado Catalogue no: **42015**
**Album:** Released May '88, on Coldrado Catalogue no: **22015**

**HAPPY HOLIDAY**
Tracks: / Adeste fideles / Jingle bells / I dream of you / I'm making believe / Slip of the lip / What a difference a day made / Beautiful saviour / God is beside me / Silent night / Happy holiday / Let's start the New Year right / God rest ye merry gentlemen / Let it snow, let it snow, let it snow / I'll be home for Christmas / White Christmas.
**Album:** Released Feb '88, on Spokane (USA) by Kiner Ents.(USA). Catalogue no: **SPOKANE 6**

**HAVIN' FUN (Live Broadcasts 1949-50) (Crosby, Bing & Louis Armstrong)**
**Cass:** Released 11 Apr '87, on Jasmine by Hasmick Promotions. Catalogue no: **JASMC 2508**
**Album:** Released Jan '88, on Sounds Rare Catalogue no: **SR 5009**
**Album:** Released 11 Apr '87, on Jasmine by Hasmick Promotions. Catalogue no: **JASM 2508**

**HERE LIES LOVE (A Selection of Love Songs)**
Tracks: / Very thought of you, The / Love thy neighbour / June in January / You've got me crying again / May I? / With every breath I take / Temptation / Let me call you sweetheart / Sweet and lovely / Love in bloom / You're getting to be a habit with me / I love you truly / Someday, sweetheart / You're beautiful tonight, my dear / Love is just around the corner / Just a-wearyin' for you / It must be true / Here lies love.
**Cass:** Released 1 Oct '86, on Living Era by Academy Sound & Vision Records. Catalogue no: **ZC AJA 5043**
**Album:** Released 1 Oct '86, on Living Era by Academy Sound & Vision Records. Catalogue no: **AJA 5043**

**HOLIDAY INN AND THE BELLS OF ST. MARY'S (Radio Adaptations)**
Tracks: / White Christmas / Happy holiday / Abraham / Be careful, it's my heart / Easter parade / Aren't you glad you're you / Bells of St. Mary's.
**Album:** Released May '79, on Spokane (USA) by Kiner Ents.(USA). Catalogue no: **SPOKANE 15**

**IN A LITTLE SPANISH TOWN**
Tracks: / In a little Spanish town.
**7" Single:** Released Apr '56, on Brunswick by Decca Records. Deleted Apr '59. Catalogue no: **05543**

**IN DEMAND**
Tracks: / Getting to know you / Love walked in / Isle of Innisfree / Waltz you saved for me, The / Dearly beloved / Golden earrings / Out of this world / Rosalie / Vaya con dios / La vie en rose

/ Beautiful love / Indian summer / It had to be you / Rose of Tralee, The / Story of Sorrento, The / I'll remember April / One rose (that's left in my heart) / Yours in my heart alone / Granada.
Note: The first album from the Crosby catalogue in some time finds twenty memorable performances coming to light. The selection has been especially chosen by the Bing Crosby Appreciation Society and endorsed by Radio 2's David Jacobs.
**Album:** Released May '86, on MCA by MCA Records. Deleted Jan '88. Catalogue no: **MCG 6004**

**ISLE OF INNISFREE**
Tracks: / Isle of Innisfree.
**7" Single:** Released Nov '52, on Brunswick by Decca Records. Deleted Nov '55. Catalogue no: **04900**

**JAZZIN' BING CROSBY, THE**
Tracks: / I'm comin', Virginia / Dinah / Shine / Some of these days / My honey's loving arms / Somebody stole Gabriel's horn / Stay on the right side of the road / Someday, sweetheart / Moonburn / I'm an old cowhand / Basin Street blues / You must have been a beautiful baby.
**Album:** Released Apr '81, on Joker (USA) by Lifetime Records (USA). Catalogue no: **SM 3053**

**JOIN BING AND SING ALONG**
**Album:** Released Oct '60, on Warner Bros. by WEA Records. Deleted Oct '65. Catalogue no: **WM 4021**

**JUST BREEZIN' ALONG**
Tracks: / Breezin' along with the breeze / How are things in Glocca Morra / Heatwave / Best things in life are free, The / My heart stood still / I got rhythm / Good old times, The / Cabaret / Send in the clowns / Only way to go, The / Have a nice day / Some sunny day / At my time of life / With a song in my heart / Razzle dazzle / That's what life is all about.
**Cass:** Released Oct '87, on EMI by EMI Records. Deleted Oct '89. Catalogue no: **TCEMS 1274**
**Album:** Released Oct '87, on EMI by EMI Records. Deleted Jun '89. Catalogue no: **EMS 1274**
**CD:** Released Oct '87, on EMI by EMI Records. Catalogue no: **CDP 748 272 2**
**CD:** Released Oct '87, on EMI by EMI Records. Catalogue no: **CZ 5**

**KRAFT MUSIC HALL MAY 27, 1937**
Tracks: / How could you? / My melancholy baby / You're here, you're there / Land of the sky blue water / Time on my hands / My little buckaroo / Forgotten waltz / Lullaby for a bazooka / Flight of the bumble bee / Where are you?.
**Album:** Released Feb '88, on Spokane (USA) by Kiner Ents.(USA). Catalogue no: **SPOKANE 7**

**KRAFT MUSIC HALL MAY 29, 1941**
Tracks: / Can't you tell? / Kerry dance, The / You're a double lovely / It was wonderful then / Stomp Caprice / Frankie and Johnny / All through the night / Hut sut song, The / Maria Elena / Things I love, The / Because of you.
**Album:** Released Feb '88, on Spokane (USA) by Kiner Ents.(USA). Catalogue no: **SPOKANE 17**

**KRAFT MUSIC HALL JANUARY 29, 1942**
Tracks: / Caisson's go rolling along, The / Chattanooga choo choo / You made me love you / Deep in the heart of Texas / Blue Danube, The / Blues in the night / Rose O'Day / Gypsy airs / Home on the range / Who calls?.
**Album:** Released Feb '88, on Spokane (USA) by Kiner Ents.(USA). Catalogue no: **SPOKANE 11**

**KRAFT MUSIC HALL MARCH 12, 1942**
Tracks: / I like it, how about you? / MacNamara's band / I don't want to walk without you / Story of Jenny, The / My darling Nellie Gray / That's a plenty / Three young fillies / We're the gang that feeds the army / Anvil chorus / Miss you.
**Album:** Released Feb '88, on Spokane (USA) by Kiner Ents.(USA). Catalogue no: **SPOKANE 2**

**KRAFT MUSIC HALL APRIL 16, 1942**
Tracks: / K-K-K-Katy / Arthur Murray taught me dancing in a hurry / Miss you / He comes from timbuckthree / Make believe / I'll be with you in apple blossom time / Little Bo Peep has lost her Jeep / Pass the bisquits Mirandy / It's Mary / Way you look tonight / Song of the islands.
**Album:** Released Feb '88, on Spokane (USA) by Kiner Ents.(USA). Catalogue no: **SPOKANE 4**

**KRAFT MUSIC HALL APRIL 30, 1942**
Tracks: / Hey Mable, Wait for me / He's wonderful / Friendship / It's Mary / It's somebody else's moon not mine / I'll be with you in apple blossom time / Malaguena / Blues in the night / Oh how I miss you tonight / Embraceable you / I remember you.
**Album:** Released Feb '88, on Spokane (USA) by Kiner Ents.(USA). Catalogue no: **SPOKANE 3**

**KRAFT MUSIC HALL DECEMBER 24, 1942**
Tracks: / Adeste fideles / Steam is on the beam, The / Why don't you fall in love with me? / Red river valley / God rest ye merry gentlemen / You'd be so nice to come home to / Silent night.
**Album:** Released May '79, on Spokane (USA) by Kiner Ents.(USA). Catalogue no: **SPOKANE 13**

**LEGENDARY BING CROSBY AND FRIENDS, THE**
Tracks: / That old gang of mine / On top of old Smokey / I can dream, can't I / Rosie / Lazy river / Paper doll.
**Cass:** Released Sep '89, on Nostalgia by Mainline Records. Catalogue no: **MRT 40051**

**LEGENDARY PERFORMER, A**
Tracks: / Ol' man river / Three little words / It must be true / Wrap your troubles in dreams / Just a gigolo / I'm thru with love / Just one more chance / Some sunny day / I'm gonna sit right down and write myself / Mack the knife / Dream a little dream of me / Whispering / Down among the sheltering palms.
**Album:** Released '79, on RCA by BMG Records (UK). Deleted '84. Catalogue no: **PL 12086**
**Cass:** Released '79, on RCA by BMG Records (UK). Deleted '84. Catalogue no: **PK 12086**

**LEGENDARY,THE**
**Cass:** Released Mar '90, on Silva Screen by Silva Screen Records. Catalogue no: **MRT 40045**

**LIVE AT THE LONDON PALLADIUM**
**Album:** Released Nov '77, on K-Tel by K-Tel Records. Deleted Nov '82. Catalogue no: **NE 951**

**MANY HAPPY RETURNS**
Tracks: / Where the blue of the night / Out of nowhere / If you should ever need me / Were you sincere / Just one more chance / I'm through with love / Many happy returns of the day / I found a million dollar baby / At your command / I apologise / Dancing in the dark / Stardust / Sweet and lovely / Too late / I'm sorry dear / Goodnight sweetheart.
**Album:** Released Jan '76, on Vocalion by Vocalion Records. Deleted '80. Catalogue no: **VLP 1**

**MERRY CHRISTMAS**
**CD:** Released Jun '88, on MCA (USA) by MCA Records (USA). Catalogue no: **31143**

**MR. CROSBY AND MR. MERCER**
Tracks: / Mr. Gallagher & Mr. Shean / Too marvellous for words / Blues in the night / Bob White / You must have been a beautiful baby / On behalf of the visiting fireman / In the cool cool cool of the evening / I'm an old cowhand / Autumn leaves / Accentuate the positive / When the world was young / Waiter, the porter and the upstairs maid.
**Album:** Released May '82, on MFP by EMI Records. Deleted '84. Catalogue no: **MFP 50554**
**Cass:** Released May '82, on MFP by EMI Records. Deleted '84. Catalogue no: **TCMFP 50554**

**MUSIC HALL HIGHLIGHTS (Crosby, Bing & John Scott Trotter Orchestra)**
Tracks: / My minds on you / Moonlight on the Ganges / Moon won't talk, The / Maria Ellena / Last night's gardenias / Yours / Play fiddle, play / Goodbye now / It was wonderful then / You walked by / Say si si / Fool's rush in / May I never love again / Loch Lomond / My heart tells me / It makes no difference now.
**Album:** Released Oct '86, on Spokane (USA) by Kiner Ents.(USA). Catalogue no: **SPOKANE 19**

**MUSIC, MUSIC, MUSIC**
Tracks: / Music music music / Marta / Copper cayon / Wedding samba, The / Yes sir that's my baby / Whispering hope / I'll walk alone / Hoop and holler / Heart and soul / Dipsey doodle / Till I waltz

again with you / Why don't you believe me / Enjoy yourself / Candy and cake / Everybody loves my baby / From the vine.
**Album:** Released '81, on Grappenhauser Catalogue no: **GRAP 1001**
**Album:** Released Jun '88, on Meteor by Magnum Music Group. Catalogue no: **MTLP 1.016**

**NEW TRICKS (Crosby, Bing & Buddy Cole Trio)**
Tracks: / When I take my sugar to tea / On the Alamo / I'm confessin' / Between the devil and the deep blue sea / Georgia on my mind / Chicago / You're driving me crazy / Avalon / Chinatown, my Chinatown / If I could be with you / Softly as in a morning sunrise / Alabamy bound.
**Album:** Released Nov '89, on Memoir by Memoir Records. Catalogue no: **MOIR 202**
**Cass:** Released Dec '87, on Memoir by Memoir Records. Catalogue no: **CMOIR 202**

**ON THE AIR (1934)**
**Album:** Released Jan '89, on Silva Screen by Silva Screen Records. Catalogue no: **SH 2002**

**OUT OF NOWHERE**
Tracks: / Were you sincere / Snuggled on your shoulder / I would if I could, but I can't / Dinah / Now that you're gone / I've got to sing a torch song / Out of nowhere / At your command / Brother, can you spare a dime / Try a little tenderness / How deep is the ocean / Sweet Georgia Brown / Lazy day / Black moonlight / Street of dreams / George White's scandals (medley) / This is the missus / Thrill is gone, The / My song / That's love / Life is just a bowl of cherries.
**CD:** Released Nov '88, on London Records by London Records Ltd. Catalogue no: **820 553 2**

**PEACE ON EARTH / LITTLE DRUMMER BOY (Crosby, Bing & David Bowie)**
Tracks: / Peace on Earth / Little drummer boy / Fantastic voyage.
**12" Single:** Released Dec '82, on RCA by BMG Records (UK). Catalogue no: **BOWT 12**
**7" Single:** Released Nov '82, on RCA by BMG Records (UK). Catalogue no: **BOW 12**

**RADIO MEMORIES**
Tracks: / When the blue of the night / Little lady make believe / My heart is taking lessons / Gypsy in my soul, The / Whistle when you work.
**Cass:** Released Sep '89, on Radio Memories Catalogue no: **TRM 20029**

**RADIO YEARS, THE**
**CD:** Released '88, on GNP Crescendo (USA) by GNP Crescendo Records (USA). Catalogue no: **GNPD 9051**

**RADIO YEARS, VOL. 1**
**Cass:** Released '87, on PRT by Castle Communications Records. Catalogue no: **PYM 6036**
**Album:** Released '87, on PRT by Castle Communications Records. Catalogue no: **PYL 6036**
**Cass:** Released Nov '85, on PRT by Castle Communications Records. Catalogue no: **ZCN 704**
**Cass:** Released '88, on GNP Crescendo (USA) by GNP Crescendo Records (USA). Catalogue no: **GNP5 9044**
**Album:** Released Nov '85, on PRT by Castle Communications Records. Catalogue no: **NCP 704**
**Album:** Released '88, on GNP Crescendo (USA) by GNP Crescendo Records (USA). Catalogue no: **GNPS 9044**

**RADIO YEARS, VOL. 2**
**Album:** Released '88, on GNP Crescendo (USA) by GNP Crescendo Records (USA). Catalogue no: **GNPS 9046**
**Cass:** Released Jun '86, on PRT by Castle Communications Records. Catalogue no: **ZCNCP 707**
**Cass:** Released '88, on GNP Crescendo (USA) by GNP Crescendo Records (USA). Catalogue no: **GNP5 9046**
**Album:** Released Jun '86, on PRT by Castle Communications Records. Catalogue no: **NCP 707**
**Album:** Released '87, on PRT by Castle Communications Records. Catalogue no: **PYL 6037**
**Cass:** Released '87, on PRT by Castle Communications Records. Catalogue no: **PYM 6037**

**RADIO YEARS, VOL. 3**
Tracks: / Zip a dee doo dah / Takes two to tango / Valencia / How are things in Glocca Morra / On top of Old Smokey / Great day / If this is love / Luck old sun / Louise / Mimi / Don't let the stars get in your eyes.
**Album:** Released '88, on GNP Crescendo (USA) by GNP Crescendo Records (USA). Catalogue no: **GNPS 9047**
**Album:** Released Jan '87, on PRT by Castle Communications Records. Catalogue no: **NCP 710**
**Album:** Released '87, on PRT by Castle Communications Records. Catalogue no: **PYL 6038**
**Cass:** Released '88, on GNP Crescendo (USA) by GNP Crescendo Records (USA). Catalogue no: **GNP5 9047**
**Cass:** Released Jan '87, on PRT by Castle Communications Records. Catalogue no: **ZCNCP 710**
**Cass:** Released '87, on PRT by Castle Communications Records. Catalogue no: **PYM 6038**

**RADIO YEARS, VOL. 4**
Tracks: / Hello Hello / Moonlight Bay / Cuanto Lagusta / Lullaby of Broadway / I can dream, can't I / Hand holdin' music / Surrey with the fringe on top / May The Good Lord Bless And Keep You / If I knew you were coming I'd've baked a cake / You've gotta start each day with a song / I Don't Know Why, I Just Do.
**Album:** Released '87, on PRT by Castle Communications Records. Catalogue no: **PYL 6039**
**Cass:** Released Jan '87, on PRT by Castle Communications Records. Catalogue no: **ZCNCP 711**
**Cass:** Released '87, on PRT by Castle Communications Records. Catalogue no: **PYM 6039**
**Album:** Released '88, on GNP Crescendo (USA) by GNP Crescendo Records (USA). Catalogue no: **GNPS 9048**
**Cass:** Released '88, on GNP Crescendo (USA) by GNP Crescendo Records (USA). Catalogue no: **GNP5 9048**
**Album:** Released Jan '87, on PRT by Castle Communications Records. Catalogue no: **NCP 711**

**REMEMBERING**
Tracks: / Please / Did you ever see a dream walking / I've got the world on a string / Sweet Georgia Brown / I don't stand - a ghost of a chance with you / My honey's loving arms / Down the old ox road / How deep is the ocean / Temptation / St. Louis blues / Dinah / Somebody stole Gabriel's horn / Stay on the right side of the road / Someday, sweetheart / Some of these days / Shine / I'm coming Virginia / There's a cabin in the pines.
**Album:** Released Jan '86, on Conifer Happy Days by Conifer Records. Catalogue no: **CHD 123**
**Cass:** Released Jan '86, on Conifer Happy Days by Conifer Records. Catalogue no: **MCHD 123**
**CD:** Released '89, on Conifer Happy Days by Conifer Records. Catalogue no: **CDHD 123**

**REPLAY ON BING CROSBY**
**Album:** Released May '86, on Sierra by Sierra Records. Catalogue no: **FEDB 5034**
**Cass:** Released May '86, on Sierra by Sierra Records. Catalogue no: **CFEDB 5034**

**SEASONS**
Tracks: / Seasons / On the very first day of the year / June in January / Spring will be a little late this year / April showers / June is bustin' out all over / In the good old summertime / Summer wind / Autumn in New York / September song / Sleigh ride / Yesterday when I was young.
**Album:** Released Jan '83, on Polydor by Polydor Ltd. Deleted Jan '88. Catalogue no: **2384 125**
**Album:** Released Dec '77, on Polydor by Polydor Ltd. Deleted Dec '82. Catalogue no: **2442 151**

**SENTIMENTAL BING**
Tracks: / There's nothing that I haven't sung about / I'm getting sentimental over you / Nevertheless / What's new / As time goes by / Old fashioned love / Time on my hands / That of black magic / Way we were / Once in a while / Rose in her hair / Night is young and you're so beautiful / At last / When I leave the world behind.
**Album:** Released Nov '81, on Decca by Decca International. Deleted Nov '85. Catalogue no: **TAB 31**

**SHE LOVES ME NOT NOVEMBER 8, (Crosby, Bing / Joan Blondell)**
Tracks: / I'm whistlin', I'm singin' / Straight from the shoulder / Love in bloom.
**Album:** Released Jun '79, on Totem

Catalogue no: **TOTEM 1004**

**SHHH VOL. 4**
Tracks: / Love thy neighbour / May I? / Straight from the shoulder / Hang your heart on a hickory limb / Skylark / All you want to do is dance / Door will open, A / Hello mom / Road to Morocco, The / Who three the overalls in Mrs Murphy's Chowder / You belong to my heart / Three caballeros / I only want a buddy not a sweetheart / Jingle bells / Christmas greeting to New York employees / Duke the spook.
**Album:** Released Oct '86, on Crosbyana Catalogue no: **LLM 023**

**SILENT NIGHT**
Tracks: / Silent night.
**7" Single:** Released Dec '52, on Brunswick by Decca Records. Deleted Dec '55. Catalogue no: **03929**

**SING YOU SINNERS JANUARY 15, 1940**
Tracks: / I've got a pocketful of dreams / Don't let that moon get away.
**Album:** Released Feb '88, on Spokane (USA) by Kiner Ents.(USA). Catalogue no: **SPOKANE 8**

**SINGS AGAIN**
**CD:** Released Apr '87, on MCA by MCA Records. Catalogue no: **MCAD 5764**

**SINGS MORE GREAT SONGS**
**CD:** Released Feb '89, on Pickwick by Pickwick Records. Catalogue no: **PWK 088**
**Album:** Released Feb '89, on Hallmark by Pickwick Records. Catalogue no: **SHM 3259**
**Cass:** Released Feb '89, on Hallmark by Pickwick Records. Catalogue no: **HSC 3259**

**SONGS OF A LIFETIME**
Tracks: / Ain't misbehavin' / At sundown / Don't blame me / I can't get started / I wish you love / I've grown accustomed to her face / Keepin' out of mischief now / Little man you've had a busy day / Love's old sweet song / Misty / Nice work if you can get it / She's funny that way / Straight down the middle / They didn't believe me / Try a little tenderness / Way down yonder in New Orleans / You'll never know / You're the top.
Note: 36 previously unreleased recordings.
**2 LP Set:** Released Apr '79, on Philips by Phonogram Ltd. Catalogue no: **6641 923**

**SPECIAL MAGIC OF BING CROSBY, THE**
**Album:** Released Dec '79, on Polydor by Polydor Ltd. Catalogue no: **2353 101**

**SPECIAL MAGIC OF BING & SATCHMO, THE (Crosby, Bing & Louis Armstrong)**
Tracks: / Way down yonder in New Orleans / Brother Bill / Little ol' tune / At the Jazz Band Ball / Rocky Mountain moon / Bye bye blues / Muskrat ramble / Sugar / Preacher, The / Dardanella / Let's sing like a Dixieland band.
**Album:** on Polydor by Polydor Ltd. Catalogue no: **2353 084**

**STRANGER IN PARADISE**
Tracks: / Stranger in paradise.
**7" Single:** Released Apr '55, on Brunswick by Decca Records. Deleted Apr '58. Catalogue no: **05410**

**THAT OLD FEELING (Crosby, Bing & Louis Armstrong)**
**Cass:** Released Feb '82, on Polydor (Import) by Polydor Ltd. Catalogue no: **3472 217**
**Album:** Released Feb '82, on Polydor (Import) by Polydor Ltd. Catalogue no: **2872 217**

**THAT TRAVELIN' TWO-BEAT (Crosby, Bing & Rosemary Clooney)**
Tracks: / Vienna Woods / Mother Brown / Roamin' in the gloamin' / Come to the Mardis Gras / Hear that band / Daughter of Molly Malone, The / Poor people of Paris, The / I get ideas / Ciao, ciao bambina / That travelin' two beat.
**Album:** Released Jan '78, on Capitol by EMI Records. Deleted '87. Catalogue no: **CAPS 1017**

**THAT'S WHAT LIFE IS ALL ABOUT**
**Album:** Released Sep '75, on United Artists by EMI Records. Deleted Sep '80. Catalogue no: **UAG 2973**
**7" Single:** Released Aug '75, on United Artists by EMI Records. Deleted Aug '78. Catalogue no: **UP 35852**

**THIS IS...**
Tracks: / Some sunny day / Down among the sheltering palms / I can't get started / Whispering / Slow boat to China / Along the way to Waikiki / Let a smile be your umbrella / Fancy meeting you here / Brazil / Dream a little dream of me / How about you? / Love won't let you get away / It happened in Monterey / Calcutta / Last night on the back porch / Say si si / Mama loves papa / Hindustan / Tell me / You came a long way from St Louis / I'm gonna sit right down and write myself a letter / Exactly like you.
**2 LP Set:** Released Sep '75, on RCA by BMG Records (UK). Catalogue no: **DPS 2066**

**TRIBUTE TO...**
Tracks: / Sweet Sue / I surrender, dear / Gonna love you / Brother, can you spare a dime? / Somebody stole Gabriel's horn / Moonburn / Please / St. Louis blues / Lazybones / Just a gigolo / She reminds me of you / Sweet Georgia Brown.
**Album:** Released May '80, on SRT by SRT Records. Catalogue no: **SRTX 79/CUS 565**

**TRUE LOVE**
Tracks: / Yes sir, that's my baby / Moonglow and theme from Picnic / Love is the sweetest thing / True love / It's alright with me / You're sensational / Manhattan / Unchained melody / Way down yonder in New Orleans / You'll never know / Lady is a tramp, The / I've got a crush on you / She's funny that way / At sundown.
Note: Recorded in Hollywood between 1954 and 1960 with the Buddy Cole Quartet; orchestral backings recorded in London between November 1978 and February, 1979. Rosemary Clooney duets on the title track.
**Cass:** Released Dec '83, on Philips (Holland) by PolyGram UK Ltd. Catalogue no: **8126 604**
**Album:** Released Dec '83, on Philips (Holland) by PolyGram UK Ltd. Catalogue no: **8126 601**

**TRUE LOVE (SINGLE) (Crosby, Bing & Grace Kelly)**
Tracks: / True love.
**7" Single:** Released Nov '56, on Capitol by EMI Records. Deleted Nov '59. Catalogue no: **CL 14645**
**7" Single:** Released Nov '83, on Capitol by EMI Records. Deleted Nov '88. Catalogue no: **CL 315**

**WHERE THE BLUE OF THE NIGHT**
Tracks: / Where the blue of the night / Mexicali rose / Just one more chance / Sweet and lovely / Bob White / Don't let that moon get away / Way you look tonight / When you dream about Hawaii / Sweet Leilani / I have eyes / Let me whisper I love you / Stardust / In a little hula heaven / Funny old hills, The / Can I forget you / Basin street blues / Songs of the Islands / Dancing under the stars / Folks who live on the hill, The / Let me call you sweetheart / Just a wearyin' for you / Sail along silv'ry moon / Dancing in the dark / Goodnight sweetheart.
**Cass set:** Released May '89, on Ditto by Pickwick Records. Catalogue no: **DTO 10299**
**CD:** on London Records by London Records Ltd. Catalogue no: **820 552-2**
**Album:** Released Apr '87, on Meteor by Magnum Music Group. Catalogue no: **MTLP 1007**

**WHITE CHRISTMAS**
**Album:** Released Dec '74, on MCA by MCA Records. Deleted Dec '79. Catalogue no: **MCF 2568**
**Album:** Released '88, on Joker (USA) by Lifetime Records (USA). Catalogue no: **SM 3930**
**Album:** Released '88, on Joker (USA) by Lifetime Records (USA). Catalogue no: **SM 4048**
**Album:** Released Jun '82, on MFP by EMI Records. Deleted '87. Catalogue no: **MFP 5590**
**Cass:** Released Jun '82, on MFP by EMI Records. Deleted '87. Catalogue no: **TCMFP 5590**

**WHITE CHRISTMAS (RADIO SHOW)**
**Album:** on Black Lion Catalogue no: **BLM 52099**

**WHITE CHRISTMAS (RE-ISSUE)**
**CD:** Released Dec '88, on Lotus Catalogue no: **CD 50001**

**WHITE CHRISTMAS (SINGLE)**
Tracks: / White christmas / God rest ye merry gentlemen.
**7" Single:** Released Dec '85, on MCA by MCA Records. Deleted Dec '88. Catalogue no: **BING 1**
**7" Single:** Released Dec '88, on MCA

**Bobcats (1938-'42) - Bob Crosby (Swaggie)**

by MCA Records. Catalogue no: **MCA 111**

**WRAP YOUR TROUBLES IN DREAMS**
Tracks: / Mary (what are you waiting for?) / Ol' man river / Make believe / Loveable / I'm afraid of you / It must be true / Fool me some more / Little things in life, The / I surrender, dear / Wrap your troubles in dreams / Just a gigolo / One more time / Thanks to you / I'm gonna get you / I'm through with love / Just one more chance.
**Album:** Released '79, on RCA Victor by BMG Records (UK). Catalogue no: **LSA 3094**

**YESTERDAY WHEN I WAS YOUNG**
Tracks: / Yesterday when I was young / Sleight ride.
**7" Single:** Released Jan '78, on Polydor by Polydor Ltd. Catalogue no: **2058958**

**ZING A LITTLE ZONG (Crosby, Bing & Jane Wyman)**
Tracks: / Zing a little zong.
**7" Single:** Released Dec '52, on Brunswick by Decca Records. Deleted Dec 55. Catalogue no: **04981**

## Crosby, Bob

**Biographical details:** A pop singer, brother of Bing. Born in 1913, he had worked for Anson Weeks and the Dorsey brothers; he was hired as a front man by musicians who had mostly played for Ben Pollock and who had formed a co-operative. They included Gil Rodin (1906-74), an arranger and reed player. Key members from New Orleans had grown up with jazz; the excellent dance band played within a band, played the real stuff. The original lineup included Yank Lawson on trumpet and Bob Haggart on bass, who later (in the 50's) co-led a jazz band which evolved into a band called The World's Greatest Jazz Band, which made many albums. There were also Ray Baudoc on drums, Nappy Lamare on guitar, arranger Deane Kincaide, reed players Matty Matlock and Eddie Miller; others passing through included many of the best white musicians of the era. The band had dozens of hits; among the best were *South Rampart Street Parade* backed with *Dogtown Blues*, both written by Haggart. Crosby coudn't conduct, but was a good pop singer who got better, and valued the company he was keeping: the band was satisfied with the deal. (Donald Clarke, April 1989) .

**20 GOLDEN PIECES: BOB CROSBY (Crosby, Bob & His Orchestra)**
Tracks: / Washington and Lee swing / When the saints go marching in / Ja da / Love's got me in a lazy mood / Tiger rag / Gin mill blues / High society / Pennies from Heaven / Tin roof blues / Georgy girl / Thoroughly modern Millie / Big noise from Winnetka / Winchester Cathedral / Ballin' the jack / Java / Summertime / Little Rock getaway / March of the Bobcats / Mame / Patricia.
**Cass:** Released Nov '81, Catalogue no: **AJKL 2026**
**Album:** Released Nov '81, on Bulldog Records by President Records. Catalogue no: **BDL 2026**

**ACCENT ON SWING (Crosby, Bob & His Ochestra)**
Note: Quig Quigley/J Hopkins.
**Album:** Released Jun '86, on Giants of Jazz by Hasmick Promotions. Catalogue no: **GOJ 1021**

**AT THE RAINBOW GRILL (Crosby, Bob & The Bop Cats)**
**Album:** Released Mar '79, on Monmouth Evergreen Catalogue no: **MES 6815**

**BAND AND SMALL (Crosby, Bob and Bing Crosby)**
**Album:** Released '88, on Blu-Disc (USA) Catalogue no: **T 5004**

**BIG APPLE, THE (1936 - 40) (Crosby, Bob & His Orchestra)**
**Album:** Released Jun '88, on Bandstand Catalogue no: **BS 7111**

**BOB CROSBY**
**Album:** Released Aug '81, on Kings Of Jazz Catalogue no: **KLJ 20015**

**BOB CROSBY & HIS ORCHESTRA (Crosby, Bob & His Orchestra)**
Tracks: / Theme - Introduction / Over the waves / Sister Kate / We're in the Money / Big noise from Winnetka / Yancey special / It's a long way to Tipperary / Diga diga doo / Smokey Mary / Theme - close / Swing concert / In a minor mood / Dogtown blues / Between the devil and the deep blue sea / South Rampart Street Parade / Gin Mill Blues.
**Album:** Released May '88, on Jasmine by Hasmick Promotions. Catalogue no: **JASM 2512**
**Cass:** Released May '88, on Jasmine by Hasmick Promotions. Catalogue no: **JASMC 2512**

**BOB CROSBY & HIS ORCHESTRA (Crosby, Bob & His Orchestra)**
Tracks: / Roll, roll, rolling along / Oh my goodness / Dixieland shuffle / I'd rather lead a band / Farewell blues / It's you I'm talking about, baby / I'm just beginning to care / It ain't right / Glory of love / Here comes your pappy / There'll be some changes made / Let's make up again / I'll never say "never again" again / Tin roof blues / Fidgety feet / Muscrat ramble / But definitely / Eeny meeny miney mo / Rockin' chair / When Icky Morgan plays his organ.
**Album:** Released Apr '81, on Rarities Catalogue no: **RARITIES 41**

**BOB CROSBY (JAZZ CLASSICS IN DIGITAL STEREO)**
Tracks: / South Rampart Street parade / Gin Mill blues / Squeeze me / Stumbling / Who's sorry now / Coquette / Fidgety feet / You're driving me crazy / Can't we be friends / Dogtown blues / March of the bob cats / Slow mood / Big foot jump / Big crash from China / Five point blues / Big noise from Winnetka / Swingin' at the sugar bowl / Honky tonk train blues.
**Album:** Released 4 Sep '88, on BBC by BBC Records & Tapes. Catalogue no: **REB 688**
**CD:** Released 4 Sep '88, on BBC by BBC Records & Tapes. Catalogue no:

**BBC CD688**
**Cass:** Released 4 Sep '88, on BBC by BBC Records & Tapes. Catalogue no: **ZCF 688**

**BOB CROSBY ON THE AIR (1940) (Crosby, Bob & His Orchestra)**
Tracks: / Summertime / Skaters Waltz / Shake down the stars / Vous tout de vey, a vous, A / Complainin' / In the mood / Where the blue of the night / It's you, you darlin' / It's a small world / Wolverine blues / Boogie woogie Maxine / Fools rush in / Cecilia / Old county down, The / Jazz me blues / Reminiscing time / Ooh what you said / Starlight hour, The / Sugarfoot stomp.
**Album:** Released Apr '79, on Aircheck (USA) by Kiner Ents.(USA). Catalogue no: **AIRCHECK 17**

**BOB CROSBY AND HIS ORCHESTRA (1937-42) (Crosby, Bob Orchestra)**
Note: Yank Lawson etc.
**Album:** Released Jan '88, on Swingfan Catalogue no: **SWINGFAN 1016**

**BOB CROSBY VOL. 1 (1935)**
**Album:** Released Apr '79, on Ajax (USA) Catalogue no: **AJAX 144**

**BOB CROSBY VOL. 2 (1935)**
**Album:** Released Apr '79, on Ajax (USA) Catalogue no: **AJAX 151**

**BOB CROSBY VOL. 3 (1936/7)**
**Album:** Released Apr '79, on Ajax (USA) Catalogue no: **AJAX 159**

**BOB CROSBY'S BOB CATS (Volume 1)**
Tracks: / Stumbling / Who's sorry now / Coquette / Fidgety feet / You're driving me crazy / Can't we be friends / Loopin' the loop / Mama's gone, goodbye / March of the bob cats / Palesteena / Slow mood / Big foot jump / Big crash from China, The / Five point blues / Way down yonder in New Orleans / Do you ever think of me.
**Album:** Released Jan '86, on Swaggie (Australia) Catalogue no: **S 1245**

**BOB CROSBY'S BOB CATS (1938-42) (Volume 2) (See panel on previous page)**
Tracks: / Hindustan / Mournin' blues / Till we meet again / Love nest, The / All by myself / Jazz me blues / Speak to me of love / Big bass viol / I hear you talking / Call me a taxi / Big noise from Winnetka / Peruna / Spain / That da da strain / Tin roof blues.
Note: 1938, a year, depending on where you were (if you were), in which some good things and a whole lot of bad things happened on this planet Earth. With a shooting war already a reality in Asia and in Spain and the rest of Europe about to be swallowed up in fully-fledged conflict, the situation was indeed pretty bad and steadily getting worse. In America, in an age of no jet aircraft, television, rockets and space exploration, it all seemed so distant and far off at the time. And so it was, that here in the USA good things were still happening and if one loved jazz music and was caught up in the height of the era of swing music, the Bob Crosby Orchestra and its "unit within the band", The Bob Cats, was one of the best happenings of all. Formed in 1935 from the remnants of the Ben Pollack band, the Bob Crosbyites had by 1938 made their mark via personal appearances from coast to coast, radio broadcasts, and on recordings. The Bob Cats themselves, though featuring successfully almost from the very beginning, did not appear as such on wax until December 1937 and March 1938. All 12 of the wonderful instrumentals cut on these two dates (plus 4 additional sides) are available on "The Bob Cats" (Swaggie S1245). By October 1938, Yank Lawson, the group's original trumpeter, had left to go with Tommy Dorsey. Matty Matlock had quit playing clarinet to devote his full time to arranging for the big band. Trumpeters Billy Butterfield and Sterling Bose were sharing the jazz chair. while the blue-tinged inspired clarinet of Irving "Faz" Fazola was added to compliment the great sounds of his fellow New Orleansian, tenor saxist Eddie Miller. Trombonist Warren Smith completed the front line, while pianist Bob Zurke, guitarist - vocalist Nappy Lamare, (also New Orleans bred), Bob Haggart on bass, and still another Delta City product, drummer Ray Bauduc, completed a homogenous personnel which took a back seat to no other similar Dixieland formated group of that period. Guitarist Lamare is absent from the 14th October, 1938 tracks, recovering from an apendectomy in a Chicago hospital. Care seems to have been taken to cover his absence by showcasing talents of some other sidemen, including the famous and unique *Big noise from Winnetka* duet of Haggart and Bauduc. The line up through 1939 and including the 6th February, 1940 date remains the same with the exception of Billy Butterfield on trumpet on all sides, Nappy Lemare back in the personnel full time, and only the pianist stool changing hands with no let down from Bob Zurke to Joe Sullivan to Jess Stacey. Unlike Bob Zurke, who made the big time after joining Crosby, the latter two were, (and still are), jazz giants on their own and well established artists before entering the Bob Crosby ranks.
Mid-1940 brought about a sudden period of temporary dissention to the band which saw the departure of many of the above named sidemen, a period of icky commercialism which included a half a dozen or so various singers, vocal groups, etc., and in many cases, poor choices of material to record.
By the summer of 1941 the wiser heads in the Crosby entourage had seen the light and it was back to less and less commercial junk and more and more of the pure jazz that the Bob Cats could play so well. Clarinettist Matlock was back in the role of hot clarinetist and Yank Lawson returned, better than ever.

Trombonist Floyd O'Brien, with the band since the dissention period of mid-1940, finally got to play some jazz, and on *Ti Roof Blues*, proves once again that h was one of the hottest and most individ ual jazz trombonists of all time. Oddl enough, this side was not issued in th USA until it came out briefly on micro groove in 1956. Flody first heard it at ou house one night over beer and pretzel and had forgotton the side was eve made. Another rare side included here with is the "Aussie" version of *The Lov Nest*, only issued down under on 78. A other Bob Cat issues of this tune in th USA and Europe are from a cut made days later, and personally observing, i not quite as good a performance. B 1942 the war had caught up with us an bad things were happening to us too wit less and less of the good things. By lat 1942, the Bob Crosby Bob Cats were thing of the past, never to be the sam again what with the change in tastes, th decline of the big bands, and of cours through the years, the loss forever o Bose, O'Brien, Fazola and Zurke. I don' have to say anything more about th music contained herein. It speaks fo itself and stands tall on its own merits Most of it is darned good and in som cases like *Mournin' Blues*, *Jazz M Blues* and *Tin Roof Blues*, its nothin short of being just great. No one has t apologise for any of it. (Jim Gordon September 1971, Chicago).
**Album:** Released Jan '83, on Swaggi (Australia) Catalogue no: **S 1288**

**CAMEL CARAVANS (THE SUMMER OF 39)**
**Album:** Released Oct '85, on Giants c Jazz by Hasmick Promotions. Catalogue no: **GOJ 1037**

**DIXIELAND BAND, THE**
**Cass:** Released Dec '86, on Halcyo (USA) by Submarine Records. Catalogue no: **CHDL 110**
**Album:** Released Dec '86, on Halcyo (USA) by Submarine Records. Catalogue no: **HDL 110**

**DIXIELAND SHUFFLE, VOL. 2 (1935-'36) (Crosby, Bob & His Orchestra)**
Tracks: / Little bit independent, A / N other one / Goody goody / I don' want t make history / Christopher Colombus You're Toots to me / You start m dreaming / Mommy / Muscrat ramble Dixieland shuffle.
**Cass:** Released Feb '89, on Halcyon (USA) by Submarine Records. Catalogue no: **CHDL 120**
**Album:** Released Feb '89, on Halcyon (USA) by Submarine Records. Catalogue no: **HDL 120**

**MARDI GRAS PARADE (Crosby, Bob & The Bop Cats)**
**Album:** Released Mar '79, on Monmouth Evergreen Catalogue no: **MES 7026**

**MORE 1938 (Crosby, Bob & His Ochestra)**
**Album:** Released Jun '86, on Circle (USA) by Jazzology Records (USA). Catalogue no: **CLP 34**

**MOURNIN' BLUES (Crosby, Bob & The Bop Cats)**
Tracks: / Mournin' blues / South rampart street parade / Washington and Lee swing / Love nest, The / Squeeze me / Spain / Call me a taxi / Yancey special / Gin mill blues / Who's sorry now / I hear you talking / All by myself / Jazz me blues / Till we meet again / Tin roof blues / I'm praying humble.
**Album:** Released Nov '85, on Affinity by Charly Records. Catalogue no: **AFS 1014**
**Cass:** Released Nov '85, on Affinity by Charly Records. Catalogue no: **TCAFS 1014**

**PLAYS (Crosby, Bob & His Ochestra)**
**Album:** Released Aug '79, on Circle (USA) by Jazzology Records (USA). Catalogue no: **CLP 1**

**SUDDENLY IT'S 1939 (Crosby Caravans) (Crosby, Bob & His Orchestra)**
Tracks: / Lady's in love with you, The / I've got the world on a string / Little Rock getaway / If I didn't care / Hindustan / Newsy blues / Pagan love song / South Rampart Street parade / Get on board and ride / Sunrise serenade / Stumbling / Memphis blues / Big noise from Winnetka / Then I'll be happy.
**Album:** Released Jan '85, on Giants of Jazz by Hasmick Promotions. Catalogue no: **GOJ 1032**
**Cass:** Released Oct '86, on Giants of Jazz by Hasmick Promotions. Catalogue no: **GOJC 1032**

**SUGARFOOT STRUT (1936 - '42) (Crosby, Bob & His Orchestra)**
**Album:** Released Jun '88, on Bandstand Catalogue no: **BS 7121**

**THAT DA DA STRAIN (Crosby, Bob & His Orchestra)**
Tracks: / That da da strain / Royal Garden blues / Squeeze me / Panama / Who's sorry now? / Big crash from China / High society / Milenberg joys / March of the Bobcats / Russian sailor's dance / Vultee special / Jimtown blues.
**Album:** Released Apr '81, on Joker (USA) by Lifetime Records (USA). Catalogue no: **SM 3243**

## Crouch, Andrae

**Biographical details:** A gospel singer, songwriter and keyboardist, born in 1942 in Los Angeles.
He has worked in groups since the early '60's with his twin sister Sandra and others such as Billy Preston; Sandra sang back-up for Diana Ross and others but rejoined her brother in 1970. Albums featured guest shots by Stevie Wonder, the Crusaders and others.
Crouch has won Grammies and written songs recorded by Elvis Presley, The Imperials and Pat Boone. (Donald Clarke, April 1989).

**AUTOGRAPH**
**Album:** Released '88, on Light by Word Records (UK). Catalogue no: **LS R 5710**
**Cass:** Released '88, on Light by Word Records (UK). Catalogue no: **LS C 5710**

**BEST OF ANDRAE CROUCH AND THE DISCIPLES (Crouch, Andrae and the Disciples)**
Tracks: / Take a little time / Everything changed / Tell them / Keep on singing / My tribute / Jesus is the answer / Through it all / Satisfied / Jesus (every hour) / I come that you might have life / Bless His holy name / I'm coming home / Just like He said He would / If heaven never was promised to me / Take me back / I don't know why / I didn't think it could be / Oh I need Him / I've got confidence / It won't be long.
**2 LP Set:** Released May '82, on Light by Word Records (UK). Catalogue no: **LS D 7034**
**Cass set:** Released May '82, on Light by Word Records (UK). Catalogue no: **LCD 7034**

**LIVE AT CARNEGIE HALL (Crouch, Andrae and the Disciples)**
Tracks: / Opening / You don't know what you're missing / He looked beyond my fault hand-writing / I didn't think it could be / Hallelujah, Hallelujah Jesus is the answer / Andrae preachin' / Can't nobody do me like Jesus / Invitation / It won't be long.
**Album:** Released May '82, on Light by Word Records (UK). Catalogue no: **LS 7018**
**Cass:** Released May '82, on Light by Word Records (UK). Catalogue no: **LC 7018**

**LIVE IN LONDON: ANDRAE CROUCH (Crouch, Andrae and the Disciples)**
Tracks: / Introduction / Perfect peace / I surrender all / Greetings by Andrae / You don't have to jump no pews (I've been born again) / Take a little time / Tell them / If I was a tree (the highest praise) / Hallelujah / Revive us again / Power in the blood / Reprise / I just want to know you / Andrae talking / Just like he said he would / I'll keep on loving you lord / You gave to me / Oh taste and see / Praise god, praise god / This is another day / Praise God reprise / Well done / My tribute.
**Cass set:** Released May '82, on Light by Word Records (UK). Catalogue no: **LCD 7048**
**2 LP Set:** Released May '82, on Light by Word Records (UK). Catalogue no: **LSD 7048**

**MORE OF THE BEST...**
Tracks: / Soon and very soon / I'll be thinking of you / They shall be mine / Please come back / Quiet times / It's gonna rain / Sweet love of Jesus, The / Jesus is Lord / Praises / I just wanna know you.
**Cass:** Released May '82, on Light by Word Records (UK). Catalogue no: **LC 7061**
**Album:** Released May '82, on Light by Word Records (UK). Catalogue no: **LS 7061**

**NO TIME TO LOSE**
**Cass:** Released Jan '85, on Myrrh by Word Records (UK). Catalogue no: **MC 1188**
**Album:** Released Jan '85, on Myrrh by Word Records (UK). Catalogue no: **MYR 1188**

**TAKE ME BACK (Crouch, Andrae and the Disciples)**
Tracks: / I'll still love you / Praises / Just like he said he would / All I can say (I really love you) / You can depend on me / Take me back / Sweet love of Jesus, The / It ain't no new thing / They shall be mine / Oh saviour / Tell them.
**Album:** Released May '82, on Light by Word Records (UK). Catalogue no: **LSX 7025**
**Cass:** Released May '82, on Light by Word Records (UK). Catalogue no: **LC 7025**

**THIS IS ANOTHER DAY (Crouch, Andrae and the Disciples)**
Tracks: / Perfect peace / My peace I leave with you / This is another day / Quiet times / Soon and very soon / We expect you / You gave to me / All that I have / Choice, The / Polynesian praise song (I love you).
**Album:** Released Feb '77, on DJM Deleted '80. Catalogue no: **DJF 20496**
**Cass:** Released May '82, on Light by Word Records (UK). Catalogue no: **LC 7042**
**Album:** Released May '82, on Light by Word Records (UK). Catalogue no: **LSX 7042**

**YOU GAVE TO ME (Crouch, Andrae and the Disciples)**
Tracks: / You gave to me / Polynesian praise song.
**7" Single:** Released Jan '77, on DJM Deleted '80. Catalogue no: **DJS 10736**

## Crouch End All Stars

**CROUCH END ALL STARS**
**Album:** Released Aug '87, on Jazzology (USA) by Jazzology Records (USA). Catalogue no: **J 148**

## Crouch, Sandra

**WE'RE WAITING**
Note: Brother Andrae featured on the title track and his presence is in evidence as co-producer and occasional instrumentalist.
Like many of the best recordings of black gospel music this was recorded live and then enhanced in the recording studio. Thus the freshness and infectious joy of the live sound is retained but with the rough edges taken off and a first rate sound mix given to bring out the punch in the rhythms.
**Album:** Released Apr '86, on Light by Word Records (UK). Catalogue no: **LSR 7079**
**Cass:** Released Apr '86, on Light by Word Records (UK). Catalogue no: **LSC 7079**

## Crudup, Arthur 'Big

**Biographical details:** Blues singer and songwriter (1905-74) best known for songs recorded by Elvis Presley: *That's Alright Mama* on his first release in 1954 and *So Glad You're Mine* and *My Baby Left Me* in 1956. He recorded for *Bluebird/Victor* 1941-52 and other labels in the '50's. Like other bluesmen he was rediscovered, in his case through the Presley connection; his music is an interesting link between country and urban blues. His songs were published by Hill and Range; he never saw the Presley royalties. (Donald Clarke, April 1989).

### BIG BOY CRUDUP AND LIGHTNIN' HOPKINGS (Crudup, Arthur Big Boy & Lightnin' Hopkins)

Tracks: / Shake that thing / I'm leaving with you now / Walk a long time / Bring me my shotgun / Just picking / If I get lucky / Death valley blues / Angel child / My mama don't allow me / I'm in the mood / I love her just the same / Looka there, she's got no hair / Last night.

**Album:** Released Nov '83, on Krazy Kat by Interstate Music. Catalogue no: **KK 7410**

### CRUDUP'S MOOD

**Album:** on Delmark (USA) by Delmark Records (USA). Catalogue no: **DS 621**

**Album:** Released Dec '88, on Delmark (USA) by Delmark Records (USA). Catalogue no: **DL 621**

### CRUDUP'S ROCKIN'

Tracks: / My baby left me / If I get lucky / Mean old frisco blues / Who's been fooling you / So glad you're mine / Shout sister shout / Cool disposition / I don't know it / That's alright / She's just like Caledonia / Rock me mama / Hand me down my walking cane / I love you / Gonna dig myself a hole / She's got no hair / Never no more / Too much competition.

**Album:** Released Oct '85, on RCA by BMG Records (UK). Deleted May '89. Catalogue no: **NL 89385**

**Cass:** Released Oct '85, on RCA by BMG Records (UK). Deleted May '89. Catalogue no: **NK 89385**

### GIVE ME A 32-20

Tracks: / Give me a 32-20 / Kind lover blues / I don't know it / Raised to my hand / That's your red wagon / Boyfriend blues / Hoodoo lady blues / Black pony blues / That's why I'm lonesome / Roberta blues / Just like a spider / Someday / She's just like Caledonia / Behind closed doors / Tired of worry / Nelvina.

**Album:** Released 19 Feb '88, on Crown Prince (Sweden) Catalogue no: **IG 403**

### I'M IN THE MOOD

Tracks: / Second man blues / Standing at my window / Come back, baby / Katie Mae / Crudup's Vicksburg blues / Gonna follow my baby / Hey, mama, everything's alright / Mercy blues / Mama don't allow / Nobody wants me / Pearly Lee / Hand me down my walking cane / Looking for my baby / Do it if you want to / You know that I love you / I'm in the mood.

**Album:** Released Jul '83, on Krazy Kat by Interstate Music. Catalogue no: **KK 7416**

### LOOK ON YONDERS WALL

**Album:** Released Dec '88, on Delmark (USA) by Delmark Records (USA). Catalogue no: **DL 614**

**Album:** on Delmark (USA) by Delmark Records (USA). Catalogue no: **DS 614**

### MEAN OL' FRISCO

Tracks: / Mean ol' Frisco / I'm in the mood / That's alright / Standing at my window / Angel child / Katie Mae / Look on yonder wall / Dig myself a hole / If I get lucky / Death valley / I love her just the same / Angel child (take 2) / Rock me Mama / Ethel Mae / My Mama don't allow me.

**Album:** Released Jun '89, on Charly R&B by Charly Records. Catalogue no: **CRB 1206**

### SHOUT, SISTER, SHOUT

**Album:** Released '87, on Bullwhip Catalogue no: **BWLP 1001**

### STAR BOOTLEGGER

**Album:** Released '88, on Krazy Kat by Interstate Music. Catalogue no: **KK 7402**

### THAT'S ALL RIGHT MAMA

**Album:** Released Jan '90, on Blues Master Catalogue no: **MB 901**

## Crusaders

**Biographical details:** At the time of their greatest success, this American band comprised Wilton Felder, Stix Hooper and Joe Sample. They originally came together in Texas in the early 50's, playing as the Swingsters. By the early sixties they were known as the Jazz Crusaders and consisted of the above three artists and Wayne Henderson.

The quartet released their first album *Freedom Sound* in 1961, and followed it with a prolific series of LP's during the 60's. In 1970 they dropped the word "Jazz" from their title and became simply the Crusaders.

This change was a recognition of the fact that they preferred to play a fusion of jazz, soul, blues and rock and not straight jazz.

As their music developed in the 70's, they were recognised as pioneers of jazz-funk, a style that assumed great importance in the late 70's and early 80's, particularly in discos. This acclaim led to the group's members carving out successful subsidiary careers as session players. Henderson left the group in 1975 to pursue solo activities, whereupon they continued for eight years as a trio.

Their virtuosity continued, and they often received musical assistance from fellow musicians of an equally high calibre, notable ace guitarist Larry Carlton.

The band's career moved, for the first time, in a major commercial direction in 1979 - having previously been a purely instrumental outfit, they began to hire guest vocalists for certain tracks.

The first and most successful example of this policy was 1979's *Street Life* single, on which the superb performance of the Crusaders and Randy Crawford ensured a disco smash. The song gave the band their only substantial pop hit, reaching no.36 in the US and no.5 in the UK, and made Crawford a star, especially in Britain. Further Crusaders tracks featured vocal appearances by Bill Withers and Joe Cocker. In addition, Bobby Womack lent his vocal talents to two acclaimed singles by Felder, 1980's *Inherit the Wind* and 1985's *(No Matter How High I Get) I'll Still Be Looking Up to You.* Drummer Stix Hooper quit in 1983 to be replaced by Leon Ndugu Chancler. (Bob Macdonald, 14/2/85)

An instrumental group formed in 1957, called the Modern Jazz Sextet, then the Nite Hawks, the Jazz Crusaders in 1960 and the Crusaders from 1972, adopting the jazz rock style and popularity. They had 18 albums n the Billboard chart 1969-84, many including Wayne Henderson on trombone, Joe Sample on keyboards, Wilton Felder on reeds, Larry Carlton on guitar and Stix Hooper on drums; all are extremely busy session players as well. Guest vocalists have included Randy Crawford, Joe Cocker, Bill Withers, Nancy Wilson and B.B. King. (Donald Clarke, April 1989).

### BEST OF THE CRUSADERS

Tracks: / Put it where you want it / Stomp and buck dance / Greasy spoon / Scratch / So far away / Hard times / So far away (live) / Don't let it get you down / Keep that same old feeling / That's how I feel / Soul caravan / Chain reaction / Ballad for Joe / Do you remember when / Way back home.

**2 LP Set:** Released Jan '77, on ABC Records by MCA Records. Catalogue no: **ABCD 612**

**Cass set:** Released Dec '76, on ABC Records by MCA Records. Catalogue no: **CABD 612**

### CHAIN REACTION

**Album:** Released Apr '77, on ABC Records by MCA Records. Catalogue no: **CAB 5144**

**Album:** Released Jun '79, on Mobile Fidelity Sound Lab(USA) by Mobile Fidelity Records (USA). Catalogue no: **MFSL 1-010**

### CHAIN REACTION/THOSE SOUTHERN NIGHTS

**CD:** Released May '89, on MCA (Import) by MCA Records. Deleted Dec '89. Catalogue no: **MCAD 5841**

### CRUSADERS, THE

**Cass:** Released '89, on GTD Catalogue no: **GTDC 083**

### FREE AS THE WIND

Tracks: / Free as the wind / I felt the love / Way we was, The / Nite crawler / Feel it / Sweet n sour / River rat / It happens every day.

**Album:** Released '83, on ABC Records by MCA Records. Deleted Jan '88. Catalogue no: **MCL 1764**

**Cass:** Released '83, on ABC Records by MCA Records. Deleted Jan '88. Catalogue no: **MCLC 1764**

**The Good and Bad Times - The Crusaders (MCA)**

### GHETTO BLASTER
**Album:** Released Apr '84, on MCA (USA) by MCA Records (USA). Catalogue no: **MCF 3176**
**CD:** Released Jun '88, on MCA (USA) by MCA Records (USA). Catalogue no: **MCAD 5429**

### GOOD AND BAD TIMES, THE (See panel above)
Tracks: / Good times / Way it goes, The / Sweet dreams / Mischievious ways / Sometimes you can take it or leave it / Three wishes.
Note: The first Crusader album in two years is also released to coincide with the 30th anniversary of the formation of the Jazz Crusaders by Joe Sample and Wilton Felder at the beginning of 1957. Joe and Wilton are joined by L.A. session players, as well as special guest vocalist Nancy Wilson, and guitarist (and former Crusader) Larry Carlton.
**Cass:** Released Dec '86, on MCA by MCA Records. Catalogue no: **MCFC 6022**
**Album:** Released Dec '86, on MCA by MCA Records. Catalogue no: **MCF 6022**
**CD:** Released Jun '89, on MCA by MCA Records. Catalogue no: **MCAD 5781**

### I'M SO GLAD I'M STANDING HERE
Tracks: / I'm so glad I'm standing here today.
**7" Single:** Released Sep '81, on MCA by MCA Records. Deleted Sep '84. Catalogue no: **MCA 741**
**12" Single:** Released Sep '81, on MCA by MCA Records. Catalogue no: **MCAT 741**

### IMAGES
Tracks: / Fair tales / Marcella's dream / Bayou bottoms / Merry go round / Cosmic regin / Covert action / Snow flake.
**Cass:** Released Aug '81, on ABC Records by MCA Records. Deleted Jan '88. Catalogue no: **MCLC 1625**
**Album:** Released Aug '81, on ABC Records by MCA Records. Deleted Jan '88. Catalogue no: **MCL 1625**

### LAST CALL
Tracks: / Last call / Honky tonk strutting.
**12" Single:** Released Jan '81, on MCA by MCA Records. Deleted Jan '84. Catalogue no: **MCAT 657**
**7" Single:** Released Jan '81, on MCA by MCA Records. Deleted Jan '84. Catalogue no: **MCA 657**

### LIFE IN THE MODERN WORLD
Tracks: / Passion fruit / A C / Life in the modern world / Samplin' / Mulholland nights / Let me prove myself tonight / Destiny / D C / Some people just never learn / Coulda', woulda, shoulda'.
**Cass:** Released Jun '88, on MCA by MCA Records. Catalogue no: **MCFC 3420**
**CD:** Released Jun '88, on MCA by MCA Records. Catalogue no: **DMCF 3420**
**Album:** Released Jun '88, on MCA by MCA Records. Catalogue no: **MCF 3420**

### NEW MOVES
Tracks: / New moves / Dead end / 1984 street life (on 12" only).
**12" Single:** Released Jul '84, on MCA by MCA Records. Deleted Jul '87. Catalogue no: **MCAT 894**
**7" Single:** Released Jul '84, on MCA by MCA Records. Catalogue no: **MCA 894**

### NIGHT LADIES
Tracks: / Night ladies.
**12" Single:** Released Apr '84, on MCA by MCA Records. Deleted '85. Catalogue no: **MCAT 853**
**7" Single:** Released Apr '84, on MCA by MCA Records. Catalogue no: **MCA 853**

### ONGAKU DAI-LIVE IN JAPAN
Tracks: / Introduction / Rainbow seeker / Hustler, The / Sweet gentle love / Drum introduction / Spiral / Carmel / In all my wildest dreams / Put it where you want it.
**Album:** Released Apr '82, on Crusaders (Audiophile series) by MCA Records. Catalogue no: **CRP 16002**

### RHAPSODY AND BLUES
Tracks: / Soul shadows / Honky tonk struttin' / Elegant evening / Rhapsody and blues / Last call / Sweet gentle love.
**Album:** Released Jul '80, on MCA by MCA Records. Deleted Jul '85. Catalogue no: **MCG 4010**
**Cass:** Released Sep '86, on MCA by MCA Records. Catalogue no: **MCLC 1771**
**Album:** Released Sep '86, on MCA by MCA Records. Catalogue no: **MCL 1771**

### RHAPSODY AND BLUES AND STANDING TALL
Tracks: / Soul shadows / Honky tonk struttin' / Elegant evening / Rhapsody and blues / Last call / Standing tall / I'm so glad I'm standing here today / Sunshine in your eyes / This old world's too funky for me / Luckenbach, Texas / Longest night.
**CD:** Released Oct '87, on MCA (Import) by MCA Records. Deleted Dec '89. Catalogue no: **MCAD 5840**

### RHAPSODY AND BLUES/STREET LIFE
Tracks: / Street life / My lady / Rodeo drive (high steppin') / Carnival of the night / Hustler, The / Night faces / Soul shadows / Honky tonk struttin' / Elegant evening / Rhapsody and blue / Last call / Sweet gentle love.
**Cass set:** Released Sep '84, on MCA (Twinpax Cassettes) by MCA Records. Deleted Jan '88. Catalogue no: **MCA 2 102**

### ROYAL JAM
Tracks: / I'm so glad I'm standing here today / One day I'll fly away / Fly with wings of love / Burnin' up the carnival / Last call / Thrill is gone, The / Better not look down / Hold on / Street life / I just can't leave your love alone / Never make a move too soon.
Note: With B.B King & The Royal Philharmonic Orchestra.
**CD:** Released Jul '87, on MCA by MCA Records. Deleted Apr '88. Catalogue no: **MCAD 8017**
**Cass:** Released Jun '82, on MCA by MCA Records. Catalogue no: **MCDC 455**
**Album:** Released Jun '82, on MCA by MCA Records. Deleted Apr '88. Cata-

logue no: **MCDW 455**

**SAMPLE A DECADE (1)**
**CD:** Released Jan '89, on Connoisseur Collection by Connoisseur Collection Ltd.. Catalogue no: **VSOPCD 131**
**Cass:** Released Jan '89, on Connoisseur Collection by Connoisseur Collection Ltd.. Catalogue no: **VSOPMC 131**
**Album:** Released Jan '89, on Connoisseur Collection by Connoisseur Collection Ltd.. Catalogue no: **VSOPLP 131**

**SCRATCH**
Tracks: / Scratch / Eleanor Rigby / Hard times / So far away / Way back home.
**Cass:** Released Sep '82, on Blue Thumb by MCA Records. Deleted Jan '88. Catalogue no: **MCLC 1709**
**Album:** Released Sep '82, on Blue Thumb by MCA Records. Deleted Jan '88. Catalogue no: **MCL 1709**

**STANDING TALL**
**Album:** Released Sep '81, on MCA by MCA Records. Deleted Sep '86. Catalogue no: **MCF 3122**

**STREET LIFE**
Tracks: / Street life / My lady / Rodeo drive (high steppin') / Carnival of the night / Hustler, The / Night faces / Inherit the wind.
**CD:** on MCA by MCA Records. Deleted '88. Catalogue no: **DIDX 153**
**Cass:** Released Sep '86, on MCA by MCA Records. Catalogue no: **MCLC 1815**
**Album:** Released Jul '79, on MCA by MCA Records. Deleted Jul '84. Catalogue no: **MCF 3008**
**CD:** Released '88, on MCA by MCA Records. Catalogue no: **DMCA 107**
**Album:** Released Sep '86, on MCA by MCA Records. Catalogue no: **MCL 1815**
**CD:** Released Jul '87, on MCA by MCA Records. Catalogue no: **CMCAD 31024**

**STREET LIFE (OLD GOLD)**
Tracks: / Street life / Inherit the wind.
**12" Single:** Released May '88, on Old Gold by Old Gold Records. Catalogue no: **OG 4065**

**STREET LIFE (SINGLE)**
Tracks: / Street life / Hustler, The.
**12" Single:** Released Aug '82, on MCA by MCA Records. Deleted Dec '89. Catalogue no: **MCAT 513**
**7" Single:** Released Aug '82, on MCA by MCA Records. Deleted Aug '85. Catalogue no: **MCA 513**

**THIS OLD WORLD'S TOO FUNKY FOR ME**
Tracks: / This old world's too funky for me / I'm so glad / Luckenbach, Texas (Available on 12" only.).
**12" Single:** Released Nov '81, on MCA by MCA Records. Deleted Nov '84. Catalogue no: **MCAT 754**
**7" Single:** Released Nov '81, on MCA by MCA Records. Deleted Nov '84. Catalogue no: **MCA 754**

**THOSE SOUTHERN NIGHTS**
Tracks: / Spiral / Keep that same old feeling / My Mama told me so / Till the sun shines / And then there was the blues / Serenity / Feeling funky.
**Cass:** Released Feb '82, on Bluetime (Denmark) by Contact Records (Denmark). Deleted Jan '88. Catalogue no: **MCLC 1645**
**Album:** Released Feb '82, on Bluetime (Denmark) by Contact Records (Denmark). Deleted Jan '88. Catalogue no: **MCL 1645**

**VOCAL ALBUM, THE**
Tracks: / Street life / This old world's too funky for me / Better not look down / Inherit the wind / Hold on (I feel our love is changing) / Help / Soul shadows / Way it goes, The / I'm so glad I'm standing here today / I'll still be lookin' up to you, (no matter how high I get) / Burnin' up the carnival.
**Cass:** Released Jul '87, on MCA by MCA Records. Deleted Apr '88. Catalogue no: **MCFC 3395**
**Album:** Released Jul '87, on MCA by MCA Records. Deleted Apr '88. Catalogue no: **MCF 3395**
**CD:** Released Jul '87, on MCA by MCA Records. Deleted Apr '88. Catalogue no: **DMCF 3395**

**VOCAL TAPE, THE**
**Cass:** Released Aug '83, on MCA by MCA Records. Catalogue no: **MCFC 3171**
**Album:** Released Aug '83, on MCA by MCA Records. Catalogue no: **MCF 3171**

## Cuber, Ronnie

**CUBER LIBRE (Various artists)**
**Album:** Released '88, on Xanadu Catalogue no: **XAN 135**

**ELEVENTH DAY OF AQUARIUS, THE**
Note: Featuring Ronnie Cuber, Tom Harrell, Rein de Graff, Sam Jones and Louis Hayes.
**Album:** Released '88, on Xanadu Catalogue no: **XAN 156**

**NEW YORK JAZZ**
Note: Featuring Ronnie Cuber, Tom Harrell, Rein de Graff, Sam Jones and Louis Hayes.
Tracks: / Fifty six / Monk's dream, A / Wail / Solar / 81st & 1st / Au privave.
**Album:** Released Apr '81, on Timeless by Timeless Records. Catalogue no: **SJP 130**

**PASSION FRUIT**
Tracks: / Passion fruit / You promised to be true / What it is / Love notes / Come dance with me / It's only in your mind.
Note: Ronnie Cuber, baritone sax, is best known for his work with George Benson. He also worked in the bands of Lionel Hampton and Woody Herman and spent a year on the road with King Curtis and Aretha Franklin. George Benson is featured on *Passion Fruit* and You Promised To Be True. Personnel: Ronnie Cuber - baritone sax, George Benson - guitar, George Wadenius - guitar, Richard Tee - electric piano, Rob Mounsey - synthesiser, Will Lee - bass, Dave Weckl - bass, Sammy Figueroa - percussion, Manolo Badrena - percussion.
**Album:** Released Jul '86, on King (Japan) Catalogue no: **K 28P 6347**

**PIN POINT**
**CD:** Released Oct '87, on King (Japan) Deleted '88. Catalogue no: **K32Y 6073**
**Album:** Released Nov '86, on King (Japan) Catalogue no: **K 28P 6415**

## Cugat, Xavier

**Biographical details:** Violinist, bandleader and composer born in 1900 in Spain. He moved to Cuba in the late 1920's and in the USA he formed a Latin-American dance band and was the most successful artist in the genre, appearing in more films than any other bandleader of that type. He was a populariser of Latin-American music; the rhythms were often simplified for American dancers but always showed respect for Cuban songs. His own best known composition was *My Shawl*; he had about 20 hit records 1935-49 and also recorded with Bing Crosby. After strokes, heart attacks and other problems, he formed a new band in a resort in Spain for his 87th birthday, still surrounded by pretty girls. (Donald Clarke, April 1989).

**1944-'45 (Cugat, Xavier & His Orchestra)**
**Album:** Released Jun '84, on Circle (USA) by Jazzology Records (USA). Catalogue no: **CLP 59**

**TO ALL MY FRIENDS**
Tracks: / New Cucaracha / Golden sunset / La bamba / Que lindas in Mexicanas / Despedida / Cielito lindo / Banana boat / Cuban holiday / Adius marquita Linda / Barbados baila / Diamante negro / Braziliana.
**Album:** Released Dec '86, on Intersound Catalogue no: **ISST 106**

## Culley, Frank

**ROCK AND ROLL**
Tracks: / Snap, The / Floorshow / Cole slow / Central Avenue breakdown / Waxie maxie boogie / After hour session / Rumboogie jive / Hop'n twist / My silent love / Mona Lisa / Gone after hours / Little Miss Blues / I've got you under my skin / Culley-flower.
**Album:** on Official by Official Records. Catalogue no: **OFF 6057**

## Cullum, Jim

**SUPER SATCH (Cullum, Jim Big Band)**
**CD:** Released Jan '88, on Stomp Off (USA) Catalogue no: **SOSCD 1148**
**Album:** Released Jan '88, on Stomp Off (USA) Catalogue no: **SOS 1148**

## Curson, Ted

**Biographical details:** A trumpet and flugelhorn player born in 1935 in Philadelphia, most famous for an incandescent Charles Mingus date on *Candid* in 1960, in a quartet that included Eric Dolphy: Curson held his own and is now one of those many fine musicians who is less well known than he should be at home because he has spent so much time in Europe. (Donald Clarke, April 1989).

**CANADIAN CONCERT OF, THE (Live at La' Tete de L'art)**
**Album:** Released Nov '87, on Can-Am (USA) Catalogue no: **CA 1700**

**I HEARD MINGUS**
**Album:** Released Oct '80, on Interplay (USA) by Interplay Records (USA). Catalogue no: **IP-7729**

**TED CURSON AND CO**
**Album:** Released May '84, on India Navigation Catalogue no: **IN 1054**

**TRIO, THE**
**Album:** Released Aug '79, on Interplay (USA) by Interplay Records (USA). Catalogue no: **IP 7722**

## Curtis, King

**20 GOLDEN PIECES: KING CURTIS (Curtis, King & The Noble Knights)**
Tracks: / Tequila / Night train / Java / Harlem nocturne / Honky tonk / Soul twist / Memphis / Watermelon man / Soul serenade / Swingin' shepherd blues / My last date (with you) / Wiggle wobble / Tanya / Tennessee waltz / Bill Bailey won't you please come home? / Misty / Sister Sadie / Ain't that good news? / Peter Gunn / One mint julep.
**Album:** Released Jul '82, on Bulldog Records by President Records. Catalogue no: **BDL 2009**

**BLUES AT MONTREUX (Curtis, King & Champion Jack Dupree)**
**Cass:** Released '88, on Atlantic by WEA Records. Catalogue no: **CS 1673**
**Album:** Released Nov '87, on Atlantic by WEA Records. Catalogue no: **SD 1637**

**DIDN'T HE PLAY**
**Album:** Released Oct '88, on Red Lightnin' by Red Lightning Records. Catalogue no: **RL 0074**
**Album:** Released Jun '88, on Red Lightnin' by Red Lightning Records. Catalogue no: **RL 074**

**INSTANT GROOVE**
**Album:** Released Feb '90, on Edsel by Demon Records. Catalogue no: **ED 315**

**IT'S GREAT TO BE RICH (EP)**
Tracks: / It's great to be rich / Lester's comet / La Cucaracha / Don't know where I've been / Sweet home Chicago.
**12" Single:** Released Jun '83, on Red Lightnin' by Red Lightning Records. Deleted Jun '89. Catalogue no: **RLEP 0045**

**IT'S PARTY TIME WITH KING CURTIS**
Tracks: / Free for all / Easy like / Hot saxes / I'll wait for you / Party time twist, The / Low down / Keep movin' / (Let's do) the hully gully twist / Slow motion / Firefly / Something frantic.
Note: The late King Curtis is best known for his work with the *Atlantic* label from his greasy low-down solos on the Coasters records through to his sterling work with Aretha Franklin. This album was cut in 1961/'62 for *Tru-Sound*, a subsidiary of *Prestige*, and features another tenor sax legend, Sam 'The Man' Taylor and Billy Butler on guitar. The album opens with a real 'hot pastrami' of a track with Curtis and Sam blowing out on *Free For All*.
It continues through some low down blues and hot R&B rockers with some cool dance craze riffin' and the funky organ sound of Ernie Hayes vamping up a storm, as Pinetop Smith said 'When I say git it, you shake that thing. (Ace Records, August 1989)
**Album:** Released 29 Aug '89, on Ace by Ace Records. Catalogue no: **CH 262**

Ted Curson

**JAZZ GROOVE**
Tracks: / Da duh dah / Have you heard / Willow weep for me / Little brother soul / In a funky groove / Soul meeting / Lazy soul / All the way / Jeep's blues / What is this thing called love / Do you have soul now.
**2 LP Set:** Released Sep '80, on Prestige Catalogue no: **PR 24033**

**KING CURTIS LIVE AT FILLMORE WEST**
Note: Reissue in original sleeve.
**Album:** Released Jun '88, on WEA (Canada) by WEA Records. Catalogue no: **SD 33359**

**LIVE IN NEW YORK**
Tracks: / Jaywalk / Trouble in mind / African waltz / What'd I say / I have to worry / Twist / Canadian sunset / How high the moon / K.C. special.
**Album:** Released Aug '85, on JSP by JSP Records. Catalogue no: **JSP 1091**

**MEMPHIS SOUL STEW (Curtis, King and Rex Garvin)**
Tracks: / Memphis soul stew / Sock it to 'em JB.
**12" Single:** Released Apr '80, on Atlantic by WEA Records. Catalogue no: **ATM 10**

**SINGS THE BLUES/TROUBLE IN MIND**
**Album:** Released Jan '88, on OBC Catalogue no: **OBC 512**

**SOUL GROOVE**
Tracks: / Blowin' off steam / Dark eyes / Who's sorry now / Sweet Georgia Brown / Sometimes I'm happy / Pickin' chicken / Soul groove part 1 / Soul groove part 2 / Clementine / Take me out to the ball game.
**Album:** Released Jul '87, on Blue Moon (1) by Magnum Music Group. Catalogue no: **BMLP 1036**

**SOUL TWIST (Curtis, King & Others)**
**Album:** Released Jul '88, on Collectables (USA) by Gotham Distributing Co.(USA). Catalogue no: **COL 5119**

**THAT'S ALRIGHT**
**Album:** Released May '83, on Red Lightnin' by Red Lightning Records. Deleted Jun '89. Catalogue no: **RL 042**

## Cuttin' The Boogie

**CUTTIN' THE BOOGIE (Various artists)**
Tracks: / Chicago stomp: *Blythe, Jimmy* / Mr. Freddie blues: *Blythe, Jimmy* / Suitcase blues: *Thomas, Hersal* / Pinetop's boogie woogie: *Smith, Clarence Pinetop* / Jump steady blues: *Smith, Clarence Pinetop* / Honky tonk train: *Lewis,*

*Meade Lux* / Yancey special: *Lewis, Meade Lux* / Mr. Freddie blues: *Lewis, Meade Lux* / Boogie woogie stomp: *Ammons, Albert* / Bass goin' crazy: *Ammons, Albert* / Mellow blues, The: *Yancey, Jimmy* / Tell 'em about me: *Yancey, Jimmy* / Climin' and screamin': *Johnson, Pete* / Blues on the downbeat: *Johnson, Pete* / Kaycee on my mind: *Johnson, Pete* / Cuttin' the boogie: *Ammons, Albert* (With Pete Johnson on piano and James Hoskins on drums.).
Note: Recorded in mono. Piano blues and Boogie-Woogie (1926-1941).
**Album:** Released Mar '87, on New World (USA) by New World Records (USA). Catalogue no: **NW 259**

## Cylinder Jazz

**CYLINDER JAZZ (Various artists)**
Tracks: / Hungarian rag: *Various artists* / Clarinet squawk: *Louisiana Five* / Dardanella: *Raderman, Harry's Jazz Orchestra* / Meadow lark: *Yellman, Duke/his orchestra* / Where's my sweetie hiding?: *Merry Sparklers* / Blue-eyed Sally: *Various artists* / Ain't she sweet: *Various artists* / She's a cornfed Indiana gal: *Oliver, Earl's Jazz Babies* / Make that trombone laugh: *Raderman, Harry's Jazz Orchestra* / Night time in Little Italy: *Frisco Jazz Band* / I'm going to park myself in your arms: *Yellman, Duke/his orchestra* / That certain feeling: *Tennessee Happy Boys* / Do it again: *Various artists* (Intro, drifting along with the tide.) / Louisville Lou: *Various artists.*
Note: 53 minutes, 14 tracks, taken from Edison Blue Amberol phonograph cylinders from 1913-1927; transcriptions by John R. T. Davies. Full colour sleeve of phonograph horns and cylinders.
**Cass:** Released '82, on Saydisc by Amon Ra Records. Catalogue no: **CSDL 334**
**Album:** Released '82, on Saydisc by Amon Ra Records. Catalogue no: **SDL 334**

## Cyrille, Andrew

**Biographical details:** A brilliant avant-garde jazz percussionist and composer, born in 1939 in Brooklyn. He studied at Julliard and worked and recorded with such big names as Coleman Hawkins, but hit his stride with Cecil Taylor 1965-1975, including the *Blue Note* album *Conquistador* and a period as Artist in Residence at Antioch College, Ohio. Like Taylor he was an outcast, ideas far ahead of his time. He has worked with the Jazz Composers Orchestra and with Jimmy Lyons; his solo album *What About?* in 1969 was originally on the *Byg* label in France. *Celebration,* from 1975 is by a septet with Ted Daniel (trumpet, flugelhorn), vocalist Jennie Lee and a poet; *Junction,* the next year has a group with Daniel now called Maono (the *IPS* label is *Institute of Percussive Studies*). *Nuba,* from 1979 is a trio with Lyons and Lee. Like many fine American musicians, he finds a lot of work in Europe. (Donald Clarke, April 1989)

**CELEBRATION**
**Album:** Released '80, on IPS Catalogue no: **ST 002**

**JUNCTION**
**Album:** Released '80, on IPS Catalogue no: **ST 003**

**NUBA**
**Album:** Released '79, on Black Saint (Italy) Catalogue no: **BSR 0030**

**WHAT ABOUT?**
Tracks: / What about / From whence I came / Rhythmical space / Rims and things / Pioneering.
Note: A drums-only album -- first recording of its kind.
**Album:** Released '82, on Affinity by Charly Records. Deleted '88. Catalogue no: **AFF 75**

# D

The following information was taken from the Music Master database on April 14th, 1990.

## Da Costa, Paulino

**AGORA**
Tracks: / Simbora / Terra / Toledo bagel / Berimbau variations / Belisco / Ritmo number one.
**Album:** Released Jan '77, on Pablo Jazz (USA) by Pablo Records (USA). Deleted '81. Catalogue no: **2335 747**
**Album:** Released '82, on Pablo Jazz (USA) by Pablo Records (USA). Catalogue no: **2310 785**
**Cass:** Released '82, on Pablo Jazz (USA) by Pablo Records (USA). Catalogue no: **K10 785**

**HAPPY PEOPLE**
Tracks: / Deja vu / Put your mind on vacation / Take it on up / Love till the end of time / Seeing is believing / Dreamflow / Carnival of colours / Let's get together / Happy people.
**Album:** Released '82, on Pablo Jazz (USA) by Pablo Records (USA). Catalogue no: **231 2102**
**Cass:** Released '82, on Pablo Jazz (USA) by Pablo Records (USA). Catalogue no: **K 12 102**

**SUNRISE**
Tracks: / Taj Mahal / I'm going to Rio / African sunrise / Walkman / O mar e meu chao / You came into my life / My love / You've got a special kind of love / Carioca / Groove.
Note: Fantastic new album from Brazilian percussionist Paulino Da Costa.
**CD:** Released Apr '87, on Pablo Jazz (USA) by Pablo Records (USA). Catalogue no: **CD 231 2143**
**Album:** Released Sep '84, on Verve (USA) by Polydor Ltd. Catalogue no: **2312 143**
**Cass:** Released Sep '84, on Verve (USA) by Polydor Ltd. Catalogue no: **K 12 143**

**TAJ MAHAL**
Tracks: / Taj Mahal.
**12" Single:** Released Sep '84, on Pablo Jazz (USA) by Pablo Records (USA). Catalogue no: **5155**

**TUDO BEM (Da Costa, Paulino & Joe Pass)**
Tracks: / Corcovado / Tears / Wave / Voice / If you went away / Que que ha / Gentle rain, The / Barquinho / Luciana / I live to love.
**Cass:** Released '82, on Pablo Jazz (USA) by Pablo Records (USA). Catalogue no: **K10 824**
**Album:** Released '82, on Pablo Jazz (USA) by Pablo Records (USA). Catalogue no: **231 0824**

## Dailey, Albert

**TEXTURES**
**Album:** Released '88, on Muse by Black & Blue Records. Catalogue no: **MR 5256**

## Dallwitz, Dave

**CINDERELLA GIRL (Dallwitz, Dave Jazz Band)**
**Album:** Released '88, on Swaggie (Australia) Catalogue no: **S 1407**
**Album:** Released Jan '88, on Swaggie (Australia) Catalogue no: **S 1413**

**DAVE DALLWITZ EUPHONIC RAGTIME (Dallwitz, Dave Euphonic Ragtime Ensemble)**
**Album:** Released Jun '86, on Stomp Off (USA) Catalogue no: **SOS 1098**

**DAVE DALLWITZ & SCHAMPUS ALL (Dallwitz, Dave & The Schampus All Stars)**
**Album:** Released May '79, on Dawn Club by Cadillac Music. Catalogue no: **DCS 33 002**

**ELEPHANT STOMP (Dallwitz, Dave Jazz Band)**
**Album:** Released Mar '87, on Stomp Off (USA) Catalogue no: **SOS 1112**

**ERN MALLY JAZZ SUITE (Dallwitz, Dave Jazz Band)**
**Album:** Released '88, on Swaggie (Australia) Catalogue no: **S1360**

**FLOATING PALAIS (Dallwitz, Dave Jazz Band)**
**Album:** Released Mar '87, on Swaggie (Australia) Catalogue no: **S 1409**

**GOLD FEVER (1977) (Dallwitz, Dave Jazz Band)**
**Album:** Released Jan '83, on Swaggie (Australia) Catalogue no: **S 1377**

**GULGONG SHUFFLE (1977) (Dallwitz, Dave Jazz Band)**
**Album:** Released Jan '83, on Swaggie (Australia) Catalogue no: **S 1378**

**ILLAWARRA FLAME(1974) (Dallwitz, Dave Jazz Band)**
**Album:** Released Jan '83, on Swaggie (Australia) Catalogue no: **S 1354**

**MELBOURNE SUITE(1973) (Dallwitz, Dave Jazz Band)**
**Album:** Released Jan '83, on Swaggie (Australia) Catalogue no: **S 1342**

**RAGTIME (Dallwitz, Dave Euphonic Ragtime Ensemble)**
**Album:** Released Jan '83, on Swaggie (Australia) Catalogue no: **S 1393**

**SUNDAY MORNING RAG (Dallwitz, Dave & The Schampus All Stars)**
**Album:** Released Dec '86, on Dawn Club by Cadillac Music. Catalogue no: **DC 33002**

## Dalto, Jorge

**URBAN OASIS**
Tracks: / Samba all day / Love of my life / Killer Joe / Ease my pain / Skydive / La costa / Sentido de sete.
Note: You may remember Jorge Dalto's piano introduction to George Benson's This Masquerade. He has also recorded with Tito Puento, Grover Washington and Spyro Gyra. Now this dynamic pianist, composer and arranger has assembled his own Inter American Band, fusing the music of two continents - the best of North and South America. With spicy percussion and tender ballads, Urban Oasis offers great crossover potential for jazz, Latin and urban contemporary markets.
**Cass:** Released Sep '85, on Concord Jazz by Concord Jazz Records (USA). Catalogue no: **CJPC 275**
**Album:** Released Sep '85, on Concord Jazz by Concord Jazz Records (USA). Catalogue no: **CJP 275**

## D'Ambrosia, Meredith

**IT'S YOUR DANCE**
Tracks: / Giant steps / Once upon a tempo / Listen little girl / Devil may care / August moon / Nobody else but me / Humpty dumpty heart / It's your dance / Underdog / It isn't so good it couldn't be better / Off again on again / No one remembers but me / Miss Harper goes bizarre / Strange meadowlark.
Note: Meredith D'Ambrosio - Vocals & piano / Harold Danko - Piano / Kevin Eubanks - Electric guitar
**CD:** Released Feb '86, on Sunnyside Jazz(USA) Catalogue no: **SSC 1011 D**
**Album:** Released Jan '86, on Sunnyside Jazz(USA) Catalogue no: **SSC 1011**

**LITTLE JAZZ BIRD**
**Album:** Released Jan '84, on Palo Alto Catalogue no: **PA 8019**

**MEREDITH....ANOTHER TIME**
Tracks: / All of us in it together / Aren't you glad you're you / It's so peaceful in the country / Rain rain (don't go away) / Dear Bix / Lazy afternoon / Where's the child I used to hold / Love is a simple thing / You are there / While we're young / Small day tomorrow / Child is born, A / Piano player / Some day my prince will come / Such a lonely girl am I / Wheelers and dealers / I was doin' all right / Skylark.

**Album:** Released Feb '87, on Sunnyside Jazz(USA) Catalogue no: **SSC 1017**

## Dance Band Years

### DANCE BAND YEARS, THE 1920's (Various artists)

Tracks: / Charleston: *Savoy Orpheans* / Yes sir, that's my baby: *Hylton, Jack & His Orchestra* / I wonder where my baby is tonight: *Mackey, Percival & His Band* / Paddlin' Madelin' home: *Hylton, Jack & His Orchestra* / Five foot two eyes of blue: *Firman, Bert & His Dance Orchestra* / Fascinating rhythm: *Mackey, Percival & His Band* / Breezing along with the breeze: *Hylton, Jack Kit Cat Band* / Clap hands here comes Charley: *Savoy Orpheans* / My cutey's due at two-to two today: *Firman, Bert & His Dance Orchestra* / When the red red robin comes bob bob bobbin along: *Hylton, Jack & His Orchestra* / Black bottom: *Firman, Bert & His Dance Orchestra* / Let's all go to Mary's house: *Whidden, Jay & His New Midnight Follies Band* / Baby face: *Savoy Orpheans* / I never see Maggie alone: *Ralton, Bert & His Havana Band* / Ain't she sweet: *Payne, Jack & His Hotel Cecil Orchestra* / Here am I broken-hearted: *Kit Kat Band* / Deed I do: *Payne, Jack & His Hotel Cecil Orchestra* / Ain't that a grand and glorious feeling?: *Firman, Bert & His Dance Orchestra* / Crazy words-crazy tune: *Payne, Jack & His Hotel Cecil Orchestra* / Varsity drag, The: *Hylton, Jack & His Orchestra*.

**Cass:** Released '88, on Saville by Conifer Records. Catalogue no: **CSVL 169**

**Album:** Released '88, on Saville by Conifer Records. Catalogue no: **SVL 169**

### DANCE BAND YEARS, THE 1930's (Various artists)

Tracks: / It's d' lovely: *Geraldo & His Orchestra* / Dipsy doodle, The: *Fox, Roy & His Orchestra* / Born to love: *Lipton, Sydney & His Grosvenor House Orchestra* / I go for that: *Geraldo & His Orchestra* / Heavenly party, A: *Fox, Roy & His Orchestra* / La-de-de, la-de-da: *Lipton, Sydney & His Grosvenor House Orchestra* / Raindrops: *Geraldo & His Gaucho Tango Orchestra* / Little robin told me so, A: *Liter, Monia & His Orchestra* / Change partners: *Geraldo & His Orchestra* / Goodbye to summer: *Lipton, Sydney & His Grosvenor House Orchestra* / Piccolino, The: *Liter, Monia & His Orchestra* / And the angels sing: *Geraldo & His Orchestra* / Smarty: *Lipton, Sydney & His Grosvenor House Orchestra* / Two shadows: *Fox, Roy & His Orchestra* / Jam sessions: *Lipton, Sydney & His Grosvenor House Orchestra* / I love you with all my heart: *Geraldo & His Orchestra* / Shoe shine boy: *Liter, Monia & His Orchestra* / Blue Caribbean sea: *Geraldo & His Orchestra* / Bob white (whatcha gonna swing tonight): *Fox, Roy & His Orchestra* / Pennies from heaven: *Liter, Monia & His Orchestra* / You can't stop me from dreaming: *Lipton, Sydney & His Grosvenor House Orchestra* / Harbour lights: *Geraldo & His Orchestra* .

**Cass:** Released '88, on Saville by Conifer Records. Catalogue no: **CSVL 168**

**Album:** Released '88, on Saville by Conifer Records. Catalogue no: **SVL 168**

### DANCE BAND YEARS, THE 1940's (Various artists)

Tracks: / I've got a girl in Kalamazoo: *Geraldo & His Orchestra* / Indian summer: *Geraldo & His Orchestra* / In the mood: *Geraldo & His Orchestra* / I hear a rhapsody: *Geraldo & His Orchestra* / South American way: *Geraldo & His Orchestra* / Do I worry: *Geraldo & His Orchestra* / You gorgeous dancing girl: *Geraldo & His Orchestra* / Swingin on Lennox avenue: *Skyrockets Dance Orchestra* / So dumb, but so beautiful: *Skyrockets Dance Orchestra* / Is you is or is you ain't my baby?: *Skyrockets Dance Orchestra* / Shoo shoo baby: *Preager, Lou & His Band* / I heard you cried last night: *Preager, Lou & His Band* / Boy is jumping, The: *Skyrockets Dance Orchestra / My prayer: Skyrockets Dance Orchestra / San Fernado valley: Skyrockets Dance Orchestra* / It jumps like mad: *Skyrockets Dance Orchestra* / Do you believe in dreams?: *Skyrockets Dance Orchestra*.

**Album:** Released Jun '82, on Saville by Conifer Records. Catalogue no: **SVL 145**

**Cass:** Released '88, on Saville by Conifer Records. Catalogue no: **CSVL 145**

## Dance Bands

### DANCE BANDS ON THE AIR - VOLUME 1 (Various artists)

Tracks: / On the air: *Gibbons, Carroll & The Savoy Hotel Orphans* / Happy feet: *Hylton, Jack & His Orchestra* / I like a little girl like that: *Payne, Jack & The BBC Dance Orchestra* / If I didn't have you: *Fox, Roy & His Band* / What a little moonlight can do: *Roy, Harry & His Orchestra* / Heart of gold: *Kunz, Charlie & The Casani Club Orchestra* / Lazy rhythm: *Stone, Lew & The Monseigneur Band* / Hors d'ouvres: *Various artists* / Sweetest music this side of heaven, The: *Winninck, Maurice & His Orchestra* / Glory of love: *Hall, Henry & The BBC Dance Orchestra* / Moon of Manakoora: *Various artists* / I double dare you: *Harris, Jack & His Orchestra* / That lovely weekend: *Loss, Joe & His Orchestra* / You're dancing on my heart: *Sylvester, Victor & His Ballroom Orchestra* / Don't say goodbye: *Sylvester, Victor & His Ballroom Orchestra*.

**Album:** Released Nov '76, on BBC by BBC Records & Tapes. Deleted '88. Catalogue no: **REC 139**

### DANCE BANDS ON THE AIR - VOLUME 2 (Various artists)

Tracks: / Stagecoach: *Winstone, Eric & His Band* / Tangerine: *Squadronaires* / Moonlight cocktail: *Geraldo & His Orchestra* / Cruising down the river: *Preager, Lou & His Orchestra* / Fanfare boogie: *Stapleton, Cyril & His Show Band* / Copacabana: *Ross, Edmundo & His Rumba Band* / Creep, The: *Mackintosh, Ken & His Orchestra* / Why worry?: *Cotton, Billy & His Band* / Hot toddy: *Heath, Ted & His Music* / Midnight in Moscow: *Ball, Kenny & His Jazzmen* / Lady is a tramp, The: *Miller, Bob & The Millermen* / Pennsylvania 6 5000: *Various artists* / Come dancing: *McVay, Ray & His Orchestra*.

**Album:** Released Nov '76, on BBC by BBC Records & Tapes. Deleted '88. Catalogue no: **REC 140**

### DANCE BANDS THROUGH THE YEARS (Various artists)

Tracks: / Too beautiful for words: *Various artists* / She wore a little jacket of blue: *Various artists* / Boo hoo: *Various artists* / It's the natural thing to do: *Various artists* / There's something in the air: *Various artists* / Rainbow on the river: *Various artists* / Little old lady: *Various artists* / So many memories: *Various artists* / Sweet someone: *Various artists* / Love walked in: *Various artists* / Says my heart: *Various artists* / Tears in my heart: *Various artists* / Whistle while you work: *Various artists* / Lambeth walk: *Various artists* / Tisket a tasket, A: *Various artists* / Heigh ho: *Various artists* / Doing the Blackpool walk: *Various artists* / Meet me down in the Sunset Valley: *Various artists* / Little lady make believe: *Various artists* / Over Wyoming: *Various artists* / Shoo shoo baby: *Various artists* / Gal in Calico, A: *Various artists* / Another spring is on the way: *Various artists* / You belong to me: *Various artists*.

**Cass set:** Released May '89, on Ditto by Pickwick Records. Catalogue no: **DTO 10311**

### IRVING BERLIN - CENTENARY (Various artists)

Note: Medley: When the midnight choo choo leaves for Alabam/That mysterious rag/When I leave the world behind/Alexanders ragtime band. Medley 2: I want to be in Dixie/Ragtime violin/When I lost you/Everybodys doing it now/How many times/Blue skies. Waltz medley: Because I love you/All alone/Always. Waltz medley 2: What'll I do?/The song is ended/You forgot to remember/Heat wave/A pretty girl is like a melody/Let's face the music and dance.

**Cass:** Released 16 May '88, on Retrospect by EMI Records. Deleted Aug '89. Catalogue no: **TC SH 512**

**Album:** Released 16 May '88, on Retrospect by EMI Records. Deleted Aug '89. Catalogue no: **SH 512**

### MUSIC OF IRVING BERLIN (Played by the great British dance bands) (Various artists)

**2 LP Set:** Released Feb '77, on World by World Records. Deleted '80. Catalogue no: **SHB 35**

### WE'LL MEET AGAIN (The music of Hugh Charles 1938-45) (Various artists)

Tracks: / I won't tell a soul: *Fox, Roy & His Orchestra* / Blue skies are just around the corner: *Hylton, Jack/his orchestra* / I shall always remember you smiling: *Hylton, Jack/his orchestra* / There'll always be an England: *Loss, Joe Concert Orchestra* / We'll meet again: *Hylton, Jack/his orchestra* / I shall be waiting: *Lipton, Sydney & His Grosvenor House Orchestra* / I'm in love for the last time: *Johnson, Ken 'Snakehips' & his West Indian Orchestra* / Little king without a crown: *Loss, Joe & His Orchestra* / Moonlight And mimosa: *Loss, Joe & His Orchestra* / Where the waters are blue / Get into the spirit of Spring: *Lipton, Sydney & his Orchestra* / Memories live longer than dreams: *Lipton, Sydney & his Orchestra* / When your train has gone: *Loss, Joe & His Orchestra* / King is still in London, The: *Gibbons, Carroll & Savoy Hotel Orpheans* / There's a land of begin again: *Winstone, Eric Accordion Band* / Let the bands play: *Loss, Joe & His Orchestra* / Russian Rose: *Geraldo/his Orchestra* / Potato Pete: *Roy, Harry & His Band* / Silver wings in the moonlight: *Gibbons, Carroll & Savoy Hotel Orpheans* / Till all our prayers are answered: *Payne, Jack Orchestra.*
**Album:** Released '88, on Reid Catalogue no: **RD 1**

## Dance Bands USA 1925

**DANCE BANDS USA 1925 TO 1935 (Various artists)**
Note: Artists include: Ace Brigode, Coon-Sanders, Jan Garber, Jean Goldkette, Benny Goodman, Glen Gray, Ipana Troubadours, Roger Wolf Kahn, Ted Lewis, Guy Lombardo, George Olsen, Slatz Randall, Leo Reisman, Waring's Pennsylvanians, Ted Weems, Paul Whiteman
**Album:** Released Oct '87, on BBC by BBC Records & Tapes. Catalogue no: **REB 650**
**CD:** Released Oct '87, on BBC by BBC Records & Tapes. Catalogue no: **BBC CD 650**
**Cass:** Released Oct '87, on BBC by BBC Records & Tapes. Catalogue no: **ZCF 650**

## Dane, Barbara

**GIPPER GATE BLUES**
Tracks: / Gipper gate blues.
**12" Single:** Released '88, on Arhoolie (USA) by Arhoolie Records (USA). Catalogue no: **ARHOOLIE 1600**

## Daniels, Billy

**Biographical details:** A cabaret singer (1915-88) who sang every day of 1937 on the radio for a dozen different sponsors and became famous in the '40's for his version of *That old black magic* to the point of being impersonated by comics. He always did well in clubs and had many fans. His double act from 1950 of comedy and vocalising with pianist Benny Payne was one of the first black acts to appear on USA TV; He made many films and stage appearances including the all-black *Hello Dolly* (with Pearl Bailey) in 1975 and the UK edition of *Bubbling brown sugar* in 1977 (more than 700 performances. (Donald Clarke, April 1989).

**AT THE CRESCENDO**
Tracks: / Them there eyes / Love is a many splendoured thing / Sway / Autumn leaves / Easy to love* / My blue Heaven* / It's all right with me* / My yiddishe momme / You were meant for me / Lady of the evening / If I should lose you / How deep is the ocean / I can dream, can't I / I live for you / Introduction & that old black magic.
Note: *Medley.
**Album:** Released '88, on Pathe Marconi (France) Catalogue no: **T 1278**
**Album:** Released '88, on GNP Crescendo (USA) by GNP Crescendo Records (USA). Catalogue no: **GPNS 16**
**Album:** Released May '78, on Pye Catalogue no: **PKL 5569**

## Daniels, Joe

**STEPPIN' OUT TO SWING (Daniels, Joe & His Hotshots)**
Tracks: / Good to me / Steppin' out to swing / Southern fried / Eep-ipe wanna piece of pie / Whirlwind / Abbey road hop / Red light / Red robin rag / Fats in the fire / When you're smiling / Lady be good / Time on my hands / Down beat / Canzonetta / Snug as a bug / Alike as two peas / Shandy / Don't be that way / It's the talk of the town / Nice going.
**Album:** Released Sep '84, on Saville by Conifer Records. Catalogue no: **SVL 167**

**SWING HIGH, SWING LOW 1935-37**
Tracks: / I got rhythm / It don't mean a thing / Chinatown my chinatown / Twelfth St. rag / Wabash blues / Swing high, swing low / After you've gone / Big boy blues / Sheik of Araby, The / In the shade of the old apple tree / Farewell blues / Who / I can't give you anything but love / Drummer goes to town.
**Album:** Released Jul '88, on Harlequin by Interstate Music. Catalogue no: **HQ 3023**

## Daniels, Maxine

**BEAUTIFUL FRIENDSHIP, A (Daniels, Maxine & Ted Taylor Trio)**
Tracks: / I've got it bad / I'm always chasing rainbows / Foggy day, A / I can't give you anything but love / Dancing on the ceiling.
Note: Tracks include those listed above.
**Cass:** Released Oct '87, on Maxam Catalogue no: **MAXAM 001**

**EVERY NIGHT ABOUT THIS TIME**
**Album:** Released Mar '86, on Calligraph Catalogue no: **CLGLP 007**

**MAXINE DANIELS**
**Album:** Released Sep '89, on Calligraph Catalogue no: **MC 589**

**POCKET FULL OF DREAMS**
Tracks: / I've got a pocketful of dreams / With you in mind / Deep purple / Seems like old times / Change partners / Sunshine of love / Something 'bout you baby / When you wish upon a star / Leaning on a lamp post / Into each life some rain must fall / Broken doll / For all we know / Over the rainbow / Talk to the animals.
**Album:** Released 15 Jan '88, on Calligraph Catalogue no: **CLGLP 016**
**Cass:** Released 15 Jan '88, on Calligraph Catalogue no: **ZCLG 016**

## Daniels, Mike

**1957-1959 (Daniels, Mike Delta Jazzmen)**
Tracks: / Milenberg joys / You're just my type / At a Georgia camp meeting / Riverboat shuffle / Weather bird rag / Baby doll / Aunt Hagar's blues / I'm confessin' / You made me love you / Blues are brewin' / When you and I were young, Maggie / That's my weakness now / Don't forget to mess around.
**Album:** Released Jun '86, on Harlequin by Interstate Music. Catalogue no: **HQ 3007**

## Danish Radio Big Band

**BY JONES, I THINK WE'VE GOT IT**
**Album:** Released Jun '81, on Metronome (Denmark) Catalogue no: **MLP 15629**

**CRACKDOWN (1st UK tour 1987)**
**Album:** Released Jan '88, on Hep Jazz by Hep Records. Catalogue no: **HEP 2041**

**GOOD TIME WAS HAD BY ALL, A (Danish Radio Big Band & Thad Jones)**
**Album:** Released Jun '81, on Metronome (Denmark) Catalogue no: **MLP 15644**

## Danko, Harold

**INK AND WATER**
Tracks: / Snow blossoms / Sand storms / Dew and petals / High mountain pines / Children's walking song / Footbridge over the rushing stream / Animals on a four-screen landscape / Leaves in a rock garden / Play song / Across the cliffs / Sunrise watch / Walk at dawn / Willow, wind and water / Roots and vines / Icicles in the cave / Reflections in a pond.
**Album:** Released Feb '86, on Sunnyside Jazz(USA) Catalogue no: **SSC 1008**

**MIRTH SONG (Danko, Harold & Rufus Reid)**
**Album:** Released Apr '84, on Sunnyside Jazz (USA) Catalogue no: **SSC 1001**

## Dankworth, John

**1953-58, FEATURING CLEO LAINE**
Tracks: / Experiments with mice / Somebody loves me / Honeysuckle rose / It's the talk of the town / I got rhythm / Idaho / I got it bad and that ain't good / Take the 'A' train / Big jazz story / Runnin' wild / Easy living / Get happy / You go to my head / Ain't misbehavin' / All Clare / I know you're mine / Adios.
**Cass:** Released Aug '84, on Retrospect by EMI Records. Deleted Jun '88. Catalogue no: **EG 2601874**

Harold Danko - Ink and Water (Sunnyside)

**Album:** Released Aug '84, on Retrospect by EMI Records. Deleted Nov '88. Catalogue no: **EG 2601871**

**AFRICAN WALTZ**
Tracks: / African waltz.
**7" Single:** Released Feb '61, on Columbia by EMI Records. Deleted Feb '64. Catalogue no: **DB 4590**

**BOP AT CLUB 11 (Dankworth, John Quartet / Ronnie Scott Boptet)**
Note: The complete 1949 concert.
**Album:** Released Jun '86, on Esquire by Titan Int. Prod.. Catalogue no: **ESQ 315**

**EXPERIMENTS WITH MICE**
Tracks: / Experiments with mice.
**7" Single:** Released Jun '56, on Parlophone by EMI Records. Deleted Jun '59. Catalogue no: **R 4185**

**FAIR OAK FUSIONS (Dankworth, John & Julian Lloyd Webber)**
Note: The work was commissioned by Fair Oak for its open air theatre in Sussex, England, after cellist Webber, having been invited to perform there, said he would like to play something written specially for him by Dankworth. John responded with a nine-movement work accommodating various musical styles and composing techniques. The album, recorded live at the Stables at Wavendon, features Julian Lloyd Webber on cello, and John on alto and soprano saxophones and clarinet, the Myrha Saxophone Quartet (John Harle, Irite Kutchmy, David Roach and Andrew Findon) playing a total of 11 instruments, Paul Hart on bass guitar and violin and Allan Ganley on drums.
**Album:** Released Jan '83, on Sepia Catalogue no: **RSR 1007**
**Cass:** Released Jan '83, on Sepia Catalogue no: **ZCRRT 1007**

**GET HAPPY (Dankworth, John Seven & Cleo Laine)**
**Album:** Released May '86, on Esquire by Titan Int. Prod.. Catalogue no: **ESQ 317**

**GONE HITCHIN' (Dankworth, John Quintet)**
Tracks: / First time, last time / Thigh boots / Gone hitchin' / Son of Sparky / Triple Tyne / Layoff / Silver ray / Key stone corner.
**Album:** Released May '83, on Sepia Catalogue no: **RSR 2012**
**Cass:** Released May '83, on Sepia Catalogue no: **ZC RRT 2012**

**INNOVATIONS (Dankworth, John & The London Symphony Orchestra)**
Tracks: / Take five / We've only just begun / Here there and everywhere.
**CD:** Released Apr '88, on Pickwick by Pickwick Records. Catalogue no: **PWK 059**

**LOVER & HIS LASS, A (Dankworth, John & Cleo Laine)**
**Album:** Released Dec '76, on Esquire by Titan Int. Prod.. Catalogue no: **ESQ 301**

**METRO**
**Album:** Released Nov '83, on Repertoire (Germany) Catalogue no: **RSR 2013**

**OCTAVIUS (Dankworth, John & Paul Hart Octet)**
**Album:** Released Apr '83, on Sepia Catalogue no: **RSR 1001**

**SYMPHONIC FUSIONS (Dankworth, John & The London Symphony Orchestra)**
Tracks: / Every time we say goodbye / Decline and fall of a bridge / Afterglow / Sing, sing, sing / Further experiments with mice / Shadow of your smile / African waltz / Fantasia enigma / Paganini in perpetuo.
**CD:** Released Jan '86, on Pickwick by Pickwick Records. Catalogue no: **PCD 842**
**Cass:** Released Aug '86, on Pickwick by Pickwick Records. Catalogue no: **HSC 3191**
**Album:** Released Aug '86, on Hallmark by Pickwick Records. Deleted '88. Catalogue no: **SHM 3191**

**TELFORD'S CHANGE (Dankworth, John & His Orchestra)**
Tracks: / Telford's change / Serenade for Sylvia.
**7" Single:** Released Jan '79, on BBC by BBC Records & Tapes. Deleted '82. Catalogue no: **RESL 63**

**WHAT THE DICKENS? (Dankworth, John & His Orchestra)**
Tracks: / Prologue / Weller never did / Little Nell / Infant phenomenon / Damdest little fascinator / Dotheboys hall / Ghosts / David and the bloaters / Please sir I want some more / Artful Dodger / Waiting for something to turn up / Dodson and Fogg / Pickwick Club / Sgt. Buzfuz.
**Album:** Released Jul '83, on Sepia Catalogue no: **RSR 2010**

**ZODIAC VARIATIONS (Dankworth, John & His Orchestra)**
Tracks: / Way with the stars / Aquarius / Pisces / Aries / Taurus / Gemini / Cancer / Leo / Virgo / Libra / Scorpio / Sagittarius / Capricorn & Coda.
**Album:** Released Jul '83, on Sepia Catalogue no: **RSR 2011**

## Dapogny, Jim

**BACK HOME IN ILLINOIS (Dapogny, Jim Chicago Jazz Band)**
**Album:** Released '88, on Jazzology (USA) by Jazzology Records (USA). Catalogue no: **J 140**

**HOW COULD WE BE BLUE**
**Album:** Released '89, on Stomp Off (USA) Catalogue no: **SOS 1183**

**JIM DAPOGNY'S CHICAGO JAZZ BAND (Dapogny, Jim Chicago Jazz Band)**
**Album:** Released Jun '86, on Jazzology (USA) by Jazzology Records (USA). Catalogue no: **J 120**

## Darby, Blind Terry

**ST. LOUIS COUNTRY BLUES**
**Album:** Released Jan '87, on Earl Archives Catalogue no: **BD 611**

## Darktown Strutters

### JAZZ THE WAY IT USED TO BE
**Cass:** Released May '84, on Kiwi-Pacific (New Zealand) Catalogue no: **TC TRL 026**
**Album:** Released May '84, on Kiwi-Pacific (New Zealand) Catalogue no: **TRL 026**

## Darnell, Larry

### I'LL GET ALONG SOMEHOW
Tracks: / I'll get along somehow (parts 1 & 2) / For you my love / Pack your rags and go / My kind of baby / My baby don't love me / Sundown / Christmas blues / I love my baby / What more do you want me to do ? / Ramblin' man / Just tell me when.
**Album:** Released Aug '87, on Route 66 (Sweden) Catalogue no: **KIX 19**

## Davenport, Cow Cow

### ALABAMA STRUT
Note: With Dora Carr, Ivy Smith, B.T. Wingfield, Leroy Pickett.
**Album:** Released Apr '79, on Magpie by Interstate Music. Deleted '88. Catalogue no: **PY 1814**

### COW COW BLUES
**Album:** Released '88, on Oldie Blues Catalogue no: **OL 2811**

### COW COW DAVENPORT 1926-38
**Album:** Released Jun '88, on Best Of Blues (USA) by Blue Island Records (USA). Catalogue no: **BOB 7**

### COW COW DAVENPORT 1927-29
**Album:** Released Aug '89, on Document Catalogue no: **DLP 557**

## Davenport, Wallace

### DARKNESS ON THE DELTA
**Album:** Released '88, on GHB by Jazzology Records (USA). Catalogue no: **GHB 146**
**Album:** Released Jan '88, on Storyville by Storyville Records AB. Catalogue no: **SLP 512**

## Davern, Kenny

### EL RADO SCHUFFLE: (A TRIBUTE TO JIMMIE NOONE)
**Album:** Released Jul '82, on Kenneth Catalogue no: **KS 2050**

### I'LL SEE YOU IN MY DREAMS
**CD:** Released '89, on Music Masters by Music Masters Records. Catalogue no: **CIJD 60212**

### LIVE HOT JAZZ (Davern, Kenny, Dick Wellstood, Chuck Riggs)
**Cass:** Released '88, on Statiras (USA) by Statiras(USA) Records. Catalogue no: **SC 8077**
**Album:** Released May '86, on Statiras (USA) by Statiras(USA) Records. Catalogue no: **SLP 8077**

### LIVE AND SWINGING (Davern, Kenny & John Peters)
Tracks: / That's a plenty / Man I love, The / Poor butterfly / Royal Garden blues / Blue monk / Love me or leave me.
**CD:** Released '88, on CMJ Catalogue no: **CMJCD 001**
**Cass:** Released '88, on CMJ Catalogue no: **CMJMC 001**

### ONE HOUR TONIGHT (Davern, Kenny Quartet / Dick Wellstood)
Tracks: / Elsa's dream / Pretty baby / Love is the thing / If I could be with you.
**Album:** Released Jan '89, on Music Masters by Music Masters Records. Catalogue no: **MMD 20148 A**
**Cass:** Released Jan '89, on Music Masters by Music Masters Records. Catalogue no: **CIJD 40148 Z**
**CD:** Released Jan '89, on Music Masters by Music Masters Records. Catalogue no: **CIJD 60148 Y**

### THIS OLD GANG OF OURS (Davern, Kenny & Humphrey Littleton)
Tracks: / Mood Hollywood / Porters love song to a chamber maid, A / My mama socks me / Jackass blues / Undecided / Of all the wrongs you've done to me.
**Album:** Released Nov '86, on Calligraph Catalogue no: **CLGLP 012**

## Davies, Cyril

**Biographical details:** One of the pioneers of British blues, born in Buckinghamshire in 1932. He had played banjo in trad and skiffle, then harmonica with Alexis Korner, jamming with visiting black Americans; in the early '60's they went electric and formed Blues Incorporated: future Rolling Stones and Cream passed through; Davies left and formed his own All-Stars, taking over Screaming Lord Sutch's Savages; he employed Nicky Hopkins and others. After his death from leukemia in 1964 vocalist Long John Baldry took over most of All Stars. *Country Line Special* is a 3-track 12" EP. (Donald Clarke, April 1989).

### COUNTRY LINE SPECIAL
Tracks: / Country line special / Chicago calling / Preachin' the blues.
**7" Single:** Released Jun '84, on PRT by Castle Communications Records. Catalogue no: **7P 308**
**12" Single:** Released Jun '84, on PRT by Castle Communications Records. Catalogue no: **12P 308**

## Davis, Blind Joe

### BLIND JOE DAVIS VOL 1 (Imcomparable, The)
**Album:** Released '88, on Oldie Blues Catalogue no: **OL 2803**

## Davis, Blind John

### BLIND JOHN DAVIS 1938
**Album:** Released '89, on Document Catalogue no: **DLP 505**

### BLIND JOHN DAVIS WITH JEANNE CARROLL (Davis, Blind John & Jeanne Carroll)
**Album:** on L&R Catalogue no: **LR 42.056**

### IN MEMORIAM 1938
**Album:** Released Jul '87, on Document Catalogue no: **DOC 505**

## Davis, Eddie 'Lockjaw'

### AFRO-JAWS
Tracks: / Wild rice / Guanco lament / Tin tin deo / Jazz-A (samba) / Alma alegre / Star eyes / Afro-jaws.
**Album:** Released Feb '88, on Riverside (USA) by Fantasy Inc (USA). Catalogue no: **RSLP 373**

### BEST OF EDDIE 'LOCKJAW' DAVIS
Tracks: / Wave / Lover / I'll never be the same / Chef, The / On a clear day / Angel eyes / Telegraph / Land of dreams / Blue Lou.
**Cass:** Released '82, on Pablo Jazz (USA) by Pablo Records (USA). Catalogue no: **K10 858**
**Album:** Released '82, on Pablo Jazz (USA) by Pablo Records (USA). Catalogue no: **2310 858**

### CHEWIN' THE FAT
Tracks: / Cherokee / Stompin' at the Savoy / Ghost of a chance / On Green Dolphin Street / Avalon / Wave / Tangerine / Oh gee.
**Album:** Released '83, on Spotlite by Spotlite Records. Catalogue no: **SPJ LP15**

### COUNTIN' WITH BASIE
**Album:** Released Apr '84, on Vogue by Vogue Records. Catalogue no: **500118**

### EDDIE 'LOCKJAW' DAVIS FOUR
Tracks: / This can't be love / I wished on the moon / Breeze and I, The / Telegraph / Land of dreams / Blue Lou.
**Album:** Released '82, on Pablo Jazz (USA) by Pablo Records (USA). Catalogue no: **2308 214**
**Cass:** Released '82, on Pablo Jazz (USA) by Pablo Records (USA). Catalogue no: **K 08 214**

### EDDIE'S FUNCTION
Tracks: / People will say we're in love / You are too beautiful / All the things you are / Ladybird / Scotty boo / Tia juana / I wished on the moon / Ebb tide / Eddie's function / Out of nowhere.
**Album:** Released Jul '86, on Affinity by Charly Records. Deleted May '88. Catalogue no: **AFF 153**

### HEAVY HITTER, THE
Tracks: / When your lover has gone / Just one of those things / Old folks / Out of nowhere / Secret love / Comin' home baby / You stepped out of a dream / Jim dog.
**Album:** Released Apr '81, on Muse by Black & Blue Records. Catalogue no: **MR 5202**

### HEY LOCK!
Tracks: / My blue Heaven / Bewitched, bothered and bewildered / Blues in my heart / Hey lock / I only have eyes for you / Chihuahua / Secret love / Nightingale / Metalmouth / Locked in / Hey Jim / Beano / Marchin' / I can't get started / S.O.S. / Jaws.
**Album:** Released May '83, on Vogue Jazz (France) by Vogue Records. Catalogue no: **VJD 548**

**JAWS**
**Album:** Released Apr '86, on Original Jazz Classics (USA) by Fantasy Inc (USA). Catalogue no: **OJC 218**

**JAWS BLUES**
**Album:** Released Jan '82, on Enja (Germany) by Enja Records (West Germany). Catalogue no: **ENJA 3097**

**MODERN JAZZ**
Tracks: / Dizzy atmosphere / It's the talk of the town / Leaping on Lenox / This is always / Bean-o / I'll remember April / Moonlight in Vermont / Johnny come lately / You go to my head / Foggy day / Tenderly / Way you look tonight.
**CD:** Released Mar '90, on King Catalogue no: **KCD 506**
**Album:** Released '88, on Sing Catalogue no: **SING 506**

**MPS JAZZ TIME VOL 8**
Tracks: / Again 'n' again / Tin tin deo / If I had you / Jim Dawg / When we were one / Gigi.
**Album:** Released Jun '79, on MPS Jazz (France) Catalogue no: **5C 064 61174**

**RAREST SESSIONS OF THE '40'S,**
Tracks: / Surgery / Lockjaw / Foxy / Real gone guy / But beautiful / Black pepper.
**Album:** Released Jul '82, on Pinnacle by Pinnacle Records. Catalogue no: **FC 5009**

**SAVE YOUR LOVE FOR ME**
Tracks: / On Green Dolphin Street / Oh gee / Speak low / Save your love for me / Good life / I wished on the moon / When your lover has gone / Bye bye blackbird / Call me / Day by day / Out of nowhere / Man with the horn, The / Weaver of dreams, A / We'll be together again.
**Cass:** Released Apr '89, on Bluebird (2) by BMG Records (UK). Catalogue no: **NK 86463**
**CD:** Released Apr '89, on Bluebird (2) by BMG Records (UK). Catalogue no: **ND 86463**
**Album:** Released Apr '89, on Bluebird (2) by BMG Records (UK). Catalogue no: **NL 86463**

**STRAIGHT AHEAD**
Tracks: / Lover / Wave / On a clear day / Chef, The / Gigi / Last train from Overbrook / Good life / I'll never be the same / Watch what happens / Lucky so and so / I may be wrong but I think you're wonderful / Smoke gets in your eyes / Stompin' at the Savoy / Time after time / Secret love / It could happen to you / Slow drag.
**Cass:** Released '82, on Pablo Jazz (USA) by Pablo Records (USA). Catalogue no: **K10 778**
**Album:** Released '82, on Pablo Jazz (USA) by Pablo Records (USA). Catalogue no: **2310 778**

**SWEETS AND JAWS (Davis, Eddie "Lockjaw"/Harry Edison)**
**Album:** Released '88, on Vogue (France) by Vogue Records. Catalogue no: **502601**

**SWINGIN' TIL GIRLS**
**CD:** Released Jul '88, on Steeplechase (USA) Catalogue no: **SCCD 31058**
**Album:** Released Feb '77, on Steeplechase (USA) Catalogue no: **SCS 1058**

**TENOR OF EDDIE 'LOCKJAW' DAVIS, THE**
**CD:** Released Dec '86, on Vogue by Vogue Records. Catalogue no: **VG 600 123**

**THAT'S ALL**
Tracks: / Exactly like you / L'amour est une drole de chose / Pitch-tree thing, The / Out of nowhere / That's all / Chef, The / George / Satin doll.
**Album:** Released Jun '86, on Kingdom Jazz by Kingdom Records. Catalogue no: **GATE 7019**
**Album:** Released Feb '87, on Pathe Marconi (France) Catalogue no: **2400601**
**Cass:** Released Jun '86, on Kingdom Jazz by Kingdom Records. Catalogue no: **CGATE 7019**

**TOUGH TENORS (Davis, Eddie 'Lockjaw' & Johnny Griffin)**
Tracks: / Again'n'again / Tin tin deo / If I had you / Jim dawg / When we were one / Gigi.
Note: Count Basie veteran Eddie ' Lockjaw' Davis and hard-bop extraordinaire Johnny Griffin formed their 'Tough Tenors Quintet' during the '60's when jazz was going through it's 'soul' stage and swinging 'get down and boogie' playing was the order of the day. Recorded 24 April 1970 with Kenny Clarke-Francy Boland Big Band rhythm section of Kenny Clarke, drums, Francy Boland, piano and Jimmy Woode, bass.
**CD:** Released Jun '86, on Milestone by Ace Records. Catalogue no: **821 293-2**

**UPTOWN**
**Album:** Released 7 Nov '87, on Swingtime by Contact Records (Denmark). Catalogue no: **ST 1021**
**Album:** Released Dec '88, on Syndicate Chapter Catalogue no: **SC 1021**

## Davis, Eddy

**EDDY DAVIS AND HOT JAZZ ORCHESTRA (Davis, Eddy & The Hot Jazz Orchestra)**
**Album:** Released '88, on Jazzology (USA) by Jazzology Records (USA). Catalogue no: **J 67**
**Album:** Released Jun '88, on Jazzology (USA) by Jazzology Records (USA). Catalogue no: **J 88**

**EDDIE DAVIS AND THE HOT JAZZ ORCHESTRA**
Tracks: / New Orleans shuffle / Because it's you that puts the music in my heart / Minority blues / Rene's bar-b-que / Ragtime dance / Rocking chair / Blame it on the blues / China boy / My man / I can't believe that you're in love with me.
**Album:** Released 8 Apr '89, on New York Catalogue no: **J 005**

**EDDY DAVIS AND STANLEY'S WASHBOARD 1983**
Tracks: / New Orleans shuffle / Was I to blame for falling in love with you / Sunset Cafe stomp / Hustlin' and bustlin' for baby / Doctor Heckle and Mr. Jibe / Sweet mama / Oriental man / Kiss me sweet / Dream man / Nuages / Sow a wild oat / Doin' ya good.
**Album:** Released 8 Apr '89, on New York Catalogue no: **J 007**

## Davis, Eunice

**SINGS THE CLASSIC BLUES OF VICTORIA SPIVEY**
**Album:** on L&R Catalogue no: **LR 42.016**

## Davis, Joe

**BIG BAND JAZZ 1940-1952**
**Album:** Released Jun '86, on Harlequin by Interstate Music. Catalogue no: **HQ 2047**

**R'N'B FROM JOE DAVIS 1952-53 VOL.1 (Various artists)**
**Album:** Released Sep '85, on Krazy Kat by Interstate Music. Catalogue no: **KK 795**

**R'N'B FROM JOE DAVIS 1955-56 VOL.2 (Various artists)**
Note: Mono
**Album:** Released May '86, on Krazy Kat by Interstate Music. Catalogue no: **KK 796**

## Davis, Miles

**Biographical details:** Miles Dewey Davis was born in Alton, Illinois, on 25 May 1926. A year later, his well-to-do landowning family moved to East St. Louis where he grew up. For his thirteenth birthday, his father gave him his first trumpet. At 16 he married. Two years later, after playing in Billy Eckstine's band in St.Louis (along with Charlie Parker, Dizzy Gillespie and Dexter Gordon), he left for New York where his father paid for his studies at the Julliard School of Music. He began playing clubs with Parker, later recording some interesting sides with his mentor, for Dial and Savoy, in the 1945-47 period. His original and lyrical virtuosity made up for some rather noticeable technical limitations. In 1948, he met arranger Gil Evans, and formed the Miles Davis Nontette (otherwise known as The Tuba Band). The journey from bebop into the "cool" had begun. His playing was highly emotive and sensitive but Miles was having problems with drug-related illnesses and although making excellent music, was not meeting with great commercial success. After an important Newport festival appearance in 1955, he formed what critics believed his most interesting band - Philly Joe Jones on drums, Red Garland on piano, Paul Chambers on bass and John Coltrane on saxophone. Not only has Miles Davis helped to change the face of of jazz but he also launched some great sidesmen - Sonny Rollins, John Coltrane, Herbie Hancock, among others. In the 'sixties and 'seventies he delved into "jazz-rock" - the album "Bitches Brew" is an excellent early example of the genre. He has continued, throughout an outstanding career, to make important records and to undertake successful concert tours.

This American trumpeter is one of the most impotant figures in the history of jazz. He is widely regarded as the father of modern jazz, both for his series of stylistic innovations and for his tutoring and training of some of the genre's most accomplished latterday greats. His British chart track record is somewhat farcical - his solitary week at No 71 in July 1970 with the *Bitches Brew* LP represents Davis' only foray into the UK national charts, and underlines the fact tht even the greatest jazz players have difficulty in overcoming the 'specialist' and 'minority interest' tags.

Born in Illinois in 1926, Miles Davis gaines his musical apprenticeship through playing in the band of the legendary alto saxophonist, Charlie Parker. The first important stage of Davis' solo career was his late Forties decision to enlist the talents of arranger Gil Evans. The previously underrated Evans underpinned the trumpeter's playing with lush orchestral arrangements, thereby inventing a new form of jazz. In the mid-Fifties, Davis assembled what proved to be one of the most acclaimed quintets of all time: tenor saxophonist John Coltrane, keyboards player Red Garland, bassist Paul Chambers and drummer Philly Joe Jones helped to bring his career to a new level of popularity amongst jazz pundits and punters alike. By the end of the decade, however, Davis' roster of musicians was forever changing, and this flexibility has remained in force throughout the remainder of his career. 'Flexibility' was a key word in the late Fifties for another reason - in keeping with his innovative character, he began to break free from conventional chord structures and progressions, and pioneered a looser, more spacious sound known as 'model improvisation'.

The 1968 album *Miles In The Sky* saw Davis, at the age of 42, moving into the rock sphere and, for the first time, adding electric instruments to his band. Tracks such as *Big Stuff* brought him a cross over audience from the realms of the drug-influenced hippie rock fraternity of the late Sixties. The lengthy solos and free, improvised sounds now employed by the trumpeter and his group were not dissimilar to those used by such rock heavyweights as Cream and Jefferson Airplane. This clear musical parallel led to the major success of two jazz-rock fusion bands, Blood, Sweat and Tears and Chicago. The list of musicians who passed through Davis' band during the late Sixties and early Seventies, gives a clear indication of his influence and importance in relation to the future development of jazz: George Benson, Billy Cobham, Chich Corea, Herbie Hancock and John McLaughlin all played with him - a phenomenon which later led to an even more durable and important fusion, jazz-funk.

Davis followed *Miles In The Sky* with a series of rocky albums, such as 1969's *In A Silent Way* and 1971's *Jack Johnson*. A road accident interrupted his output in the early Seventies, but returned to full activity with 1974's *Get Up With It* LP. After a slight lull in his popularity, Davis then released one of his most successful latterday LPs, 1981's *The Man With The Horn*. The striking simplicity of this title seemed apt for the master trumpeter at this stage in his career. After 35 years as a jazz innovator, during which time he had single-handedly re-defined the genre, he was still at the top of his profession, happy in the knowledge that many of his younger fellow musicians owed their success to him. (Bob MacDonald, 14 March 1985.).

**1954- THE MASTERPIECES**
**Album:** Released Sep '87, on Giants of Jazz by Hasmick Promotions. Catalogue no: **LPJT 55**

**1958 MILES**
**Album:** Released May '79, on Japanese Import Catalogue no: **20 AP 1401**

**AGHANTHA (IMPORT)**
**Album:** Released '88, on CBS (import) by CBS Records. Catalogue no: **CBS 88158**

**AGHANTHA (SET)**
**2 LP Set:** Released Jan '87, on CBS by CBS Records. Catalogue no: **CBS 88159**

**AMANDLA**
Tracks: / Catembe / Big time / Jo Jo / Jilli / Cobra / Hannibal / Amandla / Mr. Pastorius.
**Album:** Released May '89, on WEA by WEA Records. Catalogue no: **WX 250**
**CD:** Released May '89, on WEA by WEA Records. Catalogue no: **K 925873-2**
**Cass:** Released May '89, on WEA by WEA Records. Catalogue no: **WX 250 C**

**ARTISTRY IN JAZZ (Greatest hits)**
**CD:** Released May '87, on JVC/Fantasy Catalogue no: **VDJ 1586**

**ASCENSEUR POUR L'ECHAFAUD (Davis, Miles/Art Blakey Jazz Messengers)**
Tracks: / Generique / L'assassinat de carala / Sur l'autoroute / Julien dans l'ascenseur / Florence sur les Champs Elysees / Diner au motel / Evasion de Julien / Visite du vigile / Au bar du petit bac / Chez le photographe du motel.
Note: Three original sound tracks composed by Miles Davis and Art Blakey "Asenseur Pour L'Echafaud" (Miles Davis) "Des Femmes Disparaissent" (Art Blakey's Jazz Messengers) and "Les Liaisons Dangereuses" (Art Blakey's Jazz Messengers and participation from Barney Wilen).
**CD:** Released '88, on Phonogram by Phonogram Ltd. Catalogue no: **822 566-2**

**AT BIRDLAND, 1951**
**Album:** Released Jun '76, on Beppo Deleted '88. Catalogue no: **BEP 501**

**AT BIRDLAND: MILES DAVIS (Davis, Miles Sextet)**
Tracks: / Hot house / Embraceable you / Ouverturia / 52nd Street theme / Wee Chubb's blues.
**Album:** Released Apr '81, on Jazz Live (Italy) Catalogue no: **BLJ 8023**

**AT HIS RAREST OF ALL RARE**
**Album:** on Kings Of Jazz Catalogue no: **KLJ 20025**

**AT LAST (Davis, Miles & The Lighthouse All Stars)**
Tracks: / Infinity promenade / Round midnight / Night in tunisia / Drum conversation / At last.
**Album:** Released May '85, on Boplicity by Ace Records. Deleted '88. Catalogue no: **COP 001**

**AURA**
Tracks: / Intro / White / Yellow / Orange / Red / Green / Blue / Electric red / Indigo / Violet.
**CD:** Released Oct '89, on CBS by CBS Records. Catalogue no: **463 351 2**
**2 LP Set:** Released Oct '89, on CBS by CBS Records. Catalogue no: **463 351 1**
**Cass:** Released Oct '89, on CBS by CBS Records. Catalogue no: **463 351 4**

**BAGS' GROOVE (Davis, Miles & the Modern Jazz Giants)**
Tracks: / Bag's groove / Bag's groove (Take 2) / Airegin / Oleo / But not for me (Take 2) / Doxy / But not for me (Take 1).
**Cass:** Released Mar '88, on Prestige Deleted Jan '90. Catalogue no: **PRC 7109**
**CD:** Released Nov '86, on JVC/Fantasy Deleted '88. Catalogue no: **VDJ 1531**
**Album:** Released Mar '88, on Prestige Catalogue no: **PR 7109**
**Album:** Released Jan '87, on Original Jazz Classics (USA) by Fantasy Inc (USA). Catalogue no: **OJC 245**

**BALLADS**
Tracks: / Baby won't you please come home / I fall in love too easily / Bye bye blackbird / Basin Street blues / Once upon a summertime / Song no.2 / Wait till you see her / Corcovado.
**Cass:** Released Apr '89, on CBS (import) by CBS Records. Catalogue no: **461 099 4**
**CD:** Released Apr '89, on CBS (import) by CBS Records. Catalogue no: **461 099 2**
**Album:** Released Apr '89, on CBS (import) by CBS Records. Catalogue no: **461 099 1**

**BIRTH OF THE COOL**
Tracks: / Move / Jeru / Moon dreams / Venus De Milo / Budo / Deception / Darn that dream (CD only.) / Godchild / Boplicity / Rocker / Israel / Rouge.
**CD:** Released Apr '90, on Pacific Jazz by EMI Records. Catalogue no: **CDP 792 862 2**

**Album:** Released Jul '78, on Capitol by EMI Records. Catalogue no: **CAPS 1024**
**CD:** Released Apr '90, on Pacific Jazz by EMI Records. Catalogue no: **CZ 274**

**BITCHES BREW**
Tracks: / Pharaoh's dance / Bitches brew / Spanish key / John McLaughlin / Miles runs down the voodoo down / Sanctuary.
**Cass:** Released Apr '88, on CBS (import) by CBS Records. Catalogue no: **451126 4**
**Album:** Released Apr '88, on CBS (import) by CBS Records. Catalogue no: **451126 1**
**2 LP Set:** Released Jul '87, on CBS by CBS Records. Catalogue no: **CBS 66236**

**BLUE CHRISTMAS**
Tracks: / Little Melonae / Budo / Sweet Sue / On Green Dolphin Street / Fran dance / Stella by starlight / Blue Christmas.
**Cass:** Released May '83, on CBS by CBS Records. Deleted Nov '87. Catalogue no: **40 21070**
**Album:** Released May '83, on CBS by CBS Records. Catalogue no: **CBS 21070**

**BLUE HAZE**
**Album:** Released Jun '86, on Original Jazz Classics (USA) by Fantasy Inc (USA). Catalogue no: **OJC 093**

**BOPPING THE BLUES**
Tracks: / Don't sing me the blues (Take 1) / Don't sing me the blues (Take 2) / I've always got the blues (Take 1, incomplete) / I've always got the blues (Take 2) / I've always got the blues (Take 3) / Don't explain to me, baby (Take 1) / Don't explain to me, baby (Take 2) / Don't explain to me, baby (Take 3) / Don't explain to me, baby (Take 4) / Baby, won't you make up your mind? (Take 1) / Baby, won't you make up your mind? (Take 2) / Baby, won't you make up your mind? (Take 3).
Note: Recorded in Hollywood, 18 October 1946.
**Album:** Released Jun '88, on Black Lion Catalogue no: **BLP 60102**
**CD:** Released Jun '88, on Black Lion Catalogue no: **BLCD 760102**

**CARNEGIE HALL 1961 (Davis, Miles & Gil Evans)**
**CD:** Released Mar '90, on Giants of Jazz by Hasmick Promotions. Catalogue no: **GOJCD53023**

**CBS YEARS 1955-85**
Tracks: / Generique / All blues / Eighty-one / Blues for Pablo / Summertime / Straight, no chaser / Footprints / Florence sur les Champs Elysees / I thought about you / Some day my prince will come / Bye bye blackbird / My funny valentine / Love for sale / Budo / Miles / Files de Kilimanjaro / Fran dance / Seven steps to heaven / Flamenco sketches / So what / Water babies / Saeta / Masqualero / Pinocchio / Summer night / Fall / It's about that time / Sivad / What it is / Ms. Morrisine / Shout / Honky Tonk / Star on Cicely / Thinkin' one thing and doin' another / Miles runs the voodoo down.
**CD:** Released Feb '89, on Jam Today by Jam Today Records. Catalogue no: **463 246 2**
**Cass:** Released Feb '89, on Jam Today by Jam Today Records. Catalogue no: **463 246 4**
**Album:** Released Feb '89, on Jam Today by Jam Today Records. Catalogue no: **463 246 1**

**CHRONICLE: THE COMPLETE PRESTIGE**
Tracks: / Ahmad's blues / Airegin / Bag's Groove / Bemsha swing / Bitty ditty / Blue haze / Blue 'n' boogie / Blue room / Blues by five / Bluing / But not for me / Changes / Compulsion / Conception / Denial / Diane / Dig / Doctor Jackle / Down / Doxy / Ezz-thetic / Floppy / For adults only / Four / Gal in Calico, A / Green haze / Half nelson / Hibeck / How am I to know? / I could write a book / I know / I didn't / I see your face before me / I'll remember April / If I were a bell / In your own sweet way / It could happen to you / It never entered my mind / It's only a paper moon / Just squeeze me / Love me or leave me / Man I love, The / Miles ahead / Minor march / Morpheus / My funny valentine / My old flame / Night in Tunisia / No line / Odjenar / Old devil moon / Oleo / Out of the blue / Round about midnight / Salt peanuts / Serpent's tooth / Smooch / Solar / Something I dreamed last night / S'posin' / Stablemates / Surrey with the fringe on top / Swing spring / Tasty pudding / Theme / There is no greater love / 'Trane's blues / Tune up / Vierd blues / Walkin' / Well you needn't / When I fall in love / When lights are low / Whispering / Will you still be mine? / Willie the wailer / Wouldn't you? / Yesterdays / You don't know what love is / You're my everything.
**LP Set:** Released Dec '80, on Prestige Deleted '89. Catalogue no: **P 012**

**CIRCLE IN THE ROUND**
Tracks: / Circle in the round / Two bass hit / Love for sale / Blues No. 2 / Teo's bag / Side car / Splash sanctuary / Guinnervere.
**2 LP Set:** Released '88, on CBS by CBS Records. Catalogue no: **CBS 22132**
**2 LP Set:** Released Feb '80, on CBS by CBS Records. Deleted '85. Catalogue no: **CBS 88471**

**CLASSICS**
**2 LP Set:** Released Aug '84, on CBS (import) by CBS Records. Catalogue no: **88138**

**COLLECTION: MILES DAVIS**
Tracks: / My funny valentine / So what? / Straight, no chaser / Milestones / Some day my prince will come / Autumn leaves / Oleo / Fran dance / Oh-leu-cha / Walkin' / Theme.
**CD:** Released Sep '87, on Deja Vu Catalogue no: **DVCD 2039**
**Cass:** Released Aug '85, on Deja Vu Catalogue no: **DVMC 2039**

**COLLECTOR'S ITEM**
Tracks: / Compulsion / Serpent's tooth / Round about midnight / In your own sweet way / Wierd blues / No line / My old flame / Nature boy / There's no you / Easy living / Alone together.
**CD:** Released Apr '87, on Carrere (France) Catalogue no: **98406**
**2 LP Set:** Released '79, on Prestige Deleted '84. Catalogue no: **PR 24022**
**2 LP Set:** Released Feb '84, on Prestige (USA) by Fantasy Inc (USA). Catalogue no: **OJC 071**

**COMPLETE AMSTERDAM CONCERT, THE**
**Album:** Released Jul '85, on Celluloid (France) Catalogue no: **CEL 6745**
**Cass:** Released Jul '85, on Celluloid (France) Catalogue no: **CEL 6746**

**CONCERTO DE ARANJUEZ (Davis, Miles & Gil Evans)**
**CD:** Released Aug '88, on Giants of Jazz by Hasmick Promotions. Catalogue no: **CD 53023**

**COOKIN' AT THE PLUGGED NICKEL**
Tracks: / If I were a Bell / Stella by starlight / Walkin' / Miles.
**Album:** Released Apr '88, on CBS (import) by CBS Records. Catalogue no: **4606071**

**COOKIN' WITH THE MILES DAVIS QUINTET**
**CD:** Released '88, on Fantasy (import) by Fantasy Inc (USA). Catalogue no: **FCD 6367094**
**CD:** on JVC/Fantasy Catalogue no: **VDJ 1512**

**COPENHAGEN 1960 (Davis, Miles & John Coltrane)**
**Album:** Released Jan '90, on Royal Jazz Catalogue no: **RJ 501**

**DECOY**
Tracks: / Decoy / Robot 415 / Code MD / Freaky deaky / What is it? / That's right / That's what happened.
**CD:** Released Jun '84, on CBS by CBS Records. Deleted Jan '89. Catalogue no: **CD 25951**
**Cass:** Released Jun '84, on CBS by CBS Records. Catalogue no: **40 25951**
**Album:** Released Jun '84, on CBS by CBS Records. Catalogue no: **CBS 25951**

**DIRECTIONS**
Tracks: / Song of our country / Round midnight / So near so far / Limbo / Water on the pond / Fun / Directions / Ascent / Duran / Londa / Willie Nelson.
**2 LP Set:** Released May '81, on CBS by CBS Records. Deleted '86. Catalogue no: **88514**

**EARLY YEARS, THE**
**Album:** Released Sep '85, on Saar Giants Of Jazz (Italy) Catalogue no: **LPJT 24**
**Cass:** Released Sep '85, on Saar Giants Of Jazz (Italy) Catalogue no: **MCJT 24**

**EVOLUTION OF A GENIUS 1945-1954**

Tracks: / Now's the time / Donna Lee / Milestones / Jeru / Boplicity / Rocker / Ezz-thetic / Yesterdays / Compulsion / Tempus fugit / Tune up / It never entered my mind / Old devil moon / I'll remember April / Walkin' / But not for me.
**CD:** Released '88, on Giants of Jazz by Hasmick Promotions. Catalogue no: **GOJCD 0221**

**EZZ-THETIC (Davis, Miles & Lee Konitz)**
**Album:** Released Feb '86, on Fantasy Inc (USA) by Fantasy Inc (USA). Catalogue no: **1902119**

**FOUR AND MORE**
**Album:** Released '88, on CBS (import) by CBS Records. Catalogue no: **CBS 85560**

**FRIDAY NIGHT AT THE BLACK HAWK VOL. 1**
**CD:** Released May '89, on CBS (import) by CBS Records. Catalogue no: **463 334 2**
**Album:** Released May '89, on CBS (import) by CBS Records. Catalogue no: **463 334 1**
**Cass:** Released May '89, on CBS (import) by CBS Records. Catalogue no: **463 334 4**

**GET UP WITH IT**
Tracks: / He loved him madly / Maiysha / Honky tonk / Rated X / Calypso frelimo / Red China blues / Mtume / Billy Preston.
**Album:** Released '87, on CBS by CBS Records. Catalogue no: **88092**

**GOLDEN HIGHLIGHTS OF MILES DAVIS**
**Cass:** Released Jun '86, on CBS (import) by CBS Records. Catalogue no: **40 54733**
**Album:** Released Jun '86, on CBS (import) by CBS Records. Catalogue no: **54733**

**GREATEST HITS: MILES DAVIS**
Tracks: / Seven steps to Heaven / All blues / Some day my prince will come / Walkin' / My funny valentine / E.S.P. / Round midnight / So what.
**Album:** Released Jul '87, on CBS by CBS Records. Catalogue no: **CBS 63620**

**GREEN HAZE**
Tracks: / Will you still be mine / I see your face before me / I didn't / Gal in Calico, A / Night in Tunisia, A / Green haze / Just squeeze me (but don't tease me) / No greater love / How am I to know / S'posin' / Theme, The / Stablemates.
**Album:** Released '79, on Prestige Deleted '84. Catalogue no: **PR 24064**

**HEARD 'ROUND THE WORLD**
Tracks: / If I were a bell / My funny valentine / So what / Walkin' / All of you / Milestones / Autumn leaves.
**Album:** Released Apr '84, on CBS by CBS Records. Deleted '89. Catalogue no: **CBS 88626**

**IMMORTAL CONCERTS (Davis, Miles & John Coltrane)**
Tracks: / So what? / Fran dance / All blues / Theme / On green Dolphin Street / Walkin' / Theme.
**CD:** Released Jan '86, on AVI (USA) by AVI Record Production Inc.(USA). Catalogue no: **AVI 2004**
**2 LP Set:** Released Jun '86, on Dragon by Dragon Records. Catalogue no: **DRLP 90/91**
**2 LP Set:** Released Feb '87, on Dragon by Dragon Records. Catalogue no: **DRLP 129/130**

**IN A SILENT WAY**
Tracks: / Ssh peaceful / In a silent way / It's about that time.
**CD:** Released 27 Feb '88, on CBS (import) by CBS Records. Catalogue no: **450 982 2**
**Album:** Released Jul '87, on CBS by CBS Records. Catalogue no: **CBS 63630**
**Cass:** Released 27 Feb '88, on CBS (import) by CBS Records. Catalogue no: **450 982 4**
**Album:** Released 27 Feb '88, on CBS (import) by CBS Records. Catalogue no: **450 982 1**

**IN EUROPE (Antibes 1964)**
**Album:** Released Jun '86, on CBS (import) by CBS Records. Catalogue no: **CBS 62390**
**Album:** Released Jun '75, on CBS (import) by CBS Records. Catalogue no: **F 1028**
**CD:** Released Jun '86, on CBS (import) by CBS Records. Deleted 17 Apr '89. Catalogue no: **CD 62390**

**KIND OF BLUE**
Tracks: / So what / Freddie Freeloader / Blue in green / Al blues / Flamenco sketches.
**Album:** Released '83, on CBS by CBS Records. Catalogue no: **CBS 62066**
**CD:** Released Mar '87, on CBS by CBS Records. Catalogue no: **CBS CD 62066**
**Album:** Released Apr '88, on CBS (import) by CBS Records. Catalogue no: **460 603 1**
**Cass:** Released Apr '88, on CBS (import) by CBS Records. Catalogue no: **460 603 4**

**KONSERTHUSET, STOCKHOLM (March 22, 1960) (Davis, Miles & John Coltrane)**
Note: with Winton Kelly, Jimmy Cobb etc.
**CD:** Released Jan '88, on Giants of Jazz by Hasmick Promotions. Catalogue no: **GOJCD 0233**

**LEGENDARY MASTERS, THE (SET) (Unissued or rare1948-1960)**
**LP Set:** Released Apr '88, on Recording Arts Ref. Edition Catalogue no: **RARELP 08/10**
**CD Set:** Released Apr '88, on Recording Arts Ref. Edition Catalogue no: **RARECD 08/10**

**LEGENDARY MASTERS, THE (Unissued or rare 1948-52) (See panel below)**
Tracks: / Why do I love you? / Godchild / Moon dreams / Hallucinations / Darn that dream / Move (mood) / Conceptions (deceptions) / Opmet (out of the blue) / Chase, The / Why do I love you / S'il vous plait / Move / Max is making wax / Tune up / Bye bye blackbird / Rollin' blowin'

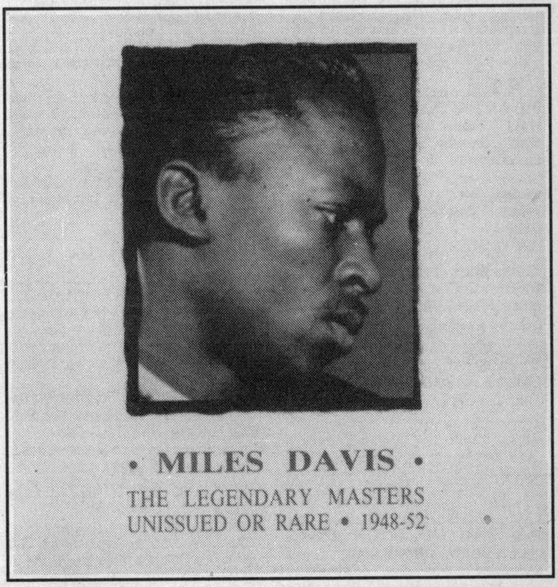


**Miles Davis - Legendary Masters 1948-1952 (Recording Arts Ref. Edition)**

walkin' / But not for me / Night in Tunisia / Fran dance / Godchild / Walkin' / It never entered my mind / Round about midnight / What's new / Blues for pablo / On Green Dolphin Street.
Note: Also available as a set - 1948-1960.
**CD:** Released '88, on Recording Arts Ref. Edition Catalogue no: **RARECD 08**
**Album:** Released '88, on Recording Arts Ref. Edition Catalogue no: **RARELP 08**

**LEGENDARY MASTERS, THE (Unissued or rare 1956-59)**
Tracks: / Tune up / Walkin' / Bye bye blackbird / It never entered my mind / Rollin' blowin' walkin' / Round about midnight / But not for me / What's new? / Night in Tunisia / Blues for Pablo.
**CD:** Released '88, on Recording Arts Ref. Edition Catalogue no: **RARECD 09**
**Album:** Released '88, on Recording Arts Ref. Edition Catalogue no: **RARELP 09**

**LEGENDARY MASTERS, THE (Unissued or rare 1960)**
Tracks: / Walkin' (theme) / Fran dance / On green dolphin street / So what?.
**CD:** Released '88, on Recording Arts Ref. Edition Catalogue no: **RARECD 10**
**Album:** Released '88, on Recording Arts Ref. Edition Catalogue no: **RARELP 10**

**LIVE AT CARNEGIE HALL: MILES DAVIS**
Tracks: / Concierto de Aranjuez (part 1) / Concierto de Aranjuez (part 2) / Teo / Walkin' / I thought about you.
**Album:** Released 27 Feb '88, on CBS (import) by CBS Records. Catalogue no: **4600641**
**Cass:** Released 27 Feb '88, on CBS (import) by CBS Records. Catalogue no: **4600644**

**LIVE AT THE PLUGGED NICKEL**
Tracks: / Walkin' / Agitation / On Green Dolphin Street / So what / Theme / 'Round about midnight / Stella by starlight / All blues / Yesterdays.
**2 LP Set:** Released '83, on CBS by CBS Records. Deleted '88. Catalogue no: **88606**

**LIVE IN COPENHAGEN, 1960 (Davis, Miles Quintet)**
**CD:** Released '89, on Royal Jazz Catalogue no: **CDRJ 501**

**LIVE IN EUROPE 1960 AND 1967 (Davis, Miles Quintet)**
**CD:** Released Mar '90, on Jazz-Up Catalogue no: **JU 320**

**LIVE: MILES DAVIS (Davis, Miles & John Coltrane)**
Tracks: / Green Dolphin Street / Walkin' / Theme / So what / Round midnight.
**Album:** Released Nov '86, on Unique Jazz by Spotlite Records. Catalogue no: **UJ 19**

**MAN WITH THE HORN (Davis, Miles & John Coltrane)**
Tracks: / Fat time / Back seat Betty / Shout Aida / Man with the horn, the / Ursula.

**Miles Davis - Miles Ahead (CBS)**

**Album:** Released Aug '81, on CBS by CBS Records. Deleted Aug '86. Catalogue no: **CBS 84708**
**CD:** Released '83, on CBS by CBS Records. Catalogue no: **CD 84708**
**Cass:** Released Sep '86, on Prix D'Ami (France) Catalogue no: **40 84708**

**MILES AHEAD (CBS) (See panel above)**
Tracks: / Springsville / Maids of cadiz, The / Duke, The / My ship / Miles ahead / Blues for pablo / New rhumba / Meaning of the blues, The / Lament / I don't wanna be kissed.
**Album:** Released Jun '86, on CBS (import) by CBS Records. Catalogue no: **62496**
**Album:** Released Apr '88, on CBS (import) by CBS Records. Catalogue no: **4606061**

**MILES AHEAD (PRESTIGE)**
Tracks: / Compulsion / Maids of cadiz, the / My ship / Meaning of the blues, the / I don't wanna be kissed / Round midnight / Duke, the / Miles ahead / New rhumba / Lament.
**Cass:** Released May '88, on Prestige Deleted Jan '90. Catalogue no: **PRC 7822**
**Album:** Released May '88, on Prestige Catalogue no: **PR 7822**

**MILES AND COLTRANE (Davis, Miles & John Coltrane)**
Tracks: / Ah-leu-cha / Straight, no chaser / Fran dance / Two bass hit / Bye bye blackbird / Little Melonae / Budo.
**Album:** Released 14 Aug '88, on CBS (import) by CBS Records. Catalogue no: **4608241**
**Cass:** Released 14 Aug '88, on CBS (import) by CBS Records. Catalogue no: **4608244**

**MILES DAVIS (Walkman/Compact jazz)**
Tracks: / Jitterbug waltz, The / Django / Wild man blues / Round midnight / Generique / L'assassinat de Carala / Sur l'autoroute / Julien dans l'asceseur / Florence sur les champs elysees / Diner au motel / Evasion de Julien / Visite du vigile / Au bar du petit bac / Chez le photographe du motel / Au privave / She rote / K.C. blues / Star eyes.
**CD:** Released Jan '90, on Verve Catalogue no: **838 254-2**
**Album:** Released '79, on Prestige Deleted '82. Catalogue no: **PR 24001**
**Cass:** Released Jan '90, on Verve Catalogue no: **838 254-4**
**Cass:** Released Sep '87, on CBS by CBS Records. Catalogue no: **441132 4**
**Album:** Released May '84, on Prestige (USA) by Fantasy Inc (USA). Catalogue no: **OJCD 507**

**MILES DAVIS 1945-51 VOL 1 (The early days)**
**Album:** Released Sep '87, on Giants of Jazz by Hasmick Promotions. Catalogue no: **LPJT 24**

**MILES DAVIS ALL STARS AND GIL EVANS (Davis, Miles & Gil Evans)**
**Album:** Released Jun '76, on Beppo Deleted '88. Catalogue no: **BEP 502**

**MILES DAVIS ALLSTARS Feat.John Coltrane / Cannonball Adderley**
**Cass:** Released Nov '88, on Jazz Band

by Flyright Records. Catalogue no: **EBC 409**
**Album:** on Jazz Band by Flyright Records. Catalogue no: **EB 409**

**MILES DAVIS AND JAZZ HOOFER (VIDEO) (Davis, Miles & Jazz Hoofer)**
**VHS:** Released '88, on Kay Jazz (video) by Kay Jazz. Catalogue no: **KJ 021**

**MILES DAVIS AT CARNEGIE HALL, 1961**
**CD:** Deleted 10 Jul '89. Catalogue no: **CD 85554**

**MILES DAVIS, DIZZY GILLESPIE & CHARLIE PARKER (Davis, Miles / Dizzy Gillespie / Charlie Parker)**
**2 LP Set:** Released Nov '76, on Vogue by Vogue Records. Catalogue no: **VJD 529**

**MILES DAVIS IN L.A., 1946**
**Album:** Released '79, on Joker (USA) by Lifetime Records (USA). Catalogue no: **SM 3717**

**MILES DAVIS & THE HI-HAT ALL-STARS**
**Album:** Released Feb '88, on Fresh Sounds (Spain) by Fresh Sounds Records (Spain). Catalogue no: **FS 280**

**MILES DAVIS & THE LIGHTHOUSE ALLSTARS (Davis, Miles & Lighthouse Allstars)**
**CD:** Released Apr '87, on Carrere (France) Catalogue no: **98610**

**MILES DAVIS & THE MODERN JAZZ JAZZ GIANT (Davis, Miles & the Modern Jazz Giants)**
**CD:** Released Jan '89, on JVC/Fantasy Catalogue no: **VDJ 1605**

**MILES DAVIS, VOL 1**
Tracks: / Tempus fugit / Kelo / Enigma / Ray's idea / How deep is the ocean? / C.T.A. / Dear old Stockholm / Chance it / Yesterdays / Donna / Woody 'n you / Woody 'n you (alt. take).
**Album:** Released Jul '89, on Blue Note by EMI Records. Catalogue no: **BST 81501**
**Album:** Released Aug '82, on Blue Note by EMI Records. Deleted Jan '88. Catalogue nø: **BLP 1501**
**Cass:** Released Mar '86, on Blue Note by EMI Records. Catalogue no: **TCBST 81501**

**MILES DAVIS VOL. 1 (CD)**
Tracks: / Dear old Stockholm / Chance it (Alternative take) / Chance it (alt. take) / Donna (alt. take) / Donna / Woody 'n you / Yesterdays / How deep is the ocean / Take off / Lazy Susan / Leap, The / Well you needn't / Weirdo / It never entered my mind.
**CD:** Released Nov '88, on Blue Note by EMI Records. Catalogue no: **BNZ 111**
**CD:** Released Nov '88, on Blue Note by EMI Records. Catalogue no: **CDP 781 501 2**

**MILES DAVIS, VOL 2**
Tracks: / Take off / Weirdo / Woodyn' you / I waited for you / Ray's idea / Donna / Well you needn't / Lazy Susan / Tempus fugit / It never entered my head.
Note: Miles' quartet session with Horace Silver and Art Blakey, performing 'Well you needn't', 'Weirdo' and 'It never entered my head' among others, is the centrepiece of this classic album. Also included is additional material that completes the sextet sessions featured on Volume one with J.J. Johnson, Jackie McLean, Art Blakey.
**Album:** Released Jul '89, on Blue Note by EMI Records. Catalogue no: **BST 81502**
**Album:** Released Aug '82, on Blue Note by EMI Records. Deleted Jan '88. Catalogue no: **BLP 1502**
**Cass:** Released Aug '85, on Blue Note by EMI Records. Deleted Jun '88. Catalogue no: **4BN 81502**

**MILES DAVIS VOL. 2 (C.D.)**
Tracks: / Kelo (alt.) / Kelo / Enigma (alt.) / Enigma / Ray's idea (alt.) / Ray's idea / Tempus fugit / Tempus fugit (alt.) / C.T.A. (alt.) / C.T.A. / I waited for you.
**CD:** Released Apr '90, on Blue Note by EMI Records. Catalogue no: **BNZ 240**
**CD:** Released Apr '90, on Blue Note by EMI Records. Catalogue no: **CDP 781 502 2**

**MILES IN BERLIN**
**CD:** Released May '87, on CBS by CBS Records. Deleted Jan '89. Catalogue no: **CD 62976**

**MILES IN ST LOUIS (Davis, Miles Quintet)**
Tracks: / I thought about you / All blues / Seven steps to Heaven / Trio, The.
Note: Recorded 25 June 1961.
**Album:** Released Apr '81, on VGM (Import) Catalogue no: **VGM 0003**

**MILES OF FUN**
Tracks: / Moose the mooche / Yardbird suite / Ornithology / Night in Tunisia / Bird's nest / Bird of paradise.
**Album:** Released Jul '80, on Manhattan Records by President Records. Catalogue no: **MAN 5028**

**MILES OF JAZZ (Davis, Miles & Charlie Parker)**
**Album:** Released '88, on Star Jazz (USA) by Charly Records. Catalogue no: **SJAZZ 7**
**Cass:** Released '88, on Star Jazz (USA) by Charly Records. Catalogue no: **S JAZZ C7**

**MILESTONES**
Tracks: / Doctor Jekyll / Sid's ahead / Two bass hit / Miles / Billy boy / Straight, no chaser.
**Cass:** Released 14 Aug '88, on CBS (import) by CBS Records. Catalogue no: **4608274**
**Album:** Released 14 Aug '88, on CBS (import) by CBS Records. Catalogue no: **4608271**

**MUSINGS OF MILES, THE**
Tracks: / I didn't / Will you still be mine / Green haze / I see your face before me / Night in Tunisia / Gal in Calico, A.
**Album:** Released Jun '84, on Original Jazz Classics (USA) by Fantasy Inc (USA). Catalogue no: **OJC 004**

**MY FUNNY VALENTINE**
**CD:** Released May '87, on CBS by CBS Records. Catalogue no: **CD 85558**

**NIGHT IN TUNISIA, A**
Tracks: / Embraceable you / Bird of paradise / Out of nowhere / My old flame / Don't blame me / Scrapple from the apple.
Note: With Charlie Parker, Lucky Thompson, Dodo Marmarosa, Arv Garrison, Victor McMilland, Roy Potter, Los Angeles, 28.3.46; Charlie Parler, Duke Gordon, Tommy Porter, Max Roach, New York, 28.10.47.
: by Chase Music Group (USA).
**Cass:** Released Apr '86, on Star Jazz (USA) by Charly Records. Catalogue no: **SJAZZC 2**
**Album:** Released Apr '86, on Star Jazz (USA) by Charly Records. Catalogue no: **SJAZZ 2**

**ON THE CORNER**
**Album:** Released Dec '88, on Beat Goes On by Andy's Records. Catalogue no: **BGOLP 30**
**Album:** Released Jan '87, on CBS by CBS Records. Catalogue no: **CBS 85549**

**PORGY & BESS (Davis, Miles & Gil Evans Orchestra)**
Tracks: / Buzzard song / Bess, you is my woman now / Gone gone gone / Summertime / Bess, oh where's my Bess? / Prayer / O Doctor Jesus / Fisherman / Strawberry and devil crab / My man's gone now / It ain't necessarily so / Here comes de honey man / I loves you, Porgy / There's a boat that's leaving shortly for New York.
**CD:** Released '88, on CBS (import) by CBS Records. Catalogue no: **35DP 61**
**Cass:** Released 27 Feb '88, on CBS (import) by CBS Records. Catalogue no: **4509854**
**Album:** Released 27 Feb '88, on CBS (import) by CBS Records. Catalogue no: **4509851**
**Cass:** Released Sep '82, on CBS by CBS Records. Catalogue no: **40 32188**
**Album:** Released Sep '82, on CBS by CBS Records. Catalogue no: **CBS 32188**

**PORTRAIT OF MILES DAVIS, A**
Tracks: / Bye bye blackbird / On Green Dolphin Street / Oleo / Autumn leaves / Sanctuary / Spanish key / Konda / Come get it / Jean Pierre / Decoy / Time after time / Something's on your mind.
**Album:** Released 5 Feb '88, on CBS (import) by CBS Records. Catalogue no: **4505931**
**Cass:** Released 5 Feb '88, on CBS (import) by CBS Records. Catalogue no: **4505934**

**PRE-BIRTH OF THE COOL (Davis, Miles & His Tuba Band)**
Tracks: / Why do I love you? / Godchild / S'il vous plait / Moon dreams / Hallucinations / Darn that dream / Move.
**Album:** Released Apr '81, on Jazz Live (Italy) Catalogue no: **BLJ 8003**

**QUIET NIGHTS**

**CD:** Deleted 10 Jul '89. Catalogue no: **CD 85556**

**RELAXIN' WITH MILES (Davis, Miles Quintet)**
**CD:** Released Apr '86, on JVC/Fantasy Catalogue no: **VDJ 1503**

**ROUND ABOUT MIDNIGHT**
Tracks: / Round about midnight / Ah leu cha / All of you / Bye bye blackbird / Tadd's delight' / Dear old stockholm.
**Cass:** Released Apr '88, on CBS (import) by CBS Records. Catalogue no: **4606054**
**Album:** Released Jun '86, on CBS (import) by CBS Records. Catalogue no: **62323**
**Album:** Released Apr '88, on CBS (import) by CBS Records. Catalogue no: **4606051**
**CD:** Released May '87, on CBS by CBS Records. Catalogue no: **CD 62323**

**SATURDAY NIGHT AT THE BLACK HAWK**
**Cass:** Released '88, on CBS by CBS Records. Catalogue no: **465 191 4**
**CD:** Released '88, on CBS by CBS Records. Catalogue no: **465 191 2**
**Album:** Released '88, on CBS by CBS Records. Catalogue no: **465 191 1**

**SEVEN STEPS TO HEAVEN**
**Album:** Released Jun '86, on CBS (import) by CBS Records. Catalogue no: **CBS 62170**

**SIESTA (Original Soundtrack) (Davis, Miles/Marcus Miller)**
Tracks: / Lost in Madrid part 1 / Kitt's kiss / Theme for augustine / Seduction, The / Submission / Conchita / Lost in Madrid part 4 / Clair / Afterglow / Siesta / Lost in Madrid part 2 / Wind / Kiss / Lost in Madrid Part 3 / Lament / Rat dance - the call / Lost in Madrid part 5 / Ls Felez.
Note: See under Siesta
**CD:** Released Feb '88, on Warner Bros. by WEA Records. Catalogue no: **K 925655 2**
**Cass:** Released Feb '88, on Warner Bros. by WEA Records. Catalogue no: **K 925655 4**
**Album:** Released Feb '88, on Warner Bros. by WEA Records. Catalogue no: **K 925655 1**

**SKETCHES OF SPAIN**
Tracks: / Concierto de Aranjuez / Amor brujo / Pan piper / Saeta / Solea.
**Album:** Released Apr '88, on CBS (import) by CBS Records. Catalogue no: **460 604 1**
**CD:** Released Dec '85, on CBS by CBS Records. Catalogue no: **CD 62327**
**Album:** Released Mar '81, on CBS by CBS Records. Catalogue no: **CBS 32023**
**Cass:** Released Mar '81, on CBS by CBS Records. Catalogue no: **40 32023**
**Cass:** Released Feb '83, on CBS by CBS Records. Catalogue no: **40 22146**
**Cass:** Released Apr '88, on CBS (import) by CBS Records. Catalogue no: **460 604 4**

**SOME DAY MY PRINCE WILL COME**
**CD:** Released Jan '86, on Mobile Fidelity Sound Lab(USA) by Mobile Fidelity Records (USA). Catalogue no: **MFCD 828**
**Album:** Released Jun '86, on CBS (import) by CBS Records. Catalogue no: **CBS 62104**

**SOMETHING ELSE (Davis, Miles & Cannonball Adderley)**
**Album:** Released May '79, on Blue Note by EMI Records. Catalogue no: **NS 40036**

**SORCERER**
Tracks: / Prince of darkness / Vonetta / Limbo / Masqualero / Pee Wee / Sorcerer, The.
**Cass:** Released Jul '87, on CBS by CBS Records. Deleted Jan '89. Catalogue no: **40 21143**
**Album:** Released Jul '87, on CBS by CBS Records. Deleted Jan '89. Catalogue no: **CBS 21143**

**STAR PEOPLE**
Tracks: / Come get it / It gets better / Speak / Star people / U'un I / Star on Cicely.
**Album:** Released Jun '83, on CBS by CBS Records. Deleted Jun '88. Catalogue no: **25395**
**CD:** Released May '87, on CBS by CBS Records. Deleted Jan '89. Catalogue no: **CD 25395**

**STEAMIN' WITH THE MILES DAVIS QUINTET**
**CD:** Released '88, on JVC/Fantasy Catalogue no: **VDJ 1522**

**TALLEST TREES**
Tracks: / Bag's groove / Smooch / Miles ahead / Airegin / Oleo / But not for me / Doxy / Man I love, The / Swing spring / Blue haze / Round midnight / Bemsha swing.
**2 LP Set:** Released '73, on Prestige Catalogue no: **PR 24012**

**TIME AFTER TIME**
Tracks: / Time after time / Katia.
**7" Single:** Released May '85, on CBS by CBS Records. Deleted May '88. Catalogue no: **A 4871**
**12" Single:** Released May '85, on CBS by CBS Records. Deleted May '88. Catalogue no: **TA 4871**

**TUNE UP**
Tracks: / When lights are low / Tune up / Four / That old devil moon / Solar / You don't know what love is / Love me or leave me / I'll remember April / Walkin' / Blue 'n' boogie / But not for me / Bags' groove / Man I love.
**2 LP Set:** Released '79, on Prestige Deleted '84. Catalogue no: **PR 24077**

**TUTU**
Tracks: / Tutu / Tomaas / Portia / Splatch / Backyard ritual / Perfect way / Don't lose your mind / Full nelson.
**CD:** Released Oct '86, on Warner Bros. by WEA Records. Catalogue no: **925490 2**
**Cass:** Released Oct '86, on Warner Bros. by WEA Records. Catalogue no: **925490 4**
**Album:** Released Oct '86, on Warner Bros. by WEA Records. Catalogue no: **925490 1**

**UNIQUE VOL 2, THE**
**Album:** Released Sep '87, on Giants of Jazz by Hasmick Promotions. Catalogue no: **LPJT 43**

**WALKIN' (Davis, Miles All Stars)**
Tracks: / Walkin' / Blue'n'boogie / Solar / You don't know what love is / Love me or leave me.
**CD:** Released Sep '89, on Riverside (USA) by Fantasy Inc (USA). Catalogue no: **CDRIVM 004**
**Album:** Released Apr '86, on Original Jazz Classics (USA) by Fantasy Inc (USA). Catalogue no: **OJC 213**
**CD:** Released Apr '87, on Carrere (France) Catalogue no: **98437**
**CD:** Released May '87, on JVC/Fantasy Catalogue no: **VDJ 1541**

**WATER BABIES**
Tracks: / Water babies / Sweet pea / Duel Mr.Tillman Anthony / Two faced / Capricorn.
**Cass:** Released Jul '86, on CBS by CBS Records. Deleted Jun '88. Catalogue no: **40 21136**
**Album:** Released Jul '86, on CBS by CBS Records. Deleted Jan '89. Catalogue no: **CBS 21136**

**WE WANT MILES**
Tracks: / Jean Pierre / Back seat Betty / Fast track / My man's gone now / Kix.
**Album:** Released May '82, on CBS by CBS Records. Catalogue no: **88579**

**WORKIN' AND STEAMIN'**
Tracks: / It never entered my mind / Four / In your own sweet way / Theme, The (take 1) / Trane's blues / Ahmad's blues / Half Nelson / Theme, The (take 2) / Surrey with the fringe on top / Salt peanuts / Something I dreamed last night / Diane / Well you needn't / When I fall in love.
**Album:** Released '79, on Prestige Deleted '82. Catalogue no: **PR 24034**

**WORKIN' WITH THE MILES DAVIS**
**CD:** Released Apr '86, on JVC/Fantasy Catalogue no: **VDJ 1521**

**WORLD OF JAZZ**
Tracks: / Yardbird suite / Cool blues / Lover's theme / Hot lips / Mr. Lucky.
**Album:** Released Jul '80, on Manhattan Records by President Records. Catalogue no: **MAN 5022**

**YOU'RE UNDER ARREST**
Tracks: / One phone call / Street scenes / Human nature / Ms. Morrisine / Katia prelude / Time after time / You're under arrest / Then there were none / Something's on your mind.
**CD:** Released '88, on CBS (import) by CBS Records. Catalogue no: **32DP 230**
**Cass:** Released Jun '85, on CBS by CBS Records. Catalogue no: **40 26447**
**CD:** Released May '87, on CBS by CBS Records. Catalogue no: **CD 26447**

**Album:** Released Jun '85, on CBS by CBS Records. Catalogue no: **CBS 26447**

## Davis, Nathan

**LONDON BY NIGHT**
Note: With Dusko Goykovich, Kenny Drew, Jimmy Woode, Al Levitt.
**Album:** Released '88, on Hot House by Hot House Records. Catalogue no: **HH 1004**

**RULES OF FREEDOM (Davis, Nathan Quartet)**
Note: With Hampton Hawes, Jimmy Garrison, Art Taylor.
**Album:** Released Dec '86, on Hot House by Hot House Records. Catalogue no: **HH 1002**

## Davis, Rev.Blind Gary

**BEST OF GARY DAVIS IN CONCERT**
Tracks: / I'm going to sit on the banks of the river / Twelve gates to the city / Angels singing / Twelve sticks / It's a long long way to Tipperary / I'll meet you at the station / Come down and meet me sometime / Buck dance / Soldier's drill.
**Album:** Released Sep '79, on Kicking Mule by Sonet Records. Catalogue no: **SNKF 152**

**BLIND GARY DAVIS (At Allegheny College, Meadville PA, 1964)**
**Album:** Released Jul '88, on Document Catalogue no: **DLP 527**
**Album:** Released Apr '88, on Document Catalogue no: **DLP 521**

**CHILDREN OF ZION (IN CONCERT)**
Tracks: / I'm going to sit down on the banks / Twelve gates to the city / I heard the angels singing / Twelve sticks / Tipperary / When the train comes along / Come down and see me sometime / Buck dance / Soldier's drill.
**Album:** Released Jul '85, on Heritage by Interstate Music. Catalogue no: **HT 308**

**GOSPEL BLUES AND STREET SONGS (Davis, Rev. Gary/Pink Anderson)**
**Album:** Released Jan '88, on OBC Catalogue no: **OBC 524**

**I AM A TRUE VINE (1962-63)**
Tracks: / I am a true vine / Lord stand by me / Won't you hush? / Mean old world / Moon is goin' down / Sportin' life blues / Get right church / Blow Gabriel / Slippin' til my gal comes in partner / Wall hollow blues / Blues in E / Piece without words / Whoopin' blues / I want to be saved.
**Album:** Released Mar '85, on Heritage by Interstate Music. Catalogue no: **HT 307**

**LET US GET TOGETHER**
Tracks: / Oh glory / How happy I am / Cocaine blues / Death don't have no mercy / Let us get together / There's destruction in that land / Tired my soul needs a'restin' / Georgia camp meeting / Blues in A / Fox chase, The / You're gonna' quit me baby.
**Album:** Released '74, on Kicking Mule by Sonet Records. Catalogue no: **SNKF 103**

**LIVE: BLIND GARY DAVIS 1964**
**Album:** Released '88, on Wolf Catalogue no: **WOLF 120.915**

**LO, I BE WITH YOU ALWAYS**
**Album:** Released '73, on Kicking Mule by Sonet Records. Catalogue no: **SNKD 1**

**NEW BLUES AND GOSPEL**
Tracks: / How happy I am / I heard the angels singing / Samson and Delilah / Children of zion / Soon my work will be done / Talk on the corner / Sally where'd you get your whiskey / Hesitation blues / Whistling blues / Lost John.
**Album:** Released Apr '88, on Blue Moon (1) by Magnum Music Group. Catalogue no: **BMLP 1040**

**O GLORY**
**Album:** Released May '81, on Adelphi (1) Catalogue no: **AD 1008**

**RAGTIME GUITAR**
**Album:** Released Oct '85, on Heritage by Interstate Music. Catalogue no: **HT 309**
**Album:** Released Mar '89, on Kicking Mule by Sonet Records. Catalogue no: **KM 106**

**REVEREND BLIND GARY DAVIS 1935-49**
**Album:** Released Dec '88, on Yazoo (USA) by Shanachie Records (USA). Catalogue no: **L1023**

**REVEREND BLIND GARY DAVIS 1962**
**Album:** Released '88, on Wolf Catalogue no: **120 915**

**REVEREND BLIND GARY DAVIS**
**CD:** Released Oct '89, on Heritage by Interstate Music. Catalogue no: **HTCD 02**

**SAY NO TO THE DEVIL**
**Album:** Released Jan '88, on OBC Catalogue no: **OBC 519**

## Davison, Wild Bill

**WILD BILL DAVISON AND PAPA BUE'S VIKING JAZZ BAND (Davison, Wild Bill & Papa Bue)**
**Album:** Released '88, on Storyville by Storyville Records AB. Catalogue no: **SLP 264**

**SWEET AND LOVELY**
**Album:** Released Feb '90, on Storyville by Storyville Records AB. Catalogue no: **SLP 4060**
**CD:** Released Feb '90, on Storyville by Storyville Records AB. Catalogue no: **STCD 4060**

## Dawkins, Jimmy

**Biographical details:** Blues singer and guitarist born in 1936 in Mississippi, known as 'Fast Fingers' for his prize winning album of that name on Delmark. A modern bluesmen with his own style, yet still in the mainstream of tradition. (Donald Clarke, April 1989).

**ALL BLUES**
Note: With Phil Guy and Professor Eddie Lusks.
**Album:** Released Jun '86, on JSP by JSP Records. Catalogue no: **JSP 1102**

**ALL FOR BUSINESS**
**Album:** on Delmark (USA) by Delmark Records (USA). Catalogue no: **DS 634**

**BLISTERSTRING (Dawkins, Jimmy Band)**
**Album:** Released Mar '90, on Delmark (USA) by Delmark Records (USA). Catalogue no: **DS 641**

**FAST FINGERS**
**Album:** on Delmark (USA) by Delmark Records (USA). Catalogue no: **DS 623**

**FEEL THE BLUES (1985 Chicago studio recording)**
Tracks: / Feel the blues / Highway man blues / Last days / Love somebody / Christmas time blues / Have a little mercy.
**CD:** Released Jan '88, on JSP by JSP Records. Catalogue no: **JSP CD 206**
**Album:** Released Oct '85, on JSP by JSP Records. Catalogue no: **JSP 1093**

**TRANSATLANTIC 770**
Tracks: / Things I used to do, The / May my way in this world / Think twice before you speak / 1011 Woodland / Mighty hawk, The / All for business / High cost of living / Stoned dead / Love and understanding / No more trouble.
**Album:** Released Aug '78, on Sonet by Sonet Records. Catalogue no: **SNTF 758**

## De Franco, Buddy

**Biographical details:** Clarinettist, born in 1923 in New Jersey. He played with Gene Krupa, Charlie Barnet, Tommy Dorsey and others; with a Count Basie septet in 1950, his own big band and then a wonderful quartet with Sonny Clark on piano, its recordings collected in a box on the USA Mosaic label. He settled in California in 1955, tired of touring, but continued to record; the clarinet had gone out of fashion in jazz and DeFranco has never had the credit he deserves except among musicians and the more perceptive fans. *Blues bag* was made for Vee Jay in 1964 with Lee Morgan, Curtis Fuller, Victor Feldman, Art Blakey, bassist Victor Sproles and trumpeter Freddy Hill. *Like someone in love* was made in 1977 with a quintet including Tal Farlow and George Duvivier; *The liveliest* was recorded with local musicians in Argentina in 1980 and *Groovin'* on Hep is a quintet that toured the UK in 1985. (Donald Clarke, April 1989).

**BLACK MAGIC (De Franco, Buddy & Helen Forest)**
**Album:** Released '78, on Shamrock (Ireland) Catalogue no: **LP 1801**

**BORN TO SWING**
Note: with Al Raymond All Star Big Jazz Band.
**Album:** Released Feb '89, on Star Satellite Catalogue no: **SS 711**

**GARDEN OF DREAMS (De Franco, Buddy & Martin Taylor)**
**Album:** on Hep Jazz by Hep Records. Catalogue no: **HEP 2039**

**GROOVING (De Franco, Buddy Quintet)**
**Album:** on Hep Jazz by Hep Records. Catalogue no: **HEP 2030**

**HARK (De Franco, Buddy & Oscar Peterson Quartet)**
Tracks: / All too soon / Summer me, winter me / Llovisna (Light rain) / By myself / Joy spring / This is all I ask / Hark / Why am I?.
Note: Buddy De Franco, clarinet; Oscar Peterson, piano; Joe Pass, guitar; Niel Pedersen, bass; Martin Drew, drums.
**CD:** Released Apr '87, on Pablo Jazz (USA) by Pablo Records (USA). Catalogue no: **CD 231 0915**
**Album:** Released Sep '85, on Pablo Jazz (USA) by Pablo Records (USA). Catalogue no: **231 0915**
**Cass:** Released Sep '85, on Pablo Jazz (USA) by Pablo Records (USA). Catalogue no: **K10 915**

**LIKE SOMEONE IN LOVE (De Franco, Buddy Quintet)**
Tracks: / Like someone in love / Melancholy Stockholm / Playa Del Sol / How long has this been going on? / Coasting at the Palisades / I love you, Porgy.
Note: Buddy De Franco, clarinet; Derek Smith, piano; Tal Farlow, guitar; George Duvivier, bass; Ronnie Bedford, drums.
**Album:** Released '79, on Progressive (USA) by Jazzology Records (USA). Catalogue no: **PRO 7014**

**LIVELIEST, THE**
Tracks: / Billie's bounce / Triste / Ja da / Yesterdays.
Note: Recorded at Municipal theatre, Buenos Aires - 27th November 1980.
**Album:** Released '82, on Hep Jazz by Hep Records. Catalogue no: **HEP 2014**

**MOOD INDIGO**
**Album:** Released '88, on Hep Jazz by Hep Records. Catalogue no: **HEP 2018**

**ON TOUR UK (De Franco, Buddy Quintet)**
**Album:** on Hep Jazz by Hep Records. Catalogue no: **HEP 2023**

## De Graaff, Rein

**CHASIN' THE BIRD**
**Album:** Released '88, on Timeless by Timeless Records. Catalogue no: **SLP 159**

**DRIFTIN' ON A REED (De Graaff, Rein)**
Tracks: / Drifting on a reed / I waited for you / For Lennie & Lee / Blue possa / Anthropology / Alone together / Lonely Friday blues / Sunrise.
**Album:** Released Apr '81, on Timeless by Timeless Records. Catalogue no: **SJP 105**

**DUO (De Graaff, Rein & Koosserierse)**
**Album:** Released '88, on Timeless by Timeless Records. Catalogue no: **SJP 213**

**MODAL SOUL (De Graaff, Rein & Dick Vennick Quartet)**
Tracks: / Sweet Basil / Detour ahead / Short rainbow / Lonely hunter / Modal soul.
**Album:** Released Apr '81, on Timeless by Timeless Records. Catalogue no: **SJP 117**

## De Johnette, Jack

**Biographical details:** Jazz/fusion drummer, pianist and composer, born in Chicago in 1942. He went to NYC in 1966 and became well-known with Charles Lloyd; he played on Miles Davis' *Bitches brew* in 1969 and joined Davis 1970-1, demonstrating eclectic power. He led the group Compost for one album on CBS in 1972, recorded for ECM as a leader since 1976, from 1979 with varying personnel as Jack DeJohnette's Special Edition. He also made *The piano album* in 1985 on Landmark, with Eddie Gomez and Fred Waits; *Irresistable Force* '87 on MCA/Impulse has Lonnie Plaxico on electric and acoustic bass, Nana Vasconcelos on vocals and percussion, and three others. Many albums as a sideman include Chico Freeman's *Destiny dance* and *Song X* by Ornette Coleman and Pat Metheny. (Donald Clarke, April 1989).

**ALBUM ALBUM**
Tracks: / Festival / New Orleans strut / Zoot suite / Ahmad the terrible / Monk's mood / Third world anthem.
Note: Personnel: John Purcell - alto and soprano sax/David Murray- tenor sax / Howard Johnson - tuba, baritone sax / Rufus Reid - acoustic and electric bass / Jack De Johnette - drums and keyboards. Once again DeJohnette demonstrates the amalgamation of tradition and avantgarde; "Album, Album" creates an irresistable tongue- in cheek charm and reaffirms the band's premise that jazz is rooted in the tradition of entertainment.
**Album:** Released '84, on ECM Catalogue no: **ECM 1280**
**CD:** Released Feb '86, on ECM Deleted '88. Catalogue no: **823 467 2**

**AUDIO VISUALSCAPES (DeJohnette, Jack's Special Edition)**
**2 LP Set:** Released May '89, on MCA (Import) by MCA Records. Catalogue no: **MCA 2-8029**
**CD:** Released May '89, on MCA (Import) by MCA Records. Catalogue no: **MCAD 8029**

**IRRESISTIBLE FORCES (DeJohnette, Jack's Special Edition)**
**CD:** Released May '89, on MCA (Import) by MCA Records. Catalogue no: **MCAD 5992**
**Album:** Released May '89, on MCA (Import) by MCA Records. Catalogue no: **MCA 5992**

**JACK DE JOHNETTE / WENER PIRCHER / HARRY PEPL (DeJohnette, Jack / Wener Pircher / Harry Pepl)**
Tracks: / African godchild / Air, love and vitamins / Goodbye, baby post / Better times in sight.
Note: Digital recording
**Album:** Released '83, on ECM Catalogue no: **ECM 1237**

**JACK DE JOHNETTE'S SPECIAL EDITION**
**Album:** Released '83, on ECM Catalogue no: **ECM 1244**

**NEW DIRECTIONS**
**Album:** Released Jan '89, on ECM Catalogue no: **ECM 1128**
**CD:** Released Jan '89, on ECM Catalogue no: **829 374-2**

**NEW DIRECTIONS IN EUROPE**
Tracks: / Salsa for Eddie / Bayou Fever / Where or Wayne / Multo spillagio.
Note: Personnel: Jack De Johnette - drums piano / Lester Bowie - trumpet / John Abercrom- bie - guitar, mandolin guitar / Eddie Gomez - Bass.
**Album:** Released Jan '89, on ECM Catalogue no: **ECM 1157**
**CD:** Released '88, on ECM Catalogue no: **829 158-2**

**PIANO ALBUM, THE**
**CD:** Released Aug '88, on Polygram by PolyGram UK Ltd. Catalogue no: **LCD 1504**

**SPECIAL EDITION (DeJohnette, Jack's Special Edition)**
Tracks: / One for Eric / Zoot suite / Central park west / India / Journey to the twin planet.
Note: Personnel: Jack De Johnette - drums, piano, melodica / David Murrray - tenor sax, bass clarinet / Arthur Blythe - alto sax, / Peter Warren - bass.
**Album:** Released Jan '89, on ECM Catalogue no: **ECM 1152**
**CD:** Released Jan '89, on ECM Catalogue no: **827 694-2**

**TIN CAN ALLEY (DeJohnette, Jack's Special Edition)**
**Album:** Released '81, on ECM Catalogue no: **ECM 1189**

**WORKS: JACK DE JOHNETTE**
Tracks: / Bayou fever / Gri gri man, The / To be continued / One for Eric / Unshielded desire / Blue.
Note: Personnel: Jack DeJohnette, John Abercrombie, Lester Bowie, Eddie Gomez, Terje Rypdal, Miroslav Vitous, Dave Holland.
**Album:** Released Jun '89, on ECM Catalogue no: **825 427-1**
**CD:** Released Jun '89, on ECM Catalogue no: **825 427-2**

**ZEBRA**
Note: Originally composed by Jack DeJohnette as soundtrack to Japanese film Zebra.
**Album:** Released Jun '89, on MCA (Jazz Today) Catalogue no: **MCA 42160**
**CD:** Released Jun '89, on MCA (Jazz Today) Catalogue no: **MCAD 42160**

## Dean, Elton

**BOLOGNA TAPE, THE (Dean's, Elton Quintet)**
**Album:** Released '88, on Ogun by Cadillac Music. Catalogue no: **OG 530**

**CHEQUE IS IN THE MAIL**
**Album:** Released Aug '77, on Ogun by Cadillac Music. Catalogue no: **OG 610**

**HAPPY DAZE (Dean's, Elton Ninesense)**
**Album:** Released '88, on Ogun by Cadillac Music. Catalogue no: **OG 910**

**OH FOR THE EDGE (Dean's, Elton Ninesense)**
**Album:** Released '88, on Ogun by Cadillac Music. Catalogue no: **OG 900**

## Dean, Roger

**CYCLES (Dean, Roger / Lysis)**
**Album:** Released Aug '77, on Mosaic by Mosaic Records (UK). Catalogue no: **GCM 774**

**LYSIS LIVE (Dean, Roger / Lysis)**
**Album:** Released Jan '77, on Mosaic by Mosaic Records (UK). Catalogue no: **GCM 762**

**SOMETHING BRITISH MADE IN HONG KONG**
Note: Also featuring Geoff Warren, Ed Speight, Ashley Brown live.
**Album:** Released Apr '88, on Mosaic by Mosaic Records (UK). Catalogue no: **GCM 871**

## Dearie, Blossom

**Biographical details:** Singer, pianist and songwriter born in 1926 in New York State. She played cocktail piano and accompanied vocal group; whe worked in Paris 1952-56 with Annie Ross, then formed vocal group the Blue Stars (had a hit with *Lullaby in birdland* sung in French). Back in the USA leading a trio she has been a cabaret favourite ever since, with an endearing piping voice and witty songs, some by Dave Frishberg. She recorded on Verve, then on her own Daffodil label. (Donald Clarke, April 1989).

**BLOSSOM DEARIE**
Tracks: / Lover man / Deed I do / I won't dance / It might as well be spring / Thou swell.
**Album:** Released May '83, on Verve (USA) by Polydor Ltd. Catalogue no: **2304 357**

**BLOSSOM DEARIE SINGS: 1973**
**Album:** Released Apr '79, on Daffodil Catalogue no: **DAFFODIL 101**

**BLOSSOM DEARIE SINGS: 1975**
**Album:** Released Apr '79, on Daffodil Catalogue no: **DAFFODIL 102**

**ET TU BRUCE, VOL. 8**
Tracks: / Bruce / Hey John / Someone's been sending me flowers / You have lived in autumn / Alice in Wonderland / Satin doll / Riviera, The / Inside a silent tear.
**CD:** Released Aug '89, on Master Mix Catalogue no: **CDCHE 5**
**Cass:** Released Aug '89, on Master Mix

Elaine Delmar

Catalogue no: **ZCHE 5**
**Album:** Released Aug '89, on Master Mix Catalogue no: **CHELP 5**

**FEATURING BOBBY JASPAR**
**Album:** Released Feb '88, on Fresh Sounds (Spain) by Fresh Sounds Records (Spain). Catalogue no: **FS 215**

**MAY I COME IN?**
**Album:** Released Apr '81, on Capitol by EMI Records. Catalogue no: **SM 2066**

**MY NEW CELEBRITY IS YOU**
**2 LP Set:** Released Apr '79, on Daffodil Catalogue no: **DAFFODIL 103**

**NEEDLEPOINT MAGIC**
**Album:** Released Aug '89, on Master Mix Catalogue no: **CHELP 3**
**Album:** Released '88, on Daffodil Catalogue no: **CDCHE 3**

**SONGS OF CHELSEA**
**CD:** Released May '88, on Master Mix Catalogue no: **CDCHE 2**
**Album:** Released May '88, on Master Mix Catalogue no: **DAF 1**
**Cass:** Released May '88, on Master Mix Catalogue no: **ZCDAF 1**

**WINCHESTER IN APPLE BLOSSOM TIME**
**2 LP Set:** Released Apr '79, on Daffodil Catalogue no: **DAFFODIL 104**

## Dejan's Olympia Brass

**DEJAN'S OLYMPIA BRASS BAND 1968**
**Album:** Released Apr '79, on Nola Catalogue no: **NOLA LP 4**

**JAZZY YOURS**
**Cass:** Released '87, on Maison de Soul(USA) by Flat Town Music Co.(USA). Catalogue no: **1011 TC**
**Album:** on Maison de Soul(USA) by Flat Town Music Co.(USA). Catalogue no: **1011**

## Delmar, Elaine

**ELAINE DELMAR AND FRIENDS (Delmar, Elaine & Friends)**
Tracks: / I've got the world on a string / My funny valentine / Honeysuckle rose / When the world was young / I got it bad / September song / Basin Street blues / Mountain greenery / More than you know / Don't get around much anymore / Stardust / I gotta right to sing the blues / Puttin' on the Ritz / Tea for two / Boy next door / I'm glad there is you / Just one of those things / It amazes me / Bewitched / He was too good to me / Looking for a boy / Little girl blue / Spring is here / Nobody else but me.
**2 LP Set:** Released Sep '80, on Polydor by Polydor Ltd. Deleted Sep '85. Catalogue no: **268 101 0**

**IN TOWN**
**Album:** Released Sep '87, on Hep Jazz by Hep Records. Catalogue no: **HEP 2035**

**I'VE GOT THE WORLD ON A STRING**
Tracks: / When the world was young / I've got the world on a string / My funny valentine / Honeysuckle rose / I've got it bad and that ain't good / September song / Basin Street blues / Mountain

greenery / More than you know / Don't get around much anymore / Stardust / I gotta right to sing the blues.
**Album:** Released Aug '77, on Retrospect by EMI Records. Catalogue no: **WRS 1004**

## Delta Blues

**DELTA BLUES, VOL 1 Various artists (Various artists)**
Note: With Charlie Patton, Son House, Tommy Johnson, Ishman Bracey.
**Album:** Released Jul '88, on Document Catalogue no: **DLP 532**

**DELTA BLUES VOL 2 (29-39) (Various artists)**
Note: Various artists including: Kid Bailey, Garfield Akers, Joe Calicott, Jim Thompkins, Sam Collins & Bukka White.
**Album:** Released '88, on Document Catalogue no: **DLP 533**
**Album:** Released Oct '88, on Roots (Germany) Catalogue no: **RL 339**

## Delta Blues Band

**SUNNYLAND SLIM'S BLUES JAM**
**Album:** Released May '77, on Storyville by Storyville Records AB. Catalogue no: **SLP 245**

## Delta Experimental

**DELTA EXPERIMENTAL PROJECTS (Blues, The) (Various artists)**
**Album:** Released Sep '88, on Fan Club by New Rose Records. Catalogue no: **FC 044**

## Deluxe Blues Band

**DELUXE BLUES BAND**
Tracks: / Avocado Eldorado / Something inside of me / Mary, Mary / Calling in the flag / Cold cold feeling / Steel truckin' man / I held my baby last night / Freight house blues / One way out / Sun went down, The.
**Album:** Released Mar '88, on Blue Horizon by Ace Records. Catalogue no: **BLUH 004**

**LIVE: DELUXE BLUES BAND**
**7" Single:** Released Jul '81, on Hot Box by Armageddon Records. Catalogue no: **HOT BOX 1**

**STREET CAR NAMED DELUXE, A**
**Album:** Released Dec '83, on Appaloosa Catalogue no: **AP 020**

## Demolition Blues

**DEMOLITION BLUES (Various artists)**
**Album:** Released '87, on Insane Catalogue no: **INSANELP 1**

## Denon Jazz

**DENON JAZZ SAMPLER VOL.1**
Note: Another splendid way of advertising Denon's fast-growing catalogue of contemporary jazz material recorded for CD release. Among the list of luminaries present are long-established major talents like Benny Golson and Freddie Hubbard (breathing new life into 'Love is a Many Splendored Thing'), Jim Hall, ably assisted by Tom Harrell ('With a Song in My Heart'), and Steve Khan (sharing top billing with Rob Mounsey during 'Tafiya'). But there are also delightful contributions from talented musicians/singers of more recent vintage, including tenorist Bennie Wallace (in tandem with Yosuke Yamashita, from Japan, on 'P.S. I Love You'), the irrestible Eliane Elias ('Cross Currents'), and the highly promising vocal-instrumental group The Ritz (sounding suitably uplifted by Charlie Parker's 'Scrapple from the Apple'). (Denon 11/88).
**CD:** Released '88, on Denon Catalogue no: **GES 9107**

## Derise, Joe

**BLUES ARE OUT OF TOWN**
**Album:** Released Aug '88, on Audiophile (USA) by Jazzology Records (USA). Catalogue no: **AP 174**

**HOUSE OF FLOWERS**
**Album:** Released Aug '88, on Audiophile (USA) by Jazzology Records (USA). Catalogue no: **AP 153**

**JOE DERISE SINGS AND PLAYS THE JIMMY VAN HEUSEN VOL 1**
**Album:** Released May '88, on Audiophile (USA) by Jazzology Records (USA). Catalogue no: **AP 231**

**TENTETTE IS MAD ABOUT YOU**
**Album:** Released Aug '88, on Jazzology (USA) by Jazzology Records (USA). Catalogue no: **AP 215**

## Des Plantes, Ted

**Biographical details:** see under - Frank Powers..

**SHOUT, SISTER, SHOUT (Des Plantes', Ted Washboard Wizards)**
**Album:** Released Nov '88, on Stomp Off (USA) Catalogue no: **SOS 1174**

**SWEDISH AMERICAN HOT JAZZ**
**Album:** Released Jan '88, on Stomp Off (USA) Catalogue no: **SOS 1136**

## Desanto, Sugar Pie

**DOWN IN THE BASEMENT**
**CD:** Released Feb '90, on CBS by CBS Records. Catalogue no: **CHD 9275**
**Album:** Released '89, on Chess by Vogue Records. Catalogue no: **LPM 7001**

**LOVIN' TOUCH**
**Album:** Released Jul '87, on Diving Duck (Holland) Catalogue no: **DD 4310**

## Descloux, Lizzy

**LIZZY MERCIER DESCLOUX**
Tracks: / It's all my imagination / Abyssinia / Gazelles / Dolby sisters / Saliva brothers / Eclipse / Les dents de l'amour / Wakwazulu kwezizulu rock / Mono on my mind / I'm liquor / Queen of overdub kisses / Sun's jive / All the same.
**Album:** Released Sep '84, on CBS by CBS Records. Deleted Sep '89. Catalogue no: **CBS 25936**

**ONE FOR THE SOUL**
Tracks: / One for the soul / Simply beautiful / Fog horn blues / Women don't like me / My funny valentine / Sound of Leblon beach / Garden of Alas / God-spell me wrong / Off off pleasure / Long voodoo ago / Love streams.
Note: French cult artist Lizzy Mercier Descloux's three previous albums have been praised by the English music press. Recorded in Brazil, 'One for the soul' is a collection of ten songs all in English. Special guest artist, American trumpeter Chet Baker plays on five songs. The CD has three extra songs, 'Queen of overdub kisses', 'A word is A whah' and 'Scala saga scamba'.
**CD:** Released Jul '86, on Polydor (France) by Polydor Ltd. Catalogue no: **827 910-2**
**Cass:** Released Jul '86, on Polydor (France) by Polydor Ltd. Catalogue no: **827 910-4**
**Album:** Released Jul '86, on Polydor (France) by Polydor Ltd. Catalogue no: **827 910-1**

**PRESS COLOR**
Tracks: / Fire / Torso corso / Mission impossible / No golden throat / Jim on the move / Wawa / Tumour / Aya mood.
**Album:** Released Feb '80, on Island by Island Records. Deleted '86. Catalogue no: **ILPS 7001**

**ZULU ROCK**
Tracks: / Zulu rock / Sun's jive.
**7" Single:** Released Apr '84, on CBS by CBS Records. Catalogue no: **A 4359**
**12" Single:** Released Apr '84, on CBS by CBS Records. Catalogue no: **TA 4359**

## Desmond, Paul

**Biographical details:** The alto saxophonist (1924-77) was a star in the Dave Brubeck Quartet until it broke up in 1967; he wrote Brubeck's biggest hit, *Take five*. His lyrical style and light, airy tone was liked even by people who were not Brubeck fans. He recorded as a leader for Fantasy in 1954 and 1956; the quartet set *Blues in time* with Gerry Mulligan was made in 1957; *Paul Desmond Quartet live* was made in Toronto in 1975 with Ed Bickert on guitar. The complete Desmond/Jim Hall quartet tracks from two labels have been compiled in a boxed set on the American Mosaic label. He was going to write a book about the Brubeck years called *How many of you are there in the quartet* but he died of lung cancer. (Donald Clarke, April 1989).

**EAST OF THE SUN**
Tracks: / I get a kick out of you / Time after time / For all we know / 2 degrees east / 3 degrees west.
Note: Paul Desmond-alto sax, Jim Hall-guitar, Percy Heath-bass, Connie Kay-drums.
**Cass:** Released '88, on Discovery (USA) by Discovery Records (USA). Catalogue no: **DSC 840**
**Album:** Released '88, on Discovery (USA) by Discovery Records (USA).

Catalogue no: **DS 840**
**CD:** Released Dec '86, on Discovery (USA) by Discovery Records (USA). Catalogue no: **DSCD 840**

**GREATEST HITS: PAUL DESMOND**
Tracks: / Take ten / I've grown accustomed to her face / Black orpheus / Hi lili hi lo / Desmond blue / Embarcadero / All the things you are / El prince / Alone together / Taste of honey, A / O Gato.
**Album:** Released Jun '86, on RCA by BMG Records (UK). Catalogue no: **CL 89809**
**Cass:** Released Jun '86, on RCA by BMG Records (UK). Catalogue no: **CK 89809**

**IF IT FEELS GOOD**
Tracks: / If it feels good / Have faith in your love.
**12" Single:** Released Mar '81, on Flamingo by Airwave Records (USA). Deleted Mar '84. Catalogue no: **FMT 14**
**7" Single:** Released Mar '81, on Flamingo by Airwave Records (USA). Deleted Mar '84. Catalogue no: **FM 14**

**LATE LAMENT**
Tracks: / My funny valentine / Like someone in love / I should care / Then I'll be tired of you / Ill wind / Desmond blue / Body and soul / I've got you under my skin / Imagination.
**Cass:** Released Sep '87, on RCA by BMG Records (UK). Deleted May '89. Catalogue no: **NK 85778**
**CD:** Released Sep '87, on RCA by BMG Records (UK). Catalogue no: **ND 85778**
**Album:** Released Sep '87, on RCA by BMG Records (UK). Catalogue no: **NL 85778**
**CD:** Released Apr '89, on Bluebird (2) by BMG Records (UK). Catalogue no: **ND 90207**

**MASTER OF JAZZ**
**Album:** Released Aug '83, on RCA (Germany) Catalogue no: **CL 42790**

**ONLY RECORDED PERFORMANCE, THE (Desmond, Paul Quartet)**
Tracks: / Greensleeves / You go to my head / Blue dove / Jesus Christ superstar / Here's that rainy day / East of the sun / Bags new groove.
**Cass:** Released Nov '84, on Finesse Deleted '87. Catalogue no: **ZCFIN 6050**
**Album:** Released Nov '84, on Finesse Deleted '87. Catalogue no: **FINLP 6050**

**PAUL DESMOND**
**Album:** Released May '81, on Artists House Catalogue no: **AH 2**

**PAUL DESMOND, JIM HALL, PERCY HEATH, CONNIE KAY (Desmond, Paul / Jim Hall / Percy Heath / Connie Kay)**
Tracks: / Greensleeves / You go to my head / East of the sun / Time after time / I get a kick out of you / For all we know / Two degrees east, three degrees west.
**Album:** on Warner Bros. by WEA Records. Catalogue no: **K 56294**

**PAUL DESMOND QUARTET LIVE (Desmond, Paul Quartet)**
Tracks: / Wendy / Wave / Things ain't what they used to be / Nancy / Manha de carnival / Here's that rainy day / My funny valentine / Take five.
**2 LP Set:** Released Jul '76, on Horizon by A&M Records. Catalogue no: **AMLJD 850**

**PURE DESMOND**
**Album:** Released Feb '84, on CTI (Musidisc France) by Polydor Ltd. Catalogue no: **CTI 9007**

**SKYLARK**
**CD:** Released Feb '84, on CTI (Musidisc France) by Polydor Ltd. Catalogue no: **CTI 9006**
**CD:** Released Feb '84, on CBS by CBS Records. Deleted 17 Apr '89. Catalogue no: **450572 2**

**TWO OF A MIND (Desmond, Paul & Gerry Mulligan)**
Tracks: / All the things you are / Stardust / Two of a mind / Blight of the fumble bee / Way you look tonight / Out of nowhere.
**Cass:** Released Aug '89, on Bluebird (2) by BMG Records (UK). Catalogue no: **NK 90364**
**CD:** Released Jul '89, on Bluebird (2) by BMG Records (UK). Catalogue no: **ND 89654**
**Album:** Released Jul '89, on Bluebird (2) by BMG Records (UK). Catalogue no: **NL 89654**
**Album:** Released Aug '89, on Bluebird (2) by BMG Records (UK). Catalogue no: **NL 90364**
**Cass:** Released Jul '89, on Bluebird (2) by BMG Records (UK). Catalogue no: **NK 89654**
**CD:** Released Aug '89, on Bluebird (2) by BMG Records (UK). Catalogue no: **ND 90364**

## Detroit Blues...

**DETROIT BLUES-EARLY 50'S**
**Album:** Released '88, on Blues Classics(USA) by Arhoolie Records (USA). Catalogue no: **BC 12**

## Detroit Gospel

**DETROIT GOSPEL (Various artists)**
**Album:** Released Sep '86, on Heritage by Interstate Music. Catalogue no: **HT 311**

## Detroit Jazz Tradition

**ALIVE AND WELL**
Note: With J.C. Heard, Claude Black, George Benson, Dave Young.
**Album:** Released Jul '88, on Parkwood Catalogue no: **PARKWOOD 102**

## Deuchar, Jimmy

**SCOTS CONNECTION, THE (Deuchar, Jimmy Quintet)**
**Album:** Released Apr '81, on Hep Jazz by Hep Records. Catalogue no: **HEP 2006**

**THOU SWELL (Deuchar, Jimmy/ Alan Clare/ Victor Feldman/ Tony Kinsey)**
Tracks: / They can't take that away from me / Close as pages in a book / Folks who live on the hill, The / Thou swell / Why do I love you? / Things we did last summer, The / This can't be love / Just one of those things.
**Album:** Released Jul '87, on Esquire by Titan Int. Prod.. Catalogue no: **ESQ 330**

## Di Meola, Al

**Biographical details:** The guitarist and composer was born in 1954 in New Jersey, began on guitar at age 9 and was inspired to play fusion by hearing Miles Davis with Chick Corea. He attended Berklee in Boston and joined Corea's Return To Forever in 1974, led his own groups and toured and recorded in a guitar trio with John McLaughlin and Paco DeLucia. He plays both acoustic and electric guitars. His albums on CBS all made the top 200 USA albums; he switched to Manhattan for the acoustic solo *Cielo e terra* then formed the Al Di Meola Project, with percussionist Airto, Phil Markowtz on keyboards, Danny Gottlieb on drums and bassist Chip Jackson for *Soaring through a dream.* (Donald Clarke, April 1989)..

**CASINO**
Tracks: / Egyptian danza / Chasin' the voodoo / Dark eye tango / Senor mouse / Fantasia suite for two guitars / Viva la danzarina / Guitars of the exotic isle / Rhapsody Italia / Bravoto fantasia / Casino.
**Album:** Released Mar '82, on CBS by CBS Records. Deleted '87. Catalogue no: **CBS 32071**
**Cass:** Released Mar '82, on CBS by CBS Records. Deleted '87. Catalogue no: **40 32071**
**CD:** Released May '87, on CBS by CBS Records. Deleted Jan '89. Catalogue no: **CD 82645**

**CIELO E TERRA**
Tracks: / Traces of a tear / Vertigo shadow / Cielo e Terra / Enigma of desire / Atavism of twilight / Coral / When your gone / Etude / Solace.
Note: Debut album for the Manhattan label from guitar virtuoso Al Di Meola. He produces the album and composes all tunes with the exception of one, written by Keith Jarrett. Underlining Manhattan Records comitment to the more specialist areas of the market, the addition of Di Meola to the roster will undoubtedly serve to broaden further the appeal of this already well established artist.
**Album:** Released May '85, on EMI-Manhattan by EMI Records. Deleted Jul '87. Catalogue no: **EJ 2403321**
**Cass:** Released May '85, on EMI-Manhattan by EMI Records. Deleted Jul '87. Catalogue no: **EJ 2403324**

**ELECTRIC RENDEZVOUS**
Tracks: / God bird / Change / Electric rendezvous / Passion, grace and fire / Cruisin' / Black cat shuffle / Ritmo de la noche / Somalia / Jewel inside a dream.
Note: Al Dimeola is a unique craftsman- he can turn his talents to any style of guitar playing from classical to heavy

electric, "Electric Rendezvous" is a celebration of these two very distinct musical styles. Steve Gaad, Paco de Lucia and Jan Hammer join Al on this LP.
**CD:** Released May '87, on CBS by CBS Records. Deleted Jan '89. Catalogue no: **CD 85437**
**Album:** Released Mar '82, on CBS by CBS Records. Deleted '85. Catalogue no: **CBS 85437**
**Cass:** Released Mar '82, on CBS by CBS Records. Deleted '85. Catalogue no: **40 85437**

**ELEGANT GYPSY**
Tracks: / Flight over Rio / Midnight tango / Mediterranean sundance / Race with devil on Spanish highway / Lady of Rome / Sister of Brazil / Elegant gypsy suite.
**Cass:** Released '79, on CBS by CBS Records. Catalogue no: **40 81845**
**Album:** Released May '77, on CBS by CBS Records. Deleted '85. Catalogue no: **CBS 81845**
**CD:** Released '88, on CBS by CBS Records. Deleted Jan '89. Catalogue no: **CD CBS 81845**

**FRIDAY NIGHT IN SAN FRANCISCO**
Tracks: / Mediterranean sundance / Rio ancho / Short tales of the black forest / Frevo resgado / Fantasia suite for two guitars / Guardian angel.
**Cass:** Released Jun '81, on CBS by CBS Records. Deleted Aug '87. Catalogue no: **40 84962**
**Album:** Released Jun '81, on CBS by CBS Records. Deleted '86. Catalogue no: **CBS 84962**
**CD:** Released '88, on Philips by Phonogram Ltd. Catalogue no: **800 047 2**

**LAND OF THE MIDNIGHT SUN**
Tracks: / Wizard / Sarabande from violin sonata in B minor / Pictures of the sea (love theme) / Land of the midnight sun / Golden dawn suite (morning fire) / Calmer of the tempests / From ocean to the clouds / Short tales of the Black Forest.
**CD:** Released '88, on CBS by CBS Records. Deleted Jan '89. Catalogue no: **CD 81220**
**Album:** Released '86, on CBS by CBS Records. Catalogue no: **CBS 32027**

**SCENARIO**
Tracks: / Mata hari / African night / Island dreamer / Scenario / Seqencer / Cachaca / Hypnotic conviction / Calliope / Scroundrel.
**CD:** Deleted 10 Jul '89. Catalogue no: **CD 25718**

**SOARING THROUGH A DREAM**
Tracks: / Capoeira / Traces (of a tear) / Ballad / July / Marina / Soaring through a dream.
Note: Acclaimed guitarist Al Di Meola releases a second album for Manhattan records this being an electric project in contrast to his last accoustic work on Cielo E Terra. Joining Di Meola on this new project is noted Brazillian percussionist Airto moreira who assists in the compositions of three of the albums six cuts. the group performed live in Britain, at the Apollo Manchester on September 28th and the Odeon Hammersmith on September 29th as part of a European tour.
**Album:** Released Oct '85, on EMI-Manhattan by EMI Records. Deleted Aug '89. Catalogue no: **EJ 2403981**
**Cass:** Released Oct '85, on EMI-Manhattan by EMI Records. Deleted Jul '87. Catalogue no: **EJ 2403984**

**SPANISH EYES**
Tracks: / Spanish eyes.
**7" Single:** Released Oct '82, on CBS by CBS Records. Deleted Oct '85. Catalogue no: **CBS 8946**

**SPLENDIDO HOTEL**
Tracks: / Alien chase on an Arabian desert / Silent story in her eyes / Roller jubilee / Two to tango / Al Di's dream.
**Album:** Released Aug '80, on CBS by CBS Records. Deleted '85. Catalogue no: **CBS 88468**

**TIRAMI SU**
Tracks: / Beijing demons / Arabella / Smile from a stranger / Rhapsody of fire / Song of the pharoah kings / Andonea / Maraba / Song with a view.
**CD:** Released Apr '88, on EMI-Manhattan by EMI Records. Deleted Aug '89. Catalogue no: **CDP 746 995 2**
**Album:** Released Apr '88, on EMI-Manhattan by EMI Records. Catalogue no: **MTL 1019**
**Cass:** Released Apr '88, on EMI-Manhattan by EMI Records. Deleted Aug '89. Catalogue no: **TCMTL 1019**
**CD:** Released Apr '88, on EMI-Manhattan by EMI Records. Deleted Aug '89. Catalogue no: **CDMTL 1019**

**TOUR DE FORCE (LIVE)**
Tracks: / Elegant gypsy suite / Nena / Advantage / Egyptian danza / Race with the devil on Spanish highway / Cruisin'.
**Album:** Released May '89, on CBS by CBS Records. Catalogue no: **CBS 25121**

## Dial Masters

**DIAL MASTERS 2 (BOX SET) Modern jazz (Various artists)**
Note: Companion piece to Charlie Parker collection. Spotlite SPJ 127-133.
**LP Set:** Released '83, on Spotlite by Spotlite Records. Catalogue no: **SPJ BOX 7**

## Dickenson, Vic

**Biographical details:** American jazz trombonist (1906-84), one of the best, a master of the traditional hot syles and a mellow ballad sound as well. He played mostly the dixieland style in post-war years with Eddie Condon, Red Allen, Bobby Hackett, but remained a fluent and versatile veteran admired by the young and old. (Donald Clarke, April 1989).

**ESSENTIAL VIC DICKENSON**
Tracks: / Russian lullaby / Keep out of mischief / Sir Charles at home / Jeepers creepers / I cover the waterfront / Runnin' wild / When you and I were young Maggie / Nice work if you can get it / Old fashioned love / Everybody loves m baby / Suspension blues / You brough a new kind of love to me.
**Album:** Released May '83, on Vogu Jazz (France) by Vogue Records. Cata logue no: **VJD 551**

**JUST FRIENDS**
Note: Featuring Red Richards/John Wi liams
**Album:** Released Jun '86, on Sackvill by Spotlite Records. Catalogue no: **201**

**TROMBONE CHOLLY**
**Album:** Released Aug '87, on Sonet b Sonet Records. Catalogue no: **SNT 720**

**VIC DICKENSON'S QUARTE (Dickenson, Vic Quartet)**
Note: Mono production. Featurin Buddy Tate/G.Duvivier/O.Jackson
**Album:** Released Jun '86, on Storyvill by Storyville Records AB. Catalogue no **SLP 4021**

**YACHT CLUB SWING 1964-196 (Dickenson, Vic All Stars)**
**Album:** Released May '86, on Harlequi by Interstate Music. Catalogue no: **H 2045**

## Dickerson, Walt

**I HEAR YOU JOHN (Dickerson Walt & Jimmi Johnson)**
**Album:** Released Jun '81, on Steeple chase (USA) Catalogue no: **SCS 1146**

**SHADES OF LOVE**
**Album:** Released Feb '79, on Steeple chase (USA) Catalogue no: **SCD 1700**

**VISIONS (Dickerson, Walt & Sur Ra)**
**Album:** Released Sep '79, on Steeple chase (USA) Catalogue no: **SCS 1126**

## Dickie, Neville

**EYE OPENER**
**Album:** Released '88, on Stomp Of (USA) Catalogue no: **SOS 1052**

**NEVILLE DICKIE MEETS FATS, THE LION AND THE LAMB**
**Album:** Released '88, on Stomp Of (USA) Catalogue no: **SOS 1176**

**ROBIN'S RETURN**
Tracks: / Robin's return.
**7" Single:** Released Oct '69, on Major Minor Deleted '72. Catalogue no: **MM 644**

**TAKEN IN STRIDE 2**
**Album:** Released '88, on Stomp Off (USA) Catalogue no: **SOS 1096**

## Diddley, Bo

**Biographical details:** This American singer, guitarist and songwriter, born Ellas McDaniel in Mississippi in 1928, is one of the most influential figures in the history of rock. He studied the classical violin for twelve years before making the guitar his primary instrument but, during his formative years, he also absorbed some very important influences from the rhythm and blues and church music spheres. In 1955 he gained a contract with Chess Records, the same label that

**Bo Diddley**

simultaneously launched the career of Chuck Berry. Diddley soon gave the company a Top 10 success on the US R&B charts with an eponymous single, *Bo Diddley.* This seminal track incorporated all of the man's talents - an original, cheeky and witty theme and title (how many other artists had written a song about themselves?), enthusiastic vocals and, most importantly, an inventive and wildly exciting guitar style; the reverse side of the record, *I'm A Man,* was equally invigorating. Several more R&B hits followed during the remainder of the Fifties, and he also played on some of Berry's famous tracks. 1959 saw Diddley reach No 20 in the US with his novelty single *Say Man* - incredibly, this was the only pop hit of his entire career. Diddley's influence really began to show itself in the early/mid-Sixties, particularly in Britain. Having been a part of the original mid-Fifties rock 'n' roll explosion, he played an important role in rock's next vital revolution - the Beatles-led British boom. The early repertoire of the Rolling Stones featured a host of Diddley numbers, and that up-and-coming group also helped to foster UK record buyers' interest in Chuck Berry. At about the same time, in the summer of '63, a superb version of *Bo Diddley* by the late Buddy Holly was issued and hit No 4 on the British charts. This paved the way for Diddley himself to score four UK chart albums in quick succession, plus a minor hit single with *Pretty Thing.* That song inspired the name of the Pretty Things, a British hitmaking group of the mid-Sixties. He also inspired another rising UK R&B combo, the Animals, to record *The Story Of Bo Diddley,* a lengthy and amusing account of their somewhat awkward meeting with him. Acts such as the Who and the Yardbirds also owed Diddley a considerable debt. The guitar riff on his self-titled song became one of the most imitated sounds in all of rock music, and formed the basis of many classic tracks by a variety of artists. He continued to record numerous albums during the sixties and seventies, but with very little success. It is very ironic that such an important figure has never enjoyed major record success as a performer on either side of Atlantic; he has always been seriously underrated in the public mind. One of his mid-fifties R&B singles, *Who Do You Love,* became a UK Top 20 hit for Juicy Lucy in 1970, and has been covered by many other artists. Diddley still tours regularly, but is not a rich man. Bob MacDonald, 30 March 1985.

R&B singer, composer, guitarist, born Elias McDaniel in 1928 in Mississippi; one of the most influential R&B artists of the mid 50's, despite a surprisingly small number of chart entries, whose trademark 'hambone' or 'shave-and-a-haircut, six bits' beat has been imitated by countless lesser acts. He recorded for Checker/Chess 1955-74 and had eight R&B hits beginning with the two sided *Bo Diddley/I'm a man* in 1955. *Roadrunner* on Black Lion UK was made at Joyous Lake, Woodstock in the late '70's . (Donald Clarke, April 1989).

**AIN'T IT GOOD TO BE FREE?**
Tracks: / Ain't it good to be free? /
Swamp funk.
**CD:** Released 20 Feb '88, on New Rose (1) by New Rose Records. Catalogue no: **ROSE 34CD**
**Album:** Released Jun '84, on New Rose (1) by New Rose Records. Catalogue no: **ROSE 34**

**BO DIDDLEY BOX SET**
**Cass set:** Released Nov '89, on Charly by Charly Records. Catalogue no: **TCBOX 257**
**LP Set:** Released Nov '89, on Charly by Charly Records. Catalogue no: **BOX 257**
**CD Set:** Released Nov '89, on Charly by Charly Records. Catalogue no: **CDBOX 257**

**BO DIDDLEY (CD SINGLE)**
Tracks: / Bo diddley / Road runner / You can't judge a book by the cover / Mona (I need you baby).
**CD Single:** Released Feb '89, on Charly by Charly Records. Catalogue no: **CDS 11**

**BO DIDDLEY - I'M A MAN**
**Album:** Released Oct '88, on Vogue (France) by Vogue Records. Catalogue no: **515027**

**BO DIDDLEY IS A GUNSLINGER**
**Album:** Released Oct '63, on Pye Deleted '68. Catalogue no: **NJL 33**

**BO DIDDLEY (LP)**
Tracks: / Bo diddley / I'm a man / Bring it to Jerome / Bring it to Jerome / Before you accuse me / Hey Bo Diddley / Dearest darling / Hush your mouth / Say bossman / Diddley daddy / Diddy wah diddy / Who do you love.
**CD:** Released Dec '86, on Vogue by Vogue Records. Catalogue no: **VGCD 600114**
**Album:** Released Oct '63, on Pye International Deleted '68. Catalogue no: **NPL 28026**
**Album:** Released Apr '87, on Chess by Vogue Records. Catalogue no: **GCH 8026**
**Cass:** Released Apr '87, on Chess by Vogue Records. Catalogue no: **GCHK 78026**

**BO DIDDLEY RIDES AGAIN**
**Album:** Released Nov '63, on Pye International Deleted '68. Catalogue no: **NPL 28029**

**BO DIDDLEY (SINGLE)**
Tracks: / Bo Diddley / Pretty thing / Road runner / Say man.
**7" Single:** Released Jul '85, on Chess (PRT) Deleted '88. Catalogue no: **CHES 4001**

**BO DIDDLEY'S BEACH PARTY**
Tracks: / Memphis / Gunslinger / Hey Bo Diddley / Old smokey / Bo Diddley's dog / I'm all right / Mr.Custer / Bo's waltz / What's buggin' you / Roadrunner.
**Cass:** Released '89, on Chess by Vogue Records. Catalogue no: **GCHK 78111**
**Album:** Released Feb '64, on Pye Deleted '69. Catalogue no: **NPL 28032**
**Album:** Released '89, on Chess by Vogue Records. Catalogue no: **GCH 8111**

**CHESS MASTERS**
Tracks: / Mona / Hey Bo Diddley / Road runner / Bring it to Jerome / Pretty thing / Pills / I'm a man / Hush your mouth / Sax man / Cops and robbers / Mumblin' guitar / Diddley Biddley / Memphis / She's alright / You can't judge a book by the cover / Who do you love.
**Album:** Released Apr '81, on Chess (PRT) Deleted '88. Catalogue no: **CXMD 4003**
**Cass:** Released 19 Mar '88, on Stylus by Stylus Music Records. Catalogue no: **SMC 849**
**CD:** Released '88, on Stylus by Stylus Music Records. Catalogue no: **SMD 849**
**Album:** Released 19 Mar '88, on Stylus by Stylus Music Records. Catalogue no: **SMR 849**

**CHESS MASTERS VOL. 2**
Tracks: / Crackin' up / Blues inst / Great grandfather / You don't love me / What do you know about love / Lazy woman / Come on baby / Dancing girl / Diddy wah diddy / Little girl / Nursery rhyme / Clock strikes 12 / She's fine she's mine / Down home special / Say boss man / Bo meets the monster / Willie & Lillie / Oh yea / Mama keep your big mouth shut / You're looking good / Greatest lover in the world / Let me in / Little girl / Bo's guitar.
**2 LP Set:** Released May '82, on Chess by Vogue Records. Catalogue no: **CXMD 4009**

**DIDDLEY DADDY**
Tracks: / Bo Diddley / I'm a man / You don't love me / Diddley daddy / She's fine, she's mine / Pretty thing / Bring it to Jerome / Diddy wah diddy / I'm looking for a woman / Who do you love / Cops and robbers / Hey Bo Diddley / Mona (I need you baby) / Before you accuse me / Say man / Hush your mouth / Bo's guitar / Willie and Lillie / Crackin' up / I'm sorry / Nursery rhyme / Story of Bo Diddley / Road runner / You can't judge a book by the cover.
**CD:** Released Aug '88, on Chess by Vogue Records. Catalogue no: **CDRED 2**

**GIVE ME A BREAK**
Tracks: / Give me a break.
**Album:** Released Oct '87, on Checkmate Catalogue no: **CHECKMATE 1960**

**GO BO DIDDLEY**
Tracks: / Crackin' up / I'm sorry / Bo's guitar / Willie and lillie / You don't know me / Say man / Great grandfather, The / Oh yeah / Don't let it go / Little girl / Dearest darling / Clock struck twelve, The.
**Album:** Released Apr '87, on Chess by Vogue Records. Catalogue no: **GCH 8021**
**Cass:** Released Apr '87, on Chess by Vogue Records. Catalogue no: **GCHK 78021**

**GOT MY OWN BAG OF TRICKS**
**2 LP Set:** Released Oct '88, on Vogue by Vogue Records. Catalogue no: **427011**

**HAVE GUITAR,WILL TRAVEL**
Tracks: / She's alright / Cops and robbers / Diddley daddy / Mumblin' guitar / I need you baby / Say man / Back again / Nursery rhyme / I love you so / Spanish guitar / Dancing girl / Come on baby / Run.
**Album:** Released Aug '86, on Chess by Vogue Records. Catalogue no: **GCH 8002**
**Cass:** Released Aug '86, on Chess by Vogue Records. Catalogue no: **GCHK 78002**

**HEY, BO DIDDLEY**
Tracks: / Mess around / Somebody's crying / Hong Kong / Can I go home with you / I'm going home / Rhyme song / Cracklin' / Rockin' on.
**Cass:** Released May '88, on Jazz Life Catalogue no: **2173022**
**Cass:** Released Jul '88, on Conifer Catalogue no: **MCFRC 507**
**CD:** Released May '88, on Jazz Life Catalogue no: **2473022**
**Album:** Released Jul '88, on Conifer Catalogue no: **CFRC 507**
**Album:** Released May '88, on Jazz Life Catalogue no: **2273022**
**Album:** Released Aug '86, on Magnum Force by Magnum Music Group. Catalogue no: **MFM 021**

**HEY GOOD LOOKIN'**
Tracks: / Hey good lookin'.
**7" Single:** Released Mar '65, on Chess by Vogue Records. Deleted '68. Catalogue no: **CHESS 8000**

**HIS GREATEST SIDES VOL.1**
Tracks: / Bo Diddley / Pretty thing / Bring it to Jerome / I'm a man / Mona / Diddley daddy / Dearest darling / Who do you love / Roadrunner / Say man / Bo's bounce / You can't judge a book by it's cover / Crackin' up / Hey Bo Diddley.
**Album:** Released Aug '86, on Chess by Vogue Records. Catalogue no: **GCH 8005**
**Cass:** Released Aug '86, on Chess by Vogue Records. Catalogue no: **GCHK 78005**

**I'M A MAN**
Tracks: / Bo Diddley / I'm a man / You all green / Mr. Kruschev / Somebody beat me / Tonight is ours / I'm sorry / Little girl.
**Album:** Released Oct '82, on Black Lion Catalogue no: **BLM 52004**

**IN THE SPOTLIGHT**
Tracks: / Roadrunner / Story of Bo Diddley / Scuttle bug / Signifying blues / Let me in / Limber / Love me / Craw-dad / Walkin' and talkin' / Travelin' west / Deed and deed I do / Live my life.
**Cass:** Released Oct '87, on Chess by Vogue Records. Catalogue no: **GCHK 78038**
**Album:** Released Aug '87, on Chess by Vogue Records. Catalogue no: **GCH 8038**
**CD:** Released Feb '90, on MCA by MCA Records. Catalogue no: **CHD 9264**

**IT'S GREAT TO BE RICH (EP) (Diddley, Bo & Billy Boy)**
Tracks: / It's great to be rich.
**12" Single:** Released Jun '83, on Red Lightnin' by Red Lightning Records. Deleted Jun '89. Catalogue no: **RLEP 12 045**

**LIVE '77**
**Album:** on Fan Club by New Rose Records. Catalogue no: **FC 009**

**LIVING LEGEND**
**CD:** Released Sep '89, on New Rose (1) by New Rose Records. Catalogue no: **ROSE 188CD**
**Album:** Released Sep '89, on New Rose (1) by New Rose Records. Catalogue no: **ROSE 188**
**Cass:** Released Sep '89, on New Rose (1) by New Rose Records. Catalogue no: **ROSE 188C**

**PRETTY THING**
Tracks: / Pretty thing.
**7" Single:** Released Oct '63, on Pye International Deleted '66. Catalogue no: **7N 25217**

**ROAD RUNNER**
Tracks: / Hey Bo Diddley / Say bossman / Bring it to Jerome / Mona / Before you accuse me / You can't judge a book by the cover / Road runner.
**Album:** Released Jul '84, on Black Lion Catalogue no: **BLM 52014**

**ROAD RUNNER (INSTANT)**
Tracks: / Bo Diddley / I'm a man / Pretty thing / Who do you love / Mona (I need you baby) / Say man / Hush your mouth / Road runner / You can't judge a book by the cover / Cops and robbers / Hey Bo Diddley / Crackin' up / Diddley Daddy / Bring it to Jerome.
**Album:** Released Jul '89, on Instant (2) by Charly Records. Catalogue no: **INS 5004**
**CD:** Released Jul '89, on Instant (2) by Charly Records. Catalogue no: **CDINS 5004**
**Cass:** Released Jul '89, on Instant (2) by Charly Records. Catalogue no: **TCINS 5004**

**ROCK 'N' ROLL JAM (VIDEO) (Diddley, Bo & Friends)**
Note: An all star jam featuring Ron Wood, Kenny Jones, Mick Fleetwood, John Mayall and Ronnie Lane amongst others ... a superstar backing band for one of the great legends of rock'n'roll. Running time: 60 mins.
**VHS:** Released Nov '89, on Hendring Video Catalogue no: **HEN 2188 G**

**SUPER BLUES (Diddley, Bo & Muddy Waters)**
**Album:** on Blues Rock Project Catalogue no: **BRP 2012**

**WHERE IT ALL BEGAN**
**Album:** Released Oct '88, on Vogue (France) by Vogue Records. Catalogue no: **515012**

## Dirty Dozen Brass Band

**Biographical details:** A New Orleans brass band playing hip arrangements, describing its style as 'jazz gumbo'. The octet turned to the traditional instrumentation in 1979, with only one man not from New Orleans. Their second album *Mardi Gras in Montreux live*: was described as 'one of the best in-concert recordings I've heard by Steve Lewis in *The wire*. They also sessioned with Phil Alvin on his album *Unsung stories*. (Donald Clarke, April 1989).

### LIVE: MARDI GRAS IN MONTREUX
**Cass:** Released '88, on Rounder (USA) by Rounder Records (USA). Catalogue no: **ROUNDER 2052C**
**CD:** Released '88, on Rounder (USA) by Rounder Records (USA). Catalogue no: **CD 2052**
**Album:** Released Jun '86, on Rounder Europa (USA) Catalogue no: **REU 1009**
**Album:** Released '88, on Rounder (USA) by Rounder Records (USA). Catalogue no: **ROUNDER 2052**

### MY FEET CAN'T FAIL ME NOW
Tracks: / Blackbird special / Do it fluid / I ate up the apple tree / Bongo beep / Blue Monk / Caravan / St. James' Infirmary / Li'l Liza Jane / Mary, Mary / My feet can't fail me now.
Note: Davis and Marshall play snare drums, Jones bass drum. Lewis plays soprano Sax
**Album:** Released Oct '84, on George Wein Collection(USA) by Concord Jazz Records (USA). Catalogue no: **GW 3005**
**CD:** Released Oct '84, on George Wein Collection(USA) by Concord Jazz Records (USA). Catalogue no: **CCD 43005**

### VOODOO
Tracks: / It's all over now / Oop pop a dah / Moose the mooche / Black drawers, blue piccolo / Voodoo / Gemini rising / Don't drive drunk / Santa cruz.
**Cass:** Released Jul '89, on CBS by CBS Records. Catalogue no: **465 097 4**
**CD:** Released Jul '89, on CBS by CBS Records. Catalogue no: **465 097 2**
**Album:** Released Jul '89, on CBS by CBS Records. Catalogue no: **465 097 1**

## Disley, Diz

### ZING WENT THE STRINGS (Disley, Diz & The Soho Quintette)
**Album:** Released Nov '86, on Waterfront by Waterfront Music. Catalogue no: **WF 031**

## Distel, Sacha

**Biographical details:** This French singer's only year of success on the British record charts was 1970. A self-titled album reached No 21 that year, logging 14 weeks on the LP listings. He reached No 10 on the UK singles chart with his rendition of *Raindrops Keep falling on my head*, the Oscar-winning Burt Bacharach/Hal David song featured in the successful movie "Butch Cassity and the Sundance Kid". The original film version was sung by B J Thomas, who took the song to the US No 1 slot in January '70. But in Britain, Distel was the clear winner. The Frenchman hit No 10 (compared with Thomas' No 38 and Bobbie Gentry's No 40), and logged a total of 27 weeks on the Top 50. In the best traditions of its writers, *Raindrops* was an agreeable piece of mass-appeal, middle of the road pop.

Distel's blank showing on the UK charts (apart from 1970) is not a true reflection of his fame and popularity with the older British music lover, particularly during the Seventies. His albums, containing predictable selections of mainly familiar chansons d'amour, tended to sell in small quantities over a long period of time. In addition, his discs were only one part of a successful showbusiness career, which included numerous TV, cabaret, variety and concert appearances. He is one of the few artists to break out of his country's insular music business and sustain an international career. (Bob MacDonald, 21 June 1985.).

### ADIOS AMIGO
Tracks: / Adios amigo / Wir konnten freunde sein / Blacky / Eine ist einsam wie du / Traurig schone augen / Ein paar tranen / Marie cherie / Irene von avignon / Der platz neben mir / Unsere sprache ist musik / Ein fraunfreund / Frauen und rosen / Dir frau mit dem einsamen herzeb / Eine tur fiel zu / Deine stimme am telefon / Ich kann dich so schwer vergessen.
**Album:** Released Mar '88, on Bear Family by Bear Family Records (Germany). Catalogue no: **BFX 15310**

## District Six

### AKUZWAKALE (LET IT BE HEARD)
Tracks: / Woza wena (a calling to rise) / Skokiaan / Dance of the lions / Owenda / Sivela kude (we come from far) / Ilanga / Akuzwakale (let it be heard).
Note: District Six was formed in early 1983 by three young South Afrcian musicians. The name given to the band is reference to a Cape Town township, one of the many to be destroyed under the South African governments policy of resettlement. The music is a mixture of South African folk and urban jazz. Since their appearance at the '83 Bracknell Jazz Festival, the band have attracted a great deal of interest and have undertaken a Jazz Services Tour. Personnel: Russell Herman - guitar & voice / Dill Katz - fender fretless bass / Harrison Smith - tenor, soprano sax & flute / Jim Dvorak - trumpet / Ruthie Smith - alto, soprano sax & voice.
**Cass:** Released Mar '85, on District Six Catalogue no: **DC 6001**
**Album:** Released Mar '85, on District Six Catalogue no: **D 6001**

### IMGOMA YABANTWANA
**CD:** Released Mar '90, on D6 Catalogue no: **JJCD11**

### LEAVE MY NAME AT THE DOOR
Tracks: / Leave my name at the door / Nameless one, The / In our hands / Ilanga / Koko / Drums for Nelson / Mangwane.
Note: Second album from District six, whose inspiration is drawn from South African folk music, contemporary jazz and free expression. They have gained wide recognition in the jazz world since their Jazz Service Tour, numerous appearances at major festivals and a German tour with Annie Whitehead guesting. The group has slightly changed in the line-up with the departure of Russell Herman and Ruthie Smith. *Leaving My name at the door* is an exciting second album recording a live performance at the Bass Clef Club, London, in November 1985. Personnel: Jim Dvorak, trumpet, pocket trumpet, penny whistle, vocals, percussion; Harrison Smith, saxophones, flute; Mervyn Africa, piano, vocals, cabassa, hand cymbals; Dill Katz, fretless bass guitar; Brian Abrahams, drums, vocals.
**Album:** Released Feb '86, on Wave by Wave Records. Catalogue no: **WAVE LP 29**

### TO BE FREE
Tracks: / Ke a rona (power to the people) / Into the light / Etlon tu / Reasons of the heart / Kwa tebugo (part 2 of songs for Winnie Mandela) / Unity dance (part 3 of songs for Winnie Mandela) / Mbiso / Kalimba (CD only).
**Album:** Released Aug '88, on Editions EG by E.G. Records. Catalogue no: **EGED 53**
**CD:** Released '87, on Editions EG by E.G. Records. Catalogue no: **EEGCD 53**
**Cass:** Released '87, on Editions EG by E.G. Records. Catalogue no: **EGEDC 53**

## Dixie Five

### DIXIE FIVE (Various artists)
**Album:** Released Nov '88, on Jazzology (USA) by Jazzology Records (USA). Catalogue no: **J 147**

## Dixie Four

### CHICAGO SOUTH SIDE (Dixie Four / Midnight Rounders / State Street Ramblers)
**Album:** Released Feb '87, on Collectors Items Catalogue no: **CI 019**

## Dixie Hummingbirds

### CHRISTIAN TESTIMONIAL, A
**Cass:** Released Jun '84, on MCA (USA) by MCA Records (USA). Catalogue no: **MCA 28000**

### DIXIE HUMMINGBIRDS
Tracks: / Lord come see about me / Two little fishes / Is there anyone in heaven / Search me Lord / I'll be satisfied / Move up a little higher / We shall walk through

the valley / You've got to live / What then / Down on me / Dear Lord look down upon me (Track features the Angelic Gospel Singers) / Jesus will answer prayer / Standing out on the highway / In the morning.
**Album:** Released 22 Apr '88, on Gospel Heritage by Interstate Music. Catalogue no: **HT 318**

## Dixieaires

**LET ME FLY 1948-50**
Tracks: / Will the circle be unbroken? / Poor and needy / I got to stand / If you see my Saviour / Friends let me tell you... / I got a home in that rock / Send me Jesus / God is the greatest creator / Buckle my shoe / Christ ABC / Loose the man / Let me fly / Little wooden church / You better run / I've got an interest over there / Look around you brother.
**Album:** Released Jan '88, on Heritage by Interstate Music. Catalogue no: **HT 317**

**MY TROUBLE IS HARD**
**Album:** Released Oct '89, on Heritage by Interstate Music. Catalogue no: **HT 319**

## Dixieland

**DIXIELAND (Various artists)**
**CD:** Released Jul '88, on Entertainers Catalogue no: **ENTCD 250**

**DIXIELAND COLLECTION (Various artists)**
Tracks: / Tiger rag: *Original Dixieland Jazz Band* / Tin roof blues: *New Orleans Rhythm Kings* / She's crying...: *New Orleans Rhythm Kings* / Royal Garden blues: *Beiderbecke, Bix* / Fidgety feet: *Wolverine Orchestra* / Clementine: *Goldkette, Jean & His Orchestra* / Way down yonder in New Orleans: *Trumbauer, Frankie* / That's no bargain: *Nichols, Red* / Moanin' low: *Mole, Miff* / Nobody's sweetheart: *McKenzie* / Strut Miss Lizzie: *Hotsy Totsy Gang* / There'll be some changes made: *Chicago Rhythm Kings* / Basin Street blues: *Charleston Chasers* / Eel, The: *Condon, Eddie & His Orchestra* / After you've gone: *Venuti, Joe & Eddie Lang* / Spider crawl: *Banks, Billy & His Orchestra* / Rockin' chair: *Carmichael, Hoagy* / Thinking of you: *Rhythm Cats* / Relaxin' at the Touro: *Spanier, Muggsy*.
**CD:** Released Jun '88, on Deja Vu Catalogue no: **DVCD 2119**
**Album:** Released Dec '87, on Deja Vu Catalogue no: **DVLP 2119**
**Cass:** Released Dec '87, on Deja Vu Catalogue no: **DVMC 2119**

**DIXIELAND DOWN SOUTH (Various artists)**
Note: Various artists include: Joe Capraro & Charlie Cordilla.
**Album:** Released '88, on Southland by Delta Records. Catalogue no: **SLP 220**

**DIXIELAND JAZZ CLASSICS**
**Album:** Released '88, on Herwin by Shanachie Records (USA). Catalogue no: **HERWIN 116**

**DIXIELAND JUBILEE (Various artists)**
**CD Set:** Released Oct '88, on Mainline (2) by Mainline Records. Catalogue no: **267 306 2**
**Cass:** Released May '82, on Black Lion-Intercord Catalogue no: **CAS 455 002**
**2 LP Set:** Released May '88, on Black Tulip Catalogue no: **80011**
**2 LP Set:** Released Oct '82, on Black Lion Catalogue no: **BLP 30401/2**
**Cass set:** Released May '88, on Black Tulip Catalogue no: **850111/2**
**2 LP Set:** Released May '82, on Black Lion-Intercord Catalogue no: **INT 155 002**

**DIXIELAND JUBILEE, VOL.2 (Various artists)**
Tracks: / Black and blue: *Lyttelton, Humphrey* / Barefoot days: *Welsh, Alex* / Jazz me blues: *Dutch Swing College Band* / Tiger rag: *Greene, Brian* / Making whoopee: *Barber, Chris* / St. Philip Street breakdown: *Sunshine, Monty* / I'm crazy 'bout my baby: *Collie, Max* / Careless love: *Sunshine, Monty* / Chelsea cakewalk: *Bilk, Acker* / Buddy Bolden's blues: *Various artists* / West End blues: *Bryden, Beryl & The Rod Mason Band* / All of me: *Barber, Chris* / Honeysuckle rose: *Bilk, Acker* / Tishomingo blues: *Lyttelton, Humphrey* / Just a closer walk with thee: *Sunshine, Monty* / Bill Bailey: *Dutch Swing College Band* / Tie a yellow ribbon: *Welsh, Alex* / You made me love you: *Dutch Swing College Band* / High society: *Barber, Chris* / St. Louis blues: *Bryden, Beryl & The Rod Mason Band* / Carry me back to old Virginny: *Various artists* / Ice cream: *Greene, Brian* / C jam blues: *Sunshine, Monty* / Travellin' on: *Bilk, Acker* / Wild man blues: *Various artists*.
**Cass set:** Released May '82, on Black Lion-Intercord Catalogue no: **CAS 455 005**
**2 LP Set:** Released Oct '82, on Black Lion Catalogue no: **BLP 30403/4**
**2 LP Set:** Released May '82, on Black Lion-Intercord Catalogue no: **INT 155 005**

**DIXIELAND JUBILEE, VOL.3 (Various artists)**
Tracks: / High Society: *Various artists* / Savoy blues: *Various artists* / Carolina shuffle: *Various artists* / Memphis blues: *Various artists* / Loch Lomond: *Various artists* / When the saints go marching in: *Various artists* / Theo, wir fahr'n nach lodz: *Various artists* / Lazy river: *Various artists* / Nobody knows the trouble I've seen: *Various artists* / Creole love call: *Various artists* / Saturday night function: *Various artists* / Over in the gloryland: *Various artists* / Meet me tonight in dreamland: *Various artists* / Little brown jug: *Various artists* / Lonesome Road: *Various artists* / Makin' whoopee: *Various artists* / Smokey mokes: *Various artists* / Just a little while to stay here: *Various artists* / New Orleans function: *Various artists* / Oh didn't he ramble: *Various artists* / Margie: *Various artists* / King of the Zulus, The: *Various artists* / Swanee River: *Various artists* / Mood indigo: *Various artists* / Tie a yellow ribbon: *Various artists.*
**Cass set:** Released May '82, on Black Lion-Intercord Catalogue no: **CAS 455 013**
**2 LP Set:** Released May '82, on Black Lion-Intercord Catalogue no: **INT 155 013**

**DIXIELAND JUBILEE, VOL.4 (Various artists)**
Tracks: / Panama rag: *Various artists* / I'm going home: *Various artists* / Chinatown: *Various artists* / Davenport blues: *Various artists* / Darktown strutters' ball: *Various artists* / Back home again in Indiana: *Various artists* / Original Charleston strut: *Various artists* / Gisela: *Various artists* / Cheek to cheek: *Various artists* / Hello Dolly: *Various artists* / Carry me back: *Various artists* / I can't give you anything but love: *Various artists* / Rovin', A: *Various artists* / Does your chewing gum lose its flavour?: *Various artists* / Dear old Southland: *Various artists* / Dippermouth blues: *Various artists* / Isle of Capri: *Various artists* / I'm crazy 'bout my baby: *Various artists* / New Orleans stomp: *Various artists* / Sweethearts on parade: *Various artists* / Go tell it on the mountain: *Various artists* / Avalon: *Various artists* / Mack the knife: *Various artists* / Wochenend und sonnenschein: *Various artists.*
**Cass set:** Released May '82, on Black Lion-Intercord Catalogue no: **CAS 455 024**
**2 LP Set:** Released May '82, on Black Lion-Intercord Catalogue no: **INT 155 024**

**DIXIELAND JUBILEE, VOL.5 (Various artists)**
Tracks: / Wolverine blues: *Various artists* / Sugar foot stomp: *Various artists* / Jenny's ball: *Various artists* / Georgia on my mind: *Various artists* / Kassiam: *Various artists* / Careless love: *Various artists* / Struttin' with some barbecue: *Various artists* / Higher ground: *Various artists* / Ole miss: *Various artists* / 'S wonderful: *Various artists* / Terrible blues: *Various artists* / When it's sleepy time down South: *Various artists* / My blue Heaven: *Various artists* / Black and blue: *Various artists* / Dardanella: *Various artists* / Old rugged cross, The: *Various artists* / Blue and sentimental: *Various artists* / Big Bill: *Various artists* / My bucket's got a hole in it: *Various artists* / Egyptian fantasy: *Various artists* / When you wore a tulip: *Various artists* / Whistling Rufus: *Various artists* / Light from the lighthouse: *Various artists* / Clarinet marmalade: *Various artists.*
**Cass set:** Released May '82, on Black Lion-Intercord Catalogue no: **CAS 455 032**
**2 LP Set:** Released May '82, on Black Lion-Intercord Catalogue no: **INT 155 032**

**DIXIELAND JUBILEE, VOLS. 1 & 2 (Various artists)**
**2 LP Set:** Released May '88, on Black Tulip Catalogue no: **80029**

**Cass set:** Released May '88, on Black Tulip Catalogue no: **850291/2**

**DIXIELAND STORY, THE (Various artists)**
Tracks: / Tiger bag: *Various artists* / Look at 'em doing it now: *Various artists* / Copenhagen: *Various artists* / Careless love: *Various artists* / She's crying for me: *Various artists* / That's no bargain: *Various artists* / Way down yonder in New Orleans: *Various artists* / I'm more than satisfied: *Various artists* / Royal Garden blues: *Various artists* / Nobody's sweetheart: *Various artists* / Coquette: *Various artists* / I found a new baby: *Various artists* / There'll be some changes made: *Various artists* / Shake your can: *Various artists* / Moanin' low: *Various artists* / Strut Miss Lizzie: *Various artists* / Georgia on my mind: *Various artists* / Georgia grind: *Various artists* / After you've gone: *Various artists* / Spider crawl: *Various artists* / Eel, The: *Various artists* / When the saints go marching in: *Various artists* / At the jazz band ball: *Various artists* / Relaxin' at the Touro: *Various artists* / Muskrat ramble: *Various artists*.
**CD:** Released May '89, on Deja Vu Catalogue no: **DVRE CD 20**
**Cass:** Released May '89, on Deja Vu Catalogue no: **DVRE MC 20**

**EDDIE CONDON, GEORGE WETTING (Various artists)**
**CD:** Released Mar '90, on Giants of Jazz by Hasmick Promotions. Catalogue no: **GOJCD53041**

**GOLDEN ERA OF DIXIELAND (Various artists)**
**Album:** Released Feb '90, on Storyville by Storyville Records AB. Catalogue no: **SLP 805**

**HOLIDAY IN DIXIELAND (Various artists)**
**Album:** Released Mar '90, on Intersound Catalogue no: **ISST116**

## Dixieland Sound

**AT THE JAZZBAND BALL**
**Album:** Released Feb '86, on Fantasy Inc (USA) by Fantasy Inc (USA). Catalogue no: **1902124**

## Dixon, Bill

**LIVE IN NEW MORNING-LEGENDARY (Dixon, Bill Trio)**
**2 LP Set:** Released Oct '88, on Leo by Leo Records. Catalogue no: **LR 412/13**

## Dixon, Floyd

**EMPTY STOCKING BLUES**
Tracks: / Doin' the town / You need me now / Milky white way / Walkin' and talkin' blues / I saw stars / Married woman / Don't cry now baby / Precious Lord / Empty stocking blues / She's understanding / Time and place / Red cherries / I'm so worried / San Francisco blues / Hard living alone / Do I love you.
**Album:** Released Aug '85, on Route 66 (Sweden) Catalogue no: **KIX 27**

**HOUSTON JUMP**
Tracks: / Houston jump / Red head 'n' Cadillac / Mississippi blues / Girl fifteen / Sad journey / Tired broke and busted / It's getting foggy / Pleasure days / River, The / Rockin' at home / Come back baby / Roll baby roll / Is it true / Alarm clock blues / I'm ashamed of myself / Tight skirts.
**Album:** Released Jun '80, on Route 66 (Sweden) Catalogue no: **KIX 11**

**OPPORTUNITY BLUES**
Tracks: / Dallas blues / Shuffle boogie / Prairie dog hole / Broken hearted / Lovin' / Let's dance / Bad neighbourhood / Blues for Cuba / Real lovin' mama / Telephone blues / Too much jelly roll / Baby lets go down to the woods / Wine wine wine / Moonshine / Ooh little girl / Opportunity blues.
**Album:** Released Jun '80, on Route 66 (Sweden) Catalogue no: **KIX 1**

## Dixon, Willie

**Biographical details:** Bassist; also guitarist, vocalist and songwriter; born in 1915 in Mississippi: as house bassist, composer and talent scout at Chicago record labels in the '50's he was one of the most important figures in the golden age of Chicago blues. He first moved to Chicago in the late '20's; he was a boxer and a good one, but turned to pro music in 1937. He worked for Chess 1952-6 other Chicago labels 1956-60, played on and otherwise contributed to hits by Muddy Waters, Bo Diddley, Howlin' Wolf, Otis Rush and many others: he wrote *Hoochie coochie man, I just want to make love to you, Little red rooster, Wang dang doodle, Seventh son* and scores more. *Willie's blues* with Memphis Slim was made for Prestige Bluesville in 1959. (Donald Clarke, April 1989).

**COLLECTION: WILLIE DIXON (20 blues greats)**
Tracks: / Little red rooster / Built for comfort / Wang dang doodle / Ain't superstitious / Evil / Walking the blues / Fiery love / Alone / Mannish boy / All aboard / Rock me / I love the life I live / Sugar sweet / Thunderbird / One more / Teenage beat / Snake dancer / Temperature / Rock bottom / Black angel blues.
**Cass:** Released Jan '87, on Deja Vu Catalogue no: **DVMC 2092**
**Album:** Released Jan '87, on Deja Vu Catalogue no: **DVLP 2092**

**GINGER ALE AFTERNOON**
**Cass:** Released 2 Oct '89, on Colosseum (West Germany) Catalogue no: **VSC 5234**
**CD:** Released 2 Oct '89, on Colosseum (West Germany) Catalogue no: **VSCD 5234**
**Album:** Released 2 Oct '89, on Colosseum (West Germany) Catalogue no: **VS 5234**

**I AM THE BLUES**
**CD:** on Mobile Fidelity Sound Lab(USA) by Mobile Fidelity Records (USA). Catalogue no: **MFCD 872**

**WILLIE'S BLUES (Dixon, Willie & Memphis Slim)**
Tracks: / Nervous / Good understanding / That's my baby / Slim's thing / That's all I want baby / Don't you tell nobody / Youth to you / Sittin' and cryin' the blues / Bluit for comfort / I got a razor / Go easy / Move me.
**Album:** Released May '84, on Original Blues Classics (USA) by Fantasy Inc (USA). Catalogue no: **OBC 501**

## Dizrhythmia

**DIZRHYTHMIA**
Tracks: / Dizrhythmia / Standing in the rain / It will only end in tears / Walking on the cracks / 8000 miles / What Katy did next / Grown man, A.
Note: West / East collaboration featuring The Lodge's guitarist Jakko together with drummer Gavin Harrison, bassist Danny Thompson & the Indian percussionist Pandit Dinesh.
**CD:** Released Jul '88, on Antilles/New Directions by Island Records. Catalogue no: **ANCD 8727**
**Album:** Released Jul '88, on Antilles/New Directions by Island Records. Catalogue no: **AN 8727**
**Cass:** Released Jul '88, on Antilles/New Directions by Island Records. Catalogue no: **ANC 8727**

**IT WILL ONLY END IN TEARS**
Tracks: / It will only end in tears / Dizrhythmia.
**7" Single:** Released Jun '88, on Antilles/New Directions by Island Records. Catalogue no: **ANN 6**

## Docker, Bob

**QUINTETTE DU HOT CLUB**
Tracks: / What this thing called love / Djangology / I'm confessin' / What kind of a friend / Anouman / Sweet Georgia Brown / Baby won't you please come home / Manoir de mes reeves / I saw stars / Finesse.
**Album:** Released Jan '88, on Spotlite by Spotlite Records. Catalogue no: **SPJ 534**

## Doctor Dixie Jazz Band

**BEST OF DOCTOR DIXIE JAZZ BAND**
**CD:** Released 16 Jan '88, on Timeless (Import) by Timeless Records. Catalogue no: **CDTTD 521**

## Doctor John

**BRIGHTEST SMILE IN TOWN, THE**
Tracks: / Saddled the cow / Boxcar boogie / Brightest smile in town / Waiting for a train / Monkey puzzle / Average kind of guy / Pretty Libby / Marie Le Veau / Come rain or come shine / Suite home New Orleans.
**Cass:** Released '87, on Demon by Demon Records. Catalogue no: **FIEND-CASS 9**
**Album:** Released Nov '83, on Demon by Demon Records. Catalogue no: **FIEND 9**

**CITY LIGHTS**
Tracks: / Dance the night away with you / Street side / Wild honey / Rain / Snake

eyes / Fire of love / Sonata / He's a hero / City lights.
**Album:** Released Jan '79, on Horizon by A&M Records. Deleted Jan '84. Catalogue no: **AMLJ 732**

**DOCTOR JOHN AND CHRIS BARBER (Live at the Marquee Club, London) (Doctor John & Chris Barber)**
Tracks: / Stack a lee / New Orleans memories / In the right place / You lie too much / Boogie woogie / Blues down in San Antone / Oh Eliza / Wicked shall cease, The / Panorama / When the saints go marching in.
**VHS:** Released '86, on Jettisoundz by Jettisoundz Records. Catalogue no: **JE 145**

**DOCTOR JOHN PLAYS MAC REBENNACK**
Tracks: / Dorothy / Mac's boogie / Memories of Professor Longhair / Nearness of you / Delicado / Honey dripper / Big Mac / New island midnight / Saints / Pinetop / Silent night (Available on CD only) / Dance a la negres (Available on CD only) / Wade in the water (Available on CD only).
Note: Recorded in August 1981. This album is the one that Dr. John said he had 'always wanted to make'. Unaccompanied piano in the New Orleans tradition and a typically gritty vocal performance on 'The nearness of you'. Licensed from Clean Cut Records of Baltimore.
**Cass:** Released '87, on Demon by Demon Records. Catalogue no: **FIEND-CASS 1**
**CD:** Released '88, on Clean Cuts (USA) by Clean Cuts Records (USA). Catalogue no: **CD 705**
**CD:** Released '88, on Demon by Demon Records. Catalogue no: **FIENDCD 1**
**Album:** Released Sep '82, on Demon by Demon Records. Catalogue no: **FIEND 1**

**GRIS GRIS**
Tracks: / Gris gris gumbo ya ya / Danse Kalinda ba doom / Mama roux / Danse fambeaux / Croker courtbullion / Jump sturdy / I walk on gilded splinters.
**Album:** Released Aug '87, on Alligator (Sonet) by Alligator Records (USA). Catalogue no: **AL 3904**
**Album:** on Atlantic by WEA Records. Catalogue no: **K 40168**

**GUMBO**
**Album:** Released Nov '87, on Alligator (Sonet) by Alligator Records (USA). Catalogue no: **AL 3901**

**HOLLYWOOD BE THY NAME**
**Album:** Released 2 Oct '89, on Beat Goes On by Andy's Records. Catalogue no: **BGOLP 62**
**CD:** Released 2 Oct '89, on Beat Goes On by Andy's Records. Catalogue no: **BGOCD 62**

**I BEEN HOODOOD**
Tracks: / Right place wrong time / Same old, same old / Qualified / Travelling mood / Such a night / I been hoodood / Cold, cold, cold / Quitters never win / What comes around (goes around) / (Everybody wanna get rich) rite away / R U 4 real / Can't get enuff / Destively bonnaroo.
**Album:** Released Apr '84, on Edsel by Demon Records. Catalogue no: **ED 128**

**IN A SENTIMENTAL MOOD**
**CD:** Released Apr '89, on Warner Bros. by WEA Records. Catalogue no: **K 9258892**
**Cass:** Released Apr '89, on Warner Bros. by WEA Records. Catalogue no: **K 9258894**
**Album:** Released Apr '89, on Warner Bros. by WEA Records. Catalogue no: **K 9258891**

**IN THE NIGHT**
Tracks: / Bald head / Bring your love / Did she mention my name / Go ahead / Grass is greener / I pulled the cover off you two lovers / In the night / Just like America / Tipitina / Zu zu man / Mean cheatin' woman / New Orleans / Shoo-rah / Time has come, The / One night late / Ear is on strike, The.
**Album:** Released Jan '85, on Topline by Charly Records. Catalogue no: **TOP 118**
**Cass:** Released Jan '85, on Topline by Charly Records. Catalogue no: **KTOP 118**

**IN THE RIGHT PLACE**
Tracks: / Right place wrong time / Same old same old / Just the same / Qualified / Travelling mood / Peace brother peace / Life / Such a night / Shoo fly marches on / I been hoodood / Cold cold cold.
**Album:** on Atlantic by WEA Records. Catalogue no: **K 50017**

**JETSET**
Tracks: / Jetset.
**7" Single:** Released Feb '84, on Beggars Banquet by Beggars Banquet Records. Deleted Feb '87. Catalogue no: **BEG 107**
**12" Single:** Released Feb '84, on Beggars Banquet by Beggars Banquet Records. Deleted Feb '87. Catalogue no: **BEG 107T**

**LOSER FOR YOU, BABY**
Tracks: / Time had come, The / Loser for you baby / Ear is on strike, The / Little closer to my home, A / I pulled the cover off you two lovers / New Orleans / Go ahead on / Just like a mirror / Bring your love / Bald head.
**Album:** Released Oct '82, on Fontana Import Catalogue no: **F 80023**
**Cass:** Released Oct '82, on Fontana Import Catalogue no: **MF 80023**
**Album:** Released Nov '88, on Thunderbolt by Magnum Music Group. Catalogue no: **THBL 066**
**CD:** Released Nov '88, on Thunderbolt by Magnum Music Group. Catalogue no: **CDTB 66**

**LOSER FOR YOU, BABY (FONTANA)**
Tracks: / Loser for you, baby / Go ahead on / Just like a mirror / Time had come, The.
**Cass:** Released Oct '82, on Fontana Import Catalogue no: **MF 80023**
**Album:** Released Oct '82, on Fontana Import Catalogue no: **F 80023**

**MACK REBENNACK/BRIGHTEST SMILE**
**Cass:** Released Feb '86, on Demon by Demon Records. Catalogue no: **FIEND-CASS 9**

**MAKIN' WHOOPEE**
Tracks: / Makin' whoopee / More than you know / In a sentimental mood.
**12" Single:** Released Jun '89, on Warner Bros. by WEA Records. Catalogue no: **W 2976T**
**7" Single:** Released Jun '89, on Warner Bros. by WEA Records. Catalogue no: **W 2976**

**NEARNESS OF YOU**
Tracks: / Nearness of you.
**7" Single:** Released Sep '82, on Demon by Demon Records. Catalogue no: **D 1015**

**NIGHT TRIPPER AT HIS BEST**
**Album:** Released Jul '88, on Bellaphon Catalogue no: **BID 8014**

**RIGHT PLACE, WRONG TIME**
Tracks: / Right place, wrong time.
**7" Single:** Released Jan '77, on Atlantic by WEA Records. Deleted '80. Catalogue no: **K 10877**

**SUCH A NIGHT. LIVE IN LONDON**
**Cass:** Released Jun '84, on Spindrift by Celtic Music. Catalogue no: **SPIC 107**
**Album:** Released Jun '84, on Spindrift by Celtic Music. Catalogue no: **SPIN 107**

**ULTIMATE DR JOHN**
**CD:** Released Jun '88, on Warner Super Savers (USA) Catalogue no: **WSP 27612**

**ZU ZU MAN**
Tracks: / Cat and mouse game / She just a square / Bald headed / In the night / Helping hand / Zu zu man / Mean cheatin' woman / Woman's the root of all evil / Trader John / Shoo-rah / Ti-pi-ti-na / One night late.
**CD:** Released May '89, on Thunderbolt by Thunderbolt Records. Catalogue no: **CDTB 069**
**Album:** Released May '89, on Thunderbolt by Thunderbolt Records. Catalogue no: **THBL 069**
**CD:** Released Apr '87, on Topline by Charly Records. Catalogue no: **TOP CD 504**

## Dodds, Baby

**JAZZ A LA CREOLE DONEWELL (Dodds, Baby Trio)**
**Album:** Released Jun '88, on GHB by Jazzology Records (USA). Catalogue no: **GHB 50**

## Dodds, Johnny

**Biographical details:** Clarinettist from New Orleans (1892-1940) who also played some alto sax. He demonstrated the classic New Orleans clarinet style on the first important jazz records ever made, by King Oliver in 1923, then with

Louis Armstrong's Hot Fives and Hot Sevens. He played on two dates with Jelly Roll Morton's Red Hot Peppers, and Oliver hired him specially for a solo on *Someday sweetheart* in 1926, with Oliver's Dixie Syncopators. He was playing in a quartet with his brother, drummer baby Dodds, in 1940. (Donald Clarke, April 1989)4.

**1926-28 (See panel below)**

Tracks: / Perdido street blues / Gatemouth / Too tight / Papa dip / Mixed salad / I can't say / Flatfoot / Mad dog / Ballin' the jack / Grandma's ball / My baby / Oriental man / Get 'em again blues / Brush stomp / My girl / Sweep 'em clean / Lady love / Brown bottom Bess.

Note: The jazzmen who survived the turbulent 1920's, forgotten 1930's and wartime 1940's have for most of their lives fairly well documented. Not so those who died in the 1930's and early 1940's. Johnny Dodds - probably the greatest clarinetist to come out of jazz - left little of his life behind other than the legacy of well over 200 recorded sides. The few facts which can be researched regarding Johnny Dodds' movements are usually rehashings of the Baby Dodds Story as told to Lary Gara, published in 1959 by Contemporary Press, (California USA) and a study of the King Oliver Band, 1921 to 1923. G.E. Lambert's *Johnny Dodds* (in Cassell's 1961 Kings of jazz series) offered nothing new historically although worth reading for some excellent observations about Dodd's contribution to music. Johnny Dodds was born on 12th April, 1892 but whether in Waverley, Mississippi or New Orleans, Louisiana, we have not established for certain. One of six children from a musical family he was encouraged by his father to take up clarinet and took lessons from the legendary Lorenzo Tio Senior and Charlie McCurdy (McCurdis)? While in his teens Dodds was playing semi-professionally and it is known that at this time he played with Frankie Dusen's Eagle Band. Full time fame came when the young John joined Kid Ory's band about 1911-12. It was while with Ory that Dodds came into close musical contact with King Joe Oliver. The association with Ory's band was to last intermittently until 1917-18 when Dodds toured with Billy and Mary Macks Merrymakers minstrel show, which also included Mutt Carey. What appears to have been regular engagements with Fate Marable's band on the riverboats 'S.S. Sidney Streckfus' and S.S. Capitol also occurred about this time and, apart from Johnny Dodds, included Louis Armstrong, Johnny St Cyr, Baby Dodds and Pops Foster. In 1920 Johnny Dodds returned to Chicago to replace Jimmy Noone in the King Oliver band which was playing nightly at both the Dreamland and the Pekin Cafe. A six month tour to California from June to December, 1921 followed and the band played regularly at the Pergola Dancing Pavilion in San Francisco's lower Market Street. Dodds was to make a permanent home in Chicago at this time apparantly jouneying once to New York in 1938 and never returning to New Orleans.

Johnny Dodd's period with the King Oliver Creole Jazz Band hasbeen well documented from the time of the successful, but eventful West Coast tour in 1921 to the band's break up in late 1924. We have yet to verify and publish the disenchantment over recording royalites which led to the resignation in late 1923 of half the band including the Dodds brothers and the subsequent union troubles which plagued Oliver in 1924, the resultant personnel changes and the 'myth' of the Lincoln Gardens fire late in December 1924 on the day a newly formed Oliver band was to open there. Following their resignation in 1923 Johnny and Baby Dodds formed a small group which held a permanent job at Burt Kelly's Stables until New Year's Day 1930 when the police closed it down for an alleged liquor violation. The 1930's were even leaner years for all including Johnny Dodds and although he managed to hold more or less regular engagements over this period, the once great clarinetist like many of his peers, was to become relatively unknown, except to a handful, during the emerging swing music boom. While Benny Goodman and other young white musicians rose to popular heights, legendary musicians like Dodds, Bechet, Morton, King Oliver and Jimmie Noone were forgotten relics of the 1920's jazz age. The full account of Dodd's activities during this period, so far as we can research it, has been given on the companion volume to this release - Johnny Dodds, SWAGGIE 808. The untimely death of Johnny Dodds on the morning of 8th August 1940, at the age of 48, left jazz music so much poorer and we can only speculate on the course of the jazz revival had he lived to recieve the adulation later given to Sidney Bechet, Barney Bigard and George Lewis. The mid 1920's are now regarded as the golden age of classic jazz, and rightly so, for during this brief 3 to 4 year period the greatest of jazz recordings were made. It is to Johnny Dodds' credit that almost 60 years later the sides including him as sideman and occasional leader are considered to be among the best from this era. The New Orleans Wanderers and Bootblacks recordings have for many years been accepted as among the greatest jazz records ever made. Organised by Columbia, apparently to cash in on the popularity of Louis Armstrong's Hot Five recordings, the Wanderers-Bootblack sessions were arranged by Louis Armstrong, with his name in large type on the label giving the impression that he was on the recordings. Louis, already broken his contractual agreement with Okeh when he recorded *Georgia Bo Bo* and *Drop that sack* in May 1926 for Vocalion, was reluctant to take part, so Lil composed the tunes, credited them to her husband and took the royalties. Lil Armstrong was leading the band at the Dreamland when the Wanderers-Bootblacks were made which included Mitchell, Louis Armstrong, Joe Walker, alto, Jimmy Strong, clarinet; Sudi Bernard, bass and Baby Dodds.

**Johnny Dodds - 1926 - 28 (Swaggie)**

For the recording session George Mitchell from Lil's band was used on cornet, Kid Ory, Johnny Dodds, Johnny St. Cyr and Lil Armstrong were from the regular Hot Five recording group and an unknown alto was included on all sides except *Perdido Street Blues*. The identity of the alto player has always been a mystery. Stomp Evans was for many years the usual candidate, to be replaced by Joe Walker, probably on the evidence of his alleged presence in Lil's Dreamland band. The name Joe Clark credited in our personnel listing is by courtesy of Brian Rust's *Jazz Records* in the confident knowledge that so diligent a researcher has finally unearthed irrefutable proof from Columbia's files or some other positive source. George Mitchell was born in Louisville, Kentucky on 8th March 1899, toured early in his career with the Rabbits Foot Minstrel Show and moved to Chicago in 1919. Over the next few years Mitchell toured constantly, returning to Chicago from to time to time to play with Carol Dickerson, Dock Cook, Jimmy Noone, Lil Armstrong and Earl Hines - but that is another story in itself. The sides featuring the Chicago Footwarmers represent the entire recorded output of this small group, generally thought to have been arranged by Jimmy Blythe, the pianist. We know very little about Jimmy Blythe in spite of many years of research. Like George Mitchell, he was born in Louisville, Kentucky about 1901. He died in Chicago on 21st June, 1931. Blythe's recorded output was enormous and covered most of the major studios, and included such greats as Ma Rainey, Louis Armstrong, and Freddy Keppard, yet he appears to have had little impact on the memories of the musicians who played with him. As Baby Dodds recalled in Larry Gara's *The Baby Dodds story*, Blythe was a very quiet fellow, not the boisterous type at all. In appearance he was dark and short. And everything he did was always to the best of his ability. The 18 tracks on this album (like the companion *Johnny Dodds* release on SWAGGIE 808) have been re-issued before but have since been deleted and it is our pleasure to release remastered versions of these classic recordings. (Bill Haesler, December 1981)

**Album:** Released Jan '83, on Swaggie (Australia) Catalogue no: **S 807**

**1927 (Dodds, Johnny with his Trio)**
Tracks: / Weary blues / New Orleans stomp / Wild man blues / Melancholy / Come on & stomp, stomp, stomp / After you've gone / Joe Turner blues / When Erastus plays his old kazoo / Oh Lizzie / Clarinet wobble / New St Louis blues.
**Album:** Released Jan '83, on Swaggie (Australia) Catalogue no: **S 808**

**BLUE CLARINET STOMP 1926-1928**
Tracks: / Weary blues / New Orleans Stomp / Wild man blues / Melancholy / Come on & stomp, stomp, stomp / After you've gone / Joe Turner blues / When Erastus plays his old kazoo / Blue clarinet stomp / Blue piano stomp / Bucktown stomp / Weary city / Bull fiddle blues / Blue washboard stomp / Sweet Lorraine / Pencil papa / My little Isabel-A / Heah' me talking / Goober dance / Too tight-A.
Note: Johnny Dodds' Black Bottom Stompers, Trio, Washboard Band & Orchestra
**Album:** Released Mar '87, on VJM (Vintage Jazz Music) by Vintage Jazz Music Society(VJM). Catalogue no: **VLP 61**

**IMMORTAL, THE**
**Album:** Released Mar '83, on VJM (Vintage Jazz Music) by Vintage Jazz Music Society(VJM). Catalogue no: **VLP 48**

**JOHNNY DODDS 1928-9**
**Album:** Released Apr '88, on Swaggie (Australia) Catalogue no: **S 848**

**JOHNNY DODDS VOL 1**
**Album:** Released Dec '86, on Classic Jazz Masters Catalogue no: **CJM 32**

**MYTH OF NEW ORLEANS, THE**
Note: Featuring Kid Ory, Charlie Shavers.
**Album:** Released Sep '87, on Giants of Jazz by Hasmick Promotions. Catalogue no: **LPJT 47**

**STOMP TIME**
Tracks: / Bohunkus blues / Buddy Burton's jazz / East Coast trot / Chicago buzz / Apeman / Your folks / Steal away / Salty dog / Stomp time blues / It must be the blues / Loveless love / 119th Street blues / There'll come a day / Weary way blues / Oriental man / Sock that thing.
Note: The legendary clarinettist is accompanied by such outfits as Blythe's Washboard Band, Junie Cobb's Home Town Band, Paramount Pickers, Jasper Taylor & His State Street Boys.
**Album:** Released Apr '83, on Rhapsody by President Records. Catalogue no: **RHA 6024**

## Doggett, Bill

**Biographical details:** Pianist, organist and arranger born in 1916 in Philadelphia; he worked for Lucky Millinder, the Ink Spots, Lionel Hampton, Count Basie and others, and played on many records; with an R&B combo he had a huge classic hit with *Honky tonk* in 1956, with Clifford Scott on tenor sax, guitar by Billy Butler linking choruses, and Doggett playing a boogie woogie-like slow shuffle on the organ: it was in the top ten in the USA for 14 weeks, rising to number 2; number one in the R&B chart. Seven Hot 100 hits until 1960 included *Slow walk* (Sil Austin also had an R&B hit). He arranged and conducted the album *Rhythm is our business* for Ella Fitzgerald on Verve in 1963. (Donald Clarke, April 1989).

**14 ORIGINAL GREATEST HITS : BILL DOGGETT**
**Album:** Released Mar '88, on King (USA) Catalogue no: **K 5009**

**16 BANDSTAND FAVOURITES**
**Album:** Released Apr '87, on Starday (USA) by Gusto Records (USA). Catalogue no: **SLP 3023**
**Cass:** Released Apr '87, on Starday (USA) by Gusto Records (USA). Catalogue no: **GT 53023**

**AS YOU DESIRE ME**
Tracks: / I hadn't anyone till you / Yesterdays / Alone / As time goes by / Dedicated to you / Sweet and lovely / Cottage for sale / As you desire me / Dream / Don't blame me / This love of mine / Fools rush in.
**Album:** Released '88, on Sing Catalogue no: **SING 523**
**CD:** Released Mar '90, on King Catalogue no: **KCD 523**

**BILL DOGGETT**
**Album:** Released Jul '88, on Bellaphon Catalogue no: **BID 8009**

**DAME DREAMING**
Tracks: / Sweet Lorraine / Diane / Dinah / Kamona / Cherry / Cynthia / Jeannine / Tangerine / Nancy / Estrellita / Laura / Marcheta.
**Album:** Released '88, on Sing Catalogue no: **SING 532**

**DANCE A WHILE**
Tracks: / Flying home / Misty moon / Bone tones / Tailor made / Chelsea bridge / Kid from Franklin Street, The / Pied piper of Islip / Passion flower / Song is ended, The / Autumn leaves / How could you? / Smoochie.
**CD:** Released Mar '90, on King Catalogue no: **KCD 585**
**Album:** Released Jul '88, on Sing Catalogue no: **SING 585**

**DOGGETT BEAT FOR HAPPY FEAT, THE**
Tracks: / Soft / And the angels sing / Ding dong / Honey / Easy / Hammer head / Ram-bunk-shush / Chloe / Hot ginger / King Bee / What a diff'rence a day made / Shinding.
**Album:** Released '88, on Sing Catalogue no: **SING 557**
**CD:** Released Mar '90, on King Catalogue no: **KCD 557**

**GOIN' DOGGETT**
Tracks: / Honky tonk (part 1) / Honky tonk (part 2) / Big boy / Slidin' / Buttered popcorn / Backwoods / Slow walk / Quaker city / Night train / Ram-bunk-shush / Peacock alley / Hold it / Rainbow riot.
Note: A contemporary of Earl Bostic, keyboard playing Bill Doggett also had a substantial career before he joined King in the early fifties. Most noteably he had been pianist/arranger with Lucky Millinder's orchestra (in fact he formed the original band and then gave control to Millinder) and pianist/organist with Louis Jordan & The Tympany Five. Along with Wild Bill Davis he was a pioneer in the 'legitimizing' of the Hammond organ as a recognised jazz/R & B instrument. Like Bostic he recorded prolifically for King and in several musical styles, but none more successful than his small

combo R&B sessions, as typified by the smash hit 'Honky Tonk' (both parts included here). The album contains many similarly rhythmic R & B instrumentals such as Ram-bunk-shush, Hold it, Slow walk, Rainbow riot, etc, featuring tenor sax work by Clifford Scott & Ray Felder and other notable accompanists such as guitarists Bill Jennings & Billy Butler, bassists Carl Pruitt & Edwyn Conley and drummers Shep Shepherd & Calvin Shields. Solid, infectious R & B all the way.
**Cass:** Released Jul '85, on Charly R&B by Charly Records. Catalogue no: **TCCRB 1094**
**Album:** Released Jul '85, on Charly R&B by Charly Records. Catalogue no: **CRB 1094**

**MANY MOODS OF, THE**
**CD:** Released Mar '90, on King Catalogue no: **KCD 778**

**MR. HONKY TONK**
Note: Mono.
**Album:** Released Nov '85, on Black & Blue (2) by BMG Records (UK). Catalogue no: **33562**

## Doherty, Jim

**SPONDANCE (Jazz Ballet, A) (Doherty, Jim with Louis Stewart & Bob Sheppard)**
**Cass:** Released Jun '88, on Livia Catalogue no: **LRCS 10**

## Dolphy, Eric

**Biographical details:** The alto saxist, clarinettist, bass clarinettist, flautist and composer led one of the great unfinished careers in the history of music, and may ultimately be more influential than John Coltrane. Born in Los Angeles in 1928, he died of the complications of diabetes in Berlin, Germany in 1964. He was a member of the Chico Hamilton quintet 1958-59; In New York in 1960 he joined a Charles Mingus quartet with Ted Curson and Danny Richmond for an astonishing album on Candid and led his own quintet at the Five Spot with Booker Little, Mal Waldron, Ed Blackwell and Richard Davis in 1961. He played with Coltrane in 1961, led a group with Freddie Hubbard in 1962 and went to Europe with Mingus in 1964. He had a need to express himself spiritually that extended the frontiers of the music. Dolphy was inspired by Bird calls, marching bands, etc. as well as by deeper mysteries, and the hard-won and distinctive tonal beauty in his playing remained a hallmark. Every scrap that Dolphy recorded is being issued, and every one of them is priceless. (Donald Clarke, April 1989).

**ARTISTRY IN JAZZ (Greatest hits)**
**CD:** Released May '87, on JVC/Fantasy Catalogue no: **VDJ 1594**

**AT THE FIVE SPOT VOL 1**
**CD:** Released Apr '86, on JVC/Fantasy Catalogue no: **VDJ 1504**

**AT THE FIVE SPOT VOL 2**
**CD:** Released Apr '86, on JVC/Fantasy Catalogue no: **VDJ 1525**

**BERLIN CONCERTS**
**Album:** Released Jul '88, on Enja (Germany) by Enja Records (West Germany). Catalogue no: **ENJA 3007 9**

**CANDID DOLPHY**
**CD:** Released Mar '90, on Candid Catalogue no: **CCD79033**
**Album:** Released Mar '90, on Candid Catalogue no: **CS9033**

**COLLECTION: ERIC DOLPHY**
Tracks: / Prophet, The / Like someone in love / Booker's waltz / Bee vamp / Fire waltz.
**Cass:** Released Aug '86, on Deja Vu Catalogue no: **DVMC 2077**

**ERIC DOLPHY QUARTET (1961)**
Note: With L.Schifrin / B.Cunningham / M.Lewis) (Dolphy, Eric Quartet
**Album:** Released Jun '81, on Jazz Connoisseur by Spotlite Records. Catalogue no: **JC 107**

**ERIC DOLPHY AND THE CHAMPS ELYSEES ALL STARS (Dolphy, Eric & The Champs Elysees All Stars)**
Tracks: / Springtime / GW / 245 / Serene.
**Album:** Released Dec '88, on West Wind Catalogue no: **WW 016**
**CD:** Released Dec '88, on West Wind Catalogue no: **WWCD 016**

**ESSENTIAL, THE**
**CD:** Released Apr '87, on Fantasy (import) by Fantasy Inc (USA). Deleted '88. Catalogue no: **FCD 60022**

**FAR CRY**
**CD:** Released Jan '89, on JVC/Fantasy Catalogue no: **VDJ 1613**

**FIRE WALTZ**
Tracks: / Lautir / Curtsy / Geo's tune / They all laughed / Head shakin' / Dianna / Warm canto / Warp and woof / Fire waltz / Duquility / Thirteen / We diddit / Status seeking.
**2 LP Set:** Released '79, on Prestige Deleted '84. Catalogue no: **PR 24085**

**LIVE AT GASLIGHT INN (Dolphy, Eric Quintet)**
**Album:** Released Jul '82, on Ingo Catalogue no: **INGO 14**

**LIVE AT THE FIVE SPOT II**
**Album:** Released Jan '87, on Original Jazz Classics (USA) by Fantasy Inc (USA). Catalogue no: **OJC 247**

**MUSIC MATADOR**
Tracks: / Jitterbug waltz / Music matador / Alone together / Love me.
**Album:** Released Jan '81, on Affinity by Charly Records. Catalogue no: **AFF 47**

**OTHER ASPECTS**
Tracks: / Jim Crow / Inner flight 1 / Dolphy'n / Inner flight 2 / Improvisations and tukras.
Note: Blue Note announce the discovery and release of a variety of tapes from the private libary of the late, great Eric Dolphy. These recordings have been carefully remixed to digital tape for the best possible sound reproduction. This extraordinary find actually reveals three sides of the amazing reedman and composer. Jim Crow, with a classical ensemble, shows Dolphy's previously unrecorded talents as a classical player and composer. *Improvisations and Tukras* is an authentic excursion into the music of India. His two unaccompanied flute solos, Inner Flight 1 & 2, and his duet with bassist Ron Carter, *Dolphy'n*, are masterful jazz improvisations. These diverse and exciting discoveries add a wealth to the legacy of an under-recorded genius who died all too young.
**CD:** Released Aug '89, on Blue Note by EMI Records. Deleted Jan '90. Catalogue no: **CDP 748 041 2**
**Album:** Released Mar '87, on Blue Note by EMI Records. Deleted Nov '88. Catalogue no: **BT 85131**
**CD:** Released Aug '89, on Blue Note by EMI Records. Deleted Jan '90. Catalogue no: **BNZ 182**

**OUT TO LUNCH**
Tracks: / Hat and bread / Something sweet, something tender / Gazzellioni / Out to lunch / Straight up and down.
**CD:** Released May '87, on Blue Note by EMI Records. Deleted Aug '89. Catalogue no: **BNZ 23**
**Album:** Released Nov '85, on Blue Note by EMI Records. Deleted Nov '88. Catalogue no: **BST 84163**
**Album:** Released '79, on Blue Note by EMI Records. Deleted '84. Catalogue no: **BNS 40017**
**CD:** Released May '87, on Blue Note by EMI Records. Deleted Aug '89. Catalogue no: **CDP 746 524 2**
**Cass:** Released Sep '87, on Blue Note by EMI Records. Deleted Aug '89. Catalogue no: **4BN 84163**

**QUINTET U.S.A.**
Tracks: / Miss Ann / Left alone / G.W. / 2.45.
**Album:** Released Apr '81, on Unique Jazz by Spotlite Records. Catalogue no: **UJ 10**

**STATUS**
Tracks: / Status seeking / God bless the child / Miss Ann / Laura / Way you look tonight, The / Don't blame me / Don't blame me (take 2) / April fool.
**Album:** Released '79, on Prestige Deleted '84. Catalogue no: **PR 24070**

**STOCKHOLM SESSIONS**
**Album:** Released Jan '82, on Enja (Germany) by Enja Records (West Germany). Catalogue no: **ENJA 3055**

**THREE DOLPHY GROUPS**
**Album:** Released Nov '86, on Unique Jazz by Spotlite Records. Catalogue no: **UJ 26**

**UNREALISED TAPES**
**CD:** Released Oct '88, on West Wind Catalogue no: **WWCD 016**

**VINTAGE DOLPHY**
**CD:** on Enja (Germany) by Enja Records (West Germany). Catalogue no: **ENJA 5045-24**
**Album:** Released Jan '88, on Enja (Germany) by Enja Records (West Germany). Catalogue no: **ENJA 5045**

**Fats Domino**

## Domino, Fats

**Biographical details:** This American singer, pianist and songwriter, born in New Orleans into a small family of nine children, became interested in the piano as a child. While a teenager, he suffered a factory injury which restricted the use of some of his fingers. After much perseverance, he regained full control of his wounded hand, and, at the age of 17, he played with Billy Diamond's band at the local Hideaway Club. It was Diamond who bestowed the nickname Fats upon young Antoine Domino; with the latter's 16 stone weght showing no sign of diminishing, the monicker stuck with him for his entire career. In the late Forties, when Fats Domino was just entering his twenties, the young pianist met another local bandleader named Dave Bartholemew. The two became inseparable musical colleagues and Bartholemew served as his long-term co-writer, bandleader and trumpeter.

Fats Domino's first recording session took place in December 1949. It yielded his first smash hit, aptly titled *The Fat Man*. During the Fifties, he became a key figure in rhythm and blues music, thanks to his influential boogie-woogie piano style, his appealing voice (which somehow managed to combine the smoothness of a ballad singer with a hint of Louis Armstrong-style gruffness) and his band's infectiously rolling rhythms. He was not only an R&B great but also a rock 'n' roll pioneer, helping to lay the groundwork for the mid-Fifties rock revolution.

Domino's sales statistics were phenomenal. Of the singles that he released between 1949 and 1960, 23 became million sellers; 17 of those were written by the Domino/Bartholemew partnership. His first major success on the US pop charts - i.e. his first record to cross over from the black to the white audience - was 1955's *Ain't That A Shame*, which reached No 10; but it was beaten to the top by a watered down No 1 cover version from the ultra-wholesome white singer Pat Boone. Nevertheless, *Ain't That A Shame* established Domino in the pop market, and the hits flowed endlessly until the early Sixties. His American Top 10 pop hits included *I'm In Love Again* (1956), *Blue Monday* (from one of his several rock 'n' roll movie appearances, "The Girl Can't Help It"), *I'm Walkin'* and *Valley Of Tears* (1957), *Whole Lotta Loving*, *I Want To Walk You Home* and *Be My Guest* (1959) and *Walking To New Orleans* (1960).

The biggest success of Domino's career was one of his few non-original hits. His 1957 smash hit *Blueberry Hill* - a song originally associated with Gene Autry in 1941 - took him to No 2 in the US; this strolling, reflective rendition of the song remains one of the greatest classics of the Fifties. In Britain, *Blueberry Hill* reached No 6, thus becoming his only UK Top Tenner; however, he chalked up 18 subsequent British hits, all of which fell short of the Top 10.

Estimates of Domino's worldwide sales figures vary between 60 million and 70 million records. The respect that he has always commanded in the rock and pop world is such that one star - Chubby Checker - was even stage named after him. On both sides of the Atlantic, Domino's final Top 40 hit was *Red Sails In The Sunset* in late 1963. His recording career went down hill, although he remained an active live performer, as shown by his long overdue UK concert debut in 1967. He never really returned to the limelight. The Seventies and eighties saw him performing a less hectic schedule of concert, cabaret and film work, plus a rare return to the recording studio with 1979's critically acclaimed album *Sleeping On The Job*. (Bob MacDonald, 24 June 1985.)

R&B singer, pianist and bandleader, born in New Orleans in 1928; one of the earliest and most popular of the '50's rock'n'rollers: 36 USA top 40 hits in eight years; 66 altogether in the Hot 100. His first language was French; discovered as a teenager by Dave Bartholomew, his first recording session in 1949 included the traditional *Hey la bas*, indicating the coming together of many decades of New Orleans history and musical influences *La bas* was originally a voodoo god of luck, then identified in French/Catholic Louisiana with St Peter, finally became an R&B standard. Domino's first release was a cleaned-up drug song called *The fat man* for an R&Bhit in 1950; his fifth release *Every night about this time* used the piano triplet for which he became famous, showing the influence of Little Willie Littlefield. Fats became a crossover act in 1955 with *Ain't that a shame*: Pat Boone covered it for a number one pop hit, but Fat's own record made the top ten and days of the white cover/rip off were numbered. *Blue Monday* in 1957 was featured in the film *The girl can't help it* probably the best rock'n'roll movie ever made; *I'm walkin'* was covered by teenage TV star Ricky Nelson the same year and was the beginning of his career in music. Most hits were Domino-Bartholomew compositions, though standards included *Blueberry Hill, What's the reason I'm not pleasin' you, Red sails in the sunset*, Hank Williams *Jambalaya* and the Beatles *Lady Madonna*. His smoky, blues tinged voice with a trace of French accent was instantly likeable; the party-music formula perfectly captured the innocent pleasure of early pop-rock with riffing saxes, rocking tenor solo (often by Lee Allen or Herb Hardesty) and the rolling New Orleans style piano; the band rocked hard but made it sound easy. Domino is still a huge draw whenever he chooses to tour. (Donald Clarke, April 1989).

### 16 GREATEST HITS: FATS DOMINO

Tracks: / Blueberry Hill / I'm in love again / Ain't that a shame / I'm walking / Blue Monday / Whole lotta loving / I want to walk you home / I'm ready / My blue Heaven / I'm gonna be a wheel someday / Jambalaya / So long / When the saints go marching in / Heartbreak Hill / Kansas

City / Walking to New Orleans.
**CD:** Released May '87, on Bescol Catalogue no: **CD 32**

### 20 GREATEST HITS: FATS DOMINO
**Cass:** Released Dec '88, on Masters (Holland) Catalogue no: **MAMC 9251185**
**CD:** Released Oct '88, on Fun (Holland) Catalogue no: **FUNCD 9011**
**Album:** Released '88, on Masters (Holland) Catalogue no: **MA 251185**
**Cass:** Released Oct '88, on Fun (Holland) Catalogue no: **FUNC 9011**
**Album:** Released Oct '88, on Fun (Holland) Catalogue no: **FUN 9011**

### 20 ROCK'N'ROLL HITS: FATS DOMINO
**Album:** Released Jan '83, on EMI (Germany) by EMI Records. Catalogue no: **IC 064 82750**

### 24 GREATEST HITS: FATS DOMINO
**CD:** Released '88, on Silver Line Catalogue no: **SLCD 804**

### AIN'T THAT A SHAME?
Tracks: / Ain't that a shame / Fat man.
**7" Single:** Released Jan '57, on London-American Deleted '60. Catalogue no: **HLU 8173**
**7" Single:** Released May '84, on EMI Golden 45's by EMI Records. Catalogue no: **G45 17**

### BACK TO BACK (Domino, Fats / Chuck Berry)
Tracks: / Reelin' and rockin' / School days / My ding a ling / Too much monkey business / Memphis Tennessee / Maybelline / Nadine / Fat man / Blueberry hill / Oh, what a price / Domino twist / Let the four winds blow / I'm in the mood for love / Please don't leave me / I'm ready / I'm in love again / Be my guest.
**CD:** on Magnum Force by Magnum Music Group. Catalogue no: **CDMFD 001**

### BE MY GUEST
Tracks: / Blueberry Hill / Whole lotta lovin' / I'm in love again / Blue Monday / I want to walk you home / Ain't that a shame / Be my guest / My girl Josephine / Let the four winds blow / I'm ready.
**Cass:** Released May '86, on Bulldog Records by President Records. Catalogue no: **BCD 1059**
**Album:** Released May '86, on Bulldog Records by President Records. Catalogue no: **BDL 1059**

### BE MY GUEST (SINGLE)
Tracks: / Be my guest.
**7" Single:** Released Dec '59, on London-American Deleted '62. Catalogue no: **HLP 9005**

### BEST OF FATS DOMINO
Tracks: / Blueberry Hill / Whole lotta lovin' / Fat man / Blue Monday / I'm walking / I'm in love again / Be my guest / When my dreamboat comes home / Let the four winds blow / I'm gonna be a wheel someday / Walking to New Orleans / Ain't that a shame / I want to walk you home / My blue Heaven / Valley of tears.
**CD:** Released Apr '88, on MFP by EMI Records. Catalogue no: **CDP 746 581 2**
**CD:** Released Apr '88, on MFP by EMI Records. Catalogue no: **CDMFP 6026**
**Album:** Released Dec '85, on Liberty by EMI Records. Catalogue no: **EG 2607621**

### BEST OF FATS DOMINO (2)
**CD:** Released Jul '88, on EMI by EMI Records. Catalogue no: **CDP 790 294 2**
**CD:** Released Jul '88, on EMI by EMI Records. Catalogue no: **CZ 111**

### BEST OF FATS DOMINO (LIBERTY)
Tracks: / Blueberry Hill / Ain't that a shame / Please don't leave me / Blue Monday / Fat man / I'm in love again / I'm walking / I'm ready / I'm gonna be a wheel someday / I want to walk you home / Whole lotta lovin' / Be my guest / My girl Josephine / Walkin' to New Orleans / Let the four winds blow / Jambalaya.
**Cass:** Released Oct '85, on Liberty by EMI Records. Catalogue no: **EG 2607624**
**Album:** Released Oct '85, on Liberty by EMI Records. Catalogue no: **EG 2607621**

### BEST OF THE FAT MAN
**Cass:** Released Jun '89, on Spectrum (CD) by M.S.D.. Catalogue no: **U3016-2**
**CD:** Released Jun '89, on Spectrum (CD) by M.S.D.. Catalogue no: **K3016-2**

### BIG BEAT, THE
Tracks: / Big beat, The.
**7" Single:** Released Mar '58, on London-American Deleted '61. Catalogue no: **HLP 8575**

### BLUE MONDAY
Tracks: / Blue monday.
**7" Single:** Released Mar '57, on London-American Deleted '60. Catalogue no: **HLP 8377**

### BLUEBERRY HILL (ALBUM)
Tracks: / Blue Monday / Whole lotta lovin' / Red sails in the sunset / I'm ready / Jambalaya / Blueberry Hill / Yes it's me, and I'm in love again / Ain't that a shame / I'm in the mood for love / I want to walk you home.
**Cass:** Released '84, on Premier by Premier Records. Catalogue no: **KCBR 1003**
**Album:** Released '84, on Premier by Premier Records. Catalogue no: **CBR 1003**
**Cass:** Released May '88, on Black Tulip Catalogue no: **2136012**
**CD:** Released May '88, on Black Tulip Catalogue no: **2436012**
**Album:** Released May '88, on Black Tulip Catalogue no: **2236012**

### BLUEBERRY HILL (PICTURE DISC)
**LP Pic:** Released May '88, on Picture Disc Catalogue no: **PD 50001**

### BLUEBERRY HILL (SINGLE)
Tracks: / Blueberry Hill.
**7" Single:** Released Nov '56, on London-American Catalogue no: **HLU 8330**
**7" Single:** Released Apr '76, on United Artists by EMI Records. Deleted '79. Catalogue no: **UP 35797**
**7" Single:** Released Sep '79, on United Artists by EMI Records. Catalogue no: **UP 36524**
**7" Single:** Released Apr '83, on EMI (Europe) by EMI Records. Catalogue no: **2C 008 83272**
**7" Single:** Released Jun '84, on SMP (2) Catalogue no: **SKM 06**

### BLUEBERRY HILL (PICKWICK CD)
**CD:** Released '88, on Pickwick by Pickwick Records. Catalogue no: **PWK 021**

### BLUEBERRY HITS
**Cass:** Released Dec '88, on Capitol (Specials) Catalogue no: **4XLL 8347**

### BOOGIE WOOGIE BABY
Tracks: / Rockin' chair / Sometimes I wonder / Nobody loves me / Dreaming / Careless love / I've got eyes for you / Right from wrong / No no baby / My baby's gone / Boogie woogie baby / How long / Rose Mary / Fats Domino blues / What's the matter baby / Stay away / 9th ward blues / Hey la bas boogie.
**Album:** Released Sep '85, on Ace by Ace Records. Catalogue no: **CHD 140**

### COLLECTION : FATS DOMINO
**CD:** Released '88, on Spectrum (CD) by M.S.D.. Catalogue no: **SPEC 85015**

### COUNTRY BOY
Tracks: / Country boy.
**7" Single:** Released Mar '60, on London-American Deleted '63. Catalogue no: **HLP 9073**

### EASYRIDING: FATS DOMINO
Tracks: / Intro. / Blueberry Hill / Jambalaya / Oh, what a price / Domino twist / Let the four winds blow / Whole lotta loving / Blue Monday / I'm walking / Walking to New Orleans / I'm gonna be a wheel someday / I'm in the mood for love / Please don't leave me / Ain't that a shame / So long / My blue Heaven / I want to walk you home / When the saints go marching in.
**Cass:** Released Jul '88, on Knight by Knight Records Ltd.. Catalogue no: **KNMC 11006**
**Album:** Released Jul '88, on Knight by Knight Records Ltd.. Catalogue no: **KNLP 11006**

### FABULOUS MR D, THE
**Album:** Released Jan '83, on Imperial by K-Tel Records. Catalogue no: **2C 068 83296**

### FAT MAN LIVE, THE
Tracks: / Fat man / Blueberry hill / Oh, What a price / Domino twist / Let the four winds blow / I'm in the mood for love / Please don't leave me / I'm ready / I'm in love again / Be my guest.
**Album:** Released Mar '86, on Magnum Force by Magnum Music Group. Catalogue no: **MFM 023**

### FAT MAN, THE
Tracks: / I'm gonna be a wheel someday / I want to walk you home / Whole lotta

loving / Fat man / Blueberry Hill / Please don't leave me / Blue Monday / Jambalaya / I'm in love again / Be my guest / Red sails in the sunset / Going home.
**Album:** Released Nov '84, on Topline by Charly Records. Catalogue no: **TOP 110**
**Cass:** Released Nov '84, on Topline by Charly Records. Catalogue no: **KTOP 110**

**FATS DOMINO**
Tracks: / Introduction / Blueberry Hill / Please don't leave me / Domino twist / Let the four winds blow / Whole lotta loving / Blue Monday / You win again / I'm walking / I'm gonna be a wheel someday / I'm in the mood for love / Jambalaya / O what a price / Ain't that a shame / So long / When the saints go marching in / Deep in the heart of Texas.
**Cass:** Released Jul '85, on Mercury (Holland) Catalogue no: **824 318-4**
**Album:** Released Jul '85, on Mercury (Holland) Catalogue no: **824 318-1**
**Cass:** Released Oct '84, on Audio Fidelity(USA) by Audio Fidelity (USA). Catalogue no: **ZCGAS 727**
**Album:** Released '88, on Joker (USA) by Lifetime Records (USA). Catalogue no: **SM 3897 2**

**FATS DOMINO (MFP)**
Tracks: / Be my guest / Margie / Ain't that a shame / I hear you knocking / When my dreamboat comes home / All by myself / Honey chile / Jambalaya / I'm in love again / What a party / Blueberry hill / I've been around / My blue heaven / My girl Josephine / Natural born lover.
**Cass:** Released Apr '86, on MFP by EMI Records. Catalogue no: **MFP 41 5747 4**
**Album:** Released Apr '86, on MFP by EMI Records. Catalogue no: **MFP 41 5747 1**

**FATS DOMINO (PICTURE DISC)**
**LP Pic:** Released Dec '85, on Astan (USA) Catalogue no: **PD 50003**

**FATS DOMINO COLLECTION (20 golden greats)**
Tracks: / Blueberry Hill / Blue Monday / So long / Whole lotta loving / Jambalaya / Ballin' the jack / Please don't leave me / When the saints go marching in / Yes it's me and I'm in love again / I'm walking / My blue Heaven / Heartbreak Hill / Walkin' to New Orleans / Let the four winds blow / Kansas City / Why don't you do right? / I'm gonna be a wheel someday / Ain't that a shame / I'm ready / Domino twist.
**CD:** Released Jul '87, on Deja Vu Catalogue no: **DVCD 2030**
**Album:** Released Nov '85, on Deja Vu Catalogue no: **DVLP 2030**
**Cass:** Released Nov '85, on Deja Vu Catalogue no: **DVMC 2030**

**FATS DOMINO AND FRIENDS (Domino, Fats & Friends)**
**VHS:** Released Nov '88, on Video Collection by Video Collection. Catalogue no: **VC 4049**

**FATS DOMINO LIVE (VIDEO)**
Note: Running time: 44 mins.
**VHS:** Released Jun '88, on MSD Catalogue no: **V 9053**

**FATS DOMINO VOL. 1**
**Cass:** Released '88, on Joker (USA) by Lifetime Records (USA). Catalogue no: **MC 3895**
**Album:** Released '88, on Joker (USA) by Lifetime Records (USA). Catalogue no: **SM 3895**

**FATS DOMINO, VOL. 2**
**Album:** Released '88, on Joker (USA) by Lifetime Records (USA). Catalogue no: **SM 3896**

**FATS IS BACK**
**Album:** Released Nov '81, on Mercury (USA) by PolyGram Rec.Inc.(USA). Catalogue no: **6463 043**
**Cass:** Released Nov '81, on Mercury (USA) by PolyGram Rec.Inc.(USA). Catalogue no: **7145 043**

**GETAWAY WITH**
Tracks: / When my dreamboat comes home / Wigs / Trouble in mind / Man that's all / Kansas city / Reelin and rockin / On a slow boat to china / Monkey business / Heartbreak hill / Girl I'm gonna marry / Why don't you do right / Ballin' the jack.
**Album:** Released Dec '83, on Ace by Ace Records. Deleted '88. Catalogue no: **CH90**

**GOLDEN GREATS: FATS DOMINO**
**Album:** Released Dec '79, on Hammer Deleted '84. Catalogue no: **HMR 9002**

**GREATEST HITS: FATS DOMINO**
Tracks: / I'm walking / Blue Monday / Blueberry Hill / When the saints go marching in.
**Album:** Released Aug '88, on Philips by Phonogram Ltd. Catalogue no: **927 910 1**
**CD:** Released Jun '88, on Spectrum (1) Catalogue no: **U 4043**
**CD:** Released Apr '87, on DRG (USA) by DRG Records (USA). Deleted '88. Catalogue no: **CD 860705**

**GREATEST HITS - LIVE**
**Cass set:** Released Jun '88, on Spectrum (1) Catalogue no: **M 10174**

**HERE STANDS FATS DOMINO**
**Album:** Released '83, on EMI (France) by EMI Records. Catalogue no: **2C 068 82621**

**HONEY CHILE**
Tracks: / Honey chile.
**7" Single:** Released Feb '57, on London-American Deleted '60. Catalogue no: **HLU 8356**

**I MISS YOU SO**
**Album:** Released '83, on Imperial by K-Tel Records. Catalogue no: **2C 068 83295**

**I WANT TO WALK YOU HOME**
Tracks: / I want to walk you home.
**7" Single:** Released Oct '59, on London-American Deleted '62. Catalogue no: **HLP 8942**

**I'M IN LOVE AGAIN**
Tracks: / I'm in love again.
**7" Single:** Released Jul '56, on London-American Deleted '59. Catalogue no: **HLU 8280**

**I'M WALKIN'**
Tracks: / I'm walking.
**7" Single:** Released Apr '57, on London-American Deleted '60. Catalogue no: **HLP 8407**

**JAMBALAYA**
**Album:** Released Nov '84, on Astan (USA) Catalogue no: **20083**
**Cass:** Released Nov '84, on Astan (USA) Catalogue no: **40083**

**JAMBALAYA (SINGLE)**
Tracks: / Jambalaya.
**7" Single:** Released Mar '62, on London-American Deleted '65. Catalogue no: **HLP 9520**

**LET'S DANCE WITH DOMINO**
**Album:** Released '81, on EMI (France) by EMI Records. Catalogue no: **2C 068 83031**

**LIL' BIT OF GOLD: FATS DOMINO**
Tracks: / Blueberry Hill / I'm walking / Ain't that a shame / Walking to New Orleans.
**CD Single:** Released May '88, on Rhino by Creole Records. Catalogue no: **R 373007**

**LIVE AT MONTREUX**
Tracks: / Hello Josephine / I'm in love again / Blueberry hill / Jambalaya / Walking to New Orleans / I'm gonna be a wheel someday / Blue Monday / Mardi gras in New Orleans / Stagger Lee / I want to walk you home / Let the four winds blow / I'm walking / When the saints go marching in / Sentimental journey.
**Album:** on Atlantic by WEA Records. Catalogue no: **K 50107**

**LIVE IN CONCERT**
Tracks: / Fat man / Blueberry Hill / Domino twist / What a price / Let the four winds blow / Jambalaya / Medley: I'm in love again / Honey chile / Red sails in the sunset / Ain't that a shame / So long / Natural born lover / C.C. rider / I'm in the mood for love / I want to walk you home.
**Album:** Released Jan '85, on Charly R&B by Charly Records. Catalogue no: **CRB 1053**

**LOT OF DOMINOS, A**
**Album:** Released '83, on EMI (France) by EMI Records. Catalogue no: **2C 068 64146**

**MARGIE**
Tracks: / Margie.
**7" Single:** Released May '59, on London-American Deleted '62. Catalogue no: **HLP 8942**

**MILLION RECORDS HITS**
**Album:** Released '83, on Imperial by K-Tel Records. Catalogue no: **2C 068 83297**

**MOTIVE SERIES**
Tracks: / My blue Heaven / Blueberry Hill / When the saints go marching in / Deep in the heart of Texas / I left my heart in San Francisco / Blue Monday / You win again / Walking to New Orleans / Mardi Gras in New Orleans / I'm walking / I don't get over it.
**Album:** Released Sep '82, on Polygram (Import) .Catalogue no: **6463 141**

**MY BLUE HEAVEN**
**Album:** Released Nov '84, on Astan (USA) Catalogue no: **20082**
**Cass:** Released Nov '84, on Astan (USA) Catalogue no: **40082**

**MY GIRL JOSEPHINE**
Tracks: / My girl Josephine.
**7" Single:** Released Jan '61, on London-American Deleted '64. Catalogue no: **HLP 9244**

**MY TOOT TOOT (Domino, Fats & Doug Kershaw)**
Tracks: / My toot toot / Diggy liggy lo.
**7" Single:** Released Aug '85, on Magnum Force by Magnum Music Group. Catalogue no: **MFS 004**

**NEW ORLEANS ROCK 'N' ROLL**
**Album:** Released '85, on Pathe Marconi (France) Catalogue no: **PM 1551833**

**ONLY ROCK AND ROLL**
Tracks: / Fat man, The / Please don't leave me / All by myself / Ain't it a shame / I can't go on / My blue heaven / When my dreamboat comes home / I'm walkin' / Don't deceive me / Big beat, The / Sick and tired / I'm gonna be a wheel some day / Margie / Lil' Liza Jane / When the saints go marching in / When I was young / Shurah / My girl Josephine.
**Album:** on Official by Official Records. Catalogue no: **OFF 6036**

**RED SAILS IN THE SUNSET**
Tracks: / Red sails in the sunset.
**7" Single:** Released Oct '63, on H.M.V. by EMI Records. Deleted '66. Catalogue no: **POP 1219**

**REELIN' AND ROCKIN'**
Tracks: / When I'm walking (let me walk) / Kansas City / I'm living right / Land of make believe / Who cares / I'm a fool to care / Love me / Land of a thousand dances / Heartbreak hill / Wigs / Girl I'm gonna marry, The / Something you got / Packin' up / Reelin' and rockin' / Red sails in the sunset.
**Album:** Released Jun '83, on Charly R&B by Charly Records. Catalogue no: **CRB 1054**

**ROCK AND ROLLIN'**
Tracks: / Reelin' and rockin' / School days / My ding a ling / Too much monkey business / Memphis, Tennessee / Maybellene / Nadine / Fat man / Blueberry Hill / Oh, what a price / Domino twist / Let the four winds blow / I'm in the mood for love / Please don't leave me / I'm ready / I'm in love again / Be my guest.
**Album:** Released Jan '83, on EMI (France) by EMI Records. Catalogue no: **2C 068 83092**
**Album:** Released Jan '83, on EMI (France) by EMI Records. Catalogue no: **2C 068 62438**

**ROCK 'N' SLOW**
**Cass:** Released '88, on EMI (Holland) by EMI Records. Catalogue no: **1A222 1583484**
**Album:** Released '88, on EMI (Holland) by EMI Records. Catalogue no: **1A022 1583481**

**SICK AND TIRED**
Tracks: / Sick and tired.
**7" Single:** Released Jul '58, on London-American Deleted '61. Catalogue no: **HLP 8628**

**SINGLES ALBUM**
Tracks: / Blueberry Hill / Be my guest / My girl Josephine / I hear you knocking / Fat man / Blue Monday / Walking to New Orleans / Ain't that a shame / My blue heaven / I want to walk you home / Whole lotta loving / Country boy / Let the four winds blow / It keeps rainin' / Goin' home / I'm gonna be a wheel someday.
**Album:** Released Nov '82, on Fame by EMI Records. Deleted Jan '88. Catalogue no: **FA 3046**
**Album:** Released Apr '81, on United Artists by EMI Records. Deleted Apr '86. Catalogue no: **UAG 30254**

**SLEEPING ON THE JOB**
Tracks: / Sleeping on the job / After hours / When I lost my baby / Something about you baby / Move with the groove / Any old time / Shame on you / I just can't get / Girl I love / Love me.
**Album:** Released May '79, on Sonet by Sonet Records. Catalogue no: **SNTF 793**

**THIS IS FATS DOMINO**
**Album:** Released Jan '83, on Imperial by K-Tel Records. Catalogue no: **2C 068 83298**
**Album:** Released Jan '83, on Imperial by K-Tel Records. Catalogue no: **2C 068 62383**

**THREE NIGHTS A WEEK**
Tracks: / Three nights a week.
**7" Single:** Released Nov '60, on London-American Deleted '63. Catalogue no: **HLP 9198**

**TWENTY GREATEST HITS**
Tracks: / Blueberry Hill / Be my guest / My girl Josephine / I hear you knocking / Fat man / Blue Monday / Walkin' to New Orleans / Ain't that a shame / My blue Heaven / I want to walk you home / Whole lotta lovin' / Country boy / Let the four winds blow / It keeps rainin' / Jambalaya / I'm ready / Going to the river / I'm walking / Going home / I'm gonna be a wheel someday.
**Album:** Released Mar '77, on United Artists by EMI Records. Catalogue no: **UAS 29967**
**Album:** Released '86, on UNKNOWN Deleted Jun '89. Catalogue no: **TW 50032**

**VALLEY OF TEARS**
Tracks: / Valley of tears.
**7" Single:** Released Jul '57, on London-American Deleted '60. Catalogue no: **HLP 8449**

**VERY BEST OF FATS DOMINO, THE (Play it again)**
Tracks: / Blueberry Hill / Ain't that a shame / Fat man.
**Album:** Released Jan '83, on Liberty (import) by EMI Records. Catalogue no: **IC 064 94442**
**Album:** Released May '70, on Liberty by EMI Records. Deleted '75. Catalogue no: **LBS 83331**

**WALKIN' TO NEW ORLEANS (LP)**
**Album:** Released Sep '84, on Pathe Marconi (France) Catalogue no: **PM 1546621**

**WALKIN' TO NEW ORLEANS (SINGLE)**
Tracks: / Walkin' to New Orleans / Fat man.
**7" Single:** Released Jul '60, on London-American Deleted '63. Catalogue no: **HLP 9163**
**7" Single:** Released Oct '80, on United Artists by EMI Records. Catalogue no: **UP 36525**

**WHAT A NIGHT (SINGLE)**
Tracks: / What a night.
**7" Single:** Released Nov '61, on London-American Deleted '64. Catalogue no: **HLP 9456**

**WHAT A PARTY**
**Album:** Released Sep '84, on Pathe Marconi (France) Catalogue no: **PM 1546631**

## Donaldson, Lou

**Biographical details:** Alto saxist and leader born in 1926 in North Carolina. He recorded with Milt Jackson and Thelonious Monk, then as a leader for Blue Note 1952-74 as well as other labels during that period and since. His funky, bluesy post-Parker style was typical of Blue Note; he paved the way for the David Sanborns of this world. (Donald Clarke, April 1989).

**ALLIGATOR BOGALOO**
Tracks: / Alligator bogaloo / One cylinder / Thang, The / Aw shucks / Rev. Moses / I want a little girl.
**CD:** Released Aug '89, on Blue Note by EMI Records. Catalogue no: **BNZ 183**
**CD:** Released Aug '89, on Blue Note by EMI Records. Catalogue no: **CDP 784 263 2**

**BLUES WALK**
Tracks: / Move / Masquerade is over, The / Play Ray / Autumn nocturne / Callin' all cats / Blues Walk.
**Album:** Released Aug '85, on Blue Note by EMI Records. Catalogue no: **BST 81593**
**CD:** Released May '87, on Blue Note by EMI Records. Catalogue no: **BNZ 24**
**CD:** Released May '87, on EMI-Manhattan by EMI Records. Catalogue no: **CDP 746 525 2**

**FORGOTTEN MAN (Donaldson, Lou Quartet)**
**Album:** Released '88, on Timeless by Timeless Records. Catalogue no: **SJP 153**
**CD:** Released 16 Jan '88, on Timeless (Import) by Timeless Records. Catalogue no: **CDSJP 153**

**HERE 'TIS**
Tracks: / Foggy day / Here 'tis / Cool blues / Watusi jump / Walk wid me.
**Cass:** Released Sep '84, on Blue Note by EMI Records. Deleted '87. Catalogue no: **BST 84066**

**LUSH LIFE**

Tracks: / Sweet slumber / You've changed / Good life / Stardust / What will I tell my heart / It might as well be spring. / Sweet and lovely.

**CD:** Released Mar '89, on Blue Note by EMI Records. Catalogue no: **BNZ 124**

**CD:** Released Mar '89, on Blue Note by EMI Records. Catalogue no: **CDP 784 254 2**

**Album:** Released Jul '86, on Blue Note by EMI Records. Catalogue no: **BST 84254**

### NATURAL SOUL

Tracks: / Funky Mama / Love walked in / Spaceman twist / Sow belly blues / That's all / Nice 'n' greasy.

Note: Produced by Alfred Lion.

**CD:** Released Jun '89, on Blue Note by EMI Records. Catalogue no: **BNZ 194**

**CD:** Released Jun '89, on Blue Note by EMI Records. Catalogue no: **CDP 784 108 2**

**Album:** Released Nov '86, on Blue Note by EMI Records. Catalogue no: **BST 84108**

### QUARTET, QUINTET AND SEXTET

Tracks: / If I love again / Down home / Best things in life are free, The / Lou's blues / Cheek to cheek / Sweet ice / Stroller, The / Roccus / Caracas / Moe's bluff / Roccus (alt. take) (CD only.) / Cheek to cheek (alt. take) (CD only.) / Lou's blues (alt. take) (CD only.) / Things we did last summer, The (CD only.) / After you've gone (CD only.).

**Album:** Released Apr '89, on Blue Note by EMI Records. Catalogue no: **B1 81537**

**CD:** Released Apr '89, on Blue Note by EMI Records. Catalogue no: **CDP 781 537 2**

**CD:** Released Apr '89, on Blue Note by EMI Records. Catalogue no: **BNZ 159**

### SWEET POPPA LOU

Tracks: / Mambo Inn / You'll never know / Mo' Gravy / If I should lose you / Shuckin blues / Don't take your love from me.

Note: Artists: Herman Foster, Calvin Hall, Idris Muhammad (Recorded 7th January, 1982)

**Album:** Released Jan '81, on Muse by Black & Blue Records. Catalogue no: **MR 5247**

## Donegan, Dorothy

### EXPLOSIVE, THE

**Album:** Released Aug '88, on Audiophile (USA) by Jazzology Records (USA). Catalogue no: **AP 209**

## Donegan, Lonnie

**Biographical details:** This British singer, guitarist and banjoist, born in Glasgow, was christened Anthony Donegan but adopted the name Lonnie in 1952, in deference to Lonnie Johnson, the noted American blues artist whom he idolised. Donegan began playing the guitar as a 15 year old during the mid-Forties; by this time, his family was based in London. Between 1949 and 1951, he underwent National Service in Army where, during his spare time, he took up banjo and also drums. Soon after discharge, he joined Ken Colyer's jazz band; in 1954 the entire combo, including Lonnie, deserted their leader and became the Chris Barber Band. With Donegan on guitar and banjo, they became a regular fixture at Humphrey Lyttleton's club in London's Oxford Street. The Chris Barber Band included in their act a skiffle interlude, which gave Lonnie a chance to espouse his favourite music.

*Rock Island line*, a LP track recorded in 1954 featuring Donegan (guitar), Barber (string bass) and Beryl Bryden (washboard), was later issued as a single and jumped into the UK Top 10 in early '56. Even more surprisingly, it became a similar success in the US (then a rare feat for a British act), peaking at No 8 on both sides of the Atlantic. The success of this record prompted Donegan to quit Barber and begin a full-time solo career.

Donegan never looked back. He quickly became Britain's 'King of Skiffle', popularising this intriguing offshoot of jazz. The main attractions of skiffle were its sheer straightforwardness and the cheapness of the necessary instruments - washboards, tea chests and broom handles were used by numerous improvised groups up and down the UK, either as additions to or substitutes for the guitar/banjo/bass/drums line-up. This UK boom, which happened at the same time as the arrival of rock 'n' roll, found favour with rock, folk and jazz fans.

Prior to the 1958 arrival of Cliff Richard, Donegan was Britain's top homegrown act. Even after that, the hits kept on coming until late 1962. During his seven year chart life, Donegan chalked up no less than 30 UK hits; even as late as 1985, the "Guinness Book Of British Hit Singles" still ranked him as Britain's 4th biggest domestic chart act of all time, despite his 23 year absence. In 1957 he managed two consecutive UK No 1 hits, with the traditional *Cumberland Gap* and the double A sided smash *Gamblin' man* (adapted from a Woody Guthrie number)/*Putting on the style* (a traditional song). His status as a leading folk music expert was exemplified by his inspired choice of material, which included adaptations of songs by Leadbelly (*Rock Island line* and *Bring a little water, Sylvie*), Woody Guthrie, the Carter Family and Jimmie Driftwood. His third UK No 1 single, 1960's *My Old Man's A Dustman*, confirmed that he was moving into the world of music hall comedy and showbiz variety; also in this category was *Does your Chewing gum lose its flavour (on the bed post overnight)*, his only American Top 5 hit. The arrival of Beatlemania immediately knocked Donegan's chart career on the head; but his TV and concert appearances kept the star of skiffle, who had inspired so many young UK musicians, in steady money. (Bob MacDonald, 28 June 1985.)

Born Anthony Donegan in 1931 in Glasgow, he changed his name in homage to guitarist and blues singer Lonnie Johnson. He sang and played banjo with Chris Barber's trad group and launched skiffle pratically single handed, playing onstage between sets: he plundered the

**Lonnie Donegan**

USA country/folk heritage, using songs by Woody Guthrie and Leadbelly etc. for 31 top 30 UK hits 1958-1962 not counting re-entries but including an EP and an album which sold so well they reached the singles chart. His *Rock Island line* was a transatlantic top ten in 1956 and inspired satires (by Stan Freberg and Jim Dale), a sure sign of his deep influence. His beat was rock-solid; the hits were well-recorded and are still listenable. (Donald Clarke, April 1989).

**BATTLE OF NEW ORLEANS**
Tracks: / Battle of New Orleans.
**7" Single:** Released Jun '59, on Pye Deleted '62. Catalogue no: **7N 15206**

**BEST OF LONNIE DONEGAN, THE**
Tracks: / Rock Island line / Tom Dooley / Putting on the style.
**CD:** Released Jan '89, on Pickwick by Pickwick Records. Catalogue no: **PWK 076**

**BRING A LITTLE WATER SYLVIE**
Tracks: / Bring a little water Sylvie / Dead or alive.
**7" Single:** Released Sep '56, on Pye Deleted '59. Catalogue no: **N 15071**

**COMANCHEROS, THE**
Tracks: / Comancheros, The.
**7" Single:** Released Jan '62, on Pye Deleted '65. Catalogue no: **7N 15410**

**CUMBERLAND GAP**
Tracks: / Cumberland gap.
**7" Single:** Released Apr '57, on Pye Deleted '60. Catalogue no: **B 15087**

**DOES YOUR CHEWING GUM LOSE ITS FLAVOUR**
Tracks: / Does your chewing gum lose its flavour.
**7" Single:** Released Feb '59, on Pye Deleted '62. Catalogue no: **7N 15181**

**DON'T YOU ROCK ME DADDY-O**
Tracks: / Don't you rock me daddy-o.
**7" Single:** Released Jan '57, on Pye Deleted '60. Catalogue no: **N 15080**

**FORT WORTH JAIL**
Tracks: / Fort Worth jail.
**7" Single:** Released Jun '59, on Pye Deleted '62. Catalogue no: **7N 15198**

**GAMBLIN' MAN**
Tracks: / Gamblin' man / Putting on the style.
**7" Single:** Released Jun '57, on Pye Deleted '60. Catalogue no: **N 15093**

**GAMBLIN' MAN (OLD GOLD)**
Tracks: / Gamblin' man / Puttin' on the style.
**7" Single:** Released Jul '82, on Old Gold by Old Gold Records. Deleted Jul '88. Catalogue no: **OG 9131**

**GOLDEN AGE OF LONNIE DONEGAN VOL. 1**
**Album:** Released Sep '62, on Golden Guinea Deleted '67. Catalogue no: **GGL 0135**

**GOLDEN AGE OF LONNIE DONEGAN VOL. 2**
**Album:** Released Feb '63, on Golden Guinea Deleted '68. Catalogue no: **GGL 0170**

**GOLDEN HOUR OF GOLDEN HITS**
**Cass:** Released '74, on PRT by Castle Communications Records. Catalogue no: **ZCGH 514**

**GOLDEN HOUR OF GOLDEN HITS, VOL. 2**
Tracks: / Mule skinner blues / Pick a bale of cotton / Times are getting hard boys / Sal's got a sugar lip / My dixie darling / Ham 'n' eggs / Lively / Stewball / Fort Worth Jail / Dead or live / I'm just a rolling stone / Aunt Rhody / Rock o' my soul / Golden vanity / Corina Corina / Seven golden daffodils / Lumbered / Very good year, A.
**Album:** Released '73, on Golden Hour Catalogue no: **GH 565**

**GRAND COULEE DAM**
Tracks: / Grand Coulee dam.
**7" Single:** Released Apr '58, on Pye Deleted '61. Catalogue no: **N 15129**

**GREATEST HITS: LONNIE DONEGAN**
**Cass:** Released Mar '83, on Ditto by Pickwick Records. Catalogue no: **DTO 10048**
**Cass:** Released Feb '80, on Bravo by Pickwick Records. Deleted '88. Catalogue no: **BRC 2530**

**HAVE A DRINK ON ME**
Tracks: / Have a drink on me.
**7" Single:** Released May '61, on Pye Deleted '64. Catalogue no: **7N 15354**

**HIT SINGLES COLLECTION, THE**
Tracks: / Rock Island line / Stewball / Lost John / Railroad Bill / Old Riley / Bring a little water, Sylvie / Dead or alive / Don't you rock me daddy-o / Cumberland Gap / Gamblin' man / Putting on the style / My dixie darling / Jack o' diamonds / Grand Coulee dam / Sally don't you grieve / Betty, Betty, Betty / Lonesome traveller / Tom Dooley / Does your chewing gum lose its flavour? / Fort Worth Jail / Battle of New Orleans / Sal's got a sugar lip / San Miguel / My old man's a dustman / I wanna go home / Lorelei / Lively / Virgin Mary / Have a drink on me / Michael row the boat ashore / Lumbered / Comancheros, The / Party's over, The / Pick a bale of cotton / Lonnie's skiffle party (Parts 1 & 2).
**CD Set:** Released Sep '87, on PRT by Castle Communications Records. Catalogue no: **PYC 7003**
**2 LP Set:** Released Oct '87, on PRT by Castle Communications Records. Catalogue no: **PYL 7003**
**Cass set:** Released Oct '87, on PRT by Castle Communications Records. Catalogue no: **PYM 7003**

**I WANNA GO HOME**
Tracks: / I wanna go home.
**7" Single:** Released May '60, on Pye Deleted '63. Catalogue no: **7N 15267**

**JACK O' DIAMONDS**
Tracks: / Jack o' diamonds.
**7" Single:** Released Dec '57, on Pye Deleted '60. Catalogue no: **N 15116**

**JUBILEE CONCERT**
Tracks: / Ace in the hole / Isle of Capri / Going home / Shine / Jenny's ball / One sweet letter from you / Hush-a-bye / Bugle call march / Ice cream / John Henry / Take this hammer / Railroad Bill / Tom Dooley / New burying ground / Grand Coulee dam / New York town / Miss Otis regrets / Does your chewing gum lose its flavour? / One night of love / Rock Island line / Gloryland / Corina Corina / Goodnight Irene.
Note: In 1981 Lonnie Donegan was enjoying an enormous revival with his new single and live appearances. This 15th anniversary album which features many hits - such as Rock Island Line and Does Your Chewing Gum Lose It's Flavour?, was recorded in Berlin, Hamburg and London, with such notable jazzers as Chris Barber, Ken Colyer and Monty Sunshine.
**Cass:** Released Dec '81, on Dakota Catalogue no: **ZCICSD 2001**
**Album:** Released Dec '81, on Dakota Catalogue no: **ICSD 2001**

**LIVELY**
Tracks: / Lively.
**7" Single:** Released Nov '60, on Pye Deleted '63. Catalogue no: **7N 15312**

**LONESOME TRAVELLER**
Tracks: / Lonesome traveller.
**7" Single:** Released Sep '58, on Pye Deleted '61. Catalogue no: **N 15158**

**LONNIE DONEGAN**
Tracks: / Rock Island line / Lost John / Nobody's child / Bring a little water Sylvie / Frankie and Johnny / Cumberland gap / Mule skinner blues / Putting on the style / My Dixie darling / Ham 'n' eggs / Grand coulee dam / Times are getting hard boys / Long summer day / Does your chewing gum lose it's flavour / Whoa buck / Battle of New Orleans / Fancy talking tinker / Miss Otis regrets / Talking guitar blues / My old man's a dustman / Have a drink on me / Keep on the sunny side / Pick a bale of cotton / This train.
**Album:** Released Sep '89, on Castle Collector Series by Castle Communications Records. Catalogue no: **CCSLP 223**
**CD:** Released Sep '89, on Castle Collector Series by Castle Communications Records. Catalogue no: **CCSCD 223**
**Cass:** Released Sep '89, on Castle Collector Series by Castle Communications Records. Catalogue no: **CCSMC 223**

**LONNIE DONEGAN FILE, THE**
**Cass:** Released Nov '77, on PRT by Castle Communications Records. Catalogue no: **ZCFLD 011**

**LONNIE DONEGAN SHOWCASE**
Tracks: / Wabash cannonball / How long how long blues / Nobody's child / I shall not be moved / I'm Alabamy bound / I'm a ramblin' man / Wreck of the old '97 / Frankie and Johnny.
**Album:** Released Dec '56, on Pye Deleted '59. Catalogue no: **NPT 19012**

**LONNIE'S SKIFFLE PARTY**
Tracks: / Lonnie's skiffle party.
**7" Single:** Released Nov '58, on Pye Deleted '61. Catalogue no: **N 15165**

**LORELEI**
Tracks: / Lorelei.
**7" Single:** Released Aug '60, on Pye Deleted '63. Catalogue no: **7N 15275**

**LOST JOHN**
Tracks: / Lost John / Stewball.
**7" Single:** Released Apr '56, on Pye Deleted '59. Catalogue no: **7N 15036**

**MICHAEL ROW THE BOAT**
Tracks: / Michael row the boat
**7" Single:** Released Aug '61, on Pye Deleted '64. Catalogue no: **7N 15371**

**MY DIXIE DARLING**
Tracks: / My dixie darling.
**7" Single:** Released Oct '57, on Pye Deleted '60. Catalogue no: **7N 15108**

**MY OLD MAN'S A DUSTMAN**
Tracks: / My old man's a dustman / Does your chewing gum lose its flavour.
**7" Single:** Released May '79, on Flashback by Mainline Records. Deleted '82. Catalogue no: **FBS 10**
**7" Single:** Released Mar '60, on Pye Deleted '63. Catalogue no: **7N 15256**

**PARTY'S OVER,THE**
Tracks: / Party's over, The.
**7" Single:** Released Apr '62, on Pye Deleted '65. Catalogue no: **7N 15424**

**PICK A BALE OF COTTON**
Tracks: / Pick a bale of cotton.
**7" Single:** Released Aug '62, on Pye Deleted '65. Catalogue no: **7N 15455**

**PUTTIN' ON THE STYLE**
Tracks: / Rock Island line / Have a drink on me / Ham 'n' eggs / I wanna go home / Diggin' my potatoes / Nobody's child / Putting on the style / Frankie and Johnny / Drop down baby / Lost John.
**Album:** Released Feb '78, on Chrysalis by Chrysalis Records. Catalogue no: **CHR 1158**
**Cass:** Released '79, on Chrysalis by Chrysalis Records. Catalogue no: **ZCHR 1158**

**RARE AND UNISSUED GEMS**
Tracks: / Cajun Joe / Louisiana moon / There's a big wheel / Fisherman's luck / Lovey told me goodbye / Bad news / Nothing to gain / Five hundred miles / Tiger rag / Keep on the sunny side / Red beret / Kevin Barry / Comancheros, The / Just a-wearyin' for you / Ding ding / Leavin' blues.
**Album:** Released Jun '85, on Bear Family by Bear Family Records (Germany). Catalogue no: **BFX 15170**

**ROCK ISLAND LINE (LP)**
Tracks: / My old man's a dustman / Pick a bale of cotton / Bring a little water Sylvie / Cumberland Gap / Michael row the boat ashore / Rock Island line / It takes a worried man / Don't you rock me daddy-o / Does your chewing gum lose its flavour? / Putting on the style / Battle of New Orleans / Have a drink on me.
**Album:** Released Oct '85, on Flashback by Mainline Records. Catalogue no: **FBLP 8071**
**Cass:** Released Oct '85, on Flashback by Mainline Records. Catalogue no: **ZCFBL 8071**

**ROCK ISLAND LINE (OLD GOLD)**
Tracks: / Rock island line / Last train to San Fernando.
**7" Single:** Released '89, on Old Gold by Old Gold Records. Catalogue no: **OG 9902**

**ROCK ISLAND LINE (SINGLE)**
Tracks: / Rock Island line / John Henry.
**7" Single:** Released Mar '82, on Decca by Decca International. Deleted '88. Catalogue no: **F 10674**

**SALLY DON'T YOU GRIEVE**
Tracks: / Sally don't you grieve / Betty Betty Betty.
**7" Single:** Released Jul '58, on Pye Deleted '61. Catalogue no: **N 15148**

**SAL'S GOT A SUGAR LIP**
Tracks: / Sal's got a sugar lip.
**7" Single:** Released Sep '59, on Pye Deleted '62. Catalogue no: **7N 15223**

**SAN MIGUEL**
Tracks: / San Miguel.
**7" Single:** Released Dec '59, on Pye Deleted '62. Catalogue no: **7N 15237**

**SKIFFLE SESSION**
Tracks: / Skiffle session.
**7" Single:** Released Jul '56, on Pye Deleted '59. Catalogue no: **NJE 1017**

**STEWBALL**
Tracks: / Stewball.
**7" Single:** Released Apr '56, on Pye Deleted '59. Catalogue no: **N 15036**

**TOM DOOLEY**
Tracks: / Tom Dooley.
**7" Single:** Released Nov '58, on Pye Deleted '61. Catalogue no: **7N 15172**

**VIRGIN MARY**
Tracks: / Virgin Mary.
**7" Single:** Released Dec '60, on Pye Deleted '63. Catalogue no: **7N 15315**

## Dorge, Pierre

**BALLAD ROUND THE LEFT CORNER**
**Album:** Released Jul '88, on Steeplechase (USA) Catalogue no: **SCS 1132**
**CD:** Released Jul '88, on Steeplechase (USA) Catalogue no: **SCCD 31132**

## Dorham, Kenny

**Biographical details:** Trumpeter, composer and bandleader (1924-72) who also played other instruments. A highly rated soloist in modern jazz. His best known album in *Afro Cuban*, originally a 10" album on Blue Note (the CD combines it with another, similar session but without Patato Valdez' congo drums). A 1958 session with John Coltrane and Cecil Taylor has been marketed under several titles, such as *Coltrane Time*. He played in the soundtrack of *A star is born* in 1954 and wrote French film scores *Witness in the city* and *Dangerous liasons* in 1959; he was also active in music education. (Donald Clarke, April 1989).

**AFRO-CUBAN**
Tracks: / Afrodisia / Lotus flower / Minor's holiday / Minor's holiday (alternate take) / Basheer's dream / K.D.'s motion / La villa / Venita's dance / K.D.'s cab ride.
**CD:** Released Sep '87, on Blue Note by EMI Records. Deleted Feb '90. Catalogue no: **CDP 746 815 2**
**CD:** Released Sep '87, on Blue Note by EMI Records. Catalogue no: **BNZ 28**

**BUT BEAUTIFUL**
**2 LP Set:** Released Sep '76, on Milestone by Ace Records. Catalogue no: **M 47036**

**DEXTER GORDON / KENNY DORHAM (Dorham, Kenny & Dexter Gordon)**
Tracks: / Billie's bounce / Just friends / Summertime / Scrapple from the apple.
**Album:** Released Jul '82, on Jazz Reactivation Catalogue no: **JR 159**

**EASE IT**
Tracks: / Alvars / Stella by starlight / Why not? / Ease it / Samba de Orfeu / East 42nd Street.
**Album:** Released Apr '81, on Muse by Black & Blue Records. Catalogue no: **MR 5053**

**HOT STUFF FROM BRAZIL**
Tracks: / Wee dot / Red door, The / Autumn leaves / Halley's comet / Night in Tunisia / It's alright with me.
**Album:** Released Dec '88, on West Wind Catalogue no: **WW 015**
**CD:** Released Dec '88, on West Wind Catalogue no: **WWCD 015**

**MEMORIAL ALBUM**
**CD:** Released '88, on Xanadu Catalogue no: **FDC 5164**

**MUSIC OF KENNY DORHAM**
**Album:** Released Feb '88, on Reservoir Catalogue no: **RSR 117**

**QUIET KENNY**
**Album:** Released Jan '87, on Original Jazz Classics (USA) by Fantasy Inc (USA). Catalogue no: **OJC 250**
**CD:** Released Apr '87, on Carrere (France) Catalogue no: **98348**
**CD:** Released Nov '86, on JVC/Fantasy Deleted '88. Catalogue no: **VDJ 1535**

**ROUND MIDNIGHT AT THE CAFE**
Tracks: / Mexico City / Night in Tunisia / Autumn in New York / Hill's edge / Monaco / Round Midnight.
Note: After leaving the Jazz Messengers trumpeter Kenny Dorham decided to put togethera similar ensemble called Jazz Prophets with saxophonist J.R Montrose and pianist Bobby Timmons. Although the group was short-lived we are fortunate that Blue Note was present one evening at the Cafe Bohemia to preserve this outstanding band with guest artist Kenny Burrell on several titles. Aside from the title tune highlights include such Dorham originals as Monaco, Mexico City and Hill's Edge.
**Album:** Released Jul '89, on Blue Note by EMI Records. Catalogue no: **BST 81524**

**ROUND ABOUT MIDNIGHT AT THE CAFE VOL.1**
Tracks: / Monaco / Round midnight / Mexico city / Night in Tunisia / Autumn in New York / Hill's edge / K.D.'s blues /

Who cares? / Mexico city (alternate take).
**CD:** Released May '87, on EMI-Manhattan by EMI Records. Catalogue no: **BNZ 25**
**CD:** Released Jul '87, on EMI-Manhattan by EMI Records. Catalogue no: **CDP 746 541 2**

### ROUND ABOUT MIDNIGHT AT THE CAFE VOL. 2
Tracks: / Royal roost / My heart stood still / Prophet, The / K.D.'s Blues / Riffin' / Who cares? / Monaco / N.Y. (theme).
**CD:** Released Jul '87, on EMI-Manhattan by EMI Records. Catalogue no: **BNZ 26**
**CD:** Released May '87, on EMI-Manhattan by EMI Records. Catalogue no: **CDP 746 542 2**

### SCANDIA SKIES
**Album:** Released Apr '81, on Steeplechase (USA) Catalogue no: **SCS 6011**

### TROMPETA TOCCATA
Tracks: / Trompeta toccata / Night watch / Mamacita / Fox, The.
**Album:** Released Jul '89, on Blue Note by EMI Records. Catalogue no: **BST 84181**
**CD:** Released May '89, on Blue Note by EMI Records. Catalogue no: **CDP 784 181 2**
**CD:** Released May '89, on Blue Note by EMI Records. Catalogue no: **BNZ 166**

### UNA MAS
Tracks: / Una mas / Straight ahead / Sao Paulo / If ever I would leave you.
Note: P 1987 Manhattan Records,a division of Capitol Records Inc.
**CD:** Released May '87, on EMI-Manhattan by EMI Records. Catalogue no: **BNZ 27**
**CD:** Released May '87, on EMI-Manhattan by EMI Records. Catalogue no: **CDP 746 515 2**

### WEST 42ND STREET
**Album:** Released 10 Jul '89, on Black Lion Catalogue no: **BLP 60119**

### WHISTLE STOP
Tracks: / Philly twist / Buffalo / Sunset / Whistle stop / Sunrise in mexico / Windmill / Dorham's epitaph.
**Album:** Released Dec '84, on Blue Note by EMI Records. Catalogue no: **BLP 4063**

## Dorsey, Georgia Tom

### COME ON MAMA DO THAT DANCE
**Album:** Released Dec '88, on Yazoo (USA) by Shanachie Records (USA). Catalogue no: **L 1041**

## Dorsey, Jimmy

**Biographical details:** Alto saxist, clarinettist and bandleader (1904-57) who sometimes played trumpet or cornet in the early years. He co-led a successful band with his brother Tommy; when they split in 1935 he took over and had 100 pop hits in fifteen years. The band also backed Bing Crosby, Francis Longford, the Andrews Sisters and others on records. The band were less jazz orientated than brother Tommy's, but the level of musicianship was always very high; the biggest hits were all vocals: the number one hits included *Change partners, The breeze and I* (adapted from Lecuona's *Andalucia*), *I hear a rhapsody, High on a windy hill, My sister and I* and *Blue champagne* (all vocals by Bob Eberly, a much better singer than his brother Ray Eberly who sang with Glenn Miller); also duets *Amapola, Green eyes* and *Tangerine* (Eberly and Helen O Connell) and *Besame mucho* (Eberly and Kitty Kallen). The hits were all on USA Decca and are now owned by MCA, which had never reissued them properly as of early 1989. Jimmy Dorsey's fine alto sax had one more memorable hit with *So rare* in 1957, an instrumental version of a pop song from 1937. (Donald Clarke, April 1989).

### 1939: JIMMY DORSEY (Dorsey, Jimmy & His Orchestra)
**Album:** Released Aug '88, on Circle (USA) by Jazzology Records (USA). Catalogue no: **CLP 30**

### CAN ANYONE EXPLAIN?
Tracks: / Diz does everything / See-saw / I can't get started / McGee's closet / Grand central getaway / I'm in love again / Moon of Manakoora / Can anyone explain? / Heatwave / Let's fall in love / Big butter and egg man / This can't be love / Alto tude / Sing a song / Great lie, The.
**Cass:** Released Sep '89, on Big Band Era Catalogue no: **40130**
**Album:** Released Mar '85, on Astan (USA) Catalogue no: **F 21030**

### CONTRASTS 1945 (Dorsey, Jimmy Orchestra)
**Album:** Released Jul '87, on Magic (1) by Submarine Records. Catalogue no: **AWE 27**

### DON'T BE THAT WAY 1935 - 40 (Dorsey, Jimmy & His Orchestra)
**Cass:** Released Jun '88, on Bandstand Catalogue no: **BS 7120C**
**Album:** Released Jun '88, on Bandstand Catalogue no: **BS 7120**

### DORSEYLAND BAND
Tracks: / That's a plenty / Basin Street blues / Stars fell on Alabama / Charlie my boy / Beale Street blues / Indiana / Rosetta / Royal Garden blues / Levee blues / Chicago / Way down yonder in New Orleans / Farewell blues.
**Album:** Released Apr '85, on Hindsight (UK) by Michele International Records. Catalogue no: **HUK 203**
**Album:** Released '88, on Hindsight (UK) by Michele International Records. Catalogue no: **HSR 203**

### EARLY YEARS, THE 1936 - 41 (Dorsey, Jimmy & His Orchestra)
**Album:** Released Jun '88, on Bandstand Catalogue no: **BS 7104**

### HEAT WAVE (Dorsey, Jimmy Orchestra)
**Album:** Released Aug '89, on Golden Era by Delta Records. Catalogue no: **GELP 15011**

### JIMMY DORSEY
**Album:** Released Mar '90, Catalogue no: **Q028**

### JIMMY DORSEY, 1939-40
Tracks: / Contrasts / Shine on harvest moon / Imagination / Blue Lou / Just for a thrill / Fools rush in / Carolina in the morning / At least you could say hello / Moonlight on the river / I'm stepping out with a memory tonight / Julia / Nearness of you / Shoot the meatball to me Dominick boy / You, you darlin' / Blueberry hill / Flight of the jitterbug.
Note: Jimmy Dorsey, Helen O'Connell, Bob Eberly and the great Dorsey orchestra are at their best on this album taken from direct-to-disc radio transcriptions. Only two selections--Tottie Camarata's "Shoot the meatball to me", "Dominick boy" and "Flight of the jitterbug", which was composed and arranged for Dorsey by Don Redman--were recorded commercially but in different versions. Fourteen numbers never before have been available on records. Ms. O'Connell and Eberly, two of the best and most popular of all band singers, each performs four songs with the band that brought them radio, disc and film fame. (Hindsight catalogue - 1989)
**Album:** Released Apr '89, on Hindsight Catalogue no: **HSR 101**

### JIMMY DORSEY AND HIS ORCHESTRA 1939/40 (Dorsey, Jimmy & His Orchestra)
Tracks: / Contrasts / Shine on harvest moon / Imagination / Blue Lou / Just for a thrill / Fools rush in / Carolina in the morning / At least you could say hello / Moonlight on the river / I'm stepping out with a memory tonight / Julia / Nearness of you / Shoot the meatball to me Dominick boy / You, you darlin' / Blueberry Hill / Flight of the jitterbug.
**Album:** Released Feb '79, on London Records by London Records Ltd. Deleted Feb '84. Catalogue no: **HMP 5042**

### JIMMY DORSEY AND HIS ORCHESTRA, VOL. 3 1949-51 (Dorsey, Jimmy Orchestra)
**Album:** Released '88, on Hindsight Catalogue no: **HSR 165**

### JIMMY DORSEY COLLECTION (20 golden greats)
Tracks: / Contrasts / Flight of the jitterbug / Fools rush in / Shine on, harvest moon / Moonlight on the river / Blueberry Hill / Carolina in the morning / Imagination / You, you darlin' / Just for a thrill / St. Louis blues / Basin Street blues / Tailspin / Dese, dem, dose / Blue Lou / Julia / Nearness of you, The / Shoot the meatball to me Dominick boy / At least you could say hello / I'm stepping out with a memory tonight.
**Cass:** Released Jul '88, on Deja Vu Catalogue no: **DVMC 2063**
**Album:** Released Jul '88, on Deja Vu Catalogue no: **DVLP 2063**

### JIMMY DORSEY AND HIS ORCHESTRA (Dorsey, Jimmy & His Orchestra)

Tracks: / Theme / Moonlight serenade / Shine on harvest moon / Comes love / So many times / Dixieland detour / It's funny to everyone but me / Go fly a kite / Pagan love song / Theme - close / Jug music / Where do I go from you / One o'clock jump / As time goes by / I would do anything for you / Jumpin' jimmy.
**Cass:** Released May '88, on Jasmine by Hasmick Promotions. Catalogue no: **JASMC 2513**
**Album:** Released May '88, on Jasmine by Hasmick Promotions. Catalogue no: **JASM 2513**

**JIMMY DORSEY AND HIS ORCHESTRA, 1944-47 (Dorsey, Jimmy & His Orchestra)**
**Album:** Released Apr '79, on First Heard by Submarine Records. Catalogue no: **FH 19**

**JIMMY DORSEY ORCHESTRA (Dorsey, Jimmy Orchestra)**
Tracks: / Wolverine blues / Stuff is here, The / Sandman / Beele / Dorsey stomp / Top hat, white tie and tails / Tap dancer's nightmare / Peanut vendor / Sunset strip / Together / Oh what a beautiful morning / Perdido / I can't believe that you're in love with me / Hi poppin / King Porter stomp.
**Album:** Released Apr '81, on Queendisc (Italy) Catalogue no: **QU 028**

**JIMMY DORSEY PLAYS GREATEST HITS**
**CD:** Released '88, on Gusto (USA) by Gusto Records (USA). Catalogue no: **CD 1003**

**JIMMY DORSEY, VOL 1, 1935-36**
**Album:** Released Apr '79, on Ajax (USA) Catalogue no: **AJAX 103**

**JIMMY DORSEY, VOL 2, 1936**
**Album:** Released Apr '79, on Ajax (USA) Catalogue no: **AJAX 114**

**JIMMY DORSEY, VOL 3, 1936-37**
**Album:** Released Apr '79, on Ajax (USA) Catalogue no: **AJAX 117**

**JIMMY DORSEY, VOL 4, 1937-38**
**Album:** Released Apr '79, on Ajax (USA) Catalogue no: **AJAX 118**

**JIMMY DORSEY, VOL 5, 1938**
**Album:** Released Apr '79, on Ajax (USA) Catalogue no: **AJAX 124**

**JIMMY DORSEY, VOL 6, 1938**
**Album:** Released Apr '79, on Ajax (USA) Catalogue no: **AJAX 128**

**JIMMY DORSEY, VOL 7, 1938**
**Album:** Released Apr '79, on Ajax (USA) Catalogue no: **AJAX 134**

**JIMMY DORSEY, VOL 8, 1938-39**
**Album:** Released Apr '79, on Ajax (USA) Catalogue no: **AJAX 141**

**JIMMY DORSEY, VOL 9, 1939**
**Album:** Released Apr '79, on Ajax (USA) Catalogue no: **AJAX 148**

**JIMMY DORSEY, VOL 10, 1939**
**Album:** Released Apr '79, on Ajax (USA) Catalogue no: **AJAX 156**

**MOSTLY 1940 (Dorsey, Jimmy Orchestra)**

Tommy Dorsey

**Album:** Released Mar '84, on Circle (USA) by Jazzology Records (USA). Catalogue no: **CLP 46**

**MUSKRAT RAMBLE (Dorsey, Jimmy & His Dorseylanders)**
Tracks: / Muskrat ramble / Royal Garden blues / Sweet Lorraine / Charley my boy / Memphis blues / That's a-plenty / Johnson rag / Wolverine blues / Beale Street blues / Panama / Jazz me blues.
**Cass:** Released Mar '87, on Swing House by Submarine Records. Catalogue no: **CSWH 22**
**Album:** Released Mar '87, on Swing House by Submarine Records. Catalogue no: **SWH 22**

**PENNIES FROM HEAVEN**
Tracks: / It's the natural thing to do / Slap that bass / Love bug will bite you, The / Dorsey Dervish / Pick yourself up / Moon got in my eyes, The / In a sentimental mood / Rap-tap on wood / I love to sing / All you want to do is dance / They can't take that away from me / Serenade to nobody in particular / Let's call a heart a heart / Swingin' the jinx away / Stompin' at the Savoy / After you / Listen to the mocking bird / Pennies from Heaven.
**Cass:** Released 1 May '88, on Living Era by Academy Sound & Vision Records. Catalogue no: **ZC AJA 5052**
**Album:** Released 1 May '88, on Living Era by Academy Sound & Vision Records. Catalogue no: **AJA 5052**

**SPOTLIGHTING THE FABULOUS DORSEYS**
**Album:** Released Oct '84, on Giants of Jazz by Hasmick Promotions. Catalogue no: **GOJ 1023**

## Dorsey, Tommy

**Biographical details:** This American trombonist and bandleader holds the unique and important distinction of having the first No.1 record on the world's first record sales chart. Published by Billboard magazine (still America's leading chart source) in July 1940 , he was No.1 with *I'll never smile again.* To add to his triumph, he also held the US No.8 position that week with *Imagination*; his equally famous bandleading brother, Jimmy Dorsey, was No.2 with *The breeze and I.* Tommy, who first led his own orchestra in 1935, died in November 1956 at the age of 51; his elder brother passed away mere months later. After Tommy's death, the trombone player Warren Covington took over the Tommy Dorsey Orchestra. It was this set-up that scored a major hit on the British charts at the end of 1958. *Tea for two cha cha,* an updated dance version of the 1924 standard *Tea for two* reached No.3 and spent 19 weeks on the UK Top 30. In the States, the tune got to No.7. (Bob MacDonald, 1st July 1985)
Trombonist and one of the Swing Era's most successful bandleaders (1905-56). Also see biography for Dorsey Brothers. After the split from brother Jimmy he took over the band of his old friend Joe Haymes; among the excellent sidemen who passed through were trumpeters Bunny Berigan, Yank Lawson, Charlie Shavers, Max Kaminsky, Sterling Bose,

Charlie Spivak, Pee Wee Erwin and Ziggy Elman; also see Buddy DeFranco on clarinet; Bud Freeman on tenor sax; Dave Tough, Buddy Rich and Louis Bellson on drums; arrangers Paul Weston, Axel Stordahl, Sy Oliver, Deane Kincaide; vocalists Edythe Wright, Jack Leanord, Dick Haymes, Connie Haines, Joe Stafford, Frank Sinatra ... The parade of talent seemed endless, and the band could play sweet or hot as well as almost any other. Dorsey was not only a talent scout, but one of the best trombonists in music, with a seamless legato, beautiful tone and phrasing; Sinatra admitted learning about phrasing and dynamics from Dorsey. The band's theme *I'm getting sentimental over you* had first been recorded in 1932 by the Dorsey Brothers band and led to Tommy's title as 'The sentimental gentlemen of swing'. There were more than 180 hits in less than 15 years, including some of the biggest of the era: *Marie* featured a vocal by Leonard against a chant by the band of a paraphrase of the lyrics; the Swing Choir device was invented by Don Redman, but Dorsey apparently got the arrangement from Doc Wheeler's Sunset Serenaders, who once cut him in a ballroom battle of the bands. *Marie* was backed with *Song of India* (from Rimsky-Korsakov) and both featured Berigan, the era's greatest white trumpeter. *Boogie woogie* was an arrangement of the Pinetop Smith classic; Sy Oliver (poached from Jimmie Lunceford) was responsible for *Opus No.1* and *On the sunny side of the street* (again using the Swing Choir effect); Oliver and Stafford say on *Yes indeed*; *Indian summer* and *All the things you are* were number one hits featuring Leonard, and *Polka dots and moonbeams, I'll never smile again, Delores, There are such things, In the blue of the evening* and many more featured Sinatra. The very name of Tommy Dorsey is synonymous with the whole era. (Donald Clarke, April 1989).

**16 HITS (Dorsey, Tommy Orchestra / Frank Sinatra)**
Note: Featuring Frank Sinatra, Bunny Berigan & Buddy Rich.
**Album:** Released Sep '87, on Giants of Jazz by Hasmick Promotions. Catalogue no: **LPJT 18**

**1935 SESSIONS**
**Album:** Released Jun '86, on Halcyon (USA) by Submarine Records. Catalogue no: **HDL 103**

**1940 MEADOWBROOK BROADCAST**
**CD:** Released Jun '89, on Tax Catalogue no: **TAXCD 3705-2**

**1937-1946 (Dorsey, Tommy & His Orchestra)**
**Cass:** Released '88, on Joker (USA) by Lifetime Records (USA). Catalogue no: **MC 3615**
**Album:** Released '88, on Joker (USA) by Lifetime Records (USA). Catalogue no: **SM 3615**

**1950-1952 (Dorsey, Tommy & His Orchestra)**
Tracks: / Picalily dilly / Let me love you tonight / Isn't it romantic (medley) / I kiss your hand Madame / This is romance / Sleepy lagoon / Wagon wheels / Nondrastic / Life is just a bowl of cherries / Sweet Georgia Brown / Bells of St. Mary's / I'm in the mood for love / Shaver's shivers / Maybe / Taking a chance on love / My sweetie went away.
Note: Featuring Charlie Shavers, Sam Donahue, Boomie Richman, Walt Levinsky, Louis Bellson.
**Album:** Released Apr '81, on Solid Sender Catalogue no: **SOL 511**

**ALL TIME GREATEST HITS, VOLUME 1 (Dorsey, Tommy & Frank Sinatra)**
Tracks: / Sky fell down, The / I'll be seeing you / Fools rush in / Imagination / I'll never smile again / Our love affair / Look at me now / Without a song / Lets get away from it all / Blue skies / Street of dreams / Take me / Be careful, it's my heart / These are such things / Light a candle in the chapel.
**CD:** Released Feb '89, on RCA by BMG Records (UK). Catalogue no: **ND 90310**
**Cass:** Released Feb '89, on RCA by BMG Records (UK). Catalogue no: **NK 90310**
**Album:** Released Feb '89, on RCA by BMG Records (UK). Catalogue no: **NL 90310**

**AT THE FAT MAN'S**
Tracks: / Blue skies / Dawn on the desert / At the Fat Man's / Bingo bango boffo / Marie / Chloe / Well git it / At sundown / Opus one / Candy / Continental / Call you sweetheart / Feels so good / Pussy Willow / Broadcasts from 1945-1948.
**Album:** Released '81, on Hep Jazz by Hep Records. Catalogue no: **HEP 9**

**BEAT OF THE BIG BANDS (Dorsey, Tommy Orchestra)**
Tracks: / Do do do / It started all over again / I dream of you / Moonlight in Vermont / There are such things / Melancholy serenade / Autumn in New York / I should care / This love of mine / Rain.
**Album:** Released Oct '84, on CBS by CBS Records. Catalogue no: **32508**

**BEST OF TOMMY DORSEY**
Tracks: / Maria / Star dust / Little white lies / I'll never smile again / Yes Indeed / Boogie woogie / Opus one / Song of India / Who / Royal Garden blues / Once in a while / I'm getting sentimental over you.
**Cass:** Released '84, on RCA by BMG Records (UK). Catalogue no: **NK 81087**
**Album:** Released '84, on RCA by BMG Records (UK). Catalogue no: **NL 81087**

**BIG BAND BASH (Dorsey, Tommy Orchestra)**
**CD:** Released Mar '90, on Giants of Jazz by Hasmick Promotions. Catalogue no: **GOJCD53082**

**BIG REUNION PART 1**
**Album:** Released '84, on First Heard by Submarine Records. Catalogue no: **FH 53**
**Cass:** Released '84, on First Heard by Submarine Records. Catalogue no: **CFH 53**

**DIAMOND SERIES: TOMMY DORSEY (Dorsey, Tommy & His Orchestra)**
Tracks: / I get a kick out of you / Why shouldn't I? / You do something to me / It's de-lovely / Love for sale / Just one of those things / It still suits me / Make believe / Bill / Why do I love you? / Can't help lovin' dat man / Nobody else but me / Everything happens to me / Summertime / I'll be seeing you / Once in a while.
**CD:** Released Apr '88, on Diamond Series by RCA Records. Catalogue no: **CD 90127**

**DORSEY-SINATRA SESSIONS, 1940-42 (Dorsey, Tommy & Frank Sinatra)**
Tracks: / Sky fell down, The / Too romantic / Shake down the stars / Moments in the moonlight / I'll be seeing you / Say it / Polka dots and moonbeams / Fable of the rose / This is the beginning of the end / Hear my song, Violetta / Fools rush in / Devil may care / April played the fiddle / I haven't time to be a millionaire / Imagination / Yours is my heart alone / You're lonely and I'm lonely / East of the sun / Head on my pillow / It's a lovely day tomorrow / I'll never smile again / All this and Heaven too / Where do you keep your heart? / Whispering trade winds / One I love, The / Call of the canyon, The / Love lies / I could make you care / World in my arms, The / Our love affair / Looking for yesterday / Tell me at midnight / We three / When you awake / Anything / Shadows on the sand / You're breaking my heart all over again / I'd know you anywhere / Do you know why? / Not so long ago / Stardust / Oh, look at me now / You might have belonged to another / You lucky people / It's always you / I tried / Dolores / Without a song / Do I worry? / Everything happens to me / Let's get away from it all / I'd never let a day pass by / Love me as I am / This love of mine / I guess I'll have to dream the rest / You and I / Neiani / Free for all / Blue skies / Two in love / Pale moon / I think of you / How do you do without me? / Sinner kissed an angel, A / Violets for your furs / Sunshine of your smile, The / How about you? / Snootie little cutie / Poor you / I'll take Tallulah / Last call for love / Somewhere a voice is calling / Just as though you were here / Sweet dreams / Take me / Be careful, it's my heart / In the blue of the evening / Dig down deep / There are such things / Daybreak / It started all over again / Light a candle in the chapel.
**LP Set:** Released Nov '72, on RCA by BMG Records (UK). Catalogue no: **SD 1000**

**FORD V8 SHOWS AT TEXAS**
Tracks: / Theme / On the beach at Bali Bali / But definitely / I'm an old cowhand / Ja da / It's a sin to tell a lie / Weary blues / Dancing with you (once in a while) / Big John special / Song of India / Shine on Harvest Moon / Would you? / Happy as

the day is long.
**Album:** Released Jan '88, on Jasmine by Hasmick Promotions. Catalogue no: **JASM 2509**
**Cass:** Released 12 Feb '88, on Jasmine by Hasmick Promotions. Catalogue no: **JASMC 2509**

**FOREVER (Dorsey, Tommy & His Orchestra)**
Tracks: / What'll I do / Sweet Sue / Night in Sudan / Too romantic / Say it / Imagination / Devil may care / Swanee river / Yes indeed / Who can I turn to / Embraceable you / Sleepy lagoon / Summertime / Dedicated to you / Will you still be mine / Violets for your furs / Do you know why.
**2 LP Set:** Released Aug '86, on RCA by BMG Records (UK). Catalogue no: **NL 89859**

**FRANK SINATRA SINGS THE STANDARDS (Dorsey, Tommy & His Orchestra with Frank Sinatra)**
Tracks: / I'll be seeing you / Whispering / Somewhere a voice is calling / Blue skies / Stardust / Without a song / Hear my song, Violetta / Yours is my heart alone / East of the sun / One I love / Let's get away from it all / Fools rush in / I'll never smile again / Polka dots and moonbeams / Imagination / Daybreak / Violets for your furs / Everything happens to me / How about you? / This love of mine.
**Album:** Released Jan '82, on RCA by BMG Records (UK). Deleted Jan '87. Catalogue no: **INTS 5098**
**Album:** Released '84, on RCA by BMG Records (UK). Deleted Jul '89. Catalogue no: **NL 89102**
**Cass:** Released '84, on RCA by BMG Records (UK). Deleted Nov '88. Catalogue no: **NK 89102**

**FRANK SINATRA WITH THE TOMMY DORSEY ORCHESTRA (Dorsey, Tommy & His Orchestra)**
Tracks: / Sinner kissed an angel, A / Polka dots and moonbeams / Fools rush in / Imagination / I could make you care / This love of mine / Without a song / Everything happens to me / Violets for your furs / Sky fell down, The / Be careful, it's my heart / In the blue of the evening.
**Album:** Released Feb '77, on RCA by BMG Records (UK). Catalogue no: **NL 11586**

**INDISPENSABLE TOMMY DORSEY, VOLS.. 1/2 (1935-37) (Dorsey, Tommy & His Orchestra)**
Tracks: / Weary blues / I'm getting sentimental over you / Music goes around and around, The / Rhythm in my nursery rhymes / I'm shooting high / Day I let you get away, The / Rhythm saved the world / Stardust / Royal garden blues / Jada / At the codfish ball / Mary had a little lamb / You've gotta eat your spinach baby / On the beach at Bali / San Francisco / That's a plenty / After you've gone / Head over heels in love / Sleep / Maple leaf rag / Keepin' out of mischief now / Melody in F / Song of India / Marie / Liebestraum / Mendelssohn's Spring song / Jammin' / They can't take that away from me / Humoresque / Beale street blues / Blue Danube / Dark eyes.
**Cass set:** Released '87, on RCA by BMG Records (UK). Deleted May '89. Catalogue no: **NK 89752**
**2 LP Set:** Released '87, on RCA by BMG Records (UK). Deleted May '89. Catalogue no: **NL 89752**

**INDISPENSABLE TOMMY DORSEY, VOLS. 3/4 (1937-38) (Dorsey, Tommy & His Orchestra)**
Tracks: / Posin' / That stolen melody / All you want to do is dance / After you / Stardust on the moon / Night and day / Smoke gets in your eyes / Canadian capers / Good bye Jonah / Big apple, The / Lady is a tramp, The / Tears in my heart / If the man in the moon were a coon / Getting some fun out of life / Nice work if you can get it / Who? / Dipsy doodle, The / Big dipper / Shine on harvest moon / When the midnight choo choo leaves for Alalabama / Music, Maestro please / Tisket a tasket, A / Stop beatin' around the Mulberry bush / Panama / Washboard blues / Chinatown, my Chinatown / Sheik of Araby, The / Copenhagen / Symphony in riffs / Boogie woogie / Tin roof blues / Sweet Sue.
**2 LP Set:** Released Aug '84, on RCA by BMG Records (UK). Deleted May '89. Catalogue no: **NL 89163**
**Cass set:** Released Aug '84, on RCA by BMG Records (UK). Deleted May '89. Catalogue no: **NK 89163**

**INDISPENSABLE TOMMY DORSEY, VOLS. 5/6 (1938-39) (Dorsey, Tommy & His Orchestra)**
Tracks: / Cocktails for two / Old black Joe / Down home rag / Hawaiian war chant / Davenport blues / It's all yours / Milenberg joys (parts 1 & 2) / Hold tight / Honolulu / Blue moon / Peckin' with the penguins / Got no time / Little skipper / Our love / Tea for two / By the river Sainte Marie / Asleep or awake / You grow sweeter as the years go by / If you ever change your mind / To you / This is no dream / Marcheta / Lamp is low, The / Dawn on the desert / Why begin again? / Lonesome road / Rendezvous time in Paree / How am I to know? / Is it possible? / Well, all right / La Rosita / All I remember is you.
**Cass set:** Released Aug '88, on RCA by BMG Records (UK). Deleted May '89. Catalogue no: **NK 89589**
**2 LP Set:** Released Aug '88, on RCA by BMG Records (UK). Deleted May '89. Catalogue no: **NL 89589**

**INDISPENSABLE TOMMY DORSEY VOLS. 7/8 (Dorsey, Tommy & His Orchestra)**
**Cass:** Released '87, on RCA by BMG Records (UK). Deleted Jul '89. Catalogue no: **NK 90028**
**2 LP Set:** Released '87, on RCA by BMG Records (UK). Deleted Jul '89. Catalogue no: **NL 90028**

**JAMBOREE 1935-6 (Dorsey, Tommy & His Orchestra)**
**Album:** Released Jul '87, on Halcyon (USA) by Submarine Records. Catalogue no: **HDL 114**
**Cass:** Released Jul '87, on Halcyon (USA) by Submarine Records. Catalogue no: **CHDL 114**

**LEGEND VOLUMES I-III, THE**
Tracks: / On the sunny side of the street / Chicago / Chloe / Hucklebuck, The / It's de-lovely / I get a kick out of you / I'm getting sentimental over you / Stardust / That's a plenty / After you've gone / Keepin' out of mischief now / Liebestraum / Satan takes a holiday / Stop, look and listen / Beale Street blues / Night and day / Smoke gets in your eyes / Once in a while / Lady is a tramp, The / Who? / Little white lies / Shine on harvest moon / What'll I do? / I hadn't anyone till you / Tisket a tasket, A / Boogie woogie / You must have been a beautiful baby / Sweet Sue / Hawaiian war chant / Milenberg joys / tea for two / Night in Sudan / March of the toys / I'll be seeing you / Say it / This is the beginning of the end / Devil may care / East of the sun / I'll never smile again / Whispering / One I love belongs to somebody else, The / Do you know why? / Song of India / Marie / For you / Whatcha know Joe? / Yes indeed / Will you still be mine / Swing low sweet chariot / This love of mine / I guess I'll have to dream the rest / Loose lid special / Blue skies / Hallelujah / What is this thing called love? / Snooty little cutie / Well, git it / Street of dreams / Sleepy lagoon / Opus one.
**CD:** Released Jan '87, on RCA by BMG Records (UK). Deleted Nov '88. Catalogue no: **PD 89810**

**LITTLE WHITE LIES**
Tracks: / I've got a note / Royal Garden blues / Ja da / Maple leaf rag / Who / Little white lies / Symphony in Riffs / Copenhagen / Old black Joe / Well alright / Back to back / Stomp off.
**Album:** Released Apr '81, on Joker (USA) by Lifetime Records (USA). Catalogue no: **SM 3062**

**LIVE AT THE MEADOWBROOK**
**Album:** Released Apr '79, on Fanfare by Captain Billy's Music. Catalogue no: **FANFARE 29-129**

**LIVE IN NEW YORK, 1955-6 (Dorsey, Tommy & Jimmy Orchestra)**
Tracks: / I'm getting sentimental over you / My brother is the leader of the band / Teach me tonight / I've got the world on a string / Alexander's ragtime band / Wagon wheels / Don't worry about me / Stereophonic / Always in my heart / Stella by starlight / I'm glad there is you / Bells of Saint Mary's, The / Quiet please.
Note: With guests Duke Ellington, Mindy Carson and Johnny Ray. Featuring

Buddy Rich. Duke Ellington Medley: Don't get around much anymore / In a sentimental mood / Mood indigo / I'm beginning to see the light / Sophisticated lady / Caravan / Solitude / Do nothing till you hear from me / I let a song go out of my heart / Don't get around much anymore / It don't mean a thing if it ain't got that swing. Medley of Dorsey favourites: Brazil / Once in a while / The breeze and I / This love of mine / All of me / Opus No. 1 / Amapola / There are such things / Yours / On the sunny side of the street / Mare Elena / Song of India / Tangerine / I'll never smile again / Green eyes / Marie.
**CD:** Released Oct '89, on Magic (1) by Submarine Records. Catalogue no: **DAWE 37**
**Cass:** Released Oct '89, on Magic (1) by Submarine Records. Catalogue no: **CAWE 37**

**MAKING BIG BAND HISTORY (1944)**
**Album:** Released Feb '81, on First Heard by Submarine Records. Catalogue no: **FH 1003**

**MAPLE LEAF RAG 1936 - 39 (Dorsey, Tommy & His Orchestra)**
**Album:** Released Jun '88, on Bandstand Catalogue no: **BS 7116**

**ON THE SUNNY SIDE OF THE STREET (Dorsey, Tommy/ Jimmy Dorsey/ Coleman Hawkins)**
**Album:** Released May '88, on Nostalgia by Mainline Records. Catalogue no: **NOST 7653**
**Cass:** Released Sep '85, on Saar Giants Of Jazz (Italy) Catalogue no: **MCJT 18**
**Album:** Released Sep '85, on Saar Giants Of Jazz (Italy) Catalogue no: **LPJT 18**

**ONE NIGHT STAND 1940**
**Album:** Released Apr '79, on Sandy Hook (USA) Catalogue no: **SH 2001**

**RADIO DAYS VOL.1**
**CD:** Released Aug '89, on Starline (Jazz) Catalogue no: **CDSG 405**

**REED ALBUM VOL. 2 (Dorsey, Tommy & Various Artists)**
**Album:** Released '88, on Meritt (USA) Catalogue no: **MERITT 11**

**SENTIMENTAL JOURNEY**
**Cass set:** Released Apr '85, on Cambra by Cambra Records. Deleted '88. Catalogue no: **CRT 5142**
**2 LP Set:** Released Apr '85, on Cambra by Cambra Records. Deleted '88. Catalogue no: **CR 5142**

**SOLID SWING**
Tracks: / Chez faire / Capital idea / Swanee River / Continental / Chloe / On the sunny side of the street / Puddle wump / Non drastic / Sweet Georgia Brown / Hollywood hat / Lullaby in boogie / Song of India / Swing to me up in Harlem / Why begin again? / Summertime / At the Fat Man's / Brotherly jump / Harlem express / I'm beginning to see the light / Midriff / Swing high / Dry bones / Another one of them things / Coming through the Rye.
Note: Featuring a super - band with super - sound and super soloists: Louis Bellson / Tommy Dorsey / Irving Josephs / Walt Levinsky / Boomie Richman / Doc Severinson / Charlie Shavers. Mono....
**Album:** Released '84, on First Heard by Submarine Records. Catalogue no: **FH 47**
**Cass:** Released '84, on First Heard by Submarine Records. Catalogue no: **CFH 47**

**SONG OF INDIA (Dorsey, Tommy & His Orchestra)**
Tracks: / They didn't believe me / Cheek to cheek / Opus one / Tico tico / Blue skies / I'll never smile again / Begin the beguine / There's no you / Midriff / Cuttin' out blues / Pussy willow / Hollywood hat / Then I'll be happy / Lovely weather for ducks / And the angels sing / Somebody loves me / Boogie woogie / Song of India / On the sunny side of the street / Non drastic / Swanee river.
**Album:** Released Oct '87, on Dance Band Days by Prism Leisure. Catalogue no: **DBD 08**
**CD:** Released Jul '87, on Dance Band Days by Prism Leisure. Catalogue no: **DBCD 08**
**Cass:** Released Oct '87, on Dance Band Days by Prism Leisure. Catalogue no: **DBDC 08**

**STORY**
**Album:** Released Oct '79, on Big Band International Catalogue no: **BB 12707**

**SWING HIGH**
Tracks: / Swing high / Always / Pussy willow / That's it / Swing time up in harlem / Why begin again / Summertime / At the fat man's / Brotherly jump / Harlem express / I'm beginning to see the light / Midriff / Swing high / Dry bones / Another one of them things / Coming through the rye.
**Cass:** Released May '88, on Big Band Era Catalogue no: **40127**
**Album:** Released Mar '85, on Astan (USA) Catalogue no: **F 20127**
**Album:** Released May '88, on Big Band Era Catalogue no: **20127**

**SWINGING BIG BANDS, THE 1937-46 (Dorsey, Tommy & His Orchestra)**
Tracks: / Boogie woogie / Copenhagen / Lonesome road / Hawaiian war chant / Sleepy lagoon / L.A. April 1946 / Then I'll be happy / Liebestraum / Song of India / Opus NR / I'm getting sentimental over you / Once in a while / Music, maestro please.
**Album:** Released Apr '81, on Joker (USA) by Lifetime Records (USA). Catalogue no: **SM 3615**

**TEA FOR TWO CHA CHA (Dorsey, Tommy & His Orchestra)**
Tracks: / Tea for two cha cha.
**7" Single:** Released Oct '58, on Brunswick by Decca Records. Deleted Oct '61. Catalogue no: **05757**

**THIS IS TOMMY DORSEY**
**Album:** Released '83, on RCA (Germany) Catalogue no: **26 28033**

**THIS IS TOMMY DORSEY VOL.2**
**Album:** Released '83, on RCA (Germany) Catalogue no: **26 28041**

**TOMMY AND JIMMY DORSEY (Dorsey, Tommy & His Orchestra)**
**Album:** Released Apr '79, on Bright Orange Catalogue no: **BO 714**

**TOMMY DORSEY**
**Album:** Released Apr '79, on Bright Orange Catalogue no: **BO 711**

**TOMMY DORSEY COLLECTION (20 Golden Greats)**
Tracks: / Song of India / Sleepy lagoon / I'm getting sentimental over you / Hawaiian war chant / Boogie woogie / Copenhagen / Then I'll be happy / Liebestraum / Opus one / Lover is blue, A / After all / Polka dots and moonbeams / Fable of the rose / Marie / Whispering (medley) / I'll get by (medley) / Deep night / Sky fell down, The / Music, Maestro, please / Do I love you.
Note: Whispering medley: Whispering/ Avalon/ Japanese sandman. I'll get by medley: I'll get by/ Talk of the town/ If I had you. Do I love you? medley: Do I love you?/ Careless/ Say si si.
**Album:** Released Aug '85, on Deja Vu Catalogue no: **DVLP 2019**
**Cass:** Released Aug '85, on Deja Vu Catalogue no: **DVMC 2019**

**TOMMY DORSEY AND COMPANY (Dorsey, Tommy & Company)**
**Album:** Released '84, on First Heard by Submarine Records. Catalogue no: **FH 24**
**Cass:** Released '84, on First Heard by Submarine Records. Catalogue no: **CFH 24**

**TOMMY DORSEY AND FRANK SINATRA (Dorsey, Tommy & Frank Sinatra)**
**Album:** Released '88, on Joker (USA) by Lifetime Records (USA). Catalogue no: **SM 3878**
**Cass:** Released '88, on Joker (USA) by Lifetime Records (USA). Catalogue no: **MC 3878**

**TOMMY DORSEY AND HIS ORCHESTRA (Dorsey, Tommy & His Orchestra)**
Note: Featuring Frank Sinatra, Jo Stafford, Connie Haines.
**Album:** Released Mar '89, on Jasmine by Hasmick Promotions. Catalogue no: **JASM 2523**
**2 LP Set:** on RCA Victor by BMG Records (UK). Catalogue no: **DPM 2026**
**Cass:** Released Mar '89, on Jasmine by Hasmick Promotions. Catalogue no: **JASMC 2523**

**TOMMY DORSEY AND HIS ORCHESTRA (Dorsey, Tommy & His Orchestra with Frank Sinatra)**
Tracks: / Marie / Too romantic / Polka dots and moonbeams / This is the beginning of the end / Hear my song, Violetta / I haven't time to be a millionaire / Head on my pillow / I'll never smile again / One I love, The / Call of the canyon, The / Shadows on the sand / Do you know why / Yearnin' / Not so long ago / Stardust / How am I to know / Look at me now / You lucky people you / Without a song / Everything happens to me / Let's get away from it all / Love me as I am / This love of mine / Blue skies / How do you do without me? / Violets for your furs / How about you / My melancholy baby / Dig down deep / It started all over again / I'll take Tallulah / Song is you, The.
**2 LP Set:** Released '83, on RCA (France) by BMG Records (France). Catalogue no: **PM 43685**

**TOMMY DORSEY IN CONCERT**
**Album:** Released May '84, on RCA (Germany) Catalogue no: **NL 45154**
**Cass:** Released May '84, on RCA (Germany) Catalogue no: **NK 45154**

**TOMMY DORSEY ORCHESTRA (Dorsey, Tommy & His Orchestra)**
Tracks: / Jump time / Milenberg joys / Sweet potato / Hawaiian war chant / Song of India / Blues no more / Swing low sweet chariot / I say I'm sorry / Quiet please / Easy does it / March of the toys / I know that you know.
**Album:** Released Apr '81, on Jazz Live (Italy) Catalogue no: **BLJ 8012**

**TOMMY & JIMMY DORSEY ORCHESTRA (Dorsey, Tommy & Jimmy Orchestra)**
Tracks: / By heck / Stop, look and listen / Milenberg joys / St. Louis blues / Honeysuckle rose / Basin street blues / Weary blues / Tailspin / That eccentric rag / Dese dem dose / Dippermouth blues.
**Album:** Released Apr '81, on Kings Of Jazz Catalogue no: **KLJ 20009**

**TOMMY DORSEY AND HIS ORCHESTRA VOL 1**
**Album:** Released '89, on Echo Jazz Catalogue no: **EJLP 01**
**Cass:** Released '89, on Echo Jazz Catalogue no: **EJMC 01**
**CD:** Released '89, on Echo Jazz Catalogue no: **EJCD 01**

**TOMMY DORSEY AND HIS ORCHESTRA VOL. 2**
**Cass:** Released '89, on Echo Jazz Catalogue no: **EJMC 09**
**Album:** Released '89, on Echo Jazz Catalogue no: **EJLP 09**
**CD:** Released '89, on Echo Jazz Catalogue no: **EJCD 09**

**WELL, GIT IT (Dorsey, Tommy Orchestra)**
**CD:** Released '88, on Jass Catalogue no: **JASSCD 14**

**YES INDEED**
Tracks: / Lonesome road (part 1) / Lonesome road (part 2) / Well, all right / Stomp it off / Easy does it / Quiet please / Swing high / Swanee river / Yes, indeed / Loose lid special / Swingin' on nothin' / Moonlight on the Ganges / Well git it / Opus 1 / Chloe (song of the swamp) / Minor goes muggin', The.
**CD:** Released Apr '90, on RCA by BMG Records (UK). Catalogue no: **ND 90449**
**Album:** Released Apr '90, on RCA by BMG Records (UK). Catalogue no: **NL 90449**
**Cass:** Released Apr '90, on RCA by BMG Records (UK). Catalogue no: **NK 90449**

## Douglas, K.C.

**BIG ROAD BLUES**
Tracks: / Big road blues / Buck dance / Tore your playhouse down / Whisky headed woman / Catfish blues / Howlin' blues / Kansas City blues / Bottle up and go / K.C. blues / Key to the highway.
**Album:** Released Oct '88, on Ace by Ace Records. Catalogue no: **CH 254**

**COOL DOWN AMENA**
Tracks: / Cool down amena.
**12" Single:** Released Mar '82, on Fashion by Fashion Records. Catalogue no: **FAD 011**

**COUNTRY BOY, THE**
**Album:** Released '81, on Arhoolie (USA) by Arhoolie Records (USA). Catalogue no: **ARHOOLIE 1073**

**MERCURY BOOGIE**
**Album:** Released Apr '88, on Oldie Blues Catalogue no: **OL 2812**

## Down South

**DOWN SOUTH (Various artists)**
**Album:** Released Oct '88, on Roots (Germany) Catalogue no: **RL 313**

## Down South Blues

**BLUES SINGERS (Various artists)**
**Album:** Released '88, on Wolf Catalogue no: **WBJ 003**

## Down Town Jazzband

**HEAR US TALKIN' TO YA**
**Album:** Released '88, on Timeless by Timeless Records. Catalogue no: **TTD 514**

## Downes, Wray

**AU PRIVAVE (Downes, Wray/Dave Young/Ed Bickert)**
Tracks: / Anthropology / My romance / I'm hip / Portrait of Jennie / Sweet Georgia Brown / Au privave / Spanish fandango / Yours is my heart alone / Falling in love with love.
**Album:** Released Jul '86, on Sackville by Spotlite Records. Catalogue no: **4003**

## Downhome Blues

**DOWNHOME BLUES (Various artists)**
**Album:** Released Apr '84, on JSP by JSP Records. Catalogue no: **JSP 1068**

## Drag's Half Fast

**DRAG'S HALF FAST JAZZ BAND (Drag's Half Fast Jazz Band)**
**Album:** Released Jul '87, on GHB by Jazzology Records (USA). Catalogue no: **GHB 54**

## Draper, Ray

**TUBA JAZZ**
**Album:** Released Feb '88, on Fresh Sounds (Spain) by Fresh Sounds Records (Spain). Catalogue no: **FS 308**

## Dreamland Syncopators

**TERRITORY JAZZ**
Note: with Keith Nichols & Claus Jacobi
**Album:** Released Jan '88, on Stomp Off (USA) Catalogue no: **SOS 1150**

## Drew, Kenny

**AFTERNOON IN EUROPE (Drew, Kenny Trio)**
Tracks: / Golden striker, The / Midnight sun / Jeg gik mig ud en sommerday at hore / Tivoli strool / Ach varmeland,du skona / Afternoon in Paris / Quiet cathedral, The.
**Album:** Released '83, on RCA by BMG Records (UK). Catalogue no: **PL 45373**

**AND FAR AWAY (Drew, Kenny Quartet)**
**CD:** Released Jan '86, on Soul Note Catalogue no: **SN 1081**

**BY REQUEST**
Note: With Neils-Henninning Orsted Pederson.
**CD:** Released Jan '86, on RCA Jazz (Japan) Catalogue no: **886 007**

**KENNY DREW TRIO (Drew, Kenny Trio)**
**CD:** Released '88, on Fantasy (import) by Fantasy Inc (USA). Catalogue no: **FCD 631224**
**CD:** Released Apr '86, on Vanguard (USA) by CBS Records. Deleted '88. Catalogue no: **VDJ 1507**

**MORNING**
**Album:** Released Jul '88, on Steeplechase (USA) Catalogue no: **SCS 1048**
**CD:** Released Jul '88, on Steeplechase (USA) Catalogue no: **SCCD 31048**

**PRIZE WINNERS (Drew, Kenny / Henning / Pedersen / Asmussen / Thigpen)**
Tracks: / Django / Pretty girl / Golgatha / Bridgetown Baby / Hush-a-bye / Donna Lee / You are the sunshine of my life / Evening in the park / Careless love.
**Album:** Released Apr '81, on Matrix (Denmark) Catalogue no: **MTX 1001**

**THIS IS NEW**
Tracks: / This is new / Carol / It's you or no one / You're my thrill / Little / Paul's pal / Why do I love you.
**Album:** Released Feb '88, on Riverside (USA) by Fantasy Inc (USA). Catalogue no: **RLP 236**

**UNDERCURRENT**
Tracks: / Undercurrent / Funk cosity / Lion's den / Pot's on, The / Groovin' the blues / Ballade.
**CD:** Released Aug '89, on Blue Note by EMI Records. Catalogue no: **BNZ 184**

CD: Released Aug '89, on Blue Note by EMI Records. Catalogue no: **CDP 784 059 2**

**YOUR SOFT EYES (Drew, Kenny Trio)**
**CD:** Released Jan '86, on Soul Note Catalogue no: **SNCD 1031**

## Drew, Martin

**BRITISH JAZZ ARTISTS VOL 3 (Drew, Martin, Band)**
**Album:** Released May '80, on Lee Lambert by Lee Lambert Records. Catalogue no: **LAM 003**

## Dry Throat Five

**MY MELANCHOLY BABY - 100% 20'S**
**Album:** Released Nov '88, on Stomp Off (USA) Catalogue no: **SOS 1151**

**WHO'S BLUE**
**Album:** Released Oct '86, on Stomp Off (USA) Catalogue no: **SOS 1114**

## Duke, George

**Biographical details:** This American keyboards player, singer and producer gained experience during the mid-sixties by playing in West Coast nightclubs. His career began in earnest in 1968, when he joined the band of up-and-coming violinist Jean-Luc Ponty as a jazz keyboardist. After 3 albums with Ponty, he joined Frank Zappa's Mothers of Invention and remained with the notorious madman from 1970-75; he managed to add a degree of stability to zany Zappa's work, whose music and personnel were an ever-changing phenomenon. While with Zappa, Duke mastered the new synthesiser technology and began releasing solo LP's. Duke's fusion of jazz with funk and soul, for which he later became well-known, started to emerge in 1976 while he was collaborating with drummer Billy Cobham. During 1977-79 the prolific Duke issued five solo albums within three years, on which he consolidated his funky approach. 1980 brought him his only solo entries into the UK charts: *Brazilian love affair* reached no.36 on the singles chart; meanwhile, the album of the same name, recorded in Brazil and featuring local accompanying musicians, climbed to no.33 on the UK LP listings. For his only American Top 40 single, Duke teamed up in 1981 with a fellow jazz-funk fusionist, the brilliant bassist Stanley Clarke. Their LP *The Clarke/Duke project* yielded the US no.19 hit *Sweet baby*. At the same time as *Sweet baby* was climbing the Billboard Hot 100, Duke was doing even better as a producer. A Taste of Honey's 1981 revival of *Sukiyaki* was a million-selling US no.3 hit; on this single, Duke went for a delicate, understated, summery soul sound. 1984 brought him his first US no.1 single, plus a UK no.2 as producer of Deniece Williams' *Let's hear it for the boy*. He continued to release his own classy and polished, but somewhat underrated, albums, such as 1982's *Dream on* and 1983's *Guardian of the light*. (Bob Macdonald, 7/7/85)
Keyboardist and composer born in 1946 in California. He sessioned with Don Ellis, Frank Zappa, Cannonball Adderley and co-led a group with Billy Cobham in 1975; since then he led various groups of his own and did festival, TV and film work, also producing records (a number one USA hit in 1984 with Deniece Williams' *Let's hear it for the boy*, etc. His versatile success has been mainly in a soft-fusion mode and he is best-known for the Clarke-Duke project with the bassist Stanley Clarke. (Donald Clarke, April 1989).

**1976 SOLO KEYBOARD ALBUM**
Tracks: / Mr. McFreeze / Love reborn / Excerpts from the opera Tzina / Spock gets funky / Pathways / Vulcan mind probe / Dream that ended.
**Album:** Released '83, on Epic by CBS Records. Deleted '88. Catalogue no: **EPC 25021**

**BORN TO LOVE YOU**
Tracks: / Born to love you / You are the light.
**7" Single:** Released Aug '83, on Epic by CBS Records. Deleted '86. Catalogue no: **A 3612**

**BRAZILIAN LOVE AFFAIR**
Tracks: / Brazilian love affair / Summer breezin' / Cravo E Canela / Alone / 6 AM / Brazilian sugar / Sugar loaf mountain / Love reborn / Up from the sea it arose and ate Rio in one / I need you now / Ao que vai Nascer.
**Album:** Released Jul '80, on Epic by CBS Records. Deleted '85. Catalogue no: **EPC 84311**
**7" Single:** Released Jul '80, on Epic by CBS Records. Deleted Jul '83. Catalogue no: **EPC 8751**
**Cassingle:** Released Aug '82, on CBS by CBS Records. Deleted Aug '85. Catalogue no: **A40 2630**

**DREAM ON**
Tracks: / Shine on / You / Dream on / I will always be your friend / Framed / Ride on love / Someday / Son of reach for it / Positive energy / Let your love shine.
**CD:** Released '88, on Epic (import) by CBS Records. Catalogue no: **35 8P 8**
**Album:** Released Mar '82, on Epic by CBS Records. Deleted Mar '87. Catalogue no: **EPC 85215**

**FOLLOW THE RAINBOW**
Tracks: / Party down / Say that you will / Funkin' for the thrill / Sunrise / Festival / I am for real / Straight from the heart / Corine / Pluck / Follow the rainbow.
**Album:** Released Apr '79, on Epic by CBS Records. Deleted Apr '84. Catalogue no: **EPC 83336**

**GEORGE DUKE**
Tracks: / Broken glass / I just want to be in your life / Good friends / So mean to me / Stand with your man / Island girl / King for a day / Morning, you and love / I can make it better / African violet.
**Cass:** Released Oct '86, on Elektra by Elektra Records (UK). Catalogue no: **960 480-4**
**Album:** Released Oct '86, on Elektra by Elektra Records (UK). Catalogue no: **960 480-1**
**Album:** Released Sep '83, on Epic by CBS Records. Deleted Jan '88. Catalogue no: **EPC 32348**

**GUARDIAN OF THE LIGHT**
Tracks: / Overture / Light / Shane / Born to love you / Silly fightin' / You / War fugue interlude / Reach out / Give me your love / Stand / Soon / Celebrate / Fly away.
**CD:** Released '88, on Import (label unknown) Catalogue no: **35 8P 20**
**Cass:** Released May '83, on Epic by CBS Records. Catalogue no: **40 25262**
**Album:** Released May '83, on Epic by CBS Records. Deleted '85. Catalogue no: **EPC 25262**

**I LOVE THE BLUES, SHE HEARD MY CRY**
Tracks: / Chariot / Look into her eyes / Sister serene / That's what she said / Mashavu / Rokkinrowl / Prepare yourself / Giant child within us / Someday / I love the blues she heard my cry.
**Album:** Released Sep '84, on MPS Jazz (Germany) Catalogue no: **817 488-1**
**CD:** Released Sep '84, on Polydor by Polydor Ltd. Deleted Aug '87. Catalogue no: **817 488-2**

**I SURRENDER**
Tracks: / I surrender / Jam.
**12" Single:** Released Jul '85, on Elektra by Elektra Records (UK). Deleted Jul '88. Catalogue no: **EKR 15T**
**7" Single:** Released Jul '85, on Elektra by Elektra Records (UK). Deleted Jul '88. Catalogue no: **EKR 15**

**I WANT YOU FOR MYSELF**
Tracks: / I want you for myself / Dog man.
**7" Single:** Released Jan '80, on CBS by CBS Records. Deleted Jan '85. Catalogue no: **CBS 8137**

**I WILL ALWAYS BE YOUR FRIEND**
Tracks: / I will always be your friend / Framed.
**7" Single:** Released Aug '82, on Epic by CBS Records. Deleted Aug '85. Catalogue no: **EPCA 2661**

**I'M JUST THE PIANO PLAYER**
**CD:** Released Feb '89, on Elektra by Elektra Records (UK). Catalogue no: **K 660778-2**
**Album:** Released Feb '89, on Elektra by Elektra Records (UK). Catalogue no: **EKT 52**
**Cass:** Released Feb '89, on Elektra by Elektra Records (UK). Catalogue no: **EKT 52 C**

**MASTER OF THE GAME**
Tracks: / Look what you find / Every step I take / Games / I want you for myself / In the distance / I love you more / Dog man / Everybody's talkin'.
**Album:** Released Jan '80, on Epic by CBS Records. Deleted Jan '85. Catalogue no: **EPC 83951**

**NIGHT AFTER NIGHT**
Tracks: / Miss wriggle / Children of the night / Love ballad / Guilty / Same ole

love / Say hello / You are the only one in my life / Brazilian coffee / This lovin' / Mystery eyes.
**Album:** Released Feb '89, on Elektra by Elektra Records (UK). Catalogue no: **EKT 52**
**CD:** Released Feb '89, on Elektra by Elektra Records (UK). Catalogue no: **960 778 2**
**CD:** Released Feb '89, on Elektra by Elektra Records (UK). Catalogue no: **EKT 52 CD**
**Cass:** Released Feb '89, on Elektra by Elektra Records (UK). Catalogue no: **EKT 52 C**

**PRIMAL**
Tracks: / Second time around / Night has a thousand eyes / Days of wine and roses / Jeannine / Little girl blue / Secret love.
**Album:** Released '79, on MPS Jazz Deleted '84. Catalogue no: **5C 064 61170**

**REACH OUT**
Tracks: / Reach out.
**7" Single:** Released Apr '83, on Epic by CBS Records. Catalogue no: **A 3267**
**12" Single:** Released Apr '83, on Epic by CBS Records. Catalogue no: **TA 3267**

**RIDE ON LOVE**
Tracks: / Ride on love / Son of reach for it.
**7" Single:** Released May '82, on Epic by CBS Records. Deleted May '85. Catalogue no: **EPCA 2372**
**12" Single:** Released May '82, on Epic by CBS Records. Deleted May '85. Catalogue no: **EPCA 132372**

**SAY THAT YOU WILL**
Tracks: / Say that you will / I'm for real.
**7" Single:** Released May '79, on Epic by CBS Records. Deleted '82. Catalogue no: **EPC 7095**

**SECRET RENDEZVOUS**
Tracks: / Got to get back to love / Stay awhile / Thinking of you / Secret rendezvous / Take it on / She can wait forever / Better ways / Your life / Ipanema lady.
**Album:** Released Sep '89, on Epic by CBS Records. Catalogue no: **EPC 26059**

**SHINE ON**
Tracks: / Shine on / Positive energy.
**7" Single:** Released May '80, on Epic by CBS Records. Deleted May '85. Catalogue no: **EPC A2072**
**12" Single:** Released May '80, on Epic by CBS Records. Deleted May '85. Catalogue no: **132072**

**THIEF IN THE NIGHT**
**Cass:** Released May '85, on Elektra by Elektra Records (UK). Catalogue no: **EKT 3C**
**Album:** Released May '85, on Elektra by Elektra Records (UK). Deleted Aug '87. Catalogue no: **EKT 3**
**CD:** Released '88, on Elektra by Elektra Records (UK). Catalogue no: **960 398-2**

**THIEF IN THE NIGHT (SINGLE)**
Tracks: / Thief in the night / La la.
**12" Single:** Released Apr '85, on Elektra by Elektra Records (UK). Deleted Apr '88. Catalogue no: **EKR 5T**
**7" Single:** Released Apr '85, on Elektra by Elektra Records (UK). Deleted Apr '88. Catalogue no: **EKR 5**

## Dukes Of Dixieland

**Biographical details:** A second rate jazz band, surprisingly made up on New Orleans residents including the Assunto family, who once sold a lot of records because they were among the first stereo records. (Donald Clarke, April 1989)

**DIXIELAND FAVOURITES**
**Cass:** Released Dec '88, on Capitol (Specials) Catalogue no: **4XLL 57001**

**DUKES OF DIXIELAND**
**Cass:** Released Oct '84, on Audio Fidelity(USA) by Audio Fidelity (USA). Catalogue no: **ZCGAS 714**

## Dukes Of Rhythm

**DUKES OF RHYTHM 1960 Featuring Joe Carl (Various artists)**
Tracks: / Those eyes: *Various artists* / For love: *Various artists* / Before I grow too old: *Various artists* / Ooh poo pah doo: *Various artists* / Holy one: *Various artists* / Tell it like it is: *Various artists* / Don't leave me again: *Various artists* / One little dream: *Various artists* / Somebody's cheatin': *Various artists* / You broke my heart: *Various artists* / Everybody's rockin': *Various artists* / I've found my love: *Various artists* / Defeated: *Various artists* / Don't leave me again: *Various artists.*
**Album:** Released Dec '88, on Krazy Kat by Interstate Music. Catalogue no: **KK 788**

## Dunbar, Ted

**JAZZ GUITARIST**
Tracks: / Winding blues / Total conversation / Trees and grass and nice things / Nica's dream / Hi-fly / Bougie / Epistrophy.
**Album:** Released Jan '83, on Xanadu Catalogue no: **XAN 196**

**OPENING REMARKS**
**Album:** Released Mar '79, on Xanadu Catalogue no: **X 155**

## Duncan, Johnny

**Biographical details:** This American singer and guitarist, born in Tennessee, enjoyed brief British fame in 1957 while remaining unknown in his home country. His first important musical experience occurred in his early teens when he sang in a gospel quartet. He started playing guitar at the age of 16 (1947) and soon joined Bill Monroe's Blue Grass Boys, Monroe being a noted country/blues fusionist. Duncan was drafted into the US Army and, in 1953, was posted in Britain; later that year he married a British girl. He then decided to settle in the UK after his discharge. In 1956 his musical career received a boost, when he replaced the fast-rising star Lonnie Donegan as skiffle singer in the Chris Barber Band; with *Rock Island Line* becoming a transatlantic Top 10 hit, Donegan was in the process of spearheading the UK's skiffle boom. Because of his nationality and his experience in bluegrass music, Duncan's style was more authentic than Donegan's, and he therefore attracted a credibility tag. By the start of 1957, Duncan felt confident enough to leave Barber and form his own combo, Johnny Duncan & The Blue Grass Boys. Later that year, Duncan and his group achieved their first and only major UK hit - *Last train to San Fernando*, an evocative and enjoyable single, was a no.2 smash. However, the two follow-up singles, *Blue blue heartaches* and *Footprints in the snow*, both peaked at no.27, and subsequent attempts failed to make the British charts. They continued to be a successful live group for a while, but Duncan was fading into obscurity by the end of the 50's. Duncan returned to the States in the early 60's, and tried to refine and perfect his country round. From 1967 onwards, he enjoyed hits from time to time on the US country charts, but he never became one of the genre's major artists. (Bob Macdonald, 8/7/85).

**BLUE BLUE HEARTACHES (Duncan, Johnny & The Blue Grass Boys)**
Tracks: / Blue blue heartaches.
**7" Single:** Released Oct '57, on Columbia by EMI Records. Deleted '62. Catalogue no: **DB 3996**

**FOOTPRINTS IN THE SNOW (Duncan, Johnny & The Blue Grass Boys)**
Tracks: / Footprints in the snow.
**7" Single:** Released Nov '57, on Columbia by EMI Records. Deleted '62. Catalogue no: **DB 4029**

**GREATEST HITS: JOHNNY DUNCAN**
Tracks: / Stranger / Sweet country woman / Atlanta Georgia stray / She can put her shoes under my bed / Come a little bit closer / Song in the night / It counldn't have been any better / Jo and the cowboy / Thinkin' of a rendezvous / Scarlet water.
**Album:** Released Apr '79, on CBS by CBS Records. Deleted Apr '84. Catalogue no: **CBS 83486**

**LAST TRAIN TO SAN FERNANDO (single) (Duncan, Johnny & The Blue Grass Boys)**
Tracks: / Last train to San Fernando.
**7" Single:** Released Jul '57, on Columbia by EMI Records. Deleted '62. Catalogue no: **DB 3959**

**LAST TRAIN TO SAN FERNANDO**
Tracks: / Last train to San Fernando / Itching for my baby / Geisha girl / Jig along home / Railroad, steamboat, river and canal / I heard the bluebirds sing / Git along home Cindy / Raise a ruckus tonight / Rockabilly baby / Detour / Which way did he go / Blue, blue heartaches / Footprints in the snow / My little baby / Yellow moon / Pan American / I'm

movin' on / Dang me.
**Album:** Released '86, on Bear Family by Bear Family Records (Germany). Catalogue no: **BFX 15169**

**NICE 'N' EASY (Duncan, Johnny / Janie Fricke)**
Tracks: / He's out of my life / Nice 'n' easy / There's nothing stronger than our love / Baby / Loving arms / Come a little closer / It couldn't have been any better / Atlanta Georgia stray / Thinkin' of a rendezvous / Stranger.
**Album:** Released Sep '81, on CBS by CBS Records. Deleted Sep '86. Catalogue no: **CBS 85111**

**WORLD OF COUNTRY MUSIC VOL 2**
Tracks: / Mustang prang / Life can be beautiful / Hello heartache / If it feels good, do it / Wild side of life / Just for what I am / Salty dog blues / Just a little lovin' / Footprints in the snow / Blue, blue heartaches / Someone to give my love to / Hey good lookin' / I can't help it / Jambalaya / Smoke, smoke, smoke / Tom Dooley / Last train to San Fernando / Mustang prang (revisited).
**Album:** Released '73, on World Of Learning by World Of Learning Records. Catalogue no: **SPA 295**

## Duncan, Sammy

**SWINGIN' JAZZ (Duncan, Sammy & His All-Stars)**
**Album:** Released '88, on Jazzology (USA) by Jazzology Records (USA). Catalogue no: **J 84**

**WHEN THE SAINTS GO MARCHING IN (Duncan, Sammy & His All-Stars)**
**Album:** Released Dec '87, on Jazzology (USA) by Jazzology Records (USA). Catalogue no: **J 118**

**WHEN YOU'RE SWINGING (Duncan, Sammy & His All-Stars)**
**Album:** Released Dec '87, on Jazzology (USA) by Jazzology Records (USA). Catalogue no: **J 119**

## Dunham, Andrew

**DETROIT BLUES VOL.2 1948-9 (Dunham, Andrew & Friends)**
Tracks: / Wife lovin' blues / Stranger in your town / I tried / Waterlee blues / Single man blues / Thanksgiving blues / Big chested mama blues / Stormy weather blues / When I'm gone / Pay day blues / Christmas blues / Brownskin woman / Cottonfield blues / 3 cent stamp blues.
**Album:** Released Dec '84, on Krazy Kat by Interstate Music. Catalogue no: **KK 7423**

## Dunham, Sonny

**1943-1944 (Dunham, Sonny & His Orchestra)**
Note: Mono.
**Album:** Released Jan '87, on Circle (USA) by Jazzology Records (USA). Catalogue no: **CLP 85**

**HALF PAST JUMPING TIME (Dunham, Sonny & His Orchestra)**
**Album:** Released Aug '89, on Golden Era by Delta Records. Catalogue no: **GELP 15008**

**SONNY DURHAM ON THE AIR (Durham, Sonny & His Orchestra)**
Tracks: / Mocassin Glide / Besame mucho / Shoo shoo baby / Old acquaintance / Holiday for strings / When they ask about you / I'll be around / Don't worry mom / You're blase / Body and soul / Do nothing till you hear from me / With a sweetheart like you / Matinee at the meadowbrook / Blue moon.
**Album:** Released May '79, on Aircheck (USA) by Kiner Ents.(USA). Catalogue no: **AIRCHECK 25**

**SONNY DUNHAM ORCHESTRA (Dunham, Sonny & His Orchestra)**
**Album:** Released Aug '89, on Golden Era by Delta Records. Catalogue no: **GELP 15044**

## Dunn, Johnny

**JOHNNY DUNN'S ORIGINAL JAZZ HOUNDS (Dunn, Johnny Original Jazz Hounds)**
**Album:** Released Apr '79, on VJM (Vintage Jazz Music) by Vintage Jazz Music Society(VJM). Catalogue no: **VLP 11**

## Dupree, Champion Jack

**Biographical details:** A blues singer and songwriter, born in 1910 in New Orleans; he played guitar and drums, but described himself as the last of the barrelhouse piano players. Orphaned by a fire, he learned piano in the same Coloured Waifs Home where Louis Armstrong earlier learned cornet. His nickname from his days as a boxer (107 bouts). He began recording in 1940 on Okeh and recorded almost every year thereafter, on Savoy with Brownie McGhee in 1947, on Apollo 1949-50, King and others 1951-5, Atlantic in 1958; he lived in Europe from 1959. (Donald Clarke, April 1989).

**1940-50**
**Album:** Released '89, on Best Of Blues (USA) by Blue Island Records (USA). Catalogue no: **BOB 14**

**1944-1945: THE OTHER TAKES**
Tracks: / She makes good jelly / Rum cola blues / Lovers Lane / Black wolf / Outside man, The / Forget it mama / You've been drunk / G.R. boogie / Santa Claus blues / Love strike blues / Wet deck mama / Big-legged mama / I'm a doctor for waman.
Note: Mono Recording
**Album:** Released Jun '86, on Krazy Kat by Interstate Music. Catalogue no: **KK 801**

**BEST OF THE BLUES**
Note: Mono production.
**Album:** Released May '86, on Storyville by Storyville Records AB. Catalogue no: **SLP 4010**
**Album:** Released '88, on Storyville by Storyville Records AB. Catalogue no: **SLP 151**

**BIGTOWN PLAYBOYS BURNLEY**
**CD:** Released Oct '89, on JSP by JSP Records. Catalogue no: **JSPCD 231**

**BLUES FOR EVERYBODY (BEL-**

Jack Dupree

**LAPHON)**
**Album:** Released Jul '88, on Bellaphon Catalogue no: **BID 8020**

**BLUES FOR EVERYBODY (Dupree, Jack)**
**Cass set:** Released Mar '88, on Gusto (USA) by Gusto Records (USA). Catalogue no: **GD 5037**
**2 LP Set:** Released Oct '79, on Gusto (USA) by Gusto Records (USA). Catalogue no: **GD 0037**

**CHAMPION JACK DUPREE (Dupree, Champion Jack/Ken Lending Blues Band)**
**CD:** Released '86, on Hi Grade (MCS Hi Grade) Catalogue no: **105 011**

**CHAMPION JACK DUPREE 1944-1945**
Tracks: / Rum cola blues / She makes good jelly / Johnson street boogie woogie / I'm going down with you / F.D.R. blues / God bless our new president / Gin mill sal / County jail special / Fisherman's blues / Lover's lane / Black wolf / Walkin' by myself / Outside man / Forget it mama / You've been drunk / Santa Claus blues.
**Album:** Released Jul '82, on Red Pepper by Interstate Music. Catalogue no: **RP 701**

**CHAMPION JACK DUPREE AND HIS BLUES**
Tracks: / Barrelhouse woman / Louise / One dirty woman / When things go wrong / Cut down on my overheads / Troubles / Tee nah nah / Caldonia / Under your hood / Come back baby / Baby let me go with you / Garbage man / I feel like a millionare / Right now / Georgianna / Shake, baby, shake.
**CD:** Released Mar '89, on London by London Records Ltd. Catalogue no: **820 569 2**

**DEATH OF LOUIS ARMSTRONG**
**CD:** Released Dec '86, on Vogue by Vogue Records. Catalogue no: **VGCD 600096**

**FROM NEW ORLEANS TO CHICAGO**
Tracks: / Third degree / T.V. mama / He knows the rules / Ain't it a shame / Ooh-la-la / (Going down to) big leg Emma's / Won't be a fool no more / Take it slow and easy / She's all in my life / Poor poor me / Pigfoot and a bottle of beer / Down the valley / Too early in the morning / Shim-sham-shimmy.
**CD:** Released Oct '88, on Decca by Decca International. Catalogue no: **820 568 2**
**Album:** Released Jul '85, on Crosscut by Topic Records. Catalogue no: **CCR 1009**

**HAPPY TO BE FREE**
**Album:** Released May '89, on GNP Crescendo (USA) by GNP Crescendo Records (USA). Catalogue no: **GNPS 10005**

**INCREDIBLE CHAMPION JACK DUPREE, THE**
Tracks: / Big fat mama / 41 Highway / Old woman blues / President Kennedy blues / I'm goin' to look the world over / Poor boy blues / Miss Ada blues / Gravier Street special / You're so fine / Rock me, mama / Don't worry / Driving me mad.
**Album:** Released '87, on Sonet by Sonet Records. Catalogue no: **SNTF 614**

**JUBILEE ALBUM**
Tracks: / Freedom / Ramblin' boogie / Jump for Jack / Nobody loves me / Blues for champ / Married man / I hate to be alone / When Victoria Spivey was living / Rocky Mountain / New York City / Move me, baby / Shineberger boogie / Thank you, God / Happy birthday / Rockin' the house / One more time / Blues ad lib, The / Bye bye blues / Mother in law / Gergiana / One scotch, one bourbon, one beer.
Note: Live recording of 75th birthday concert in Hamburg. Guests include Memphis Slim, Louisiana Red, Monty Sunshine.
**2 LP Set:** Released 21 Jul '89, on Blue Moon (1) by Magnum Music Group. Catalogue no: **BMLP 2.074**

**JUNKER BLUES 1940-41**
**Album:** Released Oct '85, on Travelin' Man by Interstate Music. Catalogue no: **TM 807**

**LEGACY OF THE BLUES-3**
Tracks: / Vietnam blues / Drunk again / Found my baby gone / Anything you want / Will it be? / You're the one / Down and out / Roamin' special / Life I lead, The / Jitterbug jump.
**Album:** Released May '89, on GNP Crescendo (USA) by GNP Crescendo Records (USA). Catalogue no: **GNPS 10013**
**Album:** Released '87, on Sonet by Sonet Records. Catalogue no: **SNTF 626**
**CD:** Released '87, on Sonet by Sonet Records. Catalogue no: **SNTCD 626**

**ROCKIN' THE BOOGIE**
Tracks: / My baby's coming back / Rockin' the boogie / I don't know / You better kick the habit / I had that dream / I hate to be alone / Be a man / Old old woman / Good Lord born on Christmas Day / Baby please don't go.
Note: Bar code : Album : 5099882 225812
**Album:** Released 19 Mar '88, on Blue Moon (1) by Magnum Music Group. Catalogue no: **BMLP 058**

**RUN A LITTLE BOOGIE 1945-53**
**Album:** Released Dec '88, on Krazy Kat by Interstate Music. Catalogue no: **KK 7401**

**SHAKE BABY SHAKE**
Tracks: / Ups, The / Lonely road blues / Story of my life / When I get married / Dirty woman / Old time rock'n'roll / Down the lane / Rocky mountain / Just like a woman / Shake baby shake / Wrong woman, The / You're always cryin' the blues / Woman trouble again / My baby's like a clock / Hello darlin' / Lollipop baby.
Note: A complete anthology of Dupree's recordings from RCA's VIK and Groove subsiduary labels 1956-57, including many unissued titles.
**Album:** Released Jul '87, on Detour by Detour Records. Catalogue no: **DT 33007**

**SINGS THE BLUES**
**CD:** Released Mar '90, on King Catalogue no: **KCD 735**

**THE BLUES OF CHAMPION JACK DUPREE**
**Album:** Released Feb '90, on Storyville by Storyville Records AB. Catalogue no: **SLP 240**

**TRICKS, THE**
**Album:** Released May '89, on GNP Crescendo (USA) by GNP Crescendo Records (USA). Catalogue no: **GNPS 10001**
**Album:** Released Oct '88, on Vogue (France) by Vogue Records. Catalogue no: **512502**

**TROUBLE, TROUBLE**
**Album:** Released Jan '88, on Storyville by Storyville Records AB. Catalogue no: **SLP 4139**

**WON'T BE A FOOL NO MORE**
Tracks: / Third degree / T.V. mama / He knows the rules / Ain't it a shame? / Ooh-la-la / Big-Leg Emma's / Won't be a fool no more / Calcutta blues / Take it slow and easy / She's all in my life / Poor poor me / 24 hours / Pigfoot and a bottle of beer / Down in the valley / Too early in the morning / Shim-sham-shimmy.
**Album:** Released Jan '86, on See For Miles by See For Miles Records. Catalogue no: **SEE 44**

## Duran, Elena

**BRANDENBURG BOOGIE (Duran, Elena with Grappelli, Holloway, Walley & Ganley)**
Tracks: / Brandenburg boogie / Jesu, joy of man's desiring / Groovy gavotte 1 / Fascinating fugue / Groovy gavotte II / Sleeper's awake / Aria / D minor double / Minuet / Jig / Air on a G string / Groovy gavotte III / Sicilienne / Funky flute.
**Album:** Released Nov '80, on EMI by EMI Records. Catalogue no: **EMD 5536**
**Cass:** Released Nov '80, on EMI by EMI Records. Catalogue no: **TC EMD 5536**

**MARY ROSE**
Tracks: / Mary Rose / Walaichu.
**7" Single:** Released Jun '82, on RCA by BMG Records (UK). Catalogue no: **RCA 237**

**VIVA ELENA**
Tracks: / Song of the Andes / La paloma / River song / Black orpheus theme / Brazilian serenade / Guantanamera / Mexican hat dance / Mary Rose / La cucaracha / Walaychu / Totoras / Cielito lindo / Benedito pretinho / Inca dance / Frog song.
**Album:** Released Jun '82, on RCA by BMG Records (UK). Catalogue no: **RCALP 6030**
**Cass:** Released Jun '82, on RCA by BMG Records (UK). Catalogue no: **RCAK 6030**

## Duskin, Big Joe

### CINCINNATI STOMP
**Album:** Released Dec '88, on Arhoolie (USA) by Arhoolie Records (USA). Catalogue no: **ARHOOLIE 1080**

### DON'T MESS WITH THE BOOGIE MAN
**Cass:** Released Aug '88, on Special Delivery by Topic Records. Catalogue no: **SPDC 1017**
**CD:** Released Nov '88, on Special Delivery by Topic Records. Catalogue no: **SPDCD 1017**
**Album:** Released Aug '88, on Special Delivery by Topic Records. Catalogue no: **SPD 1017**

## Dutch Swing College

### 40 YEARS, 1945-1985, AT ITS BEST
**Album:** Released Sep '86, on Timeless by Timeless Records. Catalogue no: **TTD 616**
**CD:** Released '89, on Timeless by Timeless Records. Catalogue no: **CDTTD 516**

### 1960
**CD:** Released Mar '90, on Philips by Phonogram Ltd. Catalogue no: **JJCD12**

### BAND'S BEST, THE
Tracks: / Way down yonder in New Orleans / Weary blues / South / Doctor Jazz / I've found a new baby / Alexander's ragtime band / King Porter stomp / Buddy's habits / Quena blues / Besame mucho / Wilhelm Tell / Tennessee waltz rock / Mack the knife / Milenberg joys / At the jazz band ball / Fidgety feet / Royal Garden blues / Basin Street blues / Ice cream / See see rider / Tiger rag / When the saints go marching in / Big butter and egg man / High society / I wish I could shimmy like my sister Kate / Clarient marmalade / Struttin' with some barbecue / Please don't talk about me when I'm gone.
**Cass:** Released Oct '84, on Verve (USA) by Polydor Ltd. Catalogue no: **7588 024**
**Album:** Released Oct '84, on Verve (USA) by Polydor Ltd. Catalogue no: **6601 024**

### DIGITAL ANNIVERSARY
Tracks: / Bourbon Street parade / Wabash blues / Caribbean parade / Is it true what they say about Dixie? / Clarinet games / Saturday night is the loneliest night of the week / Coal black shine / Third Street blues / Gladiolus rag / Columbus stockade blues / Devil in the moon / Original Dixieland one-step.
**Album:** Released Apr '86, on Phonogram (Import) Catalogue no: **824 585 1**
**CD:** on Phonogram by Phonogram Ltd. Catalogue no: **824 585-2**
**Cass:** Released Apr '86, on Phonogram (Import) Catalogue no: **824 585 4**

### DIGITAL DATE
Tracks: / That's a plenty / I remember Johnny / Stockyards strut / I'm coming Virginia / Chimes blues / (Back home again in) Indiana / Sweetie dear / Somewhere somehow / Alabama jubilee / Murkeys / Tat da da strain / That's my desire / Lulu's back in town / Crazy sticks / When my sugar walks down the street / Kaper's up / South Rampart Street parade / Jamaican brew.
**Cass:** Released Mar '88, on Philips (Holland) by PolyGram UK Ltd. Catalogue no: **8340874**
**CD:** Released Mar '88, on Philips (Holland) by PolyGram UK Ltd. Catalogue no: **8340872**
**Album:** Released Mar '88, on Philips (Holland) by PolyGram UK Ltd. Catalogue no: **8340871**

### DIGITAL DIXIE
Tracks: / Way down yonder in New Orleans / Kneedrops / West End blues / At a Georgia camp meeting / I want a little girl / China boy / Creole belles / Sugar / Kazoos / Down home rag / On Green Dolphin Street / Everybody loves my baby.
**Cass:** Released Feb '82, on Philips (Import) by PolyGram UK Ltd. Catalogue no: **7111 472**
**Album:** Released Feb '82, on Philips (Import) by PolyGram UK Ltd. Catalogue no: **6433 472**
**CD:** on Philips by Phonogram Ltd. Deleted Mar '88. Catalogue no: **800 065-2**

### DIGITAL DUTCH
Tracks: / West Side stomp / Buddy Bolden's blues / Papa Dip / Sidewalk blues / Clarinet case / Louisiana / My gal Sal / Coney Island washboard / Perdido street blues / Tailspin / Gatemouth / Perdido / Do you know what it means to miss New Orleans? / Chicago / Drum blues.
**CD:** on Philips by Phonogram Ltd. Catalogue no: **814 068 2**

### DUTCH SAMBA
Tracks: / Corro / Velas blancas / Girl from Ipanema / Samba de Orfeu / Menina flor meditacao / Manana / Corcovado / Poinciana / Samba de Quena / Eso es el Amor / La adelita.
**CD:** Released Jun '89, on Timeless by Timeless Records. Catalogue no: **CDTTD 552**
**Album:** Released Jun '89, on Timeless by Timeless Records. Catalogue no: **TTD 552**

### DUTCH SWING COLLEGE BAND LIVE (The Best of Dixieland)
**Album:** Released Jan '90, on Verve Catalogue no: **838 765 1**
**CD:** Released Jan '90, on Verve Catalogue no: **838 765 2**

### JUBILEE CONCERT
**Cass:** Released Nov '80, on Pablo Jazz (USA) by Pablo Records (USA). Catalogue no: **7588 003**

### MUSIC FOR THE MILLIONS
Tracks: / Ice scream / Memphis blues / Take your pick / Just a closer walk with thee / Tennessee waltz rock / March of the Indians / Marina / I ain't gonna give nobody none of this jelly roll / Black and tan fantasy / Tiger rag / You don't know how much you suffer / High society.
**Album:** Released Apr '83, on Philips (Import) by PolyGram UK Ltd. Catalogue no: **6375 463**
**Cass:** Released Apr '83, on Philips (Import) by PolyGram UK Ltd. Catalogue no: **7174 463**

### ON TOUR
**Album:** Released Aug '81, on Philips (Import) by PolyGram UK Ltd. Catalogue no: **9279 368**
**Cass:** Released Aug '81, on Philips (Import) by PolyGram UK Ltd. Catalogue no: **7259 368**

### SWING STUDIO SESSIONS
Tracks: / At the Jazz Band Ball / Savoy blues / Fidgety feet / See see rider / Royal Garden blues / Some of these days / Tiger rag / Just a closer walk with thee / March of the Indians / Mood indigo / I wish I could shimmy like my sister Kate / I've been working on the railroad / East St. Louis toodle-oo / Cornet chop suey / When it's sleepy time down South / Dippermouth blues / Davenport blues / Shake it and break it.
**CD:** Released May '85, on Philips by Phonogram Ltd. Catalogue no: **824 256 2**

### WHEN THE SWING COMES MARCHING IN
Tracks: / High school cadets / High society / Swanee / Liberty bell / Copenhagen / Stars and stripes forever / Anchors aweigh / Original Dixieland one-step / Semper Fidelis / Ory's Creole trombone / Sensation rag / Officer of the day.
Note: With the Marine Band of the Royal Netherlands Navy.
**Album:** Released Mar '85, on Philips (Holland) by PolyGram UK Ltd. Catalogue no: **6375 424**
**Cass:** Released Mar '85, on Philips (Holland) by PolyGram UK Ltd. Catalogue no: **7174 424**

### ...WITH GUESTS, VOLUME 1
Tracks: / Mandy make up your mind / I got the right to sing the blues / I wanna be happy / Keepin' out of mischief now / I got rhythm / Lotus blossom / Swing that music / Poor butterfly / As long as I live / Nobody knows you (when you're down and out) / Shimme-sha-wabble / Wild dog.
**CD:** Released Oct '87, on Polydor (Germany) by Polydor Ltd. Catalogue no: **830 771-2**

# E

The following information was taken from the Music Master database on April 14th, 1990.

## Eagle Brass Band

### LAST OF THE LINE, THE

Note: Mono.

**Album:** Released Jun '86, on GHB by Jazzology Records (USA). Catalogue no: **GHB 170**

## Eaglin, Snooks

**Biographical details:** New Orleans guitarist, singer and songwriter, born in 1936 and blind since infancy. He wrote *Lucille* a big hit for Little Richard. He made R&B singles for Imperial 1960-61, his own inimitable covers of Fats Domino, Dave Bartholemew, Jesse Belvin but they didn't sell; an all round entertainer being type cast as a blues singer and preferring to work with a combo, he was semi-retired for a while, but was talked back into the studio for the delightful 1971 album now on Sonet in the UK, and has also made more records including demos with Professor Longhair. (Donald Clarke, April 1989).

### BABY YOU CAN GET YOUR GUN

Tracks: / You give me nothing but the blues / Oh sweetness / Lavinia / Baby you can get your gun / Drop the bomb / That certain door / Mary Joe / Nobody knows / Pretty girls everywhere.

**Cass:** Released '88, on Black Top (USA) by Rounder Records (USA). Catalogue no: **BT 1037C**

**CD:** Released '88, on Black Top (USA) by Rounder Records (USA). Catalogue no: **BT 1037CD**

**Album:** Released Jun '87, on Demon by Demon Records. Catalogue no: **FIEND 96**

**Album:** Released '88, on Black Top (USA) by Rounder Records (USA). Catalogue no: **BT 1037**

### DOWN YONDER

Tracks: / Down yonder / No more doggin' / Talk to your daughter / Going to the river / Oh red / Yours truly / Travelling mood / St. Pete Florida blues / Teeny bit of your love, A / Mustang Sally / Let the four winds blow / San Jose.

**Album:** Released Aug '78, on Sonet by Sonet Records. Catalogue no: **SNTF 752**

**Album:** Released May '89, on GNP Crescendo (USA) by GNP Crescendo Records (USA). Catalogue no: **GNPS 10023**

### LEGACY OF THE BLUES-2

Tracks: / Boogie children / Who's loving you? / Lucille / Drive it home / Good news / Funky Malaguena / Pinetop's boogie woogie / That same old train / I get the blues / Young boy blues / Tomorrow night / Little girl of mine.

**Album:** Released May '89, on GNP Crescendo (USA) by GNP Crescendo Records (USA). Catalogue no: **GNPS 10012**

**CD:** Released '88, on Sonet by Sonet Records. Catalogue no: **SNTCD 625**

**Album:** Released '88, on Sonet by Sonet Records. Catalogue no: **SNTF 625**

### NEW ORLEANS 1960-61

**Album:** Released '88, on Sundown by Magnum Music Group. Catalogue no: **CG 709-04**

### OUT OF NOWHERE

**CD:** Released Mar '90, on Black Top (USA) by Rounder Records (USA). Catalogue no: **JJCD13**

**CD:** Released Oct '89, on Demon by Demon Records. Catalogue no: **FIENDCD 146**

**Album:** Released Oct '89, on Demon by Demon Records. Catalogue no: **FIEND 146**

### PORTRAITS IN BLUES VOL. 1

**Album:** Released Jan '88, on Storyville by Storyville Records AB. Catalogue no: **SLP 146**

### POSSUM UP A SIMMON TREE

**Album:** Released May '81, on Arhoolie (USA) by Arhoolie Records (USA). Catalogue no: **ARHOOLIE 2014**

## Eardley, Jon

### JON EARDLEY-MICK PYNE (Eardley, Jon/Mick Pyne)

Tracks: / Crazy rhythm / Basin Street blues / Emily / My funny valentine / You don't know what love is / My old flame / You'd be so nice to come home to / Nightingale sang in Berkeley Square, A.

**Album:** Released '83, on Spotlite by Spotlite Records. Catalogue no: **SPJ LP 16**

### NAMELY ME

Tracks: / Andree / Namely me / Sabam / Laugh little boy / Konigawenz / Bell and bugle / Horshoe curve.

**Album:** Released '83, on Spotlite by Spotlite Records. Catalogue no: **SPJ LP 17**

## Earland, Charles

**Biographical details:** This American keyboards player came to prominence in the jazz market in 1970 with his *Black talk* album. Throughout the early Seventies, his urgent organ style attracted considerable acclaim because it broke away from the ponderous blues approach that had come to be associated with jazz organists. Adding synthesisers and electric piano to his range of instruments, Earland went disco in the mid-Seventies. In this capacity, he achieved his sole UK chart entry - *Let the music play*, which featured an unnamed male vocalist, reached No.46 on the singles chart in 1978. He continued to release albums into the Eighties, although his wavering between jazz and dance styles tended to lessen his chances of maintaining a loyal audience. (Bob MacDonald, 21.7.85).

An orgainist and compser, born in 1941 in Philadelphia. He also plays soprano sax. He started on alto-sax, played tenor at 17 with organist Jimmy McGriff, switched to organ in 1963 and has become one of the most popular organists, his walking or rolling bass lines fitting either jazz or rockish settings. (Donald Clarke, April 1989).

### COMING TO YOU LIVE

Tracks: / Cornbread / Take me to heaven / Good question / I will never tell / Zee funkin' space / It's the woman in you / Coming to you live / Spend the night with me.

**Album:** Released Feb '81, on CBS by CBS Records. Deleted '86. Catalogue no: **CBS 84815**

### DOGGIE BOOGIE BABY

Tracks: / Doggie boogie baby.

**12" Single:** on MCA by MCA Records. Catalogue no: **MCAT 880**

**7" Single:** on MCA by MCA Records. Catalogue no: **MCA 880**

### IN THE POCKET

Tracks: / Tackhead / In the alley / Grant's groove / Ballad for Mom / Good date, A.

Note: Artists include Charlie Earland, Houston Person, Melvin (Hassan) Sparks, Idris Muhammad.

**Album:** Released Aug '82, on Muse by Black & Blue Records. Catalogue no: **MR 5240**

### INFANT EYES

Tracks: / We are not alone / Blues for Rudy / Thang, The / Infant eyes / Is it necessary?.

Note: Charlie Earland, organ; Bill Hardman, trumpet; Frank Wess, flute and tenor sax; Mack Goldsbury, tenor sax; Jimmy Ponder, guitar; Melvin Sparks, guitar; Grady Tate, drums; Lawrence Killian, percussion.

**Album:** Released Apr '81, on Muse by Black & Blue Records. Catalogue no: **MR 5181**

**LET THE MUSIC PLAY**
Tracks: / Let the music play.
**7" Single:** Released Aug '78, on Mercury by Phonogram Ltd. Deleted '83. Catalogue no: **6167 703**

**PLEASANT AFTERNOON**
**Album:** Released '81, on Muse by Black & Blue Records. Catalogue no: **MR 5201**

## Early Black Swing

**EARLY BLACK SWING (Various artists)**
Tracks: / Louis shuffle: *Henderson, Fletcher & His Orchestra* / Sugar foot stomp: *Henderson, Fletcher & His Orchestra* / Jimtown blues: *Henderson, Fletcher & His Orchestra* / Diga diga doo: *Ellington, Duke/his Cotton Club Orchestra* / Saratoga swing: *Ellington, Duke/his Cotton Club Orchestra* / Blue feeling: *Ellington, Duke/his Cotton Club Orchestra* / South: *Moten, Bennie Kansas City Orchestra* / Moten swing: *Moten, Bennie Kansas City Orchestra* / Milenberg joys: *McKinney's Cotton Pickers* / Plain dirt: *McKinney's Cotton Pickers* / Grand piano blues: *Hines, Earl & His Orchestra* / Everybody loves my baby: *Hines, Earl & His Orchestra* / Hot tempered blues: *Johnson, Charlie Paradise Ten* / Boy in the boat (the rock): *Johnson, Charlie Paradise Ten* / Market Street stomp: *Missourians* / Prohibition blues: *Missourians.*
**Cass:** Released Jul '89, on Bluebird (2) by BMG Records (UK). Catalogue no: **NK 89583**
**CD:** Released Jul '89, on Bluebird (2) by BMG Records (UK). Catalogue no: **ND 89583**
**Album:** Released Jul '89, on Bluebird (2) by BMG Records (UK). Catalogue no: **NL 89583**
**Album:** Released Aug '89, on Bluebird (2) by BMG Records (UK). Catalogue no: **NL 90365**
**Cass:** Released Aug '89, on Bluebird (2) by BMG Records (UK). Catalogue no: **NK 90365**
**CD:** Released Aug '89, on Bluebird (2) by BMG Records (UK). Catalogue no: **ND 90365**

## Early Glenn Miller

**EARLY GLENN MILLER (Various artists)**
**Album:** Released '88, on Collectors Must Catalogue no: **M 8003**

**EARLY GLENN MILLER - VOL. 2 (Miller, Glenn)**
**Album:** Released Feb '89, on Collectors Must Catalogue no: **M 8004**

## East Coast Blues

**EAST COAST BLUES (Various artists)**
Tracks: / So many days / That gal's no good / Foolin' me / Don't be funny baby / Goin' to Chattanooga / New goin' down slow / Number writer / Laughing blues / Somebody changed the lock / You're a little too slow / Driving that thing / I can shake it / I will never love again / No love blues / Lizzie Lou.
**Album:** Released Jan '88, on Krazy Kat by Interstate Music. Catalogue no: **KK 824**

**EAST COAST BLUES 1924-37 (Various artists)**
**Album:** Released Dec '88, on Yazoo (USA) by Shanachie Records (USA). Catalogue no: **L 1013**
**Album:** Released Apr '89, on Blues Document Catalogue no: **BD 2038**

## East Side Stompers

**ALGIERS STRUT 1985**
Tracks: / Bourbon Street parade / Curse of an aching heart, The / China boy / Flat foot / Algiers strut / Stevedore stomp / Savoy blues / Coney Island washboard / Double dare you / Tuxedo rag / Freddie Moore rag / Chimes blues.
**Album:** Released Jul '86, on VJM (Vintage Jazz Music) by Vintage Jazz Music Society(VJM). Catalogue no: **LC 37**

**ORIGINAL EAST SIDE STOMPERS, THE**
**Album:** Released Apr '79, on VJM (Vintage Jazz Music) by Vintage Jazz Music Society(VJM). Catalogue no: **LC 21S**

## Easton, Ted

**KIDNEY STEW (Easton, Ted & His Band)**
Note With Eddie 'Cleanhead' Vinson.
**Album:** Released Aug '88, on Circle (USA) by Jazzology Records (USA). Catalogue no: **CLP 57**

**PEANUTS HUCKO WITH TED EASTON'S BAND (Easton, Ted & His Friends)**
**Album:** Released Aug '88, on Circle (USA) by Jazzology Records (USA). Catalogue no: **CLP 21**

**SALUTE TO SATCHMO (Easton, Ted & His Friends)**
**Album:** Released Jun '86, on Circle (USA) by Jazzology Records (USA). Catalogue no: **CLP 12**

## Easy Riders Jazz Band

**RED WING**
Note: Features the Easy Riders Jazz Band with Kid Thomas & Sammy Rimington)
**Album:** Released Jun '86, on GHB by Jazzology Records (USA). Catalogue no: **GHB 189**

## Eaton, Cleveland

**Biographical details:** This American bass guitarist and keyboards player played bass with Ramsey Lewis' band during the late 60's and early 70's. Lewis, a renowned keyboardist, also employed future Earth Wind & Fire leader Maurice White for a considerable portion of this era. Eaton eventually went solo and issued a series of nondescript albums. He achieved his sole British chart entry in 1978 - *Bama boogie woogie*, a dreary disco offering, transferred itself from the dance floor to the no.35 slot on the pop chart, despite a dearth of radio airplay. His LP's have include *Half and half*, *Instant hip* and *Keep love alive*, all featuring his brand of jazz-funk. (Bob Macdonald, 21/7/85).

**BAMA BOOGIE WOOGIE**
Tracks: / Bama boogie woogie / West coast disco / Funky funky music / Pure love / Whammy omy / Flying high / Chitown theme / Funky cello.
**Album:** Released Jan '79, on Miracle by Gull Records. Deleted '88. Catalogue no: **MLP 3001**

**IT'S A SHAME (Eaton, Cleveland & Cinnamon)**
Tracks: / It's a shame / Cryin' tears for you.
**7" Single:** Released Jan '80, on Miracle by Gull Records. Deleted '83. Catalogue no: **M 14**

**KEEP LOVE ALIVE**
Tracks: / Birmingham train / I'm lonely tonight / Burnin' / I don't know / Get off / Flyin' high / Free at last / Keep love alive.
**Album:** Released Mar '80, on Miracle by Gull Records. Deleted '88. Catalogue no: **MLP 3008**

## Echoes Of New Orleans

**ECHOES OF NEW ORLEANS (Various artists)**
**Album:** Released Jun '88, on GHB by Jazzology Records (USA). Catalogue no: **GHB 139**

## Eckstine, Billy

**Biographical details:** This American singer, born in Pittsburgh, Pennsylvania in 1913, took up singing at the age of 11. After his family moved to Washington DC, he developed his contrasting interests in music and football. He could not decide which of these talents would make a better career; but the choice was made for him when, after gaining an athletic scholarship to a university, he broke his collar bone. His big break as a singer came in 1939, when bandleader Earl Hines spotted him performing in a Chicago club. Eckstine became the ensemble's regular vocalist, and stayed with them for four years. During his time with Hines, Eckstine was joined on vocals by a young protege named Sarah Vaughan. When Billy formed his own band in 1944, he employed Sarah plus a host of talented musicians: his orchestra proved to be a training ground for such future jazz stars as Art Blakey, Miles Davis, Dizzy Gillespie and Charlie Parker. Billy and his band scored two smash hits in the mid-forties with *Cottage for sale* and *Prisoner of love.* The orchestra disbanded in 1947, and Eckstine became a solo recording artist and performer. During the late forties and early fifties, his baritone crooning made him one of America's top singers. His string of jazzy hits included *Everything I have is yours*, *Blue moon*, *Caravan*, *My foolish heart* and *I apologise* - many of these numbers were drawn from the Thirties. These American hits took place before the British charts were inaugurated, but Eckstine enjoyed a big UK chart hit at the end of '54 - *No-one but you* reached no.3. in 1959 he reached the UK no.8 position with his

rendition of *Gigi*, the theme from the smash musical. In duet with Sarah Vaughan, he achieved a belated British no.17 hit in 1969 with their 1957 recording of *Passing strangers*. Mr. B, as he was known, influenced many singers with his individual style of phrasing, and was one of the first jazz vocalists to achieve a worldwide reputation. (Bob Macdonald, 22/7/85)
The American jazz-balladeer with the deep velvet voice was born William Clarence Eckstein in 1914 in Pittsburgh; he also played trumpet, valve trombone and guitar. He sang with Earl Hines 1939-43, then led one of the most influential bands of the day 1944-47 with tenor saxist / arranger Budd Johnson. Sidemen at various times including Gene Ammons, Art Blakey, Miles Davies, Kenny Dorham, Dizzy Gillespie, Dexter Gordon, Fats Navarro, Lucky Thompson, Charlie Parker, singing partners Lena Horne and Sara Vaughan, arrangements by Tadd Dameron and others as well as Johnson (who by the way worked for all the most influential bands of the day--Woody Herman, Hines, Eckstine and Body Raeburn--and whose influence is underrated). This fine outfit was unsuccessful commercially: the music business didn't give a damn and musicians' union strikes hurt studio recording *Together* on Spotlite for example in an Armed Forces Network recording). Eckstine led an octet briefly then took his big beautiful voice to market and had many hits, including duets with Sassy. He is still one of the USA's favourite entertainers and there was recently a flurry of record activity in the USA: a two-disc compilation *Everything I have is yours* of 1949-57 hit tracks and a new album *Billy Eckstine sings with Benny Carter* with guest Helen Merrill (nominated for a Grammy); whether Polygram will be bothered to let the UK see them is the question. (Donald Clarke, April 1989).

**BLOWING THE BLUES AWAY (Eckstine, Billy & His Orchestra)**
**Album:** Released Dec '87, on Swingtime by Contact Records (Denmark). Catalogue no: **ST 1015**

**GIGI**
Tracks: / Gigi.
**7" Single:** Released Feb '59, on Mercury (EMI) Deleted '64. Catalogue no: **AMT 1018**

**GOLDEN HOUR: BILLY ECKSTINE**
Tracks: / Just a little lovin' / What the world needs now is love / My Cherie amour / Taste of my tears, The / Remembering / I am yours / Maybe this time / Sophisticated lady / We've only just begun / Make it with you / If she walked into my life / Very thought of you, The / Loving arms / All in love is fair / Walk a mile in my shoes / Feel the warm / Mixed-up girl.
**Album:** Released Oct '75, on Golden Hour Catalogue no: **GH 842**

**GREATEST HITS: BILLY ECKSTINE**
Tracks: / I apologise / Love me or leave me / St. Louis blues / Here comes the blues / Life is just a bowl of cherries / Tenderly / Taking a chance on love / Everything I have is yours / How high the moon / Laura / You're driving me crazy / No one but you / I left my hat in Haiti / As long as I love.
**Album:** Released Mar '84, on Polydor by Polydor Ltd. Deleted Dec '89. Catalogue no: **SPELP 64**
**Cass:** Released Mar '84, on Polydor by Polydor Ltd. Catalogue no: **SPEMC 64**

**I AM A SINGER**
**Album:** Released Mar '87, on Kim Catalogue no: **KIM 1**

**IMAGINATION**
Tracks: / It was so beautiful / I gotta right to sing the blues / Love is just around the corner / I don't stand a ghost of a chance / Faded summer love, A / What a little moonlight can do / Imagination / Lullaby of the leaves / I cover the waterfront / I wished on the moon / That's all.
**Album:** Released Jun '88, on Memoir by Memoir Records. Catalogue no: **MOIR 129**
**Cass:** Released Nov '89, on Memoir by Memoir Records. Catalogue no: **CMOIR 129**

**MR. B AND THE BAND - SAVOY SESSIONS**
**2 LP Set:** Released Feb '86, on Savoy by Savoy Records. Catalogue no: **WL 70552**

**NO ONE BUT YOU**
Tracks: / No one but you.
**7" Single:** Released Sep '57, on MGM by Polydor Ltd. Deleted '62. Catalogue no: **MGM 164**

**ONCE MORE WITH FEELING**
**Album:** Released Feb '88, on Fresh Sounds (Spain) by Fresh Sounds Records (Spain). Catalogue no: **FS 134**

**PASSING STRANGERS (Eckstine, Billy & Sarah Vaughan)**
Tracks: / Passing strangers.
**7" Single:** Released Mar '69, on Mercury by Phonogram Ltd. Deleted '74. Catalogue no: **MF 1082**
**78 rpm:** Released '57, on Mercury (Pye) Deleted '58. Catalogue no: **MT 164**

**SAVOY SESSIONS, THE (Eckstine, Billy/Mr B & The Band)**
**2 LP Set:** Released Mar '85, on Savoy Jazz (USA) by Malaco Records (USA). Catalogue no: **SJL 2214**

**SOMETHING MORE**
Tracks: / Something more / All in love is fair / Mixed-up girl / Song for you, A / Remembering / Sophisticated lady / Feel the warm / Think about things / Very thought of you, The / Thank you for the moment / Maybe this time, Mister / You've gone and got the blues.
**Album:** Released Oct '81, on Stax by Fantasy Inc (USA). Catalogue no: **STAXL 5007**
**Cass:** Released Oct '81, on Stax by Fantasy Inc (USA). Catalogue no: **STAXK 5007**

**TOGETHER (Eckstine, Billy Big Band)**
Tracks: / Blowing the blues away (Instrumental number.) / Deed I do (Vocal number.) / I wanna talk about you (Vocal number.) / Together (Vocal number.) / Mean to me (Vocal number.) / Without a song (Vocal number.) / Mr. Chips (Instrumental number.) / Airmail special (Instrumental number.) / Don't blame me (Vocal number.) / If that's the way you feel (Vocal number.) / Opus X (Instrumental number.) / Love me or leave me (Instrumental number.).
Note: Sarah Vaughan, Lena Horne and Billy Eckstine share the vocals and sidesmen include Fats Navarro, Bud Johnson, Gene Ammons and John Malachi.
**Album:** Released May '83, on Spotlite by Spotlite Records. Catalogue no: **SPJ 100**

## ECM Spectrum

**ECM SPECTRUM VOL.1 (Various artists)**
Note: Duration 67 minutes, 13 tracks. Unique compilation available only on CD, covers 1974-1984. Personnel include Pat Metheny, Keith Jarrett, John Surman, Charlie Haden, Terje Rypdal, Shankar, Egberto Gismonti, Nana Vasconcelos, John Abercrombie, Don Cherry, Ed Blackwell, Jack DeJohnette.
**CD:** Released Jun '89, on ECM Catalogue no: **831 623-2**

## Eddie & Sugar Lou...

**EDDIE & SUGAR LOU'S HOTEL TYLER 1929-31 (Eddie & Sugar Lou's Hotel Tyler Orchestra)**
**Album:** Released Jul '87, on Everybody's (Sweden) Catalogue no: **E-1012**

## Edison, Harry Sweets

**BEST OF HARRY EDISON**
Tracks: / Edison's lights / Ain't misbehavin' / Avalon / E / Miz Kitty's blues / Feelings / My ideal / Simply sweets.
**Cass:** Released '82, on Pablo Jazz (USA) by Pablo Records (USA). Catalogue no: **K10 847**
**Album:** Released '82, on Pablo Jazz (USA) by Pablo Records (USA). Catalogue no: **231 0847**

**BLUES FOR BASIE**
Tracks: / Blues for Piney Brown / Blues for the blues / Blues for Basie / Gee baby ain't I good to you / You're getting to be a habit with me / Taste on the place / Moonlight in Vermont.
**Album:** Released Jun '77, on Verve Catalogue no: **2332 082**

**EDISON, DAVIS & BOONE (Edison, Harry Sweets, Eddie Lockjaw Davis & Richard Boone)**
**Album:** Released '88, on Storyville by Storyville Records AB. Catalogue no: **SLP 271**

**EDISON'S LIGHTS**
Tracks: / Edison's lights / Ain't misbehavin' / Avalon / E / Helena's theme /

Homegrown / Spring is here / On the trail.
**Album:** Released '82, on Pablo Jazz (USA) by Pablo Records (USA). Catalogue no: **2310 780**
**Cass:** Released '82, on Pablo Jazz (USA) by Pablo Records (USA). Catalogue no: **K10 780**

**HARRY 'SWEETS' EDISON & EDDIE 'LOCKJAW' DAVIS (Edison, Harry Sweets & Eddie 'Lockjaw' Davis)**
**Album:** Released Feb '90, on Storyville by Storyville Records AB. Catalogue no: **SLP 276**

**INVENTIVE MR EDISON, THE (Edison, Harry Sweets Quartet)**
**Album:** Released Feb '88, on Fresh Sounds (Spain) by Fresh Sounds Records (Spain). Catalogue no: **FS 50**

**JAZZ AT THE PHILHARMONIC 1983 (Edison, Harry Sweets /Eddie "Lockjaw" Davis/Al Grey)**
**Album:** Released May '83, on Pablo Jazz (USA) by Pablo Records (USA). Catalogue no: **2310 882**
**Cass:** Released May '83, on Pablo Jazz (USA) by Pablo Records (USA). Catalogue no: **K10 882**

**JUST FRIENDS (Edison, Harry Sweets and John Haley Sims)**
**Album:** Released '82, on Pablo Jazz (USA) by Pablo Records (USA). Catalogue no: **231 0841**
**Cass:** Released '82, on Pablo Jazz (USA) by Pablo Records (USA). Catalogue no: **K10 841**

**MEETING IN STOCKHOLM (Edison, Harry Sweets & Claes Crona)**
**Album:** Released Oct '88, on Beaver (Sweden) Catalogue no: **BRLP 001**

**OPUS FUNK VOL. 2 (Edison, Harry Sweets & Eddie 'Lockjaw' Davis)**
**Album:** Released May '86, on Storyville by Storyville Records AB. Catalogue no: **SLP 4025**

**SIMPLY SWEETS (Edison, Harry 'Sweets' & Eddie 'Lockjaw' Davis)**
Tracks: / Dirty butt blues / Feelings / One for the Count / My ideal / Simply sweets / Opus funk / Lax / Miz Kitty's blues.
**Cass:** Released '82, on Pablo Jazz (USA) by Pablo Records (USA). Catalogue no: **K10 806**
**Album:** Released '82, on Pablo Jazz (USA) by Pablo Records (USA). Catalogue no: **231 0806**

**SWEET TRACKS (Edison, Harry Sweets & Jimmy Forrest)**
Tracks: / Pussy Willow / Centerpiece / Indiana / If I had you / Jive at five / Imagination / Louisiana / Candy / Harriet / Sweetnings / Paradise / It happened in Monterey / Angel eyes / Sweet cakes / It's easy to remember (so hard to forget) / Twenty forty / There is no greater love / Tea for two / They can't take that away from me / Candid sweets / Ain't misbehavin' / I'm confessin' / Blue skies / Witchcraft.
**Album:** Released Jul '78, on Vogue by Vogue Records. Catalogue no: **VJD 547**

**SWINGER, THE**
Tracks: / Pussy Willow / Nasty / Thought of you, The / Stroller, The / Sunday / Fairground.
Note: Recorded 1958 with Jimmy Forrest/Jimmy Jones/Freddie Green/Joe Benjamin.
**Album:** Released May '82, on Verve Catalogue no: **2304 538**

## Edwards, Eddie

**EDDIE EDWARDS ORIGINAL DIXELAND**
Note: With Tony Sbarbaro
**Album:** Released '87, on Commodore Class Catalogue no: **6.26170**

## Egan, Mark

**TOUCH OF LIGHT, A**
Note: GRP debut from reowned bass player Mark Egan. Having performed for years with the Pat Metheny group and other notables such as Gil Evans, David Sanborn and Michael Franks, 'A touch of light' is the culmination of Mark Egan's broad spectrum of musical experience. With Bill Evans (sop. sax); Cafe (percussion); Gil Goldstein (keyboards); Danny Gottlieb (drums); Clifford Carter (piano). CD contains an extra track.
**Album:** Released Sep '88, on GRP by GRP Records (USA). Catalogue no: **GR 9572**
**CD:** Released Sep '88, on GRP by GRP Records (USA). Catalogue no: **GRD 9572**
**Cass:** Released Sep '88, on GRP by GRP Records (USA). Catalogue no: **GRC 9572**

## Eldridge, Roy

**Biographical details:** Trumpeter, one of the most influential in history (1911-89); he also played piano, bass, drums and sang. He was nickname 'Little Jazz' around 1930. His solo of Fletcher Henderson's *Stealin' apples* made him famous among musicians; then he joined Gene Krupa, where he had vocal duet hits with Anita O'Day as well as his own trumpet features. His complete technical ability and power in reserve made him the primary model for the young Dizzy Gillespie. He toured and recorded a great deal for Norman Granz and only stopped playing in 1980 when he had a stroke. (Donald Clarke, April 1989).

**ARCADIA BALLROOM 39**
Note: Mono.
**Album:** Released Jul '86, on Jazz Archives (USA) by Jazz Archives Inc.(USA). Catalogue no: **JA 14**

**ART FORD'S JAZZ PARTY (October 1958)**
Note: With Buck Clayton/Urbie Green / Buster Bailey / Stuff Smith / Bill Henderson / Harry Sheppard. Tracks include: Basin Street / C Jam blues / Rose room / Baby please come home / Stompin' at the Savoy / Blue skies / I got rhythm / Somebody loves me, etc.
**Album:** Released Oct '87, on Jazz Connoisseur by Spotlite Records. Catalogue no: **AFJP 7**

**BEST OF ROY ELDRIDGE**
Tracks: / Recado bossa nova / Swee-

Roy Eldridge - Little Jazz Live '57 (Jazz Band)

thearts on parade / Willow,weep for me / Gofor / I want a little girl / That thing / All of me / Bye bye blackbird.
**Album:** Released '82, on Pablo Jazz (USA) by Pablo Records (USA). Catalogue no: **231 0857**
**Cass:** Released '82, on Pablo Jazz (USA) by Pablo Records (USA). Catalogue no: **K10 857**

**DALE'S WAIL**
Tracks: / Little jazz / Wrap your troubles in dreams / Roy's riff / Rockin' chair / Love for sale / Man I love / Oscar's arrangement / Dale's wail / Somebody loves me / Willow weep for me / I can't get started / When it's sleepy time down South / Don't blame me / Feeling a draft / Echoes of Harlem / When your lover has gone / Blue moon / Stormy weather / Sweethearts on parade / Foggy day / If I had you / I only have eyes for you / Sweet Georgia Brown / Song is ended.
**2 LP Set:** Released '79, on Verve Deleted '84. Catalogue no: **2632081**

**EARLY YEARS, THE**
**Album:** Released '88, on CBS (import) by CBS Records. Catalogue no: **CBS 88585**

**HAPPY TIME**
Tracks: / Sweethearts on parade / Willow weep for me / Makin' whoopee / Gee baby ain't I good to you / All of me / I want a little girl / On the sunny side of the street / I can't get started / Stormy Monday / Let me off uptown.
**Album:** Released '82, on Pablo Jazz (USA) by Pablo Records (USA). Catalogue no: **231 0746**
**Cass:** Released '82, on Pablo Jazz (USA) by Pablo Records (USA). Catalogue no: **K10 7**

**HEAT'S ON, THE (Eldridge, Roy / Howard McGhee)**
**Album:** Released Apr '79, on Esquire by Titan Int. Prod.. Catalogue no: **ESQ 307**

**JAZZ MATURITY...WHERE IT'S COMING FROM (Eldridge, Roy & Dizzy Gillespie)**
**Cass:** Released '82, on Pablo Jazz (USA) by Pablo Records (USA). Catalogue no: **K10 816**
**Album:** Released '82, on Pablo Jazz (USA) by Pablo Records (USA). Catalogue no: **231 0816**

**KRUPA YEARS 1941-2 (Sideman 1940)**
**Album:** Released '88, on Meritt (USA) Catalogue no: **MERITT 502**

**KRUPA YEARS, THE**
**Album:** Released May '88, on Nostalgia by Mainline Records. Catalogue no: **NOST 7642**

**LITTLE JAZZ**
Tracks: / King David / It don't mean a thing / Wrap your troubles in dreams / Undecided / Ain't no flies on me / Man I love, The / Easter parade / Wild driver / If I had you / Nuts / Someone to watch over me / Goliath / Bounce / I remember Harlem / Baby, don't do me like that / Une petite laitue / L'Isle Adam / Black and blue / Tue disais quetu m'aimais / Oh shut up / Hollywood pastime / I'd love him so / Heat is on, The / Wild man blues / Fireworks.
**2 LP Set:** Released May '83, on Vogue Jazz (France) by Vogue Records. Catalogue no: **VJD 533**

**LITTLE JAZZ LIVE IN 1957 (See panel on previous page)**
Tracks: / Sweet Georgia Brown / Embraceable you / Lover come back to me / Little jazz / Rockin' chair / Lady be good / Soft wind / Perdido / Long blues, The.
Note: This exciting album is a true delight for Eldridge fans and includes what is surely some of Roy's very best playing ever. The beautifully mournful *Embraceable you* is by itself enough to elevate the entire record to five stars - just gorgeous. Astonishly *Little jazz* was blowing as searingly as ever, if more sparingly, right up until his December, 1980, heart attack, which stilled his trumpet forever. I know, because I went to see him play about a dozen times a month during his last thirty months as a performer at Jimmy Ryan's Club on West 54th Street in New York City. The gig called for mostly dixieland and Roy generally played perfunctorily through the first set which always commenced a lot closer to ten than the advertised nine o' clock start. Some nights, during the balmy weather, Roy would pull his nautical deck chair and sit right in front of the club throughout the lengthy intermissions. Other nights, he would make his way the fifty yards to the corner of Broadway and 54th and the legendary Cecil Tavern. A bit dingy, but with booths, a long bar and the last bar and the last place in Manhattan where draft beer could be had for a mere thirty cents, Cecil's also boasted a juke box that included the Krupa-Eldridge collaboration on *After you've gone*. I spent a lot of intermissions with Roy in Cecil's but he always paced his straight vodka consumption very carefully and only took two big shots prior to the final set at just after two in the morning. By this time there were never more than a handful of patrons remaining and Roy would be personally in the mood to play a ballad. One per night, and only after two o'clock, but I waited for a lot of them ... *The man I love, Rocking chair, Body and soul, Embraceable you, Stardust* ... He never missed, which he had occasionally done at certain jazz festivals earlier.
At age seventy Roy still had the fire which doubtless contributed to his heart attack. Happily, he survived and is enjoying his life in contented retirement. *Little jazz* leads off our album and Roy plays with great emotion. John Faddis made a recent recording of this tune and even had me fooled that it might be Roy until I realised it was almost note-for-note the old 1945 Artie Shaw record. Roy never played anything the same twice, of course. Speaking of Shaw, I recently asked Dick Johnson why the current Shaw band doesn't play *Little jazz* 'only because we don't have all the parts anymore - I love the tune' he responded.
Bud Freeman, who just last month wowed them at Don and Sue Miller's Arizona Jazz Party, steals the spotlight on side two, both in tandem with Eldridge and as part of Dave Garroway's birthday party all-star jam session, on *Perdido*. The Goodman-Christian tune *Soft winds* is a delightful change of pace mid-tempo rocker that gives everybody space to solo. As reedman Joe Muranyi told me on many evenings before Roy's final sets: 'This is why I like the job - I live to hear Roy's ballad every night.' Fortunately, we have sufficient outstanding Eldridge ballad material that an ambition of mine to release an all ballad album by Roy is in the works. (Edgar Ward, San Diego, California, April 1988)
**Album:** Released Jun '88, on Jazz Band by Flyright Records. Catalogue no: **EB 408**

**LITTLE JAZZ SPECIAL**
**Album:** Released Jun '86, on Queen Catalogue no: **QUEEN 066**

**LITTLE JAZZ & THE JIMMY RYAN (Eldridge, Roy & The Jimmy Ryan All-Stars)**
Tracks: / Between the Devil and the deep blue sea / St. James' Infirmary / Beale Street blues / Black and blue / Sing, sing, sing / Wynola / Cute / Bourbon Street / All of me / Last call at Jimmy Ryan's.
**Cass:** Released '82, on Pablo Jazz (USA) by Pablo Records (USA). Catalogue no: **K10 869**
**Album:** Released '82, on Pablo Jazz (USA) by Pablo Records (USA). Catalogue no: **231 0869**

**NEVER TOO OLD TO SWING (Eldridge, Roy & Tiny Grimes)**
Tracks: / Romance without romance / West End Phil / T'aint what you do (it's the way that you do it) / Food for thought / One is never too old to swing / In a swinging groove / Downtown sound, The / Frantic.
**Album:** Released Jan '78, on Sonet by Sonet Records. Catalogue no: **SNTF 736**

**NIFTY CAT, THE**
Tracks: / Jolly Hollis / Cotton / 5400 North / Ball of fire / Wineola / Nifty cat, The.
Note: Roy Eldridge, trumpet (vocal on Wineola); Budd Johnson, tenor and soprano saxophones; Benny Morton, trombone; Nat Pierce, piano; Tommy Bryant, bass; Oliver Jackson, drums. Produced by Bill Weilbacher. Recording engineer: Roger Rhodes. Recorded nov 24th 1970 in New York.
**Album:** Released Jan '87, on New World (USA) by New World Records (USA). Catalogue no: **NW 349**
**CD:** Released Dec '86, on New World (USA) by New World Records (USA). Catalogue no: **NWCD 349**

**PORTRAITS IN JAZZ (Eldridge, Roy / Richie Kamuca)**
**Album:** Released Apr '79, on Pumpkin

Catalogue no: **PUMPKIN 107**

**RARE BROADCASTS**
Tracks: / Goof and I, The / Undecided / Heat is on, The / I remember / Interview / Lady Brown.
Note: With Ben Webster, Kai Winding, Dick Wellstood, Slam Stewart, Zutty Singleton, Lou Terrazzi.
**Album:** Released Jun '86, on Duke by Melodisc Records. Catalogue no: **D 1010**

**ROY ELDRIDGE**
**Album:** Released '88, on GNP Crescendo (USA) by GNP Crescendo Records (USA). Catalogue no: **GNPS 9009**

**ROY ELDRIDGE 1957**
**Album:** Released '89, on Jazz Society Catalogue no: **AA 514**

**ROY ELDRIDGE 1935-40**
**Album:** Released '88, on Tax Catalogue no: **TAX 8020**

**ROY ELDRIDGE AT JERRY NEWMAN'S**
Tracks: / Sweet and brown / Body and soul / Lemon house / Jazz rose / Sweet Lorraine / I can't give you anything but love / I surrender, dear (Two takes.) / Way you look tonight (Three takes.) / Rags (Two takes.).
Note: With Willie Smith, Herbie Fields, Tony D'Amore, Buddy Weed, Mike Bryan, George T. Simon, Margie Harris. Recorded: 19 November 1940.
**Album:** Released Jan '83, on Xanadu Catalogue no: **XAN 186**

**ROY ELDRIDGE FOUR**
Tracks: / Between the Devil and the deep blue sea / Gofor / I surrender, dear / Joie de Roy / Perdido / Bye bye blackbird.
**Cass:** Released '82, on Pablo Jazz (USA) by Pablo Records (USA). Catalogue no: **K 08 203**
**Album:** Released '82, on Pablo Jazz (USA) by Pablo Records (USA). Catalogue no: **2308 203**

**TIPPIN' OUT**
**2 LP Set:** Released Oct '85, on Affinity by Charly Records. Catalogue no: **AFSD 1016**

**UNE PETITE LAITUE**
**Album:** Released '88, on Vogue by Vogue Records. Catalogue no: **500092**
**Album:** Released Sep '79, on Jazz Legacy by Vogue Records. Catalogue no: **JL 92**

**WHAT'S IT ALL ABOUT?**
Tracks: / I still love him so / Heat's on, The / That thing / Recado bossa nova / Melange.
**Album:** Released '82, on Pablo Jazz (USA) by Pablo Records (USA). Catalogue no: **231 0766**
**Cass:** Released '82, on Pablo Jazz (USA) by Pablo Records (USA). Catalogue no: **K10 766**

## Elgert, Les

**LES ELGERT AND HIS ORCHESTRA 1946 (Elgert, Les & His Orchestra)**
**Album:** Released Dec '88, on Circle (USA) by Jazzology Records (USA). Catalogue no: **CLP 126**

## Elizalde, Fred

**VOLUME 4 1927-33**
**Cass:** Released Nov '87, on Neovox by Neovox Records. Catalogue no: **NEO 929**

## Ellington, De Lange

**NEWPORT 1958 (Ellington, De Lange & Mills)**
**Cass:** Released Jun '86, on CBS by CBS Records. Deleted Aug '87. Catalogue no: **40 84408**
**Album:** Released Jun '86, on CBS (import) by CBS Records. Catalogue no: **84408**

**NUTCRACKER SUITE (Ellington, De Lange & Mills)**
**Album:** Released Jun '86, on CBS (import) by CBS Records. Catalogue no: **84413**

## Ellington, Duke

**Biographical details:** Edward Kennedy "Duke" Ellington was the greatest composer in the history of jazz, and one of the genre's most accomplished bandleaders and pianists. Although fellow American orchestra leaders such as Glenn Miller, Jimmy Dorsey and Tommy Dorsey were bigger household names and greater record sellers, and although such figures as Louis Armstrong had a stronger public personality, the Duke's pervasive musical influence and amazing consistency made him easily one of the all-time greats. Duke Ellington moved from his native Washington to New York in 1923. During the next fifteen crucial years, he gradually assembled one of the slickest and most innovative ensembles that the burgeoning jazz world had seen. He possessed an uncanny ability to develop his players' strong points and to squeeze every last drop of talent from them, thus bringing out skills that the musicians never knew they had. Having become a regular recording artist as well as a live attraction, Ellington hired a compositional collaborator in 1939, who remained a trusted lieutenant until 1967 - Billy Strayhorn co-wrote several great pieces with Ellington, and received sole composer's credit on the 1941 song *Take the A train.* During the early forties, the Duke was probably at the very peak of his career. The war then proceeded to disrupt all of America's big bands; and although Ellington remained popular through the forties and early fifties, it was not till 1956 that he began to regain his former musical greatness. A particularly noteworthy item during the fifties was his acclaimed *Such sweet thunder*. Swinging through the 60's in fine form, Ellington did not begin to go downhill till 1971. He died in May 1974; exactly 3 years later, Stevie Wonder reached no.1 in America and no.2 in Britain with his tribute single *Sir Duke*. Ellington only chalked up two chart entries in Britain. On the UK singles chart (which was inaugurated in 1952), he reached no.7 in early '54 with *Skin deep*. On the British album listings (started in 1958), he got to no.11 in 1961 with *Nut cracker suite*. (Bob Macdonald, 28/7/85)
Edward Kennedy Ellington (1899-1974) was a pianist, bandleader, arranger and composer; he was all of these things at once, rather that wearing several hats, which made him one of the greatest composers of the century. He led a band of unruly geniuses long after big bands were no longer big business so that he could hear his own music the day after he wrote it. Born into a middle-class family in Washington DC, he went to New York twice looking for work, successful on his second trip; The Washingtonians were led by Elmer Snowden in 1923 but within a couple of years Ellington's band was playing his music. The band became famous through broadcasts from the Cotton Club 1927-31; trumpeter Bubby Miley and trombonist Joe 'Tricky' Sam Nanton practised a growling style, probably borrowed from King Oliver, which, together with the Club's floor shows have it the 'Jungle Band' identity and sound. Ellington had considered a career as an artist; he discovered a talent for tone colour and began to create a unique body of composition and wrote specifically for his own men, so that his band from the beginning had a sensual beauty and an identity as a band that others lacked. Between 1926-30 *East St Louis toodle oo* was recorded eight times on six labels with different arrangements each time as the young composer experimented. On *Mood indigo* in 1930, the classic sound of the melody played by a blend of Nanton, Barney Bigard on clarinet and trumpeter Artie Whetsol showed the formidable skill of a born arranger/composer. The band had already been billed for years as Duke Ellingon & His Famous Orchestra in 1939, when Ben Webster on tenor sax and Jimmy Blanton on bass joined, along with Ellington's amanuensis Billy Strayhorn (1915-67), like Duke a composer and arranger: their work together was so seamless that later they often could not recall who had written what. Webster was the first authoriative tenor stylist in the band, while Blanton was among a handful of the most influential musicians in the history of jazz before his early death from TB. The band began recording for Victor in early 1940 and the flood of masterpieces up to the infamous 1943 musicians unions' strike against the record companies has never been equaled. *The great Ellington units* compiles the small group tracks from 1940\41, some of the most beautiful chamber music ever recorded, especially the Johnny Hodges sides: Strayhorn wrote beautiful

erotic ballads for Hodges alto sax, and the sessions included the first appearance of the riff that would be used in Ellington's *Happy go lucky local* and borrowed in a few years for the early R&B classic *Night train*. By the end of the Forties hard times were setting in for big bands and many critics were writing Duke off, but in 1956 he played at the Newport Jazz Festival and almost started a riot with the 20-year-old arrangement *Diminuendo in blue* and *Crescendo in blue*: Paul Gonsalves on tenor was supposed to play a bridge between the two parts, but played 27 choruses and had the audience dancing in the aisles. Ellington made the cover of Time magazine and the Newport album the top 15 of the Billboard pop album chart, his status as elder statesmen of American music never again in doubt. He also wrote extended compositions, film soundtracks and works for the musical stage, much of this never recorded or even assembled properly; he was always most interested in the work at hand: once his friends presented him with a beautifully bound book of his compositions, he made a gracious speech of thanks and walked away leaving the book behind. New albums are still coming out in the USA from the private stock or from broadcasters' vaults, loving produced by his son Mercer, by Stanley Dance and/or archivist Jerry Valburn; among the late masterpieces/recent reissues are the *New Orleans suite*, 1970, *Far east suite* (1966) and *...And his mother called him Bill* (1967), a tribute to Strayhorn, who sent his last composition *Blood count* to the band from the hosptial where he lay dying of cancer. (Donald Clarke, April 1989).

**FIVE HORN GROVE**
**Album:** Released Nov '88, on Vogue by Vogue Records. Catalogue no: **500094**

**1943 : VOL. 1 (World Broadcasting Service) (Ellington, Duke/His Orchestra)**
**Album:** Released Jan '87, on Circle (USA) by Jazzology Records (USA). Catalogue no: **CLP 101**

**1943 : VOL. 2 (World Broadcasting service) (Ellington, Duke/His Orchestra)**
**Album:** Released Jan '87, on Circle (USA) by Jazzology Records (USA). Catalogue no: **CLP 102**

**1943 : VOL. 3 )World Broadcasting Service) (Ellington, Duke/His Orchestra)**
**Album:** Released Jan '87, on Circle (USA) by Jazzology Records (USA). Catalogue no: **CLP 103**

**1943 : VOL 4 (World Broadcasting Service) (Ellington, Duke/His Orchestra)**
**Album:** Released '88, on Circle (USA) by Jazzology Records (USA). Catalogue no: **CLP 104**

**1943 : VOL 5 (World Broadcasting Service) (Ellington, Duke/His Orchestra)**
**Album:** Released Aug '88, on Circle (USA) by Jazzology Records (USA). Catalogue no: **CLP 105**

**1945 : VOL. 6 (Ellington, Duke & His Orchestra)**
**Album:** Released Aug '88, on Circle (USA) by Jazzology Records (USA). Catalogue no: **CLP 106**

**1945 : VOL. 8 (Ellington, Duke & His Famous Orchestra)**
**Album:** Released '89, on Circle Catalogue no: **CLP 108**

**1945 : VOL. 9 (Ellington, Duke & His Famous Orchestra)**
**Album:** Released 10 Jul '89, on Circle Catalogue no: **CLP 109**

**1953 PASADENA CONCERT, THE**
Tracks: / Tattooed bride, The / Diminuendo and crescendo in blue / Hawk talks, The / Monologue / St. Louis blues / VIP's boogie / Without a song / Do nothing till you hear from me / Street blues / Perdido / Ellington medley.
**Album:** Released May '86, on PRT by Castle Communications Records. Catalogue no: **NP 708**
**CD:** Released '88, on Vogue by Vogue Records. Catalogue no: **VG 600 105**
**Album:** Released Oct '88, on Vogue by Vogue Records. Catalogue no: **500201**
**Cass:** Released May '86, on PRT by Castle Communications Records. Catalogue no: **ZCNCP 708**
**CD:** Released May '89, on GNP Crescendo (USA) by GNP Crescendo Records (USA). Catalogue no: **GNPD 9045**

**1954 LOS ANGELES CONCERT**
**CD:** Released May '89, on GNP Crescendo (USA) by GNP Crescendo Records (USA). Catalogue no: **GNPD 9049**
**CD:** Released Jul '87, on Vogue by Vogue Records. Catalogue no: **VG 600 142**
**Album:** Released Oct '88, on Vogue by Vogue Records. Catalogue no: **500 207**

**1927-30 (Ellington, Duke Orchestra)**
**Album:** Released Sep '87, on Giants of Jazz by Hasmick Promotions. Catalogue no: **LPJT 35**

**1928-33**
Tracks: / Black beauty / Sweet mama / When you're smiling / Admiration / Accordion Joe / Home again blues / Moon over Dixie / Baby when you aint there / Anytime, anyday, anywhere / Delta bound / Eerie moan / Bundle of blues.
**Album:** Released '87, on Joker (USA) by Lifetime Records (USA). Catalogue no: **SM 3081**

**1931-39 VOL 2**
**Album:** Released Sep '87, on Giants of Jazz by Hasmick Promotions. Catalogue no: **LPJT 42**

**1931-1932 (Ellington, Duke Orchestra)**
**CD:** Released Mar '90, on Giants of Jazz by Hasmick Promotions. Catalogue no: **GOJCD53046**

**AFRO - BOSSA (Ellington, Duke / His Orchestra)**
Tracks: / Afro-bossa / Purple gazelle / Absinthe / Moonbow / Sempre amore / Silk lace / Tigress / Angu / Volupte / Bonga pyramid / Eighth veil, The.
Note: Featuring Billy Strayhorn, "Cat" Anderson, "Cootie" Williams, Ray Nance, Buster Cooper, Russell Procope, Johnny Hodges, Paul Gonsalves.
**Album:** Released Jun '83, on Discovery (USA) by Discovery Records (USA). Catalogue no: **DS 871**

**AGE OF ELLINGTON, THE**
Tracks: / Take the A train / I got it bad (and that ain't good) / Sophisticated lady / Perdido / Solitude / Cotton tail / Concerto for Cootie / Mood indigo / C-jam blues / Prelude to a kiss / Caravan / Things ain't what they used to be / Don't get around much anymore / Jump for joy / Chelsea Bridge / Black and tan fantasy / East St. Louis toodle oo / Creole love call / Transblucency / Jack the bear / Harlem air shaft / Sepia panorama / Conga bravo / Rockabye river / Blood count / Raincheck / Lotus blossom / Twitch, The / New world a coming / Black, brown and beige / Perfume suite, The / David danced before.
**LP Set:** Released '79, on RCA by BMG Records (UK). Deleted '84. Catalogue no: **PL 42086**

**ALL STAR ROAD BAND VOL.1 (Ellington, Duke/His Orchestra)**
Tracks: / Take the 'A' train / Such sweet thunder / Frustration / Cop out / Perdido / Mood indigo / Bassment / Sophisticated lady / Stardust / Jeeps blues / All of me / Diminuendo and crescendo in blue / I got it bad and that ain't good / On the sunny side of the street.
**Cass:** Released Mar '84, on Doctor Jazz (USA) by CBS Records (USA). Catalogue no: **ZCASD 850**
**2 LP Set:** Released Mar '84, on Doctor Jazz (USA) by CBS Records (USA). Catalogue no: **ASLD 850**

**ALL STAR ROAD BAND VOL.2 (Ellington, Duke/His Orchestra)**
Tracks: / Mood indigo / Satin doll / Happy go lucky local / Things ain't what they used to be / Do nothing till you hear from me / Guitar amour / Summertime / C-jam blues / Silk lace / I got it bad and that ain't good / Isfahan / Timon of Athens / Tutti for cootie / Stompin' at the Savoy / Jeep's blues / I can't stop loving you / Diminuendo and crescendo in blue.
**2 LP Set:** Released '86, on Doctor Jazz (USA) by CBS Records (USA). Catalogue no: **ASLD 853**
**Cass:** Released '86, on Doctor Jazz (USA) by CBS Records (USA). Catalogue no: **ZCASD 853**

**ANATOMY OF A MURDER**
**Album:** Released Jun '86, on CBS (import) by CBS Records. Catalogue no: **84411**

**AND HIS MOTHER CALLED HIM BILL (Ellington, Duke/His Orchestra)**
Tracks: / Boo-dah / U.M.M.G. / Blood

count / Smada / Rock skipping at the Blue Note / Raincheck / Midriff (CD only) / My little brown book / Lotus blossom / Snibor / After all / All day long / Daydream / Intimacy of the blues, The / Charpoy.
**Album:** Released Feb '84, on RCA (France) by BMG Records (France). Deleted '89. Catalogue no: **NL 89166**
**Album:** Released '79, on RCA Victor by BMG Records (UK). Deleted '84. Catalogue no: **LSA 3073**
**CD:** Released Feb '84, on RCA by BMG Records (UK). Deleted May '89. Catalogue no: **NK 89166**
**CD:** Released Apr '88, on Bluebird (2) by BMG Records (UK). Catalogue no: **ND 86287**

**AND THE ELLINGTONIANS**
Tracks: / Cat walk / Moonlight fiesta / She / Happening, The / Swamp drums / Sultry serenade / Indian summer / Britt and butter blues / Caravan / Alternate / Hoppin' John / Jumpin' with symphony Sid / New piano roll blues, The / Perdido / Take the 'A' train / Oscalypso / Blues for Blanton / Things ain't what they used to be / Make no mistake / In a blue summer garden / Cottontail / Flamingo / Bang up blues / "C" Jam blues / Johnny come lately / Great times.
**2 LP Set:** Released May '83, on Vogue Jazz (France) by Vogue Records. Catalogue no: **VJD 525**

**ART OF DUKE ELLINGTON (Great Paris concert)**
Tracks: / Kinda dukish / On the sunny side of the street / Star crossed lovers / All of me / Asphalt jungle, The / Concerto for Cootie / Tutti for cootie / Suite Thursday / Perdido / Eighth veil, The / Rose of the Rio Grande / Cop out / Bula / Jam with Sam / Happy go lucky / Local / Tone parallel to Harlem.
**Album:** on Atlantic by WEA Records. Catalogue no: **K 60044**

**AT CARNEGIE HALL NOV 23 1946 (Ellington, Duke Orchestra)**
Tracks: / Eighth veil, The / Golden feather / Flippant flurry / Golden cress / Unbooted character, The / Sultry sunset / Deep south suite.
**Album:** Released Apr '81, on Queendisc (Italy) Catalogue no: **QU 018**

**AT HIS VERY BEST**
Tracks: / Jack the Bear / Concerto for Cootie(Do nothin' till you hear from me) / Harlem air shaft / Across the track blues / Chloe / Royal Garden blues / Warm valley / Koko / Black, brown and beige / Creole love call / Transbluecency.
**Album:** Released Jan '73, on RCA by BMG Records (UK). Catalogue no: **LSA 3071**

**AT NEWPORT**
Tracks: / Newport jazz festival suite / Festival junction / Blues to be there / Newport up / Jeep's Blues / Diminuendo And Crescendo In Blues.
**Album:** Released Jun '86, on CBS (import) by CBS Records. Catalogue no: **84403**
**Cass:** Released 27 Feb '88, on CBS (import) by CBS Records. Catalogue no: **4509864**
**Album:** Released 27 Feb '88, on CBS (import) by CBS Records. Catalogue no: **4509861**

**AT NEWPORT (II)**
**Album:** Released Jun '86, on CBS (import) by CBS Records. Catalogue no: **84420**

**AT SOUTHLAND AND COTTON CLUB**
**Album:** Released '88, on Collector's Classics Catalogue no: **CC 16**

**AT TANGLEWOOD - JULY 15, 1956 VOL. 1 (Ellington, Duke Orchestra)**
Tracks: / Newport jazz festival suite / Festival junction / Blues to be there / Newport up / Hawk talks, The / Prelude to a kiss / I got it bad / La Virgen de la Macarena / Black and tan fantasy / Harlem air shaft / Clarinet melodrama / Theme for Trambean / Sophisticated lady / Take the 'A' train.
**Album:** Released Apr '81, on Queendisc (Italy) Catalogue no: **QU 049**

**AT TANGLEWOOD - JULY 15, 1956 VOL. 2 (Ellington, Duke Orchestra)**
**Album:** Released Apr '81, on Queendisc (Italy) Catalogue no: **QU 050**

**AT THE BAL MASQUE**
Tracks: / Satin doll / Lady in red / Indian love call / Donkey serenade, The / Gypsy love song / Laugh, clown, laugh / Alice blue gown / Who's afraid of the big bad wolf? / Got a date with an angel / Poor butterfly / Satan takes a holiday / Peanut vendor.
**Cass:** Released Jul '87, on CBS by CBS Records. Deleted Jan '89. Catalogue no: **40 21144**
**Album:** Released Jul '87, on CBS by CBS Records. Deleted Aug '88. Catalogue no: **CBS 21144**
**Album:** Released Jun '86, on CBS (import) by CBS Records. Catalogue no: **84409**

**AT THE BLUE NOTE, CHICAGO (In the upper room)**
**CD:** Released '86, on Vogue by Vogue Records. Catalogue no: **VG 600 062**

**AT THE COTTON CLUB**
**Album:** Released Mar '90, on Tax Catalogue no: **TAX 8001**

**AT THE COTTON CLUB-1939 (Ellington, Duke/His Orchestra)**
Tracks: / East St. Louis toodle-oo / Jig walk / In a sentimental mood / I'm slapping Seventh Avenue with the sole of my shoe / Alabamy home / If you were in my place / I've got to be a home / I've got to be a rug cutter / Lost in meditation / Oh, babe, maybe someday / Everyday / Azure / Carnival in Caroline / Dinah's in a jam / Frolic Sam.
**Album:** Released '87, on Joker (USA) by Lifetime Records (USA). Catalogue no: **SM 3111**

**AT THE HURRICANE CLUB VOL. 1**
**Album:** Released Jan '88, on Hurricane (2) Catalogue no: **HC 6.001**

**AT THE HURRICANE CLUB VOL. 2**
**Album:** Released Jan '88, on Hurricane (2) Catalogue no: **HC 6.002**

**BACK TO BACK (Ellington, Duke / Johnny Hodges)**
Tracks: / Weary blues / St. Louis Blues / Loveless love / Royal Garden blues / Wabash blues / Basin Street blues / Beale street blues.
**Album:** Released Jun '81, on Verve (USA) by Polydor Ltd. Catalogue no: **2304 503**
**Cass:** Released Jun '84, on Verve (USA) by Polydor Ltd. Catalogue no: **3113 087**
**CD:** Released '88, on Starr by Polydor Ltd. Catalogue no: **823 637-2**

**BAND SHORTS (Ellington, Duke / His Orchestra)**
Tracks: / Black and tan fantasy / Duke steps out / Black beauty / Cotton club stomp / Hot feet / Same train / Lightning / Rockin' in rhythm / Stormy weather / Bugle call rag.
**Album:** Released Jan '87, on Meteor by Magnum Music Group. Catalogue no: **MTLP 1005**

**BEST OF DUKE ELLINGTON (JOKER) 1927 - 1941**
Tracks: / East St. Louis toodle-oo / Black and tan fantasy / Creole love call / Mooche, The / Mood indigo / Rockin' in rhythm / Echoes of the jungle / Harlem speaks / Caravan / Conga brava / Cottontail / Take the 'A' train.
**Album:** Released '87, on Joker (USA) by Lifetime Records (USA). Catalogue no: **SM 3056**

**BEST OF DUKE ELLINGTON 1942-46 (Ellington, Duke/His Orchestra)**
Tracks: / Frankie and Johnny / Diminuendo and crescendo in blue / In the shade of the old apple tree / Harlem airshift / Creole love call / It don't mean a thing / Kissing bug / Prelude to a kiss / Jam-a-ditty / Beautiful Indians:Hiawatha/Minnehaha / Happy go lucky local / Overture to a jam session / Blue skies (Trumpet no end) / Magenta haze / Golden feather / Sultry sunset / Flippant flurry.
**2 LP Set:** Released Apr '84, on Musidisc by Musidisc Records (France). Catalogue no: **ALB 130**

**BEST OF DUKE ELLINGTON (PABLO)**
Tracks: / Bateau / Sophisticated lady / Goof, The / Black butterfly / Mendoza / Layin' on mellow / Sunset and the mocking bird (From Queen's suite.) / Lightning bugs and frogs (From Queen's suite.) / Le sucrier velours (From Queen's suite.) / Northern lights (From Queen's suite.) / Single petal of a rose (From Queen's suite.) / Apes and peacocks.
**Album:** Released '82, on Pablo Jazz (USA) by Pablo Records (USA). Catalogue no: **231 0845**
**Cass:** Released '82, on Pablo Jazz (USA) by Pablo Records (USA). Catalogue no: **K10 845**

**BLACK, BROWN AND BEIGE**
**Album:** Released Jun '86, on CBS (import) by CBS Records. Cat no: **84406**

**Album:** Released Mar '79, on Monmouth Evergreen Catalogue no: **MES 7077**

**BLACK BUTTERFLY**
Tracks: / Happy reunion / Chinoiserie / Hank Cinq / Star crossed lovers / Such sweet thunder / Perdido / Black butterfly / In a sentimental mood / Mood indigo / I'm beginning to see the light / I got it bad and that ain't good / Just squeeze me / It don't mean a thing / Solitude.
**Album:** Released Jul '88, on Black Lion Catalogue no: **BLM 52041**

**BLANTON-WEBSTER YEARS, THE (Ellington, Duke/His Orchestra)**
Tracks: / You, you darlin' / Jack the bear / Koko / Morning glory / So far, so good / Conga brava / Concerto for Cootie / Me and you / Cottontail / Never no lament / Dusk / Bojangles / Portrait of Bert Williams, A / Blue goose / Harlem air shaft / At a Dixie roadside diner / All too soon / Rumpus in Richmond / My greatest mistake / Sepia panorama / There shall be no night / In a mellow tone / Five o'clock whistle / Warm valley / Flaming sword, The / Jumpin' punkins / Across the track blues / John Hardy's wife / Blue serge / After all / Chloe / Bakiff / Are you sticking? / I never felt this way before / Just a sittin' and a rockin' / Giddybug gallop, The / Sidewalks of New York, The / Chocolate shake / Flamingo / I got it bad (and that ain't good) / Clementine / Brown skin gal / Girl in my dreams tries to look like you, The / Jump for joy / Moon over Cuba / Take the 'A' train / Five o'clock drag / Rocks in my bed / Bli-blip / Chelsea Bridge / Raincheck / What good would it do? / I don't know what kind of blues I got / Perdido / C jam blues / Moon mist / What am I here for? / I don't mind / Someone / My little brown book / Main stem / Johnny come lately / Hayfoot strawfoot / Sentimental lady / Sip of the lip, A (can sink a ship) / Sherman shuffle.
**CD Set:** Released Nov '88, on Bluebird (2) by BMG Records (UK). Catalogue no: **PD 85659**
**Cass set:** Released Apr '87, on RCA by BMG Records (UK). Catalogue no: **PK 85659**
**LP Set:** Released Jan '87, on RCA by BMG Records (UK). Catalogue no: **PL 85659**

**BLUE ROSE**
**Album:** Released Jun '86, on CBS (import) by CBS Records. Catalogue no: **84402**

**BLUES IN ORBIT**
Tracks: / Blues in orbit / Track 360 / Villes ville is the place, man / Brown penny / Three J's blues / Smada / Pie eyes blues / C jam blues / Sweet and pungent / In a mellow tone / Sentimental lady / Blues in blueprint / Swingers get the blues too / Singer's jump, The.
**Album:** Released Jun '86, on CBS (import) by CBS Records. Catalogue no: **84307**
**Album:** Released 22 Aug '88, on CBS (import) by CBS Records. Catalogue no: **4608231**
**Cass:** Released 22 Aug '88, on CBS (import) by CBS Records. Catalogue no: **4608234**

**BRAGGIN' IN BRASS 1936-39**
**Album:** Released '88, on Tax Catalogue no: **TAX 8010**

**BRUNSWICK SESSIONS VOL.1 1932-35**
Tracks: / It don't mean a thing / Lazy Rhapsody / Blue tune.
**Album:** Released Sep '89, on Jazz Information (Sweden) Catalogue no: **CAH 3001**

**BRUNSWICK SESSIONS VOL.2**
Tracks: / Clouds in my heart / Ducky wucky / Jack cocktail / Lightnin' / Stars / Any time any day / Anywhere / Doin the new low down / I must have that man / Happy as the day is long.
**Album:** Released Sep '89, on Jazz Information (Sweden) Catalogue no: **CAH 3002**

**BRUNSWICK SESSIONS VOL.3**
Tracks: / Get yourself a new broom / Bundle of blues / Sophisticated lady / I'm satisfied / Saddest tale / Sumpin' about rhythm / Margie lets have a jubilee / Harlem speaks / Farewell Blues.
**Album:** Released Sep '89, on Jazz Information (Sweden) Catalogue no: **CAH 3003**

**CARNEGIE HALL CONCERT (Ellington, Duke & His Famous Orchestra)**
**Album:** Released Nov '84, on Musicraft (USA) by Discovery Records (USA). Catalogue no: **MVS 2004**

**CARNEGIE HALL CONCERTS, DECEMBER 1944**
Tracks: / New look / Blue serge / Triple play / Harlem airshift / Wonderlust / Junior hop / Jeep's blues / Squatty roo / Mood to be wooed / Mella brava / Kickapoo joy juice / On a turquoise cloud / Bakiff / Liberian suite / Cotton tail / East St.Louis / Toodle-oo / Echoes of Harlem / Black and tan fantasy / Things ain't what they used to be / Basso profundo / New York City blues / Clothed woman.
**2 LP Set:** Released Aug '80, on Prestige Deleted '85. Catalogue no: **PR 24075**
**2 LP Set:** Released Aug '80, on Prestige Deleted '85. Catalogue no: **PR 24073**

**CARNEGIE HALL CONCERTS, JANUARY 1946**
Tracks: / Caravan / In a mellotone / Solid old man / Black, brown and beige / Rugged romeo / Sono / Air conditioned jungle / Pitter panther patter / Take the 'A' train / Magenta haze / Diminuendo in blue/transluency / Crescendo in blue / Suburbanite / I'm just a lucky so and so / Riffin' drill / Tonal group.
**2 LP Set:** Released Aug '80, on Prestige Deleted '85. Catalogue no: **PR 24074**

**CLASSIC TRANSCRIPTIONS**
Tracks: / West Indian pancake / Love and I / John Hardy's wife / Clementine / Love like this can't last / After all / Girl of my dreams / Jumpin' punkins / Frankie and Johnny / Flamingo / It's sad but true / Mooche, The / Ring dem bells / Frustration / Coloratura / Rose of the Rio Grande / Love you madly / Take the 'A' train / Tone parallel to Harlem / Duet / Bounce / I hear a rhapsody / Madame will drop her shawl / Frenesi / Until tonight.
Note: Double album, double cassette. Mono.A Vee Jay recording. Licensed from Charly Records APS. This compilation (P) 1986 Charly Holdings Ltd. (C) 1986 Charly Records Ltd. Double LP.
**2 LP Set:** Released May '86, on Affinity by Charly Records. Catalogue no: **AFSD 1032**

**COMPLETE ELLINGTON 1947/52**
Note: 6 LP set.
**LP Set:** Released Jun '86, on CBS (import) by CBS Records. Catalogue no: **66607**

**CONCERT IN THE VIRGIN ISLANDS (Ellington, Duke/His Orchestra)**
Tracks: / Island virgin / Virgin jungle / Fiddler on the diddle / Jungle kitty / Things ain't what they used to be / Big fat Alice's blues / Chelsea Bridge / Opener, The / Mysterious chick / Barefoot stomper / Fade up.
Note: Features "Cat" Anderson, Johnny Hodges, "Cootie" Williams, Ray Nance, Buster Cooper, Russell Procope, Jimmy Hamilton, Paul Gonsalves, Harry Carney, and many more.
**Cass:** Released Jan '84, on Discovery (USA) by Discovery Records (USA). Catalogue no: **DSC 841**
**Album:** Released Jan '84, on Discovery (USA) by Discovery Records (USA). Catalogue no: **DS 841**

**CONCERT OF SACRED MUSIC**
Tracks: / In the beginning, God / Tell me it's the truth / Come Sunday / Will you be there? / Ain't but the one / New world a-coming / David danced before the Lord with all his might.
**Album:** Released Jan '83, on RCA (France) by BMG Records (France). Catalogue no: **PL 43663**

**CONCERTS IN CANADA**
**Album:** Released '88, on Ellington 86 Catalogue no: **E 87**

**COSMIC SCENE, THE**
**Album:** Released Jun '86, on CBS (import) by CBS Records. Catalogue no: **84407**

**COTTON CLUB DAYS**
Tracks: / Creole love call / Blues I love to sing / Black and tan fantasy / East St. Louis toodle-oo / Black beauty / Mooche, The / Cotton Club stomp / Misty morning / Duke steps out / Shout 'em aunt Tillie / Mood indigo / Old man blues.
Note: Mono.
**Album:** Released Jul '86, on RCA by BMG Records (UK). Deleted Jul '89. Catalogue no: **CL 89801**
**Cass:** Released Jul '86, on RCA by BMG Records (UK). Deleted Jul '89. Catalogue no: **CK 89801**

**COTTON CLUB STOMP 1937-39**
**Album:** Released Mar '90, on Tax Catalogue no: **TAX 8012**

**DANCE DATE (Airforce USA march 1958)**
**Album:** Released Mar '90, on Jazz Connoisseur by Spotlite Records. Catalogue no: **JC004**

**DANCE DATE (2) (Air Force 1960)**
**Album:** Released Nov '86, on Unique Jazz by Spotlite Records. Catalogue no: **UJ 27**

**DIGITAL DUKE**
Tracks: / Solitude / Sophisticated lady / Prelude to a kiss / Perdido / Take the 'A' train / Do nothing till you hear from me / Jeep's blues / In a mellow tone / Cotton trail / Satin doll / Mood indigo / Birmingham breakdown / 22 cent's stomp.
Note: An authentic recreation of original classic Ellington material, conducted by Duke's son, Mercer. The album features original band members Louis Bellson, Norris Turney, Clark Terry, Chuck Connors, Bruce Woodman, Eddie Daniels and special guest Branford Marsalis.
**CD:** Released May '87, on GRP by GRP Records (USA). Catalogue no: **GRD 9548**
**Cass:** Released May '87, on GRP by GRP Records (USA). Catalogue no: **GRPM 91038**
**Album:** Released May '87, on GRP by GRP Records (USA). Catalogue no: **GRP 91038**
**DAT:** Released Jul '88, on GRP by GRP Records (USA). Catalogue no: **GRT 9548**

**DROP ME OFF AT HARLEM (Ellington, Duke/His Orchestra)**
**CD:** Released Jun '88, on Compact Selection Catalogue no: **TQ 151**

**DRUM IS A WOMAN, A**
**Album:** Released Jun '86, on CBS (import) by CBS Records. Catalogue no: **84405**

**DUKE**
**Album:** Released Mar '79, on Varese Sarabande Records(USA) by Varese Sarabande Records (USA). Catalogue no: **VS 81007**

**DUKE - 56 / 62 VOL.1 (Ellington, Duke / His Orchestra)**
Tracks: / Black and tan fantasy / A-flat minor / Suburban beauty / Cafe au lait / West Indian dance / Cop out / Allah-bye / Piano improvisations (parts 1-4) / Commercial time / Mood indigo / Willow weep for me / Mood indigo (II) / Where or when / All the things you are / Night and day / Slamar in D flat / Track 360 / Jones / Lullaby of Birdland / Feet bone / Red carpet / Satin doll / When I trilly with my filly / Anatomy of a murder.
**2 LP Set:** Released Jul '86, on CBS by CBS Records. Catalogue no: **CBS 88653**
**Cass:** Released Jul '86, on CBS by CBS Records. Catalogue no: **40 88653**

**DUKE - 56 / 62 VOL.2 (Ellington, Duke / His Orchestra)**
Tracks: / Brown penny / Pie eyes blues / Sentimental lady / Sweet and pungent / Swinger's jump, The / Lullaby of Birdland / Dreamy sort of thing / Wailer, The / Asphalt jungle suite / Lotus blossom / Matumbe / Just a sittin' and a rockin' / Tulip or turnip? / Jingle bells / One more once / Blues in Hoss's flat / Asphalt jungle theme-Pt 1, Pt 3 / Bon amour / Paris blues- Parts 1-3 / Turkish coffee.
**2 LP Set:** Released Jul '86, on CBS by CBS Records. Catalogue no: **CBS 88654**
**Cass:** Released Jul '86, on CBS by CBS Records. Catalogue no: **40 88654**

**DUKE - 56 / 62 VOL. 3 (Ellington, Duke / His Orchestra)**
Tracks: / If you were in my place / Just a sittin' and a rockin' / Pomegranate / Rock city rock / Your love has faded / My heart, my mind, my everything / Together / Duke's place / Hand me down love / Walkin' and singin' the blues / I can't give you anything but love / To know you is to love you / Lonely one, The / Lost in loveliness / I'm just a lucky so and so / One more once / Day in, day out / Why was I born? / Love you madly / Where in the world? / Moulin Rouge.
**Cass:** Released Jul '86, on CBS by CBS Records. Catalogue no: **40 26306**
**Album:** Released Jul '86, on CBS by CBS Records. Catalogue no: **CBS 26306**

**DUKE ELLINGTON**
**CD:** Released May '89, on Object Enterprises Catalogue no: **ONN 43**
**Cass:** Released Oct '84, on Audio Fidelity(USA) by Audio Fidelity (USA). Catalogue no: **ZCGAS 749**
**Album:** Released Apr '81, on Jazz Live (Italy) Catalogue no: **BLJ 8018**
**Album:** Released Apr '81, on Kings Of Jazz Catalogue no: **KLJ 20003**

**DUKE ELLINGTON (1941)**
**Album:** Released Jul '88, on Forlane Catalogue no: **99003**
**CD:** Released Jul '88, on Forlane Catalogue no: **UCD 19003**

**DUKE ELLINGTON 1927-30**
**Album:** Released Jan '83, on Swaggie (Australia) Catalogue no: **S 1231**

**DUKE ELLINGTON 1927-34**
Tracks: / Creole love call / Black beauty / Got everything but you / Duke steps out / Jungle nights in Harlem / Blue feeling.
**CD:** Released Jan '89, on Hermes by Nimbus Records. Catalogue no: **HRM 6001**

**DUKE ELLINGTON: 1946-47**
Tracks: / Magenta haze (Recorded in New York, 28 March 1946.) / Eighth veil, The (Recorded in New York, 28 March 1946.) / Transblucency (Recorded in New York, 28 March 1946.) / Embraceable you (Recorded in New York, 28 March 1946.) / Hey baby (Recorded in Hollywood, 11 July 1946.) / Come rain or come shine (Recorded in Hollywood, 11 July 1946.) / Overture to a jam session (Recorded in New York, 7 January 1947.) / Jam-a-ditty (Recorded in New York, 7 January 1947.) / Frustration (Recorded in New York, 10 June 1947.) / Azalea (Recorded in New York, 10 June 1947.) / Orchids for madam (Recorded in New York, 10 June 1947.).
**Album:** Released Apr '81, on Queendisc (Italy) Catalogue no: **QU 036**

**DUKE ELLINGTON AND JOHN COLTRANE (Ellington, Duke/John Coltrane)**
Tracks: / In a sentimental mood / Take the Coltrane / Big Nick / Stevie / My little brown book / Angelica / Feeling of jazz, The.
Note: Recorded 1962. Personnel: Duke Ellington (piano), John Coltrane (tenor sax), Jimmy Garrison (bass), Elvin Jones (drums), Sam Woodyard (drums), Aaron Bell (bass).
**CD:** Released Jun '89, on MCA (Impulse Jazz) Catalogue no: **MCAD 39103**
**Album:** Released Jun '82, on Jasmine by Hasmick Promotions. Catalogue no: **JAS 4**
**Cass:** Released Jun '82, on Jasmine by Hasmick Promotions. Catalogue no: **JAS C4**

**DUKE ELLINGTON AND ORCHESTRA 1946 (Ellington, Duke/His Orchestra)**
Tracks: / Take the 'A' train / Crosstown / Passion flower / Magenta haze / Everything goes / Eighth veil, The / Riff'n'drill / Blue abandon / Transblucency / Rugged romeo / Jennie / Sono / Jeep is jumpin'.
Note: All the riches of mid-'40's Ellington are captured in this series, mastered magnificently from never before released radio transcriptions. The music on volume 1 was recorded at New York City, March 28, 1946, the year Ellington became the first to win both the Swinging and Sweet Band divisions of the Down Beat poll. This is the band with Johnny Hodges, Harry Carney, Otto Hardwicke, Jimmy Hamilton, Al Sears, Lawrence Brown, Joe "Tricky Sam" Nanton, Claude Jones, Wilbur DeParis, Cat Anderson, Taft Jordan, Francis Williams, Shelton Hemphill, Bernard Flood, Oscar Pettiford, Fred Guy, Sonny Greer and Duke. (Hindsight Catalogue - 1989)
**Album:** Released '88, on Hindsight Catalogue no: **HSR 125**

**DUKE ELLINGTON AND ORCHESTRA, 1946 VOL. 2 (Ellington, Duke Orchestra)**
Tracks: / Rockabye river / Pretty woman / Gathering in a clearing, A / You don't love me no more / Tip toe topic / Just squeeze me / Perdido / Hey baby / Suddenly it jumped / Come rain or come shine / Fickle fling / 9:20 special / One o'clock jump.
Note: Transcription dates in March and July '46 are the sources of this volume, a lively documentation of significant developments in Ellington's world famous orchestra. Ray Nance returned and Harold "Shorty" Baker rejoined the trumpet section between the spring and summer sessions. Russell Procope took over the

Otto Hardwicke reed chair for a stay that lasted until the end, twenty-eight years later. An abundance of good singing is heard - - Kay Davis, Al Hibbler and Nance. With this album, "Come rain or come shine" becomes Ms. Davis' first commercially released vocal performance with words and is the only recording of the band playing this number. (Hindsight Catalogue - 1989)
**Album:** Released '88, on Hindsight Catalogue no: **HSR 126**

**DUKE ELLINGTON AND REX STEWART 1943-46 (Ellington, Duke & Rex Stewart)**
**Album:** Released '89, on Jazz Society Catalogue no: **AA 501**

**DUKE ELLINGTON AND THE SMALL GROUPS**
**Album:** Released Feb '89, on Giants of Jazz by Hasmick Promotions. Catalogue no: **LPJT 70**

**DUKE ELLINGTON AT CARNEGIE HALL (November 23, 1946)**
**Album:** Released '88, on Queen Catalogue no: **QUEEN 017**

**DUKE ELLINGTON COLLECTION (20 golden greats)**
Tracks: / Take the 'A' train / I got it bad and that ain't good / Things ain't what they used to be / Black and tan fantasy / Creole love call / Mooche, The / El Gato / Rockin' in rhythm / Hawk talks, The / East St. Louis toodle-oo / Cotton Club stomp / Saratoga swing / Jungle nights in Harlem / Koko / Do nothing till you hear from me / Harlem airshaft / C jam blues / Chloe / Just a sittin' and a rockin' / Across the track blues.
**CD:** Released Jun '88, on Deja Vu Catalogue no: **DVCD 2014**
**Album:** Released Aug '85, on Deja Vu Catalogue no: **DVLP 2014**
**Cass:** Released Aug '85, on Deja Vu Catalogue no: **DVMC 2014**

**DUKE ELLINGTON CONCERT 1953**
**Album:** Released '88, on GNP Crescendo (USA) by GNP Crescendo Records (USA). Catalogue no: **GNPS 9045**
**Cass:** Released '88, on GNP Crescendo (USA) by GNP Crescendo Records (USA). Catalogue no: **GNP5 9045**

**DUKE ELLINGTON DANCE 1958**
**Album:** Released '88, on Unique Jazz by Spotlite Records. Catalogue no: **UJ 16**

**DUKE ELLINGTON AND FRIENDS (Compact/Walkman jazz) (Ellington, Duke & Friends)**
Tracks: / Take the 'A' train / Caravan / Mood indigo / I let a song go out of my heart / Prelude to a kiss / Satin doll / Stompy Jones / I got it bad (and that ain't good) / Don't get around much anymore / It don't mean a thing.
**CD:** Released Mar '88, on Verve Catalogue no: **833 291-2**
**Cass:** Released 27 Feb '88, on Verve Catalogue no: **833 291-4**

**DUKE ELLINGTON AND HIS FAMOUS ORCHESTRA 1932-38**
Note: Barney Bigard, Cootie Williams etc.
**Album:** Released Jan '88, on Swingfan Catalogue no: **SWINGFAN 1001**
**Album:** Released Apr '81, on Rarities Catalogue no: **RARITIES 29**

**DUKE ELLINGTON AND HIS ORCHESTRA 1940-41**
Tracks: / Stomp caprice / Bugle breaks / You and I / Have you changed? / Raincheck / Blue serge / Moon mist / I don't want to set the world on fire / Easy Street / Perdido.
**Album:** Released Apr '81, on Joker (USA) by Lifetime Records (USA). Catalogue no: **SM 3120**

**DUKE ELLINGTON AND HIS ORCHESTRA 1927-31 (Ellington, Duke/His Orchestra)**
**CD:** Released Feb '89, on Giants of Jazz by Hasmick Promotions. Catalogue no: **GOJCD 53030**
**CD:** Released Aug '88, on Giants of Jazz by Hasmick Promotions. Catalogue no: **CD 53030**
**Album:** Released Jul '87, on Circle (USA) by Jazzology Records (USA). Catalogue no: **CLP 104**

**DUKE ELLINGTON IN LONDON, 1958**
Note: Special double-album issued for the Ellington '88 Convention.
**2 LP Set:** Released Jul '88, on Ellington 88 Catalogue no: **E 88**

**DUKE ELLINGTON (JAZZ CLASSICS IN DIGITAL STEREO)**
Tracks: / Rockin' in rhythm / It don't mean a thing / Baby, when you ain't there / Bugle call rag / Blue harlem / Jazz cocktail / Lightnin' / Slippery horn / Drop me off at Harlem / Bundle of blues / Jive stomp / Dear old Southland / Saddest tale / Truckin' / Clarinet lament / Echoes of Harlem / In a jam / Stepping into swing society.
**CD:** Released 4 Sep '89, on BBC by BBC Records & Tapes. Catalogue no: **BBC CD686**
**Album:** Released 4 Sep '89, on BBC by BBC Records & Tapes. Catalogue no: **REB 686**
**Cass:** Released 4 Sep '89, on BBC by BBC Records & Tapes. Catalogue no: **ZCF 686**

**DUKE ELLINGTON MEETS COLEMAN HAWKINS (Ellington, Duke / Coleman Hawkins)**
Tracks: / Limbo jazz / Mood indigo / Ray Charles's place / Wanderlust / You dirty dog / Self portrait (of the bean) / Jeep is jumpin' / Recitic, The.
**Album:** Released Jun '82, on Jasmine by Hasmick Promotions. Deleted Jun '86. Catalogue no: **JAS 1**
**CD:** Released Feb '87, on Impulse by Impulse Records. Deleted Dec '89. Catalogue no: **MCAD 5650**
**Cass:** Released Jun '82, on Jasmine by Hasmick Promotions. Deleted Jun '86. Catalogue no: **JAS C1**
**Album:** Released Oct '85, on Impulse by Impulse Records. Catalogue no: **AS 26**
**Cass:** Released Aug '86, on Impulse by Impulse Records. Deleted Dec '89. Catalogue no: **ASC 26**

**DUKE ELLINGTON OCTOBER 20, 1945**
**Album:** Released '88, on Queen Catalogue no: **QUEEN 006**

**DUKE ELLINGTON ON THE AIR VOLUME 2 (Ellington, Duke / His Orchestra)**
Tracks: / Blue cellophane / Frustration / I'm beginning to see the light / Just a sittin' and a rockin' / Trumpets no end / Midriff / Candy / Black, brown and beige suit / Accentuate the positive / Way low.
**Album:** Released Feb '88, on Aircheck (USA) by Kiner Ents.(USA). Catalogue no: **AIRCHECK 29**

**DUKE ELLINGTON AND HIS ORCHESTRA (Ellington, Duke / His Orchestra)**
**Album:** Released Mar '90, on Echo Jazz Catalogue no: **EJLP 04**
**Album:** Released May '86, on Storyville by Storyville Records AB. Catalogue no: **SLP 4003**

**DUKE ELLINGTON AND ORCHESTRA (Ellington, Duke Orchestra)**
**Album:** Released '89, on Echo Jazz Catalogue no: **EJLP 02**
**Cass:** Released '89, on Echo Jazz Catalogue no: **EJMC 02**
**CD:** Released '89, on Echo Jazz Catalogue no: **EJCD 02**

**DUKE ELLINGTON AND ORCHESTRA (Ellington, Duke Orchestra)**
**Album:** Released Mar '79, on Gramercy 5 by Gramercy 5 Records. Catalogue no: **GM 7705**
**Album:** Released Apr '81, on Queendisc (Italy) Catalogue no: **QU 006**

**DUKE ELLINGTON AND ORCHESTRA 1945 (Ellington, Duke Orchestra)**
**Album:** Released May '89, on Circle Catalogue no: **CLP 7**

**DUKE ELLINGTON AND PAUL GONSALVES (Ellington, Duke / Paul Gonsalves)**
**CD:** Released Apr '87, on Carrere (France) Catalogue no: **98547**

**DUKE ELLINGTON PRESENTS (Big band bounce and boogie) (Ellington, Duke / His Orchestra)**
Tracks: / Summertime / Laura / I can't get started / My funny Valentine / Everything but you / Frustration / Cottontail / Daydream / Deep Purple / Indian Summer / Blues.
**Album:** Released Apr '85, on Affinity by Charly Records. Catalogue no: **AFS 1013**
**Cass:** Released Sep '86, on Affinity by Charly Records. Catalogue no: **TCAFS 1013**

**DUKE ELLINGTON AND THE ELLINGTONIANS**
**2 LP Set:** Released Oct '88, on Vogue by Vogue Records. Catalogue no: **400019**

**DUKE ELLINGTON VOL. 1**
**Album:** Released May '88, on Blu-Disc (USA) Catalogue no: **T 1001**

**DUKE ELLINGTON VOL. 2**
**Album:** Released May '88, on Blu-Disc (USA) Catalogue no: **T 1003**

**DUKE ELLINGTON VOL. 3 1946 (Ellington, Duke Orchestra)**
Tracks: / Unbooted character, The / Suburbanite, The / Indiana / Moon mist / In a jam / On the Alamo / I can't believe that you're in love with me / Tea for two / Just you, just me / Someone / Double ruff / Flower is a lovesome thing, A / Mooche, The.
Note: Joe "Tricky Sam" Nanton's last recorded solo, "The Mooche", cut on radio transcription July 17, 1946, four days before his death, is only one of the unique treasures in this volume of Ellingtonia. Clarinet virtuoso Jimmy Hamilton plays a rare tenor saxophone solo on "Just you, just me", the bands only known performance of Billy Strayhorn's "Double ruff" and Strayhorn interpreting his own "A flower is a lovesome thing" with Johnny Hodges soloing are on this all-instrumental album. Patricia Willard's liner notes tell the story of the music as it was told to her by Ellington and his musicians. (Hindsight Catalogue - 1989)
**Album:** Released '88, on Hindsight Catalogue no: **HSR 127**

**DUKE ELLINGTON, VOL. 4 1947 (Ellington, Duke Orchestra)**
Tracks: / Golden cress / Flippant flurry / Jam-a-ditty / Fugueaditty / Happy go lucky local / Overture to a jam session / Sultry sunset / Beale Street blues / Memphis blues / St. Louis Blues / Who struck John?.
Note: In an unprecedented indulgance of Ellington's passion for freedom of expression, radio transcriptions imposed no time limits on the Maestro's music, as did three-minute commercial recordings. The six-minute-twenty-second "Happy go lucky local" on volume 4 is the longest, uninterrupted version of this Ducal classic ever released. And "Who struck John?" - - at one minute, twenty-seven seconds probably is Ellington's and Johnny Hodges shortest tune on record. "Golden cress", with Lawrence Brown's trombone, is half again the length of the Musicraft 78. This is the only recording of the irrepressible Ray Nance singing "St. Louis Blues". (Hindsight Catalogue - 1989)
**Album:** Released '88, on Hindsight Catalogue no: **HSR 128**
**Album:** Released Jul '88, on FDC Catalogue no: **FDC 1023**

**DUKE ELLINGTON, VOL. 5 1947 (Ellington, Duke Orchestra)**
Tracks: / Swamp fire / How high the moon / Blue Lou / Violet blue / Royal Garden blues / Jumpin' punkins / Park at 106th / Frustration / Blue is the night / Jump for joy / Far away blues / Embraceable you / Frisky / Take the 'A' train.
Note: Because radio transcriptions, the source of these albums, were excempt from the January 1 - August 14, 1947 ASCAP recording ban, Volume 4 and 5 are the sole documentation of the Ellington Orchestra during those months. Duke's assemblage of brilliant soloists was awesome. Johnny Hodges, Harry Carney, Lawrence Brown, Al Sears, Ray Nance, Jimmy Hamilton, Sonny Greer, Oscar Pettiford, Shorty Baker, Russell Procope and Ellington himself are among those on Volume 5. Kay Davis' vocal, "Embraceable you", and "Come rain or come shine" on Volume 2 are the only recordings of her singing words during nearly six years with the band. (Hindsight Catalogue - 1989)
**Album:** Released '88, on Hindsight Catalogue no: **HSR 129**

**DUKE ELLINGTON WITH ALICE BABS & NILS LINDBERG (Ellington, Duke / Alice Babs)**
**Album:** Released May '79, on Phontastic (Sweden) Catalogue no: **PHON 11**

**DUKE FEATURES HODGES**
Tracks: / Ring dem bells / Daydream / Jump for joy / Warm valley / Rockabye river / Whispering grass / Mood to be wooed, The / Jeep is jumpin' / Sentimental lady / I don't mind / Passion flower / Hop, skip and jump.
**Album:** Released Jul '83, on Unique Jazz by Spotlite Records. Catalogue no: **UJ 35**

**DUKE IS ON THE AIR 1952, THE**
**Album:** Released Apr '79, on Aircheck (USA) by Kiner Ents.(USA). Catalogue no: **AIRCHECK 3**

**DUKE IS ON THE AIR: VOLUME 1, THE (Ellington, Duke/His Orchestra)**
Tracks: / Bensonality / All of me / Bakiff / Hawk talks, The / Do nothing till you hear from me / VIP's boogie / Jam with Sam / Just a sittin' and a rockin' / Mood indigo / Tulip or turnip / Ting a ling / Flamingo / Rockin' in rhythm / Sophisticated lady / Take the 'A' train / Flying home.
**Album:** Released Feb '88, on Aircheck (USA) by Kiner Ents.(USA). Catalogue no: **AIRCHECK 4**

**DUKE'S BIG FOUR (Ellington, Duke Quartet)**
Tracks: / Cottontail / Blues, The / Hawk talks, The / Prelude to a kiss / Love you madly / Just squeeze me / Everything but you.
**Cass:** Released '82, on Pablo Jazz (USA) by Pablo Records (USA). Catalogue no: **K10 703**
**CD:** on Pablo Jazz (USA) by Pablo Records (USA). Catalogue no: **J33J 20009**
**Album:** Released '82, on Pablo Jazz (USA) by Pablo Records (USA). Catalogue no: **2310 703**

**DUKE, THE 1940**
Note: Live from the Crystal Ballroom in Fargo, N.D. Mono.
**2 LP Set:** Released Mar '87, on Jazz Society Catalogue no: **AA 520/521**

**EARLY CLASSICS VOL.1, THE**
**Album:** Released Oct '79, on Nevox Catalogue no: **725**

**EARLY CLASSICS VOL.2, THE**
**Album:** Released Oct '79, on Nevox Catalogue no: **726**

**EARLY CLASSICS VOL.3, THE 1926-28**
**Cass:** Released Jan '82, on Neovox by Neovox Records. Catalogue no: **NEO 758**

**EARLY ELLINGTON**
Tracks: / Black and tan fantasy / Creole love call / East St. Louis toodle-oo / Black beauty / Mooche, The / Flaming youth / Ring dem bells / Old man blues / Mood indigo / Rockin' in rhythm / Creole rhapsody / Creole rhapsody (part 2) / Echoes of the jungle / Daybreak express / Stompy Jones / Solitude.
**Cass:** Released Jul '89, on Bluebird (2) by BMG Records (UK). Catalogue no: **NK 86852**
**CD:** Released Jul '89, on Bluebird (2) by BMG Records (UK). Catalogue no: **ND 86852**
**Album:** Released Jul '89, on Bluebird (2) by BMG Records (UK). Catalogue no: **NL 86852**

**ELEGANT MR. ELLINGTON, THE**
**Cass:** Released '84, on Swing House by Submarine Records. Catalogue no: **CSWH 4**
**Album:** Released '84, on Swing House by Submarine Records. Catalogue no: **SWH 4**

**ELLINGTON 56**
Tracks: / East St. Louis toodle-oo / Creole love call / Stompy Jones / Jeep is jumpin' / Jack the bear / In a mellow tone / Koko / Midriff / Stomp, look and listen / Unbooted character, The / Lonesome lullaby / Upper Manhattan medical group / Cottontail / Daydream / Deep purple / Indian summer / Laura / Blues.
Note: The odyssey of Duke Ellington is difficult to grasp in mere words. Even years after his death in May 1974, the realisation of his contribution is still increasing, particularly on the part of fellow musicians who now appreciate just how unique Ellington was. Nevertheless, many people seem content themselves with focusing on just one aspect of Duke's achievement. There are listeners who treat him as merely one of the great bandleaders, with an ensemble whose technical excellence (and built-in nostalgia) put him on a level with Goodman, Herman and the rest - this is no mean praise, of course, and it is amply justified by such varied pieces as *Rockin' in rhythm, Perdido* and *Take the A train.* And there are critics who see Ellington as the first and almost the only artistically successful composer in jazz, who took its most vital qualitites and, without burying them, made them the basis of involved works like *Black, brown and beige, Harlem* and the original conception of *Diminuendo and crescendo in blue.*
Equally you can find pianists (the intelligent ones) who don't accept the con-

ventional view that Duke's keyboard playing was limited, but savour the timing, and textures of even his simplest statements - and, while he was often pianistically reticent on his band recordings, certainly his few trio albums (*Duke plays Ellington, Piano in the foreground* and *Money jungle*) can provide endless fascination for piano freaks and non-specialists alike. And, finally, perhaps the largest group of Ellington fanciers are those who, without consciously placing him on the same level as Gershwin, Kern and Porter, still go around humming or whistling snatches of *Don't get around much any more, I'm beginning to see the light, Satin doll* and the numerous other great songs from the Ducal pen.

Ellington himself was well aware of the importance of his song output in keeping him in the public eye and ear, and from the mid 1940s he regularly regaled his concert audiences with a *Medley of hits*. Indeed, he openly acknowledged that, from around this date (when the bottom dropped out of the big bands as a popular and economically viable format), he subsided the continued operation of his orchestra and the payment of the salaries incurred from the earnings of his song royalties. And, even before this, it was the songs which prompted him to retrospection on record. When his manager Irving Mills started his own label at the end of 1936, Duke re-cut four of his greatest hits, and did something similar again on his last date for Mills in 1940; then in 1945, he made four 78 r.p.m. discs comprising new versions of songs such *Sophisticated lady* and *I let a song out of my heart*.

Although the 1945 sessions were later grouped on an early 10 inch LP, and several other compositions were reprised on albums recorded in the early 1950s, it was not until 1956 but Duke specifically set out to devote a whole project to his own previous works. And when he did so, whether on his own initiative or that of a producer, songs were set aside in favour of some of his classical instrumentals. Or rather, being Ellington and not wanting to make things too simple or schematic, he recorded material for two albums within a short space of time: of the 23 tracks, 14 were earlier pieces, 3 were new and 6 were popular standards by other writers, such as the band played more often at dances than in the studio (two tracks even had vocals). So, although the resulting tapes were originally divided into the serious and academic sounding *Historically speaking* on the one hand and the more show-biz seeming *Duke Ellington presents* on the other, in fact the lines were blurred, with the old flagwaver *Cotton tail* appearing in the latter album and the totally new and obscure *Lonesome lullaby* in the 'historic' collection.

Here, with the compact disc permitting the combination of most of those tracks within the maximum available playing time, the vocals and several non-Ellington tunes have been omitted, and the homogeneity of the sessions becomes clear. Specifically, the continuity between various strands of Ducal material is brough out in no uncertain fashion, so that the similarities inherent in *In a mellow tone* and *Unbooted character* are seen to be related also to the much earlier *Stompy Jones* (based on *Panama* and to the new head-arrangement *Blues* - which incidentally, makes a fascinating comparison with *Duke's jam* recorded by the band a month earlier under the leadership of Johnny Hodges. And the more dreamy and mysterious side of the repertoire outlined in *East St. Louis toodle oo* is maintained in *Lonesome lullaby* (with Ray Nance on violin) as well as being enhanced by *Day Dream* from staff writer Billy Strayhorn, who probably also arranged *DeepPurple* and *Indian Summer*. More fascinating to look at closely, especially if you're able to compare with other Ellington versions of the same tunes, is the way the bandleader builds a programme with contrasts which relate to this particular performance. Certain pieces were played faster than on their debut recordings, notably *Koko/cotton tail/mellow tone* and *Stomp, look and listen* (the evidence of airshots shows that the first two actually began speeding up soon after they were originally recorded), but in *East St. Louis, Creole love call* and *Day dream* were all slowed down to bring out their special qualities. And, of course, Ellington was as always especially adept at bringing out his current band. 1956 was to be the year in which they caused a near-riot at Newport, and the press coverage helped to increase Duke's popularity once more. But it is the enclosed material (rather than the Newport album) which shows what a fresh and invigorating sound the band was making. A lot of important things had happened during the previous year for, not only had the brass section personnel settled down to one of its classic lineups, but the arrival of Jimmy Woode and Sam Woodyard had given the band a new lease of life in the rhythm section; while the reeds had been restored to their configuration of five years earlier by the return of 'All American No. 1 saxophonist, Johnny Hodges'.

All the altos are by Hodges, apart from the *Indian summer* feature for Russell Procope; Procope is heard on clarinet in *Creole love call*, while the bulk of the clainet work is by Jimmy Hamilton who plays the tenor solo on *Blues*, the rest of the tenor being by the great Paul Gonsalves. Among the trombones, the muted solos are by Quentin Jackson (otherwise it is Britt Woodman) while the most featured trumpet is Ray Nance; but Clark Terry splits with Nance the closing segment of *Unbooted character* and takes the first two solos on *Blues*, whose final choruses (like those of Stompy Jones) are by Cat Anderson, while the trumpeter heard on Strayhorn's fine *Upper manhattan medical group* (and the second chorus of *Creole love call* is Willie Cook. The piano and baritone saxophone of the leader and Harry Carney respectively are easily identifiable because there are no other candidates but also, of course, because they were the two most essential and individual sounds in the entire band at this period. In short, the band's performance and the brilliantly detailed mono recording fully deserves its issue as a compact disc. And, whether you regard it as a deliberate excercise in re-creating some of the significant numbers from different eras of Ellington's vast output, or merely a display of his versatility in playing everything from unique compositions to straightahead blues and standards, this album represents one of the high points in Duke's career. (Brian Priestley)

**CD:** Released '86, on Charly by Charly Records. Catalogue no: **CDCHARLY 20**

## ELLINGTON INDIGOES

**Album:** Released Jun '86, on CBS (import) by CBS Records. Catalogue no: **82682**

## ELLINGTON MOODS

**Album:** Released Oct '88, on Vogue by Vogue Records. Catalogue no: **500061**

## ELLINGTON SUITES, THE

Tracks: / Sunset and the mocking bird (From Queen's suite.) / Lightning bugs and frogs (From Queen's suite.) / Le sucrier velours (From Queen's suite.) / Northern lights (From Queen's suite.) / Single petal of a rose (From Queen's suite.) / Apes and peacocks (From Queen's suite.) / Fanfare (From Goutelas suite.) / Goutelas / Get-with-it-ness (From Goutelas suite.) / Something (From Goutelas suite.) / Having at it (From Goutelas suite.) / Uwis (From Uwis suite.) / Klop / Loco madi .

**Cass:** Released '82, on Pablo Jazz (USA) by Pablo Records (USA). Catalogue no: **K10 762**

**Album:** Released '82, on Pablo Jazz (USA) by Pablo Records (USA). Catalogue no: **231 0762**

**CD:** Released Jan '89, on JVC/Fantasy Catalogue no: **VDJ 28006**

## ELLINGTON TRAIN, THE

**Album:** Released Aug '88, on La Locomotora Negra Catalogue no: **E 30 885**

## ELLINGTON UPTOWN

**Album:** Released Jun '86, on CBS (import) by CBS Records. Catalogue no: **84309**

## ESSENTIAL DUKE ELLINGTON VOL. 1, 1924-27

**Album:** Released Apr '79, on VJM (Vintage Jazz Music) by Vintage Jazz Music Society(VJM). Catalogue no: **VLP 71**

## ESSENTIAL DUKE ELLINGTON VOL. 2, (Instrumentals) (1927)

**Album:** Released Oct '88, on VJM (Vintage Jazz Music) by Vintage Jazz Music Society(VJM). Catalogue no: **VLP 72**

## ESSENTIAL DUKE ELLINGTON VOL. 4, 1928-29

**Album:** Released Dec '88, on VJM (Vintage Jazz Music) by Vintage Jazz Music Society(VJM). Catalogue no: **VLP 74**

**ESSENTIAL DUKE ELLINGTON VOL. 5, THE**
**Album:** Released May '89, on VJM (Vintage Jazz Music) by Vintage Jazz Music Society(VJM). Catalogue no: **VLP 75**

**ETERNAL DUKE ELLINGTON**
**CD:** Released Feb '89, on Phontastic (Sweden) Catalogue no: **NOSTCD 7666**

**EVENING WITH THE DUKE (Ellington, Duke Orchestra)**
**Album:** Released Aug '79, on Giants of Jazz by Hasmick Promotions. Catalogue no: **GOJ 1003**

**FABULOUS FORTIES, THE**
Tracks: / Bojangles / People will say, The / Five o'clock drag / Johnny come lately / Tonight I shall sleep / Wait for me, Mary / It's been so long / Blue skies / Don't get around much anymore / Altitude / I don't want anybody at all / Things ain't what they used to be / April in Paris / Whispering grass / Just a sittin' and a rockin' / Theme and intro.
Note: Featuring Ray Nance, Barney Bigard, Johnny Hodges, Ben Webster, Rex Stewart, Cootie Williams, Jimmy Blanton, Harry Carney, Ivie Anderson.
**Album:** Released Apr '81, on Rarities Catalogue no: **RARITIES 56**
**Album:** Released Sep '87, on Giants of Jazz by Hasmick Promotions. Catalogue no: **LPJT 66**

**FABULOUS FORTIES VOL.2, THE**
Tracks: / C jam blues / Sophisticated lady / I can't give you anything but love / It don't mean a thing / On the sunny side of the street / Moon mist / Theme and intro / Happy-go-lucky local / Jungle / Frantic fantasy / In a sentimental mood / Mood indigo / Hiawatha / Warm valley / Frustration / Air conditioned jungle / Caravan / Solitude / Don't get around much anymore.
Note: Featuring Ray Nance, Lawrence Brown, Johnny Hodges, Harry Carney, Cat Anderson and other regulars of the period. Recorded at Radio WNEW, New York, 10 May 1947; Ciro's Restaurant, Hollywood, July 1947; Carnegie Hall, New York, 19 December 1944.
**Album:** Released Apr '81, on Rarities Catalogue no: **RARITIES 59**

**FANTASTIC**
**Album:** Released Jul '84, on RCA(Special Imports Service) by BMG Records (UK). Catalogue no: **FJL 27161(2)**

**FAR AWAY STAR**
Note: Featuring Ellington, Duke / Babs / Lindberg / Orchestra
**Album:** Released '82, on Phontastic (Sweden) Catalogue no: **PHONT 7511**
**Cass:** Released '82, on Phontastic (Sweden) Catalogue no: **PHONT 8511**

**FAR EAST SUITE, THE**
Tracks: / Tourist point of view / Bluebird of Delhi (mynah) / Isfahan / Depk / Mount Harissa / Blue pepper (far east of the blues) / Agra / Amad / Ad lib on Nippon.
**CD:** Released Nov '88, on Bluebird (2) by BMG Records (UK). Catalogue no: **ND 87640**

**FARGO ENCORES**
Note: Recorded in 1940.
**Album:** Released May '88, on Nostalgia by Mainline Records. Catalogue no: **NOST 7636**

**FEELING OF JAZZ, THE**
**Album:** Released Feb '89, on Black Lion Catalogue no: **BLP 60123**

**FESTIVAL SESSION (Ellington, Duke / His Orchestra)**
Tracks: / Idiom '59 (parts 1-3) / Things ain't what they used to be / Launching pad / Perdido / Cop out estension / Duael fuel (parts 1-3).
**Album:** Released Jul '86, on CBS by CBS Records. Deleted Jun '88. Catalogue no: **CBS 21137**
**Cass:** Released Jul '86, on CBS by CBS Records. Deleted Jun '88. Catalogue no: **40 21137**

**GIANTS 3**
Note: Featuring Ellington, Duke / Holiday, Billie / Louis Armstrong
**Cass:** Released Jun '88, on Giants of Jazz by Hasmick Promotions. Catalogue no: **GOJC 1008**
**Album:** Released Jun '88, on Giants of Jazz by Hasmick Promotions. Catalogue no: **GOJ 1008**

**GIRL'S SUITE (Ellington, Duke Orchestra)**
Tracks: / Girls / Mahalia / Peg o' my heart / Juanita / Sylvia / Lena / Girl's suite / Dinah / Clementine / Diane / Under the balcony / Strange feeling / Dancers in love / Coloratura.
**Album:** Released Oct '82, on CBS by CBS Records. Deleted Oct '87. Catalogue no: **CBS 85933**

**GOIN' UP (Ellington, Duke Orchestra)**
Tracks: / Coca cola theme & intro / Perdido / Hayfoot strawfoot / Don't get around much anymore / Coca cola commercial / Going up / Things ain't what they used to be / Take the 'A' train / After a while / I ain't got nothin' but the blues / Riff staccato / I didn't know about you / Main stem.
**Album:** Released Jul '87, on Duke by Melodisc Records. Catalogue no: **D 1011**

**GOLDEN DUKE**
Tracks: / Jam-a-ditty / Diminuendo in blue / Magenta haze / Blue skies / Hiawatha / Minnehaha / Overture to a jam session / Flippant flurry / Golden feather / Tulip or turnip / It shouldn't happen to a dream / Sultry sunset / Happy-go-lucky local / Cottontail / C jam blues / Flamingo / Bang-up blues / Tonk / Johnny come lately / In a blue summer garden / Great times / Perdido / Take the 'A' train / Oscalypso / Blues for Blanton.
**2 LP Set:** Released Oct '80, on Prestige Catalogue no: **PR 24029**

**GOOD YEARS OF JAZZ VOL. 2 (VIDEO)**
**VHS:** Released Feb '90, on Storyville by Storyville Records AB. Catalogue no: **SV3002**

**GREAT DUKE ELLINGTON, THE**
Tracks: / Take the a-train / I got it bad / Perdido / Mood indigo / Black & tan fantasy / Twitch / Solitude / Do nothin' til you hear from me / Mooche / Sophisticated lady / Creole love call.
**Album:** Released May '85, on Premier by Premier Records. Catalogue no: **CBR1009**
**CD:** Released Aug '87, on The Collection by Object Enterprises. Catalogue no: **OR 0022**

**GREAT ELLINGTON UNITS, THE**
Tracks: / Daydream / Good Queen Bess / That's the blues, old man / Junior hop / Without a song / My Sunday gal / Mobile bay / Linger awhile / Charlie the chulo / Lament for Javanette / Lull at dawn, A / Ready Eddy / Some Saturday / Subtle slough / Menelik (The lion of Judah) / Poor bubber / Squatty roo / Passion flower / Things ain't what they used to be / Going out the back way / Brown suede / 'C' blues.
**CD:** Released Nov '88, on Bluebird (2) by BMG Records (UK). Catalogue no: **ND 86751**

**GREAT TIMES (Ellington, Duke / Billy Strayhorn)**
**Album:** Released Aug '84, on Riverside (USA) by Fantasy Inc (USA). Catalogue no: **OJC 108**

**GREATEST HITS: DUKE ELLINGTON**
Tracks: / Take the 'A' train / Sophisticated lady / Caravan / Perdido / Prelude to a kiss / C jam blues / Mood indigo / Mooche, The / Satin doll / Solitude.
**Cass:** Released May '83, on CBS by CBS Records. Catalogue no: **40 21059**
**Album:** Released May '83, on CBS by CBS Records. Catalogue no: **CBS 21059**

**HAPPY-GO-LUCKY LOCAL (Ellington, Duke / His Orchestra)**
**CD:** Released Jul '88, on Musicraft (USA) by Discovery Records (USA). Catalogue no: **MVSCD 52**

**HARLEM (Ellington, Duke/His Orchestra)**
Tracks: / Blow by blow / Caravan / Satin doll / Harlem / Things ain't what they used to be / All of me / Prowling cat, The / Opera, The / Happy reunion / Tutti for cootie.
**Album:** Released Aug '85, on Pablo Jazz (USA) by Pablo Records (USA). Catalogue no: **230 8245**
**CD:** Released '87, on Pablo Jazz (USA) by Pablo Records (USA). Catalogue no: **CD 230 8245**
**Cass:** Released Aug '85, on Pablo Jazz (USA) by Pablo Records (USA). Catalogue no: **K 08 245**

**HOLLYWOOD BOWL CONCERT, THE**
Tracks: / Blutopia / Overture to a jam session / Mooche, The / Jumpin' punkins / Ring dem bells / Beale Street blues / Memphis blues / St. Louis blues / Golden feather / Air conditioned jungle / Golden cress / Diminuendo in blue / Translucency / Crescendo in blue.

Note: Recorded 31 August 1947.
**Album:** Released Apr '81, on Unique Jazz by Spotlite Records. Catalogue no: **UJ 01**

**HOLLYWOOD BOWL CONCERT: VOL 2**
Tracks: / Come Sunday / Blues, The / Emancipation celebration / Dancers in love / Frankie and Johnny / Take the 'A' train / Moon mist / Jam-a-ditty / Minnehaha / Hiawatha.
**Album:** Released Apr '81, on Unique Jazz by Spotlite Records. Catalogue no: **UJ 03**

**HOT FROM HARLEM 1927-1930 (Ellington, Duke/His Orchestra)**
Tracks: / Black and tan fantasy / Chicago stomp down / Sweet mama / Bugle call rag / Take it easy / Jubilee stomp / Harlem twist / Black beauty / Swamp river / Mooch / Move over / Hot and bothered / Misty mornin' / Syncopated shuffle / Big house blues / Ring dem bells / Three little words / Old man blues / Sweet chariot / Mood indigo / Rockin' in rhythm.
**2 LP Set:** Released Nov '79, on World by World Records. Deleted '84. Catalogue no: **SHB 58**

**HOT FROM THE COTTON CLUB**
Tracks: / Mooche, The / Harlem twist (East St St Louis toodle-oo) / Hot and bothered / Diga diga doo / Black beauty / Mood indigo / Ring dem bells / Doin' the new low down / Black and tan fantasy / Jungle jamboree / Big house blues / Old man blues / Rockin' in rhythm / Blues with a feeling / Misty mornin' / Goin' to town.
**CD:** Released Oct '87, on EMI by EMI Records. Catalogue no: **CDP 748 274 2**
**Cass:** Released May '85, on Retrospect by EMI Records. Deleted Nov '88. Catalogue no: **EG 2605674**
**Album:** Released May '85, on Retrospect by EMI Records. Deleted Nov '88. Catalogue no: **EG 2605671**
**CD:** Released Oct '87, on EMI by EMI Records. Catalogue no: **CZ 7**

**IMMORTAL DUKE ELLINGTON & HIS ORCHESTRA (Broadcasts 1940/41) (Ellington, Duke/His Orchestra)**
Tracks: / Grievin' / Gal from Joe's, The / Day in, day out / I don't want to set the world on fire.
**Album:** Released Mar '88, on Delta (1) by Delta Records. Catalogue no: **20 805**

**IN A MELLOTONE**
Tracks: / Take the A train / Portrait of Bert Williams, A / Main stem / Just a settin' and a rockin' / I got it bad (and that ain't good) / Perdido / Blue serge / Flaming sword, The / In a mellow tone / Cottontail / I don't know what kind of blues I got / Rumpus in Richmond / All too soon / Sepia panorama / Rocks in my bed / What am I here for?.
**Album:** Released '79, on RCA by BMG Records (UK). Deleted '82. Catalogue no: **LSA 3069**

**IN SWEDEN (1958)**
**Album:** Released Oct '86, on Jazz Information (Sweden) Catalogue no: **CAH 4001**

**IN THE SIXTIES (Ellington, Duke / His Orchestra)**
Tracks: / Take the 'A' train / I got it bad and that ain't good / Perdido / Mood indigo / Black and tan fantasy / Twitch / Solitude / Raincheck / Do nothing till you hear from me / Mooche, The / Sophisticated lady / Creole love call / Daydream / Rock skipping at the Blue Note / All day long / After all / Snibor / U.M.M.G..
**CD:** Released '86, on RCA by BMG Records (UK). Deleted Jul '89. Catalogue no: **PD 89565**

**IN THE UNCOMMON MARKET**
Tracks: / Bula / Silk Lace / Asphalt jungle, The / Star crossed lovers / Getting sentimental over you / E.S.P. (extra sensory perception) / Paris blues / Shepherd, The (first concept) / Kinda Dukish.
Note: Previously unreleased recordings from European concerts during the 60's. With the exception of Getting Sentimental Over You
Personnel: Cootie Williams / Cat Anderson / Roy Burrowes / Ray Nance / Lawrence Brown / Buster Cooper / Chuck Connors /Johnny Hodges / Russell Procope / Jimmy Hamilton / Paul Gonsalves / Harry Carney / Ernie Shepard / Sam Woodyard.
**Album:** Released Jan '87, on Pablo Jazz (USA) by Pablo Records (USA). Catalogue no: **230 8247**
**Cass:** Released Jan '87, on Pablo Jazz (USA) by Pablo Records (USA). Catalogue no: **K 8247**

**INCOMPARABLE, THE**
**CD:** Released Dec '88, on Dance Band Days by Prism Leisure. Catalogue no: **DBCD 11**
**Cass:** Released Oct '87, on Dance Band Days by Prism Leisure. Catalogue no: **DBDC 11**
**Album:** Released Oct '87, on Dance Band Days by Prism Leisure. Catalogue no: **DBD 11**

**INDIGOS**
**CD:** Released '88, on CBS by CBS Records. Catalogue no: **463 342 2**
**Album:** Released '88, on CBS by CBS Records. Catalogue no: **463 342 1**
**Cass:** Released '88, on CBS by CBS Records. Catalogue no: **463 342 4**

**INDISPENSABLE DUKE ELLINGTON VOLS. 1/2 1927 -29**
Tracks: / Creole love call / Blues I love to sing / Black and tan fantasy / Washington wobble / Harlem river quiver / East St. Louis toodle-oo / Blue bubbles / Black beauty / Jubilee stomp / Got everything but you / Flaming youth / Saturday night function / Doin' the voom voom / Harlemania / Dicty glide, The / Hot feet / Sloppy Joe / Stevedore stomp / Cotton Club stomp / Mississippi dry / Duke steps out / Haunted nights / Swanee shuffle / Breakfast dance / Jazz lips / Mooche, The / High life / Misty mornin' / Saratoga swing.
**2 LP Set:** Released '83, on RCA (France) by BMG Records (France). Catalogue no: **PM 43687**
**Cass:** Released Sep '86, on Jazz Tribune by BMG Records (UK). Deleted May '89. Catalogue no: **NK 89749**
**2 LP Set:** Released Sep '86, on Jazz Tribune by BMG Records (UK). Deleted Jul '89. Catalogue no: **NL 89749**

**INDISPENSABLE DUKE ELLINGTON VOLS. 3/4**
Tracks: / Stomp Jones / Solitude / Blue feeling / Ebony rhapsody / Live and love tonight / I met my Waterloo / My old flame / Troubled waters / Double check stomp / Sweet dreams of love / Jungle nights in Harlem / Shout 'em Aunt Tillie / Aunt Tillie / Ring dem bells / Old man blues / Nine little miles from Ten Ten Tennessee / When a black man's blue / Mood indigo / Rockin' in rhythm / Creole rhapsody (parts 1 & 2) / Limhouse blues / Echoes of the jungle / It's glory / Mystery song, The / Dinah / Bugle call rag / Dallas doings / Sweet jazz o' mine / Rude interlude / Dear old Southland / Daybreak express / Delta serenade.
**Album:** Released Sep '86, on Jazz Tribune by BMG Records (UK). Deleted Jul '89. Catalogue no: **NL 89762**
**2 LP Set:** Released '83, on RCA (France) by BMG Records (France). Catalogue no: **PM 43697**
**Cass:** Released Sep '86, on Jazz Tribune by BMG Records (UK). Catalogue no: **NK 89762**

**INDISPENSABLE DUKE ELLINGTON VOLS. 5/6**
Tracks: / Koko (II) / Bojangles (II) / Pitter panther patter (II) / Body and soul (II) / Sophisticated lady (II) / Jack the bear / Koko / Morning glory / Conga brava / Concerto for Cootie / Bojangles / Cottontail / Never no lament / Dusk / Portrait of Bert Williams, A / Blue goose / Harlem air shaft / At a Dixie roadside diner / All too soon / Rumpus in Richmond / Sepia panorama / In a mellow tone / Five o' clock whistle / Warm valley / Across the track blues / Chloe / Sidewalks of New York, The / Pitter panther patter / Body and soul / Sophisticated lady / Mr. J.B. Blues
**Cass set:** Released Sep '86, on Jazz Tribune by BMG Records (UK). Deleted May '89. Catalogue no: **NK 89750**
**2 LP Set:** Released Sep '86, on Jazz Tribune by BMG Records (UK). Deleted Jul '89. Catalogue no: **NL 89750**
**2 LP Set:** Released '83, on RCA (France) by BMG Records (France). Catalogue no: **PM 45352**

**INDISPENSABLE DUKE ELLINGTON VOLS. 7/8**
**Cass:** Released Feb '85, on RCA by BMG Records (UK). Catalogue no: **NK 89274**
**2 LP Set:** Released Feb '85, on RCA by BMG Records (UK). Deleted Jul '89. Catalogue no: **NL 89274**

**INDISPENSABLE DUKE ELLINGTON VOLS. 9/10 (The Small Groups)**
Tracks: / Daydream / Good Queen Bess / That's the blues, old man / Junior hop / Without a song / My Sunday gal / Mobile Bay / Linger awhile / Charlie the Chulo / Lament for Javanette / Lull at dawn, A / Ready Eddy / Dear old Southland / Solitude / Some Saturday / Subtle slough / Menelik the lion of Judah / Poor bubber / Squattyroo / Passion flower / Things ain't what they used to be / Goin' out the back way / Brown suede / Noir blue / C jam blues / June / Frankie and Johnny / Jumpin' room only / Tonk / Drawing room blues.
**2 LP Set:** Released '87, on Jazz Tribune by BMG Records (UK). Deleted Jul '89. Catalogue no: **NL 89582**
**Cass:** Released '87, on Jazz Tribune by BMG Records (UK). Catalogue no: **NK 89582**

**INDISPENSABLE DUKE ELLINGTON VOLS. 11/12 (1944-46)**
Tracks: / I'm beginning to see the light / Black, brown and beige - i) Work song / Black, brown and beige - ii) Come Sunday / Black, brown and beige - iii) The blues / Black, brown and beige - iv) Three dances / Carnegie blues / Mood to be wooed, The / (Otto make that) riff staccato / Prelude to a kiss / Caravan / Black and tan fantasy / Mood indigo / In a sentimental mood / It don't mean a thing / Sophisticated lady / Tonight I shall sleep / I let a song go out of my heart / Solitude / Black beauty / Perfume suite - i) Balcony serenade / Perfume suite - ii) Strange feeling / Perfume suite - iii) Dancers in love / Perfume suite - iv) Coloratura / Time 's a wastin' / Rockabye river / Sudenly it jumped / Transblucency / Just squeeze me / Gathering in a clearing, A / Beale street blues / Memphis blues / St. Louis blues / Swamp fire / Royal garden blues.
**2 LP Set:** Released Sep '87, on RCA by BMG Records (UK). Deleted Jul '89. Catalogue no: **NL 89972**
**Cass:** Released Sep '87, on RCA by BMG Records (UK). Deleted Jul '89. Catalogue no: **NK 89972**

**INSTRUMENTALS 1927-1928**
Tracks: / Red hot band / Doin' the frog / Sweet mama / Stack o lee blues / Bugle call rag / Got everything but you / Jubilee stomp / Harlem twist / Take it easy / Black beauty / Jubilee stomp (II) / Yellow dog blues / Tishomingo blues / Diga diga doo / Doin' the new low down / Swampy river / Mooche, The.
**Album:** Released Apr '85, on VJM (Vintage Jazz Music) by Vintage Jazz Music Society(VJM). Catalogue no: **VLP 73**

**INTIMACY OF THE BLUES (Ellington, Duke-Small Bands)**
Tracks: / Combo suite / Intimacy of the blues, The / Out south / Tell me 'bout my baby / Kentucky Avenue / Near North / Soul country / Noon morning / Rockochet / Tippy-toeing through the jungle garden / Just a sittin' and a rockin' / All too soon.
Note: The material on this excellent album was recorded between March 1967 and June 1970 and features small group sessions using regular salaried musicians from the Ellington Orchestra. All these sessions were made during the orchestra's brief lay-offs and much of the material here was recorded almost as a rehearsal for later full orchestral versions. Personnel includes: Duke Ellington-piano \ Cat Anderson - trumpet \ Lawrence brown - trombone \ Johnny Hodges - alto saxophone \ John Lamb-Bass \ Rufus Jones - Drums \ PaulConsalves - tenor saxophone \ Harry Carney - baritone - saxophone \ Wild Bill Davis - organ \ Willie cook - trumpet \ Victor Kaskin, Paul Kondziela - basses \ Norris Turney - flute \ Joe Benjamin - Bass \ Harold Ashby - tenor saxophone.
**Album:** Released Aug '86, on Fantasy by Ace Records. Catalogue no: **F 9640**

**INTIMATE DUKE ELLINGTON**
**Album:** Released Jan '77, on Pablo Jazz (USA) by Pablo Records (USA). Deleted '81. Catalogue no: **2310 787**

**ISFAHAN**
Tracks: / Satin doll / Isfahan / Diminuendo and crescendo in blue / Jeep's blues / Pyramid / La plues belle / Africaine.
**Album:** Released Jul '88, on Black Lion Catalogue no: **BLM 52031**

**JAM-A-DITTY (Ellington, Duke Orchestra)**
**CD:** Released 21 Jul '89, on Jazz & Jazz Catalogue no: **CDJJ 602**
**Album:** Released Jun '89, on Jazz & Jazz Catalogue no: **JJ 602**

**JAZZ COCKTAIL**
Tracks: / Stevedore stomp / Creole love call / It don't mean a thing / Hot and bothered / Rose room / Old man blues / Jungle nights in Harlem / Tiger Bay / Sweet jazz o' mine / Mood indigo / Sing you sinners / Limehouse blues / Double check stomp / Swing low / Jazz cocktail / Creole rhapsody.
**Cass:** Released 1 Oct '83, on Living Era by Academy Sound & Vision Records. Catalogue no: **ZC AJA 5024**
**CD:** Released Oct '88, on Living Era by Academy Sound & Vision Records. Catalogue no: **CD AJA 5024**
**Album:** Released 1 Oct '83, on Living Era by Academy Sound & Vision Records. Catalogue no: **AJA 5024**

**JAZZ OF WORLD WAR 2**
Tracks: / Creole love call / It don't mean a thing / Harlem air shaft / Kissing bug / Prelude to a kiss / Ring them bells / Diminuendo and crescendo in blue / In the shade of the old apple tree / Frankie and Johnny.
**Album:** Released '87, on Joker (USA) by Lifetime Records (USA). Catalogue no: **SM 3134**

**JAZZ PARTY**
**Cass:** Released 27 Feb '88, on CBS (import) by CBS Records. Catalogue no: **4600594**
**Album:** Released 27 Feb '88, on CBS (import) by CBS Records. Catalogue no: **4600591**

**JAZZ PARTY IN STEREO**
**Album:** Released Jun '86, on CBS (import) by CBS Records. Catalogue no: **84410**

**JAZZ TIME VOL.14**
**Album:** Released '88, on Vogue (France) by Vogue Records. Catalogue no: **502714**

**JAZZ TRIBUNE VOL. 7-8 (1941-42)**
**Cass:** Released '88, on RCA by BMG Records (UK). Deleted May '89. Catalogue no: **NK 89274**

**JEEP IS JUMPIN', THE**
Tracks: / East St. Louis toodle-oo / Creole love call / Stompy Jones / Jeep is jumpin' / Jack the bear / In a mellow tone / Koko / Midriff / Stop look and listen / Unbooted character, The / Lonesome lullaby / Upper Manhattan medical group.
**Album:** Released May '82, on Affinity by Charly Records. Catalogue no: **AFF 91**

**JIMMY BLANTON YEARS**
Tracks: / Koko / Blue goose / So far so good / Cotton tail / Concerto for Cootie / Jack the bear / Boy meets horn / Sgt was shy, The / Ring dem bells / Chelsea Bridge / Jive rhapsody / Jumpin' punkins / Frankie and Johnny / Take the 'A' train.
**Album:** Released Apr '81, on Queendisc (Italy) Catalogue no: **QU 007**

**JUMP FOR JOY**
**Cass:** Released May '88, on Jazz Life Catalogue no: **46012**
**Album:** Released May '88, on Jazz Life Catalogue no: **26012**
**CD:** Released May '88, on Compact Collection Catalogue no: **15012**

**JUNGLE TRIANGLE**
Tracks: / Caravan / Jungle triangle / Sentimental lady / Guitar amour / El viti / Passion flower / Agra / What am I here for? / Flirtibird.
**Album:** Released Jul '88, on Black Lion Catalogue no: **BLM 52021**

**L.A. CONCERT 1954**
**Cass:** Released '88, on GNP Crescendo (USA) by GNP Crescendo Records (USA). Catalogue no: **GNP5 9049**
**Album:** Released '88, on GNP Crescendo (USA) by GNP Crescendo Records (USA). Catalogue no: **GNPS 9049**

**LEGENDARY DUKE ELLINGTON, THE**
**Album:** Released '88, on Vogue by Vogue Records. Catalogue no: **VG SLD0903**

**LIVE AT STUTTGART VOL.1**
**Album:** on Jazz Band by Flyright Records. Catalogue no: **EB 411**

**LIVE AT THE CLUB ZANZIBAR**
Tracks: / Take the 'A' train / Wonder of You, The / Riff 'n' Drill / Last time I saw you / How Deep Is The Ocean / Every hour on the hour / Harlem Airshaft / Light / Tell it to a star / I ain't got nothin' but the blues.

**Cass:** Released 16 Sep '88, on Giants of Jazz by Hasmick Promotions. Catalogue no: **GOJC 1020**
**Album:** Released Jul '88, on Giants of Jazz by Hasmick Promotions. Catalogue no: **GOJ 1020**

**LIVE: DUKE ELLINGTON**
**2 LP Set:** Released Aug '79, on Affinity by Charly Records. Catalogue no: **AFFD 28**

**LIVE FROM CRYSTAL BALLROOM, VOL. 1**
**CD:** Released Aug '89, on Tax Catalogue no: **TAXCD 3720-2**

**LIVE FROM CRYSTAL BALLROOM, VOL. 2**
**CD:** Released 10 Aug '89, on Tax Catalogue no: **TAXCD 3721-2**

**LIVE FROM HOTEL SHERMAN, CHICAGO VOL. 1**
**Album:** Released Dec '86, on Jazz Supreme Deleted '87. Catalogue no: **JS 704**

**LIVE IN ITALY 1967 VOL.1**
**CD:** Released Dec '89, on Musidisc by Musidisc Records (France). Catalogue no: **JU 305**

**LIVE IN ITALY 1967 VOL.2**
**CD:** Released '89, on Jazz-Up Catalogue no: **JU 306**

**LIVE IN PARISO**
Tracks: / Deep purple / All of me / What else can you do with a drum / Harlem air shaft / Such sweet thunder / Stompy Jones / Things ain't what they used to be / Fe fi fo fum / El gato.
**Album:** Released Apr '86, on Magic (1) by Submarine Records. Catalogue no: **AWE 19**
**Cass:** Released Apr '86, on Magic (1) by Submarine Records. Catalogue no: **CAWE 19**

**LOUIS ARMSTRONG & DUKE ELLINGTON VOL. 1 (Ellington, Duke / Louis Armstrong)**
Tracks: / It don't mean a thing / Solitude / Don't get around much anymore / I'm beginning to see the light / Just squeeze me / Do nothing till you hear from me / I got it bad / Azalea.
**Album:** Released Jan '82, on Jazz Reactivation Catalogue no: **JR 114**

**LOUIS ARMSTRONG & DUKE ELLINGTON VOL. 2 (Ellington, Duke / Louis Armstrong)**
Tracks: / Duke's place / I'm just a lucky so-and-so / Cotton tail / Mood indigo / Do nothin' till you hear from me / Beautiful American / Black and tan fantasy / Drop me off in Harlem / Mooch / In a mellowtone.
**Album:** Released May '83, on Jazz Reactivation Catalogue no: **JR 133**

**MAGENTA HAZE**
Tracks: / Feeling of jazz, The / Magenta haze / Dancers in love / I'm gonna go fishin' / Rockin' in rhythm / Mr. Gentle and Mr. Cool / Smada / Jump for joy / Things ain't what they used to be.
**Album:** Released Jul '88, on Black Lion Catalogue no: **BLM 52011**

**MARCH 27TH, 1959**
Tracks: / Fat mouth / Lost in the night / Little John's tune / Frou frou / Dankworth Castle / Moonstone / Night stick / Lullaby for dreamers / She was a tinkling thing / Jamaica tomboy / Still water / Jet strip.
**Album:** Released Oct '80, on From The Jazz Vault by Damont Audio Ltd.. Catalogue no: **JV 101**

**MASTERPIECES BY... (Ellington, Duke / His Orchestra)**
**Album:** Released Jun '86, on CBS (import) by CBS Records. Catalogue no: **84415**
**Cass:** Released Jun '86, on CBS (import) by CBS Records. Catalogue no: **40 84415**

**MASTERS OF JAZZ**
**Album:** Released '83, on RCA (Germany) Catalogue no: **CL 42237**

**MASTERS OF JAZZ VOL.6 (Ellington, Duke / His Orchestra)**
**CD:** Released Feb '89, on Storyville by Storyville Records AB. Catalogue no: **STCD 4106**
**Album:** Released May '86, on Storyville by Storyville Records AB. Catalogue no: **SLP 4106**

**MEMORIAL**
**2 LP Set:** Released Oct '88, on Vogue by Vogue Records. Catalogue no: **400029**

**MIDNIGHT IN PARIS**
**Album:** Released Jun '86, on CBS (import) by CBS Records. Catalogue no: **84414**

**MONKEY JUNGLE**
Tracks: / Monkey jungle / Fleurette Africaine (the African flower) / Very special / Warm valley / REM blues / Little Max, A / Wig wise / Switchblade / Caravan / Backward country boy blues / Solitude.
**Album:** Released Jul '89, on Blue Note by EMI Records. Catalogue no: **785 129 1**
**CD:** Released Jun '87, on Blue Note by EMI Records. Catalogue no: **BNZ 29**
**Album:** Released Sep '84, on Blue Note by EMI Records. Catalogue no: **BNP 25113**
**Album:** Released Jul '89, on Blue Note by EMI Records. Catalogue no: **BT 85129**
**CD:** Released Jun '87, on Blue Note by EMI Records. Catalogue no: **CDP 746 398 2**

**MUSIC IS MY MISTRESS**
Tracks: / C jam blues / All of me / Black and tan fantasy / Danske onje (Danish eyes) / Queenie pie reggae / Azure / Jack the bear / Sweet Georgia Brown / Flower is a lovesome thing, A / Music is my mistress suite.
**Album:** Released '89, on Music Masters by Music Masters Records. Catalogue no: **MMC 40185Z**
**Cass:** Released '89, on Music Masters by Music Masters Records. Catalogue no: **MMD 20185Y**
**CD:** Released '89, on Music Masters by Music Masters Records. Catalogue no: **CIJD 60185K**
**CD:** Released Nov '89, on Limelight Catalogue no: **820 801-2**

**MY PEOPLE (Ellington, Duke/His Orchestra)**
Tracks: / Ain't but the one / Will you be there? / Come Sunday / David danced before the Lord with all his might / My mother and my father / Montage / My people / Blues ain't / Workin' blues / My man sends me / Jail blues / Lovin' lover / King fit the battle of Alabam' / What colour is virtue?.
Note: Conceived, written and staged by the Duke Ellington Orchestra under the supervision of Billy Strayhorn.
**Album:** Released Apr '81, on Joker (USA) by Lifetime Records (USA). Catalogue no: **SM 3257**

**NEW ORLEANS SUITE**
Tracks: / Blues for New Orleans / Bourbon Street jingling jollies / Portrait of Louis Armstrong / Thanks for the beautiful land on the delta / Portrait of Wellman Braud / Second line / Portrait of Sidney Bechet / Aristocracy a la Jean Lafitte / Portrait of Mahalia Jackson.
**Album:** Released '87, on Atlantic by WEA Records. Catalogue no: **K 50403**
**CD:** Released Jul '87, on Atlantic Jazz by WEA Records. Catalogue no: **781 376-2**

**NIGHT TRAIN**
**Album:** Released May '88, on Big Band Era Catalogue no: **20132**
**Cass:** Released May '88, on Big Band Era Catalogue no: **40132**

**NUTCRACKER SUITE (Ellington, Duke / His Orchestra)**
Tracks: / Nutcracker suite / Peer Gynt suite No. 1 / Peer Gynt suite No. 2.
**Album:** Released Jun '80, on CBS by CBS Records. Deleted '85. Catalogue no: **CBS 61899**
**Album:** Released Apr '61, on Philips by Phonogram Ltd. Deleted '66. Catalogue no: **BBL 7418**

**OCTOBER 20TH 1945**
**Album:** Released Mar '90, Catalogue no: **Q006**

**ON THE AIR (Ellington, Duke / His Orchestra)**
Tracks: / Harlem speaks / Caravan / One, two, button your shoe / Sophisticated lady / Rockin' in rhythm / East St. Louis toodle-oo / Grievin' / Little Posey / Gal from Joe's, The / Tootin' through the roof / Day in, day out / Merry go round.
**Album:** Released Sep '82, on Bulldog Records by President Records. Catalogue no: **BDL 1046**
**Cass:** Released Sep '82, on Bulldog Records by President Records. Catalogue no: **AJKL 1046**

**ON THE ROAD WITH DUKE ELLINGTON**
**VHS:** Released '88, on Kay Jazz (video) by Kay Jazz. Catalogue no: **KJ 017**

**ONE NIGHT STAND**
**Album:** Released Jul '82, on Joyce Catalogue no: **JLP 1023**

**PARIS JAZZ PARTY**
**Album:** Released Mar '81, on Affinity by Charly Records. Deleted May '88. Catalogue no: **AFF 57**

**PIANO IN THE BACKGROUND (Ellington, Duke/His Orchestra)**
**Album:** Released Jun '86, on CBS (import) by CBS Records. Catalogue no: **84418**

**PIANO IN THE FOREGROUND (Ellington, Duke/His Orchestra)**
**Album:** Released Jun '86, on CBS (import) by CBS Records. Catalogue no: **84419**

**PIANO REFLECTIONS**
Tracks: / Who knows? / Retrospective / B flat blues / Passion flower / Dancers in love / Reflections in D / Melancholia / Prelude to a kiss / In a sentimental mood / Things ain't what they used to be / All too soon / Janet / Kinda Dukish / Night time / December blue (CD only.).
**CD:** Released Feb '90, on Capitol by EMI Records. Catalogue no: **CDP 792 863 2**
**Album:** Released May '84, on MFP (France) by EMI Records. Catalogue no: **2M 056 80802**
**CD:** Released Feb '90, on Capitol by EMI Records. Catalogue no: **CZ 277**
**Cass:** Released May '84, on MFP (France) by EMI Records. Catalogue no: **2M 256 80802**

**PIANO REFLECTIONS 1953 (Ellington, Duke Trio)**
**Album:** Released Jan '83, on Swaggie (Australia) Catalogue no: **S 1346**

**POPULAR DUKE ELLINGTON, THE**
Tracks: / Take the 'A' train / I got it bad and that ain't good / Perdido / Mood indigo / Black and tan fantasy / Twitch / Solitude / Do nothing till you hear from me / Mooche, The / Sophisticated lady / Creole love call.
**Cass:** Released Nov '84, on RCA by BMG Records (UK). Catalogue no: **NK 89095**
**Album:** Released '79, on RCA by BMG Records (UK). Deleted '84. Catalogue no: **9LSA 3072**
**Album:** Released Nov '84, on RCA by BMG Records (UK). Catalogue no: **NL 89095**

**RAINBOW ROOM BROADCASTS 1967 (Ellington, Duke Octet)**
Tracks: / Satin doll / Mood indigo / Take the 'A' train / Passion flower / Sophisticated lady / Things ain't what they used to be / Tricky's lick / Blues / Solitude / Daydream / Caravan.
**Album:** Released Apr '81, on Unique Jazz by Spotlite Records. Catalogue no: **UJ 15**

**RARE 1947-57**
**CD:** Released Sep '89, on Big Band Era Catalogue no: **2601822**

**RAREST OF ALL RARE PERFORMANCES**
**Album:** Released Jul '82, on Kings Of Jazz Catalogue no: **KLJ 20034**

**REFLECTIONS IN ELLINGTON**
**Album:** Released '88, on Everybody's (USA) Catalogue no: **EV 3005**

**REPLAY ON DUKE ELLINGTON**
**Cass:** Released Nov '88, on Sierra by Sierra Records. Catalogue no: **FEDC 5020**
**Album:** Released Nov '88, on Sierra by Sierra Records. Catalogue no: **FEDB 5020**

**REUNION CONCERT (Ellington & Armstrong)**
**CD:** Released Oct '86, on Mobile Fidelity Sound Lab(USA) by Mobile Fidelity Records (USA). Catalogue no: **MFCD 2-807**

**ROCKIN' IN RHYTHM**
Tracks: / Shoe shine boy / Trumpet in spades / Solitude / Happy as the day is long / Cootle's concerto / In a jam / Uptown beat / Yearning for love / Love is like a cigarette / Exposition swing / Show boat shuffle / Barney's concerto / It was a sad night in Harlem / East St. Louis toodle-oo / Mooche, The / It don't mean a thing / Rockin' in rhythm / Black and tan fantasy.
**Cass:** Released 1 Nov '88, on Living Era by Academy Sound & Vision Records. Catalogue no: **ZC AJA 5057**
**CD:** Released 1 Nov '88, on Living Era by Academy Sound & Vision Records. Catalogue no: **CD AJA 5057**
**Album:** Released 1 Nov '88, on Living Era by Academy Sound & Vision Records. Catalogue no: **AJA 5057**

**ROCKIN' IN RHYTHM (2) (Ellington, Duke/His Orchestra)**
Tracks: / Rockin' in rhythm / Mood indigo / Double check stomp / Awful sad / Yellow dog blues / Louisiana / Black and tan fantasy / Creole rhapsody (parts 1 & 2) / Immigration blues / East St. Louis toodle-oo / New Orleans low down / Rent party blues / Cotton club stomp No. 1 / Home again blues / Sweet Mama / Harlem flat blues / Jungle Jamboree.
**Album:** Released Mar '87, on Affinity by Charly Records. Catalogue no: **AFS 1034**

**ROYALTY**
Tracks: / Mooche, The / Someone / I can't believe that you're in love with me / Indiana / Fickle fling / One o'clock jump / Tip toe topic / Tea for two / Gathering in a clearing, A / Suddenly it jumped.
**Album:** Released Sep '85, on Sierra by Sierra Records. Catalogue no: **FEDB 5027**
**Cass:** Released Jul '84, on Allegience Catalogue no: **ZCALB 2310**
**Album:** Released Jul '84, on Allegience Catalogue no: **ALEB 2310**

**SEATTLE CONCERT, THE**
Tracks: / Skin deep / How could you do a thing like that to me? / Perdido / Caravan / Harlem / Hawk talks, The / Ellington medley / Jam with Sam.
**Album:** Released Nov '87, on RCA by BMG Records (UK). Deleted Jul '89. Catalogue no: **NL 90071**

**SERENADE TO SWEDEN**
Tracks: / Take the 'A' train / Taffy twist / Black and tan fantasy / Stompy Jones / Sophisticated lady / C jam blues / Seren-

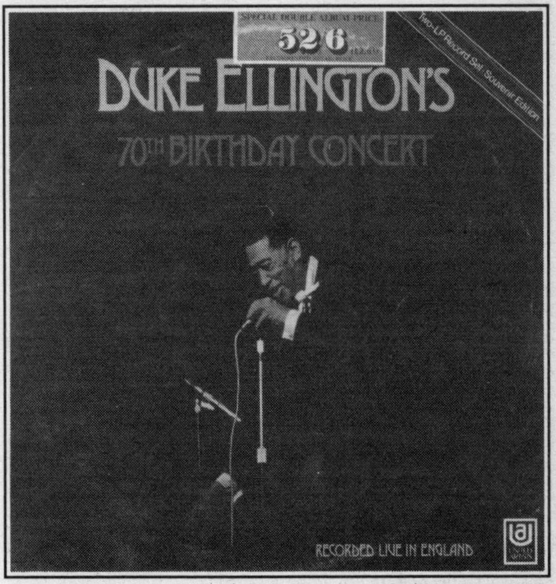


**Duke Ellington - Seventieth birthday concert (United Artists)**

ade / Boo-dah / I let a song go out of my heart.
**Album:** Released Oct '82, on Black Lion Catalogue no: **BLM 52001**
**Cass:** Released '83, on Black Lion Catalogue no: **BLM 52001C**

**SEVENTIETH BIRTHDAY CONCERT (See panel on previous page)**
Note: Prelude to a kiss medley includes the following tracks - Prelude to a kiss / I'm just a lucky so and so / I let a song go out of my heart / Do nothin' til you hear from me / Just squeeze me / Don't get around much anymore / Mood indigo / Sophisticated lady / Caravan.
Special souvenir edition.
Tracks: / Rockin' in rhythm / B.P. / Take the 'A' train / Tootie for cootie / 4.30 blues / El gato / Black butterfly / Things ain't what they used to be / Laying on mellow / Satin doll / Azure / In triplicate / Perdido / Fifi / Prelude to a kiss meldey / Black swan / Final ellington speech.
**LP Set:** Released '70, on United Artists Catalogue no: **UAD 60001**

**SHOWCASE**
Tracks: / Satin doll / C Jam blues / In a sentimental mood.
**LP Set:** Released Dec '84, on Pathe Marconi (France) Catalogue no: **PM 155189-3**

**SIDE BY SIDE (Ellington, Duke / Johnny Hodges)**
Tracks: / Stompy Jones / Squeeze me / Big shoe / Going up / Just a memory / Let's fall in love / Ruin / Bend one / You need go rock.
**Album:** Released Feb '86, on Polydor by Polydor Ltd. Deleted Oct '88. Catalogue no: **821 578-1**
**CD:** Released Feb '86, on Polydor by Polydor Ltd. Deleted Jul '88. Catalogue no: **821 578-2**
**Cass:** Released Feb '86, on Polydor by Polydor Ltd. Deleted Jul '88. Catalogue no: **821 578-4**

**SKIN DEEP**
Tracks: / Skin deep.
**7" Single:** Released Mar '54, on Philips by Phonogram Ltd. Deleted '59. Catalogue no: **PB 243**

**SOPHISTICATED LADY (16 Ellington classics) (Ellington, Duke/His Orchestra)**
Tracks: / Take the 'A' train / Perdido / In a mellow tone / Happy go lucky local / Sophisticated lady / I got it bad and that ain't good / Mood indigo / It don't mean a thing / Things ain't what they used to be / I let a song go out of my heart / Something to live for / Black beauty / Caravan / Dancers in love / Solitude / Black and tan fantasy.
**Album:** Released Jul '86, on CBS by CBS Records. Catalogue no: **CBS 25742**
**Cass:** Released Jan '84, on CBS (import) by CBS Records. Catalogue no: **40 25742**

**SOUNDTRACK (Ellington, Duke (USA) Catalogue no: 40024**
**Album:** Released Nov '84, on Astan (USA) Catalogue no: **20024**

**Album:** Released '88, on Storyville by Storyville Records AB. Catalogue no: **SLP 702**

**S.R.O**
Tracks: / Take the 'A' train / I got it bad and that ain't good / Things ain't what they used to be / West Indian pancake / Black and tan fantasy / Creole love call / Mooche, The / Soul call / El gato / Open house / Rockin' in rhythm / Jam with Sam / Adlib on Nippon / C jam blues / Hawk talks, The.
**CD:** Released Apr '89, on Denon Catalogue no: **DC 8540**
**Cass:** Released Apr '89, on Denon Catalogue no: **MC 7680**
**CD:** Released '88, on Denon Catalogue no: **C38-7680**

**STEREO AIR FORCE DANCE 1958 VOL.2**
**Album:** Released '88, on Unique Jazz by Spotlite Records. Catalogue no: **UJ 34**

**STEREO EXCURSION WITH DUKE (1953-73)**
**Album:** Released '88, on Ellington 86 Catalogue no: **E 86**

**STUDIO RECORDINGS 1 (1937-47)**
**Album:** Released '88, on Up To Date Catalogue no: **UTD 2002**

**STUDIO RECORDINGS 2 (1947-49)**
**Album:** Released '88, on Up To Date Catalogue no: **UTD 2003**

**STUDIO RECORDINGS 3 (1926-52)**
**Album:** Released '88, on Up To Date Catalogue no: **UTD 2004**

**STUDIO RECORDINGS 4 (1947-51)**
**Album:** Released '88, on Up To Date Catalogue no: **UTD 2005**

**STUDIO RECORDINGS 5 1929-56**
**Album:** Released '88, on Up To Date Catalogue no: **UTD 2006**

**STUDIO RECORDINGS 6 (1930-58)**
**Album:** Released May '86, on Up To Date Catalogue no: **UTD 2007**

**STUDIO RECORDINGS 7 (1929-62)**
**Album:** Released May '86, on Up To Date Catalogue no: **UTD 2008**

**STUDIO RECORDINGS 8 (1933-1967) (Ellington, Duke/His Orchestra)**
**Album:** Released Jan '87, on Up To Date Catalogue no: **UTD 2009**

**SWEET THUNDER**
**Cass:** Released May '88, on Jazz Life Catalogue no: **2673724**
**Album:** Released May '88, on Jazz Life Catalogue no: **2673721**
**CD:** Released May '88, on Jazz Life Catalogue no: **2673722**

**SYMPHONIC ELLINGTON**
**Album:** Released Jun '83, on Trend (USA) by Trend Records (USA). Catalogue no: **TR 529**

**TAKE THE 'A' TRAIN**
**CD:** Released 10 Jul '89, on Vogue by Vogue Records. Catalogue no: **VGCD 670208**
**Cass:** Released Nov '84, on Astan (USA) Catalogue no: **40024**
**Album:** Released Nov '84, on Astan (USA) Catalogue no: **20024**

**TANGLEWOOD July 15, 1956**
**Album:** Released '88, on Queen Catalogue no: **QUEEN 049**

**TENDERLY (Ellington, Duke/His Orchestra)**
Tracks: / Nutcracker suite overture / Such sweet thunder / Black and tan fantasy / Creole love call / Mooche, The / Tulip or turnip / Tenderly / All of me / Jeeps blues.
**Cass:** Released Apr '86, on Castle Showcase by Castle Communications Records. Catalogue no: **SHTC 110**
**Album:** Released Apr '86, on Castle Showcase by Castle Communications Records. Catalogue no: **SHLP 110**

**THIS ONE'S FOR BLANTON (Ellington, Duke/Ray Brown)**
Tracks: / Do nothing till you hear from me / Pitter panther patter / Things ain't what they used to be / Sophisticated lady / See see rider / Fragmented suite for piano and bass.
Note: Booklet included with record.
**Cass:** Released '82, on Pablo Jazz (USA) by Pablo Records (USA). Catalogue no: **K10 721**
**CD:** Released '88, on Pablo Jazz (USA) by Pablo Records (USA). Catalogue no: **J33J 20010**
**Album:** Released '82, on Pablo Jazz (USA) by Pablo Records (USA). Catalogue no: **231 0721**

**TRANSCRIPTION YEARS, THE VOL. 1 1941-45**
**Album:** Released Aug '87, on Tax Catalogue no: **M 8037**
**Album:** Released Mar '90, on Tax Catalogue no: **TAX 8037**

**TRANSCRIPTIONS YEARS, THE**
**Album:** Released Jan '83, on Swaggie (Australia) Catalogue no: **S 1388**

**TREASURY SERVICE, 2 APRIL 1945**
**Album:** Released '88, on Phontastic (Sweden) Catalogue no: **NOST 7662**

**TREASURY SHOW VOL.1**
Tracks: / Take the 'A' train / Blutopia / Midriff / Creole love call / Suddenly it jumped / Frustration / I'm beginning to see the light / Love / Perfume suite / Violence / Dancers in love / Coloratura / Air conditioned jungle / I ain't got nothin' but the blues / Subtle slough / Passion flower.
**Album:** Released '82, on Nostalgia by Mainline Records. Catalogue no: **NOST 7621**

**TREASURY SHOW VOL.2**
Tracks: / Take the 'A' train / Mood to be wooed / If you are but a dream / Riff staccato / I'm beginning to see the light / Black brown and beige / Stomp look and listen / Frantic fantasy / It don't mean a thing / Sentimental lady.
**Album:** Released '82, on Nostalgia by Mainline Records. Catalogue no: **NOST 7622**

**TREASURY SHOW VOL.3**
Tracks: / Take the 'A' train / Midriff / Carnegie blues / Someone / My little brown book / Kissing bug / Ring dem bells / I'm beginning to see the light / Black brown and beige / Candy / Teardrops in the rain / Accentuate the positive / Way low.
**Album:** Released '82, on Nostalgia by Mainline Records. Catalogue no: **NOST 7623**

**TREASURY SHOW VOL.4**
Tracks: / Blutopia / Clementine / Sentimental journey / I got it bad / Three cent stomp / Black and tan fantasy / Blue skies / Passion flower / Air conditioned jungle / Frantic fantasy / I'm beginning to see the light / Main stem / Everything but you / Carnegie blues / Jump for joy / Things ain't what they used to be / Take the 'A' train / My heart sings.
**Album:** Released '82, on Nostalgia by Mainline Records. Catalogue no: **NOST 7624**

**TREASURY SHOW VOL.5**
Tracks: / Take the 'A' train / Carnegie blues / Riff staccato / All at once / Yesterdays / I kiss your kiss / Accentuate the positive / Blue cellophane / Prelude to a kiss / Caravan / Sophisticted lady / I'm beginning to see the light / Solitude / I ain't got nothin' but the blues / I don't mind / Jeep is jumpin'.
**Album:** Released '82, on Nostalgia by Mainline Records. Catalogue no: **NOST 7631**

**TREASURY SHOW VOL.6**
Tracks: / Take the 'A' train / Teardrops in the rain / Everything but you / Perdido / If you are but a dream / Pitter panther patter / Emancipation celebration / I should care / In a sentimental mood / It don't mean a thing / Solitude / I'm beginning to see the light / Bond promo / Subtle slough / C jam blues / Don't you know I care / Stomp look and listen / Things ain't what they used to be.
**Album:** Released '82, on Nostalgia by Mainline Records. Catalogue no: **NOST 7632**

**TREASURY SHOW VOL.7**
Tracks: / Take the 'A' train / Sugar hill penthouse / Suddenly it jumped / Candy / Friend of yours, A / Kissing bug / Hollywood hangover / Laura / In the shade of the old apple tree / Frankie and Johnny / I'm beginning to see the light / Bond promo / Midriff / I ain't got nothin' but the blues / My honey's loving arms / Rockin' in rhythm.
**Album:** Released '82, on Nostalgia by Mainline Records. Catalogue no: **NOST 7633**

**TREASURY SHOW VOL.8**
Tracks: / Take the 'A' train / Mood to be wooed, The / Jack the bear / More I see you, The / Way low / Blues on the double / Summertime / Come Sunday / Light / I'm beginning to see the light / On the Alamo / Carnegie blues / Riff staccato / Blue skies / Things ain't what they used to be / Moon maiden / Edward the first / Symphonette / Intimate interlude / Some summer fun / Layin' on mellow / Eulb / Tenz / I got it bad and that ain't good / Sophisticated lady / Edward the second.
**Album:** Released '82, on Nostalgia by Mainline Records. Catalogue no: **NOST 7634**

**TWO GREAT CONCERTS IN EUROPE**
Tracks: / Take the A train / Caravan / Do nothing till you hear from me / Fancy dance / Hawk talks, The / Swamp drum / Main stem / Tattooed bride / Threesome / Take the A train (version) / Satin doll/Sophisticated lady / Meow, shorted encore / I got it bad and that ain't good / Harmong in Harlem / Things ain't what they used to be / Perdido / New concerto for Cootie, The / Carolina shout rockin' in rhythm / Take the A train.
**CD:** Released Dec '89, on Accord (France) by Musidisc Records (France). Catalogue no: **302284**
**Cass:** Released Dec '89, on Accord (France) by Musidisc Records (France). Catalogue no: **302282**

**UNDOCUMENTED ELLINGTON, THE**
**Album:** Released '88, on Up To Date Catalogue no: **UTD 2001**

**UNFORGETTABLE DUKE ELLINGTON,**
Tracks: / H'ya Sue / It's mad mad mad / You gotta crawl before you walk / Brown Penny / Boogie bop blues / Three cent stomp / Progressive gavotte / Take it easy / Singing in the rain / Don't get around much anymore / I can't believe that you're in love with me.
**Cass set:** Released Jan '83, on Ditto by Pickwick Records. Catalogue no: **DTO 10045**

**UNKNOWN SESSION**
Tracks: / Everything but you / Black beauty / All too soon / Something to live for / Mood indigo / Creole blues / Don't you know I care / Flower is a lovesome thing / Mighty like the blues / Tonight I shall sleep / Dual highway / Blues.
**Album:** Released '79, on CBS by CBS Records. Deleted '84. Catalogue no: **CBS 82819**

**UNUSUAL ELLINGTON, THE**
Tracks: / Stomp look and listen / Warm valley / Sultry serenade / Hiya Sue / Passion flower / Primping for the prom / Cobb's tune / Coffee and kisses / Easy to love / Change my ways / Liza / Body and soul.
**Album:** Released '82, on Nostalgia by Mainline Records. Catalogue no: **NOST 7614**

**UP IN DUKE'S WORKSHOP**
Tracks: / Blem / Goof, The / Love is just around the corner / Bateau / Wanderlust / Neo-Creole / Black butterfly / Mendoza.
**Album:** Released '82, on Pablo Jazz (USA) by Pablo Records (USA). Catalogue no: **231 0815**
**Cass:** Released '82, on Pablo Jazz (USA) by Pablo Records (USA). Catalogue no: **K10 815**

**UPTOWN**
Tracks: / Take the 'A' train / Mooche, The / Tone parallel to Harlem / Perdido / Controversial suite part 1 / Before my time / Controversial suite part 2 / Skin deep.
**Cass:** Released 14 Aug '88, on CBS (import) by CBS Records. Catalogue no: **4608304**
**Album:** Released 14 Aug '88, on CBS (import) by CBS Records. Catalogue no: **4608301**

**VINTAGE PERFORMANCES (Ellington, Duke / His Orchestra)**
**CD:** Released Jan '88, on London by London Records Ltd. Catalogue no: **820 592-2**

**VIP (Rare live performances)**
**Album:** Released '84, on Swing House by Submarine Records. Catalogue no: **SWH 28**

**WASHINGTON D.C. ARMORY CONCERT, THE**
Tracks: / Perdido / All the things you are / Just squeeze me / La virgen de la Macarena / Happy go lucky local / Tone parallel to Harlem / Take the 'A' train / John Sander's blues.
**Album:** Released '82, on Nostalgia by Mainline Records. Catalogue no: **NOST 7611**

**WASHINGTON WOBBLE**
**CD:** Released Mar '90, on Saville by Conifer Records. Catalogue no: **JJCD14**

**WAY LOW - LANGLEY FIELDS BROADCAST (Ellington, Duke Orchestra)**
Note: Broadcasts from 8th December 1943, 19th November 1942 & May 1943 are featured on this album.
**Album:** Released Jul '87, on Duke by Melodisc Records. Catalogue no: **D 1017**

**WEST COAST TOUR**
**Album:** Released '82, on Jazz Bird Catalogue no: **JAZ 2010**
**Cass:** Released '82, on Jazz Bird Catalogue no: **ZCJAZ 2010**

## Ellington, Mercer

**Biographical details:** Trumpeter, composer, arranger and bandleader, born in 1919 in Washington DC, son of Duke Ellington and always in his shadow. He led his own bands at various times, also working off and on for his father: he wrote *Blue serge, John Hardy's wife, Things ain't what they used to be, Moon mist* etc. for Duke 1955-59; he resumed playing and had his own band in Birdland in 1959; then he was a D.J. for several years and rejoined Duke in 1965, managing the band and playing trumpet. Mercer backed Diahann Carroll on *A tribute to Ethel Waters* in 1978. He leads the popular Ellington ghost band; albums made in the '80's like *Continuum* on Fantasy, *Hot & bothered* on Dr Jazz, *Digital Duke* on GRP (the band including

Branford Marsalis, Louis Bellson, Clark Terry) are Mercer albums, though often listed as Duke's. The Affinity album is compilation of tracks made in the late 50's. Mercer also led the band for the musical *Sophisticated ladies* in 1980-1 based on Duke's music. (Donald Clarke, April 1989).

**STEPPIN' INTO SWING SOCIETY (Ellington, Mercer & his orchestra)**
Tracks: / Steppin' into swing society / Frolic Sam / Ruint / Be patient / Gal from Joe's, The / Indelible / Broadway babe / Black butterfly / Got my foot in the door / If you were in my place / Yearning for love / Afternoon moon / Black and tan fantasy / Maroon / Azure / Mood indigo.
**Album:** Released Aug '88, on Affinity by Charly Records. Catalogue no: **AFF 194**

## Ellington, Ray

**GOON SHOW HITS (Ellington, Ray & Quartet)**
Tracks: / Framed / Three bears, The / I've got a gal in Kalamazoo / Signora-Bueno sera (medley) / Lady's in love with you, The / Little girl / That's my girl / Teddy bears' picnic / Ol' man river / Miss Otis regrets / Old Mother Hubbard / My very good friend the milkman / It's a sin to tell a lie / I want a little girl / From this moment on.
**Album:** Released '74, on BBC by BBC Records & Tapes. Deleted '88. Catalogue no: **REC 172**

**LONG BLACK NYLONS**
Tracks: / Long black nylons.
**7" Single:** on Northwood by Northwood Records. Catalogue no: **NW 45 003**

**MADISON, THE**
Tracks: / Madison, The.
**7" Single:** Released Nov '62, on Ember by Bulldog Records (UK). Catalogue no: **S 102**

## Elliot, Don

**MELLOPHONE**
**Album:** Released Feb '88, on Fresh Sounds (Spain) by Fresh Sounds Records (Spain). Catalogue no: **FS 200**

## Ellis, Chris

**VOCAL WITH HOT ACCOMPANIMENT**
Note: Accompanied by Digby-Fairweather / Martin Litton / Paul Sealey / Tiny Winters. Tracks include: You can't stop me from dreaming / The bathtub ran over / Melancholy baby / I'll never say never again again.
**Album:** Released Sep '87, on Dormouse Catalogue no: **DM 15**

## Ellis, Don

**Biographical details:** Trumpeter and bandleader, composer and teacher (1934-78) who worked in dance bands, with Maynard Ferguson, recorded with George Russell in 1961, was a trumpet soloist in modern compositions played by the New York Philharmonic and from 1965 did very interesting big band work on CBS under the influence of Indian music, bizarre time changes etc. at one point using a custom made horn that would play quarter tones. His film music included the Grammy winning theme *The French Connection* in 1973. He had a serious heart attack in 1975 and was recovering and took up the superbone (slide/valve trombone) but had another, final attack. *How time passes* was recorded in 1960 with a quartet including Jaki Byard, Ron Carter and Charlie Persip. (Donald Clarke, April 1989).

**HOW TIME PASSES**
Tracks: / How time passes / Sallie / Simplex one, A / Waste / Improvisational suite.
Note: Recorded 1960. Tracks include: How time passes / Sallie / A simplex one / Waste / Improvisational suite.
**Album:** Released Dec '85, on Candid Catalogue no: **CS 9004**
**CD:** Released Sep '87, on Candid Catalogue no: **CCD 9004**

**LIVE AT MONTREUX**
Tracks: / Open wide / Loneliness / Future feature / Go no go / Sporting dance / Niner two.
**Album:** Released '79, on Atlantic by WEA Records. Catalogue no: **K 50496**

**OUT OF NOWHERE**
**CD:** Released May '89, on Candid Catalogue no: **CCD 9032**
**Album:** Released May '89, on Candid Catalogue no: **CS 9032**

## Ellis, Herb

**Biographical details:** Jazz guitarist born in 1921 in Texas. Working for Jimmy Dorsey, he left with bassist John Frigo and pianist Lou Carter as the trio Soft Winds 1947-52: using Nat Cole's trio format but with all three singing original arrangements in hip harmony, they were ahead of their time (Carter later became TV's 'Lou the taxi driver', a popular guest of the USA Perry Como show). Ellis joined Ray Brown in Oscar Peterson trio 1953-58, perhaps the greatest piano trio of all time; he accompanied Ella Fitzgerald, Julie London and others; he has toured in guitar duos with Joe Pass and Barney Kessell. When he complained in the mid-'70's to local car dealer Carl Jefferson in Concord, California about lack of opportunities to record he was instrumenal in setting up the extremely successful Concord Jazz label: Jefferson soon sold his car business. (Donald Clarke, April 1989).

**AFTER YOU'VE GONE (Ellis, Herb & Ray Brown)**
**CD:** Released Jul '88, on Concord Jazz by Concord Jazz Records (USA). Catalogue no: **CCD 6006**

**DOGGIN' AROUND (Ellis, Herb & Red Mitchell)**
**Cass:** Released 12 Apr '89, on Concord by Concord Jazz Records (USA). Catalogue no: **CJ 372C**
**Album:** Released 12 Apr '89, on Concord by Concord Jazz Records (USA). Catalogue no: **CJ 372**
**CD:** Released 12 Apr '89, on Concord by Concord Jazz Records (USA). Catalogue no: **CCD 4372**

**HERB ELLIS & JOE PASS (Ellis, Herb & Joe Pass)**
**CD:** Released Jul '88, on Concord Jazz by Concord Jazz Records (USA). Catalogue no: **CCD 6001**

**HERB MIX**
Tracks: / It's a small world after all / Tenderly / Girl from Ipanema / It could happen to you / Deep / Moonlight in Vermont / Give my regards to Broadway / Way we were, The / Preacher, The.
**Album:** Released Apr '82, on Concord Jazz by Concord Jazz Records (USA). Catalogue no: **CJ 181**

**HOT TRACKS (Ellis, Herb & Ray Brown Sextet)**
**CD:** Released Dec '88, on Concord by Concord Jazz Records (USA). Catalogue no: **CCD 6012**

**RHYTHM WILLIE (Ellis, Herb & Freddie Green)**
**CD:** Released Jul '88, on Concord Jazz by Concord Jazz Records (USA). Catalogue no: **CCD 6010**

**SEVEN COME ELEVEN (Ellis, Herb & Joe Pass)**
**CD:** Released Jul '88, on Concord Jazz by Concord Jazz Records (USA). Catalogue no: **CCD 6002**

**SOFT AND MELLOW**
**CD:** Released Aug '88, on Bel Catalogue no: **CCD 4077**
**Album:** Released Mar '79, on Concord Jazz by Concord Jazz Records (USA). Catalogue no: **CJ 77**

**SOFT SHOE (Ellis, Herb & Ray Brown)**
**CD:** Released Jul '88, on Concord Jazz by Concord Jazz Records (USA). Catalogue no: **CCD 6003**

**TWO FOR THE ROAD (Ellis, Herb & Joe Pass)**
Tracks: / Love for sale / Am I blue? / Seven come eleven / Guitar blues / Lady be good / Cherokee (concept 1) / Cherokee (concept 2) / Gee baby ain't I good to you / Try a little tenderness / I found a new baby / Angel eyes.
**CD:** Released May '86, on Pablo Jazz (USA) by Pablo Records (USA). Catalogue no: **CD 20029**
**CD:** Released Jan '89, on JVC/Fantasy Catalogue no: **VDJ 28015**
**Cass:** Released '82, on Pablo Jazz (USA) by Pablo Records (USA). Catalogue no: **K10 714**
**Album:** Released '82, on Pablo Jazz (USA) by Pablo Records (USA). Catalogue no: **231 0714**

## Elman, Ziggy

**1947: ZIGGY ELMAN (Elman, Ziggy & His Orchestra)**
Note: With Virginia Maxey, Bob Manning.
**Album:** Released Jun '86, on Circle (USA) by Jazzology Records (USA). Catalogue no: **CLP 70**

## Elsdon, Alan

**JAZZ JOURNEYMEN**
Tracks: / Lord Randal / Saturday afternoon blues / Diga diga doo / There's yes yes in your eyes / Panama rag / Four or five times / Two deuces / Come back, sweet Papa / Lovely Rita, meter maid / Satisfaction.
**Album:** Released Aug '77, on Black Lion Catalogue no: **BLP 12163**

## Engbarth, Gerhard

**BLUES VOM FRIEDEN (Engbarth, Gerhard with Louisiana Red)**
**Album:** on L&R Catalogue no: **LR 44.011**

## Englund, Ernie

**ERNIE ENGLUND HIS TRUMPET AND THE VISBY BIG BAND**
**Album:** Released May '86, on Phontastic (Sweden) Catalogue no: **PHONT 7567**

**VISBY DOMKYRKA (Englund, Ernie & Ola Hoglund)**
**Album:** Released '88, on Four Leaf Clover Catalogue no: **FLC 5071**

## Entertainers Of The Jazz...

**ENTERTAINERS OF THE JAZZ AGE SERIES 5 (Various artists)**
Note: Artists include; Charles Hamp, Eddie Walters.
**Cass:** Released Jul '86, on Emporium Cassettes Catalogue no: **046**

## Erskine, Peter

**MOTION POET**
Tracks: / Erskoman / Not a word / Hero with a thousand faces / Dream clock / Exit up right / New regalia, A / Boulez / Mysery man, The / In walked Maya.
Note: A veritable summit meeting involving most of today's leading jazz-fusion protagonists, Motion Poet is a splendidly consistent set which can only further enhance the ever growing reputation of leader Peter Erskine as a record-maker under his own name. Not surprisingly, Erskine's superior drumming is a major factor throughout - he also contributes four of the nine numbers - but there is no lack of creative impact from his talented colleagues. Including Eliane Elias, John Abercrombie, Will Lee, Marc Johnson and the Brecker brothers, Randy and Mike. a fine horn section augments the various permutations of leading personnel: the whole is skilfully knitted together by Vince Mendoza - composer of three other titles - who performed a similar arranging assistance on Erskine's previous Denon CD release: Transition. (Denon 11/88).
**Album:** Released '89, on Denon Catalogue no: **INLP 803**
**CD:** Released Oct '88, on Denon Catalogue no: **CY 72582**

**PETER ERSKINE**
Tracks: / Leroy street / E.S.P. / All's well that ends / Coyote blues / In statu nascendi / Change of mind / My ship.
Note: Peter Erskine-drums / Michael Brecker - tenor sax / Randy Brecker-trumpet / Eddie Gomez - bass / Mike Mainieri-vibes / Don Grolnick - electric piano / Bob Mintzer - tenor sax / Don Alias - congas / Kenny Kirkland - piano.
**Album:** Released Mar '83, on Polydor (Import) by Polydor Ltd. Catalogue no: **1014 010**

**TRANSITION**
Tracks: / Osaka castle / Rabbit in the moon, The / Corazon / Suite / King Richard II / Hard speaks hold, The / My foolish heart / Orson Welles and others.
Note: Peter Erskine (Drums), John Abercrombie (Guitar), Marc Johnson (Bass), Joe Lovano (Tenor/soprano saxes), Bob Mintser (Tenor sax), Kenny Werner (Piano / Synthesisers), Peter Gordon (French Horn).
**CD:** Released '88, on Denon Catalogue no: **CY-1484**

## Erstrand, Lars

**MINE FOREVER (Erstrand, Lars Trio)**
**Album:** Released '88, on PHM Catalogue no: **PHM 1010**

## Ervin, Booker

**Biographical details:** Tenor saxist (1930-70), like Booker Little and Eric Dolphy a fine talent who died much too young (of kidney disease). He had a virile Texas tenor style on both blues and ballads; he played on several Charles Mingus albums 1958-62 and on Randy Weston's *African cookbook* as well as making several fine small group sets of his own. (Donald Clarke, April 1989).

**BOOK COOKS**
Tracks: / Blue book, The / Git it / Little Jane / Book cooks, The / Largo / Poor butterfly.
**Album:** Released May '82, on Affinity by Charly Records. Deleted '88. Catalogue no: **AFF 88**

**FREEDOM AND SPACE SESSIONS**
Tracks: / Lunar tune / Dry me not / Day to mourn / Grant's stand / Stella by starlight / Al's in / Mojo / I can't get started / Number two / Second 2 / There is no greater love.
**2 LP Set:** Released Jan '80, on Prestige Deleted Jan '85. Catalogue no: **PR 24091**

**LAMENT FOR BOOKER ERVIN**
**Album:** Released Jan '82, on Enja (Germany) by Enja Records (West Germany). Catalogue no: **ENJA 2054**

**SONG BOOK, THE**
**Album:** Released Apr '76, on Prestige Catalogue no: **PR 7318**

**THAT'S IT (See panel below)**
Tracks: / Mojo / Uranus / Poinciana / Speak low / Booker's blues / Boo.
Note: I first heard Booker Ervin at the beginning of 1959 when he was with Charles Mingus' turbulent Jazz Workshop. Mingus' problem with sidemen is usually that of finding musicians who can match or at least come reasonably close to equalling his own volcanic feelings and musical daring. In appearance, Ervin looked as if he might. I saw a broad,

**Booker Ervin - That's it (Candid)**

muscular man with a moustache that would have won the respect of a Mexican revolutuionary and the implacable stance of a man for whom taking care of business was first and not second nature. Then Booker began to play. I felt as if I had been hit by a blast of heat. Unmasked, un-inhibited, boilingly honest emotions exploded from his horn. He played moreover, with a huge tone and a beat that might have even moved Barry Goldwater into this century. His ideas were fiercly his own and yet he understood Mingus' road and had no trouble commiting himself to that challenging journey without losing his strong sense of self-identification.

My admiration for Booker has steadily increased since then, all the more since I've come to know him off the stand. Booker is shy, intransigently honest, and is possessed of seemingly inexhaustible determination.His career as a musician has had several detours,but he's come back each time.He was born Booker Telleferro Ervin II in Denison, Texas, October 31, 1930. His father was a trombonist and played for a time with Buddy Tate in a Texas band. His mothers music was reserved for the vivid meetings for her "sanctified" church. As a boy ,Booker wanted a saxaphone, but his mother couldn't afford to buy him one, and accordingly gave him his fathers trombone. He played the instrument from the age of eight to thirteen, became proficient at it, then finally put it down. "That wasn't it", he says. When he joined the Air Force in 1950, he started to express himself musically again after seven years away from playing. Borrowing a tenor from Special Services, he taught himself the horn and by the time he was stationed in Okinawa, he was leading his own combo.

Booker was discharged in 1953, and the next year he went to Boston to study at Schillinger House (now the Berklee School of Music). There he was trained by Joe Viola and became more technically fluent on the horn. He planned to go on to New York, but illness disabled him for a time.

By 1955 he was back in music and was touring the south, southwest and west with Ernie Fields' rhythm and blues band. The next year he was working around Dallas with James Clay, played in Chicago with bluesmen Lowell Fulson, returned to Dallas, and then set out for Oregon. He stopped in Denver for what he had hoped to be a brief visit, but he remained eighteen months. For a while he played, then he gave up the horn again. "I was getting disgusted. I started to study and then work on mechanical drafting. I got pretty good at it, but that wasn't it. So I went to work in the post-office. There I felt secure economically, but that wasn't it either." At the end of 1957 he started journeying again. He played in Pittsburgh for six months, but union rules limited him to only a week of playing during that time. Finally he made New York in May 1958 after four years of trying. Shafi Hadi, then with Mingus, had heard Ervin at a session and told Mingus, "I just a tenor who cuts just about everybody. He doesn't play just changes; he plays music." Mingus' pianist Horace Parlan invited Booker to sit with Charlie, and Mingus was strongly impressed.

Ervin, after a period of washing dishes at Horn & Hardart so that he could stay in New York. He joined Mingus in November 1958, and stayed until February 1960 and then rejoined for the Newport Rebellion led by Mingus and Max Roach, a trip to France, and occasional other jobs. Essentially, however, he had been freelancing and leading his own combo. "Being with Mingus", he recalls, "was very important to me. I became aware of harmonic possibilities that I'd never heard before, and having to play his charts freed me imaginatively and technically. I became much more flexible over horn."

Ervin has inexorably been building a style of his own. Lester Young had been his first major influence; and later there were Dexter Gordon, Sonny Stitt, Sonny Rollins & John Coltrane. "But he never imitated Coltrane", Mingus emphasizes. "He was playing this way before he'd ever heard of Coltrane, and the two in any case are quite dissimilar." Ervin feels:" I'm playing, or trying to, like myself now.It's the only way to make playing worthwile.Music means so much to me that it would not figure to play like anyone but myself."

For his first album on *Candid*, Ervin suggested a free-blowing date largely based, however, on new material. "I had done some other recording sessions, but I had been saving these songs for the right time, and I felt this was it." For his rhythm section, he chose drummer Al Harewood ("he keeps perfect time and never gets in your way"); pianist Felix Krull (a nom-de-date); and a remarkable bassist, george Tucker, who has worked with Earl Bostic, John Coltrane, Jackie McClean, Kenny Furrell, Lou Donaldson, and others.

All the originals are by Booker. He named the opener *Mojo* (a vintage voodoo charm) because the song connoted to him "afeeling of mystery, of out-of-the-ordinary power". Contributing to that feeling is the fact that the piece is played in two keys simultaneously- the pianist is in one, and Booker and Tucker are in the other. As is usual with Booker, the piece came to him from working out ideas on the piano. "I heard it and it seemed to be right just this way". From the beginning, the seizing *Cry Of Jazz* in Bookers playing is clearly evident. Also evident are a definiteness in execution, an absorbing sense of thematic and rhythmic continuity and enveloping pulsation. Note the strength sound and taste of George Tucker's bass throughout on this track and the record as a whole plus Mr. Krull's intensity.

Uranus is so titled because the piece seemed to Booker to be "airy, sort of suggestive of limitless space". The interpretation indicate Ervin's capacity for reflective gentleness, but his is a lyricism that communicates fierce,underlying passions.

Booker chose *Poinciana* because he likes the changes. In other hands, the tune has often conveyed to me a vista of wistfully swaying palms, but Booker turns the song into exclamatory,blues-timbered autobiography and instills extraordinary heat into its lines. George Tucker takes an intriguingly developed, powerful solo.

*Speak Low* was also selected because of its provocative changes. Booker plays it with a bursting vitality of sound, beats and ideas- a total absorbtion in the music that has led Charles Mingus to call him one of the "trance" players. "Nearly everybody I've worked with whom I've liked", Mingus explains, "seems to get into a trance when they are their best. I remember when Booker was really going, I'd say something to him and he just didn't hear me. He was somewhere else - inside the music". This is playing of such energetic, leaping spontaneity that to this listener it is a surgingly exciting experience and is evidence that the most liberating source of jazz's future is still within the improviser.

*Booker's Blues* is as basic and deeply relaxed a blues performance as I've heard by any of the "new" modernists . "Sure I keep working on a lot of differnt harmonic things", says Booker, "but I feel the blues and keep coming back to them." Here the speech-like directness of Booker's message recalls what Fred Ramsey has called the "singing horns" of the earliest years of jazz. Also impressively personal are the solos of Mr.Krull and especially George Tucker. Booker has a son , Booker Telleferro Ervin III whose nickname is 'Mr. Boo Boo' The tune *Boo* is named for him and expresses some of that childs playfulness. Mr. Ervin obviously is capable of high spirits as well as burning blues.

"Booker means a lot to me", Charlie Mingus summarizes. "I prefer the musician-composers like Lester, Charlie Parker, Sonny Rollins and Booker to the guys who race through changes and scale exercises and to those other inflicted with infantilesoulysis. Booker is more of my school, I think. I mean he goes for himself". And finally the title of the album came from Booker. Listening to a playback, he nodded "Yes, Thats it!" - Nat Hentoff

**Album:** Released Jun '86, on Candid Catalogue no: **CS 9014**

**CD:** Released Jun '88, on Candid Catalogue no: **CCD 9014**

## Esquire All American...

### ESQUIRE ALL AMERICAN HOT JAZZ SESSIONS, THE (Various artists)

Tracks: / Long long journey: *Esquire All American ...* / Snafu: *Esquire All American ...* / One that got away: *Esquire All American ...* / Gone with the wind: *Esquire All American ...* / Indiana winter:

*Esquire All American...* / Indian summer: *Various artists* / Blow me down: *Various artists* / Buckin' the blues: *Various artists* / Blues after hours: *Teagarden, Jack Big Eight* / Low flame: *Fifty Second Street All Stars* / Allen's alley: *Fifty Second Street All Stars* / Just one more chance: *Thompson, Lucky & Lucky Seven* / From Dixieland to Be-bop: *Thompson, Lucky & Lucky Seven* / Boulevard bounce: *Thompson, Lucky & Lucky Seven* / Boppin' the blues: *Thompson, Lucky & Lucky Seven* / Ain't misbehavin': *Tatum, Art* / Cherokee: *Tatum, Art* / Erroll's bounce: *Garner, Erroll* / Erroll's blues: *Garner, Erroll* / I don't wanna miss Mississippi: *Bailey, Mildred.*
**CD:** Released Jul '89, on Bluebird (2) by BMG Records (UK). Catalogue no: **ND 86757**
**Album:** Released Jul '89, on Bluebird (2) by BMG Records (UK). Catalogue no: **NL 86757**
**Cass:** Released Jul '89, on Bluebird (2) by BMG Records (UK). Catalogue no: **NK 86757**

## Esquire Jazz All Stars

**ON THE AIR 1944**
Tracks: / Esquire bounce / Rockin' chair / Basin street blues / I'll get by / Rachel's dream / Tea for two / Get happy / My silent love / Surrey with the fringe on top / Esquire blues / Honeysuckle rose.
**Album:** Released May '79, on Aircheck (USA) by Kiner Ents.(USA). Catalogue no: **AIRCHECK 27**

## Esquire Jazz Concert

**ESQUIRE JAZZ CONCERT, METROPOLITAN OPERA HOUSE (Various artists)**
**CD:** Released Jan '89, on Giants of Jazz by Hasmick Promotions. Catalogue no: **GOJCD 53035**

## Estes, Sleepy John

**Biographical details:** Blues singer, guitarist and songwriter (1899-1977), blind in one eye from a childhood accident and totally blind by about age 50. His nickname was from a tendency to doze due to low blood pressure. He first recorded in 1929 and was one of those who lived long enough to be rediscovered and feted at festivals around the world. (Donald Clarke, April 1989).

**1929-30**
**Album:** Released '89, on Document Catalogue no: **DLP 564**

**1929-30 SESSIONS**
**Album:** Released May '86, on Roots (Germany) Catalogue no: **RSE 4**

**BLUES OF SLEEPY JOHN ESTES 1**
**Album:** Released Jan '82, on Swaggie (Australia) Catalogue no: **S 1219**

**BLUES OF SLEEPY JOHN ESTES 2**
**Album:** Released Jan '83, on Swaggie (Australia) Catalogue no: **S 1220**

**BROKE AND HUNGRY**
**Album:** Released Dec '88, on Delmark (USA) by Delmark Records (USA). Catalogue no: **DL 608**

**BROWNSVILLE BLUES**
**Album:** Released Dec '88, on Delmark (USA) by Delmark Records (USA). Catalogue no: **DL 613**

**ELECTRIC SLEEP**
**Album:** on Delmark (USA) by Delmark Records (USA). Catalogue no: **DS 619**
**Album:** Released Dec '88, on Delmark (USA) by Delmark Records (USA). Catalogue no: **DL 619**

**LEGEND OF...**
**Album:** Released Dec '88, on Delmark (USA) by Delmark Records (USA). Catalogue no: **DL 603**

**LIVE IN AUSTRIA, 1966 (Estes, Sleepy John and Yank Rachell)**
**Album:** Released Jul '88, on Wolf Catalogue no: **120 913**

**SOUTHERN BLUES (Various artists)**
**Album:** Released '88, on Wolf Catalogue no: **WOLF 120.916**

## Eugene, Wendell

**WENDELL EUGENE \ TEDDY RILEY, MICHAEL WHITE, KID SHEIK COLA**
**Album:** Released Sep '86, on 504 Catalogue no: **LPS 4**
**Cass:** Released Sep '86, on 504 Catalogue no: **TCS 4**

**WEST INDIAN BLUES (Eugene, Wendell New Orleans Band 1968)**
Tracks: / Everybody loves somebody / West Indies blues / Muskrat ramble / Blues / Liza Jane / Pagan love song / Should I / Bourbon Street parade / Boogie / I can't give you anything but love / China boy / Exactly like you / Fidgety feet.
**Album:** Released Apr '79, on Nola Catalogue no: **NOLA LP 20**

**WEST INDIES BLUES (Eugene, Wendell New Orleans Band 1968)**
**Album:** Released '88, on 504 Catalogue no: **LPS 8**

## Europe, Jim

**1907-1919 (Europe, Jim & Arthur Pryor Bands)**
**Album:** Released Apr '81, on Saydisc by Amon Ra Records. Catalogue no: **SDL 221**

## European Classic Jazz Trio

**THAT'S LIKE IT OUGHT TO BE**
Note: Featuring Ornberg / Smith / Rau
**Album:** Released Apr '88, on Stomp Off (USA) Catalogue no: **SOS 1142**

**WHIP ME WITH PLENTY OF...**
**Album:** Released '88, on Stomp Off (USA) Catalogue no: **SOS 1070**

## European Jazz...

**EUROPEAN JAZZ QUINTET (European Jazz Quintet)**
**Album:** Released Sep '79, on Ego Catalogue no: **EGO 4012**

**LIVE AT MOERS FESTIVAL '77 (European Jazz Quartet)**
**Album:** Released Jul '78, on Ring Catalogue no: **RING 01018**

## Evans, Bill

**Biographical details:** Pianist and composer (1929-80). His debut album leading a trio in 1956 was the first of a long series of lyrical albums which found many fans in and outside jazz: often solo or duo but usually with a trio, he created intimate moods of distinctive delicacy and harmonic approach. Lalo Schifrin compared Oscar Peterson and Evans to Liszt and Chopin: Peterson / Liszt conquered the piano, Evans / Chopin seduced it. He practised a kind of Zen on the piano, such as trying to draw vibrato out of it: impossible, 'but trying for it affects what comes before it in the phrase'. His career was marked by a loyal following among critics and public alike. His duo album with Jim Hail, *Undercurrent* in 1959, had one of the best known sleeve photos of the LP era, an underwater shot of a woman floating in a lake taken by Toni Frissell. On *Conversations with myself* in 1963 he accompanied himself by means of double - and triple tracking; he had a complete composition in mind for each take and knew what he was going to do before he did it: onlookers were astonished, and he later made similar albums. *Affinity* in 1978 was a quintet with Toots Thielmans, one of his many Grammy nominations, included a Joe Markowitz tune *Sno pea.* Gene Lees wrote lyrics for Evans' tunes, including *Waltz for Debby.* Some of Evans' titles were anagrams: 'Re': *Person I knew* for Orrin Keepnews, the boss at Riverside; *N.Y.C.'s No lark* for Sonny Clarke, who Evans said was an influence. His collaborator on bass 1966-79 was Eddie Gomez; they also performed and recorded as a duo. His other bassists included Gary Peacock; the trio with bassist Scott LaFaro and a drummer Paul Motian was legendary; at the end it was Marc Johnson on bass and Joe La Barbera on drums. (Donald Clarke, April 1989).

**ALTERNATIVE MAN**
Tracks: / Alternative man, The / Path of least resistance / Let the juice loose / Gardiners garden / Survival of the fittest / Jo Jo / Cry in her eyes, The / Miles away / Flight of the falcon.
Note: Bill Evans is one of a new breed of jazz-orientated musicians whose music, built on a solid jazz basis, appeals to an ever-widening audience, examples being Wynton Marsalis and Stanley Jordan. A multi-talented reed player, Evans played with Miles Davis' band during miles' comeback. He has also played on albums by David Sanborn, Ron Carter and Michael Franks as well as a spell as a member of The Mahavishnu Orchestra. Personnel on *The Alternative Man* encapsulates most of the Mahavishnu Orchestra together with special guest John McLaughlin. The rhythm section of Danny Gottlieb and Mark Egan are ex-

members of the Pat Metheny Group and Gottlieb just finished a european tour with Al Di Meola while Mark Egan appeared on the new Duran Duran project-Arcadia. Chuck Loeb and Mitchell Forman have both played with Stan Getz at different times. Hiram Bullock and Lew Soloffare top flight session musicians with credits too numerous to list. Al Foster and Marcus Miller both played with Bill Evans in the Miles Davis band and Miller is fast becoming a very well known name through his work with Luther Vandross. Altogether a first class line-up of talent on an album with a very wide range of appeal.

**Album:** Released Dec '85, on Blue Note by EMI Records. Deleted Jun '89. Catalogue no: **BT 85111**

**CD:** Released Jul '87, on Blue Note by EMI Records. Catalogue no: **CDP 746 336 2**

**Cass:** Released Dec '85, on Blue Note by EMI Records. Catalogue no: **TCBT 85111**

**CD:** Released Jul '87, on Blue Note by EMI Records. Catalogue no: **BNZ 30**

**ARTISTRY IN JAZZ (Greatest hits)**
**CD:** Released May '87, on JVC/Fantasy Deleted '88. Catalogue no: **VDJ 1585**

**AT THE MONTREUX JAZZ FESTIVAL**
Tracks: / One for Helen / Sleeping bee / Mother of pearl / Nardis / O loves you Porgy / Touch of your lips, The / Embraceable you / Some day my prince will come / Walkin' up / Quiet now.
Note: Personnel: Bill Evans - piano \ Eddie Gomez - bass \ Jack DeJohnette - drums. Recorded in 1968, two years before Bill Evans' death, this is one of the great jazz performances- winning a Grammy award for best instrumental jazz performance (small group). With a generous 58 minutes playing time, the CD benefits from twoadditional tracks which were never available on the original album. These are: Bill Evans playing solo piano on "I loves you Porgy" and "Quiet now".

**Album:** Released Mar '81, on Verve Catalogue no: **2304 152**

**CD:** on Verve Catalogue no: **827 844-2**

**AT THE VILLAGE VANGUARD (Evans, Bill Trio)**
**CD:** Released Apr '87, on London Records by London Records Ltd. Catalogue no: **FCD 60017**

**AUTUMN LEAVES**
**Album:** Released Jun '86, on Crusader Jazz Masterworks Catalogue no: **CJZ LP 7**

**AUTUMN LEAVES (LOTUS)**
**Album:** Released Apr '81, on Lotus Catalogue no: **LPPS 111 11**

**BILL EVANS (Compact / Walkman jazz)**
Tracks: / I believe you / Spartacus (love theme) / Granados / My foolish heart / I loves you Porgy / How about you / I've got you under my skin / Round midnight / Elsa / Sleeping bee / Pavane / Little Lulu.

**CD:** Released Jun '87, on Verve Catalogue no: **831 366-2**

**Cass:** Released Jun '87, on Verve Catalogue no: **831 366-4**

**BILL EVANS - A TRIBUTE (Various artists)**
**Album:** Released Jan '84, on Palo Alto Catalogue no: **PA 8028**

**BILL EVANS GOLDEN TRIO (Evans, Bill Golden Trio)**
Tracks: / Come rain or come shine / Autumn leaves (mono) / Autumn leaves (stereo) / Witchcraft / When I fall in love / What is this thing called love / Spring is here / Some day my prince will come / Blue in green / Peri's scope / Nardis / Israel / I wish I knew / Sweet and lovely / How deep is the ocean / Haunted heart / Beautiful love / Elsa / Boy next door / My foolish heart / My romance / Some other time / Solar / Gloria's step / My man's gone now / All of you / Alice in Wonderland / Porgy / Milestones / Detour ahead / Waltz for Debbie / Jade visions.

**Album:** Released Jun '88, on Riverside (1) Catalogue no: **RIV 4000**

**BILL EVANS LIVE IN PARIS, 1965**
**Album:** Released '89, on Royal Jazz Catalogue no: **RJ 503**

**BILL EVANS TRIO AT SHELLEY'S MANNEHOLE (Evans, Bill Trio)**
Tracks: / Isn't it romantic / Boy next door / Wonder why / Swedish pastry / Love is here to stay / Blues in f / 'Round midnight / Stella by starlight.

**Album:** Released Jan '87, on Original Jazz Classics (USA) by Fantasy Inc (USA). Catalogue no: **OJC 263**

**BILL EVANS WITH SYMPHONY ORCHESTRA**
**Album:** Released Apr '89, on Polydor by Polydor Ltd. Catalogue no: **821 938 1**

**Cass:** Released Apr '89, on Polydor by Polydor Ltd. Catalogue no: **821 938 4**

**CALIFORNIA HERE I COME**
Tracks: / California here I come / Polka dots and moonbeams / Turn out the stars / Stella by starlight / You're gonna hear from me / In a sentimental mood / G waltz / On Green Dolphin Street / Gone with the wind / If you could see me now / Alfie / Very early / Round midnight / Emily / Wrap your troubles in dreams.
Note: Bill Evans - piano, Eddie Gomez - bass and Philly Joe Jones - drums.

**2 LP Set:** Released Apr '83, on Verve Catalogue no: **811 674-1**

**COLLECTION: BILL EVANS**
Tracks: / Autumn leaves / Waltz for Debbie / Milestones / My romance / All of you / Alice in Wonderland / Time remembered / My foolish heart / My man's gone now / Detour ahead / Solar.

**Cass:** Released Nov '85, on Deja Vu Catalogue no: **DVMC 2042**

**CONVERSATION WITH MYSELF**
Tracks: / 'Round midnight / How about you? / Spartacus love theme / Blue Monk / Stella by starlight / Hey there / N.Y.C.'s no lark / Just you, just me.

**CD:** on Verve Deleted Mar '88. Catalogue no: **821 984-2**

**CREATIVE PROCESS (VIDEO)**
**VHS:** Released '88, on Kay Jazz (video) by Kay Jazz. Catalogue no: **KJ 045**

**ELOQUENCE (Evans, Bill & Eddie Gomez)**
**CD:** Released May '87, on JVC/Fantasy Catalogue no: **VDJ 1569**

**EMPATHY**
**CD:** Released Jan '90, on Verve Catalogue no: **837757 2**

**EVERYBODY DIGS BILL EVANS**
Tracks: / Minority / Young and foolish / Lucky to be me / Night and day / Epilogue / Tenderly / Peace piece / What is there to say? / Oleo.

**Album:** Released 5 Feb '88, on Riverside (USA) by Fantasy Inc (USA). Catalogue no: **RSLP 291**

**CD:** Released Apr '86, on JVC/Fantasy Catalogue no: **VDJ 1517**

**CD:** Released Apr '87, on Carrere (France) Catalogue no: **98944**

**CD:** Released '88, on Fantasy (import) by Fantasy Inc (USA). Catalogue no: **FCD 6431129**

**EXPLORATIONS**
**CD:** Released May '87, on JVC/Fantasy Catalogue no: **VDJ 1527**

**GREEN DOLPHIN STREET (Evans, Bill & Philly Joe Jones)**
**CD:** Released May '87, on JVC/Fantasy Catalogue no: **VDJ 1576**

**HOW MY HEART SINGS (Evans, Bill Trio)**
**CD:** Released Jan '89, on JVC/Fantasy Catalogue no: **VDJ 1618**

**IN YOUR OWN SWEET WAY**
**Album:** Released Mar '81, on Affinity by Charly Records. Deleted '88. Catalogue no: **AFF 58**

**INTERMODULATION (Evans, Bill & Jim Hall)**
**CD:** Released Jun '89, on Verve Catalogue no: **837 434-2**

**Album:** Released Jun '89, on Verve Catalogue no: **833 771 1**

**Cass:** Released Jun '89, on Verve Catalogue no: **833 771 4**

**INTERPLAY (Evans, Bill & Freddie Hubbard)**
**CD:** Released May '87, on JVC/Fantasy Catalogue no: **VDJ 1546**

**IT HAPPENED IN PESCARA 1969-89 (Evans, Bill/Art Pepper)**
**2 LP Set:** Released '89, on Philology Catalogue no: **214W 100/101**

**JAZZHOUSE**
**CD:** Released Jan '89, on JVC/Fantasy Catalogue no: **VDJ 1118**

**LIVE IN EUROPE**
Tracks: / How my heart sings / Time to remember / Twelve-toned tune / Waltz for Debbie / Stella by starlight / Some day my prince will come / Round midnight.

**Album:** Released '81, on Unique Jazz by Spotlite Records. Catalogue no: **UJ 24**

**LIVE IN PARIS 1972 VOL 1**
Tracks: / Re person I knew / Gloria's

step / Waltz for Debbie / Turn out the stars / Two lonely people / What are you doing the rest of your.
**Album:** Released Jun '88, on France's Concert Catalogue no: **FC 107**
**CD:** Released Jun '88, on Esoldun Catalogue no: **FCD 107**

**LIVE IN PARIS 1972 VOL 2**
**CD:** Released Jun '89, on France's Concert Catalogue no: **FCD 125**
**Album:** Released Jun '89, on France's Concert Catalogue no: **FC 125**

**LIVE IN PARIS VOL 2**
Tracks: / Twelve tone tune / Sugarplum / Quiet now / Very early / Autumn leaves / Time remembered / My romance / Some day my prince will come.
**CD:** Released Jun '88, on France's Concert Catalogue no: **FCD 114**
**Album:** Released Jun '88, on France's Concert Catalogue no: **FC 114**

**LIVING ON THE CREST OF A WAVE**
Tracks: / Reef carnival / When it's a good thing / Dawn / Young and old / Past thoughts / Living on the crest of a wave.
**Album:** Released Jun '84, on Elektra by Elektra Records (UK). Deleted Jun '89. Catalogue no: **9603491**

**MONTREUX 2**
**Cass:** Released Feb '84, on CTI (Musidisc France) by Polydor Ltd. Catalogue no: **CTK 9511**

**MOONBEAMS (Evans, Bill Trio)**
**CD:** Released Jan '89, on JVC/Fantasy Catalogue no: **VDJ 1617**

**MY ROMANCE**
**Album:** Released '88, on Zeta Catalogue no: **ZET 702**

**NEW JAZZ CONCEPTIONS**
Tracks: / I love you / Five / I got it bad and that ain't good / Conception / Easy living / Displacement / Speak low / Waltz for Debbie / Our delight / My romance / No cover, no minimum (2 takes).
**Album:** Released Jun '86, on Original Jazz Classics (USA) by Fantasy Inc (USA). Catalogue no: **OJC 025**
**CD:** Released Oct '89, on Riverside (USA) by Fantasy Inc (USA). Catalogue no: **CDRIVM 005**

**PARIS CONCERT, THE (EDITION ONE)**
Tracks: / I do it for your love / Quiet now / Noelle's theme / My romance / I loves you Porgy / Up with the lark / All mine / Beautiful love.
**Album:** Released '88, on Elektra by Elektra Records (UK). Catalogue no: **E 0164**

**PORTRAIT IN JAZZ**
Tracks: / Come rain or come shine / Autumn leaves / Witchcraft / When I fall in love / Peri's scope / What is this thing called love? / Spring is here / Some day my prince will come / Blue in green.
**Album:** Released Feb '84, on Riverside (USA) by Fantasy Inc (USA). Catalogue no: **OJC 088**
**CD:** Released May '87, on JVC/Fantasy Deleted '88. Catalogue no: **VDJ 1506**
**CD:** Released '88, on Fantasy (import) by Fantasy Inc (USA). Catalogue no: **FCD 6301162**

**QUIET NOW**
Tracks: / Very airy / Sleeping bee / Quiet now / Turn out the stars / Autumn leaves / Nardis.
**CD:** on Charly by Charly Records. Catalogue no: **CDCHARLY 25**
**Album:** Released Dec '81, on Affinity by Charly Records. Catalogue no: **AFF 73**

**QUINTESSENCE**
**CD:** Released Apr '87, on Carrere (France) Catalogue no: **98545**
**CD:** Released Nov '86, on Fantasy (import) by Fantasy Inc (USA). Deleted '88. Catalogue no: **FCD 6119529**

**RE: PERSON I KNEW**
Tracks: / Re: Person I knew / Sugar plum / Alfie / T.T.T. / Excerpt from Dolphin dance / Very early / 34 skidoo / Emily / Are you all the things?.
**Album:** Released Sep '81, on Fantasy by Ace Records. Catalogue no: **F 9608**

**SUNDAY AT THE VILLAGE VANGUARD**
**CD:** Released Dec '86, on Carrere (France) Catalogue no: **CA 98 957**

**SUNDAY NIGHT AT THE VILLAGE VANGUARD (Evans, Bill Trio)**
**CD:** Released May '87, on JVC/Fantasy Deleted '88. Catalogue no: **VDJ 1519**

**SYMBIOSIS**
**Album:** Released Apr '81, on MPS Jazz Catalogue no: **MPS 68 052**

**TIME REMEMBERED**
**Album:** Released Apr '84, on Carrere (France) Catalogue no: **68150**

**TOWN HALL**
**CD:** Released Feb '87, on Polydor by Polydor Ltd. Deleted Jul '88. Catalogue no: **831 271-2**

**TRIO 64 (Evans, Bill Trio)**
Tracks: / Little Lulu / Sleeping bee / Santa Claus is coming to town / I'll see you again / For Heaven's sake / Dancing in the dark / Everything happens to me. Note: Bill Evans -- piano Gary Peacock -- bass Paul Motion -- drums
**Album:** Released Jul '84, on Verve (France) Catalogue no: **815 057-1**
**CD:** on Verve Deleted Aug '87. Catalogue no: **815 057-2**

**TRIO '65 (Evans, Bill Trio)**
Tracks: / Israel / Elsa / Round midnight / Our love is here to stay / How my heart sings / Who can I turn to / Come rain or come shine / If you could see me now.
**Album:** Released Aug '83, on Verve Deleted '88. Catalogue no: **2304517**

**TRIO/DUO**
Tracks: / Little Lulu / Sleeping bee / Always / Santa Claus is coming to town / I'll see you again / For Heaven's sake / Dancing in the dark / Everything happens to me / I've got you under my skin / My man's gone now / Turn out the stars / Angel face / Jazz samba / All across the city.
**Album:** on Polydor by Polydor Ltd. Catalogue no: **2632 054**

**UNDERCURRENT (Evans, Bill & Jim Hall)**
Tracks: / My funny valentine / I hear a rhapsody / Dream gypsy / Romain / Skating in Central Park / Darn that dream / My funny valentine (alt. take) (CD only.) / Stairway to the stars (CD only.) / I'm getting sentimental over you (CD only.) / Romaine (alt. take) (CD only.).
**Album:** Released Mar '87, on Memoir by Memoir Records. Catalogue no: **MOIR 504**
**Cass:** Released Mar '87, on Memoir by Memoir Records. Catalogue no: **CMOIR 504**

**UNDERCURRENT (BLUENOTE) (Evans, Bill & Jim Hall)**
**CD:** Released Jun '89, on Blue Note by EMI Records. Catalogue no: **CDP 790 583 2**
**CD:** Released Jun '89, on Blue Note by EMI Records. Catalogue no: **BNZ 167**
**Album:** Released Jul '89, on Blue Note by EMI Records. Catalogue no: **B1 90583**

**WALTZ FOR DEBBY (Evans, Bill Trio)**
**CD:** Released Dec '86, on JVC/Fantasy Catalogue no: **VDJ 1536**

**WE WILL MEET AGAIN**
**Album:** Released Jul '85, on WEA (France) by WEA Records. Catalogue no: **WB 56807**

**WHAT'S NEW ? (Evans, Bill & Jeremy Steig)**
**Album:** Released Apr '81, on IMS by Polydor Ltd. Catalogue no: **2304 285**

**WITH SYMPHONY ORCHESTRA (Evans, Bill Trio)**
Tracks: / Granados / Valse / Prelude / Time remembered / Pavane / Elegie / My bells / Blue interlude.
**Album:** Released Apr '89, on Verve (USA) by Polydor Ltd. Catalogue no: **821 983-1**
**Album:** Released Sep '84, on Verve (USA) by Polydor Ltd. Catalogue no: **230 452-5**
**Cass:** Released Sep '84, on Verve (USA) by Polydor Ltd. Catalogue no: **821 983-4**
**CD:** Released Sep '84, on Verve (USA) by Polydor Ltd. Deleted Mar '88. Catalogue no: **821 983-2**

**YOU'RE GONNA HEAR FROM ME**
Tracks: / You're gonna hear from me / Waltz for Debbie / Time remembered / Emily / Some day my prince will come / Round midnight / Nardis / Who can I turn to / Love is here to stay.
**Album:** Released Jan '89, on Milestone by Ace Records. Catalogue no: **MX 9164**

## Evans, Doc Jazzband

**AT THE GAS LIGHT**
**Album:** Released '89, on Audiophile (USA) by Jazzology Records (USA). Catalogue no: **AP 95**

**DOWN IN JUNGLE TOWN**
**Album:** Released Dec '87, on Audio-

phile (USA) by Jazzology Records (USA). Catalogue no: **AP 4**
**Album:** Released Aug '88, on Jazzology (USA) by Jazzology Records (USA). Catalogue no: **AP 8**

## Evans, Gil

**Biographical details:** Pianist, arranger and bandleader. With Claude Thornhill's innovatory band 1941-48 except for military service; later his basement flat in NYC was a meeting place for George Russell, Charlie Parker, Gerry Mulligan (who'd also worked for Thornhill) and others. Both Evans and Mulligan contributed to Miles Davis's 1949 *Birth of the cool*; Evans wrote for Peggy Lee, Tony Bennett, Benny Goodman; he arranged and conducted albums *Look to the rainbow* with Astrud Gilberto and *Guitar forms* with Davis: *Miles ahead, Porgy & Bess, Sketches of Spain, At Carnegie Hall* and *Quiet nights*, playing piano on some sessions. (Donald Clarke, April 1989).

**BIG BAND LUMIERE (Evans, Gil & Laurent Cugny)**
**Album:** Released Jan '89, on Polygram (France) by PolyGram UK Ltd. Catalogue no: **836 401-1**
**CD:** Released Jan '89, on Polygram (France) by PolyGram UK Ltd. Catalogue no: **836 401-2**

**BLUES IN ORBIT**
**Album:** Released Jan '82, on Enja (Germany) by Enja Records (West Germany). Catalogue no: **ENJA 3069**

**BRITISH ORCHESTRA, THE**
Tracks: / Hotel me / Friday thirteenth / London / Little wing.
Note: Musicians include John Surman (baritone and soprano saxes, bass clarinet and synthesisers), Don Weller (tenor and soprano saxes), John Taylor, Henry Lowther, Guy Barker, Malcolm Griffiths, Chris Hunter.
**Album:** Released May '83, on Mole Catalogue no: **MOLE 8**
**CD:** Released May '83, on Mole Catalogue no: **MOLECD 8**

**BUD & BIRD (Evans, Gil & The Monday Night Orchestra)**
**2 LP Set:** Released Sep '88, on Electric Bird Catalogue no: **K 19 P 6455**
**CD:** Released Sep '88, on Electric Bird Catalogue no: **K32Y 6171**

**CARNEGIE HALL 1961 (See also under Davis, Miles) (Evans, Gil & Miles Davis)**
**CD:** Released Mar '90, on Giants of Jazz by Hasmick Promotions. Catalogue no: **GOJCD 53023**

**FAREWELL (Evans, Gil & The Monday Night Orchestra)**
Note: The fourth issue in the series of legendary performances recorded at New York's Sweet Basil. Recorded in December 1986.
**CD:** Released Sep '88, on King (Japan) Catalogue no: **K32Y 6250**
**Album:** Released Sep '88, on Paddlewheel/King Catalogue no: **K 28P 6486**

**GIL EVANS**
**CD Set:** Released Jan '90, on Verve Catalogue no: **8387942**

**GIL EVANS LIVE**
Tracks: / Angel / Parabola / Orange was the colour / Silk blue / Stone free / Fugue / Cheryl / Birdhead / Relaxing at Carnarillo.
**Album:** Released '79, on RCA by BMG Records (UK). Deleted '84. Catalogue no: **PL 25209**

**GREAT JAZZ STANDARDS**
Tracks: / Davenport blues / Straight no chaser / Ballad of the sad young man / Joy spring / Django / Chant of the weed / La nevada.
**CD:** Released Mar '89, on Blue Note by EMI Records. Catalogue no: **CZ 51**
**CD:** Released Jan '89, on Pacific Jazz by EMI Records. Catalogue no: **CDP 746 856 2**

**GUITAR FORMS (Evans, Gil & Kenny Burrell)**
**Album:** Released Aug '81, on Verve Catalogue no: **2304 158**

**INTO THE HOT (Evans, Gil Orchestra)**
**CD:** Released May '89, on MCA (Import) by MCA Records. Catalogue no: **MCAD 39104**

**LITTLE WING**
**Album:** Released May '79, on Circle (USA) by Jazzology Records (USA). Catalogue no: **RK 23578/13**

**LIVE 1976**
**Album:** Released '88, on Zeta Catalogue no: **ZET 714**

**LIVE AT SWEET BASIL (Evans, Gil & The Monday Night Orchestra)**
Tracks: / Parabola / Voodoo chile / Orange was the colour of her dress, then silk blue / Prince of darkness / Blues in 'C' (John's memory) / Cheryl / Bird feathers / Relaxin' at Camarillo / Goodbye pork pie hat / Up from the skies.
Note: Legendary composer, arranger and orchestra leader Gil Evans recorded live at Sweet Basil with 14 piece orchestra. Compositions by Jimi Hendrix, Herbie Hancock and Charles Mingus. Gil Evans is probably best known for his work with Miles Davis between 1957-60 and was associated with the nine piece Miles had during this period that was dubbed the 'Birth of The Cool'. Personnel: Gil Evans - acoustic and electric pianos \ Lew Soloff - trumpet \ Hannibal Marvin Peterson - trumpet \ Shunzo Ohno - trumpet \ Miles Evans - trumpet \ George Adams - tenor sax \ Chris Hunter - alto sax \ Howard Johnson - tuba, baritone sax, bass clarinet \ Tom Malone - trombone \ Hiram Bullock - Pete Levin - synthesizer \ Mark Egan - bass \ Adam Nussbaum - drums \ Minò Cinelu - percussion.
**CD:** Released Oct '87, on King (Japan) Catalogue no: **K32Y 6017**
**Album:** Released Jul '86, on King (Japan) Catalogue no: **K 23P 6355**

**LIVE AT SWEET BASIL. VOL.2 (Evans, Gil & The Monday Night Orchestra)**
**CD:** Released Oct '87, on King (Japan) Catalogue no: **K32Y 6018**
**2 LP Set:** Released Apr '87, on King (Japan) Catalogue no: **K 19P 6421**

**LIVE AT THE PUBLIC THEATRE**
**CD:** Released Oct '87, on Black Hawk (USA) by Blackhawk Records (USA). Catalogue no: **CDBKH 525**
**Album:** Released Oct '87, on Black Hawk (USA) by Blackhawk Records (USA). Catalogue no: **BKH 525**

**LIVE AT THE PUBLIC THEATRE VOL. 2**
**Album:** Released Oct '87, on Black Hawk (USA) by Blackhawk Records (USA). Catalogue no: **BKH 526**
**CD:** Released Oct '87, on Black Hawk (USA) by Blackhawk Records (USA). Catalogue no: **CDBKH 526**

**NEW BOTTLE, OLD WINE (Evans, Gil Orchestra)**
Tracks: / St. Louis blues / King Porter stomp / Willow tree / Struttin' with some barbecue / Lester leaps in / Round midnight / Manteca / Bird feathers.
**CD:** Released Aug '88, on EMI-Manhattan by EMI Records. Catalogue no: **CDP 746 855 2**
**CD:** Released Aug '88, on EMI-Manhattan by EMI Records. Catalogue no: **CZ 50**

**OUT OF THE COOL**
Tracks: / La Nevada / Where flamingos fly / Bilbao song / Stratusphunk / Sunken treasure.
**CD:** Released May '87, on MCA by MCA Records. Catalogue no: **MCAD 5653**
**Album:** Released Sep '82, on Jasmine by Hasmick Promotions. Catalogue no: **JAS 52**
**Cass:** Released May '87, on MCA by MCA Records. Deleted Dec '89. Catalogue no: **ASC 4**
**Album:** Released Dec '85, on Impulse by Impulse Records. Catalogue no: **AS 4**
**Cass:** Released Sep '82, on Jasmine by Hasmick Promotions. Catalogue no: **JAS C52**

**PACIFIC STANDARD TIME**
**2 LP Set:** Released '79, on Blue Note by EMI Records. Deleted '84. Catalogue no: **BND 4024**

**PARABOLA**
**Album:** Released Oct '79, on Horo Catalogue no: **HDLP 31/32**

**PARIS BLUES**
**CD:** Released Jul '88, on Owl (France) Catalogue no: **OWLC 049**
**Cass:** Released Jul '88, on Owl (France) Catalogue no: **OWLM 749**
**Album:** Released Jul '88, on Owl (France) Catalogue no: **OWLL 049**

**PLAYS THE MUSIC OF JIMI HENDRIX (Evans, Gil Orchestra)**
Tracks: / Angel / Crosstown traffic / Castles made of sand / Up from the skies

(take 1) / 1983 - A merman I should turn to be / Voodoo chile / Gypsy eyes / Little wing / Up from the skies (take 2) / Little Miss Lover.
**CD:** Released Nov '88, on Bluebird (2) by BMG Records (UK). Catalogue no: **ND 84809**

**PRIESTESS**
**Album:** Released May '87, on Antilles / New Directions by Island Records. Deleted Dec '88. Catalogue no: **AN 8717**
**CD:** Released May '87, on Antilles / New Directions by Island Records. Catalogue no: **ANCD 8717**
**CD:** Released '86, on Polystar (Japan) Catalogue no: **J33D 20001**
**Cass:** Released May '87, on Antilles / New Directions by Island Records. Deleted Jun '88. Catalogue no: **ANC 8717**

**REST OF GIL EVANS LIVE AT THE RFH 1978**
**Album:** Released Feb '81, on Mole Catalogue no: **MOLE 3**

**THERE COMES A TIME (Evans, Gil Orchestra)**
Tracks: / King Porter stomp / Thre comes a time / Makes her move / Little wing / Meaning of the blues / Aftermath the fourth movement / Children of the fire / Anita's dance.
**Album:** Released '79, on RCA by BMG Records (UK). Deleted '84. Catalogue no: **PL 11057**
**CD:** Released Apr '88, on Bluebird (2) by BMG Records (UK). Catalogue no: **ND 85783**

## Evans, Margie

**ANOTHER BLUES DAY**
**Album:** Released Dec '88, on L&R Catalogue no: **LR 42.060**

**MISTREATED WOMAN**
**Album:** on L&R Catalogue no: **LR 42.050**

## Ewans, Kai

**DANISH JAZZ VOL 1**
**Album:** Released Jul '82, on Storyville by Storyville Records AB. Catalogue no: **SLP 410**

## Ewell, Don

**Biographical details:** Traditional jazz pianist (1916-83). He played revival music with Bunk Johnson, Kid Ory, Doc Evans; later toured with Jack Teagarden; he was a very good player in the style of his favourites Fats Weller and Jelly Roll Morton. (Donald Clarke, April 1989) .

**DENVER CONCERT (Ewell, Don & Barbara Dane)**
**Album:** Released Mar '90, on Pumpkin Catalogue no: **PUMPKIN120**

**DON EWELL AND BARBARA DANE 1966 (Ewell, Don & Barbara Dane)**
**Album:** Released Nov '88, on Pumpkin Catalogue no: **P 120**

**DON EWELL & HIS ALL STARS (Ewell, Don, Conger and Thompson)**
**Album:** Released Jun '88, on Jazzology (USA) by Jazzology Records (USA). Catalogue no: **J 29**

**DON EWELL QUINTET (Ewell, Don Quintet)**
**Album:** Released Jun '86, on Jazzology (USA) by Jazzology Records (USA). Catalogue no: **J 69**

**IN NEW ORLEANS**
**Album:** Released Oct '86, on GHB by Jazzology Records (USA). Catalogue no: **GHB 30**
**Album:** Released Sep '86, on New Orleans Catalogue no: **NOR 7209**

**JAZZ ON A SATURDAY AFTERNOON**
**Album:** Released Feb '90, on Storyville by Storyville Records AB. Catalogue no: **SLP 502**

**PIANO SOLOS**
**Album:** Released '88, on Eighty-Eight Upright Catalogue no: **88 UR 002**

**TOGETHER (Ewell, Don/Bob Green)**
**Album:** Released Aug '79, on Jazzology (USA) by Jazzology Records (USA). Catalogue no: **JCE 84**

**YELLOW DOG BLUES (Ewell, Don Quintet)**
**Album:** Released Aug '88, on Jazzology (USA) by Jazzology Records (USA). Catalogue no: **AP 66**

## Excelsior Brass Band

**EXCELSIOR BRASS BAND**
**Album:** Released Apr '79, on Wizard (USA) by Adam Productions Inc.(USA). Catalogue no: **WIZARD 3**

# F

The following information was taken from the Music Master database on April 14th, 1990.

## Faddis, Jon

**GOOD AND PLENTY**
**CD:** Released '86, on Dunhill Compact Classics (USA) Catalogue no: **DZS 025**

**JON & BILLY (Faddis, Jon & Billy Harper)**
**Album:** Released Oct '87, on Black Hawk (USA) by Blackhawk Records (USA). Catalogue no: **BKH 532**
**CD:** Released Oct '87, on Black Hawk (USA) by Blackhawk Records (USA). Catalogue no: **CDBKH 532**

**LEGACY**
Tracks: / West end blues / Little jazz / Night in Tunisia / Instigator, The / Things to come / Child is born, A / L'il darlin' / Whisper not.
**Cass:** Released Feb '86, on Concord Jazz by Concord Jazz Records (USA). Deleted '88. Catalogue no: **CJC 291**
**Album:** Released Feb '86, on Concord Jazz by Concord Jazz Records (USA). Deleted '88. Catalogue no: **CJ 291**
**CD:** Released Dec '86, on Concord Jazz by Concord Jazz Records (USA). Deleted '88. Catalogue no: **CCD 4291**

**YOUNG BLOOD**
**Album:** Released '82, on Pablo Jazz (USA) by Pablo Records (USA). Deleted '88. Catalogue no: **231 0765**
**Cass:** Released '82, on Pablo Jazz (USA) by Pablo Records (USA). Deleted '88. Catalogue no: **K10 765**

## Fairweather, Digby

**GOING OUT STEPPIN'**
Tracks: / She's funny that way / Jeepers creepers / Moanin' in the mornin' / Run rabbit run / Small fry / Looking at you / Going out steppin' / Very thought of you / If I had rhythm in my nursery rhymes / Blues for the depression / What a little moonlight can do / As long as I love.
**Album:** Released Apr '80, on Black Lion Deleted '85. Catalogue no: **BLP 12190**

**HAVIN' FUN**
Tracks: / Indiana / Georgia on my mind / It don't mean a thing / I've got the world on a string / Sing / Cherokee / Some of these days / Moon country / At sundown / Black butterfly / Havin' fun.
**Album:** Released '88, on Black Lion Catalogue no: **BLP 12175**

**SONGS FOR SANDY**
Tracks: / Prologue / Sandy and Al / Singing away the cold in Edinburgh / Hi-life in Hampstead / Sandy's blues / Requiem for a weeping willow / Singing away the cold in Edinburgh (reprise) / It's always Fairweather / Pal Sandy / Rosetta / Blue turning grey over you / One for Sandy.
**Album:** Released '83, on Hep Jazz by Hep Records. Catalogue no: **HEP 2016**

**VELVET**
**Album:** Released Oct '79, on Black Lion Catalogue no: **BLP 12187**

## Fame, Georgie

**Biographical details:** This British singer, keyboards player and songwriter was born Clive Powell in Lancashire. In 1959, at the age of 16, he moved to London and was spotted by Larry Parnes, a showbusiness entrepreneur who was currently enjoying success with Billy Fury and Marty Wilde. Having re-christened those two stars, Parnes came up with a similarly eye-catching and ridiculous stage name for young Clive - he became Georgie Fame. However, the teenage pianist did not live up to his new surname for several years. After a spell in Fury's backing group, the Blue Flames, Georgie broke away from Fury and took the Blue Flames with him. That was in late 1961. Early in the following year, Georgie Fame & The Blue Flames secured a residency at London's Flamingo Club in Soho. They gradually built up a cult following in that increasingly important musical haunt, thanks to the group's electric blend of various blues, jazz and Caribbean styles, and thanks also to the burgeoning popularity of the general London rhythm-and-blues scene. Georgie's first taste of chart success occurred in late 1964, when an aptly titled LP *Fame at last* entered the UK Top 20. Then, in January '65, came the smash success of the first hit single - *Yeh yeh* surged unexpectedly to the UK No.1 position. With Fames's vocals heavily influenced by US R&B singer Mose Allison, there were further British hits in store for Fame and the Flames. After achieving smaller successes plus a second No.1 with 1966's Fame-penned *Get away*, Georgie disbanded the Blue Flames and opted for a big band sound. This yielded his third UK No.1 and only US Top Tener in the shape of *The ballad on Bonnie & Clyde*, a slice of watered down, middle-of-the-road jazz (1968). As the Sixties became the Seventies, Fame drifted out of the record charts and into the steadier, less exciting world of cabaret and television. A 1971 duet with fellow singer/keyboardist/ex-bluesman Alan Price brought forth a UK No.11 hit with the irritating *Rosetta*, but the remainder of the Seventies saw George banished permanently from the charts and toying with TV commercials, radio jingles, Blue Flames revivals and further cabaret and club work. (Bob MacDonald, 16th August 1985)

Singer and keyboardist, born Clive Powell in 1943 in Leigh. He was renamed by impresario Larry Parnes on joining Billy Fury's backing group the Blue Flames, retaining both name and group when Fury quit rock'n'roll for ballads in 1962 (though Fury once fired Fame for refusing to stick to simple rock'n'roll piano). At London's Flamingo Club black USA servicemen were among the customers: 'GIs would come up and say, Hey man have you heard Mose Allison? Eddie Jefferson? Booker T? They even lent me their own records so I could hear it for myself.' Fame aquired a Hammond organ in 1962 and the influence of Jimmy Smith crept in. He had hit albums and a number one single *Yeh yeh* in 1964. He left the band in '66, sang with a big band, worked with strings and ballads on CBS, had a two year partnership in the late '60's with former Animal Alan Price as Fame and Price Together in TV and cabaret and on a hit record *Rosetta*; he worked on TV jingles, worked in Europe and re-formed the Flames in 1974; he tours with a Hoagy Carmichael song show *Stardust road*; he packed Ronnie Scott's for a week in 1986 and starred that year in *Swingin' on 10th Avenue*, a celebration of George Gershwin's music with the LSO at the Royal Albert Hall. 'Really what I've been doing is rehearsing for 25 years.' As a result he is never short of work. (Donald Clarke, April 1989).

**20 BEAT CLASSICS**
Tracks: / Yeh yeh / Getaway / Do-re-mi / My girl / Sweet things / Point of no return / Get on the right track / Baby / Ride your pony / Moody's mood for love / Funny how time slips away / Sunny sitting in the park / Green onions / In the meantime / Papa's got a brand new bag / Blue Monday / Pride and joy / Pink champagne / Let the sun shine in / I love the life I live.
**Album:** Released Mar '82, on RSO by Polydor Ltd. Deleted Mar '87. Catalogue no: **RSX 1**
**Cass:** Released Sep '83, on RSO (USA) by Polydor Ltd. Deleted 30 May '89. Catalogue no: **SPEMC 45**
**Album:** Released Sep '83, on RSO (USA) by Polydor Ltd. Catalogue no: **SPELP 45**

**BACK AGAIN (Fame, Georgie / Blue Flames)**
**Album:** Released Oct '87, on K-Tel by K-Tel Records. Catalogue no: **NE 1372**
**CD:** Released Oct '87, on K-Tel by K-Tel Records. Catalogue no: **NCD 5143**

**Cass:** Released Oct '87, on K-Tel by K-Tel Records. Catalogue no: **CE 2372**

**BALLAD OF BONNIE AND CLYDE**
**Album:** Released '88, on Castle Showcase by Castle Communications Records. Catalogue no: **SHLP 149**
**Cass:** Released '88, on Castle Showcase by Castle Communications Records. Catalogue no: **SHTC 149**

**BALLAD OF BONNIE AND CLYDE (OLD GOLD)**
Tracks: / Ballad of Bonnie and Clyde / Rosetta.
**7" Single:** Released Sep '84, on Old Gold by Old Gold Records. Catalogue no: **OG 9554**

**BALLAD OF BONNIE AND CLYDE (SINGLE)**
Tracks: / Ballad of Bonnie and Clyde.
**7" Single:** Released Jul '84, on CBS by CBS Records. Deleted '85. Catalogue no: **CBS A4599**
**7" Single:** Released Dec '67, on CBS by CBS Records. Deleted '70. Catalogue no: **CBS 3124**

**BECAUSE I LOVE YOU**
Tracks: / Because I love you.
**7" Single:** Released Mar '67, on CBS by CBS Records. Deleted '70. Catalogue no: **CBS 202587**

**CLOSING THE GAP**
Tracks: / Give a little more / Run away with me / I love Jamaica / Eros hotel / Everything I own / Lean on me / Upright / Bring back my love.
**Album:** Released Sep '80, on Piccadilly Deleted '86. Catalogue no: **N 137**
**Cass:** Released Sep '80, on Piccadilly Deleted '86. Catalogue no: **ZCN 137**

**DRIP DROP (Fame, Georgie/Annie Ross)**
Tracks: / Drip drop / One morning in may.
**7" Single:** Released Jul '81, on Bald Eagle Deleted Jul '84. Catalogue no: **BE 181**

**FIRST THIRTY YEARS, THE**
Tracks: / Do the dog / Yeh yeh / Getaway / Ballad of Bonnie & Clyde, The / Rosetta / Daylight / Samba (toda menina baiana) / In crowd, The / C'est la vie / Fully booked / That ol' rock and roll / Sitting in the park / Do-re-mi / Like we used to be / Sunny / Seventh son / Ali shuffle, The / Hurricane, The / Moody's mood for love / Dawn yawn / Mellow yellow / Woe is me / Funny how time slips away / Old music master, The.
**Cass:** Released Dec '89, on Connoisseur Collection by Connoisseur Collection Ltd.. Catalogue no: **VSOPMC 144**
**CD:** Released Dec '89, on Connoisseur Collection by Connoisseur Collection Ltd.. Catalogue no: **VSOPCD 144**
**2 LP Set:** Released Dec '89, on Connoisseur Collection by Connoisseur Collection Ltd.. Catalogue no: **VSOPLP 144**

**GEORGIE FAME AND THE BLUE FLAMES (Fame, Georgie / FBlue Flames)**
**CD:** Released '86, on Delta (1) by Delta Records. Deleted '88. Catalogue no: **11 048**

**GEORGIE FAME WITH ALAN PRICE (Fame, Georgie /Alan Price)**
**Cass:** Released May '84, on Ditto by Pickwick Records. Catalogue no: **DTO 10069**

**GEORGIE FAME / LENA ERICSON / LASSE SAMUELSON (Fame, Georgie / Lena Ericson / Lasse Samuelson)**
**Cass:** Released '88, on Four Leaf Clover Catalogue no: **FLCK 15901**
**Album:** Released Jul '86, on Four Leaf Clover Catalogue no: **FLC 5091**

**GET AWAY**
Tracks: / Get away.
**7" Single:** Released Jun '66, on Columbia by EMI Records. Deleted '69. Catalogue no: **DB 7946**

**GIVE A LITTLE MORE**
Tracks: / Give a little more / Give a little more (part 2).
**7" Single:** Released Aug '80, on Piccadilly Deleted '83. Catalogue no: **7P 194**

**GO FOR IT**
Tracks: / Go for it / Still care about us.
**7" Single:** Released Mar '90, on Food For Thought by Music For Nations Records. Catalogue no: **YUM 119**

**HALL OF FAME**
**Album:** Released Mar '67, on Columbia by EMI Records. Deleted '70. Catalogue no: **SX 6120**

**HONG KONG BLUES (Fame, Georgie / Annie Ross)**
Tracks: / Hong kong blues / Old music master.
**7" Single:** Released Feb '82, on Bald Eagle Deleted Feb '87. Catalogue no: **BEE 182**

**HURRICANE**
Tracks: / Huricane.
**7" Single:** Released Aug '82, on My Records Deleted Aug '85. Catalogue no: **MY 001**

**IN GOODMAN'S LAND (Fame, Georgie / Sylvia Vrethammar)**
Tracks: / Flying home / Makin' whoopee / King Porter stomp / Limehouse blues / Just one of those things / Don't be that way / Alexander's ragtime band / Sweet Georgia Brown / You turned the tables on me / Airmail special / Memories of you / In Goodmansland medley.
**Album:** Released Nov '83, on Sonet by Sonet Records. Catalogue no: **SNTF 908**

**IN THE MEANTIME**
Tracks: / In the meantime.
**7" Single:** Released Mar '65, on Columbia by EMI Records. Deleted '68. Catalogue no: **DB 7494**

**LIKE WE USED TO BE**
Tracks: / Like we used to be.
**7" Single:** Released Jul '65, on Columbia by EMI Records. Deleted '68. Catalogue no: **DB 7633**

**MY FAVOURITE SONGS (Fame, Georgie / Blue Flames)**
Tracks: / Rosetta / Ballad of Bonnie and Clyde / Barefootin' / That old rock 'n' roll / Get away / Yeh yeh / Bring it on home to me / Saturday night fish fry / Someday / Lawdy Miss Clawdy.
Note: Featuring Zoot Money and Andy Fairweather-Low.
**Album:** Released Feb '84, on Teldec (1) by ASV (Academy Sound & Vision). Catalogue no: **LF6 25646**
**Cass:** Released Feb '84, on Teldec (1) by ASV (Academy Sound & Vision). Catalogue no: **PF4 25646**

**NO WORRIES (Fame, Georgie & The Australian Blue Flames)**
Tracks: / Lady be good / Ole buttermilk sky / Eros Hotel / Little Samba / It ain't right / On a misty night / Cats' eyes / Parchman farm / Zulu / Saturday night fish fry / Try na get along with the blues / Yeh yeh / Get away.
Note: "The legendary Georgie Fame returns to vinyl with this superb album, which will appeal to loyal followers and young fans alike. On all his hit singles Georgie was backed by the Blue Flames. On No Worries, recorded in Australia, he has a new group, the Australian Blue Flames." (IMS Records, May 1988.)
**Cass:** Released May '88, on Four Leaf Clover Catalogue no: **FLCK 5099**
**Album:** Released May '88, on Four Leaf Clover Catalogue no: **FLC 5099**
**CD:** Released May '88, on Four Leaf Clover Catalogue no: **FLCD 5099**

**PEACEFUL**
Tracks: / Peaceful.
**7" Single:** Released Jul '69, on CBS by CBS Records. Deleted '72. Catalogue no: **CBS 4295**

**RHYTHM AND BLUES AT THE FLAMINGO**
Tracks: / Night train / Let the good times roll / Do the dog / Eso beso / Work song / Parchman farm / You can't sit down / Humpty Dumpty / Shop around / Baby please don't go.
**Cass:** Released Nov '84, on RSO (USA) by Polydor Ltd. Deleted '86. Catalogue no: **SPEMC 80**
**Album:** Released Nov '84, on RSO (USA) by Polydor Ltd. Deleted '87. Catalogue no: **SPELP 80**

**RIGHT NOW**
Tracks: / Different dream / Funny how tiem slips away / Little samba / I'm in love with ya baby / Ollie's party / Eros Hotel / 'Cross a lazy afternoon / Country girl / Don't you worry 'bout a thing / Too shy to say / Zulu / Last song.
**Album:** Released Apr '79, on Pye Deleted Apr '84. Catalogue no: **NSPH 18600**

**ROSETTA (Fame, Georgie/Alan Price)**
Tracks: / Rosetta.
**7" Single:** Released Apr '71, on CBS by CBS Records. Deleted '74. Catalogue no: **CBS 7108**
**7" Single:** Released Jul '84, on CBS by CBS Records. Catalogue no: **A 4599**

**SAMBA**
Tracks: / Samba / Willow King.
**7" Single:** Released Oct '86, on Ensign by Ensign Records. Catalogue no: **ENY 605**
**12" Single:** Released Oct '86, on Ensign by Ensign Records. Catalogue no: **ENYX 605**

**SELECTION OF STANDARDS... (Fame, Georgie, Hoagy Carmichael & Annie Ross)**
**CD:** Released '88, on DRG (USA) by DRG Records (USA). Catalogue no: **CDSL 5197**

**SEVENTH SON**
Tracks: / Seventh son.
**7" Single:** Released Dec '69, on CBS by CBS Records. Deleted '72. Catalogue no: **CBS 4659**

**SITTING IN THE PARK**
Tracks: / Sitting in the park.
**7" Single:** Released Dec '66, on Columbia by EMI Records. Deleted '69. Catalogue no: **DB 8096**

**SOMETHING**
Tracks: / Something.
**7" Single:** Released Oct '65, on Columbia by EMI Records. Deleted '68. Catalogue no: **DB 7727**

**SOUND VENTURE**
**Album:** Released Oct '66, on Columbia by EMI Records. Deleted '69. Catalogue no: **SX 6076**

**SUNNY**
Tracks: / Sunny.
**7" Single:** Released Sep '66, on Columbia by EMI Records. Deleted '69. Catalogue no: **DB 8015**

**SWEET THINGS**
**Album:** Released May '66, on Columbia by EMI Records. Deleted '69. Catalogue no: **SX 6043**

**THAT'S WHAT FRIENDS ARE FOR**
Tracks: / Maybe tomorrow / Lovely day / L in L.A. / You / I don't care who I can dance with / That's what friends are for / Don't hit me when I'm down / Sitting in the park / If I didn't mean you well / Cat's eyes.
**Cass:** Released Oct '79, on PRT by Castle Communications Records. Catalogue no: **ZCN 119**
**Album:** Released Nov '79, on Pye Deleted '84. Catalogue no: **N 119**

**TRY MY WORLD**
Tracks: / Try my world.
**7" Single:** Released Sep '67, on CBS by CBS Records. Deleted '70. Catalogue no: **CBS 2945**

**TWO FACES OF FAME**
**Album:** Released Jul '67, on CBS by CBS Records. Deleted '70. Catalogue no: **SBPG 63018**

**YEAH YEAH (COLUMBIA)**
Tracks: / Yeah yeah
**7" Single:** Released Dec '64, on Columbia by EMI Records. Deleted '67. Catalogue no: **DB 7428**

**YEAH YEAH (OLD GOLD)**
Tracks: / Get away / Yeah yeah.
**7" Single:** Released Mar '86, on Old Gold by Old Gold Records. Catalogue no: **OG 9588**

**YEAH YEAH (RSO)**
Tracks: / Yeah yeah / Getaway.
**7" Single:** Released May '80, on RSO by Polydor Ltd. Deleted May '83. Catalogue no: **RSO 58**

## Famous Blackbirds

**FAMOUS BLACKBIRDS REVUES (Various artists)**
Tracks: / Silver rose: *Plantation Orchestra, The* / Arabella's wedding day: *Plantation Orchestra, The* / Smiling Joe: *Plantation Orchestra, The* / For baby and me: *Plantation Orchestra, The* / Bandana babies: *Leslie, Lew Blackbirds Orchest* / Magnolia's wedding: *Leslie, Lew Blackbirds Orchest* / You're lucky to me: *Ellington, Duke/His Orchestra* / Memories of you: *Ellington, Duke/His Orchestra* / I can't give you anything but love: *Mills Brothers* / Diga diga doo: *Mills Brothers/Duke Ellington* / St. Louis blues: *Waters,Ethel/Cecil Mack Choir* / Doin' the new lowdown: *Robinson, Bill 'Bojangles'* / I must have that man: *Hall, Adelaide with Duke Ellington & His Orchestra* / Baby: *Hall, Adelaide with Duke Ellington & His Orchestra* / Shuffle your feet-Banadana babies: *Mills, Harry & Donald.*
Note: Blackbirds finale: I can't give you anything but love / Doin' the new lowdown / I must have that man / Baby / Dixie / Diga diga do / Porgy / I can't give you anything but love.
**Cass:** Released '88, on Saville by Conifer Records. Catalogue no: **CSVL 195**
**Album:** Released '88, on Saville by Conifer Records. Catalogue no: **SVL 195**

## Farlow, Tal

**Biographical details:** Jazz guitarist, born in 1921 in South Carolina, who began playing in 1943 inspired by Charlie Christian. He had an enthusiastic following in the '50's, then was semi-retired, teaching and playing for pleasure; he became more active again in the second half of the 70's. He made his own shorter fingerboard for looser tuning and softer sound, and a dividing device that allowed an extra line while playing single notes; he published an instruction book. *Autumn in New York* was made in 1954; he also recorded on Prestige and Xanadu. (Donald Clarke, 1989).

**AT ED FUERST'S**
**CD:** Released '88, on Xanadu Catalogue no: **FDC 5160**

**AUTUMN IN NEW YORK**
Tracks: / Strike up the band / Have you met Miss Jones? / Cherokee / Autumn in New York.
Note: Tal Farlow - guitar Jerry Wiggins - piano Ray Brown - bass Chico Hamilton - drums
**Album:** Released May '83, on Verve (USA) by Polydor Ltd. Catalogue no: **2304 321**

**CHROMATIC PALETTE**
**Album:** Released Aug '81, on Concord by Concord Jazz Records (USA). Catalogue no: **CJ 154**

**COOKIN' ON ALL BURNERS**
Tracks: / You'd be so nice to come home to / If I should lose you / I've got the world on a string / Love letters / Lullaby of the leaves / I thought about you / I wished on the moon / Why shouldn't I? / Just friends.
Note: Tal Farlow - guitar James Williams - piano Gary Mazzaropi - bass Vinnie Johnson - drums
**Album:** Released Mar '83, on Concord Jazz by Concord Jazz Records (USA). Catalogue no: **CJ 204**

**LEGENDARY TAL FARLOW, THE**
Tracks: / You stepped out of a dream / When your lover has gone / I got it bad and that ain't good / When lights are low / Who cares? / I can't get started / Prelude to a kiss / Everything happens to me.
Note: Art Farmer - Trumpet, Ernie Royal - Trumpet, Jimmy Cleveland - Trombone, Oscar Estelle - Alt/Ten/Bar, Harold Mabern - Piano, Jimmy Woode - Bass, Roy McCurdy - Drums.
**CD:** Released '88, on IMS by Polydor Ltd. Catalogue no: **CJ 266 390**
**Album:** Released Apr '85, on Concord Jazz by Concord Jazz Records (USA). Catalogue no: **CJ 266**

**ON STAGE**
**Album:** Released Mar '81, on Concord by Concord Jazz Records (USA). Catalogue no: **CJ 143**

**RED NORVO TRIO (Farlow, Tal & Charles Mingus)**
Tracks: / Swedish pastry / Take 1 / I can't believe you're in love with me / Time and tide / Those little white lies / Prelude to a kiss / Move / Godchild take 2 / September song / This can't be love (take 1) / I'm yours / I get a kick out of you / Zing went the strings of my heart / Cheek to cheek / Night and day / Godchild / Mood indigo / This can't be love (take 2) / If I had you / Deed I do / I'll remember April / This can't be love (master) / I've got you under my skin / Have you met Miss Jones.
**Album:** Released '82, on Arista by BMG Records (UK). Deleted '87. Catalogue no: **SJL 2212**

**RETURN OF TAL FARLOW, THE**
Tracks: / Straight No Chaser / Darn That Dream / Summertime / Sometime Ago / I'll Remember April / My Romance / Crazy she calls it.
**Cass:** Released Mar '88, on Prestige Deleted Jan '90. Catalogue no: **PRC 7732**
**Album:** Released Mar '88, on Prestige Catalogue no: **PR 7732**

**SWINGING GUITAR OF TAL FARLOW, THE**
Tracks: / Taking a chance on love / Yardbird suite / You stepped out of a dream / They can't take that away from me / Like someone in love / Meteor / I love you.

Note: Tal Farlow - guitar Eddie Costa - piano Vinnie Burke - bass
**Album:** Released Aug '82, on Verve (USA) by Polydor Ltd. Catalogue no: **2304 211**

**TALMAGE FARLOW (VIDEO)**
**VHS:** Released '88, on Kay Jazz (video) by Kay Jazz. Catalogue no: **KJ 015**

## Farmer, Art

**Biographical details:** Trumpeter, then switching to flugelhorn since mid-'60's, born in 1928. He went to L.A. in 1945 with his twin brother Addison, a fine bassist who died in 1963. He played in the Lionel Hampton band in 1952-53, settled in New York and led his own groups with Gigi Gryce, Horace Silver, then Gerry Mulligan (including film soundtracks; co-led the popular Jazztet with Benny Golson 1959-62, then had a quartet with Jim Hall; he settled in Vienna in 1968 and has become a master of the beautiful warm-toned flugelhorn, a frequent and valued visitor to Britain. (Donald Clarke, April 1989).

**AMBROSIA**
Tracks: / Windmills of your mind / Once upon a summertime / Watch what happens / What are you doing the rest of your life / You must believe in Spring / Years of my youth, The / Summer knows, The / I will wait for you.
**CD:** Released '88, on Denon Catalogue no: **C38-7091**

**ART FARMER QUINTET (Farmer, Art Quintet)**
**Album:** Released Jan '87, on Original Jazz Classics (USA) by Fantasy Inc (USA). Catalogue no: **OJC 241**

**ART FARMER SEPTET (Farmer, Art Septet)**
**Album:** Released Jun '86, on Original Jazz Classics (USA) by Fantasy Inc (USA). Catalogue no: **OJC 054**

**ARTWORKER**
Note: Art Farmer - trumpet Ernie Royal - trumpet Jimmy Cleveland - trombone Oscar Estelle - 'alt;ten;bar' Harold Mabern - piano Jimmy Woode - bass Roy McCurdy - drums
**Album:** Released Apr '81, on Lotus Catalogue no: **ORL 8293**

**BACK TO THE CITY (Farmer, Art & Benny Golson Jazztet)**
**CD:** Released May '87, on JVC/Fantasy Deleted '88. Catalogue no: **VDJ 1043**

**BIG BLUES (Farmer, Art & Jim Hall)**
Tracks: / Whisper not / Child is born / Big blues / Pavane for a dead princess.
**Album:** Released Mar '79, on CTI (1) by Polydor Ltd. Deleted '84. Catalogue no: **CTI 7083**

**CRAWL SPACE**
**Album:** Released Feb '84, on CTI (Musidisc France) by Polydor Ltd. Catalogue no: **CTI 9008**

**ELOQUENT**
Tracks: / Cascavelo / Day after / Con fab / Gap sealer / Cocodrilo / Whole tone stomp.
**Album:** Released '79, on MPS Jazz Deleted '84. Catalogue no: **5C 064 61176**

**FOOLISH**
Tracks: / Larry's delight / Al-leu-cha / D's dilemma / In a sentimental mood / Foolish memories / Farmer's market.
**Album:** Released Dec '88, on L&R Catalogue no: **LR 45008**
**CD:** Released Dec '88, on L&R Catalogue no: **CDLR 45008**

**HERE'S THAT RAINY DAY**
**CD:** Released May '88, on Mobile Fidelity Sound Lab(USA) by Mobile Fidelity Records (USA). Catalogue no: **MFCD 886**

**INTERACTION (Farmer, Art, Quartet, featuring Jim Hall)**
Tracks: / Days of wine and roses / By myself / My little suede shoes / Embraceable you / My kinda love / Sometime ago.
**Album:** Released Nov '80, on Atlantic by WEA Records. Catalogue no: **K 50728**

**JAZZ AT THE SMITHSONIAN VOL.1**
Tracks: / You know I care / Red cross / Cherokee sketches / Recorda me / Blue monk / Firm roots.
Note: Art Farmer came to prominence at a time when many trumpet players, following the lead of Dizzy Gillespie, were bold and extrovert. Farmer however, developed a different style that was wistful and lyrical, which ended in his switching from the more strident trumpet to the mellower and deeper flugelhorn. In this hour long concert, Art Farmer demonstrates that he is master of both instruments. Essential viewing for all jazz followers. Running time: 58 mins. (Parkfield Publishing)
**VHS:** Released Sep '89, on Parkfield Publishing Catalogue no: **MKJ 0003**

**MAIDEN VOYAGE**
Tracks: / Nica's dream / Ruby my dear / Blue bossa / Goodbye pork pie hat / Blue in green / Maiden voyage / Naima.
Note: Art Farmer (Flugelhorn), Jack De Johnette (Drums), Ron Carter (bass), Masahiko Satoh (Keyboard).
**CD:** Released '88, on Denon Catalogue no: **C38-7071**

**MANHATTAN (Farmer, Art Quintet)**
Note: With Sahib Shihab, Kenny Drew, Mads Vinding, Ed Thigpen.
**CD:** Released '86, on Soul Note Catalogue no: **SNCD 1026**
**Album:** Released Jul '82, on Soul Note Catalogue no: **SN 1026**

**MEET THE JAZZTET (Farmer, Art & Benny Golson)**
Tracks: / Serenata / It ain't necessarily so / Avalon / I remember Clifford / Blues march / It's alright with me / Park Avenue petite / Mox Nix / Easy living / Killer Joe.
**Cass:** Released Aug '88, on Chess by Vogue Records. Catalogue no: **GCHK 78092**
**Album:** Released Aug '88, on Chess by Vogue Records. Catalogue no: **GCH 8092**

**MIRAGE (Farmer, Art Quintet)**
Note: With Clifford Jordan.
**CD:** Released '86, on Soul Note Catalogue no: **SNCD 1046**

**ON THE ROAD**
Tracks: / Downwind / My funny valentine / Namely you / What am i here for / I can't get started / Will you still be mine.
**Album:** Released Aug '87, on Boplicity by Ace Records. Deleted '88. Catalogue no: **COP 009**

**PORTRAIT OF ART FARMER**
Tracks: / Back in the cage / Stablemates / Very thought of you, The / And now.... / Nita / By myself / Too late noe / Earth.
**Album:** Released Aug '86, on Contemporary (USA) Catalogue no: **COP 029**
**CD:** Released Jan '89, on JVC/Fantasy Catalogue no: **VDJ 1627**
**Album:** Released Mar '79, on Contemporary (USA) Catalogue no: **S 7554**

**SING ME SOFTLY OF THE BLUES (Farmer, Art Quartet)**
Tracks: / Sing me softly of the blues / Ad infinitum / Petite belle / Tears / I waited for you / Ore for Majid.
**Album:** Released Aug '80, on Atlantic by WEA Records. Catalogue no: **K 50725**

**SLEEPING BEE, THE**
**Album:** Released '76, on Sonet by Sonet Records. Catalogue no: **SNTF 715**

**SOMETHING TO LIVE FOR (Music of Billy Strayhorn)**
**CD:** Released Jan '89, on JVC/Fantasy Catalogue no: **VDJ 1112**

**SOMETHING YOU GOT**
**Album:** Released Feb '84, on CTI (Musidisc France) by Polydor Ltd. Catalogue no: **CTI 9016**

**TWO TRUMPETS (Farmer, Art & Donald Byrd)**
**Album:** Released Jun '86, on Original Jazz Classics (USA) by Fantasy Inc (USA). Catalogue no: **OJC 018**

**WARM VALLEY**
Tracks: / Moose the mooche / And now there's you / Three little words / Eclipso / Sad to say / Upper Manhattan medical group / Warm valley.
**Cass:** Released May '83, on Concord Jazz by Concord Jazz Records (USA). Catalogue no: **CJC 212**
**Album:** Released May '83, on Concord Jazz by Concord Jazz Records (USA). Catalogue no: **CJ 212**

**WHEN FARMER MET GRYCE (Farmer, Art & Gigi Gryce)**
Tracks: / Night at Tony's, A / Blue concept / Stupendous - lee / Deltitnu / Capri / Blue lights / Infant's song / Social call.
**Album:** Released Feb '84, on Prestige (USA) by Fantasy Inc (USA). Catalogue no: **OJC 072**

**WORK OF ART, A**
Tracks: / She's funny that way / Love

walked in / Change partners / Red cross / You know I care.
**Album:** Released Apr '82, on Concord by Concord Jazz Records (USA). Catalogue no: **CJ 179**

**YAMA (Farmer, Art / Joe Henderson)**
**Album:** Released Feb '84, on CTI (Musidisc France) by Polydor Ltd. Catalogue no: **CTI 9019**

**YOU MAKE ME SMILE (Farmer, Art Quintet)**
Note: With Clifford Jordan.
**CD:** Released '86, on Soul Note Catalogue no: **SN 1076**

## Farrell, Al

**LIVE IN KANSAS CITY (Farrell, Al & Crescent City Statement)**
**Cass:** Released Apr '88, on Nola Catalogue no: **STC 1001**

## Farrell, Joe

**JOE FARRELL AND PAUL HORN (Farrell, Joe & Paul Horn)**
**CD:** Released Jul '89, on Cleo Catalogue no: **CLCD 5018**

**NIGHT DANCING**
Tracks: / Night dancing / Silver lace.
**7" Single:** Released Dec '78, on Atlantic by WEA Records. Deleted '81. Catalogue no: **LV 2**

**QUINTET / COREN / HANCOCK**
**CD:** Released '88, on CBS by CBS Records. Deleted Jan '89. Catalogue no: **450559-2**

## Fathers & Sons

**FATHERS AND SONS (Original soundtrack) (Various artists)**
Tracks: / All aboard: *Various artists* / Mean disposition: *Various artists* / Blow wind blow: *Various artists* / You can't lose what you ain't never had: *Various artists* / Walkin' thru the park: *Various artists* / Forty days and forty nights: *Various artists* / Standin' round cryin': *Various artists* / I'm ready: *Various artists* / Twenty four hours: *Various artists* / Sugar sweet: *Various artists* / Long distance call: *Various artists* / Baby please don't go: *Various artists* / Honey bee: *Various artists* / Same thing, The: *Various artists* / Got my mojo working (pt 1): *Various artists* / Got my mojo working (pt 2): *Various artists.*
Note: Artists include R.H. Harris & The Soul Stirrers, Original Blind Boys of Mississippi, Sensational Nightingales.
**Album:** Released Aug '87, on Spirit Feel by Shanachie Records (USA). Catalogue no: **ACH 013**
**CD:** Released Feb '90, on MCA by MCA Records. Catalogue no: **CHD 92522**

## Fathers & Sons (Group)

**FATHERS & SONS**
Tracks: / Twelve's it / Joy forever / Nostalgic / Impressions / Futuristic / Lush life / Jug ain't gone / Time marches on / I can't get started / Tribute to our fathers.
**Album:** Released Jul '82, on CBS by CBS Records. Deleted Jul '87. Catalogue no: **CBS 85786**

## Fatool, Nick

**SPRING OF '87 (Fatool, Nick Jazzband)**
**Album:** Released 8 Apr '89, on Jazzology (USA) by Jazzology Records (USA). Catalogue no: **J 158**

## Fawkes, Wally

**JUICY AND FULL TONED**
Tracks: / Sheik of Araby / Summertime / Monday date / Fishmouth / Exactly like you / That's what it's all about / Lullaby of the leaves / Bodgers blues / Polka dot rag / Mobile blues / Avalon / Lazy bones / Petite fleur / Baby Brown.
**Cass:** Released Jun '89, on Lake by Lake Records. Catalogue no: **LA 5012C**
**Album:** Released Jun '89, on Lake by Lake Records. Catalogue no: **LA 5012**

**OCTOBER SONG (Fawkes, Wally & Friends)**
Tracks: / Avalon / Rent party blues / Lucky duck / Dallas blues / Viper mad.
**Album:** Released Sep '86, on Calligraph Catalogue no: **CLGLP 010**

**WALLY FAWKES AND THE RHYTHM KINGS (Fawkes, Wally & The Rhythm Kings)**
**Album:** Released Jun '86, on Stomp Off (USA) Catalogue no: **SOS 1060**

**WALLY FAWKES NEO-TROGLODYKES (Fawkes, Wally & The Neo-Troglodykes)**
**Album:** Released May '79, on Dawn Club by Cadillac Music. Catalogue no: **DCS 33 001**

**WHATEVER NEXT (Fawkes, Wally & Soho Shakers)**
**Album:** Released Jan '88, on Stomp Off (USA) Catalogue no: **SOS 1144**

## Feather, Leonard

**LEONARD FEATHER PRESENTS**
**Album:** Released Apr '88, on VSOP Catalogue no: **VSOP 12**

**PRESENTS 'JAZZ FROM 2 SIDES'**
**Album:** Released Jun '87, on Concept (1) Catalogue no: **VL 5**

## Feldman, Vic

**Biographical details:** An all round jazz musician, born in London in 1934, who died in L.A. in 1987. He was a self-taught prodigy, playing drums, piano and vibes. He recorded in the UK 1948-57 with John Dankworth, Stan Tracey, drummers Phil Seamen and Tony Crombietc; larger groups 1955-57 with Ronnie Scott, Tubby Hayes and others. He went to the USA in 1955 and worked mainly on the West Coast; the number of records he made as a sideman is huge. Cannonball Adderly wanted to hire Feldman (1960-1) and introduced him to the group by playing a record; when they all raved about it he told them that Feldman was white, English and Jewish. He went to Russia with Benny Goodman in 1962; he gigged and recorded with Miles Davis in 1963; he wrote *Seven steps to heaven*, title track of a Davis album, and was offered a permanent job by Davis, but it went to Herbie Hancock because Feldman didn't want to leave his wife. Marylin died in 1984 and he never really got over it. (Donald Clarke, April 1989).

**VIC FELDMAN WITH MALLETS A FORE THOUGHT**
**Album:** Released Apr '88, on VSOP Catalogue no: **VSOP 13**

## Felix, Lennie

**PIANO SOLOS**
**Album:** Released '88, on Eighty-Eight Upright Catalogue no: **88 UR 003**

## Female Blues

**FEMALE BLUES 1940/42 (Various artists)**
**Album:** Released Feb '89, on Document Catalogue no: **DLP 548**

## Female Country Blues

**FEMALE COUNTRY BLUES VOL.1 - 1924 / 28 (Various artists)**
**Album:** Released Mar '89, on Blues Document Catalogue no: **BD 2040**

## Fenix Jazz Band

**GRANDPA'S SPELLS**
Note: Buenos Aires, Argentina.
**Album:** Released Mar '87, on Stomp Off (USA) Catalogue no: **SOS 1129**

## Ferguson, Allyn

**PICTURES AT AN EXHIBITION FRAMED**
Note: Moussorgsky's compositions arranged and conducted by Allyn Ferguson. Featuring Bud Shank, Bill Perkins, Tommy Tedesco, Howard Roberts, Frank Capp, Bill Hood and Paul Horn.
**Album:** Released '88, on Discovery (USA) by Discovery Records (USA). Catalogue no: **DS 810**

**WITH THE CHAMBER JAZZ SEXTET (Ferguson, Allyn & Kenneth Patchen)**
Note: An album of Patchen's poetry set to jazz. Music composed by Allyn Ferguson.
**Album:** Released '88, on Discovery (USA) by Discovery Records (USA). Catalogue no: **DS 858**

## Ferguson, Maynard

**Biographical details:** Trumpeter and bandleader born in 1928 in Montreal. He also plays other horns. He was a high note specialist with Stan Kenton 1950-3; formed his own big band 1956-65, alternately leading a sextet toward the end of that period. The 1956 *Birdland Dreamband* on Bluebird is a great edition of the band with stars in it such as Ernie Wilkins, Al Cohn and Hank Jones. He was respected by other musicians for technique and versatility, but as time went by the band was more popular with the public than critics; he formed a bigger band in England and recorded for CBS and other labels in the '70's; the band shrunk to 13, then 11 pieces; most recently he plays arrangement of pop/rock songs, loud as ever. (Donald Clarke, April 1989).

**BEST OF MAYNARD FERGUSON**
Tracks: / Gonna fly now / McArthur Park / Star Trek / Birdland / Give it one / Stella by starlight / Battleship Galactica, Theme from / Pagliacci / Main title (theme from Star Wars) / Airegin.
**Album:** Released Jul '80, on CBS by CBS Records. Catalogue no: **CBS 84200**

**BIG BOP NOUVEAU**
Tracks: / Blue birdland / Cherokee / Caught in a current / But beautiful / Cruisin' for a bluesin'.
Note: Contains medley:- Chameleon/Macarthur Park/Frame For The Blues/Maria/Birdland.
**Album:** Released Feb '90, on Intima (EMI) Catalogue no: **773 390 1**
**CD:** Released Feb '90, on Intima (EMI) Catalogue no: **CDP 773 390 2**
**CD:** Released Feb '90, on Intima (EMI) Catalogue no: **CDINTM 73390**
**Album:** Released Feb '90, on Intima (EMI) Catalogue no: **INTM 73390**

**BIRDLAND DREAMBAND, THE**
Tracks: / Lady bug / Still water stomp / Blue birdland / Great guns / Button nose / Maynard the fox / Somebody wants me down there / More west / Wailing boat, the / Mogo / Early hours / Geller's cellar / Say it with trumpets / You said it / Everybody moan / Sleep softly / Cervezita / Little girl Kimbi.
**CD:** Released Jun '88, on Bluebird (2) by BMG Records (UK). Catalogue no: **ND 86455**

**BLUES ROAR, THE**
**CD:** Released '86, on Mobile Fidelity Sound Lab(USA) by Mobile Fidelity Records (USA). Catalogue no: **MFCD 843**

**BODY AND SOUL**
Tracks: / Expresso / Body and soul / M.O.T. / Mira Mira / Last dive / Beautiful hearts / Central park.
Note: Super trumpet star Maynard Ferguson's brand new album "Body and Soul" is the first recording of his reorganized young band that has turned on large audiences in the US and abroad during the past year. It introduces a hot 11-piece road band with a powerful sound. Personnel:Maynard Ferguson-MF Horn Trumpets, Flugelhorn / Wayne Bergeron - Lead Trumpet, Flugelhorn / Alan Wise - Trumpet - Flugelhorn / Alex Iles - Trombones / Tim Ries-Alto, Tenor & Soprano Saxophones, Flute / Rick Margitza-Tenor, Soprano, Saxophones / Todd Carlon-Keyboards / Dave Miller-Drums / Dave Carpenter-Bass / Steve Fisher-Percussion/Michael Higgins-Guitar.
**Album:** Released Sep '86, on Black Hawk (USA) by Blackhawk Records (USA). Catalogue no: **BKH 50101**
**Cass:** Released Sep '86, on Black Hawk (USA) by Blackhawk Records (USA). Catalogue no: **BKHMC 50101**
**CD:** Released Mar '87, on Black Hawk (USA) by Blackhawk Records (USA). Catalogue no: **CDBKH 50101**

**CONDUCTS THE BIRDLAND DREAMBAND**
Tracks: / Wailing boat, (The) / Somebody wants me down there / Maynard the fox / Blue Birdland / Great guns / Lady bug / More west / Stillwater stomp / That Jones boy / Button nose / Little girl Kimbi / Straight up / Cervezita / Mogo / Sleep softly / Geller's cellar / Free Lee / Say it with trumpets / Everybody moan / Tell me funky / You said it / Early hours / Nightmare Alley.
**2 LP Set:** Released '83, on RCA (France) by BMG Records (France). Catalogue no: **PM 43841**

**HIGH VOLTAGE**
**CD:** Released Feb '89, on Enigma by Enigma Records (USA). Catalogue no: **CDENV 517**
**Album:** Released Feb '89, on Enigma by Enigma Records (USA). Catalogue no: **ENVLP 517**
**CD:** Released Oct '87, on Enigma by Enigma Records (USA). Catalogue no: **3279 2**
**Cass:** Released Feb '89, on Enigma by Enigma Records (USA). Catalogue no: **TCENV 517**

**HOLLYWOOD**
Tracks: / Don't stop till you get enough / Deja vu / Hollywood / Nine to five / For your eyes only / Here today / Portuguese love / Touch & go.
**Album:** Released Jul '82, on CBS by CBS Records. Deleted Jul '87. Catalogue no: **CBS 85503**

**LIVE IN ITALY, VOL.1 (Ferguson, Maynard Big Band)**
Note: Recorded at the Donizettie Theatre, Bergamo on March 22nd 1969. Maynard Ferguson, Martin Drover, Ernie Garside and Hank Shaw (trumpets); Wally Aldred and Paul Keepwhiteman (trombones); Gary Cox, Danny Moss, Brian Smith and Bob Watson (saxophones); Pete Jackson (piano); Kenny Knepper (bass) and Bob Gillespie (drums). 51 minutes playing time.
**CD:** Released Nov '89, on Jazz-Up Catalogue no: **JU 308**

**LIVE IN ITALY, VOL.2 (Ferguson, Maynard Big Band)**
Note: Recorded at the Donizettie Theatre, Bergamo on March 22nd 1969. Maynard Ferguson, Martin Drover, Ernie Garside and Hank Shaw (trumpets); Wally Aldred and Paul Keepwhiteman (trombones); Gary Cox, Danny Moss, Brian Smith and Bob Watson (saxophones); Pete Jackson (piano); Kenny Knepper (bass) and Bob Gillespie (drums). 56 minutes playing time.
**CD:** Released Nov '89, on Jazz-Up Catalogue no: **JU 309**

**MAYNARD '61 (ROULETTE)**
**Album:** Released Feb '90, on Roulette (EMI) by EMI Records. Catalogue no: **793 900 1**
**Album:** Released Feb '90, on Roulette (EMI) by EMI Records. Catalogue no: **ROU 1010**
**CD:** Released Feb '90, on Roulette (EMI) by EMI Records. Catalogue no: **CDP 793 900 2**
**CD:** Released Feb '90, on Roulette (EMI) by EMI Records. Catalogue no: **CDROU 1010**

**MAYNARD '61**
Tracks: / Ole / New blue / Blues for Kapp (AKA Coldwater Canyon blues) / Ultimate rejection / Pharaoh, The / Goodbye / Saturday night (is the loneliest night of the week) (CD only.) / This is my lucky day (CD only.) / Go east, young man (CD only.).
**Album:** Released Feb '88, on Fresh Sounds (Spain) by Fresh Sounds Records (Spain). Catalogue no: **FS 103**

**MAYNARD '62**
Tracks: / Have you met Miss Jones? / Maria / Zip'n'zap / Lazy afternoon / Go east young man / This my lucky day / 'X' stream / Four / Pretty little Nieda / 'Round about the blues.
**Album:** Released Feb '88, on Fresh Sounds (Spain) by Fresh Sounds Records (Spain). Catalogue no: **FS 104**
**Album:** Released Sep '89, on Fresh Sounds (Spain) by Fresh Sounds Records (Spain). Catalogue no: **FS 364**

**MAYNARD FERGUSON & HIS ORIGINAL DREAMBAND (Ferguson, Maynard & His Original Dreamband)**
**Album:** Released Sep '86, on Artistry Catalogue no: **AR 104**

**MESSAGE FROM BIRDLAND**
**Album:** Released Feb '88, on Fresh Sounds (Spain) by Fresh Sounds Records (Spain). Catalogue no: **FS 228**

**MESSAGE FROM NEWPORT, A (Ferguson, Maynard Orchestra)**
Tracks: / Fugue, The / Fan it, Janet / Waltz, The / Tag team / And we listened / Slide's derangement / Frame for the blues / Humbug / Three little foxes.
**CD:** Released Oct '89, on Roulette (EMI) by EMI Records. Catalogue no: **CDP 793 272 2**
**CD:** Released Oct '89, on Roulette (EMI) by EMI Records. Catalogue no: **CZ 237**
**Album:** Released Oct '89, on Roulette (EMI) by EMI Records. Catalogue no: **793 272 1**
**Album:** Released Oct '89, on Roulette (EMI) by EMI Records. Catalogue no: **ROU 1004**

**NEWPORT SUITE**
**Album:** Released Feb '88, on Fresh Sounds (Spain) by Fresh Sounds Records (Spain). Catalogue no: **FS 94**

**SI! SI! - M.F.**
**Album:** Released Feb '88, on Fresh Sounds (Spain) by Fresh Sounds Records (Spain). Catalogue no: **FS 84**

**STAIGHT AWAY JAZZ THEMES**
Tracks: / Straight away / Apprehension / Mambo la mans / Cocky Scott / Up shift / Last lap / Melancholia / Pit stop / Stroking / After the race.
**Album:** Released Sep '89, on Fresh Sounds (Spain) by Fresh Sounds Records (Spain). Catalogue no: **FS 365**

**SWINGING MY WAY THROUGH COLLEGE**
**Album:** Released Jun '88, on Fresh Sounds (Spain) by Fresh Sounds Records (Spain). Catalogue no: **FS 320**

**THREE KENTON'S BE BOPPERS GROUPS (Ferguson, Maynard / Vido Musso / Eddie Safranski)**
**Album:** Released Jul '83, on Unique Jazz by Spotlite Records. Catalogue no: **UJ 36**

**TRUMPETS OUT FRONT (Ferguson, Maynard & Herb Pomeroy)**
Tracks: / Fugue / Fan it Janet / Waltz / Tag team / And we listened / Slide's derangement / Frame for the blues / Humbug / Three little foxes / Blue grass / Wolafunt's lament / Jack Spratt / Aluminium baby / It's sandman / Our delight / Theme for Terry / No one will room with me / Feather merchant / Bit man / Less talk.
**2 LP Set:** Released May '83, on Vogue Jazz (France) by Vogue Records. Catalogue no: **VJD 567**
**Cass set:** Released May '83, on Vogue Jazz (France) by Vogue Records. Catalogue no: **ZCVJD 567**

**TWO'S COMPANY (Ferguson, Maynard / Conner, Chris)**
**Album:** Released Feb '88, on Fresh Sounds (Spain) by Fresh Sounds Records (Spain). Catalogue no: **FS 93**

## Ferre, Boulou

**GYPSY DREAMS**
**Album:** Released May '81, on Steeplechase (USA) Catalogue no: **SCS 1140**

**TRINITY**
**Album:** Released Jul '88, on Steeplechase (USA) Catalogue no: **SCS 1171**
**CD:** Released Jul '88, on Steeplechase (USA) Catalogue no: **SCCD 31171**

## Fessor's Big City Band

**FEELIN' GOOD**
**Album:** Released Feb '90, on Storyville by Storyville Records AB. Catalogue no: **SLP 426**

**HAMBA NAMI**
**Album:** Released '88, on Storyville by Storyville Records AB. Catalogue no: **SLP 261**

**HOT BISCUITS**
**Album:** Released Jul '81, on Storyville by Storyville Records AB. Catalogue no: **SLP 406**

**JUNGLE BLUES**
**Album:** Released Feb '90, on Storyville by Storyville Records AB. Catalogue no: **SLP 440**

**LIVE**
**Album:** Released Feb '90, on Storyville by Storyville Records AB. Catalogue no: **SLP 424**

**STOLEN SUGAR**
**Album:** Released Feb '90, on Storyville by Storyville Records AB. Catalogue no: **SLP 427**

**THIRD FLOOR RICHARD**
**Album:** Released Feb '90, on Storyville by Storyville Records AB. Catalogue no: **SLP 433**

**WILD BILL DAVISON**
**Album:** Released '88, on Storyville by Storyville Records AB. Catalogue no: **SLP 421**

## Festa New Orleans

**ASCONA**
**Album:** Released '88, on Festa Nor Catalogue no: **FESTA 934**

**FESTA NEW ORLEANS MUSIC ASCONA (Various artists)**
Note: Featuring: The King Oliver Centennial band, Lillian Boutte & Her Music Friends, Storyville Shakers, Louis Nelson N.O. Band, Al Rapone & The Zydeco Express, Jambalaya Four & Freddie Kohlman, S.Rimmington Band, Thomas Jefferson, Papa Toms Lamentation Jazz Band, New Orleans Blue Serenade.
**Album:** Released Nov '86, on Festa New Orleans Catalogue no: **LP 30**

## Fifties...

**50'S: JUKE JOINT BLUES, THE (Various artists)**
Tracks: / 3 o'clock blues: *King, B.B.* / Long tall woman: *James, Elmore* / Ramblin' on my mind: *Gilmore, Boyd* / Gonna let you go: *Turner, Babyface* / Love my baby: *Bland, Bobby & Junior Parker* / Riding in the moonlight: *Howlin' Wolf* / 44 blues: *Dudlow & Peck Curtis* / Step back baby: *Blair, Sunny* / This is the end: *Reed, James* / Jake head boogie: *Lightnin' Hopkins* / Down in New Orleans: *Smith, Little George* / Monte Carlo: *Dixie Blues Boys* / Doin' the town: *Dixon, Floyd* / Just got in from Texas: *Gordon, Roscoe* / Big mouth: *Nelson, Jimmy* / Have you ever: *Dee, Mercy* / Sputterin' blues: *Robertson, Walter* / Prowling blues: *Fuller, Johnny* / Going to New Orleans: *Tanner, Kid* / Good morning little angel: *Louis, Joe Hill* / Panic's on, The: *McCracklin, Jimmy* (Available on CD only) / What's the matter with you: *Horton, Walter "Shakey"* (Available on CD only).
**Album:** Released Jun '87, on Ace by Ace Records. Catalogue no: **CHA 216**
**Cass:** Released Jun '87, on Ace by Ace Records. Deleted Jan '90. Catalogue no: **CHC 216**
**CD:** Released Jul '87, on Ace by Ace Records. Catalogue no: **CDCH 216**

## Firehouse Five

**DIXIELAND (Firehouse Five Plus Two)**
**CD:** Released Apr '87, on Carrere (France) Catalogue no: **98605**

**DIXIELAND FAVOURITES**
**CD:** Released Apr '87, on London Records by London Records Ltd. Catalogue no: **FCD 60008**

**GOOD TIME JAZZ (Firehouse Five Plus Two)**
Tracks: / Runnin' wild / Five foot two, eyes of blue / When you wore a tulip (and I wore a red red rose) / I can't give you anything but love / Swanee River / Alabama jubilee / Muskrat ramble / That's a plenty / Frankie and Johnny / Yes sir, that's my baby / Tiger rag / Sheik of Araby, The / California here I come / Isle of Capri / Everybody loves my baby / St. Louis blues / Just a stomp at twilight / Sweet Georgia Brown / Doctor Jazz / 12th Street rag.
**Album:** Released Feb '82, on MFP by EMI Records. Deleted '87. Catalogue no: **MFP 50533**
**Cass:** Released Feb '82, on MFP by EMI Records. Deleted '87. Catalogue no: **TCMFP 50533**

## First British ...

**FIRST BRITISH R & B FESTIVAL, (An historic artefact) (Various artists)**
Tracks: / Introduction by Bob Wooler: *Davis, Spencer R & B Quartet* / Dimples: *Road Runners* / You can make it if you try: *Road Runners* / Mary Ann: *Road Runners* / Bright lights big city: *Stewart, Rod* / 2.19 blues, The: *Baldry, Long John* / Night time is the right time: *Davis, Spencer R & B Quartet* / Slow walk: *Williamson, Sonny Boy & The Yardbirds* / Pontiac blues: *Williamson, Sonny Boy & The Yardbirds* / Lonesome cabin: *Williamson, Sonny Boy & The Yardbirds* / Bye bye bird: *Williamson, Sonny Boy & The Yardbirds* / Got my mojo working: *All Star Jam.*
**Album:** Released Mar '89, on Decal by Charly Records. Catalogue no: **LIK 54**

## First Revolution...

**NEW ORLEANS GOSPEL - RHYTHM & BLUES (First Revolution Singers)**
Tracks: / Anonymous love / It's gonna rain / Down by the riverside / Please remember me / There's room at the cross / Mary don't you weep / I'm gonna serve the Lord.
Note: with Cherry Blossom Band.
**Album:** Released Dec '87, on Five O Four Records Catalogue no: **504 LPS 24**

**RUNNING FOR JESUS NEW ORLEANS GOSPEL - RHYTHM AND BLUES (First Revolution Of New Orleans)**
**Cass:** Released Sep '87, on Entertainers Catalogue no: **504 TCS 101G**

## First Time

**FIRST TIME I MET THE BLUES (Best of Chess Blues Vol 1) (Various artists)**

Tracks: / Don't start me talkin': *Williamson, Sonny Boy* / Key to the highway: *Little Walter* / Hoochie coochie man: *Waters, Muddy* / Walkin' the boogie: *Hooker, John Lee* / Smokestack lightning: *Howlin' Wolf* / So many roads, so many trains: *Rush, Otis* / When the lights go out: *Witherspoon, Jimmy* / Worried life blues: *Berry, Chuck* / First time I met the blues: *Guy, Buddy* / Off the wall: *Little Walter* / Third degree: *Boyd, Eddie* / I'm leaving you: *Spann, Otis* / Sun is shining, The: *James, Elmore* / Reconsider baby: *Fulson, Lowell* / I don't know: *Mabon, Willie* / Red rooster, The: *Howlin' Wolf* / Fattening frogs for snakes: *Williamson, Sonny Boy* / Sugar mama: *Hooker, John Lee* / Be careful: *Brim, John* / Wee wee hours: *Berry, Chuck* / Walking the blues: *Dixon, Willie* / Howlin' for my darling: *King, Albert* / Guess I'm a fool: *Slim, Memphis* / Got my mojo working: *Waters, Muddy*.
**CD:** Released Jun '89, on Chess by Vogue Records. Catalogue no: **CDRED 11**

## Fischer, Clare

**2+2 (Fischer, Clare & His Latin Jazz Sextet)**
**CD:** Released '88, on Discovery (USA) by Discovery Records (USA). Catalogue no: **DSCD 921**

**ALONE TOGETHER**
Tracks: / Yesterdays / Tahila / Touch of your lips, The / Everything happens to me.
**Album:** Released '88, on Discovery (USA) by Discovery Records (USA). Catalogue no: **DS 820**

**AND SOMETIMES VOICES (Fischer, Clare & Salsa Picante & Two Plus Two)**
Tracks: / Malibu glide / Country / Canto / Shake out all those blues / One night (in a dream) / Renacimiento / La ronde / Como come.
Note: 1982 Grammy nomination. All original compositions by Grammy Award winner Clare Fischer. Featuring Gary Foster-flute & soprano sax, Danny Embrey-guitar, Brent Fischer-electric bass, Poncho Sanchez-congas, Luis Conte-percussion, Armand Grimaldi-drums. 2+2 singers: Darlene Koldenhoven, Mary Hulan, Armick Byram & John Laird.
**Cass:** Released '88, on Discovery (USA) by Discovery Records (USA). Catalogue no: **DSC 852**
**Album:** Released Jan '84, on Discovery (USA) by Discovery Records (USA). Catalogue no: **DS 852**

**BLUES TRILOGY (Fischer, Clare & Woodwinds)**
**CD:** Released '88, on Discovery (USA) by Discovery Records (USA). Catalogue no: **DSCD 936**

**BY AND WITH HIMSELF (Clare Fischer plays)**
Tracks: / Giant steps / Jeru / Counterall / Fugue / Turn out the stars / Last night when we were young / Mememto.
Note: Clare Fischer-piano.
**Album:** Released '88, on Discovery (USA) by Discovery Records (USA). Catalogue no: **DS 934**

**CRAZY BIRD (Fischer, Clare & Salsa Picante)**
Tracks: / Bernie's tune / Where are the children? / Serenidade / La mucura / Pajaro loco / Solar patrol / Canto Africano / Pavillion.
Note: Featuring Bill Watrous and Jeff Berlin
**CD:** Released Sep '86, on Discovery (USA) by Discovery Records (USA). Catalogue no: **DSCD 914**
**Album:** Released '88, on Discovery (USA) by Discovery Records (USA). Catalogue no: **DS 914**
**Cass:** Released '88, on Discovery (USA) by Discovery Records (USA). Catalogue no: **DSC 914**

**DUALITY (Fischer, Clare Big Band)**
Tracks: / Come Sunday / This is always / Old folks.
Note: All-star band featuring Bud Shank, Bill Perkins and Conte Candoli.
**Album:** Released '88, on Discovery (USA) by Discovery Records (USA). Catalogue no: **DS 807**

**EASY LIVIN'**
Tracks: / In your own sweet way / Glad to be unhappy / Aquarius / My pretty girl / Kerry dancer / Goodbye / I'll take romance / Easy living.
Note: Clare Fischer, piano; Bobby West, bass.
**Album:** Released Apr '81, on Revelation (USA) by Hit Record Entertainment Inc.(USA). Catalogue no: **REV 2**

**EXTENSION (Fischer, Clare Orchestra, featuring Jerry Coker)**
Tracks: / Ornithology / Quiet dawn / Bittersweet / Igor / Extension / Coker's blues / Running mate / Soloette / Passacaglia / Canto Africano.
**Album:** Released Apr '84, on Discovery (USA) by Discovery Records (USA). Catalogue no: **DS 902**

**FREE FALL (Fischer, Clare & His Latin Jazz Sextet/2 + 2 Plus)**
Tracks: / Samba Claro / Novios / Blues bossa / Night we called it a day, The / You and I.
Note: Clare Fischer - keyboards; Dick Mitchell - flute, soprano sax; Brent Fischer - electric bass, Walfredo Reyes - drums; Luis Conte & Michito Sanchez - latin percussion. Singers: Darlene Kolden - hoven, Mary Hylan, John Laird, Darryl Phinnessee, Angie Jaree, David & Bob Joyce.
**Album:** Released '88, on Discovery (USA) by Discovery Records (USA). Catalogue no: **DS 921**
**Cass:** Released '88, on Discovery (USA) by Discovery Records (USA). Catalogue no: **DSC 921**

**GREAT WHITE HOPE**
Tracks: / After you've gone / Autumn leaves / Western airlines / Fuzz blues / Music of the spheres / You call it madness / C minor theme.
**Album:** Released Apr '81, on Revelation (USA) by Hit Record Entertainment Inc.(USA). Catalogue no: **REV 13**

**JAZZ SONG**
Tracks: / Spring is here / Suerte / Here's that rainy day / Moon mist / Autumn lines / Love locked out / Serenidade / Just friends.
Note: Solo piano. Recorded 9th May 1973.
**Album:** Released Mar '87, on Revelation (USA) by Hit Record Entertainment Inc.(USA). Catalogue no: **REV 31**

**LEMBRANCAS (REMEMBRANCES)**
Tracks: / C.P. (Charlie Palmieri) / Fina / Coco B. / Curumim / Endlessly / On Green Dolphin Street / Xapun / Gilda / Pan pipe dance / And miles to go / Strut, The (CD only.).
**CD:** Released Mar '90, on Concord by Concord Jazz Records (USA). Catalogue no: **CCD 4404**
**Cass:** Released Mar '90, on Concord by Concord Jazz Records (USA). Catalogue no: **CJP 404C**

**MACHACHA (IMPORT) (Fischer, Clare & Salsa Picante)**
Note: Featuring Gary Foster-flute, Rick Zunigar-guitar, Alex Acuna-drums, Poncho Sanchez-congas, David Troncoso-bass.
**Cass:** Released '88, on Discovery (USA) by Discovery Records (USA). Catalogue no: **DSC 835**
**Album:** Released '88, on Discovery (USA) by Discovery Records (USA). Catalogue no: **DS 835**

**ONE TO GET READY**
Tracks: / Liz Anne / In memoriam: J.F.K. & R.F.K. / You stepped out of a dream / Lover man / Free ways.
Note: Clare Fischer -- piano. Gary Foster -- tenor sax. Bobby West -- bass. Jim Kelthner -- drums. Recorded Autumn 1963, March 1964, Spring 1965.
**Album:** Released Apr '81, on Revelation (USA) by Hit Record Entertainment Inc.(USA). Catalogue no: **REV 6**

**RECLAMATION ACT OF 1972**
Tracks: / Blues reclaimed, The / Soon / Sometimes I feel this way / Meade Lux Lewis, I love you / Pensativa / W.P.A. work chant.
Note: Recorded: 3 January 1970, 9 May 1971.
**Album:** Released Apr '81, on Revelation (USA) by Hit Record Entertainment Inc.(USA). Catalogue no: **REV 15**

**SALSA PICANTE**
Note: Arranged and conducted by by Clare Fischer. Clare Fischer-piano, Rick Zunigar-guitar, David Acuna-flute, David Troncosso-bass, Pete Riso-drums, Alex Acuna-timbales.
**Cass:** Released '88, on Discovery (USA) by Discovery Records (USA). Catalogue no: **DSC 817**
**Album:** Released '88, on Discovery (USA) by Discovery Records (USA). Catalogue no: **DS 817**

**STARBRIGHT (Fischer, Clare & Gary Foster)**
Tracks: / Cherokee / Some day my prince will come / Brazilian waltz / Bluesome / Starbright / I love you / If you could see me now / Slippin' at Bells.
**Album:** Released Jan '84, on Discovery (USA) by Discovery Records (USA). Catalogue no: **DS 885**
**Cass:** Released Jan '84, on Discovery (USA) by Discovery Records (USA). Catalogue no: **DSC 885**

**STATE OF HIS ART**
Tracks: / Duke, The / Some day my prince will come / Woodyn' you? / Free improvisation / Basic blues / Proto-blues / Phrygian blues / Out-of-tempo blues.
Note: Recorded in May 1973.
**Album:** Released Apr '81, on Revelation (USA) by Hit Record Entertainment Inc.(USA). Catalogue no: **REV 26**

**T' DA-A-A-A-A (Fischer, Clare & Yamaha Quartet)**
Tracks: / Soon / Round midnight / Lennie's pennies / Blues in F / Crystal sunrise.
Note: Clare Fischer -- organ. Gary Foster -- alto sax. Andy Simpkins -- bass. Larry Bunker -- drums.
**Album:** Released Apr '81, on Revelation (USA) by Hit Record Entertainment Inc.(USA). Catalogue no: **REV 23**

**WALTZ (Fischer, Clare Big Band)**
**CD:** Released '88, on Discovery (USA) by Discovery Records (USA). Catalogue no: **DSCD 948**

**WHOSE WOODS ARE THESE?**
Tracks: / Blues trilogy / Basic blues / Blues in G / Blues bossa / If / Da vida bel / Long time ago, A / Free prelude / Lennie's pennies.
**Cass:** Released '88, on Discovery (USA) by Discovery Records (USA). Catalogue no: **DSC 880**
**Album:** Released Feb '84, on Discovery (USA) by Discovery Records (USA). Catalogue no: **DS 880**

## Fitzgerald, Ella

**Biographical details:** This American singer is commonly referred to as the First Lady of Jazz. Born in Newport News, Virginia in 1918, she ran away from home at the age of 16 to compete in a talent contest. In the following year (1935), she became the resident singer with Chick Webb's orchestra. It was in this capacity that she achieved her first big-selling record *A tisket, a tasket* - this adaptation of an old nursery rhyme was recorded in New York in 1938. Fitzgerald embarked upon a solo career in 1940 and, over the next 25 years, became a living legend. Her pitch, diction and phrasing were as close to perfection as any jazz singer has ever reached. Whether scatting a jazz standard or calmly interpreting a middle-of-the-road ballad, she transformed her repertoire into a serene sequence of veritable vignettes. The main criticism levelled at her was that her sheer coolness and imperturbaility meant boredom for some listeners - Ella put technical brilliance before emotion. Fitzgerald was with Decca until the late Fifties, but then switched to Verve Records, a label founded by her manager Norman Granz. Many aficionados argued that she reached her artistic peak during this later period. 1960 was certainly a successful year in disc terms: the singer reached the pop Top 40 on both sides of the Atlantic with her distinctive rendition of the standard *Mack the knife*; in Britain, she gained Top 20 successes with three EP's and three LP's during 1960. Between 1958 and 1964, she chalked up five UK Top 40 singles. Ella's remarkable voice was still holding up well when she turned 60 years old in 1978, and was used by Memorex in their commercials for blank tape. That climatic last note broke the glass, but was withstood intact by the cassette! In his epic 1983 rap *The crown*, Gary Byrd suggested that you should 'Sing like Ella and make them guess, Is it you or is it Memorex'. (Bob MacDonald, 26th August 1985)
One of the century's favourite singers. She was an orphan,born in 1918; she won talent contests and joined Chick Webb in 1934 (he adopted her) and had a big hit with the rhythmic novelty *A tisket a tasket* in 1938. She fronted the band after Webb died in 1939, went solo in 1942 and toured with JATP from 1946. The question of whether she's a jazz singer is pointless; she transcends category. She had hits in the Billboard charts on USA Decca (now MCA) 1940-51 including three with the Ink Spots and one with Louis Jordan, but soon switched to Norman Granz's labels and has been selling albums ever since: it was rare for two records sets to chart in the '50's but hers did. She made several films of which the best known is *Pete Kelly's blues*; the soundtrack album in 1955 was shared with Peggy Lee. (Donald Clarke, April 1989).

**16 ORIGINAL HITS: ELLA**
**Cass:** Released Sep '87, on Timeless Treasures Catalogue no: **MC 1629**

**30 BY ELLA**
**CD:** on EMI by EMI Records. Deleted Jun '89. Catalogue no: **CDP 748 333 2**

**70 MINUTES OF JAZZ WITH THE**
**CD:** Released '88, on Entertainers Catalogue no: **ENT CD 226**

**ALL THAT JAZZ**
**Cass:** Released Apr '90, on Pablo by Ace Records. Catalogue no: **PBDC 006**
**CD:** Released Apr '90, on Pablo by Ace Records. Catalogue no: **CDPBD 006**

**ANTONIO CARLOS JOBIM SONG-BOOK,**
Tracks: / Somewhere in the hills / Girl from Ipanema / Dindi / Off key / Water to drink / Triste / How insensitive / He's a carioca / Felicidade / This love that I've found / Dreamer / Quiet nights of quiet stars / Bonita / One-note samba / Wave / Don't ever go away / Song of the jet / Useless landscape.
**Cass set:** Released May '82, on Pablo Jazz (USA) by Pablo Records (USA). Catalogue no: **K 30 201**
**2 LP Set:** Released May '82, on Pablo Jazz (USA) by Pablo Records (USA). Catalogue no: **263 0201**

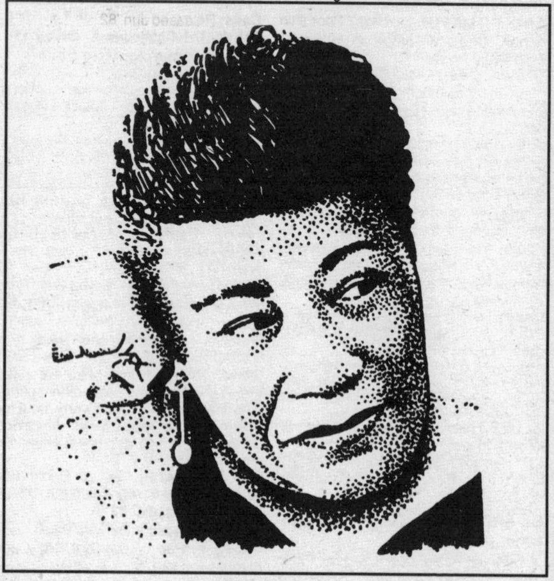

**Ella Fitzgerald**

**AT THE MONTREUX JAZZ FESTIVAL 1975**
Tracks: / Caravan / Satin doll / Teach me tonight / Wave / It's all right with me / Let's do it / How high the moon / Girl from Ipanema / T'aint nobody's business if I do.
**CD:** Released '86, on Pablo Jazz (USA) by Pablo Records (USA). Catalogue no: **J33J20032**
**Cass:** Released '82, on Pablo Jazz (USA) by Pablo Records (USA). Catalogue no: **K10 751**
**Album:** Released '82, on Pablo Jazz (USA) by Pablo Records (USA). Catalogue no: **2310 751**

**AT THE OPERA HOUSE**
Tracks: / It's all right with me / Don'cha go 'way mad / Bewitched, bothered and bewildered / Stompin' at the Savoy / These foolish things / Ill wind / Goody goody / Moonlight in Vermont / Lady be good.
Note: Coleman Hawkins, Lester Young, Stan Getz, Illinois Jacquet, Flip Phillips -- tenor saxes; Sonny Stitt -- alto sax; Roy Eldridge -- trumpet; Jay Jay Johnson -- trombone; Oscar Peterson -- piano; Herb Ellis -- guitar; Ray Brown -- bass; Jo Jones, Connie Kay -- drums. Recorded 1963.
**CD:** Released Jun '87, on Polydor by Polydor Ltd. Deleted Oct '88. Catalogue no: **831 269-2**
**Album:** Released Oct '84, on Verve (USA) by Polydor Ltd. Catalogue no: **821 554-1**

**AT THE SOUTHLAND OF BOSTON (Fitzgerald, Ella/Chick Webb)**
Tracks: / Let's get together / Poor little rich girl / New moon and an old serenade / Breaking 'em down / If I didn't care / Stars and stripes forever / I never knew Heaven could speak / My wild Irish rose / Chew, chew, chew, chew (your bubble gum) / Blue Lou / Deep in a dream / One o'clock jump / That was my heart.
Note: Recorded: 4 May 1939 and 2 October 1939.
**Album:** Released Apr '81, on Jazz Live (Italy) Catalogue no: **BLJ 8010**

**BASIN STREET BLUES**
**Cass:** Released Jul '88, on Vanstory Catalogue no: **VSK 3406**
**Album:** Released Jul '88, on Vanstory Catalogue no: **VS 3406**

**BEST IS YET TO COME (Fitzgerald, Ella & Nelson Riddle)**
Note: See also under Nelson Riddle.
**CD:** Released Apr '87, on Pablo Jazz (USA) by Pablo Records (USA). Catalogue no: **CD 231 2138**

**BEST OF ELLA FITZGERALD**
**Cass:** on Pablo Jazz (USA) by Pablo Records (USA). Catalogue no: **PBMC 001**
**Cass:** Released Aug '81, on MCA by MCA Records. Catalogue no: **MCLC 1611**
**Album:** on Pablo Jazz (USA) by Pablo Records (USA). Catalogue no: **PBM 001**
**Album:** Released Aug '81, on MCA by MCA Records. Catalogue no: **MCL 1611**
**CD:** on Pablo Jazz (USA) by Pablo Records (USA). Catalogue no: **CDPBM 001**

**BEST OF ELLA FITZGERALD (2)**
Tracks: / Dreamer / Fine and mellow / Street of dreams / This love that I've found / How long has this been going on / You're blase / Honeysuckle rose / I'm walking / I'm getting sentimental over you / Don't be that way.
**CD:** Released Jan '89, on Pablo Jazz (USA) by Pablo Records (USA). Catalogue no: **CDPEM 001**
**Cass:** Released Jan '89, on Pablo Jazz (USA) by Pablo Records (USA). Catalogue no: **PEMC 001**
**Album:** Released Jan '89, on Pablo Jazz (USA) by Pablo Records (USA). Catalogue no: **PEM 001**

**BEST YEARS OF...**
Tracks: / Tisket a tasket, A / Take another guess / I've got a guy / Gotta pebble in my shoe / Undecided / Chew, chew, chew, chew (your bubble gum) / You'll have to swing it / Big boy blues / Dedicated to you / This time it's for real.
Note: Recorded in 1936, 1937 and 1938 with the Chick Webb Orchestra and Chick Webb's Savoy Eight.
**Album:** Released Apr '81, on Joker (USA) by Lifetime Records (USA). Catalogue no: **SM 3054**

**BEWITCHED**
Tracks: / Bewitched / Begin the beguine / My funny valentine / 'S wonderful / Let's do it / Manhattan / Night and day.
**Album:** Released Jun '82, on Polydor by Polydor Ltd. Catalogue no: **3236 233**
**Cass:** Released Jun '82, on Polydor by Polydor Ltd. Catalogue no: **2475 233**

**BUT NOT FOR ME**
Tracks: / But not for me.
**7" Single:** Released Oct '59, on H.M.V. by EMI Records. Deleted Oct '62. Catalogue no: **POP 657**

**CAN'T BUY ME LOVE**
Tracks: / Can't buy me love.
**7" Single:** Released Apr '64, on Verve Deleted Apr '67. Catalogue no: **VS 519**

**CLAP HANDS, HERE COMES CHARLIE**
**CD:** Released Mar '90, on Polydor by Polydor Ltd. Catalogue no: **835 646 2**

**CLASSY PAIR, A (Fitzgerald, Ella / Count Basie)**
Tracks: / I'm getting sentimental over you / Organ grinder's swing / Just a sittin' and a rockin' / My kind of trouble is you / Ain't misbehavin' / Some other spring / Teach me tonight / Don't worry 'bout me / Honeysuckle rose / Sweet Lorraine / Please don't talk about me when I'm gone.
**CD:** Released Apr '86, on Pablo Jazz (USA) by Pablo Records (USA). Catalogue no: **J33J 20057**
**Cass:** Released '82, on Pablo Jazz (USA) by Pablo Records (USA). Catalogue no: **K12 132**
**Album:** Released '82, on Pablo Jazz (USA) by Pablo Records (USA). Catalogue no: **231 2132**

**COLE PORTER SONG BOOK VOLS. 1 & 2**
Tracks: / All through the night / Anything goes / Miss Otis regrets / Too darn hot / In the still of the night / I get a kick out of you / Do I love you / Always true to you in my fashion / Let's do it / Just one of those things / Every time we say goodbye / All of you / Begin the beguine / Get out of town / I am in love / From this moment on / I love Paris / You do something to me / Ridin' high / Easy to love / It's all right with me / Why can't you behave / What is this thing called love / You're the top / Love for sale / It's delovely / Night and day / Ace in the hole / So in love / I've got you under my skin / I concentrate on you / Don't fence me in.
**2 LP Set:** Released Jul '84, on Verve Catalogue no: **2683 044**
**CD Set:** on Verve Catalogue no: **821 989-2/990-2**
**Cass set:** Released Jul '84, on Verve Catalogue no: **31 12 054**

**COLE PORTER SONGBOOK VOL.2**
**CD:** Released '88, on Polygram by PolyGram UK Ltd. Catalogue no: **821 990 2**

**DESAFINADO**
Tracks: / Desafinado.
**7" Single:** Released Nov '62, on Verve Deleted Nov '65. Catalogue no: **VS 502**

**DIGITAL III AT MONTREUX (Fitzgerald, Ella / Count Basie / Joe Pass)**
Tracks: / I can't get stated / Good mileage / Ghost of a chance / Flying home / I cover the waterfront / Li'l darlin' / In your own sweet way / Oleo.
**CD:** Released Apr '87, on Pablo Jazz (USA) by Pablo Records (USA). Catalogue no: **CD 230 8223**
**Cass:** Released May '82, on Pablo Jazz (USA) by Pablo Records (USA). Catalogue no: **K 08 223**
**Album:** Released May '82, on Pablo Jazz (USA) by Pablo Records (USA). Catalogue no: **D 230 8223**

**DREAM DANCING (Fitzgerald, Ella / Cole Porter)**
Tracks: / Dream dancing / I've got you under my skin / I concentrate on you / My heart belongs to daddy / Love for sale / So near and yet so far / Down in the depths / After you / Just one of those things / I get a kick out of you / All of you / Anything goes / At long last love / C'est megnifique / Without love.
**Album:** Released '82, on Pablo Jazz (USA) by Pablo Records (USA). Catalogue no: **2310 814**
**Cass:** Released '82, on Pablo Jazz (USA) by Pablo Records (USA). Catalogue no: **K10 814**
**Cass:** Released May '82, on Pablo Jazz (USA) by Pablo Records (USA). Catalogue no: **K10 814**

**EASY LIVIN (Fitzgerald, Ella & Joe Pass)**
**Cass:** Released Apr '87, on Pablo Jazz

(USA) by Pablo Records (USA). Catalogue no: **K10 921**
**Album:** Released Apr '87, on Pablo Jazz (USA) by Pablo Records (USA). Catalogue no: **231 0921**

**ELLA**
**Album:** Released '88, on Joker (USA) by Lifetime Records (USA). Catalogue no: **SM 3976-2**
**CD:** Released May '86, on Pablo Jazz (USA) by Pablo Records (USA). Catalogue no: **CD 20032**

**ELLA A NICE**
Tracks: / Night and day / Get out of town / Easy to love / You do something to me / Body and soul / Man I love, The / Porgy / Bossa scene, The / Girl from Ipanema / Fly me to the moon / O nosso amor / Cielito lindo / Magdalena / Aqua de beber / Summertime / They can't take that away from me / Mood indigo / Do nothing till you hear from me / It don't mean a thing / Something / St. Louis blues / Close to you / Put a little love in your heart.
**Cass:** Released Mar '84, on Pablo Jazz (USA) by Pablo Records (USA). Catalogue no: **K 08 234**
**Album:** Released Mar '84, on Pablo Jazz (USA) by Pablo Records (USA). Catalogue no: **230 8234**

**ELLA AND HER FELLAS**
Tracks: / You won't be satisfied (until you break my heart) / That's the way it is / Stone cold dead in the market (he had it done coming) / I gotta have my baby back / Sentimental journey / Frim fram sauce / It's only a paper moon / Dream a little dream of me / Baby it's cold outside / Tisket a tasket, A / Would you like to take a walk / Don'cha go way mad.
**Album:** Released Aug '82, on MCA by MCA Records. Catalogue no: **MCL 1705**
**Cass:** Released Aug '82, on MCA by MCA Records. Catalogue no: **MCLC 1705**

**ELLA AT THE OPERA HOUSE**
**Album:** Released Jun '60, on Columbia by EMI Records. Deleted '65. Catalogue no: **3SX 10126**

**ELLA & BASIE (Fitzgerald, Ella / Count Basie)**
Tracks: / Honeysuckle rose / Deed I do / Into each life some rain must fall / Them there eyes / Dream a little dream of me / Tea for two / Satin doll / I'm beginning to see the light / Shiny stockings / My last affair / Ain't misbehavin' / On the sunny side of the street.
**Album:** Released Oct '84, on Verve (USA) by Polydor Ltd. Catalogue no: **2304 049**
**CD:** Released '88, on Polydor by Polydor Ltd. Catalogue no: **821 576 2**
**Cass:** Released Oct '84, on Verve (USA) by Polydor Ltd. Catalogue no: **3113 108**

**ELLA & DUKE AT THE COTE D'AZUR (Fitzgerald, Ella / Duke Ellington)**
**2 LP Set:** Released Jan '90, on Verve Catalogue no: **833 562 1**

**ELLA & ELLIS (Fitzgerald, Ella / Ellis Larkin)**
Tracks: / I'm glad there is you / What is there to say / People will say we're in love / Please be kind / Until the real thing comes along / Makin' whoopee! / Imagination / Stardust / My heart belongs to daddy / You leave me breathless / Baby, what else can I do / Nice work if you can get it / Someone to watch over me / My one and only (what am I gonna do) / But not for me / Looking for a boy / I've got a crush on you / How long has this been going on / Soon / Maybe.
**Album:** Released Feb '84, on MCA by MCA Records. Deleted Apr '88. Catalogue no: **MCL 1775**
**Cass:** Released Feb '84, on MCA by MCA Records. Deleted Apr '88. Catalogue no: **MCLC 1775**

**ELLA FITZGERALD**
**Album:** Released '88, on Lotus Catalogue no: **LOP 14,015**
**Album:** Released Sep '87, on Entertainers Catalogue no: **ENT LP 13008**
**Cass:** Released Jul '87, on Verve Catalogue no: **831 367-4**
**Cass:** Released '88, on Entertainers Catalogue no: **ENT MC 13008**
**CD:** Released Jul '87, on Verve Catalogue no: **831 367-2**
**Album:** Released Sep '87, on Lotus Catalogue no: **LOP 14 088**

**ELLA FITZGERALD AND HER ORCHESTRA (Fitzgerald, Ella & Her Orchestra)**
**CD:** Released Oct '89, on Jazz Anthology by Musidisc Records (France). Catalogue no: **550032**

**ELLA FITZGERALD COLLECTION**
**CD:** Released Oct '89, on Collection by K-Tel Records. Catalogue no: **OR 0077**
**Cass:** Released Aug '85, on Deja Vu Catalogue no: **DVMC 2004**
**CD:** Released Dec '87, on Deja Vu Catalogue no: **DVCD 2004**
**Album:** Released Aug '85, on Deja Vu Catalogue no: **DVLP 2004**

**ELLA FITZGERALD & HER ORCHESTRA From Roseland ballroom (Fitzgerald, Ella/her Famous Orchestra)**
**Album:** Released Mar '88, on Delta (1) by Delta Records. Catalogue no: **20 804**

**ELLA FITZGERALD LIVE (Compact / Walkman jazz)**
Tracks: / Oh lady be good / Summertime / Honeysuckle Rose / Body and soul / Squeeze me / These foolish things / Stompin' at the Savoy.
**Cass:** Released 27 Feb '88, on Verve Catalogue no: **833 294-4**
**CD:** Released Mar '88, on Verve Catalogue no: **833 294-2**

**ELLA FITZGERALD & LOUIS (Compact / Walkman Jazz) (Fitzgerald, Ella & Louis Armstrong)**
Tracks: / They can't take that away from me / Gee baby ain't I good to you / I won't dance / It ain't necessarily so / Fine romance, A / Stompin' at the Savoy / Foggy day, A / Don't be that way / Summertime / Cheek to cheek / Can't we be friends / Let's call the whole thing off.
**CD:** Released Aug '88, on Verve Catalogue no: **835 313-2**
**Cass:** Released Aug '88, on Verve Catalogue no: **835 313-4**

**ELLA FITZGERALD SINGS THE ELLINGTON SONGBOOK**
Tracks: / Rockin' in rhythm / Take the 'A' train / I ain't got nothing but the blues / Clementine.
**CD Set:** Released Apr '89, on Verve Catalogue no: **837 035-2**

**ELLA FITZGERALD SINGS THE JOHNNY MERCER SONGBOOK**
Tracks: / Too marvellous for words / Early autumn / Day in, day out / Laura / This time the dream's on me / Skylark / Single-O / Something's gotta give / Travelling light / Midnight sun / Dream / I remember you / When a woman loves a man / Let's begin / Fine romance, A / All the things you are / I'll be hard to handle / You couldn't be cuter / She didn't say yes / I'm old fashioned / Remind me / Way you look tonight / Yesterdays / Can't help lovin' dat man / Why was I born?.
**Cass:** Released Oct '84, on Verve Deleted May '89. Catalogue no: **TWOMC 11**

**ELLA FITZGERALD SONGBOOK, THE**
Tracks: / Begin the beguine / Every time we say goodbye / Fascinating rhythm / Stormy weather.
**Cass set:** Released Dec '81, on World Records by EMI Records. Catalogue no: **CASSETTE 58**
**LP Set:** Released Dec '81, on World Records by EMI Records. Catalogue no: **ALBUM 58**

**ELLA FITZGERALD STORY, THE**
Tracks: / You'll have to swing it / Big boy blues / Take another guess / Dedicated to you / Cryin' mood / Just a simple melody / Holiday in harlem / I've got a guy / Tisket a tasket, A / Ella / Gotta pebble in my shoe / I let a tear fall in the river / I found my yellow basket / Undecided / Chew, chew, chew, chew (your bubble gum) / Vote for Mr. Rhythm / Everybody step / It's foxy / Lover come back to me / Angel eyes / I'm beginning to see the light / My heart belongs to daddy / Just one of those things / I can't give you anything but love, baby / Sophisticated lady.
**CD:** Released May '89, on Deja Vu Catalogue no: **DVRE CD 05**
**Cass:** Released May '89, on Deja Vu Catalogue no: **DVRE MC 05**

**ELLA FITZGERALD & THE CHICK WEBB ORCHESTRA (Fitzgerald, Ella & The Chick Webb Orchestra)**
Tracks: / Blue Lou / Cryin' mood / Clap hands, here comes Charlie / I've got a guy / Strictly jive / Just a simple melody / Holiday in Harlem / Rock it for me / Harlem congo / Midnight in Harlem / Spinnin' the web / Chew, chew, chew, chew (your bubble gum) / I let a tear fall in the river / Sugar pie.
**Album:** Released Apr '81, on Joker (USA) by Lifetime Records (USA). Catalogue no: **SM 3613**

**ELLA FITZGERALD-VOLUME 1**
**Album:** Released Jun '86, on Swingtime by Contact Records (Denmark). Catalogue no: **ST 1006**

**ELLA IN BERLIN**
**CD:** Released Apr '87, on Verve Deleted Oct '88. Catalogue no: **825 670-2**

**ELLA IN LONDON**
Tracks: / Sweet Georgia Brown / They can't take that away from me / Every time we say goodbye / It don't mean a thing / You've got a friend / Lemon drop / Very thought of you, The / Happy blues / Man I love, The.
Note: Ella Fitzgerald / Tommy Flanagan/Joe Pass / Keeter Betts / Bobby Durham.
**Cass:** Released '82, on Pablo Jazz (USA) by Pablo Records (USA). Catalogue no: **K10 711**
**Album:** Released '82, on Pablo Jazz (USA) by Pablo Records (USA). Catalogue no: **2310 711**
**CD:** Released Jul '86, on Pablo Jazz (USA) by Pablo Records (USA). Catalogue no: **J33J 20033**

**ELLA IN ROME**
**Album:** Released '85, on Verve Deleted Oct '89. Catalogue no: **835 454 1**

**ELLA & LOUIS (Fitzgerald, Ella & Louis Armstrong)**
Tracks: / Can't we be friends? / Isn't this a lovely day / Moonlight in Vermont / They can't take that away from me / Under a blanket of blue / Foggy day, A / Tenderly / Stars fell on Alabama / Nearness of you, The / April in Paris / Cheek to cheek.
**Cass:** Released '88, on Entertainers Catalogue no: **ENT MC 13023**
**Album:** Released Apr '89, on Verve Catalogue no: **825 373-1**
**Album:** Released '88, on Entertainers Catalogue no: **ENT LP 13023**
**LP Set:** Released Mar '81, on Verve Catalogue no: **2615 034**
**CD:** Released Sep '85, on Verve Catalogue no: **825 373-2**
**Cass:** Released Apr '89, on Verve Catalogue no: **825 373-4**

**ELLA & LOUIS AGAIN (Fitzgerald, Ella & Louis Armstrong)**
**CD:** Released '86, on Polygram (Germany) by PolyGram UK Ltd. Catalogue no: **825 374-2**

**ELLA LOVES COLE**
Tracks: / I get a kick out of you / Down in the depths / At long last love / I've got you under my skin / So near and yet so far / All of you / Without love / My heart belongs to Daddy / Love for sale / Just one of those things / I concentrate on you / Anything goes / C'est magnifique.
**Album:** on Atlantic by WEA Records. Catalogue no: **K 40450**

**ELLA & OSCAR (Fitzgerald, Ella & Oscar Peterson)**
Tracks: / Mean to me / How long has this been going on / When your lover has gone / More than you know / There's a lull in my life / Midnight sun / I hear music / Street of dreams / April in Paris / Hear music.
**Cass:** Released '82, on Pablo Jazz (USA) by Pablo Records (USA). Catalogue no: **10 759**
**Album:** Released '82, on Pablo Jazz (USA) by Pablo Records (USA). Catalogue no: **2310 759**
**CD:** Released Jul '86, on Pablo Jazz (USA) by Pablo Records (USA). Catalogue no: **J33J 20030**

**ELLA & RAY (Fitzgerald, Ella & Ray Brown)**
Tracks: / Ool-ya-koo / Love that boy / Mr. Paganini / Too soon to know / I never knew / How high the moon / Heatwave / Old Mother Hubbard / Pop goes the weasel / Flying home.
**Album:** Released Apr '81, on Jazz Live (Italy) Catalogue no: **BLJ 8035**

**ELLA SINGS ARLEN VOL. 1**
**CD:** Released Oct '88, on Polydor by Polydor Ltd. Catalogue no: **817 527-2**

**ELLA SINGS ARLEN VOL. 2**
**CD:** Released Oct '88, on Polydor by Polydor Ltd. Deleted Dec '89. Catalogue no: **817 528-2**

**ELLA SINGS GERSHWIN**
Tracks: / Someone to watch over me / My one and only (what am I gonna do) / But not for me / Looking for a boy / Nice work if you can get it / Oh lady be good / I've got a crush on you / How long has this been going on / Maybe / Soon / I'm just a lucky so and so / I didn't mean a word I said.
Note: A welcome rerelease of a classic album. Ella Fitzgerald singing Gershwin will prove to be immensely popular with many people.
**Cass:** Released Sep '86, on MCA by MCA Records. Catalogue no: **MCLC 1820**
**Album:** Released May '86, on MCA by MCA Records. Catalogue no: **MCL 1820**
**Album:** Released Jun '60, on Brunswick by Decca Records. Deleted '65. Catalogue no: **LA 8648**

**ELLA SINGS GERSHWIN VOL.5**
**Album:** Released Jul '60, on H.M.V. by EMI Records. Deleted '65. Catalogue no: **CLP 1353**

**ELLA SINGS JOBLIM**
**CD Set:** Released Jan '89, on JVC/Fantasy Catalogue no: **VDJ 25006-7**

**ELLA SWINGS LIGHTLY**
Tracks: / Little white lies / You hit the spot / What's your story, morning glory? / Just you, just me / As long as I live / Teardrops from my eyes / Gotta be this or that / Moonlight on the Ganges / My kinda love / Blues in the night / If I were a bell / You're an old smoothie / Little Jazz / You brought a new kind of love to me / Knock me a kiss / 720 in the books.
**Album:** Released Dec '79, on Verve Catalogue no: **2304 134**

**ELLA (VERVE)**
Tracks: / Sweet and lovely / Let's fall in love / Makin' whoopee / That old feeling / I remember you / Moonlight serenade / Gone with the wind / Can't we be friends / Out of this world / My old flame / East of the sun / Lullaby of Broadway.
**Album:** Released Feb '77, on Verve Deleted '80. Catalogue no: **2352 170**

**ELLA WITH... (Fitzgerald,Q Ella / Savoy 8 / Benny Goodman / Chick Webb / Mills bros)**
Tracks: / All over nothing at all / If you ever should leave / It's my turn now / Everyone's wrong but me / Bei mir bist du schon / Little bit later on, A / I want to be happy / Hallelujah! / Crying my heart out for you / You'll have to swing it / Holiday in Harlem / Cryin' mood / Devoting my time / Rock it for me / Darktown strutters' ball / Sing me a swing song / Vote for Mr. Rhythm / Just a simple melody / Swinging on the reservation / Under the spell of the blues / I got the spring fever blues / Rhythm and romance / If dreams come true / Take another guess / Dipsy doodle, The / I got a guy / When I get low I get high / Did you mean it? / Dedicated to you / Big boy blues / Goodnight my love.
Note: Ella with Her Savoy Eight, The Mills Brothers, Chick Webb & His Orchestra, Benny Goodman & His Orchestra. 32 track collection includes the famous 1936/37 recordings that 19 year old Ella Fitzgerald made with the Chick Webb Orchestra.
**Cass set:** Released 1 Feb '88, on Living Era by Academy Sound & Vision Records. Catalogue no: **ZC AJD 055**
**2 LP Set:** Released 1 Feb '88, on Living Era by Academy Sound & Vision Records. Catalogue no: **AJD 055**
**CD Set:** Released 1 Feb '88, on Living Era by Academy Sound & Vision Records. Catalogue no: **CD AJD 055**

**EVERYTIME WE SAY GOODBYE**
Tracks: / Every time we say goodbye / Manhattan.
**7" Single:** Released Mar '88, on Honeybee by Stylus Music Records. Catalogue no: **HONEY 5**
**7" Single:** Released May '80, on Verve Deleted May '83. Catalogue no: **200901-7**
**12" Single:** Released Mar '88, on Honeybee by Stylus Music Records. Catalogue no: **HONEY 5 12**

**FINE AND MELLOW**
Tracks: / Fine and mellow / I'm just a lucky so and so / Ghost of a chance /

Rockin' in rhythm / I'm in the mood for love / Round midnight / I can't give you anything but love / Man I love, The / Polka dots and moonbeams.
Note: With Harry Edison, Clark Terry, Zoot Sims, Eddie Davis, Tommy Flanagan, Joe Pass, Ray Brown, Louis Benson.
**Album:** Released '82, on Pablo Jazz (USA) by Pablo Records (USA). Catalogue no: **2310 829**
**Cass:** Released '82, on Pablo Jazz (USA) by Pablo Records (USA). Catalogue no: **K10 828**

## FIRST LADY OF SWING
**Album:** Released '88, on Entertainers Catalogue no: **ENT LP 13034**
**Cass:** Released '88, on Entertainers Catalogue no: **ENT MC 13034**

## FITZGERALD AND PASS...AGAIN (Fitzgerald, Ella & Joe Pass)
Tracks: / Ain't got nothin' but the blues / T'is autumn / My old flame / That old feeling / Rain / I didn't know about you / You took advantage of me / I've got the world on a string / All too soon / One I love, The / Solitude / Nature boy / Tennessee waltz / One-note samba.
**Album:** Released May '82, on Pablo Jazz (USA) by Pablo Records (USA). Catalogue no: **231 0772**
**Cass:** Released May '82, on Pablo Jazz (USA) by Pablo Records (USA). Catalogue no: **K10 772**

## FOR THE LOVE OF ELLA
**Cass set:** Released Jan '90, on Verve Catalogue no: **841 766 4**
**2 LP Set:** Released Jan '90, on Verve Catalogue no: **841 766 1**
**CD Set:** Released Jan '90, on Verve Catalogue no: **841 766 2**

## FOREVER YOUNG VOL.1
Tracks: / My melancholy baby / All my life.
**Album:** Released '86, on Swingtime by Contact Records (Denmark). Deleted Jun '89. Catalogue no: **ST 1006**

## FOREVER YOUNG VOL.2
**Album:** Released Jun '86, on Swingtime by Contact Records (Denmark). Deleted Jun '89. Catalogue no: **ST 1007**

## GEORGE GERSHWIN SONG BOOK, THE
Tracks: / Sam and Delilah / But not for me / My one and only / Let's call the whole thing off / I've got beginner's luck / Lady be good / Nice work if you can get it / Things are looking up / Just another rhumba / How long has this been going on? / 'S wonderful / Man I love, The / That certain feeling / By Strauss / Who cares? / Someone to watch over me / Real American folk song / They all laughed / Looking for a boy / My cousin from Milwaukee / Somebody from somewhere / Foggy day, A / Clap yo' hands / For you, for me, for evermore / Stiff upper lip / Strike up the band / Soon / I've got a crush on you / Bidin' my time / Aren't you kind of glad we did? / Of thee I sing / Half it dearie blues, The / I was doing it right / He loves and she loves / Love is sweeping the country / Treat me rough / Love is here to stay / Slap that bass / Isn't it a pity / Shall we dance? / Love walked in / You've got what gets me / They can't take that away from me / Embraceable you / I can't be bothered now / Boy, what love has done to me / Fascinating rhythm / Oh so nice / Lorelei / Let's kiss and make up / I got rhythm.
**CD:** on Verve Deleted Jan '89. Catalogue no: **825 024-2**
**Cass:** Released Aug '85, on Verve Catalogue no: **VRVC 9**
**Album:** Released Aug '85, on Verve Catalogue no: **VRV 9**

## GERSHWIN SONGBOOK 1
Tracks: / Sam and Delilah / But not for me / My one and only / Let's call the whole thing off / Beginner's luck / Embraceable you / Lady be good / Nice work if you can get it / Things are looking up / Just another rhumba / How long has this been going on? / I can't be bothered now / 'S wonderful / Man I love, The / That certain feeling / By Strauss / Someone to watch over me / Real American folk song / Funny face / They all laughed / My cousin in Milwaukee / Somebody from somewhere / They can't take that away from me / Let's kiss and make up.
**2 LP Set:** on Polydor by Polydor Ltd. Deleted 30 Jun '89. Catalogue no: **2682 004**

## GET HAPPY
Tracks: / Somebody loves me / Cheerful little earful / You make me feel so young / Beat me daddy, eight to the bar / Like young / Cool breeze / Moonlight becomes you / Blue skies / You turned the tables on me / Gypsy in my soul / Goody goody / St. Louis blues.
Note: Recorded in Los Angeles between 1957 and 1959 with four different orchestras ---Nelson Riddle, Frank Duval, Paul Weston, Russell Garcia.
**Album:** Released Oct '83, on Polydor (France) by Polydor Ltd. Catalogue no: **813 391-1**

## GOLDEN GREATS: ELLA FITZGERALD
Tracks: / Tisket a tasket, A / Stairway to the stars / It's only a paper moon / That old black magic / Tender trap, The / Into each life some rain must fall / Flying home / (I love you) for sentimental reasons / O lady be good / How high the moon / Basin Street blues / My one and only love / I've got the world on a string / Walkin' by the river / Lover come back to me / Mixed emotions / Smooth sailing / (If you can't sing it) you'll have to swing it / I wished on the moon.
**Cass:** Released Jul '85, on MCA by MCA Records. Catalogue no: **MCMC 5009**
**Album:** Released Jul '85, on MCA by MCA Records. Catalogue no: **MCM 5009**

## GREATEST HITS: ELLA FITZGERALD
**Album:** Released May '88, on Music Power Catalogue no: **33004**
**Cass:** Released May '88, on Music Power Catalogue no: **63004**

## GREATEST HITS: ELLA FITZGERALD VOL.2
**Cass:** Released May '88, on Music Power Catalogue no: **63005**
**Album:** Released May '88, on Music Power Catalogue no: **33005**

## HELLO DOLLY
Tracks: / Hello Dolly / People / Sweetest sounds, The / Can't buy me love / Miss Otis regrets / My man / How high the moon / Volare / Thrill is gone, The / Memories of you / Lullaby of the leaves / Pete Kelly's blues.
**Album:** Released Jun '88, on Memoir by Memoir Records. Catalogue no: **MOIR 128**
**Cass:** Released Nov '89, on Memoir by Memoir Records. Catalogue no: **CMOIR 128**

## HELLO LOVE
Tracks: / You go to my head / Willow weep for me / I'm through with love / Spring will be a little late this year / Everything happens to me / Lost in a fog / I've grown accustomed to his face / I'll never be the same / So rare / Tenderly / Stairway to the stars / Moonlight in Vermont.
**Album:** Released Nov '89, on Memoir by Memoir Records. Catalogue no: **MOIR 124**
**Cass:** Released Nov '89, on Memoir by Memoir Records. Catalogue no: **CMOIR 124**

## HOW HIGH THE MOON
Tracks: / How high the moon.
**7" Single:** Released Oct '60, on H.M.V. by EMI Records. Deleted Oct '63. Catalogue no: **POP 782**

## INCOMPARABLE ELLA, THE
Tracks: / Lady is a tramp / Manhattan / Very thought of you / From this moment on / I've got you under my skin / Foggy day / With a song in my heart / Cheek to cheek / I've got a crush on you / Night and day / Every time we say goodbye / It's only a paper moon / I get a kick out of you / I got rhythm / My funny valentine / That old black magic.
**Album:** Released May '80, on Polydor by Polydor Ltd. Deleted '85. Catalogue no: **POLTV 9**
**CD:** Released '89, on Polygram by PolyGram UK Ltd. Catalogue no: **835 610 2**
**Cass:** Released Apr '80, on Polydor by Polydor Ltd. Catalogue no: **POLVM 9**

## INTIMATE ELLA, THE
**CD:** Released Mar '90, on Polydor by Polydor Ltd. Catalogue no: **839 838 2**

## IRVING BERLIN SONGBOOK, THE
Tracks: / Let's face the music and dance / You're laughing at me / Let yourself go / You can have him / Puttin' on the Ritz / Get thee behind me, Satan / Alexander's ragtime band / Top hat, white tie and tails / How about me? / Cheek to cheek / I used to be colour blind / Lazy / How deep is the ocean? / All by myself / You forgot to remember / Blue skies / Supper time / How's chances? / Heatwave / Isn't this

a lovely day / You keep coming back like a song / Reaching for the moon / Slumming on Park Avenue / Song is ended, The / I'm putting all my eggs in one basket / Now it can be told / Always / It's a lovely day today / Change partners / No strings / I've got my love to keep me warm.
**2 LP Set:** Released '88, on Polydor by Polydor Ltd. Catalogue no: **2683 027**

**IRVING BERLIN SONGBOOK VOL.1**
Tracks: / Reaching for the moon / Slumming on Park Avenue / Song is ended, The / I'm putting all my eggs in one basket / Now it can be told / Always / It's a lovely day today / Change partners / No strings / I've got my love to keep me warm / Let's face the music and dance / Your laughing at me / Let yourself go / You can have him / Russian lullaby / Puttin' on the Ritz / Get thee behind me satan / Alexander's ragtime band / Top hat, white tie and tails / How about me / Cheek to cheek / I used to be colour blind / Lazy / How deep is the ocean / All by myself / (You forgot to) remember / Suppertime / How's chances / Heatwave / Isn't this a lovely day / You keep coming back like a song.
**CD:** Released Nov '86, on Polydor by Polydor Ltd. Deleted Oct '88. Catalogue no: **829 534-2**

**IRVING BERLIN SONGBOOK VOL.2**
**CD:** Released Nov '86, on Polydor by Polydor Ltd. Deleted Oct '88. Catalogue no: **829 535-2**

**JAZZ AT THE PHIL**
**CD:** Released Feb '89, on Tax Catalogue no: **TAXCD 3703-2**

**JEROME KERN SONGBOOK**
Tracks: / Let's begin / Fine romance, A / All the things you are / I'll be hard to handle / You couldn't be cuter / She didn't say yes / I'm old fashioned / Remind me / Way you look tonight / Yesterdays / Can't help lovin' dat man / Why was I born?.
**CD:** on Polydor by Polydor Ltd. Deleted Oct '88. Catalogue no: **825 669-2**

**JOHNNY MERCER SONGBOOK, THE**
Tracks: / Too marvellous for words / Early autumn / Day in, day out / Laura / This time the dream's on me / Skylark / Single-o / Something's gotta give / Travellin' light / Midnight sun / Dream / I remember you / When a woman loves a man.
**2 LP Set:** Released Oct '76, on Verve Deleted Jan '89. Catalogue no: **2610 025**
**CD:** Released Oct '86, on Verve Deleted '88. Catalogue no: **823 247-2**

**LADY BE GOOD VOL. 2**
**Album:** Released '88, on Joker (USA) by Lifetime Records (USA). Catalogue no: **SM 3976**

**LADY TIME**
Tracks: / I'm walking / All or nothing at all / I never had a chance / I cried for you / What will I tell my heart? / Since I fell for you / And the angels sing / I'm confessin' / Mack the knife / That's my desire / I'm in the mood for love.
**Cass:** Released May '82, on Pablo Jazz (USA) by Pablo Records (USA). Catalogue no: **K10 825**
**Album:** Released May '82, on Pablo Jazz (USA) by Pablo Records (USA). Catalogue no: **231 0825**

**LIKE SOMEONE IN LOVE**
Tracks: / There's a lull in my life / More than you know / What will I tell my heart? / I never had a chance / Close your eyes / We'll be together again / Then I'll be tired of you / Like someone in love / Midnight sun / I thought about you / You're blase / Night wind / What's new? / Hurry home / How long has this been going on?.
**Album:** Released Oct '75, on Verve Catalogue no: **2352 097**

**LIVE AT CARNEGIE HALL (5/7/73) (See panel below)**
**Album:** Released Apr '84, on CBS (import) by CBS Records. Catalogue no: **CBS 88621**

**LIVE FROM ROSEMAN BALLROOM, NEW YORK 1940 (Fitzgerald, Ella / her Famous Orchestra)**
**CD:** Released '88, on Delta (1) by Delta Records. Catalogue no: **11 104**

**LOVE SONGS: ELLA FITZGERALD**
Tracks: / I can't get started / It might as well be spring / You'll never know / I wished on the moon / Please be kind / Someone to watch over me / My one and only love / I'm glad there is you / Angel eyes / Walkin' by the river / How long has this been going on / Old devil moon / Baby doll.
**Album:** Released Nov '89, on Memoir by Memoir Records. Catalogue no: **MOIR 111**
**Cass:** Released Nov '89, on Memoir by Memoir Records. Catalogue no: **CMOIR 111**

**LOVER COME BACK TO ME**
**Album:** Released Mar '84, on MFP (France) by EMI Records. Catalogue no: **2M 056 64868**
**Cass:** Released Mar '84, on MFP (France) by EMI Records. Catalogue no: **2M 256 64868**

**LULLABIES OF BIRDLAND**
Tracks: / Lullaby of Birdland / Rough ridin' / Angel eyes / Smooth sailing / Lady be good / Later / Ella hums the blues / How high the moon / Basin Street blues / Airmail special / Flying home.
**Album:** Released Aug '83, on Jasmine by Hasmick Promotions. Catalogue no: **JASM 1027**

**MACK THE KNIFE**
Tracks: / Mack the knife.
**7" Single:** Released Apr '60, on H.M.V. by EMI Records. Deleted Apr '63. Catalogue no: **POP 736**

**MR PAGANINI VOL. 1**
**Album:** Released '88, on Joker (USA) by Lifetime Records (USA). Catalogue no: **SM 3974**

**Ella Fitzgerald - Live at Carnegie Hall (CBS)**

**NICE WORK IF YOU CAN GET IT (Fitzgerald, Ella/Andre Previn)**
Tracks: / Let's call the whole thing off / How long has this been going on / Who cares / I got a crush on you / Someone to watch over me / Embraceable you / They can't take that away from me / Foggy day, A / But not for me / Nice work if you can get it.
Note: All songs by George Gershwin. Recorded: 1983.
**Album:** Released May '84, on Pablo Jazz (USA) by Pablo Records (USA). Catalogue no: **231 2140**
**Cass:** Released May '84, on Pablo Jazz (USA) by Pablo Records (USA). Catalogue no: **K 12 140**
**CD:** Released Sep '86, on Verve (USA) by Polydor Ltd. Catalogue no: **131 1250**

**ON THE SUNNY SIDE OF THE STREET (Fitzgerald, Ella/Count Basie)**
Tracks: / Honeysuckle rose / Deed I do / Into each life some rain must fall / Them there eyes / Dream a little dream of me / Tea for two / Satin doll / I'm beginning to see the light / Shiny stockings / My last affair / Ain't misbehavin' / On the sunny side of the street.
**CD:** on Verve Deleted Jan '89. Catalogue no: **821 576-2**

**PERFECT MATCH, A (Fitzgerald, Ella / Count Basie)**
Tracks: / Please don't talk about me when I'm gone / Sweet Georgia Brown / Some other spring / Make me rainbows / After you've gone / Round midnight / Fine and mellow / You've changed / Honeysuckle rose / St. Louis blues / Basella.
**CD:** Released '88, on Pablo Jazz (USA) by Pablo Records (USA). Catalogue no: **131 125 3**
**Cass:** Released May '82, on Pablo Jazz (USA) by Pablo Records (USA). Catalogue no: **K 12 110**
**Album:** Released May '82, on Pablo Jazz (USA) by Pablo Records (USA). Catalogue no: **231 2110**

**PORTRAIT OF ELLA FITZGERALD, A**
Tracks: / Mack the knife / But not for me / Begin the Beguine / Manhattan / Every time we say goodbye / Desafinado / Embraceable you / Moonlight in Vermont / How high the moon / Someone to watch over me / Lullaby of Broadway / Very thought of you, The / Where or when / Georgia on my mind / Foggy day, A / Can't buy me love.
**Album:** Released 4 Mar '88, on Stylus by Stylus Music Records. Catalogue no: **SMR 847**
**Cass:** Released 4 Mar '88, on Stylus by Stylus Music Records. Catalogue no: **SMC 847**
**CD:** Released 4 Mar '88, on Stylus by Stylus Music Records. Catalogue no: **SMD 847**

**RAREST OF ALL RARE PERFORMANCES**
**Album:** Released May '82, on Kings Of Jazz Catalogue no: **KLJ 20032**

**RAREST, THE 1936-39**
Tracks: / Vote for Mr. Rhythm / Everybody step / Swinging on the reservation / I got the spring fever blues / I'm just a jitterbug / It's foxy / If dreams come true / F.D.R. Jones / Love, you're just a laugh / Pack up your sins and go to the devil / I love each move you make / I can't stop loving you.
**Cass:** Released '87, on Joker (USA) by Lifetime Records (USA). Catalogue no: **MC 3281**
**Album:** Released '87, on Joker (USA) by Lifetime Records (USA). Catalogue no: **SM 3281**

**RHYTHM IS MY BUSINESS**
**Album:** Released Nov '82, on Verve (USA) by Polydor Ltd. Catalogue no: **2304 558**

**RODGERS & HART SONGBOOK**
Tracks: / Have you met Miss Jones? / You took advantage of me / Ship without a sail / To keep my love alive / Dancing on the ceiling / Lady is a tramp, The / With a song in my heart / Manhattan / Johnny One Note / I wish I were in love again / Spring is here / It never entered my mind / This can't be love / Thou swell / My romance / Where or when / Little girl blue / Give it back to the Indians / Ten cents a dance / There's a small hotel / I didn't know what time it was / Everything I've got / I could write a book / Blue room / My funny valentine / Betwitched / Mountain greenery / Wait till you see her / Lover / Isn't it romantic? / Here in my arms / Blue moon / My heart stood still / I've got five dollars.
**CD:** Released '85, on Verve Deleted Jan '89. Catalogue no: **8215 79-2**
**2 LP Set:** Released Feb '75, on Verve Catalogue no: **2683 053**

**RODGERS & HART SONGBOOK II**
**CD:** Released Jul '85, on Verve Deleted Jan '89. Catalogue no: **821 580-2**

**SENTIMENTAL JOURNEY**
Tracks: / Sentimental journey / Dream a little dream of me / Someone to watch over me.
**Album:** Released Apr '88, on Pickwick by Pickwick Records. Catalogue no: **SHM 3232**
**Cass:** Released Apr '88, on Pickwick by Pickwick Records. Catalogue no: **HSC 3232**

**SILVER COLLECTION**
**CD:** on Verve Catalogue no: **823 445-2**

**SINGS CHRISTMAS**
Tracks: / O holy night / It came upon a midnight clear / Hark the herald angels sing / First Noel, The / Silent night / O come all ye faithful / Sleep my little Jesus / O little town of Bethlehem / We three kings of Orient are / God rest ye merry gentlemen.
**Cass:** Released Dec '82, on MFP by EMI Records. Deleted '87. Catalogue no: **TCMFP 5587**
**Album:** Released Dec '82, on MFP by EMI Records. Deleted '87. Catalogue no: **MFP 5587**

**SINGS RODGERS AND HART VOL 2**
**Cass:** Released Jan '90, on Verve Catalogue no: **3112015**

**SINGS THE GEORGE AND IRA**
**LP Set:** Released Apr '83, on Verve (USA) by Polydor Ltd. Catalogue no: **2615 063**

**SONGBOOKS, THE**
Tracks: / Lady be good / Nice work if you can get it / Fascinating rhythm / All the things you are / Yesterdays / Can't help lovin' dat man / Come rain or come shine / It's only a paper moon / Over the rainbow / Laura / Skylark / This time the dream's on me / Puttin' on the Ritz / Alexander's ragtime band / Cheek to cheek / My funny Valentine / Lady is a tramp, The / Have you met Miss Jones / Manhattan.
**CD:** Released Nov '84, on Verve Catalogue no: **823 445-2**

**SPEAK LOVE**
Tracks: / Speak low / Come love / There's no you / I may be wrong but I think you're wonderful / At last / Thrill is gone, The / Gone with the wind / Blue and sentimental / Girl talk / Georgia on my mind.
**CD:** Released '88, on Pablo Jazz (USA) by Pablo Records (USA). Catalogue no: **3112 47**
**Album:** Released Oct '84, on Pablo Jazz (USA) by Pablo Records (USA). Catalogue no: **2310 888**

**SPECIAL MAGIC OF ELLA FITZGERALD (Fitzgerald, Ella & Louis Armstrong)**
**Cass:** Released Jan '90, on Verve Catalogue no: **3113168**
**Album:** Released Aug '77, on Verve Catalogue no: **2317 145**

**STOCKHOLM CONCERT, 1966 (Fitzgerald, Ella/Duke Ellington)**
Tracks: / Imagine my frustration / Duke's place / Satin doll / Something to live for / Wives and lovers / So dance samba / Let's do it / Lover man / Cottontail.
**Album:** Released Feb '85, on Pablo Jazz (USA) by Pablo Records (USA). Catalogue no: **230 8242**
**Cass:** Released Feb '85, on Pablo Jazz (USA) by Pablo Records (USA). Catalogue no: **K 8242**
**CD:** Released Aug '86, on Pablo Jazz (USA) by Pablo Records (USA). Catalogue no: **J33J 20006**

**SUMMERTIME**
Tracks: / Summertime / Every time we

say goodbye / Mack the knife.
**12" Single:** Released Jun '89, on Polydor by Polydor Ltd. Deleted Dec '89. Catalogue no: **PZ 48**
**7" Single:** Released Jun '89, on Polydor by Polydor Ltd. Deleted Dec '89. Catalogue no: **PO 48**

**SUNSHINE OF YOUR LOVE**
Tracks: / Hey Jude / Sunshine of your love / This girl's in love with you / Watch what happens / Alright, OK you win / Give me the simple life / Useless landscape / Old devil moon / Don'cha go 'way mad / House is not a home, A / Trouble is a man / I love you madly.
Note: Tommy Flanagan -- piano. Frank De La Rosa -- bass. Ed Thigpen -- drums.
**Album:** Released Sep '84, on MPS Jazz (Germany) Catalogue no: **821 290-1**

**SWEET AND HOT**
Tracks: / Thanks for the memory / It might as well be spring / You'll never know / I can't get started / Moanin' low / Taking a chance on love / That old black magic / Old devil moon / Lover come back to me / Between the Devil and the deep blue sea / You'll have to swing it.
**Album:** Released Oct '84, on Jasmine by Hasmick Promotions. Deleted Jun '87. Catalogue no: **JASM 1045**

**SWINGIN' SHEPHERD BLUES**
Tracks: / Swingin' shepherd blues.
**7" Single:** Released May '58, on H.M.V. by EMI Records. Deleted May '61. Catalogue no: **POP 486**

**SWINGING CHRISTMAS**
Tracks: / Jingle bells / Winter wonderland / Santa Claus is coming to town.
**Album:** Released Dec '81, on Verve Catalogue no: **2304 445**

**TAKE LOVE EASY (Fitzgerald, Ella & Joe Pass)**
Tracks: / Take love easy / Once I loved / Don't be that way / You're blase / Lush life / Foggy day, A / Gee baby ain't I good to you / You got to my head / I want to talk about you.
**CD:** Released Jan '89, on JVC/Fantasy Catalogue no: **VDJ 28003**
**CD:** Released Jul '86, on Pablo Jazz (USA) by Pablo Records (USA). Catalogue no: **J33J 20031**
**Cass:** Released May '82, on Pablo Jazz (USA) by Pablo Records (USA). Catalogue no: **K10 702**
**Album:** Released May '82, on Pablo Jazz (USA) by Pablo Records (USA). Catalogue no: **231 0702**

**THANKS FOR THE MEMORY**
**Cass:** Released Apr '90, on Pickwick by Pickwick Records. Catalogue no: **HSC 3302**
**Album:** Released Apr '88, on Platinum Music by Prism Leisure. Catalogue no: **PLAT 305**
**CD:** Released Apr '90, on Pickwick by Pickwick Records. Catalogue no: **PWKS 573**
**Cass:** Released Apr '88, on Platinum Music by Prism Leisure. Catalogue no: **PLAC 305**
**Album:** Released Apr '90, on Pickwick by Pickwick Records. Catalogue no: **SHM 3302**

**THAT OLD ELLA MAGIC**
Tracks: / A-tisket, a-tasket / Hard hearted hannah / Angel eyes / But not for me.
**Cass:** Released Sep '83, on MFP by EMI Records. Deleted '87. Catalogue no: **TCMFP 5623**
**Album:** Released Sep '83, on MFP by EMI Records. Deleted '87. Catalogue no: **MFP 5623**

**THESE ARE THE BLUES**
**CD:** Released Nov '86, on Polydor by Polydor Ltd. Deleted Oct '88. Catalogue no: **829 536-2**
**Album:** Released Aug '89, on Verve Catalogue no: **829 536 1**
**Cass:** Released Aug '89, on Verve Catalogue no: **829 536 4**

**VERY THOUGHT OF YOU**
**Album:** Released May '87, on Contour by Pickwick Records. Catalogue no: **CN 2087**

**WEBB ON THE AIR**
**Cass:** Released May '82, on Jazz Bird Catalogue no: **ZCJAZ 2021**
**Album:** Released May '82, on Jazz Bird Catalogue no: **JAZ 2021**

**WHISPER NOT**
**Album:** Released Jun '81, on Verve (USA) by Polydor Ltd. Catalogue no: **2304 393**

**WITH CHICK WEBB**
**Album:** Released Nov '84, on Astan (USA) Catalogue no: **20077**
**Cass:** Released Nov '84, on Astan (USA) Catalogue no: **40077**

**WITH THE TOMMY FLANAGAN TRIO (Fitzgerald, Ella & Tommy Flanagan Trio)**
Tracks: / Too close for comfort / I ain't got nothin' but the blues / My man / Come rain or come shine / Day by day / Ordinary fool / One-note samba / I let a song go out of my heart / Billie's bounce / You are the sunshine of my life.
**Album:** Released May '82, on Pablo Jazz (USA) by Pablo Records (USA). Catalogue no: **2308 206**
**Cass:** Released May '82, on Pablo Jazz (USA) by Pablo Records (USA). Catalogue no: **K 08 206**

## Five Birds And A Monk

**FIVE BIRDS AND A MONK**
Tracks: / Billie's bounce / 'Round midnight / Confirmation / Yardbird suite / Relaxin' at Camarillo / Bloomdido.
**Album:** Released Sep '81, on Galaxy (1) by President Records. Catalogue no: **GXY 5134**

## Five A Slide

**FIVE A SLIDE (Various artists)**
Note: Artists include: Roy Williams/Pete Strange/Jim Shepherd/John Beecham/ Campbell Burnap.
**Album:** Released Jun '86, on Audiophile (USA) by Jazzology Records (USA). Catalogue no: **AP 180**

## Five Blind Boys Of Alabama

**FIVE BLIND BOYS OF ALABAMA**
Tracks: / I want my crown / What more can Jesus do / Don't wonder about him / I've an interest over there / Death has taken mother home / What manner of man is this / Living on Mother's prayer / Honey in the rock / Jesus won't deny me / Anyhow / Blessed be the name / Good religion / No more tears no more dying / Come over here / Canaan's land / Leave your burden there.
**Album:** Released 11 Apr '87, on Heritage by Interstate Music. Catalogue no: **HT 315**

## Flanagan, Ralph

**HOT TODAY (Flanagan, Ralph Orchestra)**
**Album:** Released Dec '88, on Golden Era by Delta Records. Catalogue no: **GOLDEN 15043**

## Flanagan, Tommy

**Biographical details:** Jazz pianist and nonpariel accompanist, born in 1930 in Detroit. He made his pro debut with Dexter Gordon in 1945, moved to NYC and accompanied Ella Fitzgerald and Tony Bennett, and has played with just about everybody, including Coltrane on his epochal *Giant steps*. His own many albums as leader always yield tasty results. (Donald Clarke, April 1989).

**3**
Note: Montreux 1977
**CD:** Released May '86, on Pablo Jazz (USA) by Pablo Records (USA). Catalogue no: **CD 20036**

**ALONE TOO LONG (Music for piano)**
Tracks: / Parisian thoroughfare / In your own sweet way / Like a butterfly / Billie Holiday medley / Glad to be unhappy / No more / That ole devil called love / Alone too long / Maybe September / Strollin / Here's that rainy day.
Note: Recorded at Sound Ideas Studios, New York City, 8th December, 1977
**CD:** Released '88, on Denon Catalogue no: **C38-7260**
**Album:** Released Mar '82, on Denon Deleted '88. Catalogue no: **YX 7523**

**BALLADS AND BLUES**
**Album:** Released Jan '82, on Enja (Germany) by Enja Records (West Germany). Catalogue no: **ENJA 3031**

**BEST OF TOMMY FLANAGAN**
Tracks: / All day long / U.M.M.G. / Intimacy of the blues, The / Main stem / Star crossed lovers / Jump for joy / Woodyn' you / Blue bossa.
**Album:** Released Jan '82, on Pablo Jazz (USA) by Pablo Records (USA). Catalogue no: **231 0854**
**Cass:** Released Jan '82, on Pablo Jazz (USA) by Pablo Records (USA). Catalogue no: **K10 854**

**CATS, THE (Flanagan, Tommy, John Coltrane, Kenny Burrell)**
Tracks: / Minor mishap / How long has this been going on / Eclipso / Solacium /

Tommy's time.
**Album:** Released Jun '86, on Original Jazz Classics (USA) by Fantasy Inc (USA). Catalogue no: **OJC 079**

**CONFIRMATION**
**Album:** Released Jan '82, on Enja (Germany) by Enja Records (West Germany). Catalogue no: **ENJA 4014**

**ECLYPSO**
**Album:** Released Jan '82, on Enja (Germany) by Enja Records (West Germany). Catalogue no: **ENJA 2088**

**HOME COOKING (Flanagan, Tommy / Nisse Sandstrom / Red Mitchell)**
Tracks: / I remember you / Painter's blues / Karin / I could happen to you / Minor mishap / Way you look tonight / Indian Summer.
Note: Also featuring Nisse Sandstrom - tenor sax
**Album:** Released Jan '82, on Phontastic (Sweden) Catalogue no: **PHONT 7530**

**IN STOCKHOLM 1957**
Note: With Wilbur Little and Elvin Jones.
**Album:** Released Jun '86, on Dragon by Dragon Records. Catalogue no: **DRLP 87**

**JAZZ POET**
Tracks: / Raincheck / Lament / Willow weep for me / Caravan / That tired routine called love / Glad to be happy / St Louis blues / Mean streets.
**Cass:** Released Mar '90, on Timeless by Timeless Records. Catalogue no: **MCSJP 301**
**Album:** Released Nov '89, on Timeless by Timeless Records. Catalogue no: **SJP 301**
**CD:** Released Nov '89, on Timeless by Timeless Records. Catalogue no: **CDSJP 301**

**MAGNIFICENT TOMMY FLANAGAN, THE**
**Album:** Released Jul '82, on Progressive (USA) by Jazzology Records (USA). Catalogue no: **PRO 7059**

**NIGHTS AT THE VANGUARD**
Note: With George Mraz and Al Foster.
**Album:** Released Jun '88, on Uptown (USA) Catalogue no: **UP 27 29**

**OUR DELIGHTS (Flanagan, Tommy & Hank Jones)**
Tracks: / Our delight / Autumn leaves / Robbins nest / Jordu / Confirmation / Ladybird / Child is born, A.
Note: Tommy Flanagan and Hank Jones - pianos
**CD:** Released Jan '87, on Fantasy (import) by Fantasy Inc (USA). Deleted '88. Catalogue no: **FCD 6145113**

**SOMETHING BORROWED, SOMETHING BLUE**
**Album:** Released '79, on Galaxy (1) by President Records. Deleted '84. Catalogue no: **GXY 5110**

**SUPER JAZZ TRIO, THE (Flanagan, Tommy and Reggie Workman and Joe Chambers)**
**Album:** Released Jan '83, on RCA (France) by BMG Records (France). Catalogue no: **PL 45367**

**SUPER SESSION**
**Album:** Released Jan '82, on Enja (Germany) by Enja Records (West Germany). Catalogue no: **ENJA 3059**

**TOGETHER (Flanagan, Tommy & Kenny Barron)**
Tracks: / Dig / If I should lose you / Stella by starlight / I can't get started / Darn that dream / Way you look tonight.
Note: Tommy Flanagan (piano) & Kenny Barron (piano).
**CD:** Released '89, on Denon Catalogue no: **C38 7263**
**Album:** Released Mar '82, on Denon Deleted '88. Catalogue no: **YX 7544**

**TOKYO RECITAL (Flanagan, Tommy Trio)**
Tracks: / All day long / U.M.M.G. / Something to live for / Main stem / Daydream / Intimacy of the blues, The / Caravan / Chelsea Bridge / Take the 'A' train.
**Cass:** Released Jan '82, on Pablo Jazz (USA) by Pablo Records (USA). Catalogue no: **K10 724**
**Album:** Released Jan '82, on Pablo Jazz (USA) by Pablo Records (USA). Catalogue no: **231 0724**
**CD:** Released Jan '89, on JVC/Fantasy Catalogue no: **VDJ 28013**

**TOMMY FLANAGAN THREE**
Tracks: / Barbados / Some other spring / Easy living / Star crossed lovers / Jump for joy / Woodyn' you? / Blue bossa.
**Cass:** Released Jan '82, on Pablo Jazz (USA) by Pablo Records (USA). Catalogue no: **K 08 202**
**Album:** Released Jan '82, on Pablo Jazz (USA) by Pablo Records (USA). Catalogue no: **2308 202**

**YOU'RE ME**
Tracks: / You're me / Darn that dream / What am I here for / When I have you / All the things you are / Milestones / Whisper not / There'll never be another you.
**Album:** Released Jan '82, on Phontastic (Sweden) Catalogue no: **PHONT 7528**

## Flash of '29

**FLASH OF '29 (Portrait in music of 1929) (Various artists)**
Tracks: / Some of these days: *Various artists* / If I had a talking picture of you: *Various artists* / Messa stomp: *Various artists* / Louise: *Various artists* / Dinah: *Various artists* / Button up your overcoat: *Various artists* / Honey: *Various artists* / Won't you get off it, please?: *Various artists* / Muskrat ramble: *Various artists* / After you've gone: *Various artists* / Black and blue: *Various artists* / When you're smiling: *Various artists* / Wang wang blues: *Various artists* / I'm a dreamer, aren't we all?: *Various artists* / Everybody loves my baby: *Various artists* / Bashful baby: *Various artists.*
Note: With, among others, Louis Armstrong, Bing Crosby, Annette Hanshaw, Red Nichols, Fletcher Henderson, Earl Hines, Duke Ellington, Fats Waller.
**Cass:** Released '82, on Nostalgia by Mainline Records. Catalogue no: **NOST 8608**
**Album:** Released '82, on Nostalgia by Mainline Records. Catalogue no: **NOST 7608**

## Flat Foot Stompers

**FLAT FOOT STOMPERS & FRIENDS VOL.2 (Various artists)**
**Album:** Released '88, on Timeless by Timeless Records. Catalogue no: **TTD 529**

## Fleury Trio

**CONCERT BY THE FLEURY TRIO, A**
**Album:** Released Apr '89, on Audiophile (USA) by Jazzology Records (USA). Catalogue no: **AP 53**

## Flory, Med

**JAZZ WAVE (Flory, Med & His Orchestra)**
**Album:** Released Feb '88, on Fresh Sounds (Spain) by Fresh Sounds Records (Spain). Catalogue no: **FS 107**

**SUPERSAX (Flory, Med Five Saxophone Band)**
Tracks: / Just friends / Night in Tunisia / Stareyes / Donna Lee / Tempus fugit / Around midnite / Scrapple from the apple.
**VHS:** Released Sep '86, on Chris Wellard by Chris Wellard Distribution. Catalogue no: **LJB 501**

## Flyin' saxophones

**THOSE FLYIN', JUMPIN' AND GRUNTIN' SAXOPHONES (Various artists)**
Tracks: / Blow, Illinois, blow: *Jacquet, Illinois* / Illinois blows the blues: *Jacquet, Illinois* / Still flyin': *Cobb, Arnett* / Cobb's idea: *Cobb, Arnett* / Queen bee blues: *Vinson, Eddie* / Jump and grunt: *Vinson, Eddie* / Old maid boogie: *Vinson, Eddie* / Kidney stew: *Vinson, Eddie* / Lavender coffin: *Thomas, Joe* / Backstage at the Apollo: *Thomas, Joe* / Every man to his own profession: *Jordan, Louis* / Chicky-Mo, Craney Crow: *Jordan, Louis* / Coleslaw: *Jordan, Louis* / My baby says yes: *Crosby, Bing & Louis Jordan* / Your socks don't match: *Crosby, Bing & Louis Jordan.*
Note: Featuring Illinois Jacquet, Arnett Cobb, Eddie "Cleanhead" Vinson, Joe Thomas, Louis Jordan, Bing Crosby.
**Album:** Released Nov '83, on Queendisc (Italy) Catalogue no: **QU 058**

## Foehner, Gale

**RHYMS IN RAGTIME**
**Album:** Released Jun '86, on Stomp Off (USA) Catalogue no: **SOS 1023**

## Folk & Blues...

**FOLK AND BLUES FESTIVAL (Various artists)**
**Album:** Released '88, on Joker (USA) by Lifetime Records (USA). Catalogue no: **SM 3588**
**Cass:** Released '88, on Joker (USA) by Lifetime Records (USA). Catalogue no: **MC 3588**

## Fontana, Carl

**GREAT FONTANA, THE**
Note: With Al Cohn and Ray Drummond.
**Album:** Released Jun '88, on Uptown (USA) Catalogue no: **UP 27 28**

## For Sentimental Reasons

**FOR SENTIMENTAL REASONS 1942-49 (Various artists)**
Tracks: / Golden earrings: *Lee, Peggy* / Manana: *Lee, Peggy* / I love you for sentimental reasons: *Cole, Nat "King"* / Christmas song,The: *Cole, Nat King Trio* / Blue moon: *Various artists* / Again: *Various artists* / Tampico: *Kenton, Stan & His Orchestra* / Tree in the meadow, A: *Whiting, Margaret* / Long ago and far away: *Stafford, Jo* / Dream: *Pied Pipers* / Hurry on down: *Lutcher, Nellie* / Personality: *Merçer, Johnny & The Pied Pipers* / On the Atchison, Topeka and Santa Fe: *Mercer, Johnny & The Pied Pipers* / Buttons and bows: *Dinning Sisters* / Cow-cow boogie: *Slack, Freddie & His Orch.* / Temptation: *Ingle, Red & The Natural Seven.*
Note: From the Hit Parade, 1942-49. Mele Torme/Peggy Lee/Margret Whiting/Stan Kenton & June Christie/Johnny Mercer etc.
**Album:** Released Jan '87, on Memoir by Memoir Records. Catalogue no: **MOIR 502**
**Cass:** Released Jan '87, on Memoir by Memoir Records. Catalogue no: **CMOIR 502**

## Ford, Ricky

**FLYING COLORS**
Tracks: / Jordanian walk / Chelsea Bridge / Take the Coltrane / Bye-ya / Olympic glaze / Portrait of Mingus / Flying color.
Note: Ricky Ford -- tenor sax . John Hicks -- piano. Walter Booker -- bass. Jimmy Cobb -- drums. Recorded: 24 April 1980.
**Album:** Released Apr '81, on Muse by Black & Blue Records. Catalogue no: **MR 5227**

**INTERPRETATIONS**
Tracks: / Interpretations, opus 5 / Moon mist / Seabea / Fix or repair / Daily / Lady A / Bostonova / Dexter.
Note: With John Hicks, Walter Booker, Jimmy Cobb, Wallace Roney, Robert Watson.
Recorded: 22 February 1982.
**Album:** Released Nov '82, on Muse by Black & Blue Records. Catalogue no: **MR 5275**

**LOXODONTA AFRICANA (The Jazz Sound)**
Tracks: / Loxodonta Africana / UCIL / Blues Peru / Dexter / My romance / One up one down / Aerolinos.
**Album:** Released Jul '86, on New World (USA) by New World Records (USA). Catalogue no: **NW 204**

**MANHATTAN BLUES**
**Album:** Released Mar '90, on Candid Catalogue no: **CS9036**
**CD:** Released Mar '90, on Candid Catalogue no: **CCD79036**

**MANHATTAN PLAZA**
Tracks: / Fadism / Afternoon in New York / Diane's melody / Ceal's place / On the Plaza / If you could see me now / Olean visit.
Note: Ricky Ford -- tenor sax . Oliver Beener -- trumpet. Jaki Byard -- piano. David Frissen -- bass. Danny Richmond -- drums. Recorded 1 August 1978.
**Album:** Released Apr '81, on Muse by Black & Blue Records. Catalogue no: **MR 5188**

**SHORTER IDEAS (See panel below)**
Tracks: / Yes or no / Miyako / Dance cadaverous / Pinocchio / Tabloid blues / Wolf trap / Happy reunion.
Note: Produced by Michael Cuscana. Arranged by Ricky Ford. Engineer: Rudy Van Gelder. Cover photo: Clarence Eastmond. Black liner photos: J. Flint. Art direction: Dick Smith. Recorded at the Van Gelder Studio, Englewood Cliffs, on 28.8.84. Mastered by Rudy Van Gelder.
**Album:** Released May '86, on Muse by Black & Blue Records. Catalogue no: **MR 5314**

## Foretich, Herman

**FORETICH FOUR (Foretich, Herman Four)**
**Album:** Released Apr '89, on Jazzology (USA) by Jazzology Records (USA). Catalogue no: **J 144**

**HERMAN FORETICH AND THE ATLANTA SWING QUARTET (Foretich, Herman & The Atlanta Swing Quartet)**
**Album:** Released Aug '88, on Audiophile (USA) by Jazzology Records (USA). Catalogue no: **AP 124**

## Forman, Bruce

**BRUCE FORMAN 20-20**
**Album:** Released '88, on Muse by Black & Blue Records. Catalogue no: **MR 5273**

**DYNAMICS (Forman, Bruce & George Cables)**
**Album:** Released Nov '85, on Concord Jazz by Concord Jazz Records (USA). Catalogue no: **CJ 279**

**FULL CIRCLE (Forman, Bruce Quintet)**
Tracks: / Marshall arts / Helen's song / On the sunny side of the street / Skylark / Circular / Giant steps / Desert rain / Summertime.
Note: Bruce Forman -- guitar. George Cables -- piano. Bobby Hutcherson --

**Ricky Ford - Shorter ideas (Muse)**

vibes. Jeff Carney -- bass. Eddie Marshall -- drums.
**Album:** Released Oct '84, on Concord Jazz by Concord Jazz Records (USA). Catalogue no: **CJ 251**

**IN TRANSIT**
**Album:** Released '88, on Muse by Black & Blue Records. Catalogue no: **MR 5299**

**PARDON ME (Forman, Bruce Quartet)**
Note: Combine virtuosity and musicality and you have the guitar artistry of Bruce Forman. Also an accomplished composer, Bruce presents four contemporary originals in addition to a set of tasty standards he has arranged for this date. Forman is internationally popular performing regularly in Europe and has recently completed tours in Australia and Japan. Pardon Me is his fourth and most adventurous Concord release to date. Personnel: Bruce Forman (guitar), Billy Childs (piano), Jeff Carney (bass), Eddie Marshall (drums).
**Album:** Released Feb '89, on Concord by Concord Jazz Records (USA). Catalogue no: **CJ 368**
**CD:** Released Feb '89, on Concord by Concord Jazz Records (USA). Catalogue no: **CCD 4368**
**Cass:** Released Feb '89, on Concord by Concord Jazz Records (USA). Catalogue no: **CJ 368 C**

**RIVER JOURNEY**
Tracks: / River journey / Simple waltz, A / Two bits / St. Thomas / Chances / I just got back in town / Nature boy.
Note: Richie Cole, Russell Ferrants, Scott Morris, Bob Magnusson, Frank Martin, Rich Girard, Babatunde
**Album:** Released '81, on Muse by Black & Blue Records. Catalogue no: **MR 5251**

**THERE ARE TIMES**
**CD:** Released Dec '87, on Concord Jazz by Concord JazzRecords (USA). Catalogue no: **CCD 4332**

## Formative Years

**FORMATIVE YEARS: BENNY GOODMAN (1927-1934) (Various artists) (See panel)**
Tracks: / That's a plenty: *Goodman, Benny* / Clarietitis: *Goodman, Benny* / Wolverine Blues: *Goodman, Benny Boys* / Room 1411: *Goodman, Benny Boys* / Blue: *Goodman, Benny Boys* / Crazy 'bout my gal: *Mills, Irving & His Hotsy Totsy Gang* / Railroad man: *Mills, Irving & His Hotsy Totsy Gang* / Carolina in the morning: *Nichols, Red & Orchestra* / How come you do me like you do?: *Nichols, Red & Orchestra* / Basin Street blues: *Charleston Chasers* / I gotta right to sing: *Goodman, Benny & His Orchestra* / Your mother's son in law: *Goodman, Benny & His Orchestra* / Georgia jubilee: *Goodman, Benny & His Orchestra* / Junk man: *Goodman, Benny & His Orchestra* / Ol' pappy: *Goodman, Benny & His Orchestra* / Moonglow: *Goodman, Benny & His Orchestra* / Nitwit serenade: *Goodman, Benny & His Orchestra* / Bugle call rag: *Goodman, Benny & His Orchestra.*
Note: Benny Goodman did not compose or orchestrate; he never possessed the innate blues sense of Barney Bigard or Pee Wee Russell; he became the world's most popular clarinettist but founded no influential reed "school" and the stage personality was competent if not flamboyant.
Yet in the mid-thirties this Chicago-born clarinettist was to release forces transmitting the listening patterns of America and shattering partitions both musical and social. It is difficult to give an exact reason for the Goodman explosion; it was probably a combination of his uncanny prediction of public taste combined with a relentless jazz idealism and intolerance of shoddy work both in himself and in the musicians around him......and the influence on Goodman of the very sound and environment of Chicago in the twenties. There is no greater Goodman scholar than D.R. Connor and he once observed penetratingly, "Had Goodman been given celestial choice of the time and place of his birth he could not have chosen more wisely".
B.G. was born on May 30th, 1909, and as he approached his teens jazz came up the river from New Orleans. Amstrong, Teschmacher, Rapollo, Bix, Johnny Dodds, Bessie Smith - these and many other great musicians were around singing and playing. Jazz was part of the social scene and before he reached the age of ten Goodman's ultrasensitive musical mind was absorbing, peering, translating and creating.
He got his union card at the astonishing age of thirteen and this precocious youngster made his first solo recording (*That's a-plenty* and *Clarinetitis*) when nearly seventeen; and this was his fourth recording session! From the opening bars of *That's a-plenty* we sense a free-edged, unflagging enthusiasm. There are hints of Dodds and Tesch but already the embryonic stirrings of a master are perceptible; just a few weeks later he recorded and had published One hundred jazz breaks by Benny Goodman!
Benny joined the Ben Pollack band in 1926. The association lasted four years and was most important in giving Benny the opportunity to develop his style in the company of a nucleus of jazz musicians. Pollack was occasionally to object when the young musician engaged some of his men for his own recording date - *Wolverine blues* is a case in point, where in Jelly Roll Morton's classic forms an excellent theme for the variations of Glenn Miller, Jimmy McPartland and the clarinet leader.
Pollack "sits in" on Goodman's first New York recording date. It is fascinating to find B.G. playing incisive baritone sax on *Room 1411* and lovely, dreamy alto on *Blue*. Unlike Benny Carter, Goodman was never to develop a natural multi-instrumental technique; in future years he was only to reach for a saxophone to demonstrate a phrase to an erring reed section.
In addition to sides made under his own name Goodman soon became most eagerly sought after for both jazz and popular music record sessions. In 1930

**Formative Years - Benny Goodman (1927-1934) (Decca)**

Irving Mills obtained his services for one of the Hotsy Totsy Gang sessions and the clarinettist duly delivered phrases of exciting vehemence in *Crazy 'bout my gal.*

Similar confidence and mastery is revealed in the two sides made under the direction of Red Nichols. Critic Hector Stewart was so excited by *Carolina in the morning* that he wrote, "This must surely rate as the most definitive hot statement of the theme on clarinet." Glenn Miller's arrangement of *Carolina* is fine and reminds one how different were the paths of the two musicians in the thirties. Both made a lot of money but Goodman stuck to jazz and gave well paid employment to scores of jazz musicians while Miller formed his soporific band which serenaded without a single jazz soloist.

By the turn of the thirties Goodman's unique style was nearing final development and its virtues were clearly recognised by recording companies - in the first seven months of 1931 he record 175 78rpm sides that were issued: how much time he spent on rejects and alternative takes we shall never know.

The B.G. style may be said to hang between the nervous tension of Teschmacher and the poised serenity of Noone. It was a style of taste and elegance distinguished by a clear pure tone and subtle use of ornamentation; all was dependent on supreme technical authority and consistent level of inspiration.

It is interesting to note that while classical composers have written works for B.G. his style is not suitable for what is loosely termed a "jazz concerto" a la *Barney's concerto* (Ellington) and *Concerto for clarinet* (Shaw). Like Hodges he was also not completely happy in collective improvisation, and was supreme in providing a fine chorus which enhanced the contributions of great musicians around him and the quality of arrangement; the virtuosity was basically one of humility.

In theory it would see that the lazy nonchalant drawl of Teagarden has no communication with the pointed authority of B.G.; but abstract theory plays little part in the meeting of jazz minds and the two formed a great partnership in the early thirties. Goodman directed the last session of the Charleston Chasers and *Basin Street* is a jazz masterpiece which somehow typifies natural, unselfconscious jazz.

When Goodman first met critic and promoter John Hammond in September 1933 he was in no way impressed by a suggestion to record four sides for the British market only but John's sheer enthusiasm won him over and four sides were cut of which *Gotta right* (a delightful arrangement by Arthur Schutt) quickly established itself as a firm favourite with British and (later) American jazz fans.

Hammond continued to influence recording activity and on November 27th, 1933, walked into the studio with a seventeen-year-old coloured singer. This time Goodman needed no persuasion and the greatest jazz vocalist made her first record *Your mother's son-in-law.* The young Holiday revealed already her worldly cynicism and rasping attack as she tore into the doggerel-like word progressions which passed as lyrics.

Mildred Bailey's style is in complete contrast to the astonishingly mature young Holiday. The voice bubbles with innocence and the musicianship is pretty rather than profound. *Junk man* and *Ol' pappy* are captivating and the quality of these tracks and *Georgia jubilee* is enhanced by the contribution of the master Coleman Hawkins. *Moonglow* is the first recorded example of the great partnership of Goodman and Teddy Wilson and the brilliant "single note" exposition of the pianist makes a fine impact on the track. Many executive eyebrows were raised a little about Goodman using coloured musicians in the studio; such a happening was then uncommon. It was not that Goodman was initiating social changes but that he was simply a musical idealist who insisted on the best regardless of colour and 'ware anyone who might protest (as indeed they did!). Becoming more and more influenced by negro musicians, Goodman became eager and anxious to form his own big band, increasingly obsessed with the idea of fronting a unit which could be to white audiences what Ellington, Webb and Redman were to the black ones.

Glimmerings of the swing era dawned (if faintly) when Goodman was successful in winning an audition to provide a band for Billy Rose's Music Hall. He obtained the contrast by only one vote and this was probably due to the glamorous presence of singer Helen Ward. The Goodman big band **was** formed and played with limited and praiseworthy success.

Goodman was still searching for a big band style and used three arrangers for four titles recorded in August 1934 by the "Billy Rose" band. Will Hudson provided a stock figuration for the amusing *Nit wit serenade* and Dean Kincaide gives us a fine *Bugle call rag.* The band really swings in both tracks.

Had Goodman deserted the jazz scene in 1934 his achievements would still have been prodigious. Let us give the last word to D.R. Connor: "His distinctive tone, his masterful technique, his fiery inventiveness developed and grew firm in the years 1926 to 1934, and at the end of them his reputation as a jazz musician was fully established with the orchestra leaders, the record contractors and the knowing musicians of that time. It took dancing and listening America - and the rest of the world - just a little longer to catch on." (Vic Bellerby)

**Album:** Released Jun '86, on Decca by Decca International. Deleted '88. Catalogue no: **RAL 508**

## Forrest, Helen

**Biographical details:** One of the best loved vocalists of the Big Band Era, who sang with Artie Shaw, Benny Goodman and Harry James; she made films and sang on the radio, and in the mid '40's her hits included duets with Dick Haymes, another of the era's best white singers. She was still active in clubs in the '70's and came back in 1983 with a new album on Stash. (Donald Clarke, April 1989)e.

### DOUBLE DATE WITH HELEN FORREST & CHRIS CONNOR (Forrest, Helen/Chris Connor)

**CD:** Released Aug '89, on Stash (USA) Catalogue no: **STCD 14**

### NOW AND FOREVER

Tracks: / I've heard that song before / I don't want to walk without you / Happiness is just a thing called Joe / But not for me / I cried for you / I had the craziest dream / You made me love you / I didn't want to do it / You'll never know more than you know.

Note: Artists: Helen Forrest / Bob Zottola / Clint Sherman / Frank Wess / Hank Jones / George Duvivier / Jim Mitchell / Grady Tate.

**Album:** Released Jul '83, on Stash (USA) Catalogue no: **ST 225**

**Album:** Released Mar '87, on Stash (USA) Catalogue no: **ST 129**

### SUNNY SIDE OF THE STREET, THE

**Album:** Released Aug '88, on Audiophile (USA) by Jazzology Records (USA). Catalogue no: **AP 47**

## Fort Valley Blues

### GEORGIA 1941-43

**Album:** Released '88, on Flyright by Interstate Music. Catalogue no: **FLY 250**

## Forty Years Of Women...

### FORTY YEARS OF WOMEN IN JAZZ (Various artists)

**LP Set:** Released May '89, on Stash (USA) Catalogue no: **STB 001**

**CD Set:** Released Jul '89, on Milan Catalogue no: **CD 505/6**

**CD Set:** Released Aug '89, on Jass Catalogue no: **JASSCD 9/10**

## Forward Motion

### BERKLEE TAPES, THE

**Album:** on Hep Jazz by Hep Records. Catalogue no: **HEP 2026**

### PROGRESSIONS

**Album:** Released Mar '87, on Hep Jazz by Hep Records. Catalogue no: **HEP 2033**

## Foster, Chuck

### 1945-1946 (Foster, Chuck & His Orchestra)

**Album:** Released Jun '86, on Circle (USA) by Jazzology Records (USA). Catalogue no: **CLP 68**

### CHUCK FOSTER, 1940

Tracks: / Oh, you beautiful doll / Friendly tavern polka / My sister and I / You tell me your dream / Dixie girl / Knee deep in stardust / Sunshine of my heart / No foolin' / Little brown jug / Little bit south of North Carolina, A / Dark eyes / Dream affair, A / These things you left me /

Listen to my heart / I've been drafted / Goodbye now.
Note: Saxophonist Chuck Foster's sweet orchestra, whose continuous existence since 1932 was interrupted only briefly during World War II, sounds today much as it did when these radio transcriptions were made in Hollywood, according to author Irving Townsend's liner notes which quote the longtime leader. Legendary pianist Hal Pruden, around whom the band's immaculate phrasing and impeccable dynamics were fashioned, arranged most of the numbers on this album. Some are by Harry Lewis. Foster's dancing fans enjoyed hearing their music embellished by able and attractive singers so every selection on this LP is complete with vocal refrain. (Hindsight Catalogue - 1989)
**Album:** Released '88, on Hindsight Catalogue no: **HSR 115**

**LONG OVERDUE (Foster, Chuck & Pete Christlieb)**
**Album:** Released Nov '88, on Sea Breeze Catalogue no: **SB 2023**

**MUSIC IN THE FOSTER FASHION (Foster, Chuck & His Orchestra)**
Tracks: / Oh you beautiful doll / Little girl / Shake down the stars / I've told every little star / Give a little whistle / Glow worm / How high the moon / Angel / Let there be love / Isle of May / Five foot two, eyes of blue / Singing hills, The / I've got my eyes on you / Majorette / Love song of Renaldo / Too romantic / Where was I? / It's a blue world.
**Album:** Released Feb '78, on Aircheck (USA) by Kiner Ents.(USA). Catalogue no: **AIRCHECK 22**

## Foster, Frank

**2 FRANKS PLEASE (Foster, Frank/Frank Wess)**
**2 LP Set:** Released Mar '85, on Savoy Jazz (USA) by Malaco Records (USA). Catalogue no: **SJL 2249**

**FRANKLY SPEAKING (Foster, Frank & Frank Weiss)**
Tracks: / When did you leave heaven? / Up and coming / One morning in May / Two Franks / This is all I ask / Blues backstage / An' all such stuff as'dat / Summer knows, The.
**CD:** Released Sep '86, on Concord Jazz by Concord Jazz Records (USA). Catalogue no: **CCD 4276**
**Album:** Released Sep '86, on Concord Jazz by Concord Jazz Records (USA). Catalogue no: **CJ 276**

**MANHATTAN FEVER (Foster, Frank/Loud Minority)**
Tracks: / Thruway traffic / Four five six / Manhattan fever / Marie Jean.
Note: Recorded at Sound Ideas Studios, New York City, November, 29th & 30th, 1977.
**Album:** Released Mar '82, on Denon Deleted '88. Catalogue no: **YX 7521**

**SHINY STOCKINGS (Foster, Frank/Loud Minority)**
Tracks: / Shiny stockings / Love scene / Tomorrow's blues today / Day spring / Hills of the north rejoice.
**CD:** Released Jun '89, on Denon Catalogue no: **DC 8545**
**Album:** Released Mar '82, on Denon Deleted '88. Catalogue no: **YX 7545**

**TWO FOR THE BLUES (Foster, Frank/Frank Wess)**
Tracks: / Two for the blues / Nancy / Send in the clowns / Your beauty is a song of love / But for the likes of you / Spring can really hang you up the most / Time for love, A / Heat of winter / Bay street.
Note: Two tenor giants who were both members of the Basie Band during the 50's and 60's. They carried on the tradition set by former Basie men Hershel and Lester Young for contrasting styles. Frank Foster representing the "modern" trend and Frank Wess the Coleman Hawkins school. Recorded 1983.
**Album:** Released Sep '84, on Pablo Jazz (USA) by Pablo Records (USA). Catalogue no: **231 0905**
**Cass:** Released Sep '84, on Pablo Jazz (USA) by Pablo Records (USA). Catalogue no: **K10 905**

## Foster, Herman

**LIVE IN BOLOGNA VOLUME 2 (Foster, Herman & Lou Donaldson Quartet)**
Note: See under Donaldson,Lou Quartet
**Album:** Released Oct '86, on Timeless by Timeless Records. Catalogue no: **SJP 207**

**ONE AND ONLY, THE (Herman Foster Trio)**
**Album:** Released Oct '86, on Timeless by Timeless Records. Catalogue no: **SJP 201**

## Foster, Teddy

**MELODY MAN 1936-37**
Tracks: / Melody man / Sing, sing, sing / Skeleton in the cupboard, The / Harlem / Jerry the junker / Where the lazy river goes by / When a lady meets a gentleman down south / Breakfast in harlem / St. Louis blues / Sugar rose / Pennies from Heaven / T'ain't no use / With a banjo on my knee / Rhythm's OK in Harlem, The / Poor Dinah / Take another guess.
**Album:** Released Feb '88, on Harlequin by Interstate Music. Catalogue no: **HQ 3020**

## Foundations Of...

**FOUNDATIONS OF MODERN JAZZ (Various artists)**
**CD:** Released '86, on Dunhill Compact Classics (USA) Catalogue no: **DZS 022**

## Fountain, Pete

**ALIVE IN NEW ORLEANS**
**Album:** Released Apr '79, on First American Catalogue no: **FA 7706**

**SUPER JAZZ 1 (Fountain, Pete & Al Hirt)**
**2 LP Set:** Released May '76, on Monument Catalogue no: **MNT 22009**

## Four...

**FOUR DECADES OF JAZZ Various artists (Various artists)**
**2 LP Set:** Released Mar '79, on Xanadu Catalogue no: **X 5001**

## Four Freshmen

**Biographical details:** Vocal group formed in 1948 in Indianapolis, Indiana as the Toppers. They were discovered in 1950 by Stan Kenton who helped get a Capitol contract; good signing with modern harmonies sold albums. Lineup was lead singer Bob Flanigan, second voice Don Barbour, third Ross Barbour, bass Hal Kratzch was replaced by Ken Errair in 1953, who replaced by Ken Albers '56; Don Barbour was replaced by Bill Comstock in 1960, who was replaced by Ray Brown in 1973. (Donald Clarke, April 1989).

**LIVE AT BUTLER UNIVERSITY (Four Freshmen & The Stan Kenton Orchestra)**
Tracks: / There will never be another you / After you / Byrd Avenue / Surfer girl / Girl talk / When the feeling hit you / Walk on by / What are you doing the rest of your life? / Brand new key / Teach me tonight / Beautiful friendship / Summer has gone / Hymn to her / Come back to me / It's not unusual / Coming round the mountain / Walk softly / Artistry in rhythm.
**2 LP Set:** Released Oct '87, on Creative World(USA) by GNP Crescendo Records (USA). Catalogue no: **STD 1059**
**Cass:** Released Oct '87, on Creative World(USA) by GNP Crescendo Records (USA). Catalogue no: **STC 1059**
**CD:** Released Oct '87, on Creative World(USA) by GNP Crescendo Records (USA). Catalogue no: **STCD 1059**

**STARS IN OUR EYES**
Tracks: / Shangri-la / Sentimental me / Standing on the corner / Lamplighter's serenade, The / Teach me tonight / Tom dooley / Opus one / I thought about you / Love is a many splendoured thing / Green fields / In apple blossom time / Imagination.
Note: Following close on the heels of the imported album "Voices In Fun" which re-kindled the public interest in thr group, this album brings another fine selection of songs from The Four Freshmen. Again,the Freshmen salute outstanding vocal group as The Andrews Sisters,The Mills Brothers and The King Sisters.These unique interpretations of vocal classics are completmented perfectly by the orchestral arrangements directed by Dick Reynolds.
**Cass:** Released May '86, on Capitol by EMI Records. Catalogue no: **TCEMS 1152**
**Album:** Released May '86, on Capitol by EMI Records. Catalogue no: **EMS 1152**

**VOICES IN FUN**
Tracks: / I want to be happy / Ole buttermilk / I can't give you anything but love

/ You make me feel so young / Save the bones for henry Jones / Swinging on a star / On sunny side of the street / Manana / On the Atchison, Topeka and Santa Fe / Aren't you glad you're you / Happy talk / Accentuate the positive.
Note: A fantastic album featuring the Four Freshmen singing all time favourites such as 'I want to be happy'and'On the sunny side of the street'.All the swinging and often humourous arrangements are by ever popular Billy May, who also conducts the orchestra.
**Cass:** Released Jan '86, on Capitol by EMI Records. Deleted Jul '87. Catalogue no: **TCEMS 1131**
**Album:** Released Jan '86, on Capitol by EMI Records. Deleted Oct '89. Catalogue no: **EMS 1131**

## Four-Four Sax

### FOUR-FOUR SAX (Various artists)
Tracks: / I'll remember April: *Konitz, Lee* / Record shop suey: *Konitz, Lee* / Lee tchee: *Konitz, Lee* / Young Lee: *Konitz, Lee* / You'd be so nice to come home to: *Konitz, Lee* / 4 pm: *Konitz, Lee* / Lost Henri: *Konitz, Lee* / Toot's suite: *Sims, John Haley 'Zoot'* / Late Tiny Kahn, The: *Sims, John Haley 'Zoot'* / Call it anything: *Sims, John Haley 'Zoot'* / Zoot suite: *Sims, John Haley 'Zoot'* / Once in a while: *Sims, John Haley 'Zoot'* / Great drums: *Sims, John Haley 'Zoot'* / Escale a Victoria: *Foster, Frank* / Things we did last summer, The: *Foster, Frank* / Just 40 bars: *Foster, Frank* / My heart stood still: *Foster, Frank* / Fat shoes: *Foster, Frank* / I'll take romance: *Foster, Frank* / Eleanore: *Jaspar, Bobby* / Capri: *Jaspar, Bobby* / Schabozz: *Jaspar, Bobby* / Simplicity: *Jaspar, Bobby* / Up in Quincy's room: *Jaspar, Bobby* / Consultation: *Jaspar, Bobby* / Au tabour: *Jaspar, Bobby* / Expansion: *Jaspar, Bobby*.
Note: Featuring -- on individual tracks -- four great reedmen, Lee Konitz (alto sax), Zoot Sims, Frank Foster, Bobby Jaspar (tenor saxes), plus Henri Renaud (piano), Frank Rosolino (trombone), Jimmy Gourlay (guitar), Jean Marie Ingrand, Don Bagley (basses), Stan Levy, Jean Louis Viale (drums).
**Album:** Released Apr '82, on Vogue Jazz (France) by Vogue Records. Catalogue no: **VJD 577**

## Fox, Roy

### AT MONSEIGNEUR RESTAURANT, PICCADILLY (Fox, Roy & His Band)
Tracks: / Whispering / Minnie the moocher / Kickin' the gong around / Jig time / I got rhythm / Nobody's sweetheart / Georgia on my mind / Yes yes / Old man of the mountain, The / If I didn't have you / How'm I doin' / She didn't say yes / You're my everything / Oh Monah.
**Album:** Released '64, on Ace Of Clubs by Decca Records. Deleted '88. Catalogue no: **ACL 1172**

### BANDS THAT MATTER, THE
Tracks: / Londonola, The / Build a little home / June in January / May 1 / Lovable / Jungle drums / Goodnight Vienna / Living in clover / Corrina / Japanese sandman / Everything I have is yours / Drowsy blues / What a perfect combination / Goodnight lovely little lady.
**Album:** on Eclipse Catalogue no: **ECM 2045**

### DANCE MUSIC OF THE 30'S (Fox, Roy & His Band)
**Album:** Released '89, on Joy by President Records. Catalogue no: **JOY 266**

### FOX FAVOURITES (Fox, Roy & His Orchestra)
Tracks: / Keep young and beautiful / Black-eyed Susan Brown / I cover the waterfront / Over my shoulder / Maybe I'm wrong again / You ought to be in pictures / Sweet and hot / Every little moment / When the robin sings his song again / Blue moments / Without that certain thing / We've got to put that Sun back in the sky / Rhythm lullaby / Everything stops for tea.
**Album:** Released Mar '83, on Jasmine by Hasmick Promotions. Deleted Jun '87. Catalogue no: **JASM 2019**

### GOLDEN AGE OF ROY FOX
Tracks: / Love is a dancing thing / Play orchestra play / Let's face the music / South sea island / Whispering / Night is young / Love and learn / I've got beginners luck / I've got my love to keep me warm / 50000000 robins can't be wrong / Can i forget you / Things are looking up / Roses in december / You leave me breathless / You went to my head / If it rains who cares.
**Cass:** Released Apr '85, on Golden Age by EMI Records. Catalogue no: **GX 41 2528 4**
**Album:** Released Apr '85, on Golden Age by EMI Records. Catalogue no: **GX 41 2528**

### I'LL STRING ALONG WITH YOU
**2 LP Set:** Released Sep '87, on Saville by Conifer Records. Catalogue no: **SVLD 004**
**Cass:** Released '88, on Saville by Conifer Records. Catalogue no: **CSVLD 004**

### INVITATION TO A DANCE (Fox, Roy & His Band)
Tracks: / Swaller tail coat / True / One morning in May / Drowsy blues / Fair and warmer / You oughta be in pictures / Jungle drums / Soon / I'll string along with you / I saw stars / What a difference a day made / I'm in love / Out in the cold again / Dream man (make me dream some more) / I've got an invitation to a dance / If the moon turns green / Accent on youth / San Felipe / Do you ever have a feeling you're flying / Echo of a song, The.
**Cass:** Released '88, on Saville by Conifer Records. Catalogue no: **CSVL 179**
**Album:** Released Sep '86, on Saville by Conifer Records. Catalogue no: **SVL 179**

### RISE 'N' SHINE (Fox, Roy Orchestra)
Tracks: / Rise 'n' shine / It's been so long / Your heart and mine / Quicker than you can say Jack Robinson / Miracles sometimes happen / Saddle your blues to a wild mustang / Moon for sale / Bird on the wing / Star and the rose, The / You / You do the darndest things, baby / Carelessly / It's the natural thing to do / Moon got in my eyes, The / Let's call the whole thing off / They can't take that away from me / Whispers in the dark / Too marvellous for words / That old feeling / Stop, you're breaking my heart.
**Cass:** Released Nov '88, on Saville by Conifer Records. Catalogue no: **CSVL 197**
**Album:** Released Nov '88, on Saville by Conifer Records. Catalogue no: **SVL 197**

### ROY FOX, 1928-32 (Fox, Roy & Al Bowlly)
**Album:** Released Nov '89, on Harlequin by Interstate Music. Catalogue no: **HQ 3026**

### ROY FOX & HIS BAND (Fox, Roy & His Band featuring Al Bowlly)
Tracks: / Ya got love / Betty co-ed / Maybe it's love / Oh Monah / I'd rather be a beggar with you / That lindy hop / One more time / Smile darn ya, smile / Thank you father / Your forgot your gloves / Roll on, Mississippi, roll on / Bathing in the sunshine / Ten cents a dance / Between the Devil and the deep blue sea / My temptation / Sing another chorus please / You forgot your gloves.
**Album:** Released Nov '82, on Joy by President Records. Catalogue no: **JOYD 266**
**Cass:** Released Nov '82, on Joy by President Records. Catalogue no: **TCJOYD 266**

### ROY FOX & HIS BAND: VOLUME 2 (Fox, Roy & His Band)
Tracks: / You're telling me / My romance / Roll on, Kentucky moon / I don't want to go to bed / What would happen to me? / Love, you funny thing / Lady I love, The / Time alone will tell / When the waltz was through / Guilty / Goodnight Vienna / Stardust / Blue moon in the sky / Echo of a song, The / Put that sun back in the sky.
**Album:** Released Jul '86, on Joy by President Records. Catalogue no: **JOYD 275**

### ROY FOX & HIS ORCHESTRA (1938) (Fox, Roy & His Orchestra)
Tracks: / Nice work if you can get it / Gypsy in my soul / Who? / College swing / Let's all dance / Rockin' the town / Meanest thing you ever did, the / What a fool I've been / I double dare you / You took the words right out of my heart / Rhythm in me, the / Mamma, I wanna make rhythm / Me, myself and I / You appeal to me / Rosalie / Love walked in / You went to my head / Sweet someone / Just a simple melody / Snake charmer / It's the natural thing to do.
**Album:** Released Mar '79, on Halcyon (USA) by Submarine Records. Catalogue no: **HAL 9**

### ROY FOX & HIS ORCHESTRA, 1936-1938 (Fox, Roy & His Orches-

**tra)**
Tracks: / Love is a dancing thing / Play, orchestra, play / But where are you? / Let's face the music and dance / South sea island magic / Did your mother come from Ireland? / What will I tell my heart? / I've got my love to keep me warm / Things are looking up / Roses in December / Dearest love / I could use a dream / I fall in love with you every day / You leave me breathless / It rains, who cares? / Rose Marie / Calling me home / Miller's daughter, Marianne / Merry-go-round, The / Broken down / Night is young and you're so beautiful, The / Where are you? / Gone with the wind / Can I forget you? / When the sun says goodnight to the mountain / You do the darndest things baby / Baby / Love and learn / I've got beginner's luck / You went to my head / Fifty million robins can't be wrong / Whispering / Alone / Music goes round and around, The / Sweetheart, let's grow old together / Cheek to cheek / On Treasure Island / Poor little Angeline / It's a sin to tell a lie / Is it true what they say about Dixie? / Ramona / Wedding of the painted doll, The / Dancing with tears in my eyes / Goodnight sweetheart / Let's put out the lights / Stormy weather / Isle of Capri / When I grow too old to dream / Alone / September in the rain.
**2 LP Set:** Released Oct '75, on Retrospect by EMI Records. Catalogue no: **SHB 33**

**STRICTLY INSTRUMENTAL (Fox, Roy & His Orchestra)**
Tracks: / I got rhythm / Black eyes / Way down yonder in New Orleans / You're the cream in my coffee / Lady be good / Birth of the blues / Happy feet / Mean to me / That's a plenty / Someday, sweetheart / Everybody loves my baby / On the sunny side of the street / Tiger rag / Let's do it / Impressions of Harlem / China boy / Chicago / Ain't she sweet / Congo / Mr. Sweeney's learned to swing / Song of India.
**Cass:** Released May '87, on Halcyon (USA) by Submarine Records. Catalogue no: **CHAL 1**
**Album:** Released Dec '82, on Halcyon (USA) by Submarine Records. Catalogue no: **HAL 1**

**TEN CENTS A DANCE**
Tracks: / Maybe it's love / One more time / Peanut vendor / Lady play your mandolin / Dancing through the ages (part 1) / My sweet Virginia / Between the devil and the deep blue sea / What made you so adorable / Thank you father / Hurt / Ten cents a dance / Writing a letter to you / That Lindy hop / Dancing through the ages (part 2) / If I have to go on without you / Ya got love / Betty loved / Bathing in the sunshine.
**Album:** Released Dec '88, on Burlington Records by Plant Life Records. Catalogue no: **BUR 015**
**Cass:** Released Dec '88, on Burlington Records by Plant Life Records. Catalogue no: **4 BUR 015**

**THIS IS ROMANCE (At the Kit Cat Restaurant 1933) (Fox, Roy & Kit-Cat Band)**
Tracks: / Look what you've done / There's a ring around the Moon / Girl in the little green hat / This is romance / Something came and got me in the spring / That's what life is made of / Oh Johanna / Without that certain thing / Blue moments / Happy & contented / Louisiana lullaby / My hat's on the side of my head.
**Album:** Released Jul '85, on Joy by President Records. Catalogue no: **JOYD 285**
**Album:** Released '88, on Saville by Conifer Records. Catalogue no: **SVL 166**

**THIS IS ROY FOX**
Tracks: / Singin' in the rain / Bye bye blackbird.
Note: Tracks include: Singin' in the rain, Bye bye blackbird etc... Previously unissued 1938 recordings with vocals by Denny Dennis, Mary Lee and Sid Buckman.
**Album:** Released Dec '82, on Halcyon (USA) by Submarine Records. Catalogue no: **HAL 7**

**WHISPERING (Fox, Roy & His Band)**
Tracks: / Whispering / Out of nowhere / We'll all go riding on a rainbow / I wished on the moon / Lazy day / Cobra and the flute, The / My sweet / Truckin' / It must be true / To be worthy of you / All I do is dream of you / In the middle of a kiss / Poor kid / Alexander's ragtime band / I'm gonna get you / La majestica / You didn't know the music (I didn't know the words) / Little man you've had a busy day.
Note: Eight tracks feature the band which was resident at London's Monseigneur Club after it opened in 1931. Vocals on some tracks are by the legendary Al Bowlly.
**Album:** Released Sep '81, on Decca by Decca International. Deleted '88. Catalogue no: **RFL 13**

## Francis, Panama

**GET UP AND DANCE (Francis, Panama & The Savoy Sultans)**
**CD:** Released '88, on Stash (USA) Catalogue no: **STCD 5**

**GROOVING (Francis, Panama & The Savoy Sultans)**
**Album:** Released Aug '88, on Stash (USA) Catalogue no: **ST 218**

**PANAMA FRANCIS ALL STARS 1949 (Various artists)**
**Album:** Released Sep '87, on Krazy Kat by Interstate Music. Catalogue no: **KK 813**

## Franco, Buddy De

**BORINQUIN**
**Album:** Released Aug '77, on Sonet by Sonet Records. Catalogue no: **SNTF 724**

**LIKE SOMEONE IN LOVE (Franco, Buddy De Quintet)**
**Album:** Released Apr '81, on Progressive (USA) by Jazzology Records (USA). Catalogue no: **PRO 7014**

**MR LUCKY**
Tracks: / Mr. Lucky / Bye, bye blackbird / Mar descancado / In a sentimental mood / Your smile / Close enough for love / Danielle / Lolita's theme.
Note: Personnel: Buddy De Franco - clarinet/Joe Cohn - guitar/Albert Daily - piano/George Duvivier - bass/Ronnie Bedford - drums.
**Cass:** Released Sep '84, on Pablo Jazz (USA) by Pablo Records (USA). Catalogue no: **K10 906**
**Album:** Released Sep '84, on Pablo Jazz (USA) by Pablo Records (USA). Catalogue no: **231 0906**

## Frank, Ed

**NEW NEW ORLEANS MUSIC, VOL. 1 (Frank, Ed Quintet)**
**CD:** Released '88, on Rounder (USA) by Rounder Records (USA). Catalogue no: **CD 2065**
**Cass:** Released '88, on Rounder (USA) by Rounder Records (USA). Catalogue no: **ROUNDER 2065C**
**Album:** Released '88, on Rounder (USA) by Rounder Records (USA). Catalogue no: **ROUNDER 2065**

## Franklin, Phil

**PHIL FRANKLIN JAZZ BAND (Franklin, Phil Jazz Band)**
**Album:** Released Sep '86, on Timeless by Timeless Records. Catalogue no: **TTD 501**

## Frazier, Calvin

**CALVIN FRAZIER & SAM PITMAN (1938 Detroit) (Frazier, Calvin/Sam Pitman)**
**Album:** on Flyright by Interstate Music. Catalogue no: **FLY 542**

## Fredriksson, Borje

**FREDRIKSSON SPECIAL**
**Album:** Released Apr '89, on Dragon by Dragon Records. Catalogue no: **DRLP 167**

## Freeflight

**BEYOND THE CLOUDS**
**Album:** Released Jan '85, on Palo Alto Catalogue no: **PA 8075**

**JAZZ, THE Classical union**
**Cass:** Released Jan '84, on Palo Alto Catalogue no: **PAC 8042**
**Album:** Released Jan '84, on Palo Alto Catalogue no: **PA 8042**

**SOARING**
**Album:** Released Jun '84, on Palo Alto Catalogue no: **PA 8050**

## Freeman, Bud

**Biographical details:** Born in 1906 in Chicago, Bud Freeman was the first great white player of jazz tenor sax, his light tone preceeding Lester Young and providing the only stylistic alternative to Coleman Hawkins until Young came along. He played with dance and jazz bands including Tommy Dorsey, then with Chicago sidekick Benny Goodman during his classic period (1936-9) and always with small groups, recording under his own name as well as visiting Europe as early as 1928. his Summa Cum Laude Orchestra recorded 1939-40 on several labels, notably Bluebird (Victor) in July 1939, with Eddie Condon, Pee Wee Russell, Max Kaminsky and four others, tracks now on the Bluebird CD compilation *At the jazz band ball.* He published an autobiography called *You don't look like a musician* and was a founder member of the World's Greatest Jazz Band. (Donald Clarke, July 1989).

**BUD FREEMAN**
**Album:** Released Mar '79, on Monmouth Evergreen Catalogue no: **MES 7022**

**BUD FREEMAN & FAMOUS CHICAGOANS**
Note: with Teagarden, Pee Wee Russell, Max Kaminsky, Eddie Condon.
**Album:** Released Jan '88, on Family Catalogue no: **SFR 742**

**BUD FREEMAN & HIS ALL STARS (Freeman, Bud & His All Stars)**
**Album:** Released '84, on Swing House by Submarine Records. Catalogue no: **SWH 32**

**BUD FREEMAN TAPES, THE (Freeman, Bud with the Cambridge City Jassband)**
Tracks: / Hindustan / Once in a while / Wolverine blues / Sunday / 'S wonderful / Tea for two / That's a plenty / I found a new baby.
**Album:** Released Nov '81, on Plant Life Jazz by Plant Life Records. Catalogue no: **PLJ 001**

**BUD FREEMAN WITH THE BOB BARNARD JAZZ BAND (Freeman, Bud with the Bob Barnard Jazzband)**
**Album:** Released Jan '83, on Swaggie (Australia) Catalogue no: **S 1367**

**CHICAGO**
Tracks: / Saturday night fish fry / Meet you in San Juan / Basin Street blues / Chicago / School days / All by myself / Loveless love / One for the money.
Note: With Roy Eldridge, Ray Bryant, Bob Haggart, Jo Jones.
**Album:** Released Jan '85, on Black Lion Catalogue no: **BLP 30108**

**CHICAGOANS IN NEW YORK**
**Album:** Released Jun '79, on Dawn Club by Cadillac Music. Catalogue no: **DC 12009**

**CHICAGO-STYLED, 1935-40, VOL 1**
**Album:** Released Jan '83, on Swaggie (Australia) Catalogue no: **S 1216**

**COMMODORE STYLE (Freeman, Bud & George Wettling)**
**Album:** Released '87, on Commodore Class Catalogue no: **6.25894**

**COMPLEAT BUD FREEMAN**
**Album:** Released Apr '89, on Jazzology (USA) by Jazzology Records (USA). Catalogue no: **J 165**

**DOLPHIN HAS A MESSAGE, THE**
**Album:** Released Mar '82, on JSP by JSP Records. Catalogue no: **JSP 1011**

**KEEP SMILIN' AT TROUBLE**
Tracks: / Keep smilin' at trouble / Sail fish, The / What is there to say / Oh! baby / Big boy / That da da strain / Wailing blues / Copenhagen / As long as I live / Sensation rag / Sunday / Satanic Blues / Buzzard, The / I need some pettin' / Fidgety feet / Tillie's downtown now / Tia juana / Susie.
**Album:** Released Apr '87, on Affinity by Charly Records. Catalogue no: **AFS 1036**

**LAST NIGHT WHEN WE WERE YOUNG**
**Album:** Released '78, on Black Lion Catalogue no: **BLP 30189**

**STOP LOOK & LISTEN TO BUD FREEMAN (Freeman, Bud / various)**
Tracks: / Newport news / At sundown / Exactly like you / Let's do it / But not for me / Stop, look & listen / Hanid / Dave's blues / I remember you / Perdido / You took advantage of me.
**Album:** Released Dec '88, on Affinity by Charly Records. Catalogue no: **AFF 112**

**SUPERBUD (Freeman, Bud & The Keith Ingham Trio)**
**Album:** Released Jul '88, on 77 by 77 Records. Catalogue no: **77 S 55**

**SWINGING TENORS (Freeman, Bud & Eddie Miller)**
**Album:** Released Apr '81, on Affinity by Charly Records. Deleted '88. Catalogue no: **AFF 64**

**THREE'S NO CROWD (Freeman, Bud Trio)**
Tracks: / You took advantage of me / Three's no crowd / I got rhythm / Keep smiling at trouble / At sundown / My honey's loving arms / I don't believe it / Three little words / Swingin' without Mazz / Blue room / Exactly like you.
Note: Personnel:Bud Freeman-Tenor Sax/Jess Stacy-Piano/George Wetting-Drums. All sessions from New York in 1938, MONO recording
**Album:** Released Jul '82, on Commodore Class Catalogue no: **AG6 24061**

**TWO BEAUTIFUL (Freeman, Bud & Buddy Tate)**
**Album:** Released Jun '86, on Circle (USA) by Jazzology Records (USA). Catalogue no: **CLP 69**

## Freeman, George

**BIRTH SIGN**
**Album:** Released '86, on Delmark (USA) by Delmark Records (USA). Catalogue no: **DS 424**

**NEW IMPROVED FUNK**
**Album:** Released '87, on UNKNOWN Deleted Jun '89. Catalogue no: **PLEO 22**

## Friedman, Don

**FUTURES PASSED (Friedman, Don Quartet)**
**Album:** Released Jan '82, on Enja (Germany) by Enja Records (West Germany). Catalogue no: **ENJA 2068**

**HOT KNEPPER AND PEPPER**
Tracks: / Audobon / I'm getting sentimental over you / Hellure / Groovin' high / Alfie / Laura / Prelude to a kiss / I got it bad and that ain't good / Beautiful love.
Note: Artists include Jimmy Knepper, Pepper Adams, George Mraz, Billy Hart. Recorded 26th June, 1978.
**Album:** Released '81, on Progressive (USA) by Jazzology Records (USA). Catalogue no: **PRO 7036**

**OF THE WIND'S EYE (Friedman, Don Quartet)**
**Album:** Released Jan '82, on Enja (Germany) by Enja Records (West Germany). Catalogue no: **ENJA 3089**

## Friends Of Fats

**FRIENDS OF FATS (Various artists)**
Note: Artists include: Herman Autrey/Fred Robinson/Rudy Powell/Etc.
**Album:** Released Jul '86, on Collectors Items Catalogue no: **CI 007**

## Friesen, David

**AMBER SKIES**
**Album:** Released Jul '84, on Palo Alto Catalogue no: **UNKNOWN**

**PATHS BEYOND TRACING**
**Album:** Released Apr '81, on Steeplechase (USA) Catalogue no: **SCS 1138**

**WEST COAST REPORT**
**CD:** Released Oct '88, on West Wind Catalogue no: **WWCD 015**

## Frisco Jazz Band

**GOOD MAN IS HARD TO FIND, A**
**Album:** Released Dec '86, on Dawn Club by Cadillac Music. Catalogue no: **DC 12005**

## From Boogie To Bop

**FROM BOOGIE TO BOP 1939-1956 (Blue Note 50th anniversary collection vol. 1) (Various artists)**
Tracks: / Two's and fews: *Ammons, Albert & Meade Lux Lewis* / Summertime: *Bechet, Sidney* / Profoundly blue: *Hall, Edmond* / Blue harlem: *Quebec, Ike* / 'Round midnight: *Monk, Thelonious* / Criss cross: *Monk, Thelonious* / Ladybird: *Dameron, Tadd & Fats Navarro* / Tin tin deo: *Moody, James* / Un poco loco: *Powell, Bud* / Glass enclosure: *Powell, Bud* / Bag's groove: *Jackson, Milt* / Tempus fugit: *Davis, Miles* / Easy living: *Brown, Clifford* / Preacher, The: *Silver, Horace* / Avila and tequila: *Mobley, Hank* / Decision: *Rollins, Sonny* / Champ, The: *Smith, Jimmy (USA).*
**CD:** Released Jul '89, on Blue Note by EMI Records. Catalogue no: **CDP 792 465 2**

**Cass:** Released Jul '89, on Blue Note by EMI Records. Catalogue no: **TCBST2 92465**

## Fruscella, Tony

**DEBUT**
**Album:** Released '88, on Spotlite by Spotlite Records. Catalogue no: **SPJ 126**

**FRU & BREW (Fruscella, Tony / Brew Moore)**
Tracks: / Sometimes I'm happy / Blue Lester / Hackensack / Imagination / Donna.
**Album:** Released '83, on Spotlite by Spotlite Records. Catalogue no: **SPJ 151**

## Full Faith

**DEBUT (Full Faith & Credit Big Band)**
**Album:** Released Jan '84, on Palo Alto Catalogue no: **PA 8001**

**JAZZFAIRE (Full Faith & Credit Big Band)**
**Album:** Released Jan '84, on Palo Alto Catalogue no: **PA 8003**

## Fuller, Blind Boy

**Biographical details:** The blues singer and guitarist (1908-41) was one of 10 children and went blind in the late 20's. From North Carolina, he was one of them most influential in the Piedmont blues style, more eclectic than that of the Mississippi delta and with a strong folk element. (Donald Clarke, July 1989).

**1935-40**
**Album:** Released '89, on Best Of Blues (USA) by Blue Island Records (USA). Catalogue no: **BOB 12**

**BLIND BOY FULLER 1935-1940**
**Album:** Released '88, on Blues Classics(USA) by Arhoolie Records (USA). Catalogue no: **BC 11**

**BLIND BOY FULLER & BROWNIE 1936-41 (Fuller, Blind Boy & Brownie McGhee)**
Tracks: / Black and tan / Red's got the piccolo blues / If you don't give me what I want / Black bottom blues / Me and my dog / Picking up tomatoes / Money spending woman / Double trouble.
**Album:** Released 10 Jul '89, on Flyright by Interstate Music. Catalogue no: **FLY 105**

**BLUE AND WORRIED MAN**
Tracks: / I'm a good stem winder / It doesn't matter, baby / Jivin' Big Bill blues / Blue and worried man / Woman you better wake up / You can't hide from The Lord / Twelve gates to the city / Baby, you gotta change your mind / You got to have your dollar / Bye bye baby / No stranger now / Must have been my Jesus / Jesus is a holy man.
**Album:** Released Jan '84, on Travelin' Man by Interstate Music. Catalogue no: **TM 801**

**DEATH VALLEY**
**Album:** Released '88, on Oldie Blues Catalogue no: **OL 2809**

**GREAT CAROLINA BLUESMAN**
**Album:** Released Dec '88, on Old Tramp Catalogue no: **OT 1202**

**ON DOWN 1937-40**
**Album:** Released Oct '79, on Magpie by Interstate Music. Deleted '88. Catalogue no: **PY 1811**

**TRUCKIN' MY BLUES AWAY**
**Album:** Released May '79, on Yazoo (USA) by Shanachie Records (USA). Catalogue no: **L 1060**

## Fuller, Curtis

**Biographical details:** A first rate modern jazz trombonist born in Detroit in 1934. He played in the US army and in Detroit, went to the NYC in 1957 and has been a leading player on the instrument ever since. (Donald Clarke, July 1989).

**ALL STAR SEXTETS**
**2 LP Set:** Released Mar '85, on Savoy Jazz (USA) by Malaco Records (USA). Catalogue no: **SJL 2239**

**BLUESETTE**
Note: Artists include:Curtis Fuller-Trombone/Benny Golson-Tenor Sax./Tommy Flanagan- Piano/Jimmy Garrison-Bass/Al Harewood-Drums. The excellent trombonist, Curtis Fuller, aged 24, followed success with LP's on Prestige and Blue Note, and musicans Kenny Burrell, Sonny Clarke and Lee Morgan to record this superb album as a leader for Savoy in 1959 and that year he was rewarded by winning the Trom-bone New Star Category' in the 'down beat' critics' poll. At the same time, Benny Golson - also featured in this album - won the 'down beat' Outstanding New Arranger Award. Recorded in New Jersey 1959.
**Album:** Released Dec '85, on Savoy (France) Deleted May '89. Catalogue no: **WL 70502**

**CURTIS FULLER MEETS ROMA JAZZ (Fuller, Curtis & Roma Jazz Trio)**
**Album:** Released '88, on Timeless by Timeless Records. Catalogue no: **SJP 204**

**FIRE & FILIGREE**
**Album:** Released Dec '79, on Beehive (USA) Catalogue no: **BH 7007**

**FOUR ON THE OUTSIDE**
Tracks: / Four on the outside (Adams plays baritone sax.) / Kathy (Adams plays baritone sax.) / Hello, young lovers (Adams plays baritone sax.) / Little dreams (Adams plays baritone sax.) / Ballad for Gabe-Wells (Adams plays baritone sax.) / Corrida del terro (Adams plays baritone sax.).
Note: With Pepper Adams/J.Williams/Etc.
**Album:** Released Sep '86, on Timeless (Import) by Timeless Records. Catalogue no: **SJP 124**

**NEW TROMBONE**
Tracks: / Vonce and 5 / Transportation blues / Namely you / What is this thing called love?.
**Album:** Released Feb '84, on Prestige (USA) by Fantasy Inc (USA). Catalogue no: **OJC 077**

**WITH FRENCH HORNS**
**Album:** Released Feb '86, on Fantasy Inc (USA) by Fantasy Inc (USA). Catalogue no: **1902112**

## Fuller, Jesse

**Biographical details:** This singer, songwriter and guitarist (1896-1976) was also known as the Lone Cat; he was essentially the last of the Negro Minstrels, his work tinged with folk-blues and country music. He ran away from home in Georgia and spent most of his life on the West Coast; he worked as a film extra in the mid-'20's. In the early '50's he became a one-man band, playing guitar, harmonica, kazoo and fotdella (a bass made out of a piano string and operated by a foot pedal, sometimes spelled 'footdella'). His best-known tune is *San Francisco Bay Blues*, much covered by latter-day folkies. (Donald Clarke, July 1989).

**FRISCO BLUES**
**Album:** Released May '81, on Arhoolie (USA) by Arhoolie Records (USA). Catalogue no: **ARHOOLIE 2009**

**JAZZ FOLKSONGS,SPIRITUALS & BLUES**
**Album:** Released Sep '81, on Good Time Jazz(USA) by Fantasy Inc (USA). Catalogue no: **1010 031**

**MOVE ON DOWN THE LINE**
Tracks: / Move on down the line / Stealing / Ninety-nine years and one dark day / Animal fair / Sleeping in the midnight cold / Stack o lee / Railroad worksong / Lining up the track / Hanging 'round a skin game / Railroad blues / San Francisco Bay blues.
Note: Veteran bluesman Fuller sings and plays 12-string guitar, harmonica, kazoo, fotdella and sock cymbals.
**Album:** Released '81, on Topic by Topic Records. Catalogue no: **12T 134**

**SAN FRANCISCO BAY BLUES**
Tracks: / San Francisco Bay blues / Jesse's new midnight special / Morning blues / Little black train / Midnight cold / Whoa mule / John Henry / I got a mind to ramble / Crazy about a woman (you're no good) / Where could I go but to the Lord / Stealin' back to my old time used to be / Brownskin girl (I've got my eye on you).
**Album:** Released Sep '82, on Contemporary (Import) Catalogue no: **1010 051**
**Album:** Released Sep '87, on Ace by Ace Records. Catalogue no: **CH 226**

## Fullerton College

**LOVE YA (Fullerton College Jazz Band)**
**Album:** Released '88, on Am-Pm (USA) Catalogue no: **AM 17**

**PRIMARILY JAZZ (Fullerton College Jazz Band)**
Tracks: / Licks and tricks / Shadow of a doubt / Four play / Shuffle this / Bop brothers' beach party / Say it, Roger /

Why not? / Morning sun.
**Album:** Released Apr '84, on Am-Pm (USA) Catalogue no: **AM 13**

**TIME TRIPPING (Fullerton College Jazz Band)**
Tracks: / Straight tone and strive ahead / Sienna / Cozumel rendezvous / Umpire strikes back, The / Battle of the bop brothers / Soft summer breeze / Beach bum memories / Yo mombo.
**Album:** Released Apr '84, on Am-Pm (USA) Catalogue no: **AM 10**

**UNFORGETTABLE (Fullerton College Big Band)**
Tracks: / In the mood / Sweet Georgia Brown / Easy living / Some day my prince will come / That's all and more / But beautiful.
Note: Winner of the 1985 National Association of Jazz Educator's Disney-world-competi-tion and opening band for the 1985 Playboy Jazz Festival: Tom Ranier/Jim Linahon/Jeff Tower/Doug Gregan/Tim Grindheim:
**CD:** on Am-Pm (USA) Catalogue no: **AMCD 15**
**Album:** Released '88, on Am-Pm (USA) Catalogue no: **AM 15**

## Fun On The Frets

**FUN ON THE FRETS (Early jazz guitar) (Various artists)**
**Album:** Released Dec '88, on Yazoo (USA) by Shanachie Records (USA). Catalogue no: **L 1061**

## Funk And Blues

**FUNK AND BLUES 1956-1967 (Blue Note 50th anniversary collection vol. 3) (Various artists)**
Tracks: / Senor blues: *Silver, Horace* / Song for my father: *Silver, Horace* / Moanin': *Blakey, Art\Jazz Messengers* / Back at the chicken shack: *Smith, Jimmy (USA)* / Cristo redentor: *Byrd, Donald* / Blue bossa: *Henderson, Joe/Kenny Dorham* / Funjii mama: *Mitchell, Blue* / Sidewinder, The: *Morgan, Lee* / Alligator Bogaloo: *Donaldson, Lou.*
**CD:** Released Jul '89, on Blue Note by EMI Records. Catalogue no: **CDB1 92471**
**2 LP Set:** Released Jul '89, on Blue Note by EMI Records. Catalogue no: **BST2 92471**
**Cass:** Released Jul '89, on Blue Note by EMI Records. Catalogue no: **TCBST2 92471**
**CD:** Released Jul '89, on Blue Note by EMI Records. Catalogue no: **CDBST2 92471**
**CD:** Released Jul '89, on Blue Note by EMI Records. Catalogue no: **CDP 792 471 2**

## Fylde Coast Jazzmen

**RUNNING WILD**
Tracks: / Indiana / Big butter and egg man / In a mellow tone / Royal garden blues / Bourbon Street parade / Mood indigo / Running wild / Doctor Jazz / Tiger rag.
**Album:** Released Jul '82, on Folk Heritage by Folk Heritage Records. Catalogue no: **FHR 088**

# G

This information was taken from the Music Master database on April 14th, 1990.

## Gadd, Steve

**Biographical details:** Born in 1954 in Rochester, New York, Gadd became the ultimate session drummer, his solos transcribed and published; the list of jazz, rock and pop records he has played on is just ridiculously long.
His sextet called Stuff included Richard Tee on keyboards and Cornell Dupree on guitar; albums on WB sold well in Japan. With Tee, Dupree, Eddie Gomez and Ronnie Cuber on reeds he recorded as the Gadd Gang, a more friendly group in which everybody solos on eclectic material. There is also an album called Gaddabout on *Projazz* in the USA. (Donald Clarke, July 1989).

### GADDABOUT

Tracks: / Gaddabout / My little brother / Montauk moon / Duke, The / Lucky 13 / Leavin' tomorrow.
Note: Steve Gadd's first album as leader. Strong rhythmic fusion jazz with R & B / Soul undertones. Music to dance to. All compositions by Steve Gadd and David Matthews. Personnel: Steve Gadd / Richard Tee / Jeff Mironov / Neil Jason / George Young/ Lew Soloff / Ronnie Cuber.
**Album:** Released Jul '86, on King (Japan) Catalogue no: **K 28P 6314**

## Gaillard, Slim

**Biographical details:** Vocalist, songwriter, multi-instrumentalist born in Detroit in 1916. Slim & Slam (duo with bassist Slam Stewart) had huge novelty hits in the late '30's including *Flat foot floosie*, covered by Fats Waller, Benny Goodman and many others. Postwar Gaillard hits included *Cement mixer (put-ti, put-ti)* in 1946.
He invented the jive *Vout Oreenie* language, and recorded with Charlie Parker. A square deejay declared *Yep roc heresay* as degenerate; it was a recitation of a menu from a Middle-Eastern restaurant. He lives in the UK; *Anytime, anyplace, anywhere* on Hep was made in London in 1982. (Donald Clarke, July 1989).

### ANYTIME, ANYPLACE, ANYWHERE

Tracks: / How high the moon / Anytime, anyplace, anywhere / I can't get started / Slim's jam No.2 / Everything's OK in the UK / Music goes round and around, The / Satin doll / Honeysuckle rose.
Note: Featuring Buddy Tate, Jay McShann.
**Album:** Released May '83, on Hep Jazz by Hep Records. Catalogue no: **HEP 2020**

### AT BIRDLAND: SLIM GAILLARD

Tracks: / Flat foot floosie No 1 / Cement mixer / Imagination / Sabroso / Flat foot floosie No 2 / Lady be good / Fine and dandy / Serenade in sulpher / Serenade in vout.
**Album:** Released Apr '81, on Hep Jazz by Hep Records. Catalogue no: **HEP 21**

### CEMENT MIXER PUT-TI PUT-TI

**Album:** Released Dec '86, on Folklyric (USA) by Arhoolie Records (USA). Catalogue no: **FL 9038**

### LAUGHING IN RHYTHM, 1945-51

**Album:** Released Oct '89, on Official by Official Records. Catalogue no: **OFF 3050**
**CD:** Released Oct '89, on Official by Official Records. Catalogue no: **OFF 83050CD**

### LEGENDARY MCVOUTY

**CD:** Released Oct '89, on Hep Jazz by Hep Records. Catalogue no: **HEPCD 6**

### OPERA IN VOUT

**Album:** Released Jun '82, on Verve Catalogue no: **2304 554**

### ROOTS OF VOUTY

Tracks: / Slim's jam / I don't know why / Dizzy boogie / School kids' hop / Poppity pop / Chicken rhythm / Riff City / Mean mama blues / Peanut vendor / Mean pretty mama / Santa Monica jump.
**Album:** Released Nov '83, on Putti-Putti Catalogue no: **PUT 01**

### SLIM GAILLARD, HELEN HUMES AND WILD BILL MOORE

**Album:** Released May '85, on Savoy Jazz (USA) by Malaco Records (USA). Catalogue no: **SJL 2242**

### SLIM GAILLARD ORIGINAL 1938

**CD:** Released 10 Aug '89, on Tax Catalogue no: **TAXCD S-1-2**

### TUTTI FRUTTI

**Album:** Released 7 Nov '87, on Swingtime by Contact Records (Denmark). Catalogue no: **ST 1018**
**Cass:** Released Dec '88, on Syndicate Chapter Catalogue no: **SC 1018**

### VOUTEST, THE

Tracks: / Tee say malee / Gaillard special / Dynamite / Yep roc heresy / Poppity pop / Gaillard special no. 2 / Bow tie Jim / Eastwood, Voutwood / Ya ha ya / Dunkin bagel / Laguna / Gaillard special no. 3 / Cement mixer.
**Album:** Released Jan '83, on Hep Jazz by Hep Records. Catalogue no: **HEP 28**

## Gainen, Maury

### JAZZ SUNRISE

Tracks: / Jazz sunrise / To the sea / In a sentimental mood / Out of the night came you / Night has a thousand eyes, The / Three for Bob / Little Linda / Mr. Wind / Spring can really hang you up the most.
Note: Maury Gainen - sax & flute, Roy McCurdy - drums, Bob Magnusson - bass, Milcho Leviev - keyboards.
**Album:** Released Jun '83, on Discovery (USA) by Discovery Records (USA). Catalogue no: **DS 855**

## Gaines, Roy

### GAINELINING

Tracks: / First rule of cheating / Low-down and funky / Baby, what you want me to do? / It's too late, brother / It came on time / Hell of a night tonight / Houston, Texas / Short-haired woman / Roy's new 6 am 3 o'clock blues / Okie dokie stomp.
**Album:** Released May '86, on Red Lightnin' by Red Lightning Records. Catalogue no: **RL 035**

## Galbraith, Charlie

### PORTRAIT OF CHARLIE GALBRAITH

Tracks: / Jeepers creepers / Lover come back to me / Days of wine and roses / I surrender dear / Limehouse blues / Stars fell on Alabama / I'll remember April / Struttin' with some barbeque.
Note: Charlie is one of the stalwarts of the British jazz scene, having led the Charlie Galbraith Allstars as well as playing trombone in other well known bands. On this record he is joined by Al Gay, Clarinet / tenor, Jack Parnell, drums, Keith Rolt, piano and Pip Hallman, bass.
**Album:** Released Nov '81, on Plant Life by Plant Life Records. Catalogue no: **PLR 006**

## Gallivan, Joe

### EXPRESSION TO WINDS (Gallivan, Joe & Charles Austin)

**Album:** Released May '78, on Spitball Deleted '86. Catalogue no: **SB 6**

### MERCY DASH (Gallivan, Joe, Keith Tipett, Elton Dean, Hugh Hopper)

Note: For full information see under: Tippett, Keith/Gallivan, Joe/Dean, Elton/Hopper, Hugh.
**Album:** Released '87, on UNKNOWN Deleted Jun '89. Catalogue no: **CP 2001**

## Galloway, Jim

### BOJANGLES

**Album:** Released Mar '81, on Hep Jazz by Hep Records. Catalogue no: **HEP 2008**

**METRO STOMPERS**
Tracks: / Blues my naughty sweetie gives to me.
Note: Recorded live in Toronto, 15 September, 1973.
**Album:** Released Apr '81, on Sackville by Spotlite Records. Catalogue no: **4002**

**THOU SWELL (Galloway, Jim Quartet & Jay McShann)**
Tracks: / Thou swell / Someone to watch over me / Wrap your troubles in dreams / Black butterfly / Sweet Sue / I've got the world on a string / Just a gigolo / Humoresque / I only have eyes for you.
Note: Recorded 15 and 16 June, 1981.
**Album:** Released May '83, on Sackville by Spotlite Records. Catalogue no: **4011**

**THREE IS COMPANY (Galloway, Jim/Dick Wellstood and Pete Magadini)**
Tracks: / Minor drag / Lulu's back in town / Broken windmill / Sunday morning / Blues Alley bump / After you've gone / Buddy Bolden's blues / I'd climb the highest mountain / Let's get away from it all / Everything I've got.
Note: Recorded 22 September, 1973.
**Album:** Released Apr '79, on Sackville by Spotlite Records. Catalogue no: **2007**

## Gambale, Frank

**BRAVE NEW GUITAR**
Note: A former pupil and teacher at the Guitar Institute of Technology in LA, Frank Gambale is without doubt one of the most technically accomplished guitarists in the world. After spells with both Jeff Berlin and Jean Luc Ponty, he realised a life's ambition by joining Chick Corea's Electric Band.
**Album:** Released May '89, on Music Maker Catalogue no: **UNKNOWN**

**PRESENT FOR THE FUTURE**
**Album:** Released May '89, on Music Maker Catalogue no: **UNKNOWN**
**CD:** Released May '89, on Music Maker Catalogue no: **UNKNOWN**

## Ganelin Trio

**Biographical details:** A Soviet jazz trio combining Russian soul with the influence of the avant-garde of the '60's: formed in Vilnius, Lithuania c. 1947 by pianist Vyacheslav Ganelin, Vladimir Chekasin on reeds and drummer Vladimir Tarasov (all are multi-instrumentalists). Now that the artists are allowed to use structure as a tool in their kit instead of joining a category, 'jazz' has become a truly international language; like all the best Russian, then Soviet artists, the trio were unafraid of eclecticism, borrowing from chamber music, folk and ethnic musics, as well as indulging in some zany humour. They have now broken up. Ganelin emigrated to Israel. (Donald Clarke, July 1989).

**ANCORA DA CAPO**
**Album:** Released Sep '84, on Leo by Leo Records. Catalogue no: **LR 108**

**ANCORA DA CAPO (2)**
**Album:** Released Sep '84, on Leo by Leo Records. Catalogue no: **LR 109**

**BALTIC TRIANGLE**
**Album:** Released 1 Mar '88, on Leo by Leo Records. Catalogue no: **LR 125**

**CON AFFETTO**
**Album:** Released Oct '85, on Leo by Leo Records. Catalogue no: **LR 137**

**CON FUOCO**
**Album:** Released Sep '84, on Leo by Leo Records. Catalogue no: **LR 106**

**GANELIN TRIO**
**Album:** Released Jun '89, on Leo by Leo Records. Catalogue no: **LR 168**

**GREAT CONCERTS OF NEW JAZZ**
**2 LP Set:** Released Jan '87, on Leo by Leo Records. Catalogue no: **LR 400/401**

**LIVE IN EAST GERMANY**
**Album:** Released Sep '84, on Leo by Leo Records. Catalogue no: **LR 102**

**NEW WINE**
**Album:** Released Sep '84, on Leo by Leo Records. Catalogue no: **LR 112**

**POCO A POCO**
**CD:** Released Feb '89, on Leo by Leo Records. Catalogue no: **CDLR 101**

**STRICTLY FOR OUR FRIENDS**
**Album:** Released Sep '84, on Leo by Leo Records. Catalogue no: **LR 120**

**VIDE**
**Album:** Released Sep '84, on Leo by Leo Records. Catalogue no: **LR 117**

## Ganeling Duos

**GREAT CONCERTS OF NEW JAZZ (Ganeling Duos, Chekasin & Tarasov)**
**2 LP Set:** Released Oct '88, on Leo by Leo Records. Catalogue no: **LR 410/11**

## Gant, Cecil

**Biographical details:** A blues based pianist and a crooner of considerable crossover appeal (1913-51). His ballad *Wonder* in late 1944, billed as *Pvt. Cecil Grant*, made No. 1 on the Harlem Hit Parade, (as the 'race' chart was called then), and sold impressively nationwide. He toured as The G I Singsation dressed in army khaki, breaking attendance records at major venues, attracting both black and white audiences, but was unlucky, perhaps too early: it was left to Nat Cole and Billy Eckstine to find the lucrative 'Sepia Sinatra' market. He died of pneumonia. (Donald Clarke, July 1989)

**CECIL BOOGIE**
**Album:** Released Sep '76, on Flyright by Interstate Music. Catalogue no: **FLY 4714**

**I'M STILL SINGING THE BLUES**
**Album:** Released '88, on Oldie Blues Catalogue no: **OL 8004**

**KILLER DILLER BOOGIE**
**Album:** Released Jun '79, on Magpie by Interstate Music. Catalogue no: **PY 1816**

**ROCK LITTLE BABY**
**Album:** Released Oct '76, on Flyright by Interstate Music. Catalogue no: **FLY 4714**

**ROCK THIS BOOGIE**
Tracks: / Cecil boogie / Hit that jive Jack / Hogan's alley / I gotta gal / Boogie blues / Little baby you're running wild / Long distance / Am I to blame / Rock the boogie / Blues in LA / Cecil boogie No. 2 / What's on your worried mind / Stuff you gotta watch / Syncopated boogie / Time will tell / Cecil's mop mop.
**Album:** Released May '83, on Krazy Kat by Interstate Music. Catalogue no: **KK 7413**

## Garbarek, Jan

**Biographical details:** Jazzman playing reeds and flute, born in Norway in 1947. Self-taught after hearing John Coltrane on the radio, he played with the George Russell Orchestra (then resident in Scandinavia) and soon began recording for ECM. He is unique in not being derivative at all; he plays a blend of new and old, but plays his own thoughts instead of other people's licks; his style is influenced by folk music and it's sound is ascetic, but the feeling behind it is not. (Donald Clarke, July 1989).

**AFTENLAND**
**CD:** Released Nov '89, on ECM Catalogue no: **839 304 2**
**Album:** Released Nov '89, on ECM Catalogue no: **ECM 1169**

**ALL THOSE BORN WITH WINGS**
Tracks: / Last clown, The / Yellow fever / Soulful Bill / La divetta / Cool train / Loop, The.
Note: Saxophonist Jan Garbarek's first solo album and released on the eve of his first British tour. After years of experimenting with all sorts of electronic sounds in group formats, he has created an album that is hauntingly beautiful with a sound structure that has a strong visual component.
**Album:** Released Feb '87, on ECM Catalogue no: **ECM 1324**
**CD:** Released Mar '87, on ECM Catalogue no: **831 394 2**

**DANSERE**
**CD:** Released Oct '86, on ECM Catalogue no: **829 193 2**

**DIS**
Tracks: / Vandrere / Krusning / Viddene / Skygger / YR / Dis.
Note: Personnel: Jan Garbarek - tenor and soprano sax, wood flute / Ralph Towner - 12 string and classical guitars.
**CD:** Released Feb '86, on ECM Catalogue no: **827 408-2**

**ESOTERIC CIRCLE**
Tracks: / Traneflight / Rabalder / Esoteric circle / VIPs / S.A.S. 644 / Nefertiti / Gee / Karin's mode / Breeze ending.
**CD:** Released Dec '87, on Freedom Catalogue no: **FCD 41031**
**Album:** Released Sep '87, on Freedom Catalogue no: **FLP 41031**

**EVENTYR**
**CD:** Released Aug '88, on ECM Catalogue no: **829 384 2**

Jan Garbarek

**Album:** Released Nov '81, on ECM Catalogue no: **ECM 1200**

**FOLK SONGS**
Tracks: / Folk songs / Bodas De Prata / Cego Aderaldo / Veien / Equilibrista / For Turiya.
Note: Personnel: Charlie Haden - bass / Jan Garbarek - tenor and soprano sax/Egberto Gismonti - 8 string guitar, super 8 guitar, piano.
**CD:** Released Jul '86, on ECM Catalogue no: **827 702 2**

**GRAY VOICE, THE**
**CD:** Released Aug '88, on ECM Catalogue no: **825 406-2**

**LEGEND OF THE SEVEN DREAMS**
Tracks: / He comes from the north / Aichuri, the song man / Tongue of secrets / Brother wind / It's name is secret road / Send word / Voy cantado / Mirror store.
Note: This album features solo, trio & quartet performances.
The supporting musicians are Eberhard Weber, Nana Vasconcelos & Rainer Bruninghaus.
**Album:** Released Oct '88, on ECM Catalogue no: **ECM 1381**
**CD:** Released Oct '88, on ECM Catalogue no: **837 344-2**

**LISTEN TO THE GRAY VOICE**
**Album:** Released Nov '85, on ECM Catalogue no: **ECM 1294**

**PATHS, PRINTS**
**Album:** Released Dec '82, on ECM Deleted Dec '87. Catalogue no: **ECM 1223**

**PLACES**
**CD:** Released Oct '86, on ECM Catalogue no: **829 195 2**

**WAYFARER**
Tracks: / Gesture / Wayfarer / Gentle / Pendulum / Spor / Singsong.
Note: Personnel: Jan Garbarek - tenor and soprano sax / Bill Frisell - guitar / Eberhard Weber - bass / MichaelDiPasquad-drums,percussion
For the last decade, Jan Garbarek has been recognised, as the perhaps most important and influential European soloist. With his current group, that has already toured the USA, Canada and Europe, he might achieve a similiar status as a bandleader.
This new album with guitarist Bill Frisell, bassist Eberhard Weber and drummer MichaeL Di Pasqua has the potential to attract a large audience that could range from jazz listeners to the followers of sophisticated rock, as it represents Garbarek's most explosive and driving music to date.
**Album:** Released Sep '83, on ECM Catalogue no: **ECM 1259**
**CD:** Released Aug '86, on ECM Catalogue no: **8119682**

**WITCHI-TAI-TO**
Tracks: / A.I.R. / Kukka / Hasta simpre / Witchi-tai-to / Desireless.
**CD:** Released Mar '88, on ECM Catalogue no: **8333302**

**WORKS: JAN GARBAREK**
Tracks: / Folk songs (From Folk Songs ECM 1170) / Skirk and hyl (From Dansere ECM 1075) / Passing (From Places ECM 1118) / Selje (From Tryptykon ECM 1029) / Viddene (From Dis ECM 1093) / Snipp, snapp, snute (From Eventyr ECM 1200) / Beast of Kommode (From Afric Pepperbird ECM 1007) / Svevende (From Dansere ECM 1075).
Note: Personnel: Jan Garbarek, Charlie Haden, Egberto Gismonti, Jack Dejohnette, Terje Rypdal, Nana Vasconcelos.
**CD:** Released Jun '89, on ECM Catalogue no: **823 266-2**
**Album:** Released Jun '89, on ECM Catalogue no: **823 266-1**

## Garber, Jan

**Biographical details:** An American dance band leader (1897-1977) who alternated between sweet and hot styles. He had over 60 (mostly sweet) hits between 1923-51 and continued popular in hotel work. (Donald Clarke, July 1989)d.

**JAN GARBER 1939-41**
Tracks: / My dear / It's a wonderful world / Rose room / Tumbling tumbleweeds / Do you ever think of me / Oh what you said / Siren's song, The / Lady be good / Stardust / Because of you / Birth of the blues / I hear a rhapsody / Whispering / Love song of Renaldo / Somebody loves me / I'll see you in my dreams.

Note: Jan Garber earned his title of "Idol of the Air Lanes" both from live broadcasts and from the beaming of such top-notch radio transcriptions as the ones which are the source of this album. Alto saxophonist-musical director Freddie Large, whose band merged with Garber's in the early 30's, trumpeter Fritz Heilbron and trombonist Don Shoup are the principal instrumental soloists.
Heilbron and Lee Bennett split the vocal interpretations four each of tunes that, for the personable Garber, became repeatedly requested "standards" although he never recorded most of them commercially.
(Hindsight Catalogue - 1989)
**Album:** Released '88, on Hindsight Catalogue no: **HSR 130**

**JAN GARBER AND ORCHESTRA 1944 (Garber, Jan & His Orchestra)**
Note: Featuring Liz Tilton/Bob Davis
**Album:** Released Jun '88, on Circle (USA) by Jazzology Records (USA). Catalogue no: **CLP 99**

**JAN GARBER & ORCHESTRA PLAY 22 (Garber, Jan & His Orchestra)**
**Album:** Released Jun '84, on Hindsight Catalogue no: **HSR 403**

**UNCOLLECTED JAN GARBER & HIS ORCHESTRA (Garber, Jan & His Orchestra)**
Tracks: / Who / Maria Elena / Things we did last summer, The / Paper moon / More than you know / Bye bye blues / Dancing in the dark / Prisoner of love /

Diane / Old buttermille sly / Over the rainbow / Cherokee.
**Album:** Released Apr '85, on Hindsight Catalogue no: **HUK 204**

## Garcia, Russell

### I LEAD A CHARMED LIFE
Note: Arranged and conducted by Garcia. Features Bill Watrous-trombone, Mike Wofford - piano, Jim Plank - drums and percussion, Chuck Findley - flugelhorn & trumpet, Teddy Edwards - tenor sax, Jopel Di Bartolo - bass.
**Album:** Released '88, on Discovery (USA) by Discovery Records (USA). Catalogue no: **DS 814**

### JAZZ VARIATIONS
**CD:** Released '88, on Trend (USA) by Trend Records (USA). Catalogue no: **TRCD 542**

### JOHNNY EVER GREEN'S, THE (Garcia, Russell Orchestra)
Tracks: / Body and soul / Who do you think you are / Living in dreams / Out of nowhere / I wanna be loved / Steam is on the beam, The / Trembling of a leaf / Easy come, easy go / I cover the waterfront / Coquette / You're mine you / Not bad / Hello, my lover, goodbye / There's a ring around the Moon / I'm yours / With you, with me.
Note: With Sue Allen, Eddie Robertson, The Jud Conlon Rhythmaires, John T. Williams and Don Fagerquist
**Album:** Released Feb '88, on Fresh Sounds (Spain) by Fresh Sounds Records (Spain). Catalogue no: **FS 240**

### VARIATIONS FOR FLUGELHORN,
Note: Featuring Chuck Findley - flugelhorn, the Di Vinci String Quartet, Bob Magnusson - bass, Steve Schaeffer - drums.
**Album:** Released '88, on Trend (USA) by Trend Records (USA). Catalogue no: **TR 522**

## Gardner, Freddy

### 1935-37
**Album:** Released Mar '89, on Harlequin by Interstate Music. Catalogue no: **HQ 3018**

### FREDDY GARDNER AND SWING ORCHESTRA (Gardner, Freddy & His Swing Orchestra)
**Album:** Released Mar '90, on Harlequin by Interstate Music. Catalogue no: **HQ3027**

### MUSIC MAESTRO PLEASE (Gardner, Freddy & His Swing Orchestra)
Tracks: / Music maestro please / Dipsy doodle / Limehouse blues / Nobody's sweetheart / Bugle call rag / My sweetie went away / You can't stop me from dreaming / I double dare you / Jeepers creepers / They say / Hold tight, hold tight / Snake charmer, The / Tiger rag / Dinah / Temptation rag / Have you got any castles, baby? / Tom, Tom, the piper's son / I want to be happy.
**Album:** Released Aug '84, on Recollections (Decca) by Decca Records. Catalogue no: **RFL 44**

## Garland, Red

**Biographical details:** Texas-born pianist (1923-84) most famous for membership in classic Miles Davies Quintet of 1956-58, but always a stylish and influential player. He made over 30 albums on *Prestige* and other labels, almost all trio sets. (Donald Clarke, July 1989).

### ARTISTRY IN JAZZ
**CD:** Released Jul '87, on JVC/Fantasy Catalogue no: **VDJ 1591**
**Album:** Released '88, on Timeless by Timeless Records. Catalogue no: **SJP 179**

### BRIGHT AND BREEZY
**Album:** Released Jan '87, on Original Jazz Classics (USA) by Fantasy Inc (USA). Catalogue no: **OJC 265**

### CROSSINGS
**Album:** Released '79, on Galaxy (1) by President Records. Deleted '84. Catalogue no: **GXY 5106**

### FEELIN' RED
Tracks: / It's alright with me / You better go now / On a clear day / Going home / Second time around / I wish I knew / Cherokee.
**Album:** Released Apr '81, on Muse by Black & Blue Records. Catalogue no: **MR 5130**

### GROOVY (Garland, Red Trio)
**CD:** Released May '89, on Carrere (France) Catalogue no: **98439**
**Album:** Released Jun '86, on Original Jazz Classics (USA) by Fantasy Inc (USA). Catalogue no: **OJC 061**

### I LEFT MY HEART
Tracks: / Will you still be mine / Please send me someone to love / Bye bye Blackbird / Body and soul / Bag's Groove / I left my heart in San Francisco.
Note: Produced by: Todd Barkan / Assistant Producer - Michael Bloom / Recorded live at Keystone Korner / San Fransisco, Calif. MaY, 1978. Red Garland - Piano / Leo Wright - Alto sax. (Side two only) Chris Amberger - Bass / Eddie Moore - drums.
**Album:** Released Jan '86, on Muse by Black & Blue Records. Catalogue no: **MR 5311**

### MISTY RED (Garland, Red Trio)
**CD:** Released '86, on RCA Jazz (Japan) Catalogue no: **886 000**

### MOODSVILLE 6 (Garland, Red Trio)
**Album:** Released Apr '86, on Original Jazz Classics (USA) by Fantasy Inc (USA). Catalogue no: **OJC 224**

### RED ALERT
**Album:** Released '79, on Galaxy (1) by President Records. Deleted '84. Catalogue no: **GXY 5109**

### RED GARLAND'S PIANO
Tracks: / Please send me someone to love / Stompin' at The Savoy / Very thought of you, The / Almost like being in love / If I were a bell / I know why / But not for me / I can't give you anything but love.
**Album:** Released Feb '84, on Prestige (USA) by Fantasy Inc (USA). Catalogue no: **OJC 073**

### SAYING SOMETHING
Tracks: / Undecided / What is there to say / Two bass hit / Billie's bounce / Soft winds / Solitude / Lazy Mae / On Green Dolphin Street / If you could see me now.
**Album:** Released Apr '80, on Prestige Deleted '85. Catalogue no: **PR 24090**

### SOUL JUNCTION (Garland, Red Quintet & John Coltrane)
**CD:** Released May '87, on JVC/Fantasy Catalogue no: **VDJ 1523**

### STEPPING OUT
Tracks: / Yours is my heart alone / You stepped out of a dream / I wish I knew / Have you met Miss Jones / Daahound / Here's that rainy day.
**Album:** Released Aug '81, on Galaxy (1) by President Records. Deleted Aug '86. Catalogue no: **GXY 5129**

## Garnas, Agnes Buen

### ROSENSFOLE (Garnas, Agnes Buen and Jan Garbarek)
**CD:** Released Jun '89, on ECM Catalogue no: **839 293 2**
**Cass:** Released Jun '89, on ECM Catalogue no: **839 293 4**
**Album:** Released Jun '89, on ECM Catalogue no: **ECM 1402**

## Garner, Erroll

**Biographical details:** This American jazz pianist and composer was dubbed one of the great romantics of the genre. His melodic instincts and rich chords were exemplified by his best known tune *Misty*, which he composed in 1954. *Misty* was initially performed as an instrumental by the Erroll Garner Trio. Lyrics were added by Johnny Burke in 1955. The song was made famous in the pop market by Johnny Mathis, who took it to no. 12 in the US in 1959 and the same position in the UK in 1960. Fifteen years later, Ray Stevens scored a countrified hit with it. As a performer, Garner's only taste of UK chart success occurred in July 1962, when the *Close up in swing* LP reached no. 20. This meagre track record was a scant reflection of his importance, and underlined the fact that even the bast jazz artists have difficulty in overcoming the "specialist" and "minority interest" tags. Garner died in January 1957 at the age of 53. (Bob MacDonald, 16/9/85)
Also affectionately called the Elf, Errol Garner (1923-77) was self taught and could not read music; his irrepressible humour, swing and gift for melody made him one of the most popular jazz musicians of all. His most famous composition was *Misty* in 1954, repeatedly honoured by ASCAP as one of the most-played standards of past decades. His *Concert by the sea*, made live in Carmel, California in 1956, is one of the best-selling jazz records of all time, but listen to other CBS records before you buy: some of them have slushy orchestras dubbed

on them. (Donald Clarke, July 1989).

**1945**
**Album:** Released '88, on Zeta Catalogue no: **ZET 713**

**AT THE PIANO**
Tracks: / Caravan / No greater love / Avalon / Lullaby of Birdland / Memories of you / Will you still be mine.
**Album:** Released Aug '86, on Avan-Guard Catalogue no: **BVL 040**
**Album:** Released Jun '86, on CBS (import) by CBS Records. Catalogue no: **62311**

**BEST OF COMPACT JAZZ**
**CD:** Released Jan '90, on Mercury by Phonogram Ltd. Catalogue no: **830 695 2**
**Cass:** Released Jan '90, on Mercury by Phonogram Ltd. Catalogue no: **830 695 4**

**CLASSIC PIANOS**
Tracks: / Blueberry rhyme / Blues for Fats / Honeysuckle rose / Squeeze me / My fate is in your hands / I've got a feeling I'm falling / I've found a new baby / Four or five times / Yesterdays / Loot to boot / Gaslight.
Note: In addition to Garner, this album / tape features three other great jazz pianists - Earl Hines, James P. Johnson and Art Hodes - plus Rod Cless (clarinet).
**Cass:** Released Mar '84, on Doctor Jazz (USA) by CBS Records (USA). Catalogue no: **ZCAS 802**

**CLOSEUP IN SWING**
**Album:** Released Feb '85, on RCA (France) by BMG Records (France). Catalogue no: **NL 89431**
**Album:** Released Jul '62, on Philips by Phonogram Ltd. Deleted '67. Catalogue no: **BBL 7579**

**COMPACT JAZZ: ERROLL GARNER**
Tracks: / Misty / Oh lady be good / Begin the beguine.
**Cass:** Released Jul '87, on Phonogram by Phonogram Ltd. Catalogue no: **831 695-4**
**CD:** Released Jul '87, on Phonogram by Phonogram Ltd. Catalogue no: **831 695-2**

**COMPLETE SAVOY SESSIONS 1 (1945 - 49)**
Tracks: / Play fiddle play / Dark eyesky / Laff slam laff / Jumpin' at the deuces / Laura / Stardust / Somebody loves me / Back home again in Indiana / I cover the waterfront / It's easy to remember / Penthouse serenade / Love walked in / September song / Body and soul.
**Cass:** Released Nov '86, on RCA by BMG Records (UK). Deleted Nov '89. Catalogue no: **WK 70521**
**Album:** Released Jan '87, on RCA by BMG Records (UK). Deleted Nov '89. Catalogue no: **WL 70521**

**COMPLETE SAVOY SESSIONS 2 (1949)**
**Album:** Released '87, on Jazz Tribune by BMG Records (UK). Deleted Nov '89. Catalogue no: **WL 70542**
**Cass:** Released '87, on Jazz Tribune by BMG Records (UK). Deleted Nov '89. Catalogue no: **WK 70542**

**COMPLETE SAVOY SESSIONS 3**
Tracks: / This can't be love / Man I love, The / Moonglow / I want a little girl / She's funny that way / Until the real thing comes along / Confessin' / Stormy weather / On the sunny side of the street / Rosalie / Everything happens to me / Stairway to the stars.
**Album:** Released Feb '87, on RCA by BMG Records (UK). Deleted Nov '89. Catalogue no: **WL 70833**
**Cass:** Released Feb '87, on RCA by BMG Records (UK). Deleted Nov '89. Catalogue no: **WK 70833**

**CONCERT BY THE SEA**
Tracks: / I'll remember April / Teach me tonight / Mambo Carmel / It's all right with me / Red top / April in Paris / They can't take that away from me / Where or when / Erroll's theme.
**Cass:** Released 27 Feb '88, on CBS (import) by CBS Records. Catalogue no: **4510424**
**Album:** Released 27 Feb '88, on CBS (import) by CBS Records. Catalogue no: **4510421**
**Cass:** Released Jun '86, on CBS (import) by CBS Records. Catalogue no: **4062310**

**DREAMY**
**Album:** Released Jun '86, on CBS (import) by CBS Records. Catalogue no: **84267**

**EASY TO LOVE**
**Album:** Released Jun '88, on Emarcy Catalogue no: **832 994 1**
**CD:** Released Jun '88, on Emarcy Catalogue no: **832 994 2**

**ELF, THE**
Tracks: / Cover the waterfront / Love walked in / I don't stand a ghost of a chance / Indiana / Somebody loves me / Body and soul / Penthouse serenade / Undecided / Red sails in the sunset / I can't believe that you're in love with me / Stompin' at the Savoy / Stardust / More than you know / Over the rainbow / Laura / This can't be love / Man I love, The / Moonglow / I want a little girl / It's easy to remember / Goodbye / She's funny that way / Until the real thing comes along / Confessin' / Stormy weather / I surrender dear / I'm in the mood for love / All of me.
**Album:** Released Mar '85, on Savoy Jazz (USA) by Malaco Records (USA). Catalogue no: **SJL 2207**

**ENCORES IN HI FI**
Tracks: / Moonglow / Sophisticated Lady / Robbins' nest / Creme De Menthe / Humouresque / How high the moon / Fancy / Groovy day / Man I love,The.
**Album:** Released Jun '86, on CBS by CBS Records. Deleted Jun '88. Catalogue no: **CBS 21134**
**Cass:** Released Jun '86, on CBS by CBS Records. Catalogue no: **40 21134**

**ERROLL GARNER & ART TATUM Vol. 1 (Garner, Erroll & Art Tatum)**
**Album:** Released Aug '81, on Kings Of Jazz Catalogue no: **KLJ 20020**

**ERROLL GARNER COLLECTION (20 Golden Greats)**
Tracks: / Misty / Girl from Ipanema / Rosalie / I'm in the mood for love / All of me / September song / Stardust / Body and soul / I only have eyes for you / There will never be another you / Man I love, The / It's easy to remember / On the sunny side of the street / This can't be love / Red sails in the sunset / All the things you are / She's funny that way / Over the rainbow / Until the real thing comes along / Stormy weather.
**Album:** Released Aug '85, on Deja Vu Catalogue no: **DVLP 2016**
**Cass:** Released Aug '85, on Deja Vu Catalogue no: **DVMC 2016**
**CD:** Released Jun '88, on Deja Vu Catalogue no: **DVCD 2016**

**ERROLL GARNER GEMS**
Tracks: / Laura / Indiana / I'm in the mood for love / Way you look tonight / Penthouse serenade / Frenesi / Play, piano, play / Body and soul / I cover the waterfront / Oh lady be good / Mean to me / Easy to love.
**Album:** Released Jul '86, on CBS by CBS Records. Catalogue no: **CBS 21062**
**Cass:** Released Jul '86, on CBS by CBS Records. Deleted Jan '89. Catalogue no: **40 21062**

**ERROLL GARNER PLAYS GERSHWIN AND KERN**
Tracks: / Strike up the band / I got rhythm / Foggy day, A / Can't help lovin' dat man / Ol' man river / Fine romance, A / Love walked in / Someone to watch over me / Lovely to look at / Only make believe.
**Album:** Released Sep '83, on Bulldog Records by President Records. Catalogue no: **BDL 4004**

**ERROLL GARNER QUARTET (Garner, Erroll Quartet)**
**Album:** Released '88, on Joker (USA) by Lifetime Records (USA). Catalogue no: **SM 3911**

**ERROLL GARNER: Vol. 1**
Tracks: / Body and soul / All of me / More than you know / Penthouse serenade / I only have eyes for you / September song / Red sails in the sunset / I can't believe that you're in love with me / Stardust / All the things you are / On the sunny side of the street.
Note: Erroll Garner -- piano; John Simmons -- bass; Alvin Stoller -- drums. Recorded in Los Angeles, 1949.
**Cass:** Released '88, on Joker (USA) by Lifetime Records (USA). Catalogue no: **MC 3718**
**Album:** Released Apr '81, on Joker (USA) by Lifetime Records (USA). Catalogue no: **SM 3718**

**ERROLL GARNER: Vol. 2**
**Album:** Released Apr '81, on Joker (USA) by Lifetime Records (USA). Catalogue no: **SM 3719**

**ERROLL'S A GARNER**
**CD:** Released Dec '86, on Vogue by Vogue Records. Catalogue no: **VGCD 600110**

**GARNER CONCERT, THE**
**Album:** Released Jul '82, on Jazz Groove Catalogue no: **JG 008**

**GEMINI**
Tracks: / How high the moon / It could happen to you / Gemini / When a gypsy makes his violin cry / Tea for two / Something / Eldorado / These foolish things.
**Cass:** Released Jun '85, on Bulldog Records by President Records. Catalogue no: **BDC 4007**
**Album:** Released Jun '85, on Bulldog Records by President Records. Catalogue no: **BDL 4007**

**GREAT GARNER, THE**
Tracks: / Way you look tonight / Turquoise / Pavanne / Impressions / Confessin' / I may be wrong / Skylark / Summertime / Flamingo / Reverie / Blue and sentimental / I can't give you anything but love.
**Album:** Released '79, on Atlantic by WEA Records. Catalogue no: **50243**

**HISTORIC FIRST RECORDING, THE**
**CD:** Released Oct '89, on Jazz Anthology by Musidisc Records (France). Catalogue no: **550 042**

**IMMORTAL CONCERTS (Carmel, California, Sept 1955 and Seattle March, 1963)**
**CD:** Released '88, on Giants of Jazz by Hasmick Promotions. Catalogue no: **GOJCD 53034**

**JAZZ TIME VOL 7**
**Album:** Released '88, on Vogue (France) by Vogue Records. Catalogue no: **502707**

**KING OF THE JAZZ PIANO**
Tracks: / Moonglow / Stardust / Confessin' / Over the rainbow / All of me / I surrender dear / Undecided / Stormy weather / Stompin' at the savoy / I'm in the mood for love / Red sails in the sunset / I can't believe you're in love with me.
**Album:** Released May '85, on Meteor by Magnum Music Group. Catalogue no: **MTM 011**

**LIVE: ERROLL GARNER TRIO (Garner Trio, Erroll)**
Tracks: / Theme...Tippin' out and introduction / Just too marvellous for words / Misty / Stompin' at the Savoy / 7-11 jump, The / Lover / I'll remember April / Dreamin' / Passin' through / Two handed blues / I only have eyes for you / Theme...Tippin' out / It's alright with Met / Where or when / Tea for three.
**Album:** Released Sep '87, on Flyright by Interstate Music. Catalogue no: **EB 404**

**LONG AGO AND FAR AWAY**
Tracks: / When Johnny Comes Marching Home / It Could Happen To You / I Don't Know Why / It Could Happen To You / My Heart Stood Still / When you're smiling / Long Ago And Far Away / Poor Butterfly / Spring Is Here / Petite waltz / Petite waltz bounce, The / Lover / How high the moon / People Will Say We're In Love / Laura / I Cover The Waterfront / Penthouse Serenade.
**Album:** Released Apr '88, on CBS (import) by CBS Records. Catalogue no: **4606141**

**MAMBO MONES**
**CD:** Released Jan '90, on Verve Catalogue no: **8349092**

**MISTY**
Tracks: / Misty / Very thought of you, The / It might as well be spring / Dreamy / I didn't know what time it was / Moment's delight / On the street where you live / Other voices / This is always / Solitaire / St. Louis blues / Summertime / 'S wonderful / Easy to love / Way you look tonight / I'm in the mood for love.
**Cass:** Released Mar '83, on CBS Cameo by CBS Records. Deleted Jan '89. Catalogue no: **40-32260**
**Album:** Released Mar '83, on CBS Cameo by CBS Records. Deleted Aug '88. Catalogue no: **CBS 32260**

**MISTY/CONCERT BY THE SEA**
Tracks: / Misty / Very thought of you, The / It might as well be spring / Dreamy / I didn't know what time it was / Moment's delight / On the street where you live / Other voices / This is always / Solitaire / St. Louis blues / Summertime / 'S wonderful / Easy to love / I'll remember April / Teach me tonight / Mambo Carmel / Autumn leaves / It's alright with me / Red top / April in Paris / They can't take that away from me / How could you do a thing like this to me? / Where or when / Erroll's theme / Way you look tonight / I'm in the mood for love.
**Album:** Released Jun '85, on CBS (Blue Diamond) by CBS Records. Catalogue no: **CBS 22185**
**Cass:** Released Jun '85, on CBS (Blue Diamond) by CBS Records. Catalogue no: **40 22185**

**MOONGLOW**
**Album:** Released Dec '84, on Pathe Marconi (France) Catalogue no: **PM 1652401**
**Cass:** Released Dec '84, on Pathe Marconi (France) Catalogue no: **1652404**

**MOST HAPPY PIANO**
Tracks: / But not for me / Alexander's ragtime band / Time on my hands / Girl of my dreams / Mambo 207 / Way back blues / Ol' man river / Full moon and empty arms / Passing through.
**Cass:** Released Jul '87, on CBS by CBS Records. Deleted Jan '89. Catalogue no: **450306 4**
**Album:** Released Jul '87, on CBS by CBS Records. Deleted Aug '88. Catalogue no: **450306 1**

**NIGHT AT THE MOVIES, A**
Tracks: / You made me love you / As time goes by / Sonny boy / Charmaine / I found a million dollar baby / I'll get by / Three o'clock in the morning / Stella by starlight / Jeannine I dream of lilac time / Schoner gigolo, armer gigolo / How deep is the ocean? / It's only a paper moon / Paramount on parade.
**Album:** Released '86, on Bulldog Records by President Records. Catalogue no: **BDL 4005**

**OTHER VOICES**
Tracks: / Misty / Very thought of you, The / It might as well be spring / Dreamy / I didn't know what time it was / Moment's delight / On the street / Where you live / Other voices / This is always / Solitaire.
**Album:** Released Mar '86, on CBS by CBS Records. Deleted Aug '87. Catalogue no: **CBS 32736**
**Cass:** Released Mar '86, on CBS by CBS Records. Deleted Aug '87. Catalogue no: **40 32736**

**OVERTURE TO DAWN**
Tracks: / I hear a rhapsody / You were born to be kissed / Overture to dawn / Autumn mood / Erroll's concerto / Floating on a cloud / I surrender dear / I got rhythm / On the sunny side of the street / Yesterdays / Fast company / Duke for dinner / Fighting cocks, The / Erroll's reverie / Lick and a promise, A / All the things you are / Gas light / Opus 1 / Clock stood still, The.
**CD:** on Official by Official Records. Catalogue no: **OFF 83016-3**
**LP Set:** on Official by Official Records. Catalogue no: **OFF 3016-3**

**PLAY PIANO, PLAY**
Tracks: / Play piano, play / Love is the strangest game / Blues Garni / Don't worry 'bout me / Loose nut / Love for sale / Frankie and Johnny / Sloe gin fizz / Pastel / Trio.
**2 LP Set:** Released Oct '88, on Vogue by Vogue Records. Catalogue no: **400028**
**CD:** Released 10 Jul '89, on Vogue by Vogue Records. Catalogue no: **VGCD 670215**
**Album:** Released '83, on Spotlite by Spotlite Records. Catalogue no: **SPJ 129**

**PLAYS GERSHWIN AND KERN**
Tracks: / Strike up the band / Love walked in / I got rhythm / Someone to watch over me / Foggy day, A / Nice work if you can get it / Lovely to look at / Can't help lovin' dat man / Only make believe / Ol' man river / Dearly beloved / Why do I love you / Fine romance, A.
Note: Personnel: Erroll Garner - Piano /Eddie Calhoun - Bass /Kelly Martin - Drums / Charles Isaacs - Bass /Jimmy Smith - Drums /Jose Mangual - Congas. Recorded between 1964-1968 in New York. Erroll Garner's only recording dedicat-ed to the works of two great American song-writers and previously unreleased(he died in 1977 aged 55). Garner was one of the most popular jazz artists internat-ionally appearing in concerts and festivals around the world. His best known composition is Misty which he re-recorded for use in the film, Play Misty For Me starring Clint Eastwood. Misty was also a major hit for Ray Stevens. These recordings were made in one takes and completely ad lib. The

tracks Nice work if youcan get it and Why do I love you are previously unreleased.
**CD:** Released Jun '86, on Mercury by Phonogram Ltd. Catalogue no: **826 224-2**

**QUARTET**
**Cass:** Released '88, on Joker (USA) by Lifetime Records (USA). Catalogue no: **MC 3911**
**Album:** Released '88, on Joker (USA) by Lifetime Records (USA). Catalogue no: **SM 3911**

**RELAXIN'**
**Album:** Released Mar '84, on Vogue by Vogue Records. Catalogue no: **500117**

**ROMANTIC AND SWINGING**
Tracks: / That old feeling / Lady be good / Exactly like you / I'll never smile again / Love in bloom / Solitaire / All of a sudden / Misty / You are my sunshine / St. James' Infirmary.
**Cass:** Released Oct '83, on Mercury (USA) by PolyGram Rec.Inc.(USA). Catalogue no: **7259 113**
**Album:** Released Oct '83, on Mercury (USA) by PolyGram Rec.Inc.(USA). Catalogue no: **9279 113**

**SAVOY COMPLETE VOLUME 2**
**Album:** Released Feb '86, on RCA by BMG Records (UK). Catalogue no: **NL 70542**
**Cass:** Released Feb '86, on RCA by BMG Records (UK). Catalogue no: **NK 70542**

**SHADOW OF YOUR SMILE**
Tracks: / Shadow of your smile / Girl from Ipanema / Misty / There will never be another you / Variations on misty / Yesterdays / I'll remember April / Tell it like it is.
**Album:** Released Apr '81, on Up International Catalogue no: **LPUP 5115**

**STARDUST**
**Album:** Released Nov '84, on Astan (USA) Catalogue no: **20105**
**Cass:** Released Nov '84, on Astan (USA) Catalogue no: **40105**

**THAT'S MY KICK**
**Album:** Released Oct '85, on RCA (France) by BMG Records (France). Catalogue no: **NL 89433**

## Garrett, Kenny

**GARRETT FIVE**
Tracks: / Feeling good / But beautiful / Computer 'G' / Lee Hall's blues / Odoriko / Little Dixie / Little melonae / La bamba / Tokyo tower / United we waltz.
**CD:** Released Jun '89, on Paddlewheel/King Catalogue no: **K32Y 6280**
**Album:** Released Jun '89, on Paddlewheel/King Catalogue no: **K28P 6494**

**INTO (Featuring Woody Shaw (Garrett, Kenny Quintet)**
**Album:** Released '88, on Criss Cross Catalogue no: **CRISS 1014**

## Garrick, Michael

**KRONOS**
**Album:** on Hep Jazz by Hep Records. Catalogue no: **HEP 2013**

**Michael Garrick**

**YOU'VE CHANGED**
Tracks: / You've changed / Rhythm a ning / Like someone in love / Soft awakening.
**Album:** Released May '81, on Hep Jazz by Hep Records. Catalogue no: **HEP 2011**

## Gatemouth

**BOGALUSA BOOGIE MAN**
**Album:** Released Nov '79, on Barclay (France) by Decca Records. Catalogue no: **90035**

## Gateway Jazz Band

**GATEWAY JAZZ BAND WITH GEORGE CHISHOLM (Gateway Jazz Band & George Chisholm)**
Tracks: / Struttin' with some barbecue / Nobody knows you (when you're down and out) / Ain't misbehavin' / Creole love call / Sweet Georgia Brown / Shine / I got it bad / Surrey with the fringe on top / Black and blue / Just a closer walk with thee.
**Album:** Released Apr '81, on Fellside by Fellside Records. Deleted Feb '90. Catalogue no: **FE 016**

**LIVE JAZZ FROM THE SOLENT AREA**
**Cass:** Released Jun '86, on All That's Jazz Catalogue no: **VOL 4**

## Gauthe, Jacques

**CASSOULET STOMP (Gauthe, Jacques & His Creole Rice Jazzband)**
**Album:** Released Feb '89, on Stomp Off (USA) Catalogue no: **SOS 1170**

**RIZ A LA CREOLE (Gauthe, Jacques & His Creole Rice Jazzband)**
**Album:** Released Dec '87, on GHB by Jazzology Records (USA). Catalogue no: **GBH 179**

## Gee, Matthew

**JAZZ BY GEE**
**Album:** Released Sep '88, on Riverside (1) Catalogue no: **RLP 221**

## Gelato, Ray

**GIANTS OF JIVE (Gelato, Ray's Giants of Jive)**
Tracks: / Sing sing sing / Ain't what you do (it's the way that you do i / Please Mr. Policeman / Late night blues / Eel, The / On the sunny side of the street / Flying home / All the jive is gone / Big fat mamas are back in style.
**Album:** Released 27 Feb '89, on Blue Horizon by Ace Records. Catalogue no: **BLUH 006**

## Geller, Herb

**BIRDLAND STOMP**
Tracks: / Birdland stomp / Come rain or come shine / Our love is here to stay / Princess,The / Summer serenade / Confirmation.
**Album:** Released Jan '88, on Enja (Germany) by Enja Records (West Germany). Catalogue no: **ENJA 5019**

**FIRE IN THE WEST**
**Album:** Released Feb '88, on Fresh Sounds (Spain) by Fresh Sounds Records (Spain). Catalogue no: **FS 139**

**JAZZ SONG BOOK, A**
**CD:** Released Nov '89, on Tiptoe Catalogue no: **6006-2**

**RHYME AND REASON (Geller, Herb Octet)**
Tracks: / Rhyme and reason (our birthday party) / Sudden senility.
**Album:** Released Aug '83, on Discovery (USA) by Discovery Records (USA). Catalogue no: **DS 874**

**STAX OF SAX (Geller, Herb Quintet)**
**Album:** Released Feb '88, on Fresh Sounds (Spain) by Fresh Sounds Records (Spain). Catalogue no: **FS 101**

**WEST COAST SCENE**
**2 LP Set:** Released Sep '77, on Vogue by Vogue Records. Catalogue no: **VJD 536**

## Gem Lucky Jazz

**KENYAFRICA (VOL. 2)**
**Album:** Released '74, on Playasound Catalogue no: **PS 33002**

## Genius Jazz

**GENIUS JAZZ (Various artists)**
**Cass set:** Released 7 Nov '87, on Warwick by Warwick Records. Catalogue no: **WW 6037**

## Genova Jazzband

**GENOVA JAZZBAND AND GEORGE MASSO (Genova Jazzband and George Masso)**
**Album:** Released May '88, on FDC Catalogue no: **FDC 3004**

## George Gershwin Collection

**GEORGE GERSHWIN COLLECTION (16 Golden Greats) (Various artists)**
Tracks: / Rhapsody in blue: *Gershwin, George & Paul Whiteman* / Fascinating rhythm: *Astaire, Fred & George Gershwin* / Love walked in: *Various artists* / Swanee: *Jolson, Al* / Summertime: *Bailey, Mildred* / I got rhythm: *Waller, Fats* / Foggy day, A: *Shaw, Artie* / Porgy: *Holiday, Billie* / Our love is here to stay: *Various artists* / Someone to watch over me: *Fitzgerald, Ella* / Embraceable you: *Vaughan, Sarah* / It ain't necessarily so: *Robeson, Paul* / They can't take that away from me: *Garland, Judy* / Do it again: *Monroe, Marilyn* / Lady be good: *Gillespie, Dizzy*.
**Album:** Released Dec '87, on Deja Vu Catalogue no: **DVLP 2105**
**Cass:** Released Dec '87, on Deja Vu Catalogue no: **DVMC 2105**

## Georgia Blues

**GEORGIA BLUES (Various artists)**
**Album:** Released '88, on Rounder (USA) by Rounder Records (USA). Catalogue no: **ROUNDER 2008**

**GEORGIA BLUES (1924-35) (Various artists)**
**Album:** Released Dec '88, on HK Catalogue no: **HK 4005**

**GEORGIA BLUES 1927-33 (Various artists)**
**Album:** Released Dec '88, on Yazoo (USA) by Shanachie Records (USA). Catalogue no: **L 1012**

**GEORGIA BLUES GUITARS (1926-35) (Various artists)**
**Album:** Released '88, on Earl Archives Catalogue no: **BD 2015**

**GEORGIA BLUES TODAY (Various artists)**
**Album:** Released '88, on Flyright by Interstate Music. Catalogue no: **FLY 576**

## Georgia Grinders

**GEORGIA GRINDERS AND JIM SNYDER (Georgia Grinders & Jim Snyder)**
**Album:** Released Jun '86, on Stomp Off (USA) Catalogue no: **SOS 1068**

## Georgia Melodians

**GEORGIA MELODIANS (1924 VOL. 1)**
**Album:** Released Apr '79, on Fountain by Retrieval Records. Catalogue no: **FG 402**

**GEORGIA MELODIANS (1924-6 VOL. 2)**
**Album:** Released Apr '79, on Fountain by Retrieval Records. Catalogue no: **FG 405**

## Georgia Stomp...

**GEORGIA STOMP 1925-35 (Various artists)**
**Album:** Released Sep '87, on Harlequin by Interstate Music. Catalogue no: **HQ 2031**

## Georgians

**GEORGIANS WITH FRANK GUARENTE**
**Cass:** Released Aug '89, on VJM (Vintage Jazz Music) by Vintage Jazz Music Society(VJM). Catalogue no: **VC 12**

## Geraldo

**Biographical details:** Gerald Bright was a UK dance band leader who adopted a Latinised name opening at the Savoy Hotel in 1930 with his Gaucho Tango Orchestra, suitably dressed in someone's idea of native costume; he soon added conventional strict tempo fare and was one of the few UK leaders of the era who never played hot at all. After WWII he organised bands for transatlantic P&O liners and hired young boppers like Ronnie Scott, who were willing to play sweet for the free trip to NYC so they could hear the real thing on 52nd Street: the gig was known as Geraldo's Navy. (Donald Clarke, July 1989).

**GERALDO AND HIS MUSIC WITH CYRIL GRANTHAM**
Tracks: / What's the reason / What a difference a day made / Rose in her hair, The / Too beautiful for words / Geraldo nights / Outside of you / Bonjour Mam'selle / Sorrento by the sea / Whispering trees / My heart jumped over the moon / Paris in the spring / With all my heart and soul / Moon was yellow, The / Rose of Italy / There's a bit of Paree in you / Chestnut man / Where an old Spanish town used to be.
**Cass:** Released Jan '89, on Burlington Records by Plant Life Records. Catalogue no: **4 BUR 021**
**Album:** Released Jan '89, on Burlington Records by Plant Life Records. Catalogue no: **BUR 021**

**GERALDO AND HIS ORCHESTRA (Geraldo and His Orchestra)**
Tracks: / Let the people sing / Jealousy / You're as pretty as a picture / Deep purple / It's d'lovely / You're a sweet little headache / In the blue of the evening / Sunday, monday or always / I want to be in dixie / Blues in the night / Russian salad / Don't sit under the apple tree / I'm old fashioned / My guy's come back / Shoo-shoo baby / Moonlight mood.
**Album:** Released Mar '84, on Retrospect by EMI Records. Deleted Mar '89. Catalogue no: **SH 215**

**GERALDO: THE MAN AND HIS MUSIC (Geraldo and His Orchestra)**
Tracks: / British Grenadiers, The / But not for me / Oh baby mine / Lisa / Ding dong the witch is dead / After you get what you want you don't want it / Cottontail / On the waterfront / Clock on the wall / Jungle mambo / April in Portugal / I lived when I met you / Velvet glove, The / Look out the window / Love me always / Latin lady / Hi lili hi lo / Shifting, whispering sands.
**Album:** Released Feb '84, on President by President Records. Catalogue no: **PLE 511**
**Cass:** Released Jun '85, on President by President Records. Catalogue no: **TC-PLE 511**

**GERRY'S MUSIC SHOP (Geraldo & His Orchestra)**
Tracks: / Nice work if you can get it / Mardi gras / Sunset in Vienna / Foggy day / You turned the tables on me / Lonely troubadour / Does your heart beat for me / When the sun says "goodnight" to the mountain / Sweet Louise / "Swing Time" melody / My cabin of dreams / Celebratin' / Melody of love / To Mary with love / When evening comes / Music shop.
**Album:** Released Nov '80, on Decca by Decca International. Deleted Nov '85. Catalogue no: **RFL 2**

**GOLDEN AGE OF GERALDO**
**Album:** Released Mar '86, on Golden Age by EMI Records. Catalogue no: **GX 41 2540 1**
**Cass:** Released Mar '86, on Golden Age by EMI Records. Catalogue no: **GX 41 2540 4**

**HEART AND SOUL (Geraldo and His Orchestra)**
Tracks: / Heart and Soul / World is waiting for the sunrise / Two sleepy people / How do you do Mr. Right / And the angels sing / Same old story / What goes up must come down / Two dreams met / I miss you in the morning / I'd know you anywhere / How beautiful you are / My

heart is taking lessons / Where or when / Deep in a dream / I hear a dream / Thanks for everything / Room 504 / Could be / When the sun comes out / Between a kiss and a sigh.
**Album:** Released Apr '83, on Saville by Conifer Records. Catalogue no: **SVL 153**

**JEALOUSY (Geraldo & His Gaucho Tango Orchestra)**
**Album:** Released Mar '90, on Joy by President Records. Catalogue no: **JOY276**
**Album:** Released Aug '83, on Joy by President Records. Catalogue no: **JOYD 276**

**MEMORIES OF GERRY (Geraldo & His Orchestra)**
**Cass:** Released Aug '85, on Old Bean by Submarine Records. Catalogue no: **COLD 4**
**Album:** Released Aug '85, on Old Bean by Submarine Records. Catalogue no: **OLD 4**

**MILESTONES OF MELODY (Irving Berlin introduces) (Geraldo & His Concert Orchestra)**
**Album:** Released Jun '88, on Reid Catalogue no: **RD 3**

**PENNY SERENADE (Geraldo & His Orchestra)**
Tracks: / Penny serenade / Continental / Stormy weather / Nobody's sweetheart / Love in bloom / It's a sin to tell a lie / Pennies from heaven / Star fell out of heaven / At the cafe continental / Scrapin' the toast / Robins & roses / One, two, button your shoe / I get a kick out of you / Fine romance / You're a sweet little headache / Goodnight my love.
**Album:** Released Mar '84, on President by President Records. Deleted Mar '89. Catalogue no: **JOYD 278**

**SERENADE IN THE NIGHT (Geraldo & His Gaucho Tango Orchestra & Monte Rey)**
Tracks: / Te quiere dijiste / Serenade in the night / Melody of love / Noche de reves / Let us be sweethearts over again / No more you / You needn't have kept it a secret / Waltz of the gipsies / When the sun says goodnight to the mountain / Lady of Spain / Margarita / Sunset in Vienna / At the balalaika / Dolores / Red roof of Brittany / Our song / Pour que? / If the world were mine.
**Album:** Released Jul '84, on Recollections (Decca) by Decca Records. Catalogue no: **RFL 43**

**SINCERELY YOURS (Geraldo & His Orchestra)**
**Album:** Released Feb '82, on Reflections by Decca Records. Catalogue no: **RFL 16**

**TAKE THE 'A' TRAIN (Geraldo & His Dance Orchestra)**
Tracks: / Rose of Washington Square / How about you? / Flamingo / He's my guy / Lonesome road / Smoke gets in your eyes / I'll get by / Take the 'A' train / Don't get around much anymore / Keep your sunny side up / I'm so all alone / Zoot suite / Concerto for drums / I cover the waterfront / Hey good lookin' / Ragtime cowboy Joe / I'm ridin' for a fall / I dream of Jeannie with the light brown hair / Kentucky / G'bye now.
Note: 20 memories of radio broadcasts of 1944-6 made by the top British band of the period, Geraldo and his Dance Orchestra. Vocalists are Carole Carr, Dick James, Sally Douglas, Archie Lewis, Dorothy Carless, Doreen Villiers and Johnny Green.
**Album:** Released 1 Mar '88, on Living Era by Academy Sound & Vision Records. Catalogue no: **AJA 5051**
**Cass:** Released 1 Mar '88, on Living Era by Academy Sound & Vision Records. Catalogue no: **ZC AJA 5051**

**TIP-TOP TUNES**
Tracks: / In a little Spanish town / Nearness of you / Top hat / Autumn concerto / Hallelujah / Signature tune / My heart stood still / There's a small hotel / Heather of the hill / Rockin' through Dixie / Nature boy / What is this thing called love? / I'm on a see-saw / So many times have I cried over you / When Johnny comes marching home / Begin the beguine / Isle of Innisfree / Arkansas traveller.
**Album:** Released Sep '86, on Conifer Happy Days by Conifer Records. Catalogue no: **CHD 135**
**Cass:** Released Sep '86, on Conifer Happy Days by Conifer Records. Catalogue no: **MCHD 135**
**CD:** Released '89, on Conifer Happy Days by Conifer Records. Catalogue no: **CDHD 135**

**UNISSUED RECORDINGS (Geraldo & His Orchestra)**
**Album:** Released Sep '84, on Halcyon (USA) by Submarine Records. Catalogue no: **HAL 14**

## Gershwin (Composer)

**Biographical details:** Probably the most popular American composer of all time (1898-1937), his early death from a brain tumour was one of the greatest losses to music of this century. Influenced by ragtime and jazz, he was also an excellent concert pianist; he wrote some of the most popular songs of this century (*Lady be good, The man I love, Someone to watch over me, I got rhythm, A foggy day* etc. most with lyrics by brother Ira) as well as concert pieces (*Rhapsody in blue, An American in Paris*) and the opera *Porgy and Bess.* (Donald Clarke, July 1989).

**50TH ANNIVERSARY**
**Album:** Released May '87, on Halcyon (USA) by Submarine Records. Catalogue no: **HDD 001**
**Cass:** Released May '87, on Halcyon (USA) by Submarine Records. Catalogue no: **CHDD 001**

**AMERICAN IN PARIS (Utah Symphony Orchestra)**
Note: Conducted by Maurice Abravanel.
**CD:** Released Aug '89, on Start by Start Records Ltd.. Catalogue no: **VECD 7518**
**Cass:** Released Aug '89, on Start by Start Records Ltd.. Catalogue no: **VETC 6518**

**AMERICAN IN PARIS; PIANOFORTE CONCERTO (Bogas/ Ljubljana Symphony Orchestra/ Nice)**
**CD:** Released Sep '89, on Stradivarii by Michele International Records. Catalogue no: **SCD 6048**

**AMERICAN IN PARIS/CUBAN**
**CD:** Released '83, on RCA by BMG Records (UK). Deleted May '89. Catalogue no: **RCD 14551**

**GEORGE GERSHWIN REMEMBERED (Various artists)**
**CD:** Released Jan '89, on Silva Screen by Silva Screen Records. Catalogue no: **FCD 8100**

**GERSHWIN'S BEST (Various artists)**
**Album:** Released Sep '89, on AVM by AVM Records. Deleted Jan '90. Catalogue no: **BES 1001**
**CD:** Released Aug '89, on AVM by AVM Records. Catalogue no: **BESCD 1001**
**Cass:** Released Aug '89, on AVM by AVM Records. Catalogue no: **BESC 1001**

**GERSWHIN'S GREATEST HITS (Various artists)**
**Cass:** Released '83, on CBS by CBS Records. Catalogue no: **40 79024**

**HITS OF GEORGE GERSHWIN (50th Anniversary album) (Various**

**artists)**
Note: 50th anniversary album. Mono.
**Cass:** Released Feb '87, on Halcyon (USA) by Submarine Records. Catalogue no: **CHDL 112**
**Album:** Released Feb '87, on Halcyon (USA) by Submarine Records. Catalogue no: **HDL 112**

**PLAYS GERSHWIN**
**Cass:** Released '82, on Orchid Music Catalogue no: **ORC 015**

**PORGY AND BESS (Various artists)**
Note: Porgy - Williard White; Bess - Cynthia Haymon; Clara - Harolyn Blackwell; Sportin' Life - Damon Evans; Jake - Bruce Hubbard. Glyndbourne Chorus, the London Philharmonic conducted by Simon Rattle.
**LP Set:** Released May '89, on H.M.V. by EMI Records. Catalogue no: **EX 749 568 1**
**LP Set:** Released May '89, on H.M.V. by EMI Records. Catalogue no: **PORGY 1**
**Cass set:** Released May '89, on H.M.V. by EMI Records. Catalogue no: **EX 749 568 4**
**Cass set:** Released May '89, on H.M.V. by EMI Records. Catalogue no: **TCPORGY 1**
**CD Set:** Released May '89, on H.M.V. by EMI Records. Catalogue no: **CDS 749 568 2**
**CD Set:** Released May '89, on H.M.V. by EMI Records. Deleted Aug '89. Catalogue no: **CDPORGY 1**

**RHAPSODY IN BLUE; AMERICAN IN PARIS ; PORGY AND BESS (Jando/ Budapest PO/ Sandor)**
**CD:** Released Sep '89, on Laserlight Catalogue no: **15 606**

**RHAPSODY IN BLUE (Various artists)**
Note: Perfromed by the Newton Wayland Denver Symphony Pops
**CD:** Released '88, on K-Tel by K-Tel Records. Catalogue no: **NCD 3414**
**Cass:** Released Aug '89, on Deutsche Grammophon by PolyGram Classics. Catalogue no: **427 806 4**
**CD:** Released Aug '89, on Deutsche Grammophon by PolyGram Classics. Catalogue no: **427 806 2**

**RHAPSODY IN BLUE (2) (Various artists)**
Tracks: / Rhapsody in blue: *Various artists* / Piano concerto in F: *Various artists* / Rhapsody on a theme of Paganini (Rachmaninov): *Various artists.*
Note: Artists: Daniel Wayenberg/Orchestre de la Societe des Concerts du Conservatoire/Georges Pretre/Philharonia Orchestra/Christoph von Dohnanyi.
**Cass:** Released '89, on EMI Studio by EMI Records. Catalogue no: **769 113 4**
**CD:** Released '89, on EMI Studio by EMI Records. Catalogue no: **CDM 769 113 2**

**'S WONDERFUL (Brilliant two-piano arrangements from the '30s & '40s) (Grierson, Ralph/Artie Kane)**
Tracks: / An American in Paris / Oh, lady be good / Embraceable you / Man I love, The / Fascinating rhythm / Strike up the band / 'S wonderful.
**CD:** Released '89, on EMI Studio by EMI Records. Deleted '89. Catalogue no: **CDM 769 119 2**

**SELECTIONS FROM... (Gershwin, George & Kurt Weill)**
**Album:** Released '88, on DRG (USA) by DRG Records (USA). Catalogue no: **MRS 904**

**SONG IS...GERSHWIN, THE Gershwin 50th anniversary tribute (Various artists)**
Tracks: / I got rhythm: *Waller, Fats* / Man I love, The: *Welch, Elisabeth* / Half of it, dearie, blues, The: *Astaire, Fred* / Oh lady be good: *Hylton, Jack/his orchestra* / Little jazz bird: *Hylton, Jack/his orchestra* / Do what you do: *O'Neal, Zelma* / Funny face: *Smith, Jack* / My one and only / I found a four leaf clover: *Hart, Audrey/Irene/Charles* / Nashville nightingale: *Waring's Pennsylvanians* / Sweet and low down: *Selvin, Ben Orchestra* / That certain feeling: *Selvin, Ben Orchestra* / Liza: *Jolson, Al* / When do we dance / Someone to watch over me: *Lawrence, Gertrude* / 'S wonderful: *Winter, Marius B Dance Band* / Fascinating rhythm: *Edwards, Cliff* / I'll build a stairway to paradise: *Whiteman, Paul & His Orchestra* / I got plenty o' nuttin': *Tibbett, Lawrence.*
**Album:** Released Jul '87, on Living Era by Academy Sound & Vision Records. Catalogue no: **AJA 5048**
**Cass:** Released Jul '87, on Living Era by Academy Sound & Vision Records. Catalogue no: **ZC AJA 5048**

**TRIBUTE BY THE GIANTS OF JAZZ (Various artists)**
**CD:** Released Mar '90, on Giants of Jazz by Hasmick Promotions. Catalogue no: **GOJCD53015**

**TWO SIDES OF GEORGE GERSHWIN, THE**
Tracks: / Rhapsody in blue / Three piano preludes / Andante from Rhapsody in blue / American in Paris, An / Sweet and low down / That certain feeling / Looking for a boy / When do we dance? / Do do do / Someone to watch over me / Clap yo' hands / Maybe / My one and only / 'S wonderful / Funny face.
Note: Gershwin on piano, backed by the Paul Whiteman Concert Orchestra and the Victoria Symphony Orchestra. Recorded: London and New York, 1926-29.
**Cass:** Released Nov '88, on Halcyon (USA) by Submarine Records. Catalogue no: **CHDL 101**
**CD:** Released Nov '88, on Halcyon (USA) by Submarine Records. Catalogue no: **CDDHDL 101**
**Album:** Released '83, on Halcyon (USA) by Submarine Records. Catalogue no: **HDL 101**

## Get Right With God

**GET RIGHT WITH GOD (Hot Gospel 1947-53) (Various artists)**
**CD:** Released Jan '89, on Heritage by Interstate Music. Catalogue no: **HTCD 01**
**Album:** Released '83, on Krazy Kat by Interstate Music. Catalogue no: **KK 7417**

**GET RIGHT WITH GOD VOL 2 (Various artists)**
**Album:** Released '88, on Krazy Kat by Interstate Music. Catalogue no: **KK 7424**

## Get Wise

**GET WISE (Various artists)**
Tracks: / Mission impossible / Long remembered thunder / Yellow hill / Childhood meditations / Others / Throw it away / Samba ingles / Vanessa / King of the fools / Get wise / We'll be back / That's why it isn't love (Extra track on cassette) / So coole (Extra track on cassette).
**Album:** Released Aug '86, on Portrait by CBS Records. Catalogue no: **PRT 57122**

## Getz, Stan

**Biographical details:** One of the greats of modern jazz, the veteran tenor saxophone of Stan Getz has occasionally graced the pop charts. In 1962 he teamed with well-known jazz guitarist Charlie Byrd, and released a bossa nova instrumental single called *Desafinado.* It reached the Top 20 on both sides of the Atlantic, as did the duo's album *Jazz samba.* The single and LP sparked off a whole bossa nova craze - literally meaning "new style", the Brazilian bossa nova was accompanied by a suddenly fashionable dance. The composer of *Desafinado.*, Brazil's Antonio Carlos Jobim, was also responsible for Getz's other foray into popdom. *The girl from Ipanema,* which featured the sax of Getz plus a plaintive and slightly eerie vocal performance from Brazilian singer Astrud Gilberto, surged to no 5 on the American singles chart in 1964. In Britain it peaked at no 29 but had a second wind 20 years later when it got to no 55. The parent LP featured Getz in duet with Astrud's husband, Joso Gilberto, a lead-

Stan Getz

ing singer on Brazil's bossa nova scene. Getz, always a romantic player at heart, has dabbled in a variety of jazz styles during his mammoth career. He was born in 1927, and comes from Philadelphia. His parents were Russian-Jewish immigrants, Stan's real surname being Gayetsky. He gained his first big break in the late forties with Woody Herman's band; down the years, he also played with Jimmy Dorsey, Benny Goodman and Stan Kenton. Getz's finest decade was the 60's but he was still making worthy records in the 70's. (Bob Macdonald, 19/9/85)

Born in 1927 in Philadelphia, the tenor saxophonist played with big-name bands while still a teenager, then was one of the Four Brothers reed section in 1947-49 that gave the Woody Herman band it's real sound, the most exciting of any white band of it's era; his solo on *Early Autumn* brought more fame: with Zoot Sims, Lee Konitz, Gerry Mulligan, Art Pepper and a few others, he led a new generation of first-class white jazz reedmen popular round the world, Getz's tone and gift for beauty making him a particularly fine ballad player. His long association with Norman Granz began in 1952; *Jazz Samba* in 1962 with guitarist Charlie Byrd introduced bossa nova and reached No. 1 on Billboard's top pop albums chart; *Getz/Gilberto* '64 with Joao Giberto and his wife Astrud reached No. 2 and included the top five hit single *The girl from Ipenema*: six hit albums in the USA pop chart in two years made him one of the era's most popular jazz musicians and won him Grammies, but when the bossa nova fad was played out the beauty of his treatment was still fresh as paint, and he's never stopped making beautiful records. (Donald Clarke, July 1989).

**ANNIVERSARY**
**CD:** Released Mar '90, on Emarcy Catalogue no: **JJCD17**

**ANOTHER WORLD**
Tracks: / Pretty city / Keep dreaming / Sabra / Anna / Another world / Sum, sum / Willow weep for me / Blue serge / Brave little Pernille / Club Seven and other places.
**Album:** Released Apr '79, on CBS by CBS Records. Deleted Apr '84. Catalogue no: **CBS 88315**

**AT STORYVILLE '51 (Getz, Stan Quintet)**
**Album:** Released Oct '88, on Vogue by Vogue Records. Catalogue no: **500079**
**CD:** Released Dec '86, on Vogue by Vogue Records. Catalogue no: **VGCD 600093**

**AT THE OPERA HOUSE (Getz, Stan & J J Johnson)**
Tracks: / Billie's bounce / My funny valentine / Crazy rhythm / Blues in the closet / Yesterdays / It never entered my mind.
Note: Classic Norman Granz production. With these concert recordings, Granz started the highly successful but short-lived Getz/Johnson discography. It's a major triumph of his formula: "Put the soloists together then get out of the way and let them play". Recorded September & October 1957. Digitally remastered. 73 minutes playing time.
**CD:** Released May '87, on Verve (USA) by Polydor Ltd. Catalogue no: **831 272-2**

**BEST OF STAN GETZ**
Tracks: / Times lie / La fiesta / Street tattoo / Ligia / Don't cry for me Argentina / Club 7 and other wild places / Skylark.
**Album:** Released '80, on CBS by CBS Records. Catalogue no: **CBS 84236**

**BIG BAND BOSSA NOVA**
**CD:** Released Aug '87, on Polydor by Polydor Ltd. Deleted Jan '89. Catalogue no: **825 771-2**

**BOSSA NOVA YEARS**
**Cass set:** Released Jan '90, on Verve (USA) by Polydor Ltd. Catalogue no: **823 611 4**
**CD Set:** Released Jan '90, on Verve (USA) by Polydor Ltd. Catalogue no: **823 611 2**
**LP Set:** Released '85, on Verve (USA) by Polydor Ltd. Catalogue no: **823 611-1**

**BROTHERS, THE**
**CD:** Released Apr '87, on Carrere (France) Catalogue no: **98426**

**CHILDREN OF THE WORLD**
Tracks: / Don't cry for me Argentina / Children of the world / Livin' it up / Street tattoo / Hop scotch / On rainy afternoons / You, me and the spring / Summer poem / Dreamer / Around the day in eighty worlds.
**Album:** Released Nov '79, on CBS by CBS Records. Deleted '84. Catalogue no: **CBS 83642**

**COMMUNICATIONS**
**Album:** Released Aug '89, on Polydor by Polydor Ltd. Catalogue no: **837 437 1**
**Cass:** Released Aug '89, on Polydor by Polydor Ltd. Catalogue no: **837 437 4**
**CD:** Released Aug '89, on Polydor by Polydor Ltd. Catalogue no: **837 437 2**

**COMPLETE ROOST SESSIONS, VOL 1**
**CD:** Released Oct '88, on Vogue by Vogue Records. Catalogue no: **VGCD 600 128**

**COMPLETE ROOST SESSIONS, VOL 2**
**CD:** Released Jun '88, on Vogue by Vogue Records. Catalogue no: **VGCD 600174**

**COOL JAZZ**
Tracks: / S'cool boy / Prelude to a kiss / I only have eyes for you / Ack, varmeland du skona / Night and day / Flamingo / Don't get scared / I'm getting sentimental over you / On the Alamo / You go to my head / Strike up the band / Out of nowhere / S'wonderful / Best thing for you, The / Fools rush in / Sometimes I'm happy.
**CD:** on Official by Official Records. Catalogue no: **OFF 83022**
**Album:** on Official by Official Records. Catalogue no: **OFF 3022**

**DESAFINADO (Getz, Stan & Charlie Byrd)**
Tracks: / Desafinado.
**7" Single:** Released Nov '62, on H.M.V. by EMI Records. Deleted '65. Catalogue no: **POP 1061**

**DOLPHIN,THE**
Note: This was Getz's first album for Concord and recorded about 1980. Supported by Lou Levy, piano; Monty Budwig, bass and Jake Hanna on drums. Featured tracks are: *A Time For Love* - Johnny Mandell, *Joy Spring* - Clifford Brown, *Close Enough For Love* the theme used in the film Agatha, and the title track *The Dolphin*, a great bossa-nova track.
**CD:** Released Jul '87, on Concord Jazz by Concord Jazz Records (USA). Catalogue no: **CCD 4158**
**Album:** Released '81, on Concord Jazz by Concord Jazz Records (USA). Catalogue no: **CJ 158**

**DYNASTY**
Tracks: / Dum Dum / Ballad for Leo / Our kind of Sabi / Mona / Emmanuel, Theme from / Invitation / Ballad for my dad / Song Martine / Dynasty.
Note: Recorded live at Ronnie Scott's, London, March 1971.
**Cass:** Released Feb '84, on Verve (France) Catalogue no: **2615 054**
**CD:** Released Aug '89, on Verve Catalogue no: **839 117 2**

**EARLY DAYS, THE (SCANDINAVIA) (Getz, Stan & Oscar Pettiford)**
Tracks: / Out of nowhere / Yesterdays / Fireplace blues / My funny valentine / Laverne walk / I remember Clifford / Stuffy.
**Album:** Released '81, on Rarities Catalogue no: **RARITIES 53**

**EARLY DAYS, VOL 2 (SCANDINAVIA)**
Tracks: / Bound to be blue / Ack varmeland du Skona / Amore / Move / Spring can really hang you up the most / I like to recognise the tune / Land's end / Love walked in.
**Album:** Released '81, on Rarities Catalogue no: **RARITIES 64**

**EARLY GETZ (Getz, Stan & Friends)**
Tracks: / Michelle / T. & S. / Terry's tune / Cuddles / Speedway / Battleground / Four and one Moore / Five brothers / Skull buster / Ante room / Pennies from heaven / Poop deck / Marcia / Pinch bottle / Earless engineering / Be still / TV / Short P not LP / I've got you under my skin / What's new / You stepped out of a dream / My old flame / Lady in red / Signal / Lee / 'Round midnight / Motion.
**2 LP Set:** Released Apr '80, on Prestige Deleted '85. Catalogue no: **PR 24088**

**FOCUS**
Tracks: / I'm late / Her / Pan / I remember when / Night rider / Once upon a time / Summer afternoon.
**CD:** Released Oct '84, on Verve Deleted Mar '88. Catalogue no: **821 982-2**

**FOR MUSICIANS ONLY (Getz, Stan & Sonny Stitt)**
**Album:** Released Aug '89, on Verve Catalogue no: **837 435 1**

**GETZ AU GO GO**
Tracks: / Singing song, The / Telephone song / One mote samba / Only trust your heart / Carcovado / It might as well be spring / Eu e voce / Summertime / Six mix pix flix / Here's that rainy day.
Note: Live debut performance of what was then the New Stan Getz Quartet, plus singer Astrud Gilberto. Recorded in New York, August 1964.
**CD:** Released '85, on Verve (USA) by Polydor Ltd. Deleted Aug '88. Catalogue no: **821 725-2**
**Album:** Released '85, on Verve (USA) by Polydor Ltd. Catalogue no: **2304 173**
**Cass:** Released '88, on Verve Catalogue no: **3112008**

**GETZ-GILBERTO COLLECTION (20 golden greats) (Getz, Stan & Joao Gilberto)**
Tracks: / It might as well be spring / Corcovado / Here's that rainy day / Samba da minha terra / Un abraco no bonfa / One-note samba / Stan's blues / Tonight I shall sleep / Telephone song / Only trust your heart / O pato / Rosa Moreno / Singing song, The / Voce e eu / Grandfather's waltz / Meditation / Six mix pix flix / They all fall in love / All God's chillun got rhythm.
**CD:** Released Nov '87, on Deja Vu Catalogue no: **DVCD 2024**
**Album:** Released Nov '85, on Deja Vu Catalogue no: **DVLP 2024**
**Cass:** Released Nov '85, on Deja Vu Catalogue no: **DVMC 2024**

**GETZ-GILBERTO STORY, THE (Getz, Stan & Joao Gilberto)**
Tracks: / Diaper pin / Interlude on bebop / Stan's mood / Always / Night and day / I got it bad / Pot luck / All God's chillun got rhythm / They all fall in love / East of the sun (and west of the moon) / Telephone song, The / Eu e voce / Singing song, The / Corcovado / Only trust your heart / It might as well be spring / One note samba / Here's that rainy day / Tonight I shall sleep / Stan's blues / Grandfather's waltz.
**CD:** Released Apr '89, on Deja Vu Catalogue no: **DVRE CD 17**
**Cass:** Released Apr '89, on Deja Vu Catalogue no: **DVRE MC 17**

**GIRL FROM IPANEMA, THE (Getz, Stan & Astrud Gilberto)**
Tracks: / Girl from Ipanema.
**7" Single:** Released Jul '64, on Verve Deleted '67. Catalogue no: **VS 520**

**HAMPTON & GETZ (Getz, Stan & Lionel Hampton)**
**CD:** Released Aug '87, on Polydor by Polydor Ltd. Deleted 30 May '89. Catalogue no: **831 672 2**

**IMMORTAL CONCERTS (Stan Getz meets Joao & Astrud Gilberto) (Getz, Stan/Joao Gilberto/Astrud Gilberto)**
Tracks: / Corcovado / O Pato / It might as well be spring / Samba da minha terra / One note samba / Tonight I shall sleep / Bim bom / Singing song, The / Telephone song, The / Here's that rainy day / Eu e Voce / Rosa moreno / Grandfather's waltz / Only trust your heart / Um abraco no bonfa / Stan's blues / Meditation / Summertime / Six mix pix flix.
**CD:** Released Jun '88, on Giants of Jazz by Hasmick Promotions. Catalogue no: **GOJCD 53021**

**IN CONCERT (Getz, Stan & Joe Farrell)**
Tracks: / Heartplace / Kali-au / Chappaua / Nature boy / 500 miles high / Lady day / Autumn leaves / Billie's bounce.
**CD:** Released '89, on Kingdom Jazz by Kingdom Records. Catalogue no: **CDGATE 7022**

**IT MIGHT AS WELL BE SPRING**
Tracks: / On the Alamo / Gone with the wind / Yesterdays / Sweetie pie / You go to my head / Hershey bar / Tootsie roll / Strike up the band / Imagination / For stompers only / Navy blue / Out of nowhere / S' wonderful / Penny / Split kick / It might as well be Spring / Best thing for you / Melody express / Yvette / Potter's luck / Song is you / Wildwood / Lullaby of Birdland / Autumn leaves / Fools rush in / These foolish things.
**2 LP Set:** Released Jun '81, on Vogue by Vogue Records. Deleted '86. Catalogue no: **VJD 573**

**JAZZ SAMBA (Getz, Stan & Charlie Byrd)**
**Cass:** Released Apr '89, on Verve Catalogue no: **810 061-4**
**Album:** Released Feb '63, on Verve Deleted '68. Catalogue no: **SULP 9013**
**CD:** Released Apr '89, on Verve Catalogue no: **810 061-2**
**Album:** Released Apr '89, on Verve Catalogue no: **810 061-1**

**JAZZ SAMBA ENCORE (Getz, Stan & Luis Bonfa)**
Tracks: / Sambalero / So danco samba / O morro noa tem vez / Insensatez / Samba de duas notas / Mania de Maria / Saudade vem correndo / Um abraco no Getz / Ebony samba / Menina flor.
**Album:** Released '84, on Verve (USA) by Polydor Ltd. Catalogue no: **V 68523**
**CD:** Released Apr '86, on Verve Deleted Jul '88. Catalogue no: **823 613-2**

**JAZZ SUMMET (Getz, Stan & Dave Brubeck)**
**2 LP Set:** Released Oct '88, on Vogue by Vogue Records. Catalogue no: **400015**

**LAURINDO ALMEIDA**
Tracks: / Minima moca / Once again / Winter moon / Do what you do do well / Sambra de Sahra / Maracuta-too.
**CD:** Released '84, on Verve Catalogue no: **823 149-2**

**LINE FOR LYONS (Getz, Stan & Chet Baker)**
Tracks: / Just friends / Stella by starlight / Airegin / My funny valentine / Milestones / Dear old Stockholm / Line for Lyons.
**CD:** Released Jul '87, on Sonet by Sonet Records. Catalogue no: **SNTCD 899**
**Album:** Released '83, on Sonet by Sonet Records. Catalogue no: **SNTF 899**
**CD:** Released '86, on Vogue by Vogue Records. Catalogue no: **VG 600 034**

**LIVE AT MONTMATRE**
**CD:** Released on Steeplechase (USA). Catalogue no: **SCCD 31073**
**CD:** Released on Steeplechase (USA). Catalogue no: **SCCD 31074**

**LIVE AT THE VILLAGE VANGUARD**
Tracks: / Feather merchant / Polka dots and moonbeams / Jordu / Is it true what they say about Dixie? / Time after time / To the ends of the earth / Stars fell on Alabama.
**Album:** Released '81, on Ingo Catalogue no: **INGO 1**

**LYRICAL STAN GETZ, THE**
Tracks: / Willow weep for me / La fiesta / Captain Marvel / Ligia / Misty / Lover man (oh where can you be).
**Album:** Released Aug '88, on CBS (import) by CBS Records. Catalogue no: **4608191**
**Cass:** Released Aug '88, on CBS (import) by CBS Records. Catalogue no: **4608194**

**MIDEM - LIVE,'80 (Getz, Stan & Paul Horn)**
Tracks: / Heartplace / Kali-au / Chappaqua / Nature boy / Impromptur / Samba de Orfeu / Work song.
**Album:** Released '83, on Kingdom Jazz by Kingdom Records. Catalogue no: **GATE 7004**
**Cass:** Released '89, on Kingdom Jazz by Kingdom Records. Catalogue no: **CGATE7004**

**MOONLIGHT IN VERMONT (Getz, Stan & Johnny Smith)**
Tracks: / Moonlight in Vermont / Taboo / Tenderly / Jaguar / Stars fell on Alabama / Where or when / Foggy day, A / I didn't know what time it was / It might as well be spring / On the Alamo / Lullaby of Birdland / These foolish things / Autumn leaves / Imagination / Dear old Stockholm / When I fall in love / Nearness of you, The / Satin doll / Deep purple / Sentimental journey.
**Album:** on Vogue Jazz (France) by Vogue Records. Catalogue no: **VJD 539**

**OPUS DE BOP**
**Album:** Released '85, on Savoy (France) Deleted May '89. Catalogue no: **WL 70516**

**PEACOCK (Getz, Stan & Jimmy Rowles)**
Tracks: / I'll never be the same / Lester left town / Body and soul / What am I here for / Serenade to Sweden / Chess players / Mosaic / Peacocks / My buddy / Hour of parting / Rose Marie / This is all I ask / Skylark / Would you like to take a walk.
**Album:** Released Aug '86, on CBS by CBS Records. Catalogue no: **CBS 21138**

**POETRY (Getz, Stan & Albert Dailey)**
Tracks: / Confirmation / Child is born, A / Tune up / Lover man / Night in Tunisia / Spring can really hang you up the most / Round midnight.
**Album:** Released '84, on Elektra (Musician) by Elektra Records (USA). Deleted Aug '87. Catalogue no: **960 370-1**

**PORTRAITS (Getz, Stan Quartet)**
Tracks: / Sweet rain / Wee / Lush life / Night time street / La fiesta.
**Album:** Released '81, on Lotus Catalogue no: **LPPS 111 09**

**PURE GETZ (Getz, Stan Quartet)**
Tracks: / On the up and up / Blood count / Very early / Sippin' at bells / I wish I knew / Come rain or come shine / Tempus fugit.
**Cass:** Released '82, on Concord Jazz by Concord Jazz Records (USA). Catalogue no: **CJC 188**
**CD:** Released Dec '86, on Concord Jazz by Concord Jazz Records (USA). Catalogue no: **CCD 4188**
**Album:** Released '82, on Concord Jazz by Concord Jazz Records (USA). Catalogue no: **CJ 188**

**QUINTET AND QUINTET (1950/1951)**
**CD:** Released Oct '89, on Jazz Anthology by Musidisc Records (France). Catalogue no: **550102**

**SILVER COLLECTION, THE (Getz, Stan & Oscar Peterson)**
**CD:** Released '86, on Polydor by Polydor Ltd. Catalogue no: **827 826-2**

**SONG AFTER SUNDOWN, A (Getz, Stan & Arthur Fiedler)**
Tracks: / Love is for the very young / Song after sundown, A / Three ballads for Stan / Where do you go? / Tanglewood concerto / Girl from Ipanema.
**CD:** Released Apr '88, on Bluebird (2) by BMG Records (UK). Catalogue no: **ND 86284**

**SPECIAL Vol. 2 (Ellington)**
**Album:** Released '88, on Raretone Catalogue no: **RARETONE 5002**

**STAN GETZ**
Tracks: / Lover come back to me / Yesterdays / There will never be another you / How high the moon / Strike up the band / Get happy / Dear old Stockholm / Pernod.
**Album:** Released '81, on Queendisc (Italy) by Queendisc Records. Catalogue no: **QU 013**
**Album:** Released '88, on Joker (USA) by Joker Records. Catalogue no: **SM 3967**
**CD:** Released Jul '89, on Cleo by Cleo Records. Catalogue no: **CLCD 5011**

**STAN GETZ (Prestige)**
Tracks: / Five brothers / Battle of the saxes / Preservation / Crazy chords / Intoit / Long Island sound / Indian summer / There's a small hotel / Too marvellous for words / Wrap your troubles in dreams / My old flame / Lady in red / Ginza samba / I've grown accustomed to her face / For all we know / Crow's nest / Liz Anne / Big bear / My buddy.
**2 LP Set:** Released Sep '79, on Prestige by Prestige Records. Catalogue no: **PR 24019**

**STAN GETZ (Compact/Walkman Jazz)**
**Cass:** Released Jun '87, on Polydor. Catalogue no: **831 368-4**
**CD:** Released Jun '87, on Polydor. Catalogue no: **831 368-2**

**STAN GETZ AND FRIENDS (Compact/Walkman jazz) (Getz, Stan & Friends)**
**CD:** Released Aug '88, on Verve Catalogue no: **835 317 2**
**Cass:** Released Aug '88, on Verve Catalogue no: **835 317 4**

**STAN GETZ AND JAOA GILBERTO (Getz, Stan & Jaoa Gilberto)**
Tracks: / Girl from Ipanema / Doralice / Para vachuchar / Meu coracao / Desafinado / Corcovado / So dance smba / O grande amor / Vivo sohando.
**Album:** Released Sep '81, on Verve Catalogue no: **2304071**
**CD:** Released Sep '81, on Verve Catalogue no: **8100482**

**STAN GETZ AT STORYVILLE**
**Album:** Released '78, on Vogue by Vogue Records. Catalogue no: **VJD 554**

**STAN GETZ AND BOB BROOKMEYER (Getz, Stan & Bob Brookmeyer)**
Tracks: / Minuet circa / Who could care? / Nice work if you can get it / Thump, thump, thump! / Nightingale sang in Berkeley Square, A / Love jumped out.
**Album:** Released '84, on Verve (France) Catalogue no: **8133 591**

**STAN GETZ IN PARIS 1956**
**Album:** Released May '88, on Fresh Sounds (Spain) by Fresh Sounds Records (Spain). Catalogue no: **FS 7**

**STAN GETZ IN PARIS 1958**
**Album:** Released Feb '89, on Royal Catalogue no: **ROYALLD 4002**

**STAN GETZ IN STOCKHOLM**
Tracks: / Honeysuckle rose (take 2) / They can't take that away from me / Topsy / Celebrating (Janne's blues) (take 2) / Cabin in the sky (take 2) / Like someone in love (take 3) / Speak low (take 5) / Stockholm street (take 2) / Bengt's blues (take 2) / Gold rush / Stockholm street / Cabin in the sky (rehearsal take) / Cabin in the sky / Celebrating (Janne's blues) / Speak low (take 3) / Like someone in love / Like someone in love (take 2) / Gold rush.
Note: Stan Getz was strongly related to Sweden during the 1950s. Not only did

he visit us a number of times, the first of which was early in 1951 when he recorded, among other things, the Swedish folk song *Ack Varmeland du skona* (retitled Dear old Stockholm) for the US release). He also married a Swedish girl. In 1958, Getz made an extensive tour of Sweden, mostly in the company of bassist Gunnar Johnson's quintet, based in Gothenburg and including young talents such as pianist Jan Johansson and tenor saxophonist Erik Notstrom. Both Erik and Jan enjoyed writing arrangements that were sometimes pretty and sometimes funny or even wierd. Their cooperation with Getz lasted about half a year and included a tour in Norway, but it was mostly one nighters at dance-spots all over Sweden (although they played some concerts as well). Stan was living in the South of Sweden at the time and, eventually, moved to Copenhagen. There were no American type jazz clubs in Sweden at that time. Jazz was played mainly at "folk parks" (amusement parks that have dance spots) all over the country. The jazz enthusiasts used to gather in the dance floor in front of the stage, while the dancers did their stuff on what was left of the space. Not seldom, the dancers moved around to swingers like *Honeysuckle Rose* or ballads such as *Like Someone In Love*, sometimes extended to 10 or even 15 minutes by the length of improvisations. And there were seldom any complaints.

In 1958, I heard Stan Getz playing for dancers in a small village outside my home town Sundsvall some 450 kilometers north of Stockholm. I was a 15 year old school boy, contributing articles on jazz to the weekly "Juniors Page". One of the people I met was Benny Bailey, the excellent American trumpet player who had been living in Stockholm for a few years and was slowly becoming a big name in Swedish jazz. When we saw each other in Stockholm, he said he was going to record a date with Stan Getz and asked if I would like to come along. I sure did. Thus, I happened to visit the recording studio at Europa Film in Sundbyberg, just outside Stockholm, and meet some of my big idols. It was August 25, 1958. At the first date, the all star band was rehearsing, concentrating on Jan Johansson's tricky version of *Honeysuckle Rose*. Simon Brehm, bass player and owner of the Karusell record label, aceted as a producer on behalf of Norman Granz. After a couple of hours, Brehm suggested an intermission. Nice, big sandwiches were brought along with bottles of Johnny Walker (Red label). This created a happy feeling with lots of jokes and laughter. As we sat in a small cinema, connected to the Europa Film movie studios, the recording engineer, Bengt Runsten suddenly said it was time for a little picture show.

The lights were turned out and an old silent black and white started to roll on the screen. We were all quite amused to see an artistically well-done hard core and, after 30 years, I still remember every bit of it. In those days, such pictures were unknown to 15 year old school boys and, being an innocent myself, I thought it was just a little bit too much for me. But also the more experienced viewers in the studio all of a sudden got other things than music on their minds, so everybody agreed to call it a day and try it again tomorrow.

Only two days in the studio, altogether, were planned for this production, the first of which was for Jan Johansson's arrangements and the second for Bengt Hallberg's. As nothing had been put onto tape on the first date, however, Simon Brehm called Hallberg and asked him not to be too early the next day. For me, this was an occasion of a lifetime, so again, I went with Benny Bailey to the studio on August 26th. Now, the recording actually started, and *Honeysuckle rose* was the first take. It came out beautifully, everybody raised their eyebrows during Benny's powerful trumpet solo and the whole performance had a tremendous swing. But after the take, Simon Brehm came out from the recording booth with a stopwatch in his hand. "Great, but too long", he said. "Let's make another one". Brehm planned to release the music in Sweden on EP's that couldn't take more than six or seven minutes per side. Stan and Benny and the gang had wailed a few choruses too many. Unfortunately, that longer take seems to have been erased, so we just have the second take, which is good enough. Jan Johansson's arrangement of *Honeysuckle rose* was at that time almost avant garde, at least in "cool" Sweden. Until this date, Jan had mostly been writing for the two saxes and rhythm in the Gunnar Johnson Quintet.

During 1958, he was commisioned by his friend, band leader and saxophonist Hacke Bjorksten, to write for his new septet with five horns, bass and drums - similar to the group on these records. Hacke told Jan to write "difficult" and he took up a few old standards and treated them with his very special imagination. Jan had always musical ideas of his own, and he became one of the most important Swedish jazz musicians of the sixties. 1959 to 1961, he worked regularly with Getz in Sweden and abroad. He was killed in a car crash in 1968. His work for this session gives interesting examples of "early" Jan Johansson, with his score on *Honeysuckle Rose* as the outstanding item. The solo work on this number is also peak performances, Getz showing his mastership from the start, even if a few of his favourite licks appear in spots. Some time ago, I happened to listen to his 1952 recording of *Mosquito knees*, based on the chords of *Honeysuckle Rose*, and was surprised to notice that Stan citates himself at a certain moment here, even if the two solos are completely. When three tunes had been successfully made - no whiskey or dirty movies this time - Bengt Hallberg and extra tenor man Bjarne Nerem entered the studio.

They started to rehearse Hallberg's arrangements, but it was late and the musicians were getting tired. Brehm decided to call it off and get one or two extra dates to complete the LP. All the men involved couldn't get together until three weeks later - at which time I had returned to school and couldn't be there. Anyhow, Hallberg's scores are in a way very typical for Swedish jazz of the fifties: nice tunes and fat, well-sounding ensemble parts. *Cabin in the sky* is a wonderfully interpreted with a sax section that has three tenors and one baritone - a true "Four Brothers" combination. Stan's solo-playing is beautiful and Lars Gullin contributes nicely with his baritone. This performance was never on LP before, just on a Swedish EP. On the two September dates, the band added more music than necessary to complete an LP. *Janne's Blues* and *Gold Rush* were not used at all.

The former is previously unissued and the latter was included in a Getz sampler some 25 years later. *Janne's blues* is also called *Celebrating*, most probably so because Jan Johansson celebrated his 27th birthday during the recording. The same number and almost identical arrangement was also played by the aforementioned Hacke Bjorksten Septet under the name of *166: ans blues*. *Gold rush* is a tune by Gerry Mulligan, also known as *Turnstyle*. The Gunnar Johnson band played it, arranged by Erik Norstrom, and Stan asked Erik to re-write it for this recording band. Erik, a great admirer of Getz and an excellent soloist at his own, used to take turns with Getz in tenor battles at concerts and dance hall stages but, unfortunately, doesn't solo at all here. Neither does Bjarne Nerem, the third tenor man. This was Getz recording, no doubt about it.

Lars Gullin, however, is heard in many solos, although his playing is not always up to his usual high standards. On this date, Gullin came up with a score of rather peculiar composition *Stockholm street*. It has a lot of Lars' personality to it, but here is also a more sad and dark atmosphere and most of his works from these years. Getz is the only soloist on this rather advanced harmonic structure. Notify the bass line, a part which LArs always was very particular about. Still, it was Bengt Hallberg who made the strongest impact on these September dates. His arrangements are superb as is his solo playing (on *Bengt Blues*, for example). Hallberg was and is a key figure in Swedish music. Throughout the album, we can also enjoy the powerful two man brass section of Benny Bailey and Ake Persson, both also contributing several fine solos. One year later, they were adopted by Quincy Jones and went abroad with his big band - both remained abroad, playing in different bands all over Europe. Imported from Denmark for these sessions was the strong and swinging drummer William Schioppfe. His drums have a nice clean sound, well recorded by Bengt Runsten, who was one of the leading sound engineers in Sweden during the monaural era. At the

restoration of these sessions, many alternate takes were found. Strangely enough, though, a couple of the released takes couldn't be found at all on the master tapes. The original versions of *Speak Low* and *Stockholm Street* had to be dubbed from a mint copy of the old LP. This was called "Imported from Europe" and the cover had a street picture of a French policeman directing the traffic, probably in Paris. No information was given about the recording or the music, except for the names of the musicians. Reading the liner notes, you got the impression that it was a Danish recording, the text being mostly about Getz' approval of living in Denmark. There have been many confusing errors regarding the dates, arrangers and participating musicians published in discographies over the years. This is straightened out here. Sides A and B and the first two tracks on side C are selected takes, the rest being previously unissued alternates. To my ears, 30 years later, this is still fresh and exciting.
**2 LP Set:** Released Jun '88, on Dragon by Dragon Records. Catalogue no: **DRLP 157/158**

**STAN GETZ AND MILES DAVIS (Getz, Stan & Miles Davis)**
**Album:** Released '81, on Kings Of Jazz Catalogue no: **KLJ 20013**

**STAN GETZ QUARTET AND SHELLY MANNE QUINTET (Getz, Stan Quartet & Shelly Manne Quintet)**
Tracks: / Some blues (bronx blues) / Polka dots and moonbeans / Theme / Jordu / Lover man / Ain't you a mess / Theme - introduction / Dart game, The / Parthenia / B's flat / Gem from tiffany, A / Little girl blue / Lover come back to me.
Note: On a warm Spring day in 1986, the city of Los Angeles held a special event in honour of the late Shelly Manne and his famous jazz club, the 'Manne-Hole'. The hip spot had opened in 1960 and enjoyed a 12 year reign as Los Angeles' pre-eminent location for mainstream jazz before lease difficulties caused Shelly to move across town in a short-lived effort to sustain the club in a new location. As the mayor dedicated a bronze marble manhole cover in front of the club's former location, Bill Holman, Conte Condoli, Jack Sheldon, Betty Bennett, Bob Cooper, Alvin Stoller, Dave Pell, Al Aarons, Leroy Vinnegar and many more of Shelly's friends looked on. Afterward there was a full-blown jam session right in the street paid for by the city. It was my all time favourite jazz club and Shelly was one of my favourite people - he used to nightly risk his liquor licence by allowing me to slip in from the alley through the back door and sit in a corner of the quaint bar so that I could dig the scent and drink the marvellous Tuborg draught beer which was still actually imported in those days. This was the summer of 1965 and while I was not yet 18, thanks to Mr. Manne, I had already dug more truly great, live jazz those few wonderful months than most aficianadoes see in a lifetime.

The first side of this remarkable album features some of the most relaxed and lyrical Stan Getz you'll ever hear, as well as absolutely exquisite brush, cymbal and bass pedal work by Shelly. Stan first worked with Shelly during a July, 1955 engagement at Zardi's in Hollywood and this 1956 reunion on side two from the club Basin Street in New York City was clearly a mutually stimulating occasion. The announcer on side one gives Stan's theme as *Some Blues* but it was commercially recorded as *Bronx Blues*. The house band at Shelly's 'Manne-hole' used *A gem from Tiffany* as their theme from the very beginning and throughout the club's existence. The tune was written by the great Bill Holman in honour of a jazz club of the same name on West 8th Street in downtown Los Angeles that flourished for awhile in the 1950's. *Parthenia*, Shelly's own tune, commemorates the street in Northridge, California, where Mr and Mrs Manne bought a home a few miles northwest of Hollywood. The haunting ballad features Charlie Mariano on alto sax, who had just joined Shelly's regular combo after two years with Stan Kenton. The ubiquitous Russ Freeman takes the tasty piano solo and shows why he was asked to do so many record dates in the '50s and '60s. Russ was a Shelley regular, logging service from 1954. Although only 23 at the time of these recordings, Stu was already a verteran of tours with Stan Kenton and Woody Herman. His clean, articulated style is heard to advantage on *B's flat*.
A great period in jazz was the mid-1950's, and on this album, representing a synthesis of bop and the 'cool', or West Coast sound, it is piquantly brought back to us by these unique artists. Who can forget Shelly's powerful drumming on Woody's 1949 *More Moon* or on Kenton's 1951 *Viva Prado* and happily Stan Getz, who has been ill has just recently reappeared after an early summer, 1987 operation. Stan now lives comfortably in Palo Alto, California, where he invited some of us for a backyard barbeque in the summer of 1986. He is on the faculty at Stanford University and has a tour in progress as I write these notes with his phenomenally popular protege, vocalist Dianne Schurr. With the recent passing of Al Cohn, Stan is the last of the Woody Herman 'Four brothers' - long may he live and continue to delight us with his magnificent artistry. (Edgar Ward, San Diego, California, May 1988)
**Album:** Released Jun '88, on Jazz Band by Flyright Records. Catalogue no: **EB 407**

**Stan & Shelley Live - Stan Getz (Jazz Band)**

**STAN GETZ SPECIAL, VOL 2**
Tracks: / Everything happens to me / I'll remember April / Strike up the band / All God's chillun got rhythm / Love walked in / We'll be together again.
**Album:** Released '83, on For Collectors Catalogue no: **FC 5012**

**STEAMER, THE**
Tracks: / Blues for Mary Jane / There will never be another you / You're blase / Too close for comfort / Like someone in love / How about you?.

STAN GETZ
Bengt Hallberg · Jan Johansson · Lars Gullin · Åke Persson · Benny Bailey

**Stockholm Sessions '58 - Stan Getz (Dragon)**

Note: With Lou Levy, Leroy Vinnegar, Stan Levey. Recorded: 1956.
**Album:** Released '82, on Verve Catalogue no: **2304 533**

**STOCKHOLM SESSIONS '58 (See panel above)**
**Album:** Released Oct '89, on Sonet by Sonet Records. Catalogue no: **SNTF 1019**
**CD:** Released Oct '89, on Sonet by Sonet Records. Catalogue no: **SNCD 1019**

**SWEET RAIN**
Tracks: / Litha / O grande amor / Sweet rain / Con aima / Windows / There will never be another you.
**CD:** Released '84, on Verve Deleted Mar '88. Catalogue no: **815 054-2**
**Album:** Released '76, on Verve Catalogue no: **2317.115**

**TWO SIDES OF STAN GETZ**
**Album:** Released Nov '86, on Unique Jazz by Spotlite Records. Catalogue no: **UJ 33**

**VOYAGE**
Tracks: / I wanted to say / I thought about you / Yesterdays / Dreams / Falling in love / Voyage.
Note: Personnel: Stan Getz, Kenny Barron, George Mraz, Victor Lewis
**Cass:** Released Sep '88, on Black Hawk (USA) by Blackhawk Records (USA). Catalogue no: **BKHMC 51101**
**Album:** Released Sep '88, on Black Hawk (USA) by Blackhawk Records (USA). Catalogue no: **BKH 51101**
**CD:** Released Mar '87, on Black Hawk (USA) by Blackhawk Records (USA). Catalogue no: **BKH 51101 CD**

**WEST COAST JAZZ**
**Album:** Released '81, on Verve (USA) by Polydor Ltd. Catalogue no: **2304 330**

**WITH EUROPEAN FRIENDS**
Tracks: / All God's chillun got rhythm / Broadway / Ladybird / Dear old Stockholm / East of the sun / They all fall in love / Theme for Manuel / Our kind of sabi.
Note: Personnel: Stan Getz (Tenor sax), Martial Solal (Piano), Pierre Michelot (Bass), Kenny Clarke (Drums), and other European musicians.
**CD:** Released '88, on Denon Catalogue no: **C38-7679**
**Cass:** Released '89, on Denon Catalogue no: **MC 7679**

**WITH LAURINDO ALMEIDA**
**CD:** Released '88, on Polydor by Polydor Ltd. Catalogue no: **823 149 2**

**YESTERDAYS**
Tracks: / Sweetness / Long Island sound / Yesterdays / Strike up the band / Pernod / Get happy / Dear old Stockholm.
Note: Recorded at Carnegie Hall, New York, 14 December 1949: Stan Getz (tenor sax), Kai Winding (trombone), Al Haig (piano), Tommy Potter (bass), Roy Haynes (drums). Recorded at Birdland, New York, 20 January 1953 and 23 January 1953: Stan Getz (tenor sax), Duke Jordan (piano), Bill Crow (bass), Kenny Clarke (drums).
**Album:** Released '81, on Jazz Live (Italy) Catalogue no: **BLJ 8036**

## Giants of Jazz

**GIANTS OF JAZZ IN BERLIN**
**CD:** Released Feb '90, on Emarcy Catalogue no: **834 567 2**

**GIANTS OF JAZZ, THE**
Tracks: / Straight, no chaser / Thelonious / Sweet and lovely / Don't blame me / I'll wait for you / Epistrophy.
Note: Personnel: Dizzy Gillespie/Thelonius Monk/Kai Winding/Sonny Stitt/Art Blakey/ Al McKibbon.
**Album:** Released Jul '84, on George Wein Collection (USA) by Concord Jazz Records (USA). Catalogue no: **CCD 4304**
**CD:** Released Jan '87, on Concord Jazz by Concord Jazz Records (USA). Catalogue no: **CCD 43004**

**GIANTS OF JAZZ VOL.1 (Various artists)**
Tracks: / Brown eyed woman: *Various artists* / Bottles empty: *Various artists* / Groovin' gates: *Various artists* / Ma cherie amour: *Various artists* / Save it pretty mama: *Various artists* / Bad dude: *Various artists.*
**Album:** Released May '80, on Manhattan Records by President Records. Deleted '85. Catalogue no: **MAN 5006**

**GIANTS OF JAZZ VOL.2 (Various artists)**
Tracks: / Empanada: *Various artists* / Gee but it's good: *Various artists* / Yesterme, yesteryou, yesterday: *Various artists* / Nightime in the switching yard: *Various artists* / Too bad: *Various artists* / Wedding bell blues: *Various artists.*
**Album:** Released May '80, on Manhattan Records by President Records. Deleted '85. Catalogue no: **MAN 5008**

**GIANTS OF JAZZ VOL.3**
Tracks: / Wave / Boogie nights / Crying blind / Shake it well / Big legged woman / Nightime in the switching yard. **Album:** Released May '80, on Manhattan Records by President Records. Deleted '85. Catalogue no: **MAN 5012**

**GIANTS OF JAZZ VOL.4 (Various artists)**
Tracks: / After you've gone: *Various artists* / Close to you: *Various artists* / Out to lunch: *Various artists* / Willow weep for me: *Various artists* / In the hush of the night: *Various artists* / Nobody:

*Various artists.*
**Album:** Released Nov '80, on Manhattan (USA) by Capitol (USA) Records. Deleted Nov '85. Catalogue no: **MAN 5015**

**GIANTS OF JAZZ VOL.5**
Tracks: / Misty / Dancing in the sun / Jimmy Reed blues / Over the hump / Sweet Ginny / I put a spell on you.
**Album:** on Manhattan Records by President Records. Catalogue no: **MAN 5018**

**GIANTS OF JAZZ: VOLUME 1 (Various artists)**
Tracks: / Ain't misbehavin': *Various artists* / Sleepy time down south: *Various artists* / Hamp rich dido blues: *Various artists* / Limelight: *Various artists* / Buddy's rock: *Various artists* / My funny valentine: *Various artists* / Walking shoes: *Various artists.*
Note: Musicians include Gerry Mulligan, Lionel Hampton, Hank Jones, Buddy Rich, John Hendricks, Bucky Pizzareli.
**Album:** Released '84, on Kingdom Jazz by Kingdom Records. Catalogue no: **GATE 7015**
**Cass:** Released '89, on Kingdom Jazz by Kingdom Records. Catalogue no: **CGATE 7015**

**GIANTS OF TRADITIONAL JAZZ (Various artists)**
Note: Mutt Carey & His Group, Sidney Bechet & His Group, Joe Marsala & His Group, Wild Bill Davison & His Group, Ben Pollack & His Group.
**Album:** Released Feb '85, on Savoy (France) Catalogue no: **WL 70513**
**2 LP Set:** Released Mar '85, on Savoy Jazz (USA) by Malaco Records (USA). Catalogue no: **SJL 2251**

## Giants Of Jazz & Blues

**GIANTS OF JAZZ AND BLUES (Various artists)**
**Cass:** Released Jan '87, on Masters (Holland) Catalogue no: **MAMC 281285**
**Album:** Released Jan '87, on Masters (Holland) Catalogue no: **MA 28 1285**
**CD:** Released '88, on Spectrum (CD) by M.S.D.. Catalogue no: **SPEC 85013**

## Gibbons, Carroll

**Biographical details:** British dance band leader born in 1903 in the USA; he died in 1954. He came to England in 1924 and took over the Savoy Orpheans in 1927; he went to HMV as director of Light Music in 1928 and recorded as the New Mayfair Dance Orchestra. With various small groups he accompanied Noel Coward, Paul Robeson, Gracie Fields and others including George Metaxa, Romanian born musical comedy star. His assistant Ray Noble took over when Gibbons went to the USA to work in films; he returned to England in 1931, re-formed the Orpheans and led them for the rest of his life. The band within a band was Carroll Gibbons and his Boy Friends. Records and broadcasts were extremely popular and his drawing sign off 'G'night everybody' was very familiar. (Donald Clarke, July 1989).

**BODY AND SOUL (Gibbons, Carroll & Savoy Hotel Orpheans)**
Tracks: / Body and soul / I don't know why (I just do) / She's funny that way / I apologise / Who am I? / Mean to me / Faded summer love, A / Sweet and lovely / Mona Lisa / Moonbeam dance / There's a time and place for everything / You're blase / Reaching for someone (and not finding anyone there) / Alone with my dreams / Oh Monah.
Note: Featuring singers Al Bowlly and Jack Plant.
**Cass:** Released Jun '85, on Joy by President Records. Catalogue no: **TC-JOY B 268**
**Album:** Released Nov '82, on Joy by President Records. Catalogue no: **JOY 268**

**BRIGHTER THAN THE SUN (Gibbons, Carroll & Savoy Hotel Orpheans)**
Tracks: / You're gonna lose your gal / One morning in May / May I? / Beat O' my heart / So help me / I saw stars / For all we know / All my life / You're the kind of a baby for me / Kiss by kiss / Sailin' on the Robert E. Lee / One hour with you / What makes you so adorable / By special permission of the copyright owners / After tonight we say goodbye / I wish I knew a bigger word than love / What more can I ask / Brighter than the sun / It's gonna be you / Oceans of time.
**Album:** Released Jan '86, on Saville by Conifer Records. Catalogue no: **SVL 174**
**Cass:** Released Jan '86, on Saville by Conifer Records. Catalogue no: **CSVL 174**

**CARROLL GIBBONS STORY (Carroll Gibbons & Savoy Hotel Orpheans)**
Tracks: / Mama's gone goodbye / Where'd you get those eyes? / Garden in the rain / Can't we talk it over? / When we're alone / I'll never be the same / Isn't it romantic? / I guess I'll have to change my plan / Shuffle off to Buffalo / On the air / Living in dreams / Easy come, easy go / Piccolino, The / Broadway rhythm / I got a feelin' you're foolin' / These foolish things / Midnight in Mayfair / Goodnight my love / There's a lull in my life / So rare / Can I forget you? / Folks who live on the hill, The / Foggy day, A / Remember me / Sing my heart / There goes my dream / I don't want to talk without you / I'll get by / Don't you know I care / It was swell while it lasted / Moment I saw you, The.
**Cass:** Released Feb '84, on Retrospect by EMI Records. Catalogue no: **TC2 SH 167/8**
**2 LP Set:** Released Feb '84, on Retrospect by EMI Records. Deleted Jul '87. Catalogue no: **SH 167/8**

**CARROLL RE-CALLS THE TUNES**
Tracks: / Lady is a tramp, The / Sweet Sue / California here I come / Babette / I can't give you anything but love / Dinah / Ain't misbehavin' / Stormy weather / Exactly like you / Oh me, oh my / They didn't believe me / Cheek to cheek / In the still of the night / Two sleepy people / Rosalie / Solitude / Time on my hands / Manhattan holiday / Bubbling over / I cried for you / Somebody loves me / These foolish things / I'll see you in my dreams / Diane / I'll see you again / Kiss me again / Alice blue gown / Speak to me love / Marcheta / Honeysuckle rose / I've got a feeling I'm falling / Keepin' out of mischief now / Summer rain / Smoke gets in your eyes / Way you look tonight / Moonbeams dance / I want the waiter.
**Album:** Released Jul '86, on Retrospect by EMI Records. Deleted Jun '89. Catalogue no: **SH 509**
**Cass:** Released Nov '86, on Retrospect by EMI Records. Deleted Jun '89. Catalogue no: **TCSH 509**

**DANCING IN THE DARK (Gibbons, Carroll & Savoy Hotel Orpheans)**
Tracks: / What a life / Dancing in the dark / Sweet and lovely / Keepin' out of mischief now / Actions speak louder than words / My silent love / I heard / Bidin' my time / I wanna be loved / Great big bunch of you / As time goes by / Snuggled on your shoulder / All of a sudden / Old man of the mountain, The / Love me tonight / Blues in my heart / Goopy Geer (He plays piano & he plays by ear) / With love in my heart.
Note: The Cat And The Fiddle medley.
**Album:** Released '86, on Saville by Conifer Records. Catalogue no: **SVL 157**
**Cass:** Released '86, on Saville by Conifer Records. Catalogue no: **CSVL 157**

**GOLDEN AGE OF CARROLL GIBBONS, (Gibbons, Carroll & The Savoy Hotel Orpheans)**
Tracks: / On the air / Dancing in the dark / Home / Tony's wife, with thee I swing / I double dare you / Sixty seconds got together / I have eyes / Wishing / Nightingale sang in Berkeley Square, A / I'm nobody's baby / Room 504 / Come happy day / Let's be sensible / When day is done / I'm going to get lit up when the

lights go up in London.
**Album:** Released Apr '85, on Golden Age by EMI Records. Deleted '87. Catalogue no: **GX 412 526-1**
**Cass:** Released Apr '85, on Golden Age by EMI Records. Catalogue no: **GX 412 526-4**

### I SAW STARS
Note: Featuring Savoy (hotel) orpheans
**Cass set:** Released '88, on Saville by Conifer Records. Catalogue no: **CSVLD 001**
**2 LP Set:** Released Sep '87, on Saville by Conifer Records. Catalogue no: **SVLD 001**

### MUSIC MAESTRO PLEASE
Tracks: / You were there / Play, orchestra, play / There isn't any limit to my love / This'll make you whistle / Did you mean it? / I'm in a dancing mood / I've got my love to keep me warm / This year's kisses / Too marvellous for words / It looks like rain in Cherry Blossom Lane / Foggy day, A / Nice work if you can get it / With a smile and a song / One song / Love walked in / Love is here to stay / Music, maestro, please / It's d'lovely / My heart is taking lessons / On the sentimental side.
**Album:** Released May '89, on Saville by Conifer Records. Catalogue no: **SVL 200**
**Cass:** Released May '89, on Saville by Conifer Records. Catalogue no: **CSVL 200**

### ON THE AIR (Gibbons, Carroll & The Savoy Hotel Orpheans)
Tracks: / On the air / Have you met Miss Jones / Comes love / Stairway to the stars / What's new / My heart belongs to Daddy / I don't want to set the world on fire / F.D.R. Jones / Shake down the stars / Accentuate the positive / Tomorrow's sunrise / Cynthia's in love / Over Wyoming / Silver wedding waltz / Francesca / Wandering along / I can dream, can't I / So ends my search for a dream.
**Cass:** Released Jun '85, on President by President Records. Catalogue no: **TC-PLE 513**
**Album:** Released Oct '86, on World Records by EMI Records. Deleted Jul '88. Catalogue no: **SH 360**
**Album:** Released Jul '84, on President Evergreen by President Records. Catalogue no: **PLE 513**
**Cass:** Released Oct '86, on Retrospect by EMI Records. Deleted Jul '88. Catalogue no: **TC SH 360**

### ON THE WIRELESS AT 7 PM EACH (Hartley's Jam Broadcasts)
Tracks: / My lips and your lips / You've got to admit / I'm so misunderstood / Swing on the gait / Life of the party, The / While there's a 'you' about / Love is just around the corner / Say when / Needle in a haystack / Wrapped around your finger / Body and soul / You fit into the picture / College rhythm / Blue moon / I got rhythm / In my country that means love.
Note: Includes medley 1: I wish I were twins/Sweetheart, I'm dreaming of you/I can't give you anything but love/You mother's son in law. Medley 2: Who do you think you are/Let's be sensible/Auf wiedersehn, my dear/Pop goes your heart.
**CD:** Released May '90, on Retrospect by EMI Records. Catalogue no: **CDP 794 321 2**
**Cass:** Released May '90, on Retrospect by EMI Records. Catalogue no: **TCSH 519**
**CD:** Released May '90, on Retrospect by EMI Records. Catalogue no: **CZ 307**
**Album:** Released May '90, on Retrospect by EMI Records. Catalogue no: **SH 519**
**Album:** Released May '90, on Retrospect by EMI Records. Catalogue no: **794 321 1**
**Cass:** Released May '90, on Retrospect by EMI Records. Catalogue no: **794 321 4**

### TOO MARVELLOUS FOR WORDS
Tracks: / Too marvellous for words / Night is young and you're so beautiful, The / Seal it with a kiss / Here comes the sandman / Goodnight my love / Foggy day, A / I don't want to make history / Never gonna dance / Take my heart / I stumbled over love / This years kisses / Moon got in my eyes / Nice work if you can get it / Roses in December / Can I forget you / You're not the kind / Remember me? / Put me behind bars.
**Album:** Released Dec '88, on Burlington Records by Plant Life Records. Catalogue no: **BUR 016**
**Cass:** Released Dec '88, on Burlington Records by Plant Life Records. Catalogue no: **4 BUR 016**

## Gibbs, Mike

### BIG MUSIC (Gibbs, Mike Orchestra)
Tracks: / Wall to wall / Pride aside / Kosasa / Almost ev'ry day / Watershed / Mopsus / Adult / Pride outside.
Note: For nearly twenty years Mike Gibbs has been at the forefront of the jazz movement, and has also worked outside the jazz sphere with artists such as Peter Gabriel and Joni Mitchell. (Virgin Records, Oct 1988)
**CD:** Released Oct '88, on Venture (2) by Virgin Records. Catalogue no: **CDVE 27**
**Cass:** Released Oct '88, on Venture (2) by Virgin Records. Catalogue no: **TCVE 27**
**Album:** Released Oct '88, on Venture (2) by Virgin Records. Catalogue no: **VE 27**

## Gibbs, Terry

**Biographical details:** Born Julius Gubenko in 1924 in Brooklyn, the vibist and bandleader has always been an under-rated jazzman. He played in name bands, then Benny Goodman small groups; he has made some wonderful big band albums, and two volumes of previously unreleased *Dream Band* from 1959 were recently re-issued in the USA on Contemporary. *Terry* is a quartet album made for Brunswick in 1954; *Take it from me* on Impulse 10 years later; *February 19th 1963* was originally called *The Family album*; all are quartet records. An album on Palo Alto with Buddy De Franco was ecstatically reviewed; excellent work from both veterans. No relation to Terry Gibbs, a blind soulful country singer whose USA albums on MCA haven't done as well as they deserved. (Donald Clarke, July 1989) .

### CHICAGO FIRE (Gibbs, Terry & Buddy De Franco)
Tracks: / Rockin' in rhythm / Please send me someone to love / Sister Sadie / This is always / Cherokee / Giant steps / Bopstacle course / Stella by starlight / 52nd street theme.
**CD:** Released Jan '89, on JVC/Fantasy Catalogue no: **VDJ 1133**
**Album:** Released '88, on Contemporary by Ace Records. Catalogue no: **C 14036**

### FAMILY ALBUM, THE
**Album:** Released Oct '88, on Vogue by Vogue Records. Catalogue no: **500072**

### FEBRUARY 19TH, 1963 (Gibbs, Terry Quartet)
Tracks: / Burton up your lips / Up at Logue's place / One for my uncle / Ballad for Barbara / Sherry bossa nova / El cheapo / Henny time / Many moons ago / Better to be richie than poor / Sunny girl / Sol right with me / Half stuie.
**Album:** Released Oct '80, on From The Jazz Vault by Damont Audio Ltd.. Catalogue no: **JV 110**

### JAZZ PARTY - FIRST TIME TOGETHER (Gibbs, Terry & Buddy De Franco)
**Album:** Released Jan '84, on Palo Alto Catalogue no: **PA 8011**
**Cass:** Released Jan '84, on Palo Alto Catalogue no: **PAC 8011**

### TAKE IT FROM ME (Gibbs, Terry Quartet)
Tracks: / Take it from me / El Fatso / OGE / Pauline's place / 8lb 10oz / Gee dad, it's a deacan / All the things you are / Honeysuckle rose.
**Cass:** Released Sep '82, on Jasmine by Hasmick Promotions. Catalogue no: **JAS C60**
**Album:** Released Sep '82, on Jasmine by Hasmick Promotions. Deleted Feb '88. Catalogue no: **JAS 60**

### TERRY
Tracks: / Temporary / Tremendez / Old man Newman / What ho / Fatty / Baby doll / Peaches / Jazz mambo / Where are you / That feeling / Love is just around the corner / Trotting.
**Album:** Released Feb '83, on Jasmine by Hasmick Promotions. Deleted Feb '88. Catalogue no: **JASM 1005**

### TERRY GIBBS AT THE PIANO
**Album:** Released Feb '88, on Fresh Sounds (Spain) by Fresh Sounds Records (Spain). Catalogue no: **FS 217**

## Gibson, Banv

**BANV GIBSON ON TOUR**
**Album:** Released Nov '88, on Jazzology (USA) by Jazzology Records (USA). Catalogue no: **J 154**

**JAZZ BABY (Gibson, Banv & NOR Hot Jazz)**
**Album:** Released '88, on Stomp Off (USA) Catalogue no: **SOS 1073**

## Gibson Brass Band

**NON-UNION MUSICIANS OF NEW ORLEANS Louisiana vol. 1**
**Album:** Released Dec '87, on GHB by Jazzology Records (USA). Catalogue no: **GHB 215**

**NON-UNION MUSICIANS OF NEW ORLEANS Louisiana vol. 2**
**Album:** Released 8 Apr '89, on GHB by Jazzology Records (USA). Catalogue no: **GHB 216**
**Gibson, Clifford**

**BEAT YOU DOING IT**
**Album:** Released Dec '88, on Yazoo (USA) by Shanachie Records (USA). Catalogue no: **L 1027**

## Gibson, Harry

**BOOGIE WOOGIE IN BLUE (Gibson, Harry "Hipster")**
Tracks: / Barrelhouse boogie / Stop that dancin' up there.
Note: From the mid-1940's, the original compositions of the Hipster, plus his piano and vocals.
**Album:** Released '88, on Musicraft (USA) by Discovery Records (USA). Catalogue no: **MVS 2003**

**EVERYBODY'S CRAZY BUT ME (Gibson, Harry "Hipster")**
**Album:** Released Aug '88, on Progressive Catalogue no: **PRO 7042**

## Gilberto, Astrud

**Biographical details:** This Brazilian singer had had virtually no musical experience when she shot to brief stardom in 1964. Her husband Joao Gilberto, one of the leading figures on Brazil's bossa nova scene, was in the process of recording a bossa nova LP with himself on vocals and US tenor saxophonist Stan Getz providing the main accompaniment. For one song, *The Girl From Ipanema*, it was decided that Astrud might sound suitable for some of the lyrics (she was a native of the Ipanema beach area). When the album track was issued as a single, it was in an edited form and only Astrud's section (not Joao's) could be heard. *The Girl From Ipanema* was one of the year's surprise smashes, reaching no. 5 on the American chart. The untrained straightforwardness of the vocal performance was riveting - the natural quality of Astrud's voice were plaintive and slightly eerie. Although there were no further US hit singles, she became a cult figure in American jazz circles during the mid-sixties and rivalled her husband's status in their native country. In Britain *The Girl From Ipanema* peaked at no. 29. Two decades later, in one of pop music's more surprising quirks, it was reissued and reached no. 55. This 1984 reappearance was due to a mini-boom in jazz that was taking place in Britain, led by such acts as Sade, Everything but the Girl and Working Week. (Bob Macdonald, 21/9/85).

**ASTRUD GILBERTO (Compact/Walkman jazz)**
**Cass:** Released Jul '87, on Verve Catalogue no: **831 369 4**
**Cass:** Released Oct '84, on Audio Fidelity(USA) by Audio Fidelity (USA). Catalogue no: **ZCGAS 737**
**CD:** Released Jul '87, on Verve Catalogue no: **831 369 2**

**ASTRUD GILBERTO ALBUM**
Tracks: / Once I loved / Agua de beber / How insensitive / Meditation / Roses and roses / O morro nao tem vez / Dindi / Photograph / Dreamer / So finha de ser com voce / All that's left is to say goodbye.
**Album:** Released Jan '90, on Verve Catalogue no: **823 009 1**
**CD:** Released Nov '84, on Verve Deleted Oct '88. Catalogue no: **823 451-2**

**BEST OF ASTRUD GILBERTO**
Tracks: / Stay / Call me / Meditation / Light of my life / How insensitive / It might as well be spring / Here's that rainy day / Agua de beber / Beach samba / One note samba / My foolish heart / Certain smile, A / Girl from Ipanema / Shadow of your smile.
**Cass:** Released Oct '82, on Verve (Import) Catalogue no: **3201 729**
**Album:** Released Nov '85, on Verve (Holland) Catalogue no: **825 791-1**
**Cass:** Released Nov '85, on Verve (Holland) Catalogue no: **825 792-4**
**Album:** Released Oct '82, on Verve (Import) Catalogue no: **2482 559**

**ESSENTIAL ASTRUD GILBERTO**
Tracks: / Take me to Aruanda / Bim bom / So nice (summer samba) / One note samba / O Ganso / Tristeza / Fly me to the moon / It might as well be spring / Manha de carnival / Girl from Ipanema / Meditation / O morro nao tem vez / Corcovado / Certain smile, A / Beach samba / Agua de beber / Goodbye sadness.
**Cass:** Released Sep '84, on Verve Catalogue no: **VRVC 6**
**Album:** Released Sep '84, on Verve Catalogue no: **VRV 6**

**GETTING OVER YOU**
Tracks: / Young love of my life.
**7" Single:** Released Sep '84, on PRT by Castle Communications Records. Catalogue no: **7P 317**

**GILBERTO**
**Cass:** Released '87, on Verve Catalogue no: **8230094**

**GILBERTO/GETZ (Gilberto, Astrud & Stan Getz)**
Tracks: / Girl from Ipanema / Doralice / Paro muchachar / Desafinado / Meu Caracado / Corcovado / So danco samba / O grande amor / Viva sohando.
**CD:** Released '83, on Verve Catalogue no: **810 048-2**

**GIRL FROM IPANEMA, THE**
Tracks: / Girl from Ipanema / Take me to Aruanda.
**7" Single:** Released Aug '84, on Verve Deleted '87. Catalogue no: **IPA 1**
**CD:** Released '86, on Bellaphon Catalogue no: **CDBID 11001**
**12" Single:** Released Aug '84, on Verve Deleted '87. Catalogue no: **IPAX 1**
**Album:** Released Oct '82, on Phoenix (2) by Audio Fidelity Enterprises. Catalogue no: **PHX 1022**

**LOOK TO THE RAINBOW**
Tracks: / Berimbau / Once upon a summertime / Felicidade / I will wait for you / Frevo / Maria Quiet (Marie Moita) / Look at the rainbow / Bim bom / Lugar bonito / El preciso aprender a ser so (learn to live alone).
**CD:** Released Aug '86, on Polydor by Polydor Ltd. Deleted Mar '88. Catalogue no: **821 556-2**
**Cass:** Released Aug '86, on Polydor by Polydor Ltd. Deleted Mar '88. Catalogue no: **821 556-4**
**Album:** Released Aug '86, on Polydor by Polydor Ltd. Deleted Mar '88. Catalogue no: **821 556-1**

**MUSIC FOR THE MILLIONS**
Tracks: / Once I loved / Auga de beber / Meditation / And roses and roses / How insensitive / O morro / Dindi / Photograph / Dreamer / So tinha de ser com voce / All that's left is to say goodbye.
**Cass:** Released Jul '84, on Verve (Holland) Catalogue no: **817 852-4**
**Album:** Released Jul '84, on Verve (Holland) Catalogue no: **817 852-1**

**ONCE UPON A SUMMERTIME**
Tracks: / One note samba / Meditation / My foolish heart / Berimbau / Frevo / Once upon a summertime / How insensitive / Stay / Light my fire / Call me / I will wait for you / She's a carioca.
**Album:** Released Jan '77, on Verve Deleted '81. Catalogue no: **2352 172**

**SHADOW OF YOUR SMILE**
Tracks: / Shadow of your smile / Fly me to the moon / Gentle rain, The / Who can I turn to / Day by day.
**Album:** Released Jun '82, on Verve (USA) by Polydor Ltd. Catalogue no: **2304 540**

**SO AND SO (Mukai meets Gilberto) (Gilberto, Astrud & Shigeharu, Mukai)**
Tracks: / Champagne & caviar / Velas / Noos dois / Berimbau / Miracle of the fishes / Terrafirme / Keep on riding / Hold me.
Note: Musicians include: Astrud Gilberto (Vocal), Shigeharu, Makui (Trombone), Jorge Dalto (Piano), Jeff Mironov (Guitar), Antony Jackson (Bass), Omar Hakim (Drums), Denny Morouse (Flute).
**CD:** Released '88, on Denon Catalogue no: **C38-7582**

**THIS IS ASTRUD GILBERTO**
**Album:** Released Apr '85, on Verve (Germany) Catalogue no: **825 064-1**

## Gilberto, Joao

**Biographical details:** This Brazilian singer and guitarist came to fame in the early 60's as one of the leading exponents of his country's bossa nova sound. This style with its accompanying dance, sparked off a craze in the Western world when introduced to US audiences by Stan Getz and Charlie Byrd in 1962. Getz teamed with Gilberto in 1964 for a bossa nova LP - but its stand out track *The Girl From Ipanema* featured only the vocals of wife Astrud Gilberto when released on single. Joao's material was largely composed by Antonio Carlos Jobim, who helped him to popularise the bossa nova movement in Brazil. (Bob Macdonald, 21/9/85)
Guitarist and composer, born in Brazil in 1931. He showed his songs to composer Antonio Carlos Jobim (born in 1937) and began recording them in the late '50's; they were among the inventors of bossa nova, a fusion of the samba, the Baiao of North Brazil and North American cool jazz. ('Bossa' is the hump on the back of an ox; 'bossa nova' means 'new disturbance'.) It was disliked by the young left in Brazil because too American, but swetp the USA (see entry for Stan Getz). Astrud Gilberto, Joaos wife at the time, was a songwriter and lyricist, launching a singing career with *The Girl From Ipenema*, a huge hit in 1964. (Donald Clarke, July 1989).

**BRAZIL**
**Album:** Released Apr '82, on Mercury by Phonogram Ltd. Catalogue no: **6328 382**

**GILBERTO AND JOBIM**
Tracks: / Manha de Carnaval / O pato / Corcovado / Trevo de quarto folhas / Un abraco no bonfa / Se e tarde me pardoa / Discussao / A felicidade / Amor certinho / Outra vez / Samba de una nota so / Doralice / So em teus bracos / Meditacao / Felicidade.
**Cass:** Released '88, on EMI (Italy) by EMI Records. Catalogue no: **3C254 81353**
**Album:** Released Dec '86, on EMI (Italy) by EMI Records. Catalogue no: **3C 054 81353**

**JOAO AND ASTRUD GILBERTO MEET STAN GETZ (Gilberto, Joao/Astrud Gilberton/Stan Getz)**
**Cass:** Released Jul '88, on Entertainers Catalogue no: **ENT MC 13051**
**Album:** Released Jul '88, on Entertainers Catalogue no: **ENT LP 13051**

## Gill, John

**FINGER BUSTER**
**Album:** Released Jun '86, on Stomp Off (USA) Catalogue no: **SOS 1066**

## Gillespie, Dizzy

**Dizzy Gillespie**

**Biographical details:** Born John Birks Gillespie in 1917 in South Carolina, the trumpeter, composer, bandleader and vocalist was with Charlie Parker one of the inventors of modern jazz. He was influenced by Roy Eldridge; his repuation for pranks and zany humour led to his nickname, but he understood the importance of technical ability and became one of the greatest musicians in the world. Famous for his upturned trumpet, resulting from an accident: he liked the better sound dispersal and has been playing a bent horn ever since. Apart from his harmonic and rhythmic advances in jazz itself, his other innovations included modern jazz for big band in the late '40's and the Afro Cuban movement, inspired by roommate Mario Bauza, who played trumpet and was music director for Machito, and by the sensational Cuban drummer Chano Pozo, who played in Dizzy's band. Dizzy formed his own label in Detroit; it went broke but the music hold up extremely well and was well recorded for the time: the excellent Savoy set *Dee Gee Days* collects 1951-2 tracks including an early John Coltrane date and vocals with Joe 'Bebop' Carroll. A big band orgainised for Dizzy by Quincy Jones toured Europe and Latin America in the '50's for the USA State Department: it was popular around the world and and excellent advertisement for USA, but money was cut off partly because of complaints about using taxpayers' money to support a jazz band. He has led combos since except for one-off events. He ran for President in 1963 and the write-in vote almost got him on the California ballot. (Donald Clarke, July 1989) .

**20 GOLDEN PIECES: DIZZY GILLESPIE**
Tracks: / Night and day / Man I love, The / When it's sleepy time down South / Sweet and lovely / Very thought of you, The / Jealousy / Blue and sentimental / My old flame / Pennies from Heaven / Blue moon / Blue 'n' boogie / Hot house / Groovin' high / Dizzy atmosphere / All the things are are / Things to come / Emanon / Ray's idea / Our delight / Good dues blues.
**Cass:** Released Jul '82, on Bulldog Records by President Records. Catalogue no: **BDC 2006**
**Album:** Released Jul '82, on Bulldog Records by President Records. Catalogue no: **BDL 2006**

**1948-52 (Gillespie, Dizzy Big Band)**
Tracks: / Cubana be, Cubana bop / Groovin' high / Candido bongos / On the sunny side of the street / Ooh-shoo-be-doo-bee.
**Album:** Released Apr '81, on Queendisc (Italy) Catalogue no: **QU 045**

**AFRO-CUBAN BOP (Gillespie, Dizzy & His Orchestra)**
Tracks: / Oop-pop-a-da / One bass hit / Guarachi guaro / Relaxin' at Camarillo / I should care / Squirrel, The / Dizzier and dizzier / Taboo.
**Album:** Released Apr '81, on Jazz Live (Italy) Catalogue no: **BLJ 8028**

**AFRO-CUBAN JAZZ MOODS (Gillespie, Dizzy & Machito)**
Tracks: / Oro, incienso y mirra / Calidoscopico / Pensativo / Exuberante.
**Cass:** Released '82, on Pablo Jazz

(USA) by Pablo Records (USA). Catalogue no: **K10 771**

**Album:** Released '82, on Pablo Jazz (USA) by Pablo Records (USA). Catalogue no: **2310 771**

**ANONYMOUS MR. GILLESPIE, THE**

Tracks: / My melancholy baby / Cherokee / You're only happy when I'm blue / Ten lessons with Timothy / Who / Way you look tonight, The / Why do I love you / All the things you are / Night and day / Weeping Willie / Everytime I think of you / Baranco boogie / Shades of twilight / Once in a lovetime / Worried life / Empty bed blues.

**Album:** on Official by Official Records. Catalogue no: **OFF 3032**

**AT DOWNBEAT CLUB, SUMMER 47**

**Album:** Released '88, on Jazz Guild (USA) Catalogue no: **JG 1010**

**AT NEWPORT**

**Album:** Released Aug '81, on Verve Catalogue no: **2304 348**

**AT THE MONTREUX JAZZ FESTIVAL (Gillespie, Dizzy Big Seven)**

Tracks: / Lover come back to me / What's new? / Cherokee.

**Cass:** Released '82, on Pablo Jazz (USA) by Pablo Records (USA). Catalogue no: **K10 749**

**Album:** Released '82, on Pablo Jazz (USA) by Pablo Records (USA). Catalogue no: **2310 749**

**BEBOP ENTERS SWEDEN 1947-49 (Gillespie, Dizzy Big Band)**

**Album:** Released Jul '82, on Dragon by Dragon Records. Catalogue no: **DRLP 34**

**BEST OF DIZZY GILLESPIE**

Tracks: / Unicorn / Free ride / Pensavito / Exuberante / Behind the moonbeam / Shim-sham-shimmy.

**Album:** Released '82, on Pablo Jazz (USA) by Pablo Records (USA). Catalogue no: **231 0855**

**Cass:** Released '82, on Pablo Jazz (USA) by Pablo Records (USA). Catalogue no: **K10 855**

**BIG BAND 1968**

**Album:** Released Mar '77, on Beppo Deleted '88. Catalogue no: **BEPPO 509**

**BIRK'S WORKS**

Tracks: / Birk's works / Good bait / Oop-pop-a-da / Woodyn' you / Champ, The / I can't get started / Caravan.

Note: With Dexter Gordon, Milt Jackson, Billy Taylor, Joe Carroll, Bud Powell, CharlieMingus, Max Roach, Bill Graham, Lou Hackney, Al Jones.

**Album:** Released May '83, on Duke by Melodisc Records. Catalogue no: **D 1019**

**BODY AND SOUL (Gillespie, Dizzy & His Orchestra)**

Tracks: / Rhumbop concerto / Relaxin' at Camarillo / Guarachi guaro / Soulphony in three hearts / Love me or leave me / Body and soul / Oop-pop-a-do / Ool-ya-koo / I'm beboppin' too.

Note: Sarah Vaughan sings on two tracks, *Love Me or Leave Me* and *Body and Soul*.

**Album:** Released Oct '85, on Bulldog Records by President Records. Catalogue no: **BDL 1057**

**Cass:** Released Oct '85, on Bulldog Records by President Records. Catalogue no: **BDC 1057**

**BOP SESSION, THE (Gillespie, Dizzy/Sonny Stitt/John Lewis/Max Roach)**

Tracks: / Blues 'n' boogie / Confirmation / Groovin' high / Loverman / All the things you are / Ladybird.

**CD:** Released Jun '88, on Sonet by Sonet Records. Catalogue no: **SNTCD 692**

**CD:** Released '88, on Vogue by Vogue Records. Catalogue no: **VG 600 039**

**Album:** Released Jun '88, on Sonet by Sonet Records. Catalogue no: **SNTF 692**

**CHAMP 1951-1952, THE**

Tracks: / Champ, The / Birk's works / Caravan / Time on my hands / On the sunny side of the street / Tin tin deo / Stardust / They can't take that away from me / Bluest blues / Swing low sweet Cadillac / Ooh-shoo-be-doo-bee.

Note: Musicians featured on the various tracks include Dizzy Gillespie (trumpet), J.Johnson (trombone), John Coltrane (tenor sax), Budd Johnson (tenor sax), Bill Graham (baritone sax), Milt Jackson (vibes), Wynton Kelly (piano), Kenny Burrell (guitar), Percy Heath (bass), Bernie Griggs (bass), Kansas Fields (drums), Art Blakey (drums), Al Jones (drums), Joe Carroll (vocals).

**Album:** Released Mar '85, on Jazz Anthology by Musidisc Records (France). Catalogue no: **JA 5183**

**CD:** Released Jul '89, on Vogue by Vogue Records. Catalogue no: **VG 670213**

**CLOSER TO THE SOURCE**

Tracks: / Could it be you / It's time for love / Closer to the source / You're No.1 in my book / Iced tea / Just before dawn / Textures.

**Album:** Released Jul '86, on Atlantic by WEA Records. Deleted Aug '87. Catalogue no: **781 646-1**

**Cass:** Released Jul '86, on Atlantic by WEA Records. Deleted Aug '87. Catalogue no: **781 646-4**

**COMPLETE PLEYEL CONCERT**

**2 LP Set:** Released Mar '84, on Vogue by Vogue Records. Catalogue no: **429002**

**CONCERT - MASSEY HALL, TORONTO (15 May 1953) (Gillespie, Dizzy & Charlie Parker)**

Tracks: / Perdido / Salt peanuts / All the things you are / Wee / Hot house.

Note: Dizzy Gillespie / Charlie Parker / Bud Powell / Charlie Mingus / Max Roach.

**Album:** Released Apr '84, on Joker (USA) by Lifetime Records (USA). Catalogue no: **SM 3784**

**CONFIRMATION (See under Berman, Sonny) (Gillespie, Dizzy & Sonny Berman)**

Tracks: / Confirmation / Diggin' for Diz / Dynamo / When I grow too old to dream / Round midnight / Nocturne / Curbstone scuffle / Woodchopper's holiday / Somebody loves me / Blue serge.

**Album:** Released '83, on Spotlite by Spotlite Records. Catalogue no: **SPJ 132**

**DEE GEE DAYS**

**Album:** Released Sep '78, on Savoy Jazz (USA) by Malaco Records (USA). Catalogue no: **SJL 2209**

**DEEGEE DAYS**

Tracks: / Tin Tin Deo / Birk's works / We love to boogie / Lady be good / Champ, The / I'm in a mess / School days / Swing low sweet cadillac / Bopsie's blues / I couldn't beat the rap / Caravan / Nobody knows / Bluest blues / On the sunny side of the street / Stardust / Time on my hands / Blue skies / Umbrella man / Confessin' / Ooh-shoo-be-doo-bee / They can't take that away from me.

**2 LP Set:** Released Feb '85, on Savoy (France) Deleted Jun '88. Catalogue no: **WL 70517**

**CD:** Released Mar '86, on RCA by BMG Records (UK). Deleted Nov '89. Catalogue no: **ZD 70517**

**DIGITAL AT MONTREUX 1980**

Tracks: / Christopher Columbus / I'm sitting on top of the world / Manteca / Get that booty / Kisses.

**Cass:** Released '82, on Pablo Jazz (USA) by Pablo Records (USA). Catalogue no: **K 08 226**

**Album:** Released '82, on Pablo Jazz (USA) by Pablo Records (USA). Catalogue no: **D 2308 226**

**DIZ DELIGHTS (Gillespie, Dizzy & His Orchestra)**

Tracks: / 52nd street theme / Night in Tunisia / Anthropology / Ow / Oop-pop-a-da / Two bass hit / Stay on it / Woodyn' you / Cool breeze / Manetca / Good bait / Ool-ya-koo.

**Cass:** Released Jul '86, on RCA by BMG Records (UK). Deleted Jul '89. Catalogue no: **CK 89804**

**Album:** Released Jul '86, on RCA by BMG Records (UK). Deleted Jul '89. Catalogue no: **CL 89804**

**DIZZY (Live at Carnegie Hall 1947) (Gillespie, Dizzy & His Legendary Big Band)**

**Album:** Released Sep '87, on Artistry Catalogue no: **AR 110**

**CD:** Released May '86, on Pablo Jazz (USA) by Pablo Records (USA). Catalogue no: **CD 20038**

**Album:** Released '88, on GNP Crescendo (USA) by GNP Crescendo Records (USA). Catalogue no: **GNPS 9028**

**DIZZY AND DOUBLE SIX OF PARIS**

**CD:** Released '86, on Philips (Germany)

by PolyGram UK Ltd. Catalogue no: **830 224-2**

**DIZZY GILLESPIE... (Various artists)**
**Album:** Released Sep '86, on Lotus Catalogue no: **LPPS 111 14**
**Cass:** Released '88, on Mercury by Phonogram Ltd. Catalogue no: **832 574-4**
**CD:** Released Jul '88, on Mercury by Phonogram Ltd. Catalogue no: **825 574-2**

**DIZZY GILLESPIE (1946-1949)**
**Album:** Released '83, on RCA (France) by BMG Records (France). Catalogue no: **PM 42408**
**Cass:** Released Sep '86, on Jazz Tribune by BMG Records (UK). Deleted May '89. Catalogue no: **NK 89763**
**Album:** Released Sep '86, on Jazz Tribune by BMG Records (UK). Deleted May '89. Catalogue no: **NL 89763**

**DIZZY GILLESPIE (1948-1953)**
**Album:** Released '88, on Vogue (France) by Vogue Records. Catalogue no: **502002**

**DIZZY GILLESPIE AND GIANTS OF JAZZ (Gillespie, Dizzy & Giants of Jazz)**
Tracks: / Straight, no chaser / Thelonious / Sweet and lovely / Don't blame me / I'll wait for you / Epistrophy.
**Album:** Released Sep '84, on Concord by Concord Jazz Records (USA). Catalogue no: **GW 3004**

**DIZZY GILLESPIE AND CHARLIE PARKER (Gillespie, Dizzy & Charlie Parker)**
**Cass:** Released Jun '84, on EMI (Europe) by EMI Records. Catalogue no: **2M 256 64847**
**Album:** Released Jun '84, on EMI (Europe) by EMI Records. Catalogue no: **2M 056 64847**

**DIZZY GILLESPIE COLLECTION**
**CD:** Released Oct '89, on Collection by K-Tel Records. Catalogue no: **OR 0083**
**Album:** Released Nov '85, on Deja Vu Catalogue no: **DVLP 2028**
**Cass:** Released Nov '85, on Deja Vu Catalogue no: **DVMC 2028**

**DIZZY GILLESPIE AND HIS BAND IN CONCERT (Gillespie, Dizzy & His Band)**
**Album:** Released '88, on GNP Crescendo (USA) by GNP Crescendo Records (USA). Catalogue no: **GNPS 23**

**DIZZY GILLESPIE AND HIS ORCHESTRA (Gillespie, Dizzy & Orchestra)**
**Album:** Released Sep '87, on Giants of Jazz by Hasmick Promotions. Catalogue no: **LPJT 37**

**DIZZY GILLESPIE JAM**
Tracks: / Girl of my dreams / Get happy / Once in a while / But beautiful / Here's that rainy day / Champ, The.
**Cass:** Released '82, on Pablo Jazz (USA) by Pablo Records (USA). Catalogue no: **K 08 211**
**Album:** Released '82, on Pablo Jazz (USA) by Pablo Records (USA). Catalogue no: **2308 211**

**DIZZY GILLESPIE MEETS PHIL WOODS**
**Album:** Released Jan '88, on Timeless by Timeless Records. Catalogue no: **SFP 250**
**Album:** Released May '89, on Timeless by Timeless Records. Catalogue no: **SJP 250**
**CD:** Released Jan '88, on Timeless (Import) by Timeless Records. Catalogue no: **CDSJP 250**

**DIZZY GILLESPIE QUINTET IN EUROPE (Gillespie, Dizzy Quintet)**
Tracks: / Lady be good / No greater love / Mooche, The / Night in Tunisia / Long, long summer.
Note: With Leo Wright, Lalo Schifrin, B. Cunningham, Mel Lewis.
**Album:** Released '81, on Unique Jazz by Spotlite Records. Catalogue no: **UJ 30**

**DIZZY GILLESPIE SEXTET (Gillespie, Dizzy Sextet)**
**Album:** Released May '84, on Vogue Jazz (France) by Vogue Records. Catalogue no: **429 002**

**DIZZY GILLESPIE AND THE DOUBLE SIX**
**Album:** Released Oct '82, on Mercury (Import) Catalogue no: **6337 203**

**DIZZY GILLESPIE (VIDEO)**
**VHS:** Released '88, on Kay Jazz (video) by Kay Jazz. Catalogue no: **KJ 078**

**DIZZY GILLESPIE VOL1**
Tracks: / Emanon / Ool-ya-koo / 'Round midnight / Stay on it / Good bait / One bass hit / I can't get started / Manteca.
**Album:** Released Jan '82, on Jazz Reactivation Catalogue no: **JR 120**

**DIZZY GILLESPIE VOL 2**
Tracks: / Champ, The / Tin tin deo / They can't take that away from me / Good bait / Mon homme / Bluest blues / Birk's works / On the sunny side of the street / Swing low sweet Cadillac / School days / Shoo-be-doo-be-doo.
**Album:** Released May '83, on Jazz Reactivation Catalogue no: **JR 137**

**DIZZY GILLESPIE VOL 3**
Tracks: / Oop-pop-a-da / Round midnight / Algo bueno / I can't get started / Two bass hit / Good bait / Afro-Cuban suite / Ool-ya-koo / Things to come.
**Album:** Released May '83, on Jazz Reactivation Catalogue no: **JR 141**

**DIZZY GILLESPIE WITH CHARLIE PARKER (Gillespie, Dizzy & Charlie Parker)**
**Cass:** Released '88, on Joker (USA) by Lifetime Records (USA). Catalogue no: **MC 3784**
**Album:** Released '88, on Joker (USA) by Lifetime Records (USA). Catalogue no: **SM 3784**

**DIZZY GILLESPIE'S BIG FOUR**
Tracks: / Frelimo / Hurry home / Russian lullaby / Be bob (Dizzy's fingers) / Birk's works / September song / Jitterbug.
**CD:** Released Jan '89, on JVC/Fantasy Catalogue no: **VDJ 28008**
**Album:** Released '82, on Pablo Jazz (USA) by Pablo Records (USA). Catalogue no: **2310 719**
**Cass:** Released '82, on Pablo Jazz (USA) by Pablo Records (USA). Catalogue no: **K10 719**

**DIZZY GILLESPIE, SARAH VAUGHAN AND CHARLIE PARKER (Gillespie, Dizzy, Sarah Vaughan, Charlie Parker)**
**CD:** Released Apr '87, on Delta (1) by Delta Records. Deleted '88. Catalogue no: **11 064**

**DIZZY IN PARIS**
**CD:** Released Dec '85, on Vogue by Vogue Records. Catalogue no: **VGCD 600047**

**DIZZY ON THE FRENCH RIVIERA**
**Album:** Released Sep '84, on Philips (Timeless) by PolyGram UK Ltd. Catalogue no: **TIME 09**
**Cass:** Released Sep '84, on Philips (Timeless) by PolyGram UK Ltd. Catalogue no: **TIMEC 09**

**DIZZY'S DELIGHT**
**Album:** Released May '79, on Phoenix (USA) by All Star Talent Inc.(USA). Catalogue no: **LP 4**

**DIZZY'S PARTY**
Tracks: / Dizzy's party / Shim-sham-shimmy / Harlem samba / Land of milk and honey.
**Album:** Released May '82, on Pablo Jazz (USA) by Pablo Records (USA). Catalogue no: **231 0784**
**Cass:** Released May '82, on Pablo Jazz (USA) by Pablo Records (USA). Catalogue no: **K10 784**

**ELECTRIFYING EVENING**
Tracks: / Kush / Salt peanuts / Night in Tunisia / Mooche, The.
Note: Recorded live in 1961.
**Album:** Released May '82, on Verve Catalogue no: **2304 349**

**ENDLESSLY**
**Album:** Released May '89, on MCA (Import) by MCA Records. Catalogue no: **MCA 42153**
**CD:** Released May '89, on MCA (Import) by MCA Records. Catalogue no: **MCAD 42153**
**Cass:** Released May '89, on MCA (Import) by MCA Records. Catalogue no: **MCAC 42153**

**ENDURING MAGIC**
Tracks: / Blue and boogie / Thrill is gone, The / Yale blue blues / Take the 'A' train / Love for sale / Street of dreams / Jew's harp.
Note: Live recordings made between 1970 and 1985 and dedicated to the memory of Billy Strayhorn and Duke Ellington. Personnel: Dizzy Gillespie - trumpet and Jew's harp / Dwike Mitchell-piano / Willie Ruff - bass and French horn.
**Album:** Released Jan '87, on Black

Hawk (USA) by Blackhawk Records (USA). Catalogue no: **BKH 51801**

**FREE RIDE**
Tracks: / Unicorn / Incantation / Wrong number / Free ride / Ozone madness / Love poem for Donna / Last stroke of midnight.
**Cass:** Released May '82, on Pablo Jazz (USA) by Pablo Records (USA). Catalogue no: **K10 794**
**Album:** Released May '82, on Pablo Jazz (USA) by Pablo Records (USA). Catalogue no: **231 0794**

**GIANT, THE**
Note: With Johnny Griffin etc.
**CD:** Released '86, on Accord (France) by Musidisc Records (France). Catalogue no: **139 217**

**GILLESPIE JAM SESSIONS, THE**
**2 LP Set:** Released Aug '76, on Verve Catalogue no: **2610 023**

**GOOD BAIT**
Tracks: / Good bait / Algo bueno / Minor walk / Half nelson / Cool breeze / Squirrel, The / Oop-pop-a-da / S'posin' / Taboo.
**Album:** Released May '83, on Spotlite by Spotlite Records. Catalogue no: **SPJ 122**

**GREAT DIZZY GILLESPIE, THE**
Tracks: / Blue and boogie / Groovin' high / Dizzy atmosphere / All the things you are / Salt peanuts / Hot house / Oop bop sh'bam / That's Earl's brother / Our delight / One bass hit / Things to come / Ray's idea.
Note: Vintage bop from the Dizzy Gillespie Sextet -- featuring the incomparable Charlie Parker on alto -- and the Dizzy Gillespie Orchestra. Recorded between February 1945 and November 1946.
**Album:** Released Apr '81, on Joker (USA) by Lifetime Records (USA). Catalogue no: **SM 3541**

**GROOVIN' HIGH (Gillespie, Dizzy & His Sextets)**
**Album:** Released Oct '86, on Musicraft (USA) by Discovery Records (USA). Catalogue no: **MVS 2009**

**IN CONCERT 1956**
**Album:** Released Aug '89, on Artistry Catalogue no: **AR 111**

**IN THE BEGINNING**
Tracks: / Blue 'n' boogie / Groovin' high / All the things you are / Dizzy atmosphere / Salt peanuts / Shaw 'nuff / Lover man / Hot house / One bass hit / Oop bop sh'bam / Hand fulla gimme / That's Earl, brother / Things to come / Good dues blues / Our delight / Ray's idea / Emanon / he beeped when he shoulda bopped / I waited for you / Nice work if you can get it / She's gone again / Thinking of you.
**2 LP Set:** Released '79, on Prestige Deleted '84. Catalogue no: **PR 24019**

**INCREDIBLE**
**Album:** Released '79, on MPS Jazz Deleted '84. Catalogue no: **5C 064 99400**

**JAZZ MATURITY...WHERE ITS COMING FROM (Gillespie, Dizzy/Roy Eldridge)**
**Album:** Released May '82, on Pablo Jazz (USA) by Pablo Records (USA). Catalogue no: **231 0816**
**Cass:** Released May '82, on Pablo Jazz (USA) by Pablo Records (USA). Catalogue no: **K10 816**

**JAZZ TIME VOL.5**
**Album:** Released '88, on Vogue (France) by Vogue Records. Catalogue no: **502705**

**JIVIN' IN BEBOP**
**CD:** Released '89, on Jazz-Up Catalogue no: **JU 304**

**JUST BOP (Gillespie, Dizzy Sextet)**
**Album:** Released Apr '81, on Queendisc (Italy) Catalogue no: **QU 039**

**LEGENDARY, THE**
**2 LP Set:** Released Oct '88, on Vogue by Vogue Records. Catalogue no: **400018**

**LIVE: AT BIRDLAND 1956 (Gillespie, Dizzy Big Band)**
**Album:** Released '88, on Fanfare by Captain Billy's Music. Catalogue no: **LP 46-146**

**LIVE AT THE SHRINE AUDITORIUM (Gillespie, Dizzy Big Band)**
**Album:** Released Apr '81, on Queendisc (Italy) Catalogue no: **QU 003**

**LIVE AT THE VILLAGE VANGUARD**
**Album:** Released '79, on Blue Note by EMI Records. Deleted '84. Catalogue no: **BNS 40035**

**MONTEREY 1961**
**Album:** Released Sep '79, on Jazz Legacy by Vogue Records. Catalogue no: **JL 90**

**MONTREUX 1980**
**CD:** Released Apr '87, on Pablo Jazz (USA) by Pablo Records (USA). Catalogue no: **CD 230 8226**

**MOST IMPORTANT RECORDINGS**
**CD:** Released Mar '90, on Ogun by Cadillac Music. Catalogue no: **CD OFF 83056-2**

**NEW FACES**
Tracks: / Birk's works / Lorraine / Tin Tin Deo / Tenor song / Ballad fiesta mojo / Every morning / Ballad / Fiesta mojo.
**Album:** Released Sep '88, on GRP by GRP Records (USA). Catalogue no: **GRP 91012**
**Cass:** Released Sep '88, on GRP by GRP Records (USA). Catalogue no: **GRPM 91012**
**CD:** Released Sep '88, on GRP by GRP Records (USA). Catalogue no: **GRD 9512**
**Album:** Released Aug '85, on GRP by GRP Records (USA). Catalogue no: **GRPA 1012**

**NIGHT IN HAVANA, A**
Tracks: / Night in Tunisia (ext.) / Mantega / Gillespiana suite (blues segment) / Swing low sweet chariot / Gee baby.
Note: Running time: 86 minutes.
**VHS:** Released Feb '90, on Castle Hendring Video by Castle Communications Records. Catalogue no: **HEN 2 193**

**NIGHT IN TUNISIA**
**Album:** Released Jul '89, on Jazz & Jazz Catalogue no: **JJ 606**
**CD:** Released Jul '89, on Jazz & Jazz Catalogue no: **CDJJ 606**

**N.Y.C. 1952**
Tracks: / Champ, The / Good bait / Tin tin deo / Perdido.
**Album:** Released Apr '81, on Lotus Catalogue no: **LPPS 111 10**

**ONE BASS HIT (Gillespie, Dizzy & His Orchestra)**
**Album:** Released Oct '86, on Musicraft (USA) by Discovery Records (USA). Catalogue no: **MVS 2010**

**ONE NIGHT IN WASHINGTON**
Tracks: / Afro suite / Hob nail boogie / Caravan / Tin tin deo / Ups 'n' downs / Wild bills boogie.
**Album:** Released '84, on WEA by WEA Records. Deleted '89. Catalogue no: **K960300-1**

**OO POP A DA (Gillespie, Dizzy Quartet)**
**Album:** Released Oct '85, on Affinity by Charly Records. Catalogue no: **AFF 142**

**OOP-BOP SH'BAM**
Tracks: / I waited for you / Groovin' high / Oop-pop-a-da / Cool breeze / Stay on it / Ladybird / Wouldn't you? / Two bass hit / Oop bop sh'bam / Hot house / Ray's idea / Pan dameronium.
Note: Important broadcasts from the Dowbeat Club, New York, during the summer of 1947, featuring Dizzy on trumpet, Milt Jackson (vibes), Ray Brown (bass) and James Moody (drums).
**Album:** Released Oct '82, on Nostalgia by Mainline Records. Catalogue no: **NOST 7629**

**PARIS CONCERT**
**Album:** Released '88, on GNP Crescendo (USA) by GNP Crescendo Records (USA). Catalogue no: **GNPS 9006**

**PASADENA 1948 (Legendary big band concerts)**
**CD:** Released Oct '88, on Vogue by Vogue Records. Catalogue no: **VG 600 125**
**Album:** Released Oct '88, on Vogue by Vogue Records. Catalogue no: **500060**

**PLAYS AND RAPS IN HIS GREATEST CONCERT**
**Cass:** Released Jul '82, on Pablo Jazz (USA) by Pablo Records (USA). Catalogue no: **K20 116**
**Album:** Released Jul '82, on Pablo Jazz (USA) by Pablo Records (USA). Catalogue no: **D 2620 116**

**PLEYEL CONCERT 1953**
Tracks: / Champ, The / Tin tin deo / They can't take that away from me / Good bait / Bluest blues / Birks works / I can't get started / On the sunny side of the street / Mon homme / Swing low sweet Cadillac

/ School days / Oo-shoo-be-do-be.
**Album:** Released Oct '88, on Vogue (France) by Vogue Records. Catalogue no: **509173**
**CD:** Released Dec '86, on Vogue by Vogue Records. Catalogue no: **VG 600 031**

**PORTRAIT OF DUKE ELLINGTON, A (Gillespie, Dizzy & His Orchestra)**
Tracks: / In a mellow tone / Things ain't what they used to be / Serenade to Sweden / Chelsea Bridge / Upper Manhattan medical group / Do nothing till you hear from me / Caravan / Sophisticated lady / Johnny come lately / Perdido / Come Sunday.
**CD:** Released Nov '84, on Verve Deleted Mar '88. Catalogue no: **817 107-2**
**Album:** Released Jun '84, on Verve (USA) by Polydor Ltd. Catalogue no: **817 107-1**

**PROFESSOR BOP**
Tracks: / Blue and boogie / Groovin' high / Dizzy atmosphere / All the things you are / Hot house / Oop bop sh'bam / Our delight / Things to come / Ray's idea / Emanon / Good dues blues.
**Album:** Released '87, on Atlantis by Charly Records. Deleted '88. Catalogue no: **ATS 11**
**Cass:** Released Mar '87, on Atlantis by Charly Records. Catalogue no: **TCATS 11**

**SAVOY SESSION, THE (Gillespie, Dizzy & Dee Dee Days)**
**2 LP Set:** Released Mar '85, on Savoy Jazz (USA) by Malaco Records (USA). Catalogue no: **SJL 2209**

**SHAW 'NUFF (Gillespie, Dizzy & His Sextets & Orchestra)**
**CD:** Released Jul '88, on Musicraft (USA) by Discovery Records (USA). Catalogue no: **MVSCD 53**

**SMALL COMBOS**
Note: Featuring Dexter Gordon, Charly Parker, John Coltrane, Stuff Smith, etc.
**Album:** Released Sep '87, on Giants of Jazz by Hasmick Promotions. Catalogue no: **LPJT 32**

**SMALL GROUPS, 1945-46, THE**
Tracks: / Melancholy baby / On the Alamo / Cherokee / Blue 'n' boogie / One bass hit / Ooh bob sh'bam / Handful of gimme / That's Earl's brother / Groovin' high / All the things you are / Dizzy atmosphere / Salt peanuts / Shaw 'nuff / Lover man.
Note: Classic bop tracks featuring Gillespie, Charlie Parker, Milt Jackson, Dexter Gordon, Al Haig and other major jazzmen.
**Album:** Released Apr '81, on Phoenix (USA) by All Star Talent Inc.(USA). Catalogue no: **LP 2**

**SONNY SIDE UP (Gillespie, Dizzy & Sonny Rollins)**
**CD:** Released Feb '87, on Polydor by Polydor Ltd. Catalogue no: **825 674-2**

**SUMMERTIME (Gillespie, Dizzy & Mongo Santamaria)**
Tracks: / Virtue / Afro-blue / Summertime / Mambo Mongo.
**Cass:** Released '82, on Pablo Jazz (USA) by Pablo Records (USA). Catalogue no: **K 08 229**
**Album:** Released Mar '83, on Pablo Jazz (USA) by Pablo Records (USA). Deleted Mar '87. Catalogue no: **D230 8229**
**CD:** Released '88, on Pablo Jazz (USA) by Pablo Records (USA). Catalogue no: **103 1123**

**SWEET SOUL**
**Cass:** Released Jan '85, on Pathe Marconi (France) Catalogue no: **2M 256 64825**
**Album:** Released Jan '85, on Pathe Marconi (France) Catalogue no: **2M 056 64825**
**Album:** Released Nov '79, on Gateway (USA) by Gemcom Inc.(USA) Records. Catalogue no: **GSLP 7025**

**SWING LOW SWEET CADILLAC**
Tracks: / Swing low sweet Cadillac / Mas que nada / Something in your smile / Kush.
**Cass:** Released Oct '85, on Impulse by Impulse Records. Deleted Dec '89. Catalogue no: **ASC 9149**
**Album:** Released Oct '85, on Impulse by Impulse Records. Deleted Dec '89. Catalogue no: **AS 9149**
**Cass:** Released Jun '82, on Jasmine by Hasmick Promotions. Catalogue no: **JAS C5**
**Album:** Released Jun '82, on Jasmine by Hasmick Promotions. Deleted Jun '86. Catalogue no: **JAS 5**

## Gills, John

**BIG CITY BLUES (Gills, Johnny California Sunset Five)**
**Album:** Released '88, on Stomp Off (USA) Catalogue no: **SOS 1157**

**DOWN HOME BLUES**
**Album:** Released Nov '87, on Stomp Off (USA) Catalogue no: **SOS 1126**

**I LOST MY HEART (Gills, John Original Sunset Five)**
**Album:** Released '88, on Stomp Off (USA) Catalogue no: **SOS 1094**

**SOME SWEET DAY (Vol 1)**
**Album:** Released Apr '88, on Stomp Off (USA) Catalogue no: **SOS 1156**

## Gillum, Bill 'Jazz'

**JAZZ GILLUM 35-47**
Note: With Bill Broonzy, Boyd, Sykes, Washboard Sam etc.
**Album:** Released Apr '88, on Document Catalogue no: **DLP 522**

**JAZZ GILLUM 1935-46**
**Album:** Released '88, on Best Of Blues (USA) by Blue Island Records (USA). Catalogue no: **BOB 4**

**ME AND MY BUDDY 1938-42**
**Album:** Released Jun '88, on Bluetime (Denmark) by Contact Records (Denmark). Catalogue no: **BT 2013**

**ROLL DEM BONES 1938-49**
**Album:** Released Jun '88, on Wolf Catalogue no: **WBJ 002**

## Giordano, Steve

**DAYBREAK**
Tracks: / Daybreak / Stages / Prissy / Moment's notice / Summer landscape.
Note: Giordano - guitar; Barry Miles - piano; synthesizer; Mike Richmond - bass; Billy Hart - drums; Joe Nero - conga; bongo; percussion; June 22, 1979:
**Album:** Released Apr '81, on Muse by Black & Blue Records. Catalogue no: **MR 5211**

## Giuffre, Jimmy

**Biographical details:** Born in 1921 in Texas, Jimmy Giuffre is a composer, bandleader and reedplayer who has been highly regarded yet taken for granted for decades. His composition often takes the form of little tone poems, as in his most famous piece, *The Train and the River*, played by his trio in the TV special *The Sound of Jazz* in 1957 and at the Newport Jazz Festival in 1958 (and in the Newport film *Jazz on a Summer's Day*). He played in big bands in the '40's, wrote *Four Brothers* and much else for Woody Herman, and later was a regular at the Lighthouse in Hermosa Beach, California. The keynote of everything he does is tonal beauty, as in the 1959 album *Lee Konitz Meets Jimmy Giuffre* on Verve: he contributed arrangements and tunes and played baritone sax, with Konitz and Hal McKusik on altos and Warne Marsh and Ted Brown on tenors. Having won polls on clarinet in the late '50's he gave up the other reeds, but returned to them in the mid-'60's, on later albums playing soprano, alto, tenor and flute. (Donald Clarke, July 1989).

**AD LIB (Giuffre, Jimmy)**
**Album:** Released Mar '81, on Verve Catalogue no: **2304 490**

**EASY WAY, THE (Giuffre, Jimmy Three)**
Tracks: / Easy way, The / Mack the knife / Come rain or come shine / Careful / Ray's time / Dream, A / Off centre / Montage / Time enough.
**Album:** Released Mar '82, on Verve (USA) by Polydor Ltd. Catalogue no: **2304 491**

Jimmy Giuffre

**FOUR BROTHERS**
Tracks: / Do it / All for you / I only have eyes for you / Four brothers / Sultana / Nutty pine / Wrought iron / Someone to watch over me / Ring-tail monkey / Ironic.
**Album:** Released Dec '81, on Affinity by Charly Records. Deleted '88. Catalogue no: **AFF 70**

**JIMMY GIUFFRE IN CONCERT (Giuffre, Jimmy Trio)**
Tracks: / Flight / Goodbye / Used to be hiptus / Venture / This time, this time.
**Album:** Released Apr '81, on Unique Jazz by Spotlite Records. Catalogue no: **UJ 18**

**JIMMY GIUFFRE QUARTET IN PERSON (Giuffre, Jimmy Quartet)**
Tracks: / Quiet time / Crab, The / My funny valentine / We see / What's new? / Two for Timbuctu.
Note: Recorded in New York, 1960.
**Album:** Released Mar '83, on Verve (USA) by Polydor Ltd. Catalogue no: **2304 492**

**QUASAR (Giuffre, Jimmy)**
**CD:** Released '86, on UNKNOWN Catalogue no: **N 1108**

**TANGENTS IN JAZZ**
**Album:** Released Apr '81, on Affinity by Charly Records. Deleted '88. Catalogue no: **AFF 60**

**TENORS WEST (Giuffre, Jimmy & The Marty Paich Octet)**
**Album:** Released '88, on GNP Crescendo (USA) by GNP Crescendo Records (USA). Catalogue no: **GNPS 9040**

**THESIS (Giuffre, Jimmy Three)**
**Album:** Released Jun '81, on Verve (USA) by Polydor Ltd. Catalogue no: **2304 499**

**WEST COAST SCENE (Giuffre, Jimmy & The Marty Paich Octet)**
Tracks: / There's no you / Dragon / Shorty George / Paichence / At the Mardi Gras / Take the 'A' train / Ballet du bongo / Line for Lyons / Jacqueline / Con spirito / On Green Dolphin Street / I'm also a person / I had the craziest dream / Arrivederci / Brown cow / Anyhow / Julie is her name / Aplomb / Sunset eyes / Tenors west.
**2 LP Set:** Released Sep '77, on Vogue by Vogue Records. Catalogue no: **VJD 536**

## Gleason, Jackie

**Biographical details:** The USA TV and film comedian (1916-87) was also a composer and conductor; he loved big band jazz and was behind *Stageshow*, a variety show fronted by Tommy and Jimmy Dorsey, and on which Elvis Presley made his first network TV appearance in 1955. Gleason couldn't read or write music, but picked out tunes on the piano for others to write down and arrange; he composed some of his own TV themes, and his mood music albums were hits, some of them featuring jazzmen of the calibre of conettist Bobby Hackett. (Donald Clarke, July 1989).

**JACKIE GLEASON PLAYS ROMANTIC JAZZ**
Tracks: / I've got my eyes on you / Lady is a tramp, The / There'll be some changes made / My blue Heaven / Soon / Petite waltz / Love next / How about you? / Crazy rhythm / Don't blame me / Best things in life are free, The / Who cares? / I never knew / Most beautiful girl in the world, The / You can't pull the wool over my eyes.
**Cass:** Released Oct '84, on Pathe Marconi (France) Catalogue no: **PM 1552954**
**Album:** Released Oct '84, on Pathe Marconi (France) Catalogue no: **PM 1552951**

**SILK'N'BRASS**
Tracks: / One of those songs / Girl from Ipanema / It's such a happy day / Everything's coming up roses / Real live girl / Starry eyed and breathless / You're nobody till somebody loves you / Begin to love / Shangri-la / If I ruled the world / Somebody else is taking my place.
Note: Orchestra conducted by: Jackie Gleason:
**Album:** Released Oct '86, on Capitol by EMI Records. Deleted Nov '88. Catalogue no: **EMS 1182**
**Cass:** Released Oct '86, on Capitol by EMI Records. Deleted Nov '88. Catalogue no: **TCEMS 1182**

**SONGS AND STORY OF JACKIE GLEASON**
**Album:** Released '83, on EMI (Germany) by EMI Records. Catalogue no: **IC 134 85230/1**

**TORCH WITH THE BLUE FLAME, THE**
Tracks: / Let's face the music and dance / Just in time / But beautiful / Love letters / My heart reminds me / Again / I've grown accustomed to her face / Careless / My silent love / Fascination / Alone in the crown / Time.
Note: Jackie Gleason, conductor, actor and comedian of the 50's/60's presents a selection of much loved, easy listening tracks including tracks by the famous writers of the day, plus some Gleason originals. This previously rare album makes excellent late night listening.
**Album:** Released Dec '85, on Capitol by EMI Records. Deleted Jul '88. Catalogue no: **EMS 1136**
**Cass:** Released Dec '85, on Capitol by EMI Records. Deleted Jan '88. Catalogue no: **TCEMS 1136**

## Glenn, Lloyd

**Biographical details:** He went to California in 1942, becoming one of the shapers of West Coast rhythm'n'blues, as well as playing New Orleans style jazz with the Kid Ory Band. He backed vocalist Red Miller for a No.1 R&B hit *Bewildered* in 1948, had his own chart topper with *Chica boo* in 1950, backed Lowell Fulson on hits and toured with Big Joe Turner in the 1980s. (Donald Clarke, July 1989).

**AFTER HOURS**
**Album:** Released '88, on Oldie Blues

Catalogue no: **OL 8002**
**Album:** Released Sep '84, on Pathe Marconi (France) Catalogue no: **PM 154661**

### BLUE IVORIES
Tracks: / Pinetop's boogie woogie / Blue ivories / In the mood / Topsy / Swing time shuffle / Hep cat shuffle / Now is the time / Jungletown jubilee / Night time / Savage boy / Boogie woogie on St. Louis blues / Blues / Ugh.
**Album:** Released Feb '85, on Stockholm (Sweden) Catalogue no: **RJ 203**

### BLUES AND BOOGIE
**Album:** Released Jan '85, on Black & Blue (1) by Black & Blue Records. Catalogue no: **BB 33563**

### TEXAS MAN
Tracks: / Texas man / All alone blues / Advice to a fool / Still my love is your / Midnight boogie / Brazos bottom / Dedicated to you / Honky tonk train / Joymakers boogie / It moves me / Angora / Levee blues / Stranger / It's you I'm thinking of / Cute-tee / Where or when.
**Album:** Released Mar '88, on Mr.R&B (Sweden) Catalogue no: **JB 608**

## Glenn Miller Story

### GLENN MILLER STORY (Original soundtrack)
Tracks: / Moonlight serenade / Tuxedo Junction / Little brown jug / St. Louis blues / In the mood / String of pearls / Pennsylvania 6 5000 / American patrol / Basin street blues / Otchi-tchor-hi-ya.
Note: Louis Armstrong and The All Stars. Conducted by Joseph Gershenson. Pre-1957.
**Album:** Released Aug '85, Catalogue no: **MCF 3273**
**CD:** Released Jul '88, on MCA by MCA Records. Catalogue no: **DMCL 1665**
**Cass:** Released Apr '82, on MCA by MCA Records. Catalogue no: **MCLC 1665**
**Album:** Released Apr '82, on MCA by MCA Records. Catalogue no: **MCL 1665**
**CD:** Released Oct '85, on MCA by MCA Records. Catalogue no: **DMCF 3273**

## Glinn, Lillian

### COLUMBIA BLUES ISSUES 1927-29
Tracks: / All alone and blue / Come home Daddy / Man I love is worth talkin' about / Doggin' me blues / Brown skin blues / Best friend blues / Lost letter blues / Packing house blues / Shake it down / I'm a front door woman with a back door man / Where have all the black men gone? / Atlanta blues / All the week blues / Wobble it a little / Daddy / Black man blues.
**Album:** Released '87, on VJM (Vintage Jazz Music) by Vintage Jazz Music Society(VJM). Catalogue no: **VLP 31**

### LILLIAN GLINN AND MAE GLOVER 1929-31 (Glinn, Lillian & Mae Glover)

**Live In Leipzig - Harry Gold (Lake)**

**Album:** Released Jan '88, on Blues Document Catalogue no: **BD 2009**

## Goebbels, Heiner

### MAN IN THE ELEVATOR, THE (Goebbels, Heiner & Heiner Muller)
Note: German composer Heiner Goebbels has set to music a text by Germany's most prolific contemporary playwright, Heiner Muller. For this he has used the finest 'avant-garde' musicians such as Don Cherry, George Lewis, Arto Lindsay and Fred Firth. *The Man in the Elevator* was premiered in Frankfurt, 1987 at the first 'Art-Rock Festival' and was the highlight of the three day event. Heiner Goebbels has also just completed a successful tour through some of Europe's major cities with this project. Reviews have been ecstatic. Personnel:- Arto Lindsay, voice & guitar / Ernst Stotzner, voice / Don Cherry, voice, trumpet, doussin' gouni / Fred Firth, guitar, bass / Charles Hayward, drums, metal / George Lewis, trombone / Ned Rothenburg, saxophones, bass clarinet / Heiner Goebbels, piano, synthesizer, programming / Heiner Muller, the author. (New Note, 1988).
**Album:** Released Nov '88, on ECM Catalogue no: **ECM 1369**
**CD:** Released Nov '88, on ECM Catalogue no: **837 110-2**

## Going Away...

### GOING AWAY BLUES 1926-35 (Various artists)
**Album:** Released Dec '88, on Yazoo (USA) by Shanachie Records (USA). Catalogue no: **L 1018**

## Going Back On The Farm

### GOING BACK ON THE FARM CHICAGO BLUES (Various artists)
**Album:** Released Nov '85, on Travelin' Man by Interstate Music. Catalogue no: **TM 809**

### GOING BACK TO NEW ORLEANS (Various artists)
**Album:** Released Jan '79, on Sonet by Sonet Records. Catalogue no: **SNTF 5021**

## Gold, Harry

### BOUNCING BACK (Gold, Harry & His Pieces Of Eight)
Tracks: / Bouncing back / Ostrich walk / Look at em doing it / Little rock getaway / Temptation blues / Panama rag / I wanna be like you / Since my best gal turned me down / Meander in the minor / Honky tonk train blues / Birth of the blues / There'll be some changes made / Dixieland shuffle / Tiger rag.
**Album:** Released Feb '89, on Lake by Lake Records. Catalogue no: **LA 5011**
**Cass:** Released Feb '89, on Lake by Lake Records. Catalogue no: **LA 5011 C**

### DIXIE (Gold, Harry & His Famous Pieces Of Eight)
Tracks: / If you wore a tulip / Blue and brokenhearted / Dixie / After you've gone / Rosie / Sensation rag / Walk right back

/ Ostrich walk / At the jazz band ball / Basin Street blues / Old man time / Copenhagen.
**Album:** Released '88, on Harlequin by Interstate Music. Catalogue no: **HQ 3001**

**LIVE IN LEIPZIG (Gold, Harry & His Pieces Of Eight) (See panel on previous page)**
Tracks: / Dixieland jamboree / Davenport blues / That's a plenty / Blue / Riverboat shuffle / At the jazz band ball / Paper doll / Farewell blues / Maryland / Jazz me blues / Some of these days / Big chief battle axe.
Note: Recorded at Leipzig, G.D.R. 4/9/84.
**Cass:** Released Jan '88, on Lake by Lake Records. Catalogue no: **LA 5003C**
**Album:** on Lake by Lake Records. Catalogue no: **LA 5003**

**OCTAGONAL GOLD (Gold, Harry & His Pieces Of Eight)**
Tracks: / If you knew Susie / Mississippi mud / Ory's Creole trombone / Stumbling / You turned the tables on me / Washington and Lee swing / I want a big butter and egg man / Poor butterfly / That da da strain / Watford Gap / Ida, sweet as apple cider / Dippermouth blues.
**Album:** Released Jul '80, on Black Lion Catalogue no: **BLP 12118**

## Golden Age Of...

**GOLDEN AGE OF BRITISH DANCE (Various artists)**
Tracks: / South American Joe: *Roy, Harry & His Band* / Avalon: *Roy, Harry & His Band* / Build a little home: *Roy, Harry & His Band* / Limehouse blues: *Roy, Harry & His Band* / Spanish shawl: *Roy, Harry & His Band* / Margie: *Roy, Harry & His Band* / Music, Maestro, please: *Roy, Harry & His Band* / Piano madness: *Roy, Harry & His Band* / I ain't got nobody: *Stone, Lew & His Band* / Red sails in the sunset: *Stone, Lew & His Band* / Dinner for one please, James: *Stone, Lew & His Band* / She's a Latin from Manhattan: *Stone, Lew & His Band* / She wore a little jacket of blue: *Stone, Lew & His Band* / Continental, The: *Stone, Lew & His Band* / Cheek to cheek: *Stone, Lew & His Band* / Afraid to dream: *Fox, Roy & His Band* / These foolish things: *Fox, Roy & His Band* / Let's call the whole thing off: *Fox, Roy & His Band* / This year's kisses: *Fox, Roy & His Band* / Too marvellous for words: *Fox, Roy & His Band* / That old feeling: *Fox, Roy & His Band* / Harbour lights: *Fox, Roy & His Band* / I let a song go out of my heart: *Fox, Roy & His Band* / Maybe it's because I love you too much: *Noble, Ray & His Band* / Lazy day: *Noble, Ray & His Band* / You ought to see Sally on Sunday: *Noble, Ray & His Band* / How could we be wrong?: *Noble, Ray & His Band* / Close your eyes: *Noble, Ray & His Band* / Time on my hands: *Noble, Ray & His Band* / Mad about the boy: *Noble, Ray & His Band* / One morning in May: *Noble, Ray & His Band.*
**Cass set:** Released '81, on World Records by EMI Records. Catalogue no: **CASSETTE 32**
**2 LP Set:** Released '69, on Retrospect by EMI Records. Catalogue no: **SH 118/9**
**LP Set:** Released '81, on World Records by EMI Records. Catalogue no: **ALBUM 32**
**Album:** Released Jan '79, on Retrospect by EMI Records. Catalogue no: **SH 277**

**GOLDEN AGE OF CHICAGO BLUES (Various artists)**
**CD:** Released Jan '86, on Vogue by Vogue Records. Catalogue no: **VG 600 048**

**GOLDEN AGE OF FEMALE VOICE (Various artists)**
Tracks: / Nightingale sang in Berkeley Square, A: *Welch, Elisabeth* / There goes that song again: *Carless, Dorothy* / When I grow too old to dream: *Laye, Evelyn* / I've told every little star: *Ellis, Mary* / That old feeling: *Hall, Adelaide* / Stormy weather: *Langford, Frances* / Pu-leeze Mr. Hemingway: *Carlisle, Elsie* / Moment I saw you, The: *Courtneidge, Cicely* / Spread a little happiness: *Hale, Binnie* / When you've got a little springtime in your heart: *Matthews, Jessie* / Says my heart: *Becke, Eve* / Night was made for love, The: *Wood, Peggy* / These foolish things: *Welch, Elisabeth* / Nightingale sang in Berkely Square, A: *Welch, Elisabeth* / You've done something to my heart: *Jones, Gwen* / Moon got in my eyes: *Lenner, Anne / Try a little tenderness: Williams, Frances* / Wish me luck (as you wave me goodbye): *Fields, Gracie.*
**Cass:** Released Mar '87, on Golden Age by EMI Records. Deleted '88. Catalogue no: **TCGX 2553**
**Cass:** Released Jun '88, on MFP by EMI Records. Deleted '89. Catalogue no: **TCMFP 5826**
**Album:** Released Jun '88, on MFP by EMI Records. Deleted '89. Catalogue no: **MFP 5826**
**Album:** Released Mar '87, on Golden Age by EMI Records. Deleted '88. Catalogue no: **GX 41 2553**

**GOLDEN AGE OF GEORGE GERSHWIN (Various artists)**
Tracks: / Delishious: *Savoy Hotel Orpheans with Jack Plant* / Bidin' my time: *Savoy Hotel Orpheans with The Carlyle Cousins* / Let's call the whole thing off: *Savoy Hotel Orpheans with Carroll Gibbons, Anne Lerner* / Shall we dance?: *Savoy Hotel Orpheans with Carroll Gibbons, Anne Lerner* / Nice work if you can get it: *Savoy Hotel Orpheans with George Melacrino* / Strike up the band: *Savoy Hotel Orpheans with Anne Lenner* / They can't take that away from me: *Fox, Roy & His Orchestra* / Things are looking up: *Fox, Roy & His Orchestra* / They all laughed: *Hall, Henry & The Dance Orchestra with Leslie Douglas* / Slap that bass: *Six Swingers with Sam Costa* / Beginner's luck (I've got): *Six Swingers with Sam Costa* / Foggy day, A: *Loss, Joe & His Band with Chick Henderson* / Love is here to stay: *Harris, Jack & His Orchestra* / Love walked in: *Harris, Jack & His Orchestra* / Rhapsody in blue: *Roy, Harry & His Orchestra.*
**Album:** Released Nov '87, on Golden Age by EMI Records. Catalogue no: **GX 2557**
**Cass:** Released Nov '87, on Golden Age by EMI Records. Catalogue no: **TCGX 2557**
**Album:** Released Jul '84, on Golden Age by EMI Records. Catalogue no: **GX 41 2524-1**
**Cass:** Released Jul '84, on Golden Age by EMI Records. Catalogue no: **GX 41 2524-4**

**GOLDEN AGE OF GOSPEL SINGING (Various artists)**
Note: Featuring: Bessie Griffin, Angelic Gospel Singers etc.
**Album:** Released Jul '87, on Folklyric (USA) by Arhoolie Records (USA). Catalogue no: **FL 9046**

**GOLDEN AGE OF JAZZ OF THE 30'S (Various artists)**
Tracks: / Pink elephants: *Venuti, Joe* / Hiawatha's lullaby: *Venuti, Joe* / Charlie's home: *Rollini, Adrian* / Gin mill blues: *Sullivan, Joe* / Sweet Lorraine: *Venuti, Joe* / I got a right to sing the blues: *Goodman, Benny* / Ain't ya glad?: *Goodman, Benny* / Texas tea party: *Goodman, Benny* / Hell's bells and hallelujah: *Venuti, Joe* / Barrelhouse: *Stacy, Jess* / Buzzard, The: *Freeman, Bud* / Last round-up, The: *Various artists* / Chicken and waffles: *Berigan, Bunny* / Blues of Israel: *Krupa, Gene.*
**Album:** Released Jul '83, on Golden Age by EMI Records. Catalogue no: **GX 2509**

**Cass:** Released Jul '83, on Golden Age by EMI Records. Catalogue no: **TC GX 2509**

## GOLDEN AGE OF MALE VOICE (Various artists)

Tracks: / Goodnight Vienna: *Buchanan, Jack* / Don't let that moon get away: *Trent, Bruce* / Music goes round and around, The: *Elrick, George* / Me and my girl: *Cooper, Jack* / My melancholy baby: *Bowlly, Al* / Best things in life are free, The / Only a glass of champagne: *Askey, Arthur* / On the Amazon: *Howes, Bobby* / Puttin' on the Ritz: *Astaire, Fred* / Change partners: *Henderson, Chick* / Let's face the music and dance: *Dennis, Denny* / Sixty seconds got together: *Melachrino, George* / Dancing in the dark: *Browne, Sam* / I'll see you again: *Coward, Noel* / What a little moonlight can do: *Hulbert, Jack* / You brought a new kind of love to me: *Chevalier, Maurice.*

**Album:** Released Jun '88, on MFP by EMI Records. Deleted '89. Catalogue no: **MFP 5825**

**Album:** Released Mar '87, on Golden Age by EMI Records. Deleted '88. Catalogue no: **GX 41 2552**

**Cass:** Released Jun '88, on MFP by EMI Records. Deleted '89. Catalogue no: **TCMFP 5825**

**Cass:** Released Mar '87, on Golden Age by EMI Records. Deleted '88. Catalogue no: **TCGX 2552**

## GOLDEN AGE OF MUSIC HALL (Various artists)

Tracks: / Wait till the work comes round: *Elen, Gus* / Riding on top of a motor car: *Victoria, Vesta* / My old dutch: *Chevalier, Albert* / When I take my morning promenade: *Lloyd, Marie* / Robin, The: *Leno, Dan* / My first cigar: *Bradfield, Louis* / Coster girl in Paris: *Lloyd, Marie* / Bang went the chance of a lifetime: *Robey, George* / Where's the count?: *Roberts, Arthur* / When I marry Amelia: *Lytton, Henry* / Fallen star, A: *Chevalier, Albert* / Tower of London: *Leno, Dan* / Territorial, The: *Little Tich* / Anona: *Forde, Florrie.*

**Album:** Released '82, on Rhapsody by President Records. Catalogue no: **RHA 6014**

## GOLDEN AGE OF THE CHARLESTON (Various artists)

Tracks: / Black bottom charleston: *Various artists* / Mississippi mud: *Various artists* / Ain't she sweet?: *Various artists* / My pet: *Various artists* / Barcelona: *Various artists* / Everybody stomp: *Various artists* / Painting the clouds with sunshine: *Various artists* / Miss Annabelle Lee: *Various artists* / Paddlin' Madelin' home: *Various artists* / Brown sugar: *Various artists* / Didn't I tell you?: *Various artists* / Kansas City Kitty: *Various artists* / All by yourself in the moonlight: *Various artists* / Charleston Charley: *Various artists.*

Note: Featuring Birt Firman & His Orchestra, the Savoy Havana Band, the Carlton Hotel Dance Orchestra.

**Cass:** Released Jul '83, on Golden Age by EMI Records. Catalogue no: **TC GX 2507**

**Album:** Released Jul '83, on Golden Age by EMI Records. Catalogue no: **GX 2507**

## GOLDEN AGE OF THE DANCE BAND (Various artists)

Tracks: / You and the night and the music: *Somer's, Deboy Band* / Blue skies are round the corner: *Hylton, Jack/his orchestra* / Yes yes (my baby says yes) / She had to go and lose it at the Astor: *Roy, Harry & His Orchestra* / Solitude: *Stone, Lew & His Orchestra* / You gorgeous dancing doll: *Geraldo & The Savoy Hotel Orchestra* / Hold my hand: *Noble, Ray & His Orchestra* / Pennies from Heaven: *Levy, Louis & His Gaumont British Symphony Orchestra* / Dancing in the dark: *Gibbons, Carroll & The Savoy Hotel Orpheans* / Let's dance at the make believe ballroom: *Loss, Joe & His Orchestra* / Happy days are here again: *Payne, Jack & His BBC Dance Orchestra* / Half of it dearie blues, The: *Mackey's, Percival Band* / I've got my love to keep me warm: *Fox, Roy & His Orchestra* / Lambeth walk: *Munro, Ronnie & His Orchestra* / I took my harp to a party: *Cotton, Billy & His Band* / Here's to the next time: *Hall, Henry & The BBC Dance Orchestra.*

**Album:** Released Jun '87, on Golden Age by EMI Records. Catalogue no: **GX 2556**

**Cass:** Released Jun '87, on Golden Age by EMI Records. Catalogue no: **TCGX 2556**

## THOSE DANCE BAND YEARS-VOL 1 (Various artists)

Tracks: / Paddlin' Madelin' home: *New Prince Toronto Band* / Everybody stomp: *Savoy Havana Band* / At sundown: *Savoy Havana Band* / Charleston Charley: *Carlton Hotel Dance Orchestra* / Valencia: *Various artists* / Vo-do-do-de-o blues: *Various artists* / You've got those wanna-go-back-again blues: *Whidden, Jay & His New Midnight Follies Band* / Up and at 'em: *Whidden, Jay & His New Midnight Follies Band* / Hello, aloha, how are you?: *Munro, Ronnie & His Dance Orchestra* / Crazy quilt: *Hylton, Jack Kit Cat Band* / Jig walk: *Devonshire restaurant Dance Band* / Brainstorm: *Somers, Debroy & His Band* / Ain't she sweet?: *Piccadilly Revels Band* / Just the same: *Piccadilly Revels Band* / I need lovin': *Sylvans* / Devil is afraid of music, The: *London Radio Dance Band.*

**Album:** Released Oct '76, on Retrospect by EMI Records. Deleted '88. Catalogue no: **SH 361**

## THOSE DANCE BAND YEARS-VOL 2 (Various artists)

Tracks: / Mississippi mud: *Sylvians* / Nebrasca: *Munro, Ronnie & His Dance Orchestra* / Kiss and make up: *Piccadilly Players* / You wouldn't fool me, would you?: *Piccadilly Players* / Blue butterfly: *Rhythm Band* / There's a blue ridge 'round my heart, Virginia: *Rosebery, Arthur & His Kit Kat Dance Band* / Broadway melody: *Rosebery, Arthur & His Kit Kat Dance Band* / You went away once too often: *Kunz, Charlie & His Chez Henri Club Band* / Wake up, chillun, wake up: *Starita, Ray & His Ambassadors' Club Band* / Do something: *Payne, Jack & His BBC Dance Orchestra* / Everyday away from you: *Four Bright Sparks* / Eleven-thirty, Saturday night: *Arcadian Dance Orchestra* / Tap your feet: *Hylton, Jack & His orchestra* / If I could be with you one hour tonight / Time on my hands: *Mackay, Percival & His Band* / Got the bench, got the park: *Noble, Ray & The New Mayfair Orchestra* / Would you like to take a walk?: *Noble, Ray & The New Mayfair Orchestra* / Reaching for the moon: *Noble, Ray & The New Mayfair Orchestra* / Hello beautiful: *Noble, Ray & The New Mayfair Orchestra.*

**Album:** Released Oct '76, on Retrospect by EMI Records. Deleted '88. Catalogue no: **SH 362**

## THOSE DANCE BAND YEARS-VOL 3 (Various artists)

Tracks: / Miss Elizabeth Brown: *Noble, Ray & The New Mayfair Orchestra* / Sil'vry Rio Grande: *Noble, Ray & The New Mayfair Orchestra* / River stay 'way from my door: *Noble, Ray & The New Mayfair Orchestra* / Oh Rosalita: *Noble, Ray & The New Mayfair Orchestra* / Down Sunnyside Lane: *Payne, Jack & His BBC Dance Orchestra* / That's my desire: *Kyte, Sidney & his Piccadilly Hotel Band* / All of me: *Blue Lyres* / You rascal you: *Blue Lyres* / Clouds will soon roll by, The / Mean music: *Brown, Philip's Grosvenor Band* / Sadie the shaker: *Lipton, Sydney & His Grosvenor House Orchestra* / You're an old smoothie: *Somers, Debroy & His Band* / I like to go back in the evening: *Jackson, Jack & His Orchestra* / Japanese sandman: *Noble, Ray & His Orchestra* / April in Paris: *Hall, Henry & The BBC Dance Orchestra* / We'll make hay while the sun shines: *Merrin, Billy & His Commanders*

/ Annie doesn't live here any more: *Cotton, Billy & His Band* / Better think twice: *Gibbons, Carroll & Savoy Hotel Orpheans.*
**Album:** Released Oct '76, on Retrospect by EMI Records. Deleted '88. Catalogue no: **SH 363**

**THOSE DANCE BAND YEARS-VOL 4 (Various artists)**
Tracks: / Carioca: *Geraldo's Gaucho Tango Orchestra* / Deep forest: *Foresythe, Reginald* / Tina: *Stone, Lew & His Band* / Pop, goes your heart: *Stone, Lew & His Band* / What a little moonlight can do: *Levy, Louis & The Gaumont British Dance Band* / June in January: *Joyce, Teddy & His Orchestra* / Holiday express: *Joyce, Teddy & His Orchestra* / Buchanan stomp: *Perritt, Harry & His Orchestra* / Medley: *Roy, Harry & His Orchestra* / Footloose and fancy free: *Hylton, Jack/his orchestra* / St. Louis blues: *Daniels, Joe & His Hotshots* / Roll along, prairie moon: *Jackson, Jack & His Band* / From the top of your head: *Gibbons, Carroll & Savoy Hotel Orpheans* / Love is a dancing thing: *Winnick, Maurice* / My sweetie went away: *Leader, Harry & His Band.*
**Album:** Released Oct '76, on Retrospect by EMI Records. Deleted '88. Catalogue no: **SH 364**

**THOSE DANCE BAND YEARS-VOL 5 (Various artists)**
Tracks: / Moon over Miami: *Winnick, Maurice* / Woe is me: *Rabin, Oscar & His Romany Band* / Oh by jingo, oh by gee: *Krakajax* / Pretty girl is like a melody, A: *Fox, Roy & His Orchestra* / Free: *Cotton, Billy & His Band* / When my dreamboat comes home: *Martin, Bram & His Band* / West End blues: *Various artists* / Boo hoo: *Gonella, Nat/his Georgians* / Swing high, swing low: *Firman, Bert & His Dance Orchestra* / Never in a million years: *Bissett, Billy & His Orchestra* / Love is good for anything that ails you: *Orlando & His Orchestra* / Swing session in Siberia: *Elrick, George & His Swing Music Makers* / Getting some fun out of life: *Jacobs, Howard & His Golden Tone Sax & Orchestra* / Chinese laundry blues: *Seymour, Syd & His Mad Hatters* / You started something: *Ternant's Rhythm, Billy* / She's the daughter of the old grey mare: *Donovan, Dan & His Music.*
**Album:** Released Oct '76, on Retrospect by EMI Records. Deleted '88. Catalogue no: **SH 365**

**THOSE DANCE BAND YEARS-VOL 6 (Various artists)**
Tracks: / Someday, sweetheart: *Millward, Sid & His Band* / Sweet as a song: *White, Jack & His Collegians* / Mama, I wanna make rhythm: *Harris, Jack & His Orchestra* / Plain Jane: *Harris, Jack & His Orchestra* / How'd ja like to love me: *Fox, Roy & His Orchestra* / Love makes the world go round: *Hall, Henry & His Orchestra* / Penny serenade: *Geraldo/his Orchestra* / My own: *Carroll, Eddie & His Music* / There's a new apple tree: *Thorburn, Billy & His Dance Band* / You must have been a beautiful baby: *Rignold, Hugo & His Orchestra* / I'm madly in love with you: *Williams, Reginald & His Futurists* / Heaven can wait: *Thorburn, Billy & His Dance Band* / South of the border (down Mexico way): *Loss, Joe & his band* / Begin the beguine: *Loss, Joe & his band* / Lady's in love with you, The: *Stratton, Von & His Music* / Wishing (will make it so): *Darewski, Herman & His Band.* **Album:** Released Oct '76, on Retrospect by EMI Records. Deleted '88. Catalogue no: **SH 366**

**THOSE DANCE BAND YEARS-VOL 7 (Various artists)**
**Album:** Released Jan '77, on Retrospect by EMI Records. Deleted '88. Catalogue no: **SH 367**

## Golden Big Band

**GOLDEN BIG BAND VOL 1 (Various artists)**
**CD:** Released May '89, on Object Enterprises Catalogue no: **ONN 29**

**GOLDEN BIG BAND VOL 2 (Various artists)**
**CD:** Released May '89, on Object Enterprises Catalogue no: **ONN 30**

## Golden Days Of...

**GOLDEN DAYS OF JAZZ (Various artists)**
**Album:** Released '83, on RCA (Germany) Catalogue no: **26.21001**

**GOLDEN DAYS OF ROCK (Various artists)**
**Cass:** Released Sep '81, on Ampro Catalogue no: **AMP 016**

## Golden Eagle...

**GOLDEN EAGLE GOSPEL SINGERS, (Golden Eagle Gospel Singers)**
**Album:** Released Jul '88, on Eden by Balaclava Records. Catalogue no: **ELE 4-200**

## Golden Eagle Jazz Band

**GOLDEN EAGLE JAZZ BAND**
**Album:** Released Jun '86, on Stomp Off (USA) Catalogue no: **SOS 1192**

## Golden Gate Quartet

**GOLDEN GATE QUARTET 1937-9**
**Album:** Released '88, on Joker (USA) by Lifetime Records (USA). Catalogue no: **SM 4043**

**JUBILEE**
**Album:** Released Aug '84, on Ibach (France) Catalogue no: **60558**
**Cass:** Released Aug '84, on Ibach (France) Catalogue no: **C 60558**

**NEGRO SPIRITUALS**
Tracks: / Rock my soul / Joshua fit de battle of Jerico / Sometimes I feel like a motherless child / Hard trials and great tribulations / Jezebel / Only believe / Michael / Didn't it rain / Nobody knows the trouble I've seen / Put your hand / Down by the riverside / When saints go marching in.
Note: Features 12 gospel songs. This is the group in which Brook Benton started his career.
**Album:** Released Jun '83, on Happy Bird (Germany) Catalogue no: **B 90069**

**NO. 1'S (GREATEST HITS), THE**
**Album:** Released May '84, on Ibach (France) Catalogue no: **60587**
**Cass:** Released May '84, on Ibach (France) Catalogue no: **C 60587**

**SPIRITUALS**
Tracks: / King of kings / Old time religion / Take my hand precious Lord / My Lord, what a morning / Precious memories / For the rest of my life / Casey Jones / Somebody's knocking at your door / Rocks don't fall on me / Roll Jordan roll / Skip to my lou / When they ring the golden bells / Peace in the valley.
**Cass:** Released Nov '86, on EMI (Italy) by EMI Records. Catalogue no: **3C 254 10534**
**Album:** Released Nov '86, on EMI (Italy) by EMI Records. Catalogue no: **3C 054 10534**

## Golden Greats

**GOLDEN GREATS: 20 BIG BANDS (Various artists)**
Tracks: / Skyliner: *Various artists* / Undecided: *Various artists* / South rampart street parade: *Various artists* / Flying home: *Various artists* / I get a kick out of you: *Various artists* / One o'clock jump: *Various artists* / Moonlight bay: *Various artists* / T.D.'s boogie woogie: *Various artists* / Comanche war dance: *Various artists* / Washington whirligig: *Various artists* / Woodchoppers ball: *Various artists* / In the mood: *Various artists* / When the saints go marching in: *Various artists* / Gambler's blues: *Various artists* / Liza: *Various artists* / Organ grinder's swing: *Various artists* / John Silver: *Various artists* / Wednesday night hop: *Various artists* / Casa loma stomp: *Various artists* / Down south camp meeting: *Various artists.*
**Cass:** Released Oct '85, on MCA by MCA Records. Catalogue no: **MCMC 5025**
**Album:** Released Oct '85, on MCA by MCA Records. Catalogue no: **MCM 5025**

## Golden Hits...

**GOLDEN HITS OF THE 40'S (Various artists)**
Note: 32 Golden Oldies
**2 LP Set:** Released '88, on BR Music/BR Music (Holland) by BR Music Records. Catalogue no: **BRLP 63/64**
**Cass:** Released Mar '86, on MCA by MCA Records. Deleted Apr '88. Catalogue no: **MCMC 5031**
**Cass set:** Released '88, on BR Music/BR Music (Holland) by BR Music Records. Catalogue no: **BRMC 63/64**
**Album:** Released Mar '86, on MCA by MCA Records. Deleted Apr '88. Catalogue no: **MCM 5031**

**GOLDEN HITS OF THE 50'S (Various artists)**
**Cass set:** Released '88, on BR Music/BR Music (Holland) by BR Music Records. Catalogue no: **BRMC 65/66**
**Cass:** Released Mar '86, on MCA by MCA Records. Deleted Apr '88. Catalogue no: **MCMC 5032**
**2 LP Set:** Released '88, on BR Music/BR Music (Holland) by BR Music Records. Catalogue no: **BRLP 65/66**
**Album:** Released Mar '86, on MCA by MCA Records. Deleted Apr '88. Catalogue no: **MCM 5032**

**GOLDEN HITS OF THE 60'S (Various artists)**
Note: 32 Golden Oldies (Only 20 tracks on CD)m
**CD:** Released '88, on BR Music/BR Music (Holland) by BR Music Records. Catalogue no: **BRCD 38**
**2 LP Set:** Released '88, on BR Music/BR Music (Holland) by BR Music Records. Catalogue no: **BRLP 67/68**
**Cass set:** Released Dec '88, on BR Music/BR Music (Holland) by BR Music Records. Catalogue no: **BRMC 67/68**

**GOLDEN HITS OF THE 60'S VOLUME 1 (Various artists)**
Tracks: / Sweet nothin's: *Lee, Brenda* / Johnny will: *Boone, Pat* / Little bitty tear, A: *Ives, Burl* / Ginny come lately: *Hyland, Brian* / Sheila: *Roe, Tommy* / Our day will come: *Ruby And The Romantics* / Bo diddley: *Holly, Buddy* / Wipe out: *Surfaris* / Grazing in the grass: *Maskela, Hugh* / Clapping song, The: *Ellis, Shirley* / Eve of destruction: *McGuire, Barry* / 1-2-3: *Barry, Len* / Monday Monday: *Mamas & Papas* / If only I had time: *Rowles, John* / Midnight confessions: *Grass Roots* / Born to be wild: *Steppenwolf.*
**Album:** Released Mar '86, on MCA by MCA Records. Deleted Apr '88. Catalogue no: **MCM 5033**
**Cass:** Released Mar '86, on MCA by MCA Records. Deleted Apr '88. Catalogue no: **MCMC 5033**

**GOLDEN HITS OF THE 60'S Volume 2 (Various artists)**
Tracks: / Speedy Gonzales / Sealed with a kiss / All alone I am / Brown eyed handsome man / Mr Bass man / Deck of cards / Pipeline / Red sails in the sunset / Like a baby / Dedicated to the one I love / Bend me, shape me / What a wonderful world / MacArthur Park / Little arrows / Dizzy / Tracy.
**Album:** Released Mar '86, on MCA by MCA Records. Deleted Apr '88. Catalogue no: **MCM 5034**
**Album:** Released Mar '86, on MCA by MCA Records. Deleted Apr '88. Catalogue no: **MCMC 5034**

**GOLDEN HITS OF THE 70'S (Various artists)**
**2 LP Set:** Released '88, on BR Music/BR Music (Holland) by BR Music Records. Catalogue no: **BRLP 69/70**
**Cass:** Released Mar '86, on MCA by MCA Records. Deleted Apr '88. Catalogue no: **MCMC 5035**
**Cass set:** Released '88, on BR Music/BR Music (Holland) by BR Music Records. Catalogue no: **BRMC 69/70**
**Album:** Released Mar '86, on MCA by MCA Records. Deleted Apr '88. Catalogue no: **MCM 5035**

## Golden Hour Of Brass

**GOLDEN HOUR OF BRASS BANDS (Various artists)**
**Cass:** Released Jan '72, on PRT by Castle Communications Records. Catalogue no: **ZCGH 521**

**GOLDEN HOUR OF CLARINET JAZZ (Various artists)**
Tracks: / Petite fleur: *Sunshine, Monty* / Boodle am shake: *Lightfoot, Terry, Acker Bilk & Sandy Brown* / Satin doll: *Coe, Tony* / A'rowing: *Bilk, Acker* / That old feeling: *Brown, Sandy & Archie Semple* / Wild cat blues: *Sunshine, Monty* / Here today: *Fawkes, Wally* / My journey to the sky: *Bilk, Acker & Terry Lightfoot* / Love for sale: *Brown, Sandy* / Hiawatha: *Bilk, Acker & Terry Lightfoot* / Last western, The: *Brown, Sandy* / Sweet Georgia Brown: *Coe, Tony* / Hush-a-bye: *Sunshine, Monty* / Louise: *Brown, Sandy & Archie Semple* / Elephant stomp: *Lightfoot, Terry* / I'm in the market for you: *Semple, Archie* / Times a wastin': *Coe, Tony* / Slab's blues: *Brown, Sandy & Acker Bilk.*
**Album:** Released '79, on Pye Catalogue no: **GH 649**
**Cass:** Released '79, on PRT by Castle Communications Records. Catalogue no: **ZCGH 649**

**GOLDEN HOUR OF TRADITIONAL JAZZ (Various artists)**
**Cass:** Released Mar '79, on PRT by Castle Communications Records. Catalogue no: **ZCGH 669**
**Cass:** Released Sep '72, on PRT by Castle Communications Records. Catalogue no: **ZCGH 526**

## Golden Memories...

**GOLDEN MEMORIES OF THE GREAT SWING ERA (Various artists)**
Tracks: / Blueberry Hill: *Dorsey, Jimmy* / I'm stepping out with a memory tonight: *Various artists* / All of me: *James, Harry* / G.I. jive: *Herman, Woody* / Got a penny, Jenny: *Kenton, Stan* / Sentimental journey: *Various artists* / I'll get by: *Baron, Paul* / I double dare you: *Clinton, Larry* / It's funny to everyone but me: *Various artists* / Cuddle up a little closer: *Various artists* / Little brown jug: *Various artists* / I may be wrong: *Various artists* / Answer to love, The: *Various artists* / You and me that used to be, The: *Various artists* / Rain, rain, go away: *Various artists* / Boo hoo: *Various artists.*
**CD:** Released Oct '87, on Teldec (Germany) by ASV (Academy Sound & Vision). Catalogue no: **8.26528**

## Goldie, Don

**JAZZ EXPRESS**
Note: Mono
**Album:** Released Jun '86, on Jazzology (USA) by Jazzology Records (USA). Catalogue no: **J 135**

## Golson, Benny

**Biographical details:** He grew up in Philadelphia with John Coltrane & the Heath Brothers, and was influenced by Tadd Dameron as a composer/arranger. Coltrane took Golson's 'Stablemates' to recording sessions with the Miles Davis Quintet and Mal Waldron in 1955-6; it became a jazz classic along with *Whisper not, I remember Clifford,* and others. Golson and Art Farmer led the Jazztet 1959-62; his writing and studio activities included work with Peggy Lee, Lou Rawls and Nancy Wilson. Since the late 1970s he has returned to performing, including re-forming the Jazztet with Farmer. (Donald Clarke 1989).

**... WITH BOBBY TIMMONS (Golson, Benny/Guerin, Roger)**
**Album:** Released Feb '88, on Fresh Sounds (Spain) by Fresh Sounds Records (Spain). Catalogue no: **FS 187**

**BENNY GOLSON IN PARIS**
**CD:** Released Jan '89, on DRG (USA) by DRG Records (USA). Catalogue no: **CDSW 8418**

**BENNY GOLSON'S NEW YORK SCENE**
Tracks: / Something in B flat / Step lightly / Blues it / Capri / Whisper not / Just be myself / You're mine you.
**Album:** Released Feb '89, on Contemporary by Ace Records. Catalogue no: **COP 043**

**BLUES ON DOWN**
**2 LP Set:** Released Apr '79, on Milestone by Ace Records. Catalogue no: **M 47048**

**CALIFORNIA MESSAGE**
**Album:** Released '88, on Timeless by Timeless Records. Catalogue no: **SFP 177**

**GROOVIN' WITH GOLSON**
**Album:** Released Apr '86, on Original Jazz Classics (USA) by Fantasy Inc (USA). Catalogue no: **OJC 226**

**KILLER JOE RAP**
Tracks: / Killer Joe rap / Walkin' and stalkin'.

**12" Single:** Released May '81, on CBS by CBS Records. Deleted May '84. Catalogue no: **TA 1223**

**ONE MORE MEMORY (Golson, Benny Quintet with Curtis Fuller)**
**Album:** Released Apr '84, on Timeless by Timeless Records. Catalogue no: **SJP 180**

**PARIS/NEW YORK 1958**
**Album:** Released May '87, on Swing Disque Catalogue no: **SW 8418**

**STARDUST (Golson, Benny & Freddie Hubbard)**
Tracks: / Stardust / Double bass / Gipsy jingle-jangle / Povo / Love is a many splendoured thing / Sad to say / Far away.
Note: The superior talents of tenorist *(Benny Golson)* and trumpeter/flugelhornist *(Freddie Hubbard)* are brought together on this recording of superbly crafted small group jazz playing. Not only is it a perfect showcase for these two fine instrumentalists but also a reminder of the composing/arranging skills of Golson. (Denon 10/88). Other musicians are: Ron Carter (Bass), Marvi 'Smitty' Smith (Drums), Mulgrew Miller (Piano).
**CD:** Released Oct '88, on Denon Catalogue no: **CY 1838**
**Cass:** Released Oct '88, on Denon Catalogue no: **CC 23**

**THIS IS FOR YOU JOHN**
**Album:** Released '88, on Timeless (Import) by Timeless Records. Catalogue no: **SJP 235**
**CD:** Released Jan '88, on Timeless (Import) by Timeless Records. Catalogue no: **CDSJP 235**

**TIME SPEAKS**
Tracks: / I'll remember April / Time speaks / No dancin' / Jordu / Blues for Duane / Theme for Maxine.
Note: An album dedicated to the memory of trumpeter Clifford Brown. Personnel: Benny Golson - tenor sax / Freddie Hubbard - trumpet / Woody Shaw - trumpet / Kenny Barron -piano / Cecil McBee - bass / Ben Riley - drums.
**CD:** Released Jan '87, on Timeless by Timeless Records. Catalogue no: **CDSJP 187**
**Album:** Released Aug '85, on Timeless by Timeless Records. Catalogue no: **SJP 187**

## Gomez, Eddie

**DOWN STRETCH**
**Album:** Released Oct '87, on Black Hawk (USA) by Blackhawk Records (USA). Catalogue no: **BKH 531**
**CD:** Released Oct '87, on Black Hawk (USA) by Blackhawk Records (USA). Catalogue no: **CDBKH 531**

**GOMEZ (Gomez, Eddie & Chick Corea)**
Tracks: / Dabble vision / Santurce / Japanese waltz / Zimmermann (for Toru Takemitsu) / Mez-ga / Ginkakuji / Pops and Alma / Row, row, row your tones / We will meet again.
Note: Chick Corea (Piano), Eddie Gomez (bass), Steve Gadd (Drums).
**Cass:** Released Oct '88, on Denon Catalogue no: **CC 17**
**CD:** Released Oct '88, on Denon Deleted '89. Catalogue no: **C38 7189**

**MEZGO**
Tracks: / Me too / Capricious fantasy / Puccini's walk / Delgado / Caribbean morning / Scott David / Cello sonata in G Minor / 1st movement.
**Cass:** Released Sep '86, on Epic by CBS Records. Deleted Nov '87. Catalogue no: **40 57084**
**Album:** Released Sep '86, on Epic by CBS Records. Catalogue no: **EPC 57084**

**POWER PLAY**
Tracks: / Power play / Loco motive / Mel / Spanish flower / Mr. Go / Amethyst / W.110th.St / Forever.
**CD:** Released Jul '88, on Epic by CBS Records. Deleted Jan '90. Catalogue no: **461184 2**
**Album:** Released Jul '88, on Epic by CBS Records. Deleted Oct '89. Catalogue no: **461184 1**
**Cass:** Released Jul '88, on Epic by CBS Records. Deleted Oct '89. Catalogue no: **461184 4**

**STREET SMART**
Tracks: / Street smart / Lorenzo / I'caramba / It was you all along / Blues period / Double entendre / Carmen's song / Bella horizonte / Besame mucho.
**Cass:** Released Apr '90, on Epic by CBS Records. Catalogue no: **466225 4**
**Album:** Released Apr '90, on Epic by CBS Records. Catalogue no: **466225 1**
**CD:** Released Apr '90, on Epic by CBS Records. Catalogue no: **466225 2**

## Gonella, Nat

**CRAZY VALVES (Gonella, Nat/his Georgians)**
Tracks: / How'm I doin? / Capri caprice / Skeleton in the cupboard, The / I can't dance, I got ants in my pants / Crazy valves / Bessie couldn't help it / Take another guess / Nagasaki / Just a crazy song / Sheik of Araby, The / Tiger rag / Copper coloured gal / Ol' man mose / Trumpetuous / I'm gonna clap my hands / Makin' a fool of myself / 'Bill' Tell / Georgia on my mind / Amor, amor, amor / Cu-cu-rru-cu-cu-paloma / Summer samba / Besame mucho / Mas que nada / One note samba / La felicidad / Desafinado / Brazil / Amorada / Amapola / El cumbanchero.
Note: An exhilarating, entertaining showcase of one of the great personalities of British jazz, Nat Gonella, enjoying his 80th birthday this year. *Crazy Valves* presents 18 vintage tracks from his great little band, the Georgians, from 1934 to 1937. (ASV Records October, 1988).
**Album:** Released Sep '88, on Living Era by Academy Sound & Vision Records. Catalogue no: **AJA 5055**
**Cass:** Released Sep '88, on Living Era by Academy Sound & Vision Records. Catalogue no: **ZC AJA 5055**

**GEORGIA ON MY MIND (Gonella, Nat/his Georgians)**
Tracks: / E flat blues / Tiger rag / Wabash blues / Someone stole Gabriel's horn / Ol' man Mose / Bye bye blues / Jeepers creepers / Spooky takes a holiday / Flat foot Floogie / Mahogany Hall blues stomp / When you're smiling / You must have been a beautiful baby / I must see Anne tonight / Just a kid named Joe / Georgia on my mind.
**Album:** Released Aug '81, on Decca by Decca International. Deleted Aug '86. Catalogue no: **RFL 12**
**Album:** Released Jul '80, on World by World Records. Deleted Jul '85. Catalogue no: **SH 369**

**GOLDEN AGE OF NAT GONELLA**
**Cass:** Released Jul '85, on Golden Age by EMI Records. Catalogue no: **GX 41 2536 4**
**Album:** Released Jul '85, on Golden Age by EMI Records. Catalogue no: **GX 41 2536 1**

**HOW'M I DOIN'? (Gonella, Nat/his Georgians)**
Tracks: / How'm I doin'? / Mama don't allow it / Blue turning grey / Lazy rhythm / Fan it / You rascal you / Get hot / Kickin' the gong around / Bye bye blues / Music goes round and around, The / Confessin' / Somebody stole Gabriel's horn / Lady be good / His old cornet / How long how long blues / I want to be happy / Sweet music man / Ol' man river / Swingin' to those lies (it's a sin to tell a lie).
Note: 1936.
**Album:** Released Mar '87, on Old Bean by Submarine Records. Catalogue no: **OLD 11**
**Cass:** Released Mar '87, on Old Bean by Submarine Records. Catalogue no: **COLD 11**

**MISTER RHYTHM MAN (Gonella, Nat/his Georgians)**
Tracks: / Don't let your love go wrong / Moonglow / Troublesome trumpet / Dinah / Let him live / Oh mo'nah / Georgia on my mind / Sing / E flat blues / Georgia's a gorgeous gal / Basin street blues / I'm gonna wash my hands of you / Mister rhythm man / Stardust / Earful of music / Down at uncle bill's / Smoke rings / Beale street blues / Rockin' chair / I heard / St louis blues / Runnin' wild / Rhythm is our business / Breakin' the ice.
**Cass:** Released Oct '84, on Retrospect by EMI Records. Deleted Jan '88. Catalogue no: **EG 2601884**
**Album:** Released Oct '84, on Retrospect by EMI Records. Deleted Jan '88. Catalogue no: **EG 2601881**

**NAT GONELLA AND HIS TRUMPET**
Tracks: / Georgia on my mind / Sweet Sue / Moon country / Nobody's sweetheart / Troublesome trumpet / I heard / That's my home / When you're smiling / Rockin' chair / I can't believe that you're in love with me / Stormy weather / I can't dance, I got ants in my pants / Carolina.

**Naturally Gonnella - Nat Gonnella (Conifer)**

**Album:** Released '67, on Ace Of Clubs by Decca Records. Deleted '88. Catalogue no: **ACL 1241**

**NAT GONELLA SCRAPBOOK, THE**
Tracks: / Gotta pebble in my shoe / Solitude / Blue skies / Begin the beguine / If I didn't care / This night / Ain't ya comin out / T'aint what you do (it's the way that you do it) / He stole my heart away / Louis blues / Meet me down in sunset valley / Harlem speaks / Tiger rag / Never break a promise / Music maestro please / On the sentimental side / Spider and the fly, The.
**Album:** Released May '85, on Joy by President Records. Catalogue no: **JOY 284**

**NAT GONELLA STORY**
Tracks: / Georgia on my mind / Wild man blues / Bessie couldn't help it / Miss Otis regrets (she's unable to lunch today) / Them there eyes / O Mo'nah / Nagasaki / Honeysuckle rose / Just a kid named Joe / Ain't misbehavin' / Stompin' at the Savoy / It's a pair of wings for me / Don't get around much anymore / Five minutes more.
**Album:** Released Feb '78, on Note by EMI Records. Catalogue no: **NTS 146**

**NATURALLY GONELLA (Gonella, Gonella & His Georgians) (See panel above)**
Tracks: / Yeah man / Truckin' / Hot lips / Sheik of Araby, The / Black coffee / Blow, Gabriel, blow / Capri caprice (isle of Capri) / Oh Peter (you're so nice) / Georgia rockin' chair / Lazy river / Sweet and hot / Pidgin English hula / Square-face / Japanese sandman / Ghost of Dina / Jig time / Gonna wed that gal o' mine / Peanut vendor / Sophisticated lady.
**Album:** Released '86, on Conifer Happy Days Catalogue no: **CHD 129**

**RUNNING WILD (Gonella, Nat & His Georgians)**
**Album:** Released '88, on Harlequin by Interstate Music. Catalogue no: **HQ 3003**

**YEAH MAN 1935-1937**
Tracks: / Georgia rockin' chair / St. Louis blues / Yeah man / Mahogany hall stomp / I'm getting sentimental over you / Japanese sandman / I'm gonna kiss myself goodbye / Big apple / Whatcha gonna do when there ain't no swing? / Swingin' the jinx away / Someday, sweetheart / I don't like / Peckin' / Farewell blues / You can't swing a love song / Taint good (like a nickel made of wood).
**Album:** Released Jan '88, on Harlequin by Interstate Music. Catalogue no: **HQ 3019**

## Gonsalves, Paul

**Biographical details:** He played with Count Basie in 1946, then with Dizzy Gillespie, joining Duke Ellington in 1950 to stay for the rest of his life. A drug addict and alcoholic, sometimes unreliable, he never hurt anyone but himself and Ellington always forgave his transgressions. He was unsurpassed as a ballad player. At the 1956 Newport Jazz Festival, he played the bridge between the two parts of *Diminuendo in Blue* and *Crescendo in Blue*, blowing chorus after chorus over the hard-swinging band; he was thus partly responsible for a classic and best-selling live jazz album, also gaining (overdue) recognition as a grandfather of American music, and resulting in Ellington's picture appearing on Time magazine's cover. When Gonsalves died in London, Ellington, also dying, was not told. (Donald Clarke, 1989).

**CLEOPATRA FEELIN' JAZZY**
Tracks: / Action in Alexandria / Cleo's asp / Cleopatra's lament.
**Cass:** Released Aug '82, on Jasmine by Hasmick Promotions. Catalogue no: **JAS C47**
**Album:** Released Aug '82, on Jasmine by Hasmick Promotions. Deleted Feb '88. Catalogue no: **JAS 47**

**GETTIN' TOGETHER**
**CD:** Released '86, on Carrere (France) Catalogue no: **CA 98 946**

**JAZZ TILL MIDNIGHT (Gonsalves, Paul & Eddie "Lockjaw" Davis)**
**CD:** Released Feb '90, on Storyville by Storyville Records AB. Catalogue no: **STCD 4123**

**JUST A-SITTIN' AND A-ROCKIN' (Gonsalves, Paul & Ray Nance)**
Tracks: / BP blues / Lotus blossom / Don't blame me / Just a sittin' and a rockin' / Hi ya, Sue / Angel eyes / I'm in the market for you / Tea for two.
**Album:** Released Jul '88, on Black Lion Catalogue no: **BLP 30138**

**MEXICAN BANDIT MEETS PITSBURGH PIRATE (Gonsalves, Paul & Roy Eldridge)**
Tracks: / 1.5400 North / I cover the waterfront / C jam blues / Body and soul / It's the talk of the town / Somebody loves me.
Note: The first collaboration between these two important jazz soloists. Paul Gonsalves was a key member of Duke Ellington's Orchestra for most of his working life (he died in 1974, ten days after Ellington). Having started with Ellington as an average tenor player, he emerged as one of the greats. He is one of the most important trumpet soloists in jazz history. Having worked with Fletcher Henderson, Teddy Wilson, Benny Goodman, Gene Krupa, Artie Shaw and countless small groups, his wealth of experience is unrivalled. Recorded in New York, 1973.
**Album:** Released Oct '86, on Fantasy by Ace Records. Catalogue no: **F 9646**
**Cass:** Released Oct '86, on Fantasy by Ace Records. Catalogue no: **5F 9646**

**RARE PAUL GONSALVES SEXTET IN EUROPE 1963 (Gonsalves, Paul Sextet)**
**Album:** Released Apr '79, on Jazz Connoisseur by Spotlite Records. Catalogue no: **JC 109**

**TELL IT THE WAY IT IS**
Tracks: / Tell it the way it is / Things ain't what they used to be / Duke's place / Impulsive / Rapscallion in Babs Canyon

/ Body and soul.
**Cass:** Released Jun '82, on Jasmine by Hasmick Promotions. Catalogue no: **JAS C27**
**Album:** Released Jun '82, on Jasmine by Hasmick Promotions. Deleted Feb '88. Catalogue no: **JAS 27**

## Good Morning

**GOOD MORNING BLUES "VAR GOD DROJ" (Featuring Claes Jansson etc) (Various artists)**
Tracks: / Good morning blues: *Various artists* / Riding in the moonlight: *Various artists* / Breaking up is hard to do: *Various artists* / Little by little: *Various artists* / Everyday I have the blues: *Various artists* / Almost grown: *Various artists* / Hard times got me: *Various artists* / I got my mojo working: *Various artists* / That's alright mama: *Various artists* / Sporting life: *Various artists.*
**Album:** Released '82, on Phontastic (Sweden) Catalogue no: **PHONT 7507**

**GOOD MORNING MR PRESLEY (Various artists)**
**Album:** Released Jul '85, on Grunt Grunt A Go-Go Catalogue no: **GGAGG 1**

## Good News

**GOOD NEWS (22 GOSPEL GREATS) (Various artists)**
Tracks: / I'm going through: *Caravan* / It's Jesus in me: *Caravan* / I'm a rollin': *Five Blind Boys Of Mississippi* / Where there's a will: *Five Blind Boys Of Mississippi* / Wade in the water: *Harmonizing Four* / Father I stretch my hand to thee: *Harmonizing Four* / Nobody knows: *Highway QC'S* / Working on the building: *Highway QC'S* / Uncloudy day: *Staple Singers* / This may be the last time: *Staple Singers* / Going away: *Staple Singers* / Good news: *Staple Singers* / Don't drive me away: *Staple Singers* / Will the circle be unbroken: *Staple Singers* / Too close: *Staple Singers* / Great day in December: *Swan Silvertones* / Oh Mary don't you weep: *Swan Silvertones* / How I got over: *Swan Silvertones* / What about you: *Swan Silvertones* / Brighter day ahead: *Swan Silvertones* / Seek, seek: *Swan Silvertones* / I'll search heaven: *Swan Silvertones.*
**CD:** Released Dec '87, on Charly by Charly Records. Catalogue no: **CDCHARLY 98**

## Goodman, Benny

**Biographical details:** The King of Swing. One of the most famous names in the history of jazz, he did much to evolve and popularize the dance band phenomenon of the swing era. Benny was born into a poor working-class environment, being the 12th child of his Russian-born parents. He took up the clarinet at the age of six, having previously dabbled in harmonica playing. His father was impressed by his musical instincts and, as Benny grew up, fixed him up with lessons in a local synagogue band followed by training and experience in local boys' bands. During his teens he became interested in the increasingly popular jazz genre. He turned professional in 1926, working for various bandleaders and also as a radio studio musician for a time. In 1934, now based in New York, he decided to form his own ensemble. After overcoming the initial teething problems, Goodman and his band jumped into top gear in 1935. His dynamic, tight, danceable yet rhythmically complex jazz sound became a sensation following the band's acclaimed residencies in Los Angeles and Chicago. Goodman was a household name by 1938, the year that he performed the first ever jazz concert at New York's Carnegie Hall. He hit his commercial peak during the late 30's and early 40's, during which time his flexible roster of musicians appeared variously as a trio, a quartet, a sextet and a Big Band. His most famous records of the era included such numbers as *Stardust, Royal Garden blues, I found a new baby* and, in 1942, his US Top 5 hit *Why don't you do right?*, which featured vocals by Peggy Lee. Many of the most respected jazz musicians played in Goodman's bands. These included, among others: guitarist Charlie Christian, vibraphonist Lionel Hampton, drummer Gene Krupa and pianist Teddy Wilson. Goodman's rendition of Frank Loesser's *On a slow boat to China* (which featured vocals by Al Hendrickson) was released in 1948 and helped to make the song a standard. A biographical movie came out in 1956; the film yielded a US Top 20 single in the shape of *Memories of you*, performed by the Benny Goodman Trio with singer Rosemary Clooney. The British record charts were not inaugurated until the fifties, and Goodman's UK chart track record is thus somewhat farcical - his only entry occurred in April 1971, when the *Benny Goodman today* LP reached no. 49. His albums continue to sell in steady quantities, although the vast choice of available catalogue negates the possibility of an LP selling sufficiently to garner a chart position. (Bob Macdonald, 25/9/88)

Benjamin David Goodman became one of the most famous and best-loved stars of the twentieth century, as well as one of the greatest jazzmen, first in the Chicago style of small-group jazz and then as the King of Swing. His first recorded solo was made in 1926 with Ben Pollock's band; producer John Hammond (whose sister Goodman married) became an early champion, and Goodman's busy freelance career included in 1933 both Bessie Smith's last and Billie Holiday's first recording sessions. He formed a big band in 1934 for an unsuccessful engagement at Billy Rose's Music Hall, then played on a radio dance music programme called Let's Dance, Goodman's big band jazz alternating with Xavier Cugat (latin) and Kel Murray (sweet music). He took this big band on tour starting in May 1935, initially without success, but when they got to Oakland, California a large audience of young people was waiting - the Swing Era had begun years before in the black community, but now it began in commercial terms, and a jazz-based style dominated

Benny Goodman

popular music for 15 years. Goodman had 164 hit records between 1931 and 1953. The 1930s produced 75 of them on the Victor label, with the classic band, sidemen including Bunny Berigan, Bud Freeman, and Harry James, Martha Tilton and Helen Forrest being among the vocalists. The arrangements of Fletcher Henderson, Jimmy Mundy, and Edgar Sampson (all black) were important, and the Carnegie Hall concert of 1938 was a milestone in jazz history. The band improved when Gene Krupa left it, and in the 1940s the hits were on the CBS label, Eddie Sauter writing some of the best arrangements and vocalists including Peggy Lee. Goodman was one of the first to employ black sidemen, getting away with it in the late 1930s by presenting them in small groups as an added attraction rather than as full band members. The trio included Teddy Wilson (piano) and Gene Krupa (drums), the quartet added Lionel Hampton , and the sextet (CBS 1939-41) added Charlie Christian (electric guitar), and often Count Basie or Fletcher 'Smack' Henderson on piano, and these records had a more modern feeling, with Georgie Auld (tenor saxophone), who incidentally played on the soundtrack of the Scorsese film *New York, New York* in 1977. Goodman flirted with modern jazz in 1949 on Capitol, employing, among others, Wardell Gray (Tenor saxophone), but never liked the style, which led many musicians to conclude that he simply didn't have a good enough ear for it. He spent the rest of his life playing his classic style and making enemies - Helen Forrest described him as the rudest man she had ever met - but his place in history is secure. (Donald Clarke, 1989).

**20 GREATEST HITS: BENNY GOODMAN**
**Album:** Released Nov '84, on Astan (USA) Catalogue no: **20121**
**Cass:** Released Nov '84, on Astan (USA) Catalogue no: **40121**

**40TH ANNIVERSARY CONCERT**
**Cass:** Released May '78, on London Records by London Records Ltd. Catalogue no: **KDBC 3/4**

**1938 CARNEGIE HALL JAZZ CONCERT**
Tracks: / Don't be that way / One o'clock jump / Sensation rag / I'm coming, Virginia / When my baby smiles at me / Shine / Blue reverie / Life goes to a party / Honeysuckle rose / Body and soul / Man I love, The / Avalon / I got rhythm / Blue skies / Loch Lomond / Blue room / Swingtime in the Rockies / Bei mir bist du schon / China boy / Stompin' at The Savoy / Dizzy spells / Sing, sing, sing / Big John's special.
**Album:** Released '88, on CBS by CBS Records. Deleted Jul '89. Catalogue no: **66202**

**1939**
**Album:** Released Mar '90, on Tax Catalogue no: **TAX 8021**

**1939 VOL 2**
**Album:** Released Mar '90, on Tax Catalogue no: **TAX8033**

**1937-38 3 LP box set**
**Album:** Released Dec '81, on Verve Catalogue no: **2615 060**

**1937-39 (Goodman, Benny & His Orchestra)**
Tracks: / Blue Hawaii / Veni, veni / All of me / Yam, The / Moten swing / Clap hands, here comes Charlie / Hartford stomp / Trees / Begin the beguine / Sly mongoose / Hot foot shuffle / Hold tight.
**Album:** Released Mar '85, on Jazz Anthology by Musidisc Records (France). Catalogue no: **JA 5114**

**1936-1939**
**Cass:** Released '88, on Joker (USA) by Lifetime Records (USA). Catalogue no: **MC 3870**
**Album:** Released '88, on Joker (USA) by Lifetime Records (USA). Catalogue no: **SM 3870**

**1938-1939: NEWHOUSE PRESENT (Goodman, Benny His Orchestra,Trio & Quartet)**
**2 LP Set:** Released May '86, on Nostalgia by Mainline Records. Catalogue no: **NOST 7625/26**

**ALL OF ME**
Tracks: / In the mood / Yam, The / Moten swing / Begin the beguine / Blue Hawaii / All of me / Hartford stomp / Trees / Clap hands, here comes Charlie / Sly mongoose / Hot foot shuffle / Hold tight.
Note: With Harry James, Ziggy Elman, Vido Musso, Jess Stacy, Gene Krupa, Dave Tough. Recorded: 1939.
**Cass:** Released '82, on Black Lion-Intercord Catalogue no: **CAS 427 034**
**Album:** Released '82, on Black Lion-Intercord Catalogue no: **INT 127 034**

**ALL THE CATS JOIN IN**
Tracks: / Clarinade / All the cats join in / Mad boogie / Remember / Somebody stole my gal / Darktown strutters' ball / Lucky / Rattle and roll / Body and soul / Lady be good.
**Album:** Released Oct '85, on Bulldog Records by President Records. Catalogue no: **BDL 1056**
**Cass:** Released Oct '85, on Bulldog Records by President Records. Catalogue no: **BDC 1056**
**Cass:** Released May '85, on First Heard by Submarine Records. Catalogue no: **CFH 37**
**Album:** Released May '85, on First Heard by Submarine Records. Catalogue no: **FH 37**

**ALTERNATIVE GOODMAN 9**
**Album:** Released Mar '90, on Nostalgia by Mainline Records. Catalogue no: **NOST7648**

**BASLE, SWITZERLAND, 1959**
**Album:** Released Nov '86, on Artistry Catalogue no: **AR 108**

**BASIN STREET BLUES**
**Album:** Released Nov '84, on Astan (USA) Catalogue no: **20084**
**Cass:** Released Nov '84, on Astan (USA) Catalogue no: **40084**

**BENNY GOODMAN 1943**
**Album:** Released '88, on Queen Catalogue no: **QUEEN 042**
**Album:** Released May '88, on Blu-Disc (USA) Catalogue no: **T 1002**
**Album:** Released '88, on Lotus Catalogue no: **LOP 14,081**
**CD:** Released Mar '88, on Verve Catalogue no: **820 543 2**
**Album:** Released Jul '82, on Jazz Reactivation Catalogue no: **JR 155**
**Cass:** Released Feb '88, on Verve Catalogue no: **820 543 4**

**BENNY GOODMAN, 1946**
**Album:** Released '89, on Jazz Society Catalogue no: **AA 505**

**BENNY GOODMAN COLLECTION (20 golden greats)**
Tracks: / Let's dance / Bugle call rag / King Porter stomp / St. Louis blues / Stealin' apples / Stompin' at the Savoy / Dinah / Alexander's ragtime band / Dear old Southland / Get happy / Body and soul / Christopher Columbus / One o'clock jump / Chloe / Rosetta / My melancholy baby / Sometimes I'm happy / Three little words / I want to be happy / Goodbye.
**Album:** Released Aug '85, on Deja Vu Catalogue no: **DVLP 2011**
**Cass:** Released Aug '85, on Deja Vu Catalogue no: **DVMC 2011**

**BENNY GOODMAN AND FRIENDS**
**CD:** Released Mar '87, on London Records by London Records Ltd. Deleted Feb '89. Catalogue no: **820 179-2**

**BENNY GOODMAN AND HIS ORCHESTRA (Goodman, Benny & His Orchestra)**
**CD:** Released '86, on Delta (1) by Delta Records. Catalogue no: **11 042**
**Album:** Released Sep '87, on Giants of Jazz by Hasmick Promotions. Catalogue no: **LPJT 38**

**BENNY GOODMAN AND HIS ORCHESTRA (Goodman, Benny & His Orchestra)**
**CD:** Released Jan '89, on Giants of Jazz by Hasmick Promotions. Catalogue no: **GOJCD 53042**

**BENNY GOODMAN, HIS STARS AND HIS**
Tracks: / I cried for you / Lady be good / Opus one/two / Memories of you / Lamp is low, The / Gone with "what" wind / Jack hits the road / Southpaw serenade / Fiesta in blue / There'll be some changes made / Chonk, Charlie, chonk / Superman / Flying home / Rose room / Let the doorknob hitcha.
**Album:** Released Apr '81, on Queendisc (Italy) Catalogue no: **QU 016**

**BENNY GOODMAN IN STOCKHOLM (1959) (Goodman, Benny/Flip Phillips)**
**CD:** Released '88, on Phontastic (Sweden) Catalogue no: **PHONTCD 8801**

**BENNY GOODMAN -- LIVE IN LAS VEGAS (December 31, 1966) (Goodman, Benny Sextet)**
Note: New Year's Eve concert from the Hotel Tropicana, with supporting musicians including Doc Cheatham, Mousie Alexander and Ross Tompkins playing Sweet Georgia Brown, Rose Room, Airmail Special, Memories of You.
**Album:** Released Apr '88, on Sounds Great Catalogue no: **SG 8010**

**BENNY GOODMAN ON THE AIR 1940 (Goodman, Benny & His Orchestra)**
Tracks: / Lets dance / Big John special / Hour of parting / Seven come eleven / Where do I go from you? / Goodbye / These foolish things / After you've gone / Board meeting / Six appeal / Stardust / Goodbye / Idaho.
**Album:** Released Apr '79, on Aircheck (USA) by Kiner Ents.(USA). Catalogue no: **AIRCHECK 16**

**BENNY GOODMAN ON THE AIR VOL 2 (Goodman, Benny & His Orchestra)**
Tracks: / Don't be that way / Louise Tobin blues / Make believe / Sheik of Araby, The / Alexanders ragtime band / It's never too late / Sent for you yesterday / Goodbye / Let's dance / Blue skies / If you ever change your mind / Russian lullaby / Boy meets horn / I got rhythm / Sugar foot stomp / Three little words / Don't worry 'bout me / In a little Spanish town / Tea for two / Indianapolis speedway race.
**Album:** Released Feb '88, on Aircheck (USA) by Aircheck Records. Catalogue no: **AIRCHECK 32**

**BENNY GOODMAN ON THE AIR VOL 3 (Goodman, Benny & His Orchestra)**
Tracks: / Stompin' at the Savoy / Louise / Bugle call rag / Love me or leave me / Lady's in love with you, The / Without a song / Memories of you / And the angels sing / King Porter stomp / Jumpin' at the woodside / There'll be some changes made / China boy / Class of '39, The / Wrappin' it up / Goodbye / Moonlight serenade / Mozart matriculates / Stealin' apples / Pic-a-rib / One o'clock jump.
**Album:** Released Feb '88, on Aircheck (USA) by Kiner Ents.(USA). Catalogue no: **AIRCHECK 34**

**BENNY GOODMAN ORCHESTRA AND GROUPS (Goodman, Benny & His Orchestra)**
Tracks: / Blue Hawaii / Veni, veni / All of me / Yam, The / Moten swing / Clap hands, here comes Charlie / Sly mongoose / Hot foot shuffle / Hold tight / Hartford stomp / Begin the beguine / September song / World is waiting for the sunrise / Bill Bailey / I want to be happy / Runnin' wild / Mission to Moscow / Clarinet a la King / King Porter stomp / World is waiting for the sunrise / Poor butterfly / Let's dance / I walk with you / Yesterday / Great day / Shadow of your smile / Air mail special / String of pearls.
**Album:** Released Apr '81, on Kings Of

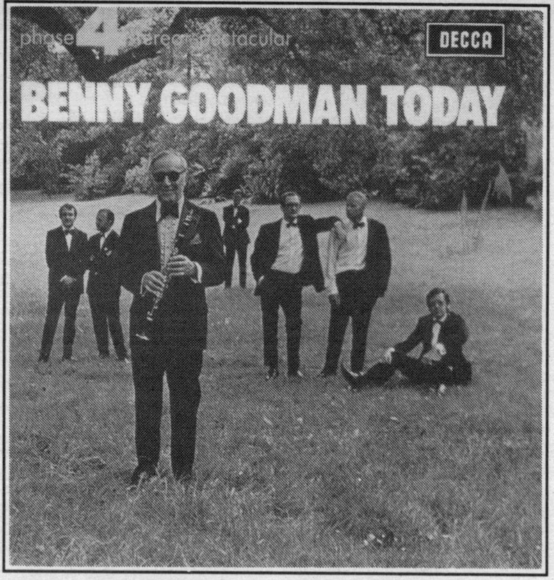


**Benny Goodman Today - Benny Goodman (Decca)**

Jazz Catalogue no: **KLJ 20005**

**BENNY GOODMAN PLAYS CLASSICS**
**CD Set:** Released Mar '87, on Teldec (1) by ASV (Academy Sound & Vision). Catalogue no: **8 48262**
**Cass:** Released Mar '87, on Teldec (1) by ASV (Academy Sound & Vision). Catalogue no: **4 48262**
**2 LP Set:** Released Mar '87, on Teldec (1) by ASV (Academy Sound & Vision). Catalogue no: **6 48262**

**BENNY GOODMAN PLAYS GERSHWIN**
Tracks: / I got rhythm / Man I love, The / Nice work if you can get it / Who cares? / How long has this been going on? / Love walked in / Embraceable you / Liza / Fascinating rhythm / Oh lady I love / Lady be good / Somebody loves me.
**Cass:** Released May '83, on CBS by CBS Records. Catalogue no: **40 21064**
**Album:** Released May '83, on CBS by CBS Records. Catalogue no: **CBS 21064**

**BENNY GOODMAN STORY, THE**
Tracks: / Blue skies / King Porter stomp / Goodbye / Stompin' at the Savoy / Get happy / Christopher Columbus / St. Louis blues / Alexander's ragtime band / Dear old southland / So rare / Big John special / I've got my love to keep me warm / Smiles / Chloe / I got rhythm / Don't be that way / One o'clock jump / My melancholy baby / Whispering / Bach goes to town (a fugue in swing tempo) / If dreams come true / AC/DC current / Bugle call rag / Don't be that way / Sing, sing, sing.
**CD:** Released Apr '89, on Deja Vu Catalogue no: **DVRE CD 08**
**Cass:** Released Apr '89, on Deja Vu Catalogue no: **DVRE MC 08**

**BENNY GOODMAN SWINGS**
**Album:** Released Jun '85, on Pathe Marconi (France) Catalogue no: **PM 155 1563**

**BENNY GOODMAN -- THE KING SWINGS (December 8, 1973)**
**Album:** Released Apr '88, on Sounds Great Catalogue no: **SG 8006**

**BENNY GOODMAN TODAY (See panel above)**
**Album:** Released Apr '71, on Decca by Decca International. Deleted '76. Catalogue no: **DDS 3**

**BENNY GOODMAN TRIO PLAYS.... (Fletcher Henderson Fund WNEW New York 1951) (Goodman, Benny Trio)**
**Album:** Released Aug '87, on Tax Catalogue no: **M 8041**

**BENNY GOODMAN TRIO & QUARTET (Goodman, Benny Trio & Quartet)**
Tracks: / After you've gone / Body and soul / Who? / Someday, sweetheart / China boy / More than you know / All my life / Lady be good / Nobody's sweetheart / Too good to be true / Moonglow / Dinah / Exactly like you / Vibraphone blues / Sweet Sue / My melancholy baby / Tiger rag / Stompin' at The Savoy / Whispering / Ida / Tea for two / Runnin' wild.
**CD:** Released Apr '88, on Bluebird (2)

by BMG Records (UK). Catalogue no: **ND 85631**

**BENNY GOODMAN VOL.1**
Tracks: / Sweet Georgia Brown / Broadway / Blue room.
Note: Never before released recordings from his private collection. Teddy Wilson / Zoot Zims / Ruby Braff / Roland Hanna & Urbie Green.
**CD:** Released Jan '89, on Music Masters by Music Masters Records. Catalogue no: **CIJ 60142 Z**
**Cass:** Released Jan '89, on Music Masters by Music Masters Records. Catalogue no: **CIJ 20142 F**
**Album:** Released Apr '79, on Bright Orange Catalogue no: **BO 704**
**Album:** Released Jan '89, on Music Masters by Music Masters Records. Catalogue no: **CIJ 40142 A**

**BENNY GOODMAN VOL.2 (Big band)**
**Album:** Released May '88, on Blu-Disc (USA) Catalogue no: **T 1004**

**BENNY GOODMAN VOL.3**
**Album:** Released Nov '88, on Blu-Disc (USA) Catalogue no: **T 1006**

**BENNY GOODMAN VOL.4**
**Album:** Released Nov '88, on Blu-Disc (USA) Catalogue no: **T 1009**

**BENNY GOODMAN VOL.5 (Small-group)**
**Album:** Released Nov '88, on Blu-Disc (USA) Catalogue no: **T 1011**

**BENNY GOODMAN VOL.6 (Small-group 1939/45)**
**Album:** Released Nov '88, on Blu-Disc (USA) Catalogue no: **T 1012**

**BENNY GOODMAN: VOLUME 2 (Goodman, Benny & His Orchestra)**
Tracks: / Can't we be friends? / Bugle call rag / Indiana / I surrender, dear / Life is a song / Sweet little you / Between the Devil and the deep blue sea / Royal Garden blues / Sweet and lovely / Three little words / Sugar foot stomp / When we're alone / There must have been a devil in the Moon / Restless. **Album:** Released Apr '79, on Bright Orange Catalogue no: **BO 718**
**Album:** Released Mar '85, on Jazz Anthology by Musidisc Records (France). Catalogue no: **JA 5152**

**BENNY GOODMAN - WHEN SWING WAS KING**
Note: Broadcasts, April 27-29, 1937, April 7, 1938. Rare performances with some of the greatest names of the big band era, including Harry James, Gene Krupa, Teddy Wilson, Lionel Hampton, Ziggy Elman and Jess Stacy. This great swing aggregation play *Johnny One Note, That Foolish Feeling, More Than You Know, Camel Hop, Big John Special, Lullaby In Rhythm* and eight more.
**Album:** Released Apr '88, on Sounds Great Catalogue no: **SG 8004**

**BENNY GOODMAN WITH RED NICHOLS' ORCHESTRA (Goodman, Benny & Red Nichols)**
Tracks: / How come you do me like you do? / Making faces at the man in the moon / East St. Louis toodle-oo.
**Album:** Released '79, on Decca by Decca International. Deleted '88. Catalogue no: **V 5001**

**BENNY GOODMANS 1934 BILL DODGE**
**2 LP Set:** Released Jun '88, on Circle (USA) by Jazzology Records (USA). Catalogue no: **CLP 111/112**

**BENNY RIDES AGAIN**
Tracks: / Mission to Moscow / Benny rides again / Earl,The / Oh baby / Fascinating rhythm / Everything I've got / Whispering / All the things you are / You do something to me / It could happen to you / Stereo stomp.
**CD:** Released Jun '88, on MCA (USA) by MCA Records (USA). Catalogue no: **31264**
**Album:** on Chess by Vogue Records. Catalogue no: **GCH 8096**

**BENNY'S BOP**
Tracks: / Mary's idea / Bye bye blues bop / There's a small hotel / Blue views / I can't give you anything but love / You took advantage of me / Where oh where has my little dog gone / Pepper (Patsy's idea) / String of pearls / I'll see you in my dreams / Undercurrent blues.
**Album:** Released Jan '88, on Hep Jazz by Hep Records. Catalogue no: **HEP 36**

**BEST OF BENNY GOODMAN**
Tracks: / Don't be that way / Sing, sing, sing / And the angels sing / Loch Lomond / King Porter stomp / Stompin' at The Savoy / One o'clock jump / After you've gone / Goodnight my love / Goodbye.
**Album:** Released '84, on RCA by BMG Records (UK). Catalogue no: **NL 89323**
**Album:** Catalogue no: **INTS 5079**
**Cass:** Released Mar '86, on RCA by BMG Records (UK). Catalogue no: **NK 89323**

**BEST OF NEWHOUSE (Camel Caravan broadcasts 1938-39)**
Tracks: / One o'clock jump / Moonglow / Stardust / Lullaby in rhythm / Alexander's ragtime band / Shine on harvest moon / Diga diga doo / I know that you know / I've found a new baby / Swingtime in the Rockies / Clarinet marmalade / I hadn't anyone till you / Minnie the moocher's wedding day / Dinah / Runnin' wild / Sugar foot stomp / Honeysuckle rose / Shine / You're driving me crazy / Sing, sing, sing / Dizzy spells / Smoke house / It had to be you / Bach goes to town / I'm a ding dong daddy / Whispering / Undecided / Sent for you yesterday / Kingdom of swing / Who'll buy my bublitchki? / Goodbye.
**Album:** Released '82, on Nostalgia by Mainline Records. Catalogue no: **NOST 726526**

**BEST OF, THE**
**Album:** Released Mar '90, Catalogue no: **SM3973/2**

**BG 1938**
Tracks: / Don't be that way / House hop / Sampson stomp / I can't give you anything but love / I've found a new baby / One o'clock jump / I let a song go out of my heart / Jazz me blues / King Porter stomp / I never knew / Flat foot floogie / Diga diga doo / Shine on harvest moon.
**Album:** Released May '83, on Queendisc (Italy) Catalogue no: **QU 060**

**B.G.IN HI FI**
Tracks: / Let's dance / Jumpin' at The Woodside / Stompin' at The Savoy / What can I say, after I say I'm sorry? / When I grow too old to dream / Get happy / You brought a new kind of love to me / Rock rimmon / Somebody stole my gal / Blue Lou / Sent for you yesterday / You're a sweetheart / Big John's special / Jersey bounce / Airmail special / Ain't misbehavin' (CD only.) / Slipped disc (CD only.) / Rose room (CD only.) / I would do anything for you (CD only.).
**CD:** Released Apr '90, on Pacific Jazz by EMI Records. Catalogue no: **CDP 792 864 2**
**Cass:** Released Mar '85, on Capitol by EMI Records. Deleted Nov '88. Catalogue no: **ED 2604264**
**CD:** Released Apr '90, on Pacific Jazz by EMI Records. Catalogue no: **CZ 273**
**Album:** Released Mar '85, on Capitol by EMI Records. Deleted Nov '88. Catalogue no: **ED 2604261**

**BIG BAND 1936-39**
**Album:** Released '88, on Joker (USA) by Lifetime Records (USA). Catalogue no: **SM 3870**

**BIG BAND EUROPE (Benny Goodman vol. 3)**
Tracks: / Pennies from heaven / Fine romance, A.
**Album:** Released '89, on Denon Catalogue no: **CIJ 40157Y**
**Cass:** Released '89, on Denon Catalogue no: **CIJ 20157Z**
**CD:** Released '89, on Denon Catalogue no: **CIJ 60157X**

**BIG BAND SOUND, THE**
Tracks: / Let's dance / King Porter stomp / Christopher Columbus / Sing, sing, sing / You turned the tables on me / Bugle call rag / It had to be you / Bach goes to town / There's a small hotel / Rose of Washington Square.
**CD:** Released Aug '87, on The Collection by Object Enterprises. Catalogue no: **OR 0030**

**BIG CITY SWING**
Tracks: / Let's dance / Roll 'em / Don't be that way / Stompin' at The Savoy / And the angels sing / Why don't you do right? / String of pearls / Where or when / Jersey bounce / Poor butterfly / Please don't talk about me when I'm gone / How high the moon.
**Album:** Released Oct '80, on Decca by Decca International. Deleted '88. Catalogue no: **TAB 5**

**BLUE SKIES (Goodman, Benny & His Orchestra) (See panel on next page)**
Tracks: / Hooray for love / Get rhythm in your feet (and music in your soul) / Blue skies / Jingle bells / Santa Claus came

**Blue Skies - Benny Goodman (Conifer)**

in the spring / Goodbye / Yankee doodle never went to town / No other one / Eeny meeny miney mo / Basin Street blues / It's been so long / Stompin' at the Savoy / Goody-goody / Breakin' in a pair of shoes / Get happy / Christopher Columbus / I know that you know / Star dust / You can't pull the wool over my eyes / Glory of love, The.
**CD:** Released Jun '88, on Compact Selection Catalogue no: **TQ 131**

**BREAKFAST BALL, 1934 (Goodman, Benny & His Orchestra)**
Tracks: / Georgia jubilee / Junk man / Ol' pappy / Emaline / I ain't lazy - I'm just dreamin' / As long as I live / Moon glow / Breakfast ball / Take my word / It happens to the best of friends / Nitwit serenade / Bugle call rag / Learning / Stars fell on Alabama / Solitude / I'm getting sentimental over you / I'm a hundred per cent for you / Cokey / Like a bolt from the blue / Music hall rag.
**Album:** Released Jul '88, on Saville by Conifer Records. Catalogue no: **SVL 172**
**Cass:** Released '88, on Saville by Conifer Records. Catalogue no: **CSVL 172**

**CAMEL CARAVAN BROADCASTS 1938 (Goodman, Benny & His Orchestra)**
**Album:** Released Nov '86, on Soundcraft (USA) Catalogue no: **LP 1019**

**CAMEL CARAVAN BROADCASTS, VOL 2 (Goodman, Benny & His Orchestra)**
**Album:** Released Nov '86, on Soundcraft (USA) Catalogue no: **LP 1020**
**Album:** Released Nov '86, on Soundcraft (USA) Catalogue no: **LP 1021**

**CAMEL CARAVAN BROADCASTS/CAFE (Goodman, Benny & His Orchestra)**
**Album:** on Jasmine by Hasmick Promotions. Catalogue no: **JASM 2518**
**Cass:** Released '88, on Jasmine by Hasmick Promotions. Catalogue no: **JASMC 2518**

**CAMEL CARAVAN, VOL 1**
Tracks: / Let's dance / I can't give you anything but love / Hurry home / Songwriter's story, The / You must have been a beautiful baby / Honky tonk train blues / Cuckoo in the clock / Roll 'em / Goodbye / Let's dance / Sweet Sue / Could be / Softly as in a morning sunrise / Ciribiribin / I have eyes / Umbrella man / Sent for you yesterday / Goodbye.
Note: Original broadcasts, 3 January 1939 and 10 January 1939.
**Album:** Released Mar '85, on Giants of Jazz by Hasmick Promotions. Catalogue no: **GOJ 1030**

**CAMEL CARAVAN VOL.2**
**Album:** Released Mar '85, on Giants of Jazz by Hasmick Promotions. Catalogue no: **GOJ 1033**

**CAMEL CARAVAN VOL.3 (One o' clock jump)**
**Album:** Released Oct '85, on Giants of Jazz by Hasmick Promotions. Catalogue no: **GOJ 1036**

**CARNEGIE HALL ENCORE**
**Album:** Released Jun '88, on Sounds Great Catalogue no: **SG 8020**

**CLARINET A LA KING (Alternate Goodman, Vol 6)**
Tracks: / This autumn / That's the way it goes / Clarinet a la King / I'm here / Shady ladybird / Buckle down Winsocki / Let's do it / I'll get by / If I had you / Limehouse blues / Someone else is taking my place / Somebody nobody loves / How long has this been going on? / That did it, Marie / Winter weather.
Note: Recorded in 1941.
**Album:** Released '82, on Nostalgia by Mainline Records. Catalogue no: **NOST 7617**

**CLARINET A LA KING (CBS)**
Tracks: / How deep is the ocean / Zaggin' with Zig / It never entered my mind / Henderson stomp / Superman / Yes, my darling daughter / Bewitched / Scarecrow / Solo flight / Cherry / I found a million dollar baby / When the sun comes out / Pound ridge / Earl, The / Caprice XXIV Paganini / Clarinet a la king.
**Cass:** Released 14 Aug '88, on CBS (import) by CBS Records. Catalogue no: **4608294**
**Album:** Released 14 Aug '88, on CBS (import) by CBS Records. Catalogue no: **4608291**

**CLARINETITIS**
Tracks: / Clarinetitis / After a while / Dinah / Jazz holiday, A / Jungle blues / Sheik of Araby, The / Shimme-sha-wabble / How come you do me like you do? / Blue / Muskrat ramble / Room 1411 / That's a-plenty / Indiana / Shirt-tail stomp / Sugar / Crazy 'bout my gal / Woverine blues / Railroad man.
**Cass:** Released Jan '86, on Affinity by Charly Records. Catalogue no: **TCAFS 1018**
**Album:** Released Jan '86, on Affinity by Charly Records. Catalogue no: **AFS 1018**

**CLASSICS IN JAZZ**
**Album:** Released Jan '83, on Swaggie (Australia) Catalogue no: **S 1381**

**COMMAND PERFORMANCE**
Note: With Miff Mole / Peggy Lee / Jess Stacey / Bill Harris etc. 1943/44. Tracks include *I'm just wild about Harry / Stealin' apples / Improvisation / Why don't you do right*, etc...
**Cass:** Released Oct '87, on Swing House by Submarine Records. Catalogue no: **CSWH 46**
**Album:** Released '84, on Swing House by Submarine Records. Catalogue no: **SWH 46**

**COMPLETE SMALL COMBINATIONS (1935-1937)**
Tracks: / After you've gone (2 takes) / Body and soul (2 takes) / Who? / Someday, sweetheart / China boy / More than you know / All my life / Lady be good / Nobody's sweetheart / Too good to be true / Moonglow / Dinah / Vibraphone blues / Sweet Sue / My melancholy baby / Tiger rag / Stompin' at the savoy (2 takes) / Whispering / Ida sweet as apple cider / Tea for two / Runnin' wild / Avalon (2 takes) / Handful of keys (2 takes) /

Man I love, The / Exactly like you.
**Cass set:** Released Sep '86, on Jazz Tribune by BMG Records (UK). Deleted Jul '89. Catalogue no: **NK 89753**
**2 LP Set:** Released Sep '86, on Jazz Tribune by BMG Records (UK). Deleted Jul '89. Catalogue no: **NL 89753**

**COMPLETE SMALL COMBINATIONS VOLS 3/4 (1937-1939)**
Tracks: / Sugar / Dizzy spells / Opus 1/2 / I must have that man / Sweet Georgia Brown / 'S wonderful / Pick-a-rib (parts 1 & 2) / I cried for you (2 takes) / I know that you know / Opus 3/4 / Smiles / Liza / Where or when / Silouetted in the moonlight / Vieni, vieni / I'm a ding dong daddy / Bei mir bist du schon (parts 1 & 2) / Sweet Lorraine / Blues in your flat (3 takes).
**2 LP Set:** Released '86, on RCA. Deleted Jul '89. Catalogue no: **NL 89754**
**Cass Set:** Released '86, on RCA. Deleted May '89. Catalogue no: **NK 89754**

**COMPOSITIONS AND COLLABORATORS (collectors' edition)**
**Album:** Released '88, on CBS by CBS Records. Catalogue no: **CBS M 42227**

**DANCE AND SWING WITH BENNY**
Tracks: / Let's dance / Don't be that way / You was right, baby / Seven come eleven / Come to baby, do / Lucky / It's the talk of the town / Somebody stole my gal / Rattle and roll / Who's sorry now? / Ain't misbehavin' / And the angels sing / All the cats join in / I got the sun in the morning / Sing, sing, sing.
Note: Recorded 1945-46.
**Album:** Released '82, on Nostalgia by Mainline Records. Catalogue no: **NOST 7603**

**DIAMOND SERIES: BENNY GOODMAN**
Tracks: / Let's dance / Mission to Moscow / Meet the band / I got it bad and that ain't good / Why you? / Titter pipes / Feathers / On the Alamo / Midgets / One o'clock jump / Bei mir bist du schon / Stealin' apples / Swift as the wind / Fontainbleau / Meadowland / Goodbye.
**CD:** Released Apr '88, on Diamond Series by RCA Records. Catalogue no: **CD 90129**

**DURING THE FABULOUS FIFTIES**
**Album:** Released Aug '79, on Giants of Jazz by Hasmick Promotions. Catalogue no: **GOJ 1010**

**EARL, THE (The alternate Goodman, Vol 5) (Goodman, Benny & His Orchestra)**
Tracks: / Cherry / Good evenin' good lookin' / Something new / I found a million dollar baby / Don't be that way / When the sun comes out / Smoke gets in your eyes / Tuesday at ten / Soft as spring / Down, down, down / Pound Ridge / Elmer's tune / Clarinet a la King / My old flame / How deep is the ocean? / Earl, The.
Note: Recorded in 1941.
**Album:** Released '82, on Nostalgia by Mainline Records. Catalogue no: **NOST 7616**

**FAMOUS LIVE BROADCASTS 1937/44 (Goodman, Benny & His Orchestra)**
Tracks: / Let's dance / Memories of you / Bugle call rag.
**Album:** Released Mar '88, on Delta (1) by Delta Records. Catalogue no: **20 807**

**FASCINATING RHYTHM**
**Album:** Released Oct '88, on Vogue by Vogue Records. Catalogue no: **500202**
**CD:** Released Jul '89, on Vogue by Vogue Records. Catalogue no: **VG 670211**

**FIRST BIG BANDS, THE**
**CD:** Released Mar '90, on BBC by BBC Records & Tapes. Catalogue no: **BBCD 759**
**Album:** Released Mar '90, on BBC by BBC Records & Tapes. Catalogue no: **REN 766**
**Cass:** Released Mar '90, on BBC by BBC Records & Tapes. Catalogue no: **ZCF 759**

**FLYING HOME (The alternate Goodman, Vol 2)**
Tracks: / I've been there before / Homeward bound (flying home) / Make with the kisses / Soft winds / Darn that dream / Beyond the moon / I'm confessin' / Squeeze me / King Porter stomp / I can't love you anymore / Nostalgia / Nobody / Man I love, The / Henderson stomp / Benny rides again / Cabin in the sky.
**Album:** Released '82, on Nostalgia by Mainline Records. Catalogue no: **NOST 7610**

**FRENESI (The alternate Goodman, Vol 3)**
Tracks: / Frenesi / Hard to get / Moonlight on the Ganges / Yes my darling daughter / I'm always chasing rainbows / Somebody stole my gal / Let the doorknob hitcha / I hear a rhapsody / Corn silk / Birds of a feather / Breakfast feud / Gone with what draft / I'm not complaining / Time on my hands / You're dangerous / Memory of a rose.
Note: Recorded, with Goodman's Orchestra and Sextet, 1940-41.
**Album:** Released '82, on Nostalgia by Mainline Records. Catalogue no: **NOST 7612**

**GET HAPPY**
Tracks: / Hooray for love / Get rhythm in your feet / Blue skies / Jingle bells / Santa Claus came in the spring / Goodbye / Yankee Doodle never went to town / No other one / Eeny meeny miney mo / Basin Street blues / It's been so long / Stompin' at the Savoy / Goody-goody / Breakin' in a pair of shoes / Get happy / Christopher Columbus / I know that you know / Star dust / You can't pull the wool over my eyes / Glory of love, The.
**Cass:** Released Apr '87, on Saville by Conifer Records. Catalogue no: **CSVL 185**
**Album:** Released Apr '87, on Saville by Conifer Records. Catalogue no: **SVL 185**

**GOODMAN, BENNY 1943**
**Album:** Released Mar '90, on Vogue by Vogue Records. Catalogue no: **Q042**

**GOODMAN ON THE AIR**
Tracks: / Airmail special / After you've gone / Flying home / Slipped disc / Clarinade / Oomph fah fah / Clarinet a la King / It's only a paper moon / Rachel's dream / Something new / Tiger rag / Rattle and roll / Rose room / King Porter stomp.
Note: Broadcasts from 1945, with Goodman's Orchestra and Sextet.
**Album:** Released '82, on Nostalgia by Mainline Records. Catalogue no: **NOST 7605**

**GOODMAN TOUCH, THE**
**Album:** Released Jan '83, on Swaggie (Australia) Catalogue no: **S 1380**

**GOTTA BE THIS OR THAT (The alternate Goodman, Vol 10)**
**Album:** Released Mar '87, on Nostalgia by Mainline Records. Catalogue no: **NOST 7650**

**GREATEST HITS: BENNY GOODMAN**
**Album:** Released May '88, on Music Power Catalogue no: **33006**
**Cass:** Released May '88, on Music Power Catalogue no: **63006**

**HALL OF FAME: BENNY GOODMAN & ORCHESTRA (Goodman, Benny & Orchestra)**
Tracks: / In the mood / Yam / Moten swing / Clap hands, here comes Charlie / Blue Hawaii / Vieni vieni / All of me / Hartford stomp / Trees / Begin the beguine / Sly mongoose / Hot foot shuffle / Hold tight.
**Album:** Released Jan '77, on Black Lion Deleted '81. Catalogue no: **BLPS 20151**

**HALLELUJAH 1944-46**
**Album:** Released Jan '88, on Sounds Great Catalogue no: **SG 8016**

**HISTORY OF JAZZ**
Tracks: / Sometimes I'm happy / Basin Street blues / Stompin' at The Savoy / Swingtime in the Rockies / Pick yourself up / He ain't got rhythm / Roll 'em / One o'clock jump / Ooh, oh boom / Undecided / And the angels sing / Jumpin' at The Woodside.
**Album:** Released Apr '81, on Joker (USA) by Lifetime Records (USA). Catalogue no: **SM 3057**

**I GOT RHYTHM The alternate Goodman, Vol 11**
**Album:** Released Mar '87, on Nostalgia by Mainline Records. Catalogue no: **NOST 7652**

**INDISPENSABLE BENNY GOODMAN VOLS 1/2 (1935-36) (Goodman, Benny & His Orchestra)**
Tracks: / Blue skies / Dear old Southland / Sometimes I'm happy / King Porter stomp / Between the devil and the deep blue sea / Madhouse / If I could be with you one hour tonight / When Buddha smiles / Stompin' at the Savoy / Breakin' in a pair of shoes / I hope Gabriel likes my music / Mutiny in the parlour / I'm gonna clap my hands / Swing is here /

Get happy / Christopher Columbus / I know that you know / Stardust / You forgot to remember / House hop / I would do anything for you / I've found a new baby / Swingtime in the Rockies / Pick yourself up / Love me or leave me / Bugle call rag (2 takes) / Organ grinder's swing / Riffin' at the Ritz / Somebody loves me.
**Cass set:** Released Sep '86, on RCA by BMG Records (UK). Deleted May '89. Catalogue no: **NK 89755**
**2 LP Set:** Released Sep '86, on RCA by BMG Records (UK). Deleted Jul '89. Catalogue no: **NL 89755**

**INDISPENSABLE BENNY GOODMAN VOLS. 3/4 (1936-37) (Goodman, Benny & His Orchestra)**
Tracks: / T'ain't no use / Bugle call rag / Jam session / Goodnight my love / (Oh yes) take another guess / Did you mean it? / When you and I were young, Maggie / Swing low sweet chariot / He ain't got rhythm / I want to be happy / Chloe / Rosetta / Peckin' / Can't we be friends? / Sing,Sing,Sing & Christopher columbus / When it's sleepy time down South / Roll 'em / Changes / Bob White / Sugar foot stomp / I can't give you anything but love / Minnie the moocher's wedding day / Let that be a lesson to you.
**Cass:** Released '86, on RCA by BMG Records (UK). Deleted May '89. Catalogue no: **NK 89756**
**2 LP Set:** Released '86, on RCA by BMG Records (UK). Deleted Jul '89. Catalogue no: **NL 89756**

**INDISPENSABLE BENNY GOODMAN VOLS. 5/6 (1938-39) (Goodman, Benny & His Orchestra)**
Tracks: / Don't be that way / One O'Clock jump / Please be kind / Ti-pi-tin / Oooooh-boom / Always and always / Make believe / Blue room / Lullaby in rhythm / I never knew / Sweet Sue / Feelin' high and happy / Why'd ya make me fall in love? / Big John special / Wrappin' it up / Flat foot floogie / Margie / Russian lullaby / Bumble bee stomp / Topsy / Smoke house / My honey's loving arms / Farewell blues / It had to be you / Louise / Whispering / Bach goes to town (a fugue in swing tempo) / I'll always be in love with you / Undecided / And the angels sing / Sent for you yesterday / Kingdom of swing / Pick-a-rib.
**2 LP Set:** Released Aug '86, on RCA by BMG Records (UK). Deleted Jul '89. Catalogue no: **NL 89587**
**Cass:** Released Aug '86, on RCA by BMG Records (UK). Deleted Jul '89. Catalogue no: **NK 89587**

**JAM**
Tracks: / I want to be happy / When you're smiling / Rachel's dream / Jam on the brakes / Sunny side of the streets / Rose room / Moonglow / Sing, sing, sing.
**Cass:** Released '84, on Swing House by Submarine Records. Catalogue no: **CSWH 37**
**Album:** Released '84, on Swing House by Submarine Records. Catalogue no: **SWH 37**

**JAM SESSION (Goodman, Benny, All Stars)**
**Cass:** Released Sep '86, on Ditto by Pickwick Records. Catalogue no: **DTO 10250**

**JAZZ CLASSICS**
**Cass:** Released Mar '90, on BBC by BBC Records & Tapes. Catalogue no: **ZCF 759**
**Album:** Released Mar '90, on BBC by BBC Records & Tapes. Catalogue no: **REB 759**
**CD:** Released Mar '90, on BBC by BBC Records & Tapes. Catalogue no: **BBCCD 759**

**JENNY (The alternate Goodman, Vol 4)**
Tracks: / This is new / Jenny / Perfidia / Bewitched / Afraid to say hello / Lazy river / Scarecrow / Yours / You lucky people / Oh, look at me now / Take it / Solo flight / Good enough to keep / Amapola / Intermezzo / Fiesta in blue.
**Album:** Released '82, on Nostalgia by Mainline Records. Catalogue no: **NOST 7615**

**JUMPIN' AT THE WOODSIDE (The alternate Goodman, Vol 1)**
Tracks: / Jumpin' at The Woodside / There'll be some changes made / Stealin' apples / Comes love / Bolero blues / What's new? / Spring song / Night and day / Blue orchids / One sweet letter / Boy meets horn / I didn't know what time it was / Love never went to college / Scatterbrain / Down by the old mill stream.
**Cass:** Released Jan '87, on Giants of Jazz by Hasmick Promotions. Catalogue no: **GOJC 1042**
**Album:** Released '82, on Nostalgia by Mainline Records. Catalogue no: **NOST 7606**
**Album:** Released Jan '87, on Giants of Jazz by Hasmick Promotions. Catalogue no: **GOJ 1042**

**KING OF JAZZ**
**CD:** Released Nov '87, on Entertainers Deleted '88. Catalogue no: **ENTCD 240**

**KING OF SWING**
**Album:** Released Dec '89, on Accord (France) by Musidisc Records (France). Catalogue no: **300152**
**CD:** Released Dec '89, on Accord (France) by Musidisc Records (France). Catalogue no: **300154**

**KING OF SWING 1958-67**
Tracks: / September song / World is waiting for the sunrise, The / Mission to Moscow / Clarinet a la King / King Porter stomp / Poor butterfly / World is waiting for the sunrise, The / Let's dance / I walk with you / Great day / Shadow of your smile / Airmail special / String of pearls / Avalon / It's alright with me / Whispering / Diga diga doo / After you've gone / Where or when / I got rhythm / These foolish things / That's a plenty / Slipped disc / I can't give you anything but love / Sheik of Araby, The / There'll be some changes made / I've found a new baby.
**Album:** Released Aug '86, on Meteor by Magnum Music Group. Catalogue no: **MTM 020**
**2 LP Set:** Released Oct '83, on Musidisc by Musidisc Records (France). Catalogue no: **ALB 246**
**Album:** Released Jun '86, on CBS (import) by CBS Records. Catalogue no: **66420**

**KING OF SWING (PICKWICK)**
**CD:** Released '88, on Pickwick by Pickwick Records. Catalogue no: **PWK 027**
**Cass:** Released Jun '89, on Hallmark by Pickwick Records. Catalogue no: **HSC 3273**

**KING OF SWING, THE**
**Cass:** Released Sep '87, on Entertainers Deleted '88. Catalogue no: **ENT MC 13022**
**Album:** Released Oct '85, on Giants of Jazz by Hasmick Promotions. Catalogue no: **GOJ 1017**
**Album:** Released Sep '87, on Entertainers Deleted '88. Catalogue no: **ENT LP 13022**

**KING OF SWING, THE (2)**
**CD:** Released Apr '87, on Bridge (MCS Bridge) Catalogue no: **100 021**

**KING OF SWING, THE (GIANTS OF JAZZ)**
**Album:** Released Sep '87, on Giants of Jazz by Hasmick Promotions. Catalogue no: **LPJT 34**

**KING PORTER STOMP Vol. 1**
**Album:** Released '88, on Joker (USA) by Lifetime Records (USA). Catalogue no: **SM 3971**
**Cass:** Released Jun '86, on Saville by Conifer Records. Catalogue no: **CSVL 176**
**CD:** Released Oct '87, on Dance Band Days by Prism Leisure. Catalogue no: **DBCD 02**
**Cass:** Released Jun '86, on Dance Band Days by Prism Leisure. Catalogue no: **DBDC 02**
**Album:** Released Jun '86, on Saville by Conifer Records. Catalogue no: **SVL 176**
**CD:** Released Oct '87, on Saville by Conifer Records. Catalogue no: **CDSVL 176**
**Album:** Released Jun '86, on Dance Band Days by Prism Leisure. Catalogue no: **DBD 02**

**LEGENDARY PERFORMER, A**
Tracks: / Don't be that way / One o'clock jump / Loch Lomond / After you've gone / Sing, sing, sing / Stompin' at the savoy / Goodnight my love / King Porter stomp / Avalon / And the angels sing / Bei mir bist du schon / Goodbye.
**Album:** Released '79, on RCA by BMG Records (UK). Deleted '84. Catalogue no: **PL 12470**
**Cass:** Released '79, on RCA by BMG Records (UK). Deleted '84. Catalogue no: **PK 12470**

**LET'S DANCE (Goodman, Benny & His Orchestra)**
Tracks: / Blue Hawaii / Vieni, vieni / All of me / Yam, The / Moten swing / Clap hands, here comes Charlie / Sly mon-

goose / Hot foot shuffle / Hold tight / Hartford stomp / Trees / Begin the beguine / Let's dance / I know that you know.
Note: Recorded between 1937 and 1942.
**Cass:** Released Jan '89, on Music Masters by Music Masters Records. Catalogue no: **MMC 40112 Y**
**Album:** Released Apr '81, on Jazz Live (Italy) Catalogue no: **BLJ 8013**
**Album:** Released Jan '89, on Music Masters by Music Masters Records. Catalogue no: **MM 20112 Z**
**CD:** Released Jan '89, on Music Masters by Music Masters Records. Catalogue no: **MM 60112 X**
**Cass:** Released Jun '84, on EMI (Europe) by EMI Records. Catalogue no: **2 M 256 64869**
**Album:** Released Jun '84, on EMI (Europe) by EMI Records. Catalogue no: **2 M 056 64869**
**CD:** Released Sep '89, on Big Band Era Catalogue no: **2601792**

**LIVE AT BASIN STREET (Benny Goodman vol 2)**
Tracks: / Let's dance / Memories of you / Air mail special.
**CD:** Released Jan '89, on Music Masters by Music Masters Records. Catalogue no: **CIJ 60156 Z**
**Cass:** Released Jan '89, on Music Masters by Music Masters Records. Catalogue no: **CIJ 20156 F**
**Album:** Released Jan '89, on Music Masters by Music Masters Records. Catalogue no: **CIJ 40156 A**

**LIVE AT CARNEGIE HALL (40th Anniversary concert)**
Tracks: / Let's Dance / I've found a new baby / Send in the clowns / Loch Lomond / Stardust / I love a piano / Roll 'em / King Porter stomp / Rocky raccoon / Yesterday / That's a plenty / How high the moon / Moonglow / Oh lady be good / Jersey bounce / Someone to watch over me / Please don't talk about me when I'm gone / Benny Goodman Medley / Sing, Sing, Sing & Christopher columbus / Goodbye.
**CD:** Released Jun '86, on London Records by London Records Ltd. Deleted May '89. Catalogue no: **820 349.2**
**Album:** Released Feb '88, on CBS (import) by CBS Records. Catalogue no: **4509831**
**Cass:** Released Feb '88, on CBS (import) by CBS Records. Catalogue no: **4509834**

**LIVE AT THE INTERNATIONAL WORLD EXHIBITION (Brussels 1958: Unissued recordings) (Goodman, Benny & His Orchestra)**
Tracks: / Let's dance / When you're smiling / Sent for you yesterday (and here you come today) / Pennies from heaven / Going to Chicago / Soon / Who cares / Deed I do / I hadn't anyone till you / I've got you under my skin / There no fool like an old fool / Sometimes I'm happy / Oh boy I'm lucky / Song is ended, The / I'm coming Virginia / Fine romance, A / Harvard blues / If I had you / Goodbye theme.
Note: Featured vocalists Jimmy Rushing and Ethel Ennis.
**CD:** Released '89, on Magic (1) by Submarine Records. Catalogue no: **DAWE 36**
**Album:** Released '89, on Magic (1) by Submarine Records. Catalogue no: **AWE 36**
**Cass:** Released '89, on Magic (1) by Submarine Records. Catalogue no: **CAWE 36**

**LIVE IN STOCKHOLM 1970**
**CD:** Released Aug '87, on London Records by London Records Ltd. Catalogue no: **820 471-2**

**LONDON DATE**
**Album:** Released Jul '76, on Sonic Catalogue no: **SON 011**

**MANHATTAN MEMORIES**
**Cass:** Released Jan '88, on Starline (Jazz) Catalogue no: **SLC 61095**

**MEMORIAL**
Note: Unissued recordings 1943-46-61
**Cass:** Released Jul '86, on Magic (1) by Submarine Records. Catalogue no: **CAWE 23**
**Album:** Released Jul '86, on Magic (1) by Submarine Records. Catalogue no: **AWE 23**

**MEMORIES OF THE SIXTIES (Goodman, Benny & His Orchestra)**
Tracks: / You've made me so very happy / Romeo and Juliet love theme / Good morning, starshine / I'll never fall in love again / Both sides now / Watch what happens / Monday, Monday / Bluesette / Aquarius / Up, up and away / Spinning wheel / Windy.
**Cass:** Released Mar '82, Catalogue no: **AJKL 1038**
**Album:** Released Mar '82, on Bulldog Records by President Records. Catalogue no: **BDL 1038**

**MORE OF THE FABULOUS FIFTIES**
**Album:** Released Aug '79, on Giants of Jazz by Hasmick Promotions. Catalogue no: **GOJ 1011**

**NIGHT WITH BENNY GOODMAN, A**
Tracks: / Blue skies / With all my heart / Walk, Jenny, walk / Rosetta / Bugle call rag / Thanks a million / Truckin' / Alamo, The / Eeny meeny miney mo / Madhouse.
**Album:** Released Oct '86, on Jazz Live (Italy) Catalogue no: **BLJ 8026**

**O'CLOCK JUMP (Vol. 2)**
**Album:** Released '88, on Joker (USA) by Lifetime Records (USA). Catalogue no: **SM 3972**

**OH LADY BE GOOD (The alternate Goodman, Vol 12)**
**Album:** Released May '86, on Nostalgia by Mainline Records. Catalogue no: **NOST 7654**

**OH MR GOODMAN**
**Cass:** Released Oct '84, on Swing House by Submarine Records. Catalogue no: **CSWH 3**
**Album:** Released Apr '79, on Swing House by Submarine Records. Catalogue no: **SWH 3**

**ORCHESTRAS AND GROUPS**
Tracks: / Poor butterfly / Avalon / It's all right with me / Whispering / Diga diga doo / Where or when / I got rhythm / These foolish things / That's a plenty / Slipped disc / After you've gone / Body and soul / China boy / I can't give you anything but love / Sheik of Araby, The / There'll be some changes made / I've found a new baby.
Note: Personnel feature: Russ Freeman, Bobby Hackett, Lionel Hampton, Zoot Sims, Gene Krupa. Teddy Wilson, Barney Kessel, Jess Stacey, Andre Previn. Recorded: Hollywood, New York and Washington, 1958-1963.
**Album:** Released Apr '81, on Rarities Catalogue no: **RARITIES 30**

**ORIGINAL SOUNDS OF THE SWING ERA**
**Album:** Released '83, on RCA (Germany) Catalogue no: **CL 05515**
**Album:** Released Sep '82, on Conifer Deleted Jan '88. Catalogue no: **26 28130**

**PERMANENT GOODMAN-KING OF SWING (vol. 2 1939-45)**
**CD:** Released Feb '89, on Phontastic (Sweden) Catalogue no: **PHONTCD 7660**
**CD:** Released Feb '89, on Phontastic (Sweden) Catalogue no: **PHONTCD 7659**

**RARE BROADCASTING (Goodman, Benny & His Orchestra)**
Tracks: / I know that you know / Changes / Yes, we have no bananas / I never knew / Stompin' at The Savoy / Farewell blues / Pardon my love / St. Louis blues / Jingle bells / Rosetta / King Porter stomp / Stardust / If I could be with you / Poor butterfly.
Note: Benny Goodman - clarinet, Pee Wee Erwin, Nate Kazebier, Jerry Neary - trumpets, Red Ballard, Jack Lacey - trombones, Toots Mondello, Hymie Schertzer - alto saxes, Art Rollini, Dick Clark - tenor saxes, Frank Froeba - piano, Allan Reuss - guitar, Harry Goodman - bass and Gene Krupa - drums.
**Album:** Released Apr '85, on Jazz Anthology by Musidisc Records (France). Catalogue no: **JA 5151**

**REHEARSAL SESSIONS 1940**
**Album:** Released Jul '82, on Jazz Document Catalogue no: **VA 7997**

**RIFFIN' AT THE RITZ (Goodman, Benny & His Orchestra)**
Tracks: / St. Louis blues / Love me or leave me / Moon glow / Dinah / Exactly like you / Vibraphone blues / When a lady meets a gentleman down south / You're giving me a song and a dance / Organ grinder's swing / Peter Piper /

Riffin' at the Ritz / Alexander's ragtime band / Somebody loves me / Tain't no use / Bugle callrag / Jam session / Goodnight my love / Take another guess / Did you mean it? / Sweet Sue, just you.
**Cass:** Released Jul '89, on Saville by Conifer Records. Catalogue no: **CSVL 203**
**Album:** Released Jul '89, on Saville by Conifer Records. Catalogue no: **SVL 203**

**ROLL 'EM (Goodman, Benny/Sid Catlett)**
**Album:** Released '88, on Honeysuckle Rose (USA) Catalogue no: **HR 5004/5**
**Album:** Released Mar '87, on Swing House by Submarine Records. Catalogue no: **SWH 7**
**Cass:** Released Mar '87, on Swing House by Submarine Records. Catalogue no: **CSWH 7**

**ROLL 'EM VOL.1**
**Cass:** Released Feb '88, on CBS (import) by CBS Records. Catalogue no: **4600624**
**Album:** Released Feb '88, on CBS (import) by CBS Records. Catalogue no: **4600621**

**ROYAL FLUSH (The alternate Goodman, Vol 7)**
Tracks: / Everthing I love / Someone's rocking my dreamboat / Let's give love a chance / Not mine / Not a care in the world / You don't know what love is / Where or when / On the sunny side / Royal flush / When / On the sunny side of the street / Dear old Southland / At the darktown strutters' ball / Zoot suite / String of pearls / My little cousin / Ramona.
**Album:** Released '82, on Nostalgia by Mainline Records. Catalogue no: **NOST 7620**

**ROYAL FLUSH (ASTAN)**
**Album:** Released Nov '84, on Astan (USA) Catalogue no: **20085**
**Cass:** Released Nov '84, on Astan (USA) Catalogue no: **40085**

**SECOND CARNEGIE HALL JAZZ CONCERT 6 OCTOBER 1939**
**Album:** Released Aug '87, on Jazz Band by Flyright Records. Catalogue no: **EB 401**

**SELECTET (Goodman, Benny (Quintet & Sextet))**
**Album:** on Swing House by Submarine Records. Catalogue no: **SWH 17**

**SESSION (Goodman, Benny, All Stars)**
Tracks: / Go, Margot, go / Get happy / Raising the riff / Billie's bounce / Tenbone / Honeysuckle rose / Slipped disc / Breakfast feud.
**Album:** Released Mar '87, on Swing House by Submarine Records. Catalogue no: **SWH 24**
**Cass:** Released Mar '87, on Swing House by Submarine Records. Catalogue no: **CSWH 24**

**SEXTET**
**CD:** Released Feb '88, on CBS (import) by CBS Records. Catalogue no: **450 411 2**
**Album:** Released Feb '88, on CBS (import) by CBS Records. Catalogue no: **450 411 1**
**Cass:** Released Feb '88, on CBS (import) by CBS Records. Catalogue no: **450 411 4**

**SING ME A SWING SONG**
Tracks: / You forgot to remember / Walk, Jennie, walk / China boy / More than you know / All my life / Oh, lady be good / Nobody's sweetheart / Too good to be true / Sing me a swingsong (and let me dance) / I would do anything for you / These foolish things / In a sentimental mood / I've found a new baby / Swingtime in the Rockies / House hop / There's a small hotel / You turned the tables on me / Here's love in your eyes / Pick yourself up / Down South camp meeting.
**Cass:** Released Jul '88, on Saville by Conifer Records. Catalogue no: **CSVL 192**
**Album:** Released Jul '88, on Saville by Conifer Records. Catalogue no: **SVL 192**

**SING SING SING (Goodman, Benny & His Orchestra)**
Tracks: / King Porter stomp / Sometimes I'm happy / Basin Street blues / If I could be with you / Goody goody / Christopher Columbus / Sing me a swing song / I would do anything for you / These foolish things / Down south camp meeting / Bugle call rag / Goodnight my love / He ain't got rhythm / I want to be happy / Roll 'em / Thanks for the memory / Don't be that way / One o'clock jump / Ti-pi-tin / Sing, sing, sing / Goodbye.
**CD:** Released Jun '88, on Bluebird (2) by BMG Records (UK). Catalogue no: **ND 85630**

**SLIPPED DISC**
**CD:** Released May '89, on CBS (import) by CBS Records. Catalogue no: **463 337 2**
**Album:** Released May '89, on CBS (import) by CBS Records. Catalogue no: **463 337 1**
**Cass:** Released May '89, on CBS (import) by CBS Records. Catalogue no: **463 337 4**

**SMALL GROUPS 1941/45**
**CD:** Released May '89, on CBS (import) by CBS Records. Catalogue no: **463 341 2**
**Cass:** Released May '89, on CBS (import) by CBS Records. Catalogue no: **463 341 4**
**Album:** Released May '89, on CBS (import) by CBS Records. Catalogue no: **463 341 1**

**SMALL GROUPS (1947-49)**
**Album:** Released Jan '83, on Swaggie (Australia) Catalogue no: **S 1364**

**SMALL GROUPS, VOLUME 1**
Tracks: / Softly as in a morning sunrise / Umbrella man / I've found a new baby / Deep purple / Exactly like you / Pagan love song / Opus 3-4 / Chicago / Lady be good / Old-fashioned love / Memories of you / Wishing.
**Album:** Released Jan '85, on Giants of Jazz by Hasmick Promotions. Catalogue no: **GOJ 1034**

**SO RARE (Goodman, Benny & Tommy Dorsey)**
**Album:** Released '88, on Jass Catalogue no: **JA 49**

**STARS FELL ON ALABAMA (Goodman, Benny & Orchestra)**
**2 LP Set:** Released Sep '87, on Saville by Conifer Records. Catalogue no: **SVLD 005**
**Cass:** Released '88, on Saville by Conifer Records. Catalogue no: **CSVLD 005**

**STOMPIN' AT THE SAVOY**
**CD:** Released 21 Jul '89, on Jazz & Jazz Catalogue no: **CDJJ 609**
**Album:** Released 21 Jul '89, on Jazz & Jazz Catalogue no: **JJ 609**

**SWING WITH BENNY GOODMAN AND HIS ORCHESTRA**
**Cass:** Released May '85, on CBS (import) by CBS Records. Deleted Nov '87. Catalogue no: **40 21124**
**Album:** Released May '85, on CBS (import) by CBS Records. Catalogue no: **21124**

**SWINGIN' THROUGH THE YEARS**
**Album:** Released Aug '79, on Giants of Jazz by Hasmick Promotions. Catalogue no: **GOJ 1005**
**Cass:** Released Sep '88, on Giants of Jazz by Hasmick Promotions. Catalogue no: **GOJC 1005**

**SWINGS**
**Album:** Released May '85, on Pathe Marconi (France) Catalogue no: **PM 1551563**

**S'WONDERFUL SWING**
Tracks: / Seven come eleven / Great day / Lonely moments / Oh baby / Moonfaced and starry-eyed / Cu-tu-gu-ru / 'S wonderful / Linda / Clarinet a la King / Maybe you'll be there / Mahzel / Sing, sing, sing.
**Cass:** Released Jul '86, on First Heard by Submarine Records. Catalogue no: **CFH 23**
**Album:** Released Jul '86, on First Heard by Submarine Records. Catalogue no: **FH 23**

**THIS IS BENNY GOODMAN**
Tracks: / King Porter stomp / Sometimes I'm happy / When Buddha smiles / Stompin' at the Savoy / I know that you know / These foolish things / Down South camp meeting / You turned the tables on me / Moonglow / Goodnight my love / Never should have told you / Sing, sing, sing / Changes / Afraid to dream / Avalon / Sugarfoot Stomp / Don't be that way / One o'clock jump / I let a song go out of my heart / And the Angels sing.
**Album:** Released Jul '86, on RCA by BMG Records (UK). Deleted Nov '88. Catalogue no: **NL 89224**
**Cass:** Released Jul '86, on RCA by BMG Records (UK). Deleted Nov '88. Catalogue no: **NK 89224**

**THIS IS BENNY GOODMAN VOL 1**
**Album:** Released '83, on RCA (Germany) Catalogue no: **26 28035**

**THIS IS BENNY GOODMAN VOL 2**
**Album:** Released '83, on RCA (Germany) Catalogue no: **26 28040**

**TOGETHER AGAIN (Quartet reunion)**
Tracks: / Who cares / Dearest / Seven come eleven / I've found a new baby / Somebody loves me / I'll get by / Say it isn't so / Runnin' wild / I got it bad and that ain't good / Four once more.
**Cass:** Released '85, on RCA by BMG Records (UK). Deleted Jul '89. Catalogue no: **NK 89304**
**Album:** Released '85, on RCA by BMG Records (UK). Catalogue no: **NL 89304**
**CD:** Released '88, on Bluebird (2) by BMG Records (UK). Catalogue no: **ND 86283**

**UNFORGETTABLE BENNY GOODMAN**
**Album:** Released '88, on Unforgettable by Castle Communications Records. Catalogue no: **UNLP 018**
**Album:** Released '88, on Unforgettable by Castle Communications Records. Catalogue no: **UNMC 018**

**UNHEARD BENNY GOODMAN, THE - VOL 7 (1941-1942)**
**Album:** Released Jan '87, on Blu-Disc (USA). Catalogue no: **T 1014**

**UNHEARD BENNY GOODMAN, THE - VOL 8 (1936-1955)**
**Album:** Released Jan '87, on Blu-Disc (USA). Catalogue no: **T 1015**

**UNHEARD BENNY GOODMAN, THE - VOL 9 (1947-1955)**
**Album:** Released Jan '87, on Blu-Disc (USA). Catalogue no: **T 1016**

**UNISSUED RADIO MATERIAL (1943) (Goodman, Benny & His Orchestra)**
Tracks: / Sugar foot stomp / Sweet Georgia Brown / Mission to Moscow / You're driving me crazy / Henderson stomp / Do nothing till you hear from me / Lady be good / Don't be that way / Stealin' apples / I'm just wild about Harry / Minnie's in the money / I'm here / Honeysuckle rose / Seven come eleven.
**Album:** Released Apr '81, on Queendisc (Italy) Catalogue no: **QU 042**

**V DISCS 1943/44**
**Album:** Released Mar '87, on Jazz Society Catalogue no: **AA 509**

**VOL 3 - ALL THE CATS JOINED IN**
Tracks: / Not mine / You're easy to dance with / Why don't you do right? / Mission to Moscow / Fascinating rhythm / Rattle and roll / All the cats join in / Fly by night / Darktown strutters' ball / Six flats unfurnished / After you've gone / Clarinade / Lucky (you're right, I'm wrong) / Swing angel / Oh, baby / Put that kiss back where you found it.
**CD:** Released Apr '89, on CBS (import) by CBS Records. Catalogue no: **461100-2**
**Album:** Released Apr '89, on CBS (import) by CBS Records. Catalogue no: **461100-1**
**Cass:** Released Apr '89, on CBS (import) by CBS Records. Catalogue no: **461100-4**

**WAR YEARS, 1943/44/45**
Tracks: / Stealin' apples / After you've gone / Three little words / Minnie's in the money / I've found a new baby / Mission to Moscow / Mr. Five by five / Gotta be this or that / Seven come eleven / Frenesi / Every time / Downhearted blues / Airmail special / World is waiting for the sunrise, The.
Note: Johnny Dee, Frank Berardi, Mickey Mangano, Yank Lawson, Roy Eldridge, Mickey McMickle - trumpets; Bill Harris, Al Mastren, Vernon Brown, Mard Silloway - trombones; Benny Goodman - clarinet; Heinie Beau, Eddie Ross, Hymie Schertzer, Reggie Merrill - alto saxes; Al Klink, Jack Simms, Art Rollini, Wolfe Tayne - tenor saxes; Eddie Beau, Ernie Carceres - baritone saxes; Teddy Wilson - piano; Jess Stacy, Allan Reuss, Tommy Kay - guitars.
**Album:** Released Apr '85, on Jazz Anthology by Musidisc Records (France). Catalogue no: **JA 5226**

**WAR YEARS, THE (1942-45)**
**Album:** Released '89, on Jazz Society Catalogue no: **AA 510**

**WORLD IS WAITING FOR THE SUNRISE, THE**
**CD:** Released Jun '88, on Spectrum (1) Catalogue no: **U 4026**

**YALE ARCHIVES VOL.1**
Tracks: / Sweet Georgia Brown (live) / Macedonia lullaby / Soft lights and sweet music / Broadway / Marching and swinging (live) / Batunga train / Cherokee / Slipped disc (live) / Diga diga doo / Lullaby in rhythm (live) / Blue room.
**CD:** Released Nov '89, on Limelight Catalogue no: **820 802-2**

**YALE ARCHIVES VOL.2**
Tracks: / Let's dance / Honeysuckle Rose / Runnin' wild / Mean to me / Memories of you / Stompin' at the Savoy / Blue and sentimental / One o'clock jump / Ive found a new baby / Stairway to the stars / Body and soul / Air mail special / Nice work if you can get it / Sing, sing, sing / Goodbye.
**CD:** Released Nov '89, on Limelight Catalogue no: **820 803-2**

**YALE UNIVERSITY LIBRARY TAPES**
**CD:** Released '89, on Music Masters by Music Masters Records. Catalogue no: **CIJ 60201**

## Goodson, Ida

**IDA GOODSON SINGS AND PLAYS CHURCH MUSIC**
**Album:** Released Jan '87, on Storyville by Storyville Records AB. Deleted '88. Catalogue no: **CLPS 1015**

## Goofus Five

**GOOFUS FIVE 1924-5, THE**
**Album:** on Fountain by Retrieval Records. Catalogue no: **FJ 118**

## Gordon, Dexter

**Biographical details:** A doctor's son, he left school in 1940 and joined Lionel

Dexter Gordon

Hampton's big band, in 1945 he played with Billy Eckstine. In 1947 he recorded for the Dial label in Los Angeles; *The Chase* (with Wardell Gray) and *The Duel* (with Teddy Edwards), among the most exciting records of their era, outsold even Charlie Parker, to become the biggest hits for Dial (since re-released on Spotlite UK). He freelanced, and led various combos, covering rhythm'n'blues, jazz, rock'n'roll, and some styles beyond category. His sextet backed Helen Humes in 1950 (tracks re-released on Savoy), and he was one of the first to play bop on the tenor sax, developing a beautiful ballad style with subtle tonal experimentation. He lived in Europe from 1962-76, being a profound influence on Sonny Rollins and John Coltrane, but wider fame came in the 1960s with the success of his albums on Blue Note. He had an acting/playing role in a production of *The connnection* in 1960, and received rave reviews (and an Oscar nomination) for his part in Bertrand Tavernier's 1986 film *Round midnight*. Dale Turner was based on Bud Powell and Lester Young, but Gordon played his naturalistic self - not only a great American musician but a great American actor. (Donald Clarke, 1989).

**AFTER HOURS**
**CD:** Released '88, on Steeplechase (USA) Catalogue no: **SCCD 31224**

**AFTER MIDNIGHT**
**CD:** Released Jul '88, on Steeplechase (USA) Catalogue no: **SCCD 31226**
**Album:** Released Jul '88, on Steeplechase (USA) Catalogue no: **SCS 1226**

**BEST OF DEXTER GORDON (Blue Note years)**
Tracks: / It's you or no one / Society red / Smile / Cheese cake / Three o'clock in the morning / Soy califa / Don't explain / Tanya (CD only.).
**CD:** Released Dec '88, on Blue Note by EMI Records. Catalogue no: **BNZ 142**
**Album:** Released Dec '88, on Blue Note by EMI Records. Catalogue no: **B1 91139**
**CD:** Released Dec '88, on Blue Note by EMI Records. Catalogue no: **CDP 791 139 2**

**BLUES AND BALLADS**
**Album:** Released '87, on Sonet by Sonet Records. Catalogue no: **SNTF 639**

**BLUES WALK**
Tracks: / Like someone in love / Body and soul / There will never be another you / Blues walk (loose walk).
**Album:** Released Sep '85, on Black Lion Catalogue no: **BLP 30157**

**BODY AND SOUL**
**Album:** Released Feb '89, on Black Lion Catalogue no: **BLP 60118**

**BOTH SIDES OF MIDNIGHT**
**Album:** Released Dec '88, on Black Lion Catalogue no: **BLP 60103**
**CD:** Released Dec '88, on Black Lion Catalogue no: **BLCD 760103**

**BOUNCIN' WITH DEX**
**Album:** Released Mar '77, on Steeplechase (USA) Catalogue no: **SCS 1060**

**CHARLIE PARKER MEMORIAL (Gordon, Dexter & Lee Konitz)**
Tracks: / Billie's bounce / Just friends / Scrapple from the apple / Summertime / Orinthology / Groovin' high / Yardbird suite / Now's the time / Parker's mood / Disappointed / Oh lady be good.
**Cass:** Released Jun '88, on Chess by Vogue Records. Catalogue no: **GCHK 2-6026**
**2 LP Set:** Released Jun '88, on Chess by Vogue Records. Catalogue no: **GCH 2-6026**

**CHASE, THE**
Tracks: / Chase, The / Mischievous lady / Lullaby in rhythm / Horning in / Chromatic aberration / Talk of the town / Blues bikini / Ghost of a chance / Sweet and lovely / Duel.
Note: With Wardell Gray, Teddy Edwards, Jimmy Rowles, Melba Liston, Jimmy Bunn.
**Album:** Released '83, on Spotlite by Spotlite Records. Catalogue no: **SPJ 130**

**CLUBHOUSE**
Tracks: / Hanky panky / I'm a fool to want you / Devilette / Clubhouse / Jodi / Lady Iris B.
**Album:** Released Jun '80, on Liberty by EMI Records. Catalogue no: **LBR 1022**

**DADDY PLAYS THE HORN**
Tracks: / Daddy plays the horn / Confirmation / Number four / Darn that dream / Autumn in New York / You can depend on me.
**CD:** Released Jan '87, on Charly by Charly Records. Catalogue no: **CDCHARLY 57**
**Album:** Released '83, on Affinity by Charly Records. Catalogue no: **AFF 103**

**DAY IN COPENHAGEN, A (Gordon, Dexter & Slide Hampton)**
Tracks: / My blues / You don't know what love is / New thing, A / What's new / Shadow of your smile / Day in Vienna, A.
Note: Recorded in 1969 this was the first Dexter album to be arranged around the frame of three horns, drafted by Slide Hampton. Features three Slide Hampton original compositions and three standards. Dexter Gordon has received much acclaim in recent months for his performance in the film 'Around Midnight' in which he starred.
**CD:** Released May '87, on MPS Jazz (Germany) Catalogue no: **821 288-2**

**DEXTER BLOWS HOT AND COLD**
Tracks: / Silver plated / Cry me a river / Rhythm mad / Don't worry 'bout me / I hear music / Bonna Rue / I should care / Blowin' for Dootsie / Tenderly.
Note: With Carl Perkins / Jimmy Robinson / Chuck Thompson / Leroy Vinnegar. Tracks include: *Cry me a river / Silver plated / Don't worry about me / Tenderly / Blowin for dootsie* etc.
**Album:** Released Feb '89, on Boplicity by Ace Records. Catalogue no: **BOP 006**
**CD:** Released Feb '89, on Boplicity by Ace Records. Catalogue no: **CDBOP 006**

**DEXTER CALLING**
Tracks: / Soul sister / I want more / End of a love affair, The / Clear the dex / Ernie's tune / Smile / Landslide / Modal mood.
**CD:** Released Jun '87, on Blue Note by EMI Records. Catalogue no: **CDP 746 544 2**
**CD:** Released Jun '87, on Blue Note by EMI Records. Catalogue no: **BNZ 36**

**DEXTER GORDON QUARTET (Gordon, Dexter Quartet)**
**Album:** Released '88, on Zeta Catalogue no: **ZET 705**

**DEXTER: THE DIAL SESSIONS**
**Album:** Released Jan '88, on Storyville by Storyville Records AB. Catalogue no: **SLP 814**

**DOIN' ALRIGHT**
Tracks: / I was doin' alright / You've changed / For regulars only / Society Red / It's you or no one / For regulars only (alternate version) / I want more (Not on album.).
Note: With Freddie Hubbard and the Horace Parlan Trio.
**CD:** Released Nov '88, on Blue Note by EMI Records. Catalogue no: **BNZ 113**
**CD:** Released Nov '88, on Blue Note by EMI Records. Catalogue no: **CDP 784 077 2**
**Cass:** Released Apr '87, on Blue Note by EMI Records. Deleted Jan '88. Catalogue no: **4BN 84077**
**Album:** Released '79, on Blue Note by EMI Records. Deleted '84. Catalogue no: **BNS40014**
**Album:** Released Aug '85, on Blue Note by EMI Records. Catalogue no: **BST 84077**

**FOR ALL WE KNOW**
**Cass:** Released May '88, on Jazz Life Catalogue no: **2173232**
**Album:** Released May '88, on Jazz Life Catalogue no: **2273232**
**CD:** Released May '88, on Jazz Life Catalogue no: **2473232**

**GETTIN' AROUND**
Tracks: / Manha de carnaval / Who can I turn to? / Heartaches / Shiny stockings / Everybody's somebody's fool / Le coiffeur / Very saxily yours / Flick of a trick.
Note: * Extra tracks on CD only.
**Album:** Released Jul '89, on Blue Note by EMI Records. Catalogue no: **BST 84204**
**CD:** Released Jun '87, on Blue Note by EMI Records. Deleted Jan '90. Catalogue no: **CDP 746 681 2**
**CD:** Released Jun '87, on Blue Note by EMI Records. Deleted Jan '90. Catalogue no: **BNZ 32**

**GO (See panel on next page)**
Tracks: / Cheesecake / Guess I'll hang my tears out to dry / Second balcony jump / Love for sale / Where are you? / Three o'clock in the morning.
Note: Dexter Gordon - tenor sax, Sonny

**Go - Dexter Gordon (Blue Note)**

Clark - piano, Butch Warren - bass, Billy Higgins - drums.
**CD:** Released Mar '87, on Blue Note by EMI Records. Catalogue no: **BNZ 33**
**CD:** Released Mar '87, on EMI by EMI Records. Catalogue no: **CDP 746 094 2**
**Album:** Released Jul '89, on Blue Note by EMI Records. Catalogue no: **BST 84112**
**Album:** Released '79, on Blue Note by EMI Records. Deleted '84. Catalogue no: **BNS 40032**
**Cass:** Released Sep '87, on Blue Note by EMI Records. Deleted Jun '88. Catalogue no: **4BN 84112**

**GOTHAM CITY**
Tracks: / Hi-fly / Nightingale sang in Berkeley Square, A / Blues walk (loose walk) / Gotham City.
**Album:** Released Feb '81, on CBS by CBS Records. Catalogue no: **CBS 84825**

**GREAT ENCOUNTERS**
Tracks: / Blues up and down / Cake / Diggin in' / Ruby, my dear / It's only a paper moon.
**Album:** Released May '80, on CBS by CBS Records. Deleted '85. Catalogue no: **83643**

**I WANT MORE**
**Album:** Released May '81, on Steeplechase (USA) Catalogue no: **SCC 6015**

**LIVE AT THE AMSTERDAM PARADISO**
Tracks: / Fried bananas / What's new / Good bait / Rhythm-a-ning / Willow weep for me / Junior / Scrapple from the apple / Closing announcement / Introduction.
**CD:** Released Sep '89, on Affinity by Charly Records. Catalogue no: **CDAFF 751**
**2 LP Set:** Released Aug '79, on Affinity by Charly Records. Deleted '88. Catalogue no: **AFFD 27**

**LIVE: DEXTER GORDON AND SONNY GREY (With the Georges Arvanitas Trio) (Gordon, Dexter & Sonny Grey)**
Tracks: / Caloon blues / Fried bananas / No matter how / Dexter leaps out.
**Album:** Released '83, on Spotlite by Spotlite Records. Catalogue no: **SPJ LP 10**

**LONG TALL DEXTER**
Tracks: / Blow Mr. Dexter / Dexter's deck / Dexter's cuttin' out / Dexter's minor mad / Long tall Dexter / Dexter rides again / I can't escape from you / Dexter digs in / Settin' the pace / So easy so easy / Dexter's riff / Dexter's mood / Dextrose index / Dextivity / Wee dot / Lion roars / After hours bop.
**Album:** Released Mar '85, on Savoy Jazz (USA) by Malaco Records (USA). Catalogue no: **SJL 2211**

**MANHATTAN SYMPHONIE**
Tracks: / As time goes by / Moment's notice / Tanya / Body and soul / LTD.
**Album:** Released Feb '79, on CBS by CBS Records. Deleted Feb '84. Catalogue no: **CBS 83184**

**MONTMARTRE COLLECTION, VOL 1**
Tracks: / Sonnymoon for two / For all we know / Devilette / Doxy.
**Album:** Released Jan '85, on Black Lion Catalogue no: **BLP 30102**

**MORE THAN YOU KNOW**
**Album:** Released Jul '88, on Steeplechase (USA) Catalogue no: **SCS 1030**
**CD:** Released Jul '88, on Steeplechase (USA) Catalogue no: **SCCD 31030**
**Cass:** Released Jul '88, on Steeplechase (USA) Catalogue no: **SCM 51030**

**MOVE**
Tracks: / Move / As time goes by / Stranger in town / Yardbird suite / Guilty / Mischievous lady / Lullaby in rhythm / Chromatic aberration / Talk of the town / Ghost of a chance / Sweet and lovely / Blues in Teddy's flat / Intersection / Mop mop / Stardust.
**Album:** Released '83, on Spotlite by Spotlite Records. Catalogue no: **SPJ 133**

**MPS JAZZ TIME VOL 12 (Gordon, Dexter & Slide Hampton)**
Tracks: / My blues / You don't know what love is / New thing / What's new / Shadow of your smile / Day in Vienna.
**Album:** Released '79, on MPS Jazz Deleted '84. Catalogue no: **5C 064 60411**

**NIGHTS AT THE KEYSTONE**
Tracks: / Sophisticated lady / It's you or no one / Antabus / Easy Living / Tangerine / More than you know / Come rain or come shine.
Note: Double Album, Double Cassette. Dexter Gordon released a string on the Blue Note label in the sixties. Recorded in 1978 and 1979 at San Francisco's famous Keystone Korner, this live 2-record set captures the Dexter Gordon Quartet in top form responding to the warm crown with incredible musicianship. The quartet features George Cable on piano, Rufus Reid on bass and Eddie Gladden on drums, andthis album will be the first release from Dexter Gordon for a number of years.
**Cass set:** Released Dec '85, on Blue Note by EMI Records. Catalogue no: **TCBABB 85112**
**2 LP Set:** Released Jul '89, on Blue Note by EMI Records. Catalogue no: **BABB 85112**

**ONE FLIGHT UP**
Tracks: / Tanya / Coppin' the haven / Darn that dream / King Neptune (CD only.).
Note: The tenor saxophone pioneer Dexter Gordon is accompanied by Donald Byrd and Kenny Drew in this, his second Paris session for Blue Note.The three performances are lengthy and swinging with a special aura of intimacy.This album introduced Byrd's *Tanya* which remains in Gordon's repertoire to this day.
**CD:** Released Jun '89, on Blue Note by EMI Records. Deleted Jan '90. Catalogue no: **BNZ 195**
**Album:** Released Dec '85, on Blue Note by EMI Records. Catalogue no: **BST 84176**
**CD:** Released Jun '89, on Blue Note by EMI Records. Deleted Jan '90. Catalogue no: **CDP 784 176 2**

**OTHER SIDE OF ROUND MIDNIGHT, THE**
Tracks: / Round midnight / Berangere's nightmare / Call sheet blues / What is this thing called love.. / Tivoli / Society red / As time goes by / It's only a paper moon.
**CD:** Released Mar '87, on Blue Note by EMI Records. Catalogue no: **BNZ 35**
**CD:** Released Mar '87, on Blue Note by EMI Records. Catalogue no: **CDP 746 397 2**
**Album:** Released Dec '86, on Blue Note by EMI Records. Catalogue no: **BT 85135**

**OUR MAN IN PARIS**
Tracks: / Scrapple from the apple / Willow weep for me / Stairway to the stars / Night in Tunisia / Our love is here to stay / Like someone to love / Broadway.
**Cass:** Released Sep '87, on Blue Note by EMI Records. Deleted Jan '88. Catalogue no: **4BN 84146**
**CD:** Released Jun '87, on Blue Note by EMI Records. Catalogue no: **CDP 746 394 2**
**Album:** Released Nov '84, on Blue Note by EMI Records. Catalogue no: **BST 84146**
**CD:** Released Jun '87, on Blue Note by EMI Records. Catalogue no: **BNZ 34**

**POWER**
Tracks: / Montmartre / Sticky wicket / Lady bird / Rainbow people / Stanley the steamer / Those were the days / Fried bananas / Meditaion / Boston Bernie.
**2 LP Set:** Released '79, on Prestige Deleted '84. Catalogue no: **PR 24087**

**SAVOY MASTER TAKES 1945-47**
Tracks: / Dexter's cuttin' out / Dexter's Minor Mad / Long tall Dexter / Dexter rides again / I can't escape from you / Dexter digs in / Settin'the pace / So easy / Dexter's riff / Dexter's mood / Dextrose / Index / Dextivity / Blow Mr. Dexter / Dexter's Deck.
**Album:** Released Mar '86, on RCA by BMG Records (UK). Catalogue no: **WL 70814**
**Cass:** Released Mar '86, on RCA by BMG Records (UK). Deleted Nov '89. Catalogue no: **WK 70814**

**SOMETHING DIFFERENT**
**CD:** Released Jul '88, on Steeplechase (USA) Catalogue no: **SCCD 31136**
**Album:** Released Jul '88, on Steeplechase (USA) Catalogue no: **SCS 1136**

**SOPHISTICATED GIANT**
Tracks: / Laura / Moontrane, The / Red top / Fried bananas / You're blase / How insensitive.
**Album:** Released Jul '87, on CBS by CBS Records. Deleted Jan '89. Catalogue no: **450316 1**
**Cass:** Released Jul '87, on CBS by CBS Records. Deleted Jan '89. Catalogue no: **450316 4**

**STRINGS AND THINGS**
**Album:** Released Jun '81, on Steeplechase (USA) Catalogue no: **SCS 1145**

**SWINGIN' AFFAIR, A**
Tracks: / Soy Califas / Don't explain / You stepped out of a dream / Backbone, The / Until the real thing comes along, (It will have to do) / McSplivens.
**CD:** Released Apr '88, on Blue Note by EMI Records. Catalogue no: **BNZ 31**
**CD:** Released Apr '88, on Blue Note by EMI Records. Catalogue no: **CDP 784 133 2**
**Album:** Released Sep '84, on Blue Note by EMI Records. Deleted '87. Catalogue no: **BST 84133**

**SWISS NIGHTS VOL.3**
**Album:** Released Sep '79, on Steeplechase (USA) Catalogue no: **SCS 1110**

**TEDDY WILSON**
**CD:** Released Jul '89, on Cleo Catalogue no: **CLCD 5025**

**CHASE, THE (WITH WARDELL GRAY) (see also under Gray, Wardell) (Gordon, Dexter & Wardell Gray)**
**CD:** Released Mar '90, on Giants of Jazz by Hasmick Promotions. Catalogue no: **GOJCD53064**

**TRUE BLUE (Gordon, Dexter & Al Cohn)**
**CD:** Released '88, on Xanadu Catalogue no: **FDC 5158**

## Gospel At Christmas

**GOSPEL AT CHRISTMAS (Various artists)**
**Album:** Released '88, on Malaco Gospel by Malaco Records (UK). Catalogue no: **MAL 04404**

## Gospel Collection

**GOSPEL COLLECTION Gospels and spirituals (Various artists)**
Tracks: / Take my mother home: *Belafonte, Harry* / I'm glad salvation: *Jackson, Mahalia* / Gospel train: *Golden Gate Quartet* / Every time I feel the spirit: *Robeson, Paul* / Lord's Prayer, The: *Vaughan, Sarah* / I believe: *Jackson, Mahalia* / What more can my Jesus do?: *Mitchell's Christian Singers* / I'm on my way: *Golden Gate Quartet* / Motherless child: *Vaughan, Sarah* / Move on up a little higher: *Jackson, Mahalia* / Didn't my Lord deliver Daniel?: *Robeson, Paul* / My mother died a-shoutin': *Mitchell's Christian Singers* / Go tell it on the mountain: *Jackson, Mahalia* / Rock Daniel: *Tharpe, Sister Rosetta.*
**CD:** Released Sep '88, on Deja Vu Catalogue no: **DVCD 2116**
**Album:** Released Dec '87, on Deja Vu Catalogue no: **DVLP 2116**
**Cass:** Released Dec '87, on Deja Vu Catalogue no: **DVMC 2116**

## Gospel Piano ...

**GOSPEL PIANO AND GUITAR CLASSICS (Various artists)**
**Album:** Released Sep '87, on Earl Archives Catalogue no: **BD 2003**

## Gospel Ship

**GOSPEL SHIP (Various artists)**
Tracks: / Amazing Grace: *Various artists* (Howard Adams leading the congretation of the Thornton Regular Baptist Ch) / Poor Pilgrim: *Various artists* / Testimony: *Various artists* / Why must I wear this shroud?: *Various artists* (Congregation of the Thornton Regular Bapist Church.) / When Jesus Christ was here on Earth: *Various artists* / Old gospel ship, The: *Various artists* / When the stars begin to fall: *Various artists* / Hick's Farewell: *Various artists* / See that my grave is kept clean: *Various artists* / I am a poor way faring stranger: *Various artists* / Little family, The: *Various artists* / Jim and Me: *Various artists* / Airplane Ride, The: *Various artists* / Guide me o thou great Jehovah: *Various artists* (Ike Caudill leading the congregation of the Mount Olivet Regular Baptist) / Testimony of pioneer religion: *Various artists.*
**Album:** Released Jul '86, on New World (USA) by New World Records (USA). Catalogue no: **NW 294**

## Graham, Kenny

**CARIBBEAN SUITE/AFRO KADABRA (Graham, Kenny)**
Tracks: / Jump for Joe / Night in Tunisia / Take the 'A' train / Flamingo / Keni B'sindika / Afro-Kadabra / Mango walk / Bongo chant / Saga boy / Dance of the zombies / Wha' huppin' sah? / Tempo medio lento / Beguine / Haitian ritual.
**Album:** Released Jul '87, on Esquire by Titan Int. Prod.. Catalogue no: **ESQ 329**

**MANGO WALK (Graham, Kenny)**
**Album:** Released Apr '79, on Esquire by Titan Int. Prod.. Catalogue no: **ESQ 308**

## Grahamophones

**CHINESE LAUNDRY BLUES**
Tracks: / Chinese laundry blues / I would sooner be a crooner.
**7" Single:** Released Jul '87, on President by President Records. Catalogue no: **PT 563**

**MAD DOGS AND ENGLISHMEN**
**Cass:** Released Dec '88, on President by President Records. Catalogue no: **PTLC 1097**
**Album:** Released Dec '88, on President by President Records. Catalogue no: **PTLS 1097**
**CD:** Released Feb '89, on President by President Records. Catalogue no: **PCOM 1097**

**VO DO DO DE O DODO**
Tracks: / Vo do do de o dodo / Deep secret.
**7" Single:** Released Jul '89, on President by President Records. Catalogue no: **PT 581**

**WE'RE TOPS ON SATURDAY NIGHT**
Tracks: / Chinese laundry blues / Blue moon / We're tops on Saturday night / I would sooner be a crooner / Isn't this a lovely day / Who stole my heart away / Nobody's sweetheart / You rascal you / Stars fell on Alabama / When can I have a banana again / Room with a view / Deep purple / Puttin' on the ritz / Mr. Wu's xylophone blues.
**Cass:** Released Jun '87, on President by President Records. Catalogue no: **PTLC 1086**
**Album:** Released Jun '87, on President by President Records. Catalogue no: **PTLS 1086**

## Grand Dominion Jazz

**AIN'T NOBODY GOT THE BLUES LIKE ME**
Tracks: / Old folks at home / Ain't nobody got the blues like me / Bedelia / Snag it / Worn out blues / Panama / Yearning (just for you) / Saratoga swing / Joe Avery's piece / Trog's blues / Georgia grind.
**Album:** Released May '89, on Stomp Off (USA) Catalogue no: **SOS 1189**

**COME BACK, SWEET PAPA**
Tracks: / One sweet letter from you / Ponchatrain / Perdido St blues / Make me a pallet on the floor / Bogalusa strut / Come back, sweet papa / Friendless blues / Martha / J'ai de la fievre / Minor drag, The.
**Album:** Released '88, on Triangle by Triangle Records. Catalogue no: **T 106**

**DON'T GIVE UP THE SHIP**
**Album:** Released Nov '87, on Stomp Off (USA) Catalogue no: **SOS 1139**

**GRAND DOMINION JAZZ BAND, THE**
**Album:** Released Jun '86, on GHB by Jazzology Records (USA). Catalogue no: **GHB 174**

## Granz, Norman

**JAM SESSION NUMBER 3**
**Album:** Released Sep '81, on Verve (USA) by Polydor Ltd. Catalogue no: **2304 421**

## Grappelli, Stephane

**Biographical details:** One of the few non-USA jazz musicians to become world-famous, and with half-a-dozen others one of the very few to 'make it' on the violin. Originally spelling his name 'Grappelly', he became famous with Django Reinhardt in the Quintet of the Hot Club of France 1934-39, also playing piano on a 1937 Paris session with Django and Coleman Hawkins. He spent World War 2 in England and recorded with Reinhardt again in 1946. His unabashed romanticism, balanced by his ability to swing and his logic in improvisation were long taken for granted, but duets with Yehudi Menuhin on TV and EMI albums have ensured new fame. (Donald Clarke, 1989).

**80**
**Cass:** Released Mar '83, on Barclay (France) by Decca Records. Catalogue no: **MB 990104**
**Album:** Released Mar '83, on Barclay (France) by Decca Records. Catalogue no: **B 90104**

**AFTERNOON IN PARIS**
Tracks: / Autumn leaves / This can't be love / Time after time / Undecided / You were only passing by / Tangerine / Chicago / Manoir de mes rev / Daphne / Misty / Afternoon in Paris.
**Album:** Released May '81, on MPS Jazz Catalogue no: **MPS 68 156**
**CD:** Released May '85, on MPS Jazz (Germany) Deleted Jul '88. Catalogue no: **821 865-2**

**AT THE WINERY**
Tracks: / You are the sunshine of my life / Love for sale / Angel's camp / Willow weep for me / Chicago / Talking a chance on love / Minor swing / Let's fall in love / Just you, just me.
Note: Personnel: Stephane Grappelli - violin & electric viola / John Etheridge - guitar / Martin Taylor - guitar / Jack Sewing - bass.
**CD:** Released Jul '87, on Concord Jazz by Concord Jazz Records (USA). Catalogue no: **CCD 4139**
**CD:** Released Sep '86, on Concord Jazz by Concord Jazz Records (USA). Catalogue no: **CCD 4131**
**Album:** Released Mar '81, on Concord by Concord Jazz Records (USA). Catalogue no: **CJ 139**

**BEST OF STEPHANE GRAPPELLI**
**Cass:** Released May '88, on Black Tulip Catalogue no: **48052**
**Album:** Released '82, on Black Lion-Intercord Catalogue no: **INT 147 013**

**CONVERSATIONS**
**CD:** Released Nov '86, on Fantasy (import) by Fantasy Inc (USA). Deleted '88. Catalogue no: **FCD 6229130**

**CRAZY RHYTHM (Grappelli, Stephane & His Trio)**
**CD:** Released '86, on Vogue by Vogue Records. Catalogue no: **VG 600 102**

**FASCINATING RHYTHM**
**Album:** Released May '88, on Jazz Life Catalogue no: **26013**
**CD:** Released May '88, on Compact Collection Catalogue no: **15013**
**Cass:** Released May '88, on Jazz Life Catalogue no: **46013**

**FEELING AND FINESSE**
Tracks: / Django / Nuages / Alabamy bound / You better go now / Daphne / Le tien / Minor swing / Makin' whoopee / How about you / Soft winds.
**Album:** Released '85, on Atlantic by WEA Records. Catalogue no: **790 140-1**

**GIANTS, THE (Grappelli, Stephane & Earl Hines)**
Tracks: / Fine and dandy / Over the rainbow / Manhattan / Moonlight in Vermont / I can't get started / You took advantage of me / Sometimes I'm happy.
**Album:** Released Sep '87, on Black Lion Catalogue no: **BLP 30193**

**GOLDEN HOUR OF STEPHANE G**
**Cass:** Released Mar '78, on PRT by Castle Communications Records. Catalogue no: **ZCGH 650**

**HOMAGE TO DJANGO**
Tracks: / Sweet Sue / Tears / Avalon / Manoir de mes reves / Clopin clopant / Daphne blues / Swing guitars / Are you in the mood? / I wonder where my baby is tonight.
**CD:** Released Dec '89, on Accord (France) by Musidisc Records (France). Catalogue no: **401204**
**Cass:** Released Dec '89, on Accord (France) by Musidisc Records (France). Catalogue no: **401202**
**Album:** Released Apr '81, on Joker (USA) by Lifetime Records (USA). Catalogue no: **SM 3510**

**HOMAGE TO DJANGO, VOL 2**
Tracks: / Djangology / Sweet chorus / Swing '39 / Oriental shuffle / Minor swing / Venez donc chez moi / Nuages / I saw stars / Fantasie / Dark eyes.
**Album:** Released Apr '81, on Joker (USA) by Lifetime Records (USA). Catalogue no: **SM 3511**

**HOT CLUB DE FRANCE (Grappelli, Stephane/Django Reinhardt)**
**LP Set:** Released Jul '88, on Forlane Catalogue no: **99001**
**CD:** Released '88, on Vogue by Vogue Records. Catalogue no: **VG 651**
**CD:** Released Jul '88, on Forlane Catalogue no: **UCD 19001**
**Cass set:** Released '88, on Ditto by Pickwick Records. Catalogue no: **DTO 10245**

**I GOT RHYTHM (Grappelli, Stephane/Hot Club)**
Tracks: / Dinah / I'm confessin' / Tiger rag / Heavenly music / Someday, sweetheart / Stephane Blues / When I look at you / After you've gone / Star eyes / Stephane's tune / Don't you know I care / Sweet Sue / Jive bomber / Weep no more / My lady / Liza (all the clouds will roll away) / Three o'clock in the morning / Folks who live on the hill, The / That old black magic / Noel brings the swing / It's a hap hap happy day / I got rhythm / My heart tells me / Bluebirds in the moonlight / Oh Johnny, oh Johnny oh / I never mention your name / Oh lady be good / You made me love you / Alexander's rag time band / Playmates / In the mood / Ting a ling / Oh by jingo, oh by gee / Sheik of Araby, The / I said no / Scatterbrain / Rose room / This can't be love / I can't believe that you're in love with me / Misty / Tea for two / After you've gone.
**Album:** Released '83, on Black Lion Catalogue no: **BLP 30158**
**Cass:** Released Mar '87, on Decca by Decca International. Deleted Feb '89. Catalogue no: **RECDC 12**
**Cass:** Released '83, on Black Lion Catalogue no: **BLP 30158C**
**2 LP Set:** Released Mar '87, on Decca by Decca International. Deleted Feb '89. Catalogue no: **RECDL 12**

**I HEAR MUSIC**
Tracks: / Tea for two / Danny boy / Let's do it / Dear Ben / I hear music / Dany / Smoke gets in your eyes / Body and soul / Gary / Flowers for Kenny.
**Album:** Released Oct '80, on RCA by BMG Records (UK). Catalogue no: **INTS 5047**
**Cass:** Released Oct '80, on RCA by BMG Records (UK). Catalogue no: **INTK 5047**

**I REMEMBER DJANGO (Grappelli, Stephane/Barney Kessel)**
Tracks: / I remember Django / Honeysuckle rose / I can't get started / What a difference a day made / More than you know / Et maintenant / I found a new baby / It's only a paper moon.
Note: With the New Hot Club Quintet.
**Album:** Released Jan '85, on Black Lion Catalogue no: **BLP 30101**

**IMPROVISATIONS**
Tracks: / Body and soul / Fascinating rhythm / My funny valentine.
**2 LP Set:** Released Mar '83, on Barclay (France) by Decca Records. Catalogue no: **BARC 96069/70**

**INTIMATE**
**Cass:** Released May '88, on Jazz Life Catalogue no: **2173032**
**Album:** Released May '88, on Jazz Life Catalogue no: **2273032**
**CD:** Released May '88, on Jazz Life Catalogue no: **2473032**

**JOUE GEO GERSHWIN ET C.PORTER**
**CD:** Released Dec '85, on Musidisc by Musidisc Records (France). Catalogue no: **139 004**

**JUST ONE OF THOSE THINGS**
Tracks: / Cheek to cheek / Are you in the mood? / Just one of those things / There's a small hotel / Pent-up house / I'll remember April / Surrey with the fringe on top / I get a kick out of you / Blue moon / Them there eyes / I can't give you anything but love / How high the moon / Waltz du passe / My one and only love.
Note: Stephane Grappelli, violin (piano on *My one and only love*); Martin Taylor, electric guitar; Marc Fossett; acoustic guitar; Patrick Caratini, bass; Allan Ganley, drums; Chris Karan, tabla.
**CD:** Released Feb '88, on EMI Studio by EMI Records. Catalogue no: **CDM 769 172 2**
**Album:** Released Apr '84, on H.M.V. by EMI Records. Deleted Mar '89. Catalogue no: **EMD 143 643 1**
**Cass:** Released Apr '84, on H.M.V. by EMI Records. Catalogue no: **TCEMD 1436434**

**JUST ONE OF THOSE THINGS (BLACK LION)**
Tracks: / Just one of those things / Misty / More / Que rest et il de nos amours? / Don't get around much anymore / Them there eyes / Honeysuckle rose.
Note: Recorded live at the Montreux Jazz Festival.
**Album:** Released Sep '85, on Black Lion Catalogue no: **BI P 30152**

**LIVE IN COPENHAGEN (Grappelli, Stephane/Joe Pass)**
**CD:** Released Aug '86, on Pablo Jazz (USA) by Pablo Records (USA). Catalogue no: **J33J 20041**

**LIVE IN SAN FRANCISCO (Grappelli, Stephane & His Trio)**
Tracks: / I've got rhythm / Fascinating rhythm / Let's fall in love / Swing '42 / Honeysuckle Rose / You are the sunshine of my life / Minor swing / Here, there and everywhere / St. Louis blues / Them there eyes / After you've gone.
Note: Personnel: Stephane Grappelli - violin / Martin Taylor - electric guitar / Diz Disley - acoustic guitar / Jack Sewing - bass.
**Album:** Released Jul '87, on Black Hawk (USA) by Blackhawk Records (USA). Catalogue no: **BKH 51601**

**LIVE IN SAN FRANCISCO (VIDEO)**
Tracks: / I've got rhythm / Fascinating rhythm / Let's fall in love / Swing '42 / Honeysuckle rose / You are the sunshine of my life / Minor swing / Here, there and everywhere / St. Louis blues / Tea for two / Them there eyes / After you've gone / Sweet Georgia Brown.
Note: Running time: 60 minutes.
**VHS:** Released Feb '90, on Castle Hendring Video by Castle Communications Records. Catalogue no: **HEN 2 192**

**MAGIC OF STEPHANE GRAPPELLI, THE**
**Cass:** Released Jun '85, on Spot by Pickwick Records. Catalogue no: **SPC 8563**
**Album:** Released Jun '85, on Spot by Pickwick Records. Catalogue no: **SPR 8563**

**MEETS THE RHYTHM SECTION**
Tracks: / Love for sale / Perugia / Two cute / Fascinating rhythm / Parisian thoroughfare / Improvisation on prelude in E minor / Wave / Hallelujah.
**Album:** Released Sep '87, on Black Lion Catalogue no: **BLP 30183**

**NORWEGIAN WOOD (Grappelli, Stephane/Elena Duran)**
Tracks: / Yesterday / All my loving / Eleanor Rigby / Norwegian wood / Can't buy me love / Here, there and everywhere / Michelle / Hey Jude / Long and winding road, The / Hard day's night, A.
**Album:** Released Oct '81, on RCA by BMG Records (UK). Catalogue no: **RCALP 6007**
**Cass:** Released Oct '81, on RCA by BMG Records (UK). Catalogue no: **RCAK 6007**

**PARIS ENCOUNTER (Grappelli, Stephane/Garry Burton)**
Tracks: / Daphne / Blue in green / Falling grace / Here's that rainy day / Coquette / Sweet rain / Night has a thousand eyes, The / Arpege / Eiderdown.
**Album:** Released '87, on Atlantic by WEA Records. Catalogue no: **K 40378**

**PARISIAN THOROUGHFARE**
Tracks: / Love for sale / Perugia / Two cute / Parisian thoroughfare / Improvisation on prelude in E minor / Wave / Hallelujah.
**Album:** Released Jul '88, on Black Lion Catalogue no: **BLM 51502**

**PLAYS GERSHWIN**
**Cass:** Released Dec '89, on Accord (France) by Musidisc Records (France). Catalogue no: **402052**
**CD:** Released Dec '89, on Accord (France) by Musidisc Records (France). Catalogue no: **402054**

**PLAYS GERSHWIN AND PORTER**
**CD:** Released '88, on Accord (France) by Musidisc Records (France). Catalogue no: **MCD 139 004**

**PLAYS JEROME KERN (Grappelli, Stephane & His Trio)**
Note: Legendary jazz violinist Stephane Grapelli's first album for GRP celebrates the music of Jerome Kern. CD contains 2 extra tracks.
**CD:** Released May '87, on GRP by GRP Records (USA). Catalogue no: **GRD 9542**
**Cass:** Released May '87, on GRP by GRP Records (USA). Catalogue no: **GRPM 91032**
**Album:** Released May '87, on GRP by GRP Records (USA). Catalogue no: **GRP 91032**

**QUINTETTE DU HOT CLUB DE FRANCE (Grappelli, Stephane / Django Reinhardt)**
**CD:** Released Jan '86, on Vogue by Vogue Records. Catalogue no: **VGCD 60070**

**REUNION, THE (Grappelli, Stephane/George Shearing)**
Tracks: / I'm coming Virginia / Time after time / La chanson de rue / Too marvellous for words / It don't mean a thing / Makin' whoopee / After you've gone / Flamingo / Star eyes / Folks who live on the hill, The.
**CD:** Released Nov '84, on Verve Deleted Jul '88. Catalogue no: **821 868-2**
**Album:** Released Apr '85, on MPS Jazz (Germany) Catalogue no: **821 868-1**
**Album:** Released May '81, on MPS Jazz Catalogue no: **MPS 68 162**

**STARDUST**
**Album:** Released Feb '89, on Black Lion Catalogue no: **BLP 60117**

**STEFF AND SLAM (Grappelli, Stephane & His Trio)**
Note: With Slam Stewart - bass.
**CD:** Released '86, on Black & Blue (1) by Black & Blue Records. Catalogue no: **233 076**

**STEPHANE GRAPPELLI**
**Album:** Released '88, on Black Lion Catalogue no: **BLP 60132**
**CD:** Released Jul '89, on Cleo Catalogue no: **CLCD 5021**
**CD:** Released '88, on Black Lion Catalogue no: **BLCD7 60132**
**CD:** Released Jul '87, on MPS Jazz Catalogue no: **831 370-2**
**Cass:** Released Jun '87, on MPS Jazz Catalogue no: **831 370-4**

**STEPHANE GRAPPELLI 1973**
Tracks: / It don't mean a thing / I've got the world on a string / What are you doing the rest of your life? / Birth of the blues / Opportunity / Just a gigolo / Didn't we? / Crazy rhythm / It might as well be spring / Emotion / Three little words / Avalon.
**Album:** Released '73, on Pye Catalogue no: **NSPL 18403**

**STEPHANE GRAPPELLI COLLECTION**
**CD:** Released Oct '89, on Collection by K-Tel Records. Catalogue no: **OR 0082**

**STEPHANE GRAPPELLI IN CONCERT**
Tracks: / Just one of those things / Misty / More / Que reste t'il de nos amours / Don't get around much anymore / Them there eyes / Honeysuckle rose.
**Album:** Released Jun '80, on Black Lion Deleted '85. Catalogue no: **BLP 12183**

**STEPHANE GRAPPELLI LIVE AT THE CARNEGIE HALL**
Tracks: / I can't give you anything but love / As time goes by / Crazy rhythm / Golden green / Chattanooga choo choo / Blues in B for BT / Nuages.
**Album:** Released Oct '83, on Doctor Jazz (USA) by CBS Records (USA). Catalogue no: **ASLP 1001**
**Cass:** Released Oct '83, on Doctor Jazz (USA) by CBS Records (USA). Catalogue no: **ZCAS 1001**

**STEPHANE GRAPPELLI PLAYS COLE PORTER**
Tracks: / It's all right with me / You're the top / Anything goes / In the still of the night / You've got a thing / Miss Otis regrets / I've got you under my skin / Love for sale / Easy to love / You'd be so nice to come home to / Let's do it / My heart belongs to daddy.
**2 LP Set:** Released Oct '83, on Musidisc by Musidisc Records (France). Catalogue no: **ALB 240**

**STEPHANE GRAPPELLI PLAYS GERSHWIN**
**Cass:** Released Dec '89, on Musidisc by Musidisc Records (France). Catalogue no: **402054**

**STEPHANE GRAPPELLI WITH JEAN LUC PONTY (Grappelli, Stephane/Jean-Luc Ponty)**
**CD:** Released '88, on Accord (France) by Musidisc Records (France). Catalogue no: **MCD 139 139**
**CD:** Released '86, on Accord (France) by Musidisc Records (France). Catalogue no: **139 210**

**STEPHANOVA**
Tracks: / Tune up / Thou swell / Norwegian dance / Fulton Street samba / My foolish heart / Lover / Way you look tonight / Stephanova / Smoke rings and wine / Tangerine / Waltz for Queenie / Sonny boy.
**Album:** Released Oct '83, on Concord Jazz by Concord Jazz Records (USA). Catalogue no: **CJ 225**
**CD:** Released Jan '90, on Concord Jazz by Concord Jazz Records (USA). Catalogue no: **292E 6033**
**CD:** Released '89, on Concord Jazz by Concord Jazz Records (USA). Catalogue no: **CCD 4225**
**CD:** Released Oct '83, on Concord Jazz by Concord Jazz Records (USA). Catalogue no: **CJC 225**

**SWINGING AFFAIR (Grappelli, Stephane/Django Reinhardt)**
Tracks: / I wonder where my baby is tonight / If I had you / Hungaria / Tornerai / After you've gone / It had to be you / Tea for two / Dinah / Body and soul / Time on my hands / Stardust / Margie / Henderson stomp / You're the cream in my coffee.
**Album:** Released Mar '81, on Decca by Decca International. Deleted '86. Catalogue no: **MOR 530**

**TALK OF THE TOWN, THE**
Tracks: / Talk of the town / Amanda / Stardust / Can't help lovin' dat man / We'll be together again / Nature boy / Nearness of you, The / Tournesol / Greensleeves / You go to my head.
**Album:** Released Sep '85, on Black Lion Catalogue no: **BLP 30165**

**TEA FOR TWO (Grappelli, Stephane/Yehudi Menuhin)**
Tracks: / Crazy rhythm / Man I love, The / Tea for two / Air on a shoestring / Foggy day, A / Viva Vivaldi / My funny valentine / Limehouse blues / Thou swell / Yesterdays / Between the Devil and the deep blue sea.
**Cass:** Released Jan '78, on EMI by EMI Records. Catalogue no: **TC EMD 5530**
**Album:** Released Jan '78, on EMI by EMI Records. Catalogue no: **EMD 5530**

**TIVOLI GARDENS, COPENHAGEN (Grappelli, Stephane/Joe Pass/Niels Pedersen)**
Tracks: / It's only a paper moon / Time after time / Let's fall in love / Crazy rhythm / How deep is the ocean? / I'll remember April / I can't get started / I get a kick out of you.
**Album:** Released '82, on Pablo Jazz (USA) by Pablo Records (USA). Catalogue no: **2308 220**
**Cass:** Released '82, on Pablo Jazz (USA) by Pablo Records (USA). Catalogue no: **K 08 220**

**TOGETHER AT LAST (Grappelli, Stephane/Vassar Clements)**
**CD:** Released Oct '89, on Flying Fish (USA) by Flying Fish Records (USA). Catalogue no: **FF 70421**
**Album:** Released May '88, on Flying Fish (USA) by Flying Fish Records (USA). Catalogue no: **FF 421**

**TOP HAT (Grappelli, Stephane/Yehudi Menuhin)**
Tracks: / Puttin' on the Ritz / Way you look tonight / He loves and she loves / Isn't this a lovely day / Piccolino / Alison / Change partners / Top Hat / They can't take that away from me / Continental / They all laughed / Amanda / Funny face / Carioca.
Note: For full details see under 'Menuhin,Sir Yehudi and Stephane Grappelli'. Made famous by Fred Astaire.
**Album:** Released Feb '82, on H.M.V. by EMI Records. Deleted Feb '87. Catalogue no: **EMD 5539**

**TRIBUTE TO DJANGO**
**Album:** Released Feb '83, on Barclay (France) by Decca Records. Catalogue no: **B 90103**
**Cass:** Released Feb '83, on Barclay (France) by Decca Records. Catalogue no: **MB 90103**

**TWO-FER, A (Grappelli, Stephane/Hank Jones)**
Tracks: / Thou swell / These foolish things / September in the rain / You better go now / Hallelujah / Yesterdays / Mellow grapes / I'll never be the same.
Note: With Jimmy Woods, Alan Dawson.
**Album:** Released May '83, on Muse by Black & Blue Records. Catalogue no: **MR 5297**

**VENUPELLI BLUES (Grappelli, Stephane/Joe Venuti)**
Tracks: / I can't give you anything but love / My one and only love / After you've gone / Undecided / Venupelli blues / I'll never be the same / Tea for two.
**CD:** Released Mar '87, on Charly by Charly Records. Catalogue no: **CDCHARLY 73**
**Album:** Released Aug '79, on Affinity by Charly Records. Catalogue no: **AFF 29**
**Album:** Released Feb '87, on Pathe Marconi (France) Catalogue no: **260 229-1**

**VINTAGE 1981**
Tracks: / If I had you / I can't get started / Blue moon / But not for me.
Note: With Martin Taylor, Mike Gari and Jack Sewing.
**Album:** Released Dec '81, on Concord by Concord Jazz Records (USA). Catalogue no: **CJ 169**

**VIOLIN SUMMIT**
**Album:** Released Sep '84, on MPS Jazz (Germany) Catalogue no: **821 303-1**

**VIOLINS NO END (Grappelli, Stephane/Stuff Smith)**
Tracks: / Don't get around much anymore / Chapeau blues / No points today / Lady is a tramp, The / Desert sands / How high the moon / Moonlight in Vermont.
**Cass:** Released Mar '85, on Pablo Jazz (USA) by Pablo Records (USA). Catalogue no: **K10 907**
**Album:** Released Mar '85, on Pablo Jazz (USA) by Pablo Records (USA). Catalogue no: **2310 907**

**VIOLINSPIRATION (Grappelli, Stephane/Diz Disley Trio)**
Tracks: / Lover come back to me / Sweet Lorraine / Shine / Solitude / Ain't misbehavin / Souvenir de villinger / Hot lips / My heart stood still / Nearness of you, The / Joy / Nightingale sang in Berkely square, A / Cherokee / Lover man.

**Album:** Released May '81, on MPS Jazz Catalogue no: **MPS 68 058**
**Cass:** Released Nov '89, on Memoir by Memoir Records. Catalogue no: **CMOIR 110**
**Album:** Released Dec '85, on Memoir by Memoir Records. Catalogue no: **MOIR 110**

**WE'VE GOT THE WORLD ON A STRING (Grappelli, Stephane / Martin Taylor)**
Tracks: / She's funny that way / Don't get around much anymore / Manhattan tea party / Here, there and everywhere / I can't believe that you're in love with me / Ol' man river / It had to be you / I've got the world on a string.
**CD:** Released Feb '88, on EMI Studio by EMI Records. Catalogue no: **CDM 769 173 2**

**YOUNG DJANGO**
Tracks: / Djangology / Sweet chorus / Minor swing / Are you in the mood / Galerie St. Hubert / Tears / Swing guitars / Oriental Shuffle / Blues for Django and Stephane.
**Album:** Released May '81, on MPS Jazz Catalogue no: **MPS 68 230**
**CD:** Released May '84, on Polydor by Polydor Ltd. Deleted Mar '88. Catalogue no: **815 672-2**

## Gray, Bruce

**BRUCE GRAY'S VINTAGE JAZZ-BAND 1973**
**Album:** Released '88, on Swaggie (Australia) Catalogue no: **S 1418**

## Gray, Glen

**GLEN GRAY, 1939 (Gray, Glen & The Casa Loma Orchestra)**
**Album:** Released Jun '86, on Circle (USA) by Jazzology Records (USA). Catalogue no: **CLP 36**

**GLEN GRAY, 1943-46**
Tracks: / Sitting on the third rail / Blue rhapsody / Don't take your love from me / Fifth avenue sax / From the blue / Flat third jive / Dancing on the ceiling / Featuring the boys / Maybe / Lion and the mouse, The / I don't care who knows it / Who ray / After you've gone / Savage / If I love again / Hold the phone.
Note: Despite the personnel transiency enforced by World War II, some remarkable musicians filled the 1943-46 Casa Loma Orchestra. Here, Bobby Hackett solos on "Maybe", "After you've gone", "Savage" and "If I love again". Herb Ellis guitar is a solo voice on "Flat third jive" and "Featuring the boys". Eugenie Baird and Skip Nelson are the singers, and the charts are outstanding the work of Ray Conniff, Bill Challis and Lou Carter. Lou Fromm, Jackie Mills, Ray Grien, Fats Daniel and Lon Doty are among the principal instrumentalists. Music historian Dave Dexter, Jr. chronicles the Casa Lomans from their 1920's beginnings. (Hindsight Catalogue - 1989)
**Album:** Released '88, on Hindsight Catalogue no: **HSR 120**

**GLEN GRAY AND CASA LOMA ORCHESTRA 1939-40 (Gray, Glen and the Casa Loma Orchestra)**
Tracks: / Smoke rings / Wrap your troubles in dreams / Hindustan / Hour of parting / It's funny to everyone but me / Sometimes I'm happy / No-name jive / Meet me tonight in dreamland / Memories of you / What's the matter with me / Little brown jug / In the mood / Tuxedo Junction / Day in, day out / High society / Sassin' the boss.
Note: Only such impeccable soloists as the Casa Loma Orchestra's Murray McEachern, Billy Rauch, Sonny Dunham and Clarence Hutchenrider could produce the calibre performances captured on the radio transcriptions from which this album was mastered. The bands legendary ensemble precision and frequent flexibility for jazz all are here, along with vocals by both Kenny Sargent and Pee Wee Hunt. Probably the only major trombonist who has distinguished himself as an alto saxophonist, McEachern is a mellow voice in the bone trio on "No name jive", a newer, six-and-a-half minute extension of the band's big hit.
**Album:** Released '88, on Hindsight Catalogue no: **HSR 104**

**GLEN GRAY AND THE CASA LOMA ORCHESTRA 1940 (Gray, Glen & The Casa Loma Orchestra)**
**Album:** Released Aug '88, on Circle (USA) by Jazzology Records (USA). Catalogue no: **CLP 61**

**GLEN GRAY AND THE CASA LOMA ORCHESTRA (Gray, Glen & The Casa Loma Orchestra)**
Tracks: / Theme - introduction / Lovely come back / Should I / Sheik of Araby, The / Chant of the jungle / Zonky / I never knew / I found a new baby / I got rhythm / Closing / Way down yonder in New Orleans / Truckin' / Weary blues / Walking the dog / I may be wrong / My blue Heaven / Dardanella / Farewell blues / Theme - close.
**Album:** Released May '88, on Jasmine by Hasmick Promotions. Catalogue no: **JASM 2516**
**Album:** Released Oct '79, on London Records by London Records Ltd. Catalogue no: **HMP 5050**
**Cass:** Released May '88, on Jasmine by Hasmick Promotions. Catalogue no: **JASMC 2516**

**MOONGLOW 1930 - 36 (Gray, Glen & His Orchestra)**
**Album:** Released Jun '88, on Bandstand Catalogue no: **BS 7126**

**ONE NIGHT STAND WITH GLEN GRAY AND THE CASA LOMA ORCHESTRA (Gray, Glen & The Casa Loma Orchestra)**
**Album:** Released Apr '79, on Sandy Hook (USA) Catalogue no: **SH 1005**

**SHALL WE SWING (Gray, Glen & The Casa Loma Orchestra)**
**Album:** Released '87, on Creative World(USA) by GNP Crescendo Records (USA). Catalogue no: **ST 1055**

**SOLO SPOTLIGHT (Gray, Glen & The Casa Loma Orchestra)**
Tracks: / Golden earrings / Street of dreams / Blue star (The Medic theme) / My foolish heart / Love letters / Around the world in 80 days / Was I to blame for falling in love with you / Stella by starlight / Beautiful love / When I fall in love / I don't stand a ghost of a chance with you / Love me.
Note: Spectacular big band sound consisting of a variety of powerful uptempo swingers and mellow mood arrangments. Featuring individually talented instrumentalists who each have their own reputation as a star performer. As the title suggest the album showcased Glen Gary's various instrumentalists in solo spotlight. deal for both listening and dancing.
**Album:** Released Jan '86, on Capitol by EMI Records. Deleted Jun '89. Catalogue no: **EMS 1147**
**Cass:** Released Jan '86, on Capitol by EMI Records. Deleted Jan '88. Catalogue no: **TCEMS 1147**

**SOUNDS OF THE GREAT BANDS IN LATIN (Gray, Glen & The Casa Loma Orchestra)**
Tracks: / String of pearls / Lean baby / Take the 'A' train / Casa Loma stomp / Stardust / No name jive / Frenesi / Collaboration / Mole, The / Early autumn / King Porter stomp.
**Cass:** Released Aug '88, on Capitol by EMI Records. Deleted Jan '90. Catalogue no: **TCEMS 1303**
**Album:** Released Aug '88, on Capitol by EMI Records. Catalogue no: **EMS 1303**

**SWING GOES ON, VOL 1**
Tracks: / Bugle call rag / Symphony in riffs / Floyd's guitar blues / Well git it / Opus one / Two o'clock jump / Swingin' the blues / New no-name jive / 720 in the books / Uptown blues / Baubles, bangles and beads / Night train / Dippermouth blues / Flying home.
**Album:** Released '83, on EMI (Germany) by EMI Records. Catalogue no: **IC 054 52710**

**SWINGIN DECADE (Gray, Glen & The Casa Loma Orchestra)**
Tracks: / Apple honey / Midnight sun / Mission to Moscow / Harlem Nocturne / Jack the bear / Champ,The / Blues Rhapsody / Malibu / Opus one / Sherwood Forest / Oh what a beautiful morning / Intermission riff.
Note: Glen Gary and the Casa Loma Orchestra bring us a selection of well recorded big band arrangements. This was one of the few post-war, genuine stereo recordings by a big band.
**Cass:** Released Dec '85, on Capitol by EMI Records. Deleted '86. Catalogue no: **TCEMS 1133**
**Album:** Released Dec '85, on Capitol by EMI Records. Deleted '86. Catalogue no: **EMS 1133**

**THEMES OF THE GREAT BANDS (Gray, Glen & The Casa Loma Orchestra)**

Tracks: / Let's dance / Getting sentimental over you / Redskin rhumba / Moonlight serenade / Leapfrog / I can't get started / Nightmare / Ciribiribin / Blue flame / Quaker city / Tuxedo Junction / Artistry in rhythm.
**Album:** Released Jun '83, on Capitol T (USA) Catalogue no: **2C 068 54578**
**Cass:** Released Mar '84, on Capitol (import) Catalogue no: **2C 068 54574**

## Gray, Jerry

### BIG DANCE TONIGHT (Gray, Jerry & His Orchestra)
Tracks: / Thou swell / Swanee / Champagne boogie / Off limits / Way you look tonight / Off the wall / Adios / Darktown strutters' ball / Kettle drum hop / Oompchuck / Coronado cruise / Baby's lullaby.
**Album:** Released Mar '84, on Jasmine by Hasmick Promotions. Deleted Feb '88. Catalogue no: **JASM 1039**

### UNCOLLECTED (1952), THE
**Album:** Released Jun '86, on Hindsight (UK) by Michele International Records. Catalogue no: **HUK 212**

## Gray, Wardell

### 1947-52
**Album:** Released Sep '87, on Giants of Jazz by Hasmick Promotions. Catalogue no: **LPJT 27**

### ALUMNI MASTERS, THE (Gray, Wardell & Ben Webster)
Tracks: / Jumpin' at The Woodside / Golden bullet / How high the moon / One o'clock jump / Cottontail / Audiology / Honeysuckle rose / Loverman / Main stem.
Note: Gray is featured on the first five tracks, Webster on the remaining six.
**Album:** Released Apr '81, on Jazz Live (Italy) Catalogue no: **BLJ 8038**

### CENTRAL AVENUE
Tracks: / Twisted / Twisted (unissued take) / Easy living / Southside / Southside (unissued take) / Sweet Lorraine / Scrapple from the apple / Move / Siner kissed an angel, A / Blue gray / Grayhound / Teadin' / April skies / Bright boy / Jackie / Farmer's market / Sweet and lovely / Lover man (oh where can you be) / Man I love, The / Lavonne / So long, Broadway / Paul's case.
**Album:** Released '79, on RCA by BMG Records (UK). Deleted '84. Catalogue no: **PR 24062**

### HUNT, THE (Gray, Wardell & Dexter Gordon)
Tracks: / Disorder at the border / Cherokee / Byas a drink / Hunt, The.
**2 LP Set:** Released '78, on Savoy Jazz (USA) by Malaco Records (USA). Catalogue no: **SJL 2222**

### LIVE JAM SESSION AT TRADEWINDS
Tracks: / Out of nowhere / Strike up the band / Pennies from Heaven.
**Album:** Released Apr '81, on Jam Session (USA) Catalogue no: **JAM 103**

### ONE FOR PREZ
**Album:** Released Feb '89, on Black Lion Catalogue no: **BLP 60106**

### SWEDISH PASTRY See under Hasselgard, Stan (Gray, Wardell/Stan Hasselgard)
**Album:** Released Jun '86, on Dragon by Dragon Records. Catalogue no: **DRLP 16**

### THIN MAN MEETS FAT BOY (Gray, Wardell/Don Lamphere Quintet)
Note: With Al Haig, Max Roach.
**Album:** Released Aug '88, on Misterioso Catalogue no: **MLP 1981**

### THIN MAN MEETS FAT BOY VOL. 2 (Gray, Wardell/Don Lamphere Quintet)
Note: Al Haig, Max Roach.
**Album:** Released Aug '88, on Misterioso Catalogue no: **MLP 1982**

### THIN MAN MEETS MAD LAD (Gray, Wardell/Leo Parker Quartet)
**Album:** Released Aug '88, on Misterioso Catalogue no: **MLP 1983**

### WARDELL GRAY
Tracks: / Bebop / Hot house / Groovin' high / King, The / It serves me right / Little dog / Spasmodic / X-1 / Good bait / C jam blues / How high the moon.
Note: With Howard McGhee, Sonny Criss, Clark Terry, Stan Hasselgard, Dodo Marmarosa.
**Album:** Released '83, on Spotlite by Spotlite Records. Catalogue no: **SPJ 134**

### WARDELL GRAY AND THE BIG BANDS
Tracks: / Let's get started / Blue keys / Straight life / Now that you're mine / Bamby / At El Grotto / Nonchalant man / Blues for sale / Having a wonderful wish / Hucklebuck, The / Egg head / Nails / Little pony / Jeep is jumpin' / Caxton Hall swing / For europeans only.
**Album:** on Official by Official Records. Catalogue no: **OFF 3029**

## Great Big Bands

### GREAT BIG BANDS (Various artists)
Tracks: / Jumpin' at The Woodside: *Basie, Count* / Sandman: *Basie, Count* / I found a new baby: *Basie, Count* / Take the 'A' train: *Ellington, Duke* / Tea for two: *Ellington, Duke* / Black and tan fantasy: *Ellington, Duke* / Honeydripper: *Calloway, Cab* / Let's go, Joe: *Calloway, Cab* / Jumpin' jive: *Calloway, Cab* / Body and soul: *Lunceford, Jimmie* / For dancers only: *Lunceford, Jimmie* / Blues in the night: *Lunceford, Jimmie* / Artistry in rhythm: *Kenton, Stan* / Harlem folk dance: *Kenton, Stan* / Tampico: *Kenton, Stan* / Etude for saxophone: *Kenton, Stan* / Goof and I, The: *Herman, Woody* / Baby I need you: *Herman, Woody* / My pal Gonzales: *Herman, Woody* / In the mood: *Miller, Glenn* / Moonlight serenade: *Miller, Glenn* / Tuxedo Junction: *Miller, Glenn* / Moten swing: *Goodman, Benny* / Clap hands, here comes Charlie: *Goodman, Benny* / Begin the beguine: *Goodman, Benny*.
Note: Featuring Count Basie, Duke Ellingon, Benny Goodman, Woody Herman, Stan Kenton, Cab Calloway, Jimmy Lunceford, Glenn Miller.
**2 LP Set:** Released Aug '63, on Musidisc by Musidisc Records (France). Catalogue no: **ALB 371**

## Great Bluesmen

### GREAT BLUESMEN (Various artists)
Tracks: / Midnight boogie: *Williams, Robert Pete* / Levee camp blues: *Williams, Robert Pete* / My baby done changed the lock on the door: *Terry, Sonny & Brownie McGhee* / Tupelo: *Hooker, John Lee* / Bus station blues: *Hooker, John Lee* / Son's blues: *House, Son* / Death letter blues: *House, Son* / Pony blues: *House, Son* / Mailman blues: *Estes, Sleepy John* / Clean up at home: *Estes, Sleepy John* / Hey rattler: *Reese, Dock* / Oh my Lord: *Reese, Dock* / Sliding Delta: *Hurt, Mississippi John* / Trouble, I've had it all my days: *Hurt, Mississippi John* / Hard times: *James, Skip* / Killing floor blues: *James, Skip* / Cherry ball blues: *James, Skip* / Illinois blues: *James, Skip* / Death don't have no mercy: *Davis, Rev. Gary* / Catfish blues: *Doss, Willie* / I had a woman: *Doss, Willie* / I'm going down south: *McDowell, Mississippi Fred* / If the river was whisky: *McDowell, Mississippi Fred* / Cottonfield blues: *Hopkins, Lightnin'* / Shake that thing: *Hopkins, Lightnin'*.
Note: Recorded live at the Newport Folk Festivals, Rhode Island, 1959 - 1965.
**2 LP Set:** Released Dec '83, on Vanguard (France) by CBS Records. Catalogue no: **VSD 77**

### GREAT BLUES MEN: VOL. 2 (Various artists)
Tracks: / Candy man: *Various artists* / Highway '61: *Various artists* / Death letter: *Various artists* / Midnight boogie: *Various artists* / My baby done gone changed to lock my door: *Various artists* / I had a woman: *Various artists* / Sporting life blues: *Various artists* / Bus station blues: *Various artists* / Clean up at home: *Various artists* / Shake that thing: *Various artists* / Death don't have no mercy: *Various artists* / Cotton crop blues: *Various artists* / Burning fire: *Various artists* / Poison ivy: *Various artists* / I can't quit you baby: *Various artists* / Messing with the kid: *Various artists* / I got mine in time: *Various artists* / Please help: *Various artists* / Set a date: *Various artists* / Dynaflow blues: *Various artists* / Everyday: *Various artists*.
**Cass:** Released Jun '79, on PRT by Castle Communications Records. Catalogue no: **ZCGH 879**
**Album:** Released '79, on Golden Hour Deleted '84. Catalogue no: **GH 879**

**NEWPORT**
**Cass set:** Released Sep '89, on Start by Start Records Ltd.. Catalogue no: **MCCVSD 77/78**
**CD:** Released Sep '89, on Start by Start Records Ltd.. Catalogue no: **CDVCD 78**

## Great British...

**GREAT BRITISH DANCE BANDS PLAY COLE PORTER (Various artists)**
Tracks: / Let's do it: *Various artists* / What is this thing called love: *Various artists* / Love for sale: *Various artists* / Night and day: *Various artists* / Experiment: *Various artists* / Miss Otis regrets (she's unable to lunch today: *Various artists* / Anything goes: *Various artists* / I get a kick out of you: *Various artists* / You're the top: *Various artists* / Easy to love: *Various artists* / I'm in love again: *Various artists* / Banjo, The: *Various artists* / What is this thing called love?: *Various artists* / Looking at you: *Various artists* / They all fall in love: *Various artists* / After you, who?: *Various artists* / How could we be wrong?: *Various artists* / It's bad for me: *Various artists* / All through the night: *Various artists* / Blow, Gabriel, blow: *Various artists* / Thank you so much, Mrs Lowsborough: *Various artists* / Goodbye, little dream, goodbye: *Various artists*.
Note: Featuring the bands of Jack Hylton, Harry Roy, Henry Hall, Ray Noble, Nat Gonella, Lew Stone, Ronnie Munro, Billy Ternent, Carroll Gibbons, Geraldo, Victor Sylvester.
**Album:** Released Aug '85, on Retrospect by EMI Records. Deleted Jun '89. Catalogue no: **EG 2604431**
**Cass:** Released Aug '85, on Retrospect by EMI Records. Catalogue no: **EG 2604434**
**2 LP Set:** Released Aug '80, on Retrospect by EMI Records. Deleted '88. Catalogue no: **SHB 66**

**GREAT BRITISH DANCE BANDS PLAY GEORGE GERSHWIN (Various artists)**
Tracks: / Swanee: *Savoy Quartet* / Drifting along with the tide: *Queens Dance Orchestra* / Please do it again: *Queens Dance Orchestra* / Yankee doodle blues: *Savoy Havana Band* / I'll build a stairway to Paradise: *Savoy Havana Band* / My fair lady: *Savoy Havana Band* / Nice baby: *Savoy Havana Band* / Sweetheart: *Hylton, Jack/his orchestra* / Innocent, lonesome, blue baby: *Hylton, Jack & His Orchestra* / Someone: *Hylton, Jack & His Orchestra* / Lady be good: *Hylton, Jack/his orchestra* / Clap yo' hands: *Hylton, Jack & His Orchestra* / Do do do: *Hylton, Jack & His Orchestra* / 'S wonderful: *Hylton, Jack & His Orchestra* / My one and only: *Hylton, Jack & His Orchestra* / Virginia: *Midnight Follies Orchestra* / Wait a bit: *Various artists* / Susie: *Various artists* / Why do I love you?: *Various artists* / Tell me more: *Various artists* / Hang on to me: *Various artists* / So am I: *Various artists* / Someone to watch over me: *Various artists* / Somebody loves me: *Darewski, Max & His Band* / I'd rather Charleston: *Mackey, Percival & His Band* / Half of it dearie blues, The: *Mackey, Percival & His Band* / Looking for a boy: *Mackey, Percival & His Band* / When do we dance?: *Mackey, Percival & His Band* / That certain feeling: *Cabaret Novelty Band* / Man I love, The: *Piccadilly Revels Band* / Funny face: *Piccadilly Players* / He loves and she loves: *Piccadilly Players*.
Note: Featuring the Savoy Quartet, Queens Dance Orchestra, Savoy Havana Band, Jack Hylton, Midnight Follies Orchestra, Savoy Orpheans, Max Darewski, Percival Mackey, Cabaret Novelty Band, Piccadilly Revels, Piccadilly Players.
**2 LP Set:** Released Oct '77, on Retrospect by EMI Records. Catalogue no: **SHB 45**

**GREAT BRITISH DANCE BANDS PLAY THE MUSIC OF IRVING BERLIN (Various artists)**
**Album:** on Retrospect by EMI Records. Catalogue no: **SH 353**

**GREAT BRITISH DANCE BANDS PLAY THE MUSIC OF NACIO HERB (Various artists)**
**Album:** on Retrospect by EMI Records. Catalogue no: **SH 267**

**GREAT BRITISH DANCE BANDS PLAY THE MUSIC OF NOEL COWARD (Various artists)**
Tracks: / I'll see you again: *Hylton, Jack & His Orchestra* / Kiss me: *Hylton, Jack & His Orchestra* / Zigeuner: *Hylton, Jack & His Orchestra* / If love were all: *Hylton, Jack & His Orchestra* / Dear little cafe: *Hylton, Jack & His Orchestra* / Russian skies: *Hylton, Jack & His Orchestra* / Specially for you: *Various artists* / Poor little rich girl: *Various artists* / Mad about the boy: *Various artists* / I'm mad about you: *Starita, Ray & The Piccadilly Band* / Teach me to dance like grandma: *Starita, Ray & His Ambassadors* / Half caste woman: *Various artists* / Try to learn to love: *Various artists* / Dance little lady: *Various artists* / Lover of dreams: *Payne, Jack & His BBC Dance Orchestra* / Mirabelle waltz: *Payne, Jack & His BBC Dance Orchestra* / Something to do with spring: *Noble, Ray & His New Mayfair Orchestra* / Let's live dangerously: *Noble, Ray & His New Mayfair Orchestra* / Let's say goodbye: *Noble, Ray & His New Mayfair Orchestra* / Children of the Ritz: *Noble, Ray & His New Mayfair Orchestra* / Party's over, The: *Noble, Ray & His New Mayfair Orchestra* / Younger generation, The: *Noble, Ray & His New Mayfair Orchestra* / Most of ev'ry day: *Jackson, Jack & His Orchestra* / Room with a view: *Jackson, Jack & His Orchestra*.
**Album:** Released '78, on Retrospect by EMI Records. Catalogue no: **SH 278**

**GREAT BRITISH DANCE BANDS PLAY VIVIAN ELLIS (Various artists)**
Note: Featuring the Savoy Havana Band, Savoy Orpheans, Jack Hylton & His Orchestra, Ray Starita & His Ambassadors' Club Band, Carroll Gibbons & The New Mayfair Dance Orchestra, Jack Hylton & His Orchestra, Harry Roy & His Orchestra, Ronnie Munro & His Orchestra.
**Album:** on Retrospect by EMI Records. Catalogue no: **SH 260**

**VOICES OF GREAT BRITISH DANCE (Various artists)**
Tracks: / Let's call a heart a heart: *Stediford, Marjorie* / I've got you under my skin: *Stediford, Marjorie* / Greatest mistake of my life: *Henderson, Chick* / Bottoms up: *Logan, Ella* / Bigger and better than ever: *Logan, Ella* / You go to my head: *Donovan, Don* / On the sentimental side: *Donovan, Don* / Mine alone: *Lynn, Vera* / Here comes the sandman: *Lynn, Vera* / Gee gee: *Mallin, Bob* / You must have been a beautiful baby: *Carless, Dorothy & Sam Costa* / I'll see you in my dreams: *Rosing, Val & His Swing Stars* / I can't give you anything but love: *Rosing, Val & His Swing Stars* / Broken record, The: *Costa, Sam* / Did your mother come from Ireland?: *Dell, Peggy* / With every breath I take: *Fitzgerald, Gerry*.
**Album:** on Retrospect by EMI Records. Catalogue no: **SH 336**

## Great British Blues

**GREAT BRITISH BLUES (1962-68) (Various artists)**
**Album:** Released Oct '82, on Decca by Decca International. Catalogue no: **TAB 53**

## Great Harp Players

**GREAT HARP PLAYERS (1927-30) (Various artists)**
Tracks: / John Henry blues: *Francis, William & Richard Sowell* / Roubin' blues: *Francis, William & Richard Sowell* / Pot licker blues: *Watson, El* / Narrow gauge blues: *Watson, El* / El Watson's fox chase: *Watson, El* / Bay rum blues: *Watson, El* / Sweet bunch of daisies: *Watson, El* / One sock blues: *Watson, El* / Lost boy blues: *McAbee, Palmer* / McAbee's railroad piece: *McAbee, Palmer* / Railway blues: *Stowers, Freeman* / Texas wild cat chase: *Stowers, Freeman* / Medley of blues: *Stowers, Freeman* / Sunrise on the farm: *Stowers, Freeman* / Mean low blues: *Blues Birdhead* / Harmonica blues: *Blues Birdhead* / Mississippi swamp moan: *Lewis, Alfred* / Friday moan blues: *Lewis, Alfred*.
**Album:** Released May '83, on Matchbox (Bluesmaster) by Saydisc Records. Catalogue no: **MSE 209**

## Great Jazz...

**GREAT JAZZ LADIES VOL.1 (Vari-**

**ous artists)**
**Album:** Released Jul '82, on Kings Of Jazz Catalogue no: **KLJ 20036**

**GREAT JAZZ LEGENDS (Various artists)**
**CD Set:** Released Oct '88, on Mainline (2) by Mainline Records. Catalogue no: **267 333 2**

**GREAT JAZZ PIANOS (1926-1940) (Various artists)**
Note: Artists include Fats Waller, Cow Cow Davenport, Jelly Roll Morton & Montana Taylori
**Album:** Released Apr '81, on Joker (USA) by Lifetime Records (USA). Catalogue no: **SM 3121**

**GREAT JAZZ SOLOS REVISITED (Various artists)**
**Album:** Released Apr '79, on Wave by Wave Records. Catalogue no: **WAVE LP 18**

**GREAT JAZZ TRUMPETS (1924-1937) (Various artists)**
Tracks: / Deep down south: *Bix Beiderbecke Orchestra* / I'm more than satisfied: *Chicago Loopers* / Clorinda: *Various artists* / Three blind mice (takes 1 & 2): *Various artists* / I need some pettin': *Wolverines, The* / Out where the blues begin: *Mills, Irving & His Hotsy Totsy Gang* / New twister, The: *Original Wolverines, The* / Shimme-sha-wabble: *Various artists* / Good man is hard to find, A: *Various artists* / Swanee river: *Berigan's, Bunny Rhythm Makers* / San Francisco: *Various artists.*
**Album:** Released Apr '81, on Joker (USA) by Lifetime Records (USA). Catalogue no: **SM 3122**

## Great Jazz Trio

**CHAPTER 11**
**Album:** Released Sep '81, on East Wind Catalogue no: **6315 069**

**CLUB NEW YORKER, THE**
Tracks: / 'S wonderful / Autumn in New York / Our love is here to stay / I've got a crush on you / Manhattan / Someone to watch over me / They can't take that away from me / Isn't it romantic / Embraceable you / But not for me.
Note: The Great Jazz Trio are: Hank Jones (Piano), Eddie Gomez (Bass), Jimmy Cobb (Drums), and feature Lewis Eley on violin.
**CD:** Released '88, on Denon Catalogue no: **C38-7072**

**GREAT JAZZ TRIO AT THE VILLAGE**
Tracks: / Confirmation / Wind flower / Nardis / Lawra.
**CD:** Released '88, on East Wind Catalogue no: **32JD-107**

**GREAT JAZZ TRIO FROM LA**
Tracks: / Night in Tunisia / Round about midnight / Satin doll / My funny valentine.
**CD:** Released '88, on East Wind Catalogue no: **32JD-112**

**GREAT JAZZ TRIO, THE**
Tracks: / Milestones / Lush life / Wave / Eighty-one / Remember Clifford / Hormone / Mr. Biko.
**CD:** Released '88, on East Wind Catalogue no: **32JD-113**

**MONK'S MOODS**
Tracks: / Round about midnight / Blue Monk / Bemsha swing / Misterioso / I mean you / Ruby my dear / Monk's dream / Jackie-ing / Monk's mood.
Note: The Great Jazz Trio are: Hank Jones (Piano), Eddie Gomez (Bass), Jimmy Cobb (Drums) and featuring Terumasa Hino on cornet.
**CD:** Released '88, on Denon Catalogue no: **C38-7323**

**N.Y. SOPHISTICATE**
Tracks: / Tribute to Duke Ellington / In a sentimental mood / C jam blues / Mood indigo / Satin doll / Lush life / Sophisticated lady / Take the 'A' train / I got it bad / Caravan / Solitude.
Note: Hank Jones (Piano), Eddie Gomez (bass), Jimmy Cobb (Drums) and featuring The String Quartet.
**CD:** Released '88, on Denon Catalogue no: **C38-7097**

**STANDARD COLLECTION**
Tracks: / Autumn in New York / Caravan / 'S wonderful / Our love is here to stay / Someone to watch over me / Isn't it romantic / Embraceable you / In a sentimental mood / Satin doll / Lush life / Sophisticated lady / Take the 'A' train / Blue monk / Ruby my dear / Monk's dream / Monk's mood.
Note: Hank Jones (Piano), Eddie Gomez (bass), Jimmy Cobb (Drums).
**CD:** Released May '86, on Denon Catalogue no: **C38 7854**
**Cass:** Released Oct '88, on Denon Catalogue no: **CC 18**

**THREESOME**
**CD:** Released '88, on Toshiba-EMI (Japan) Catalogue no: **TEC 2016**

## Great Jazz Vocalists

**GREAT JAZZ VOCALISTS (Singin' The Blues Vol. 1)**
**Cass:** Released Jan '88, on Starline (Jazz) Catalogue no: **SLC 61127**

## Great Moments...

**GREAT MOMENTS IN JAZZ (Various artists)**
Tracks: / Martians go home: *Rogers, Shorty* / Train & the river, The: *Giuffre, Jimmy* / Golden striker, The: *Modern Jazz Quartet* / Spirit feel, The: *Jackson, Milt* / Wednesday night prayer meeting: *Mingus, Charles* / Memphis underground: *Mann, Herbie* / Comin' home baby: *Torme, Mel* / Just a little lovin': *McRae, Carmen* / Bright moments song: *Kirk, Rahsaan Roland* / Compared to what: *Macann, Les & Eddie Harris* / Up jumped spring: *Hubbard, Freddie* / Stratus: *Cobham, Billy* / In walked bud: *Blakey, Art/Thelonious Monk* / My favourite things: *Coltrane, John* / Ramblin': *Coleman, Ornette* / Hard times: *Newman, David 'Fathead'* / Whispering grass: *Crawford, Hank* / Your mind is on vacation: *Various artists* / Listen here: *Harris, Eddie* / Live humble: *Lateef, Yusef* / Cosmic messenger: *Ponty, Jean-Luc* / Birdland: *Manhattan Transfer* / Rockport: *Passport* / Softly at sunrise: *Albright, Gerald* / Perigia: *Jamal, Ahmad.*
**LP Set:** Released Dec '88, on Atlantic by WEA Records. Catalogue no: **K 781 907 1**
**Cass set:** Released Dec '88, on Atlantic by WEA Records. Catalogue no: **K 781 907 4**
**CD Set:** Released Dec '88, on Atlantic by WEA Records. Catalogue no: **K 781 907 2**

## Great Singers...

**GREAT SINGERS OF THE 30'S (Various artists)**
**Album:** Released '88, on Fanfare by Captain Billy's Music. Catalogue no: **LP 40-140**

**GREAT SINGERS OF THE FIFTIES (Various artists)**
**Album:** Released Jan '79, on Jazz Greats Catalogue no: **GP 703**

## Great Swing Jam Sessions

**GREAT SWING JAM SESSIONS VOL.2 (Various artists)**
Tracks: / China boy: *Various artists* / Body and soul: *Various artists* / Honeysuckle rose: *Various artists* / Stardust: *Various artists* / Intermezzo: *Various artists* / Song of the islands: *Various artists* / Flying home: *Various artists* / Tempo and swing: *Various artists* / With a twist of the wrist: *Various artists* / Lower register: *Various artists* / Jazz me blues: *Various artists* / Floyd's guitar blues: *Various artists.*
**Album:** Released Apr '81, on Joker (USA) by Lifetime Records (USA). Catalogue no: **SM 3115**

## Great Trumpet Legends

**GREAT TRUMPET LEGENDS (Various artists)**
**Album:** Released May '88, on Jazz Life Catalogue no: **2673711**
**CD:** Released May '88, on Jazz Life Catalogue no: **267 371 2**
**Cass:** Released May '88, on Jazz Life Catalogue no: **2673714**

## Great Vocalists

**GREAT VOCALISTS (Various artists)**
Tracks: / Whispering: *Sinatra, Frank & Tommy Dorsey* / Dedicated to you: *Fitzgerald, Ella & Mills Brothers* / Take another guess: *Chick Webb, Ella W.* / Basin Street blues: *Crosby, Bing & J. Trotter Orch.* / Swing brother swing: *Holiday,*

*Billie & Count Basie* / What is this thing called swing: *Armstrong, Louis & His Orchestra* / Flat foot floogie: *Armstrong & The Mills Brothers* / St. Louis blues: *Crosby, Bing & P.Whiteman* / I'm coming Virginia: *Crosby, Bing & P.Whiteman* / Yesterdays: *Holiday, Billie* / Baby won't you please come home: *Hall, Juanita & Coleman Hawkins* / St. Louis blues: *Witherspoon, Jimmy & Gerry Mulligan.*
**Album:** Released '81, on Joker (USA) by Lifetime Records (USA). Catalogue no: **SM 3278**

**GREAT VOCALISTS, THE**
**LP Set:** Released '88, on Joker (USA) by Lifetime Records (USA). Catalogue no: **C 10-3 BOX 3**

## Greatest Boogie Woogie

**GREATEST BOOGIE WOOGIE 1 (Various artists)**
**Cass:** Released May '88, on Flashback by Mainline Records. Catalogue no: **64028**

**GREATEST BOOGIE WOOGIE 2 (Various artists)**
**Cass:** Released May '88, on Flashback by Mainline Records. Catalogue no: **64029**

## Greatest Esquire ...

**GREATEST ESQUIRE SWING SESSIONS (Jazz of World War II) (Various artists)**
Tracks: / Mop mop: *Esquire All Stars* / I've got a feeling I'm falling: *Esquire All Stars* / Flyin' home: *Esquire All Stars* / My ideal: *Esquire All Stars* / Blues: *Esquire All Stars* / I can't give you anything but love: *Esquire All Stars* / Downhearted blues: *Bailey, Mildred & Ensemble* / World is waiting for the sunrise, The: *Goodman, Benny Quintet* / Airmail special: *Goodman, Benny Quintet* / Rachel's dream: *Goodman, Benny Quintet* / Tea for two: *Various artists.*
Note: Featuring the Esquire All Stars -- Louis Armstrong and Roy Eldridge (trumpets), Jack Teagarden (trombone), Coleman Hawkins (tenor sax), Lionel Hampton (vibes), Teddy Wilson and Art Tatum (pianos) -- Mildred Bailey & Ensemble --Benny GoodmanQuintet -- Duke Ellington Orchestra, featuring Willie Smith.
**Album:** Released Apr '81, on Joker (USA) by Lifetime Records (USA). Catalogue no: **SM 3132**

## Greatest Jazz Concert

**GREATEST JAZZ CONCERT EVER, THE (Various artists)**
Tracks: / Perdido: *Various artists* / Salt peanuts: *Various artists* / All the things you are: *Various artists* / Wee: *Various artists* / Hot house: *Various artists* / Night in Tunisia, A: *Various artists* / Embraceable you: *Various artists* / Sure thing: *Various artists* / My devotion: *Various artists* / Polka dots and moonbeams: *Various artists* / Cherokee: *Various artists* / Jubilee: *Various artists* / I've got you under my skin: *Various artists* / My heart stood still: *Various artists* / I want to be happy: *Various artists* / Lullaby of Birdland: *Various artists.*
**Album:** Released '79, on Prestige Deleted '84. Catalogue no: **PR 24024**

**GREATEST JAZZ CONCERT IN THE WORLD (Various artists)**
Tracks: / Smedley: *Peterson, Oscar Trio* / Some day my prince will come: *Peterson, Oscar Trio* / Daytrain: *Peterson, Oscar Trio* / Now's the time: *Peterson, Oscar Trio* / Memories of you: *Peterson, Oscar Trio* / Misty: *Peterson, Oscar Trio* / I can't get started: *Peterson, Oscar Trio* / Moonglow: *Hawkins, Coleman & Oscar Peterson Trio* / Sweet Georgia Brown: *Hawkins, Coleman & Oscar Peterson Trio* / C-jam blues: *Hawkins, Coleman & Oscar Peterson Trio* / Woman you must be crazy: *Walker, T-Bone* / Stormy Monday: *Walker, T-Bone* / Swamp goo: *Ellington, Duke/His Orchestra* / Hurdle gurdle: *Ellington, Duke/His Orchestra* / Night flock: *Ellington, Duke/His Orchestra* / Rue bleu: *Ellington, Duke/His Orchestra* / Salome: *Ellington, Duke/His Orchestra* / Chromatic love affair: *Ellington, Duke/His Orchestra* / Mount Harissa: *Ellington, Duke/His Orchestra* / Blood count: *Ellington, Duke/His Orchestra* / Rockin' in rhythm: *Ellington, Duke/His Orchestra* / Very tenor: *Ellington, Duke/His Orchestra* / Onions: *Ellington, Duke/His Orchestra* / Take the 'A' train: *Ellington, Duke/His Orchestra* / Satin doll: *Ellington, Duke/His Orchestra* / Tutti for cootie: *Ellington, Duke/His Orchestra* / Up jump: *Ellington, Duke/His Orchestra* / Prelude to a kiss: *Ellington, Duke/His Orchestra* / Mood indigo: *Ellington, Duke/His Orchestra* / I got it bad: *Ellington, Duke/His Orchestra* / Things ain't what they used to be: *Ellington, Duke/His Orchestra* / Don't be that way: *Fitzgerald, Ella/Jimmy Jones/Duke Ellington* / You've changed: *Fitzgerald, Ella/Jimmy Jones/Duke Ellington* / Let's do it: *Fitzgerald, Ella/Jimmy Jones/Duke Ellington* / On the sunny side of the street: *Fitzgerald, Ella/Jimmy Jones/Duke Ellington* / It's only a paper moon: *Fitzgerald, Ella & Jimmy Jones Trio* / Daydream: *Fitzgerald, Ella & Jimmy Jones Trio* / If I could be with you: *Fitzgerald, Ella & Jimmy Jones Trio* / Between the devil and the deep blue sea: *Fitzgerald, Ella & Jimmy Jones Trio* / Cottontail: *Fitzgerald, Ella/Jimmy Jones/Duke Ellington* (Featuring Paul Gonsalves.).
**2 LP Set:** Released '82, on Pablo Jazz (USA) by Pablo Records (USA). Catalogue no: **262 5704**

## Greatest Ragtime

**GREATEST RAGTIME OF THE CENTURY (Various artists)**
**CD:** Released Jan '88, on Biograph (USA) by Biograph Records (USA). Catalogue no: **BCD 103**

## Greco, Buddy

**Biographical details:** Born in Philadelphia, this American singer and pianist made his radio debut at the age of four (1931). He came to prominence with his 1948 recording of a 1933 song, *Ooh look-a there, ain't she pretty.* In 1949 he began a two-year spell at the forefront of Benny Goodman's band. After building up a cabaret career, Greco achieved a one-off UK chart entry in 1960 - he reached no. 26 with his version of Rodgers & Hart's 1937 standard *The lady is a tramp.* With a piano style heavily influenced by jazz great Art Tatum, Greco continued to earn a steady living as a live performer without ever becoming a major star. (Bob Macdonald, 30/9/85).

**AT MISTER KELLY'S**
Tracks: / Welcome to Mr Kelly's / But not for me / They can't take that away from me / Polka dots and moonbeams / They didn't believe me / Foggy day, A / Here I am in love again / My baby just cares for me / My ship / Dancing on the ceiling / Will you still be mine? / One for my baby / Nearness of you, The / Give me the simple life.
**Album:** Released Jun '83, on Jasmine by Hasmick Promotions. Deleted Feb '88. Catalogue no: **JASM 1013**

**FOR ONCE IN MY LIFE**
Tracks: / In the still of the night / More I see you, The / What now my love? / Moment truth, The / Tenderly (Instrumental.) / Very thought of you, The / Satin doll / Sherry / Lady is a tramp, The / I didn't know what time it was / Look of love, The / Watch what happens / Day in the life of a fool, A / For once in my life / I had a ball.
**Album:** Released Jul '82, on Bulldog Records by President Records. Catalogue no: **BDL 1034**

**GREATEST HITS: BUDDY GRECO**
Tracks: / Lady is a tramp / My kind of girl / Around the world / Like young / Roses of Picardy / Taking a chance on love / To be or not to be in love / Mr. Lonely / Ain't she pretty / At long last love / But not for me / You're nobody 'til somebody loves you.
**Album:** Released Nov '84, on CBS by CBS Records. Catalogue no: **CBS 32522**

**LADY IS A TRAMP**
Tracks: / Lady is a tramp, The.
**7" Single:** Released Jul '60, on Fontana by Phonogram Ltd. Deleted '63. Catalogue no: **H 225**

## Green, Grant

**BORN TO BE BLUE**
Tracks: / Some day my prince will come / Born to be blue / If I should lose you / Back in your own back yard / My one and only love / Count every star / Born to be blue (alt. take) (CD only.) / Cool blues (CD only.) / Outer space (CD only.).
**Cass:** Released Sep '87, on Blue Note by EMI Records. Deleted Jun '88. Catalogue no: **4BN 84432**
**CD:** Released Aug '89, on Blue Note by EMI Records. Catalogue no: **CDP 784 432 2**
**Album:** Released Sep '85, on Blue Note by EMI Records. Deleted Nov '88. Catalogue no: **BST 84432**

**CD:** Released Aug '89, on Blue Note by EMI Records. Catalogue no: **BNZ 196**

**FEELIN' THE SPIRIT**
Tracks: / Just a closer walk with thee / Joshua fit de battle of Jerico / Nobody knows the trouble I've seen / Go down Moses / Sometimes I feel like a motherless child / Deep river.
**CD:** Released Aug '87, on Blue Note by EMI Records. Deleted Aug '89. Catalogue no: **CDP 746 822 2**
**CD:** Released Aug '87, on Blue Note by EMI Records. Deleted Aug '89. Catalogue no: **BNZ 38**

**GRANTSTAND**
Tracks: / Grantstand / My funny valentine / Blues in Maude's flat / Old folks / Green's greenery.
**Album:** Released Nov '86, on Blue Note by EMI Records. Deleted Nov '88. Catalogue no: **BST 84086**
**CD:** Released Sep '87, on Blue Note by EMI Records. Deleted Nov '88. Catalogue no: **BNZ 37**
**CD:** Released Aug '89, on Blue Note by EMI Records. Catalogue no: **BNZ 208**
**Album:** Released Nov '86, on Blue Note by EMI Records. Deleted '87. Catalogue no: **BST 84036**
**CD:** Released Aug '89, on Blue Note by EMI Records. Catalogue no: **CDP 746 430 2**

**IDLE MOMENTS**
Tracks: / Idle moments / Jean De Fleur / Django / Nomad.
**CD:** Released Nov '88, on Blue Note by EMI Records. Catalogue no: **BNZ 115**
**CD:** Released Nov '88, on Blue Note by EMI Records. Catalogue no: **CDP 784 154 2**
**Album:** Released Sep '87, on Blue Note by EMI Records. Catalogue no: **BST 84154**

**IRON CITY**
Tracks: / Iron city / Black Orpheus / Old man (let my people go) / High heel sneakers / Motherless child / Work song.
**Album:** Released Apr '81, on Muse by Black & Blue Records. Catalogue no: **MR 5120**

**LAST SESSION**
Tracks: / Wave / Just the way you are (Composer / Easy / Empanada / Night time in the switching yard / Three times a lady.
**Cass:** Released Apr '87, on Atlantis by Charly Records. Deleted May '88. Catalogue no: **TCATS 9**
**Album:** Released Apr '87, on Atlantis by Charly Records. Catalogue no: **ATS 9**

## Green, Urbie

**BLUES AND OTHER SHADES OF GREEN (Green, Urbie Quintet)**
**Album:** Released Feb '88, on Fresh Sounds (Spain) by Fresh Sounds Records (Spain). Catalogue no: **FS 61**

**MESSAGE, THE (Green, Urbie And His Orchestra)**
**Album:** Released Feb '88, on Fresh Sounds (Spain) by Fresh Sounds Records (Spain). Catalogue no: **FS 178**

## Greger, Max

**BEST OF GLENN MILLER**
Tracks: / String of pearls / Little brown jug / I know why / Chattanooga choo choo / American patrol / Moonlight Serenade / St. Louis blues march / Tuxedo Junction / Stairway to the stars / Pennsylvania 6 5000 / Johnson rag / Moonlight sonata / Song of the volga boatmen / Boatman / Bungle call rag / Anvil chorus / Tiger rag / In the mood / Serenade in blue / Sunrise serenade.
**CD:** Released Sep '85, on Polydor by Polydor Ltd. Deleted Jul '88. Catalogue no: **825 992-2**

**EUROPEAN JAZZ SOUNDS (Greger, Max & His Orchestra)**
Tracks: / Discussion / Bluer than blue / Revelation / You're the one / Sax life / Carrera / Portrait in smoke / Meet BB / M G blues / Boomerang.
**Album:** Released Nov '86, on Polydor (Germany) by Polydor Ltd. Catalogue no: **829 257-1**
**Cass:** Released Nov '85, on Polydor (Germany) by Polydor Ltd. Catalogue no: **825 992-4**
**Album:** Released Nov '85, on Polydor (Germany) by Polydor Ltd. Catalogue no: **825 992-1**

**HALLO MAX**
**Album:** Released Dec '86, on Polygram (Germany) by PolyGram UK Ltd. Catalogue no: **829 126.1**

**MANIMUM (BIG BAND JAZZ)**
Tracks: / Salute to Miles / Falling in love / One for Cann / Piece for two / Senor Bailey / Bossa flute / Early blues / Take the 'A' train.
**CD:** Released Feb '86, on Polydor (Germany) by Polydor Ltd. Catalogue no: **827 087-2**

**MAX GREGER**
Tracks: / Little brown jug / Don't sit under the apple tree / Sun valley jump / American patrol / Sunrise serenade / Stairway to the stars / At last / Tuxedo Junction / Pennsylvania 65000 / Chattanooga choochoo / I know why / Nightingale sang in Berkeley square, A / In the mood / Blue skies / Johnson rag / It happened in Sun valley / Sonata / Song of the volga boatmen / Ida, sweet as apple cider / Bugle call rag / Anvil chorus / Tiger rag / Serenade in blue / String of pearls / St. Louis blues march / Moonlight serenade.
Note: 26 popular tunes in dance tempo from German orchestra leader Max Greger.
**Album:** Released Jun '83, on Polydor (Holland) by Polydor Ltd. Catalogue no: **2482 583**
**Cass:** Released Jun '83, on Polydor (Holland) by Polydor Ltd. Catalogue no: **3201 425**

**MAXIMUM (Greger, Max Big Band)**
Tracks: / Salute to miles / Bossa flute / Piece for two / One for Cann / Senor Bailey / Falling in love / Early blues / Take the 'A' train.
**Album:** Released Sep '85, on Polydor (Germany) by Polydor Ltd. Catalogue no: **825 703-1**
**CD:** Released '88, on Polydor by Polydor Ltd. Catalogue no: **827 157 2**

**SWING DIAMONDS (Greger, Max Big Band)**
Tracks: / Trumpet blues and cantabile / Caravan / Mood indigo / Creole love call / Mr. Anthony's boogie / Hey ba ba re bop / Two o'clock jump / Eager beaver / Begin the beguine / Opus one / I've got my love to keep me warm / On the sunny side of the street / I'm beginning to see the light / April in Paris / Let's dance / Don't be that way / I'm gettin' sentimental over you / Moonlight serenade / Perfidia / Woodchopper's ball / Jumping at the woodside / C jam blues / Skyliner / Sentimental journey / Memories of you / You made me love you / Take the 'A' train / In the mood.
**CD:** Released Mar '88, on Polydor (Germany) by Polydor Ltd. Catalogue no: **833 658-2**
**Album:** Released Feb '85, on Polydor (Holland) by Polydor Ltd. Catalogue no: **823 440-1**
**Cass:** Released Feb '85, on Polydor (Holland) by Polydor Ltd. Catalogue no: **823 440-4**

## Greko, Keith

**LAST TRAIN OUTTA FLAGSTAFF**
Note: Artists include Louie Bellson / Bud Shank / David Friesen.
**Album:** Released Oct '86, on Concept (1) Catalogue no: **VL 4**

## Grey, Al

**AL GREY AND JESPER THILO QUINTET (Grey, Al & Jesper Thilo Quintet)**
**Album:** Released Jan '88, on Storyville by Storyville Records AB. Catalogue no: **SLP 4136**

**AL GREY'S ALL STARS**
**Album:** Released Apr '79, on Traveller's Products Deleted '83. Catalogue no: **TP 3001**

**BASIC GREY**
Tracks: / Things ain't what they used to be / Open wider please / I got bad and that ain't good / Don't get around much anymore / How come you do me like you do / Bluish grey / Elder, The / Bewitched / Kenie-Konie / Bluish grey / Wild deuce / Green dolphin street / Bantu / Melba's blues / Nothing but the truth / Three-fourth blues / Just waiting / R.B.Q / Minor on top / Africa lady / Hi fly.
**2 LP Set:** Released Aug '88, on Chess by Vogue Records. Catalogue no: **GCH 2-6030**

**GET IT TOGETHER (Live at The Pizza Express) (Grey,Al & Tony Coe)**
Note: With Brian Lemon, Roger Kellaway.
**Album:** Released Aug '88, on Pizza Express by Pizza Express Records. Catalogue no: **PE 5504**

**JAZZ AT THE PHILHARMONIC 1983**
**Album:** Released May '83, on Pablo Jazz (USA) by Pablo Records (USA). Catalogue no: **2310 882**

## Grieg, Stan

**BLUES EVERY TIME**
Tracks: / Love for sale / Honky tonk train blues / Take five / Willlow weep for me / Five o'clock blues / Air to The Duke / Mop mop.
**Album:** Released Aug '86, on Calligraph Catalogue no: **CLGLP 004**
**Cass:** Released Aug '86, on Calligraph Catalogue no: **ZCLG 004**

## Griffin, Johnny

**Biographical details:** Attended Du Sable High School, where he was taught by Captain Walter Dyett, the legendary music teacher who also graduated Gene Ammons, Von Freeman and scores of other fine jazzmen. The driving hard-bop player co-led a combo with Lockjaw Davis around 1960, and lived in Europe 1964-1978. (Donald Clarke, 1989).

**BLOWING SESSION, A**
Tracks: / Way you look tonight / Ball bearing / All the things you are / Smoke stack.
**CD:** Released Jun '89, on Blue Note by EMI Records. Catalogue no: **CDP 781 559 2**
**Album:** Released Sep '84, on Blue Note by EMI Records. Catalogue no: **BLP 1559**
**Album:** Released Jul '89, on Blue Note by EMI Records. Catalogue no: **B1 81559**
**CD:** Released Jun '89, on Blue Note by EMI Records. Catalogue no: **BNZ 168**

**CONGREGATION**
Tracks: / Congregation / Latin quarter, The / I'm glad there is you / Main spring / It's you or no one.
**Album:** Released '85, on Blue Note by EMI Records. Catalogue no: **BLP 1580**

**FLY MISTER FLY (With the Joe Morris Orchestra)**
**Album:** Released Jun '85, on Saxophonograph (Sweden) Catalogue no: **BP 504**

**GRIFF AND LOCK (Griffin, Johnny & Eddie Lockjaw Davis)**
**Album:** Released Jan '87, on Original Jazz Classics (USA) by Fantasy Inc (USA). Catalogue no: **OJC 264**

**INTRODUCING JOHNNY GRIFFIN**
Tracks: / Mil dew / Chicago calling / These foolish things / Boy next door, The / Nice and easy / It's alright with me / Lover man / Way you look tonight / Cherokee.
**CD:** Released May '87, on Blue Note by EMI Records. Catalogue no: **BNZ 39**
**Album:** Released Aug '85, on Blue Note by EMI Records. Deleted '87. Catalogue no: **BST 81533**
**CD:** Released May '87, on EMI-Manhattan by EMI Records. Catalogue no: **CDP 746 536 2**

**JAMFS ARE COMING, THE (Griffin, Johnny and Art Taylor Quartet)**
**Album:** Released Apr '81, on Timeless (Import) by Timeless Records. Catalogue no: **SJP 121**

**JOHNNY GRIFFIN**
**Album:** Released Oct '79, on Horo Catalogue no: **HLL 101/10**

**JOHNNY GRIFFIN MEETS DEXTER GORDON (Griffin, Johnny and Dexter Gordon)**
**Album:** Released Apr '81, on Lotus Catalogue no: **ORL 8247**

**JOHNNY GRIFFIN QUARTET (VIDEO) (Griffin, Johnny Quartet)**
**VHS:** Released '88, on Kay Jazz (video) by Kay Jazz. Catalogue no: **KJ 058**

**JOHNNY GRIFFIN SEXTET (Griffin, Johnny Sextet)**
Tracks: / Stix' trix / What's new / Wooding you / Johnny G.G / Catharsis.
**Album:** Released Feb '88, on Riverside (USA) by Fantasy Inc (USA). Catalogue no: **RLP 264**

**LITTLE GIANT, THE**
Tracks: / Catharsis / What's new / Hot sausage / Woodyn' you / Where's your overcoat boy / Little John / 63rd Street theme / Playmates / Message / Kerry dancers / Black is the colour of my true loves hair / Green grow the rushes / Londonderry air.
**2 LP Set:** Released Apr '80, on Milestone by Ace Records. Deleted '85. Catalogue no: **M 47054**
**CD:** Released '86, on JVC/Fantasy Catalogue no: **VDJ 1547**

**MAN I LOVE, THE**
Tracks: / Man I love, The / Hush-a-bye / Blues for Harvey / Masquerade is over, The / Sophisticated lady / Wee.
**CD:** Released Jun '88, on Black Lion Catalogue no: **BLCD 760107**
**Album:** Released Jun '88, on Black Lion Catalogue no: **BLP 60107**

**NYC UNDERGROUND**
Tracks: / Yours is my heart alone / Few words from Johnny Griffin / Alone agian / Let me touch it / Sophisticated lady / Rhythm-a-ning.
**Album:** Released Aug '81, on Galaxy (1) by President Records. Deleted Aug '86. Catalogue no: **GXT 5132**

**SWINGIN', THE**
Tracks: / Foot patting / Please send me someone to love / Turk's Bolero, The / Deep eight / Handful of soul, A / Jamfs are coming, The / Lady heavy bottom's house.
**Album:** Released Jun '87, on Kingdom Jazz by Kingdom Records. Catalogue no: **GATE 7020**
**Cass:** Released '89, on Kingdom Jazz by Kingdom Records. Catalogue no: **CGATE 7020**

**TOUGHEST TENORS (Griffin, Johnny & Eddie Lockjaw Davis)**
Tracks: / Tickle toe / Save your love for me / Funky fluke / Epistrophy / Well you needn't / I mean you / Good bait / Walkin' / Blues up and down / Camp meeting / Blue Lou / How am I to know / Tin tin deo.
**Album:** on Milestone by Ace Records. Catalogue no: **M 47035**

**YOU LEAVE ME BREATHLESS**
Tracks: / Rhythm-a-ning / Old folks / Wee / You leave me breathless / Leave me alone blues.
**Album:** Released Apr '85, on Black Lion Catalogue no: **BLP 30134**

## Grimes, Carol

**AIN'T THAT PECULIAR**
Tracks: / Ain't that peculiar / Fashion passion.
**7" Single:** Released Nov '82, on Polydor by Polydor Ltd. Deleted Nov '85. Catalogue no: **POSP 417**

**CAROL GRIMES**
Tracks: / I've been used / Number one (In my heart) / You make my life / Up hill peace of mind / I betcha didn't know that / Brand new tomorrow / My baby specializes / That's the time / I feel like going home / Private number / Dynamite / No more tears.
**Album:** on Charly by Charly Records. Catalogue no: **CR 30164**

**EYES WIDE OPEN**
**Album:** Released Aug '86, on Miles Music by Miles Music Records. Catalogue no: **TM 9**
**CD:** Released '86, on TM (Temple Music) by TM Records. Catalogue no: **CDTM 09**
**CD:** Released Nov '89, on Line by Line Records (W.Germany). Catalogue no: **INCD9.00329**
**Cass:** Released Aug '86, on Miles Music by Miles Music Records. Catalogue no: **ZCTM 9**

**WHY DON'T THEY DANCE**
Tracks: / Cool fire / Turning the worm / Why don't they dance / Mind the gap / Heart in my hands / Two step / Drive me crazy / Chain of fools / Stay with me baby / Living for life / Good friends.
**CD:** Released May '89, on Line by Line Records (W.Germany). Catalogue no: **INCD 9.00668**

## Grimes, Tiny

**Biographical details:** Tiny switched from the piano to the electric guitar in group Cats and a Fiddle 1940-1941, played with Art Tatum and Slam Sewart 1941-1944, in 1944 the Tiny Grimes Quintet made four tracks with Charlie Parker, with Grimes vocals, as on *Romance without finance*. His *Midnight special* on Atlantic, with Red Prysock (tenor saxophone) was an R'n'B hit in 1948, he led the Rocking Highlanders well into the 1950s, and his albums included *Some groovy fours* in 1974 on Classic Jazz, with blues pianist/R'n'B hitmaker Lloyd Glenn (1909-1985). (Donald Clarke 1989).

**EARLY-MID 1950S (Grimes, Tiny & His Friends)**

Tracks: / Movin' out today / Things got tough again / Long lean and lanky / Keep me with you / I'm in love with you / Do you really love me / Start talking baby / I'll never let you go / I'm a wine drinker / I love to make love / I want a present for Xmas / I can't go on / Call of the wild.
Note: Tiny Grimes with Cats & The Fiddle, Dixieaires, Haji Baba, Johnny Davis, J.B. Summers, Lionel Robinson.
**Album:** Released Feb '88, on Krazy Kat by Interstate Music. Catalogue no: **KK 821**

**FRANKIE AND JOHNNY BOOGIE**
**Album:** Released Nov '85, on Black & Blue (2) by BMG Records (UK). Catalogue no: **33712**

**LOCH LOMOND (Grimes, Tiny & His Rockin' Highlanders)**
Tracks: / Blue harem / Flying high / That old black magic / Profoundly blue / Boogie woogie barbecue / Annie Laurie / Nightmare blues / Hot in Harlem / Loch Lomond / Midnight special / Jumpin' at Gleason's / Jealousy / Begin the beguine / Sidewalks of New York, The / Man I love, The / Sanctifying the blues.
**Album:** Released Aug '87, on Whiskey, Women & Song (Sweden) Catalogue no: **KM 706**

**PROFOUNDLY BLUE**
**Album:** Released Apr '81, on Muse by Black & Blue Records. Catalogue no: **MR 5012**

**ROCK THE HOUSE (Grimes, Tiny & His Rockin' Highlanders)**
**Album:** Released Sep '87, on Swingtime by Contact Records (Denmark). Catalogue no: **ST 1016**

**TINY GRIMES AND THE ROCKIN' HIGHLANDERS (Grimes, Tiny & His Rockin' Highlanders)**
Tracks: / Call of the wild / St Louis blues / Tiny's jump / Howlin' blues / Frankie and Johnny boogie / My baby's cool / Pert skirt / Hey Mr. J.B. / Drinking beer / Marie.
**CD:** Released 8 Apr '89, on Krazy Kat by Interstate Music. Catalogue no: **KKCD 01**

**TINY GRIMES VOLUME 1-1949-1952**
Tracks: / Tiny's jump / Hey Now / Why did you waste my time / St. Louis Blues / Drinking beer / My baby's left me / Frankie and Johnnie Boogie-1 / Hey Mr. J.B. / Battle of the mass / I'm in love with you baby / My baby's cool / Hawaiian boogie / No hug no kiss / Frankie and Johnnie boogie-2.
Note: Mono recording.
**Album:** Released Oct '86, on Krazy Kat by Interstate Music. Catalogue no: **KK 804**

**TINY GRIMES VOLUME 2 1949-55 (Instrumentals)**
Note: 14 Gotham cuts from 1949-55... only 4 previously issued.
**Album:** Released Oct '87, on Krazy Kat by Interstate Music. Catalogue no: **KK 817**

**TINY'S BOOGIE (Rockin' & sockin' 1948-50)**
**Album:** Released '88, on Oldie Blues Catalogue no: **OL 8009**

## Grossman, Stefan

**Biographical details:** Stefan is a virtuoso ragtime revivalist. Beginning as a student, champion and biographer of Rev. Gary Davis, he also studied with blues singers Mississippi John Hurt, Skip James, Son House, Mance Lipscombe and Fred McDowell, noting their techniques as all-round entertainers rather than as pure bluesmen, playing ragtime as much as anything, and has dedicated himself to keeping that music alive. He played in the Even Dozen Jug Band, with the Fugs in 1966 and Mitch Ryder in 1967. He also formed the Kicking Mule label with Ed Denson, recording acoustic fingerpickers including himself. (Donald Clarke, 1989).

**ANTHOLOGY: STEFAN GROSSMAN**
Tracks: / Hot dogs / Blues jumped the rabbit / Hi dum diddle / Morning comes / Satisfied and ticked too / Alibi / Candyman / Fat man / Teddy Roosevelt / Blues for Mr. Sam / Those lazy blues / Twelve string medley / Little Sally Walker / Lena Anne / Danish drone / Matesa.
**Album:** Released '79, on Transatlantic by Transatlantic Records. Deleted '84. Catalogue no: **MTRA 2006**

**AUNT MOLLY'S MURRAY FARM**
Tracks: / Aunt Molly's Murray Farm / Foregone conclusion / Religious trainfare blues / See see rider / Delilah / Sideways nowhere bound / Special rider blues / Wall hollow blues / Cow cow's 4-4 waltz / Dallas rag / All my friends are gone / Number one / Money's all gone / Big road blues / Roberta.
**Album:** Released '73, on Sonet by Sonet Records. Catalogue no: **SNTF 640**

**BOTTLENECK SERENADE**
Tracks: / Tightrope / Lullaby for Anna / Bottleneck serenade / First time I ever saw your face / Birdnest two step / Dance of the blind Minotaur / Tomorrow / Working on the new railroad / Concrete parachute / For Elvie / Delta side of 1928 / Friends forever.
**Album:** Released '79, on Transatlantic by Transatlantic Records. Deleted '84. Catalogue no: **TRA 293**

**COUNTRY BLUES GUITAR**
Tracks: / Special rider blues / Pallet on your floor / New pony blues / One kind favor / Hollerin' for my crow Jane / Hard time killin' floor blues / If you haven't any hay get on down the road / Ragtime mama blues / Some day baby / Yonder comes the blues / Weeping willow / Brownsville blues.
**Album:** Released Aug '77, on Kicking Mule by Sonet Records. Catalogue no: **SNKF 129**

**GRAMERCY PARK SHEIK**
Tracks: / Little Rock blues number two / Lena Anne / Hans Fried / Crow black squall / Gentle joys, gentle sorrows / Requiem for Patrick Kilroy / Not you or I my dear / Mississippi blues number two / Cross-eyed blues / Irene's sleepy lullaby / You'd best be gentle.
**Album:** Released '88, on Sonet by Sonet Records. Catalogue no: **SNTF 627**

**HOT DOGS**
**Album:** Released Oct '80, on Transatlantic by Transatlantic Records. Catalogue no: **TRA 257 80**

**HOW TO PLAY BLUES GUITAR**
**Album:** Released Mar '89, on Kicking Mule by Sonet Records. Catalogue no: **KM 109**
**Album:** Released '78, on Kicking Mule by Sonet Records. Catalogue no: **SNKF 150**

**HOW TO PLAY BLUES GUITAR VOL.2**
Tracks: / Man of my own / Rainy day blues / Strange city streets / Easy street / Nobody's fault but mine / Come back baby / Moon goin' down / Motherless children / Wake up Mama / Morning blues / Pallet on your floor / Jubilee jamboree / Good morning little school boy.
**Album:** Released Mar '89, on Kicking Mule by Sonet Records. Catalogue no: **KM 151**
**Album:** Released '78, on Kicking Mule by Sonet Records. Deleted '88. Catalogue no: **SNKF 148**

**HOW TO PLAY RAGTIME GUITAR**
**Album:** Released Mar '89, on Kicking Mule by Sonet Records. Catalogue no: **KM 115**

**JOHN RENBOURN AND STEFAN GROSSMAN (see Renbourn, John) (Grossman, Stefan & John Renbourn)**
**Album:** Released '78, on Kicking Mule by Sonet Records. Catalogue no: **SNKF 139**

**SHINING SHADOWS**
**Album:** Released Oct '88, on Shanachie by Shanachie Records (USA). Catalogue no: **SH 95002**

**THUNDER ON THE RUN**
Tracks: / Thunder on the run / Assassination of John Fahey, The / From Berne to Perth / Sergeant Early's dream / Red haired boy / Blind Mary / Callaghan's hornpipe / Pretty girl milking a cow / Peak's puzzle / Kicking up the dust / St. Andrews / Fiddler's contest / Silver swan / Billy in the lowgrounds / Greenfields of America.
Note: Medley: Sergeant Early's dream / Redhaired boy / Blind Mary / Callahan's hornpipe / Pretty girl milking a cow / Peak's puzzle / Kicking up the dust. Medley: St. Andrews / The Fiddler's contest / Silver swan. Medley: Billy in the lowgrounds / Greenfields of America.
**Album:** Released Oct '80, on Kicking Mule by Sonet Records. Catalogue no: **SNKF 170**

**UNDER THE VOLCANO**
**Album:** Released Mar '89, on Kicking Mule by Sonet Records. Catalogue no: **KM 162**

**Album:** Released Feb '80, on Kicking Mule by Sonet Records. Deleted '88. Catalogue no: **SNKF 161**

**YAZOO BASIN BOOGIE**
Tracks: / Adam's voice / Tickle dew / Dallas rag / I'm so glad / Katz rag / Texas lemon flavour rag / Sunday rag / Pigtown fling / Red pepper rag / House carpenter / Maple leaf rag / Colored aristocracy / Slow blues in C / Aurora's powder rag / County line / Last of Callahan / Dervish boogie / Yazoo basin boogie.
**Album:** Released Mar '89, on Kicking Mule by Sonet Records. Catalogue no: **KM 102**
**Album:** Released Jan '78, on Kicking Mule by Sonet Records. Deleted '88. Catalogue no: **SNKF 134**

## Grosz, Marty

**ACOUSTIC GUITAR DUETS (Grosz, Marty & Wayne Wright)**
**Album:** Released Apr '79, on Aviva (USA) Catalogue no: **AVIVA 6000**

**CHICAGO 1957 (Grosz, Marty & His Honoris Causa Jazz Band)**
**Album:** Released Jul '86, on Collectors Items Catalogue no: **CI 008**

**DICK WELLSTOOD AND MARTY GROSZ (Grosz, Marty/Dick Wellstood)**
**Album:** Released Apr '79, on Aviva (USA) Catalogue no: **AVIVA 6001**

**MARTY GROSZ AND HIS BLUE ANGELS (Grosz, Marty & His Blue Angels)**
**Album:** Released May '88, on Aviva (USA) Catalogue no: **AVIVA 6004**

**MARTY GROSZ AND THE KEEPERS OF THE FLAME (Grosz, Marty & The Keepers Of The Flame)**
**Album:** Released Apr '88, on Stomp Off (USA) Catalogue no: **SOS 1158**

**MARTY GROSZ AND WAYNE WRIGHT (Grosz, Marty & Wayne Wright)**
**Album:** Released May '88, on Aviva (USA) Catalogue no: **AVIVA 6003**

**SINGS OF LOVE (Grosz, Marty / Tiny Signa)**
**Album:** Released '88, on Statiras (USA) by Statiras(USA) Records. Catalogue no: **SLP 8080**

**SWING IT (Grosz, Marty & Destiny's Tots)**
Tracks: / Let's swing it / Skeleton in the closet, The / Emaline / Old man harlem / Love dropped in for tea / Little girl / Sunrise serenade / I've got a feelin' / You're foolin' / What's the use / Eye opener / Sun will shine tonight, The / It's been so long / I surrender, dear / It's the last time / Sonny boy / High hat, a piccolo and a cane, A.
**CD:** Released Apr '89, on Jazzology (USA) by Jazzology Records (USA). Catalogue no: **JCD 180**

## GRP

**GRP CHRISTMAS COLLECTION, A (Various artists)**
Tracks: / Little drummer boy: *Stuermer, Daryl* / Have yourself a merry little Christmas: *Scott, Tom* / Carol of the bells: *Benoit, David* / Christmas song, The: *Schuur, Diane* / God rest ye merry gentlemen: *Corea, Chick Elektric Band* / White Christmas: *Ritenour, Lee* / Santa Claus is coming to town: *Valentin, Dave* / This Christmas: *Yutaka* / Sleigh ride: *Daniels, Eddie* / It came upon a midnight clear: *Szakcsi* / What child is this: *Egan, Mark* / O'Tannenbaum: *Burton, Gary* / Silent night: *Special EFX* / Silver Bells: *Eubanks, Kevin* / Some children see him: *Grusin, Dave.*
Note: A very special Christmas album from the entire roster of GRP stars. They have gathered together to perform all the Christmas favourites in their own unique musical style. A powerful album that cuts across all musical categories, jazz, pop, R&B and rock with its seasonal message. Over 50 minutes of music. CD version contains 3 bonus tracks.
**CD:** Released Oct '88, on GRP by GRP Records (USA). Catalogue no: **GRP 9574-2**
**Album:** Released Oct '88, on GRP by GRP Records (USA). Catalogue no: **GRP 9574-1**
**Cass:** Released Oct '88, on GRP by GRP Records (USA). Catalogue no: **GRP 9574-4**

**GRP LIVE IN SESSION (Various artists)**
Tracks: / Rio funk: *Various artists* / St. Elsewhere: *Various artists* / Mountain dance: *Various artists* / Oasis: *Various artists* / Rit variations: *Various artists* / Reverend Lee: *Various artists* / Dolphin dreams: *Various artists.*
Note: Featuring Dave Grusin, Lee Ritenour, Dave Valentin, Diane Schuur.
**Album:** Released Dec '85, on GRP by GRP Records (USA). Catalogue no: **GRP 91023**
**Cass:** Released Dec '85, on GRP by GRP Records (USA). Catalogue no: **GRPM 91023**
**CD:** Released Dec '85, on GRP by GRP Records (USA). Catalogue no: **GRD 9532**
**DAT:** Released Jul '88, on GRP by GRP Records (USA). Catalogue no: **GRT 9532**

**GRP NEW MAGIC DIGITAL SAMPLER (Various artists)**
Note: Sampler Includes: Artists: Dave Grusin, Diane Schuur, Special EFX, Stephane Grappelli, Eddie Danies, The Duke Ellingon Orchestra, David Benoit, The Chick Corea Elektric Band.
**CD:** Released Jul '87, on GRP by GRP Records (USA). Catalogue no: **GRPD 9549**

**GRP ROADTRACKS (Various artists)**
Tracks: / Power wave: *Grusin, Dave* / Essence: *Eubanks, Kevin* / Elektrik city: *Corea, Chick* / I Can't believe that you're in love with me: *Shuur, Diane* / Uptown east: *Special EFX* / Rio funk: *Ritenour, Lee* / Circle dance: *Daniels, Eddie* / Times of my life: *Cobham, Billy* / Can't change my heart: *Valentine,Dave/Bofill, Angela* / Can't change my heart: *Bofill, Angela/Valentine,Dave* / Shuffle city: *Grusin, Dave* / Harlequin: *Desconhencido, Arlequin/Grusin,Dave/Ritenour,Lee* / Harlequin: *Grusin, Dave, Lee Ritenour, Arlequin Desconhencido.*
Note: A special cassette compilation for European release only, twelve representative tracks from GRP catalogue, 60 minutes playing time, produced on chrome tape. Distinctive packaging to ensure good visibility.
**Cass:** Released Oct '86, on GRP by GRP Records (USA). Catalogue no: **GRPM 91000**

**GRP SUPER LIVE IN CONCERT (Various artists)**
Tracks: / Deedle's blues: *Various artists* / Love dance: *Various artists* / Early AM attitude: *Various artists* / Sauce, The: *Various artists* / Water from the moon: *Various artists* / Earth run: *Various artists* / Target: *Various artists* / Actor's life, An: *Various artists* / Light years: *Various artists* / Rumble: *Various artists* / Time track: *Various artists* / No zone: *Various artists* / Overture: *Various artists.*
Note: CD version contains bonus tracks. Dave Grusin / Lee Ritenour / Diane Schuur / Tom Scott / Chick Corea Elec-tric Band.
**Cass:** Released Mar '88, on GRP by GRP Records (USA). Catalogue no: **GRC2 91650**
**CD Set:** Released Mar '88, on GRP by GRP Records (USA). Catalogue no: **GRD 291650**
**2 LP Set:** Released Mar '88, on GRP by GRP Records (USA). Catalogue no: **GRP2 91650**

**NEW AGE IN JAZZ (Various artists)**
Tracks: / Early a.m attitude: *GRP* / She could be mine: *GRP* / Heart is a lonely hunter: *GRP* / Mozaik: *GRP* / Dolphin dreams: *GRP* / Rio funk: *GRP* / Birk's works: *GRP* / Opening night: *GRP* / Very nice indeed: *GRP* / Fountain of you: *GRP.*
Note: Superb collection from the "Master of Sound" GRP Records. Featuring tracks by Dave Grusin, Lee Ritenour, Dizzy Gillespie, Billy Cobham and others, this is an ideal demonstration CD and a great introduction to the GRP sound.
**CD:** Released Jun '86, on GRP by GRP Records (USA). Catalogue no: **GRPD 9529**

## Gruntz, George

**HAPPENING NOW! (Gruntz, George Concert Jazz Band '87)**
**CD:** Released '88, on Hat Art Catalogue no: **ARTCD 6008**

**THEATRE (Gruntz, George Concert Jazz Band '83)**
Tracks: / El chancho / In the tradition of Switzerland / No one can explain it / Holy grail of jazz and joy.
**Album:** Released Jun '84, on ECM Catalogue no: **ECM 1265**

## Gryce, Gigi

**Biographical details:** He studied composition in Boston, gigging in local groups from 1946, and mounted a concert in Harford with 23 pieces including Horace Silver, and won a scholarship to Paris in 1952, but like most black musicians he played in saloons most of the time. He also played on *Monk's music* in 1957, one of Monk's best; his own best-known composition was *Nico's tempo*. (Donald Clarke, 1989).

### RAT RACE BLUES
Tracks: / Rat race blues / Strange feeling / Boxer's blues / Blues in bloom / Monday through Sunday.
**Album:** Released Feb '84, on New Jazz (USA) by Fantasy Inc (USA). Catalogue no: **OJC 081**

### SIGNALS (Gryce, Gigi/Duke Jordan / Hal Overton)
**Album:** Released Mar '85, on Savoy Jazz (USA) by Malaco Records (USA). Catalogue no: **SJL 2231**

## Guaraldi, Vince

### FLOWER IS A LOVESOME THING, A (Guaraldi, Vince & Trio)
**Album:** Released Apr '86, on Original Jazz Classics (USA) by Fantasy Inc (USA). Catalogue no: **OJC 235**

## Guarnieri, Johnny

**Biographical details:** He turned to jazz in 1937 after studying classical music, playing with Benny Goodman 1939-40, including sextet specialities *A smo-o-ooth one*, *Air mail special*, among others. On one occasion, Goodman was incredibly rude to him and he was comforted by Teddy Wilson (a big influence) who told him to pay no attention. He worked for Artie Shaw 1940-1941, playing harpsichord on Shaw's famous Gramercy Five sessions (*Summit Ridge Drive*, *Special Delivery stomp*, etc. He did staff work for NBC, made hundreds of records in the 1940s including classic smallfroup sessions on Commodore with Lester Young and Coleman Hawkins, and had long residencies in Holywood in the 1970s and 1980s. (Donald Clarke, 1989).

### JOHNNY GUARNIERI PLAYS FATS WALLER
**Album:** Released Jan '79, on Taz Jazz Deleted '83. Catalogue no: **TJZ 1002**

### SUPERSTRIDE
**Album:** Released Jan '79, on Taz Jazz Deleted '83. Catalogue no: **TJZ 1001**

## Guest Stars

### GUEST STARS, THE
Tracks: / Northern lights / You can't weep over it / Valentine's day / Tin can alley / I know I know / Wake it up / Latierra y el sol cupido.
**CD:** Released '88, Catalogue no: **ES 2027**
**Album:** Released Jul '84, on Guest Stars Catalogue no: **GS 10**
**Cass:** Released Jul '84, on Guest Stars Catalogue no: **GSC 10**

### LIVE IN BERLIN
**Cass:** Released '88, on Guest Stars Catalogue no: **GS 12C**
**Album:** Released '88, on Guest Stars Catalogue no: **ES 2033**

### OUT AT NIGHT
Tracks: / Montezuma's mother / Miles apart / Amy's bounce / What means love / Wind is getting angry, The / Song of the bridge / Uranus in jeopardy / Birds of a feather.
Note: Second album from the all girl band The Guest Stars who have been touring non-stop since their debut album release in July '84.Their first LP received excel-lent reviews and opened the eyes of various promoters who became eager to book the band.Their appeal is diverse offering music from Avant-Garde to Afro-Cuban Funk. Personnel:Deidre Cartwright / Laka Daisical / Ruthie Smith / Josefina Cupido / Linda Da Mango.
**Cass:** Released Dec '85, on Guest Stars Catalogue no: **GSC 11**
**Album:** Released Dec '85, on Guest Stars Catalogue no: **GS 11**

## Guitar Slim

**Biographical details:** Eddie Jones sang with conviction and was an influential pioneer on electric guitar, not only as a stylist but also as one of the first to move around the stage to the limit of the long lead on his instrument. *The things that I do* was a no.1 R'n'B hit in 1954 on Specialty, arranged by Ray Charles who also played piano, it remains a classic blues track. (Donald Clarke, 1989).

### ATCO SESSIONS
**Album:** Released Aug '87, on Atlantic by WEA Records. Catalogue no: **81760-1**

### BATTLE OF THE BLUES
Tracks: / Certainly all / Going down slow / Stand by me / You give me nothing but the blues / You're gonna miss me / I wanna love a you / I got sumpin' for you / Reap what you sow / I'm your best bet baby / Mothers love, A / Eating and sleeping / No one but me / Funny face / Sittin' and wondering / What can I do? / Till I say well done.
**Album:** Released Feb '87, on Ace by Ace Records. Catalogue no: **CHD 189**

### CAROLINA BLUES (Guitar Slim & Jelly Belly)
**Album:** Released '81, on Arhoolie (USA) by Arhoolie Records (USA). Catalogue no: **ARHOOLIE 2005**

### GREENSBORO ROUNDER
Note: Mono Recording.
**Album:** Released Jul '86, on Flyright by Interstate Music. Catalogue no: **FLY 538**

### RED CADILLAC AND CRAZY CHICKS
**Album:** Released May '86, on Sundown by Magnum Music Group. Catalogue no: **CG 709-08**
**Album:** Released Dec '88, on Sundown by Magnum Music Group. Catalogue no: **SG 709-08**

### THINGS THAT I USED TO DO,THE
Tracks: / Well I done got over it / Trouble don't last / Guitar slim / Story of my life / Letter to my girlfriend / Reap what you sow / Later for you baby / Things that I used to do / Quicksand / Bad luck blues / Think it over / Our only child / I got sumpin' for you / Sufferin' mind / Twenty five lies / Something to remember you by.
**Album:** Released '84, on Ace by Ace Records. Catalogue no: **CHD 110**

## Guitar Wizards...

### GUITAR WIZARDS 1926-35 (Various artists)
**Album:** Released Dec '88, on Yazoo (USA) by Shanachie Records (USA). Catalogue no: **L 1016**

## Gulda, Friedrich

### MEETING, THE (Gulda, Friedrich & Chick Corea)
Tracks: / Improvisations on two pianos / Some day my prince will come / Put your little foot out / Poem no. 3 / Wiegenlied.
**CD:** Released Aug '84, on Philips by Phonogram Ltd. Catalogue no: **410 397-2**

### MUSIC OF OUR TIME
**2 LP Set:** Released '81, on MPS Jazz Catalogue no: **MPS 88 050**

## Gunter, Arthur

### BLACK & BLUES
**Album:** Released Dec '87, on Excello (USA) Catalogue no: **LP 8017**

## Gustafsson, Rune

### HIMSELF
**Album:** Released '87, on Sonet by Sonet Records. Catalogue no: **SNTF 637**

### JUST THE WAY YOU ARE (Gustafsson, Rune & Niels-Henning Orsted-Pederson)
Tracks: / Just the way you are / Laverne walk / What are you doing the rest of your life / Slipped disc / Thrill is gone, The / Latin turkey / Seven steps to heaven / Alice in wonderland / How insensitive / Hot house / Jitterbug waltz.
**Album:** Released Oct '81, on Sonet by Sonet Records. Catalogue no: **SNTF 869**

### MOVE
**Album:** Released '88, on GNP Crescendo (USA) by GNP Crescendo Records (USA). Catalogue no: **GNPS 2118**

### SWEETEST SOUNDS, THE (Gustafsson, Rune & Zoot Sims)
**Album:** Released Jun '86, on Sonet by Sonet Records. Catalogue no: **SNTF 819**

## Guy, Barry

### ENDGAME (Guy, Barry & Howard Riley & John Stevens & Trevor Watts)
**Album:** Released Nov '79, on Japo (ECM) Catalogue no: **JAPO 60028**

### ODE FOR JAZZ ORCHESTRA (Guy, Barry & The London Jazz Comp Orchestra)
**2 LP Set:** Released Nov '79, on Incus by Incus Records. Catalogue no: **INCUS 6/7**

### SOLO BRASS IMPROVISATIONS
**Album:** Released Nov '76, on Incus by Incus Records. Catalogue no: **INCUS 22**

## Guy, Buddy

**Biographical details:** He went to Chicago in 1957, where he rose to the top as one of the finest modern bluesmen both as a sideman and in his own right. He recorded with Magic Sam and under his own name in 1958. He was a house musician at Chess and had a no.12 R'n'B hit *Stone Crazy* on that label in 1962. Live gigs with Junior Wells and Otis Rush as well as studio work were issued on Vanguard, and he appeared as 'Friendly chap' on Wells' album *Voodoo man* on Delmark in 1966. *Drinkin' TNT 'n'smokin' dynamite* includes Wells and Rolling Stone Bill Wyman on bass. *In the beginning* is a 1958-1964 compilation with Chicago bands including Rush, Otis Spann and Sonny Boy Williamson. (Donald Clarke, 1989).

### BREAKIN' OUT
**CD:** Released Jul '88, on JSP by JSP Records. Catalogue no: **JSP CD 215**

### BUDDY GUY
Tracks: / Broken hearted blues / I got my eyes on you / First time I met the blues / Let me love you baby / Hard but fair / When my left eye jumps / Stone crazy / No lie / Stick around / My time after awhile / Leave my girl / My Mother.
**Album:** Released Apr '83, on Chess (USA) Catalogue no: **CXMP 2010**

### BUDDY GUY ON CHESS VOL.1
**CD:** Released '88, on Vogue by Vogue Records. Catalogue no: **VG 600 176**

### CHESS MASTERS
Tracks: / Broken hearted blues / I got my eyes on you / First time I met the blues / Let me love you baby / Hard but fair / When my left eye jumps / Stone crazy / No lie / Stick around / My time after awhile / Leave my girl alone / My mother.
**Cass:** Released Jan '87, on Chess by Vogue Records. Catalogue no: **GCHK 8013**
**Album:** Released Jan '87, on Chess by Vogue Records. Catalogue no: **GCH 8013**

### CHICAGO GOLDEN YEARS
**2 LP Set:** Released Oct '88, on Vogue by Vogue Records. Catalogue no: **427006**

### COMPLETE D.J. PLAY MY BLUES
Note: Recorded in Chicago 1981. With Phil Guy/Doug Williams/Mike Morrison/Ray Allison.
**CD:** Released Jun '87, on JSP by JSP Records. Catalogue no: **JSP CD 203**

### DJ PLAY MY BLUES
Tracks: / Good news / Blues at my babies house / She suits me to a T / Just teasin' / All your love / D.J play my blues.
**Album:** Released Oct '82, on JSP by JSP Records. Catalogue no: **JSP 1042**

### DOLLAR DONE FELL, THE
**Album:** Released Jan '82, on JSP by JSP Records. Catalogue no: **JSP 1009**

### DRINKIN' TNT 'N' SMOKIN' DYNAMITE (Guy, Buddy & Junior Wells)
Tracks: / Ah'w baby / Everything gonna be alright / How can one woman be so mean / Checking on my baby / When you see the little tears from my eyes / My younger days.
**Album:** Released Jul '84, on Sonet by Sonet Records. Catalogue no: **SNTF 920**
**CD:** Released Aug '88, on Red Lightnin' by Red Lightning Records. Catalogue no: **RLCD 0076**
**Album:** Released '88, on Blind Pig (USA) by Blind Pig Records (USA). Catalogue no: **BP-1182**
**Album:** Released Sep '82, on Red Lightnin' by Red Lightning Records. Catalogue no: **RL 034**

### GOT TO USE YOUR HOUSE
**Album:** Released Sep '79, on Blues Ball Catalogue no: **2005**

### HOLD THAT PLANE
Tracks: / Watermelon man / I'm ready / You don't love me / Hello San Francisco / Hold that plane / My time after a while / Come see about me.
**Album:** Released Jul '89, on Start by Start Records Ltd.. Catalogue no: **VNP 5315**
**CD:** Released Jul '89, on Start by Start Records Ltd.. Catalogue no: **VNP 7315**
**Cass:** Released Jul '89, on Start by Start Records Ltd.. Catalogue no: **VNP 6315**

### HOT AND COOL
Tracks: / I got my eyes on you / Things I used to do, The / (You give me) Fever / 24 hours of the day / I had a dream last night / Hold that plane / Man and the blues, A / Sweet little angel / Worry, worry.
**Album:** Released Apr '78, on Vanguard by Start Records Ltd.. Catalogue no: **VSD 79290**

### I AIN'T GOT NO MONEY (Guy, Buddy /Blue Charlie/Joe Johnson)
**Album:** Released Mar '89, on Flyright by Interstate Music. Catalogue no: **FLY 620**

### I LEFT MY BLUES IN SAN FRANCISCO
Tracks: / Keep it to yourself / Crazy love / I suffer with the blues / When my left eye jumps / Buddy's groove / Goin' home / She suits me to a tee / Leave my girl alone / Too many ways / Mother-in-law / Every girl I see.
**CD:** Released Feb '90, on Chess by Vogue Records. Catalogue no: **CHD 31265**

### I WAS WALKING THROUGH THE WOODS
**Album:** Released Oct '86, on Chess (PRT) Deleted '88. Catalogue no: **BRP 2030**

### IN THE BEGINNING
Tracks: / Sit and cry / Try to quit you baby / You surecan't do / This is the end / Broken hearted blues / Slop around / First time / I got my eyes on you / Stone crazy / Skippin' (Inst) / When my left eye jumps / Treasure untold, The / My time after awhile / I dig your wig.
**Album:** Released Sep '82, on Red Lightnin' by Red Lightnin' Records. Deleted Jun '89. Catalogue no: **RL 001**

### LEFT MY BLUES
**CD:** Released Jun '88, on MCA (USA) by MCA Records (USA). Catalogue no: **31265**

### LIVE AT THE CHECKERBOARD LOUNGE, CHICAGO 1979
Tracks: / Buddy's blues parts 1 & 2 / I've got a right to love my woman / Tell me what's inside of you (2 versions) / Done gone over you / Things I used to do, The / You don't know how I feel / Dollar done sell, The / Don't answer the door.
**CD:** Released '88, on JSP by JSP Records. Catalogue no: **JSP CD 210**

### ORIGINAL BLUES BROTHERS - LIVE (Guy, Buddy & Junior Wells)
Tracks: / Buddy's blues / Blue monday / Everyday I have the blues / Woman blues / Satisfaction / Messin' with the kid / No use cryin' / Just to be with you / Junior's shuffle / Out of sight.
**CD:** Released Feb '89, on Blue Moon (1) by Magnum Music Group. Catalogue no: **CDBM 1.007**
**Album:** Released Sep '83, on Blue Moon (1) by Magnum Music Group. Catalogue no: **BMLP 1007**

### STONE CRAZY
Tracks: / Slop around / Broken hearted blues / I got my eyes on you / First time I met the blues / Let me love you baby / I got a strange feeling / Hully gully / Ten years ago / Watch yourself / Stone crazy / Hard, but it's fair / Baby (baby, baby) / When my left eye jumps / That's it no lie / Every girl I see / Leave my girl alone / She suits me to a tee / Mother in law blues / Goin' home / I suffer with the blues.
**CD:** Released Sep '88, on Chess by Vogue Records. Catalogue no: **CDRED 6**
**Album:** Released '88, on Alligator (Sonet) by Alligator Records (USA). Catalogue no: **AL 4723**

### TEN BLUE FINGERS
Tracks: / Girl you're nice and clean / Garbage man blues / Tell me what's inside of you / You can make it if you try / Have you ever been lonesome / She winked her eye.
**Album:** Released Feb '85, on JSP by JSP Records. Catalogue no: **JSP 1085**

# H

The following information was taken from the Music Master database on 14th April, 1990.

## Hackett, Bobby

**Biographical details:** The cornettist (1915-76) was one of the most highly regarded white jazzmen of his generation. He was a guest at Benny Goodman's famous Carnegie Hall concert early in 1938 and first recorded in the studio that year with Pee Wee Russell, Eddie Condon and other stars of the Chicago style, and the next year with Bud Freeman's Summa Cum Laude Orchestra. He joined the Glenn Miller band on guitar because he was having lip trouble, but played the famous cornet solo on Miller's hit *String of pearls*. Along with other work he became better-known in the 1950s, playing lovely solos on albums of mood music by comedian Jackie Gleason, and made studio albums for Capitol with Jack Teagarden. He was identified as a Dixieland player, a later Bix Beiderbecke, but his skill transcended category: his beautiful tone, good taste and lyrical ideas allowed him to play with anybody, endearing him to critics, public and musicians alike. (Donald Clarke, Nov 1989).

**AT NICK'S 1944 (Hackett, Bobby & His Orchestra)**
**Album:** Released '87, on Commodore Class Catalogue no: **6.26171**

**BOBBY HACKETT AND HIS ORCHESTRA (Hackett, Bobby & His Orchestra)**
Note: Mono.
**Album:** Released Jun '86, on Jazzology (USA) by Jazzology Records (USA). Catalogue no: **J 111**

**BOBBY HACKETT'S SEXTET (Hackett, Bobby Sextet)**
Tracks: / Bill Bailey / Sentimental blues / Deed I do / Struttin' with some barbecue / Swing that music / S'wonderful / Fidgety feet / There'll never be another you / String of pearls / There'll be some changes made / Sign off.
Note: Featuring Bob Wilber, Urbie Green, Dave McKenna
**Album:** Released May '86, on Storyville by Storyville Records AB. Catalogue no: **SLP 4059**

**BUTTERFLIES AIRS**
**Album:** Released Oct '79, on Honeydew Catalogue no: **HD 6617**

**GOOD YEARS OF JAZZ VOL 3 (VIDEO)**
**VHS:** Released Feb '90, on Storyville by Storyville Records AB. Catalogue no: **SV3003**

**IN A MELLOW MOOD**
Tracks: / Stars in my eyes / In a sentimental mood / All through the night.
**Cass:** Released Oct '84, on Pathe Marconi (France) Catalogue no: **PM 155 297 4**
**Album:** Released Oct '84, on Pathe Marconi (France) Catalogue no: **PM 155 297 1**

**JACK TEAGARDEN AND BOBBY HACKETT (Hackett, Bobby & Jack Teagarden)**
**Album:** Released Apr '79, on Shoestring (1) Catalogue no: **SS 102**

**JAZZ FROM THE RUSTIC LODGE, VOL.1 (Hackett, Bobby & Red Allen)**
**Album:** on Jass Catalogue no: **JASS 16**
**Cass:** on Jass Catalogue no: **JASS 16C**

**JAZZ ULTIMATE (Hackett, Bobby & Jack Teagarden)**
Tracks: / Indiana / Oh baby / It's wonderful / I found a new baby / Sunday / Baby won't you please come home / Everybody loves my baby / Mama's gone goodbye / Way down yonder in New Orleans / 55th and Broadway / 'S wonderful.
Note: From *'S wonderful* by George and Ira Gershwin to *55th and Broadway* - a Hackett/Teagarden original. A jazz LP in the Dixieland vein.
**Album:** Released Jan '86, on Capitol by EMI Records. Deleted Jul '87. Catalogue no: **EMS 1134**
**Cass:** Released Jan '86, on Capitol by EMI Records. Deleted Jul '87. Catalogue no: **TCEMS 1134**

**JULY 25TH, 1960**
Tracks: / David and Goliath / Swing low sweet chariot / I'm climbing up the mountain / Nobody knows the trouble I've seen / When the saints go marching in / Heaven's full of joy / Golden gate / Way up there / Balm in Gilead / Steal away / Better be ready / Bye and bye.
**Album:** Released Oct '80, on From The Jazz Vault by Damont Audio Ltd.. Catalogue no: **JV 108**

**LIVE FROM MANASSAS (Hackett, Bobby, Vic Dickenson, Maxine Sullivan)**
**Album:** Released Feb '87, on Jazzology (USA) by Jazzology Records (USA). Catalogue no: **J 76**

**LIVE FROM THE VOYAGER ROOM (Hackett, Bobby & His Jazz Band)**
Tracks: / Allahandra / It's all in your mind / Perdido / Spain / Stardust / Clark and Madison / Cottontail / Fidgety feet / It don't mean a thing / Swing 39 / Handel with Cary / Christopher Columbus.
Note: Airchecks of the Henry Hudson Hotel Band c. 1956-57: Bobby with Bob Wilber, Ernie Caceres, Dick Cary, John Dengler, Dick Hafer, Pinie Caceres, Buzzy Drootin, Tom Gwaltney.
**Album:** Released Apr '81, on Shoestring (1) Catalogue no: **SS 108**

**LIVE FROM THE VOYAGER ROOM - VOL.2**
Tracks: / Lullaby in rhythm / Holiday hop / I'm beginning to see the light / Cornet chop suey / Ill wind / Swiss criss / Lady with the lavender hair, The / Poor butterfly / Whisper not / Morning aire / Seal, The / I guess, I'll go back home this summer / Zig zag.
**Album:** Released Apr '81, on Shoestring (1) Catalogue no: **SS 113**

**MELODY IS A MUST VOL.1 (Live at the Roosevelt Grill)**
**Album:** Released May '86, on Phontastic (Sweden) Catalogue no: **PHONT 7571**

**MELODY IS A MUST VOL.2 (Live at the Roosevelt Grill)**
**Album:** Released Mar '87, on Phontastic (Sweden) Catalogue no: **PHONT 7572**

**RARE ITALIAN DATES/LIVE AT LOUISIANA DATES 1971 (Hackett, Bobby & Albert Nicholas)**
**Album:** Released May '88, on FDC Catalogue no: **FDC 3001**

## Haden, Charlie

**Biographical details:** The modern jazz bassist was born in 1937 in Iowa; he became prominent playing with Ornette Coleman in 1959, and the group called Old And New Dreams on EM re-creates that period, with Haden, Don Cherry, Ed Blackwell and Dewey Redman. He was also active with Carla Bley and Mike Mantler in the Jazz Composers Orchestra and on Bley albums such as *Escalator over the hill.* His film work included *Last tango in Paris* with Gato Barbieri; musical values paramount, he could also work with older men such as Red Allen and Pee Wee Russell (*College concert* on Impulse), but he is best known for his Liberation Music Orchestra: an album of that name on Impulse in 1969, by a 13 piece group including Roswell Rudd, Andrew Cyrille, Cherry, Bley, Barbieri, etč. was committed music about oppression, particularly of Spanish-speaking peoples, by generals and politicians; it was followed by *The ballad of the fallen* on ECM in 1982, as well as other sessions with various artists including Paul Motian, Hampton Hawes and many more. (Donald Clarke, November 1989).

**AS LONG AS THERE'S MUSIC (Haden, Charlie / Hampton Hawes)**
**Album:** Released May '81, on Artists House Catalogue no: **AH 4**

**BALLAD OF THE FALLEN**
Tracks: / El Segardors / If you want to write to me / Ballad of the fallen / Grandola vila morena / Introduction to people / People united will never be defeated / Silence / Too late / La pasionara / La santa espina.
Note: Digital stereo. For their 1982 tour and the recording of this album, Charlie Haden reassembled the Liberation Music Orchestra maintaining the tradition of political jazz initiated in the late sixties. Despite it's political statement this is a highly listenable album of music based around popular latin folk and political songs. .
**CD:** Released Sep '84, on ECM Catalogue no: **811 546 2**
**Album:** Released Oct '83, on ECM Catalogue no: **ECM 1248**

**CLOSENESS**
Tracks: / Ellen David / O.C. / For Turiya / For a free Portugal.
**Album:** Released Nov '76, on Horizon by A&M Records. Catalogue no: **AMLJ 710**

**CLOSENESS DUETS**
**CD:** Released 24 Jul '89, on A&M by A&M Records. Catalogue no: **CDA 0808**

**GOLDEN NUMBER, THE**
**Album:** Released Jan '78, on Horizon by A&M Records. Catalogue no: **AMLJ 727**

**LIBERATION MUSIC ORCHESTRA**
Tracks: / Introduction, The / Song of the united front / El quinto regimento / Cuatro gererals, Los (The four generals) / Ending of the first side, The / Song for Che (Including excerpt from Haste Siempre by Carlos Puebla.) / War orphans / Interlude / Circus 68, 69 / We shall overcome.
Note: Recorded 1969.
**CD:** Released Jun '89, on MCA (Impulse Jazz) Catalogue no: **MCAD 39125**
**Cass:** Released Sep '82, on Jasmine by Hasmick Promotions. Catalogue no: **JAS C55**
**Album:** Released Jun '89, on MCA (Impulse Jazz) Catalogue no: **MCA 39125**
**Album:** Released Aug '82, on Jasmine by Hasmick Promotions. Catalogue no: **JAS 55**

**QUARTET WEST**
**Album:** Released Aug '87, on Verve (Germany) Catalogue no: **831 673-1**
**Cass:** Released Aug '87, on Verve (Germany) Catalogue no: **831 673-4**
**CD:** Released Aug '87, on Verve Catalogue no: **831 673- 2**

## Haggart, Bob

**PORTRAIT OF BIX, A**
**Album:** Released Jan '87, on Jazzology (USA) by Jazzology Records (USA). Catalogue no: **J 149**

## Haggart, Lawson

**1951/52 (Haggart, Lawson Jazz Band)**
**Album:** Released Aug '87, on Tax Catalogue no: **M 8040**

## Haig, Al

**Biographical details:** Jazz pianist born in 1924 in New Jersey, one of the first and best bop pianists, a ubiquitous sideman with Charlie Parker, Dizzy Gillespie, Fats Navarro in the 1940, later suffering from the 'Jim Crow' syndrome (pressure on black leaders to hire black sidemen). Cocktail piano gigs and periods of obscurity took over, but he has made something of a comeback in recent years, often on Japanesese labels but also for Britain's Spotlite label. (Donald Clarke, Nov 1989).

**EXPRESSLY ELLINGTON (Haig, Al Quartet)**
Tracks: / Just squeeze me / Body and soul / I let a song go out of my heart / Lush life / Perdido / I got it bad and that ain't good / Flamingo / Sophisticated lady.
Note: Featuring tenor saxist Art Themen.
**Album:** Released Jan '83, on Spotlite by Spotlite Records. Catalogue no: **SPJ LP20**

**INVITATION (Haig, Al Trio)**
Tracks: / Holy Land / Enigma / Invitation / Sawbo City blues / If you could see me now / Sambalhasa / Daydream / Linear.
Note: Al Haig -- piano. Bibi Rovere -- bass. Kenny Clark -- drums.
**Album:** Released Jan '83, on Spotlite by Spotlite Records. Catalogue no: **AH 4**

**JAZZ WILL-O'-THE-WISP (Haig, Al Trio)**
**Album:** Released Feb '88, on Fresh Sounds (Spain) by Fresh Sounds Records (Spain). Catalogue no: **FS 197**

**LIVE IN HOLLYWOOD (Haig, Al & Jimmy Raney 4)**
**CD:** Released '88, on Xanadu Catalogue no: **FDC 5162**

**MANHATTAN MEMORIES (Haig, Al Trio & Quartet)**
**Album:** Released Mar '87, on Sea Breeze Catalogue no: **SB 1008**

**MEETS THE MASTER SAXES, VOL. 1**
Tracks: / Light grey / Stoned / Matter and mind / Toup, The / Shawn / Hot halavah / Bopel-ground / Cobblestones / Prelude to a kiss / Boppin' in B flat / Man with a horn / Sophisticated lady / Rifftide / Stuffy.
Note: With Wardell Gray, Coleman Hawkins, John Hardee, Al Epstein.
**Album:** Released Jan '83, on Spotlite by Spotlite Records. Catalogue no: **SPJ 139**

**MEETS THE MASTER SAXES, VOL. 2**
Tracks: / Pardon my bop, 1, 2, 3 / As I live and I bop / Interlude on bebop / Diaper pin / Diaper pin 2 / Frosty / Deedle / In the merry land of bop / Pogo stick / Alleytalk / Way you look tonight / If love is trouble / Hee haw / Laughing boy.
Note: With Stan Getz, Allan Eager, Jimmy Raney, Bennie Green.
**Album:** Released Jan '83, on Spotlite by Spotlite Records. Catalogue no: **SPJ 140**

**MEETS THE MASTER SAXES, VOL. 3**
Tracks: / Donna Lee / East of the sun / Sweet miss / Long Island sound / Medicine man / Passport to Pimlico / T'ain't no use / Sinbad the tailor / Haig 'n' Haig / Always / Bopelbaby / Talk a little bop.
Note: Featuring saxists Zoot Sims, Herbie Steward and Stan Getz, trumpeter Red Rodney and trombonist Kai Winding.
**Album:** Released Jan '83, on Spotlite by Spotlite Records. Catalogue no: **SPJ 143**

**PIANO INTERPRETATIONS**
**Album:** Released Aug '79, on Sea Breeze Catalogue no: **SB 1001**

**PORTRAIT OF BUD POWELL, A**
**Album:** Released Sep '79, on Interplay (USA) by Interplay Records (USA). Catalogue no: **IP 7707**

**QUINTET OF THE YEAR REVISITED**
Tracks: / Birk's works / I mean you / Bag's groove / Epistrophy / Lover man / Night in Tunisia.
**Album:** Released Mar '83, on Spotlite by Spotlite Records. Catalogue no: **SPJ LP 23**

**SERENDIPITY**
**Album:** Released Jan '79, on Interplay (USA) by Interplay Records (USA). Catalogue no: **IP-7713**

**SOLITAIRE**
Tracks: / Lament / Joanne / Summertime / Bess, you is my woman now / In your own sweet way / Never let me go / Here's that rainy day / Don't you know I care.
Note: Solo piano.
**Album:** Released '83, on Spotlite by Spotlite Records. Catalogue no: **SPJ LP 14**

**SPECIAL BREW (Haig, Al & Jimmy Raney 4)**
Tracks: / Freedom jazz dance / We'll be together / Marmaduke / Dolphin dance / Blues for Alice / Shaw 'nuff / Don't you know I care / Just friends.
**Album:** Released '83, on Spotlite by Spotlite Records. Catalogue no: **SPJ LP 8**

**STABLEMATES (Haig, Al & Jon Eardley)**
Tracks: / Tangerine / Speak low / Round midnight / Love walked in / Embraceable you / Don't blame me.
Note: With tenor saxist Art Themen.
**Album:** Released '83, on Spotlite by Spotlite Records. Catalogue no: **SPJ LP 11**

## Hakim, Omar

### RHYTHM DEEP

Tracks: / Crucial 2 groove / Rhythm deep / Real side, The / Love is here to stay / Tears / Isolated lonely / Take my heart / Amethyst secrets / Angel delight / Constructive criticism / Sun always shines / Mystic's glance.

Note: Omar Hakim is undoubtedly, one of the most exciting and sensational drummers playing today. His studio work with Weather Report, Sting, the David Sanborn Sunday Night TV show and his studio work on an incredible number of hits (including the recent *Giving you the best that I got* from Anita Baker) certainly attests to his extraordinary drum prowess. With solid support from co-producer Michael Bearden (keyboards), Najee (sop sax), Victor Bailey (bass) and Chieli Minucci (from Special EFX) on guitar, Rhythm Deep presents Omar Hakim as the consummate musician heard not only as lead vocalist and on most of the background vocals, but on piano, synthesizer and of course drums.

**Cass:** Released Apr '89, on GRP by GRP Records (USA). Catalogue no: **GRP 95854**

**Album:** Released Apr '89, on GRP by GRP Records (USA). Catalogue no: **GRP 95851**

**CD:** Released Apr '89, on GRP by GRP Records (USA). Catalogue no: **GRP 95852**

## Hakim, Sadik

### CRUCIAL TO GROOVE

**Cass:** Released Apr '89, on GRP by GRP Records (USA). Catalogue no: **C 4007**

**Album:** Released Apr '89, on GRP by GRP Records (USA). Catalogue no: **A 4007**

### LADYBIRD

**CD:** Released Feb '90, on Storyville by Storyville Records AB. Catalogue no: **STCD 4156**

## Halcox, Pat All Stars

### SEVENTH AVENUE

Tracks: / Flintstones / Blue and sentimental / I'm gonna lock my heart / China boy / I wanna little girl / What's the racket / Jeepers creepers / You took advantage of me / Three for the blues / Dusk.

Note: The musicians are Campbell Burnap, John Crocker, Johnny Parker, Vic Pitt, John McCullum and Pete York.

**Album:** Released Nov '81, on Plant Life Jazz by Plant Life Records. Catalogue no: **PLJ 002**

## Halcyon Dance

### MY BLUE HEAVEN

**Album:** Released Mar '79, on Halcyon (USA) by Submarine Records. Catalogue no: **HAL 10**

## Halfway House Orchestra

### HALFWAY HOUSE ORCHESTRA 1925/8, THE

**Album:** Released Apr '79, on VJM (Vintage Jazz Music) by Vintage Jazz Music Society(VJM). Catalogue no: **VLP 19**

### HALFWAY HOUSE ORCHESTRA & NEW ORLEANS OWLS VOL.2 (Halfway House Orchestra & New Orleans Owls)

**Album:** Released Apr '79, on VJM (Vintage Jazz Music) by Vintage Jazz Music Society(VJM). Catalogue no: **VLP 22**

## Hall, Adelaide

**Biographical details:** Vocalist born in 1904 in New York City. She appeared in the show *Shuffle along* in 1921 and came to Europe in the *Chocolate kiddies* revue in 1925 (which also included Josephine Baker). On the same bill with Duke Ellington back in NYC her humming backstage was picked up by an open mike; Duke asked her to record: *Blues I love to sing* and *Creole love call* in '28 with wordless vocals were landmarks in Duke's output. She recorded *I can't give you anything but love* from *Blackbirds of 1928*, a song since associated with her. She went back and forth to Europe, for the fourth time in 1938 and stayed: her husband ran clubs in Paris and London (The Old Florida was bombed in the Blitz); she had a radio show with Joe Loss, and re-established herself in cabaret at posh hotels in the 1980s, still gigging in 1988. Her films include an appearance on screen singing in Korda's *Thief of Bagdad* in 1942. (Donald Clarke, Nov 1989).

### ADELAIDE HALL

**Album:** Released Mar '79, on Monmouth Evergreen Catalogue no: **MES 7080**

### THERE GOES THAT SONG AGAIN

Tracks: / There goes that song again / How did he look? / This can't be love / My devotion / It's always you / T'aint what you do (it's the way that you do it) / Translantic lullaby / I promise you / I wanna be loved / Drummer boy / That's the moon my son / Missouri scrambler / My heart tells me / Pennsylvania polka / Infatuation / You are my sunshine / Kindergarten conga / Two pairs of shoes / You're wrong / Tzigane swing / I've got a gal in Kalamazoo / Sweetheart it's you / Victory roll rag / Our back street is Broadway / Sailor with the navy blue eyes / Singing with rig.

**Album:** Released Nov '80, on Decca by Decca International. Deleted Jun '88. Catalogue no: **RFL 3**

## Hall, Andrew

### TALK OF THE TOWN (Hall, Andrew, Society Jazz Band Of New Orleans)

**Album:** Released Jul '82, on Shalom Catalogue no: **802**

## Hall Brothers Jazz Band

### FIZZ WATER 25TH ANNIVERSARY

**Album:** Released '88, on Stomp Off (USA) Catalogue no: **SOS 1062**

### WAITING AT THE END OF THE ROAD

**Album:** Released '88, on Stomp Off (USA) Catalogue no: **SOS 1031**

## Hall, Edmond

**Biographical details:** A great New Orleans jazz man (1901-67) who played baritone sax but later mainly clarinet. He made legendary records on Blue Note as the Edmond Hall Celestial Quartet (Meade Lux Lewis playing celeste, with Charlie Christian on guitar, Israel Crosby on bass); he turned down an offer from Duke Ellington in 1942, and played with Louis Armstrong's All Stars 1955-58, touring the world. (Donald Clarke, Nov 1989).

### AT CLUB HANGOVER, 1954

Tracks: / St. Louis blues / Sweet and lovely / Keeping out of mischief / Basin Street blues / Dardanella.

Note: Veteran clarinet man Hall is joined by such musicians as Ralph Sutton, Walter Page and Charlie Lodis.

**Album:** Released Jul '82, on Storyville by Storyville Records AB. Catalogue no: **SLP 253**

### EDMOND HALL

Note: Featuring Louis Armstrong, Jimmy McPartland, Wild Bill Davidson, Jack Teagarden.

**Album:** Released Sep '87, on Giants of Jazz by Hasmick Promotions. Catalogue no: **LPJT 30**

### EDMOND HALL AT CLUB HANGOVER

**Album:** Released '88, on Storyville by Storyville Records AB. Catalogue no: **SLP 4009**

### EDMOND HALL QUARTET (Hall, Edmund Quartet)

**Album:** Released Feb '90, on Storyville by Storyville Records AB. Catalogue no: **SLP 190**

### ROMPIN' IN '44 (Hall, Edmond & His Swing Quartet)

**Album:** Released Aug '88, on Circle (USA) by Jazzology Records (USA). Catalogue no: **CLP 52**

### TAKE IT, EDMOND HALL, WITH YOUR CLARINET

Tracks: / K.K. boogie / Ol' man river / Indiana / Royal Garden blues / I got rhythm / P-flat swing / Lady be good / It's been so long / I can't believe that you're in love with me / Big city blues / Steamin' and beamin' / At the ball / Walking the dog / Blues, The.

Note: Recorded, with various outfits, in the 1940's.

**Album:** Released Apr '81, on Queendisc (Italy) Catalogue no: **QU 020**

### THIS IS JAZZ VOL.3

**Album:** Released Jun '86, on Storyville by Storyville Records AB. Catalogue no: **SLP 4069**

### TWO OF A KIND (Hall, Edmond Quartet & Teddy Wilson)

**Album:** Released May '87, on Commodore Class Catalogue no: **6.25893**

## Hall, George

### GEORGE HALL, 1937

Tracks: / It's easy to remember / Caravan / 52nd street / Tea for two / Blue skies / I can't break the habit of you / Scattin' at the Kit Kat / Satan take a holiday / Dipsy doodle / Midnight in a madhouse / Have you got any castles, baby / Two dukes on a pier / You and me that used to be, The / Dallas blues / Snake charmer, The / It looks like rain in Cherry Blossom Lane / Gandy dancer.

Note: George Hall, 1937, featuring vocals by Dolly Dawn. By 1937, the George Hall band, with Tenor saxophonist George Paxton in the section and doing a lot of the arranging, had developed immensely. In addition, some of the arrangements on this record are by Don Redman. The first five numbers are from a transcribed 15-minute broadcast, complete with opening and closing theme, announcement, etc. The remaining selections are from transcriptions recorded especially for radio broadcasting purposes, never before on record, LP or otherwise. Excellent liner notes by Frank Driggs who was well acquainted with the history of this band and who had the cooperation of Dolly Dawn. (Hindsight Catalogue - 1989)

**Album:** Released '88, on Hindsight Catalogue no: **HSR 144**

## Hall, Henry

**Biographical details:** The British bandleader (1899-1989) was effectively leading 32 bands by 1924 as music director for a railway company's chain of hotels. He took a cut in pay when offered the leadership of the BBC's house dance band 1932-37; he succeeded Jack Payne and in '37 the BBC no longer kept a resident band in London, so it went freelance until disbanding in '39. Hall was less flamboyant than Payne but the musical values were high; he recruited sidemen from the Trinity College of Music and hired Benny Carter as an arranger. At his peak he broadcast 8 times a week and received 35,000 letters a year. He later became a West End impresario, still appearing on radio and TV. (Donald Clarke, Nov 1989).

### GOLDEN AGE OF HENRY HALL, THE

Tracks: / Music goes round and around, The / Little man you've had a busy day / Man on the flying trapeze, The / Play to me, gypsy / Underneath the arches / I like bananas because they have no bones / Butterflies in the rain / Just an echo in the valley / Music hath charms / Wheezy Anna / Did you ever see a dream walking? / Oh Johanna / Rusty and dusty / Somewhere at sea / It's a sin to tell a lie / Here's to the next time.

**Album:** Released Jul '84, on Golden Age by EMI Records. Catalogue no: **GX 41 2517-1**

### HELP YOURSELF TO HAPPINESS (Hall, Henry and The BBC Dance Orchestra)

Tracks: / Help yourself to happiness / You, just wonderful you / Moon / Singing in the moonlight / Love is the sweetest thing / Maree / Always in my heart / Nobody else but Elsie / Living in the hay / Turning of the tide / Hazel eyes / Clouds will soon roll by, The / Bahama mama / Wanderer / Marching along together / How can you say no? / My extraordinary gal / Downhearted / Same old Moon / Keep your last goodnight for me.

**Album:** Released '86, on Saville by Conifer Records. Catalogue no: **SVL 156**

**Cass:** Released '88, on Saville by Conifer Records. Catalogue no: **CSVL 156**

### HENRY HALL AND BBC DANCE ORCHESTRA (Hall, Henry & BBC Dance Orchestra)

Tracks: / Five-fifteen / Have you ever been lonely / Goody-goody / Wagon wheels / Waltz in swingtime / Mine for keeps / Sun has got his hat on / Wild ride / It's just the time for dancing / Elephant never forgets / I'm putting all my eggs in one basket / Teddy bear's picnic / Life begins when you're in love / I heard a song in a taxi / One, two, button your shoe / It's time to say goodnight / Here's to the next time.

**Album:** Released '89, on Joy by President Records. Catalogue no: **JOY 298**

**Album:** Released '71, on Retrospect by EMI Records. Catalogue no: **SH 140**

**Album:** Released Mar '84, on Retrospect by EMI Records. Deleted Mar '89. Catalogue no: **SH 172**

**Cass:** Released May '79, on Retrospect by EMI Records. Catalogue no: **TC SH 140**

### HERE'S TO THE NEXT TIME (Hall, Henry and The BBC Dance Orchestra)

Tracks: / I cover the waterfront / Did my heart beat, did I fall in love? / Making conversation / I've told every little star / Dance little lady / It's the talk of the town / You've got me crying again / Aloha-oe / Learn to croon / Maybe I love you too much / Blue cloud / Moonstruck / Moon song / Let's all sing like the birdies sing / Marching along together / Five-fifteen.

Note: "Vocal refrain" on all tracks.

**Album:** Released Mar '85, on Joy by President Records. Catalogue no: **JOY D283**

### LA DI DA DI DA (Hall, Henry Orchestra)

Tracks: / La di da di da.

**7" Single:** Released Nov '82, on Music For Living by Music For Living Records. Catalogue no: **A 1**

**12" Single:** Released Nov '82, on Music For Living by Music For Living Records. Catalogue no: **AA 1**

### LOVE IS THE SWEETEST THING

Note: Featuring BBC dance orchestra

**2 LP Set:** Released Sep '87, on Saville by Conifer Records. Catalogue no: **SVLD 002**

**Cass:** Released '88, on Saville by Conifer Records. Catalogue no: **CSVLD 002**

### MY DANCE

**Cass:** Released Jul '88, on Burlington (nostalgia) by Counterpoint Distribution. Catalogue no: **4BUR 009**

**Album:** Released Jun '88, on Burlington (nostalgia) by Counterpoint Distribution. Catalogue no: **BUR 009**

**CD:** Released Sep '88, on Burlington (nostalgia) by Counterpoint Distribution. Catalogue no: **2 BUR 009**

### SEEIN' IS BELIEVIN' (Hall, Henry & His Orchestra)

Tracks: / Seein' is believin' / My dance / Every now and then / Magic / Chasing shadows / Music goes 'round and around, The / Love is a dancing thing / Broken record, The / Life begins when you're in love / We say the sea / Got a bran' new suit / I'm putting all my eggs in one basket / Goody-goody / All my life / When I'm with you / Oh my goodness / Waltz in swing time / Bye, bye baby / One, two, button your shoe / Goona goo, The.

**Cass:** Released '88, on Saville by Conifer Records. Catalogue no: **CSVL 193**

**Album:** Released '88, on Saville by Conifer Records. Catalogue no: **SVL 193**

### THIS IS HENRY HALL (Hall, Henry & The BBC Dance Orchestra)

Tracks: / It's just the time for dancing / Five-fifteen / I cover the waterfront / Here's to the next time / Lullaby of the leaves / Leave the pretty girls alone / Keep it to yourself / Talk of the town / Making conversation / It's time to say goodbye / East wind / I was in the mood / Three of us, The / Love thy neighbour / Carolina / Sweetmeat Joe, the candyman / Olga Pullofski, the beautiful spy / Many happy returns / Just little bits and pieces / Misty island of the Highlands / When the guardsman started crooning on parade / Broken record, The / Saddle your blues to a wild mustang / Buffoon / Apple blossoms / There's a goldmine in the sky / Under the double eagle / You took the words right out of my heart / Miss Annabelle Lee / Bye bye blackbird / Hi-diddle-diddle / Silver on the sage / Highland swing / Blue skies are round the corner / One man went to blow / If ever a heart was in the right place.

Note: From Radiolympia, 1933.

**2 LP Set:** Released Jun '78, on Retrospect by EMI Records. Catalogue no: **SHB 48**

### TRIBUTE TO HENRY HALL, A (Hall, Henry & The BBC Dance Orchestra)

Tracks: / Thank you Mr. Bach / I'm feeling happy / Honey coloured moon / In my heart of hearts / There's no time like the present / Merry-go-round broke down, The / What will I tell my heart / Big ship / Song without words / Seein' is believin' / Music hath charms / Just little bits and pieces / Everything's in rhythm with my heart / Many happy returns of the day / Say the word and it's yours / Le touquet / With my eyes wide open I'm dreaming

/ Moonstruck.
**Album:** Released Nov '89, on Joy by President Records. Catalogue no: **JOYD 298**

**WHAT A PERFECT COMBINATION (Hall, Henry & His BBC Dance Orchestra)**
Tracks: / Twenty million people / In a little second hand store / Day you came along, The / Thanks / Thats another Scottish story / Roaming / On a steamer over / I'll string along with you / Little valley in the mountains / Love in bloom / With my eyes wide open, I'm dreaming / How's chances? / What a perfect combination / In the moonlight / My darling / Just so you'll remember.
Note: Personnel: Henry Hall directing: Frank Wilson, Arthur Williams, Andy Hodgkiss - trumpets; Bill Mulraney, Eric Tann - trombones; Burton Gillis, Freddy Williams - clarinets and alto saxophone; Eddie Cromar - clarinet, alto & baritone saxophone; Cyril Hellier, Joseph Hitchenor, Bert Powell - violins; Jack Philips, Bert Read - pianos; George Dickinson - guitar; Theo Farrar - string bass, or brass-bass where audible; Len Bermon - drums.
**Album:** Released Oct '86, on Saville by Conifer Records. Catalogue no: **SVL 178**
**Cass:** Released Oct '86, on Saville by Conifer Records. Catalogue no: **CSVL 178**

## Hall, Herb

**OLD TYME MODERN (Hall, Herb Quartet)**
Tracks: / Old-fashioned love / All of me / Buddy Bolden's blues / Crying my heart out for you / Swinging down Shaw's Hall / Beale Street blues / How come you do me like you do? / Willow weep for me / Do you know what it means to miss New Orleans? / Sweet Georgia Brown.
**Album:** Released Apr '81, on Sackville by Spotlite Records. Catalogue no: **3003**

## Hall, Jim

**Biographical details:** Jazz guitarist, born in 1930 in Buffalo, New York; one of the most highly rated and influential on the instrument for beauty and subtlety. He played with a Chico Hamilton quintet and the Jimmy Giuffre Trio in the '50s; his duo with Bill Evans (*Undercurrents* in 1959) and his quartet albums with Sonny Rollins and with Paul Desmond are justly famous as jazz classics, as well as his own albums as a leader. (Donald Clarke, Nov 1989).

**ALL ACROSS THE CITY (Hall, Jim Quartet)**
Tracks: / Beija fior / Young one (for Debra) / All across the city / Something tells me / Prelude to a kiss / How deep is the ocean / Bemsha swing / R.E.M. State / Drop shot / Big blues / Jane.
Note: Acoustic and modern electric jazz. CD version features three bonus tracks.
**Album:** Released Sep '89, on Concord Jazz by Concord Jazz Records (USA). Catalogue no: **CJ 384**
**CD:** Released Sep '89, on Concord Jazz by Concord Jazz Records (USA). Catalogue no: **CCD 4384**
**Cass:** Released Sep '89, on Concord Jazz by Concord Jazz Records (USA). Catalogue no: **CJ 384C**

**ALONE TOGETHER (Hall, Jim & Ron Carter)**
**CD:** Released May '87, on JVC/Fantasy Catalogue no: **VDJ 1033**

**CIRCLES**
**Album:** Released Nov '81, on Concord Jazz by Concord Jazz Records (USA). Catalogue no: **CJ 161**

**CONCIERTO**
Tracks: / Two's blues / Answer is yes / Concierto de Aranjuez / You'd be so nice to come home to.
**Album:** Released Feb '84, on CTI (Musidisc France) by Polydor Ltd. Catalogue no: **CTI 9020**
**CD:** Released Feb '84, on CTI (Musidisc France) by Polydor Ltd. Catalogue no: **813 661 2**

**I'M HAPPY THAT LOVE HAS FOUND YOU**
Tracks: / I'm happy that love has found you / Touch you.
**7" Single:** Released Jan '81, on Epic by CBS Records. Deleted Jan '84. Catalogue no: **EPC 9397**

**JAZZ GUITAR (Hall, Jim Trio)**
Tracks: / Stompin' at the Savoy / Things ain't what they used to be / Things ain't what they used to be (alt. take) / Thanks for the memory / Tangerine / Stella by starlight / 9.20 special / Deep in a dream / Look for the silver lining / Seven come eleven / Too close for comfort.
**CD:** Released Mar '89, on EMI-Manhattan by EMI Records. Catalogue no: **CZ 68**
**CD:** Released Jan '89, on EMI-Manhattan by EMI Records. Catalogue no: **CDP 746 851 2**

**JIM HALL & RED MITCHELL (Hall, Jim & Red Mitchell)**
**Album:** Released May '81, on Artists House Catalogue no: **AH 5**

**JIM HALL'S THREE (Hall, Jim Trio)**
Tracks: / Hide and seek / Skylark / Bottlenose blues / And I do / All the things you are / Poor butterfly / Three.
Note: Personnel: Jim Hall - guitar; Steve LaSpina - bass; Akira Tana - drums. Jim Hall's fifth recording for Concord featuring three standards and four original compositions. The track *Bottlenose blues* features the first recording of Jim on the 12-string guitar.
**CD:** Released Mar '87, on Concord Jazz by Concord Jazz Records (USA). Catalogue no: **CCD 4298**
**Album:** Released Aug '86, on Concord Jazz by Concord Jazz Records (USA). Catalogue no: **CJ 298**

**THESE ROOMS (Hall, Jim Trio)**
Tracks: / With a song in my heart / Cross court / Something tells me / Bimini / All too soon / These rooms / Darn that dream / My funny valentine / Where or when / From now on.
Note: This guitar master's inventive yet sensitive playing matched with technical dexterity has long since made him something of a legend and this new recording does nothing to alter his elevated position among the top jazz guitarists of all time. The appearance of trumpeter Tom Harrell adds a further dimension and perfectly complements Hall's own eloquence . (Denon 10/88). Other musicians are: Steve La Spina - bass; Joey Baron - drums. Tom Harrell plays the flugelhorn as well as the trumpet.
**CD:** Released '88, on Denon Catalogue no: **CY-30002**
**Cass:** Released Oct '88, on Denon Catalogue no: **CC 24**

## Hall, Juanita

**SINGS THE BLUES**
**Album:** Released Feb '88, on Fresh Sounds (Spain) by Fresh Sounds Records (Spain). Catalogue no: **FS 133**

## Hamilton, Chico

**Biographical details:** Drummer and leader, born in 1921 in Los Angeles. He played clarinet with classmates Charles Mingus, Illinois Jacquet and Ernie Royal, studied drums during WWII with Jo Jones and was house drummer at Billy Berg's club in Hollywood. Along with studio work he became prominent in West Coast 'cool jazz' movement, with the pianoless Gerry Mulligan quartet in 1952, then his own group from 1956 with Buddy Collette, Jim Hall and Fred Katz on cello, featured in the film *Sweet smell of success* in 1957; he employed the young Eric Dolphy. Musical values were high but music perhaps too genteel for many critics. (Donald Clarke, Nov 1989).

**CHICO HAMILTON (VIDEO)**
**VHS:** Released '88, on Kay Jazz (video) by Kay Jazz. Catalogue no: **KJ 062**

**EUPHORIA**
**CD:** Released Sep '89, on Swallow (USA) by Flat Town Music Co.(USA). Catalogue no: **CHECD 7**
**Cass:** Released Sep '89, on Swallow (USA) by Flat Town Music Co.(USA). Catalogue no: **CHEMC 7**
**Album:** Released Sep '89, on Swallow (USA) by Flat Town Music Co.(USA). Catalogue no: **CHELP 7**

**GONGS EAST (Hamilton, Chico Quintet & Eric Dolphy)**
Tracks: / Beyond the blue horizon / Long ago and far away / Far east.
**Cass:** Released '88, on Discovery (USA) by Discovery Records (USA). Catalogue no: **DSC 831**
**Album:** Released '88, on Discovery (USA) by Discovery Records (USA). Catalogue no: **DS 831**

**MAN FROM TWO WORLDS**
Tracks: / Child's play / Blues for O.T. / Mallet dance / Love song to a baby.
**Cass:** Released Aug '82, on Jasmine by Hasmick Promotions. Catalogue no: **JAS C48**
**Album:** Released Aug '82, on Jasmine

by Hasmick Promotions. Deleted Feb '88. Catalogue no: **JAS 48**

**MAY 19TH AND 20TH, 1959 (Hamilton, Chico Quintet)**
Tracks: / Fat mouth / Theme for a starlet / Little lost bear / Champs Elysee / Pretty little theme / Lost in the night / Frou frou / Cawn pawn / Lullaby for dreamers / Opening / Lady E / Truth.
**Album:** Released Oct '80, on From The Jazz Vault by Damont Audio Ltd.. Catalogue no: **JV 111**

**PASSIN' THRU (Hamilton, Chico Quintet)**
Tracks: / Passin' thru / Second time around / El toro / Transfusion / Lady Gabor / Lonesome child.
**Cass:** Released Jun '82, on Jasmine by Hasmick Promotions. Catalogue no: **JAS C17**
**Album:** Released Jun '82, on Jasmine by Hasmick Promotions. Deleted Feb '88. Catalogue no: **JAS 17**

**THAT'S JAZZ (Hamilton, Chico & Friends)**
Tracks: / Miss movement / More than you know / Newport news / Different journey, A / Vulture, The / Sun yen sen / Island blues / One Sheridan Square.
**Album:** on Warner Bros. by WEA Records. Catalogue no: **K 56239**

## Hamilton, Jimmy

**Biographical details:** Clarinettist born in South Carolina in 1917 who played with Duke Ellington 1943-68. He had no superior as a clarinettist in big band jazz; among many features with Ellington were the 1952 version of *The mooche* and the introduction to the '56 Newport Festival Suite. He also came out of retirement to play on the beautiful *Clarinet summit* albums on India Navigation. (Donald Clarke, Nov 1989).

**IT'S ABOUT TIME**
**Album:** Released Feb '86, on Fantasy Inc (USA) by Fantasy Inc (USA). Catalogue no: **1902123**

**SWING LOW, SWEET CLARINET**
**Album:** Released Feb '88, on Fresh Sounds (Spain) by Fresh Sounds Records (Spain). Catalogue no: **FS 132**

## Hamilton, Scott

**Biographical details:** Tenor saxist, born in Providence Rhode Island in 1954, influenced by his father's record collection; he played harmonica, then took up the tenor at 16 and formed a quartet at 18 with whom he still plays: Chuck Riggs (drums), Chris Flory (guitar) and Phil Flanigan (bass) later reformed with (usually) John Bunch on piano. He first recorded as a sideman in 1978; he never learned to sight-read, so 'I'm forced to do what I really like'. As most tenor players are still imitating John Coltrane, who's been dead for many years, so Hamilton plays a Selmer saxophone older than he is in the swing-era style as though nothing had happened since, and does it very well. (Donald Clarke, Nov 1989).

**APPLES AND ORANGES**
**Album:** Released Dec '81, on Concord by Concord Jazz Records (USA). Catalogue no: **CJ 165**

**GRAND APPEARANCE, THE (Hamilton, Scott Quartet)**
**Album:** Released '88, on Progressive Catalogue no: **PRO 7026**
**Album:** Released Apr '81, on Progressive (USA) by Jazzology Records (USA). Catalogue no: **PRO 7026**

**MAJOR LEAGUE (Hamilton, Scott, Jake Hanna, Dave McKenna)**
Tracks: / Swinging at the Copper Rail / Pretty girl is like a melody, A / Cocktails for two / I'm through with love / Linger awhile / September in the rain / This is all I ask / It all depends on you / April in Paris.
**Album:** Released Sep '86, on Concord Jazz by Concord Jazz Records (USA). Catalogue no: **CJ 305**
**Cass:** Released Sep '86, on Concord Jazz by Concord Jazz Records (USA). Catalogue no: **CJC 305**

**RIGHT TIME, THE (Hamilton, Scott Quintet)**
Tracks: / Just in time / If I love again / Sleep / Eventide / All through the night / Skylark / Stealing port / Dropsy.
**Album:** Released Feb '87, on Concord Jazz by Concord Jazz Records (USA). Catalogue no: **CJ 311**
**CD:** Released Jul '87, on Concord Jazz by Concord Jazz Records (USA). Catalogue no: **CCD 4311**

**SCOTT HAMILTON PLAYS BALLADS**
Note: CD version features three bonus tracks.
**Album:** Released Sep '89, on Concord Jazz by Concord Jazz Records (USA). Catalogue no: **CJ 386**
**CD:** Released Sep '89, on Concord Jazz by Concord Jazz Records (USA). Catalogue no: **CCD 4386**
**Cass:** Released Sep '89, on Concord Jazz by Concord Jazz Records (USA). Catalogue no: **CJ 386C**

**SCOTT HAMILTON QUINTET IN CONCERT, THE (Hamilton, Scott Quintet)**
Tracks: / I can't believe that you're in love with me / Wrap your troubles in dreams / I've found a new baby / When I fall in love / Whispering / Sultry serenade / Stardust / One o'clock jump.
**Album:** Released Feb '84, on Concord by Concord Jazz Records (USA). Catalogue no: **CJ 233**

**SCOTT HAMILTON AND WARREN VACHE (Hamilton Scott & Warren Vache)**
**Album:** Released Apr '79, on Concord by Concord Jazz Records (USA). Catalogue no: **CJ 70**

**SCOTTS BUDDY (Hamilton Scott & Buddy Tate)**
**Album:** Released May '81, on Concord by Concord Jazz Records (USA). Catalogue no: **CJ 148**

**SECOND SET**
Tracks: / All the things you are / Time after time / Taps Miller / All too soon / How insensitive / I never knew / For all we know / Jumpin' the blues.
**Album:** Released Nov '84, on Concord by Concord Jazz Records (USA). Catalogue no: **CJ 254**
**CD:** Released May '85, on Concord Jazz by Concord Jazz Records (USA). Catalogue no: **CCD 4254**

## Hampton, Lionel

**Biographical details:** Vibraphonist, drummer, pianist, singer and bandleader, born in 1909: one of the best loved entertainers in jazz. A nun taught him to play the snare drum at school; he hit the road as a drummer in 1927 and soon discovered the vibes. He recorded with Louis Armstrong in 1930 and became famous with Benny Goodman from 1935; as a contractor with Victor 1937-41, he made a long series of classic small-group records, and has led crowd-pleasing bands ever since. (Donald Clarke, Nov 1989).

**1937-40**
**Album:** Released Sep '87, on Giants of Jazz by Hasmick Promotions. Catalogue no: **LPJT 11**

**ALIVE AND JUMPING (Hampton, Lionel / Milt Buckner / All Stars)**
**Album:** Released Jun '81, on MPS Jazz Catalogue no: **MPS 68 186**

**AS TIME GOES BY (Hampton, Lionel/Svend Asmussen)**
Tracks: / Flying home / Midnight sun / Rose room / As time goes by / Air mail special / Avalon.
**CD:** Released Jun '88, on Sonet by Sonet Records. Catalogue no: **SNTCD 779**
**Album:** Released Mar '87, on Sonet by Sonet Records. Catalogue no: **SNTF 779**

**AT NEWPORT '78 (Hampton, Lionel All Star Band)**
Tracks: / Stompin' at the Savoy / Hamp's the champ / Flying home / On the sunny side of the street / Carnegie hall blues.
Note: Personnel: Lionel Hampton (vibraphones), Cat Anderson (tpt), Doc Cheatham (tpt), Jimmy Maxwell (tpt), Joe Newman (tpt), Eddie Bert (tbn), John Gordon (tbn), Benny Powell (tbn), Bob Wilber (clt), Earl Warren (clt, flt, soprano sax), Charles MacPherson (alto sax), Paul Moen (tenor sax), Arnett Cobb (tenor sax), Pepper adams (bass sax), Billy Mackel (gtr), Ray Bryant (piano), Chubby Jackson (bass), Panama Francis (drums).
**Album:** Released Apr '81, on Timeless by Timeless Records. Catalogue no: **SJP 142**

Lionel Hampton

**CD:** Released Jun '89, on Timeless by Timeless Records. Catalogue no: **CDSJP 142**

**BAD DUDE**
Tracks: / Glad Hamp / Groovin' gates / Easy living / Flying home.
**Album:** Released Aug '80, on Manhattan Records by President Records. Deleted '85. Catalogue no: **MAN 5036**

**BLACKOUT**
Tracks: / Blackout / After you've gone / Twelfth St. rag / Birth of the blues / Glad Hamp / I can't give you anything but love / Stompin' at The Savoy.
**Album:** Released Sep '83, on Kingdom Jazz by Kingdom Records. Catalogue no: **GATE 7008**
**Cass:** Released '89, on Kingdom Jazz by Kingdom Records. Catalogue no: **CGATE 7008**

**BOOGIE WOOGIE ALBUM, THE**
Tracks: / Graffiti express / Rolling slow / Central Avenue breakdown / Whisky blues / Mr. Freddie blues / Sheik of Araby boogie / New York shuffle / Jivin' in Jazzland / Hamp's boogie woogie.
Note: Recorded in New York, 1982.
**Album:** Released Apr '83, on Telefunken (Germany) Catalogue no: **6.25427**

**CHICAGO JAZZ CONCERT**
Tracks: / Chase, The / Mark VII / Love for sale / How high the moon / Stardust / Wailin' at the moon.
**Album:** Released Apr '84, on Jasmine by Hasmick Promotions. Deleted '89. Catalogue no: **JASM 1040**

**COBB'S IDEA**
Tracks: / Cobb's idea / Vibes boogie / Bongo interlude / Airmail special / Midnight sun / T.V. special / Boogie / Who cares?.
Note: From recordings made during 1946.
**Album:** Released Jun '83, on Happy Bird (Germany) Catalogue no: **B 90116**
**Cass:** Released Jun '83, on Happy Bird (Germany) Catalogue no: **MB 990116**

**COMPLETE 1953 PARIS SESSIONS**
Tracks: / September in the rain / Free Press oui / Always / Walking at the Trocadero / Real crazy / More and more crazy / Completely crazy / I only have eyes for you / Blue panassie.
**2 LP Set:** Released Mar '77, on Vogue by Vogue Records. Catalogue no: **VJD 532**

**COMPLETE 1954 PARIS SESSIONS**
**2 LP Set:** Released Oct '88, on Vogue by Vogue Records. Catalogue no: **400068**

**COMPLETE LIONEL HAMPTON VOLS. 1 AND 2**
Tracks: / Rhythym, rhythym / China stomp / I know that you know / Confessin' / Drum stomp / Piano stomp / I surrender dear / Object of my affection, The / Ring dem bells / Don't be that way / I'm in the mood for swing / Shoe shiner's drag / Any time at all / Muskrat ramble / Down home jump / Rock hill special / Fiddle diddle / My last affair / Jivin' the vibes / Mood that I'm in, The / Hampton stomp / Buzzin' around with the bee / Whoa babe / Stompology / On the sunny side of the street / Judy / Baby wont you please come home / Everybody loves my baby / After you've gone / I just couldn't take it baby / You're my ideal / Sun will shine tonight.
**2 LP Set:** Released Dec '85, on RCA by BMG Records (UK). Deleted May '89. Catalogue no: **NL 89583**
**Cass set:** Released Dec '85, on RCA by BMG Records (UK). Catalogue no: **NK 89583**

**COMPLETE PARIS SESSION**
Tracks: / September in the rain / Free press oui / Always / Real crazy / More crazy / Completely crazy / I only have eyes for you.
Note: Tracks include those listed above.
**CD:** Released May '85, on Vogue by Vogue Records. Catalogue no: **VG 600 029**

**EASY LIVING (Hampton, Lionel & His Orchestra)**
Tracks: / Them changes / I'm so tired / Ain't no sunshine / California dreamin' / Eubie's boogie / Easy living / Flying home.
**Album:** Released Oct '80, on Manhattan (see EMI Manhattan) Deleted Jan '88. Catalogue no: **MAN 5030**

**FLYING HOME**
**CD:** Released '86, on Dunhill Compact Classics (USA) Catalogue no: **DZS 013**

**FLYING HOME (ASTAN)**
Tracks: / Hammo's jive / On the sunny side of the street / Summertime / Blue boy / Swanee River / Flying home / Stardust / How high the moon / I only have eyes for you / Lady be good.
**CD:** Released 10 Jul '89, on Vogue by Vogue Records. Catalogue no: **VG 670212**
**Album:** Released Mar '85, on Astan (USA) Catalogue no: **F 20129**

**FLYING HOME (MERCURY) (Hampton, Lionel & His Quartet)**
Tracks: / Always / 'S wonderful / Airmail special / Nearness of you, The / Soft winds / Stompin' at The Savoy / Love for sale / April in Paris / Just one of those things / Stardust / That old black magic / This can't be love / Willow weep for me / How high the moon / Blues for Norman / I can't get started / Moonglow / It's a blue world / High and mighty / When the saints go marching in / Flying home / Midnight sun / Tenderly / Hallelujah / Indiana / Man I love, The / Body and soul.
Note: Five-album box set from recordings made between 1953 and 1955, with Teddy Wilson, Oscar Peterson, Red Callender, Ray Brown, Gene Krupa and Buddy Rich.
**LP Set:** Released Nov '83, on Mercury (USA) by PolyGram Rec.Inc.(USA). Catalogue no: **8130 911**

**FLYING HOME (VERVE) (Hampton, Lionel / His Quartet)**
**Album:** Released Jun '89, on Verve Catalogue no: **837 434-1**
**Cass:** Released Jun '89, on Verve Catalogue no: **837 434-4**

**GLAD HAMP**
**CD:** Released Jul '89, on Cleo Catalogue no: **CLCD 5002**

**HAMP IN HARLEM (Hampton, Lionel / His Giants Of Jazz)**
**CD:** Released Jan '88, on Timeless (Import) by Timeless Records. Catalogue no: **CDSLP 168**
**Album:** Released Apr '81, on Timeless by Timeless Records. Catalogue no: **SJP 133**

**HAMP THE CHAMP (Hampton, Lionel & His Orchestra)**
Tracks: / Whoa babe / On the sunny side of the street / Shine / Don't be that way / I'm in the mood for swing / Muskrat ramble / Shoe shiner's drag / Shufflin' at the Hollywood / When lights are low / Hot mallets / Flying home / Jivin' with Jarvis / Three quarter boogie.
**Album:** Released Jul '86, on RCA by BMG Records (UK). Deleted Jul '89. Catalogue no: **CL 89806**
**Cass:** Released Jul '86, on RCA by BMG Records (UK). Deleted Jul '89. Catalogue no: **CK 89806**

**HAMPS BLUES**
Tracks: / Air mail special / E.G. / Psychedelic Sally / Raunchy Rita / Fum / Ham hock blues / Ring them bells / Lion's den / Here's that rainy day / Killer joe.
Note: Personnel: Lionel Hampton (Vibraphone / Vocal), Zoot Sims (Tenor sax), Teddy Wilson (Piano), George Duvivier (Bass), Buddy Rich (Drums), and others.
**CD:** Released Apr '89, on Denon Catalogue no: **DC 8538**
**CD:** Released '88, on Denon Catalogue no: **C38-7973**
**Cass:** Released Apr '89, on Denon Catalogue no: **MC 7973**

**HAMPS BOOGIE**
**CD:** Released May '88, on Jazz Life Catalogue no: **2673742**
**Album:** Released May '88, on Jazz Life Catalogue no: **2673741**
**Cass:** Released May '88, on Jazz Life Catalogue no: **2673744**

**HAMPTOLOGIA - VOL.1**
**Album:** Released Feb '82, on Polydor (Import) by Polydor Ltd. Catalogue no: **2304 527**

**HAMPTOLOGIA - VOL.2**
**Album:** Released Feb '82, on Polydor (Import) by Polydor Ltd. Catalogue no: **2304 528**

**HOT MALLETS, VOL 1 (Lionel Hampton's choice of the cream of his small-band sides)**
Tracks: / Buzzin' around with the bee / Stompology / On the sunny side of the street / I'm confessin' / Piano stomp / Everybody loves my baby / Ring dem bells / Don't be that way / I'm in the mood for swing / Shoe shiner's drag / Muskrat ramble / Down home jump / It don't mean a thing / Shufflin' at the Hollywood / Denison swing / Aintcha comin' home? / Twelfth St. rag / When lights are low / One sweet letter from you / Hot mallets / Early session hop.
**CD:** Released Apr '88, on Bluebird (2) by BMG Records (UK). Catalogue no: **ND 86458**

**IN PARIS - 1956**
**Album:** Released May '87, on Swing Disque Catalogue no: **SW 8415**

**IN THE BAG**
Tracks: / In the bag / Dig those vibes / Jack the fox boogie / How high the moon / Million dollar smile / Turkey hop / Double talk / Empty glass / Hamp's gumbo / Mingus fingers / Three minutes on 52nd Street / Hamp's got a Duke / Dancing on the ceiling / Blues for little 'T' / Memories of you / Silver slipper.
**Cass:** Released Dec '85, on Affinity by Charly Records. Catalogue no: **TCAFS 1017**
**Album:** Released Dec '85, on Affinity by Charly Records. Catalogue no: **AFS 1017**

**JAM BAND**
**Album:** Released '84, on First Heard by Submarine Records. Catalogue no: **FH 54**

**JAY BIRD**
Tracks: / Jay bird / Bebop / I cover the waterfront / Satchmo's blues / Hot house / Adam blew his hat / Calling Dr Mancuso / Brant Inn boogie / Good rockin' tonight / Dues in blues / Beulah's boogie.
Note: Joining the great vibes player are Fats Navarro, Teddy Buckner, Benny Bailey, Wes Montgomery, Charlie Mingus and Milt Buckner. Recorded in 1948.
**Cass:** Released '82, on Black Lion-Intercord Catalogue no: **CAS 427 032**
**Album:** Released '82, on Black Lion-Intercord Catalogue no: **INT 127 032**

**JAZZ AMBASSADORS, THE**
**Album:** Released '79, on Polydor by Polydor Ltd. Catalogue no: **2610 022**

**JAZZ TIME VOL.8**
**Album:** Released '88, on Vogue (France) by Vogue Records. Catalogue no: **502708**

**JIVING THE BLUES**
**Album:** Released '84, on Swing House by Submarine Records. Catalogue no: **SWH 45**

**JUST JAZZ ALL STARS (Concert)**
**Album:** Released '88, on GNP Crescendo (USA) by GNP Crescendo Records (USA). Catalogue no: **GPNS 15**
**Cass:** Released '88, on GNP Crescendo (USA) by GNP Crescendo Records (USA). Catalogue no: **GPN5 15**

**LEAPIN' WITH LIONEL (Big band bounce & boogie) (Hampton, Lionel & His Orchestra)**
Tracks: / Flying home / Hamp's boogie woogie / Tempo's boogie / Beulah's boogie / Slide, hamp, slide / Hey ba ba re bop / Rockin' in rhythm / Airmail special / Cobb's idea / Hamp's walkin' boogie / Red top / Midnight sun / Beulah's sister's boogie / Rag mop.
**Album:** Released Nov '83, on Affinity by Charly Records. Catalogue no: **AFS 1000**
**Cass:** Released '86, on Affinity by Charly Records. Catalogue no: **TCAFS 1000**

**LIGHT MY FIRE (Hampton, Lionel & His Orchestra)**
Tracks: / Them changes / I'm so tired / Ain't no sunshine / California dreamin' / You've got a friend / I / Light my fire / Bridge over troubled water.
**Album:** Released Apr '80, on Manhattan Records by President Records. Deleted '85. Catalogue no: **MAN 5004**

**LIONEL HAMPTON**
**CD:** Released Jul '89, on Cleo Catalogue no: **CLCD 5004**
**CD:** Released Mar '88, on Verve Catalogue no: **833 287-2**
**Album:** Released Apr '79, on Bright Orange Catalogue no: **BO 716**
**Cass:** Released 27 Feb '88, on Verve Catalogue no: **833 287-4**

**LIONEL HAMPTON AND JUST JAZZ ALL STARS (Hampton, Lionel & Just Jazz All Stars)**
Tracks: / Perdido / That's my desire / Central Avenue breakdown / Kaba's blues / Hamp's boogie woogie / Flying home.
**Album:** Released Jan '82, on Jazz Reactivation Catalogue no: **JR 102**

**LIONEL HAMPTON AND OTHERS (Hampton, Lionel & Others)**
**CD:** Released Jul '89, on Cleo Catalogue no: **CLCD 5012**

**LIONEL HAMPTON COLLECTION (20 golden greats)**
Tracks: / Airmail special / Hava nagila / Cool train / Lady be good / Crying / Song of the Negev / Gladysee bounce / Helpless / Railroad N.I. / I can't believe that you're in love with me / Cry of the blues / Don't feel the scene salty / Wild Bill / Hannah, Hannah / MC Ghee / Kingfish / Playboy's theme / Juice and more juice / Exodus / Kiss was just a kiss, A.
**Cass:** Released Jul '86, on Deja Vu Catalogue no: **DVMC 2065**
**Album:** Released Jul '86, on Deja Vu Catalogue no: **DVLP 2065**

**LIONEL HAMPTON IN CONCERT (CLEO)**
**CD:** Released Jul '89, on Cleo Catalogue no: **CLCD 5008**

**LIONEL HAMPTON IN CONCERT (JAZZ LIVE)**
**Album:** Released Apr '81, on Jazz Live (Italy) Catalogue no: **BLJ 8015**

**LIONEL HAMPTON IN PARIS**

**CD:** Released '88, on DRG (USA) by DRG Records (USA). Catalogue no: **CDSW 8415**

**LIONEL HAMPTON PRESENTS GERRY MULLIGAN (Hampton, Lionel / Gerry Mulligan)**
Tracks: / Apple core / Song for Johnny Hodges / Blight of the fumble bee / Gerry meets Hamp / Blues for Gerry / Line for Lyons / Walking shoes / Limelight.
**CD:** Released Jun '87, on Kingdom Jazz by Kingdom Records. Catalogue no: **CDGATE 7014**
**Album:** Released '84, on Kingdom Jazz by Kingdom Records. Catalogue no: **GATE 7014**
**Cass:** Released '89, on Kingdom Jazz by Kingdom Records. Catalogue no: **CGATE 7014**

**LIONEL HAMPTON AND THE JUST JAZZ ALL STARS (Hampton, Lionel/Just Jazz All Stars)**
**CD:** Released Dec '86, on Vogue by Vogue Records. Catalogue no: **VGCD 600099**

**LIONEL HAMPTON - VOL.2**
Tracks: / September in the rain / Free press oui / Always / Walking at the Trocadero.
**Album:** Released May '83, on Jazz Reactivation Catalogue no: **JR 126**

**LIONEL HAMPTON VOL.3**
Tracks: / Real crazy / More crazy / More and more crazy / Completely crazy / I only have eyes for you / Blue panassie.
**Album:** Released Feb '82, on Jazz Reactivation Deleted Feb '87. Catalogue no: **JR 144**

**LIVE AT CARNEGIE HALL (Lionel Hampton 50th anniversary concert) (Hampton, Lionel & His Orchestra)**
Tracks: / Tea for two / I'm confessin' / Misty / Avalon / More than you know / Runnin' wild.
Note: With Lionel Hampton, Pepper Adams, Cat Anderson, Eddie Bert, Ray Bryant, Doc Cheatham, Arnett Cob, Panama Francis, John Gordon, Chubby Jackson, Charles McPherson, Billy Mackel, Jimmy Maxwell, Paul Moen, Joe Newman, Benny Powell, Earl Warren, Bob Wilber.
**Album:** Released Feb '83, on Carosello Catalogue no: **BUDLP 9000**

**LIVE AT MUZEVAL (Hampton, Lionel / Big Band)**
**CD:** Released Mar '90, on Timeless by Timeless Records. Catalogue no: **CDSJP 120**
**Album:** Released Apr '81, on Timeless by Timeless Records. Catalogue no: **SJP 120**

**LIVE IN PARIS - VOL.1**
**Album:** Released Apr '81, on Joker (USA) by Lifetime Records (USA). Catalogue no: **SM 3543**

**LIVE IN PARIS - VOL.2**
**Album:** Released Apr '81, on Joker (USA) by Lifetime Records (USA). Catalogue no: **SM 3544**

**MADE IN JAPAN**
Tracks: / Airmail special / Advent / Stardust / Mess is here / Interpretations, opus 5 / Minor thesis / Jodo / Valve job / Armail / Big bad Henry / Moment's notice / No me esqueca / Giant steps / Rodney / Round Robin / Flying home / Hamp's boogie woogie / Glad Hamp / Ol' man river / Greasy greens / Mr. P.C. / Hamp's got the blues / Ein burgermeister de Francoise.
Note: Recorded live in Tokyo in June, 1982.
**Album:** Released Aug '85, on Timeless by Timeless Records. Catalogue no: **SJP 175**
**Cass:** Released Aug '85, on Timeless by Timeless Records. Catalogue no: **SJP 1120**

**MASTERPIECES**
**Album:** Released Sep '85, on Saar Giants Of Jazz (Italy) Catalogue no: **LPJT 29**
**Cass:** Released Sep '85, on Saar Giants Of Jazz (Italy) Catalogue no: **MCJT 29**
**Album:** Released Sep '87, on Giants of Jazz by Hasmick Promotions. Catalogue no: **LPJT 29**

**MEMORABLE SESSION, A**
**Album:** Released Oct '88, on Vogue by Vogue Records. Catalogue no: **500 752**

**MESS IS HERE, THE (Live, 1944-45) (Hampton, Lionel & His Orchestra)**
**Album:** Released Jun '78, on Solid Sender Catalogue no: **SOL 502**
**Album:** Released Oct '85, on Giants of Jazz by Hasmick Promotions. Catalogue no: **GOJ 1014**
**Cass:** Released Jan '86, on Magic (1) by Submarine Records. Catalogue no: **CAWE 18**
**Album:** Released Jan '86, on Magic (1) by Submarine Records. Catalogue no: **AWE 18**

**MOSTLY BLUES**
Tracks: / Bye bye blues / Someday my prince will come / Take the 'A' train / Blues for jazz beaux / Walkin' uptown / Honeysuckle rose / Mostly blues / Limehouse blues / Gone with the wind.
**Album:** Released '89, on Music Masters by Music Masters Records. Catalogue no: **CIJD 40168L**
**CD:** Released Nov '89, on Limelight Catalogue no: **820 805-2**
**CD:** Released '89, on Music Masters by Music Masters Records. Catalogue no: **CIJD 60168K**

**NEW YORK BLACKOUT**
**Cass:** Released Jan '85, on Pathe Marconi (France) Catalogue no: **2M 256 64824**
**Album:** Released Jan '85, on Pathe Marconi (France) Catalogue no: **2M 056 64824**

**NEWPORT UPROAR**
**Cass:** Released Feb '86, on RCA by BMG Records (UK). Deleted May '89. Catalogue no: **NK 89590**
**Album:** Released Feb '86, on RCA by BMG Records (UK). Deleted May '89. Catalogue no: **NL 89590**

**PLAY BRASSENS (Hampton, Lionel/friends)**
Tracks: / La premiere fille / Dans l'eau de la Claire Fontaine / Le vieux leon / Penelope / A l'ombre de coeur de ma mie / Oncle Archibald / La route aux 4 chansons / Les amoureux des bancs publics / L'orage / Le 22 septembre / Les passantes.
**Album:** Released Mar '84, on IMS by Polydor Ltd. Catalogue no: **8123 861**

**QUARTET**
**Cass:** Released Jul '89, on Polydor by Polydor Ltd. Catalogue no: **837 434-4**
**Album:** Released Jul '89, on Polydor by Polydor Ltd. Catalogue no: **837 434-1**

**RIDIN' ON THE L & N**
Tracks: / Ridin' on the L & N / Pencil's broke / Doublin' with Dublin / Boogie woogie Santa Claus / Royal Family, The / There will never be another you / I've been a fool (thinking you cared) / Hawk's nest / Man I love, The / Adam blew his hat / Cherokee / Wee Albert / Moonglow / Everybody's somebody's fool / Tempo's birthday / Lavender coffin / Sky blue / I'll remember April.
**Album:** Released Jun '88, on Affinity by Charly Records. Catalogue no: **AFS 1037**

**RING DEM VIBES**
**Album:** Released Nov '79, on Barclay (France) by Decca Records. Catalogue no: **80706**

**SOUL OF LIONEL HAMPTON, THE**
**Album:** Released Apr '81, on Joker (USA) by Lifetime Records (USA). Catalogue no: **SM 3539**

**STARDUST (Hampton, Lionel All Stars)**
Tracks: / Man i love / Lady be good / One o clock jump / Stardust.
**Album:** Released Jun '85, on Jasmine by Hasmick Promotions. Catalogue no: **JASM 1044**

**VIBES BOOGIE (Live 1955)**
**Album:** Released Jun '89, on Jazz & Jazz Catalogue no: **JJ 605**
**CD:** Released 21 Jul '89, on Jazz & Jazz Catalogue no: **CDJJ 605**

**YOU BETTER KNOW IT!!**
Tracks: / Ring dem bells / Vibraphone blues / Tempo's birthday / Sweetheart on parade / Pick a rib / Trick or treat / Cute swingle jingle / Taste of honey, A.
**Cass:** Released Jun '82, on Jasmine by Hasmick Promotions. Catalogue no: **JAS C19**
**Album:** Released Jun '82, on Jasmine by Hasmick Promotions. Deleted Feb '88. Catalogue no: **JAS 19**

## Hampton, Slide

**Biographical details:** Locksley Wellington Hampton is a trombonist and composer born in 1932 in Pennsylvania. He first recorded as a leader in 1959 and was later music director for Lloyd Price, but relocated to Europe; like trumpeter Benny Bailey and many others, he is less well-known at home than he ought to be, but radio work in Germany has presumably brought more peace of mind than the Stateside scuffle. (Donald Clarke, Nov 1989).

### 1969 (Hampton, Slide Quartet)

**Album:** Released Sep '84, on Pathe Marconi (France) Catalogue no: **PM 1552621**

### ROOTS (featuring Clifford Jordan)

**Album:** Released '88, on Criss Cross Catalogue no: **CRISS 1015**

### WORLD OF TROMBONES

**CD:** Released Jan '89, on Black Lion Catalogue no: **760 113**

**Album:** Released Jan '89, on Black Lion Catalogue no: **BLP 60113**

## Hancock, Herbie

**Biographical details:** This American keyboard player, composer and vocalist was born in Chicago and received classical training as a child. He studied to become an engineer, but quit his course before graduation in order to pursue a musical career. During the early sixties, he was a member of jazz trumpeter Donald Byrd's band. Hancock's debut LP *Takin' off* was released in 1963 - in that same year, just as he was celebrating his 23rd birthday, the opening track *Watermelon man* became a surprise US Top 10 hit in a cover version by Mongo Santamaria. Herbie himself did not flirt with the pop market until the mid-seventies, for the intervening years were spent playing jazz. From 1963-68 Hancock led a double life. He released acclaimed solo albums like *Empyrean Isles* and *Maiden voyage*, and played in one of the best line-ups of trumpeter Miles Davis' band.

The group's 1968 album, *Miles in the sky* saw Davis moving into the rock sphere, and for the first time, adding electric instruments to his band. Tracks such as *Big stuff* brought him a cross-over audience from the realms of the drug-influenced hippie rock fraternity of the late 60's. Herbie was inspired by this, and decided to quit Davis in order to pursue similar themes with his own band. His 1969 album *The prisoner* was the first solo Hancock record to include electric piano. During the early seventies, Hancock continued to explore the possibilities of electronic keyboards and the new synthesiser technology, and continued to garnish his jazz with rock influences; and he also began to dabble in an even more durable and important fusion, jazz-funk. Such experiments did not please jazz purists, but they enhanced his reputation as an innovative and talented artist. As the disco scene began to get off the ground in 1974, he registered his first major commercial success with the funky album *Headhunters*. Many more in similar vein followed. After a brief return to his jazz roots, Herbie emerged in 1978 with a record that was aimed at the disco and pop markets; from this point onwards, he forsook the jazz audiences altogether. *I thought it was you* reached no. 15 on the UK singles chart, and introduced the world to another piece of Herbie experimentation, the vocoder. This synthesiser-cum-voicebox made his inexperienced voice sound like a robot, which was handy for someone who couldn't sing. He repeated the trick on his 1979 disco single *You bet your love*, which also reached the Top 20. 1983 brought Hancock into the UK Top 10 and onto dancefloors all over the world with his biggest disco success yet. Teaming with Material, the New York electro-jazz-funk experimentalists, he came up with the dynamic single *Rockit*. This showed that veteran Herbie was thoroughly in tune with contemporary electro/hip hop/scratching trends, and was accompanied by an equally innovative and upfront video clip. (Bob Macdonald, 7/10/85)

Born in 1940 in Chicago, the keyboardist's tunes such as *Watermelon man* and *Maiden voyage* on various Blue Note LPs in the '60s were part of the beginning jazz-funk.

Apart from freelance work and film music he played in the Miles Davis Quintet 1963-8 (later reunited as V.S.O.P. with Freddie Hubbard replacing Miles). Having helped to invent funk he reaped the reweard with 17 pop-chart albums 1973-84, tending towards the slickly disco-ish; the single *Rockit* was a landmark (produced by Bill Laswell). He won an Oscar for his work on the film *Round midnight* in 1986. (Donald Clarke, Nov 1989).

### AUTO DRIVE

Tracks: / Autodrive / Bomb.

**12" Single:** Released Oct '83, on CBS by CBS Records. Deleted '86. Catalogue no: **TA 3802**

**7" Single:** Released Oct '83, on CBS by CBS Records. Deleted '86. Catalogue no: **A 3802**

### BEST OF HERBIE HANCOCK

Tracks: / Doin' it / I thought it was you / Chameleon / Hang up your hang ups / You bet your love / Tell everybody.

**Album:** Released Nov '84, on CBS by CBS Records. Catalogue no: **CBS 32526**

**Cass:** Released Nov '84, on CBS by CBS Records. Catalogue no: **40 32526**

### BEST OF HERBIE HANCOCK (2) (Blue Note years)

Tracks: / Watermelon man / Driftin' (CD only.) / Maiden voyage / Dolphin dance / One finger snap / Cantaloupe island / Riot / Speak like a child / King cobra (CD only.).

**CD:** Released Dec '88, on Blue Note by EMI Records. Catalogue no: **BNZ 143**

**CD:** Released Dec '88, on Blue Note by EMI Records. Catalogue no: **CDP 791 142 2**

**Album:** Released Dec '88, on Blue Note by EMI Records. Catalogue no: **B1-91142**

### BY ALL MEANS (Hancock, Herbie & Alphonse Mouzon)

Tracks: / Do I have to? / Space invaders / Next time we love, The / Jogger, The / By all means.

**CD:** Released Apr '84, on Verve Deleted Aug '87. Catalogue no: **817 485-2**

**Album:** Released Apr '81, on MPS Jazz Catalogue no: **MPS 68 266**

### BY ALL MEANS (SINGLE)

Tracks: / By all means / Do I have to.

**12" Single:** Released Jul '87, on Excaliber by Red Bus Records. Deleted '88. Catalogue no: **EXCL 509**

**7" Single:** Released Jul '87, on Excaliber by Red Bus Records. Deleted '88. Catalogue no: **EXC 509**

### CROSSINGS

Tracks: / Sleeping giant / Quasar / Water torture.

**Album:** on Warner Bros. by WEA Records. Catalogue no: **K 46164**

### EMPYREAN ISLES

Tracks: / One finger snap / Oliloqui valley / Cantaloupe Island / Egg, The / One finger snap (alt. take) (CD only.) / Oliloqui valley (alt. take) (CD only.).

**Album:** Released Jul '89, on Blue Note by EMI Records. Catalogue no: **BST 84175**

**CD:** Released Aug '89, on Blue Note by EMI Records. Catalogue no: **CDP 784 175 2**

**CD:** Released Aug '89, on Blue Note by EMI Records. Catalogue no: **BNZ 185**

### EVENING WITH ..., AN (Hancock, Herbie & Chick Corea)

Tracks: / Homecoming / Ostinato / Hook / Bouquet / Maiden voyage / La fiesta.

**2 LP Set:** Released Dec '79, on Polydor by Polydor Ltd. Deleted '84. Catalogue no: **2672049**

### EVENING WITH HERBIE HANCOCK AND CHICK COREA (Hancock, Herbie & Chick Corea)

Tracks: / Someday my prince will come / Liza / Button up / February moments / Maiden voyage / La fiesta.

**2 LP Set:** Released '79, on CBS by CBS Records. Deleted '84. Catalogue no: **CBS 88329**

### FAT ALBERT ROTUNDA

Tracks: / Wiggle waggle / Fat mama / Tell me a bedtime story / Oh' here he comes / Jessica / Fat Albert Rotunda / Lil' brother.

**Album:** Released '88, on Warner Bros. by WEA Records. Catalogue no: **K 46039**

### FEETS DON'T FAIL ME NOW

Tracks: / You bet your love / Trust me / Tell everybody / Ready or not / Honey from the jar / Knee deep.

**CD:** Released Sep '85, on CBS by CBS Records. Deleted 17 Apr '89. Catalogue no: **CD 83491**

**Album:** Released Feb '79, on CBS by CBS Records. Deleted '84. Catalogue no: **CBS 83491**

**FUTURE SHOCK**
Tracks: / Rockit / Future shock / TFS / Eath beat / Autodrive / Rough.
**Album:** Released Aug '83, on CBS by CBS Records. Catalogue no: **CBS 25540**
**Cass:** Released 11 Apr '87, on CBS by CBS Records. Deleted Jan '89. Catalogue no: **450 625 4**
**CD:** Released '88, on CBS by CBS Records. Deleted Jan '89. Catalogue no: **CDCBS 25540**
**Album:** Released 11 Apr '87, on CBS by CBS Records. Deleted Aug '88. Catalogue no: **450 625 1**
**Cass:** Released Aug '83, on CBS by CBS Records. Deleted Aug '87. Catalogue no: **40 25540**

**FUTURE SHOCK (SINGLE)**
Tracks: / Future shock.
**7" Single:** Released Jan '84, on CBS by CBS Records. Deleted '87. Catalogue no: **A 4075**

**GO FOR IT**
Tracks: / Go for it / Making love.
**7" Single:** Released Apr '80, on CBS by CBS Records. Deleted Apr '83. Catalogue no: **CBS 8529**

**HANCOCK ALLEY**
Tracks: / Jammin' with Herbie / Herbie's blues / Rock your soul / Scoochie / Cycles / Witch fire.
**Album:** Released Jun '80, on Manhattan Records by President Records. Deleted '85. Catalogue no: **MAN 5021**

**HARDROCK**
Tracks: / Hardrock / T.F.S..
**12" Single:** Released Aug '84, on CBS by CBS Records. Catalogue no: **TA 4616**
**7" Single:** Released Aug '84, on CBS by CBS Records. Catalogue no: **A 4616**

**HEADHUNTERS**
Tracks: / Chameleon / Watermelon man / Sly / Vein melter.
Note: Digital stereo.
**Album:** Released Apr '84, on CBS by CBS Records. Catalogue no: **CBS 32008**
**CD:** Released Jul '84, on CBS by CBS Records. Deleted Jan '89. Catalogue no: **CD 65928**

**HERBIE HANCOCK AND THE ROCKIT BAND (Hancock, Herbie & The Rockit Band)**
**VHS:** Released Oct '84, on CBS by CBS Records. Catalogue no: **661950**

**HERBIE HANCOCK: GREATEST HITS**
Tracks: / Doin' it / Thought it was you / Chameleon / Hang up your hang ups / You bet your love / Tell everybody.
**Album:** Released Jan '80, on CBS by CBS Records. Catalogue no: **CBS 84106**
**Cass:** Released Jan '80, on CBS by CBS Records. Catalogue no: **40 84106**

**HOT AND HEAVY**
Tracks: / Hot piano / Live and awake / Night walkers / Scoochie / Cycles / Witch fire / Jammin' with Herbie / Herbie's blues / Rock your soul / Afro boogie / Far out / Hot and heavy.
**Cass:** Released '84, on Premier by Premier Records. Catalogue no: **KCBR 1030**
**Cass:** Released Apr '86, on Star Jazz (USA) by Charly Records. Catalogue no: **SJAZZC 4**
**Album:** Released Apr '86, on Star Jazz (USA) by Charly Records. Catalogue no: **SJAZZ 4**
**Album:** Released '84, on Premier by Premier Records. Catalogue no: **CBR 1030**
**Cass:** Released Nov '84, on Chase Music (USA) by Chase Music Group (USA). Catalogue no: **SJAZC 4**

**I THOUGHT IT WAS YOU**
Tracks: / I thought it was you.
**7" Single:** Released May '82, on CBS by CBS Records. Catalogue no: **CBS 6530**

**I THOUGHT IT WAS YOU (OLD GOLD)**
Tracks: / I thought it was you / You bet your love.
**7" Single:** Released Sep '85, on Old Gold by Old Gold Records. Deleted Jul '88. Catalogue no: **OG 9561**

**INVENTIONS AND DIMENSIONS**
Tracks: / Succotash / Triangle / Jack rabbit / Mimosa / Jump ahead, A.
**Album:** Released Apr '89, on Blue Note by EMI Records. Catalogue no: **B1 84147**
**CD:** Released Apr '89, on Blue Note by EMI Records. Catalogue no: **CDP 784 147 2**
**CD:** Released Apr '89, on Blue Note by EMI Records. Catalogue no: **BNZ 154**

**LITE ME UP**
Tracks: / Lite me up / Bomb / Gettin' to the good part / Paradise / Can't hide your love / Fun tracks / Motormouth / Give it all your heart.
**Album:** Released Jul '84, on CBS by CBS Records. Deleted Jul '89. Catalogue no: **CBS 32474**

**LITE ME UP (SINGLE)**
Tracks: / Lite me up / Satisfied with love.
**7" Single:** Released Nov '82, on CBS by CBS Records. Deleted Nov '85. Catalogue no: **A 2222**

**MAGIC WINDOWS**
Tracks: / Magic number / Tonight's the night / Everybody's broke / Help yourself / Satisfied with love / Twilight clone.
**Album:** Released Nov '81, on CBS by CBS Records. Deleted Nov '86. Catalogue no: **CBS 85144**

**MAIDEN VOYAGE**
Tracks: / Maiden voyage / Eye of the hurricane / Little one / Survival of the fittest / Dolphin dance.
**Album:** Released Jul '89, on Blue Note by EMI Records. Deleted May '89. Catalogue no: **BST 84195**
**CD:** Released Jul '87, on Blue Note by EMI Records. Catalogue no: **BNZ 40**
**Cass:** Released Mar '84, on Blue Note (France) by EMI Records. Catalogue no: **BSC 841954**
**CD:** Released Jul '87, on Blue Note by EMI Records. Catalogue no: **CDP 746 339 2**
**Cass:** Released Mar '86, on Blue Note by EMI Records. Deleted Jun '89. Catalogue no: **TCBST 84195**
**CD:** Released '88, on EMI (Japan) by EMI Records. Catalogue no: **CP 353071**

**MONSTER**
Tracks: / Saturday night / Stars in your eyes / Go for it / Don't hold it in / Making love / It all comes round.
**Album:** Released Jun '80, on CBS by CBS Records. Deleted '85. Catalogue no: **CBS 84237**

**MR HANDS**
Tracks: / Spiralling prism / Calypso / Just around the corner / 4 a.m. / Shifless shuffle / Textures.
**Cass:** Released Nov '80, on CBS by CBS Records. Catalogue no: **40 84638**

**MWANDISHI**
Tracks: / Ostinato (suite for Angela) / You'll know when you get there / Wandering spirit song.
**Album:** Released '88, on Warner Bros. by WEA Records. Catalogue no: **K 46077**

**MY POINT OF VIEW**
Tracks: / Blind man, blind man / Tribute to someone, A / King Cobra / Pleasure is mine / And what if I don't?.
**CD:** Released Apr '88, on Blue Note by EMI Records. Catalogue no: **BNZ 44**
**Album:** Released Oct '84, on Blue Note by EMI Records. Deleted Jul '87. Catalogue no: **BST 84126**
**CD:** Released Apr '88, on Blue Note by EMI Records. Catalogue no: **CDP 784 126 2**

**NIGHT WITH HERBIE**
Tracks: / Hot piano / Live & awake / Night walkers / Afro boogie / Far out / Hot heavy.
**Album:** Released Aug '80, on Manhattan Records by President Records. Catalogue no: **MAN 5027**

**PERFECT MACHINE**
Tracks: / Perfect machine / Obsession / Vibe alive / Beat wise / Maiden voyage P. bop / Chemical residue.
**CD:** Released 13 Jun '88, on CBS by CBS Records. Catalogue no: **460679 2**
**Album:** Released 13 Jun '88, on CBS by CBS Records. Deleted Jan '90. Catalogue no: **460679 1**
**Cass:** Released 13 Jun '88, on CBS by CBS Records. Deleted Jan '90. Catalogue no: **460679 4**

**PIANO, THE**
**Album:** Released Jan '80, on Japanese Import Catalogue no: **30 AP 1033**

**PRISONER, THE**
Tracks: / I have a dream / Prisoner, The / Firewater / He who lives in fear /

Promise of the sun.
**CD:** Released Aug '87, on Blue Note by EMI Records. Catalogue no: **CDP 746 845 2**
**Album:** Released Sep '87, on Blue Note by EMI Records. Catalogue no: **BST 84321**
**CD:** Released Aug '87, on Blue Note by EMI Records. Catalogue no: **BNZ 43**

**QUARTET**
Tracks: / Well you needn't / Round midnight / Clear ways / Quick sketch / Eye of the hurricane / Parade / Sorcerer, The / Pee Wee / I fall in love too easily.
**Album:** Released '84, on CBS by CBS Records. Catalogue no: **22219**

**ROCKIT**
Tracks: / Rockit / Rough.
**12" Single:** Released '83, on CBS by CBS Records. Catalogue no: **TA 3577**
**7" Single:** Released '83, on CBS by CBS Records. Catalogue no: **A 3577**

**ROCKIT (OLD GOLD)**
Tracks: / Rockit / You bet your love / I thought it was you / Future shock.
**12" Single:** Released Feb '86, on Old Gold by Old Gold Records. Catalogue no: **OG 4001**

**SONGS FOR MY FATHER**
**Cass:** Released Sep '87, on Blue Note by EMI Records. Deleted Nov '88. Catalogue no: **4BN 84195**

**SOUND-SYSTEM**
Tracks: / Hardrock / Metal beat / Karabali / Junku / People are changing / Sound-system / Rockit (Extra track available on cassette only.) / Autodrive (Extra track available on cassette only.) / Future shock (Extra track available on cassette only.) / TFS (Extra track available on cassette only.) / Rough (Extra track available on cassette only.) / Chameleon (Extra track available on cassette only.).
**Cass:** Released Aug '86, on CBS by CBS Records. Catalogue no: **40 32805**
**Album:** Released Aug '86, on CBS by CBS Records. Catalogue no: **CBS 32805**
**CD:** Released Dec '85, on CBS by CBS Records. Deleted Jan '89. Catalogue no: **CD 26062**

**SPEAK LIKE A CHILD**
Tracks: / Riot / Speak like a child / First trip / Toys / Godbye to childhood / Sorcerer, The.
**CD:** Released Jun '87, on Blue Note by EMI Records. Catalogue no: **CDP 746 136 2**
**CD:** Released Jun '87, on Blue Note by EMI Records. Catalogue no: **BNZ 41**
**Album:** Released Jul '89, on Blue Note by EMI Records. Catalogue no: **BST 84279**

**SUNLIGHT**
Tracks: / I thought it was you / Come running to me / Sunlight / No means yes / Good question.
**Album:** Released Jul '78, on CBS by CBS Records. Catalogue no: **CBS 82240**
**Cass:** Released Jul '78, on CBS by CBS Records. Catalogue no: **40 82240**

**TAKIN' OFF**
Tracks: / Watermelon man / Three bags full / Empty pockets / Maze, The / Driftin' / Alone and I.
**CD:** Released May '87, on Blue Note by EMI Records. Catalogue no: **BNZ 42**
**CD:** Released May '87, on Blue Note by EMI Records. Catalogue no: **CDP 746 506 2**
**Cass:** Released Sep '87, on Blue Note by EMI Records. Deleted Nov '88. Catalogue no: **4BN 84109**
**Cass:** Released Jul '82, on Blue Note by EMI Records. Catalogue no: **BST 84109**

**TELL EVERYBODY**
Tracks: / Tell everybody / Trust me.
**7" Single:** Released Apr '79, on CBS by CBS Records. Deleted '82. Catalogue no: **CBS 7229**
**12" Single:** Released Apr '79, on CBS by CBS Records. Deleted '82. Catalogue no: **CBS 127229**

**THIRD PLANE (Hancock, Herbie / Ron Carter / Tony Williams)**
**CD:** Released '86, on Carrere (France) Catalogue no: **CA 98 134**

**THRUST**
**Album:** Released Oct '74, on CBS by CBS Records. Catalogue no: **CBS 80193**

**VIBE ALIVE**
Tracks: / Vibe alive / Vibe alive (ext. dance remix) (Available on 12" version only.) / Vibe alive (bonus beats) (Track on 12" version only.) / Maiden voyage P. bop.
**CD Single:** Released 14 May '88, on CBS by CBS Records. Deleted Jan '89. Catalogue no: **651 432 9**
**12" Single:** Released May '88, on CBS by CBS Records. Deleted Jan '89. Catalogue no: **651 432 8**
**Album:** Released Jun '88, on Columbia by EMI Records. Catalogue no: **XSS 177755**
**7" Single:** Released May '88, on CBS by CBS Records. Deleted Jan '89. Catalogue no: **651 432 7**

**VILLAGE LIFE**
Tracks: / Moonlight / Ndan ndan nyaria / Early warning / Kanatente.
**Album:** Released '86, on CBS by CBS Records. Catalogue no: **CBS 23697**

**YOU BET YOUR LOVE**
Tracks: / You bet your love / Knee deep.
**7" Single:** Released Feb '79, on CBS by CBS Records. Deleted '81. Catalogue no: **CBS 7010**

## Hancock, John

**MISSISSIPPI MOTION (A legacy in river ragtime)**
**Album:** Released Mar '87, on Stomp Off (USA) Catalogue no: **SOS 1025**

## Handy, Capt. John

**Biographical details:** The New Orleans alto saxist and clarinettist (1900-71) who had worked with Kid Ory, Kid Howard and Kid Sheik, with whom he toured Europe in the '60s. (Donald Clarke, Nov 1989).

**ALL ABOARD (Handy, Capt. John & His New Orleans Stompers)**
**Album:** Released Jun '86, on GHB by Jazzology Records (USA). Catalogue no: **GHB 42**

**ALL ABOARD WITH JIM ROBINSON**
**Album:** Released Jun '88, on GHB by Jazzology Records (USA). Catalogue no: **GHB 43**

**ALL ABOARD WITH RIMMINGTON**
**Album:** Released Jun '88, on GHB by Jazzology Records (USA). Catalogue no: **GHB 41**

**CAPTAIN JOHN HANDY, GEOFF BULL AND BARRY MARTYN'S BAND**
**Album:** Released Feb '87, on GHB by Jazzology Records (USA). Catalogue no: **GHB 166**

**WITH THE CLAUDE HOPKINS BAND**
**Album:** Released Feb '85, on RCA (France) by BMG Records (France). Catalogue no: **NL 89503**

## Handy, John

**Biographical details:** John Richard Handy II, born in 1933 in Texas, is not related to Captain John Handy, the New Orleans musician. The younger man plays alto and tenor saxophones and other instruments and is also a composer. He played clarinet at 13, won amateur featherweight boxing championship in 1947 and took up alto sax in 1949. He recorded with Charles Mingus 1958-59, worked with pianist Randy Weston, with Mingus at Monterey 1964, with his own quintet there in 1965; he has also done film/TV work and appeared with symphony orchestras. (Donald Clarke, Nov 1989).

**HARD WORK**
**Album:** Released Aug '76, on Impulse by Impulse Records. Catalogue no: **IMPL 8038**

**HARD WORK (SINGLE)**
Tracks: / Hard work / Young enough to dream.
**7" Single:** Released May '82, on MCA by MCA Records. Deleted '85. Catalogue no: **MCA 626**
**12" Single:** Released May '82, on MCA by MCA Records. Deleted '85. Catalogue no: **MCAT 626**

**LEGENDARY HANDY SESSIONS**
**Album:** Released Apr '89, on GHB by Jazzology Records (USA). Catalogue no: **GHB 251**

**RIGHT THERE**
**Album:** Released Apr '84, on Gull by Gull Records. Deleted '88. Catalogue no: **MLP 3010**

**WHERE GO THE BOATS (Handy, John & Lee Ritenour)**
**CD:** Released '88, on Inak Catalogue no: **INAK 861 CD**

## Handy, John & Mabel

**JOHN & MABEL HANDY MEMORIAL**
**Album:** Released Apr '79, on Nola Catalogue no: **NOLA LP 1**

## Hanna, Roland

**GERSHWIN, CARMICHAEL, CATS**
Tracks: / Stardust / Skylark / Memory / Nearness of you / Bess, oh where's my bess / Embraceable you.
**Album:** Released Mar '83, on CTI (1) by Polydor Ltd. Deleted Mar '88. Catalogue no: **CTI 9008**

**GLOVE**
Note: Reissue from the Japanese Trio label, with George Mraz and Motohiko Hino.
**Album:** Released Jul '88, on Black Hawk (USA) by Blackhawk Records (USA). Catalogue no: **BKH 530**
**CD:** Released Jul '88, on Black Hawk (USA) by Blackhawk Records (USA). Catalogue no: **BKH 530CD**

**INFORMAL**
**Album:** Released Dec '79, on Hi-Fly (Switzerland) Catalogue no: **P 102**

**NEW YORK JAZZ QUARTET**
**Album:** Released Apr '84, on Beehive (USA) Catalogue no: **BH 7013**

**PERUGIA**
Tracks: / Take the 'A' train / I got it bad and that ain't good / Time dust gathered / Perugia / Child is born, A / Wistful moment.
**CD:** Released Sep '87, on Freedom Catalogue no: **FCD 41010**
**Album:** Released Sep '87, on Freedom Catalogue no: **FLP 41010**

**ROLAND HANNA AND GEORGE MRAZ (Hanna, Roland & George Mraz)**
**Album:** Released Oct '87, on Black Hawk (USA) by Blackhawk Records (USA). Catalogue no: **BKH 527**

**SWING ME NO WALTZES**
**Album:** Released '79, on Storyville by Storyville Records AB. Catalogue no: **SLP 4018**

**THIS MUST BE LOVE (Hanna, Sir Roland, George Moraz, Ben Riley)**
**Album:** Released Jun '86, on Audiophile (USA) by Jazzology Records (USA). Catalogue no: **AP 157**

**TIME FOR THE DANCERS (Hanna, Roland Trio)**
**Album:** Released '88, on Progressive Catalogue no: **PRO 7012**

## Hanshaw, Annette

**ANNETTE HANSHAW - THE EARLY YEARS 1926 VOL 1 (See panel on next page)**
Tracks: / Black bottom / Six feet of Papa / Lay me down to sleep in Caroline / Falling in love with you / Don't take that black bottom away / Cherie, I love you / Calling me home / If I'd only believed in you / My baby knows how / Do do do / Everything's made for love / Kiss your little baby goodnight / One sweet letter from you / If you can't tell the world she's a good girl / I'm all alone in a palace of stone.
Note: The 1920s have been written about, maligned, over praised and condemned perhaps more than any other decade of the twentieth century. The period has been described as the Jazz Age, the Aspirin Age, the Roaring Twenties, the Sweet and Twenties, the Golden Era, and (even) the Morning After - apparently referring to the reckless but understandable optimism and gaity that followed the First World War, which no ominous political movements to Right and Left and no solemn warnings from politicians and financiers could extinguish, until the whole thing collapsed in a heap of worthless paper one autumn day in 1929 on Wall Street, New York. The last-mentioned nickname may refer, or course to the social experiment known as Prohibition which began on July 1 1919, with the passing of the Volstead Act and which was not repealed until December 6, 1933.
The reckless, lawless, whoopee-making side of life in the twenties has been so overplayed by writers, most of them were not conscious, or even born, during that era, that anyone not knowing any better might be forgiven for thinking that life was one long alcoholic orgy against a background of obstreperous so-called jazz music. In fact, most people on both sides of the Atlantic were too busy trying to pick up the pieces into which the Great War of 1914-1918 had shattered their lives, and fit them together again into something like a resonable pattern, that they had no time or money, even if they had the inclination, to indulge in waywardness of this sort. To be sure, those with money often got into papers because they did crazy, extrovert things like pogo-stick jumping, flag pole squatting, marathon-dancing and swimming the English Channel or flying the Atlantic Ocean alone, but if everyone, or nearly everyone, had indulged in these capers, obviously they would not have made the headlines because they would not have been news.
The voice on this record belongs to a young lady who can fairly claim to have merited the term 'flapper', used since the war to denote a young teenage girl, and still in common use in the mid and late twenties.
Annette Hanshaw was born in New York on October 18, 1910, partly of Virginian parentage. She was rather shy, and not in the slightest the extrovert, brash type popularly supposed to be the usual American girl of the mid-twenties. She was gifted with a naturally sweet, warm, flexible voice, and in 1926, before her sixteenth birthday, she was heard singing at a private affair by Herman Rose, the Musical Director of Pathe Records. He realised she possessed considerable talent, and asked her to come along to the recording studios.
She was to become one of the first 'pop' artists to achieve fame through recording, for she had not, like her friend and rival in later years, Ruth Etting, come up through vaudeville, and being of a diffident nature, she naturally depended on influential people to ensure that her outstanding talent was properly managed and not allowed to run to waste. Her Pathe test, in which she recorded a medley of popular songs of the day, was so successful that she was given a contract on the spot. Even so, her recording - indeed, her professional - career only spans just under eight years, for in 1934, at the height of her popularity, but weary of endless broadcasts, films, recording sessions and stage appearances, she gave up everything for marriage and became Mrs. Herman Rose.
For the next twenty five years, nothing more was heard of Miss Annette Hanshaw, as some of the original 78 rpm discs label her with quaint old worldliness. Then in 1959, one of us sailed to New York having established a contact with Mrs. Annette Rose, a widow working as a stenographer in a firm of lawyers. She was exactly as charming, shy and somewhat bewildered as might have been expected. She could not understand that anyone wanted to see and talk about her long-dead career because of a great love of her divine voice. She hated her records, she said, and had hated making most of them.
Being a perfectionist, only a perfect performance would satisfy her, but she recalled being almost in tears on several sessions when something did not turn out as she had wanted. She rememembered wistfully and with gratitude the kindly Eddie Lang, who did so much to smooth over akward situations, which arose frequently if the late Tommy Dorsey were present. Annette remembered one date - not for Pathe, but after his company had been taken over by Columbia - when the band parts had been distributed wrongly, evidently in a hurry. The director was no less a person than Dr. Euguene Ormandy, now one of the world's greatest symphony conductors, and as he signalled for the orchestra to start the rehearsal, absolute bedlam was let loose as the musicians began playing different parts of the score. Tommy Dorsey sprang to his feet, uttering the most appalling oaths, almost coming to blows with Dr. Ormandy (who was as dumbfounded as anyone else, and in no way to blame) and poor Annette, shaken by the appalling cacophony, burst into tears. It was Eddie Lang who came to her rescue, and that of the session generally. Calmly, he organised order out of chaos, and in a few moments, everything was sunny again.
Annette Hanshaw was an instant hit on both sides of the Atlantic. Her first commercially issued record in England coupled *Black bottom* with *Lay me down to sleep in Carolina*, a song with indifferent music and a perfunctory lyric, but which was nevertheless very popular in 1926. On the latter, Annette accompanies herself on piano, another pointer to her versatility, especially as she claims to be unable to read a note of music. The original labels of these self-

**Annette Hanshaw - The Early years 1926 Vol. 1 (Fountain)**

accompanied records give her full credit for this, and she smiled as she looked at one of them and said 'If you hear any ukulele strumming on anything I did with Irving Brodsky at the piano, that'll be me too'. Sure enough on *One sweet letter*, the original recording of what has since become a standard in the traditional jazz repertoire, there is a short passage on ukulele. It is interesting to compare this above average number with the other contemporary accounts of it by women singers: Kate Smith, assisted by the Charleston Chasers, another Red Nichols band, and Sophie Tucker, who was backed by Miff Mole's Molers, to all intents and purposes the same group as the Chasers. It will be seen that Red Nichols and Miff Mole, at that time the two outstanding New York jazzmen, are both present on Annette's first session, the products of which brought forth the following accolade from 'Peppering', the popular music critic in 'The Gramophone' for March 1927: 'I must draw your attention to Annette Hanshaw, whose record of *Black bottom* and *Lay me down to sleep in Carolina*, seems to me well worth possessing for the sake of its rhythm'. His concluding paragraph reads: 'Taking it all around, my first prize this month goes to Annette Hanshaw'.

Now the pseudonym 'Peppering' covered several identities, but at that time it masked that of no less a personality than the late Christopher Stone, brother-in-law of the editor and founder of the magazine (Sir) Compton MacKenzie; pioneer disc jockey, and a man of great charm wide taste and unassailable honesty. Praise for an unknown and an American unknown at that, was rare indeed, almost unknown in itself. The old established pop singers could stand back: 'Peppering' had selected an unknown fifteen year old as his star turn that month. On being told this, Annette looked incredulous. 'I suppose they (the records) were all right for those days', she said finally, 'but I hate them now'. Nevertheless, like the great trouper she is and always has been, she settled down to an evening's inquisition with as many of those very records as could be mustered. Eventually she warmed to them and said, still a little grudgingly, that perhaps this one was a bit better than some, or that one wasn't too bad. 'That little baby voice', she murmered. 'You mean there are people in England who collect these things?' She had to be assured that this was so, and not only did people collect them, but treasured them as a wealthy art-collector does his Rubens, Cuyps and Renoirs, or a philatelist his Cape Triangulars.

Listening to any track on this record, it is not difficult to understand why the performances appeal so strongly. Annette Hanshaw, as we have seen, was that rarity, a completely natural artist of outstanding talent. She could tackle lively, typically boisterous numbers such as *My baby knows how* with just the right amount of verve, and switch to wistful sentiment such as *If I'd only believed in you* or *Cherie I love you* (her French accent is commendably good, especially when compared with that of many of her compatriots who persist in singing what sounds like 'Sherry, jer tame'. She has a lively sense of humour that bubbles merrily in such things as *Everything's made for love*; she says she sometimes made up her own extra choruses, and if the final refrain on this is one of hers, she must be given credit as a first-class comedienne. Contrast this number and its originally rather dated coquetry with the distinctly saucy lyrics of 'Do-do-do', composed by the Gershwin brothers for *Oh Kay* starring Gertrude Lawrence, whose extraordinary voice sounds excruiciatingly 'camp' nowadays, whereas Miss Annette Hanshaw's advanced rhythmic phrasing of the number gives it more than it really deserves.

Another number with a surprisingly modern lyric, at least in the second chorus is *Don't take that black bottom away*, in which Annette implores the authorities not to implement their threat to ban the latest dance craze: 'Take those sexy plays, where they scream, 'The woman pays', but don't take that black bottom away!' What about the futuristic final phrase on this one?. This particular track is also interesting in that it is one of the very few sides Annette ever made by the old acoustic process, where the artists performed into a large-mouthed metal horn, ususally at top volume in an effort to activate the sluggish mechanism of the cutting stylus. Yet Annette's dulcet voice shows no signs of straining as she sings this number, even when in direct competition with the up-dated Dixieland ensemble supplied by Pathe to accompany her. Further, it does not end with her usual tag line, 'That's all'.

This can be heard on almost all the other tracks on this LP, on two of them prompted by a man's voice (probably Herman Roe's). It seems that when making her test record, she finished her song, stopped playing, and looked around, not quite sure of what to do next. Nothing suggested itself, so she said, perhaps with some relief, 'That's all'.

Herman Rose liked this so well that he had her do the same routine on pratically all her other recordings up to 1931. By that time she was being billed as the 'Personality Girl', and was broadcasting regularly, but she was evidently rather tired of the tag by then, for it comes over on some of her later sides in tones that get as near as Annette ever could to irritation. Asked to end her taped interview with her usual signing-off line, she looked puzzled for a moment, and as the tape ran out, whe suddenly remembered and giggled 'That's all' into the microphone. The last two tracks in this set are also acoustic recordings, and neither of them features the tag-line. They show the artiste in a much more sombre mood than usual, both being somewhat in the the nature of sermonettes. *If you can't tell the world she's a good little girl* is a comment on the evils of uninformed gossip and scandal, but the session-mate, also a waltz may need some explaining. It is subtitled 'The peaches and Browning song', and is a comment on an event that drew the attention of New York society that year. This was the marriage between a fifteen-year-old girl named Frances Belle Heenan and a millionaire real-estate dealer in his fiftis, named Edward West Browning. On meeting his future bride, Browning announced he was going to call her 'Peaches' because she suggested peaches and cream to him. (He had what would nowadays be termed 'a thing' about teenage girls; Lolita would have been everyday stuff to him, one feels. He liked to give them pet names, and instructed them to call him 'Daddy'.) After six months of marriage, 'Peaches' decided she had had enough of 'Daddy', so she packed her bags, jewels and fine clothes and all, and turned him in, but instead of returning to the bosom of her family, she applied to a front-rank 'ghost' writer and gave him the inside story which appeared as 'My honeymoon with Daddy'. Browing replied in kind, and gave his 'ghost' a version of life with 'Peaches', and this began a kind of tit for tat that ended in a trial that went against 'Peaches', who was suing for a legal separation involving 300 dollars a week alimony. In the recitative on this record, Annette Hanshaw plays the part of just any young girl married - in this case by the orders of her parents - to an impossibly oider man, and the thing is slanted against fathers and mothers who arrange marriages for the financial aspect above all else, rather than against either 'Peaches' Heenan or 'Daddy' Browning; nevertheless, it is an interesting, if maudlin, social comment. Jazz collectors, noting the words 'The red heads' on the labels, have been sadly disappointed to find nothing but Murray Kellner's diffident violin and Irving Brodsky's adquate piano in attendance, though surely no one could do more with this pair of homilies in popular song form than Annette Hanshaw?

In May 1928, the Pathe Company made the last records on that label by Annette. Immediately she and her manager transferred to Columbia, and on this and its various subsidiary labels she appeared in her own name and that of 'Gay Ellis', 'Dot Dare' and 'Patsy Young'. The latter two pseudonyms were reserved for labelling her impressions of Helen Kane, the girl who created the 'boop boop a doop' style of singing that has become a kind of trademark of the twenties. Annette was a close friend of the late Miss Kane, and her impressions sounded more like Helen Kane than Helen Kane, according to Helen Kane. Thus another facet of Annette Hanshaw's versatility is revealed. She was also employed as vocalist with Frank Ferera's Hawaiin Trio, and when the records were issued, her friends would tease her about them, asking if she was contemplating appearing in a lei and a grass skirt. As the twenties became the thirties, Annette's voice darkened slightly and matured into the most sweetly, wholesomely seductive sound on record or radio. She worked with Don Voorhees and his Orchestra, and had offers of film contracts, but apart from a number of short films, she did not take these up. As we have said, by now she was weary of show business; the heavy burden of responsibility grew ever heavier, and in the spring of 1934, she laid it down. Suggestions that she might attempt a come back were gently but firmly declined. Had she agreed to try, no doubt she would have made the grade, for she can still sing as delightfully as ever, but is now strictly for friends. Events have turned full circle.

It is remarkable, but significant, that no one ever succeeded in duplicating Annette Hanshaw's technique. Usually, when an artiste is huge success, there are dozens waiting to jump, however gracelessly, on the band wagon. Ruth Etting, whose husband at the time, one 'Gimp' Schneider, insisted that Annette's records did not appear on Columbia in competition with his wife's, was already established when Annette made her first record, as was Lee Morse (subtitled 'the unique') on Pathe also. Lee Wiley and Mildred Bailey relied on a much more limited, sophisticated repertoire, following as best they could in the illustrious footsteps of the great coloured artists such as Eva Taylor and Ethel Waters. Comediennes such as Helen Kane and Mae Questal were subjects for Annette's mimicry, as we have seen and the more dramatic singers such as Kate Smith and Sophie Tucker had no need to invade Annette's field of activity.

In England, Elsie Carlisle and later, Vera Lynn, occasionally sounded something like Annette, but as the first was active long before Annette was heard of, and the second did not become known until some time after Annette's last record was issued and deleted, there can be no case of copyism here. Although she never visited England, Annette is remembered clearly by those who were buying records of popular music at the time her records appeared. (She was given at least three new names on as many English labels, incidentally: on Mayfair she was Marion Lee, on Ariel 'Leila Sandford', and on Key, the label whose repertoire was selected for Selfridge's by Christopher Stone, she was re-named 'Ethel Bingham'. On being told this, she was at once horrified and yet vastly amused. 'Oh not Ethel Bingham' she cried). In the twenties, dance bands that initially were no more than that began to feature vocalists, almost always men, who sang the words of the chorus of the number through a megaphone from the bandstand. On records, these vocalists were usually trained recording artists whose voices had the necessary timbre to cut through the accompaniment of the band clustering round the recording horn, and quite a number projected the words as if they had not the slightest idea of their meaning; the sounds were all important. (One exception was Billy Murray, another Irving Kaufman). Then came Annette Hanshaw, at sixteen an experienced recording artiste accustomed to both types of recording, to sing the vocals with such bands as Lou Gold's, Willard Robison's and the Original Memphis Five. After that girls began to appear in the studios: Belle Mann recorded some archly coquettish vocals with Ben Pollack and Nat Shilkret, Lee Wiley sang with Leo Reisman, Mildred Bailey with Paul Whiteman, Edythe Wright with Tommy Dorsey, Helen Ward with Benny Goodman, ... but by now it was the rule rather than the exception that a band should include in its regular personnel what was rather childishly termed a 'fem-chirp', offering glamour and veiled sex appeal in a stylish evening gown.

It is difficult to imagine most of the sirens of the thirties and forties inventing their own musical shorthand (as Annette did), of being able to cope so convincingly with exuberant nonsense and sentimental pathos alike, or infusing their work with the same amount and quality of sheer personality. This is not to say these later arrivals on the scene were of no consequence; within their limits they were provided some first-class entertainment, but the point is that they were all strictly confined to one or two styles; Annette was the supreme mistress of all styles. The twenties may have been the Era of Wonderful Nonsense, they sometimes roared, but for every noisy extrovert there was a least one quiet, unassuming level headed type. So it was with singers: they weren't all noisy declaimers of mammy songs and bawdy blues. There were Whispering Jack Smith, who used no megaphone, and Rudy Valee, who did; there was a young chap called Bing Crosby just starting out with Paul Whiteman. There was also Annette Hanshaw. (Brian Rust and Tony Skyrme)

**Album:** Released Apr '79, on Fountain by Retrieval Records. Catalogue no: **FV 201**

### ANNETTE HANSHAW 1927 VOL 2

**Album:** Released Apr '79, on Fountain by Retrieval Records. Catalogue no: **FV 202**

### ANNETTE HANSHAW 1928 VOL 3

**Album:** Released May '86, on Fountain by Retrieval Records. Catalogue no: **FV 205**

### IT WAS SO BEAUTIFUL (Her last recordings 1932/34)

Tracks: / It was so beautiful / We just couldn't say goodbye / Love me tonight / Say it isn't so / I cover the waterfront / Don't blame me / Give me liberty or give me love / Let's fall in love.

**Cass:** Released Feb '89, on Halcyon (USA) by Submarine Records. Catalogue no: **CHDL 119**

**Album:** Released Feb '89, on Halcyon (USA) by Submarine Records. Catalogue no: **HDL 119**

### LOVABLE AND SWEET

**Album:** Released May '77, on Retrospect by EMI Records. Catalogue no: **SH 246**

### SHE'S GOT IT (1920-30'S)

**Album:** Released Oct '77, on Retrospect by EMI Records. Catalogue no: **SH 247**

### SWEETHEART OF THE TWENTIES

Note: Tracks include: 'Ain't that a grand and glorious feeling/ Get out and get under the moon/Black bottom/Song og the wanderer/Six feet of papa.etc. Fea-

**Harlem - Classic Big Band Jazz (Lake)**

turing Red Nichols, Eddie Lang, Adrian Rollini, Jimmy Lynette, Miff Mole. 1926-28.
**Album:** Released Dec '82, on Halcyon (USA) by Submarine Records. Catalogue no: **HAL 5**
**Cass:** Released Sep '87, on Halcyon (USA) by Submarine Records. Catalogue no: **CHAL 5**

## Happy Jazz Band

**LIVE AT MEMPHIS JAZZ FESTIVAL**
**Album:** Released Jun '88, on Jazzology (USA) by Jazzology Records (USA). Catalogue no: **J 132**

## Hard Luck Blues

**HARD LUCK BLUES (Lissie Miles, Susie Smith & Other Artists)**
**Album:** Released '74, on VJM (Vintage Jazz Music) by Vintage Jazz Music Society(VJM). Catalogue no: **VLP 40**

## Harlem (Band)

**CLASSIC BIG BAND JAZZ (See panel above)**
Tracks: / Pay-off, The / Shout 'em Aunt Tillie / Paducah / Do you believe in love at first sight / Black and tan fantasy / Will you, won't you be my baby? / Accordion Joe / Copenhagen / Cincinatti daddy / Beedle-um-bum / Felling drowsy / Jazznocracy / Jeeps blues / Goin' to town.
Note: A debut album from this vintage-styled Midlands based big band. Harlem specialises in the music of Duke Ellington, Fletcher Henderson, McKinney's Cottonpickers, King Oliver's Dixie Syncopaters, etc. Personnel: Tony Pipkins, Chris Williams, Brian Bates - Trumpets/ Paul Munnery - Trombones/ Zoltan Sagi - Alto - Sop.Saxes/ John Osborne - Alto - Bari - saxes/ Terry Perry - Tenor Sax/ Bruce jangman - Banjo / Fred Brownson - Piano/ Alan Robinson - Bass/ John Astle - Drums.
**Album:** Released '85, on Lake by Lake Records. Catalogue no: **LA 5002**
**Cass:** Released '85, on Lake by Lake Records. Catalogue no: **LA 5002 C**

**HARLEM SPEAKS (Various artists)**
Tracks: / Saratoga drag: *Various artists* / Stevedora stomp: *Various artists* / Hot bones and rice: *Various artists* / Sugarfoot stomp: *Various artists* / Cotton Club stomp: *Various artists* / Misty morning: *Various artists* / Harlem speaks: *Various artists* / Gee baby ain't I good to you: *Various artists.*
**Cass:** Released Aug '89, on Lake by Lake Records. Catalogue no: **LA 5013C**
**Album:** Released Aug '89, on Lake by Lake Records. Catalogue no: **LA 5013**

## Harlem ...

**A WORLD OF JAZZ (Harlem Jazz)**
**Album:** Released '88, on Vogue by Vogue Records. Catalogue no: **VG DP36**

**HARLEM (1926-57) (Various artists)**
**Album:** Released '83, on RCA (France) by BMG Records (France). Catalogue no: **PM 43249**

**HARLEM COMES TO LONDON (Original Artists) (Various artists)**
Tracks: / Silver rose: *Plantation Orchestra, The* / Arabella's wedding day: *Plantation Orchestra, The* / Smilin' Joe: *Plantation Orchestra, The* / For baby & me: *Plantation Orchestra, The* / Camp meeting day: *Sissle Noble & his Orchestra* / Sophisticated lady: *Ellington, Duke/His Orchestra* / Ike: *Ellington, Duke/His Orchestra* / Dinah: *Hatch & his Harlem Stompers* / Some of these days: *Hatch & his Harlem Stompers* / I can't dance, I got ants in my pants: *Various artists* / I must have that man: *Valaida* / Keep a twinkle in your eye: *Nicholas Brothers*/ Your heart and mine: *Nicholas Brothers* / Dixie isn't Dixie any more: *Carter, Lavaida* / Jo Jo the cannibal kid: *Carter, Lavaida* / Breakfast in Harlem: *Buck & Bubbles* / I ain't got nobody: *Buck & Bubbles* / Sweet Georgia Brown: *Buck & Bubbles* / Harlem in my heart: *Welch, Elisabeth* / Ain't misbehavin': *Waller, Fats & his Continental Rhythm* / I can't give you anything but love: *Various artists.*
**Album:** Released Mar '78, on Retrospect by EMI Records. Catalogue no: **SH 265**
**Album:** Released '88, on DRG (USA) by DRG Records (USA). Catalogue no: **SW 8444**

**HARLEM HEAVIES (R&B '54-62) (Various artists)**
**Album:** Released May '85, on Moonstone by Ampersand Music. Catalogue no: **BLP 107**

## Harlem Hamfats

**HARLEM HAMFATS: 1936/37**
Tracks: / Weed smokers dream / I'm cuttin' out / Bad luck man / Oh red / Garbage man / Little girl / Growling dog / Move your hand.
**Cass:** Released Sep '89, on Neovox by Neovox Records. Catalogue no: **NEO 850**

**HARLEM HAMFATS: 1936-39**
**Album:** Released Feb '89, on Document Catalogue no: **DLP 547**

**HOT CHICAGO JAZZ - BLUES AND JIVE**
**Album:** Released Oct '86, on Folklyric (USA) by Arhoolie Records (USA). Catalogue no: **FL 9029**

**I'M SO GLAD**
**Album:** Released '88, on Queen Catalogue no: **QUEEN 062**

## Harlem Hit Parade

**HARLEM HIT PARADE (Old town blues vol. 2) (Various artists)**
**Album:** Released Apr '87, on Ace by Ace Records. Catalogue no: **CHD 206**

## Harlem Jazz

**HARLEM JAZZ 1921-31 (Various artists)**
Note: Jimmie Johnson/Henderson, Texas Blues Destroyers, Marvin Smoley, Cab Calloway.
**Album:** Released '88, on Classic Jazz Masters Catalogue no: **CJM 1**

## Harlem Jazz & Blues

**HARLEM JAZZ AND BLUES BAND**
Note: B.Williams, E.Durham, E.Chamblee, G.Rodgers, A.Casey.
**Album:** Released '88, on Barron Catalogue no: **VLP 404**

**HARLEM BLUES AND JAZZ BAND (Harlem Jazz & Blues Band)**
**Album:** Released Oct '88, on Barron Catalogue no: **VLP 403**

## Harmonica Frank

**HARMONICA FRANK**
**Album:** Released Apr '79, on Puritan Catalogue no: **PURITAN 3003**

## Harmonicas...

**GREAT HARMONICA PLAYERS VOL.1 (Various artists)**
**Album:** Released Oct '88, on Roots (Germany) Catalogue no: **RL 320**

**GREAT HARMONICA PLAYERS VOL.2 (Various artists)**
**Album:** Released Oct '88, on Roots (Germany) Catalogue no: **RL 321**

**HARMONICAS, WASHBOARDS, FIDDLES, AND JUGS (Various artists)**
**Album:** Released Oct '88, on Roots (Germany) Catalogue no: **RL 311**

## Harmonicas Unlimited

**HARMONICAS UNLIMITED (Various artists)**
Note: Featuring Mapp, Moore, Williams, McCoy, Hays, Wilson, Stovepipe.
**2 LP Set:** Released Sep '87, on Document Catalogue no: **DLP 503/504**

## Harper, Bill

**BILLY HARPER QUINTET (Harper, Bill Quintet)**
**Album:** Released Sep '79, on Soul Note Catalogue no: **SN 1001**

**BLACK SAINT IN EUROPE (Harper, Bill Quintet)**
**Album:** Released Jul '78, on Black Saint (Italy) Catalogue no: **BSR 001**

## Harpo, Slim

**Biographical details:** The blues singer played harmonica and guitar (1924-70); he was born James Moore in Baton Rouge, Louisiana. He was one of the 'swamp blues' artists on the Excello label, the first blues label in Nashville, along with Lonesome Sundown (Cornelius Green) and Harpo's brother in law Lightnin' Slim, with whom he recorded in the mid-'50s. Harpo's best-known hits were *I'm a king bee* in 1957 and a No. 1 on the R&B chart with *Baby scratch my back* in 1966. His wife Lovell often co-wrote songs. (Donald Clarke, Nov 1989).

**BEST OF SLIM HARPO**
**Album:** Released Dec '87, on Excello (USA) Catalogue no: **LP 8010**

**BLUES HANGOVER (Jay Miller sessions)**
**Album:** Released Dec '88, on Flyright by Interstate Music. Catalogue no: **FLY 520**

**GOT LOVE IF YOU WANT IT**
**Album:** Released '88, on Flyright by Interstate Music. Catalogue no: **FLY 558**

**HE KNEW THE BLUES**
**Album:** Released Jul '88, on Sonet by Sonet Records. Catalogue no: **SNTF 769**

**I'M A KING BEE**
Tracks: / I'm a king bee / I love the life I'm livin' / Moody blues / Buzzin' / Dream girl.
**CD:** Released May '89, on Flyright by Interstate Music. Catalogue no: **FLYCD 05**

**RAININ' IN MY HEART**
**Album:** Released Dec '87, on Excello (USA) Catalogue no: **LP 8003**

**SHAKE YOUR HIPS**
Tracks: / Wonderin' blues / Baby scratch my back / I'm gonna miss you / Rainin' in my heart / We're two of a kind / I need money / Midnight blues / Harpo's blues / Buzzin' / My little queen bee / I love the life I'm livin' / Shake your hips.
**Album:** Released Oct '86, on Flyright by Interstate Music. Catalogue no: **FLY 593**

**TIP ON IN**
**Album:** Released Dec '87, on Excello (USA) Catalogue no: **LP 8008**

## Harrell, Tom

**MOON ALLEY (Harrell, Tom Quintet)**
**Album:** Released '88, on Criss Cross Catalogue no: **CRISS 1018**

**PLAY OF LIGHT, THE**
**Album:** Released Aug '86, on Black Hawk (USA) by Blackhawk Records (USA). Catalogue no: **BKH 50901**
**Cass:** Released Aug '86, on Black Hawk (USA) by Blackhawk Records (USA). Catalogue no: **BKHMC 50901**

## Harriott, Joe

**Biographical details:** Born in Jamaica in 1928, Harriott was a unique alto saxophonist who was working out his own avant-garde style at the same time, but independently of John Coltrane and Ornette Coleman, and who died in poverty in England in 1973. He sought in particular to make a fusion with jazz and Indian music, but was never recorded or produced very well in a society which doesn't like music, just the noise it makes. (Donald Clarke, Nov 1989).

**JUMP FOR ME (Harriott, Joe & The Tony Kinsey Trio)**
Tracks: / Last resort, The / Best behaviour / How deep is the ocean? / Get happy / Jump for me / Can't we be friends / Raymond / Nice work if you can get it / Chirracahaua / Teddi / Song is you, The / It don't mean a thing.
**Album:** Released Jul '87, on Esquire by Titan Int. Prod.. Catalogue no: **ESQ 326**

## Harris, Barry

**AT THE JAZZ WORKSHOP**
Note: With Sam Jones & Louis Hayes
**CD:** Released '86, on JVC/Fantasy Deleted '88. Catalogue no: **VDJ 1548**

**BARRY HARRIS PLAYS BARRY HARRIS**
**Album:** Released Mar '79, on Xanadu Catalogue no: **X 154**

**FOR THE MOMENT**
**Album:** Released '88, on Uptown (USA) Catalogue no: **UP 27.20**

**LIVE IN CONCERT**
**CD:** Released '88, on Xanadu Catalogue no: **FDC 5155**

**PASSING IT ON (VIDEO)**
**VHS:** Released '88, on Kay Jazz (video) by Kay Jazz. Catalogue no: **KJ 048**

## Harris, Eddie

**Biographical details:** Born in 1936 in Chicago, the tenor saxophonist has always been an innovator, using an electronic Varitone attachment on his tenor in the early '70s. He remains best-known for his USA Top 40 hit in 1961 with the theme from *Exodus*, and for the co-led Les McCann and Eddie Harris Quintet album *Swiss movement*, made live at Montreux in 1969, with McCann's vocal on Gene McDaniels' *Compared to what?*. (Donald Clarke, Nov 1989).

**BLACK SAX**
**2 LP Set:** Released '88, on GNP Crescendo (USA) by GNP Crescendo Records (USA). Catalogue no: **GNPS 2.2073**

**EDDIE (Harris, Eddie, Ralph Armstrong, Sherman Ferguson)**
**Album:** Released Oct '86, on Timeless by Timeless Records. Catalogue no: **SJP 244**

**EXODUS TO JAZZ**
Tracks: / Exodus / Alicia / Gone home / A.T.C. / A.M. Blues / Little girl blue / Velocity / W.P..
Note: An original Vee Jay recording.
**Album:** Released Apr '87, on Atlantis by Charly Records. Deleted '88. Catalogue no: **ATS 10**
**Cass:** Released Apr '87, on Atlantis by Charly Records. Deleted May '88. Catalogue no: **TCATS 10**

**I'M TIRED OF DRIVING**
Tracks: / Two times two equals love / You are the one / Songbird / I'm tired of driving / Loneliest monk / Theme for the foxy ladies / You stole my heart / There was a time / What's wrong with the world today.
**Album:** Released '79, on RCA by BMG Records (UK). Deleted '84. Catalogue no: **PL 12942**

**LIVE IN BERLIN**
Note: Superb set from the controversial American saxophonist, multi instrumentalist and composer Eddie Harris. Recorded live at the Quasimodo Club, Berlin, March '88. Personnel: Eddie Harris (piano, tenor sax, & vocals), Ray Peterson (electric bass fret & fretless electric bass), Norman Fearrington (drums and the tube drum).
**CD:** Released May '89, on Timeless by Timeless Records. Catalogue no: **CDSJP 289**
**Album:** Released May '89, on Timeless by Timeless Records. Catalogue no: **SJP 289**

**STEPS UP (Harris, Eddie quartet)**
**Album:** Released Sep '81, on Steeplechase (USA) Catalogue no: **SCS 1151**

**SWISS MOVEMENT (Harris, Eddie / Les McCann)**
Tracks: / Compared to what / Cold duck time / Kathleen's theme / You got it in your soulness / Generation gap, The.
**Album:** on Atlantic Jazz by WEA Records. Catalogue no: **K 50405**
**CD:** Released '88, on Atlantic Jazz by WEA Records. Catalogue no: **K781 365 2**

## Harris, Gene

**Biographical details:** Pianist, born in 1933 in Michigan. He formed the Four Sounds in 1957, became the Three Sounds '58, recorded from the late '50s to '77 for Blue Note, Verve, Limelight and then Blue Note again. On some of the albums the trio was augmented (on Verve with Anita O'Day) and Harris recorded with Lou Donaldson, Stanley Turrentine etc. but he ended up on obscure Jazzizz and Jam labels in the early '80s, with bassist John Heard and Jimmy Smith on drums: his unique bluesy piano had got lost in the shuffle until rescued by the Concord Jazz label since 1985, where he's recorded with Benny Carter and as a leader. (Donald Clarke, Nov 1989).

**GENE HARRIS AND THE PHILIP MORRIS SUPERBAND (Harris, Gene & The Philip Morris Superband)**
Tracks: / Surrey with the fringe on top, The / Creme de menthe (on CD only) / When it's sleepy time down south / Love is here to stay / I'm just a lucky so and so / Serious grease (on CD only) / Like a lover (on CD only) / Old man river / Do you know what it means to New Orleans (on 12" only) / Porgy and Bess (medley) / You're my everything / There is no greater love / Things ain't what they used to be.
Note: Recorded live in New York before embarking on their world tour, Gene Harris and his 17 piece 'Superband' pump out exciting powerhouse swinging big band jazz. Superband has an unprecedented number of legendary soloists and section players. There has never been a band with as many star players. Gene Harris (piano), Ray Brown (bass), Jeff Hamilton (drums), Herb Ellis (guitar), Jerry Dodgion (alto sax), James Moody (tenor sax & flute), Gary Smulyan (baritone sax), Urbie Green (trombone), James Morrison (trombone), Eddie Bert (trombone), Paul Faulise (bass trombone), Johnny Coles (trumpet), Harry 'Sweets' Edison (trumpet), Michael Philip Mossman (trumpet), Joe Mosello (trumpet), Ernestine Anderson (vocals) and Ernie Andrews (vocals).
**Album:** Released Nov '89, on Concord Jazz by Concord Jazz Records (USA). Catalogue no: **CJ 397**
**CD:** Released Nov '89, on Concord Jazz by Concord Jazz Records (USA). Catalogue no: **CCD 4397**
**Cass:** Released Nov '89, on Concord Jazz by Concord Jazz Records (USA). Catalogue no: **CJ 397C**

**GENE HARRIS TRIO PLUS ONE, THE**
Tracks: / Gene's lament / Misty / Uptown sop / Things ain't what they used to be / Yours is my heart alone / Battle hymn of the Republic.
Note: Gene's debut album as a leader on Concord, a joyful, soulful performance captured live at New York's blue Note. From the opening note of Ray Brown's composition "Gene's Lament", you'll find yourself rockin' and clappin' to the beat. Personnel: Gene Harris-piano / Ray Brown-bass / Mickey Roker-drums / Special guest: Stanley Turrentine-tenor saxaphone.
**Album:** Released Oct '86, on Concord Jazz by Concord Jazz Records (USA). Catalogue no: **CJ 303**
**CD:** Released Apr '87, on Jazz (USA) by Concord Jazz Records (USA). Catalogue no: **CCD 4303**

**LISTEN HERE (Harris, Gene Quartet)**
Tracks: / his masquerade / I've got a feeling I'm falling / Blues for Jezebel / Lullabye / This can't be love / Don't be that way / Listen here / Sweet and lovely / Song is ended, The / To you.
Note: CD version features two bonus tracks.
**Album:** Released Sep '89, on Concord Jazz by Concord Jazz Records (USA). Catalogue no: **CJ 385**
**CD:** Released Sep '89, on Concord Jazz by Concord Jazz Records (USA). Catalogue no: **CCD 4385**
**Cass:** Released Sep '89, on Concord Jazz by Concord Jazz Records (USA). Catalogue no: **CJ 385C**

**TRIBUTE TO COUNT BASIE (Harris, Gene All Star Big Band)**
Tracks: / Captain Bill / Night mist blues / Swingin' the blues / When did you leave Heaven? / Blue and sentimental / Riled up / Masquerade is over, The / Dejection blues.
Note: "Pianist Gene Harris and his superb big band pay tribute to the great Count Basie, performing new arrangements with all the precision, strength and subtlety that is Basie. The soloists improvise with the abandon and originality of the Count's great men. Marshal Royal, Snooky Young, Ray Brown, Plas Johnson, Jon Faddis, Bill Watrous, Bob Cooper and Conte Candoli help make up the 17-piece band which assists Gene with this heartfelt tribute." (IMS Records, May 1988.)
**CD:** Released May '88, on Concord Jazz by Concord Jazz Records (USA). Catalogue no: **CCD 4337**
**Cass:** Released May '88, on Concord Jazz by Concord Jazz Records (USA). Catalogue no: **CJC 337**
**Album:** Released May '88, on Concord Jazz by Concord Jazz Records (USA). Catalogue no: **CJ 337**

## Harris, Jack

**JACK HARRIS AND HIS ORCHESTRA (Harris, Jack & His Orchestra)**
Tracks: / Amoresque / Wake up and live / Once in a while / Toy trumpet, The / Gypsy in my soul / How many rhymes can you get / Cry baby cry / Caravan / I can't face the music / Back to back / Amazon goes a-wooing / I'm sorry for myself / It looks like rain in Cherry Blossom Lane / Snake charmer, The / Mr. Renard's nightmare.
**Album:** Released Feb '75, on Retrospect by EMI Records. Catalogue no: **SH 219**

## Harris, Phil

**Biographical details:** Born in 1904 in Indiana, the bandleader, singer and actor grew up in Nashville and began on drums, leading his own bands from the '30s. He remains best-known for novelty songs of RCA in the '40s: *That's what I like about the South, Woodman, spare that tree, The Preacher and the bear*; he had hits with *Smoke smoke smoke (that cigarette), The old master painter* and a number one novelty *The thing* in 1950. He worked on radio from the mid-'30s, with Jack Benny for many years and also with his wife, Alice Faye, a singer/dancer who became famous with Rudy Vallee in George White's *Scandals* on stage and film in the '30s. Harris also made many films and survived on TV into the '60s, something of an American institution. (Donald Clarke, Nov 1989).

**BEST OF PHIL HARRIS**
Tracks: / Darktown poker club, The / Woodman, spare that tree / That's what I like about the South / Preacher and the bear, The / Deck of cards / Is it true what they say about Dixie? / Goofus / Thing, The / Persian kitten, The / St. James Infirmary / Muskrat ramble / Row row row.
**Cass:** Released '87, on RCA by BMG Records (UK). Catalogue no: **NK 89526**
**Album:** Released Oct '80, on RCA by BMG Records (UK). Catalogue no: **INTS 5050**
**Album:** Released '87, on RCA by BMG Records (UK). Catalogue no: **NL 89526**
**Cass:** Released Oct '80, on RCA by BMG Records (UK). Catalogue no: **INTK 5050**

**PHIL HARRIS AND ORCHESTRA (The Uncollected 1933) (Harris,**

**Phil & Orchestra)**
**Album:** Released '88, on Hindsight Catalogue no: **HSR 215**
**Album:** Released Jun '86, on Hindsight (UK) by Michele International Records. Catalogue no: **HUK 215**

**THAT'S WHAT I LIKE ABOUTTHE SOUTH (Harris, Phil & Orchestra)**
**Album:** Released Aug '89, on Golden Era by Delta Records. Catalogue no: **GELP 15042**

**TWO COMPLETE BROADCASTS (Harris, Phil & Alice Faye)**
**Album:** Released Jun '79, on Radio Archives (USA) by Kiner Ents.(USA). Catalogue no: **101**

## Harris, Wynonie

**BATTLE OF THE BLUES (Harris, Wynonie & Roy Brown)**
Tracks: / Mr. Blues is coming to town / Good rockin' tonight / Rock Mr. Blues / Bloodshot eyes / Just like two drops of water / Luscious woman / Lovin' machine / Keep on churnin' (till the butter comes) / Good morning judge / Quiet whiskey / Down boy down / Cadillac baby / Too much lovin' ain't no good / Hard luck blues / My gal from kokomo / Big town / Rockabye baby / Black diamond / Ain't no rockin' no more / Fannie Brown got married / Shake 'em up baby / Good looking and foxy too.
**CD:** Released Dec '86, on Charly by Charly Records. Catalogue no: **CDCHARLY 37**
**Album:** Released Dec '87, on Sing Catalogue no: **SING 607**
**CD:** Released Mar '90, on King Catalogue no: **KCD 607**

**BATTLE OF THE BLUES VOL. 2**
**CD:** Released Oct '88, on King 1 Catalogue no: **KLP 627**

**GOOD ROCKIN' BLUES**
**Album:** Released Jul '88, on Bellaphon Catalogue no: **BID 8022**

**GOOD ROCKIN' TONIGHT**
**Cass set:** Released Mar '88, on Gusto (USA) by Gusto Records (USA). Catalogue no: **GD 5040**

**HERE COMES THE BLUES**
Tracks: / Wynonie's blues / Here comes the blues / Straighten him out / Young man's blues / Baby look at you / She's gone with the wind / Somebody changed the lock on my door / That's the stuff you gotta watch / Mr. Blues jumped the rabbit / Whiskey and jelly roll blues / Rugged road / Come back baby / Hey-ba-ra-re-bop / Good morning Corinne / In the evenin' blues.
**Album:** Released Dec '88, on Official by Official Records. Catalogue no: **OFF 6024**

**MR BLUES IS COMING TO TOWN**
Tracks: / Sittin' on it all the time / Drinkin' by myself / Wynonie's blues / Big city blues / Bite again bite again / Blowin' to California / Love untrue, A / Rock Mr. Blues / Mr. Blues is coming to town / Be mine my love / Keep-a-talking / Here comes the night / Christina / My playful baby's gone / Wine wine sweet wine / Fishtail blues.
**Album:** Released Jan '88, on Route 66 (Sweden) Catalogue no: **KIX 3**

**OH BABY**
Tracks: / Around the clock 1 - 11 / Cock a doodle doo / Yonder goes my baby / Time to change your town / Hard ridin' mama / You got to get yourself a job girl / Oh babe / My baby's barrel house / Luscious woman / Bad news baby (there'll be no...) / Stormy night blues / Down boy down / Gift to gittin' baby / Don't take my whiskey away from me / I get a thrill.
**Album:** Released Aug '87, on Route 66 (Sweden) Catalogue no: **KIX 20**

**PLAYFUL BABY**
Tracks: / I gotta lyin' woman / Playful baby / Rebecca's blues / Take me out of the rain / Everybody's boogie / Papa tree top / Lollipop mama / Ghost of a chance / Married women - stay married / Do it again, please / Triflin' woman / Night train / Bring it back / Nearer my love to thee / Git with the grits / Good mambo tonight.
**Album:** Released May '86, on Route 66 (Sweden) Catalogue no: **KIX 30**

**ROCK MR. BLUES**
Tracks: / Good morning Judge / Down boy down / Bloodshot eyes / Lovin' machine / Mr. Blues is coming to town / I like my baby's pudding / Rock Mr. Blues / Baby shame on you / Just like two drops of water / Good rockin' tonight / Blow your brains out / Sittin' on it all the time / Luscious woman / Keep on churnin' (till the butter comes) / Quiet whiskey / I feel that old age coming on.
**Cass:** Released Jul '85, on Charly R&B by Charly Records. Catalogue no: **TCCRB 1097**
**Album:** Released Jul '85, on Charly R&B by Charly Records. Catalogue no: **CRB 1097**

## Hartman, Johnny

**Biographical details:** Vocalist with a beautiful dark, deep voice (1923-83) who deserved more fame. Born in Chicago, he sang and played piano from age 8, sang with Earl Hines and Dizzy Gillespie in the late '40s, recorded on Impulse (including with John Coltrane) and on Audiophile and Chicago's Bee Hive label in 1980. (Donald Clarke, Nov 1989).

**AND I THOUGHT ABOUT YOU**
**Album:** Released Feb '88, on Fresh Sounds (Spain) by Fresh Sounds Records (Spain). Catalogue no: **FS 249**

**FROM THE HEART**
Tracks: / Blue skies / Birth of the blues / What is there to say / Ain't misbehavin' / I fall in love too easily / We'll be together again / Down in the depths / They didn't believe me / I get a kick out of you / All of me / I'm glad there's you / When your lover has gone / I'll remember April / I see your face before me / September song / Moonlight in Vermont.
**Album:** Released May '88, on Affinity by Charly Records. Catalogue no: **AFF 189**
**CD:** Released May '88, on Charly by Charly Records. Catalogue no: **CDCHARLY 116**

**JUST DROPPED BY TO SAY HELLO**
**CD:** Released May '89, on MCA (Import) by MCA Records. Catalogue no: **MCAD 39105**

**ONCE IN EVERY LIFE**
**Album:** Released Apr '84, on Beehive (USA) Catalogue no: **BH 7012**

**THIS ONE'S FOR TED**
**Album:** Released Aug '88, on Audiophile (USA) by Jazzology Records (USA). Catalogue no: **AP 181**

**UNFORGETTABLE SONGS**
Tracks: / Very thought of you, The / Fools rush in / Love is here to stay / Once in a while / Biddin' my time / Down in the depths / Ain't misbehavin' / Isn't it romantic / Unforgettable / More I see you, The / What do I owe her / Almost like being in love.
**Album:** Released Mar '85, on Jasmine by Hasmick Promotions. Deleted Feb '88. Catalogue no: **JASM 1515**

## Haskins, Chris

**CRESCENT CITY BLUES**
Tracks: / Tiger rag / Sweet Georgia Brown / Sheik of Araby, The / Poor Joe / Crescent city blues / Tenderly Hindustan / I wish I could shimmy like my sister Kate.
**Album:** Released Oct '82, on Black Lion Catalogue no: **BLM 51013**

## Hasselgard, Stan

**JAMMIN' AT JUBILEE**
Note: With B. Eckstine; Wardell Gray; Barney Kessel; Jackie Mills; J. Rowles; Benny Goodman Septet 1948.
**Album:** Released Jun '86, on Dragon by Dragon Records. Catalogue no: **DRLP 29**

**JAZZ CLARINET OF... (Hasselgard, Ake 'Stan')**
**Album:** Released Jun '86, on Dragon by Dragon Records. Catalogue no: **DRLP 25**

**PERMANENT STAN HASSELGARD WITH THE AMERICANS (1945/48)**
**CD:** Released '88, on Phontastic (Sweden) Catalogue no: **PHONTCD 8802**
**Album:** Released Sep '89, on Phontastic (Sweden) Catalogue no: **PHONT 8802**

**YOUNG CLARINET 1940-48 (Hasselgard, Ake 'Stan')**
**Album:** Released Oct '88, on Dragon by Dragon Records. Catalogue no: **DRLP 163**

## Hastings, Count

**COUNT HASTINGS PLUS DANNY TURNER (1948-50) (Hastings, Count plus Danny Turner, Eddie**

**Woodland)**
Tracks: / Diga diga doo / Sugar cane / She's funny that way / Begin the beguine / Candied jam / Patches / Baboo / Minor in the diner / Midnight moan / Jumpin' with Pio / Snap case / Danny's jump.
**Album:** Released Jan '88, on Krazy Kat by Interstate Music. Catalogue no: **KK 823**

## Hastings, Lennie

**ALWAYS THE BEST (Hastings, Lennie Quintet)**
Note: Featuring:- Digby Fairweather & J Parker.
**Album:** Released Dec '86, on Dawn Club by Cadillac Music. Catalogue no: **DC 33.004**

## Hawes, Hampton

**Biographical details:** Jazz pianist and composer who did his best work on the West Coast at a time when everybody thought that West Coast jazz added up to Dave Brubeck and Gerry Mulligan. He was born in 1928 in L.A. and died there in 1977. He led his own trios from 1954, a modern stylist influenced by Bud Powell, and an underrated composer. He recorded with Wardell Gray, Charles Mingus and others, but his *The trio* and three of *All night session* 1955-56 are mature genius. Sentenced to ten years in prison hospital for possession of heroin, a personal letter to President Kennedy got him out; he also wrote a prize winning autobiography, *Rise up off me.* (Donald Clarke, Nov 1989).

**ALL NIGHT SESSION VOL. 1**
Tracks: / Jordu / Groovin' high / Takin' care / Broadway / Hampton's pulpit.
**Album:** Released Aug '86, on Contemporary (USA) Catalogue no: **COP 027**

**ALL NIGHT SESSION VOL. 2 (Hawes, Hampton Quartet)**
Tracks: / I'll remember April / Should care, I / Woody'n you / Two bass hit / Will you still be mine / April in Paris / Blues 'n' boogie.
**Album:** Released May '87, on Contemporary (USA) Catalogue no: **COP 039**

**AN HISTORIC MEETING RECORDED IN THE EARLY HOURS, AN (Hawes, Hampton And Pedro Iturralde Quartet)**
**Album:** Released Feb '88, on Fresh Sounds (Spain) by Fresh Sounds Records (Spain). Catalogue no: **FS 229**

**CHALLENGE, THE**
**Album:** Released Jan '88, on Storyville by Storyville Records AB. Catalogue no: **SLP 1013**

**DYNAMIC**
Tracks: / Hamp's blues / Ruhythm / Black Forest blues / Autumn leaves / What is this thing called love / Sonora / Waltz for Debbie / My foolish heart.
**Album:** Released '79, on MPS Jazz Deleted '84. Catalogue no: **5C 064 61169**

**EVERYBODY LIKES HAMPTON HAWES (Vol 3: The trio)**
Tracks: / Somebody loves me / Sermon / Embraceable you / I remember you / Night in Tunisia / Lover come back to me / Polka dots and moonbeams / Billy boy / Coolin' the blues.
Note: Hampton Hawes, piano; Red Mitchell, bass; Chuck Thompson, drums.
**Album:** Released Apr '82, on Contemporary (USA) Catalogue no: **1003 523**

**FOR REAL**
Tracks: / Hip / Wrap your troubles in dreams / Crazeology / Numbers game / for real / I love you.
**Album:** Released Jan '86, on Contemporary by Ace Records. Catalogue no: **COP 013**

**FOUR**
**Album:** Released May '86, on Contemporary by Ace Records. Catalogue no: **COP 022**

**GREENLEAVES OF SUMMER, THE**
Tracks: / Vierd blues / Green leaves of summer / Ill wind / St. Thomas / Secret love / Blue skies / More I see you, The / G.K. Blues / Fly me to the moon / Sunny / Status of Maceo, The / Suite for solo piano / First, second & third movements.
**Album:** Released Nov '83, on Contemporary (Import) Catalogue no: **1007 614**

**HAMPTON HAWES**
**Album:** Released Sep '83, on Concord Jazz by Concord Jazz Records (USA). Catalogue no: **CJ 222**

**HAMPTON HAWES MEMORIAL ALBUM, THE**
**Album:** Released Jul '82, on Xanadu Catalogue no: **XANADU 161**

**HAMPTON HAWES AND THE LES MCCANN TRIO (Hawes, Hampton & The Les McCann Trio)**
**VHS:** Released '88, on Kay Jazz (video) by Kay Jazz. Catalogue no: **KJ 007**

**HAMPTON HAWES TRIO VOL. 1**
**CD:** Released May '87, on JVC/Fantasy Deleted '88. Catalogue no: **VDJ 1553**

**HAMPTON HAWES TRIO VOL. 2 (Hawes, Hampton Trio)**
**CD:** Released '86, on JVC/Fantasy Deleted '88. Catalogue no: **VDJ 1559**

**KEY FOR TWO**
**Album:** Released Aug '79, on Affinity by Charly Records. Deleted '88. Catalogue no: **AFF 31**

**LITTLE COPENHAGEN NIGHT MUSIC, A**
**Album:** Released Jan '79, on Freedom Catalogue no: **FLP 41043**

**LIVE AT THE JAZZ SHOWCASE**
**Album:** Released Jan '82, on Enja (Germany) by Enja Records (West Germany). Catalogue no: **ENJA 3099**

**SEANCE, THE**
**Album:** Released Mar '79, on Contemporary (USA) Catalogue no: **S 7621**

**SPANISH STEPS**
Tracks: / Blues enough / Sonora / Black forest / Dangerous / Spanish steps / My romance.
**Album:** Released Jan '85, on Black Lion Catalogue no: **BLP 30111**

**THIS IS HAMPTON HAWES VOL.2**
**Album:** Released Sep '81, on Contemporary (Import) Catalogue no: **1003 515**

**TRIO, THE (Hampton Hawes vol.1)**
Tracks: / I got rhythm / What is this thing called love / Blues the most / So in love / Feelin' fine / Hamp;s blues / Easy living / All the things you are / These foolish things / Carioca.
**Album:** Released Feb '89, on Contemporary by Ace Records. Catalogue no: **COP 020**

## Hawkins, Allen

**1933-34 (Hawkins, Allen Orchestra)**
**Album:** Released '88, on Gaps Catalogue no: **GAPS 070**

## Hawkins, Buddy Boy

**BUDDY BOY HAWKINS AND HIS BUDDIES (Hawkins, Buddy Boy & His Buddies)**
**Album:** Released Dec '88, on Yazoo (USA) by Shanachie Records (USA). Catalogue no: **YAZOO 1010**

## Hawkins, Coleman

**Biographical details:** The giant of the tenor saxophone was born in 1904 in St. Joseph, Missouri and died in 1969 in New York City. He made his first recordings with Mamie Smith's Jazz Hounds, but soon joined the Fletcher Henderson band: under the influence of Louis Armstrong and with arrangements by Don Redman, the band evolved from a variety / dance band into the most influential of jazz orchestras; meanwhile Hawkins overcame the tubby, moaning sound of the vaudeville saxophone, playing loud with a stiff reed to be heard over the band, and developed a rich, deep, dark tone; Probably under the influence of pianist Art Tatum, he began to improvise on the chord structure of a tune rather that just the melody. He single-handedly established the tenor as one of the most important instruments in jazz, then went to Europe in 1934; while he was gone the developing competition included Lester Young, playing a completely different style, but Hawk came back in 1939 and recorded *Body and soul*: danceable and smoochy, it was also a staggeringly impressive series of chromatic improvisations on the classic song, a top 20 hit at the time and an enduring jazz classic. He had re-established himself as the boss and dominated the instrument until his death. Always lyrical rather than a bluesman, his best records are ballads, such as *I can't believe that you're in love with me, I surrender dear, The man I love, My ideal, I only have eyes for you* all from the '40s. He never became a stick in the mud and was among the first to hire boppers for record dates, including in 1944 the young Thelonious Monk. Among Hawkins' best records are the Coleman Hawkins Sax Ensemble date for Keynote in 1944 (three reeds and rhythm) and *Duke Ellington meets Coleman Hawkins* and Benny Carter's *Further definitions*, both on Impulse from the 1960s, but any record with Hawkins on it is a priceless document. His acolyte, the great Ben Webster, was only a few months younger, but always called him 'the old man'. (Donald Clarke, Nov 1989).

**ALL STAR SESSION**
**Cass:** Released '82, on Jazz Bird Catalogue no: **ZCJAZ 2000**
**Album:** Released '82, on Jazz Bird Catalogue no: **JAZ 2000**

**ALLSTARS**
**CD:** Released Apr '87, on Carrere (France) Catalogue no: **98443**

**AT BAYOU CLUB (Hawkins, Coleman & Roy Eldridge)**
**Album:** Released '88, on Honeysuckle Rose (USA) Catalogue no: **HR 5002**

**AT BAYOU CLUB, VOL. 2 (Hawkins, Coleman & Roy Eldridge)**
**Album:** Released '88, on Honeysuckle Rose (USA) Catalogue no: **HR 5006**

**BEAN 1929-49, THE**
**Album:** Released Sep '87, on Giants of Jazz by Hasmick Promotions. Catalogue no: **LPJT 51**

**BEAN AND BEN (Hawkins, Coleman & Ben Webster)**
Tracks: / In the hush of the night / Out to lunch / Every man for himself / Look out, Jack / On the bean / Recollections / Flyin' Hawk / Drifting on a reed / Broke but happy / Blues on the bayou / Jumpin' with Judy / Blues on the delta / Bottle's only / Save it, pretty mama / For lovers only / Peach Tree Street blues.
**Album:** Released Oct '83, on Harlequin by Interstate Music. Catalogue no: **HQ 2004**

**BEAN STALKIN' (Hawkins, Coleman & Friends)**
Tracks: / Bean stalkin' / Stompin' at the savoy / Take the 'A' train / Indian summer / Crazy rhythm / Indiana.
**Album:** Released Jan '89, on Pablo Jazz (USA) by Pablo Records (USA). Catalogue no: **PAB 004**

**BEAN-A-RE-BOP**
**Album:** Released Sep '79, on Queendisc (Italy) Catalogue no: **QU 038**

**BEAN'S TALKING AGAIN**
**Album:** Released Oct '88, on Vogue by Vogue Records. Catalogue no: **500056**

**BODY AND SOUL**
Tracks: / Body and soul / Meet Doctor Foo / She's funny that way / Fine dinner.
**CD Single:** Released Oct '89, on Bluebird (2) by BMG Records (UK). Catalogue no: **ZD 43188**
**Album:** Released Feb '87, on RCA by BMG Records (UK). Deleted May '89. Catalogue no: **PL 85658**
**Cass:** Released Feb '87, on RCA by BMG Records (UK). Deleted May '89. Catalogue no: **PK 85658**

**BODY AND SOUL (CD)**
Tracks: / Meet Doctor Foo / Fine dinner / She's funny that way / Body and soul / When day is done / Sheik of Araby, The / My blue Heaven / Bouncing with Bean / April in Paris / How strange / Half step down please / Angel face / Jumping for Jane / I love you / There will never be another you / Little Girl Blue / Dinner for one please, James / His very own blues / 39" & 25" & 39" / Bean stalks again / Have you met Miss Jones? / Essence of you, The.
**CD:** Released Apr '88, on Bluebird (2) by BMG Records (UK). Catalogue no: **ND 85717**

**BODY AND SOUL (WEST WIND)**
**Album:** Released 6 Jan '89, on West Wind Catalogue no: **WW 018**
**CD:** Released Mar '89, on West Wind Catalogue no: **WWCD 018**

**CENTERPIECE**
Tracks: / Jellybean / Centerpiece / Disorder at the Border / If I had you / Bean and the boys / All the things you are.
**Album:** Released Jun '89, on Phoenix (1) by Phoenix Records. Catalogue no: **PHOENIX 13**

**CHOCOLATE DANDIES, LEONARD FEATHER'S ALL STARS**
**Album:** Released May '87, on Commodore Class Catalogue no: **624 056**
**CD:** Released May '87, on Commodore Class Catalogue no: **824 056**

**CLASSIC TENORS (Hawkins, Coleman & Lester Young)**
Tracks: / Man I love, The / Sweet Lorraine / Get happy / Crazy rhythm / How deep is the ocean? / Voodte / Hello babe / Linger awhile / I got rhythm / I'm fer it too / Hawkins barrelhouse / Stumpy.
**Album:** Released Oct '83, on Doctor Jazz (USA) by CBS Records (USA). Catalogue no: **ASLP 1004**
**Cass:** Released Oct '83, on Doctor Jazz (USA) by CBS Records (USA). Catalogue no: **ZCAS 1004**
**Cass:** Released Apr '81, on Joker (USA) by Lifetime Records (USA). Catalogue no: **MC 3259**
**Album:** Released Apr '81, on Joker (USA) by Lifetime Records (USA). Catalogue no: **SM 3259**

**COLEMAN HAWKINS**
**CD:** Released Jul '89, on Cleo Catalogue no: **CLCD 5029**

**COLEMAN HAWKINS: 1940-43**
Tracks: / Smack / I surrender, dear / I can't believe that you're in love with me / Dedication / Esquire bounce / Boff boff / My ideal / Esquire blues.
**Album:** Released Dec '84, on Commodore Class Catalogue no: **AG6 24056**

**COLEMAN HAWKINS AT THE BAYOU CLUB**
**Album:** Released '88, on Vogue (France) by Vogue Records. Catalogue no: **502005**

**COLEMAN HAWKINS AND BEN WEBSTER (Compact/Walkman jazz) (Hawkins, Coleman & Ben Webster)**
Tracks: / Blues for Yolanda / It never entered my mind / Don't get around much anymore / I'll never be the same / Budd Johnson / La Rosita / De-dar like someone in love / That's all / You'd be so nice to come home to / Maria.
**CD:** Released '88, on Verve Catalogue no: **833 296 2**
**Cass:** Released '88, on Verve Catalogue no: **833 296-4**

**COLEMAN HAWKINS COLLECTION (Retrospective)**
Tracks: / Man I love, The / Lady be good / I'm in the mood for love / Back home again in Indiana / Soft winds / All the things you are.
**Album:** Released Jun '88, on Deja Vu Catalogue no: **DVLP 2125**
**Cass:** Released Jun '88, on Deja Vu Catalogue no: **DVMC 2125**

**COLEMAN HAWKINS IN CONCERT**
Tracks: / Bean and the boys / Yesterdays / Mop mop / Sweet Georgia Brown / Blues / I cried for you / Billie's blues / He's funny that way.
Note: Recordings made by the great tenor player in Chicago and New York in 1944, 1946 and 1947 featuring, among others, Roy Eldridge, Jack Teagarden, Lester Young, Barney Bigard and -- on three tracks -- the incomparable Billie Holiday.
**Album:** Released Apr '81, on Phoenix (USA) by All Star Talent Inc.(USA). Catalogue no: **LP 8**

**COLEMAN HAWKINS PLAYS THE WINDY CITY**
Tracks: / All the things you are / Centerpiece / Body and soul / Way you look tonight / Moonglow.
Note: Live recordings from Chicago featuring the tenor giant with rhythm sections.
**Album:** Released '83, on Spotlite by Spotlite Records. Catalogue no: **SPJ 137**

**COLEMAN HAWKINS AND THE EARL HINES TRIO 1965 (Hawkins, Coleman & The Earl Hines Trio)**
**Album:** Released Apr '79, on Pumpkin Catalogue no: **PUMPKIN 105**

**DESAFINADO (IMPULSE)(Hawkins, Coleman Sextet)**
**Cass:** Released Oct '85, on Impulse by Impulse Records. Deleted Dec '89. Catalogue no: **ASC 28**
**Album:** Released Oct '85, on Impulse by Impulse Records. Catalogue no: **AS 28**

**DESAFINADO (JASMINE) (Hawkins, Coleman Sextet)**
Tracks: / Desafinado / I'm looking over a four leaf clover / Samba para bean / I remember you / One-note samba / O pato / Un abraco no bonfa / Stumpy bossa nova.
**Cass:** Released Jun '82, on Jasmine by Hasmick Promotions. Catalogue no: **JAS C12**
**Album:** Released Jun '82, on Jasmine by Hasmick Promotions. Deleted Feb '88. Catalogue no: **JAS 12**

**DISORDER AT THE BORDER**
Tracks: / Disorder at the Border / Blue room / Stuffy / Rifftide / I can't get started.

Note: Featuring, among others, Roy Eldridge, Horace Silver, Howard McGhee, Art Blakey.
**Album:** Released '83, on Spotlite by Spotlite Records. Catalogue no: **SPJ 121**

**DUTCH TREAT**
**Album:** Released Jul '82, on Xanadu Catalogue no: **XANADU 189**

**ENCOUNTERS BEN WEBSTER**
Tracks: / Blues for Yolande / It never entered my mind / Rosita / You'd be so nice to come home to / Prisoner of love / tangerine / Shine on harvest moon.
**CD:** Released Oct '84, on Verve Deleted Jul '88. Catalogue no: **823 120-2**

**ESSENTIAL COLEMAN HAWKINS, THE**
Tracks: / There's a small hotel / Sunday / Body and soul / Hanid / Picasso / How long? / In a mellow tone / Walker, The.
Note: Compilation of tracks recorded between 1948 and 1958.
**Album:** Released May '82, on Verve Catalogue no: **2304 537**

**EUROPEAN CONCERT (Hawkins, Coleman & Roy Eldridge)**
Tracks: / Joshua fit de battle of Jerico / Autumn leaves / If I had you / Disorder at the Border.
Note: Coleman Hawkins -- tenor sax. Tommy Flanagan -- piano. Major Holley -- bass. Eddie Lock -- drums.
**Album:** Released Nov '86, on Unique Jazz by Spotlite Records. Catalogue no: **UJ 31**

**FAVOURITES**
Tracks: / Disorder at the Border / Yesterdays / Bean and the boys / Stiffly / Body and soul / Man I love, The / Rifftide.
**Album:** Released Jun '89, on Phoenix (1) by Phoenix Records. Catalogue no: **PHOENIX 22**

**GENIUS OF, THE**
Tracks: / I'll never be the same / You're blase / I wished on the moon / How long has this been going on / Like someone in love / Melancholy baby / Ill wind / In a mellow tone / There's no you / World is waiting for the sunrise / Somebody loves me / Blues for Rene.
**Album:** Released Jan '86, on Verve Deleted Jan '89. Catalogue no: **825 673-1**
**CD:** Released Jan '86, on Verve Deleted Jul '88. Catalogue no: **825 673-2**
**Cass:** Released Jan '86, on Verve Deleted Oct '88. Catalogue no: **825 673-4**

**GOOD OL' BROADWAY**
**Album:** Released Jun '86, on Fantasy Inc (USA) by Fantasy Inc (USA). Catalogue no: **1902114**

**GREAT ENGLISH CONCERT, THE (Hawkins, Coleman / Stan Getz / Roy Eldridge)**
**Album:** Released Jul '82, on Jazz Groove Catalogue no: **JG 007**

**HAWK**
Tracks: / All the things you are / Centerpiece / Body and soul / Just you, just me / One o'clock jump / Lover come back to me / How high the moon.
**Album:** Released Apr '81, on Shoestring (1) Catalogue no: **SS 107**

**HAWK FLIES HIGH, THE**
Tracks: / Chant / Juicy fruit / Think deep / Laura / Blue lights / Sanctity.
**Album:** Released Feb '88, on Riverside (USA) by Fantasy Inc (USA). Catalogue no: **RLP 233**

**HAWK IN EUROPE, THE 1934-1937**
Tracks: / Lullaby / Lost in a fog / Lady be good / Avalon / What a difference a day made / Stardust / Meditation / Netcha's dream / Strange fact, A / Crazy rhythm / Honeysuckle rose / Out of nowhere / Sweet Georgia Brown / Mighty like the blues / Pardon me pretty baby / Somebody loves me / My buddy / Well all right then.
Note: "The Hawk in Europe" is a compilation of 18 of the recordings he made during 1934-7 in Europe.
**Album:** Released Jul '88, on Living Era by Academy Sound & Vision Records. Catalogue no: **AJA 5054**
**Cass:** Released Jul '88, on Living Era by Academy Sound & Vision Records. Catalogue no: **ZC AJA 5054**

**HAWK IN GERMANY (Hawkins, Coleman & Bud Powell)**
Tracks: / Shaw 'nuff / Blues in the closet / Willow, weep for me / John's abbey / Salt peanuts / All the things you are / Yesterdays / Stuffy / Just you, just me.
**Album:** Released Jan '86, on Black Lion Catalogue no: **BLP 30125**

**HAWK IN HOLLAND, THE**
Tracks: / Some of these days / After you've gone / I only have eyes for you / I wish I were twins / Chicago / Medidation / What Harlem is to me / Netcha's dream / I wanna go back to Harlem / Consolation / Strange fact, A / Original Dixieland one-step / Smiles / Something is gonna give me away.
Note: With the Ramblers Dance Orchestra.
**Album:** Released '88, on GNP Crescendo (USA) by GNP Crescendo Records (USA). Catalogue no: **GNPS 9002**
**Album:** Released Feb '83, on Jasmine by Hasmick Promotions. Deleted Jun '87. Catalogue no: **JASM 2011**

**HAWK AND ROY (Hawkins, Coleman & Roy Eldridge)**
Tracks: / It's tight like that / Easy rider / Scratch my back / Save it, pretty mama / How long blues / Shake it and break it / Pretty girl is like a melody, A / Pom pom / It's my turn now / You're a lucky guy / Plucking the bass / I'm getting sentimental over you / High society / Muskrat ramble / Who told you I cared? / Does your heart beat for me?.
Note: Coleman Hawkins -- tenor sax. Benny Carter -- alto sax. Danny Polo -- clarinet. Joe Sullivan -- piano. Ulysses Livingstone -- guitar. Art Shapiro -- bass. George Wettling -- drums. Joe Turner -- vocalist(two tracks). Recorded 14th December 1939/ January 15th 1940. Roy Eldridge Big Band recorded October 1939, December 1939.
**Album:** Released Apr '81, on Phoenix (USA) by All Star Talent Inc.(USA). Catalogue no: **LP 3**

**HAWK TALKS**
Tracks: / Lucky duck / I can't get started / Foolin' around / Man I love, The / Trust in me / Where is your heart? / Wishing / Carioca / If I could be with you one hour tonight / Ruby / Sin / Midnight sun / And so to sleep again / Lonely wine.
**Album:** Released Dec '83, on Jasmine by Hasmick Promotions. Deleted Feb '88. Catalogue no: **JASM 1031**
**Album:** Released Jun '85, on Affinity by Charly Records. Catalogue no: **AFF 139**

**HAWK AND THE HUNTER, THE**
**Album:** Released Oct '88, on Vogue by Vogue Records. Catalogue no: **500073**

**HAWK VARIATIONS**
Note: Mono.
**Album:** Released Jan '86, on Swingtime by Contact Records (Denmark). Deleted Jun '89. Catalogue no: **ST 1004**

**HAWKINS AND ELDRIDGE AT THE BAYOU CLUB VOL. 2 (Hawkins, Coleman & Roy Eldridge)**
**Album:** Released '88, on Vogue (France) by Vogue Records. Catalogue no: **502009**

**HAWKINS SET**
Tracks: / Yesterdays / Hawk's tune / Stuffy / Body and soul / Bean stalkin' / Riftide / Sophisticated lady / I can't get started / Time on my hands / Walker.
**Album:** Released May '84, on Verve Deleted Jan '89. Catalogue no: **VRV 3**

**HIGH AND MIGHTY HAWK, THE**
Tracks: / Get set / You've changed / Ooh-wee, Miss G.P.! / Vignette / My one and only love / Bird of prey blues.
Note: "One of the genuine giants amongst jazzmen, tenor saxophonist Coleman Hawkins was one of the elite players lured by Stanley Dance to record for the Felstead label in the late 50's and early 60's. This month the first trio of gems from that catalogue are promoted to Compact Disc by London and initially into the spotlight is our Missouri-born reed man". (London Records, June 1988).
**CD:** Released May '88, on London Records by London Records Ltd. Catalogue no: **820 602-2**
**Album:** Released Nov '86, on Affinity by Charly Records. Catalogue no: **AFF 163**

**HIGH STANDARDS VOL. 2 (Hawkins, Coleman & Red Allen)**
**Album:** Released Dec '87, on Jass Catalogue no: **JASS 11**

**HOLLYWOOD STAMPEDE**
Tracks: / April in Paris / Rifftide / Stardust / Stuffy / Hollywood stampede / I'm thru with love / What is there to say? / Wrap your troubles in dreams / Too much of a good thing / Bean soup / Someone to

watch over me / It's the talk of the town / Isn't it romantic? / Bean-a-re-bop / Way you look tonight, The / Phantomesque.
**Album:** Released Feb '90, on EMI by EMI Records. Catalogue no: **LP 93201**
**CD:** Released Feb '90, on Capitol by EMI Records. Catalogue no: **CZ 268**
**Cass:** Released Feb '90, on EMI by EMI Records. Catalogue no: **MC 93201**
**CD:** Released Feb '90, on Capitol by EMI Records. Catalogue no: **CDP 792 596 2**
**CD:** Released Feb '90, on EMI by EMI Records. Catalogue no: **793 201 2**

**IMMORTAL COLEMAN HAWKINS, THE**
Note: With Roy Eldridge, Earl Hines trio.
**Album:** Released Nov '86, on Pumpkin Catalogue no: **PUMPKIN 118**

**IN EUROPE 1934-39 VOLS 1, 2 & 3**
**CD Set:** Released Mar '90, on Jazz-Up Catalogue no: **JU 317**

**INDISPENSABLE COLEMAN HAWKINS, THE**
Tracks: / St. Louis shuffle / Hello Lola / Hocus pocus / She's funny that way / Body and soul / My blue heaven / One o'clock jump / Say it isn't so / You were mean't for me / April in Paris / Angel face / I love you / Essence of jazz.
**Cass set:** Released Nov '84, on RCA (France) by BMG Records (France). Deleted Jul '89. Catalogue no: **NK 89277**
**2 LP Set:** Released Nov '84, on RCA (France) by BMG Records (France). Deleted Jul '89. Catalogue no: **NL 89277**

**JAZZ TONES**
**CD:** Released '88, on Xanadu Catalogue no: **FDC 5156**

**LESTER YOUNG / COLEMAN HAWKINS (Hawkins, Coleman & Lester Young)**
**Album:** Released '83, on Spotlite by Spotlite Records. Catalogue no: **SPJ 119**

**LIVE FROM THE LONDON HOUSE (Chicago 1963) (Hawkins, Coleman Quartet)**
**Album:** Released Feb '89, on Jasmine by Hasmick Promotions. Catalogue no: **JASM 2521**
**Cass:** Released Feb '89, on Jasmine by Hasmick Promotions. Catalogue no: **JASMC 2521**

**LIVE SESSIONS AT THE SAVOY BALLROOM 1940**
**CD:** Released Oct '89, on Jazz Anthology by Musidisc Records (France). Catalogue no: **550132**

**LOVER MAN**
Tracks: / Stuffy / Willow weep for me / Undecided / Pleyel blues / Lover man / Caravan / Indian summer.
**Album:** Released Jan '88, on Esoldun Catalogue no: **FC 104**
**CD:** Released Jan '88, on Esoldun Catalogue no: **FCD 104**

**MARCH 21 AND 25, 1963 (Hawkins, Coleman & His Orchestra)**
Tracks: / Peebles / Whisper to me / Traumerei / Lazy butterfly / Not quite night / Misty morning / Easy walker / Lullaby / I knew Dana / Lonely tenor / Hawk talk / All the time.
**Album:** Released Oct '80, on Jazz Vault Catalogue no: **JV 103**

**MASTERS OF JAZZ VOL.12**
**Album:** Released May '86, on Storyville by Storyville Records AB. Catalogue no: **SLP 4112**
**CD:** Released Feb '89, on Storyville by Storyville Records AB. Catalogue no: **STCD 4112**

**MEMORIAL**
**Album:** Released '89, on Jazz Society Catalogue no: **AA 504**
**Album:** Released Apr '81, on Joker (USA) by Lifetime Records (USA). Catalogue no: **SM 3537**

**REAL THING**
Tracks: / Soul blues / Greensleeves / Until the real thing comes along / I hadn't anyone till you / It's a blue world / I want to be loved / Red beans / While we're young / For you for me for evermore / Then I'll be tired of you / Mighty like a rose / At dawning / I'll get by / Trouble is a man / Poor butterfly.
**Album:** Released '79, on Prestige Deleted '84. Catalogue no: **PR 24083**

**SIRIUS**
Tracks: / Man I love, The / Don't blame me / Just a gigolo / One I love, The / Time on my hands / Sweet and lovely / Exactly like you / Street of dreams / Sugar.
**Cass:** Released '82, on Pablo Jazz (USA) by Pablo Records (USA). Catalogue no: **K10 707**
**Album:** Released '82, on Pablo Jazz (USA) by Pablo Records (USA). Catalogue no: **2310 707**

**SOUL**
**Album:** Released Aug '84, on Prestige (USA) by Fantasy Inc (USA). Catalogue no: **OJC 096**

**STANDARDS AND WARHORSES (Hawkins, Coleman & Red Allen)**
**CD:** on Jass Catalogue no: **JASSCD 2**
**Cass:** Released May '88, on Jass Catalogue no: **JASS10/11C**

**SWINGVILLE 2005 (Hawkins, Coleman All Stars)**
**Album:** Released Apr '86, on Original Jazz Classics (USA) by Fantasy Inc (USA). Catalogue no: **OJC 225**

**TENOR TRIUMVERATE (Hawkins, Coleman / Chu Berry / Lester Young)**
Tracks: / Big head / Skippy / Platinum love / There's a small hotel / Blowin' up a breeze / Monday at Minton's / Dream girl / Get lost / Six cats and a prince / I cover the waterfront / One o'clock jump / Easy does it / Tea for two.
**Album:** Released '81, on Queendisc (Italy) Catalogue no: **QU 051**

**THANKS FOR THE MEMORY**
**CD:** Released '88, on Xanadu Catalogue no: **FDC 5159**

**TODAY AND NOW (Hawkins, Coleman Quartet)**
Tracks: / Go Li'l Liza / Quintessence / Don't love me / Love song from Apache.
**Album:** Released Aug '82, on Jasmine by Hasmick Promotions. Catalogue no: **JAS 38**
**Cass:** Released Aug '82, on Jasmine by Hasmick Promotions. Catalogue no: **JAS C38**

**TOGETHER (Hawkins, Coleman & Lester Young)**
Tracks: / Sweet Georgia Brown / I got rhythm / Lady be good.
Note: Recorded in 1946.
**Album:** Released Apr '81, on Jazz Live (Italy) Catalogue no: **BLJ 8037**

**VERY SAXY**
**Album:** Released Jun '86, on Fantasy Inc (USA) by Fantasy Inc (USA). Catalogue no: **1902111**

**WARHORSES VOL. 1 (Hawkins, Coleman & Red Allen)**
**Album:** Released Dec '87, on Jass Catalogue no: **JASS 10**

**WRAPPED TIGHT**
Tracks: / Wrapped tight / Intermezzo / Out of nowhere / Indian summer / Red roses for a blue lady / Marcheta / Beautiful girl / She's fit / And I still love you / Bean's place.
**Cass:** Released Sep '82, on Jasmine by Hasmick Promotions. Catalogue no: **JAS C50**
**Album:** Released Sep '82, on Jasmine by Hasmick Promotions. Catalogue no: **JAS 50**

## Hawkins, Dale

**Biographical details:** A rockabilly singer, born in 1938 in Louisiana, one of the first to have hits. His *Suzie Q* (a USA top 30 in 1957) was an anomaly at the time: on the Checker label, primarily a black R&B outlet, with an R&B beat using a cowbell and with a classic rockabilly guitar solo by the young James Burton. Hawkins had only one other top 40 hit (*La do dada* in 1958), but the live act was popular; many subsequent records had Roy Buchanan on guitar. Hawkins later produced records by Bruce Channel, another white blues singer: *Hey baby*, a 1962 No. 1 with a harmony vocal by Delbert McClinton was said to have influenced the Beatles. (Donald Clarke, Nov 1989).

**MY BABE**
**Album:** Released Nov '87, on Argo Jazz (USA) by Chess Records (USA). Catalogue no: **ARGO 1450**

**SUZIE Q**
**Album:** Released Nov '87, on Argo Jazz (USA) by Chess Records (USA). Catalogue no: **ARGO 1429**

## Hawkins, Edwin

**Biographical details:** This American singer, arranger, choir leader and pianist was born in Oakland, California. In April 1967 the 23 year old Hawkins co-founded the North California State Youth Choir, by recruiting the most able 17-25 year old vocalists from other church ensembles in the San Francisco area. To raise funds for the choir, they recorded an LP on a 2-track tape recorder and sold copies at the Annual Youth Congress in Cleveland, Ohio in June 1968. The choir won the singing contest at that event, and sold about 60% of the 1000 copies of their album. Suddenly in early 1969, a Cisco disc jockey began giving heavy airplay to the track *Oh happy day* from the album. It was picked up by a major record company and released under the billing of the Edwin Hawkins Singers. During the summer of '69 it became a surprise smash, reaching no 4 on the US chart and climbing to no 2 in the UK. The uplifting *Oh happy day* was thus the only black gospel record ever to become a major international pop hit. It was an exhuberant and thoroughly inspirational performance by the 46 strong choir of a traditional song that originally dated from 1755. The featured soloist on *Oh happy day*, Dorothy Combs Morrison, soon left to pursue a solo career. Hawkins never achieved another pop hit, except in a one-off collaboration with Melanie, but his name was now established in the gospel field and he became something of an institution on the genre's international touring circuit, albeit with an increasingly MoR sound. (Bob MacDonald, 12/10/85).

**BEST OF THE EDWIN HAWKINS (Hawkins, Edwin Singers)**
Tracks: / Oh happy day / Jubilation / Someday / Every man wants to be free / Lean on me / Ooh, child / I'm coming through / Blowin' in the wind.
**Cass:** Released Jul '85, on Buddah by Buddah Records Inc.(USA). Catalogue no: **252 213-4**
**Album:** Released Jul '85, on Buddah by Buddah Records Inc.(USA). Catalogue no: **252 213-1**

**IMAGINE HEAVEN**
**Album:** Released Mar '82, on IMS by Polydor Ltd. Catalogue no: **LN 1501**

**LIVE WITH THE OAKLAND SYMPHONY ORCHESTRA**
Tracks: / Fanfare overture / Worship the Lord / Come to me / Talk / Gift of song, The / Oh happy day / Call him, he'll be there / I need to pray.
**Cass:** Released May '82, on Myrrh by Word Records (UK). Catalogue no: **MC 1112**
**Album:** Released May '82, on Myrrh by Word Records (UK). Catalogue no: **MYR 1112**

**OH HAPPY DAY (OLD GOLD) (Hawkins, Edwin Singers)**
Tracks: / Oh happy day / Brand new key.
**7" Single:** Released Oct '88, on Old Gold by Old Gold Records. Catalogue no: **OG 9802**

**OH HAPPY DAY (SINGLE) (Hawkins, Edwin Singers)**
Tracks: / Oh happy day.
**7" Single:** Released May '69, on Buddah by Buddah Records Inc.(USA). Deleted '72. Catalogue no: **201 048**

## Hawkins, Erskine

**Biographical details:** Trumpeter and bandleader, born in Birmingham, Alabama in 1914, who became one of the most popular leaders in Harlem during the swing era, recording for RCA Victor from 1938 to 1950. Several national hits included the original version of *Tuxedo junction* covered by Glenn Miller, and the bluesy *After hours*, written by Avery Parrish, the band's pianist. Hawkins was a high-note specialist on trumpet, billed at 'The 20th Century Gabriel'; other solists included the excellent Dud Bascomb on trumpet and Julian Dash on tenor (who co-wrote *Tuxedo* with Hawkins). (Donald Clarke, Nov 1989).

**COMPLETE ERSKINE HAWKINS - VOLS. 1 AND 2 (1938-1939)**
Tracks: / Rockin' rollers jubilee / I'm madly in love with you / Let this be a warning to you / Miss Hallujah Brown / Weary blues / King Porter stomp / Strictly swing / Do you wanna jump, children? / What do you know about love? / Study in blue, A / Easy rider / Because of you / "I", the living "I" / Let the punishment fit the crime / Swing out / Raid the joint / Big wig in the wigwam / Polka dotty / No soap / Swingin' on Lenox Avenue / Hot platter / Gin mill special / Cherry / Tuxedo Junction / Weddin' blues / You can't escape from me / Rehearsal in love / Satan takes the rhumba / More than you know / Uptown shuffle / Hadn't anyone 'til you / Baltimore bounce / Fine and mellow / Sabou.
**2 LP Set:** Released '83, on RCA (France) by BMG Records (France). Catalogue no: **PM 43257**

**ERSKINE HAWKINS AND HIS ORCHESTRA (Hawkins, Erskine & His Orchestra)**
**Album:** Released Sep '87, on Hindsight Catalogue no: **HSR 232**

**LIVE AT THE APOLLO 1944-47 (Hawkins, Erskine & His Orchestra)**
**Album:** Released '88, on Everybody's (USA) Catalogue no: **EV 3003**

**ONE NIGHT STAND - 1946**
**Album:** Released Jul '82, on Joyce Catalogue no: **JLP 1013**

**ORIGINAL TUXEDO JUNCTION (Hawkins, Erskine & His Orchestra)**
Tracks: / Tuxedo Junction / After hours / Tippin' in / Rockin' rollers' jubilee / Weary blues / Easy rider / Swing out / Big wig in the wigwam / Swingin' on Lenox Avenue / Gin mill special / Cherry / Dolomite / Song of the wanderer / Junction blues / Sweet Georgia Brown / Five o'clock whistle / Soft winds / Nona / Blackout / Don't cry baby / Bear mash blues.
**CD:** Released Jul '89, on Bluebird (2) by BMG Records (UK). Catalogue no: **ND 89682**
**Album:** Released Jul '89, on Bluebird (2) by BMG Records (UK). Catalogue no: **NL 89682**
**Cass:** Released Jul '89, on Bluebird (2) by BMG Records (UK). Catalogue no: **NK 89682**

**SNEAKIN' OUT**
**Album:** Released Sep '79, on First Heard by Submarine Records. Catalogue no: **FH 30**
**Cass:** Released Oct '84, on First Heard by Submarine Records. Catalogue no: **CFH 30**

**SWINGIN' IN HARLEM**
**Album:** Released '88, on Tax Catalogue no: **TAX 8014**

**TUXEDO JUNCTION**
**Cass:** Released Aug '89, on RCA by BMG Records (UK). Catalogue no: **NK 90363**
**CD:** Released Aug '89, on RCA by BMG Records (UK). Catalogue no: **ND 90363**
**Album:** Released Aug '89, on RCA by BMG Records (UK). Catalogue no: **NL 90363**

## Hawkins, Walter

**1927-29 (Hawkins, Walter 'Buddy Boy')**
Tracks: / Shaggy dog blues / Number three blues / Jailhouse fire blues / Snatch it back blues / Workin' on the railroad / Yellow woman blues / Raggin' the blues / Awful fix blues / Rag blues / How come mama blues / Snatch it and grab it / Voice throwin' blues.
**Album:** Released Jan '83, on Matchbox (Bluesmaster) by Saydisc Records. Catalogue no: **MSE 202**

**JESUS CHRIST IS THE WAY (Hawkins, Walter & The Family)**
Tracks: / I'm going through / I need your spirit / Strange / You're everything to me / Someday we'll meet again / God has signed my name / Jesus Christ is the way / I love Jesus more today / He brought me / Lord, give us time.
**Cass:** Released May '82, on Light (USA) by Lexicon Music Inc.. Catalogue no: **LC 7043**
**Album:** Released May '82, on Light (USA) by Lexicon Music Inc.. Catalogue no: **LS 7043**

**LOVE ALIVE (Hawkins, Walter & The Love Centre Choir)**
Tracks: / Follow me / Dear Jesus, I love you / I love the Lord / Changed / I won't be satisfied / God is / I'm not the same / Goin' up yonder.
**Album:** Released May '82, on Light (USA) by Lexicon Music Inc.. Catalogue no: **LS 7038**
**Cass:** Released May '82, on Light (USA) by Lexicon Music Inc.. Catalogue no: **LC 7038**

**LOVE ALIVE 2 (Hawkins, Walter & The Love Centre Choir)**
Tracks: / Come by here, good Lord / He's that kind of friend / Never alone / Until I found the Lord / Be grateful / I'm goin' away / God will open doors / Right on.
**Album:** Released May '82, on Light (USA) by Lexicon Music Inc.. Catalogue no: **LSX 7050**
**Cass:** Released May '82, on Light (USA) by Lexicon Music Inc.. Catalogue no: **LC**

7050

**LOVE ALIVE 3**

**Album:** Released Apr '85, on Light (USA) by Lexicon Music Inc.. Catalogue no: **LS 7075**

**Cass:** Released Apr '85, on Light (USA) by Lexicon Music Inc.. Catalogue no: **LC 7075**

## Hayes, Clancy

**Biographical details:** Banjo player, singer and songwriter (1908-72). His unpretentious and folksy deep baritone was perfect for the West Coast imitation turn-of-the-century style of revival music (trad jazz). He was best known with the Bob Scobey band in the '50s. He wrote *Huggin' and chalkin'*, a USA chart topper in 1946 for Hoagy Carmichael. (Donald Clarke, Nov 1989).

**OH BY JINGO**

**Album:** on Delmark (USA) by Delmark Records (USA). Catalogue no: **DL 210**

## Hayes, Clifford

**CLIFFORD HAYES DIXIELAND JUG BLOWERS (Hayes, Clifford & His Jug Blowers)**

**Album:** Released Dec '88, on Yazoo (USA) by Shanachie Records (USA). Catalogue no: **L 1054**

**CLIFFORD HAYES VOL 1: 1926-31**

Note: With the Dixieland Jug Blowers, Louisville Stompers, Jimmie Rogers.

**Album:** Released Jun '88, on Wolf Catalogue no: **WBJ 1004**

**CLIFFORD HAYES VOL 2: 1924-31**

Note: With Sara Martins Jug Band, Kid Coley, John Harris.

**Album:** Released Jun '88, on Wolf Catalogue no: **WBJ 1005**

## Hayes, Edgar

**Biographical details:** USA pianist and bandleader (1905-79). His version of *Stardust* in 1938 would have made the black chart if there'd been one at the time, but the B-side, an arrangement by saxophonist Joe Garland of a time-honoured riff, was covered by Glenn Miller the next year. Kenny Clarke was the band's drummer, and Hayes' version of *In the mood* was much better that Miller's. (Donald Clarke, Nov 1989).

**1937-1938 (Hayes, Edgar & His Orchestra)**

**Album:** Released May '86, on Swingfan Catalogue no: **1003**

## Hayes, Louis

**REAL THING, THE**

**Album:** Released Apr '81, on Muse by Black & Blue Records. Catalogue no: **MR 5125**

## Hayes, Tubby

**Biographical details:** Edward Brian Hayes, a multi-instrumentalist, but mainly a tenor saxophonist, born in London in 1935, and died there during heart surgery in 1973. He turned pro age 15 and led his own groups including the Jazz Couriers 1957-9 with Ronnie Scott; he first played in the USA in 1961 and played with Duke Ellington at Royal Festival Hall in 1964. He was the best-known and best-loved British jazzman of his generation, still greatly missed, but of course badly treated by the UK record industry, most of his stuff usually out of print. (Donald Clarke, Nov 1989).

**AFTER LIGHTS OUT (Hayes, Tubby Quintet)**

Tracks: / Ode to Ernie / No I wouldn't / Foolin' myself / Nicole / Message to the messengers / Hall hears the blues.

**Album:** Released Mar '83, on Jasmine by Hasmick Promotions. Deleted Jun '87. Catalogue no: **JASM 2015**

**MEXICAN GREEN (Hayes, Tubby, Quartet)**

**Album:** Released Jan '81, on Mole Catalogue no: **MOLE 2**

**TUBBS (A tribute) (Hayes, Tubby Quintet)**

Tracks: / All of you / Don't fall off the bridge / Modes and blues / Blue flues.

**Album:** Released '83, on Spotlite by Spotlite Records. Catalogue no: **SPJ 902**

**TUBBS' TOURS**

**Album:** Released Jul '81, on Mole Catalogue no: **MOLE 4**

**TUBBY HAYES 1957-72 (Hayes, Tubby, Quartet)**

**Album:** Released '89, on I.A.J.R.C (USA) by Vintage Jazz Music Society(VJM). Catalogue no: **IAJRC 50**

**TUBBY'S GROOVE (Hayes, Tubby, Quartet)**

Tracks: / Tin tin deo / Embers / Like someone in love / Surrey with the fringe on top / Sunny Monday / Blue hayes.

**Album:** Released Feb '83, on Jasmine by Hasmick Promotions. Deleted Jun '87. Catalogue no: **JASM 2001**

**WHERE AM I GOING TO LIVE 1969**

Tracks: / Off the wagon / For heaven's sake / Where am I going / Wierd blues / Walkin'.

**Album:** Released Jan '86, on Harlequin by Interstate Music. Catalogue no: **HQ 3006**

## Haymes, Dick

**Biographical details:** USA pop singer (1916-80), star of '40s movie musicals, very popular in his day (over 40 big hits) and still highly regarded by other singers. He wrote songs and tried to sell them to Harry James, who hired him as a singer instead. Born in Argentina, his comebacks were hampered by hassles with tax and immigration bureaucrats; on one occasion a European tour with Billie Holiday was planned, but the authorities wouldn't let him leave the country so that the tour was cancelled and everybody lost. (Donald Clarke, Nov 1989).

**AS TIME GOES BY**

**Album:** Released Aug '88, on Audiophile (USA) by Jazzology Records (USA). Catalogue no: **AP 170**

**BALLAD SINGER, THE**

Tracks: / Oh look at me now / On a slow boat to China / What's new / Cheek to cheek / This time the dreams on me / Very precious love, A / You're my girl / Long hot summer / So far / Moonlight becomes you / You stepped out of a dream / Sinner kissed my angel, A / My heart stood still.

**Album:** Released Jul '89, on Jasmine by Hasmick Promotions. Catalogue no: **JASM 2525**

**Cass:** Released Jul '89, on Jasmine by Hasmick Promotions. Catalogue no: **JASC 2525**

**BEST OF DICK HAYMES**

Tracks: / You'll never know / It can't be wrong / How blue the night / Let the rest of the world go by / More I see you / I wish I knew / My sin / Love letters / Isn't it kinda fun / It might as well be spring / That's for me / It's a grand night for singing / Oh what it seemed to be / Aren't you kinda glad we did / For you for me for evermore / Another night like this / Stella by candlelight / Mam'selle / When I'm not near the girl I love / Little white lies.

**Album:** Released Feb '82, on MCA by MCA Records. Deleted Feb '87. Catalogue no: **MCL 1651**

**DICK HAYMES**

Tracks: / Oh, look at me now / What's new? / My heart stood still / Cheek to cheek.

Note: Tracks include those listed above.

**Album:** Released Jul '88, on Glendale (USA) by Glendale Records (USA). Catalogue no: **GLS 9006**

**DICK HAYMES SINGS IRVING BERLIN**

Tracks: / Girl that I marry, The / How deep is the ocean (how high is the sky) / What'll I do / Little fish in a big pond / Once upon a time today / Say it with music / Song is ended, The / Soft light and sweet music / Cheek to cheek / Say it isn't so / Girl on the magazine cover, The / All alone / Lady of the evening / Let's take an old fashioned walk / It's a lovely day today / You're just in love.

**Album:** Released Sep '86, on MCA by MCA Records. Catalogue no: **MCL 1773**

**Cass:** Released Sep '86, on MCA by MCA Records. Catalogue no: **MCLC 1773**

**FOR YOU, FOR ME, FOR EVERMORE**

**Album:** Released Jun '86, on Audiophile (USA) by Jazzology Records (USA). Catalogue no: **AP 130**

**GOLDEN GREATS: DICK HAYMES**

Tracks: / You'll never know / It can't be wrong / How blue the night / Let the rest of the world go by / More I see you, The / I wish I knew / Love letters / Isn't it kinda fun / It might as well be Spring / That's for me / It's a grand night for singing / Oh what it seemed to be / Aren't you kind of glad we did / For you, for me, for evermore / Another night like this / Stella by starlight / Mam'selle / When I'm not near

the girl I love / Little white lies / My sin.
**Cass:** Released Oct '85, on MCA by MCA Records. Catalogue no: **MCMC 5024**
**Album:** Released Oct '85, on MCA by MCA Records. Catalogue no: **MCM 5024**

### GREAT SONG STYLISTS VOL.1
Tracks: / Until you fall in love / To be with you / I only wanna laugh / I'll only miss her when I think of her / Everybody has the right to be wrong / Daybreak / That's for me / Lazy / Love will find a way / My foolish heart / Just one of those things / Do-bi-do / Just another sunset / How blue the night / My favourite colour is blue / Did we dance / Ill forget you / Time for love, A.
**Album:** Released Apr '83, on Apex Catalogue no: **SAX 4**

### IMAGINATION
**Album:** Released Jun '88, on Audiophile (USA) by Jazzology Records (USA). Catalogue no: **AP 79**

### KEEP IT SIMPLE (Haymes, Dick / Loonis McGlohon Trio)
Tracks: / More I see, The / I get along without you very well / Little white lies / Almost like being in love / Stella by starlight / Very thought of you, The / I'll remember April / That's for me / It might as well be spring / Who cares / Love is here to stay / Love walked in / You'll never know / There will never be another you.
**Album:** Released May '88, on Audiophile (USA) by Jazzology Records (USA). Catalogue no: **AP 200**

### LAST GOODBYE
Tracks: / To be with you / Far from the madding crowd / Did we dance / You are the sunshine of my life / What are you doing the rest of your life / Wave / Until you fall in love / Love will find a way / Morning after / It's nice to be with you / My favourite colour is blue / I'll remember April / I'll forget you / Where is love.
**Album:** Released Jun '83, on London Records by London Records Ltd. Catalogue no: **DHS 7**

### LOVE LETTERS
Tracks: / I could happen to you / Mam'selle / When the wind was green / What's good about goodbye / Love letters / When lights are low / Easy to love / Your home is in my arms / I'll never smile again / Lost in the stars / What'll I do / My silent love.
**Cass:** Released Oct '85, on Memoir by Memoir Records. Catalogue no: **CMOIR 107**
**Album:** Released Oct '85, on Memoir by Memoir Records. Catalogue no: **MOIR 107**

### MOONDREAMS
Tracks: / If I should lose you / You don't know what love is / Imagination / Skylark / Isn't this a lovely day / What's new? / Way you look tonight / Then I'll be tired of you / I like the likes of you / Moonlight becomes you / Between the devil and the deep blue sea.
**Album:** Released '83, on Capitol (import) Catalogue no: **2C 068 81989**

### POLKA DOTS AND MOON BEAMS
Tracks: / Too late now / Little bit independent, A / I wish I didn't love you so / Spring will be a little late this year / Count every star / Laura... / It's magic / Polka dots and moonbeams / Song is you, The / They didn't believe me / Sunday morning or always / I guess I'll have to dream the rest / How are things in Gloccamorra? / My prayer.
**Cass:** Released Nov '89, on Memoir by Memoir Records. Catalogue no: **CMOIR 120**
**Album:** Released Jul '86, on Memoir by Memoir Records. Catalogue no: **MOIR 120**

### RAIN OR SHINE
**Album:** Released Aug '78, on Capitol by EMI Records. Deleted Jul '87. Catalogue no: **CAPS 1019**

### SOMETHING TO REMEMBER YOU BY (Haymes, Dick & Helen Forrest)
Tracks: / Something to remember you by / It had to be you / In love in vain / Long ago / I'll buy that dream / You'll never know / Lost in the stars / Love letters / Little white lies / Where or when / You stole my heart / Come rain or come shine / I'm always chasing rainbows / Something old, something new / All through the day / I only have eyes for you / I'll never smile again / You'd be so nice to come home to.
**Cass set:** Released Apr '85, on Cambra by Cambra Records. Deleted '88. Catalogue no: **CRT 5141**
**2 LP Set:** Released Apr '85, on Cambra by Cambra Records. Deleted '88. Catalogue no: **CR 5141**

### SPECIAL MAGIC, THE
**Album:** Released Apr '79, on Standing Room Only(USA) Catalogue no: **SRO 1002**

### SWINGIN' SESSION
**CD:** Released Aug '89, on Starline (Jazz) Catalogue no: **CDSG 404**

### V DISC YEARS, THE
**Album:** Released Apr '79, on Standing Room Only(USA) Catalogue no: **SRO 1001**

### VIC DAMONE AND DICK HAYMES (Haymes, Dick & Vic Damone)
**Album:** Released Jan '79, on Jazz Greats Catalogue no: **GP 702**

## Haymes, Joe

### RAY NOBLE AND JOE HAYMES 1935 (Haymes, Joe & Ray Noble)
**Album:** Released Apr '79, on Aircheck (USA) by Kiner Ents.(USA). Catalogue no: **AIRCHECK 2**

## Haynes, Roy

**Biographical details:** The famous drummer, born in 1926 in Massachusetts, is one of the most versatile and tasteful in modern jazz. He has gigged and recorded with practically everybody, from Lester Young and Thelonious Monk to Gary Burton, Larry Coryell and Chick Corea. *We three* was made in 1958 with Phineas Newborn and Paul Chambers; *Out of the afternoon* in 1962 on Impulse, with Roland Kirk, Tommy Flanagan and bassist Henry Grimes. (Donald Clarke, Nov 1989).

### OUT OF THE AFTERNOON (Haynes, Roy Quartet)
Tracks: / Moon ray / Fly me to the moon / Raoul / Snap crackle / If I should lose you / Long wharf / Some other Spring.
**Cass:** Released '82, on Jasmine by Hasmick Promotions. Catalogue no: **JAS C24**
**Album:** Released Jun '82, on Jasmine by Hasmick Promotions. Deleted Feb '88. Catalogue no: **JAS 24**

### THANK YOU, THANK YOU
**Album:** Released '79, on Galaxy (1) by President Records. Deleted '84. Catalogue no: **GXY 5103**

### WE THREE (Haynes, Roy Trio)
**CD:** Released Apr '87, on Carrere (France) Catalogue no: **98401**

## Heath, Jimmy

### JIMMY
**Album:** Released Apr '81, on Muse by Black & Blue Records. Catalogue no: **MR 5138**

## Heath, Ted

**Biographical details:** To those people who only think of the former Prime Minister when the name Ted Heath is mentioned, it may come as a surprise to learn that the first famous Ted Heath was one of Britain's top conductors and bandleaders of the Forties and Fifties. The original Mr Heath was already well established by the time the UK record charts were inaugurated in 1952. His first entry on those charts was *Vanessa*, which reached No.11 in January 1953. Most of his later hits - such as *Dragnet* (No.9 in 1953), *Skin deep* (No.9 in 1954) and *Swingin' shepherd blues* (No.3 in 1958) - also provided simultaneous successes for American jazz and dance band favourites like Ray Anthony, Duke Ellington and Ella Fitzgerald. Heath, who died in November 1969, made a bow to the younger generation in 1956 when his orchestra appeared in *It's a wonderful world*, Britain's first attempt at a rock'nroll movie. Heath's final appearance on the UK singles chart occurred in late 1961, when he reached No.36 with his rendition of *Sucu sucu*. He did however, achieve a Top 20 album in 1962 with *Big band percussion* (Bob MacDonald, 15th Oct 1985)

British trombonist and bandleader (1900-69), who played for Jack Hylton and Ambrose, then left Geraldo in 1944 to form his own band for a BBC series, leading it until illness in '64 (it carried on in his name for 5 years and there have been many reunions). Well-recorded by Decca and with good arrangements (Tadd Dameron was on staff in the mid-50's) and with many of the best young UK jazzmen passing through, it was among the best mainstream big jazz bands in the world, its records selling well in the USA too. (Donald Clarke, Nov 1989).

**ALL TIME TOP TWELVE (Heath, Ted & His Music)**
Tracks: / Begin the beguine / April in Paris / 'S wonderful / Tenderly / Autumn leaves / Somebody loves me / September song / Stardust / Tea for two / On the sunny side of the street / I've got the world on a string / My blue Heaven.
**Album:** Released Dec '89, on Memoir by Memoir Records. Catalogue no: **MOIR 126**
**CD:** Released Nov '89, on Memoir by Memoir Records. Catalogue no: **CMOIR 126**

**AT THE LONDON PALLADIUM (Heath, Ted & His Music)**
Tracks: / Champ, The / Eloquence / Do nothing till you hear from me / Pick yourself up / Blue for moderns / Fourth dimension / Retrospect / Dark eyes / Solitude / Hawk talks, The / I got it bad and that ain't good / Rhapsody for drums.
**Album:** Released Feb '83, on Jasmine by Hasmick Promotions. Deleted Jun '87. Catalogue no: **JASM 2005**

**AT THE LONDON PALLADIUM, VOL 3 (Heath, Ted & His Music)**
Tracks: / Flying home / Skylark / Late night final / Our love / After you've gone / And the angels sing / Crazy rhythm / Haitian ritual / Send for Henry / Lover / Sweet Georgia Brown / Concerto for Verrell.
**Album:** Released Jun '83, on Jasmine by Hasmick Promotions. Deleted Jun '87. Catalogue no: **JASM 2021**

**BEGINNING, THE (Heath, Ted & His Music)**
Tracks: / Caravan / Opus 1 / East of the sun / Bakerloo non-stop / My heart goes crazy / Ad lib frolic / Route 66 / Taboo / Baia / London Suite / Turn on the heath / Dark eyes / Stratford water / Sophisticated lady / That lovely weekend / Euphoria / Sweet and lovely.
**2 LP Set:** Released Nov '79, on Decca by Decca International. Deleted '84. Catalogue no: **DDV 5015**

**BIG BAND**
**CD:** Released '89, on Echo Jazz Catalogue no: **EJCD 06**
**Cass:** Released '89, on Echo Jazz Catalogue no: **EJMC 06**
**Album:** Released '89, on Echo Jazz Catalogue no: **EJLP 06**

**BIG BAND BASH**
**CD:** Released Jan '90, on Polydor by Polydor Ltd. Catalogue no: **8205952**

**BIG BAND FAVOURITES (Heath, Ted & His Music)**
Tracks: / Take the 'A' train / Two o'clock jump / Sentimental journey / Harlem nocturne / Jumpin' at The Woodside / Contrasts / Jersey bounce / At the woodchoppers' ball / St. James' Infirmary blues / Song of India / Fever / Tuxedo Junction / Cherokee / Intermission riff / Skyliner / Night train / St. Louis blues / Mood indigo / Blues in the night / King Porter stomp / Peanut vendor / Lullaby of Birdland / Basin Street blues / At the Jazz Band Ball / Sing, sing, sing / String of pearls / Flying home / In the mood.
**Cass:** Released Aug '84, on Decca by Decca International. Deleted '88. Catalogue no: **KMC2 5003**

**BIG BAND PERCUSSION (Heath, Ted & His Music)**
Tracks: / Johnny one note / Blues in the night / Peanut vendor / More than you know / Poinciana / Drum crazy / Taking a chance on love / It ain't necessarily so / Daddy / Mood indigo / Thou swell / But not for me / Tumbling tumbleweeds / Close your eyes / At last / Egyptian night / They didn't believe me / Ebb tide.
**CD:** Released Nov '88, on London Records by London Records Ltd. Catalogue no: **820 593-2**
**Album:** Released Apr '62, on Decca by Decca International. Deleted '67. Catalogue no: **PFM 24004**

**BIG BAND SOUND OF TED HEATH (Heath, Ted Orchestra)**
Tracks: / Billy Bailey / Chapter two / Gentle winds / Hello Berlin / Roll on, roll off / Flight number one / Minor mambo / Try a little later / Stuttgart special / Long night / Skip to my lou / Sur le pont d'Avignon.
Note: Don Lusher directs, with Kenny Baker, Derek Healy, Ronnie Hughes, Duncan Campbell, Roy Willcox, Ray Swinfield, Tommy Whittle, Henry MacKenzie, Eddie Mordue, Wally Smith, Johnny Edwards, Rick Kennedy, Bill Geldard, Norman Stenfalt, Lennie Bush, Judd Proctor, Ronnie Verrell.
**Album:** Released Dec '86, on Intersound Catalogue no: **ISST 131**

**COAST TO COAST (Heath, Ted & His Music)**
Tracks: / St. Louis blues / Charleston / I left my heart in San Francisco / Chicago / Manhattan serenade / Alabamy bound / I've got a gal in Kalamazoo / Oh Susannah / Moonlight in Vermont / Lullaby of Broadway / Allentown jail / Jersey bounce.
**CD:** Released Jul '87, on London Records by London Records Ltd. Catalogue no: **820 355-2**

**DANCING TIME (Heath, Ted Orchestra)**
**Album:** Released Aug '89, on Golden Era by Delta Records. Catalogue no: **GELP 15032**

**DRAGNET**
Tracks: / Dragnet.
**7" Single:** Released Oct '53, on Decca by Decca International. Deleted '56. Catalogue no: **F 10176**

**FAITHFUL HUSSAR, THE**
Tracks: / Faithful Hussar, The.
**7" Single:** Released Jul '56, on Decca by Decca International. Deleted '59. Catalogue no: **F 10746**

**FATS WALLER ALBUM (Heath, Ted & His Music)**
Tracks: / Honeysuckle rose / Ain't misbehavin' / Blue turning grey over you / Jitterbug waltz / I've got a feeling I'm falling / Alligator crawl / London suite.
**Album:** Released Feb '83, on Jasmine by Hasmick Promotions. Deleted Jun '87. Catalogue no: **JASM 2007**

**FEVER**
Tracks: / Fever / More / Hello, Dolly / Summer Place, A theme from / Never on a Sunday (Jamais le Dimanche) / Wives and lovers / Mack the knife / Moon river / Misty / Blues in the night / People / Fly me to the moon.
**CD:** Released Mar '87, on London Records by London Records Ltd. Deleted Feb '89. Catalogue no: **820 180-2**

**FOCUS ON TED HEATH**
**Cass:** Released May '78, on Decca by Decca International. Deleted '88. Catalogue no: **KFOC2 8082**
**2 LP Set:** Released May '78, on Phase 4 Deleted '81. Catalogue no: **FOS 29/30**

**FROM MOIRA WITH LOVE**
Tracks: / Folks who live on the hill / Melody in F / Clair de lune / Our love / Liebestraum / Song of India / Look for the silver lining / Procession / Skylark / Retrospect (Not on CD.) / Bill / Nearness of you / Fourth dimension / Thou swell / September song / Memories of you / Birth of the blues (Not on CD.) / Sixteen going on seventeen (Not on CD.) / Hot toddy (Not on CD.) / Georgia on my mind / Harlem nocturne (Not on CD.) / Someone to watch over me (Not on CD.) / St. Louis blues (Not on CD.) / How high the moon (Not on CD.) / Tonight / Faithfull Hussar / Blues for moderns (Not on CD.) / Our waltz / Obsession / Lush slide (Not on CD.) / Eloquence / Rhapsody for drums.
**Album:** Released Oct '89, on Horatio Nelson by Horatio Nelson Records & Tapes Ltd.. Catalogue no: **SIV 106**
**CD:** Released Oct '89, on Horatio Nelson by Horatio Nelson Records & Tapes Ltd.. Catalogue no: **CDSIV 6106**
**Cass:** Released Oct '89, on Horatio Nelson by Horatio Nelson Records & Tapes Ltd.. Catalogue no: **CSIV 106**

**GERSHWIN FOR MODERNS (Heath, Ted Orchestra)**
Tracks: / Man I love, The / Love walked in / Nice work if you can get it / Love is here to stay / Clap yo hands / I got rhythm / But not for me / Someone to watch over me / That certain feeling / Embraceable you / Changing my tune / Soon.
**Album:** Released '84, on Elite (Decca) by Decca Records. Catalogue no: **TAB 76**

**GOLDEN AGE OF TED HEATH, VOL. 1 THE**
Tracks: / Opus one / Somebody loves me / Swinging shepherd blues / My favourite things / Maria / Lullaby of Broadway / Holiday for strings / Flying home / I get a kick out of you / Jumpin' at the woodside / Man I love / Hawaiian war chant / Al last / Cherokee / We'll git it / 'S wonderful / You steped out of a dream / Sabre dance / Blues in the night / Royal garden blues / Moonlight in Vermont /

Apple honey / Fly me tyo the moon / Listen to my music / Pick yourself up / Hawk talks / And the angels sing / Champ, The.
**CD:** Released Nov '85, on Horatio Nelson by Horatio Nelson Records & Tapes Ltd.. Catalogue no: **CDSIV 6102**
**2 LP Set:** Released Nov '85, on Horatio Nelson by Horatio Nelson Records & Tapes Ltd.. Catalogue no: **SIV 102**
**Cass:** Released Nov '85, on Horatio Nelson by Horatio Nelson Records & Tapes Ltd.. Catalogue no: **CSIV 102**

**GOLDEN AGE OF TED HEATH VOL.2, THE**
Tracks: / 9.20 special / East of the sun / Intermission riff / Ad lib frolic / Girl talk / South Rampart St. Parade / American patrol / That lovely weekend / Swanee river / Artistry in rhythm / Nightingale sang in Berkeley Square / Bakerloo non stop / In the mood / I had the craziest dream / Soon amapola / I can't get started / Perdido / C jam blues / Sophisticated lady / First jump / Night and day / Poor little rich girl / Swing low sweet chariot.
**CD:** Released Oct '89, on Horatio Nelson by Horatio Nelson Records & Tapes Ltd.. Catalogue no: **CDSIV 6121**
**2 LP Set:** Released Oct '89, on Horatio Nelson by Horatio Nelson Records & Tapes Ltd.. Catalogue no: **SIV 1121**
**Cass:** Released Oct '89, on Horatio Nelson by Horatio Nelson Records & Tapes Ltd.. Catalogue no: **CSIV 1121**

**GOLDEN AGE OF TED HEATH VOL.3, THE**
Tracks: / Let's dance / Chattanooga choo choo / Swinging the blues / My guy's come back / Touch of your lips, The / Chicago / Skyliner / NIghtmare / Lush slide / Serenade in blue / Woodchopper's ball / Kalamazoo / On the sunny side of the street / I got it bad and that ain't good / Sidewalks of Cuba / After you've gone / Big John special / Chloe / Jersey bounce / Contrasts / Gotton trail / Fascinatin' rhythm / Snowfall / Headin' north.
**CD:** Released Feb '90, on Horatio Nelson by Horatio Nelson Records & Tapes Ltd.. Catalogue no: **CDSIV 6135**
**Cass:** Released Feb '90, on Horatio Nelson by Horatio Nelson Records & Tapes Ltd.. Catalogue no: **CSIV 1135**
**2 LP Set:** Released Feb '90, on Horatio Nelson by Horatio Nelson Records & Tapes Ltd.. Catalogue no: **SIV 1135**

**HITS I MISSED (Heath, Ted & His Music)**
Tracks: / High noon / Ebb tide / Twelfth St. rag / Love is a many splendoured thing / Three coins in the fountain / Unchained melody / Learnin' the blues / Swedish rhapsody / Moulin Rouge / My resistance is low / My foolish heart / Secret love.
**Album:** Released Mar '83, on Jasmine by Hasmick Promotions. Catalogue no: **JASM 2201**

**HOT TODDY**
Tracks: / Hot toddy.
**7" Single:** Released Jul '53, on Decca by Decca International. Deleted '56. Catalogue no: **F 10093**

**KERN FOR MODERNS (Heath, Ted & His Music)**
Tracks: / Long ago and far away / They didn't believe me / Look for the silver lining / Bill / Can I forget you? / Song is you, The / Ol' man river / Folks who live on the hill, The / Dearly beloved / Make believe / I won't dance / Why was I born?.
**Album:** Released Jun '83, on Jasmine by Hasmick Promotions. Deleted Jun '87. Catalogue no: **JASM 2022**

**LATINO (Heath, Ted & Edmundo Ros)**
Tracks: / Cherry pink and apple blossom white / Heatwave / Mas qye nada / Malaguena / Alla en el Rancho Grande / Desafinado / La Bamba / Brazil / What a difference a day made / La paloma / Tico tico / Vaya con Dios / Tequila / La cucaracha.
**Album:** Released Mar '83, on Decca by Decca International. Deleted '88. Catalogue no: **TAB 64**

**LISTEN TO MY MUSIC**
Tracks: / Listen to my music / Dark eyes / Bewitched / Anything goes / Don't blame me / Moonlight on the Ganges / Get happy / Show me the way to go home / Mad about the boy / If I had you / Tonight / All things you are / More than you know / Jealousy / By the sleepy lagoon / Slaughter on Tenth Avenue / Rockin' in Morocco.
**Album:** Released Nov '82, on Elite (Decca) by Decca Records. Deleted '86. Catalogue no: **TAB 39**
**Cass:** Released Nov '82, on Elite (Decca) by Decca Records. Deleted '88. Catalogue no: **KTBC 39**

**MY VERY GOOD FRIEND THE BANDLEADERS (Heath, Ted & His Music)**
Tracks: / Sing, sing, sing / When it's sleepy time down south / Intermission riff / Duke-a train.
**Album:** Released Nov '89, on Memoir by Memoir Records. Catalogue no: **MOIR 214**
**Cass:** Released Nov '89, on Memoir by Memoir Records. Catalogue no: **CMOIR 214**

**OLDE ENGLYSHE (Heath, Ted & His Music)**
Tracks: / Lincolnshire poacher / Greensleeves / D'ye ken John Peel? / Drink to me only with thine eyes / There's a tavern in the town / Barbara Allen / Cherry ripe / Sweet Polly Oliver / London Bridge is falling down / Early one morning / Lass of Richmond Hill / Foggy foggy dew.
**Album:** Released Mar '83, on Jasmine by Hasmick Promotions. Deleted Jun '87. Catalogue no: **JASM 2200**

**PLAYS AL JOLSON CLASSICS**
Tracks: / Toot toot Tootsie / Rock a bye your baby with a dixie melody / Waiting for the Robert E. Lee / Swanee / My manny / Give my regards to Broadway / April showers.
**Album:** Released Sep '89, on Memoir by Memoir Records. Catalogue no: **MOIR 215**
**Cass:** Released Sep '89, on Memoir by Memoir Records. Catalogue no: **CMOIR 215**

**RODGERS FOR MODERNS (Heath, Ted & His Music)**
Tracks: / Have you met Miss Jones? / There's a small hotel / Easy to remember / My heart stood still / Down by the river / Thou swell / Lady is a tramp, The / Where or when / This can't be love / I married an angel / Blue room / Dancing on the ceiling.
**Album:** Released Dec '83, on Jasmine by Hasmick Promotions. Catalogue no: **JASM 2925**

**SENTIMENTAL JOURNEY (Heath, Ted & His Music)**
Tracks: / Lullaby of Broadway / Mack the knife / Sentimental journey / Cherokee / Mood indigo / At last / Summer Place, A theme from / Fever / Cotton fields / Blame it on the bossa nova / Norwegian wood / Canadian sunset / American patrol / Caravan.
Note: Recorded between 1961 and 1975.
**Album:** Released May '84, on Polydor (France) by Polydor Ltd. Catalogue no: **811 004-1**
**Cass:** Released May '84, on Polydor (France) by Polydor Ltd. Catalogue no: **811 004-4**

**SHALL WE DANCE? (Heath, Ted & His Music)**
Tracks: / Dancing in the dark / I could have danced all night / Dancing with my shadow / Love dance / Shall we dance? / Let's face the music and dance / Dancing time / Ten cents a dance / Dancing with tears in my eyes / Dance, ballerina, dance / All you want to do is dance / I won't dance.
**Album:** Released Jun '83, on Jasmine by Hasmick Promotions. Deleted Jun '87. Catalogue no: **JASM 2204**

**SKIN DEEP**
Tracks: / Skin Deep.
**7" Single:** Released Feb '54, on Decca by Decca International. Deleted '57. Catalogue no: **F 10246**

**SMOOTH 'N' SWINGING**
Tracks: / Lover come back to me / Summertime / How about you? / Don't get around much anymore / Smooth 'n' swinging / Don't be that way / Taking a chance on love / These foolish things / Midnight sun / Fine romance / Night & day / You're my everything / You'd be so nice to come home to.
**Album:** Released Nov '81, on Decca by Decca International. Deleted '86. Catalogue no: **TAB 33**

**SPOTLIGHT ON SIDESMEN (Heath, Ted & His Music)**
Tracks: / Ill wind / Swinging the blues / Hey baby / Idaho / I can't get started / Love for sale / Lover man / Sidewalks of Cuba / I'll never be the same / Cottontail / Lullaby of the leaves / Witch doctor.
**Album:** Released Dec '83, on Jasmine

by Hasmick Promotions. Deleted Jun '87. Catalogue no: **JASM 2026**

**STRICTLY INSTRUMENTAL (Heath, Ted & His Music)**
Tracks: / Jeanie with the light brown hair / I've got sixpence / Very thought of you, The / My guy's come back / Twilight time / First jump / Not so quiet please / Knocked 'em in the Old Kent Road / On Ilkley Moor baht'at / Donegal cradle song / Experiment / See me dance the polka / Nightingale sang in Berkeley Square, A / You go to my head / Touch of your lips, The / Two guitars / Move / So easy.
**Album:** Released Nov '84, on Decca by Decca International. Deleted '88. Catalogue no: **DVL 8**

**STRIKE UP THE BAND**
**Cass set:** Released '88, on Ditto by Pickwick Records. Catalogue no: **DTO 10224**
**Album:** Released Feb '83, on Jasmine by Hasmick Promotions. Deleted Jun '87. Catalogue no: **JASM 2006**

**SUCU SUCU**
Tracks: / Sucu sucu.
**7" Single:** Released Oct '61, on Decca by Decca International. Deleted '64. Catalogue no: **F 11392**

**SWING IS KING**
Tracks: / Flying home / Cherokee / Begin the beguine / One o'clock jump / Song of India / At the woodchopper's ball / Elks' parade / In the mood / Two o'clock jump / Contrasts / Take the 'A' train / Sing, sing, sing.
**Album:** Released '79, on Decca by Decca International. Deleted '84. Catalogue no: **DGS 6**

**SWING SESSION (Heath, Ted & His Music)**
Tracks: / Champ, The / Eloquence / Do nothing till you hear from me / Pick yourself up / Blues for moderns / Fourth dimension.
**Album:** Released Jun '83, on Jasmine by Hasmick Promotions. Deleted Jun '87. Catalogue no: **JASM 2205**

**SWING VS. LATIN (Heath, Ted & Edmundo Ros)**
**Cass:** Released Jan '88, on Memoir by Memoir Records. Catalogue no: **CMOIR 134**
**Album:** Released Dec '88, on Memoir by Memoir Records. Catalogue no: **MOIR 134**

**SWINGIN' SHEPHERD BLUES**
**7" Single:** Released Mar '58, on Decca by Decca International. Deleted '61. Catalogue no: **F 11000**

**TED HEATH AT CARNEGIE HALL (Heath, Ted Orchestra)**
Tracks: / Listen to my music / Kings Cross climax / Memories of you / R.J. boogie / Perdido / Autumn in New York / Carioca / Just one of those things / Lullaby in rhythm / Stonehenge / Procession / I remember you / Hawaiian war chant.
**Album:** Released Nov '89, on Memoir by Memoir Records. Catalogue no: **MOIR 132**
**Cass:** Released Nov '89, on Memoir by Memoir Records. Catalogue no: **CMOIR 132**

**TED HEATH AT THE BBC (Heath, Ted & His Music)**
Tracks: / From this moment on / Buttercup / Sunday kind of love, A / Gone with the wind / Morning glory / Squattyroo / Viva Verrell / Experiment / Smooth ride / I'm beginning to see the light / Seven eleven / Cuban fantasy / Listen to my music.
**Cass:** Released Sep '83, on BBC by BBC Records & Tapes. Deleted Sep '87. Catalogue no: **ZCR 483**
**Album:** Released Sep '83, on BBC by BBC Records & Tapes. Deleted Sep '87. Catalogue no: **REH 483**

**TED HEATH RECALLS THE FABULOUS DORSEYS (Heath, Ted & His Music)**
Tracks: / Opus one / I'll never smile again / Amapola / Melody in F / Oodles of noodles / Well git it / Song of India / Chloe / Green eyes / Quiet please / Marie / Liebestraum.
**Cass:** Released Mar '85, on Jasmine by Hasmick Promotions. Catalogue no: **JASMC 2027**
**Album:** Released Mar '85, on Jasmine by Hasmick Promotions. Deleted Jun '87. Catalogue no: **JASM 2027**

**TED HEATH SWINGS IN HI-STEREO (Heath, Ted & His Music)**
Tracks: / C jam blues / Three for the blues / My funny Valentine / I like to recognise the tune / Love me or leave me / Ja da / Boomsie / Big Ben / Sophisticated lady / Wrap your troubles in dreams / Over the rainbow.
**Album:** Released Mar '83, on Jasmine by Hasmick Promotions. Deleted Jun '87. Catalogue no: **JASM 2202**

**TEQUILA**
Tracks: / Tequila.
**7" Single:** Released Apr '58, on Decca by Decca International. Deleted '61. Catalogue no: **F 11003**

**THAT LOVELY WEEKEND (Heath, Ted & His Music)**
Tracks: / Strike up the band / Smoothy / Blue skies march / Dickery dock / Rag mop / You are my heart's delight / I collect / Times a wastin' / People will say we're in love / Colonel Bogey / Harlem nocturne / Open the door Richard / Big Ben bounce / Skye boat song / Any old iron / My very good friend the milkman / That lovely weekend / Auld lang syne.
**Album:** Released Aug '83, on Decca by Decca International. Deleted Aug '88. Catalogue no: **RFL 32**

**TOM HARK**
Tracks: / Tom Hark.
**7" Single:** Released Jul '58, on Decca by Decca International. Deleted '61. Catalogue no: **F 11025**

**VANESSA**
Tracks: / Vanessa.
**7" Single:** Released Jan '53, on Decca by Decca International. Deleted '56. Catalogue no: **F 9983**

**YEARS OF FAME (Heath, Ted & His Music)**
Tracks: / Kings Cross climax / Hot toddy / Hawk talks / Lullaby of Birdland / Lush slide / Send for Henry / Malaguena / Faithful Hussar / Hawaiian war chant / Walking shoes / Cool for cats / Tequila / Stardust / Champ / Eloquence / Sermonette / Limehouse blues / Bags' groove / Doodlin' / Beaulieu Abbey.
**2 LP Set:** Released Nov '79, on Decca by Decca International. Deleted '84. Catalogue no: **DPA 3077/8**

## Heavenly Gospel

**1935-1940**
Tracks: / Prodigal son / Lead me to the rock / Didn't it rain / Moving up the King's highway / I'm going to telephone to glory / Walk in the light / When the moon goes down / My Lord heard Jerusalem when she moaned.
**Album:** Released Jan '85, on Heritage by Interstate Music. Catalogue no: **HT 305**

## Heavy Heads

**CHICAGO GOLDEN YEARS**
**Album:** Released Oct '88, on Vogue (France) by Vogue Records. Catalogue no: **515005**

## Hefti, Neal

**Biographical details:** Trumpeter, pianist, composer and arranger, born in Nebraska in 1922. He wrote for several big bands, but made his mark with Woody Herman from 1944: *The good earth, Wildroot, Everywhere* and others remain classics of the period. He wrote dozens of charts for Count Basie, including the brilliant 1957 album *The atomic Mr. Basie.* Sessioned with Frank Sinatra etc; his film work included the 1966 *Batman theme.* (Donald Clarke, Nov 1989).

**BAND WITH YOUNG IDEAS, THE (Hefti, Neal & His Orchestra)**
Tracks: / Coral reef / Charmaine / Waltzing on a cloud / Lake placid / Two for a nickel, three for a dime / Why not / Sure thing / Uncle Jim / Falling in love all over again / In veradero / It's a happy holiday / Sahara's aide.
**Album:** Released Sep '83, on Jasmine by Hasmick Promotions. Deleted Feb '88. Catalogue no: **JASM 1021**

**BATMAN THEME (1966 version)**
Tracks: / Batman theme.
**12" Single:** Released Mar '88, on RCA by BMG Records (UK). Deleted Feb '90. Catalogue no: **PT 49572**
**7" Pic:** Released Jul '89, on RCA by BMG Records (UK). Catalogue no: **PB 49571 PD**

## Helfer, Erwin

**BOOGIE PIANO - CHICAGO-STYLE**
Tracks: / Hallucinating / Rubbish boogie / Rodez stomp / Inside / Sneaky Pete / Homage to AA and PJ / Dirty dozens / Thin and thirty / Big Joe / Fat city / Four o'clock blues / Oysters.
**Album:** Released '82, on Big Bear by

Big Bear Records. Deleted '88. Catalogue no: **BEAR 11**

## Hemet High Jazz Band

### TIME AFTER TIME

Tracks: / Los hermanos de bop / Nobody cares but me / Lady with the pretty legs, The / Blues for Dee / Time after time / This masquerade / Baile de la mariposa / Thank you band.

**Album:** Released Aug '84, on Am-Pm (USA) Catalogue no: **AM 11**

## Hemphill, Jessie Mae

### SHE-WOLF

**Album:** Released Oct '88, on Vogue (France) by Vogue Records. Catalogue no: **513501**

## Hemphill, Julius

**Biographical details:** An alto saxophonist and composer, born in Texas in 1940. He was a member of BAG (the Black Artists Group collective) in St Louis with Oliver Lake and Lester Bowie; his works have been presented on stage and *The orientation of sweet Willie Rollbar* was filmed in 1972. He has played and recorded with Anthony Braxton, Bowie, Kool and the Gang and others; his best-known records are still *Dogon A.D.* (1972, with drummer Philip Wilson, Abdul Wadud on cello, Baikida E.J. Carroll on trumpet and on side-long 'The hard blues' adding Hamiet Blueiett) and *Coon bid'ness* (1975, with Wadud, Blueitt, Arthur Blythe, Barry Altschul and Daniel Ben Zebulon on congo); these came out of Arista, announcing an excellent musician and an important composer, but subsequent albums have been too few. (Donald Clarke, Nov 1989).

### BUSTER BEE (Hemphill, Julius & Oliver Lake)

**Album:** Released Dec '79, on Sackville by Spotlite Records. Catalogue no: **3018**

### COON BID'NESS

**Album:** Released May '79, on Freedom Catalogue no: **FLP 41012**

### LIVE IN NEW YORK

**Album:** Released May '79, on Red Pepper by Interstate Music. Catalogue no: **VPA 138**

### RAW MATERIALS AND RESIDUALS

**Album:** Released Jul '78, on Black Saint (Italy) Catalogue no: **BSR 0015**

## Henderson, Joe

### BARCELONA

**Album:** Released Jul '88, on Enja (Germany) by Enja Records (West Germany). Catalogue no: **ENJA 3037**

### BLACK NARCISSUS

Tracks: / Black narcissus / Hindsight and forethought / Power to the people / Amoeba / Good morning heartache / Other side of right.

**Album:** Released Jan '77, on Milestone by Ace Records. Deleted '81. Catalogue no: **M 9071**

### INNER URGE

Tracks: / Inner urge / Isotope / El barrio / You know I care / Night and day.

**Album:** Released Sep '84, on Blue Note by EMI Records. Deleted '87. Catalogue no: **BST 84189**

**CD:** Released Oct '89, on Blue Note by EMI Records. Catalogue no: **CDP 784 189 2**

**CD:** Released Oct '89, on Blue Note by EMI Records. Catalogue no: **BNZ 228**

### IN 'N' OUT

Tracks: / In 'n' out / Punjab / Serenity / Short story / Brown's town.

Note: Produced by Alfred Lion

**CD:** Released Apr '87, on Blue Note by EMI Records. Catalogue no: **BNZ 45**

**CD:** Released Apr '87, on Blue Note by EMI Records. Catalogue no: **CDP 746 510 2**

**Album:** Released Sep '84, on Blue Note by EMI Records. Deleted '87. Catalogue no: **BST 84166**

### MIRROR MIRROR (Henderson, Joe & Chick Corea)

**Album:** Released May '81, on MPS Jazz Catalogue no: **MPS 69 255**

### MODE FOR JOE

Tracks: / Shade of jade, A / Mode for Joe / Black / Caribbean fire dance / Granted / Freewheelin' / Black (alt. take).

**CD:** Released Jul '89, on Blue Note by EMI Records. Catalogue no: **BNZ 209**

**Album:** Released Apr '85, on Blue Note by EMI Records. Catalogue no: **BST 84227**

**CD:** Released Jul '89, on Blue Note by EMI Records. Catalogue no: **CDP 784 227 2**

### MYSTIFIED (Henderson, Joe, Rick Laird & Ron Steen)

**Album:** Released Apr '81, on Timeless (Import) by Timeless Records. Catalogue no: **SJP 112**

### OUR THING

Tracks: / Teeter totter / Pedro's time / Our thing / Black road / Escape.

Note: The collaboration of Joe Henderson and Kenny Dorham always produced electrifying and complex, but always appealing straight ahead jazz. On this, their rarest of albums with Andrew Hill on piano, they move through Dorham's marvellous, intricate 'Escape' and the funky title tune and Latin cooker 'Pedro's Time'.

**CD:** Released Jun '89, on Blue Note by EMI Records. Catalogue no: **BNZ 197**

**Album:** Released Jul '89, on Blue Note by EMI Records. Catalogue no: **BST 84152**

**CD:** Released Jun '89, on Blue Note by EMI Records. Catalogue no: **CDP 784 152 2**

### PAGE ONE

Tracks: / Blue bossa / La mesha / Homestretch / Recorda me / Jinrikisha / Out of the night.

**Album:** Released Jul '89, on Blue Note by EMI Records. Catalogue no: **B1 84140**

**CD:** Released Jun '89, on Blue Note by EMI Records. Catalogue no: **BNZ 169**

**CD:** Released Jun '89, on Blue Note by EMI Records. Catalogue no: **CDP 784 140 2**

### RELAXIN' AT CAMARILLO

**Album:** Released Jul '81, on Contemporary Jazz Catalogue no: **1014 006**

### SOFT FOCUS (Henderson, Joe, Rick Laird & Ron Steen)

**Album:** Released Apr '81, on Timeless (Import) by Timeless Records. Catalogue no: **SJP 104**

### STATE OF THE TENOR (Live at the Village Vanguard vol. 1)

Tracks: / Beatrice / Friday the thirteenth / Happy reunion / Loose change / Ask me now / Isotope.

**Album:** Released Jul '89, on Blue Note by EMI Records. Catalogue no: **BT 85123**

**CD:** Released Jul '89, on Blue Note by EMI Records. Catalogue no: **CDP 746 296 2**

**CD:** Released Jul '89, on Blue Note by EMI Records. Catalogue no: **BNZ 210**

### STATE OF THE TENOR VOL. 2 Live at the village

Tracks: / Boo boo's birthday / Cheryl / Y ya la quiero / Soulville / Portrait / Bead game, The / All the things you are.

**Album:** Released Jul '89, on Blue Note by EMI Records. Catalogue no: **BT 85126**

**CD:** Released Jun '87, on Blue Note by EMI Records. Catalogue no: **CDP 746 426 2**

**CD:** Released Jun '87, on Blue Note by EMI Records. Catalogue no: **BNZ 46**

## Henderson, Scott

### DOCTOR HEE

**Cass:** Released '87, on Passport Jazz (USA) by Jem Records Inc.(USA). Catalogue no: **PJC 88030**

**Album:** Released '87, on Passport Jazz (USA) by Jem Records Inc.(USA). Catalogue no: **PJ 88030**
**CD:** Released '87, on Passport Jazz (USA) by Jem Records Inc.(USA). Catalogue no: **PJCCD 88030**

## Hendriks, Gijs Quartet

### CLOSE TO THE EDGE
**Album:** Released Sep '86, on Timeless by Timeless Records. Catalogue no: **SJP 113**

### DOM ROCKET
**Album:** Released Apr '81, on Timeless by Timeless Records. Catalogue no: **SJP 131**

## Herbolzheimer, Peter

### FAT MAN BOOGIE
**Album:** Released Oct '85, on East Wind Catalogue no: **EWIND 713**

### JAZZ GALA CONCERT VOL.2 (Herbolzheimer, Peter Big Band)
**CD:** Released '86, on Bellaphon Catalogue no: **CDBID 156502**

### JAZZ GALA CONCERT VOL.3
**CD:** Released '86, on Bellaphon Catalogue no: **CDBID 156503**

## Heritage Hall Jazz

### AT CARNEGIE HALL
**Album:** Released Apr '79, on Viko (USA) Catalogue no: **VIKO 20011**

### NEW ORLEANS
**Album:** Released '88, on Dixieland Jubilee (USA) by GNP Crescendo Records (USA). Catalogue no: **DJA 512**
**Album:** Released Dec '84, on Vogue by Vogue Records. Catalogue no: **LDM 30251**
**Cass:** Released '88, on Dixieland Jubilee (USA) by GNP Crescendo Records (USA). Catalogue no: **DJC 512**

## Herman, Woody

**Biographical details:** Clarinettist, singer and bandleader Woodrow Charles Herman (1913-87) was born in Milwaukee, Wisconsin, singing and dancing from age 8. He formed his own band in 1933 but failed; he worked for Gus Arnheim, then Isham Jones, assuming leadership when Jones retired and the band became a collective. The Dixielandish 'Band that plays the blues' had the Woodchoppers as a band-within-a-band, and the hits included *Woodchoppers ball* in 1939. The band began to evolve as the members were replaced by younger people, Herman buying shares as the original members left, but the musical evolution was undocumented because it occurred during the musicians' union strike against record companies, so that the 'First Herd' burst upon an astonished audience in 1945, having switched from Decca (USA) (now MCA) to CBS: the hippest, swingiest white band in the USA. Bassist Chubby Jackson and pianist/arranger Ralph Burns had joined in '43, both from the Charlie Barnett Band (another outfit always among the hip); Jackson helped to recruit the rest: trumpeter/arranger Neal Hefti; also drummer Dave Tough, tenor saxophonist Flip Phillips, trombonist Bill Harris etc. Guitarist Bill Bauer replaced the last remaining member of the old band; both Candoli brothers played trumpet mid-'44 (16-year-old Conte played on summer holiday from high school). That band disbanded '47; Herman re-formed a second Herd, known as the 'Four Brothers' band ater a composition by Jimmy Giuffre with a blend of reedmen Zoot Sims, Stan Getz, Serge Chaloff and Herbie Steward: the writing and reed sound left no doubt about the influence of Lester Young and Charlie Parker, setting the tone for the West Coast 'cool' style of the '50's. This band unfortunately included a great many junkies; disgusted with people nodding out on the bandstand, Herman disbanded again, led a smal group for a few months and formed a Third Herd in 1950, recording for Capitol. In effect he kept doing that for the rest of his life, never failing to find talented youngsters. He edited arrangements by letting them shake down on the bandstand, using an unerring sense of what was right; his men worked not for him but with him. He was one of the most generous and best-loved people in the music business. (Donald Clarke, Nov 1989).

### 2ND HERD LIVE (1948, Vol.1)
**Album:** Released '88, on Raretone Catalogue no: **RARETONE 5001**

### 40TH ANNIVERSARY CARNEGIE HALL
Tracks: / Introduction / Woody's theme (Blue flame and acknowledge.) / Apple honey / Sweet and lovely / Four brothers / Brotherhood of man / Early autumn / Wrap your troubles in dreams / Everywhere / Bijou / Cousins / Blue serge / Blue Getz blues / Finale / Caldonia.
**2 LP Set:** Released '79, on RCA Victor by BMG Records (UK). Deleted '84. Catalogue no: **PL 02203**
**CD:** Released Nov '88, on Bluebird (2) by BMG Records (UK). Catalogue no: **ND 86878**

### 50TH ANNIVERSARY TOUR (Herman, Woody Big Band)
Tracks: / It don't mean a thing / What's new / Pools / Blues for red / Conga / Central park west / Fried buzzard / Epistrophy.
**Album:** Released Aug '86, on Concord Jazz by Concord Jazz Records (USA). Catalogue no: **CJ 302**
**Cass:** Released Aug '86, on Concord Jazz by Concord Jazz Records (USA). Catalogue no: **CJC 302**

### 1937 (Herman, Woody & His Orchestra)
Tracks: / Exactly like you / Remember me / Can't we be friends / Muskrat ramble / Jazz me blues / Old man moon / Ain't misbehavin' / Someday sweetheart / Squeeze me / Weary blues / You took the words right out of my heart / I can't be bothered now / Royal Garden blues / Apache dance / Bob White / Queen Isabella.
**Album:** Released Oct '79, on London Records by London Records Ltd. Deleted '84. Catalogue no: **HMP 5048**

### 1944 AND 1946 (Herman, Woody & His Orchestra)
Tracks: / Perdido / Apple honey / Noah / Always / Half past jumping time / Two again / Golden wedding / Four or five times / Happiness is just a thing called Joe / Blowin' up a storm / Jackson fiddles / Mean to me.
**Album:** Released Apr '81, on Solid Sender Catalogue no: **SOL 506**

### 1945 BAND IN HI FI
**Album:** Released Apr '79, on Fanfare by Captain Billy's Music. Catalogue no: **FANFARE 22-122**

### 1949-THE CALIFORNIA CONCERTS (Herman, Woody & His Orchestra)
**Album:** Released '86, on Artistry Catalogue no: **AR 109**

### 1943-1946 (Herman, Woody & His Orchestra)
Tracks: / Red top / It must be jelly / Caldonia / John Hardy's wife / Apple honey / Don't worry about the mule / Dancing in the dawn / There are no wings on a foxhole / Flying home / Jones beachhead / 125th Street prophet.
Note: Featuring Sonny Berman, Neal Hefti, Bill Harris, Flip Philips, Ben Webster, Margie Hyams, Dave Tough.
**Album:** Released Apr '81, on Solid Sender Catalogue no: **SOL 503**

### 1945-1954 (Herman, Woody & His Band)
**Album:** Released '88, on Joker (USA) by Lifetime Records (USA). Catalogue no: **SM 4021**
**Cass:** Released '88, on Joker (USA) by Lifetime Records (USA). Catalogue no: **MC 4021**

### AMEN 1937 - 42 (Herman, Woody & His Orchestra)
**Album:** Released Jun '88, on Bandstand Catalogue no: **BS 7108**

### AND THE FOUR BROTHERS LIVE
**Album:** Released Apr '81, on Queendisc (Italy) Catalogue no: **QU 005**

### AT THE HOLLYWOOD PALLADIUM
**Album:** Released Apr '81, on Solid Sender Catalogue no: **SOL 515**

### AT THE WOODCHOPPERS BALL
Tracks: / At the woodchoppers ball / On the Atchison, Topeka and Santa Fe / Wild root / Bijou / Caldonia / Put that ring on my finger / There, I've said it again / Who dat up dere? / Apple honey / Goosey gander / I'll get by / Walkin' my baby back home / Spruce juice / Kiss goodnight, A / Noah.
**Album:** Released Dec '88, on Dance Band Days by Prism Leisure. Catalogue no: **DBD 09**
**Cass:** Released Dec '88, on Dance Band Days by Prism Leisure. Catalogue no: **DBDC 09**
**CD:** Released Jul '89, on Dance Band Days by Prism Leisure. Catalogue no:

DBCD 09

**BAND THAT PLAYS THE BLUES, THE (Big band bounce & boogie)**
Tracks: / At the woodchopper's ball / Dallas blues / Blues upstairs / Blues downstairs / Casbah blues / Blue prelude / Herman at the Sherman / Golden wedding / Blue flame / Fur trapper's ball / Bishop's blues / Woodsheddin' with Woody / Blues in the night / 'Tis autumn / String of pearls / Who dat up dere?.
Note: The first band ever led by Herman, recorded between 1939 - year of the smash-hit *At the woodchoppers' ball* - and 1943.
**Album:** Released Apr '84, on Affinity by Charly Records. Catalogue no: **AFS 1008**
**Cass:** Released Sep '86, on Affinity by Charly Records. Catalogue no: **TCAFS 1008**

**BLOWIN' UP A STORM**
Tracks: / Apple honey / Caldonia (CD only) / Goosey gander / Northwest passage / Good earth, The (CD only) / Bijou / Blowin' up a storm / Steps / Four men on a horse / Sidewalks of Cuba / Cherokee canyon / Keen and peachy / Goof and I, The / Four brothers / Summer sequence (part IV) / P.S. I love you / Mulligan tawny / Third herd, The.
**CD:** Released Sep '89, on Big Band Era Catalogue no: **2601822**
**CD:** Released Oct '87, on Charly by Charly Records. Catalogue no: **CDCHARLY 100**
**Album:** Released Oct '87, on Affinity by Charly Records. Catalogue no: **AFS 1043**

**BLUES GROOVE**
Tracks: / Everyday I have the blues / Trouble in mind / Smack dab in the middle / Pinetop's blues / Basin Street blues / Stormy Monday / Dupree blues / I want a little girl / Blues groove.
**Cass:** Released Mar '88, on Capitol by EMI Records. Deleted Jul '88. Catalogue no: **TCEMS 1283**
**Album:** Released Mar '88, on Capitol by EMI Records. Deleted Aug '89. Catalogue no: **EMS 1283**
**Album:** Released Mar '88, on Capitol by EMI Records. Deleted Jun '89. Catalogue no: **1599301**

**BLUES ON PARADE 1937 - 41 (Herman, Woody & His Orchestra)**
**Album:** Released Jun '88, on Bandstand Catalogue no: **BS 7122**

**CALDONIA**
Tracks: / Gold and I / I got it bad / Red top / Good Earth, The / Northwest passage / Caldonia / Your father's mustache / Mother goose jumps / There'll be some changes made / Swing low sweet chariot / Laura / Buck dance / Skylark / Baby I need you / My pal Gonzalez / Yeah man / Goof and I, The.
**Album:** Released May '88, on Big Band Era Catalogue no: **20129**
**Cass:** Released May '88, on Big Band Era Catalogue no: **40131**
**Album:** Released Mar '85, on Astan (USA) Catalogue no: **F 20131**

**CONCORD JAM VOL.1**
**Album:** Released Mar '81, on Concord by Concord Jazz Records (USA). Catalogue no: **CJ 142**

**CRAZY RHYTHM**
Tracks: / Woodchoppers ball / Caldonia / Midnight sun / Bijou / Northwest passage / Lullaby of Birdland / Carioca / I cover the waterfront / Blowin' up a storm / Crazy rhythm.
**Album:** Released Nov '82, on IMS by Polydor Ltd. Catalogue no: **F 50018**
**Cass:** Released Nov '82, on IMS by Polydor Ltd. Catalogue no: **MF 9 50018**

**CRAZY RHYTHM (SINGLE)**
Tracks: / Crazy rhythm.
**7" Single:** Released May '89, on Garland. Catalogue no: **GRZ 007**

**DANCE TIME '43**
Note: Tracks include: *Spruce juice, I don't believe in rumours, Down under, Salt Lake City blues, Who dat up dere, Four or five times*, etc.
**Cass:** Released Oct '87, on First Heard by Submarine Records. Catalogue no: **CFH 34**
**Album:** Released Oct '87, on First Heard by Submarine Records. Catalogue no: **FH 34**

**DOUBLE EXPOSURE**
Tracks: / Flying easy / I can't get next to you / Sex machine / My cherie amour / Lancaster gate / Aquarius / Hut,The / Memphis underground / Ponteio / Impression of Strayhorn / MacArthur park / Light my fire / Here I am baby / For love of Ivy / Hard to keep my mind on you / Time for love / Blues in the night / Smiling phases / Stone called Person,A.
**Cass set:** Released '89, on Chess by Vogue Records. Catalogue no: **GCHK 2-6029**
**2 LP Set:** Released Jul '88, on Chess by Vogue Records. Catalogue no: **GCH 2-6029**

**EARLY AUTUMN**
**Album:** Released Jan '85, on Pathe Marconi (France) Catalogue no: **PM 1804751**

**FAN IT**
**Album:** Released '84, on Swing House by Submarine Records. Catalogue no: **SWH 19**

**FIRST HERD 1944 (Herman, Woody & His Orchestra)**
Tracks: / Is you is or is you ain't my baby / It must be jelly / Red top / G.I. jive / Sweet Lorraine / Jones Beachhead / Four or five times / Blues on parade / 125th Street prophet / Somebody loves me / Old gold commercial / Basie's basement / Hot time in the town of Berlin / 1-2-3-4 / Apple honey.
**Album:** Released Oct '79, on London Records by London Records Ltd. Deleted '84. Catalogue no: **HMP 5058**

**FIRST HERD, THE**
**Album:** Released '88, on Fanfare by Captain Billy's Music. Catalogue no: **LP 43-143**

**FIRST SESSION 1937 (Herman, Woody & His Orchestra)**
**Album:** Released Feb '87, on Circle (USA) by Jazzology Records (USA). Catalogue no: **CLP 95**

**FOUR BROTHERS AT THE ROYAL ROOST**
**Album:** Released Oct '86, on Jazz Live (Italy) Catalogue no: **BLJ 8027**

**FOURTH HERD, THE**
**Album:** Released Oct '88, on Vogue by Vogue Records. Catalogue no: **500068**

**GIANT STEPS**
**CD:** Released Nov '86, on Fantasy (import) by Fantasy Inc (USA). Catalogue no: **FCD 6099432**

**GOLDEN FAVOURITES**
**CD:** Released Jun '88, on MCA (USA) by MCA Records (USA). Catalogue no: **31277**

**GREATEST HITS:WOODY HERMAN**
Tracks: / Apple honey / Good earth, The / Woodchopper's ball / Your father's moustache / Blue flame / Northwest passage / Caldonia / Summer sequence / Bijou / Four brothers / Wild root / Keen and peachy.
**Album:** Released '74, on Realm Catalogue no: **525 51**

**HERDMAN HERD**
**Album:** Released Apr '79, on Bright Orange Catalogue no: **BO 717**

**HEY, HEARD THE HERD**
**Album:** Released Sep '81, on Verve (USA) by Polydor Ltd. Catalogue no: **2304 509**

**HOLLYWOOD PALLADIUM 1948**
**Album:** Released Apr '81, on Hep Jazz by Hep Records. Catalogue no: **HEP 7**

**IN DISCO ORDER VOL.2**
**Album:** Released Jul '77, on Ajax (USA) Catalogue no: **AJAX 109**

**IN ENGLAND 1959**
**Album:** Released Aug '81, on Jazz Groove Catalogue no: **JG 004**

**IT POURS**
**Album:** Released '84, on First Heard by Submarine Records. Catalogue no: **FH 43**

**JUKE BOX (Herman, Woody & His First Herd)**
Tracks: / Red top / Put that ring on my finger / Great Northern / Walkin' my baby back home / Golden wedding / Atcheson, Topeka and the Santa Fe / Till the end of time / Perdido / It must be jelly / Superman with a horn / Day by day / Ee-ba-lee-ba / Wild root / Blue flame theme.
**Cass:** Released Nov '85, on First Heard by Submarine Records. Catalogue no: **CFH 36**
**Album:** Released Nov '85, on First Heard by Submarine Records. Catalogue no: **FH 36**

**JULY 30TH 1959**
Tracks: / Panatella / Lament for Linda / In a misty mood / Misery stay away from

Woody Herman - Live at Monterey (Atlantic)

my door / Catty corner / Thirteenth instant / Magpie / Blues for Indian Jim / Devil and the stoker / Swing machine / Summer nights / Johnny on the spot.
**Album:** Released Oct '80, on From The Jazz Vault by Damont Audio Ltd.. Catalogue no: **JV 104**

**JUMPIN' WITH WOODY HERMAN'S 1939 - 1942 (Herman, Woody & His Herd)**
Tracks: / Woodchoppers' ball / Blues downstairs / Blues upstairs / Casbah blues / Jumpin' blues / Blues on parade / Blue flame / Fur trappers' ball / Bishop's blues / Woodsheddin' with Woody / Hot chestnuts / Four or five times.
**Album:** Released '81, on Joker (USA) by Lifetime Records (USA). Catalogue no: **SM 3059**

**LIVE AT CONCORD '81 (Herman, Woody Big Band)**
Tracks: / Things ain't what they used to be / Dolphin, The / John Brown's other body.
Note: Guest musicians: Al Cohn, Stan Getz. Tracks include those listed above.
**Cass:** Released Sep '82, on Concord Jazz by Concord Jazz Records (USA). Catalogue no: **CJC 191**
**Album:** Released Sep '82, on Concord Jazz by Concord Jazz Records (USA). Catalogue no: **CJ 191**

**LIVE AT MONTEREY (See panel above)**
Tracks: / Four brothers / Like some blues man / Skoobeedoobee / Monterey apple tree / Skylark / Magpie.
**Album:** on Atlantic by WEA Records. Catalogue no: **K 50236**
**Album:** Released Jul '76, on Atlantic by WEA Records. Catalogue no: **ATL 50236**

**LIVE AT THE HOLLYWOOD PALLADIUM VOL. 1 (1951)**
**Album:** Released Mar '90, on Jazz Supreme Catalogue no: **JS701**

**LIVE AT THE HOLLYWOOD PALLADIUM VOL. 2 (1952)**
**Album:** Released Mar '90, on Jazz Supreme Catalogue no: **JS702**

**LIVE IN ANTIBES 1965**
**CD:** Released May '89, on France's Concert Catalogue no: **FCD 117**
**Album:** Released May '89, on France's Concert Catalogue no: **FC 117**

**LIVE IN NEW ORLEANS**
**Album:** Released Oct '84, on Giants of Jazz by Hasmick Promotions. Catalogue no: **GOJ 1022**

**NEW WORLD OF WOODY HERMAN**
**Album:** Released Oct '88, on Vogue by Vogue Records. Catalogue no: **500083**

**OMAHA NEBRASKA 1954**
Tracks: / Cohn's Allen / Off shore / Get out of town / Leo the lion / Stars fell on Alabama / Mambo the most / At the woodchopper's ball / Early autumn / Lady be good / Happiness is just a thing called Joe / Mulligan tawny / Apple honey.
**Album:** Released '84, on Swing World by Submarine Records. Catalogue no: **SWS 4**
**Cass:** Released '84, on Swing World by Submarine Records. Catalogue no: **CSWS 4**

**PRE-HERDS**
Tracks: / I've got you under my skin / It must be jelly / Basie's basement / Do nothing till you hear from me / As long as I live / Cherry / Ingie speaks / I ain't got nothin' but the blues / I get a kick out of you / I'll get by / Irresistible you / Cryin' sands / Noah / Perdido / Milkman, keep those bottles quiet / Going home.
**Album:** Released Sep '86, on Affinity by Charly Records. Catalogue no: **AFS 1027**
**Cass:** Released Sep '86, on Affinity by Charly Records. Catalogue no: **TCAFS 1027**

**PRE-HERDS (BULLDOG) (Herman, Woody & His Orchestra)**
Tracks: / Natchel blues / Don't get around much any more / Body and soul / Ready, get set, jump / At the woodchoppers' ball / Opus de funk / Park easy / Saxy.
**Album:** Released Nov '83, on Bulldog Records by President Records. Catalogue no: **BDL 1047**

**PRESENTS FOUR OTHERS**
Tracks: / Woody's lament / Goof & I / I wanna go home / Not really the blues / Tiny's blues / Loose aberrations / Four others / Tenderly.
**Album:** Released May '82, on Concord by Concord Jazz Records (USA). Catalogue no: **CJ 110**

**RHAPSODY IN WOOD**
Tracks: / Tiny's blues / I've got the world on a string / Boomsie / I ain't getting younger / I only have eyes for you / Four brothers / Rhapsody in wood.
**Album:** Released '84, on First Heard by Submarine Records. Catalogue no: **FH 29**

**ROAD BAND (Herman, Woody & His Orchestra)**
Tracks: / Opus de funk / Gina / I remember Duke / Sentimental journey / Cool cat on a hot tin roof / Where or when / Captain Ahab / I'll never be the same / Pimlico.
**Cass:** Released Jul '85, on Capitol by EMI Records. Deleted Jul '87. Catalogue no: **EG 2604254**
**Album:** Released Jul '85, on Capitol by EMI Records. Deleted Jan '88. Catalogue no: **EG 2604251**

**ROAD BAND 1948**
Tracks: / Lullaby in rhythm / You turned the tables on me / Happy song / Four brothers / I've got news for you / Keen and peachy / Wild root / Happiness is just a thing called Joe / Tiny's blues / When you're smiling / This is new / Dance, ballerina, dance / Elevation.
**Album:** Released Apr '81, on Hep Jazz by Hep Records. Catalogue no: **HEP 18**

**SECOND HERD LIVE IN HOLLYWOOD**
**Album:** Released Apr '81, on Queendisc (Italy) Catalogue no: **QU 037**

**SWING GOES ON VOL. 4**
**Album:** Released '83, on EMI (Germany) by EMI Records. Catalogue no: **IC 054 52713**

**SWINGING HERD, THE**
**Album:** Released Oct '88, on Vogue by Vogue Records. Catalogue no: **500057**

**THIRD HERD: EARLY AUTUMN**
**CD:** Released Jul '88, on Discovery (1) by Oryx Records. Catalogue no: **DSCD 944**

**THIRD HERD, THE**
Tracks: / Beau jazz / Early autumn / Mambo the most / Mother Goose jumps / Four others / Buck dance / Sorry 'bout the whole darned thing / Men from Mars / Wooftie.
**Album:** Released Jan '84, on Discovery (USA) by Discovery Records (USA). Catalogue no: **DS 845**
**Cass:** Released Jan '84, on Discovery (USA) by Discovery Records (USA). Catalogue no: **DSC 845**

**THIRD HERD, VOL.1, THE**
Tracks: / Stompin' at the Savoy / Moten swing / I love Paris / Moon is blue, The.
**Cass:** Released '88, on Discovery (USA) by Discovery Records (USA). Catalogue no: **DSC 815**
**Album:** Released '88, on Discovery (USA) by Discovery Records (USA). Catalogue no: **DS 815**

**THUNDERING HERD-LIVE**
Tracks: / Swing low sweet clarinet / I got it bad / Fan it / Apply honey / There'll be some changes made / Stardust / Northwest passage / Good earth,The / baby I need you / Half past jumping time.
**Album:** Released Aug '86, on Meteor by Magnum Music Group. Catalogue no: **MTM 019**

**THUNDERING HERDS**
Tracks: / Woodchopper's ball / Apple honey / Goosey gander / Northwest passage / Good earth, The / Jug of wine, A / Your father's moustache / Bijou / Wild root / Panacea / Backtalk / Non-alcoholic / Blues are brewin' / Goof and I, The / Four brothers / Blue flame.
Note: 3 LP set.
**Cass:** Released 14 Aug '88, on CBS (import) by CBS Records. Catalogue no: **4608254**
**Album:** Released 14 Aug '88, on CBS (import) by CBS Records. Catalogue no: **4608251**
**Album:** Released Jun '86, on CBS (import) by CBS Records. Catalogue no: **66378**

**UNCOLLECTED WOODY HERMAN AND HIS FIRST HERD**
Tracks: / It must be jelly / Sweet Lorraine / Jones beachhead / Blues on parade / Somebody loves me / There'll be a hot time in the town of Berlin / Apple honey / Red top / G.I. jive / Four or five times / 125th street prophet / Basie's basement / 1-2-3-4 jump.
Note: This LP consists of a long complete Old Gold radio show of Woody's First Herd with the best selections of their 11 shows, complete with introductions, announcements, openings, closings, etc. This is the band with Ralph Burns, Chubby Jackson, Dave Tough, Neal Hefti, Ray Wetzel, Pete Candoli, Bill Harris, Flip Philips, etc. Red Barber is the announcer and Allan Jones was the featured singer but the Jones selections have been eliminated. Even includes an Old Gold commercial; remember "latakia tobacco" and "apple honey"? Great notes by that Woody Herman discographer, George Hall. (Hindsight Catalogue - 1989)
**Album:** Released May '79, on Hindsight (UK) by Michele International Records. Catalogue no: **HSR 134**

**Woody Herman - The V Disc Years Vol. 2 (Hep Jazz)**

**V DISC YEARS VOL.1, THE**
Note: Mono
**Album:** Released Sep '86, on Hep Jazz by Hep Records. Catalogue no: **HEP 34**

**V DISC YEARS VOL.2, THE (See panel above)**
Tracks: / Don't worry 'bout that mule / 125th Street prophet / I can't put my arms around a memory / Somebody loves me / John Hardy's wife / Meshugah / Jones Beachhead / Mean to me / Caldonia / Jackson fiddles while Ralph burns / Blowin' up a storm / C jam blues and reprise.
Note: Volume 2 of the Woody Herman V Disc Years continues with the August 22nd 1945 session at the point where volume 1 ends (if you have not acquired the first volume, seek it out to complete the two-volumeHep compilation). *Don't worry 'bout that mule* is a powerful Ralph Burns arrangement with boppish trumpet section notes. Woody takes his typical 'hip' rhythm vocal followed by some truly magnificent Sonny Berman trumpet work that starts out with all jets wide open. Tony Aless takes 8 bars on the bridge. Sonny's solo leads into a short passage by Flip Phillips and band ensemble as an intro to some good Woody clarinet work. All of this is forcefully supported by a good strong rhythm section. Woody finishes the arrangement with a vocal out chorus that parodies a much heard commercial in those days for a popular American soft drink. *125th Street Prophet*, another Ralph Burns chart that features Woody's clarinet and Neal Hefti's Dizzy influenced trumpet. As in the previous title, there is very strong ensemble and rhythmic support. These two August 22nd tracks should have been recorded for Columbia records. As it is, we can be thankful they were preserved by V disc. Next we have an alternate take, the first of two presented in Volume 2. This version of *I can't put my arms around a memory* follows the same solo routine as the version presented in volume 1. *Somebody loves me* comes from the special V Disc recording session that took place at the Vanderbilt Theatre in New York in late January 1945. Ralph Burns plays the introduction that leads to Woody's soulful vocal. Bill Harris, Flip Philips and Ben Webster take solos played straight from their hearts.
Side one ends with *John Hard's wife*, an Ellington composition that features tenor great Ben Webster who was among the guests who appeared at the special V Disc session. The original V Disc label

incorrectly informs us that Flip Phillips and Marjorie Hyams are present on this performance, but don't believe it, the tenor work on both sides of Harris' solo chorus is Ben's. Just as Webster starts to come on strong he runs into trouble with a key on his horn that forces him to quit playing before he can finish his last chorus. You can plainly hear him struggling before off the microphone. Ralph Burns jumps in to conclude this unusual performance. Fortunately V Disc saw fit to issue this performance despite Webster's problem. Meshugah has always been a perplexing discographical problem. Not even V Disc expert Dick Sears could pin down the source, date and exact personnel for this title. At any rate, this recording certainly includes more musicians than listed on the V Disc label, but not to the size of the full Herman band, and Woody himself is not present. If the theme sounds familiar to you veteran Herman fans, it is because the First Herd played it often at this time as *They went that a way* and finally got around to recording it a few years later for Capitol Records as *Sonny speaks.* This performance features Sonny Berman and Neal Hefti for one chorus each then Flip Phillips and Bill Harris for two choruses each. Following some very wild trumpet section work we hear a chorus of Tony Aless' piano leading to the ensemble ride out.

Another alternate take is presented with *Jones Beachhead* which chronologically takes us back to 1944. The original V Disc issue of this number is presented on volume 1. We believe *Jones Beachhead* to be another title dedicated to a participant on the Old Gold radio show series, this time co-star Allan Jones (reference *Red Top* in volume 1). Following the completion of the radio series in October 1944, this tune was then retitled *Half past jumpin' time.* In mid-January 1946 ABC aired an excellent radio show titled *Esquire all-American jazz concert.* Featured were the bands of Duke Ellington and Woody Herman along with the extremely popular King Cole Trio with the emcee job very ably handled by Orson Welles. The remaining five tracks on this side come from this concert. *Mean to me* is a short feature for Bill Harris, who would perform it again two months alter at Carnegie Hall. *Caldonia* follows the usual Herman routine. Woody's vocal and then Flip and Bill in full flight. Tony Aless' piano is also heard. If you listen closely to the beginning of the next track you will hear the audience laughing. This was their response to the announcement of the pun title *Jackson fiddles while Ralph burns.* This is most likely the only performance of that number. Featured are Norvo, Chubby Jackson, Sonny Berman and some piano that we feel is played by guesting Ralph Burns. Although Burns quit the band in June 1945 to stay in New York and arrange full-time, he often sat in with the First Herd on special occasions.

*Blowin' up a storm* features Aless and Woody during the rhythm intro followed by Flip, Bill and Norvo with the band riffing behind each solist. The ensemble power builds to a Pete Candoli shout and as the band attacks the final blow-out the tune is truncated in a fade robbing us of a complete performance. In fact, this ending which was on the original V Disc was caused by the inclusion of a long spoken intro by Leonard Feather who advises us of all the titles and soloists you will hear on both sides of the record. An announcer's voice over the final chorus mentioning ABC I'm sure also contributed to the V Disc edit decision. The final track which ends this two volume coverage of important Woody Herman material requires an explanation. When the original broadcast was initially aired, it ended with the combined personnel of both the Herman and Ellington bands wailing on *C jam blues.* Following the final chorus and wild audience applause, the bands reprise the C jam riff and continue to play as the ABC announcer gave a summary of the broadcast participants and a plug for emcee Orson Welles. The reprise was not included on the V Disc release and it is doubtful it was heard in a transcribed version of the show. However, yours truly, as a very young jazz fan back in 1946, had recorded the broadcast on a home disc cutter. I sent a tape to Hep for their determination whether to use the extra music and to their credit they opted to include the reprise on this LP. As to the music, Woody starts off the soloing with Duke's Sonny Greer kicking everyone along on drums. Taft Jordan follows with reeds riffing behind him. Then Flip Phillips starts his solo and quite noticeably Woody's rhythm section takes over. Then it is every man for himself in a strong ride out with Duke's Cat Anderson on top. Then, as explained, the reprise has been expertly tacked on. Thank you Jack Towers and John R. T. Davies. (George Hall, 1987)

**Album:** Released Mar '87, on Hep Jazz by Hep Records. Catalogue no: **HEP 35**

## WOODCHOPPERS' BALL/ AT THE 1940 FAMOUS DOOR (Herman, Woody & Will Bradley)

**Album:** Released Jun '88, on Bandstand Catalogue no: **BS 7105**

## WOODY AND FRIENDS

**Album:** Released Dec '81, on Concord by Concord Jazz Records (USA). Catalogue no: **CJ 170**

## WOODY HERMAN

**Album:** Released Apr '79, on Bright Orange Catalogue no: **BO 707**

**CD:** Released Jul '89, on Cleo Catalogue no: **CLCD 5003**

**Album:** Released Sep '87, on Giants of Jazz by Hasmick Promotions. Catalogue no: **LPJT 5**

**Album:** Released Jul '82, on Jazz Reactivation Catalogue no: **JR 151**

## WOODY HERMAN (VERVE)

Tracks: / Good earth, The / Don't get around much anymore / Bijou / Body and soul / Leo the lion / Makin' whoopee / Camel walk / Apple honey / Pee wee blues / Preacher, The / Sidewalks of Cuba / Golden wedding, The / Caldonia / Blue flame.

**CD:** Released 14 Aug '88, on Verve Catalogue no: **835 319 2**

**Cass:** Released 15 Aug '88, on Verve Catalogue no: **835 319 4**

## WOODY HERMAN, 1937

Tracks: / Exactly like you / Remember me / Can't we be friends / Muskrat ramble / Jazz me blues / Old man moon / Ain't misbehavin' / Someday, sweetheart / Squeeze me / Weary blues / You took the words right out of my heart / I can't be bothered now / Royal Garden blues / Apache dance / Bob White / Queen Isabella.

Note: This is such vintage Herman that His pre-dates the First Herd and is a fascinating as well as somewhat swinging documentation of the evolution of Woody's style and sound. Billed as "The band that plays the blues", these September and November '37 transcriptions are its first such recordings and include then-current pop success "You took the words right out of my heart" and "Bob White". George Hall, author of a forthcoming Herman bio-discography, researched and wrote the liner notes.(Hindsight Catalogue - 1989)

**Album:** Released '88, on Hindsight Catalogue no: **HSR 116**

## WOODY HERMAN 1936-37 VOL.1

**Album:** Released Apr '79, on Ajax (USA) Catalogue no: **AJAX 102**

## WOODY HERMAN 1938-9 VOL.3

**Album:** Released Apr '79, on Ajax (USA) Catalogue no: **AJAX 123**

## WOODY HERMAN 1939 VOL.4

**Album:** Released Apr '79, on Ajax (USA) Catalogue no: **AJAX 133**

## WOODY HERMAN 1939 VOL.5

**Album:** Released Apr '79, on Ajax (USA) Catalogue no: **AJAX 135**

## WOODY HERMAN 1940 VOL.6

**Album:** Released Apr '79, on Ajax (USA) Catalogue no: **AJAX 139**

## WOODY HERMAN 1940 VOL.7

**Album:** Released Apr '79, on Ajax (USA) Catalogue no: **AJAX 145**

## WOODY HERMAN 1940 VOL.8

**Album:** Released Apr '79, on Ajax (USA) Catalogue no: **AJAX 153**

## WOODY HERMAN 1940-41 VOL.9

**Album:** Released Apr '79, on Ajax (USA) Catalogue no: **AJAX 160**

## WOODY HERMAN 1913/87

**Album:** Released '87, on Polydor by Polydor Ltd. Catalogue no: **835 231 1**

**CD:** Released '87, on Polydor by Polydor Ltd. . Catalogue no: **835 231 2**

## WOODY HERMAN COLLECTION (Twenty golden greats)

Tracks: / Blue prelude / Golden wedding / Blues in the night / At the woodchoppers' ball / Herman at the Sherman / Woodsheddin' with Woody / Casbah blues / Fur trappers' ball / Blues upstairs / Who dat up dere? / Bishop's blues / Dallas blues / Blues downstairs / Northwest passage / Pancho Maximillian Hernandez / When the red, red robin comes bob, bob, bobbin' along / Lady from 29 palms / On the sunny side of the street / Up a lazy river / Four brothers.

**Cass:** Released Nov '85, on Deja Vu Catalogue no: **DVMC 2025**
**Album:** Released Nov '85, on Deja Vu Catalogue no: **DVLP 2025**

**WOODY HERMAN AND HIS FIRST HERD**
**Album:** Released Oct '79, on London Records by London Records Ltd. Catalogue no: **HMA 5058**

**WOODY HERMAN AND HIS ORCHESTRA 1946**
**Album:** Released Apr '79, on First Heard by Submarine Records. Catalogue no: **FH 20**

**WOODY HERMAN AND HIS ORCHESTRA 1948**
**Album:** Released Apr '79, on First Heard by Submarine Records. Catalogue no: **FH 21**

**WOODY HERMAN AND HIS ORCHESTRA (Herman, Woody & His Orchestra)**
**CD:** Released '88, on Delta (1) by Delta Records. Catalogue no: **11 087**

**WOODY HERMAN AND HIS SECOND HERD 1948**
**Album:** Released Mar '90, Catalogue no: **Q 037**

**WOODY HERMAN AND HIS THIRD HERD**
**Album:** Released Apr '81, on Rarities Catalogue no: **RARITIES 42**

**WOODY HERMAN AND ORCHESTRA**
**Album:** Released '88, on Joker (USA) by Lifetime Records (USA). Catalogue no: **SM 4021**

**WOODY HERMAN PRESENTS A GREAT AMERICAN EVENING VOL. 2**
Tracks: / Woody's lament / Goof and I, The / I wanna go home / Not really the blues / Tiny's blues / Loose abberations / Four others / Tenderly.
**Album:** Released Apr '82, on Concord by Concord Jazz Records (USA). Catalogue no: **CJ 180**
**Cass:** Released Apr '82, on Concord by Concord Jazz Records (USA). Catalogue no: **CJ 180 C**

**WOODY HERMAN PRESENTS A GREAT AMERICAN EVENING VOL. 3**
Tracks: / I've got the world on a string / I cover the waterfront / Leopardskin pillbox hat / Avalon / Beautiful friendship, A / Pennies from Heaven / Wave / Caldonia.
Note: Recorded in April, 1983, with Nat Pierce, Bob Maize, Jake Hanna, Cal Collins, Scott Hamilton, Eiji Kitamura, George Masso, Ron McRoby, Jack Sheldon.
**Album:** Released Sep '83, on Concord Jazz by Concord Jazz Records (USA). Catalogue no: **CJ 220**
**Cass:** Released Sep '83, on Concord Jazz by Concord Jazz Records (USA). Catalogue no: **CJC 220**

**WOODY'S GOLD STAR (Herman, Woody Big Band)**
Tracks: / Battle royal / Woody's gold star / Mambo rockland / Round midnight / Great escape / Dig / Rose room / In a mellow tone / Watermelon man / Samba song.
**Cass:** Released Oct '87, on Concord Jazz by Concord Jazz Records (USA). Catalogue no: **CJC 330**
**Album:** Released Oct '87, on Concord Jazz by Concord Jazz Records (USA). Catalogue no: **CJ 330**
**CD:** Released Oct '87, on Concord Jazz by Concord Jazz Records (USA). Catalogue no: **CCD 4330**

**WOODY'S WINNERS**
Tracks: / 23 red / My funny valentine / Northwest passage / Poor butterfly / Greasy sack blues / Woody's whistle / Red roses for a blue lady / Opus de funk.
**Album:** Released Feb '84, on CBS by CBS Records. Catalogue no: **40 21110**
**Album:** Released Feb '84, on CBS by CBS Records. Deleted '87. Catalogue no: **CBS 21110**

**WORLD CLASS (Herman, Woody Big Band)**
Tracks: / Four brothers / Rockin' chair / Claw, The / Woody's lament / Peanut vendor / Crystal silence / Greasy sack blues / Perdido.
Note: Recorded live at Japan's Annex jazz festival in 1982. Woody's world class band features guest tenor saxophonists Al Cohn, Med Flory, Sal Nistico and Flip Philips. this Woody Herman album captures completely the real big band sound - the excitement of the solos, the section work, interplay, and the surging explosive power that one expects from this legendary band.
**CD:** Released May '85, on Concord Jazz by Concord Jazz Records (USA). Deleted '88. Catalogue no: **CCD 4240**
**Cass:** Released Jun '84, on Concord Jazz by Concord Jazz Records (USA). Catalogue no: **CJC 240**
**Album:** Released Jun '84, on Concord Jazz by Concord Jazz Records (USA). Catalogue no: **CJ 240**

## Heywood, Eddie

**BIGGEST LITTLE BIG BAND OF THE**
Tracks: / T'aint me / Back home again in Indiana / Blue Lou / Carry me back to old Virginny / I can't believe that you're in love with me / Love me or leave me / Begin the beguine / I cover the waterfront / Save your sorrow / Just you, just me / Deed I do / Lover man.
**Album:** Released Nov '83, on Telefunken (Teldec (BRD)) Deleted Nov '88. Catalogue no: **AG6 25493**

## Hibbler, Al

**DEDICATED TO YOU**
**Cass:** Released Jan '88, on Starline (Jazz) Catalogue no: **SLC 61020**

**GOLDEN GREATS: AL HIBBLER**
Tracks: / Unchained Melody / On a slow boat to china / Pennies from Heaven / Don't get around much anymore / I'll never smile again / All or nothing at all / You'll never know / Trees / Very thought of you(The) / Stardust / Stormy weather / 11th hour medley / He / After the lights go down low / September in the rain / Stella by starlight.
Note: It was during the mid-fifties the smooth voiced Al Hibbler found fame and chart success with a number of MCA recordings.A star from the decade of ballad singers(Nat Cole,Dean Martin, Perry Como, ETC)were at their height, Al Hibbler proved withhis versions of 'Unchained Melody','Stardust', 'He', 'Stormy Weather' , 'The Very Thought Of You' and many other great songs of the day, that he ranked with the very best. His versions of 'Unchained Melody' is regarded as the classic and opens this strong collection.
**Cass:** Released Feb '86, on MCA by MCA Records. Deleted Apr '88. Catalogue no: **MCMC 5026**
**Album:** Released Feb '86, on MCA by MCA Records. Deleted Apr '88. Catalogue no: **MCM 5026**

**IT'S MONDAY EVERY DAY (Hibbler, Al & The Gerald Wilson Orchestra)**
Tracks: / Baby, won't you please come home / Laughing on the outside (crying on the inside) / When the sun comes out / I'm a fool to want you.
**Album:** Released '88, on Discovery (USA) by Discovery Records (USA). Catalogue no: **DS 842**

**UNCHAINED MELODY**
Tracks: / Unchained melody.
**7" Single:** Released May '55, on Brunswick by Decca Records. Deleted '58. Catalogue no: **05420**

**UNCHAINED MELODY (OLD GOLD)**
Tracks: / Unchained melody.
**7" Single:** Released Jul '82, on Old Gold by Old Gold Records. Deleted Jul '88. Catalogue no: **OG 9207**

## Higgins, Billy

**SOLDIER, THE**
Tracks: / Sugar and spice / Midnight waltz / Just in time / If you could see me now / Peace / Sonnymoon for two.
**Album:** Released '81, on Timeless by Timeless Records. Catalogue no: **SJP 145**

## High Society Jazzband

**LASSES CANDY**
**Album:** Released Nov '88, on Stomp Off (USA) Catalogue no: **SOS 1166**

## High Water Blues

**MISSI / LOUISIANA BLUES 1965-70**
**Album:** Released '88, on Flyright by Interstate Music. Catalogue no: **FLY 512**

## Hill, Bertha 'Chippie'

**BERTHA 'CHIPPIE' HILL**
Note: Featuring Lee Collins, Lovie Austin, John Lindsay, Baby Dodds.
**Album:** Released Sep '87, on Hot Society Catalogue no: **HSLP 1005**

## Hill, Blind Joe

**ONE MAN BLUES**
**Album:** on L&R Catalogue no: **LR 42.059**

## Hill, Buck Quartet

### SCOPE
**Album:** Released Sep '79, on Steeplechase (USA) Catalogue no: **SCS 1123**

## Hill, Teddy

**Biographical details:** Bandleader (1909-78) who led his own successful band, hired Dizzy Gillespie, and later was the house leader at Minton's in NYC, lending encouragement and a place to play to the young boppers. (Donald Clarke, Nov 1989).

### TEDDY HILL AND CAB CALLOWAY
**Album:** Released Apr '81, on Queendisc (Italy) Catalogue no: **QU 021**
**Album:** Released '88, on Queen Catalogue no: **QUEEN 021**

### THAT'S ROCK 'N' ROLL
**Album:** on Jan Records Catalogue no: **33.8010**

## Hill, Tiny

**Biographical details:** Drummer, vocalist and bandleader (1906-72) who weighed more than 350 pounds and led a band described as 'swinging cornball', especially popular in USA Midwest. Beset-known record was *Angry*, used as theme; had one of several hit versions of *Slow poke* in 1952. Carried on working well into the '60's, making dancers happy and offending no one. (Donald Clarke, Nov 1989).

### 1943/4 (Hill, Tiny & his Orchestra)
**Album:** Released Mar '84, on Circle (USA) by Jazzology Records (USA). Catalogue no: **CLP 55**

## Hines, Earl

**Biographical details:** Pianist, bandleader, composer, occasional singer (1903-83) is one of the all-time greatest jazz pianist, perhaps the greatest technically except for Art Tatum, but yielding to no one in lyricism and sheer joy. He had four careers: having invented a 'trumpet style' in the right hand to be heard over a band, he became world famous with Louis Armstrong, Jimmy Noone and as a soloist in Chicago in the 1920's; he led excellent big bands 1928-47, was slowly reduced to playing Dixieland in West Coast clubs, but was then rediscovered as a soloist in the late '50s and made the world a happier place until a week before he died. (Donald Clarke, Nov 1989).

### 1965
**Album:** Released Sep '84, on Pathe Marconi (France) Catalogue no: **PM 1552611**

### AFTER YOU'VE GONE (Hines, Earl & Muggsy Spanier All Stars)
Note: Recorded live at 'Big Annies Club' San Francisco, 8th July 1956.
**Album:** Released Apr '87, on Essex by Essex Records. Catalogue no: **ZR 1021**

### ANOTHER MONDAY DATE
Tracks: / Jitterbug waltz / Darktown strutters ball / Black and blue / Blue turning grey over you / Honeysuckle rose / Squeeze me / Ain't misbehavin' / Keepin' out of mischief / I can't give you anything but love / I'm gonna sit right down / Lulu's back in town / Two sleepy people / Deep forest / Everything depends on you / Am I too late? / Blues for Tatum / In San Francisco / Ann / You can depend on me / When I dream of you / R. R. blues / Straight to love / Piano man / My Monday date.
**2 LP Set:** Released Jun '81, on Prestige Deleted '86. Catalogue no: **P 24043**

### AT CLUB HANGOVER VOL.5
**Album:** Released Sep '86, on Storyville by Storyville Records AB. Catalogue no: **SLP 4063**

### AT HOME: EARL HINES
**Album:** Released Jan '74, on Delmark (USA) by Delmark Records (USA). Catalogue no: **DS 212**

### AT THE VILLAGE VANGUARD (Hines, Earl & Roy Eldridge)
**CD:** Released '88, on Xanadu Catalogue no: **FDC 5165**

### BIG BAND
**Album:** Released Oct '88, on Vogue by Vogue Records. Catalogue no: **500111**
**Album:** Released Jul '82, on Golden Era by Delta Records. Catalogue no: **GELP 15059**

### BLUE SKIES (Hines, Earl "Fatha", Et Son Orchestre)
Tracks: / Jazz is his old lady and my old man / Just squeeze me / Yellow days / Deed I do / Blue skies / Hey love / Make it easy on yourself / Feelings.
**Album:** Released Feb '87, on MFP by EMI Records. Catalogue no: **260 236 1**

### BLUES AND THINGS (Hines, Earl with Jimmy Rushing)
**Album:** Released Jan '83, on Swaggie (Australia) Catalogue no: **S 1262**
**Album:** Released Oct '88, on Vogue (France) by Vogue Records. Catalogue no: **500076**

### BLUES FOR GARROWAY
**Cass:** Released Dec '84, on Pathe Marconi (France) Catalogue no: **PM 1652394**
**Album:** Released Dec '84, on Pathe Marconi (France) Catalogue no: **PM 1652391**

### BLUES IN THIRDS
**Album:** Released Feb '89, on Black Lion Catalogue no: **BLP 60120**

### BOOGIE WOOGIE ON THE ST LOUIS BLUES
Tracks: / Monday date, A / Blues in thirds / You can depend on me / Blue because of you / I can't trust myself alone / Boogie woogie on St. Louis blues.
**Album:** Released Jul '88, on Black Lion Catalogue no: **BLM 52032**

### BUBBLING OVER (Hines, Earl & His Orchestra)
Tracks: / That's a plenty / Fat babes / Maple leaf rag / Sweet Georgia Brown / Rosetta / Copenhagen / Angry / Wolverine blues / Rock and rye / Cavernism / Disappointed in love / Rhythm lullaby / Japanese sandman / Bubbling over / Blue / Julia.
**Album:** on Official by Official Records. Catalogue no: **OFF 3044**

### CHICAGO HIGH LIFE
Tracks: / Blues in thirds / Off time blues / Chicago high life / My Monday date / Stowaway / Chimes in blues / Panther rag / Just too soon / I know that you know / Oh, sister, ain't that hot? / Blues my naughty sweetie gives to me / Glad rag doll / Everybody loves my baby / Beaukoo Jack / Down among the sheltering palms / Love me tonight.
**Cass:** Released Oct '88, on Conifer Happy Days by Conifer Records. Catalogue no: **MCHD 137**
**Album:** Released Oct '88, on Conifer Happy Days by Conifer Records. Catalogue no: **CHD 137**

### COMES IN HANDY
**Album:** Released Aug '88, on Audiophile (USA) by Jazzology Records (USA). Catalogue no: **AP 112**

### DEEP FOREST
Tracks: / Deep forest / Lover come back to me / I can't get started / MF blues / Just you, just me / Very thought of you, The.
Note: With Budd Johnson, Bill Pemberton, Oliver Jackson.
**Album:** Released Oct '82, on Black Lion Catalogue no: **BLM 52002**
**Cass:** Released Jan '83, on Black Lion Catalogue no: **BLM 52002C**
**Album:** on Hep Jazz by Hep Records. Catalogue no: **HEP 1003**

### DINAH
**Album:** Released Oct '85, on RCA (France) by BMG Records (France). Catalogue no: **NL 70577**

### DIXIELAND BAND
**Album:** Released Dec '79, on Joker (USA) by Lifetime Records (USA). Catalogue no: **SM 3118**

### DOES HOAGY
**Album:** Released Aug '88, on Audiophile (USA) by Jazzology Records (USA). Catalogue no: **AP 113**

### EARL FATHA HINES (CLEO)
**CD:** Released Jul '89, on Cleo Catalogue no: **CLCD 5031**

### EARL FATHA HINES (GIANTS OF JAZZ)
**Album:** Released Sep '87, on Giants of Jazz by Hasmick Promotions. Catalogue no: **LPJT 46**

### EARL FATHA HINES (GNP)
**Album:** Released '88, on GNP Crescendo (USA) by GNP Crescendo Records (USA). Catalogue no: **GNPS 9042**

### EARL FATHA HINES (VOGUE)
**CD:** Released Oct '88, on Vogue by Vogue Records. Catalogue no: **VGCD 600 189**

### EARL 'FATHA' HINES VOL II
**Album:** Released '88, on GNP Crescendo (USA) by GNP Crescendo Records (USA). Catalogue no: **GNPS 9043**
**Album:** Released May '89, on Fontana by Phonogram Ltd. Catalogue no: **382 371**

### EARL HINES
**Album:** Released '88, on GNP Crescendo (USA) by GNP Crescendo Records (USA). Catalogue no: **GNPS 9010**

**EARL HINES AND HIS ALL STARS (Hines, Earl & His All Stars)**
Note: Featuring Dicky Wells.
**Album:** Released Jun '86, on Storyville by Storyville Records AB. Catalogue no: **SLP 4071**

**EARL HINES COLLECTION (20 golden greats)**
Tracks: / Honeysuckle rose / Monday date / Darktown strutters' ball / Dark eyes / Humoresque / Hollywood hop / Web, The / Nice work if you can get it / If I had you / Relaxin' at the Touro / Ain't misbehavin' / I'm gonna sit right down and write myself a letter / Lulu's back in town / Blue turning grey over you / Squeeze me / Jumpin' something / Keepin' out of mischief now / Ugly child / Blues for Garroway / I've got the world on a string.
**Cass:** Released May '86, on Deja Vu Catalogue no: **DVMC 2057**
**Album:** Released May '86, on Deja Vu Catalogue no: **DVLP 2057**

**EARL HINES CONCERT (14 February 1966)**
Tracks: / I've got the world on a string / I cover the waterfront / Rosetta / I know a little bit / Kiss to build a dream on, A / Do you know what it means to miss New Orleans? / St. Louis blues.
**Album:** Released '87, on Joker (USA) by Lifetime Records (USA). Catalogue no: **SM 3074**

**EARL HINES FEATURING MUGGSY SPANIER**
**2 LP Set:** Released Oct '88, on Vogue by Vogue Records. Catalogue no: **406501**

**EARL HINES AND FRIENDS LIVE**
Note: Features the Earl Hines Trio, the Mugsy Spanier Allstars and Clark Terry.
**Album:** Released May '88, on Musica Jazz Catalogue no: **2MJP 1050**

**EARL HINES IN NEW ORLEANS**
Tracks: / Bourbon Street parade / My Monday date / Song of the islands / Blues my naughty sweetie gives to me / Rosetta / Playing with fire / One I love belongs to somebody else, The / Bouncing for Panassie / Way down yonder in New Orleans.
**Album:** Released Jan '76, on Sonet by Sonet Records. Catalogue no: **SNTF 697**

**EARL HINES PLAYS GEORGE GERSHWIN**
Tracks: / Rhapsody in blue / Foggy day, A / Our love is here to stay / They all laughed / Somebody loves me / Embraceable you.
**Album:** Released Feb '83, on Carosello Catalogue no: **ORL 8582**
**Album:** Released Jan '83, on Swaggie (Australia) Catalogue no: **S 1339**

**EARL HINES AND WALLACE DAVENPORT VOL. 2 (Hines, Earl / Wallace Davenport)**
**Album:** Released '88, on Joker (USA) by Lifetime Records (USA). Catalogue no: **SM 3908**
**Cass:** Released '88, on Joker (USA) by Lifetime Records (USA). Catalogue no: **MC 3907**
**Album:** Released '88, on Joker (USA) by Lifetime Records (USA). Catalogue no: **SM 3907**

**EARL MEETS SWEETS AND JAWS (Hines, Earl / Harry Edison / Eddie (Lockjaw) Davis)**
Tracks: / Lax / Bye bye blackbird / In a mellow tone / Georgia on my mind / I can't get started.
Note: Earl Hines, piano; Harry Edison, trumpet; Eddie Lockjaw Davis, tenor sax; Leonard Gaskins, bass; Oliver Jackson, drums. Recorded live at the Berne Jazz Festival, 30 April 1978.
**Album:** Released Jul '83, on Mercury (USA) by PolyGram Rec.Inc.(USA). Catalogue no: **9198 205**

**EARL'S BACKROOM AND COZY'S CARAVAN (Hines, Earl Quartet & Cozy Cole Septet)**
Tracks: / Brussels' hustle (Composed by Earl Hines) / Oooh (Composed by Earl Hines) / Backroom at the villa d'este (Composed by Earl Hines) / Caravan (Composers: Ellington/Tizol/Mills) / Phatz' blues (Composers: Morris/Thompson) / Margie (Composers: Davis/Conrad/Robinson).
Note: See also under Cozy Cole Septet Tracks 1-3 Earl Hines Quartet Tracks 4-6 Cozy Cole Septet Licensed from Decca Records Ltd. A Felsted recording.
**CD:** Released Jan '88, on London by London Records Ltd. Catalogue no: **820 605 2**
**Album:** Released Nov '86, on Affinity by Charly Records. Catalogue no: **AFF 167**

**EAST OF THE SUN**
Tracks: / If I had you / One I love belongs to somebody else, The / Just friends / Can't we talk it over? / East of the sun / I cover the waterfront.
**Album:** Released Jul '88, on Black Lion Catalogue no: **BLM 52012**

**EVENING WITH EARL HINES**
Tracks: / Perdido / Boogie woogie on St. Louis blues / I got it bad and that ain't good / All of me / Things ain't what they used to be / Lil darlin' / James St. blues / Prelude to a kiss / Prisoner of love / My ship / La Rosita / Rainy day / Polka dots and moonbeams / Lester leaps in / Who / I ain't got nobody / Marie / Dinkler boogie / I wish you love.
**2 LP Set:** Released May '83, on Vogue Jazz (France) by Vogue Records. Catalogue no: **VJD 534**

**FATHA JUMPS 1940 - 42 (Hines, Earl & His Orchestra)**
**Cass:** Released Jun '88, on Bandstand Catalogue no: **BS 7115C**
**Album:** Released Jun '88, on Bandstand Catalogue no: **BS 7115**

**FATHA PLAYS CLASSICS**
**Album:** Released May '88, on Jazz Life Catalogue no: **2233012**
**CD:** Released May '88, on Jazz Life Catalogue no: **2473012**
**Cass:** Released May '88, on Jazz Life Catalogue no: **2173012**

**FATHA, VOL.1**
**Album:** Released '88, on Zeta Catalogue no: **ZET 710**

**HINES '74**
**CD:** Released May '87, on Black & Blue (1) by Black & Blue Records. Catalogue no: **233 073**

**HINES PLAYS HINES**
**Album:** Released Jan '83, on Swaggie (Australia) Catalogue no: **S 1320**

**HINE'S TUNE (Paris 1965)**
Tracks: / Hine's tune / One I love belongs to someone else, The / Bag's Groove / Blue turning grey over you / Don's blues / Tenderly / Boogie woogie on St. Louis blues / These foolish things / I'm a little brown bird / Que rest et il de nos amours / Little girl blue / You are the cream in my coffee / I can't get started / Petite laitue / Cherry / Sweet lorraine / I've got the world on a string / Body and soul / Clopin - clopant / Cest si bon.
Note: Ben Webster/Roy Eldridge/Stuff Smith etc.
**Album:** Released '87, on Esoldun Deleted Jan '88. Catalogue no: **FC 101**
**CD:** Released '88, on Esoldun Catalogue no: **FCD 101**

**IN NEW ORLEANS**
Tracks: / Someday, sweetheart / Playing with fire / Elephant stomp / Do you know what it means to miss New Orleans / Bouncing for panassie / Blues my naughty sweety gave to me / Sugar babe / If I could be with you / Someday you'll be sorry / Moonglow.
**Album:** Released Apr '81, on Up International Catalogue no: **LPUP 5058**
**Album:** Released 22 Aug '88, on Meteor by Magnum Music Group. Catalogue no: **MTLP 1.014**

**INDISPENSABLE EARL HINES, VOLS. 1 & 2**
Tracks: / Indiana / GT stomp / Ridin' and livin' / Grand terrance shuffle / Father steps in / Piano man / Riff medley / Me and columbus / XYZ / Gator swing / After all 've been to you / Lightly and politely / Rosetta / Deep forest / Number 19 / My heart / Child of a disorderd brain / Wait till it happens to ytou / Call me happy / Ann Topsy Turvy / Blue because of you / You can depend on me / Tantalizing a Cuban / Easy rhythm / In swamp lands / I'm falling for you.
**2 LP Set:** Released Jan '83, on RCA (France) by BMG Records (France). Catalogue no: **PM 42412**

**INDISPENSABLE EARL HINES, VOLS. 3 & 4**
Tracks: / Rosetta / Child of a disordered brain / Everything depends on you / Comin' home / Jelly jelly / Up jumped the Devil / Won't you come back / Jersey bounce / Julia / South side / On the sunnt side of the street / Melancholy baby / It had to be you / Windy city jive / Straight to love / Singin' on C / Water boy / Yellow fire / Somehow / I got it bad and that ain't good / I never dreamt / Father jumps,

The / Boy with the wistful eyes / Jitney man / Earl, The / You don't know what love is / She'll always remember / Shylark / Second balcony jump / Stormy Monday blues / Scoops Carry's fulough blues.
**2 LP Set:** Released Jan '83, on RCA (France) by BMG Records (France). Catalogue no: **PM 43266**

**INDISPENSABLE EARL HINES, VOLS. 5 & 6**
Tracks: / My fate is in your hands / I've got a feeling I'm falling / Honeysuckle rose / Squeeze me / Undecided / I've found a new baby / Fatha's blues / Sunday kind of love, A / Tosca's dance / Jim / Black coffee / You always hurt the one you love / Save it, pretty mama / Bye bye baby / Smoke rings / Shoeshine boy / Stanley steamer / Bernard's tune / Dream of you.
Note: Black & White series - Jazz Tribune No 36.
**2 LP Set:** Released Jan '83, on RCA (France) by BMG Records (France). Catalogue no: **PM 45358**

**IT DON'T MEAN A THING IF IT (Hines, Earl & Paul Gonsalvez)**
Tracks: / It don't mean a thing / Over the rainbow / What am I here for? / Moten swing / Blue sands / I got it bad and that ain't good.
**Album:** Released Sep '85, on Black Lion Catalogue no: **BLP 30153**

**JAZZ TIME VOL.10**
**Album:** Released '88, on Vogue (France) by Vogue Records. Catalogue no: **502710**

**JAZZ (VIDEO) (Hines, Earl & Coleman Hawkins)**
**VHS:** Released '88, on Kay Jazz (video) by Kay Jazz. Catalogue no: **KJ 068**

**LEGENDARY LITTLE THEATRE CONCERT**
Note: Includes the medley Sweet Lorraine/Mandy make up your mind..
**Album:** Released Aug '86, on Deluxe (1) Deleted '88. Catalogue no: **DE 602**

**LIVE AT THE VILLAGE VANGUARD**
Tracks: / Lover come back to me / Cavernism / Red river remembered / Out of nowhere / Moten swing / Sometimes I'm happy / Tea for two / Breezin' along with the breeze / Rosetta.
**CD:** Released Apr '89, on CBS (import) by CBS Records. Catalogue no: **462401-2**
**Album:** Released Apr '89, on CBS (import) by CBS Records. Catalogue no: **462401-1**
**Cass:** Released Apr '89, on CBS (import) by CBS Records. Catalogue no: **462401-4**

**LIVE IN MILANO, 1966**
Tracks: / Deep forest / Medley (one) / Medley (two) / Medley (three) / Medley (four) / Shiny stockings / Boogie woogie on St. Louis blues.
Note: Medley (one): I've got the world on a string; Second balcony jump; I cover the waterfront; I surrender dear. Medley (two): Blues in thirds; Birth of the blues; Memphis blues; Tin roof blues. Medley (three): You're the cream in my coffee; Tea for two; Sugar. Medley (four): Canadina sunset; Lullaby of Birdland; Satin doll.
A rare live recording made 'behind closed doors' at the Circola de la Rinascente (a private club in Milan). Solo piano performances - 5 March 1966. Recording quality good. 55:22 minutes playing time.
**CD:** Released Nov '89, on Jazz-Up Catalogue no: **JU 315**

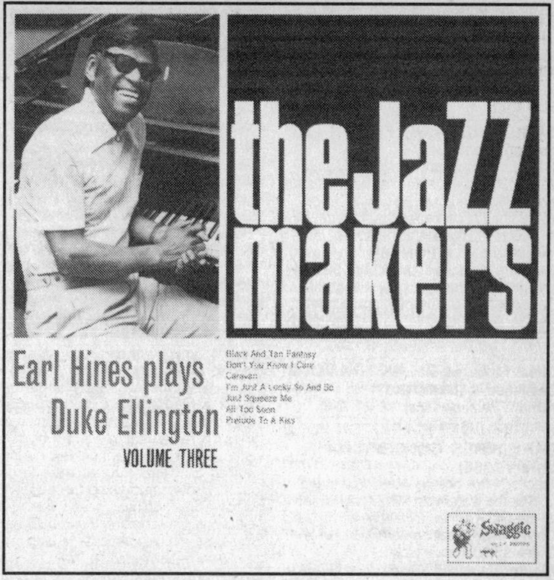


Earl Hines - Plays Duke Ellington Vol. 3 (Swaggie)

**LIVE IN ORANGE**
**Album:** Released Jun '84, on Black & Blue (1) by Black & Blue Records. Catalogue no: **33305**

**MASTER'S OF JAZZ**
**Album:** Released May '86, on Storyville by Storyville Records AB. Catalogue no: **SLP 4102**
**CD:** Released '89, on Storyville by Storyville Records AB. Catalogue no: **STCD 4102**

**MPS JAZZ TIME VOL 11 (Hines, Earl & Jaki Byard)**
Tracks: / Toodle oo, toodle oo, A / This is always / Rosetta / I can't trust myself alone / Sweet Georgia Brown / As long as I live / Genoa to Pescara / La rosita.
**Album:** Released '79, on MPS Jazz Deleted '84. Catalogue no: **5C 064 61172**

**MY TRIBUTE TO LOUIS**
**Album:** Released Aug '88, on Audiophile (USA) by Jazzology Records (USA). Catalogue no: **AP 111**

**ONCE UPON A TIME**
Tracks: / Once upon a time / Black and tan fantasy / Fantastic, that's you / Cottontail.
**Cass:** Released Aug '82, on Jasmine by Hasmick Promotions. Catalogue no: **JAS C42**
**Album:** Released Aug '82, on Jasmine by Hasmick Promotions. Deleted Feb '88. Catalogue no: **JAS 42**
**Album:** Released Oct '85, on Impulse by Impulse Records. Deleted Dec '89. Catalogue no: **AS 9108**
**Cass:** Released Aug '82, on Jasmine by Hasmick Promotions. Deleted Dec '89. Catalogue no: **ASC 9108**

**PEARLS, THE**
Tracks: / I wish I knew / Indian summer / You made me love you / Pearls, The / Wolverine blues / Mandy / Make up your mind.
**Album:** Released Jul '88, on Black Lion Catalogue no: **BLM 52022**

**PIANO 1938**
**Album:** Released '89, on Swing Classics Catalogue no: **ET 5**

**PIANO MAN**
Tracks: / Rosetta / Body and soul / Child of a disordered brain / On the sunny side of the street / My melancholy baby / Blues in thirds / G.T. stomp / Grand terrace shuffle / Father steps in / Piano man / Riff medley / Boogie woogie on St. Louis blues / Deep forest / Number 19 / Call me happy / Tantalizing a Cuban / Jelly jelly / Up jumped the devil / Windy city jive / Father jumps, The / Second balcony jump / Stormy Monday blues.

**Album:** Released Jul '89, on Bluebird (2) by BMG Records (UK). Catalogue no: **NL 86750**

**CD:** Released Jul '89, on Bluebird (2) by BMG Records (UK). Catalogue no: **ND 86750**

**Cass:** Released Jul '89, on Bluebird (2) by BMG Records (UK). Catalogue no: **NK 86750**

## PIANO PORTRAITS OF AUSTRALIA

**Album:** Released '88, on Swaggie (Australia) Catalogue no: **S 1350**

## PLAYS COLE PORTER

**Album:** Released Jan '83, on Swaggie (Australia) Catalogue no: **S 1345**

## PLAYS DUKE ELLINGTON VOL.1

**Album:** Released Jan '83, on Swaggie (Australia) Catalogue no: **S 1300**

## PLAYS DUKE ELLINGTON VOL.2

**Album:** Released Jan '83, on Swaggie (Australia) Catalogue no: **S 1323**

## PLAYS DUKE ELLINGTON VOL.3

**(See panel on previous page)**

Tracks: / Black and tan fantasy / Don't you know I care / Caravan / I'm just a lucky so and so / Just squeeze me / Prelude to a kiss / All too soon.

Note: recorded on March 18th, 1974, in New York City.

This is the third volume in a series of Earl Hines solos on the music of Duke Ellington. The project began in December of 1971 when the first volume was recorded, continues in November of 1972 with the second volume and was concluded in March of 1974 with this volume. A day or two after the 1974 recording session, Stanley Dance and I were walking down a Manhattan street together, chatting in the amiable spring sunshine. Stanley remarked that this, a three volume set of solo piano performances by a jazz artist of Hines' stature of the work of a composer of Ellington's stature was a remarkable acheivement. I agreed readily enough with this assessment, not then thinking of its full import. Later musing about it, I wondered whether any other jazz pianist had ever dedicated three LP's to one composer, and concluded that there was none that I could think of. What about two LP's? Probably that had happened, but again not that I could remember with a jazz pianist. (Bobby Short has done multiple volumes on Cole Porter, Gershwin and perhaps others, and admirable as they are in their way, they are not what I have in mind.) What pianists, then, approaching the question from a different direction, had devoted even one LP to the music of Ellington? Only three I could remember: Thelonious Monk, Oscar Peterson and McCoy Tyner. Monk's work is often described as heavily influenced by Ellington's own piano playing, and it is certain that his first solo album was of Ellington music. But McCoy Tyner, whatever influences appear in his playing, certainly would not be considered an Ellingtonian. Peteson, of course, was probably the first pianist to devote LP's to the work of individual composers. If we go back to pre-LP days, Ram Ramirez recorded a six-tune, three record, 78 album for Gotham. (And Ram, in his recent MJR album, (MJR 8122) included two Ellington numbers - *Janet* and *Prelude to a kiss*).

Come to think of it, even Ellington himself has not recorded a full LP of piano solos, and not more than three or four of his piano solos are available on LP. He has recorded on the piano with rhythmic accompaniment of one kind or another ("Piano in the foreground" - Columbia CS 8829, "Great times" - Riverside 475, "Piano reflections" - Capitol M11058, "Money jungle" - Sold State 18022) a total of only four, completely unrelated LP's. Next, I pulled out the seventy-odd piano LP's (excluding the Monk, Peterson and Tyner) in my collection that had been recorded since the early 1950s - that is since the availability of the LP gave the recording pianist the opportunity to make a purposeful selection of tunes to represent his performance style. I was startled at how few performances of Ellington tunes were to be found: not more than two or three dozen, out of a total of over seven hundred selections. One certainly thinks of Ellington as the major composer in jazz history. And he is a pianist. Why are his tunes not recorded on the piano to a greater extent by jazz musicians? The subject had come up in one way or another as we worked with Earl Hines in the Hines Plays Ellington project. It was not always easy to find tunes - even from the vast Ellington work - that Hines felt comfortable with, or familiar enough to play with facility. In the end, there were enough tunes to satisfy Earl's own exacting standards of what could, in fact, be released. But Hines aside, the fact is that Ellington does not write music that pianists play all that much, and there is more than one reason for it. First of all, is the fact that Ellington writes primarily for his orchestra. And many of the Ellington orchestral pieces are simply not adaptable - extant piano scores to the contrary - to piano playing. They somehow do not sound right. Their essential character is lost, even though the crucial notes are all there and played. This does not mean that such primarily orchestral pieces do not adapt themselves, on occasion, to the pianist. Take *Black and tan fantasy* in this set, or *Solitude* in the second volume, or *Come Sunday* in the first. But these require extra effort and very special inspiration if the pianist is to overcome this inherently orchestral quality to lend them to his own peculiar style. Secondly, many of the Ellington tunes have been created with a specific soloist in mind, and the characteristics of that soloist can not be easily converted into piano music. As we made this third volume, for example, Earl toyed with the piano score of *Boy meets horn* and finally, exasperated, said "Oh, I just can't get all of Rex's tricks out if this piano". Third, Ellington writes with a certain harmonic complexity that makes it difficult to work through one of his unfamiliar pieces very easily, and even more difficult to use it as a vehicle for improvisation. "There's too many changes in that piece to figure out exactly what to do with it", Earl would say and on we would go. Finally, when Ellington writes a particular piece for piano it is a personal statement for Ellington in his mode as a pianist. Other pianists sense this immediately and tend to shy away, almost as if in respect for Ellington's privacy. Looking, for example, at the piano score for *Dancers in love*, Hines said, "That's a pretty thing but it belongs to Duke. I used to write things like that for myself, and I played them, but no-one else would and it's the same for Duke on his pieces."

So, for all these reasons, Ellington material is performed on piano less frequently than one would expect, all other things considered. One must conclude that the pianist that undertakes to record a significant number of Ellington tunes, let alone three LP's must know what he is about, and have the courage of his convictions, besides. Maybe we should leave it that Earl Hines wanted to do three LP's on the work of Ellington for the same kind of reason other men climbc Mount Everest: because it is there. But maybe there was pride and satisfaction involved for Hines too. In the final analysis, we believe it is important to have Ellington material interpreted by a distinguished contemporary with a non-Ellington style, yet a style of classic dimension. It is on that belief that this three-volume project is founded. It must also be acknowledged that Earl Hines seems to especially enjoy a successful encounter with an Ellington tune. There is much gaiety in amongst the challenge and hard work. As this third session proceeded, he was continually commenting upon his own work with the Ellington pieces. For example, as he worked over *Just squeeze me*, noodling out what he would do with it, he stopped all at once, looked up and said: "That chord's not right you know - I changed it, I had to work out that key change - see how I went out of key and came back. And look at the boogie part - see here - (pointing at the music) it says put a little boogie into this, right here - I like that, that old Duke, he never misses a trick". On and on, bubbling, rejecting one piece, conquering another, worrying over *Black and tan fantasy* score) that's his blues, Duke's blues, I don't play that kind of blues, I'll play a couple of choruses of my blues, that's how we'll handle that. You ready in there? Let's try one with this and see what happens."

And later, "Say, you know there's some good tunes here. That fella can write them can't he? I'm going to take all this music with me over to the club tonight (he was appearing at Michael's Pub during this stay in New York City) and give all those people something new to listen to". Come to think about it, Stanley Dance was right, as he so often is. Quite an achievement for Earl Hines, this Ellington project. Bill Weilbacher 1974.

**Album:** Released Jan '83, on Swaggie (Australia) Catalogue no: **S 1341**

**PLAYS DUKE ELLINGTON VOL.4**
**Album:** Released Jan '83, on Swaggie (Australia) Catalogue no: **S 1357**

**SAN FRANCISCO- OCT. 1957**
**Album:** Released Apr '81, on Kings Of Jazz Catalogue no: **KLJ 20006**

**SPONTANEOUS EXPLORATIONS**
**Album:** Released Apr '81, on Joker (USA) by Lifetime Records (USA). Catalogue no: **SM 3258**

**SWINGIN' DOWN (Hines, Earl & His Orchestra)**
Tracks: / Blue drag / Sensational mood / Rosetta / Cavernism / We found romance / Blue / Swinging down.
**Album:** Released 8 Apr '89, on Hep Jazz by Hep Records. Catalogue no: **HEP 1018**

**TEA FOR TWO**
Tracks: / Velvet moon / Blues after midnight / Shiny stockings / Blue in thirds / When I dream of you / Sweet Lorraine.
Note: Tracks include those listed above.
**Album:** Released Jan '85, on Black Lion Catalogue no: **BLP 30106**

**TEXAS RUBY RED**
Tracks: / Cavernism / Coquette / Sometimes I'm happy / Ramona / More than you know / Texas Ruby Red / Little girl / You're mine, you.
**Album:** Released Jul '88, on Black Lion Catalogue no: **BLM 52042**

**TOUR DE FORCE**
Tracks: / When your lover has gone / Indian summer / Mack the knife / I never knew (I could love anyone like I'm loving you) / Say it isn't so / Lonesome road.
**Album:** Released Sep '85, on Black Lion Catalogue no: **BLP 30143**

**TOUR DE FORCE ENCORE**
Tracks: / Who's sorry now / Blue sands / I never knew / I'll see you in my dreams / I'm in the mood for love / There will never be another you.
**Album:** Released '88, on Black Lion Catalogue no: **BLP 30164**

**VARIETIES**
**Album:** Released '88, on Xanadu Catalogue no: **XAN 203**

**WALTZING MATILDA**
**Album:** Released Jan '83, on Swaggie (Australia) Catalogue no: **S 1338**

**WEST SIDE STORY**
Tracks: / West Side story medley / Close to you / Why do I love you? / In my solitude / Don't get around much anymore.
**Album:** Released Sep '87, on Black Lion Catalogue no: **BLP 30170**

## Hirt, Al

**Biographical details:** A New Orleans trumpet player, born there in 1922, highly regarded for technique but playing it safe and making a lot of money at pop jazz. His first combo included the fine clarinettist Pete Fountain; later Hirt had 17 USA chart albums on RCA in the '60's, and is said to have given Wynton Marsalis his first horn. (Donald Clarke, Nov 1989).

**AL HIRT**
**Cass:** Released Oct '84, on Audio Fidelity(USA) by Audio Fidelity (USA). Catalogue no: **ZCGAS 724**

**SOLID GOLD BRASS**
**Cass:** Released Jun '82, on RCA by BMG Records (UK). Catalogue no: **INTK 9007**

## Hiseman, Jon

**ABOUT TIME TOO**
**Album:** Released Sep '86, on Miles Music by Miles Music Records. Catalogue no: **TM 8**
**Cass:** Released Sep '86, on Miles Music by Miles Music Records. Catalogue no: **ZCTM 8**

## Hitch, Curtis

**CURTIS HITCH AND HOAGY CARMICHAEL (Hitch, Curtis & Hoagy Carmichael)**
**Album:** Released Apr '79, on Fountain by Retrieval Records. Catalogue no: **FJ 109**

## Hodes, Art

**Biographical details:** White blues pianist, born in Russia in 1904 and emigrated to Chicago. He edited the magazine *Jazz record* 1943-47 and made many records beginning in 1928; his solo album *Something personal* on Dawn Club, beautifully recorded in '88, is a good introduction. (Donald Clarke, Nov 1989).

**ART HODES AND MAGNOLIA JAZZBAND, VOL. 1 (Hodes, Art & Magnolia Jazzband)**
**Album:** Released Jun '86, on GHB by Jazzology Records (USA). Catalogue no: **GHB 171**

**ART HODES AND MAGNOLIA JAZZBAND, VOL. 2 (Hodes, Art & Magnolia Jazzband)**
**Album:** Released Apr '89, on GHB by Jazzology Records (USA). Catalogue no: **GHB 172**

**ART HODES PLAYS BESSIE**
**Album:** Released Mar '79, on Euphonic Catalogue no: **ESR 1213**

**ART HODES RHYTHM SECTION (Hodes, Art Rhythm Section)**
Note: With Carrie Smith, Doc Cheatham.
**Album:** Released Jul '88, on Parkwood Catalogue no: **PARKWOOD 106**

**ART OF HODES, THE**
**Album:** Released Apr '79, on Euphonic Catalogue no: **ESR 1207**

**BLUES GROOVE (Hodes, Art Blue Six)**
**Album:** Released 8 Apr '89, on Jazzology (USA) by Jazzology Records (USA). Catalogue no: **J 155**

**BLUES IN THE NIGHT**
**Album:** Released Nov '87, on Sackville by Spotlite Records. Catalogue no: **3039**

**ECHOES OF CHICAGO (Hodes, Art and His Windy City Seven)**
**Album:** Released Aug '79, on Jazzology (USA) by Jazzology Records (USA). Catalogue no: **J 79**

**GOSPEL ACCORDING TO ART**
**Album:** Released Jun '88, on Jazzology (USA) by Jazzology Records (USA). Catalogue no: **JCE 93**

**HOME COOKIN' (Hodes, Art Jazz Four plus 2)**
**Album:** Released '88, on Jazzology (USA) by Jazzology Records (USA). Catalogue no: **J 58**

**JAZZ RECORD STORY VOL 1**
**Album:** Released Jun '88, on Jazzology (USA) by Jazzology Records (USA). Catalogue no: **J 82**

**JOY TO THE WORLD**
**Album:** Released Aug '88, on Parkwood Catalogue no: **PARKWOOD 108**

**JUST THE TWO OF US (Hodes, Art & Milt Hinton)**
Tracks: / Wini' / I would do 'most anything / Low down below / By and by / Down home blues / Randolph Street blues / Here comes Cow Cow / Miss Otis regrets / Milt jumps / Willow weep for me.
Note: Recorded at the Cabbage Patch, New York City, 26 August 1981.
**Album:** Released Aug '82, on Muse by Black & Blue Records. Catalogue no: **MR 5279**

**LIVE AT HANRATTY'S, NEW YORK**
Tracks: / Liza / Exactly like you / Grandpa's spells / Someone to watch over me / St. Louis blues / Georgia on my mind / Sweet Georgia Brown / Save it, pretty mama / Plain ol' blues / Washboard blues / Struttin' with some barbecue.
**Album:** Released '81, on Must (Import) Catalogue no: **R 5252**

**MUSIC OF LOVIE AUSTIN (Hodes, Art Blue Six)**
**Album:** Released May '89, on Stomp Off (USA) Catalogue no: **SOS 1184**

**PAGIN' MR.JELLY**
**Album:** Released Mar '90, on Candid Catalogue no: **CS9037**
**CD:** Released Mar '90, on Candid Catalogue no: **CCD79037**

**SELECTIONS FROM THE GUTTER**
**Album:** Released Nov '86, on Storyville by Storyville Records AB. Catalogue no: **SLP 4057**

**SOME LEGENDARY ART (Hodes, Art Quintet)**
**Album:** Released Jul '87, on Audiophile (USA) by Jazzology Records (USA). Catalogue no: **AP 54**

**SOMETHING PERSONAL (Alone with friends) (Hodes, Art / Doug Dobel Memorial 10)**
Tracks: / Trouble in mind / Blues keep calling / Black and blue / Forty Second Street / Atlanta blues / Organ grinder blues / Old fashioned love / Lonesome blues / Bye and bye / Aunt Hager's blues / I'm coming Virginia / Russian ragout / Sweet Georgia Brown.
**Cass:** Released '88, on Dawn Club by

Cadillac Music. Catalogue no: **KDC 77/10**

**SOUTHSIDE MEMORIES**
**Album:** Released Jul '88, on Sackville by Spotlite Records. Catalogue no: **3032**

## Hodes, Bob

**JAZZ OF THE ROARING 20'S (Red Onion Jazzband)**
**Album:** Released '88, on Merry Makers Catalogue no: **MMRC 112**

## Hodges And Ellington

**SIDE BY SIDE**
**CD:** Released Jan '86, on Verve Catalogue no: **821 578-2**

## Hodges, Johnny

**Biographical details:** The alto saxophonist (1905-70) took lessons from Sidney Bechet (he also played soprano sax until about 1940), joined Duke Ellington in 1928 and stayed until his death, except for 1951-55, when he led his own small band. Nicknamed 'Rabbit' and 'Jeep', he was the most influential of all on the alto except (perhaps) Charlie Parker, who called him the 'Lily Pons' of the saxophone, a tribute to his lyricism and tonal beauty. Billy Strayhorn wrote especially effective ballads for Hodges, such as *After all, Daydream* etc. Amongst the saxophonist's freelance work was a Lionel Hampton small-group session in '37, from which *On the sunny side of the street* featured Hodges; Ellington's number one hit version of *I let a song go out of my heart* in 1938 was also a Hodges feature. The Bluebird CD of *The great Ellington units* is worth the price for the eight Hodges tracks alone, made in 1940-41. (Donald Clarke, Nov 1989)

Apart from a four year break in the fifties when he led his own small groups, Johnny Hodges was a pillar of the most distinguished orchestral edifice in jazz history - the Duke Ellington Band. Hodges joined Ellington in 1928 when he was just 22 years old. He was still with the Duke at the time of his death on May 11th 1970. Throughout the thirties there were two alto saxophonists who towered above their contemporaries. Benny Carter was one; Johnny Hodges was the other. Both had immaculate techniques, a supreme gift for melodic invention and quite ravishing tones. John Cornelius Hodges was born in Cambridge, Massachusetts, on July 25th, 1906. He started out at school playing piano and drums but he switched to saxophone when he was 14. It was the illustrious Sidney Bechet who gave Hodges his first saxophone. Bechet was courting Johnny's sister at the time and Hodges took saxophone lessons from him for a while.

Like Bechet, Hodges was a completely natural musician and he rapidly achieved remarkable command of the saxophone. When he was 18, he replaced Bechet in Willie 'The Lion' Smith's Quartet. The following year he worked with his mentor in Bechet's Club Basha. At the end of 1926 Hodges joined Chick Webb's Band at the Savoy Ballroom. Then, in 1928, he began what was to become one of the most fruitful and enduring associations in jazz when he took his seat in the saxophone section of Duke Ellington's orchestra. His work with Duke over four decades - a substantial amount of which, thankfully, is preserved on records - made him the pre-eminent voice on alto saxophone, at least until the advent of Charlie Parker. Because of his virtuosity and matchless style as a soloist, Hodges was heavily featured in the Ellington band and Duke wrote a number of showcase arrangements for him, including *Warm valley* and *The jeep is jumping*, a composition of which Johnny was co-composer. Hodges also wrote, or co wrote with Duke, such memorable originals as *Squatty roo, Juice a plenty, Wanderlust, I'm beginning to see the light* and *It shouldn't happen to a dream.* In March 1951 Hodges caused considerable surprise in the jazz world when he left the Ellington band with one or two other key figures, to embark on a career as a small group leader. His band, which at one time included the up and coming John Coltrane, had a considerable hit with a number called *Castle rock*. But, in the Spring of 1955, Hodges decided that the rigours and uncertainties of bandleading were not for him and he returned to the Ellington fold. He took engagements outside the band from time to time, making small group records and also playing with organist Wild Bill Davis and the bands of Oliver Nelson and Lawrence Welk. Hodges was a superlative saxophonist. He was an indispensable feature of the Ellington Orchestra and a major contributor to its unique character. In the words of Stanley Dance, the prodigious chronicler of things ducal. 'The flavour of his lyricism enriched the whole corpus of Ellington's music and therefore, quite directly, that of jazz itself.' (Mike Hennessey).

**2 OR 3 SHADES OF BLUE**
**Album:** Released Feb '86, on RCA by BMG Records (UK). Deleted '87. Catalogue no: **NL 89710**
**Cass:** Released Feb '86, on RCA by BMG Records (UK). Deleted '87. Catalogue no: **NK 89710**

**AT THE SPORTPALAST, BERLIN**
Tracks: / Take the 'A' train / In the kitchen / Mood indigo / Solitude / Satin doll / I got it bad and that ain't good / Rockin' in rhythm / Autumn leaves / Stompy Jones / C jam blues / Jeep is jumpin' / Good Queen Bess / Things ain't what they used to be / I'll get by / I let a song go out of my heart / Don't get around much anymore / Just squeeze me / Do nothing till you hear from me / Rose of the Rio Grande / All of me / On the sunny side of the street / Blue moon / Perdido.
**Cass set:** Released Jan '82, on Pablo Jazz (USA) by Pablo Records (USA). Catalogue no: **K 20 102**
**2 LP Set:** Released Jan '82, on Pablo Jazz (USA) by Pablo Records (USA). Catalogue no: **2620 102**

**BACK TO BACK (Hodges, Johnny & Duke Ellington)**
**Album:** Released Jun '81, on Verve Catalogue no: **2304 503**

**BIG SOUND, THE (Hodges Johnny & The Ellington Men)**
Tracks: / Don't call me, I'll call you / Ordinary thing / Waiting for Duke / Dust bowl / Little rabbit blues / Viscount / Johnny come lately / Bouquet of roses / Gone and crazy / Digits / Segdoh / Early morning rock.
**Album:** Released Feb '84, on Verve (France) Catalogue no: **2304 232**

**DUKES IN BED**
**Album:** Released Dec '79, on IMS by Polydor Ltd. Catalogue no: **2304 383**

**EVERYBODY KNOWS**
Tracks: / Everybody knows / Jeep is jumpin' / 310 blues / Main stem.
**Album:** on Jasmine by Hasmick Promotions. Catalogue no: **JAS 34**

**JOHNNY HODGES AND WILD BILL DAVISON (Hodges, Johnny & Wild Bill Davison)**
Tracks: / Blue Hodge / Hodge podge / Knuckles / Jones / I cried for you / A&R blues / Wings and things / Peg o' my heart / Spotted dog / Blues for Madeleine / Rabbit out of the hat / Hash brown / Harmony in Harlem / Blues o' mighty.
**CD:** Released Feb '90, on Verve Catalogue no: **839 288-2**
**Cass:** Released Feb '90, on Verve Catalogue no: **839 288-4**

**JOHNNY HODGES AND WILD BILL DAVISON 1965 - 66 (Hodges, Johnny & Wild Bill Davison)**
Tracks: / On the sunny side of the street / On Green Dolphin Street / Li'l darlin' / Con should and sax / Jeep is jumpin' / I'm beginning to see the light / Sophisticated lady / Drop me off in Harlem / No one / Johnny come lately / It;s only a paper moon / Taffy / Good Queen Bess / L.B. blues / In a mellow tone / Rockville / I'll always love you / It don't mean a thing / Belle of the Belmont.
**2 LP Set:** Released '83, on RCA (France) by BMG Records (France). Catalogue no: **PM 42414**

**JOHNNY HODGES, VOL 1**
Tracks: / Things ain't what they used to be / In a mellow tone / Mr. Gentle and Mr. Cool / Sophisticated lady / Jeep's blues / All of me / Passion flower / On the sunny side of the street.
**Album:** Released Jan '82, on Jazz Reactivation Catalogue no: **JR 107**

**JOHNNY HODGES, VOL 1, 1937-38**
**Album:** Released Apr '79, on Ajax (USA) Catalogue no: **AJAX 107**

**JOHNNY HODGES, VOL 2**
Tracks: / Get that geet / Perdido / That's grand / Skip it / Hop, skip and jump / Sweet Lorraine / Mix it, mix it / Jump, that's all / Mood indigo / Beau bag boogie / Time on my hands / Run about / In the shade of the old apple tree / Last legs blues.
**Album:** Released May '83, on Jazz Reactivation Catalogue no: **JR 125**

**JOHNNY HODGES, VOL 2, 1939**
**Album:** Released Apr '79, on Ajax

**Johnny Hodges - Masters Of Jazz Vol. 9 (Storyville)**

(USA) Catalogue no: **AJAX 108**

**JOHNNY HODGES, VOL 3**
**Album:** Released Apr '79, on Ajax (USA) Catalogue no: **AJAX 116**

**JOHNNY HODGES, VOL 4**
**Album:** Released Apr '79, on Ajax (USA) Catalogue no: **AJAX 120**

**LOVE IN SWINGTIME 1938-39**
**Album:** Released '88, on Tax Catalogue no: **TAX 8022**

**MAN AND HIS MUSIC, A (Hodges, Johnny & Charlie Shavers)**
**Album:** Released May '86, on Storyville by Storyville Records AB. Catalogue no: **SLP 4073**

**MASTERS OF JAZZ VOL.9 (See panel above)**
Tracks: / Cambridge blue / Brute's roots / Bouncing with Ben / One for the duke / Walkin' the frog / Rabbit pie / On the sunny side / Good Queen Bess / Jeep is jumpin' / Things ain't what they used to be.
Note: This album offers two jazz masters - masters of the saxophone - for the price of one. Ellingtonians both, John Cornelius Hodges and Benjamin Francis Webster, were superbly lyrical and magnificently authoritative saxophonists whose extemporised compositions had a serenity and authority that is only to be found among the true elite of jazz musicians. Webster was in fact, a great admirer of Hodges and it was Ben's view that no one in jazz played with more feeling. The warmth and passion that Hodges invested in his playing were in stark contrast to the demeanour of unremitting impassivity that he presented in the Duke Ellington saxophone section. Webster, also an emotional and intensely lyrical player, managed a similar look of stolid inscrutability when he played. They are a well matched pair and their musical compatibility is vividly displayed on the first Hodges session here. The 1960 date sets the two horns against a totally non ducal rhythm section and the result is informal, minimally arranged, small group mainstream jazz of the highest order. The sort of inspired music you get when six skilled musicians listen to each other and like what they hear.
*Cambridge blue* has a pleasing 16 bar theme and the spirit of it can only be described as joyous. The rhythm section really cooks and both Hodges and Webster contribute lively, hard swinging solos against Levy's rich chords and the leaping offbeat accents of Johnson. The rhythm section is quite magnificent thoughout the session and this undoubtedly helped stimulate inspired solo work from Hodges and Webster. There is no thing like an indifferent or ill-assorted rhythm section to dissipate a horn player's enthusiasm. Listen to the crispness and integrity with which Levy and Co., back the two saxophonists on *Brute's roots*, a 12 bar blues on which Hodges plays with absolute finesse and composure. Herb Ellis has two tastefully economical choruses and then gives way to Webster who delivers a breathy solo of elegance and grace. *Bouncing with Ben* is a mid-tempo blues that opens with a boisterous eight bar introduction from Johnson. The theme, played in unison, is a repeated two bar riff. Hodges builds a solo that is lyrical, lissom, light and lovely, phrasing right on top of the beat and investing the music with a tremendous 'wholesomeness'. Ellis plays prettily and then Webster takes over in gruff, gritty mood. The horns then repeat the theme and finish with an appealing diminuendo - a style of ending none too common today.
*One for the Duke* is a neat little Hodges original in B flat minor. Middlebrooks and Johnson set the rhythmic pattern for the 16 bar theme and then Hodges sails in for the first solo. Johnson's brushes and Middlebrook's bass are perfectly matched timewise and Hodges, revelling in the impeccable support, skips fluently along, giving the number plenty of air. Ellis plays an unhurried solo of lazy, wistful lines and then Ben makes a typical, sibilant contribution, full of poignant little touches and resonant glissandi. Side one ends with a pert 32 unison piece taken at a beautifully judged tempo. Johson's top cymbal is infectiously propulsive and there are fine solos from Levy and Ellis as well as the two horns. *Rabbit pie* is a good, romping 32-bar sequence and typical of the dozens of neat and tidy mainstream riff pieces that Hodges wrote for small group sessions. Hodges never swaggering but always effortlessly surefooted, rides lightly over the taut rhythm section after the unison theme statement and Webster's rasping, rough-edged outing. There are good solos again from Levy and Ellis after the reprise of the theme there's a 'sudden death' ending. On the last four tracks of this album Hodges is heard in a more familiar setting, surrounded by five stalwart Ellingtonians, plus Memphis born pianist Al Williams, a former associate of such jazz luminaries as Benny Carter and Buck Clayton. All four titles have Ellington associations. *On the sunny side of the street* the 1931 Jimmy McHugh-Dorothy Fields song, was often used a feature for Hodges in his Ellington days. Every note he plays on this speaks of the master musician he was - beautiful control, accurate pitch, creamy tone, expressive dynamics and flawless time. *Good queen Bess*, one of Rabbit's most successful compositions, was one he recorded when he made his first small group sides with fellow Ellingtonians in the late thirties. There is a fine Lawrence Brown solo on this track. *The jeep is jumping* with its rousing unison ensemble line, is a theme that Hodges co-wrote with the Duke in 1938, and *Things ain't what they used to be*, a celebrated Ellington piece of 1941 vintage, shows off Rabbit's decided flair for small group arranging.
This last track is enlivened by some solid bass backing from Aaron Bell - against Woodyard's top cymbal triplets in one passage - and a delightfully agitated Lawrence Brown trombone solo over a shuffle beat from the rhythm section. Hodges, needless to add, is in customar-

Allan Holdsworth

ily sublime form. The title *Things ain't what they used to be* has a poignant relevance in the case of Johnny Hodges because jazz will never see him nor his like again. We can be thankful, however, that we do at least have records like this one to remind us of the unfailing excellence of his music. (Mike Hennessey, 1984)
**CD:** Released May '89, on Storyville by Storyville Records AB. Catalogue no: **STCD 4109**
**Album:** Released May '86, on Storyville by Storyville Records AB. Catalogue no: **SLP 4109**

**MELLOW TONE**
Tracks: / Things ain't what they used to be / In a mellow tone / Mr. Gentle and Mr. Cool / Sophisticated lady / Jeeps' blues / All of me / Passion flower / On the sunny side of the street / Get that geet / Perdido / That's grand / Skip it / Hop, skip and jump / Sweet Lorraine / Nix it, mix it / Jump, that's all / Mood indigo / Beau bag boogie / Time on my hands / Run about / In the shade of the old apple tree / Last legs blues.
**Album:** Released May '83, on Vogue Jazz (France) by Vogue Records. Catalogue no: **VJD 528**

**NOT SO DUKISH**
**Album:** Released Dec '81, on Verve (USA) by Polydor Ltd. Catalogue no: **2304 510**

**RABBIT IN PARIS, THE**
**Album:** Released Oct '88, on Vogue by Vogue Records. Catalogue no: **500059**

**RABBITS WORK VOL 5**
**Album:** Released Jun '81, on Verve (USA) by Polydor Ltd. Catalogue no: **2304 451**

**SMOOTH ONE, THE**
Tracks: / First klass / Second klass / Straight back / Steerage / Third klass / Meet the frog / Nite life / My melancholy baby / Lotus blossom / Free for all / I told you so / Starting with you / Hare / Things you miss / Wiggle awhile / Br' rabbit / Get ready / Peaches / Hygiene.
**2 LP Set:** Released Aug '79, on Verve Catalogue no: **2632082**

**TRIPLE PLAY**
Tracks: / Take 'em off (part 1) / Take 'em off (part 2) / Nearness of you, The / Monkey on a limb / Tiny bit of blues, A / For jammers only (aka Wild onions) / On the way up / Big boy blues / Very thought of you, The / Fur piece / Sir John / Figurine / C-jam blues.
**Cass:** Released Sep '87, on RCA by BMG Records (UK). Deleted Nov '88. Catalogue no: **NK 85903**
**CD:** Released Apr '89, on Bluebird (2) by BMG Records (UK). Catalogue no: **ND 85908**
**CD:** Released Sep '87, on RCA by BMG Records (UK). Catalogue no: **ND 85903**
**Album:** Released Sep '87, on RCA by BMG Records (UK). Catalogue no: **NL 85903**

## Hoeke, Rob

**JUMPIN ON THE 88**
**Album:** Released Mar '84, on Oldie Blues Catalogue no: **OL 8005**

**ROB HOEKE AND THE REAL BOOGIE WOOGIE**
Tracks: / Rockin' my blood away / Survival boogie / Saturday evening boogie / Sunday morning blues / Real boogie woogie / Rob's home boogie / Goodbye boogie / What's going on? / Believe me / Knocking boogie / Fine and steady / For my friend / Holland boogie / Boogie woogie me.
**Album:** Released '87, on Down South Records Catalogue no: **DS 9234**

## Hokum Boys

**BROONZY, WASHBOARD SAM 1935-37**
**Album:** Released '88, on Limited Edition Catalogue no: **LE 300,003**

**CAN'T GET ENOUGH OF THAT STUFF**
**Album:** Released Dec '88, on Yazoo (USA) by Shanachie Records (USA). Catalogue no: **L 1051**

**COMPLETE RECORDINGS 1935-37**
**Album:** Released Sep '87, on Document Catalogue no: **LE 300.003**

**FAMOUS HOKUM BOYS 1930-31, THE**
**Album:** Released '88, on Matchbox by Flyright Records. Catalogue no: **MSE 1014**

**HOKUM BOYS, THE**
**Album:** Released Dec '88, on Earl Archives Catalogue no: **BD 2022**

## Holdsworth, Allan

**SAND**
**Album:** Released Aug '87, on Enigma. Catalogue no: **3293 1**

**SECRETS**
Tracks: / City nights / 54 Duncan Terrace / spokes / Perila premonition / Secrets / Joshua / Maid Marion / Endomoroh.
**Album:** Released Jul '89, on Virgin. Catalogue no: **ENVLP 536**
**CD**: Released Jul '89, on Virgin. Catalogue no: **CDENV 536**

## Holiday, Billie

**Biographical details:** Jazz singer Billie Holiday was born Eleanora Fagan in 1915 in Baltimore, Maryland, and died in 1959 in New York City. She heard records by Bessie Smith as a child and always admired Louis Armstrong, but she owed little to earlier artists: she was the first and is perhaps still the greatest of jazz singers, if the essence of jazz singing is to make the familiar sound fresh, and to make any lyric come alive with personal meaning for the listener. She had a very rough upbringing (raped as a child, then thrown into a police cell), but acquired the nickname 'Lady Day' because of her innate dignity (as well as physical beauty) which never left her in spite of everything. John Hammond produced her first record in 1933 with a 9 piece Benny Goodman band. She appeared in a short film *Rhapsody in black* early in 1935 with Duke Ellington, then

**Billie Holiday**

made a sensational debut in April at the Apollo; MC Ralph Cooper advised Frank Schiffman to book her with a famous description: 'It ain't the blues -- I don't know what it is, but you got to hear her'. In July making the first of about 100 records (1935-42), nearly all with small groups led by Teddy Wilson on which her fame mainly still rests: they were made quickly and cheaply for juke boxes, using head arrangements played by whichever sidemen happened to be in town; the songs were often second rate and even silly (black artists got songpluggers' leftovers that other artists didn't want) but she transmuted them into gold, sometimes turning a melody line inside out. She sang behind the beat, endowing lyrics with languor, irony, resignation or sexuality, depending on requirements. Her vocal texture was course, but profoundly affecting; her timbre and her time were unique. At the first session she met her life-long soulmate Lester Young, who gave her her nickname; Billie named him Prez (for President) and the nicknames stuck as long as they lived. Jazz fans, critics and musicians recognised her greatness,but she never broke through to the public at large in her lifetime, and her self-confidence was never great. She sang with Count Basie in 1937 (no studio recordings, but airchecks were later issued) and Artie Shaw in 1938 (only *Any old time*, recorded by Victor, but she didn't like life on the road and would not tolerate racism. Her record company had objected to her record with Shaw, but the former American Record Company (by then owned by CBS) allowed sessions at Commodore in 1939 because they didn't want to record *Strange fruit*, a setting of a powerful anti-lynching poem by Lewis Allen; this first Commodore record was backed with her own song *Fine and mellow* which was something of a hit. In 1942 she made a record with Paul Whiteman; after the musicians' union recording ban she began working in 1944 with Milt Gabler (who had run Commordore) at US Decca (now MCA) where she asked for and got backing with strings: an early Decca record was *Lover man*, one of her most famous, but although her lyrical interpretations are always fine, the banal arrangements and too-slow tempi of the Decca series have an overall slushy effect. She made the film *New Orleans* in 1946, a dire Hollywood version of the history of jazz saved only by its musical content, Holiday and Armstrong playing a maid and a butler. She had been introduced to opium by her first husband and to heroin by him or by another man; she kicked the habit in a clinic, but was successful only as long as she was away from the music scene; she was sentenced in 1947 to a year in a federal reformatory and her cabaret card was revoked, the NYC law not allowing anyone convicted of a felony to work in a place where liquor was served not abolished until 1967. By the mid-'50s her range had narrowed, her voice deteriorated; her unique timbre was still there and when she was in the mood she was a still a great interpreter, but years of alcohol and drugs were taking their toll. She made a poignant appearance on the CBS TV programme *Sound of jazz* with Young and many others (the best treatment jazz had received on TV until then) and began recording for Columbia: she wanted a string orchestra conducted by Ray Ellis; *Lady in satin* in 1958 was a sad document. Her health began to fail; talk of filming her autobiography came to nothing (until the disastrous 1971 version: Diana Ross did her best with an awful script). She began to spend lonely weeks in her NYC flat; in May 1959 she went to hospital; the evidence is that she was not on drugs at the time, but as she came out of a coma she was arrested for possession and fingerprinted on her deathbed. When she died there was 70 cents in her band account. (Donald Clarke, Nov 1989).

## 2 LP

**2 LP Set:** Released Apr '84, on Carrere (France) Catalogue no: **64502**

## 16 CLASSIC TRACKS: BILLIE HOLIDAY

Tracks: / Lover man / No more / That ole devil called love / Don't explain / You better go now / What is this thing called love? / Good morning heartache / No-good man / Big stuff / Baby I don't cry over you / I'll look around / Blues are brewin' / Guilty / Deep song / There is no greater love / Easy living.

Note: Accompaniment by the orchestras of Toots Camarata, Bob Haggart, Bill Stegmeyer and John Simmonds and by the Billy Kyle Trio.

**Cass:** Released Jun '82, on MCA by MCA Records. Catalogue no: **MCLC 1688**

**Album:** Released Jun '82, on MCA by MCA Records. Catalogue no: **MCL 1688**

## 16 ORIGINAL HITS: BILLIE HOLIDAY

**Cass:** Released Sep '87, on Timeless Treasures Catalogue no: **MC 1636**

## 1942 - 1951 - 1954

**Cass:** Released '88, on Pathe Marconi (France) Catalogue no: **2C 268 86527**

**Album:** Released '83, on Capitol (import) Catalogue no: **2C 068 86527**

## 1935-58

**Album:** Released '88, on Rare LPs Catalogue no: **RARE 1**

## ALL OF ME (HAPPY BIRD)

Tracks: / God bless the child / I cover the waterfront / Lover come back to me / All of me / Billie's blues / My man / Them there eyes / Lover man / Stormy weather / Willow weep for me / I only have eyes for you / Please don't talk about me when I'm gone.

Note: Issued to commemorate the 25th anniversary of the death of the greatest and most moving of all jazz singers and compiled from live radio and television broadcasts, the album covers the period between 1949 and 1958 and includes some interesting spoken introductions. The sleeve picture of Lady Day is by famous jazz photographer David Redfern.

**Album:** Released Jul '84, on Happy Bird (Germany) Catalogue no: **B 90129**

**ALL OF ME (PREMIER)**
Tracks: / My man / Them there eyes / I cover the waterfront / Lover come back to me / You're driving me crazy / All of me / I loves you, Porgy / Miss Brown to you / They can't take that away from me / Storyville / Blues are bluer / Road to love.
**Cass:** Released May '85, on Premier by Premier Records. Catalogue no: **KCBR 1021**
**Album:** Released May '85, on Premier by Premier Records. Catalogue no: **CBR 1021**

**AS TIME GOES BY**
**LP Pic:** Released 7 Nov '87, on Exclusive Picture Discs Catalogue no: **AR 30071**

**AT STORYVILLE**
Tracks: / I cover the waterfront / Too marvellous for words / I loves you, Porgy / Them there eyes / Willow weep for me / I only have eyes for you / You go to my head / He's funny that way / Billie's blues / Miss Brown to you / Lover come back to me / T'aint nobody's business if I do / You're driving me crazy.
Note: With Stan Getz, Buster Harding, John Fields, Marquis Foster, Carl Drinkard, Jimmy Woods, Peter Littman.
**Album:** Released Feb '89, on Black Lion Catalogue no: **BLP 60921**
**CD:** Released Dec '88, on Black Lion Catalogue no: **BLCD 760921**
**Album:** Released Sep '80, on Black Lion Deleted Sep '85. Catalogue no: **BLM 51007**
**Album:** Released Jan '82, on Black Lion-Intercord Catalogue no: **INT 147015**
**Album:** Released Jun '88, on Storyville by Storyville Records AB. Catalogue no: **SLP 4134**

**BILLIE, ELLA, LENA, SARAH (Various artists)**
Tracks: / Man I love, The: *Various artists* / My melancholy baby: *Various artists* / Prisoner of love: *Various artists* / Nice work if you can get it: *Various artists* / I'll never be the same: *Various artists* / East of the sun: *Various artists* / What a little moonlight can do: *Various artists* / Ain't misbehavin': *Various artists* / Out of nowhere: *Various artists* / All my life: *Various artists* / I'm gonna lock my heart: *Various artists* / Goodnight my love: *Various artists*.
Note: Featuring Billie Holliday, Ella Fitzgerald, Lena Horne and Sarah Vaughan.
**Album:** Released Mar '81, on CBS by CBS Records. Deleted '87. Catalogue no: **CBS 54303**

**BILLIE HOLIDAY**
Tracks: / When I'm gone / I loves you, Porgy / Foolin' myself.
**CD:** Released May '89, on Onn Catalogue no: **ONN 38**
**Album:** Released '88, on Joker (USA) by Lifetime Records (USA). Catalogue no: **SM 3966**
**Cass:** Released '88, on Entertainers Catalogue no: **ENT MC 13002**
**CD:** Released Jun '87, on Verve Catalogue no: **831 371-2**
**Album:** Released '88, on Entertainers Catalogue no: **ENT LP 13002**
**Cass:** Released Jun '87, on Verve Catalogue no: **831 371-4**

**BILLIE HOLIDAY 30'S**
**Album:** Released Aug '86, on Lotus Catalogue no: **LOP 14 121**
**Cass:** Released Aug '86, on Lotus Catalogue no: **LCS 14121**

**BILLIE HOLIDAY 40'S**
**Album:** Released Aug '86, on Lotus Catalogue no: **LOP 14 122**
**Cass:** Released Aug '86, on Lotus Catalogue no: **LCS 14122**

**BILLIE HOLIDAY 50'S**
**Cass:** Released Aug '86, on Lotus Catalogue no: **LCS 14123**
**Album:** Released Aug '86, on Lotus Catalogue no: **LOP 14 123**

**BILLIE HOLIDAY AT MONTEREY 1958**
Tracks: / Ain't nobody's business but my own / Willow weep for me / When your lover has gone / God bless the child / I only have eyes for you / Good morning heartache / Them there eyes / Billie's blues / What a little moonlight can do / Trav'lin light / Lover come back to me.
Note: This album is a true event! Unearthed after more than 20 years, this first-time release of Billie Holiday at the 1st Monterey Jazz Festival is a rare historic record and treat. Captured "live" in stereo outdoors in October 1958 (pre-stereo days) via an experimental stereo model recorder the quality is astounding. Remastered in digital. Personnel: Billie Holiday / Gerry Mulligan / Mal Waldron / Eddie Khan / Dick Berk.
**CD:** Released Sep '89, on Black Hawk (USA) by Blackhawk Records (USA). Catalogue no: **BKH 50701CD**
**Album:** Released Sep '86, on Black Hawk (USA) by Blackhawk Records (USA). Catalogue no: **BKH 50701**
**Cass:** Released Sep '86, on Black Hawk (USA) by Blackhawk Records (USA). Catalogue no: **BKHMC 50701**

**BILLIE HOLIDAY COLLECTION (20 golden greats)**
Tracks: / My man / Don't explain / Swing, brother, swing / Lover man / I cover the waterfront / Do you know what it means to miss New Orleans? / I'll get by / When your lover has gone / Keeps on a rainin' / Miss Brown to you / Do nothing till you hear from me / I can't get started / Fine and mellow / Yesterdays / She's funny that way / On the sunny side of the street / Strange fruit / My old flame / Lover come back to me / They can't take that away from me?.
**Album:** Released Aug '85, on Deja Vu Catalogue no: **DVLP 2018**
**Cass:** Released Aug '85, on Deja Vu Catalogue no: **DVMC 2018**
**CD:** Released Jul '87, on Deja Vu Catalogue no: **DVCD 2018**

**BILLIE HOLIDAY AND HER ORCHESTRA**
**Album:** Released Feb '89, on Giants of Jazz by Hasmick Promotions. Catalogue no: **LPJT 80**
**CD:** Released Sep '88, on Giants of Jazz by Hasmick Promotions. Catalogue no: **CD 53038**
**Cass:** Released Feb '89, on Giants of Jazz by Hasmick Promotions. Catalogue no: **MCJT 80**

**BILLIE HOLIDAY - LIVE**
Tracks: / Introduction / My man / Don't explain / Them there eyes / Swing brother swing / Lover man / I cover the waterfront / Do nothing till you hear from me / They can't take that away from me / Lover come back to me.
**Album:** Released Oct '82, on Phoenix (2) by Audio Fidelity Enterprises. Deleted Dec '89. Catalogue no: **PHX 1009**

**BILLIE HOLIDAY - LIVE 1937/56**
Tracks: / They can't take that away from me / Lover come back to me / Stormy weather / All of me.
**Album:** Released Mar '88, on Delta (1) by Delta Records. Catalogue no: **20 809**

**BILLIE HOLIDAY SONGBOOK, THE**
Tracks: / Good morning heartache / My man / Billie's blues / Don't explain / Lady sings the blues / Lover man / God bless the child / Fine and mellow / Strange fruit / Stormy blues / Trav'lin' light.
**Album:** Released Aug '85, on Verve Catalogue no: **VRV 7**
**Cass:** Released Aug '85, on Verve Catalogue no: **VRVC 7**

**BILLIE HOLIDAY STORY 1**
Tracks: / Your mother's son in law / Riffin' / Scotch, The / Them there eyes / These foolish things / Did I remember / No regrets / Fine romance, A / Easy to love / Way you look tonight / Pennies from Heaven / That's life I guess / I can't give you anything but love / This year's kisses / Why was I born / Mood that I'm in, The / I'll never be the same / Without your love / Swing brother swing / They can't take that away from me / Getting some fun out of life / Travellin' all alone / When you're smiling / If dreams come true / I can't get started / Back in your own back yard / On the sentimental side / When a woman loves a man / You go to my head / Very thought of you, The / That's all I ask of you / Dream of life / Long gone blues.
**Album:** Released Jan '73, on CBS by CBS Records. Deleted Aug '87. Catalogue no: **CBS 68228**

**BILLIE HOLIDAY STORY 2**
**2 LP Set:** Released Jan '87, on CBS by CBS Records. Catalogue no: **CBS 68229**

**BILLIE HOLIDAY STORY 3**
**2 LP Set:** Released Jan '87, on CBS by CBS Records. Catalogue no: **CBS 68230**

**BILLIE HOLIDAY STORY, THE**
Tracks: / What a little moonlight can do / Miss Brown to you / Twenty four hours a day / These n'that n'those / Let's call a heart a heart / Let's dream in the moonlight / Night and day / What is this going

to get us / Georgia on my mind / God bless the child / Until the real thing comes along / Do you know what it means to miss New Orleans / Keeps on a rainin' / He's funny that way / Fine and mellow / I cover the waterfront / Lover come back to me / Lover man / I got it bad and that ain't good / Willow weep for me / My man / Please don't talk about me when I'm gone / Don't explain / I loves you, Porgy / Billie's blues.
**Cass:** Released May '89, on Deja Vu Catalogue no: **DVREMC 03**
**CD:** Released May '89, on Deja Vu Catalogue no: **DVRECD 03**

**BILLIE HOLIDAY VOL 2**
Tracks: / Solitude / Weep no more / Girls were made to take care of boys / I loves you, Porgy / My man / T'aint nobody's business if I do / Baby get lost / Keeps on a rainin' / Them there eyes / Do your duty / Gimme a pigfoot and a bottle of beer / Now or never / You're my thrill / Crazy he calls me / Please tell me how / Somebody's on my mind / God bless the child / This is heaven to me.
**Album:** Released Feb '84, on MCA by MCA Records. Catalogue no: **MCL 1776**
**Cass:** Released Feb '84, on MCA by MCA Records. Catalogue no: **MCLC 1776**

**BILLIE HOLIDAY VOL 3**
**Album:** Released Jun '86, on Queen Catalogue no: **QUEEN 067**

**BILLIE HOLIDAY WITH LESTER YOUNG (Holiday, Billie & Lester Young)**
**CD:** Released Feb '88, on Entertainers Catalogue no: **ENTCD 218**

**BILLIE'S BLUES (ASTAN)**
**Album:** Released Nov '84, on Astan (USA) Catalogue no: **20055**
**Cass:** Released Nov '84, on Astan (USA) Catalogue no: **40055**

**BILLIE'S BLUES (BLUE NOTE)**
Tracks: / Announcement / Blue moon / All of me / My man / Them there eyes / I cried for you / What a little moonlight can do / Lover come back to me / Blue turning grey over you / Be fair to me / Rocky mountain blues / Detour ahead / Trav'lin' light / I cover the waterfront / Billie's blues.
**CD:** Released Nov '88, on Blue Note by EMI Records. Deleted Oct '89. Catalogue no: **BNZ 110**
**CD:** Released Nov '88, on Blue Note by EMI Records. Deleted Oct '89. Catalogue no: **CDP 748 786 2**

**BILLIE'S BLUES (BULLDOG VERSION)**
Tracks: / Swing, brother, swing / Do nothing till you hear from me / You're driving me crazy / Lover man / Nobody's business / My man / They can't take that away from me / He's funny that way / Don't be late / God bless the child / Lover come back to me / Don't explain / Same old story / Detour ahead / Billie's blues / Miss Brown to you.
**Album:** Released Jul '82, on Bulldog Records by President Records. Catalogue no: **BDL 1007**
**Cass:** Released Jul '82, on Bulldog Records by President Records. Catalogue no: **AJKL 1007**

**BILLIE'S BLUES (CBS)**
Tracks: / I'm a fool to want you / Glad to be unhappy / Sailboat in the moonlight / When a woman loves a man / I'll never be the same / Let's call the whole thing off / Summertime / Am I blue / I cover the waterfront / Billie's blues.
**Cass:** Released Mar '86, on CBS by CBS Records. Deleted Jan '89. Catalogue no: **40 32733**
**Album:** Released Mar '86, on CBS by CBS Records. Deleted Jan '89. Catalogue no: **CBS 32733**

**BILLIE'S BLUES (VANGUARD)**
**Cass:** Released Aug '86, on Vanguard by Start Records Ltd.. Catalogue no: **VSC 339**
**Album:** Released Aug '86, on Vanguard by Start Records Ltd.. Catalogue no: **VSLP 339**

**BODY AND SOUL**
**Album:** Released Oct '82, on Verve (Import) Catalogue no: **2304 340**

**COMPACT JAZZ: BILLIE HOLIDAY**
**CD:** Released Jul '87, on Verve Catalogue no: **831 371-2**

**ESSENTIAL BILLIE HOLIDAY, THE**
Tracks: / Lady sings the blues / It ain't nobody's business / I love my man / My man.
Note: Live recording of 1956 Carnegie Hall concert. Narration by Gilbert Millstein of extracts from the book "The lady sings the blues". Band includes Buck Clayton, Al Cohn, Kenny Burrell, Roy Eldridge, Coleman Hawkins, Chico Hamilton.
**Album:** Released Mar '83, on Verve (USA) by Polydor Ltd. Catalogue no: **2304 343**

**EVENING WITH LADY DAY**
**Album:** Released Jan '82, on Jazz Bird Catalogue no: **JAZ 2003**

**FINE AND MELLOW, 1939 & 1944**
Tracks: / Strange fruit / Yesterdays / Fine and mellow / I gotta right to sing the blues / How am I to know? / My old flame / I'll get by / I cover the waterfront.
**CD:** Released May '87, on Commodore Class Catalogue no: **824 055**
**Album:** Released May '87, on Commodore Class Catalogue no: **AG6 24055**
**CD:** Released Aug '89, on Starline (Jazz) Catalogue no: **CDSG 406**

**FINE AND MELLOW (CAMBRA)**
Tracks: / Ghost of a chance / God bless the child / I loves you, Porgy / All of me / My man / Them there eyes / Don't explain / Foolin' myself / Lover man / Tenderly / Easy to remember / Willow weep for me / Swing, brother, swing / He's funny that way.
Note: Twenty-five tracks including those listed above.
**Cass set:** Released Apr '85, on Cambra by Cambra Records. Deleted '88. Catalogue no: **CRT 139**
**2 LP Set:** Released Apr '85, on Cambra by Cambra Records. Deleted '88. Catalogue no: **CR 139**

**GOD BLESS THE CHILD**
Tracks: / God bless the child / Them there eyes / T'aint nobody's business if I do / My man / You're driving me crazy / Everything a good man needs / He's funny that way / Miss Brown to you / Detour ahead / Don't explain / lover man.
**Album:** Released Sep '87, on Meteor by Magnum Music Group. Catalogue no: **MTM 027**
**2 LP Set:** Released Jan '74, on CBS by CBS Records. Deleted '87. Catalogue no: **66 267**

**GOLDEN GREATS: BILLIE HOLIDAY**
Tracks: / That ole devil called love / Don't explain / Lover man / Easy living / Good morning heartache / No more / You better go now / What is this thing called love / No good man / Big stuff / Baby I don't cry over you / I'll look around / Blues are brewin' / Guilty / Deep song / There is no greater love.
Note: Tracks include those listed above.
**Cass:** Released Jul '85, on MCA by MCA Records. Catalogue no: **MCMC 5011**
**CD:** Released Dec '88, on MCA by MCA Records. Catalogue no: **DMCL 1688**
**Album:** Released Jul '85, on MCA by MCA Records. Catalogue no: **MCM 5011**

**GOLDEN YEARS 1933-41, THE**
Tracks: / Your mother's son in law / No regrets / This year's kisses / You go to my head / Body and soul / Georgia on my mind / Am I blue / Gloomy Sunday.
**Cass:** Released Dec '85, on CBS by CBS Records. Catalogue no: **40 66377**
**LP Set:** Released Dec '85, on CBS by CBS Records. Deleted '86. Catalogue no: **CBS 66377**

**GOLDEN YEARS OF LADY DAY**
**Album:** Released Sep '87, on Giants of Jazz by Hasmick Promotions. Catalogue no: **LPJT 10**

**GOLDEN YEARS, THE (Vol. 2 FRC 100)**
**Album:** Released '88, on Queen Catalogue no: **QUEEN 065**

**GOOD MORNING HEARTACHE**
Tracks: / Good morning heartache / What is this thing called love / God bless the child / This is heaven to me / Solitude / Don't explain / My man (mon homme) / That ole devil called love / Crazy he calls me / You're my thrill / No good man / You better go now / Weep no more / Lover man (oh where can you be).
**Album:** Released Jul '87, on Hallmark by Pickwick Records. Catalogue no: **SHM 3213**
**Cass:** Released Jul '87, on Hallmark by Pickwick Records. Catalogue no: **HSC 3213**

**GREATEST HITS: VOLUME 1**
**Album:** Released '88, on Masters (Holland) Catalogue no: **CL 27683**
**Cass:** Released '88, on Masters (Holland) Catalogue no: **CLMC 927683**

**GREATEST HITS: VOLUME 2**
**Cass:** Released '88, on Masters (Holland) Catalogue no: **CLMC 928683**
**Album:** Released '88, on Masters (Holland) Catalogue no: **CL 28683**

**HOLIDAY, BILLIE: ON THE AIR**
Tracks: / Fine and mellow / All of me / Man I love, The / You've changed / I love my man / When your lover has gone / I'm just foolin' myself / Easy to remember / Moanin' low / Don't explain.
**Album:** Released '87, on Totem Catalogue no: **TOTEM 1037**

**HOLIDAY FOR LOVERS**
Tracks: / They can't take that away from me / Don't explain / Do you know what it means to miss New Orleans / Storyville / Miss Brown to you / Them there eyes / Ain't nobody's business / My man.
**Album:** Released Jun '80, on Manhattan Records by President Records. Deleted '85. Catalogue no: **MAN 5014**

**I GOT THE RIGHT TO SING**
**Album:** Released Apr '81, on Joker (USA) by Lifetime Records (USA). Catalogue no: **SM 3289**

**I WONDER WHERE OUR LOVE HAS GONE**
**Album:** Released '88, on Giants of Jazz by Hasmick Promotions. Catalogue no: **GOJ 1001**
**Cass:** Released '88, on Giants of Jazz by Hasmick Promotions. Catalogue no: **GOJC 1001**

**I'LL BE SEEING YOU (1944)**
Tracks: / Strange fruit / Yesterdays / Fine and mellow / I gotta right to sing the blues / How am I to know? / My old flame / I'll get by / I cover the waterfront.
**Album:** Released Jan '85, on Commodore Class Catalogue no: **AG6 24291**
**CD:** Released May '87, on Commodore Class Catalogue no: **AG8 24291**

**IMMORTAL BILLIE HOLIDAY, THE**
**CD:** Released May '87, on CBS by CBS Records. Catalogue no: **CD BH 1**

**IMMORTAL SESSIONS**
**Album:** Released May '86, on Storyville by Storyville Records AB. Catalogue no: **SLP 1000**

**IMMORTAL, THE**
Tracks: / Swing brother swing / They can't take that away from me / Do nothing till you hear from me / I'll get by / I love my man / I cover the waterfront / Do you know what it means to miss New Orleans / Don't explain / Keeps on a rainin' / Lover come back to me.
**Album:** Released '87, on Joker (USA) by Lifetime Records (USA). Catalogue no: **SM 3131**
**Cass:** Released '87, on Joker (USA) by Lifetime Records (USA). Catalogue no: **MC 3131**

**IN REHEARSAL**
**CD:** Released '88, on Mobile Fidelity Sound Lab(USA) by Mobile Fidelity Records (USA). Catalogue no: **MFCD 840**

**LADY AND THE LEGEND, VOL 1 1949 - 1951**
Tracks: / My man / Miss Brown to you / Keeps on a rainin' / I cover the waterfront / All of me / Good morning heartache / Maybe you'll be there / You're driving me crazy / You're my thrill / He's funny that way / Billie's blues / Them there eyes.
**Album:** Released Sep '84, on Rhapsody by President Records. Catalogue no: **RHA 6025**

**LADY AND THE LEGEND, VOL 2 1952 - 1956**
Tracks: / My man / Tenderly / God bless the child / I cover the waterfront / Lover come back to me / Billie's blues / Them there eyes / Lover man / Stormy weather / Willow weep for me / I only have eyes for you / Please don't talk about me when I'm gone.
**Album:** Released Sep '84, on Rhapsody by President Records. Catalogue no: **RHA 6026**

**LADY AND THE LEGEND, VOL 3**
Tracks: / I cover the waterfront / Lover come back to me / Ghost of a chance / Please don't talk about me when I'm gone / Nice work if you can get it / God bless the child / Don't explain / Porgy / Fine and mellow / Foolin' myself / Easy to remember / Moanin' low / When your lover has gone.
**Album:** Released Sep '84, on Rhapsody by President Records. Catalogue no: **RHA 6027**

**LADY DAY LIVE**
**Cass:** Released Jan '88, on Demand Performance Catalogue no: **DPC 725**

**LADY DAY AND PREZ (1937-41) (Holiday, Billie & Lester Young)**
Tracks: / This year's kisses / Without your love / All of me / Me, myself and I (are all in love with you) / I'll get by / Mean to me / Sailboat in the moonlight / I'll never be the same / Getting some fun out of life / Man I love, The / Trav'lin' all alone / Time on my hands / Laughing at life / Back in your own back yard / Georgia on my mind / Let's do it / Foolin' myself / Easy living / Say it with a kiss / You can't be mine (and someone else's too) / I can't believe that you're in love with me / She's funny that way / Romance in the dark / I must have that man!.
**CD:** Released '88, on Giants of Jazz by Hasmick Promotions. Catalogue no: **GOJCD 0218**
**Album:** Released Sep '87, on Giants of Jazz by Hasmick Promotions. Catalogue no: **LPJT 45**

**LADY DAY/LADY IN SATIN**
Tracks: / Miss Brown to you / I wished on the moon / What a little moonlight can do / If you were mine / Summertime / Billie's blues / I must have that man / Foolin' myself / Easy living / Me, myself and I (are all in love with you) / Sailboat in the moonlight / I cried for you / I'm a fool to want you / For Heaven's sake / You don't know what love is / I get along without you very well / For all we know / Violets for your furs / You've changed / Easy to remember / But beautiful / Glad to be unhappy / I'll be around.
**Cass:** Released Jun '85, on CBS (Blue Diamond) by CBS Records. Catalogue no: **40 22189**
**2 LP Set:** Released Jun '85, on CBS (Blue Diamond) by CBS Records. Catalogue no: **CBS 22189**

**LADY DAY'S IMMORTAL PERFORMANCES**
**Album:** Released Sep '87, on Giants of Jazz by Hasmick Promotions. Catalogue no: **LPJT 40**

**LADY IN SATIN**
Tracks: / I'm a fool to want you / For Heaven's sake / You don't know what love is / I get along without you very well / For all we know / Violets for your furs / You've changed / Easy to remember / But beautiful / Glad to be unhappy / I'll be around / End of a love affair, The.
**Cass:** Released 27 Feb '88, on CBS (import) by CBS Records. Catalogue no: **4508834**
**Cass:** Released Mar '83, on CBS Cameo by CBS Records. Deleted Jun '88. Catalogue no: **40 32259**
**Album:** Released 27 Feb '88, on CBS (import) by CBS Records. Catalogue no: **4508831**
**Album:** Released Mar '83, on CBS Cameo by CBS Records. Deleted Jan '89. Catalogue no: **CBS 32259**

**LADY OF THE BLUES**
Tracks: / God bless the child / Them there eyes / T'aint nobody's business if I do / My man / You're driving me crazy / Billie's blues / He's funny that way / Miss Brown to you / No detour ahead / Don't explain / Lover man / All of me / Daddy he can't make no time / Tenderly.
**Album:** Released Apr '86, on Castle Showcase by Castle Communications Records. Catalogue no: **SHLP 139**
**Cass:** Released Apr '86, on Castle Showcase by Castle Communications Records. Catalogue no: **SHTC 139**

**LADY SINGS (Boxed album set)**
Tracks: / Lover man / No more / That ole devil called love / Don't explain / You better go now / What is this thing called love? / Good morning heartache / No good man / Big stuff / Baby I don't cry over you / I'll look around / Blues are brewin', The / Guilty / Deep song / There is no greater love / Easy living / Solitude / Weep no more / Girls were made to take care of boys / Porgy / My man / Ain't nobody's business if I do / Baby get lost / Keeps on rainin' / Them there eyes / Do your duty / Gimme a pigfoot and a bottle of beer / You can't lose a broken heart / Now or never / You're my thrill / Crazy he calls me / Please tell me now / Somebody's on my mind / God bless the child / This is heaven to me.
**CD:** on Official by Official Records. Catalogue no: **OFF 83017-2**
**LP Set:** on Official by Official Records. Catalogue no: **OFF 3017-3**

**LADY SINGS OF LOVE**
**Album:** Released Nov '89, on Memoir by Memoir Records. Catalogue no: **MOIR 135**
**Cass:** Released Nov '89, on Memoir by

Memoir Records. Catalogue no: **CMOIR 135**

**LADY SINGS THE BLUES**
Tracks: / Lady sings the blues / Travelling light / I must have that man / Some other spring / Strange fruit / No-good man / God bless the child / Good morning heartache / Love me or leave me / Too marvellous for words / Willow weep for me / I thought about you.
**Cass:** Released '87, on Verve Catalogue no: **3133109**
**CD:** Released Nov '87, on Entertainers Catalogue no: **ENT CD 228**
**CD:** Released Apr '87, on Card/Grand Prix Catalogue no: **CD 180002**
**Cass:** Released Oct '88, on Lotus Catalogue no: **LCS 14 151**
**Album:** Released Sep '87, on Giants of Jazz by Hasmick Promotions. Catalogue no: **LPJT 50**
**Album:** Released Apr '82, on Verve Catalogue no: **2304 124**
**Album:** Released Oct '88, on Lotus Catalogue no: **LOP 14 151**

**LADY'S DECCA DAYS VOL.1**
**CD:** Released May '89, on MCA (Import) by MCA Records. Catalogue no: **MCAD 31321**

**LADY'S DECCA DAYS VOL.2**
**CD:** Released May '89, on MCA (Import) by MCA Records. Catalogue no: **MCAD 31322**

**LAST RECORDING**
**CD:** Released Dec '89, on Verve Catalogue no: **835 370 4**
**Album:** Released Dec '79, on IMS by Polydor Ltd. Catalogue no: **2304 392**

**LEGEND OF BILLIE HOLIDAY**
Tracks: / That ole devil called love / Lover man (oh where can you be) / Don't explain / Good morning heartache / There is no greater love / Easy living / Solitude / Porgy / My man / Them there eyes / Now or never / Ain't nobody's business if I do / Somebody's on my mind / Keeps on a rainin' / You're my thrill / God bless the child.
**Cass:** Released Nov '85, on MCA by MCA Records. Catalogue no: **BHTVC 1**
**Album:** Released Nov '85, on MCA by MCA Records. Catalogue no: **BHTV 1**
**CD:** Released Nov '85, on MCA by MCA Records. Catalogue no: **DBHTV 1**

**LEGENDARY MASTERS VOL.1, THE (Unissued or rare 1935-38)**
Tracks: / What a little moonlight can do / Miss Brown to you / Twenty-four hours a day / Yankee doodle never went to town / If you were mine / These 'n' that 'n' those / Spreadin' rhythm around / Let's call a heart a heart / Please keep me in your dreams / I wish I had you / I'll never fail you / You're so desirable / You're gonna see a lot of me / Hello my darling / Let's dream in the moonlight.
**Album:** Released '88, on Recording Arts Ref. Edition. Catalogue no: **RARELP 01**
**CD:** Released '88, on Recording Arts Ref. Edition. Catalogue no: **RARECD 01**

**LEGENDARY MASTERS VOL.2, THE (Unissued or rare 1939-52)**
Tracks: / More than you know / Under a blue jungle moon / Night and day / What is this going to get us? / Loveless love / Georgia on my mind / Romance in the dark / God bless the child / Jim / Wherever you are / Until the real thing comes along / Do you know what it means to miss New orleans? / Keeps on a rainin' / He's funny that way / Fine and mellow.
**Album:** Released '88, on Recording Arts Ref. Edition. Catalogue no: **RARELP 02**

**LEGENDARY MASTERS VOL.3, THE (Unissued or rare 1952-58)**
Tracks: / I cover the waterfront / Lover come back to me / Them there eyes / Lover man / I got it bad and that ain't good / Just friends / Everything happens to me / Prelude to a kiss / I must have that man / Willow weep for me / I only have eyes for you / My man / Please don't talk about me when I'm gone / Don't explain / Porgy / Ain't nobody's business but my own / Billie's blues.
**Album:** Released '88, on Recording Arts Ref. Edition. Catalogue no: **RARELP 03**

**LEGENDARY MASTERS, THE (Unissued or rare 1935-58)**
Note: For tracks see *The Legendary Masters Vols.1, 2 & 3.*
**CD Set:** Released '88, on Recording Arts Ref. Edition. Catalogue no: **RARECD 01/02/03**
**LP Set:** Released '88, on Recording Arts. Catalogue no: **RARELP 01/02/03**

**LIVE, 1953**
Tracks: / Blue moon / All of me / My man / Them there eyes / I cried for you / What a little moonlight can do / I cover the waterfront / Billie's blues / Lover come back to me.
Note: On the first seven tracks Billie is backed by Carl Drinkard - piano; Red Mitchell - bass; Elaine Leighton - drums; while on the final two she is joined by Buddy de Franco - clarinet; Red Norvo - vibes; Beryl Booker - piano; Jimmy Raney - guitar; Gene White - bass; Elaine Leighton - drums. The album was recorded at concerts in Europe.
**Album:** Released Apr '81, on Rarities Catalogue no: **RARITIES 40**

**LIVE AND RARE 1937-56**
**CD:** Released '86, on Delta (1) by Delta Records. Catalogue no: **11 049**

**LOVER MAN**
**Album:** Released '88, on Zeta Catalogue no: **ZET 706**

**MASTERS OF JAZZ VOL.3**
**Album:** Released May '86, on Storyville by Storyville Records AB. Catalogue no: **SLP 4103**

**MISS BROWN TO YOU**
Tracks: / Good morning heartache / You're driving me crazy / Miss Brown to you / Don't explain / Man I love, The / All of me.
**Album:** Released Jan '84, on Swing House by Submarine Records. Catalogue no: **SWH 27**

**MOST IMPORTANT RECORDINGS OF BILLIE HOLIDAY, THE**
Tracks: / Did I remember? / Fine romance, A / Easy to love / Way you look tonight, The / I've got my love to keep my warm / Why was I born? / I'll get by / Easy living / I'll never be the same / He's funny that way / Nice work if you can get it / I can't believe that you're in love with me / Now they call it swing / You go to my head / Sugar / Strange fruit / Some other Spring / Night and day / You're a lucky guy / I hear music / Let's do it / Georgia on my mind / Jim / Love me or leave me / God bless the child / I'll be seeing you / On the sunny side of the street / Don't explain / Ain't nobody's business if I do / Lover come back to me / Stars fell on Alabama.
**LP Set:** Released '89, on Official by Official Records. Catalogue no: **OFF 3048-2**
**CD:** Released '89, on Official by Official Records. Catalogue no: **OFF 83048-2**

**OLD STORY, THE**
**Album:** Released '88, on CBS (import) by CBS Records. Catalogue no: **CBS 68230**

**ON HOLIDAY**
Tracks: / My man / Them there eyes / I cover the waterfront / Lover come back to me / You've drivin' me crazy / All of me / Porgy / Miss Brown.
**Album:** Released Jun '80, on Manhattan Records by President Records. Deleted '85. Catalogue no: **MAN 5013**

**PORGY**
Tracks: / I don't stand a ghost of a chance / Please don't talk about me when I'm gone / Nice work if you can get it / God bless the child / Don't explain / I loves you, Porgy / Fine and mellow / What a little moonlight can do / Foolin' myself / Easy to remember / Moanin' low / When your lover has gone.
Note: Another album to commemorate the 25th anniversary of Lady Day's death in 1959 - see notes on the album *All of me* (Happy Bird).
**Album:** Released Jul '84, on Happy Bird (Germany) Catalogue no: **B90141**

**QUINTESSENTIAL VOL.1, THE**
**Cass:** Released Feb '88, on CBS (import) by CBS Records. Catalogue no: **450 987 4**
**Album:** Released Feb '88, on CBS (import) by CBS Records. Catalogue no: **450 987 1**
**CD:** Released Feb '88, on CBS (import) by CBS Records. Catalogue no: **450 987 2**

**QUINTESSENTIAL VOL.2, THE**
**Album:** Released Feb '88, on CBS (import) by CBS Records. Catalogue no: **460 059 1**
**Cass:** Released Feb '88, on CBS (import) by CBS Records. Catalogue no: **460 059 4**

**QUINTESSENTIAL VOL.3, THE**
Tracks: / Who loves you / Pennies from Heaven / That's life I guess / I can't give

**Billie Holiday - Strange fruit (Storyville)**

you anything but love / One never knows, does one? / I've got my love to keep me warm / If my heart could only talk / Please keep me in your dreams / He ain't got rhythm / This years kisses / Why was I born / I must have that man / Mood that I'm in, The / You showed me the way / Sentimental and melancholy / My last affair.
**Album:** Released 22 Aug '88, on CBS (import) by CBS Records. Catalogue no: **4608201**
**Cass:** Released 22 Aug '88, on CBS (import) by CBS Records. Catalogue no: **4608204**

**QUINTESSENTIAL VOL.4, THE**
**CD:** Released May '89, on CBS (import) by CBS Records. Catalogue no: **463 333 2**
**Cass:** Released May '89, on CBS (import) by CBS Records. Catalogue no: **463 333 4**
**Album:** Released May '89, on CBS (import) by CBS Records. Catalogue no: **463 333 1**

**QUINTESSENTIAL VOL.5, THE**
**Cass:** Released '88, on CBS by CBS Records. Catalogue no: **465 190 4**
**Album:** Released '88, on CBS by CBS Records. Catalogue no: **465 190 1**
**CD:** Released '88, on CBS by CBS Records. Catalogue no: **465 190 2**

**RADIO AND TV BROADCASTS**
**Album:** Released Apr '81, on UNI by MCA Records. Catalogue no: **ESP 3003**

**REPLAY ON BILLIE HOLIDAY**
**Album:** Released Aug '85, on Sierra by Sierra Records. Catalogue no: **FEDB 5018**

**ROCK IT FOR ME, 1937 (Holiday, Billie & Ella Fitzgerald)**
**Album:** Released Jul '87, on Nostalgia by Mainline Records. Catalogue no: **NOST 7663**

**SILVER COLLECTION, THE**
Tracks: / I wished on the moon / Moonlight in Vermont / Say it isn't so / Love is here to stay / Darn that dream / But not for me / Body and soul / Comes love / They can't take that away from me / Let's call the whole thing off / Gee baby ain't I good to you / Embraceable you / All or nothing at all / We'll be together again.
**CD:** Released Nov '84, on Verve Catalogue no: **823 449-2**

**SONGBOOK**
**CD:** Released Jan '90, on Polydor by Polydor Ltd. Catalogue no: **8232462**
**Cass:** Released Jan '90, on Polydor by Polydor Ltd. Catalogue no: **8232464**

**SONGS FOR DISTINGUISHED LOVERS**
Tracks: / Day in, day out / Foggy day, A / Stars fell on Alabama / One for my baby / Just one of those things / I didn't know what time it was.
**CD:** Released Apr '84, on Verve Deleted Jul '88. Catalogue no: **815 055-2**
**Cass:** Released Oct '84, on Verve (USA) by Polydor Ltd. Catalogue no: **815 055-4**
**Album:** Released Oct '84, on Verve (USA) by Polydor Ltd. Catalogue no: **2304 243**

**STORYVILLE**

**Cass:** Released Nov '84, on Chase Music (USA) by Chase Music Group (USA). Catalogue no: **SJAZC 3**
**Album:** Released Apr '86, on Star Jazz (USA) by Charly Records. Catalogue no: **SJAZZ 3**
**Cass:** Released Apr '86, on Star Jazz (USA) by Charly Records. Catalogue no: **SJAZZC 3**

**STRANGE FRUIT (See panel left)**
Tracks: / Strange fruit / Yesterdays / Fine and mellow / I gotta right to sing the blues / How am I to know / My old flame / I'll get by / I cover the waterfront / I'll be seeing you / I'm yours / Embraceable you / As time goes by / She's funny that way / Lover come back to me / I love my man / On the sunny side of the street.
Note: Of the very few singers who are certain to have a lasting place in the history of jazz, there could be some disagreement about whose name comes after Louis Armstrong's and Bessie Smith's in order of importance, but there is no doubt that Billie Holiday's belongs close to the top of the list. She established herself as one of the towering originals of hot music in her first dozen years of recording, beginning in 1933, and was at the peak of her talent and emotional intensity in the two sessions, in 1939 and 1944, which produced the performances on this collection. Two of them *Strange fruit* and *Fine and mellow*, were coupled on the biggest selling record of her career; the first remains the most anguished and harrowing expression of protest against man's inhumanity to man that has ever been made in the form of vocal jazz, and the second a splended and characteristic example of the consolations that may be wrung from the blues. The others herein, only a little less than these two, are everlastingly Billie's by reason of the power and poignancy, the artistry and originality, with which she transformed them from Ordinary popular songs into extraordinary personal communications.
What Billie communicates here, better than the words or even the best of the lyrics, are such emotions as sorrow, love, hope and rage, with here and there a fleeting note of something like happiness. She does so in a style that may have been influenced, as Billie has said it might, by her listening to records of Bessie Smith and Louis Armstrong as a child of nine or ten, but that from the start was her own unique blend of the tonal phrasing, rhythmic timing and melodic improvisation that make her singing jazz. Her style has since been widely imitated, but no other singer has succeeded, or can succeed, in charging it with the private and particular passion which is the compelling force behind these classic performances.
Sometimes the words of the songs she sings parallel the feelings that she expresses through the sound of her voice, as in *I've got a right to sing the blues*, for example. But more often the emotion is a separate and strongly personal one. In the opening song of this collection, for instance, Otto Harbach has provided her

with a nostalgic ode of considerable merit in its own right and Jerome Kern with matching music. But as *Yesterdays* is written, it is a song of gentle, sentimental regret over the loss of youth's 'happy sweet sequestered days'. As sung, it expresses a far deeper sorrow than it's lyrics do and some of that rage that is in Dylan Thomas's *Do not go gentle into that good night*. The listener may hear in it an overpowering lament of longing for days that might have been, but never were, in Billie's life and perhaps the listeners own. Her art and her feeling turn sentimentality into tragedy. Similarly, what joy there is in her voice is never the sort of easy come blitheness that you are invited to find, in the words of her last song in this collection, *On the sunny side of the street*. There is instead the harsh challenging, hard won sound of exultation, of rising momentarily over the troubles of life in the act of singing itself.

'Mom and Pop were just a couple of kids when they got married. He was eighteen, she was sixteen, and I was three,' says Billie in the celebrated first lines of her autobiography, *Lady sings the blues*, written with William Dufty and published in 1956. The book describes candidly, though often with the glancing defiance of those first lines, the troubles she has seen since she was born, in Baltimore on April 7 1915, the daughter of a guitarist in the McKinney and Fletcher Henderson bands, and baptised Eleanora Fagen.

She ran errands for a madame on the corner in exchange for listening to Louis and Bessie on the victrola in the front parlor - her only musical schooling - and a few years later, in New York, began singing in Pod's and Jerry's and other Harlem joints. She made her first recording in 1933, with Benny Goodman, and from 1935 through 1938 under Teddy Wilson's and her own name, sparked some of the most explosive small-group bashes of the swing era. On those luminous dates, Billie's vocals were set off by the inspired solos of great instrumentalists. Some similarly brilliant musicians participated in the sessions preserved here, but on these occasions - for the first time on any Holiday records - they held strictly to the role of providing obbligatos and unobtrusive backgrounds for Billie's all out vocal performances. It was in this way that the fine little bands of Frankie Newton and later, Eddie Heywood accompanied Billie at Cafe Society Downtown, where (and which) she opened in 1939 and, she says, 'left two years later as a star'. The musicians took their own star turns there too, and on other Commodore records. But on these, they defer entirely to Lady Day, as she was first called by Lester Young, at about the time he was elected President of the tenor sax. What you have here is pure Lady Day, expressing not only more than her lyrics do - of love and longing and sadness and anger - but more than she was able to express in the words of her book. That is so because jazz is first and foremost a language of emotion. 'I don't think I'm singing. I feel like I'm playing a horn,' Billie quoted in *Hear me talking to ya*, the anthology compiled by Nat Shapiro and Nat Hentoff. 'I try to improvise like Les Young, like Louis Armstrong, or someone else I admire. What comes out is what I feel'.

That is what you have here, the emotional depth that underlies, but is not truly revealed in her autobiography. It is the crying tones in her voice, telling what it is to be (or to have been, and to have always in your bones) poor and black, hungry and hurt, and in terrible trouble. It is in the beat that goes on beating for dear life, fast with the up-beat of hope and desire and slow with the mourning of grief and loss, strongly and steadily like the heart of mankind. It is in the bending of melodic lines, the changing of notes and accents, into a new composition whose color and design express feelings too strong and deep for words. What is preserved in these grooves is as fresh and moving as all honest revelations of deep feeling, shaken loose by passion and tempered by art, are fresh and moving as long as they can be read or seen or heard again. (Carlton Brown)

**Album:** Released Sep '86, on Storyville by Storyville Records AB. Catalogue no: **SLP 4002**

### SWINGING HOLIDAY

Tracks: / Blues are bluer / Road to love / I can't pretend / Until the real thing comes along / Ain't nobody business / All of me / I loves you, Porgy / Miss Brown.

**Album:** Released Aug '80, on Manhattan Records by President Records. Catalogue no: **MAN 5023**

### TEN FABULOUS RECORDINGS OF THE FORTIES

**Cass:** Released '87, on Joker (USA) by Lifetime Records (USA). Catalogue no: **MC 3289**

**Album:** Released '87, on Joker (USA) by Lifetime Records (USA). Catalogue no: **SM 3289**

### TENDERLY

Tracks: / My man / Miss Brown to you / Keeps on a rainin' / Lover man / I cover the waterfront / All of me / You're my thrill / He's funny that way / Billie's blues / Tenderly.

Note: Compiled from live radio and TV broadcasts recorded between 1949 and 1958, some tracks have interesting spoken introductions. Sleeve photograph: David Redfern.

**Album:** Released Jul '84, on Happy Bird (Germany) Catalogue no: **B 90128**

### THAT OLE DEVIL CALLED LOVE

Tracks: / Them there eyes / God bless the child / Don't explain / Good morning heartache / That ole devil called love / Easy living / There is no greater love / Baby I don't cry over you / Lover man (oh where can you be) / You better go now / Deep song / Guilty / I'll look around / Blues are brewin' / What is this thing called love.

**Album:** Released Apr '88, on Platinum Music by Prism Leisure. Catalogue no: **PLAT 306**

**Cass:** Released Apr '88, on Platinum Music by Prism Leisure. Catalogue no: **PLAC 306**

### THAT OLE DEVIL CALLED LOVE (SINGLE)

Tracks: / That ole devil called love / Lover man.

**7" Single:** Released Oct '85, on MCA by MCA Records. Catalogue no: **MCA 1007**

### TOP BOX, VOLS. 1-3

Tracks: / That 'ole devil called love / I'll be seeing you / My man / Miss Brown to you / Lover man / I wonder where our love has gone / Them there eyes / I love my man (Billie's blues) / You ain't gonna bother me no more / Good morning heartache / You're drivin' me crazy / Maybe you'll be there / I love my man / Keeps on a' rainin' / Lover man.

Note: Part of CD boxed set presented in chronological order. Each set contains booklet giving details of recordings and personnel.

**CD Set:** Released '89, on Jazz-Up Catalogue no: **JUTB 3035**

### TOP BOX, VOLS. 4-6

Tracks: / He's funny that way / Them there eyes / Fine and mellow / I cover the waterfront / Lover come back to me / Tenderly / Comeback story, The / God bless the child / Too marvellous for words / I loves you Porgy.

Note: Part of CD boxed set presented in chronological order. Each set contains a booklet giving detailed information on the live recordings and personnel.

**CD Set:** Released '89, on Jazz-Up Catalogue no: **JUTB 3038**

### TOP BOX, VOLS. 7-9

Tracks: / Blue moon / Willow weep for me / Nice work if you can get it / You've changed / Stormy weather / I cried for you / What a little moonlight can do / He's funny that way / All of me.

Note: Part of CD boxed set presented in chronological order. Each set contains a booklet giving detailed information of the live recordings and personnel.

**CD Set:** Released '89, on Jazz-Up Catalogue no: **JUTB 3041**

### TOP BOX VOLS. 10-12

**CD Set:** Released Mar '90, on Jazz-Up Catalogue no: **JUTB 3044**

### WITH BARNEY KESSEL (see also under Kessel, Barney) (Holiday, Billie & orchestra with Barney, Kessel)

**CD:** Released Mar '90, on Giants of Jazz by Hasmick Promotions. Catalogue no: **GOJCD53038**

### WITH TEDDY WILSON ORCHESTRA (see also under Wilson, Teddy) (Holiday, Billie & Teddy Wilson)

**CD:** Released Mar '90, on Giants of Jazz by Hasmick Promotions. Catalogue no: **GOJCD53055**

## Holland, Dave

**Biographical details:** The bassist, born in 1946 in Wolverhampton, studied at the Guildhall School of Music, played with all the best UK Jazzmen and was hired by Miles David at age 20. His technique is impeccable and his semi-abstract contemporary jazz always highly praised. He recorded with Davis 1968-71, with Circle (Chick Corea, Anthony Braxton and Barry Altschul) and many others; he also began playing cello. Recording mostly for ECM (including a solo cello set, *Life cycle* in 1982) he formed a quintet for *Jumpin' in* in 1983 with trumpeter Kenny Wheeler, Julian Priester on trombone, Steve Coleman on alto sax and Steve Ellington on drums; *Seeds of time* in 1985 with Marvin 'Smitty' Smith replacing Ellington, and *The razor's edge* in 1987 with Robin Eubanks replacing Priester. (Donald Clarke, Nov 1989).

**JUMPIN' IN (Holland, Dave Quintet)**
**CD:** Released '88, on ECM Catalogue no: **817 437 2**
**Album:** Released Apr '84, on ECM Catalogue no: **ECM 1269**

**LIFE CYCLE (Solo cello)**
**CD:** Released Oct '86, on ECM Catalogue no: **829 200-2**
**Album:** Released Apr '83, on ECM Catalogue no: **ECM 1238**

**RAZOR'S EDGE, THE (Holland, Dave Quintet)**
Tracks: / Brother Ty / Vedana / Razor's edge / Blues for C.M. / Vortex / 5 four six / Wights waits for weights / Fight time.
**Album:** Released Oct '87, on ECM Catalogue no: **ECM 1353**
**CD:** Released Oct '87, on ECM Catalogue no: **8330482**

**SAM AND DAVE VOL. 1 (see also Sam Rivers) (Holland, Dave & Sam Rivers)**
**Album:** Released Jul '78, on Improvising Artists Catalogue no: **IAI 37.38.43**

**SAM AND DAVE VOL. 2 (see also Sam Rivers) (Holland, Dave & Sam Rivers)**
**Album:** Released Jul '78, on Improvising Artists Catalogue no: **IAI 37.38.48**

**SEEDS OF TIME (Holland, Dave Quintet)**
Tracks: / Uhren / Homecoming / Perspicuity / Celebration / World protection blues / Grid lock / Walk-a-way / Good doctor, The / Double vision.
Note: Personnel: Dave Holland - bass / Steve Coleman -alto and soprano saxophones, flutes / Julian Priester - trombone / Marvin 'Smitty' Smith -drums, percussion / Kenny Wheeler - trumpet, cornet, pocket trumpet, fluegelhorn.
**Album:** Released Aug '85, on ECM Catalogue no: **ECM 1292**
**CD:** Released Aug '85, on ECM Catalogue no: **825 322-2**

**TRIPLICATE (Holland, Dave Trio)**
Note: Dave Holland returns to the small format trio recording with Steve Coleman (alto sax) and Jack de Johnette (drums). The material ranges from compositions by the three members, to a Charlie Parker tune and a piece by Duke Ellington. (New Note, August 1988)
**Album:** Released Sep '88, on ECM Catalogue no: **ECM 1373**
**CD:** Released Sep '88, on ECM Catalogue no: **837 113-2**

## Holliday, Simon

**RAGS, BOOGIE AND SWING**
Tracks: / Should I reveal / As long as I live / Maple leaf rag / Air mail special / Climax rag / Boogie joys / All the things you are / Way down yonder in New Orleans / Winin' boy blues / Nagasaki.
**CD:** Released Mar '90, on CMJ Catalogue no: **CMJ CD 009**
**Cass:** Released Sep '89, on CMJ Catalogue no: **CMJ MC 009**

**TAKING IT EASY**
**Cass:** Released Mar '90, on CMJ Catalogue no: **CMJMC010**

## Holloway, Red

**LOCKSMITH BLUES (Holloway, Red & Clark Terry Sextet)**
**CD:** Released Nov '89, on Concord by Concord Jazz Records (USA). Catalogue no: **CCD 4390**

**RED HOLLOWAY AND COMPANY**
Tracks: / But not for me / Caravan / Passion flower / Blues for Q.M. / Well you needn't / What's new / Summertime / Tokyo express.
Note: Personnel: Red Holloway - tenor & alto saxophones / Cedar Walton - Piano / Richard Reid - bass / Jimmie Smith - drums.
**CD:** Released Jul '87, on Concord Jazz by Concord Jazz Records (USA). Catalogue no: **CCD 4322**
**Album:** Released Jul '87, on Concord Jazz by Concord Jazz Records (USA). Catalogue no: **CJ 322**
**Cass:** Released Jul '87, on Concord Jazz by Concord Jazz Records (USA). Catalogue no: **CJC 322**

## Holman, Bill

**BIG BAND JAZZ IN A JAZZ ORBIT**
**Album:** Released Apr '88, on VSOP Catalogue no: **VSOP 25**

**BILL HOLMAN BAND (Holman, Bill Band)**
Note: Veteran American composer arranger and saxophonist Bill Holman and band breathe new life into the big band sound. CD contains two extra tracks.
**Cass:** Released Sep '88, on JVC Catalogue no: **JC 3308**
**CD:** Released Sep '88, on JVC Catalogue no: **JD 3308**
**Album:** Released Feb '88, on Fresh Sounds (Spain) by Fresh Sounds Records (Spain). Catalogue no: **FS 112**
**Album:** Released Feb '89, on JVC Catalogue no: **JLP 3308**

**BILL HOLMAN'S GREAT BAND (Holman, Bill Band)**
**Album:** Released '87, on Creative World(USA) by GNP Crescendo Records (USA). Catalogue no: **ST 1053**

**FABULOUS BILL HOLMAN ORCHESTRA**
**Album:** Released Apr '81, on Sackville by Spotlite Records. Catalogue no: **2013**

**FABULOUS BILL HOLMAN, THE**
Tracks: / Airegin / Evil eyes / You and I / Bright eyes / Come rain or come shine / Big street, The.
**Album:** Released Feb '83, on Jasmine by Hasmick Promotions. Deleted Feb '88. Catalogue no: **JASM 1009**

**JIVE FOR FIVE (Holman, Eddie)**
**Album:** Released Apr '88, on VSOP Catalogue no: **VSOP 19**

## Holmes, Groove

**GOOD VIBRATIONS**
**Album:** Released Apr '81, on Muse by Black & Blue Records. Catalogue no: **MR 5167**

**NOBODY DOES IT BETTER**
Tracks: / Gonna fly now / Nobody does it better / Calypso holiday / Let's groove / Highway of life.
**Album:** Released Apr '80, on Manhattan Records by President Records. Deleted Aug '85. Catalogue no: **MAN 5005**

## Homesick James

**BLUES FROM THE SOUTHSIDE**
Tracks: / Woman I'm lovin', The / Goin' down swingin' / Cloud is crying, The / She may be your woman / Homesick's shuffle / Stones in my passway.
**Album:** Released Nov '88, on Ace by Ace Records. Catalogue no: **CH 257**

**HOMESICK JAMES AND SNOOKY PRYOR (Homesick James and Snooky Pryor)**
Tracks: / Crossroads / Nothing but trouble / Shake your moneymaker / Cross town / Careless love / After you there won't be anybody else / Woman I love, The / I feel alright / Drivin' dog / She knows how to love me / Homesick blues again.
**Album:** Released Jan '82, on Big Bear by Big Bear Records. Deleted '88. Catalogue no: **BEAR 21**

## Honda, Toshiyuki

**DREAM (Honda, Toshiyuki, Chick Corea, Miroslav Vitous, Roy Haynes)**
**CD:** Released May '87, on Toshiba-EMI (Japan) Catalogue no: **TEC 2036**

**MODERN**
**CD:** Released '86, on Eastworld Deleted '88. Catalogue no: **CP 35 5001**

**SHANGRI-LA**
**CD:** Released Feb '86, on Eastworld Deleted Feb '88. Catalogue no: **CP 35 3019**

## Honkers & Screamers

**HONKERS & SCREAMERS (Various artists)**
**Album:** Released Aug '79, on Savoy Jazz (USA) by Malaco Records (USA). Catalogue no: **SJL 2234**

John Lee Hooker

## Honsinger, Tristan

**CONCERT EXTRACTS (Honsinger, Tristan & Derek Bailey)**
**Album:** Released Nov '76, on Incus by Incus Records. Catalogue no: **INCUS 20**

## Hooker, Earl

**Biographical details:** Blues singer, songwriter, guitarist and multi-instrumentalist (1930-71), cousin of John Lee Hooker, bringing a modern feeling to roots music and becoming king of the electric slide. He wrote *Hold on, I'm comin', Two bugs and a roach* and many more. He worked the streets with Bo Diddley when they were kids, toured with Ike Turner, recorded with Steve Miller and influenced many guitarists; he died of TB. (Donald Clarke, Nov '89).

**CALLING ALL BLUES (Hooker, Earl & Magic Sam)**
Tracks: / Rockin' wild / Blue guitar / Blues in D natural / Calling all blues / Swear to tell the truth / Rockin' with the kid galloping horses / Universal rock / My love is your love / Mr. Charlie / Square dance rock / Every night about this time / Blue light boogie / You don't have to work.
**Album:** Released Aug '86, on Charly R&B by Charly Records. Catalogue no: **CRB 1134**

**EARL HOOKER**
Note: Doubleplay cassette contains albums: Two Bugs & A Roach - 1044; Hooker N' Steve - 1051.
**Cass:** Released '88, on Arhoolie (USA) by Arhoolie Records (USA). Catalogue no: **C 206**

**FIRST AND LAST RECORDINGS**
**Album:** Released May '81, on Arhoolie (USA) by Arhoolie Records (USA). Catalogue no: **ARHOOLIE 1066**

**HOOKER N STEVE**
**Album:** Released May '81, on Arhoolie (USA) by Arhoolie Records (USA). Catalogue no: **ARHOOLIE 1051**

**LEADING BRAND, THE (Hooker Earl & Jodie Williams)**
Tracks: / How long can this go on / Cotton pickin' blues / Bright sounds / Oh mama / Off the hook / You better be sure / Nothing but poison / This little voice / Leading brand, The / Nothing but good / Looking for my baby / Lonely without you / Moaning for molasses / Hide out / You may / Lucky Lou.
**Album:** Released Oct '82, on Red Lightnin' by Red Lightning Records. Deleted Jun '89. Catalogue no: **RL 018**

**PLAY YOUR GUITAR, MR. HOOKER**
**Album:** Released Dec '85, on Black Magic by Topic Records. Catalogue no: **BM 9006**

**THERE'S A FUNGUS AMUNG US**
Tracks: / Two bugs in a rug / Hold on / Off the hook / Dust my broom / Hot and heavy / Screw driver / Bertha / Foxtrot / End of the blues / Walkin' rag / Hooker special / Something you ate.
**Album:** Released Oct '82, on Red Lightnin' by Red Lightning Records. Deleted Jun '89. Catalogue no: **RL 009**

**TWO BUGS AND A ROACH**
**Album:** Released May '81, on Arhoolie (USA) by Arhoolie Records (USA). Catalogue no: **ARHOOLIE 1044**

## Hooker, John Lee

**Biographical details:** This American blues singer, guitarist and songwriter is one of the true masters of his genre and an important influence upon the development of rock music. He was born in Clarkesdale, Mississippi in 1917 and was taught to play guitar by his grandfather. During his late teens and early twenties, Hooker led a gypsy-like existence on the road, trekking from place to place without achieving much. He settled in Detroit in 1943 and began working with local blues performers. During the late Forties and early Fifties, Hooker's tenacity paid off: he rose to prominence amongst blues lovers throughout the United States with his smash hits, *Boogie chillun* and *I'm in the mood.*
With his gravel-voiced singing style, his throbbing guitar and thumping rhythms, John Lee was feverishly active in the recording studio during the Fifties; indeed, he had to adopt several pseudonyms in order to avoid flooding the burgeoning rhythm-and-blues market with John Lee Hooker discs! Having helped to sow the seeds of the rock'n'roll revolution, he earned new respect and acclaim in Britain during the early Sixties as the vital UK blues boom got underway. With groups like the Animals, the Rolling Stones, the Small Faces, the Who and the Yardbirds adopting his style and incorporating it into the new era of Sixties pop, he came to the UK to perform in 1964 and landed a surprise chart hit of his own with *Dimples* which reached the UK No.23 position. In 1967 he chalked up a British Top 40 album with *House of the blues.*
During the Seventies and Eighties, the ageing process failed to diminish Hooker's musical skill and prowess. Having been instrumental in inspiring white rockers to play the blues, his name continued to be revered, especially in Britain. A 1982 UK package show with Bobby 'Blue' Bland and B.B.King proved that the man had lost none of his infectious magic. (Bob MacDonald, 24th Oct 1985)
Born in 1917 in Mississippi and still going strong, with Lightnin' Hopkins and his cousin Earl Hooker,'the hook' is one of the most influential and successful of traditional of bluesmen with the white revivalists of the '60's. He first played electric guitar in 1948 but returned to acoustic in the early '60's. Among many songs: *Band bang bang bang, I don't want to go to Vietnam, Boogie with the hook, House rent boogie, It serves me right to suffer, 'Boogie chillen', 'One scotch, one bourbon, one beer'* (a hit for Amos Milburn). His latest and much-praised album is *The healer* on Silvertone, with many classy guests. (Donald Clarke, Nov '89).

**ALONE**
**CD Set:** Released Mar '90, on Tomato (USA) by Tomato Music Co. (USA).

Catalogue no: **JJCD23**

**BEST OF JOHN LEE HOOKER**
**2 LP Set:** Released May '89, on GNP Crescendo (USA) by GNP Crescendo Records (USA). Catalogue no: **GNPS 2-10007**
**Cass set:** Released May '89, on GNP Crescendo (USA) by GNP Crescendo Records (USA). Catalogue no: **GNP5 2-10007**
**CD:** Released Jan '88, on GNP Crescendo (USA) by GNP Crescendo Records (USA). Catalogue no: **GNPD-10007**

**BLACK RHYTHM 'N' BLUES**
Tracks: / Hey baby, you look good to me / I wanna dance all night / Mean woman / Why put me down? / My name is ringing / What the matter baby? / Baby don't you want to go? / Talk to your daughter / You move me / Things I tell you to do / I feel good / Baby baby / Daisy Mae / Stand by / Going home / Looking back over my day / Roll and tumble / Baby don't do me wrong / Come on baby.
Note: John Lee Hooker, vocals and guitar; Lowell Fulsom, guitar; Carey Bell, bass; S.P. Leary, drums.
**2 LP Set:** Released Nov '84, on Festival (France) by Musidisc Records (France). Catalogue no: **ALB 186**

**BLUES BEFORE SUNRISE**
**Album:** Released Nov '84, on Astan (USA) Catalogue no: **20052**
**Cass:** Released Jan '87, on Masters (Holland) Catalogue no: **CLMC 009231283**
**Album:** Released Jan '87, on Masters (Holland) Catalogue no: **CL 00231283**

**BLUES BEFORE SUNRISE (BULLDOG)**
Tracks: / Little wheel / I'm in the mood / Hobo blues / Crawling king snake / Blues before sunrise / Want ad blues / My first wife left me / Wednesday evening blues / Maudie / Time is marching.
**Album:** Released '86, on Bulldog Records by President Records. Catalogue no: **BDL 1011**

**BLUESWAY SESSIONS, THE**
Tracks: / Cry before I go / Boom boom / Backbiters and syndicators / Mr. Lucky / My own blues / I can't stand to leave you / Think twice before you go / I'm standing in line / Hot spring water (part 1) / Hot spring water (part 2) / Motor city is burning, The / Want ad blues / I don't wanna go to Vietnam / Mini skirts / Mean mean woman / I wanna boogaloo / Tantalizing with the blues / (Twist ain't nothin') but the old time shimmy / One room country shack / I'm just a drifter.
**2 LP Set:** Released Oct '88, on Charly by Charly Records. Catalogue no: **CDX 33**

**BOOGIE CHILLUN**
Tracks: / Dimples / Every night / Little wheel / You can lead me baby / I love you honey / Maudie / I'm in the mood / Boogie chillun / Hobo blues / Crawling king snake / Drive me away / Solid sender / No shoes / Want and blues / Will the circle be unbroken / I'm goin' upstairs / Boom boom / Bottle up and go / This is hip / Big legs, tight skirt / It serves me right to suffer / Your baby ain't sweet like mine.
**CD:** on Official by Official Records. Catalogue no: **OFF 86029**
**Album:** on Official by Official Records. Catalogue no: **OFF 6029**
**CD:** Released Mar '86, on Charly by Charly Records. Catalogue no: **CDCHARLY 4**

**BOOGIE MAN, THE**
Tracks: / Boom boom / Dirty groundhog / I'm goin' home / I love you honey / I'm in the mood / Crawling black spider / House rent boogie / Dimples / Mambo chillun / This is hip / I'm so excited / Hobo blues / Loudella / She shot me down.
**Album:** Released Aug '89, on Instant (2) by Charly Records. Catalogue no: **INS 5009**
**CD:** Released Aug '89, on Instant (2) by Charly Records. Catalogue no: **CDINS 5009**
**Cass:** Released Aug '89, on Instant (2) by Charly Records. Catalogue no: **TCINS 5009**

**BURNIN'**
Tracks: / Boom boom / Process / Lost a good girl / New leaf, A / Blues before sunrise / Let's make it / I got a letter this morning / Thelma / Drug store woman / Keep your hands to yourself / What do you say.
**Album:** Released May '87, on Topline by Charly Records. Catalogue no: **TOP 176**
**Cass:** Released May '87, on Topline by Charly Records. Catalogue no: **KTOP 176**

**CHESS MASTERS**
Tracks: / Walkin' the boogie / Love blues / Union station blues / It's my own fault / Leave my wife alone / Ramblin' by myself / Sugar mama / Down at the landing / Louise / Ground hog blues / High priced woman / Woman and money / Journey / I don;t want your money / Hey baby / Mad man blues / Bluebird / Worried life blues / Lonely boy boogie / Aplogise / Please don't go / Dreamin' blues / Hey boogie / Just me and my telephone.
**Album:** Released Apr '82, on Chess (USA) Catalogue no: **CXMD 4005**

**COLLECTION: JOHN LEE HOOKER (20 blues greats)**
Tracks: / Dimples / I'm in the mood / Hobo blues / Boogie chillun / Boom boom / Blues before sunrise / Time is marching / Tupelo / Little wheel / Shake, holler and run / Want ad blues / Crawling king snake / Whisky and wimmen / Tease me baby / Wednesday evening blues / My first wife left me / Maudie / No shoes / I love you, honey / Rock house boogie.
**Cass:** Released Nov '85, on Deja Vu Catalogue no: **DVMC 2033**
**Album:** Released Nov '85, on Deja Vu Catalogue no: **DVLP 2033**
**CD:** Released Jun '88, on Deja Vu Catalogue no: **DVCD 2033**

**CREAM, THE**
Tracks: / Hey hey / Rock steady / Tupelo / You know it ain't right / She's gone / T.B. sheets / Sugar mama / One room country shack / Drug store woman / I want you to roll me / Bar room drinking / Little girl / Louise / When my first wife left me (Available on double album only) / Boogie on (Available on double album only).
**Cass set:** Released Jan '88, on Charly R&B by Charly Records. Catalogue no: **TCCDX 22**
**Album:** Released Mar '79, on Tomato (USA) by Tomato Music Co. (USA). Deleted '88. Catalogue no: **TOM 2 7009**
**2 LP Set:** Released Jan '88, on Charly R&B by Charly Records. Catalogue no: **CDX 22**
**CD:** Released Jan '88, on Charly R&B by Charly Records. Catalogue no: **CDCHARLY 106**

**DETROIT BLUES 1950-1951 (See also under Eddie Burns)**
Tracks: / House rent boogie / Wandering blues / Making a fool out of me / Questionnaire blues / Real gone gal / Squeeze me baby / Feed her all night / Gangsters blues / Where did you stay last night / My daddy was a jockey / Little boy blue / How long must I be your slave / Grieving blues / Ground hog / Mean old train / Catfish.
**Album:** Released Nov '87, on Krazy Kat by Interstate Music. Catalogue no: **KK 816**

**DETROIT LION, THE**
**Album:** Released Feb '90, on Demon by Demon Records. Catalogue no: **FIEND 154**
**CD:** Released Feb '90, on Demon by Demon Records. Catalogue no: **FIENDCD 154**

**DIMPLES**
Tracks: / Dimples.
**7" Single:** Released Jun '64, on Stateside by EMI Records. Deleted '67. Catalogue no: **SS 297**

**DIMPLES**
Tracks: / Dimples / Boom boom / Onions.
**7" Single:** Released Jul '80, on Charly by Charly Records. Deleted '87. Catalogue no: **CTD 106**

**DO THE BOOGIE**
Tracks: / Stomp boogie / Black man blues / Helpless blues / Going mad blues / Morning blues / Rock and roll / No friend around / Low down midnight boogie / House rent boogie / Wandering blues / Landing blues / My baby's got something / Decoration day blues / Do the boogie.
Note: John Lee Hooker, vocals and guitar; James Watkins, piano; Curtis Foster, drums. Recorded between 1948 and 1951.
**Album:** Released Jul '84, on Happy Bird (Germany) Catalogue no: **B 90165**

**ENDLESS BOOGIE**
Tracks: / (I got) a good 'un / Pots on, gas on high / Kick hit 4 hit kix u / I don't need no stream heat / We might as well call it through... / Sittin' in my dark room / Endless boogie parts 27 & 28.
**Album:** Released '89, on Beat Goes On

by Andy's Records. Catalogue no: **BGOLP 70**
**CD:** Released '89, on Beat Goes On by Andy's Records. Catalogue no: **BGOCD 70**

**EVERYBODY ROCKIN'**
Tracks: / Every night / Trouble blues / Road is so rough, The / I'm so excited / Your baby ain't sweet like mine / Unfriendly woman / I'm goin' upstairs / Everybody rockin' / I'm mad again / Hard headed woman / Crawlin' black spider / Little wheel / You've taken my woman / Maudie / I'm so worried baby / Want-ad blues.
**Album:** Released Mar '81, on Charly R&B by Charly Records. Catalogue no: **CRB 1014**

**FOLK BLUES OF JOHN LEE HOOKER, THE**
Tracks: / Black snake / How long blues / Wobblin' baby / She's long, she's tall, she weeps like... / Pea vine special / Tupelo blues / I'm prison bound / I rowed a little boat / Water boy / Church bell tone / Bundle up and go / Good mornin' lil' school girl / Behind the plow.
**CD:** Released Feb '90, on Ace by Ace Records. Catalogue no: **CDCHD 927**
**Album:** Released Jan '90, on Ace by Ace Records. Catalogue no: **CH 282**

**GREATEST HITS: JOHN LEE HOOKER**
**CD:** Released May '88, on Blue City Catalogue no: **2652212**
**Cass:** Released May '88, on Blue City Catalogue no: **2652214**
**Album:** Released May '88, on Blue City Catalogue no: **2652211**

**HEALER, THE**
**CD:** Released Oct '89, on Silvertone Catalogue no: **ORECD 508**
**Album:** Released Oct '89, on Silvertone Catalogue no: **ORELP 508**
**Cass:** Released Oct '89, on Silvertone Catalogue no: **OREC 508**

**HEALER, THE (SINGLE)**
Tracks: / Healer, The / Rockin' chair / No substitute (CD only.).
**7" Single:** Released Dec '89, on Silvertone Catalogue no: **ORE 10**
**12" Single:** Released Dec '89, on Silvertone Catalogue no: **ORET 10**
**CD Single:** Released Dec '89, on Silvertone Catalogue no: **ORECD 10**

**HOOKERED ON BLUES**
Tracks: / Go back to school / It serves me right to suffer / Roll your daddy right / Jesse James blues / I'll never get out of these blues alive / Boogie chillun / Dead wagon blues.
**Cass:** Released Apr '88, on JSP by JSP Records. Catalogue no: **JSP CC 1059**
**Album:** Released Aug '83, on JSP by JSP Records. Catalogue no: **JSP 1059**

**HOOKER 'N' HEAT (CD) (See also under Canned Heat) (Hooker, John Lee & Canned Heat)**
Tracks: / Hell hound / Strut my stuff / Open up your back door / House of blue lights / It hurts me too / Wrapped up / Let's work together / Going up the country / Tease me baby / Serves me right to suffer / Nobody else but you.
Note: Legendary blues giant John Lee Hooker & seminal blues / rock group Canned Heat team up for this classic '70s concert recorded at The Fox Venice Theatre.Available for the first time on CD.
**CD:** Released Feb '88, on Rhino (USA) by Rhino Records (USA). Catalogue no: **RNCD 75776**

**HOOKER 'N' HEAT - LIVE (See also under Canned Heat) (Hooker, John Lee & Canned Heat)**
**Album:** Released Jun '88, on Rhino (USA) by Rhino Records (USA). Catalogue no: **RNLP 801**

**HOUSE OF BLUES**
**Album:** Released Oct '88, on Vogue (France) by Vogue Records. Catalogue no: **515025**

**HOUSE OF THE BLUES**
Tracks: / Louise / High priced woman / Union station blues / Ground hog blues / Leave my wife alone / Ramblin' by myself / Walkin' the boogie / Sugar mama / Love blues / Down at the landing / It's my own fault darling / Women and money / Stella Mae / Peace loving' man / Let's go out tonight / I put my trust in you / One bourbon, one scotch, one beer / You know I know / I'll never trust your love again / In the mood.
**CD:** Released May '89, on Charly by Charly Records. Catalogue no: **CDRED 6**
**Album:** Released Feb '67, on Marble Arch Deleted '72. Catalogue no: **MAL 663**
**CD:** Released Aug '88, on Chess by Vogue Records. Catalogue no: **CDRED 5**
**CD:** Released Dec '86, on Vogue by Vogue Records. Catalogue no: **VGCD 600115**
**Album:** Released Oct '87, on Chess by Vogue Records. Catalogue no: **GCH 8042**
**Cass:** Released Oct '87, on Chess (PRT) Catalogue no: **HSC 3221**

**HOUSE RENT BOOGIE**
Tracks: / Mambo chillun (All trackes composed by Hooker unless stated otherwise.) / Time is marching / Unfriendly woman / I'm so worried baby / Baby Lee / Road is so rough, The / Trouble blues / Everybody rockin' / I'm so excited / Crawlin' black spider / Little fine woman / Rosie Mae / You've taken my woman / Mama you've got a daughter / House rent boogie / I'm a stranger / I'm mad again / Hard hearted woman / I wanna walk / Run on / Blues before sunrise / Onions.
**CD:** Released Feb '87, on Charly by Charly Records. Catalogue no: **CDCHARLY 62**

**I FEEL GOOD**
**Album:** Released Sep '79, on Jewel Records Catalogue no: **JEWEL 5005**

**INFINITE BOOGIE (Hooker, John Lee & Canned Heat)**
**Album:** Released Jun '88, on Rhino (USA) by Rhino Records (USA). Catalogue no: **RNDA 71105**

**IT SERVES YOU RIGHT**
Tracks: / Sugar mama / Decoration day / Money, that's what I want / It serves you right to suffer / Shake it baby / Country boy / Bottle up and go / You're wrong.
**Album:** Released Feb '84, on Jasmine by Hasmick Promotions. Catalogue no: **JAS 74**

**JOHN LEE HOOKER BOX SET**
**CD Set:** Released Nov '89, on Charly by Charly Records. Catalogue no: **CDBOX 260**
**LP Set:** Released Nov '89, on Charly by Charly Records. Catalogue no: **BOX 260**
**Cass set:** Released Nov '89, on Charly by Charly Records. Catalogue no: **MCBOX 260**

**JOHN LEE HOOKER LIVE**
**Cass:** Released May '88, on Tomato (USA) by Tomato Music Co. (USA). Catalogue no: **2696022**
**CD:** Released May '88, on Tomato (USA) by Tomato Music Co. (USA). Catalogue no: **2696022**
**Album:** Released May '88, on Tomato (USA) by Tomato Music Co. (USA). Catalogue no: **2696021**

**JOHN LEE HOOKER STORY, THE**
Tracks: / Maudie / Shake, holler and run / Hobo blues / Crawling king snake / Blues before sunrise / Dimples / Want ad blues / Jesse James blues / I'm in the mood / Boom boom / Time is marching / Whisky and wimmen / Tease me baby / Boogie chillun / Cool little car / Gonna boogie / Hug and squeeze you / Ride till I die / Wednesday evening blues / Rock house boogie / No shoes / Roll your daddy right / Half a stranger / My first wife left me / I love you honey.
**Cass:** Released Apr '89, on Deja Vu Catalogue no: **DVRE MC 19**
**CD:** Released Apr '89, on Deja Vu Catalogue no: **DVRE CD 19**

**JOHN LEE HOOKER VOL 1**
Tracks: / Shake, holler and run / Gonna boogie / Ride 'till I die / Hobo blues / Half a stranger / Boogie chillun / Rock house boogie / Playin' the races / Cool little car / Hug and squeeze you / Tease me baby / I'm in the mood.
**Album:** Released May '81, on Ace by Ace Records. Deleted Jun '88. Catalogue no: **CH 37**

**LET'S MAKE IT**
Tracks: / Let's make it / Process / Thelma / What do you say / I got a letter this morning / I lost a good girl / New leaf, A / Keep your hands to yourself / You know I love you / Old time shimmy / Send me your pillow / Big soul / Frisco blues / She shot me down / Take a look at yourself / Good rockin' mama / I love her / I want to shout / Poor me / I want to hug you / Love is a burning thing / Birmingham blues / Don't look back / I'm leaving baby.
**CD:** Released Mar '89, on Charly by Charly Records. Catalogue no: **CDCHARLY 170**

**LIVE AT CAFE AU GO GO**
Tracks: / I'm bad like Jesse James / She's long, she's tall / When my first wife left me / Heartaches and misery / One bourbon, one scotch and one beer / I don't want no trouble / I'll never get out of these blues alive / Seven days.
**Cass:** Released Oct '88, on Beat Goes On by Andy's Records. Catalogue no: **BGOMC 39**
**Album:** Released Oct '88, on Beat Goes On by Andy's Records. Catalogue no: **BGOLP 39**
**CD:** Released Oct '88, on Beat Goes On by Andy's Records. Catalogue no: **BGOCD 39**

**LIVE AT SUGARHILL**
**Album:** Released Mar '90, on Ace by Ace Records. Catalogue no: **CH 287**

**MOANIN' AND STOMPIN' BLUES**
**Album:** Released Jul '88, on Bellaphon Catalogue no: **BID 8021**

**MOANIN' AND STOMPIN' THE BLUES (Hooker, John Lee/ Paul Harold / Ralph Wills)**
**Cass set:** Released Mar '88, on Gusto (USA) by Gusto Records (USA). Catalogue no: **GD 5032**

**MOANIN THE BLUES**
Tracks: / Drive me away / Wrong doin' woman / She left me one Wednesday / Nightmare / Sally Mae / Love me all the time / Moanin' blues / You're gonna miss me when I'm gone / Mama, you got a daughter / Wheel and deal / Tennessee blues / Baby Lee / Stop talking / I see you when you're weak / Little fine woman / Mambo chillun.
**Album:** Released Nov '81, on Charly R&B by Charly Records. Catalogue no: **CRB 1029**

**NEVER GET OUT OF THESE BLUES**
Tracks: / Bumblebee bumblebee / Hit the road / Country boy / Booggee with the hook / If you take care of me I'll take care of you (Full title: If you take xcare of me I'll take care of you (I've got a go) / T.B. sheets / Letter to my baby / Never get out of these blues alive / Baby I love you / Lonesome mood.
**CD:** Released Feb '90, on See For Miles by See For Miles Records. Catalogue no: **SEECD 89**
**Album:** Released Mar '87, on See For Miles by See For Miles Records. Catalogue no: **SEE 89**

**NO FRIEND AROUND**
Tracks: / Stomp boogie / Black man blues / Helpless blues / Going mad blues / Morning blues / Rock and roll / No friend around / Low down midnight boogie / House rent boogie / Wandering blues / Landing blues / My baby's got something / Decoration day blues / Do the boogie.
**Album:** Released Sep '82, on Red Lightnin' by Red Lightning Records. Deleted Jun '89. Catalogue no: **RL 003**
**Album:** on Charly by Charly Records. Catalogue no: **CR 30170**

**ORIGINAL AMERICAN FOLK BLUES (Hooker, John Lee & Memphis Walker)**
**CD:** on Polydor by Polydor Ltd. Deleted Mar '88. Catalogue no: **825 502-2**

**PLAYS AND SINGS THE BLUES**
Tracks: / Journey, The / I Don't want your your money / Hey baby / Mad man blues / Bluebird / Worried life blues / Apologize / Lonely boy boogie / Please don't go / Dreamin' blues / Hey boogie / Just me and my telephone.
**Cass:** Released Apr '87, on Chess by Vogue Records. Catalogue no: **GCHK 78019**
**Album:** Released Apr '87, on Chess by Vogue Records. Catalogue no: **GCH 8019**

**REAL FOLK BLUES**
Tracks: / Let's go out tonight / Peace lovin' man / Stella Mae / I put my trust in you / I'm in the mood / You know, I know / I'll never trust your love again / One bourbon, one scotch, one beer / Waterfront, The.
**Album:** Released Oct '88, on Vogue (France) by Vogue Records. Catalogue no: **515009**
**CD:** Released Feb '90, on MCA by MCA Records. Catalogue no: **CHD 9271**

**SIMPLY THE TRUTH**
Tracks: / I don't wanna go to Vietnam / I wanna boogaloo / Tantalizing with the blues / I'm just a drifter / Mini skirts / Mean mean woman / One room country shack.
**Album:** Released Feb '89, on Beat Goes On by Andy's Records. Catalogue no: **BGOLP 40**
**CD:** Released Feb '89, on Beat Goes On by Andy's Records. Catalogue no: **BGOCD 40**

**SITTIN' HERE THINKIN'**
Tracks: / I bought you a brand new home / I believe I'll lose my mind / Teasin' me / My cryin' days are over / Mean mistreatin' / How long? / How many more years? / C.C. rider / Sad and lonesome / Can't you see what you're doing to me?.
**Album:** Released Jul '83, on Happy Bird (Germany) Catalogue no: **B 90086**
**Album:** Released Apr '81, on Muse by Black & Blue Records. Catalogue no: **MR 5205**

**SOLID SENDER**
Tracks: / You can lead me, baby / Hobo blues / No shoes / I wanna walk / Canal Street blues / Run on / I'm a stranger / Whisky and wimmen / Solid sender / Sunny land / Going to California / I can't believe / I'll know tonight / Dusty road / I left my baby / Sadie Mae.
**Album:** Released Jul '84, on Charly R&B by Charly Records. Catalogue no: **CRB 1081**

**SURVIVORS - THE BLUES TODAY**
Note: Featuring the Gravenites Cipollina Band, Dr John, Archie Shepp, Ben Sidran and many more in a live concert bringing together the best of blues past and present. Running time: 87 mins.
**VHS:** Released Nov '89, on Castle Hendring Video by Castle Communications Records. Catalogue no: **HEN 2186 G**

**TANTALIZING WITH THE BLUES**
Tracks: / It serves me right to suffer / Shake it up baby / Bottle up and go / Cry before I go / Backbiters and syndicators / Think twice before you go / I don't wanna go to Vietnam / Mini skirts / Mean, mean woman / Tantalizing with the blues / I'm just a drifter / Kick hit / I'll never get out of these blues alive.
**Cass:** Released Sep '86, on MCA by MCA Records. Catalogue no: **MCLC 1686**
**Album:** Released May '82, on MCA by MCA Records. Catalogue no: **MCL 1686**

**THAT'S MY STORY**
Tracks: / I need some money / I'm wanderin' / Democrat man / I want to talk about you / Gonna use my rod / Wednesday evenin' blues / No more doggin' / One of these days / I believe I'll go back home / You're leavin' me, baby / That's my story / Black snake / How long blues / Wobblin' baby / She's long, she's tall, she weeps like... / Pea vine special / Tupelo blues / I rowed a little boat / Water boy / Church bell tone / Bundle up and go.
**Album:** Released Nov '88, on Ace by Ace Records. Catalogue no: **CH 259**

**THIS IS HIP**
Tracks: / Dimples / I love you, honey / I'm in the mood / Time is marching / Big legs, tight skirt / Onions / Take me as I am / Boom boom / This is hip / Boogie chillun / Crawling king snake / Blues before sunrise / Will the circle be unbroken? / House rent boogie / It serves me right to suffer / Bottle up and go.
**Album:** Released Jan '85, on Charly R&B by Charly Records. Catalogue no: **CRB 1004**
**Cass:** Released Jan '85, on Charly R&B by Charly Records. Catalogue no: **TCCRB 1004**

**WALKING THE BLUES**
**CD:** Released Mar '90, on Roots Catalogue no: **RTS 33016**

**WANT - AD BLUES VOL. 3**
**Album:** Released '88, on Joker (USA) by Lifetime Records (USA). Catalogue no: **SM 3963**

## Hope, Elmo

**ELMO HOPE TRIO (With Jimmy Bond & Frank Butler) (Hope, Elmo Trio)**
**Album:** Released Feb '88, on Fresh Sounds (Spain) by Fresh Sounds Records (Spain). Catalogue no: **FS 145**

## Hope, Lynn

**AND HIS TENOR SAX**
**Album:** Released Sep '84, on Pathe Marconi (France) Catalogue no: **PM 1546661**

**MORROCCO**
**Album:** Released Aug '85, on Saxophonograph (Sweden) Catalogue no: **BP 508**

## Hopkins, Claude

**Biographical details:** USA pianist, arranger, bandleader (1903-84) who led excellent bands in the swing era that employed such people as Jabbo Smith, Vic Dickenson, Edmond Hall. The band appeared in films and had a lot of airtime for a black group of the period; he disbanded in '40, occasionally re-forming later, leading small combos and working as a sideman. He was active into the '70's but never really received the fame he deserved. (Donald Clarke, Nov '89).

**CLAUDE HOPKINS**
**Album:** Released Jul '86, on Jazz Archives (USA) by Jazz Archives Inc.(USA). Catalogue no: **JA 27**

**HARLEM 1934 (Hopkins, Claude & His Orchestra)**
**Album:** Released May '86, on Swing Classics Catalogue no: **ET 2**

**SOLILOQUY**
**Album:** Released Jul '86, on Sackville by Spotlite Records. Catalogue no: **3004**

## Hopkins, Lightnin'

**AT HIS NATURAL BEST (Hopkins, Sam 'Lightnin')**
Tracks: / I don't need you woman / I wish I was a baby / Little boy blue / Crazy song / Lightnin's love / That man from New York City / Take it if you want it.
**Album:** Released Oct '80, on Rhapsody by President Records. Catalogue no: **RHAP 8**

**BAD BOOGIE**
**Album:** Released Dec '88, on Diving Duck (Holland) Catalogue no: **DD 4308**

**BIG BOY CRUDUP AND LIGHTNIN' HOPKINS (See under Crudup, Arthur)**
**Album:** Released Nov '83, on Jewel Records Catalogue no: **JEWEL 5000**

**BLUES IN MY BOTTLE**
Tracks: / Buddy Brown's blues / Wine spodee-o-dee / Sail on little girl, sail on / DC-7 / Death bells / Goin' to Dallas to see my pony run / Jailhouse blues / Blues in the bottle / Beans beans beans / Catfish blues / My grandpa is old too.
**Album:** Released Mar '90, on Ace by Ace Records. Catalogue no: **CH 290**
**Album:** Released Oct '88, on Vogue (France) by Vogue Records. Catalogue no: **512504**
**Album:** Released Jun '84, on Prestige Catalogue no: **OBC 506**

**BLUES IN MY BOTTLE AND WALKIN' THIS ROAD BY MYSELF**
**CD:** Released Mar '90, on Ace by Ace Records. Catalogue no: **CDCHD 930**

**BLUES, THE**
Tracks: / Mojo hand / Little wail / Cotton / Take me back, baby / Really nothin' but the blues / Hurricane Betsy / Guitar lightnin' / Woke up this morning / Shake yourself.
**Album:** Released Apr '81, on Joker (USA) by Lifetime Records (USA). Catalogue no: **SM 3071**
**Cass:** Released '87, on Joker (USA) by Lifetime Records (USA). Catalogue no: **MC 3071**

**BLUES UNDERGROUND**
**Album:** Released Mar '79, on D/D (US) Catalogue no: **D 8000**

**COLLECTION: LIGHTNIN' HOPKINS (20 blues greats)**
Tracks: / Change your way / Feel so bad / War news blues / House upon the hill / Honey babe / Let me play with your poodle / Black cat / Needed time / Ticket agent / Morning blues / Sis boogie / Everyday I have the blues / Bad luck and trouble / I can't stay here in your town / Appetite blues / Short-haired woman / My California / Some day baby / Mistreated blues / I just don't care.
**Cass:** Released Dec '87, on Deja Vu Catalogue no: **DVMC 2115**
**Album:** Released Dec '87, on Deja Vu Catalogue no: **DVLP 2115**

**DIRTY BLUES**
**Album:** Released Jan '73, on Mainstream Catalogue no: **MSL 1001**

**EARLY RECORDINGS**
**Album:** Released May '81, on Arhoolie (USA) by Arhoolie Records (USA). Catalogue no: **ARHOOLIE 2007**

**EARLY RECORDINGS VOL 2 (From Gold Star label, late 1940's). (Hopkins, Lightnin' & Big Boy Crudup)**
**Album:** Released May '81, on Arhoolie (USA) by Arhoolie Records (USA). Catalogue no: **ARHOOLIE 2010**

**ELECTRIC LIGHTNIN'**
Tracks: / In my mother's arms / It's mighty crazy / How have you been / I don't need you woman / Fore day creep / You're gonna miss me / This time we're gonna try / Christmas time blues / Aeroplane blues.
**Cass:** Released Jul '88, on JSP by JSP Records. Catalogue no: **JSP CC 1067**
**Album:** Released Jan '84, on JSP by JSP Records. Catalogue no: **JSP 1067**

**FLASH LIGHTNIN'**
**Album:** Released Dec '88, on Diving Duck (Holland) Catalogue no: **DD 4307**

**FREE FORM PATTERNS**
Tracks: / Mr. Charlie / Give me time to think / Fox chase, The / Mr. Ditta's grocery store / Open up your door / Baby child / Cooking done / Got her letter this morning / Rain falling / Mini skirt.
**Cass:** Released Jun '88, on Charly R&B by Charly Records. Catalogue no: **TCCRB 1190**
**Album:** Released Jun '88, on Charly R&B by Charly Records. Catalogue no: **CRB 1190**

**GOIN' AWAY**
**Album:** Released Jan '88, on OBC Catalogue no: **OBC 522**

**GREAT ELECTRIC SHOW AND DANCE, THE**
**Album:** Released Sep '79, on Jewel Records Catalogue no: **JEWEL 5002**

**GREAT SONG OF**
**Album:** Released Nov '84, on Astan (USA) Catalogue no: **20087**

**HERALD MATERIAL, 1954**
**Album:** Released Jul '88, on Collectables (USA) by Gotham Distributing Co.(USA). Catalogue no: **COL 5121**

**HOUSTON'S KING OF BLUES (Historic recordings 1952/53)**
**Album:** Released Mar '85, on Blues Classics(USA) by Arhoolie Records (USA). Catalogue no: **BC 30**

**IN BERKELEY**
**Album:** Released May '81, on Arhoolie (USA) by Arhoolie Records (USA). Catalogue no: **ARHOOLIE 1063**

**LEGACY OF THE BLUES-12**
Tracks: / Please help poor me / Way out in Abilene / Don't you call that boogie / Swing in the backyard / Hearse is parked up to the door / That meat's a little too high / Let them little things be true / I been burnin' bad gasoline / Don't you mess with my woman / Water fallin' boogie.
**Album:** Released May '89, on GNP Crescendo (USA) by GNP Crescendo Records (USA). Catalogue no: **GNPS 10022**
**Cass:** Released May '89, on GNP Crescendo (USA) by GNP Crescendo Records (USA). Catalogue no: **GNP5 10022**
**Album:** Released Jan '74, on Sonet by Sonet Records. Catalogue no: **SNTF 672**
**CD:** Released Jan '74, on Sonet by Sonet Records. Catalogue no: **SNTCD 672**

**LIGHTNIN**
**Album:** Released Mar '79, on Tomato (USA) by Tomato Music Co. (USA). Catalogue no: **TOM 2 7004**

**LIGHTNIN' HOPKINS**
Note: Doubleplay cassette contains albums: Lightnin' Hopkins & His Guitar - 1011; Po Lightnin - 1087.i
**Cass:** Released '88, on Arhoolie (USA) by Arhoolie Records (USA). Catalogue no: **C 201**

**LIGHTNIN HOPKINS AND HIS GUITAR**
**Album:** Released May '81, on Arhoolie (USA) by Arhoolie Records (USA). Catalogue no: **ARHOOLIE 1011**

**LIGHTNIN HOPKINS HIS BROTHERS AND BARBARA DANE**
**Album:** Released May '81, on Arhoolie (USA) by Arhoolie Records (USA). Catalogue no: **ARHOOLIE 1022**

**LIGHTNIN' IN NEW YORK**
Tracks: / Take it easy / Mighty crazy / Your own fault, baby, to treat me the way you do / I've had my fun if I don't get well no more / Trouble blues / Lightnin's piano boogie / Wonder why / Mister Charlie.
**Album:** Released Dec '85, on Candid Catalogue no: **CS 9010**
**CD:** Released Sep '87, on Candid Catalogue no: **CCD 9010**

**LIGHTNIN STRIKES BACK**
Tracks: / Introduction / Big car blues / Coffee house blues / Stool pigeon blues / Ball of twine / Mary Lou / Want to come home / Rolling and rolling / Devil is

watching you / Please don't quit me / Coon is hard to catch / Heavy snow / Walking round in circles / War is starting again / Got me a Louisiana woman.
**CD:** Released Nov '89, on Charly R&B by Charly Records. Catalogue no: **CD CHARLY 209**
**Album:** Released May '81, on Charly R&B by Charly Records. Catalogue no: **CRB 1031**

**LIGHTNING HOPKINS 1946-60**
**Album:** Released '89, on Blues Document Catalogue no: **BD 2066**

**LIVE AT THE BIRD LOUNGE (Hopkins, Sam 'Lightnin')**
Tracks: / I heard my children crying / Leave Jike Mary alone / You treat po' Lightnin' wrong / I'm gonna meet my baby somewhere / Don't treat that man the way you treat me / There's good rockin' tonight.
**Album:** Released Jul '82, on Bulldog Records by President Records. Catalogue no: **BDL 1010**

**LIVE AT THE BIRD LOUNGE, HOUSTON**
**Album:** Released Nov '84, on Astan (USA) Catalogue no: **20053**
**Cass:** Released Nov '84, on Astan (USA) Catalogue no: **40053**

**MAD BLUES**
Tracks: / Moonrise blues / Have to let you go / Shining moon / Mercy / Lightnin' blues / No mail blues / Baby please don't go / Another fool in town / Bold-headed blues / Mad blues / Crazy 'bout my baby / Long way from Texas / Whiskey, whiskey / Getting out of the bushes tap dance / Suicide blues / Look out / Seffegast / Here me and my partner come.
**Album:** on Official by Official Records. Catalogue no: **OFF 6054**

**MOVE ON OUT**
Tracks: / Fishing clothes / Wig wearing woman / Vietnam blues - parts 1 & 2 / Play with your poodle / Back door friend / Gamblers blues / Move on out - part 1 / Breakfast time / Mr. Charlie - parts 1 & 2 / Long way from home / Move on out - part 2 / Moaning blues / Found my baby crying / Ride in your automobile.
**Album:** Released Feb '87, on Charly R&B by Charly Records. Catalogue no: **CRB 1147**

**PO' LIGHTNIN'**
**Album:** Released Dec '88, on Arhoolie (USA) by Arhoolie Records (USA). Catalogue no: **ARHOOLIE 1087**

**SHAKE IT BABY**
**CD:** Released Oct '88, on Vogue by Vogue Records. Catalogue no: **VGCD 600 187**
**Album:** Released Oct '88, on Vogue by Vogue Records. Catalogue no: **500 891**

**SINGS THE BLUES**
**Album:** Released '83, on EMI (France) by EMI Records. Catalogue no: **2C 068 83075**

**STRUMS THE BLUES**
**Album:** Released '83, on EMI (France) by EMI Records. Catalogue no: **2C 068 83076**

**TALKING SOME SENSE**
**Album:** Released Sep '79, on Jewel Records Catalogue no: **JEWEL 5001**

**TEXAS BLUES MAN**
**Album:** Released Dec '88, on Arhoolie (USA) by Arhoolie Records (USA). Catalogue no: **ARHOOLIE 1034**

**WALKIN' THIS ROAD BY MYSELF**
Tracks: / Walkin' this road by myself / Black gal / How many more years I got to let... / Baby don't you tear my clothes / Worried life blues / Happy blues for John Glenn / Good morning little schoolgirl / Devil jumped the black man, The / Coffee blues / Black Cadillac.
**Album:** Released Oct '88, on Ace by Ace Records. Catalogue no: **CH 256**

## Horn

**HORN, THE The tenor sax in jazz (Various artists)**
Tracks: / Bird of Prey blues: *Hawkins, Coleman* / Newport news: *Freeman, Bud* (Not on CD.) / Prelude to a kiss: *Webster, Ben* / Neenah (Not on CD.) / No dues: *Cobb, Arnett* / You are too beautiful: *Davis, Eddie Lockjaw* / Hey there: *Gray, Wardell* / Darn that dream: *Gordon, Dexter* / Going south: *Ammons, Gene* (Not on CD.) / Jive at five: *Various artists* / Chase is on, The: *Rouse/Quinchette* / Way you look tonight, The: *Stitt/Holloway* / A la carte: *Kirk, Roland* / I didn't know what time it was: *Shorter, Wayne* / I want to talk about you: *Coltrane, John* / Big George: *Coleman, George* (Not on CD.).
**CD:** Released 30 Apr '88, on Charly by Charly Records. Catalogue no: **CDCHARLY 114**
**2 LP Set:** Released May '88, on Atlantis by Charly Records. Catalogue no: **ATSD 14**
**Cass set:** Released 2 Sep '88, on Atlantis by Charly Records. Catalogue no: **TCATSD 14**

## Horne, Lena

**Biographical details:** Singer and actress born in 1917 in Brooklyn. Light-skinned, very beautiful and from a prominent black family which came out of slavery with confidence and a refusal to be regarded as second rate: she surmounted obstacles to become one of the USA's best-loved entertainers. She turned pro as a singer / dancer at the Cotton Club in 1934, has appeared on stage and in many films and became a favourite in clubs.
In Paris in 1947 she married Oscar-winning film composer Lenny Hayton, who arranged Shaw's famous recording of *Stardust.* She's played the London Palladium; she appeared on Broadway in Jamaica '57-9 and has played straight dramatic roles (film *Death of a gunfighter 1969*); her one woman Broadway show *The lady and her music* was a triumph in '81 (2-disc album on Quest won a Grammy) and her latest album is *The men in my life* made in 1988 with guestra Joe Williams and Sammy Davis Jr. (Donald Clarke, Nov 1989).

**20 GOLDEN MEMORIES**
**CD:** Released Oct '89, on Black Tulip Catalogue no: **262 601 2**
**Cass:** Released Oct '89, on Black Tulip Catalogue no: **263 601 4**
**Album:** Released Oct '89, on Black Tulip Catalogue no: **253 601 2**

**20 GOLDEN PIECES: LENA HORNE**
Tracks: / Love / I wish I was back in my baby's arms / Why was I born? / Good for nothing Joe / Love me or leave me / I got it bad / Stormy weather / Poppa don't preach to me / Honeysuckle Rose / Lady is a tramp, The / Lover man / Can't help lovin' dat man / From this moment on / Take me / Night and day / Old devil moon / More / My blue Heaven / Cuckoo in the clock / Meditation.
**Cass:** Released Jul '82, on Bulldog Records by President Records. Catalogue no: **BDC 2000**
**Album:** Released Jul '82, on Bulldog Records by President Records. Catalogue no: **BDL 2000**

**...AT THE WALDORF ASTORIA**
Tracks: / Today I love everybody / Let me love you / Come running / How's your romance / After you / Love of my life / It's all right with me / Mood indigo / I'm beginning to see the light / How d'you say it / Honeysuckle rose / Day in, day out / New fangled tango / I love to love / From this moment on.
**Album:** Released Nov '80, on RCA by BMG Records (UK). Catalogue no: **INTS 5053**
**Cass:** Released Nov '80, on RCA by BMG Records (UK). Catalogue no: **INTK 5053**

**FABULOUS...., THE**
Tracks: / Stormy weather / I'm through with love / From this moment on / One for my baby / Love me or leave me / Man I love, The / I've found a new baby / What is this thing called love / I got rhythm / I gotta right to sing the blues / I wanna be loved / Day in, day out / It might as well be spring / Love / Bewitched / I'll be around / Honey in the honeycombe / Summer time / I'm confessin' / Like someone in love.
**2 LP Set:** Released Feb '85, on Cambra by Cambra Records. Deleted '88. Catalogue no: **CR 047**
**Cass set:** Released Feb '85, on Cambra by Cambra Records. Deleted '88. Catalogue no: **CRT 047**

**GIVE THE LADY WHAT SHE WANTS**
Tracks: / Diamonds are a girl's best friend / People will say we're in love / Just in time / Honey in the honeycombe / You better know it / Get out of town / Baubles, bangles and beads / Bewitched / At long last love / Speak low / Love / Let's put

Lena Horne - Lena in Hollywood (United Artists)

out the lights.
**Cass:** Released Oct '84, on RCA by BMG Records (UK). Deleted Jul '89. Catalogue no: **NK 89459**
**Album:** Released Oct '84, on RCA by BMG Records (UK). Deleted Jul '89. Catalogue no: **NL 89459**

**JAZZ MASTERS**
Tracks: / Stormy weather / Can't help loving that man / Lady is a tramp.
**Cass:** Released '88, on DRG (USA) by DRG Records (USA). Catalogue no: **MRSC 501**
**Album:** Released Aug '83, on DRG (USA) by DRG Records (USA). Deleted Jan '89. Catalogue no: **MRS 501**

**LADY AND HER MUSIC**
Tracks: / From this moment on / I got a name / I'm glad there is you / I want to be happy / Cotton Club revue / Where or when / Can't help lovin' dat man / Just one of those things / Stormy weather / Love / Push de button / Lady is a tramp / Yesterday, when I was young / Deed I do / Life goes on / Watch what happens / Surrey with the fringe on top / Fly / Bewitched / Lady must live / That's what miracles are all about / I'm gonna sit right down and write myself a letter / If you believe.
**2 LP Set:** Released Oct '81, on Qwest (USA) by Qwest Records (USA). Deleted Oct '86. Catalogue no: **K 66108**

**LENA A NEW ALBUM**
Tracks: / I've grown accustomed to his face / Someone to watch over me / My funny Valentine / Some day my prince will come / I've got the world on a string / Softly as I leave you / I have dreamed / Flower is a lovesome thing, A / I've got to have you / My ship.
**Album:** Released Nov '76, on RCA by BMG Records (UK). Catalogue no: **RS 1089**

**LENA AND GABOR (With Gabor Szabo)**
Tracks: / Watch what happens / Something / Everybody talkin / Fool on the hill, The / Yesterday when I was young / Rocky raccoon / My mood is you / Message to Michael, A / Nightwind / In my life.
**Album:** Released May '80, on Rhapsody by President Records. Catalogue no: **RHAP 1**

**LENA GOES LATIN**
Tracks: / From this moment on / Old devil moon / Falling in love with love.
**Cass:** Released '88, on DRG (USA) by DRG Records (USA). Catalogue no: **MRSC 510**
**Album:** Released '88, on DRG (USA) by DRG Records (USA). Catalogue no: **MRS 510**
**CD:** Released '88, on DRG (USA) by DRG Records (USA). Catalogue no: **CD MRS 510**

**LENA HORNE (Great performers series)**
**Cass:** Released Oct '84, on Audio Fidelity(USA) by Audio Fidelity (USA). Catalogue no: **ZCGAS 739**
**Album:** Released Jan '79, on Jazz Greats Catalogue no: **GP 704**

**LENA HORNE AND FRANK SINATRA (Horne, Lena & Frank Sinatra)**
**Album:** Released Nov '84, on Astan (USA) Catalogue no: **20037**
**Cass:** Released Nov '84, on Astan (USA) Catalogue no: **40037**

**LENA HORNE AND PEARL BAILEY**
**Album:** Released Jan '79, on Jazz Greats Catalogue no: **GP 706**

**LENA IN HOLLYWOOD (see panel left)**
Tracks: / Singin' in the rain / In love in vain / Never on Sunday / Somewhere / All the way / Wives and lovers / It had better be tonight / Moon river / Fine romance, A / I love Paris / It's a mad, mad, mad world.
**Album:** Released '66 on United Artists. Catalogue no: **SULP 1132**

**LENA....LIVE AND LOVELY**
Tracks: / I concentrate on you / I get the blues when it rains / I've grown accustomed to his face / I got rhythm / I'm confessin' / I want to be happy / I surrender dear / I've found a new baby / I understand / I let a song go out of my heart / I ain't got nobody (and nobody cares much for me) / I only have eyes for you.
**Cass:** Released Jun '87, on RCA by BMG Records (UK). Deleted Jul '89. Catalogue no: **NK 90038**
**Album:** Released Jun '87, on RCA by BMG Records (UK). Deleted Jul '89. Catalogue no: **NL 90038**

**PORTRAIT OF A SONG STYLIST**
**Cass:** Released Oct '89, on Masterpiece by Castle Communications Records. Catalogue no: **HARMC 111**
**CD:** Released Oct '89, on Masterpiece by Castle Communications Records. Catalogue no: **HAR CD 111**

**STORMY WEATHER**
Tracks: / You're my thrill / Good for nothin' Joe / Love me a little little / Don't take your love from me / Stormy weather / What is this thing called love? / Ill wind / Man I love, The / Where or when / I gotta right to sing the blues / Moanin' low / I didn't know about you / One for my baby (and one more for the road) / As long as I live / I ain't got nothin' but the blues / How long has this been goin' on / It's love / Let me love you / It's alright with me / People will say we're in love / Just in time / Get out of town.
**CD:** Released Apr '90, on RCA by BMG Records (UK). Catalogue no: **ND 90441**
**Album:** Released Apr '90, on RCA by BMG Records (UK). Catalogue no: **NL 90441**
**Cass:** Released Apr '90, on RCA by BMG Records (UK). Catalogue no: **NK 90441**

## Horton, Walter

**Biographical details:** Harmonica player, born in 1917 in Mississippi, settled in Chicago in 1940 and became a legend, recording with Muddy Waters, Johnny Shines, Otis Rush etc. as well as his own combos, an influence on younger men like Little Walter and James Cotton. (Donald Clarke, Nov

1989).

**60'S GREATEST HITS (Horton, Walter & Carey Bell)**
Tracks: / Have a good time / Christine / Lovin' my baby / Little boy blue / Can't hold out much longer / Under the sun / Tell me baby / Have mercy / That ain't it / Temptation blues / Trouble in mind.
**Album:** Released '76, on Sonet by Sonet Records. Catalogue no: **SNTF 677**

**CAN'T KEEP LOVIN' YOU**
**Album:** Released Jul '84, on Blind Pig (USA) by Blind Pig Records (USA). Catalogue no: **BP-1484**

**DEEP BLUES HARMONICA OF WALTER HORTON, THE**
Tracks: / Hard hearted woman / Sick & tired / Walter's jump / Leaving in the morning / Walter and Carey / Walking by myself / My eyes keep me in trouble.
**Album:** Released Jun '84, on JSP by JSP Records. Catalogue no: **JSP 1071**

**FINE CUTS**
Tracks: / Everybody's fishin' / Don't get around much anymore / Relaxin' / We gonna move to Kansas City / Walter's swing / Hobo blues / La cucaracha / Worried life / Put the kettle on.
**Album:** Released '88, on Blind Pig (USA) by Blind Pig Records (USA). Catalogue no: **BP-006**
**Album:** Released Aug '89, on Blue Moon (1) by Magnum Music Group. Catalogue no: **BMLP 069**

**HARMONICA BLUES KINGS (Horton, Walter & Alfred Harris)**
**Album:** Released Dec '88, on Pearl (USA) by Delmark Records (USA). Catalogue no: **PL´12**

**LITTLE BOY BLUE**
Note: Live recording - remixed.
**Album:** Released Feb '82, on JSP by JSP Records. Catalogue no: **JSP 1019**
**CD:** Released Jan '88, on JSP by JSP Records. Catalogue no: **JSP CD 208**
**Cass:** Released Apr '88, on JSP by JSP Records. Catalogue no: **JSP CC 1019**

**MOUTH HARP MAESTRO**
Tracks: / Jumpin' blues / Hard hearted woman / Cotton patch hot foot / I'm in love with you baby / What's the matter with you / Black gal / Go long woman / Little boy blues / Blues in the morning.
**Album:** Released Nov '88, on Ace by Ace Records. Catalogue no: **CHD 252**

**SOUL OF BLUES HARMONICA, THE**
Tracks: / Groove walk / Wee baby blues / It's alright / Wrinkles / Hard hearted woman / John Henry / Good moanin' blues / Friday night stomp / Gonna bring it on home / La Cucuracha.
**Cass:** Released Oct '87, on Chess by Vogue Records. Catalogue no: **GCHK 78034**
**Album:** Released Oct '87, on Chess by Vogue Records. Catalogue no: **GCH 8034**
**Album:** Released Oct '88, on Vogue (France) by Vogue Records. Catalogue no: **515028**

**WALTER HORTON**
**Album:** Released Nov '86, on Black Magic by Topic Records. Catalogue no: **BM 9010**

## Hot Aire

**HOT AIRE (American Hot Hands Of The Twenties) (Various artists)**
Tracks: / Hot aire: *Olsen, George & His Music* / If I had a girl like you: *Seattle Harmony Kings* / Darktown shuffle: *Seattle Harmony Kings* / I'm goin' out if Lizzie comes in: *Romano, Phil & His Orchestra* / Keep on croonin'a tune: *Romano, Phil & His Orchestra* / Melancholy Lou: *Lanin, Howard & His Ben Franklin Dance Orchestra* / Don't wake me up, let me dream: *Lanin, Howard & His Ben Franklin Dance Orchestra* / Paddlin' Madelin' home: *Kaufman, White & His Orchestra* / Breezin' along with the breeze: *Seattle Harmony Kings* / How many times: *Seattle Harmony Kings* / Tiger rag: *Dornberger, Charles & His Orchestra* / does she love me ? - positively. absolutely: *Garber, Jan & His Orchestra* / What do I care what somebody said: *Garber, Jan & His Orchestra* / You don't like it, not much: *Garber, Jan & His Orchestra* / Swanee shore: *Crawford, Jack & His Ochestra* / Sugar babe I'm leavin': *Steele, Blue & His Orchestra* / When the morning glories wake up in the morning: *Renard, Jacques & His Cocoanut Grove Orchestra / Baltimore: Crawford, Jack & His Ochestra.*
**Cass:** Released Mar '86, on Halcyon (USA) by Submarine Records. Catalogue no: **CHAL 16**
**Album:** Released Mar '86, on Halcyon (USA) by Submarine Records. Catalogue no: **HAL 16**

## Hot Antic Jazz Band

**HOT ANTIC JAZZ BAND VOL. 2**
**Album:** Released Jun '86, on Stomp Off (USA) Catalogue no: **SOS 1058**

**HOT ANTIC JAZZ BAND VOL. 3'**
**Album:** Released Jun '86, on Stomp Off (USA) Catalogue no: **SOS 1099**

**HOT ANTIC JAZZ BAND VOL. 4**
**Album:** Released Apr '88, on Stomp Off (USA) Catalogue no: **SOS 1154**

**I GOT THE STINGER**
**Album:** Released Jan '84, on Stomp Off (USA) Catalogue no: **SOS 1044**

## Hot Boogie Woogie

**HOT BOOGIE WOOGIE (Obscure piano blues & boogie woogie from L.A. 1945-55) (Various artists)**
**Album:** Released '88, on Oldie Blues Catalogue no: **OL 2832**

## Hot Club Of France Quintet

**SWING '35 - '39 (See panel below)**
**Album:** Released Jun '86, on GHB by JAzzology Records (USA). Catalogue no: **ECM 2051**

## Hot Cotton Jazz Band

**STOMPIN' ROOM ONLY VOL. 1**
**Album:** Released Jun '86, on GHB by Jazzology Records (USA). Catalogue no: **GHB 168**

**Hot Club of France Quintet - Swing '35 - '39 (Eclipse)**

**STOMPIN' ROOM ONLY VOL.2**
**Album:** Released '88, on GHB by Jazzology Records (USA). Catalogue no: **GHB 169**

**TAKE YOUR TOMORROW**
**Album:** on GHB by Jazzology Records (USA). Deleted Jun '86. Catalogue no: **GHB 188**

## Hot Jazz

**HOT JAZZ 1928-30 (Various artists)**
**CD:** Released Jan '89, on Hermes by Nimbus Records. Catalogue no: **HRM 6004**

**HOT JAZZ RARITIES 1926-28**
**Album:** Released '88, on Herwin by Shanachie Records (USA). Catalogue no: **HERWIN 110**

## Hot Screamin' Saxes

**BACK BAY BOOGIE (Hot screamin' saxes from New York 1941-51) (Various artists)**
Note: Featuring Benny Carter, Freddie Mitchell etc.
**Album:** Released Apr '88, on Oldie Blues Catalogue no: **OL 8013**

**SCREAMIN' BOOGIE (Hot screamin' saxes from Chicago 1947-51) (Various artists)**
Note: Featuring Jump Jackson, Chicago All Stars etc.
**Album:** Released Apr '88, on Oldie Blues Catalogue no: **OL 8014**

**TORNADO (Hot screamin' saxes from Los Angeles 1945-47) (Various artists)**
Note: Featuring Buddy Banks, Poison Gardner etc.
**Album:** Released Apr '88, on Oldie Blues Catalogue no: **OL 8012**

## Hot Trumpets

**JAZZ IN CHICAGO 1928-30**
**Album:** Released '88, on Swaggie (Australia) Catalogue no: **S 1284**

## Hotel Bands

**HOTEL BANDS (Various artists)**
**Album:** Released Aug '89, on Golden Era by Delta Records. Catalogue no: **GELP 15064**

## House, Son

**Biographical details:** Born in 1902 in Mississippi, Eddie James House Jnr, along with Skip James and one or two others was one of the greatest of the original bluesmen to live long enough to enjoy revival fame: he was inactive in music 1948 to '64 when he was rediscovered, his vitality unimpaired. (Donald Clarke, Nov 1989).

**1941-42**
**Album:** Released Oct '88, on Roots (Germany) Catalogue no: **RSE 1**

**DEATH LETTER**
Tracks: / Death letter / Pearline / Louise McGhee / John the revelator / Empire state express / Preachin' blues / Grinning in your face / Sundown / Levee camp moan.
**Album:** Released Dec '85, on Edsel by Demon Records. Catalogue no: **ED 167**

**LIBRARY OF CONGRESS SESSIONS**
**Album:** Released '88, on Folklyric (USA) by Arhoolie Records (USA). Catalogue no: **FL 9002**

**SON HOUSE IN CONCERT**
Tracks: / It's so hard / Judgement day / New York central / True friend is hard to find, A / Preachin' the blues / Change your mind.
**Album:** Released Dec '84, on Blue Moon (1) by Magnum Music Group. Catalogue no: **BMLP 1020**

## Houston Shuffle

**HOUSTON SHUFFLE 1955-66 (Various artists)**
**Album:** Released '88, on Krazy Kat by Interstate Music. Catalogue no: **KK 7425**

## Houston Jump

**HOUSTON JUMP 1946-51 (Various artists)**
**Album:** Released Dec '82, on Krazy Kat by Interstate Music. Catalogue no: **KK 7407**

## Houston Stackhouse

**HOUSTON STACKHOUSE 1910-1980 (Various artists)**
**Album:** Released Jan '88, on Wolf Catalogue no: **120 779**

## Hovington, Frank

**LONESOME ROAD BLUES**
**Album:** Released '89, on Flyright by Interstate Music. Catalogue no: **FLY 522**
**Album:** Released '88, on Rounder (USA) by Rounder Records (USA). Catalogue no: **ROUNDER 2017**

## How Blue Can You Get

**HOW BLUE CAN YOU GET (Great blues vocals in jazz tradition) (Various artists)**
Tracks: / Good morning blues: *Leadbelly* / Back o' town blues: *Armstrong, Louis/His Allstars* / St. Louis blues: *Teagarden, Jack Big Eight* / That ain't right: *Bailey, Mildred* / Crowing rooster blues: *Johnson, Lonnie* / Evil man's blues: *Bunn, Teddy/Hot Lips Page Trio* / Why don't you do right: *Green, Lil* / Corina Corina: *Manone, Wingy Orchestra* / Bessie Bessie Bessie: *Waller, Fats & his Rhythm* / St. Louis blues: *Sullivan, Maxine* / How blue can you get: *Moore, Johnny Three Blazers/Charles Brown* / Stormy Monday blues: *Eckstine, Billy* / Taxi blues: *Little Richard* / Port wine blues: *Smith, Ruby & Gene Sedric* / Brand new wagon: *Rushing, Jimmy / Count Basie & His Orchestra* / Tiny boogie, The: *Davies, Tiny* / Rocks in my bed: *Williams, Joe & Jimmy Jones* / I sing the blues: *Humes, Helen & Red Norvo Orch* / Just another woman: *Hot Lips Page Trio.*
**CD:** Released Nov '89, on Bluebird (2) by BMG Records (UK). Catalogue no: **ND 86758**
**Album:** Released Nov '89, on Bluebird (2) by BMG Records (UK). Catalogue no: **NL 86758**
**Cass:** Released Nov '89, on Bluebird (2) by BMG Records (UK). Catalogue no: **NK 86758**

## How Long..?

**HOW LONG HAS THIS BEEN GOING ON (Various artists)**
Note: Artists include: Sarah Vaughan, Oscar Peterson, Joe Pass, Louie Bellson, Ray Brown.
**CD:** Released May '86, on Pablo Jazz (USA) by Pablo Records (USA). Catalogue no: **CD 20044**

## Howard, Eddy

**Biographical details:** A singer, bandleader and songwriter (1914-63) who had hits as a vocalist with Dick Jurgens from 1934 including his own tunes, *Careless* and *My last goodbye*, then formed his own band, nearly 50 USA hits through '54 including *To each his own* and *It's no sin* (not his own songs) and active in the studio until his death. His stuff was a bit corny but well-made and patently sincere. (Donald Clarke, Nov 89).

**1949: EDDY HOWARD (Howard, Eddy & His Orchestra)**
**Album:** Released Aug '88, on Circle (USA) by Jazzology Records (USA). Catalogue no: **CLP 29**

**1949-1953 (Howard, Eddy & His Orchestra)**
**Album:** Released Oct '86, on Circle (USA) by Jazzology Records (USA). Catalogue no: **CLP 79**

**EDDY HOWARD, 1946-51**
Tracks: / Careless / To each his own / You must have been a beautiful baby / Dreamers holiday / Rose room / These foolish things / Lazy river / Toot toot tootsie, goodbye / (It's no) Sin / Our love is here to stay / Sweet Lorraine / When my dreamboat comes home / Don't take your love from me / I'll remember April / Dinner for one please, James / Ballin' the Jack / So long for now.
Note: Eddy Howard's second orchestra, heard here, regrouped at the close of World War II with many members of the original 1941-44 aggregation returning to play the top ballrooms from New York's Roosevelt to the Hollywood paladium. On this Hindsight album, Howard sings his '46 hit *To each his own* and follows it with a dozen of his superb and distinctive vocals - four with a vocal trio including saxophonist-jazz clarinetist Norman Lee and trumpeter Kenny Myers. The band's opening and closing themes, *Careless* and *So long for now* and *To each his own* were arranged by pianist Hil Radtke. (Hindsight Catologue - 1989)
**Album:** Released '88, on Hindsight Catalogue no: **HSR 119**

**HIS TOP HITS**
**Cass:** Released Sep '87, on Timeless

Treasures Catalogue no: **MC 822**

**PLAY 22 ORIGINAL BIG BAND (Howard, Eddy & His Orchestra)**
**Album:** Released '88, on Hindsight Catalogue no: **HSR 405**

**TO EACH HIS OWN (1946 - 56) (Howard, Eddy & His Orchestra)**
**Album:** Released Jun '88, on Bandstand Catalogue no: **BS 7140**
**Cass:** Released Jun '88, on Bandstand Catalogue no: **BS 7140C**

## Howard, Jim

**NO COMPROMISE (Howard, Jim & Pat Sullivan Jazz Orchestra)**
**Album:** Released Nov '88, on Sea Breeze Catalogue no: **SB 2005**

**STAIRWAY DOWN TO THE STARS (Howard, Jim & Pat Sullivan Jazz Orchestra)**
**Album:** Released Nov '88, on Sea Breeze Catalogue no: **SBWRCI 2536**
**Album:** Released Jun '89, on PJS Catalogue no: **WRC1 2536**

## Howell, Peg Leg

**Biographical details:** Blues singer and guitarist (1888-1966) in the Piedmont tradition, born in Georgia. Worked as a farmer but lost a leg due to a gunshot wound in 1916; one of the first blues singers to record, in 1926-29, then for Testament in 1963. He lost the other leg to diabetes in 1952. (Donald Clarke, Nov 1989).

**1928-29**
Tracks: / Please ma'am / Rock and gravel blues / Low down rounder blues / Fairy blues / Banjo blues / Turkey buzzard blues / Turtle dove blues / Walkin' blues / Broke and hungry blues / Rolling Mill blues / Ball and chain blues / Monkey man blues / Chittlin supper / Away from home.
**Album:** Released Jan '83, on Matchbox by Flyright Records. Catalogue no: **MSE 205**

**PEG LEG HOWELL VOL.1 1926-27**
Tracks: / Sadie Lee blues / Too tight blues / Moanin' and groanin' blues / Hobo blues / Peg Leg stomp / Doin' wrong / Skin game blues / Coal man blues / Tashomingo blues / New prison blues / Fo'day blues / New jelly roll blues / Beaver slide rag / Papa stobb blues.
Note: The 1928-29 recordings of Peg Leg Howell were issued on MSE 205 and we now complete his output with his earlier recordings. His Blues are simple and affecting but often have unusual lyrics and imaginative guitar accompaniments.He drew on country songs, ballads, white folk pieces, blue lyrics and field hollers and created a remarkably consistent repertoire. Recorded in mono.
**Album:** Released Aug '86, on Matchbox by Flyright Records. Catalogue no: **MSE 221**

## Howlin' Wolf

**Biographical details:** Born Chester Arthur Burnett in Mississippi in 1910, Howlin' Wolf was, by the time he died in Illinois in 1976, a potent rival to Muddy Waters as the most influential of black country bluesmen. As a singer, guitarist and harmonica player he became a legend with his compulsively powerful performance, named after a howl of frustration and bitterness. He worked as a farmer until 1948, performing at juke joints and learning the harmonica from Sonny Boy Williamson (Rice Miller). His first records were made for Sun in Memphis, leased to Chess and RPM; he moved to Chicago in 1952 and stayed with Chess. He had several heart attacks but would not stop working. Like Waters he had relatively few hits: his stuff was too powerful for the charts. (Donald Clarke, March 1988.)
This American blues singer, guitarist, harmonica player and songwriter was born Chester Arthur Burnett in Aberdeen, Mississippi in 1910. His original occupation was in farming, and he did not learn to play the guitar until the age of 18. Burnett spent many years as a touring performer, gradually making a name for himself as an earthy and intense artist. Burnett finally began to make records in the late Forties and early Fifties, and it was at this point that the Howlin' Wolf nickname was established - he earned this distinctive monicker for his extraordinary moaning vocals, which careered recklessly from a gruff growl to a fiery falsetto. Tracks like *How many more years* - his first real taste of disc success, a US Top 10 R&B hit in 1952 - established Howlin' Wolf as one of the most dynamic and uncompromising artists in the blues genre. His physical presence was both tall and stout; his musical prowess was equally overpowering. He was crude and emotional, and many of his songs contained abrasive sexual references.
Like several of the blues peers, Wolf earned new respect and acclaim amongst British musicians in the early Sixties. As the UK's seminal R&B boom got underway, such vital new groups as the Rolling Stones, the Who and the Yardbirds acknowledged him as a major influence. In December 1964 the Stones reached the UK No.1 slot with *Little red rooster*, a Willie Dixon song that Wolf had made famous. Wolf himself made a one-off appearance on the British charts in '64, reaching No.42 with his eight year old recording of the infectious *Smokestack lightnin*; he also reached No.16 on the special EP chart with *Tell me*. His career went through a duff period in the late Sixties but, in 1971, the 61 year-old Wolf travelled to London at the behest of the Rolling Stones and recorded an acclaimed album with an impressive array of admiring rock stars including Eric Clapton, Ringo Starr and Steve Winwood. Ill health then began to dog the singer's life. After suffering a heart attack, his problems were unfortunately compounded by a 1973 car accident in which he suffered kidney damage. He made a partial recovery and resumed his career on a part time basis; but he died from kidney failure in January 1976 at the age of 65. The Wolf was silenced, but his howl continued to be echoed in much of rock's output. (Bob MacDonald, 26th Oct 1985).

**ALL NIGHT BOOGIE**
Tracks: / Cause of it all; The / Killing floor / Little red rooster / Built for comfort / Commit a crime / Do the do / Highway 49 / Worried about my baby / Poor boy / Wang dang doodle.
**Cass:** Released Apr '87, on Masters (Holland) Catalogue no: **CL 00922983**
**Album:** Released Apr '87, on Masters (Holland) Catalogue no: **CL 0022983**
**Album:** Released Nov '84, on Blue Moon (1) by Magnum Music Group. Catalogue no: **BMLP 1019**

**BACK DOOR MAN**
**CD:** Released Feb '90, on Instant (2) by Charly Records. Catalogue no: **CDINS 5020**
**Cass:** Released Feb '90, on Instant (2) by Charly Records. Catalogue no: **TCINS 5020**
**Album:** Released Feb '90, on Instant (2) by Charly Records. Catalogue no: **INS 5020**

**BACK DOOR WOLF, THE**
**Album:** Released Oct '88, on Vogue (France) by Vogue Records. Catalogue no: **515013**

**BACK DOOR WOLF,THE**
Tracks: / Moving / Coon on the moon / Speak now woman / Trying to forget you / Stop using me / Leave here walking / Back door wolf,the / You turn slick on me / Watergate blues / Can't stay here.
**Album:** Released '89, on Chess by Vogue Records. Catalogue no: **GCH 8110**
**Cass:** Released '89, on Chess by Vogue Records. Catalogue no: **GCHK 8110**

**CADILLAC DADDY (Memphis recordings)**
**Album:** Released Apr '89, on Rounder (USA) by Rounder Records (USA). Catalogue no: **SS 28**

**CAN'T PUT ME OUT**
**Album:** Released Aug '81, on Blues Ball Catalogue no: **2002**

**CHESS MASTERS 1**
Tracks: / Fourty four / Evil / Smokestack lightning / Somebody in my home / How many more years / I'm leaving you / All night long / Moanin' for my baby / Baby how long / No place to go / I asked for water / Moanin' at midnight / Shake for me / Red rooster / You'll be mine / Who's been talking / Wang dang doodle / Little baby / Spoonful / Going down slow / Down in the bottom / Back door man / Howlin' for my baby / Tell me.
**2 LP Set:** Released Jun '81, on Chess (PRT) Deleted '88. Catalogue no: **CXMD 4004**

**CHESS MASTERS 2**
Tracks: / Killing floor / Louise / Poor boy / Sittin' on top of the world / Nature / My country sugar mama / Tail dragger / 300lbs of joy / Natchez burnin' / Built for comfort / Ooh baby hold me / Just my

kind / I've got a woman / Work for your money / I'll be around / You can't be beat / You gonna wreck my life / I love my baby / Neighbours / I'm the wolf / Rocking daddy / Who will be next / I have a little girl.
**2 LP Set:** Released Apr '82, on Chess (PRT) Deleted '88. Catalogue no: **CXMD 4007**

**CHESS MASTERS 3**
Tracks: / Mr. Airplane man / Love me darling / Change my way / I walked from Dallas / I better go now / New crawlin' king snakes / Just like I treat you / I've been abused / Don't laugh at me / I ain't superstitious / Howlin' blues / My mind is ramblin' / Do the do / Hidden charms / Come to me baby / Don't mess with me baby / So glad / Break of day / My people's gone / Long green stuff / Joy to my soul / Tell me what I've done / Dust my broom.
**Album:** Released May '83, on Chess (PRT) Deleted '88. Catalogue no: **CXMD 4014**

**CHESS MASTERS 4**
**Cass:** Released Dec '88, on Chess Masters Catalogue no: **CHXT 102**
**Album:** Released Dec '88, on Chess Masters Catalogue no: **CHXL 102**

**COLLECTION: HOWLIN' WOLF (20 blues greats)**
Tracks: / Little red rooster / My baby walked off / Killing floor / My country sugar mama / My life / Going back home / Louise / Highway 49 / Hold on to your money / Built for comfort / Ain't superstitious / My last affair / Dorothy Mae / Commit a crime / Moanin' at midnight / Wang dang doodle / Ridin' in the moonlight / Everybody's in the mood / Wolf is at your door, The / I better go now.
**Album:** Released Nov '85, on Deja Vu Catalogue no: **DVLP 2032**
**CD:** Released Aug '87, on Deja Vu Catalogue no: **DVCD 2032**
**Cass:** Released Nov '85, on Deja Vu Catalogue no: **DVMC 2032**

**GOIN' BACK HOME**
Tracks: / Saddle my pony / Worried all the time / Howlin' Wolf boogie / Wolf is at your door, The / Oh red / My last affair / Mr. Highwayman / Gettin' old and grey / Come to me baby / Don't mess with me baby / So glad / My life / Going back home / I don't know / Howlin' blues / I better go now.
**Album:** Released Sep '82, on Syndicate Chapter Deleted Jun '89. Catalogue no: **SC 003**

**GOLDEN CLASSICS: HOWLIN' WOLF**
**Cass:** Released Nov '84, on Astan (USA) Catalogue no: **40019**
**Album:** Released Nov '84, on Astan (USA) Catalogue no: **20019**

**HIS GREATEST HITS VOL.1**
Tracks: / Down in the bottom / No place to go / Sitting on top of the world / Smokestack Lightnin' / Red rooster, The / Spoonful / Evil / Killing floor / Do the do / I ain't superstitious / Who's been talkin / Three hundred pounds of joy / Back door man / Wang dang doodle.
**Album:** Released Aug '86, on Chess by Vogue Records. Catalogue no: **GCH 8009**
**Cass:** Released Aug '86, on Chess by Vogue Records. Catalogue no: **GCHK 78009**

**HOWLIN' FOR MY BABY**
Tracks: / My baby walked off / Smile at me / Bluebird blues / Everybody's in the mood / Chocolate drop / Come back home / Dorothy Mae / Highwayman / Oh Red / My last affair / Howlin for my baby / Sweet woman / C.V. wine blues / Look-a-here baby / Decoration Day blues / Well that's alright / California blues / My troubles and me / California boogie.
**CD:** Released Apr '87, on Charly by Charly Records. Catalogue no: **CDCHARLY 66**

**HOWLIN' WOLF BOX SET**
**LP Set:** Released Nov '89, on Charly by Charly Records. Catalogue no: **BOX 258**
**CD Set:** Released Nov '89, on Charly by Charly Records. Catalogue no: **CDBOX 258**
**Cass set:** Released Nov '89, on Charly by Charly Records. Catalogue no: **TCBOX 258**

**I AM THE WOLF**
**Cass:** Released '88, on Masters (Holland) Catalogue no: **CLMC 932683**
**Album:** Released '88, on Masters (Holland) Catalogue no: **CL 32683**

**LEGENDARY SUN PERFORMERS**
Tracks: / My baby walked off / Smile at me / Bluebird / Everybody's in the mood / Chocolate drop / Come back home / Dorothy Mae / Highway man / Oh Red / My lasy affair / Howlin' for my baby / Sweet woman / C.V. wine blues / Look-a-here baby / Decoration day / Well that's alright.
**Album:** Released '77, on Charly by Charly Records. Catalogue no: **CR 30134**

**LIVE IN 1975 - CHICAGO**
**Album:** Released '89, on Wolf Catalogue no: **120 000**

**LIVE IN EUROPE - 1964**
**Album:** Released '88, on Sundown by Magnum Music Group. Catalogue no: **CG 709-07**

**LONDON HOWLIN' WOLF SESSIONS, THE**
Tracks: / Rockin' daddy / I ain't superstitious / Sitting on top of the world / Worries about my baby / Built for comfort / Who's been talkin' / Red rooster (rehearsal), The / Red rooster, The / Do the do / Highway 49 / Wang dang doodle.
Note: Featuring no less than Eric Clapton, Steve Winwood, Bill Wyman and Charlie Watts, here these pop greats team up with their blues hero and get back to the roots that started them all on the road to fame and fortune.
**Cass:** Released '89, on Chess by Vogue Records. Catalogue no: **DETK 7208**
**Album:** Released '89, on Chess by Vogue Records. Catalogue no: **DET 208**
**Album:** Released Dec '85, on Chess (PRT) Deleted '88. Catalogue no: **6 24723**
**Album:** Released Apr '82, on Chess (PRT) Deleted '88. Catalogue no: **CXMP 2008**
**Album:** Released Oct '88, on Vogue (France) by Vogue Records. Catalogue no: **515004**
**Album:** on Rolling Stones(USA) by Atlantic Recording Corp.(USA). Catalogue no: **COC 49101**
**Album:** Released '88, on Blues Rock Project Catalogue no: **BRP 2004**
**CD:** Released Dec '85, on Vogue by Vogue Records. Catalogue no: **VGCD 600051**
**CD:** Released '89, on Chess by Vogue Records. Catalogue no: **CD CHESS1004**

**MEMPHIS DAYS (Definitive edition, The :Vol.1)**
Tracks: / Oh red / My last affair / Come back home / California boogie / California blues / Look-a-here baby / Smile at me / My baby walked off / Drinkin' CV wine / My troubles and me / Chocolate drop / Mr. Highwayman / Bluebird blues / Color and kind / Everybody's in the mood / Dorothy Mae / I got a woman / Decoration day blues / Well that's alright / How many more years / Baby ride with me.
**CD:** Released 6 Apr '89, on Bear Family by Bear Family Records (Germany). Catalogue no: **BCD 15460**

**MOANIN' AND HOWLIN'**
**CD:** Released Oct '88, on Chess by Vogue Records. Catalogue no: **CDRED 3**

**MOANIN' IN THE MOONLIGHT**
Tracks: / Moanin' in the moonlight / How many more years / Smokestack lightning / Baby how long / No place to go / Evil / I'm leading you / Moanin' for my baby / I ask for water / Forty four / Somebody in my home.
**Cass:** Released Apr '87, on Chess by Vogue Records. Catalogue no: **GCHK 78023**
**Album:** Released Apr '87, on Chess by Vogue Records. Catalogue no: **GCH 8023**

**MORE REAL FOLK BLUES**
**Album:** Released Oct '88, on Vogue (France) by Vogue Records. Catalogue no: **515017**

**REAL FOLK BLUES**
Tracks: / Killing floor / Louise / Poor boy / Sittin' on the top of the world / Nature / My country sugar mama (aka Sugar Mama) / Tail dragger / Three hundred pounds of joy / Natchez burning / Built for comfort / Ooh baby, hold me / Tell me what I've done.
**Album:** Released Oct '88, on Vogue (France) by Vogue Records. Catalogue no: **515011**
**CD:** Released Feb '90, on MCA by MCA Records. Catalogue no: **CHD 9273**

**RED ROOSTER**
**Cass:** Released '88, on Joker (USA) by

Lifetime Records (USA). Catalogue no: **MC 3990**
**Album:** Released '88, on Joker (USA) by Lifetime Records (USA). Catalogue no: **SM 3990**

**RIDIN' IN THE MOONLIGHT**
Tracks: / Riding in the moonlight / Crying at daybreak / Passing by blues / Driving this highway / Sun is rising, The / Stealing my clothes / I'm the wolf / Worried about my baby / House rockin' boogie / Brown skinned woman / Keep what you got / Dog me around / Moaning at midnight / I want your picture / My baby stole off.
**Album:** Released May '82, on Ace by Ace Records. Catalogue no: **CH 52**

**ROCKING CHAIR ALBUM, THE**
Tracks: / Shake for me / Red rooster, The / You'll be mine / Who's been talkin' / Wang dang doodle / Little baby / Spoonful / Going down slow / Down in the bottom / Back door man / Howlin' for my baby / Tell me.
**CD:** Released Dec '86, on Vogue by Vogue Records. Catalogue no: **VGCD 600111**

**ROCKING CHAIR ALBUM, THE (CHESS) (Off the record)**
Tracks: / Little red rooster / Wang dang doodle / Spoonful / Who's been talking / Going down slow.
**Cass:** Released Jan '87, on Chess by Vogue Records. Catalogue no: **GCHK 78012**
**Album:** Released Jan '87, on Chess by Vogue Records. Catalogue no: **GCH 8012**

**SHAKE FOR ME - THE RED ROOSTER**
**Album:** Released Oct '88, on Vogue (France) by Vogue Records. Catalogue no: **515026**

**SMOKESTACK LIGHTNIN'**
**2 LP Set:** Released Oct '88, on Vogue by Vogue Records. Catalogue no: **427016**

**SMOKESTACK LIGHTNIN' (SINGLE)**
Tracks: / Smokestack lightning.
**7" Single:** Released May '64, on Pye International Deleted '67. Catalogue no: **7N 25244**

**WE THREE KINGS (Howlin' Wolf, Little Walter & Muddy Waters)**
**Album:** Released Sep '82, on Syndicate Chapter Deleted Jun '89. Catalogue no: **SC 005**

**WOLF, THE**
Tracks: / Ain't superstitious / Going down slow / Somebody walkin' in my house / Commit a crime / My mind is ramblin' / I walked from Dallas / My country sugar mama / Louise / Hold on to your money / Streamline woman / Ridin' in the moonlight / Crying at daybreak / Passing by blues / Driving this highway / Sun is rising, The / Stealing my clothes / I'm the wolf / Worried about you baby / House rockin' boogie / Chocolate drop / Keep what you got / Dog me around / Morning at midnight / I want your picture / My baby stole off.
**Album:** Released Apr '84, on Blue Moon (1) by Magnum Music Group. Catalogue no: **BMLP 1009**

## Hubbard, Freddie

**Biographical details:** Trumpeter (also flugelhorn and piano) and composer, born in 1938 in Indianapolis. He joined Art Blakey in 1961 and became one of the brightest stars of the decade with his own series of albums, mostly on Blue Note, with fine sidemen; he became more electric and eclectic until his first pop chart entry, *Sky dive* in 1972 with Keith Jarrett and George Benson on CTI. He continued to make straight jazz records, but his accountant prefered the fusion. The pop hits ended in 1979. He also replaced Miles Davis in the reunion of Davis's classic '70s quintet called V.S.O.P. (Donald Clarke, Nov 1989).

**ARTISTRY OF FREDDIE HUBBARD, THE**
Tracks: / Caravan / Bob's place / Happy times / Summertime / Seventh day.
**Album:** Released Mar '83, on Jasmine by Hasmick Promotions. Deleted Feb '88. Catalogue no: **JAS 71**
**CD:** Released Jan '90, on MCA (Impulse Jazz) Catalogue no: **MCAD 33111**

**BACK TO BYRDLAND**
**CD:** Released '88, on Import (label unknown) Catalogue no: **RT 3005**

**BACKLASH**
Tracks: / Backlash / Return of the prodigal, The / Son / Little sunflower, The / On the que tee / Up jumped spring / Echoes of blue.
**Album:** on Atlantic by WEA Records. Catalogue no: **K 50303**

**BEST OF FREDDIE HUBBARD**
Tracks: / Red clay / One of a kind / Born to be blue / Joy spring / Summer knows, The.
Note: Recorded in The Hague and Hollywood 12 July 1980 and 14 December 1981.
Musicians: Freddie Hubbard - trumpet; David Schnitter, Harold Land - tenor saxes; Billy Childs - keyboards; Larry Klein - bass; Sinclair Lott - drums; Buck Clark - percussion.
**Album:** Released Oct '84, on Pablo Jazz (USA) by Pablo Records (USA). Catalogue no: **23 10 884**

**BEST OF FREDDIE HUBBARD (2)**
Tracks: / Outer forces / Cry me not / Hub-tones / D minor mint (CD only) / Mirrors (CD only) / Birdlike / Open sesame / Sandu / Down under (CD only).
**Album:** Released Feb '90, on Blue Note by EMI Records. Catalogue no: **793 202 1**
**Album:** Released Feb '90, on Blue Note by EMI Records. Catalogue no: **B1 93202**
**CD:** Released Feb '90, on Blue Note by EMI Records. Catalogue no: **BNZ 236**
**CD:** Released Feb '90, on Blue Note by EMI Records. Catalogue no: **CDP 793 202 2**

**BLUE SPIRITS**
Tracks: / Soul surge / Cunga black / Outer forces / Blue spirits / Jodo / Melting pot / True colors.
**CD:** Released Aug '87, on Blue Note by EMI Records. Catalogue no: **BNZ 47**
**CD:** Released Aug '87, on Blue Note by EMI Records. Catalogue no: **CDP 746 545 2**

**BORN TO BE BLUE**
Tracks: / Gibraltar / True colors / Born to be blue / Joy spring / Up jumped spring.
**Album:** Released Jul '82, on Pablo Jazz (USA) by Pablo Records (USA). Catalogue no: **D 2312 134**
**CD:** Released May '86, on Pablo Jazz (USA) by Pablo Records (USA). Catalogue no: **CD 231 2133**
**Cass:** Released Jul '82, on Pablo Jazz (USA) by Pablo Records (USA). Catalogue no: **K 12134**

**DOUBLE TAKE (Hubbard, Freddie/Woody Shaw)**
Tracks: / Sandu / Boperation / Lament for Booker / Hub-tones / Desert moonlight / Just a ballad for Woody / Lotus blossom.
**CD:** Released Jul '89, on Blue Note by EMI Records. Catalogue no: **CDP 746 294 2**
**CD:** Released Jul '89, on Blue Note by EMI Records. Catalogue no: **BNZ 211**
**Album:** Released Jul '89, on Blue Note by EMI Records. Catalogue no: **BT 85121**

**ETERNAL TRIANGLE, THE (Hubbard, Freddie/Woody Shaw)**
Tracks: / Down under / Eternal triangle, The / Moontrane, The / Calling Miss Khadija / Nostrand and Fulton / Tomorrow's destiny / Sao Paulo / Reets and I.
**CD:** Released Nov '88, on Blue Note by EMI Records. Catalogue no: **CDP 748 017 2**
**Album:** Released Jul '89, on Blue Note by EMI Records. Catalogue no: **B1 48017**
**CD:** Released Nov '88, on Blue Note by EMI Records. Catalogue no: **BNZ 112**

**FIRST LIGHT**
**CD:** Released '88, on CBS by CBS Records. Deleted Jan '89. Catalogue no: **450562-2**

**HERE TO STAY**
Tracks: / Philly mignon / Father and son / Body and soul / Nostrand and Fulton / Full moon and empty arms / Assunta.
**Album:** Released Jul '89, on Blue Note by EMI Records. Catalogue no: **BST 84135**
**CD:** Released Jan '89, on Blue Note by EMI Records. Catalogue no: **CDP 784 135 2**
**CD:** Released Jan '89, on Blue Note by EMI Records. Catalogue no: **BNZ 125**
**Cass:** Released Sep '87, on Blue Note by EMI Records. Deleted Jun '88. Catalogue no: **4BN 84135**

**HUB CAP**
Tracks: / Hub cap / Cry me not / Luan / Osie mae / Plexus / Earmon Jr. / Plexus (alt. take) (CD only).

**CD:** Released May '89, on Blue Note by EMI Records. Catalogue no: **BNZ 163**
**CD:** Released May '89, on Blue Note by EMI Records. Catalogue no: **CDP 784 073 2**
**Album:** Released Jul '89, on Blue Note by EMI Records. Catalogue no: **BST 84073**

**HUB OF HUBBARD, A**
**CD:** Released '88, on Polydor by Polydor Ltd. Catalogue no: **825 956-2**

**HUB-TONES**
Tracks: / You're my everything / Phrophet / Hub-tones / Lament for Booker / For Spee's sake / Phrophet Jennings.
**Album:** Released Jul '89, on Blue Note by EMI Records. Catalogue no: **BST 84115**
**CD:** Released Jul '87, on Blue Note by EMI Records. Catalogue no: **BNZ 48**
**CD:** Released Jul '87, on Blue Note by EMI Records. Deleted Aug '89. Catalogue no: **CDP 746 507 2**

**LIFE FLIGHT**
Tracks: / Battlescar Galorica / Saint's homecoming song, A / Melting pot / Life flight.
**CD:** Released Aug '89, on Blue Note by EMI Records. Catalogue no: **BNZ 187**
**Album:** Released Jun '87, on Blue Note by EMI Records. Catalogue no: **BT 85139**
**CD:** Released Aug '89, on Blue Note by EMI Records. Catalogue no: **CDP 746 898 2**

**LITTLE NIGHT MUSIC, A**
**CD:** Released Nov '86, on Fantasy (import) by Fantasy Inc (USA). Deleted '88. Catalogue no: **FCD 6189626**

**LIVE, THE HAGUE, 1980**
Tracks: / First light / One of another kind / One of a kind / Summer knows, The / Impressions / Happiness is now / Red clay.
**2 LP Set:** Released '82, on Pablo Jazz (USA) by Pablo Records (USA). Catalogue no: **2620 113**
**Cass set:** Released '82, on Pablo Jazz (USA) by Pablo Records (USA). Catalogue no: **K 20 113**

**LOVE CONNECTION, THE**
Tracks: / Brigitte / Love connection, The / This dream / Little sunflower / Lazy afternoon.
**Album:** Released Oct '79, on CBS by CBS Records. Catalogue no: **CBS 83660**

**MINOR MISHAP**
**CD:** Released Aug '89, on Black Lion Catalogue no: **BLCD7 60122**
**Album:** Released Feb '89, on Black Lion Catalogue no: **BLP 60122**

**MISTRAL**
**CD:** Released '88, on Toshiba-EMI (Japan) Catalogue no: **TEC 2035**

**OPEN SESAME**
Tracks: / Open sesame / Open sesame (alt. take) (CD only.) / But beautiful / Gypsy blue / Gypsy blue (alt. take) (CD only.) / All or nothing at all / One mint julep / Hub's nub.
**CD:** Released Apr '89, on Blue Note by EMI Records. Catalogue no: **CDP 784 040 2**
**Album:** Released Apr '89, on Blue Note by EMI Records. Catalogue no: **B1 84040**
**CD:** Released Apr '89, on Blue Note by EMI Records. Catalogue no: **BNZ 160**

**OUTPOST**
**Album:** Released Jan '82, on Enja (Germany) by Enja Records (West Germany). Catalogue no: **ENJA 3095**

**RED CLAY**
**Album:** Released Feb '84, on CTI (Musidisc France) by Polydor Ltd. Catalogue no: **CTI 9018**

**RIDE LIKE THE WIND**
Tracks: / Hubbard's cupboard / This is it / Condition alpha / Ride like the wind / Birdland / Brigitte / Two moods for Freddie.
**CD:** Released Jul '84, on Elektra (Musician) by Elektra Records (USA). Catalogue no: **960029-2**

**RIDE LIKE THE WIND (VIDEO)**
**VHS:** Released Sep '86, on Chris Wellard by Chris Wellard Distribution. Catalogue no: **LJB 502**

**SING ME A SONG OF SONGMY (Hubbard, Freddie & Ilhan Mimaroglu)**
Tracks: / Sing me a song of Songmy (part 1) / Threnody for Sharon Tate / This is combat I know / Crowd, The / What a good time for a Kent state / Sing me a song of Songmy (part II) / Monodrama / Black soldier / Interlude / Interlude II / And yet, there could be love / Postlude.
**Album:** on Atlantic by WEA Records. Catalogue no: **K 50235**

**SPLASH**
Tracks: / Splash / Mystic lady / I'm yours / Touchdown / You're gonna lose me / Sister Stine / Jarri.
**Album:** Released Dec '81, on Fantasy by Ace Records. Catalogue no: **F 9610**

**SWEET RETURNS**
Tracks: / Sweet return / Misty / Whistling away the dark / Calypso Fred / Heidi / Night has a thousand eyes, The.
**CD:** Released Sep '84, on Elektra (Musician) by Elektra Records (USA). Deleted Aug '87. Catalogue no: **780108 2**

**TIMES ARE CHANGIN'**
Tracks: / Spanish rose / Back to lovin' again / Was she really there? / Corason amplio (A song for Bert) / Times 'r changin' / Sabrosa / Fragile.
**Album:** Released Jul '89, on Blue Note by EMI Records. Catalogue no: **B1 90905**
**CD:** Released Jul '89, on Blue Note by EMI Records. Catalogue no: **CDP 790 905 2**

**YOU'RE GONNA LOSE ME**
Tracks: / You're gonna lose me / Listen.
**7" Single:** Released Sep '81, on Fantasy by Ace Records. Deleted '84. Catalogue no: **FTC 199**

## Hubner, Abbi

**LOW DOWN WIZZARDS**
**Album:** Released Jun '86, on Stomp Off (USA) Catalogue no: **SOS 1093**

## Hucko, Peanuts

**JAM WITH PEANUTS (Hucko, Peanuts & His All Stars)**
Tracks: / Sweet Georgia Brown / Song is ended, The / Peanut butter / Stolen Peanuts / I must have that man / Cow bell serenade / I may be wrong / Someday, sweetheart / Stand still, Stanley.
**Album:** Released '84, on Swing House by Submarine Records. Catalogue no: **SWH 33**

**PEANUTS HUCKO WITH HIS PIED-PIPER QUINTET (Hucko, Peanuts & His Pied Piper Quintet)**
Tracks: / Riverboat shuffle / Sweet one / Lonesome / Sweet spirit / Avalon / Raggedy Ann / Memories of you / East of the sun / Peter's blues / When you're smiling.
Note: Featuring Peter Appleyard, Ross Tomkins, Arnold Fishkind, Jack Sperling.
**Album:** Released Apr '81, on World Jazz Catalogue no: **WJLPS 15**

**PEANUTS HUCKO WITH HIS QUARTET AND ORCHESTRA (Hucko, Peanuts & His Quartet & Orchestra)**
Note: Plays tribute to Goodman.
**Cass:** Released Jun '86, on Holmia Cassettes Catalogue no: **HM 01**

**SOUNDS OF THE JAZZ GREATS, THE**
**Album:** Released May '81, on Zodiac by Delta Records. Catalogue no: **ZR 1014**

**STEALIN' APPLES (Hucko, Peanuts & His All Stars)**
Tracks: / Stealin' apples / First Friday / St. Louis blues / Summer's love, A / Cute / Just a closer walk with thee / Who's sorry now? / A bientot / Tremont Place / Sweet home rag.
**Album:** Released Jun '83, on Zodiac by Delta Records. Catalogue no: **ZR 1020**

**TRIBUTE TO ARMSTRONG AND GOODMAN**
Tracks: / Swing that music / Baby won't you please come home / Muskrat ramble / Summertime / Royal Garden blues / I'm confessin' / All of me / Sheik of Araby, The / Rose room / Rockin' chair / If I had you / After you've gone / Moonglow / Seven come eleven / He is funny that way / Goodnight / Sweetheart.
**2 LP Set:** Released Jan '88, on Timeless by Timeless Records. Catalogue no: **TTD 541-2**

**TRIBUTE TO BENNY GOODMAN (Hucko, Peanuts / Butterfield / Erstrand)**
**2 LP Set:** Released Sep '86, on Timeless by Timeless Records. Catalogue no: **TTD 512/13**

## Hudik Big Band

**LIVE AT MONTREUX: HUDIK BIG BAND**
**Album:** Released Jan '85, on Dragon by Dragon Records. Catalogue no: **DRLP 59**

## Hug, Armand

**1968 PIANO SOLOS**
**Album:** Released Apr '79, on Nola Catalogue no: **NOLA LP 19**

**ARMAND HUG OF NEW ORLEANS: 1971**
**Album:** Released Jan '83, on Swaggie (Australia) Catalogue no: **S 1296**

**ARMAND HUG OF NEW ORLEANS: 1974**
**Album:** Released Jan '83, on Swaggie (Australia) Catalogue no: **S 1349**

**ARMAND HUG PLAYS JELLY ROLL MORTON (See panel right)**
Tracks: / Winin' boy blues / Buddy Bolden's blues / Chicago breakdown / Sweet lips (big lip blues) / Why? / Grandpa's spells / Jelly Roll blues / My home is a Southern town / Frog-I-More rag / If you knew how I love you / Black bottom stomp / Sweet substitute.
Note: Pimp, pool hustler, braggart, self-styled 'inventor of jazz' - all these things and more was Ferdinand 'Jelly Roll' Morton. His was a life story that would make Hollywood's most fantastic stories seem mild by comparison. His musical associates respected his talent but disliked him personally. The younger generation treated him as a crazy old timer. But no matter what else Jelly Roll Morton was, there is no disagreement among jazz scholars and knowledgeable musicians concerning his musical genius. Without question he was the first true composer to write intelligent thought out music in the jazz idiom. Possibly Morton suffered professionally while he was active because the rest of the world treated jazz as a novelty - a razzamatazz type of background for bootleg booze and Charleston frenzies. Take a pop tune and play it fast and loud - but don't take it seriously. Most of the originality that makes jazz what it is was being shown only in the improvised solos of the few who had the talent. No one was consciously creating new ideas and carefully making them a part of a new form of music. No one that is except Jelly Roll. Duke Ellington came later - as did a very few others, who still remain labelled as arrangers rather than composers. But Jelly Roll was first and though he may not have 'invented jazz' as he claimed, there's no question as to his major contribution to the development of the art form itself. Morton was a pianist and his work was naturally written on that basis. He had a unique ability to arrange his music for a New Orleans styled band, however. They tell us that he was constantly admonishing his men to 'read the dots', not to mechanize the music and quench each man's individuality but rather, to give form and substance to the music as a whole. He left ample room for the improvised solo and he wrote with a full knowledge and feeling for the New Orleans style jazz musician. A careful listen to his old recordings - keeping in mind the framework of the time when the Ferde Grofes and the Challis's and the Whitemans were writing pompous adaptations of symphonic work and labelling it Jazz - will give you a clear understanding of the remarkable composing Jelly Roll was doing. Remember too that Jelly Roll Morton was a pianist in the prime days of ragtime and his departure from that mechanical, somewhat stilted music is even more impressive. There were no jazz piano players in 1904 - but Morton was becoming the first.

**Armand Hug - Armand Hug Plays Jelly Roll Morton (Swaggie)**

Armand Hug has always had a unique ability to get inside Jelly Roll's music. There are a handful of imitators that copy Morton's playing note for note - and another handful that try - but Armand had the understanding of what Morton was saying and he was able to expand and improvise on Jelly's music in a way that Morton would have approved. It is very difficult to re-arrange much of the Morton music. It was written as a progressing theme and trying to change or adapt it destroys the whole meaning. Armand consistently could maintain the weave of a Morton composition and yet add his own stylistic expansion. Armand loved Jelly Roll's music and it shows - but that alone doesn't make the offerings on this album so warm and personal. There can be no question but that Armand's being born, raised, and a permanent resident of New Orleans had made this work possible. Maybe it's something in the Louisiana air - maybe it's the subtle rhythm of the city itself - there's no way of intelligently defining it - but put that together with a masterful jazz pianist who loved and studied Jelly Roll Morton's work and the results are both unique and beautiful.
Jelly Roll Morton wrote several hundred songs at least. Many became well known and performed by jazz and swing bands all over the world (and by men who couldn't tell you a thing about Jelly Roll). *King porter stomp* was one of Benny Goodman's early big hits. *Woverine blues* - *Milneberg joys* (with the white friends from 'down home' in the New Orleans Rhythm Kings) - *Wild man blues* (with a young Louis Armstrong) - the list goes on and on. All too frequently someone will say 'Morton? I didn't know he wrote that'. The songs Armand selected for this album have no particular reason for being chosen other than Armand liked them and felt he should do them. They encompass most of Jelly Roll's life of writing and show the beauty, form and consistency he maintained throughout his career. Copyright dates are usually meaningless in Morton's music. That just happened to be the date they were written down and submitted the Copyright Office. *Jelly Roll blues* for instance, was written, according to Morton, about 1905, yet it's copyright date is 1915 and it wasn't heard much until his recording of it in 1924. *Winnin' boy blues* was copyrighted in 1939 yet he was playing itin the sporting houses of New

Orleans' Storyville before World War I. A careful study of these early dates would clearly indicate that Jelly Roll lost much of the credit in the history of jazz that has gone to others. Three is a very strong argument that W.C.Handy was not so much a writer of the blues as he was a copyrighter of simple 3 chord, 12 bar blues from the country blues singers - the Negro wandering minstrels of their day. Morton's music clearly was not that simple. Listen to *Buddy Bolden's blues* or *Sweet subsitute* or *Winin' boy blues* or *Jelly Roll blues*. These are advanced compositions yet they retain every possible essence of real blues.
Jelly Roll wrote love songs also - and very well. They weren't as repetitious or inane musically as most of the pop songs that made their authors rich, but they were beautifully written pieces of music. Listen carefully to *If you knew how I loved you* or *Why*. They offer the sweetness of the ballad with the basic jazz sense of rhythm and phrasing. Ragtime? Certainly - and extremely well written too. Jelly played - and admired - the work of the Joplins and the Scotts and the Chauvins. Remember that they were virtually contemporaries of Morton. But his own works such as *Grandpa's spells* and *Frog I more rag* are of the same calibre yet they manage to avoid the stiff 2/4 feeling of the standard ragtime repertoire. It was Jelly's own touch - that New Orleans jazz feeling that was in everything he wrote. So sit back and enjoy a truly unique album. A great New Orleans jazz pianist playing and interpreting the work of a great New Orlean jazz composer. It's not background music, it's listening music, and when you're finished, you'll tend to give some credence to Jelly Roll's claim that when men played jazz 'they were playing Jelly Roll'. Maybe he didn't invent it, but no one can deny that, without Jelly Roll Morton, jazz today would be different and possibly less interesting. (Plato Smith, New Orleans, July 1977)
**Album:** Released Jan '83, on Swaggie (Australia) Catalogue no: **S 1365**

**HUGGIN' THE KEYS**
**Album:** Released Jan '83, on Swaggie (Australia) Catalogue no: **S 1361**

**NEW ORLEANS DIXIELANDERS AND RHYTHM PALS (Hug, Armand & Eddie Miller)**
**Album:** Released '88, on Southland by Delta Records. Catalogue no: **SLP 221**
**Album:** Released 8 Apr '89, on GHB by Jazzology Records (USA). Catalogue no: **GHB 121**

**NEW ORLEANS ON SUNDAY AFTERNOON**
**Album:** Released '88, on Swaggie (Australia) Catalogue no: **S 1419**

**NEW ORLEANS PIANO**
**Album:** Released '89, on Southland by Delta Records. Catalogue no: **SLP 244**
**Album:** Released '88, on Swaggie (Australia) Catalogue no: **S 1281**

## Hughes, Spike

**Biographical details:** Patrick Cairnes Hughes (1918-87) was a British bassist, composer and bandleader. In 1933 he fulfilled a record contract by going to New York with a suitcase full of arrangements and recorded them with his 'American Orchestra', hiring the best men he could find, including Chu Berry, Coleman Hawkins, Benny Carter, Red Allen and others. His scores were ahead of their time and still make a uniquely lovely album. He became a critic (pseudonym 'Mike' in Melody Maker) and later wrote a book about Toscanini, as well as memoirs. (Donald Clarke, Nov 1989).

**1930 VOLUME 2 (Hughes, Spike & His Dance Orchestra & His Three Blind Mice)**
**Album:** Released Jun '86, on Fountain by Retrieval Records. Catalogue no: **FG 409**

**SPIKE HUGHES (Hughes, Spike & His All-American Orchestra)**
Tracks: / Nocturne / Somebody stole Gabriel's horn / Pastoral / Bugle call rag / Arabesque / Fanfare / Sweet sorrow blues / Music at midnight / Sweet Sue / Air in D flat / Donegal cradle song / Firebird / Music at sunrise / How can you do me like you do.
**Album:** Released Feb '83, on Jasmine by Hasmick Promotions. Deleted Jun '87. Catalogue no: **JASM 2012**

**SPIKE HUGHES AND DECCA-DENTS (Vol. 1) (Hughes, Spike & Decca-Dents)**
Tracks: / It's unamimous now / Body and soul / Miss is as good as a mile / Crazy feet / Boop boop a doopa doo trot / Man from the south / What wouldn't I do for that man / Fascinating devil / Zonky / Mouchi / Bottoms up / Bigger and better than ever / Ship without a sail / St. james infirmary / Crying out for the carolines / My man is on the make.
**Album:** Released '88, on Fountain by Retrieval Records. Catalogue no: **FG 407**

**SPIKE HUGHES AND HIS DANCE ORCHESTRA VOL.3 (Hughes, Spike & His Dance Orchestra & His Three Blind Mice)**
Album: Released Jun '88, on Fountain by Retrieval Records. Catalogue no: **FG 411**

## Human Arts Ensemble

**HUMAN ARTS ENSEMBLE VOL.1**
**Album:** Released May '79, on Circle (USA) by Jazzology Records (USA). Catalogue no: **RK 23578/9**

**HUMAN ARTS ENSEMBLE VOL.2**
**Album:** Released May '79, on Circle (USA) by Jazzology Records (USA). Catalogue no: **RK 23578/12**

## Human Chains

**CASHIN' IN**
Tracks: / Cashin' in / Underfelt / Lucky / Hermana guapa / Bumpa bumpa / Jaytee / Eightyfree / Mug offer extended / Freely / Rocker / Potato picker / I can't get started either.
**CD:** Released Sep '88, on Editions EG by E.G. Records. Catalogue no: **EEGCD 57**
**Cass:** Released Sep '88, on Editions EG by E.G. Records. Catalogue no: **EGEDC 57**
**Album:** Released Sep '88, on Editions EG by E.G. Records. Catalogue no: **EGED 57**

**HUMAN CHAINS**
Tracks: / Freely / My Girl / Antonia / Elderberries / La la la / Grinding to the miller men / Hollyhocks / Golden slumbers / Further away / Suguxhama / Jolobe / Ikebana / Bon / Nancy D / Death.
Note: Human Chains are Django Bates and Steve Arguelles both of whom are members of Loose Tubes. Both Django and Steve are at the forefront of a new wave of British modern jazz, creating accessible music that has potential to crossover to a mass audience. This is Human Chains' debut album and features with one exception, compositions composed by Django and Steve.
**Album:** Released Oct '86, on Loose Tubes by Loose Tubes Records. Catalogue no: **LTLP 002**
**CD:** Released Jun '89, on Loose Tubes by Loose Tubes Records. Catalogue no: **AHUM 002**

## Humes, Helen

**Biographical details:** Fine pop/jazz singer (1931-81) who first recorded in 1927 and came to fame with the classic Count Basie Band on the late '30's (dig her *Blame it on my last affair*). She never considered herself a blues singer, but had a huge R&B hit in 1945 with Bill Doggett in *Be baba leba* and was stuck in that bag into the '50's. She contributed to film soundtracks, toured the world etc. until retiring in 1967, came back in '73 and made lovely albums for Muse in later years. (Donald Clarke, Nov 1989).

**BE BABA LEBA**
**Album:** Released Aug '87, on Whiskey, Women & Song (Sweden) Catalogue no: **KM 701**

**BE BABA LEBA: THE R&B YEARS**
Tracks: / I would if I could / Keep your mind on me / Fortune tellin' man / Suspicious blues / Sad feeling / Rock me to sleep / This love of mine / He may be yours / Be baba leba / If I could be with you / Ain't gonna quit you baby / Helen's advice / Knockin' myself out / Airplane blues.
**Album:** Released Oct '86, on RCA by BMG Records (UK). Deleted Nov '89. Catalogue no: **WL 70824**
**Cass:** Released Oct '86, on RCA by BMG Records (UK). Deleted May '89. Catalogue no: **WK 70824**

**HELEN**
Tracks: / There'll be some changes made / Easy living / You brought a new kind of love to me / Evil gal blues / Why try to change me now? / Draggin' my heart around.

Note: With Buddy Tate, Joe Wilder, Norman Simmons, Billy Butler, George Duvivier, Butch Miles. Recorded 17 and 19 June 1980.
**Album:** Released '81, on Muse by Black & Blue Records. Catalogue no: **MR 5233**

**HELEN HUMES AND THE MUSE ALL STARS**
**Album:** Released Apr '81, on Muse by Black & Blue Records. Catalogue no: **MR 5217**

**HELEN HUMES WITH THE CONNIE BERRY TRIO (Humes, Helen & The Connie Berry Trio)**
**Album:** Released Aug '88, on Audiophile (USA) by Jazzology Records (USA). Catalogue no: **AP 107**

**LET THE GOOD TIMES ROLL**
**Album:** Released Nov '85, on Black & Blue (2) by BMG Records (UK). Catalogue no: **33 711**

**NEW MILLION DOLLAR SECRET**
Tracks: / Be baba leba / Fortune tellin' man / Every now and then / Central Avenue boogie / He don't love me anymore / Voo it / Pleasing man blues / It's better to give than to receive / They raided the joint / Airplane blues / I hear a rhapsody / Loud talkin' woman / You played on my piano / Helen's advice / All night long / If I could be with you one hour tonight.
**Album:** Released Jan '88, on Whiskey, Women & Song (Sweden) Catalogue no: **KM 707**

**ON THE SUNNY SIDE OF THE STREET**
Tracks: / Alright, okay, you win / If I could be with you one hour tonight / Ain't nobody's business / Kansas City / I'm satisfied / Blue because of you / On the sunny side of the street / I got it bad and that ain't good.
**Album:** Released Sep '85, on Black Lion Catalogue no: **BLP 30167**

**SWING WITH HELEN HUMES AND WYNTON KELLY (Humes, Helen & Wynton Kelly)**
Tracks: / When day is done / Home / There'll be some changes made / Some day my prince will come / I'm confessin' / S'posin' / Pennies from Heaven / Very thought of you, The / Baby won't you please come home? / Solitude / I surrender, dear / My blue Heaven.
Note: Former Basie singer Humes and pianist Kelly are joined by Joe Gordon (trumpet), Teddy Edwards (tenor sax), Al Viola (guitar), Leroy Vinnegar (bass) and Frank Butler (drums). Recorded in Los Angeles, July 1961.
**Album:** Released May '83, on Contemporary (Import) Catalogue no: **1007 598**

**T'AIN'T NOBODY'S BIZ-NESS IF I DO**
Tracks: / You can depend on me / Trouble in mind / Among my souvenirs / Ain't misbehavin' / Stardust / Bill Bailey / When I grow too old to dream / Good man is hard to find, A / Bill / T'aint nobody's business if I do / I got it bad and that ain't good / When the saints go marching in.
**Album:** Released Dec '81, on Contemporary (Import) Catalogue no: **1007 571**
**Album:** Released Mar '87, on Contemporary (USA) Catalogue no: **COP 037**

## Humphrey, Paul

**PAUL HUMPHREY SEXTET (Humphrey, Paul Sextet)**
Note: Paul Humphrey-drums, Oscar Brashear-trumpet, John Williams-bass, Buster Cooper-trombone, Herman Riley-sax, Llew Matthews-piano.
**Album:** Released '88, on Discovery (USA) by Discovery Records (USA). Catalogue no: **DS 850**

## Humphrey, Percy

**NEW ORLEANS PORTRAITS VOL.1 (Humphrey, Percy & His Crescent City Joymakers)**
**Album:** Released Feb '90, on Storyville by Storyville Records AB. Catalogue no: **SLP231**

**PERCY HUMPHREY AND HIS CRESCENT CITY JOYMAKERS (Humphrey, Percy & His Crescent City Joymakers)**
Note: Mono recording.
**Album:** Released Jun '86, on GHB by Jazzology Records (USA). Catalogue no: **GHB 85**

**PERCY HUMPHREY'S HOT SIX**
**Album:** Released Jan '87, on Storyville by Storyville Records AB. Deleted '88. Catalogue no: **CLPS 1016**

## Hunter, Alberta

**Biographical details:** Pop/jazz singer (1895-1984) from Memphis, who also worked under other names. She began recording on Black Swan in NYC with Fletcher Henderson, replaced Bessie Smith in a New York show the same year (1923) and recorded with Louis Armstrong's Jazz Babies (as Josephine Beatty) in 1924. She recorded again with Armstrong in 1926, with Fats Waller's pipe organ in 1927, and worked in London and Nice, including the Palladium in 1928 and with Paul Robeson in *Showboat* at the Drury Lane Theatre in 1928-9. Many more shows, records and films included sides with the Jack Johnson Orchestra in London in 1934. She quit music and became a nurse in 1956, but came back in 1961 on Riverside and Folkways, leading to the Newport Jazz Festival in 1978. (Donald Clarke, Nov 1989).

**BLUES WE TAUGHT YOUR MOTHER (Hunter, Alberta / Victoria Spivey / Lucille Hegamin)**
**Album:** Released Jan '88, on OBC Catalogue no: **OBC 520**

**CHICAGO-THE LIVING LEGENDS (Hunter, Alberta & Lovie Austin)**
Tracks: / St. Louis blues / Moanin' low / Downhearted blues / Now I'm satisfied / Sweet Georgia Brown / You better change / C-jam blues / Streets paved with gold / Gallion stomp / I will always be in love with you.
**Album:** Released Jun '84, on Prestige Catalogue no: **OBC 510**

**CLASSIC ALBERTA HUNTER**
Tracks: / You can't tell the difference after dark / Secondhand man / Send me a man / Chirpin' the blues / Downhearted blues / I'll see you go / Fine and mellow / Yelpin' the blues / Someday, sweetheart / Love I have for you, The / Castle's rockin', The / Boogie-woogie swing / I won't let you down / Take your big hands off / He's got a punch like Joe Louis.
Note: Recorded between 1935 and 1940 with varied outfits and musicians such as CharlieShavers (trumpet), Buster Bailey (clarinet), Lil Armstrong (piano), Leroy Jones (clarinet), Sam Clanton (piano), Al Casey (guitar), Al Matthews (bass).
**Album:** Released Apr '81, on Stash (USA) Catalogue no: **ST 115**

**GLORY OF, THE**
**Album:** Released Jun '86, on CBS (import) by CBS Records. Catalogue no: **856 06**

**LEGENDARY, THE**
**Album:** Released Jul '83, on DRG (USA) by DRG Records (USA). Deleted Jan '89. Catalogue no: **SL 5195**
**Cass:** Released Jul '83, on DRG (USA) by DRG Records (USA). Catalogue no: **SLC 5195**

**TWENTIES, THE**
**Album:** Released Aug '88, on Stash (USA) Catalogue no: **ST 123**

**YOUNG AH, THE**
**CD:** Released '88, on Jass Catalogue no: **JASSCD 6**

## Hunter, Ivory Joe

**7TH STREET BOOGIE**
Tracks: / 7th Street boogie / Boogin' in the basement / High cost low pay blues / Siesta with sonny / I quit my pretty mama / Don't fall in love with me / I got your water on / Leave her alone / Blues at sunrise / Reconversion blues / Grieving blues / Send me pretty mama / Woo wee blues / What did you do to me / S P Blues / Don't you believe her.
**Album:** Released Jun '80, on Route 66 (Sweden) Catalogue no: **KIX 4**

**ARTISTRY OF IVORY JOE HUNTER, THE**
Tracks: / If you want my love / In memories / If you were my love / Lonesome cold blooded woman / How about me / I'm cuttin' out / I need you so / My baby's gone / I'm lost without you.
**Album:** Released '82, on Bulldog Records by President Records. Catalogue no: **BDL 1016**

**HITS, THE**
Tracks: / Blues at sunrise / Pretty mama blues / Don't fall in love with me / Waiting in vain / Guess who / Landlord blues / Jealous heart / I almost lost my mind / I quit my pretty mama / S.P. blues / I need you so / It's a sin / Since I met you baby / Empty arms / Love's a hurting game / City lights.
**Album:** on Official by Official Records. Catalogue no: **OFF 6040**

**I HAD A GIRL**
Tracks: / Boogin' in the rain / I love my man / Mean woman blues / False friend blues / I like it / Stop rocking that train / Please don't cry any more / I had a girl / Let me dream / Gimme a pound o' ground / Where shall I go / It's a sin / I"m yours until eternity / U name it.
**Album:** Released Aug '87, on Route 66 (Sweden) Catalogue no: **KIX 25**

**IVORY JOE HUNTER SINGS 16 OF HIS GREATEST HITS**
Tracks: / Jealous heart / I quit my pretty mama / Waiting in vain / No money / No luck blues / Too late / I like it / I have no reason to complain / Lying woman / Guess who / In time / Code song, The / Please don't cry anymore / Don't fall in love with me / False friend blues / It's you just you / Changing blues.
**CD:** Released Oct '88, on King 1 Catalogue no: **KLP 605**
**CD:** Released Mar '90, on King Catalogue no: **KCD 605**
**Album:** Released Dec '87, on Sing Catalogue no: **SING 605**

**JUMPING AT THE DEWDROP**
Tracks: / Jumping at the dew drop / Blues at midnight / Are your hep / You're always looking for / She's a killer / We're gonna boogie / Old gal and new gal blues / Old man's boogie / If you see my baby / You lied.
**Album:** Released Aug '87, on Route 66 (Sweden) Catalogue no: **KIX 15**

**SINCE I MET YOU BABY**
**Album:** Released '88, on Mercury by Phonogram Ltd. Catalogue no: **830 897-1**

**THIS IS IVORY JOE**
Tracks: / Welcome home / City lights / Stolen moments / Cottage for sale / Guess who / Old fashioned love / Pretty mama blues / Can I forget you / I love you so much / Darling I need you / Did you mean it / My search was ended.
**Album:** Released Mar '84, on Ace by Ace Records. Deleted Jun '88. Catalogue no: **CH 97**

## Hunter, Long John

**TEXAS BORDER TOWN BLUES**
**Album:** Released Dec '88, on Double Trouble by Topic Records. Catalogue no: **DT 3011**

## Hurt, Mississippi John

**Biographical details:** A country blues / folk singer and guitarist (1892-1966) who was actually an all-round entertainer, with a little gospel and a lot of ragtime mixed in. He recorded in 1928 but the depression stopped that; he was rediscovered in time to become the darling of campus folk audiences for the last three years of his life, with his sly, gentle humour and excellent guitar playing. (Donald Clarke, Nov 1989).

**AVALON BLUES**
Tracks: / Stackolee / Coffee blues / Slidin' delta / Corina Corina / Nobody's dirty business / Monday morning blues.
**CD:** Released Jun '89, on Flyright by Interstate Music. Catalogue no: **FLYCD 06**
**Album:** Released Jan '82, on Heritage by Interstate Music. Catalogue no: **HT 301**

**BEST OF 'MISSISSIPPI' JOHN HURT**
**2 LP Set:** Released '74, on Vanguard by Start Records Ltd.. Catalogue no: **VSD 19-20**

**BEST OF MISSISSIPPI JOHN HURT**
**Cass:** Released Mar '89, on Start by Start Records Ltd.. Catalogue no: **VMTC 6304**
**Album:** Released Mar '89, on Start by Start Records Ltd.. Catalogue no: **VMLP 5304**
**CD:** Released Mar '89, on Start by Start Records Ltd.. Catalogue no: **VMCD 7304**

**LAST SESSIONS**
**CD:** Released Sep '89, on Start by Start Records Ltd.. Catalogue no: **CDVMD 79327**
**Cass set:** Released Sep '89, on Start by Start Records Ltd.. Catalogue no: **MCCV 79327**

**MISSISSIPPI JOHN HURT IN 1928**
**Album:** Released Dec '88, on Yazoo (USA) by Shanachie Records (USA). Catalogue no: **L 1065**

**MONDAY MORNING BLUES (Library of Congress Recordings Vol. 1)**
**Album:** Released Dec '87, on Flyright by Interstate Music. Catalogue no: **FLY 553**

**SACRED AND SECULAR (1963 Vol. 3 of the Library of Congress sides)**
Tracks: / Pallet on your floor / Stackolee / I'm satisfied / Ain't nobody but you babe / See see rider / Waiting for a train / Funky butt / Shortnin' bread / Mary don't you weep / Farther along / Do Lord remember me / Over in the gloryland / Glory halleluja / What a friend we have in Jesus / Where shall I be / Weeping and wailing.
**Album:** Released 22 Apr '88, on Heritage by Interstate Music. Catalogue no: **HT 320**

**SHAKE THAT THING**
Tracks: / Candy man / My creole belle / Make me a pallet on the floor / Shake that thing / I'm satisfied / Salty dog / Nobody's business but mine / Angels laid him away The / Casey Jones - talkin' Casey / Baby what's wrong with you / Lonesome blues.
Note: Legendary blues artist - Unreleased material - Extensive sleeve notes.
**Album:** Released Jan '86, on Blue Moon (1) by Magnum Music Group. Catalogue no: **BMLP 1030**

## Hutcherson, Bobby

**Biographical details:** Vibraphonist born in Los Angeles in 1941 and inspired by Milt Jackson at age 15, but before long sounded less like Jackson than most vibraphonists. He began making his own albums on Blue Note in 1965, with a fresh, personal, swinging style, often using 4 mallets and sometimes playing marimba as well. He played on *Out to lunch* (Eric Dolphy) and many other fine albums as well as his own. (Donald Clarke, Nov 1989).

**AMBOS MUNDOS (BOTH WORLDS)**
Tracks: / Pomponio / Tin tin deo / Both worlds / Street song / Beep d' bop / Poema para ravel / Yelapa / Besame mucho.
Note: Vibes player Bobby Hutcherson delivers an all acoustic set that features both Latin and North American musicians, which must qualify as one of the best latin jazz albums of the year. As well as original compositions by Hutcherson, 'Ambos Mundos' also includes superb versions of the popular 'Besame mucho' and the classic 'Tin tin deo' by Dizzy Gillespie and Chano Pozo. Bobby Hutcherson (vibes & marimba), Francisco Aguabella (congas), Randy Vincent (guitar), Smith Dobson (piano), Eddie Marshall (drums), James Spaulding (flute), Orestes Vilato (timbales & congas), Bruce Forman (guitar), Jeff Chambers (bass) and Roger Glenn (percussion & flute).
**Album:** Released Nov '89, on Landmark (USA) by Fantasy Inc (USA). Catalogue no: **LLP 15221**
**CD:** Released Nov '89, on Landmark (USA) by Fantasy Inc (USA). Catalogue no: **LCD 15221**

**COLOUR SCHEMES**
Tracks: / Recorda me / Bemsha swing / Rosemary, Rosemary / Second-hand brown / Whisper not / Colour scheme, The / Remember / Never let me go.
Note: Personnel: Bobby Hutcherson - vibraphone and marimba / Mulgrew Miller - piano / John Heard - bass / Billy Higgins - drums / Airto - percussion. Recorded Berkeley CA 1985. Recommended tracks: 'Recorda-Me' and 'Rosemary, Rosemary'.
Bobby Hutcherson has been a major exponent of the vibraphone and marimba for many years. A musician who embraces a broad musical spectrum, showing respect for both the past and present.
**Cass:** Released Jun '86, on Fantasy (import) by Fantasy Inc (USA). Catalogue no: **LLP 51508**
**Album:** Released Jun '86, on Fantasy (import) by Fantasy Inc (USA). Catalogue no: **LLP 1508**

**CRUISIN' THE BIRD**
Note: Recorded during April 1988 and features an all-star quintet. Compositions include well known standards & original pieces by Bobby, including his special title tribute to Charlie Parker. Bobby Hutcherson (vibes & marimba),

Ralph Moore (soprano & tenor sax), Buddy Montgomery (piano), Rufus Reid(bass), Victor Lewis (drums).
**CD:** Released Oct '88, on Landmark (USA) by Fantasy Inc (USA). Catalogue no: **LCD 15172**
**Album:** Released Oct '88, on Landmark (USA) by Fantasy Inc (USA). Catalogue no: **LLP 1517**

### DIALOGUE
Tracks: / Catta / Idle while / Les noirs marchant / Dialogue / Ghetto lights / Jasper.
**CD:** Released Aug '89, on Blue Note by EMI Records. Catalogue no: **BNZ 212**
**Album:** Released Nov '87, on Blue Note by EMI Records. Catalogue no: **BLJ 84198**
**CD:** Released Aug '89, on Blue Note by EMI Records. Catalogue no: **CDP 746 537 2**
**CD:** Released Jun '87, on Blue Note by EMI Records. Deleted Nov '88. Catalogue no: **BNZ 49**

### FAREWELL KEYSTONE
Tracks: / Crescent Moon / Short stuff / Prism / Starting over / Rubber man / Mapenzi.
Note: Bobby Hutcherson, vibes; Harold Land, tenor sax; Oscar Brashear, trumpet and flugelhorn; Cedar Walton, piano; Buster Williams, bass; Billy Higgins, drums. Recorded live at Keystone Korner, 1982.
**Album:** Released Jul '88, on Theresa (USA) by Theresa Records (USA). Catalogue no: **TR 124**
**CD:** Released Jul '88, on Theresa (USA) by Theresa Records (USA). Catalogue no: **TRCD 124**

### FOUR SEASONS (Hutcherson, Bobby / George Cables)
Tracks: / I mean you / All of you / Spring is here / Star eyes / If I were a bell / Summertime / Autumn leaves.
**CD:** Released Jan '87, on Timeless by Timeless Records. Catalogue no: **CDSJP 210**
**Album:** Released Aug '85, on Timeless by Timeless Records. Catalogue no: **SJP 210**

### GOOD BAIT
Tracks: / Love samba / Good bait / Highway one / Montgomery / Spring is here / Israel.
**CD:** Released '86, on JVC/Fantasy Catalogue no: **VDJ 1020**
**Album:** Released Jun '86, on Fantasy (import) by Fantasy Inc (USA). Catalogue no: **LLP 501**
**Cass:** Released Jun '86, on Fantasy (import) by Fantasy Inc (USA). Catalogue no: **LLP 5501**

### HAPPENINGS
Tracks: / Aquarian moon / Bouquet / Rojo / Maiden voyage / Head start / When you are near / Omen.
**CD:** Released Jul '89, on Blue Note by EMI Records. Catalogue no: **CDP 746 530 2**
**CD:** Released May '87, on Blue Note by EMI Records. Deleted '88. Catalogue no: **BNZ 50**

### TOTAL ECLIPSE
Tracks: / Herzog / Total eclipse / Matrix / Shame, shame / Pompeian.
**CD:** Released Jul '89, on Blue Note by EMI Records. Catalogue no: **BNZ 203**
**Album:** Released Jul '89, on Blue Note by EMI Records. Catalogue no: **BST 84291**

## Hutto, J.B.

**Biographical details:** A great Chicago blues singer and guitarist (1926-85) originally from South Carolina, raised in Georgia. He formed J.B. Hutto and the Hawks in the late '40's and was recognised 20 years later by Downbeat magazine as a rock/pop/blues act deserving wilder recognition. His nephews include Ed Williams and James 'Pookie' Young in the excellent young band Lil' Ed and the Blues Imperials on Sonet. (Donald Clarke, Nov 1989).

### BLUES FOR FONESSA
**Album:** Released Sep '79, on Amigo Catalogue no: **AMLP 823**

### BLUESMASTER
**Album:** Released Aug '85, on JSP by JSP Records. Catalogue no: **JSP 1096**

### HAWK SQUAT
**Album:** Released Dec '88, on Delmark (USA) by Delmark Records (USA). Catalogue no: **DL 617**
**Album:** Released '74, on Delmark (USA) by Delmark Records (USA). Catalogue no: **DS 617**

### J.B. HUTTO LIVE: VOL 1
**Album:** Released Apr '80, on Charly by Charly Records. Catalogue no: **CR 30182**

### LIVE AT SANDY'S JAZZ REVIVAL (Hutto, J.B. & The Housebreakers)
**Album:** Released Apr '79, on Baron Deleted '88. Catalogue no: **BARON LP 101**

### SLIDESLINGER (Hutto, J.B. & The New Hawks)
**Cass:** Released '88, on Varrick (USA) by Rounder Records (USA). Catalogue no: **VR 003C**
**Album:** Released Jan '84, on Rounder (USA) by Rounder Records (USA). Catalogue no: **VR 003**

### SLIDEWINDER
**Album:** Released '74, on Delmark (USA) by Delmark Records (USA). Catalogue no: **DS 636**

### SLIPPIN' AND SLIDIN' (Hutto, J.B. & The New Hawks)
Tracks: / Pretty baby / Why do things happen to me / New hawks walk / Eighteen year old girl / Black's ball / Soul over / Somebody loan me a dime / Jealous hearted woman / Little girl dressed in blue / I'm leaving you.
**Album:** Released '88, on Varrick (USA) by Rounder Records (USA). Catalogue no: **VR 006**
**Cass:** Released '88, on Varrick (USA) by Rounder Records (USA). Catalogue no: **VR 006C**
**Album:** Released Mar '84, on Demon by Demon Records. Catalogue no: **FIEND 17**

## Hylton, Jack

**Biographical details:** Pianist and bandleader (1892-1965) born in Lancashire. He began as a cinema organist and led a top dance band from the late '20's with Ted Heath among the sidemen: he often played hot, and hired Coleman Hawkins in the '30's, leading a band in the USA himself in the middle of that decade. He later became a theatrical producer. (Donald Clarke, Nov 1989).

### 1937-8 OH LISTEN TO THE BAND
**Album:** Released Mar '90, on Reid Catalogue no: **RD 7**

### BAND THAT JACK BUILT
**Album:** Released '73, on Retrospect by EMI Records. Catalogue no: **SH 190**

### BANDS THAT MATTER
**Album:** Released '70, on Eclipse Catalogue no: **ECM 2046**

### BREAKAWAY (Hylton, Jack/his orchestra)
Tracks: / Breakaway / On her doorstep last night / Just as we used to do / Springtime reminds me of you / That's where the South begins / Maggie's cold / Ro' ro' rollin' along / Dance of the raindrops / Steppin' out / Around the corner / Harmonica Harry / Great day / Punch and Judy show, The / Speaking of Kentucky days / Nobody's using it now / Little white lies.
**Cass:** Released Nov '82, on Joy by President Records. Catalogue no: **TCJOY D 267**
**Album:** Released Nov '82, on Joy by President Records. Catalogue no: **JOYD 267**

### GOLDEN AGE OF JACK HYLTON, THE
Tracks: / Music, maestro please / Now it can be told / One, two, button your shoe / Don't let that moon get away / Sing, baby, sing / Have you met Miss Jones / Why doesn't somebody tell me these things / Chinatown my Chinatown / She shall have music / You turned the tables on me / Get out of town / Swing is in the air / Free (Why does my heart go boom) / Blue skies are round the corner.
Note: Medley: Anything goes/You're the top / Gypsy in me
**Cass:** Released Jul '84, on Golden Age by EMI Records. Catalogue no: **GX 41 2519-4**
**Album:** Released Jul '84, on Golden Age by EMI Records. Catalogue no: **GX 41 2519-1**

### GOOD NEWS (Hylton, Jack & His orchestra)
**Album:** on Retrospect by EMI Records. Catalogue no: **SH 218**

### HITS FROM BERLIN 1927-31 (Hylton, Jack & His Orchestra)
Tracks: / When day is done / Heut war ich bei der freida / Wir wollen tun, als ob

wir freunde waren / Ja, da, die frau'n sind meine schwache Seite / Passen sie mal auf / I kiss your hand madame / When the white lilacs bloom again / O maiden, my maiden / Four words / Handsome gigolo / Thine is my whole heart / Falling in love again / Oh donna clara / White horse inn selection / Mausie / Today i feel so happy.
**Album:** Released Mar '84, on Retrospect by EMI Records. Deleted Mar '89. Catalogue no: **SH 308**

**I'M IN A DANCING MOOD (Hylton, Jack & His Orchestra)**
Tracks: / I'll never say "never again" again / She's a latin from Manhattan / About a quarter to nine / Rose room / I'm in a dancing mood / At the balalaika / Boo-hoo / September in the rain / Love live and rule my heart / Girls were made to love and kiss / Nice people / You must have been a beautiful baby / Jeepers creepers / Beer barrel polka / My prayer / Day in, day out / So deep is the night / Roadhouse revels / Rosita / Let the people sing.
Note: A brand new 20 track compilation from Jack Hylton & His Orchestra, one of the pioneers of British dance music. This selection taken from the period between 1935 and 1940, demonstrates the talent of Jack Hylton through varied tempos and well known dance tunes. Contains classic tracks such as: 'Beer Barrel Polka', 'Jeepers Creepers', 'You Must Have Been A Beautiful Baby', 'September In The Rain' and many more.
**Cass:** Released Mar '86, on Retrospect by EMI Records. Deleted 31 Jul '88. Catalogue no: **TC SH 505**
**Album:** Released Mar '86, on Retrospect by EMI Records. Deleted 31 Jul '88. Catalogue no: **SH 505**

**JACK HYLTON**
**Album:** Released '70, on Retrospect by EMI Records. Catalogue no: **SH 127**

**JACK HYLTON AND HIS ORCHESTRA (Hylton, Jack & His Orchestra)**
Tracks: / Gold diggers' song / Stormy weather / St. Louis blues / Black and tan fantasy / Mood indigo / It don't mean a thing / Bugle call rag / Happy-go-lucky you and broken-hearted me / Black and blue rhythm / Hylton stomp / 42nd Street / Young and healthy / You're getting to be a habit with me / Shuffle off to Buffalo / Nevertheless / Some of these days / You've got me crying again / Heartaches / Dinah.
**Album:** Released '66, on Ace Of Clubs by Decca Records. Deleted '88. Catalogue no: **ACL 1205**
**Album:** Released Mar '83, on Jasmine by Hasmick Promotions. Deleted Jun '87. Catalogue no: **JASM 2018**

**JACK HYLTON AND HIS ORCHESTRA (2)**
**Album:** Released '88, on GNP Crescendo (USA) by GNP Crescendo Records (USA). Catalogue no: **GNPS 9017**

**JACK HYLTON AND HIS ORCHESTRA 1935 - 40 (Hylton, Jack & His Orchestra)**
**Album:** Released May '89, on Reid Catalogue no: **RD 4**

**JACK HYLTON AND HIS ORCHESTRA: VOL. 1 (Hylton, Jack & His Orchestra)**
**Album:** Released Mar '79, on Monmouth Evergreen Catalogue no: **MES 7033**

**JACK HYLTON AND HIS ORCHESTRA: VOL. 2 (Hylton, Jack & His Orchestra)**
**Album:** Released Mar '79, on Monmouth Evergreen Catalogue no: **MES 7055**

**JACK'S BACK (Hylton, Jack & His Orchestra)**
Tracks: / Happy days are here again / Speaking of Kentucky days / My bundle of love / I'm looking over a four leaf clover / World's greatest sweetheart is you, The / Harmonica Harry / Gentlemen prefer blondes / Broadway melody / Happy feet / I wanna go places and do things / Guy that wrote 'The stein' song, The / Meadow lark / Choo choo / Life is just a bowl of cherries / Da da da / Under the ukelele tree / Hang on to me / When day is done.
Note: Tracks correct for Living Era release.
**Cass:** Released 1 Nov '82, on Living Era by Academy Sound & Vision Records. Catalogue no: **ZC AJA 5018**
**Album:** Released '88, on GNP Crescendo (USA) by GNP Crescendo Records (USA). Catalogue no: **GNPS 9018**
**Album:** Released 1 Nov '82, on Living Era by Academy Sound & Vision Records. Catalogue no: **AJA 5018**

**LOVABLE AND SWEET**
**Album:** Released Feb '85, on Old Bean by Submarine Records. Catalogue no: **OLD 1**

**PLAYS DE SYLVA, BROWN AND HENDERSON**
**Album:** Released Nov '74, on Retrospect by EMI Records. Catalogue no: **WRCSH 218**

**SONG OF HAPPINESS 1931-33**
Tracks: / Song of happiness / I apologize / Mona Lisa / Faded summer love, A / By the sycamore tree / Now's the time to fall in love / Goopy Geer (he plays piano and he plays by ear / Who's your little who-zis? / With love in my heart / Rain on the roof / With all my love and kisses / How long will it last? / Just humming along / Lawd, you made the night too long / Dream sweetheart / You're taking a chance with me / After tonight we say goodbye / Can't we meet again? (and let's be sweethearts) / You're mine, you / Did my heart beat, did I fall in love?.
**Album:** Released Sep '87, on Saville by Conifer Records. Catalogue no: **SVL 187**
**Cass:** Released '88, on Saville by Conifer Records. Catalogue no: **CSVL 187**

**SWING (Hylton, Jack & His Orchestra)**
Tracks: / Good morning / I'll never say never again again / Unbelievable / Change partners / Melody maker / Midnight blue / Do the runaround / Lovely to look at / I believe in miracles / Zing went the strings of my heart / Organ grinders swing / Lovely Liza Lee / Moanin' Minnie / If the moon turns green / September in the rain / So red the rose / Hypnotised / Drop in the next time you're passing / Give a little whistle.
**Album:** Released Jul '83, on Saville by Conifer Records. Catalogue no: **SVL 158**

**TALK OF THE TOWN (Hylton, Jack & His Orchestra)**
Tracks: / By a waterfall / Honeymoon Hotel / After you, who? / It's the talk of the town / You've got me crying again / Stormy weather / Hold me / Stay on the right side of the road / Fit as a fiddle / Happy as the day is long / I'm playing with fire / You're a smoothie / You are too beautiful / Don't blame me / 42nd Street medley / Too Much Harmony medley.
Note: 42nd Street medley: 42nd Street/You're getting to be a habit with me/Shuffle off to Buffalo/The gold diggers song/Shadow waltz. Too Much Harmony medley: Thanks/Black moonlight/The day you came along/Thanks.
**Album:** Released Jan '84, on Saville by Conifer Records. Catalogue no: **SVL 164**
**Cass:** Released Jan '86, on Saville by Conifer Records. Catalogue no: **CSVL 164**

**THIS'LL MAKE YOU WHISTLE**
Tracks: / Chasing shadows / Nothing lives longer than love / South American Joe / About a quarter to nine / She's a latin from Manhattan / Drop in the next time you're passing / Put on an old pair of shoes / Life begins at Oxford Circus / She wore a little jacket of blue / Did I remember / There isn't any limit to my love / I believe in miracles / This'll make you whistle / In the middle of a kiss / Kiss me goodnight / Can't we meet again / Did my heart beat / You've got me crying again.
**Album:** Released Jun '88, on Burlington (nostalgia) by Counterpoint Distribution. Catalogue no: **BUR 005**
**Cass:** Released Jul '88, on Burlington (nostalgia) by Counterpoint Distribution. Catalogue no: **4BUR 005**
**CD:** Released Sep '88, on Burlington (nostalgia) by Counterpoint Distribution. Catalogue no: **2 BUR 005**

## Hyman, Dick

**Biographical details:** Pianist, organist, composer and arranger, born in 1927 in New York City. He played with various jazz groups in the '40's and has done a lot of studio work; his trio record of *Moritat* was a top ten USA hit in 1956; he also set Shakespeare to music. He was among the first to record collections of Scott Joplin's rags and has always been faithful to jazz, in recent years becoming somthing of an archivist / revivalist, playing and recording collections of the music of James P.Johnson, Jelly Roll

Morton and others. (Donald Clarke, Nov 1989).

**CHARLESTON (See under J.P. Johnson) (Hyman, Dick & J.P. Johnson)**
Tracks: / Charleston / If I could be with you one hour tonight / Just before daybreak / Caprice rag / Steeplechase rag / Eccentricity / Carolina Balmoral / Snowy morning blues / Jingles / Carolina shout / You've got to be modernistic.
**Album:** Released Feb '88, on CBS (import) by CBS Records. Catalogue no: **4508641**
**Cass:** Released Feb '88, on CBS (import) by CBS Records. Catalogue no: **4508644**

**DICK HYMAN AND HIS TRIO (Hyman, Dick & His Trio)**
**Album:** Released Mar '79, on Grapevine(1) by Grapevine Records. Catalogue no: **GVR 3309**

**DICK HYMAN PIANO SOLOS**
**Album:** Released Mar '79, on Monmouth Evergreen Catalogue no: **MES 7065**

**GULF COAST BLUES (THE MUSIC OF CLARENCE WILLIAMS)**
Note: Dick Hyman plays piano.
**Album:** Released Nov '87, on Stomp Off (USA) Catalogue no: **SOS 1141**

**KING OF SWING AND THE REPUBLIC OF OPP BOP SH'BAM (Jazz in July)**
**CD:** Released '89, on Music Masters by Music Masters Records. Catalogue no: **CIJD 60200**

**SAY IT WITH MUSIC (Hyman, Dick & The Perfect Jazz Repertory Company)**
Tracks: / Mandy / How deep is the ocean / Cheek to cheek / Lazy / Say it with music / Blue skies / All alone / Puttin' on the ritz / Marie / Soft lights and sweet music.
**Album:** Released May '81, on World Jazz Deleted '86. Catalogue no: **WJLPS 16**

**STRIDE MONSTER (Duo pianos) (Hyman, Dick/Dick Wellstood)**
**Album:** Released '88, on Unisson (Canada) Catalogue no: **DDA 1006**

**THEME FROM THE 'THREEPENNY OPERA' (Hyman, Dick Trio)**
Tracks: / Theme from 'The Threepenny Opera'.
**7" Single:** Released Mar '56, on MGM by Polydor Ltd. Deleted '59. Catalogue no: **MGM 890**

# I

The following information was taken from the Music Master database on April 14th, 1990.

## I Didn't Give A Damn...

**I DIDN'T GIVE A DAMN IF WHITES (Various artists)**
**Album:** Released Oct '84, on Red Lightnin' by Red Lightning Records. Deleted Jun '89. Catalogue no: **RL 052**
**Album:** Released Oct '84, on Red Lightnin' by Red Lightning Records. Deleted Jun '89. Catalogue no: **RL 050**
**Album:** Released Oct '84, on Red Lightnin' by Red Lightning Records. Deleted Jun '89. Catalogue no: **RL 057**
**Album:** Released Oct '84, on Red Lightnin' by Red Lightning Records. Deleted Jun '89. Catalogue no: **RL 056**

## I Have To Paint My Face

**I HAVE TO PAINT MY FACE (Various artists)**
**Album:** Released May '81, on Arhoolie (USA) by Arhoolie Records (USA). Catalogue no: **ARHOOLIE 1005**

## I Love Jazz

**I LOVE JAZZ (Various artists)**
**CD:** Released Jun '88, on Spectrum (1) Catalogue no: **U 4061**

## Iai Festival

**IAI FESTIVAL (Various artists)**
**Album:** Released '78, on Improvising Artists Catalogue no: **IAI 373859**

## Ibrahim, Abdullah

**Biographical details:** Also see under *Brand, Dollar* for more information

**AFRICAN RIVER (Ibrahim, Abdullah & Ekaya)**
**Cass:** Released Nov '89, on Tiptoe Catalogue no: **6018-4**
**Album:** Released Nov '89, on Tiptoe Catalogue no: **6018-1**
**CD:** Released Nov '89, on Tiptoe Catalogue no: **6018-2**

**EKAYA**
**Album:** Released Oct '87, on Black Hawk (USA) by Blackhawk Records (USA). Catalogue no: **BKH 50205**
**CD:** Released Oct '87, on Black Hawk (USA) by Blackhawk Records (USA). Catalogue no: **CDBKH 50205**

**MOUNTAIN, THE (Ibrahim, Abdullah & Ekaya)**
Tracks: / Mountain, The / Bra timing from Phomolong / Ekaya / Sotho blue / Tuang Guru / Ntyilo ntyilo / Nelson Mandela / Wedding, The / Mannenberg (revisited) / Cape Town.
**Cass:** Released Jun '89, on Kaz by Kaz Records. Catalogue no: **KAZMC 7**
**Album:** Released Jun '89, on Kaz by Kaz Records. Catalogue no: **KAZLP 7**
**CD:** Released Jun '89, on Kaz by Kaz Records. Catalogue no: **KAZCD 7**

**WATER FROM AN ANCIENT WALL**
Tracks: / Mandela / Song for Fathima / Manenberg revisited / Tuang Guru / Water from an ancient well / Wedding / Mountain / Sameeda.
**Album:** Released Sep '88, on Black Hawk (USA) by Blackhawk Records (USA). Catalogue no: **BKH 50207**
**CD:** Released Sep '88, on Black Hawk (USA) by Blackhawk Records (USA). Catalogue no: **BKH 50207 CD**
**Cass:** Released Sep '88, on Black Hawk (USA) by Blackhawk Records (USA). Catalogue no: **KHMC 50207**

## If It's Not A Hit I'll Eat My...

**IF IT'S NOT A HIT I'LL EAT MY HAT (Various artists)**
Tracks: / Hound dog: *Thornton, Big Mama* / Pledging my love: *Various artists* / I love my baby: *Little Richard with Johnny Otis Orchestra* / I wanna ramble: *Little Junior Parker & The Blue Flames* / Farther up the road: *Bland, Bobby* / Keep on diggin': *Gordon, Roscoe* / To the end: *Sensational Nightingales* / Texas flood: *Davis, Larry* / Okie dokie stomp: *Brown, Gatemouth with Pluma Davis Orchestra* / Taxi blues: *Little Frankie Lee and the Saxons* / Spunky onions: *Davis, Billy & The Legends & Hank Moore Band* / Blue Monday: *Davis, James* / Funny how time slips away: *Hinton, Joe* / Treat her right: *Head, Roy.*
**Album:** Released Dec '88, on Ace by Ace Records. Catalogue no: **CH 154**

## Ignatzek, Klaus

**MONK'S VISIT (Ignatzek, Klaus Group) (See panel on next page)**
Note: Personnel: Klaus Ignatzek (Ldr / Acoustic piano), Bobby Watson (Alto sax / Soprano sax), Steve Wagner (Trumpet), Dieter Ilg (Acoustic bass), Joe Pulice (Drums). Recorded live at Muhle Huntziken, Switzerland, November 11th 1986.

It should come as no surprise that saxophonist Bobby Watson rather dominates this set from German pianist Klaus Ignatzeks impressive quintet - after all, Watson used to do that with the Jazz Messengers as well. Right from the opening *Pretty Soon*, when Watson steps out from the Messengers-style unison statements to deliver a driving alto solo which evolves totally organically from note to note, flawlessly constructed and exquisitely performed, it is obvious that we are in the presence of one hot player. We hear a lot of talk about the tradition these days, but Bobby Watson is in the business of copping anybody's venerable licks. He is not so much in the tradition as the tradition is in him, an ongoing absorbtion of the whole spectrum from swing to free jazz which spices his favoured bop register with all manner of exotic touches and unexpected nuances. Listen, for example, to his playing on the album's ballad cut, *Old Love, New Love* (like the rest of the music here, a Klaus Ignatzek composition). Watson comes out of the traps with a fierce, bluesy entry to a solo which goes on to slip those traces and develop into an acerbic, exhilarating wrestle with the form (well, love isn't all sweetness and light, right?).

Development is of the essence here, and everybody plays with an exceptional awareness of that essential sense of structure and purpose which Watson epitomises. The rhythm section remains acutely tuned to shifts in tempo behind young American trumpeter Steve Wagner, before the leader slides in with a poignant, powerfully embellished contribution, leaving bassman Dieter Ilg to lead everyone back into the tune. Klaus Ignatzek is a fine, fluent pianist, adaptable to the needs of the band and the music, but authoritative when pushed up front; if his playing sounds cerebral rather than intuitive, it never lacks feeling. *Monks Visit* proves to be the real showcase for his quintet's varied talents, with Watson again conjuring up a seemingly infinitely expandable solo, bursting with invention and imagination, emotion and technical accomplishment. Nothing daunted, Wagner follows this bravura display with his most impressive contribution to the set; Ilg and American drummer Joe Pulice, riding the cymbals with just the right blend of delicacy and drive, tuck in behind, while Ignatzek produces some angular, Monkish accompaniment prior to his own solo feature. In the end, everybody gets their turn to shine, and nobody wastes the chance.

Like I said, though, Watson steals the show, and the album finishes with his fertile, full-blooded soprano outing on *Caramel*. There is a lot to like in this hugely satisfying set, but nothing to like more than the saxophonist. Some justifiably ask if Watson is perhaps a shade too self-effacing, too immersed in that tradition, to really break through from respect to star status? There may be something in that, but the bottom line is simply this: the plays like a dream. Check him out, because his time is surely coming. Art Blakey, after all, doesn't make too many mistakes in choosing his musical directors. Kenny Mathieson

**Klaus Ignatzek - Monk's visit (Hep Jazz)**

(Wire Magazine)
**Album:** Released Sep '87, on Hep Jazz by Hep Records. Catalogue no: **HEP 2036**

## I'll Dance Till De Sun Breaks

**I'LL DANCE TILL DE SUN BREAKS (Various artists)**
Tracks: / Moaning saxophones rag, That: *Various artists* / Florida rag: *Various artists* / Bacchanal rag: *Various artists* / Alabama skedaddle: *Various artists* / Castle walk: *Various artists* / From soup to nuts: *Various artists* / Smokey mokes: *Various artists* / Eli Green's cake walk: *Various artists* / Cake walk, The: *Various artists* / I'll dance till de sun breaks through: *Various artists* / T'aint nobody's business if I do: *Various artists* / Whistling Rufus: *Various artists* / Wild cherries rag: *Various artists* / Bill Bailey: *Various artists* / Stomp dance: *Various artists* / Calico rag: *Various artists* / Smiles & chuckles: *Various artists* / On the Levee: *Various artists* / Trombone sneeze: *Various artists* / Two key rag: *Various artists.*
Note: 54 minutes. Ragtime, cakewalks & stomps from 1898-1923 transcribed from 78rpm records. The original cakewalk (de winner takes de cake), banjo solos, saxophone sextets, xylophone solos, etc. Artists include Ollie Oakley, Six Brown Bros, Sousa's band, Jim Europe.
**Cass:** Released Nov '83, on Saydisc by Amon Ra Records. Catalogue no: **CSDL 336**
**Album:** Released Aug '83, on Saydisc by Amon Ra Records. Deleted '86. Catalogue no: **SDL 336**

## I'm Coming From Seclusion

**I'M COMING FROM SECLUSION (Various artists)**
**Album:** Released Apr '79, on Collectors Items Catalogue no: **CI 005**

## Impulsive Jazz Dance...

**IMPULSIVE - JAZZ DANCE 5 (Various artists)**
Tracks: / Spellbinder: *Szabo, Gabor* / Hanky panky: *McFarland, Gary* / Critics choice: *Nelson, Oliver* / Cloudburst: *Pointer Sisters* / Oo oo bossa nova, The: *Jackson, Milt* / Alfie's theme: *Rollins, Sonny* / Mas que nada: *Gillespie, Dizzy* / Got my mojo working: *Hamilton, Chico* / Hard work / Caravan: *Tyner, McCoy* / See you later: *McCoy/Hamilton* / Soul sauce: *Scott, Shirley.*

**2 LP Set:** Released Jun '88, on Affinity by Charly Records. Catalogue no: **AFFD 190**
**Cass:** Released Jun '88, on Affinity by Charly Records. Catalogue no: **TCAFFD 190**

## In The Glenn Miller Mood

**IN THE GLENN MILLER MOOD (Various artists)**
**Cass:** Released Feb '83, on AIM (Budget Cassettes) Catalogue no: **AM 28**

## Ind, Peter

**Biographical details:** This jazz bassist formed the jazz record label 'Wave'. (Albums on this label include *Marsh - jazz from the east village* and *Send tape.*) Ind later played on Buddy Rich's album *The monster.* In the early Fifties he played bass in the band aboard the Queen Mary during Trans Atlantic crossings with colleagues Ronnie Ball (piano) and Brace Turner (alto sax, clarinet). (Ian Wilkins, Sept 1986).

**AT THE DEN (Ind, Peter and Sal Mosca)**
**Album:** Released Apr '79, on Wave by Wave Records. Catalogue no: **WAVE LP 2**

**IMPROVISATIONS**
**Album:** Released Apr '79, on Wave by Wave Records. Catalogue no: **WAVE LP 3**

**JAZZ BAROQUE**
**Album:** Released '88, on Wave by Wave Records. Catalogue no: **WAVE 11**

**LOOKING OUT**
**Album:** Released Apr '79, on Wave by Wave Records. Catalogue no: **WAVE LP 1**

**PETER IND SEXTET (Ind, Peter Sextet)**
**Album:** Released Apr '79, on Wave by Wave Records. Catalogue no: **WAVE LP 13**

**TIME FOR IMPROVISATIONS**
**Album:** Released Apr '79, on Wave by Wave Records. Catalogue no: **WAVE LP 4**

**TRIPLE LIBRA (Ind, Peter and Martin Taylor)**
**Album:** Released '88, on Wave by Wave Records. Catalogue no: **WAVE 24**

## Ink Spots

**Biographical details:** Ink Spots The classic line up of this American vocal group was Charles Fuqua, Orville 'Hoppy' Jones, Billy Kenny and Ivory 'Deek' Watson.
The Ink Spots were originally formed in New York in 1935. They started life as a street corner group called The Percolating Puppies, but soon realised that such a silly name would be a handicap if their career was to progress. As The Ink Spots their career cruised into top gear in 1939 when they achieved their first major disc success with *I I Didn't Care.* This introduced the world to the group's pioneering vocal style which would eventually become known as doo-wop. The Ink Spots laid down a formula - tenor, baritone and bass voices singing in polished harmony behind the lead - that was imitated by black vocal groups throughout the Forties and Fifties. Bill Kenny and Co. thus helped to lay the foundations of rhythm and blues and soul music. One of the best known numbers in their repertoire was *My Prayer* - this became a smash hit in 1956 for The Platters, who were directly influenced by the Spots. Hoppy Jones' bass lines were the prototype used by such acts as The Coasters and The Drifters and parodied in Johnny Cymbal's 1963 hit *Mr Bass Man.*

The Ink Spots teamed up with the great Ella Fitzgerald in 1944 to record *Into Each Life Some Rain Must Fall*, which proved to be a million-selling combination. Jones' death in November 1944 robbed the quartet of their most distinctive voice; but they managed to continue scoring hits for many years, including *To Each His Own* (1946), *The Gypsy* (1946) and *Melody of Love* (a UK No.10 hit in 1955). The subsequent deaths of Fuqua and Watson meant that the Ink Spots' name passed gracefully into the past tense, but their influence lived on. Via their worldwide concerts and their cameo appearance in Hollywood movies, they had introduced black music to a whole new mass white audience. (Bob MacDonald 5/11/85.)

**16 GOLDEN CLASSICS**

Tracks: / Whispering grass / Swing high swing low / Stompin' at the savoy / I don't want to set the world on fire / Maybe / You were only fooling / Sometime / White christmas / To each his own / You're breaking my heart / I'll get by / When the swallows come back to capist... / Street of dreams / We'll meet again / Coquette / Just for a thrill / Thoughtless / I cover the waterfront / Someone's rocking my dreamboat.

**Album:** Released Nov '87, on Unforgettable by Castle Communications Records. Catalogue no: **UNLP 026**
**Cass:** Released Nov '87, on Unforgettable by Castle Communications Records. Catalogue no: **UNMC 026**

**18 ORIGINAL GREATEST**

**Album:** Released Mar '88, on King (USA) Catalogue no: **K 5001**

**BEAUTIFUL EXPERIENCE**

Tracks: / Beautiful experience / Love's got a hold on you.

**7" Single:** Released Nov '80, on Splash by Splash Records. Deleted '83. Catalogue no: **SP 18**

**BEST OF THE INK SPOTS**

Tracks: / If I didn't care / We three / My prayer / Whispering grass / It's funny to everyone but me / I don't want to set the world on fire / To each his own / Do I worry? / Address unknown / Someone's rocking my dreamboat / Street of dreams / Don't get around much anymore / Gypsy, The / Maybe / When the swallows come back to Capistrane / Please take a letter, Miss Brown / Until the real thing comes along / Time out for tears / I cover the waterfront / We'll meet again / Java jive / No orchids for my lady / I'll never smile again / It is no secret.

**Cass set:** Released Mar '82, on Coral by MCA Records. Deleted Jan '88. Catalogue no: **MCLDC 607**
**2 LP Set:** Released Mar '82, on Coral by MCA Records. Deleted Jan '88. Catalogue no: **MCLD 607**
**Cass:** Released Jul '84, on Creole (Everest-Europa) by Creole Records. Catalogue no: **16 6**

**BEST OF THE INK SPOTS (MFP)**

Tracks: / If I didn't care / Bless you for being an angel / When the swallows come back to Capistrano / Whispering grass / Maybe / Java jive / Do I worry? / I don't want to set the world on fire / Every night about this time / Don't get around much anymore / To each his own / Ring, telephone, ring / I'd climb the highest mountain / Puttin' and takin' / Cow cow boogie / Into each life some rain must fall / Your feets too big / I'll never smile again / It's a sin to tell a lie / Someone's rocking my dreamboat.

**Album:** Released Nov '81, on MFP by EMI Records. Catalogue no: **MFP 50529**
**Cass:** Released Nov '81, on MFP by EMI Records. Catalogue no: **TCMFP 50529**
**CD:** Released May '89, on MFP by EMI Records. Catalogue no: **CDMFP 6064**
**CD:** Released May '89, on MFP by EMI Records. Catalogue no: **CDB 792 375 2**

**FABULOUS INK SPOTS SING THEIR**

**Cass:** Released Jan '88, on Demand Performance Catalogue no: **DPC 726**

**GOLDEN GREATS: INK SPOTS**

Tracks: / If I didn't care / When swallows come / Back to capistrano / Whispering grass / Java jive / Do I worry? / I don't want to set the world on fire / Don't get around much anymore / To each his own / I'll never smile again / Someone's rocking my dreamboat / We three / My prayer / Until the real thing comes along / No orchids for my lady / Gypsy, The / I'll get by / Maybe / You were only fooling / We'll meet again / It's a sin to tell a lie.

Note: The Ink Spots had worldwide hits during the 30's and 40's. This new twenty track "Golden Greats" collection features virtually all their many classics.
**Cass:** Released Feb '86, on MCA by MCA Records. Catalogue no: **MCMC 5029**
**Album:** Released Feb '86, on MCA by MCA Records. Catalogue no: **MCM 5029**

**GREATEST HITS: INK SPOTS**

**Cass:** Released May '88, on Nostalgia by Mainline Records. Catalogue no: **42016**
**Album:** Released May '88, on Nostalgia by Mainline Records. Catalogue no: **22016**
**Cass:** Released Sep '84, on K-Tel Goldmasters by K-Tel Records. Catalogue no: **GM 0206**

**I DIDN'T CARE**

**CD:** Released Jun '88, on Spectrum (1) Catalogue no: **U 4057**

**INK SPOTS**

**CD:** Released May '89, on Object Enterprises Catalogue no: **ONN 27**

**INK SPOTS COLLECTION (16 golden greats)**

Tracks: / Stranger in Paradise / Don't laugh at me / Keep it moving / When you come to the end of the day / Melody of love / Here in my lonely room / Changing partners / Am I too late? / Ebb tide / Flowers, Mr. Florist, please / Someone's rocking my dreamboat / I'd walk a country mile / Yesterdays / If you should say goodbye / There is something missing / Command me.

**Cass:** Released Dec '87, on Deja Vu Catalogue no: **DVMC 2107**
**Album:** Released Dec '87, on Deja Vu Catalogue no: **DVLP 2107**

**INK SPOTS: ON THE AIR**

Tracks: / Swinging on the string / Did you ever see a dream walking? / Old spinning wheel / Baby brown / Pork chops and gravy / Do I worry? / No wonder / It's so funny to everyone but me / Tiger rag / If I didn't care / Java jive / Lovely way to spend an evening, A.

**Album:** Released Feb '88, on Totem Catalogue no: **TOTEM 1020**

**INK SPOTS, THE**

Tracks: / It's the talk of the town / There goes my heart / Someone's rocking my dreamboat / Paper doll / Lazy river / In a shanty in old Shantytown / I'm confessin' / We three / Just in case you change your mind / Whispering grass.
**Album:** Released Jul '88, on Bellaphon Catalogue no: **BID 8001**
**Album:** Released '74, on Rhapsody by President Records. Catalogue no: **RHAS 9011**
**CD:** Released '86, on K-Tel by K-Tel Records. Catalogue no: **ONCD 5108**

**INKSPOTS, THE/THE PLATTERS (Ink Spots/Platters)**

**Cass set:** Released Oct '87, on Warwick by Warwick Records. Catalogue no: **WW 6047**

**JUST LIKE OLD TIMES**

Tracks: / Into each life some rain must fall / For sentimental reasons / Once in a while / On the sunny side of the street / Till then / It had to be you / Old fashioned way / I'll get by / Honeysuckle rose / Autumn leaves / Just for a thrill / Seems like old times.
**Cass:** Released Mar '85, on CBS by CBS Records. Catalogue no: **40 54876**
**Album:** Released Mar '85, on CBS by CBS Records. Deleted '87. Catalogue no: **CBS 54876**

**MELODY OF LOVE**

Tracks: / Melody of love.
**7" Single:** Released Mar '55, on Parlophone by EMI Records. Deleted '58. Catalogue no: **MSP 6152**

**SWING HIGH, SWING LOW**

Tracks: / Keep away from my doorstep / Alabama barbecue / T'ain't nobody's bizz-ness if I do / That cat is high / Swing, gate, swing / Slap that bass / Christopher Columbus / Ye suh / Your feet's too big / When the sun goes down / Swingin' on the strings / Stompin' at the Savoy / With plenty of money and you / Let's call the whole thing off / Don't let old age creep up on you / Mamma don't allow it / Oh Red / Old Joe's hittin' the jug / Whoa babe / Swing high, swing low.

**Album:** Released Apr '89, on Conifer Happy Days by Conifer Records. Catalogue no: **CHD 143**
**CD:** Released Apr '89, on Conifer Happy Days by Conifer Records. Catalogue no: **CDHD 143**
**Cass:** Released Apr '89, on Conifer Happy Days by Conifer Records. Catalogue no: **MCHD 143**

### VERY BEST OF THE INKSPOTS

**CD:** on DGR (Holland) Catalogue no: **DGC 1001**
**Cass:** Released Jun '86, on Hallmark by Pickwick Records. Catalogue no: **HSC 3194**
**Album:** Released Jun '86, on Hallmark by Pickwick Records. Catalogue no: **SHM 3194**

## Inspirational Choir...

**Biographical details:** The Inspirational Choir Of Th Pentecostal First Born Church Of The Living God gave a boost to Britain's burgeoning black gospel music scene, when they took Andrew Pryce Jackman's arrangement of the classic hymn *Abide With Me* to No.44 on the UK singles chart at Christmas 1984. (Bob MacDonald 6/11/85).

### ABIDE WITH ME

Tracks: / Sweet Holy Spirit / Abide with me.
**12" Single:** Released Nov '85, on Epic by CBS Records. Deleted Dec '86. Catalogue no: **TA 4997**
**7" Single:** Released Nov '85, on Epic by CBS Records. Catalogue no: **A 4997**
**7" Set:** on Epic by CBS Records. Deleted Dec '86. Catalogue no: **DA 4997**
**7" Single:** Released Dec '85, on Portrait by CBS Records. Catalogue no: **QA 4997**

### HIGHER AND HIGHER

**Album:** Released Dec '86, on Portrait by CBS Records. Catalogue no: **450240 1**
**Cass:** Released Dec '86, on Portrait by CBS Records. Catalogue no: **450240 4**

### I'VE GOT A FEELING

Tracks: / I've got a feeling / Right there.
**12" Single:** Released Sep '85, on Portrait by CBS Records. Catalogue no: **TX 6611**
**7" Single:** Released Sep '85, on Portrait by CBS Records. Catalogue no: **A 6611**

### ONE LOVE

Tracks: / Right there / One love.
**7" Single:** Released Feb '86, on Portrait by CBS Records. Catalogue no: **A 6902**
**12" Single:** Released Feb '86, on Portrait by CBS Records. Catalogue no: **TA 6902**

### PICK ME UP

Tracks: / Pick me up / Do not pass me by / Love lifted me (on 12" only) / Give me a clean heart (on 12" only) / Sign me up (on 12" only).
**12" Single:** Released Nov '83, on Stiff by Stiff Records. Catalogue no: **BUYIT 193**
**7" Single:** Released Nov '83, on Stiff by Stiff Records. Catalogue no: **BUY 193**

### SWEET INSPIRATION

Tracks: / Sweet inspiration / People get ready / Up where we belong / One love / Jesus dropped the charges / I've got a feeling / You light up my life / Morning has broken / Amazing grace / What a friend we have in Jesus / When He comes / God is / Abide with me.
**Album:** Released Nov '85, on Portrait by CBS Records. Catalogue no: **PRT 10048**
**CD:** Released Jan '86, on CBS by CBS Records. Catalogue no: **CD 10048**
**Cass:** Released Nov '85, on Portrait by CBS Records. Catalogue no: **40 10048**

### (YOUR LOVE HAS LIFTED ME) HIGHER

Tracks: / (your love has lifted me) Higher and higher / Amazing grace.
**12" Single:** Released Nov '86, on Portrait by CBS Records. Catalogue no: **CHOIRT 1**
**7" Single:** Released Nov '86, on Portrait by CBS Records. Catalogue no: **CHOIR 1**

## International Blue Duo

### INTRODUCING

Tracks: / Blues for real / Stanley T / Saxophone sermon / Night train / New town / Summertime / Hot cha / Please send me someone to love / 426 West Briar.
**Album:** Released Nov '84, on Crosscut by Topic Records. Catalogue no: **CCR 1007**

## International Jazz...

### IN NEW YORK 1956/57

**Album:** Released May '87, on Swing Disque Catalogue no: **SW 8416**

### IN PARIS 1956

**Album:** Released '88, on DRG (USA) by DRG Records (USA). Catalogue no: **SW 8407**

### INTERNATIONAL JAZZ BAND VOL 2

**Album:** Released Jun '88, on GHB by Jazzology Records (USA). Catalogue no: **GHB 21**

### INTERNATIONAL JAZZBAND

**Album:** Released Jun '88, on GHB by Jazzology Records (USA). Catalogue no: **GHB 20**

## Into Europe

### INTO EUROPE (Various artists)

Note: "Includes artists Simon Le Bon, Alice Cooper, Pete Townshend, Annie Lennox, Chrissie Hynde, The Clash, Twisted Sister, Black Sabbath, Jimi Hendrix, Mahalia Jackson, Joni Mitchell, Weather Report, Stryper, B.B.King, and The Alarm."
**VHS:** Released Jul '88, on Hendring Video Catalogue no: **UNKNOWN**

## Invitation To Denon

### INVITATION TO DENON PCM (digital) jazz (Various artists)

**Album:** Released '82, on Denon Deleted '88. Catalogue no: **ST 6008**

## Irakere

### CATALINA

Tracks: / Aguanile bonko / Juana 1600 / El tata / Preludio a catalina / Rucu rucu a santa clara.
Note: This Cuban All Star Band, founded in 1972, were a major attraction at the Ronnie Scott Afro-Cuban Festival last year and have been awarded a Grammy for the best Jazz Formation. Trumpet star Arturo Sandoval is featured soloist on four of the six tracks.
**Album:** Released Aug '89, on Messidor (Germany) Catalogue no: **1115955**

### CULPA DEL GUAO

Tracks: / Homenaje / Bacalao con pan / Baila mi ritmo / Por culpa del guao / Santtaguero.
**Album:** Released May '87, on Messidor (Germany) Catalogue no: **1019577**
**Album:** Released Sep '89, on Messidor (Germany) Catalogue no: **15957**

### IN LONDON

Tracks: / Bilando Asi / Johana / Estela va a estallar / Lo que va a paser / Duke, The.
Note: Irakere are regular visitors to Ronnie Scott's Club where this album was recorded in October 1987. Chucho Valdes, is its leader, pianist and major composer and arranger. The ten piece band is, by Cuban standards, ridiculously eclectic and the 'sold out' notices at the Club whenever they appear prove their popularity. This album captures their original sound live.
**Album:** Released Nov '88, on Jazz House Catalogue no: **JHR 005**

### LA CHEMIN DE LA COLLINE

**Album:** Released Mar '89, on Sterns by Sterns African Records Centre. Catalogue no: **EGR 6103**

### LEGENDARY IRAKERE LIVE IN LONDON, THE Vol. 2

Note: Recorded live at Ronnie Scott's club, June 1988. Personnel: Jesus 'Chucho' Valdes (kbds), Oscar Valdes (perc/vocals), Enrique Pia (drums/Cuban perc), Orlando Valle (flute/kbds), Javier Zaida (baritone & soprano sax/flute/clt), Cesar Lopez (alto & soprano sax), Carlos Alvares (tbn/vocals), Manuel Machado (tpt), Jorge Varona (tpt).

**Album:** Released Jun '89, on Jazz House Catalogue no: **JHR 009**

### MISA NEGRA (AFRICAN MASS)

**Album:** Released 12 Apr '89, on Messidor (Germany) Catalogue no: **15971**
**CD:** Released 12 Apr '89, on Messidor (Germany) Catalogue no: **15972**

### TIERRA EN TRANCE

**Album:** Released Mar '89, on Sterns by Sterns African Records Centre. Catalogue no: **EGR 6111**

## Isaacs, Ike

### LATIN GUITARS OF IKE ISAACS

**Album:** Released '78, on Dansan Catalogue no: **DS 004**

## Iskra Jazz In Sweden

**ISKRA JAZZ IN SWEDEN Various artists (Various artists)**
**2 LP Set:** Released Oct '77, on Caprice Records by BMG Records (UK). Catalogue no: **CAP 200679**

## It Sounds Like Bix

**IT SOUNDS LIKE BIX (Various artists)**
**Album:** Released Jan '79, on Broadway (USA) Catalogue no: **BWY 104**

# J

The following information was taken from the Music Master database on April 14th, 1990.

## Jack Teagarden Classics

**JACK TEAGARDEN CLASSICS (Various artists)**
Note: Red Nichols & 5 Pennies, Louisiana Rhythm Kings, Irving Mills.
**Album:** Released Jan '88, on Family Catalogue no: **SFR DP 649**

## Jack Walk blues

**JACK WALK BLUES (Various artists)**
**Album:** Released Apr '81, on Stash (USA) Catalogue no: **ST 110**

## Jackson Blues

**JACKSON BLUES (1928-38) (Various artists)**
**Album:** Released Dec '88, on Yazoo (USA) by Shanachie Records (USA). Catalogue no: **L 1007**

## Jackson, Bo Weavil

**1926 (Sam Butler)**
Tracks: / Devil and my brown blues / Poor boy blues / Jefferson County blues / You can't keep no brown / Christians fight on, your time ain't long / Heaven is my view / Pistol blues / Some scream high yellow / When the saints come marching home / I'm on my way to the Kingdom Land / Why do you moan?.
**Album:** Released Jan '83, on Matchbox (Bluesmaster) by Saydisc Records. Catalogue no: **MSE 203**

## Jackson, Bull Moose

**BIG FAT MAMAS ARE BACK IN STYLE**
**Album:** Released 11 Mar '88, on Route 66 (Sweden) Catalogue no: **KIX 14**

**MOOSE ON THE LOOSE**
**Album:** Released Aug '87, on Saxophonograph (Sweden) Catalogue no: **BP 506**

## Jackson, Chubby

**CHOICE CUTS**
Note: Including Chubby Jackson, Arnold Ross, George Wallington and Toots Thielemans.
**Album:** Released Nov '86, on Esquire by Titan Int. Prod.. Catalogue no: **ESQ 323**

## Jackson, Frankie

**CAN'T WAIT TILL YOU GET HOME (Jackson, Frankie 'Halfpint')**
**Album:** Released Jul '86, on Collectors Items Catalogue no: **CI 014**

**FRANKIE HALF PINT JACKSON (Jackson, Frankie 'Halfpint')**
**Album:** Released Aug '89, on Blues Document Catalogue no: **BD 2049**

## Jackson, Jack

**MAKE THOSE PEOPLE SWAY (Jackson, Jack & His Orchestra)**
Tracks: / Make those people sway / I'm playing with fire / Long may we love / I travel alone / Come on, be happy / Miss otis regrets / I'm getting sentimental over you / Two ciggarettes in the dark / Dixie lee / Two little flies on a lump of sugar / Sittin' in the dark / What a little moonlight can do / Stars fell on alabama / Blue river, roll on / Be still, my heart / Let bygones be bygones.
**Album:** Released Mar '84, on Retrospect by EMI Records. Deleted Mar '89. Catalogue no: **SH 210**

**THINGS ARE LOOKING UP (Jackson, Jack & His Orchestra)**
Tracks: / Things are looking up / Faint harmony / Soon / You turned your head / Kiss me, dear / Ache in my heart / Now that we're sweethearts again / Have a little dream on me / Don't you cry when we say goodbye / Lonely feet / I'm on a see-saw / Dancing with a ghost / Play to me gypsy / Lonely singing fool, A / What's good for the goose / Because it'slove / Ole faithful / What shall I do? / I think I can / Goodnight, lovely little lady.
**Cass:** Released '88, on Saville by Conifer Records. Catalogue no: **CSVL 173**
**Album:** Released Jul '88, on Saville by Conifer Records. Catalogue no: **SVL 173**

## Jackson, Jim

**BEST OF JIM JACKSON - 1928-1930**
**Album:** Released Jan '87, on Earl Archives Catalogue no: **BD 613**

**JIM JACKSON 1927-29**
**Album:** Released Apr '89, on Blues Document Catalogue no: **BD 2037**

**KANSAS CITY BLUES**
**Album:** Released '88, on Agram Catalogue no: **AB 2004**

## Jackson, John

**BLUES AND COUNTRY DANCE**
**Album:** Released '88, on Arhoolie (USA) by Arhoolie Records (USA). Catalogue no: **F 1025**

**BLUES FROM VIRGINIA**
**Album:** Released May '81, on Arhoolie (USA) by Arhoolie Records (USA). Catalogue no: **ARHOOLIE 1025**

**DEEP IN THE BOTTOM**
**Album:** Released '88, on Rounder (USA) by Rounder Records (USA). Catalogue no: **ROUNDER 2032**
**Cass:** Released '88, on Rounder (USA) by Rounder Records (USA). Catalogue no: **ROUNDER 2032C**

**IN EUROPE**
**Album:** Released '85, on Arhoolie (USA) by Arhoolie Records (USA). Catalogue no: **ARHOOLIE 1047**

**JOHN JACKSON (VIDEO)**
**VHS:** Released '88, on Kay Jazz (video) by Kay Jazz. Catalogue no: **KJ 076**

**JOHN JACKSON VOL.2 (More blues & country dance tunes from Virginia.)**
**Album:** Released Dec '88, on Arhoolie (USA) by Arhoolie Records (USA). Catalogue no: **ARHOOLIE 1035**

**STEP IT UP AND GO**
**Album:** Released May '79, on Rounder (USA) by Rounder Records (USA). Catalogue no: **ROUNDER 2019**

## Jackson, Lil' Son

**BLUES COME TO TEXAS**
**Album:** Released May '81, on Arhoolie (USA) by Arhoolie Records (USA). Catalogue no: **ARHOOLIE 1004**

**ROCKIN' AN' ROLLIN'**
**Album:** Released Sep '84, on Pathe Marconi (France) Catalogue no: **PM 1546671**

## Jackson, Mahalia

**20 GREATEST HITS: MAHALIA**
**Album:** Released Nov '84, on Astan (USA) Catalogue no: **20120**
**Album:** Released Sep '87, on Lotus Catalogue no: **LOP 14 029**
**Album:** Released Sep '87, on Lotus Catalogue no: **LOP 14 027**
**Album:** Released Apr '87, on Masters (Holland) Catalogue no: **U 50041**
**Cass:** Released Nov '84, on Astan (USA) Catalogue no: **40120**
**Cass:** Released Apr '87, on Masters (Holland) Catalogue no: **D 950041**

**GOSPEL**
Tracks: / Tell it, sing it, shout it / Somebody touched me / Only hope we have / There is power in the blood / I asked the Lord / Hold me / Give me that old-time religion / Leaning on the everlasting arms / He's sweet I know / Somebody bigger than you and I / Only believe / To me it's so wonderful / I'll never turn back no more / Highway up to Heaven / Trust in God / Lord search my heart / Where he leads me / Hallelujah 'tis done / Thank you, Jesus / Never look down / You can't hurry God / It's my

desire / He knows how much we can bear / My Lord.
**2 LP Set:** Released Sep '77, on Vogue by Vogue Records. Catalogue no: **VJD 537**

**IN THE UPPER ROOM**
**CD:** Released '86, on Vogue by Vogue Records. Catalogue no: **VGCD 60061**

**I'VE DONE MY WORK**
Tracks: / He's got the whole world in his hands / Every time I feel the Spirit / Upper room, The / We shall overcome / House I live in (that's America to me) / Go tell it on the mountain / Down by the riverside / Joshua fit de battle of Jerico / When the saints go marching in / Keep your hands on the plough / Nobody knows the trouble I've seen / Deep river / Holy City, The / Crying in the chapel / You'll never walk alone.
**Album:** Released May '85, on Word (UK) by Word Records (UK). Catalogue no: **WST 9630**
**Cass:** Released May '85, on Word (UK) by Word Records (UK). Catalogue no: **WC 9630**

**JAZZ TIME VOL.16**
**Album:** Released '88, on Vogue (France) by Vogue Records. Catalogue no: **502716**

**JESUS IS WITH ME**
**Cass:** Released Nov '84, on Astan (USA) Catalogue no: **40081**
**Album:** Released Nov '84, on Astan (USA) Catalogue no: **20081**

**LIVE IN ANTIBES 1968**
**Album:** Released May '89, on France's Concert Catalogue no: **FC 122**
**CD:** Released May '89, on France's Concert Catalogue no: **FCD 122**

**MAHALIA (Mahalia Jackson 1911-1972)**
Note: Running time: 72 mins.
**VHS:** Released '87, on Castle Hendring Video by Castle Communications Records. Catalogue no: **HEN 2 049 G**
**VHS:** Released Mar '90, on Castle Hendring Video by Castle Communications Records. Catalogue no: **HEN 2 049**

**MAHALIA JACKSON**
**Cass:** Released Jun '84, on CBS (import) by CBS Records. Catalogue no: **40.31383**
**Album:** Released Jun '84, on CBS (import) by CBS Records. Catalogue no: **EMB 31383**

**MAHALIA JACKSON COLLECTION (20 golden greats)**
Tracks: / Nobody knows the trouble I've seen / Go tell it on the mountain / Come to Jesus / My story / I believe / In the upper room / Run all the way / Shall I meet you over yonder? / Beautiful tomorrow / Last mile on the way, The / Walkin' to Jerusalem / Bless this house / I'm on my way to Canaan / Lord's Prayer, The / He's my light / Even me / It is no secret / Hand of God / Jesus is with me / Get away Jordan.
**Cass:** Released Aug '85, on Deja Vu Catalogue no: **DVMC 2006**
**Album:** Released Aug '85, on Deja Vu Catalogue no: **DVLP 2006**

**MAHALIA JACKSON STORY, THE**
Tracks: / Get away Jordan / Go tell it on the mountain / Lord's prayer, The / He's got the whole world in his hands / Shall I meet you over yonder / Evening prayer, An / I'm going to live the life I sing about / City called heaven / It don't cost very much / Nobody knows the trouble I've seen / Didn't it rain / He's my light / Joshua fit de battle of Jerico / I believe / Come to Jesus / My story / My God is real / Beautiful tomorrow / Last mile on the way, The / Even me / Hands of God / Walk over God's heaven / I'm on my way / Jesus is with me / Walkin' to Jerusalem.
**Cass:** Released May '89, on Deja Vu Catalogue no: **DVREMC 23**
**CD:** Released May '89, on Deja Vu Catalogue no: **DVRECD 23**

**MAHALIA JACKSON, VOL 1**
Tracks: / Tell it, sing it, shout it / Somebody touched me / Only hope we have / There is power in the blood / I asked the Lord / Hold me / Give me that old time religion / Leaning on the everlasting arm / He's sweet, I know / Somebody bigger than you / Only believe / To me it's so wonderful.
**Cass:** Released '88, on Joker (USA) by Lifetime Records (USA). Catalogue no: **MC 3609**
**Album:** Released '88, on Joker (USA) by Lifetime Records (USA). Catalogue no: **SM 3609**
**Album:** Released Jan '82, on Jazz Reactivation Catalogue no: **JR 115**

**MAHALIA JACKSON, VOL 2**
Tracks: / I'll never turn back no more / Highway up to Heaven / Lord search my soul / I trust in God / Where he leads me / Hallelujah / 'Tis done / Thank you, Jesus / Never look down / You can't hurry God / It's my desire / He knows how much we can bear / My Lord.
**Album:** Released May '83, on Jazz Reactivation Catalogue no: **JR 134**

**MEMORIAL**
**2 LP Set:** Released Oct '88, on Vogue by Vogue Records. Catalogue no: **400010**

**MY STORY**
**Album:** Released Nov '84, on Astan (USA) Catalogue no: **20080**
**Cass:** Released Nov '84, on Astan (USA) Catalogue no: **40080**

**MY TASK**
Tracks: / My task / Amazing grace / God is so good / Walk in Jerusalem / Satisfied mind, A / Whither thou goest / It is no secret / Then the answer came / My friend / Bible tells me so, The / Somebody bigger than you and I / He calmed the ocean / For my good fortune / I've done my work / How I got over / That's what he's done for me.
**Cass:** Released May '85, on Word (UK) by Word Records (UK). Catalogue no: **TCWR 3011**
**Album:** Released May '85, on Word (UK) by Word Records (UK). Catalogue no: **WRD 3011**

**NOBODY KNOWS THE TROUBLE I'VE SEEN**
**CD:** Released 10 Jul '89, on Vogue by Vogue Records. Catalogue no: **VG 670216**

**QUEEN OF GOSPEL**
**Album:** Released Nov '87, on Entertainers Catalogue no: **ENT LP 13031**
**Album:** Released Nov '87, on Entertainers Catalogue no: **ENT LP 13029**

**SILENT NIGHT**
Tracks: / Silent night / Go tell it on the mountain / Bless this house.
**Album:** Released Dec '81, on Teldec (1) by ASV (Academy Sound & Vision). Catalogue no: **6.24480**

**WARM AND TENDER SOUL OF MAHALIA JACKSON, VOL. 2**
Tracks: / In the upper room / City called Heaven / Run all the way / Go tell it on the mountain / I'm on my way to Canaan / I bow on my knees / Shall I meet you over yonder? / Beautiful tomorrow / It is no secret / Hands of God / Jesus is with me / Nobody knows the trouble I've seen / Even me / Get away Jordan / Last mile on the way, The / Bless this house / Walkin' to Jerusalem / My story / I believe / Dig a little deeper / Lord's prayer, The / Come to Jesus / He's my light.
**Album:** Released Apr '81, on Joker (USA) by Lifetime Records (USA). Catalogue no: **SM 3610**
**2 LP Set:** Released Apr '81, on Joker (USA) by Lifetime Records (USA). Catalogue no: **SM 3763/2**
**Album:** Released Apr '81, on Joker (USA) by Lifetime Records (USA). Catalogue no: **SM 3609**

**WHEN THE SAINTS GO MARCHING IN**
Tracks: / I'm going to live the life I sing about in my song / When I wake up in glory / Jesus met the woman at the well / Oh Lord is it? / I will move on up a little higher / When the saints go marching in / Jesus out of the depths / Walk over God's heaven / Keep your hands on the plough / Didn't it rain.
**Cass:** Released Jul '87, on CBS by CBS Records. Deleted Jan '89. Catalogue no: **450306 4**
**Album:** Released Jul '87, on CBS by CBS Records. Deleted Jan '89. Catalogue no: **450869 1**

## Jackson, Milt

**AIN'T BUT A FEW OF US LEFT**
Tracks: / Ain't but a few of us left / Time for love, A / If I should lose you / Stuffy / Body and soul / What am I here for?.
**Cass:** Released Sep '82, on Pablo Jazz (USA) by Pablo Records (USA). Catalogue no: **K10 873**
**CD:** Released '88, on Pablo Jazz (USA) by Pablo Records (USA). Catalogue no: **131 121 3**
**Album:** Released Sep '82, on Pablo Jazz (USA) by Pablo Records (USA).

Catalogue no: **2310 873**

**AT THE MONTREUX JAZZ FESTIVAL, 1975 (Jackson, Milt Big Four)**
Tracks: / Fungii mama / Everything must change / Speed ball / Nature boy / Stella by starlight / Like someone in love / Night mist blues / Mack the knife.
**CD:** Released Jan '89, on JVC/Fantasy Catalogue no: **VDJ 28007**
**Album:** Released Jan '82, on Pablo Jazz (USA) by Pablo Records (USA). Catalogue no: **2310 753**
**Cass:** Released Jan '82, on Pablo Jazz (USA) by Pablo Records (USA). Catalogue no: **K10 753**

**BAGS' BAG**
Tracks: / Blues for Roberta / Groovin' / How are you? / Slow boat to China / I cover the waterfront / Rev, The / Tour angel / Blues for Tomi-Oka.
**Album:** Released Jan '82, on Pablo Jazz (USA) by Pablo Records (USA). Catalogue no: **2310 842**
**Cass:** Released Jan '82, on Pablo Jazz (USA) by Pablo Records (USA). Catalogue no: **K10 842**

**BAGS MEETS WES (Jackson, Milt & Wes Montgomery)**
**Album:** Released Apr '86, on Original Jazz Classics (USA) by Fantasy Inc (USA). Catalogue no: **OJC 234**
**CD:** Released Nov '86, on JVC/Fantasy Catalogue no: **VDJ 1550**

**BALLADS AND BLUES**
Tracks: / So in love / These foolish things / Solitude / Song is ended, The / They didn't believe me / How high the moon / Gerry's blues / Hello / Bright blues.
**Album:** Released Mar '81, on Atlantic by WEA Records. Deleted '86. Catalogue no: **K 50727**

**BEBOP**
Tracks: / Au privave / Good bait / Wody 'n' you / Nows the time / Ornithology / Groovin' high / Birks works / Salt peanuts.
**Cass:** Released Oct '88, on East West Catalogue no: **790991 4**
**CD:** Released Oct '88, on East West Catalogue no: **790991 2**
**Album:** Released Oct '88, on East West Catalogue no: **790991 1**

**BEST OF MILT JACKSON**
Tracks: / Once I loved / If you went away / Yes sir, that's my baby / Three thousand miles ago / Ain't misbehavin' / My kind of trouble is you / Soul fusion / Blues for Edith.
**Album:** Released Jan '82, on Pablo Jazz (USA) by Pablo Records (USA). Catalogue no: **231 0849**
**Cass:** Released Jan '82, on Pablo Jazz (USA) by Pablo Records (USA). Catalogue no: **K10 849**

**BIG BAND, VOL 1 (Jackson, Milt & Count Basie)**
Tracks: / 9.20 special / Moonlight becomes you / Shiny stockings / Blues for me / Every tub / Easy does it / Lena and Lenny / Sunny side of the street / Back to the apple / I'll always be in love with you / Comeback / Basie / Corner pocket / Lady in lace / Blues for Joe Turner / Good time blues / Li'l darlin' / Big stuff / Blue and sentimental.
**Album:** Released '82, on Pablo Jazz (USA) by Pablo Records (USA). Catalogue no: **231 0822**
**CD:** on Pablo Jazz (USA) by Pablo Records (USA). Catalogue no: **J33J 20023**
**Cass:** Released '82, on Pablo Jazz (USA) by Pablo Records (USA). Catalogue no: **K10 822**

**BIG BAND, VOL 2 (Jackson, Milt & Count Basie)**
Tracks: / 9/20 special / Moonlight becomes you / Shiny stockings / Blues for me / Every tub / Easy does it / Lena and Lenny / Sunny side of the street / Back to the apple / I'll always be in love with you.
**Cass:** Released '82, on Pablo Jazz (USA) by Pablo Records (USA). Catalogue no: **K10 823**
**CD:** Released Apr '86, on Pablo Jazz (USA) by Pablo Records (USA). Catalogue no: **J33J 20054**
**Album:** Released '82, on Pablo Jazz (USA) by Pablo Records (USA). Catalogue no: **231 0823**

**BIG MOUTH**
Tracks: / Big mouth / Look of love, The / Bag's Groove / I love you / Days of wine and roses / Yusef / Getting sentimental over you / I owes ya.
**Album:** Released Jan '82, on Pablo Jazz (USA) by Pablo Records (USA). Catalogue no: **2310 867**
**Cass:** Released Jan '82, on Pablo Jazz (USA) by Pablo Records (USA). Catalogue no: **K10 867**

**BIG THREE, THE (Jackson, Milt/ Joe Pass/ Ray Brown)**
Tracks: / Pink panther / Nuages / Blue bossa / Come Sunday / Wave / Moonglow / You stepped out of a dream / Blues for Sammy.
**Cass:** Released May '82, on Pablo Jazz (USA) by Pablo Records (USA). Catalogue no: **K10 757**
**CD:** Released Aug '86, on Pablo Jazz (USA) by Pablo Records (USA). Catalogue no: **J33J 20021**
**Album:** Released May '82, on Pablo Jazz (USA) by Pablo Records (USA). Catalogue no: **231 0757**

**BROTHER JIM**
Tracks: / Brother Jim / Ill wind / Rhythm-a-ning / Sudden death / How high the moon / Back to Bologna / Sleeves / Lullaby of the leaves / Weasel, The.
Note: Recorded in New York City, 17 May 1965
**Album:** Released Aug '86, on Pablo Jazz (USA) by Pablo Records (USA). Catalogue no: **231 0916**
**Cass:** Released Aug '86, on Pablo Jazz (USA) by Pablo Records (USA). Catalogue no: **K10 916**

**COMPLETE MILT JACKSON (With Horace Silver)**
**Album:** Released Jun '86, on Fantasy Inc (USA) by Fantasy Inc (USA). Catalogue no: **1902118**

**DATE IN NEW YORK, A (VOL.1) (Jackson, Milt & Jay Jay Johnson)**
**Album:** Released Oct '88, on Vogue by Vogue Records. Catalogue no: **500080**

**FEELINGS**
Tracks: / Feelings / Come to me / Trouble is a man / Moody blue / Day it rained, The / My kind of troubles is you / If you went away / Tears / Blues for Edith / You don't know what love is.
Note: The great vibes man plays with string accompaniment.
**Cass:** Released Jan '82, on Pablo Jazz (USA) by Pablo Records (USA). Catalogue no: **K10 774**
**CD:** Released May '86, on Pablo Jazz (USA) by Pablo Records (USA). Catalogue no: **CD 20024**
**Album:** Released Jan '82, on Pablo Jazz (USA) by Pablo Records (USA). Catalogue no: **2310 774**

**FROM OPUS DE JAZZ TO JAZZ**
Tracks: / Opus de funk / You leave me breathless / Opus and interlude / Opus pocus / Lover / Can't help lovin' dat man / Lady is a tramp, The / Angel face / Sometimes I'm happy / What's new?.
**Album:** Released Dec '85, on Savoy (France) Deleted Nov '89. Catalogue no: **WL 70501**
**Album:** Released Jul '86, on RCA (France) by BMG Records (France). Deleted Nov '89. Catalogue no: **WL 70821**
**CD:** Released Jan '87, on RCA (France) by BMG Records (France). Deleted Nov '89. Catalogue no: **ZD 70815**

**INVITATION**
**Album:** Released Jan '87, on Original Jazz Classics (USA) by Fantasy Inc (USA). Catalogue no: **OJC 260**

**IT DON'T MEAN A THING IF YOU CAN'T TAP YOUR FOOT (Jackson, Milt Quartet)**
Tracks: / Midnight waltz / Ain't that nuthin'? / Stress and strain / Used to be Jackson / It don't mean a thing / If I were a bell / Close enough for blood.
Note: Milt Jackson (vibes), Cedar Walton (piano), Ray Brown (bass), Mickey Roker (drums). Recorded in New York, July 1984.
**Cass:** Released Mar '85, on Pablo Jazz (USA) by Pablo Records (USA). Catalogue no: **K10 909**
**Album:** Released Mar '85, on Pablo Jazz (USA) by Pablo Records (USA). Catalogue no: **2310909**
**CD:** Released Aug '86, on Pablo Jazz (USA) by Pablo Records (USA). Catalogue no: **J33J 20047**
**Album:** Released May '85, on Pablo Jazz (USA) by Pablo Records (USA). Catalogue no: **IMS 2310900**

**JACKSON**
**CD:** Released May '86, on Pablo Jazz (USA) by Pablo Records (USA). Catalogue no: **CD 20022**

**JAZZ 'N' SAMBA**
Tracks: / Blues for Juanita / I got it bad and that ain't good / Big George / Gingerbread boy.
**Cass:** Released Aug '82, on Jasmine by Hasmick Promotions. Catalogue no: **JAS C32**
**Album:** Released Aug '82, on Jasmine by Hasmick Promotions. Catalogue no: **JAS 32**

**LOOSE WALK (Jackson, Milt & Sonny Stitt)**
Tracks: / Loose walk / Parking lot blues / SKJ / Scrapple from the apple / Lover man / Star eyes.
Note: Recorded live in Milan, 11 November 1979.
**Album:** Released Jan '81, on Palcoscenico (Italy) Catalogue no: **PAL 15009**

**MEMORIES OF THELONIOUS MONK**
**CD:** Released May '86, on Pablo Jazz (USA) by Pablo Records (USA). Catalogue no: **J33J 20055**

**MILT JACKSON**
Tracks: / Lillie / Tahiti / What's new / On the scene / Willow weep for me / Criss cross / Eronel / Misterioso / Evidence / Lillie (2) / Four in one / What's new (alt. take) (Not on LP.) / Don't get around much anymore (Not on LP.) / Don't get around much anymore (alt.) (Not on LP.) / Misterioso (alt.) (Not on LP.) / Epistrophy (Not on LP.) / I mean you (Not on LP.) / All the things you are (Not on LP.) / I should care (alt.) (Not on LP.) / I should care (Not on LP.).
**CD:** Released Dec '89, on Blue Note by EMI Records. Catalogue no: **CDP 781 509 2**
**Album:** Released Nov '87, on Blue Note by EMI Records. Catalogue no: **BLJ 81509**

**MILT JACKSON (2)**
**Album:** Released '88, on GNP Crescendo (USA) by GNP Crescendo Records (USA). Catalogue no: **GNPS 9007**

**MILT JACKSON AND RAY BROWN JAM (Jackson, Milt & Ray Brown)**
Tracks: / Slippery / Beautiful friendship, A / Mean to me / You are my sunshine / CMJ.
**Album:** Released May '82, on Pablo Jazz (USA) by Pablo Records (USA). Catalogue no: **2308 205**
**Cass:** Released May '82, on Pablo Jazz (USA) by Pablo Records (USA). Catalogue no: **K 08 205**

**MILT JACKSON AND COMPANY**
Tracks: / Jaybone / Lament / Our delight / Bag's groove / Watch what happens / My one and only love / Jumpin' blues.
Note: Milt Jackson (vibes), J.J. Johnson (trombone), Tom Rainer (piano), John Collins (guitar), Ray Brown (bass), Roy McCurdy (drums). Recorded in 1983.
**Album:** Released Oct '84, on Pablo Jazz (USA) by Pablo Records (USA). Catalogue no: **2310 897**

**MILT JACKSON WITH THE THELONIUS MONK QUARTET**
Tracks: / Lillie / Tahiti / What's new / Bag's groove / On the scene / Willow weep for me / Criss cross / Eronel / Four in one / Mysterioso / Evidence.
**Album:** Released Sep '84, on Blue Note by EMI Records. Deleted '87. Catalogue no: **BLP 1509**

**NIGHT MIST**
Tracks: / Blues in my heart / Double B / Blues for Clyde / Matter of adjustment / Night mist blues / Other bag blues / D.B. blues.
**Cass:** Released Jan '82, on Pablo Jazz (USA) by Pablo Records (USA). Catalogue no: **K 12 124**
**CD:** Released '88, on Pablo Jazz (USA) by Pablo Records (USA). Catalogue no: **131 123 9**
**Album:** Released Jan '82, on Pablo Jazz (USA) by Pablo Records (USA). Catalogue no: **231 2124**

**OPUS DE FUNK**
Tracks: / Opus de funk / Buhaina / I've lost your love / Soma / Wonder why / My funny valentine / Stonewall / I should care / Nearness of you / Moon ray / Ruby my dear / Sealer / None shall wander / Ruby / Invitation / Stella by starlight / Too close for comfort / Poom a loom.
**2 LP Set:** Released Sep '79, on Prestige Deleted '84. Catalogue no: **PR 24048**

**PLENTY PLENTY SOUL**
Tracks: / Plenty plenty soul / Boogity boogity / Heartstrings / Sermonette / Spirit feel, The / Ignunt oil / Blues at twilight.
**Album:** on Atlantic by WEA Records. Catalogue no: **K 50299**

**SECOND NATURE, THE SAVOY**
Tracks: / Now's the time / In a sentimental mood / Mood indigo / Azure / Fred's mood / Flamingo / Minor conception / What's new / Sometimes I'm happy / Soul in 3/4 / Lover / Can't help lovin' / That man / Lady is a tramp, The / They can't take that away from me / Wild man / Come rain or come shine / Angel face / Soulful.
**Album:** Released Mar '85, on Savoy Jazz (USA) by Malaco Records (USA). Catalogue no: **SJL 2204**

**SOUL BELIEVER**
Tracks: / Ain't misbehavin' / Don't worry 'bout me / I've got the blues / Heartstrings / Roll 'em Pete / Yes sir, that's my baby / I've grown accustomed to her face / I've got it bad and that ain't good / Someone I love / Parking lot blues.
**Cass:** Released Jan '82, on Pablo Jazz (USA) by Pablo Records (USA). Catalogue no: **K10 832**
**Album:** Released Jan '82, on Pablo Jazz (USA) by Pablo Records (USA). Catalogue no: **231 0832**

**SOUL FUSION (Jackson, Milt & Monty Alexander)**
Tracks: / Parking lot blues / Three thousand miles ago / Isn't she lovely? / Soul fusion / Compassion / Once I loved / Yano / Bossa nova do marilla.
**Cass:** Released '82, on Pablo Jazz (USA) by Pablo Records (USA). Catalogue no: **K10 804**
**Album:** Released '82, on Pablo Jazz (USA) by Pablo Records (USA). Catalogue no: **231 0804**

**SOUL ROUTE (Jackson, Milt Quartet)**
Tracks: / Sittin' in the sandtrap / Blues for Gene / How long has this been going on? / Dejection blues / Soul route / Afterglow / In a mellow tone / My romance / Chloe.
Note: Milt Jackson (vibes), Gene Harris (piano and electric keyboards), Ray Brown (bass), Mickey Roker (drums).
**Album:** Released May '84, on Pablo Jazz (USA) by Pablo Records (USA). Catalogue no: **231 0900**
**CD:** Released May '86, on Pablo Jazz (USA) by Pablo Records (USA). Catalogue no: **CD 311254**
**Cass:** Released May '84, on Pablo Jazz (USA) by Pablo Records (USA). Catalogue no: **K10 900**

**STATEMENT (Jackson, Milt Quintet)**
Tracks: / Statement / Slowly / Thrill from the blues / Put off / Sonnymoon for two / Bad and the beautiful, The.
**Album:** Released Mar '85, on Jasmine by Hasmick Promotions. Deleted Feb '88. Catalogue no: **JAS 77**

**THAT'S THE WAY IT IS (Jackson, Milt/Ray Brown Quintet)**
Tracks: / Frankie and Johnny / Here's that rainy day / Wheelin' and dealin' / Blues in the basement / Tenderly / That's the way it is.
**CD:** Released Jan '90, on MCA (Impulse Jazz) Catalogue no: **MCAD 33112**

**TWO OF THE FEW (Jackson, Milt & Oscar Peterson)**
**Cass:** Released May '83, on Pablo Jazz (USA) by Pablo Records (USA). Catalogue no: **K10 881**
**Album:** Released May '83, on Pablo Jazz (USA) by Pablo Records (USA). Catalogue no: **2310 881**

**VERY TALL (Jackson, Milt & Oscar Peterson)**
Tracks: / On Green Dolphin Street / Work song / Heartstrings / John Browns body / Wonderful guy / Reunion blues.
**CD:** Released Jul '86, on Verve Deleted Mar '88. Catalogue no: **827 821-2**
**Album:** Released Jun '89, on Verve Catalogue no: **827 821-1**
**Cass:** Released Jun '89, on Verve Catalogue no: **827 821-4**

## Jackson, Papa Charlie

**FAT MOUTH 1924-27**
**Album:** Released Dec '88, on Yazoo (USA) by Shanachie Records (USA). Catalogue no: **L 1029**

**MOSTLY NEW TO (LP) 1924-29**
Tracks: / Salt Lake City blues / Mama don't allow it / I'm tired of fooling around with you / Bad luck woman blues / Corn

liquor blues.
**Album:** Released Apr '87, on Saydisc by Amon Ra Records. Catalogue no: **MSE 1007**

## Jackson, Willis

**COOL GATOR**
**Album:** Released Apr '86, on Original Jazz Classics (USA) by Fantasy Inc (USA). Catalogue no: **OJC 220**

**GATOR HORN, THE**
**Album:** Released Apr '81, on Muse by Black & Blue Records. Catalogue no: **MR 5146**

**GATOR'S GROOVE**
Tracks: / Soul grabber / Brother Elijah / Pool shark / Que sara sweetie / Good to the damned / Sportin' / Shuckin' / Penny serenade.
**Album:** Released Nov '88, on BGP by Ace Records. Catalogue no: **BGP 1021**

**LOCKIN' HORNS**
Tracks: / Pow / Man I love, The / Troubled times / Summertime / Shadow of your smile / Willis and Von.
Note: With Von Freeman, Carl Wilson, Joe Jones, Yusef Ali. Recorded live at the International Jazz Festival, Laren, 11 August 1978.
**Album:** Released '81, on Muse by Black & Blue Records. Catalogue no: **MR 5200**

**NOTHING BUTT**
Tracks: / Just the way you are / Nuages / Nothing butt / Hittin' and missin' / Autumn leaves / Move.
Note: With Pat Martino, Charlie Earland, Grady Tate, Buddy Caldwell. Recorded 20 June1980.
**Album:** Released Feb '83, on Muse by Black & Blue Records. Catalogue no: **MR 5294**

**NUTHER'N LIKE THUTH'N'**
Tracks: / Nuther'n like thuth'n'.
**12" Single:** Released Dec '88, on BGP by Ace Records. Catalogue no: **BGPT 004**

**ON MY OWN**
Tracks: / Later for the gator / Call of the gators, The / On my own / Dance of the lady bug / More blues at midnight / Good gliding / Wine-o-wine / Street scene / Harlem nocturne / Back door / Howling at midnight / We'll be together again / Crackerjack / Try a little tenderness / Estrellita.
**Album:** Released Aug '87, on Whiskey, Women & Song (Sweden) Catalogue no: **KM 705**

**SINGLE ACTION**
Tracks: / Evergreen / Bolita / Makin' whoopee / You are the sunshine of my life / Hittin' the numbers / Single action.
Note: With Pat Martino, Carl Wilson, Jimmy Lewis, Yusef Ali, Ralph Dorsey. Recorded 26April 1978.
**Album:** Released Apr '81, on Muse by Black & Blue Records. Catalogue no: **MR 5179**

**YA UNDERSTAND ME**
**Album:** Released '88, on Muse by Black & Blue Records. Catalogue no: **MR 5316**

## Jacobs, Little Walter

**BLUE & LONESOME**
**Album:** Released Sep '79, on Le Roi Du Blues Catalogue no: **33 2007**

**SOUTHERN FEELING**
**Album:** Released Jul '79, on Le Roi Du Blues Catalogue no: **33 2012**

## Jacobs, Paul

**BLUES, BALLADS & RAGS**
**CD:** Released '88, on Nonesuch Catalogue no: **79006 2**

## Jacquet, Illinois

**BIRTHDAY PARTY**
**Album:** Released Apr '81, on JRC Catalogue no: **JRC 11434**

**BLACK VELVET BAND**
Tracks: / Jet propulsion / King Jacquet / Try me one more time / Embryo / Riffin' at the 24th street / Mutton leg / Symphony in Sid / Jacquet for Jack the Belboy, A / Big foot / Black velvet / B-yot / Adam's alley / Blue satin / My old gal / Slow down baby / Hot rod / You gotta change / Flying home.
**CD:** Released Nov '88, on Bluebird (2) by BMG Records (UK). Catalogue no: **ND 86571**

**BLUES AND SENTIMENTAL**
**Album:** Released '82, on Jazz Bird Catalogue no: **JAZ 2002**
**Cass:** Released '82, on Jazz Bird Catalogue no: **ZCJAZ 2002**

**BLUES FROM LOUISIANA**
**Album:** Released Apr '81, on JRC Catalogue no: **JRC 11433**

**BOTTOMS UP**
**Album:** Released Nov '85, on Black & Blue (1) by Black & Blue Records. Catalogue no: **333 710**

**FABULOUS APOLLO SESSIONS, THE**
**Album:** Released Oct '88, on Vogue by Vogue Records. Catalogue no: **500 858**

**GENIUS AT WORK**
Tracks: / King, The / Easy living / C jam blues / Take the 'A' train / I wanna blow now.
Note: Recorded at Ronnie Scott's, London.
**Album:** Released Jan '85, on Black Lion Catalogue no: **BLP 30118**

**GROOVIN'**
**Album:** Released Dec '81, on Verve Catalogue no: **2304 511**

**ILLINOIS FLIES AGAIN**
Tracks: / On a clear day / Illinois Jacquet flies again / Robins nest / Watermelon man / I want a little girl / Pamela's blues / Jan / Message, The / Bassoon blues / On Broadway / Like young / Turnpike / Bonita.
**CD:** Released Mar '87, on Greenline by Charly Records. Catalogue no: **CD CHESS 75**
**CD:** Released '86, on Arco by Charly Records. Deleted May '88. Catalogue no: **ARCD 503**

**ILLINOIS JACQUET (Jacquet, Illinois & Wild Bill Davis)**
**Album:** Released Jul '82, on Jazz Reactivation Catalogue no: **JR 154**
**CD:** Released May '87, on Black & Blue (1) by Black & Blue Records. Catalogue no: **233 044**

**ILLINOIS JACQUET AND ALL STAR NEW YORK BAND**
Note: 1980 New York Studio Session with Vic Dickenson, Slam Stewart, Grady Tate.
**CD:** Released Jan '88, on JSP by JSP Records. Catalogue no: **JSP CD 212**

**ILLINOIS JACQUET FLIES AGAIN**
**Album:** Released Oct '88, on Vogue by Vogue Records. Catalogue no: **500062**

**KID AND THE BRUTE, THE (Jacquet, Illinois & Ben Webster)**
Tracks: / Saph / Mambocito mio / September song / Jacquet's dilemma / Kid and The Brute, The / I wrote this for The Kid.
Note: Webster joins Jacquet for two numbers, The Kid and The Brute and I wrote this for The Kid.
**Album:** Released May '82, on Verve Catalogue no: **2304 565**

**SWINGS THE THING**
**Album:** Released Aug '81, on Verve Catalogue no: **2304 434**

## Jacquet, Russell

**RUSS IN NICE**
**Album:** Released '88, on Jazz At Town Hall Catalogue no: **JATH 11435**

## Jailhouse Blues

**JAILHOUSE BLUES (Women's acappella songs from Parchman Penitentiary) (Various artists)**
Note: 1936 & 1939 LC rdgs.
**Album:** Released Sep '87, on Rosetta (USA) Catalogue no: **RR 1316**

## Jam For Boppers

**JAM FOR BOPPERS (JAZZ DANCE 3) (Various artists)**
Tracks: / Please don't leave me: *Shibab, Sahib* / Spanish grease: *Lewis, Ramsey Trio* / Barefoot sunday blues: *Lewis, Ramsey Trio* / Vera: *Evans,Richard Trio* / Boss Tina: *Grey, Al* / Watermelon man: *Jacquet, Illinois* / Jam for boppers: *Ammons, Gene & Sonny Stitt* / Mellow yellow: *Brown,Odell & The Organizers* / Huffin'n'puffin': *Donaldson, Lou.*
**Cass:** Released 7 Nov '87, on Argo (USA) by PolyGram Classics (USA). Catalogue no: **ARCK 7505**
**Album:** Released 7 Nov '87, on Arco by Charly Records. Catalogue no: **ARC 505**

## Jam Session

**JAM SESSION (1944-46) (Various artists)**
Tracks: / Roy meets horn: *Eldridge, Roy* / Old Rob Roy: *Eldridge, Roy* / Cocktails for two: *Tatum, Art* / Liza: *Tatum, Art* / Lester leaps in: *Young, Lester* / Rose room: *James, Harry* / Lady be good:

*Basie, Count All Stars* / Jammin' on A: *Various artists* / Blues: *Shavers, Charlie* / Stompin at the Savoy: *Shavers, Charlie* / Seven come eleven: *Shavers, Charlie* / Rose room: *Shavers, Charlie.*
**Album:** Released Apr '81, on Joker (USA) by Lifetime Records (USA). Catalogue no: **SM 3119**

**JAM SESSION VOLUME 1 (Various artists)**
**Album:** Released Jun '88, on Jammy's Catalogue no: **VPRL 1031**

**JAM SESSION VOLUME 2 (Various artists)**
**Album:** Released Aug '88, on Jammy's Catalogue no: **VPRL 1032**

## Jam Session (film)

**JAM SESSION / REVEILLE WITH BEVERLY (Original soundtrack) (Various artists)**
Note: Starring Ann Miller, Duke Ellington, Count Basie and Louis Armstrong.
**Album:** Released Jan '89, on Silva Screen by Silva Screen Records. Catalogue no: **HS 5014**

## Jam Sessions

**JAM SESSIONS (Various artists)**
Tracks: / Perdido: *Various artists* / Bye bye blues: *Various artists* / Mack the knife: *Various artists* / Milt Jackson: *Various artists* / Red top: *Brown, Ray* / That's the way it is: *Various artists* / Here 'tis: *Gillespie, Dizzy* / Freeport jump: *Basie, Count* / Sweethearts on parade: *Pablo All Stars* / Donna Lee: *Various artists.*
**Cass:** Released '82, on Pablo Jazz (USA) by Pablo Records (USA). Catalogue no: **K 20 105**
**Album:** Released '82, on Pablo Jazz (USA) by Pablo Records (USA). Catalogue no: **262 0105**

## Jamal, Ahmad

**AHMAD JAMAL**
**CD:** Released Jul '89, on Cleo Catalogue no: **CLCD 5027**

**AHMAD JAMAL AND COLEMAN HAWKINS (Jamal, Ahmad & Coleman Hawkins)**
**VHS:** Released '88, on Kay Jazz (video) by Kay Jazz. Catalogue no: **KJ 010**

**AHMAD JAMAL IN CONCERT (Jamal, Ahmad & Gary Burton)**
Tracks: / Morning of the carnival / One / Bogata / Tones for Joan's bones / Autumn leaves.
**Cass:** Released '89, on Kingdom Jazz by Kingdom Records. Catalogue no: **CGATE 7006**
**Album:** Released Jun '82, on Kingdom Jazz by Kingdom Records. Catalogue no: **GATE 7006**

**AHMED JAMAL**
Tracks: / I'll take romance / Like someone in love / Falling in love with love / Best thing for you / April in Paris / Second time around / We live in two different worlds / Night misty blues.
**Album:** Released Jul '82, on Jazz Reactivation Catalogue no: **JR 153**

**ALHAMBRA**
**Album:** Released Oct '88, on Vogue by Vogue Records. Catalogue no: **515019**

**AT THE PERSHING**
Tracks: / But not for me / Surrey with a fringe on top / Moonlight in Vermont / Music,music,music / No greater love / Poinciana / Woody'n you / Whats new.
**Album:** on Chess by Vogue Records. Catalogue no: **GCH 8032**
**Cass:** Released '89, on Chess by Vogue Records. Catalogue no: **GCHK 8032**
**CD:** Released Dec '86, on Vogue by Vogue Records. Catalogue no: **VGCD 600049**

**AT THE TOP POINCIANA REVISITED**
Tracks: / Have you met Miss Jones / Poinciana / Call me / Valley of the dolls, Theme from / Frank's tune.
**Album:** Released Jun '82, on Jasmine by Hasmick Promotions. Deleted Feb '88. Catalogue no: **JAS 15**
**Cass:** Released Jun '82, on Jasmine by Hasmick Promotions. Catalogue no: **JAS C15**

**AWAKENING, THE (Jamal, Ahmad Trio)**
Tracks: / Awakening, The / I love music / Patterns / Dolphin dance / You're my everything / Stolen moments / Wave.
**Album:** Released Apr '87, on MCA by MCA Records. Deleted Dec '89. Catalogue no: **AS 9194**
**Cass:** Released Apr '87, on MCA by MCA Records. Deleted Dec '89. Catalogue no: **ASC 9194**
**Album:** Released Aug '82, on Jasmine by Hasmick Promotions. Deleted Feb '88. Catalogue no: **JAS 44**
**Cass:** Released Aug '82, on Jasmine by Hasmick Promotions. Catalogue no: **JAS C44**
**CD:** Released Apr '87, on MCA by MCA Records. Deleted Dec '89. Catalogue no: **MCAD 5644**

**AWAKENING, THE (SINGLE)**
Tracks: / Awakening, The.
**7" Single:** Released Aug '84, on Jim White Catalogue no: **IQ PROMO 101**

**BEST OF AHMED JAMAL**
Tracks: / Black cow / Don't ask my neighbours / Swahililand / Soul girl / Dynamo / Prelude to a kiss / Genetic walk.
**Album:** Released Sep '81, on 20th Century by 20th Century Records. Catalogue no: **T 631**
**Cass:** Released Sep '81, on 20th Century by 20th Century Records. Catalogue no: **C 631**

**CHICAGO GOLDEN YEARS**
**Album:** Released Oct '88, on Vogue by Vogue Records. Catalogue no: **515002**

**DIGITAL WORKS**
Tracks: / Poinciana / But not for me / Midnight sun / Footprints / Once upon a time / One / La costa / Misty / M.A.S.H., Theme from / Biencavo / Time for love, A / Wave.
**Album:** Released Sep '87, on Atlantic by WEA Records. Catalogue no: **781 258-1**
**CD:** Released Sep '87, on Atlantic by WEA Records. Catalogue no: **781 258-2**
**Cass:** Released Sep '87, on Atlantic by WEA Records. Catalogue no: **781 258-4**

**GOODBYE MR EVANS**
Tracks: / Lament for a dying boy / Somewhere along the Nile / Close enough for love / Firefly / Mellowdrama / Goodbye Mr. Evans / Polka dots and moonbeams.
**Album:** Released Jul '88, on Black Lion Catalogue no: **BLM 52006**

**LIVE AT BUBBA'S**
Tracks: / Waltz for Debbie / House on the hill / People / Biea / It's the good life / Autumn in New York / I have never been in love before.
**Cass:** Released '89, on Kingdom Jazz by Kingdom Records. Catalogue no: **CGATE 7002**
**Album:** Released Sep '83, on Kingdom Jazz by Kingdom Records. Catalogue no: **GATE 7002**

**NIGHT SONG**
Tracks: / When you wish upon a star / Deja vu / Need to smile / Bad times / Touch me in the morning / Night song / M.A.S.H., Theme from / Something's missing in my life.
**Album:** Released Oct '81, on Motown by BMG Records (UK). Catalogue no: **STML 12145**

**ONE**
Tracks: / One / Just the way you are / Jet / Black cow / Dynamo / Sumayah / Festival 20th century.
**Album:** Released '79, on 20th Century by 20th Century Records. Deleted '83. Catalogue no: **T 555**

**POINCIANA**
**CD:** Released Jun '88, on MCA (USA) by MCA Records (USA). Catalogue no: **31266**

**PORTFOLIO**
**CD:** Released Oct '88, on Vogue by Vogue Records. Catalogue no: **VGCD 600 162**

## Jamal, Khan

**INFINITY**
**Album:** Released May '89, on Stash (USA) Catalogue no: **ST 278**

**THINKING OF YOU**
**CD:** Released Feb '89, on Storyville by Storyville Records AB. Catalogue no: **STCD 4138**
**Album:** Released Jun '88, on Storyville by Storyville Records AB. Catalogue no: **SLP 4138**

## James, Elmore

**BEST OF ELMORE JAMES**
Tracks: / Dust my blues / I was a fool / Dark and dreary / Late hours at midnight / Blue before sunrise / Goodbye baby / Standing at the crossroads / Sunnyland

/ Mean and evil / Happy home / No love in my heart / Wild about you baby.
**Album:** Released Mar '81, on Ace by Ace Records. Catalogue no: **CH 31**

**CHICAGO GOLDEN YEARS (James, Elmore & John Brim)**
**Album:** Released Oct '88, on Vogue (France) by Vogue Records. Catalogue no: **515006**

**COLLECTION: ELMORE JAMES (20 blues greats)**
Tracks: / Dust my broom / I believe / Hand in hand / Blues before sunrise / Coming home / Strange kinda feeling / I was a fool / Baby what's wrong? / Sky is crying, The / Late hours at midnight / Standing at the crossroads / Early in the morning / Rock my baby tonight / Rollin' and tumblin' / Can't stop lovin' my baby / Look on yonder wall / Dark and dreary / 1839 blues / Sinful woman / I done somebody wrong.
**CD:** Released Jul '88, on Deja Vu Catalogue no: **DVCD 2035**
**Cass:** Released Nov '85, on Deja Vu Catalogue no: **DVMC 2035**
**Album:** Released Nov '85, on Deja Vu Catalogue no: **DVLP 2035**

**COME GO WITH ME**
Tracks: / Baby please set a date / So unkind / Sunnyland train / Twelve year old boy / My kind of woman / Hand in hand (take 3) / My baby's gone / Make my dreams come true / Anna Lee / Bobby's rock / Find my kinda woman / Stranger blues / Mean mistreatin' mama / I can't stop lovin' you / She moved / I'm worried.
**CD:** Released May '89, on Charly by Charly Records. Catalogue no: **CDCHARLY 180**
**Album:** Released May '89, on Charly R&B by Charly Records. Catalogue no: **CRB 1212**

**DONE SOMEBODY WRONG**
Tracks: / Done somebody wrong.
**7" Single:** Released Mar '81, on Charly by Charly Records. Deleted '87. Catalogue no: **CTD 126**

**DUST MY BROOM**
Tracks: / Coming home / Dust my broom / Hand and hand / I believe / Done somebody wrong / It hurts me too / Pickin' the blues / Look on yonder wall / Mean mistreatin' mama / Rollin' and tumblin' / Standing at the crossroads / Sky is crying, The.
**Album:** Released Jan '85, on Topline by Charly Records. Catalogue no: **TOP 120**
**Cass:** Released Jan '85, on Topline by Charly Records. Catalogue no: **KTOP 120**

**ELMORE JAMES STORY, THE**
Tracks: / Dust my broom / Sunnyland / Hand in hand / Sho' nuff I do / Where can my baby be / Look on yonder wall / I was a fool / Wild about you baby / Sky is crying, The / Strange kinda feeling / 1839 blues / Dark and dreary / Standing at the crossroads / Coming home / Mean mistreatin' mama / My best friend / Long tall woman / My best friend - reprise / Blues before sunrise / I done somebody wrong / Make a little love / Mean and evil / Sinful woman / So mean to me / Happy home.
**CD:** Released May '89, on Deja Vu Catalogue no: **DVRECD 24**
**Cass:** Released May '89, on Deja Vu Catalogue no: **DVREMC 24**

**GOT TO MOVE**
**Album:** Released Mar '81, on Charly R&B by Charly Records. Catalogue no: **CRB 1017**

**GREATEST HITS: ELMORE JAMES**
**Cass:** Released '88, on Masters (Holland) Catalogue no: **CLMC 9271283**
**Cass:** Released May '88, on Blue City Catalogue no: **2652714**
**Album:** Released '88, on Masters (Holland) Catalogue no: **CL 271283**
**Cass:** Released Jan '87, on Masters (Holland) Catalogue no: **CLMC 009271283**
**Album:** Released May '88, on Blue City Catalogue no: **2652711**
**CD:** Released May '88, on Blue City Catalogue no: **2652712**

**JAMES - BRIM - JONES (James, Elmore, John Brim, Floyd Jones)**
**CD:** Released Dec '86, on Vogue by Vogue Records. Catalogue no: **VG 600 119**

**KING OF THE BOTTLENECK BLUES**
Tracks: / Wild about you baby / Mean and evil / My best friend / Dark and dreary / Hawaiian boogie / Blues before sunrise / Strange kinda feeling / Sho 'nuff I do / I was a fool / Long tall woman / One more drink / Wild about you.
**Cass:** Released Feb '86, on Crown by Ace Records. Deleted '88. Catalogue no: **GEMC 003**
**Album:** Released Feb '86, on Crown by Ace Records. Catalogue no: **GEM 003**

**KING OF THE SLIDE GUITAR**
Tracks: / Lost woman blues / One more drink / Strange kinda feeling / Sho nuff I do / Wild about you / Sweet little woman / Long tall woman / Where can my baby be / My baby's gone / I may be wrong / Elmo's shuffle / Please find my baby / My best friend / So mean to me / Wild about you baby / Dark and dreary.
**Album:** Released Apr '83, on Ace by Ace Records. Catalogue no: **CH 68**

**LET'S CUT IT**
Tracks: / Dust my blues / Blues before sunrise / No love in my heart / Sho' nuff I do / Standing at the crossroads / I was a fool / Sunnyland / Canton Mississippi breakdown / Happy home / Wild about you baby / Long tall woman / So mean to me / Hawaiian boogie / Mean and evil / Dark and dreary / My best friend / I believe / Goodbye baby.
**Album:** Released Nov '86, on Ace by Ace Records. Catalogue no: **CHD 192**
**Album:** Released Dec '88, on Ace by Ace Records. Catalogue no: **CH 192**
**CD:** Released Nov '86, on Ace by Ace Records. Catalogue no: **CDCH 192**

**ONE WAY OUT**
Tracks: / Talk to me baby / Shake your moneymaker / Can't stop lovin' my baby / It hurts me too / Sky is crying, The / Cry for me baby / Something inside of me / Standing at the crossroads / Coming home / Rollin' and tumblin' / Take me where you go / I need you / Person to person / One way out / Twelve year old boy, The / Dust my broom.
**Cass:** Released '85, on Charly R&B by Charly Records. Catalogue no: **TCCRB 1008**
**Album:** Released '85, on Charly R&B by Charly Records. Catalogue no: **CRB 1008**

**ORIGINAL METEOR & FLAIR SIDES (James, Elmore & his Broom Dusters)**
Tracks: / I believe / I held my baby last night / Baby what's wrong / Sinful woman / Early in the morning / Can't stop lovin' my baby / Hawaiian boogie / Hand in hand / Blues / Make a little love / Strange kinda feeling / Sho nuff I do / Make my dreams come true / Rock my baby tonight.
**Album:** Released Aug '84, on Ace by Ace Records. Catalogue no: **CH 112**

**PICKIN' THE BLUES**
Tracks: / Dust my broom / Look on yonder wall / It hurts me too / Coming home / Sky is crying, The / Standing at the crossroads / Hand in hand / Mean mistreatin' mama / I done somebody wrong / Pickin' the blues / I believe.
**Cass:** Released Apr '86, on Castle Showcase by Castle Communications Records. Catalogue no: **SHTC 140**
**Album:** Released Apr '86, on Castle Showcase by Castle Communications Records. Catalogue no: **SHLP 140**

**RED HOT BLUES**
Tracks: / Dust my broom / Look on yonder wall / It hurts me too / Coming home / Sky is crying, The / Standing at the crossroads / Hand in hand / Rollin' and tumblin' / Mean mistreatin' Mama / I done somebody wrong / Pickin' the blues / I believe.
**Album:** Released Nov '83, on Blue Moon (1) by Magnum Music Group. Catalogue no: **BMLP 008**

**SHAKE YOUR MONEYMAKER**
Tracks: / Dust my broom / Twelve year old boy, The / Coming home / It hurts me too / Elmore's contribution to jazz / Cry for me baby / Take me where you go / Sky is crying, The / Held my baby last night / Knocking at your door / Rollin' and tumblin' / Done somebody wrong / Fine little mama / Shake your moneymaker / I need you / Can't stop lovin' my baby / Something inside of me / Person to person / Baby please set a date / One way out / Got to move / Talk to me baby.
**CD:** Released Dec '86, on Charly by Charly Records. Catalogue no: **CDCHARLY 34**

### TO KNOW A MAN
**Album:** Released Feb '84, on Line by Line Records (W.Germany). Catalogue no: **OLLP 8018**

### WHO'S MUDDY SHOES ? (James, Elmore & John Brim)
Tracks: / Ice cream man / Whose muddy shoes / Madison blues / I see my baby / You got me / My best friend / Sun is shining,The / Talk to me baby / Rattlesnake / Be careful / Dust my broom / Tool bag boogie / Tough times / Stormy monday.
**Album:** on Blues Rock Project Catalogue no: **BRP 2016**
**Album:** Released '89, on Chess by Vogue Records. Catalogue no: **GCH8097**
**Album:** Released Apr '82, on Chess (USA) Catalogue no: **CXMP 2007**
**Cass:** Released '89, on Chess by Vogue Records. Catalogue no: **GCHK78097**

## James, Etta

### AVENUE D (James, Etta/David A Stewart)
Tracks: / Avenue D / My head is a city / Avenue D (Kevorkian remix) / Avenue D (Avenue dub) / Avenue D (sound assassins mix).
**7" Single:** Released May '89, on Capitol by EMI Records. Deleted Oct '89. Catalogue no: **CL 533**
**12" Single:** Released May '89, on Capitol by EMI Records. Deleted Oct '89. Catalogue no: **12CL 533**

### BLUES IN THE NIGHT (James, Etta & Eddie 'Cleanhead' Vinson)
Tracks: / Kidney stew / Railroad porter blues / Something's got a hold on me / Medley: at last / Trust in me / Sunday kind of love / I just wanna make love to you / Please send me someone to love / Love man / Misty.
Note: Exciting new album from blues veternas Etta James and Eddie Vinson recorded live at Maula's club in Los Angeles. All star support from Red Holloway saxes. Jack McDuff - organ, Shuggie Otis - guitar and Paul Humphrey on drums.
**Cass:** Released Nov '86, on Fantasy by Ace Records. Catalogue no: **5F 9647**
**Album:** Released Nov '86, on Fantasy by Ace Records. Catalogue no: **F 9647**

### CHESS MASTERS
Tracks: / Tell Mama / I'd rather go blind / Watchdog / Love of my man, The / I'm gonna take what he's got / Some rope / Security / Steal away / My mother in law / Don't lose your good thing / It hurts me so much / Just a little bit / Something's got a hold on me / Baby what you want me to do / What'd I say / Money / Seven day fool / Sweet little angel / Ooh poo pah doo / Woke up this morning.
**Album:** Released Apr '81, on Chess (PRT) Deleted '88. Catalogue no: **CXMP 2000**
**Album:** Released Apr '83, on Chess (USA) Catalogue no: **CXMD 4017**

### CHICAGO GOLDEN YEARS
**2 LP Set:** Released Oct '88, on Vogue by Vogue Records. Catalogue no: **427014**

### COME A LITTLE CLOSER
Tracks: / Out on the street again / Mama told me / You give me what I want / Come a little closer / Let's burn down the cornfield / Powerplay / Feeling uneasy / St.Louis blues / Gonna have some fun tonight / Sooki sooki.
**Album:** Released May '88, on Chess by Vogue Records. Catalogue no: **GCH 8047**
**Cass:** Released May '88, on Chess by Vogue Records. Catalogue no: **GCHK 78047**

### DEEP IN THE NIGHT
Tracks: / Laying beside you / Piece of my heart / Only women bleed / Take it to the limit / Lovesick blues / Strange man / Sugar on the floor / Sweet touch of love / I'd rather go blind.
**Album:** Released Jul '78, on Warner Bros. by WEA Records. Catalogue no: **K 56492**

### ETTA JAMES AT LAST
Tracks: / Anything to say you're mine / My dearest darling / Trust in me / Sunday kind of love / Tough Mary / I just want to make love to you / At last / All I could do was cry / Stormy weather / Girl of my dreams.
**Cass:** Released Oct '87, on Chess by Vogue Records. Catalogue no: **GCHK 78036**
**Album:** Released Oct '87, on Chess by Vogue Records. Catalogue no: **GCH 8036**

### GOOD ROCKIN' MAMA
Tracks: / Dance with me Henry / Do something crazy / Woman / I hope you're satisfied / Strange things happening / Good rockin' daddy / Hey Henry / That's all / I'm a fool.
**Album:** Released May '81, on Ace by Ace Records. Deleted Jun '88. Catalogue no: **10 CH 33**

### GOOD ROCKIN' MAMA/TUFF LOVER (SET)
Tracks: / Good rockin' mama / Dance with me Henry / Do something crazy / Woman / I hope you're satisfied / Strange things happening / Good rockin' daddy / Hey Henry / I'm a fool / That's all / Tuff lover / Pick-up / By the light of the silvery moon / Fools we mortals be / Come what may / Good lookin' / Tears of joy / Shortnin' bread rock / Baby every night / Then I'll care / Market place.
**Cass set:** Released Feb '85, on Ace by Ace Records. Catalogue no: **CHC 803**

### HER GREATEST SIDES VOL.1
Tracks: / Tell mama / Something's got a hold on me / Pushover / Only time will tell / Stop the wedding / Security / I'd rather go blind / Trust in me / Sunday kind of love / My dearest darling / At last / Waiting for Charlie to come home / All I could do was cry / Fool that I am.
**Album:** Released '87, on Chess by Vogue Records. Catalogue no: **GCH 8015**
**Cass:** Released '87, on Chess by Vogue Records. Catalogue no: **GCHK 78015**

### I GOT THE WILL
Tracks: / I got the will / Come to mamma / One night (Available on 10" and CD only).
**10" Single:** Released Jul '89, on Island by Island Records. Catalogue no: **10 IS 418**
**7" Single:** Released Jul '89, on Island by Island Records. Catalogue no: **IS 418**
**CD Single:** Released Jul '89, on Island by Island Records. Catalogue no: **CID 418**

### JUICY PEACHES
Tracks: / Next door to the blues / Pay back / Two sides to every story / Loving you more every day / That's all I want from you / It must be your love / Don't pick me for your fool / Do right woman / I worship the ground you walk on / You got it / Almost persuaded / Tighten up your own thing / Losers weepers / I found a love.
**Album:** Released '89, on Chess by Vogue Records. Catalogue no: **GCH 8116**

### ON CHESS
**CD:** Released Oct '88, on Vogue by Vogue Records. Catalogue no: **VGCD 600 175**

### R & B DYNAMITE
Tracks: / W.O.M.A.N. / Number one / I'm a fool / Strange things happening / Hey Henry / I hope you're satisfied / Good rockin' daddy / Sunshine of love / That's all / How big a fool / Market place / Tough lover / Do something crazy / Be my lovey dovey / Nobody loves you (like me) / Hickory dickory dock / You know what I mean / Wallflower, The / Baby, baby, every night / We're in love / Tears of joy (Available on CD and cassette only) / Pick-up, The (Available on CD and cassette only).
**CD:** Released May '87, on Ace by Ace Records. Catalogue no: **CDCH 210**
**Album:** Released Jun '87, on Ace by Ace Records. Catalogue no: **CH 210**
**Cass:** Released Jun '87, on Ace by Ace Records. Catalogue no: **CHC 210**

### R & B QUEEN
Tracks: / My one and only / Pick-up / I'm a fool / By the light of the silvery moon / Come what may / That's all / Tough lover / Dance with me Henry / Tears of joy / Baby baby every night / Do something crazy / Market place.
**Cass:** Released Feb '86, on Crown by Ace Records. Deleted '88. Catalogue no: **GEMC 005**
**Album:** Released Feb '86, on Crown by Ace Records. Catalogue no: **GEM 005**

Etta James - Seven Year Itch (Island)

**ROCKS THE HOUSE**
Tracks: / Somethings got a hold on me / Baby what you want me to do / What I say / Money / Seven day fool / Sweet little angel / Ooh poo pah doo / Woke up this morning.
**Album:** on Chess by Vogue Records. Catalogue no: **GCH 8030**
**Cass:** on Chess by Vogue Records. Catalogue no: **GCHK 78030**

**SEVEN YEAR ITCH (See panel above)**
Tracks: / I got the will / Jump into the fire / Shakey ground / Come to mama / Damn your eyes / Breakin' up somebody's home / Jealous kind, The / How strong is a woman / It ain't always what you do / One night.
**Album:** Released Mar '89, on Island by Island Records. Catalogue no: **ILPS 9923**
**CD:** Released Mar '89, on Island by Island Records. Catalogue no: **CID 9923**
**Cass:** Released Mar '89, on Island by Island Records. Catalogue no: **ICT 9923**

**STICKIN' TO MY GUNS**
**Album:** Released Apr '90, on Island by Island Records. Catalogue no: **ILPS 9955**
**Cass:** Released Apr '90, on Island by Island Records. Catalogue no: **ICT 9955**
**CD:** Released Apr '90, on Island by Island Records. Catalogue no: **CID 9955**

**TELL MAMA**
Tracks: / If I can't have you / Spoonful / Nobody but you / Next door to the blues / Something's got a hold on me / (You better) do right / I'm loving you more everyday / Breaking point / Mellow fellow / Steal away / Just a little bit / Don't lose your good thing / Watch dog / I'm gonna take what he's got / I'd rather go blind / Love of my man, The / It hurts me so much / Same rope, The / I got you babe / I worship the ground you walk on / You got it / Fire / Miss Pitiful.
**CD:** Released Oct '88, on Chess by Vogue Records. Catalogue no: **CDRED 7**
**CD:** Released Feb '90, on MCA by MCA Records. Catalogue no: **CHD 9269**

**TELL MAMA (SINGLE)**
Tracks: / Tell mama / Security / Something's got a hold on me / I'd rather go blind.
**7" Single:** Released Jul '85, on Chess (PRT) Deleted '88. Catalogue no: **CHES 4005**

**TUFF LOVER**
Tracks: / Tuff lover / Pick-up / By the light of the silvery moon / Fools we mortals be / Come what may / Dance with me Henry / Good lookin' / Tears of joy / Shortnin' bread rock / Baby every night / Then I'll care / Market place.
**Album:** Released Jul '83, on Ace by Ace Records. Catalogue no: **CH 73**

## James, Harry

**20 GOLDEN GREATS: HARRY JAMES LIVE (James, Harry & His Music Makers)**
Tracks: / Easy / My beloved is rugged / Rose room / King Porter stomp / Your red wagon / Lady be good / Shiny stockings / Block party / Ultra / Jumping at the woodside / Flatbush Flanagan / Carnival / Dancing in the dark / Love & weather / Rockin' in rhythm / Deep purple / Trumpet blues and cantabile / Lover come back to me / Man I love, The.
**Cass:** Released Mar '87, on Magic (1) by Submarine Records. Catalogue no: **CAWM 2**

**20 GOLDEN PIECES: HARRY JAMES (James, Harry Orchestra)**
Tracks: / Around the world in 80 days / Music makers / I don't want to walk without you / King Porter stomp / Back beat boogie / I'm beginning to see the light / Opus one / I've heard that song before / I had a craziest dream / More / Blue skies / One o'clock jump / You'll never know / My heart cries for you / Anytime / Three coins in the fountain / Taste of honey, A / You go to my head / I'll be seeing you / As long as he needs me.
Note: Vocals by Helen Forrest.
**Album:** Released Dec '81, on Bulldog Records by President Records. Catalogue no: **BDL 2023**
**Cass:** Released Feb '82, on Bulldog Records by President Records. Catalogue no: **BDC 2023**

**1954: HARRY JAMES (James, Harry & His Orchestra)**
**Album:** Released Aug '88, on Circle (USA) by Jazzology Records (USA). Catalogue no: **CLP 39**

**1943-46 (James, Harry & His Orchestra)**
Tracks: / Charmaine / Harpie's bazaar / My old flame / Blue turning grey over you / All of me / I cover the waterfront / G flat special / Blue Lou / I've found this a new baby / Ain't she sweet / I'll be around / Exactly like you / I've had this feeling before / Cinderella / How high the moon / Old folks at home.
**Album:** Released Oct '79, on London Records by London Records Ltd. Deleted '84. Catalogue no: **HMP 5052**

**1946-66**
Note: Featuring Buddy Rich.
**Album:** Released Sep '87, on Giants of Jazz by Hasmick Promotions. Catalogue no: **LPJT 68**

**1948-49 (James, Harry & His Orchestra)**
Tracks: / How high the moon / Lazy river / Better have four / New York blues / Sabre dance / You turned the tables on me / Rank Frank / Forgotten / I may be wrong / Proclamation.
**Album:** Released Oct '79, on London Records by London Records Ltd. Deleted '84. Catalogue no: **HMP 5060**

**1943-1946 BIG BAND (James, Harry & His Orchestra)**
**Album:** Released '88, on Joker (USA) by Lifetime Records (USA). Catalogue no: **SM 3872**
**Cass:** Released '88, on Joker (USA) by Lifetime Records (USA). Catalogue no: **MC 3872**

**ALL TIME STANDARDS 1938-1954 (James, Harry & His Orchestra)**
**CD:** Released '88, on Delta (1) by Delta

Harry James

Records. Catalogue no: **11 082**

**ARRANGEMENTS OF JIMMY MUNDY & ANDY GIBSON (James, Harry & Andy Gibson)**
**Album:** Released May '84, on Joyce (USA) Catalogue no: **JOYCE 2025**

**ARRANGEMENTS OF RAINS, HOLMES, BILLY MAY**
**Album:** Released May '84, on Joyce (USA) Catalogue no: **JOYCE 2026**

**BIG JOHN SPECIAL**
Tracks: / Big John special / Cherry / Don'cha go 'way mad / Stardust / I may be wrong / Bluebeard blues / Sweet Jenny Lou / Back beat boogie / Six two and even / Slap happy / Forgotten / Body and soul / Cheek to cheek / Rank Frank / Ultra.
**Album:** Released Jun '82, on Hep Jazz by Hep Records. Catalogue no: **HEP 24**

**CIRIBIRIBIN**
**Album:** Released Jun '85, on Pathe Marconi (France) Catalogue no: **PM 1551923**

**COMIN' FROM GOOD PLACE (James, Harry & His Band)**
**Album:** Released Oct '82, on Sheffield Lab.(USA) by Sheffield Lab. Inc.(USA). Deleted '86. Catalogue no: **LAB 6**

**DOUBLE FEATURE**
Tracks: / Ciribiribin / King-size blues / Shiny stockings / Lover come back to me / Harry's delight / Two o'clock jump / Jumping at the Woodside / One on the house / Rockin' in rhythm / Don't get around much anymore / Tweet tweet / Moonchild.
**Album:** Released Oct '84, on First Heard by Submarine Records. Catalogue no: **FH 48**
**Cass:** Released Oct '84, on First Heard by Submarine Records. Catalogue no: **CFH 48**

**EMBRACEABLE YOU (James, Harry & His Orchestra)**
**CD:** Released Jun '88, on Compact Selection Catalogue no: **TQ 133**

**FLASH HARRY, 1943-44**
**Album:** Released Oct '89, on Hep Jazz by Hep Records. Catalogue no: **HEP 37**

**FROM HOLLYWOOD**
**Album:** Released '84, on First Heard by Submarine Records. Catalogue no: **FH 39**

**GOLDEN TRUMPET OF HARRY JAMES, THE (James, Harry & His Orchestra)**
Tracks: / Ciribiribin / You made me love you / Two o'clock jump / I've heard that song before / Ultra / By the sleepy before / All or nothing at all / Cherry / Take the 'A' train / I heard you cried last night / Mole, The / Satin doll.
**CD:** Released Mar '87, on London Records by London Records Ltd. Deleted Feb '89. Catalogue no: **820 178-2**

**GREATEST HITS: HARRY JAMES (James, Harry Orchestra)**
**CD:** Released Apr '87, on Bridge (MCS Bridge) Catalogue no: **100 019**

**HARRY JAMES (Compact / Walkman jazz)**
Tracks: / Get off the stand / Moanin' low / My Monday date / I'm in the market for you / Harry, not Jesse / Lush life / Squeeze me / Sleepy time gal / Hot pink / Spring can really hang you up the most / Jazz connoisseur / Confessin' / Harry's delight / Weather bird rag / I cover the waterfront / Rockin' in the rhythm.
**CD:** Released Mar '88, on Verve Catalogue no: **833 285-2**
**Album:** Released Apr '79, on Giants of Jazz by Hasmick Promotions. Catalogue no: **GOJ 1009**
**Cass:** Released 27 Feb '88, on Verve Catalogue no: **833 285-4**
**Album:** Released Nov '88, on Blu-Disc (USA) Catalogue no: **T 1010**

**HARRY JAMES 1937-8**
**Album:** Released '88, on Tax Catalogue no: **TAX 8015**

**HARRY JAMES, 1943-46**
Tracks: / If that's the way you want it baby / Indiana / Body and soul / I'm satisfied / I couldn't sleep a wink last night / Rose room / All of me / Shorty George / On the sunny side of the street / Between the devil and the deep blue sea / Stardust / It's been so long / My baby just cares for me / Girl of my dreams / You go to my head / Shady ladybird.
Note: The sixteen on this album are truly outstanding performances from eleven different off-line (off the air) aircheck transcription discs.
**Album:** Released Apr '89, on Hindsight Catalogue no: **HSR 102**

**HARRY JAMES AND HIS ORCHESTRA (James, Harry & His Orchestra)**
**Album:** Released '88, on Entertainers Catalogue no: **ENT LP 13017**
**Cass:** Released '88, on Entertainers Catalogue no: **ENT MC 13017**

**HARRY JAMES AND HIS ORCHESTRA (James, Harry & His Orchestra)**
Tracks: / Theme - introduction / Shorty George / To you / King Porter stomp / From the bottom of my heart / Beer barrel Polka / White sails / Well alright / Two o'clock jump / Theme - close.
**Album:** Released May '88, on Jasmine by Hasmick Promotions. Catalogue no: **JASM 2514**
**Cass:** Released May '88, on Jasmine by Hasmick Promotions. Catalogue no: **JASMC 2514**

**HARRY JAMES AND HIS ORCHESTRA 1943-46, VOL.2 (James, Harry & His Orchestra)**
Tracks: / Joe Blow / Sweet & lovely / Easy street / Honeysuckle Rose / It can't be wrong / Nice work if you can get it / Sentimental journey / It must be jelly / I've had my moments / Do nothin' 'till you hear from me / Always / Just a sittin' a rockin' / Remember / Peg o'my heart / More than you know / Mr. Coed.
**Album:** Released Apr '80, on London Records by London Records Ltd. Deleted '85. Catalogue no: **HMA 5067**

**HARRY JAMES AND HIS ORCHESTRA 1944-45 (James, Harry**

**& His Orchestra)**
Tracks: / King porter stomp / Joe Blow / Air mail special / Six two and even / Caravan / Talk of the town / Sad sack, The / Roll 'em / Loveless love / Eightbar-riff / I may be wrong.
**Album:** Released Apr '81, on Solid Sender Catalogue no: **SOL 504**

**HARRY JAMES AND HIS ORCHESTRA, 1947-49 VOL.6 (James, Harry & His Orchestra)**
Tracks: / Who's got the ball / Lover come back to me / Pagan love song / Pppin' off / When it's sleepy down south / Little dream of me / You came a long waay from St. Louis / Ooh, look-a-there, ain't she pretty / Lover / Queer street / Tuxedo junction / Forgotten / Things ain't what they used to be / Lullaby of the leaves / One I used to love, The.
**Album:** Released '88, on Hindsight Catalogue no: **HSR 150**

**HARRY JAMES AND HIS ORCHESTRA 1948-49 (James, Harry & His Orchestra)**
Tracks: / There they go / 'Cept February which has 28 / Raffles / Snooty fruity / You turned the tables on me / Six two and even / Cottontail / Lover / Big boy / Bells.
**Album:** Released Apr '81, on Solid Sender Catalogue no: **SOL 501**

**HARRY JAMES AND HIS ORCHESTRA 1948-49 (James, Harry & His Orchestra)**
**Album:** Released Oct '79, on London Records by London Records Ltd. Catalogue no: **HMA 5050**

**HARRY JAMES COLLECTION**
**CD:** Released Oct '89, on Collection by K-Tel Records. Catalogue no: **OR 0073**
**Album:** Released '87, on Deja Vu Catalogue no: **DVLP 2086**
**Cass:** Released '87, on Deja Vu Catalogue no: **DVMC 2086**

**HARRY JAMES & HIS MUSIC MAKERS**
**Album:** Released Jul '77, on First Heard by Submarine Records. Catalogue no: **FH 14**

**HARRY JAMES IN HI-FI**
Tracks: / You made me love you / I've heard that song before / I'm beginning to see the light / My silent love / Cherry / Trumpet blues and cantabile / Music makers / Sleepy lagoon / Velvet moon / Jealousy / I cried for you / It's been a long, long time / Two o'clock jump / James session.
**Album:** Released Mar '84, on Capitol (import) Catalogue no: **1A 0381857531**

**HARRY JAMES -- LIVE IN LONDON**
Note: Telecast, 23 October, 1971. A fine live performance by Harry and the James Gang, featuring such supporting stars as Corky Corcoran, Dave Robbins and Sonny Payne in That's All, The HJ Blues, Apples, Don't Be That Way and six more, including a medley of hits.
**Album:** Released Apr '88, on Sounds Great Catalogue no: **SG 8002**

**HARRY JAMES ON THE AIR VOL.2 (James, Harry & His Orchestra)**
Tracks: / Just you, just me / Night and day / By the Shalimar / Oh brother / By the light of the silvery moon / St Louis blues / I don't want to walk without you / One dozen roses / Two O'Clock jump / Moon over Manakoora / King Porter stomp / I walk my post (in a military manner) / Pagan love song.
**Album:** Released Feb '88, on Aircheck (USA) by Kiner Ents.(USA). Catalogue no: **AIRCHECK 33**

**HARRY JAMES VOL.1 (James, Harry (Members of Orchestra))**
**Album:** Released Apr '79, on Bright Orange Catalogue no: **BO 710**

**HARRY JAMES, VOL. 2, 1943-46**
Tracks: / Charmaine / Harpie's bazaar / My old flame / Blue turning grey over you / I cover the waterfront / G-flat special / Blue Lou / All of me / I've found a new baby / Ain't she sweet / I'll be around / Exactly like you / I've had this feeling before / Cinderella / How high the moon / Old folks at home.
Note: Superb quality airchecks are the source of this album of great '40's Harry James with vocals by Helen Ward on "My old flame", "All of me", "I'll be around" and "I've had this feeling before". Arnold Ross takes the piano solo on "How high the moon", and Willie Smith is the spirited alto soloist on "Ain't she sweet". Clarinettist Eddie Rosa is featured on "Exactly like you".(Hindsight Catalogue - 1989)
**Album:** Released '88, on Hindsight Catalogue no: **HSR 123**
**Album:** Released Apr '79, on Bright Orange Catalogue no: **BO 715**

**HARRY JAMES, VOL. 4, 1943-46**
Tracks: / Sweet and lovely / Easy street / Honeysuckle rose / It can't be wrong / Nice work if you can get it / Sentimental journey / It must be jelly / I've had my moments / Do nothing till you hear from me / Always / Just a sittin' and a rockin' / Remember / Peg O' my heart / More than you know / Mr. Coed.
Note: This LP is, in effect, a continuation of selections the James Orchestra performed on their first two Hindsight LP's, HSR 102 and HSR 123. They are excerpted radio broadcasts, complete with introductions, announcements, etc. Liner notes are by Irving Townsend, based on extensive interview with tenor saxist Corky Corcoran who was with the band through this whole era. Produced by Wally Heider. Buddy Di Vito and Helen Forrest are the vocalists on this album. These broadcasts originated from the famous Hollywood Palladium. (Hindsight Catalogue - 1989)
**Album:** Released '88, on Hindsight Catalogue no: **HSR 141**

**HARRY JAMES, VOL. 5, 1943-53**
Tracks: / If I had you / Autumn in New York / Somebody loves me / Come rain or come shine / What is this thing called love / I don't know why / Blue skies / Opus one / Tree grows into Burbank, A / Moonlight bay / People's choice / My old flame / Piccadilly / Man I love, The / Sugar blues / Don't get around much anymore.
Note: The first side of this LP is more of the 1943-46 James period, being excerpted from radio broadcasts made from off-the-line airchecks, as have all Hindsight / James LP's - - thus, the fidelity. (Hindsight Catalogue - 1989)
**Album:** Released '88, on Hindsight Catalogue no: **HSR 142**

**HARRY JAMES WITH DICK HAYMES (James, Harry & Dick Haymes)**
Tracks: / Tuxedo junction / Boog it / Four or five times / Hodge podge / Exactly like you / Come and get it / Swanee river / Sheik of araby / It's the last time / Orchids for rememberance / Moon won't talk / Maybe / Alice blue gown / Million dreams ago / You've got me / How high the moon.
**Album:** on Harlequin by Interstate Music. Catalogue no: **HQ 2008**

**HARRY'S CHOICE**
Tracks: / You're my thrill / Willow weep for me / Blues for sale / I want a little girl / Moten swing / Do you know what it means to miss New Orleans? / Just for fun / New two o'clock jump.
**Cass:** Released Mar '85, on Pathe Marconi (France) Catalogue no: **PM 154575**
**Album:** Released Mar '85, on Pathe Marconi (France) Catalogue no: **2C 068 54575**

**JAMES AND HAYMES (With Dick Haymes) (James, Harry & His Orchestra)**
**Album:** Released Aug '88, on Circle (USA) by Jazzology Records (USA). Catalogue no: **CLP 5**

**KING JAMES VERSION,THE (James, Harry & His Band)**
**Album:** Released Aug '82, on Sheffield Lab.(USA) by Sheffield Lab. Inc.(USA). Catalogue no: **LAB 3**
**CD:** on Sheffield Lab.(USA) by Sheffield Lab. Inc.(USA). Catalogue no: **CD 3**

**KING PORTER STOMP**
**Album:** Released '88, on Hep Jazz by Hep Records. Catalogue no: **HEP 31**

**LIVE FROM CLEARWATER CANYON, FLORIDA VOL.1(James, Harry & His Music Makers)**
Note: Recorded 1970. Tracks include: Tuxedo junction/Summertime/Tweet tweet/Take the A train/Gigi/Opus one, etc..
**Album:** Released Oct '87, on First Heard by Submarine Records. Catalogue no: **FH 56**
**Cass:** Released Oct '87, on First Heard by Submarine Records. Catalogue no: **CFH 56**

**LIVE FROM CLEARWATER CANYON, FLORIDA VOL.2(James, Harry & His Music Makers)**
**Cass:** Released Apr '85, on First Heard by Submarine Records. Catalogue no: **CFH 57**

**Album:** Released Apr '85, on First Heard by Submarine Records. Catalogue no: **FH 57**

**LIVE FROM CLEARWATER CANYON, FLORIDA VOL.3 (James, Harry & His Music Makers)**
**Cass:** Released Aug '85, on First Heard by Submarine Records. Catalogue no: **CFH 58**
**Album:** Released Aug '85, on First Heard by Submarine Records. Catalogue no: **FH 58**

**LIVE IN CONCERT (James, Harry & The Music Makers)**
Tracks: / Opener, The / King size blues / Shiny stockings / Harry's delight / Two o'clock jump / Jumpin' at the woodside / One on the house / Rockin' in rhythm / Don't get around much anymore / Tweet tweet.
**CD:** Released Jul '89, on Dance Band Days by Prism Leisure. Catalogue no: **DBCD 03**
**Album:** Released Jun '86, on Dance Band Days by Prism Leisure. Catalogue no: **DBD 03**
**Cass:** Released Jun '86, on Dance Band Days by Prism Leisure. Catalogue no: **DBDC 03**

**LIVE IN LONDON**
**Album:** Released Mar '90, on Jasmine by Hasmick Promotions. Catalogue no: **JASM 2533**
**Cass:** Released Oct '89, on Jasmine by Hasmick Promotions. Catalogue no: **JASMC 2533**

**LIVE IN THE 1970'S VOL. 1 (See panel below)**
Tracks: / Meditation / Cherokee / Blues, The / Taste of honey, A / Satin doll / Koo koo / Sweet Georgia Brown / String of pearls / Music to watch girls by / Tie a yellow ribbon (vocal by Jeannie Stone).
Note: Since the 1940's the Harry James Band consistently toured the U.S.A. and many other venues around the world. As his many British fans will recall, Harry James made two highly successful tours here at the beginning of the 1970's. Since his sad death in 1983, we have been waiting for something new and exciting to be released by the James Band. This live recording has everything: eleven excellent numbers, three of which have not appeared on album before; good sound quality and above all, the 'Maestro' and his musicians living up to the high standard always set by one of the greatest outfits of the Big Band scene. It is a must for all collectors of James material, and for those who have a liking for Big Band music at its best. Apart from Harry's great solos, the album features many outstanding performances by his musicians, including 'Corky' Corcaran and Les De Merle. (Jim Cutler, Harry James Appreciation Society)
**Album:** Released Sep '87, on Jazz Band by Flyright Records. Catalogue no: **EB 403**

**LIVE IN THE 1940'S VOL. 2**
**Album:** Released '88, on Jazz Band by Flyright Records. Catalogue no: **EB 410**

**MEMORIAL**
Tracks: / Harry James reminisces / Back beat boogie / Close to you / Dancing in the dark / King Porter stomp / Carnival / Man I love, The / Flatbush Flanagan / Deep purple / Arrival / Harry's blues / Dear old Southland / Trumpet blues and cantabile.
Note: Originally released in 1983 after the death of James in July that year, this collection is taken from the band's radio performances.
**Album:** Released Nov '85, on First Heard by Submarine Records. Catalogue no: **FH 51**
**Cass:** Released Nov '85, on First Heard by Submarine Records. Catalogue no: **CFH 51**

**MORE HARRY JAMES IN HI-FI (James, Harry & His Orchestra)**
Tracks: / Mole / Autumn serenade / Sleepy time gal / Crazy rhythm / Melancholy rhapsody September song / Carnival / Strictly instrumental / Blue again / Don cha go way mad / These foolish things / Somebody loves me / Street scene.
**Album:** Released Mar '86, on Capitol by EMI Records. Deleted Aug '89. Catalogue no: **EMS 1148**

**MUSICMAKING**
Tracks: / Back beat boogie / Between the Devil and the deep blue sea / G Flat special / My beloved is rugged / Rose room / Talk of the town / Opus one / I'm beginning to see the light / Lady be good / Temptation / Easy / St. Louis blues.
**Album:** Released Oct '84, on First Heard by Submarine Records. Catalogue no: **FH 25**
**Cass:** Released Oct '84, on First Heard by Submarine Records. Catalogue no: **CFH 25**

**ON THE AIR (James, Harry & His Orchestra)**
Tracks: / Ciribiribin / Perdido / Wouldn't it be nice? / Rose room / And then you kissed me / St Louis blues / Amor / Don't blame me / Peg O' my heart / Maybe / Concerto for trumpet / Too romantic / Feet draggin' blues / Man I love, The / I can't begin to tell you / I'm in love with two sweethearts / Blue skies.
**Album:** Released Feb '78, on Aircheck (USA) by Kiner Ents.(USA). Catalogue no: **AIRCHECK 18**

**ONE NIGHT STAND WITH HARRY JAMES**
**Album:** Released Jan '79, on Sandy Hook (USA) Catalogue no: **SH 2004**

**PLAY 22 ORIGINAL BIG BAND RECORDINGS (James, Harry Orchestra)**
**Album:** Released '88, on Hindsight Catalogue no: **HSR 406**

**POST WAR PERIOD, THE (James, Harry & His Band)**
Tracks: / All of me / I can't begin to tell you (with Ginnie Powell) / I'm in love with two sweethearts (with Buddy DiVito) / Moonglow / Opus 1 (part only) / I still get jealous (with Buddy DiVito) / Cotton tail (small group) / Night special / Forgiving you (with Buddy DiVito) / I want to be loved (with Marion Morgan) / Blue turn-

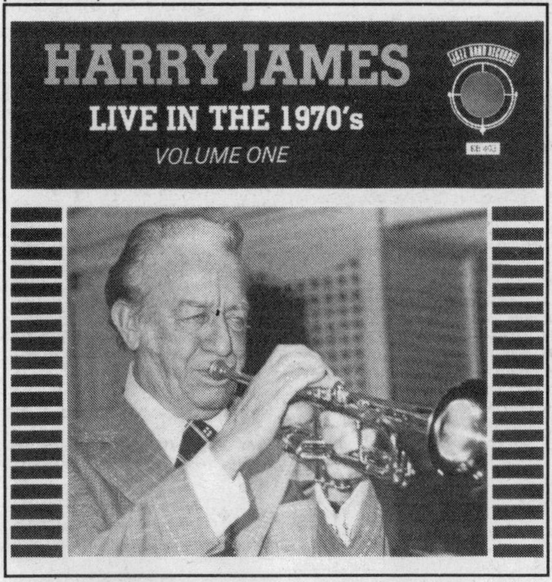

Harry James - Live in the 1970's Vol.1 (Jazz Band)

ing grey over you / Six, two and even / Nearness of you, The (with Buddy Rich) / Back beat boogie.
**Album:** Released '87, on Joyce Catalogue no: **JRC 1207**

**REMEMBER (James, Harry & His Music Makers)**
**Cass:** Released Aug '85, on Magic (1) by Submarine Records. Catalogue no: **CAWE 12**

**SATURDAY NIGHT SWING**
**Album:** Released Oct '84, on Giants of Jazz by Hasmick Promotions. Catalogue no: **GOJ 1016**

**SEPTEMBER SONG**
Tracks: / Floozie / Manhattan / Your cheatin' heart / Charmaine / Jazz me blues / Two o'clock jump / In a mellow tone / Sultry serenade / Getting sentimental over you / Pennies from Heaven / September song / If I could be with you / Cupper, The / Prince Charming / Nina / Cynthia.
**Album:** Released Mar '85, on Astan (USA) Catalogue no: **F 20133**
**Cass:** Released Sep '89, on Big Band Era Catalogue no: **40133**

**SILVER COLLECTION (James, Harry & His Orchestra)**
Tracks: / Shiny stockings / Cottontail / Lester leaps in / Take the 'A' train / Opus one / Cherokee / King Porter stomp / Flying home / In the mood / Tuxedo Junction / One o'clock jump / She's gotta go / Mae and Ray / Sentimental journey / Ultra / Strictly instrumental / Crazy rhythm / Back beat boogie.
Note: Digital stereo.
**CD:** Released Nov '84, on Verve Deleted '88. Catalogue no: **823 229-2**

**SOUNDS FAMILIAR (Live in California-1946) (James, Harry & His Orchestra)**
Tracks: / Flash / Moten swing / Five minutes more / I'd be lost without you / Blue skies / Man I love, The / Perdido / Oh but I do / Jealousy / Seems like old times / Lover come back to me / Why does it get so late so early? / Rose room / What more can I ask for? / Keb-lah / Embraceable you / Man with the horn / Shine / Two o'clock jump.
Note: Recorded live in California, 1946. Tracks include those listed above.
**Album:** Released Jun '82, on Saville by Conifer Records. Catalogue no: **SVL 151**
**Cass:** Released '88, on Saville by Conifer Records. Catalogue no: **CSVL 151**

**SPOTLIGHT ON HARRY JAMES**
**Album:** Released '88, on Magic (1) by Submarine Records. Catalogue no: **AWE 21**

**STILL HARRY AFTER ALL THESE YEARS**
**Album:** Released Dec '80, on Sheffield Lab.(USA) by Sheffield Lab. Inc.(USA). Catalogue no: **LAB 11**

**SWING GOES ON, VOL 9**
Tracks: / Moten swing / Crazy rhythm / I've heard that song before / Trumpet blues and cantabile / Sleepy lagoon / Music makers / Sleepy time gal / Ciribiribin / Two o'clock jump / Strictly instrumental / Mole, The / I'm beginning to see the light / You're my thrill / You made me love you / Just lucky.
**Album:** Released '83, on EMI (Germany) by EMI Records. Catalogue no: **IC 054 52718**

**SWINGIN' 'N' SWEET (James, Harry Octet)**
Tracks: / Ciribiribin / Perdido / Blues in the night / Honeysuckle rose / Moonlight fiesta / Two o'clock jump / Stardust / Roll 'em / Don't be that way / Cherry / Love is just around the corner / Somebody loves me / Taboo / Tenderly / Great lie, The.
**Album:** Released Jul '84, on Giants of Jazz by Hasmick Promotions. Catalogue no: **GOJ 1009**

**TEXAS CHATTER**
**Album:** Released Apr '81, on Joker (USA) by Lifetime Records (USA). Catalogue no: **SM 3058**

**TRUMPET BLUES**
**Album:** Released '84, on First Heard by Submarine Records. Catalogue no: **FH 41**
**Cass:** Released '84, on First Heard by Submarine Records. Catalogue no: **CFH 41**
**CD:** Released Sep '89, on Big Band Era Catalogue no: **2601782**

**TRUMPET TOAST (James, Harry & His Orchestra)**
**Album:** Released Feb '84, on MCA by MCA Records. Deleted '86. Catalogue no: **MCL 1774**
**Cass:** Released Feb '84, on MCA by MCA Records. Deleted '86. Catalogue no: **MCLC 1774**

**TWO O'CLOCK JUMP 1944 (James, Harry & His Orchestra)**
Tracks: / Two o'clock jump / It could happen to you / It had to be you / I'll get by / Cherry / Just you, just me / I'm beginning to see the light / I'm confessin' / I cover the waterfront / Take it easy / Love I long for, The / Back beat boogie / Jiggers / Theme - close.
Note: With Kitty Kallen, Buddy Devito, Willie Smith, Corky Corcoran, Juan Tizol.
**Cass:** Released Jun '88, on Bandstand Catalogue no: **BS 7131C**
**Album:** Released Aug '85, on Meteor by Magnum Music Group. Catalogue no: **MTM 010**
**Album:** Released Jun '88, on Bandstand Catalogue no: **BS 7131**
**Album:** Released Nov '84, on Astan (USA) Catalogue no: **20107**
**Cass:** Released Nov '84, on Astan (USA) Catalogue no: **40107**

**UNCOLLECTED HARRY JAMES & HIS ORCHESTRA, THE**
Tracks: / How high the moon / Better have four / Sabre dance / Shine / You turned the tables on me / Forgotten / I may be wrong / Lazy river / New York blues / Blue and sentimental / Rank, Frank / Proclamation.
Note: These are radio broadcast excerpts, with announcements, of the band that featured Don Lamond, Neal Hefti, Juan Tizol, Willie Smith, Corky Corcoran, etc. An all-instrumental album with liner notes by Patricia Willard based on interviews with Hefti and pianist Bruce MacDonald. There are many finger busting tunes on this album, "How high the moon" and "Up the lazy river" really demonstrate the quality of Harry's Band. Produced by Wally Heider. (Hindsight Catalogue - 1989)
**Album:** Released May '79, on Hindsight Catalogue no: **HSR 135**

**UNCOLLECTED, THE**
**Album:** Released Apr '86, on Hindsight (UK) by Michele International Records. Catalogue no: **HUK 150**

**UNFORGETTABLE, THE**
**CD:** Released Nov '87, on Entertainers Catalogue no: **ENT CD 227**

**WILD ABOUT HARRY**
Tracks: / Kinda like the blues / Blues for lovers only / Countin' / Cotton pickin' / Ring for porter / Barn 12 / What am I here for / Blues for Harry's sake / Bee gee / Blues on a count.
**Album:** Released Mar '88, on Capitol by EMI Records. Deleted Nov '88. Catalogue no: **EMS 1284**
**Cass:** Released Mar '88, on Capitol by EMI Records. Deleted 31 Jul '88. Catalogue no: **TCEMS 1284**

## James, Homesick

**HOME SWEET HOMESICK JAMES**
Tracks: / Highway 51 / Lonesome train / Homesick's original dust my broom / Kissing in the dark / Sweet home Chicago / Mailman / Shake your moneymaker / Dust my broom / Worried about my baby / Gotta move - can't stay here no more / Tin pan alley / Careless love.
**Album:** Released Jan '82, on Big Bear by Big Bear Records. Deleted '88. Catalogue no: **BEAR 10**

**SAD & LONESOME (James, Homesick and Snooky Prior)**
**Album:** Released Jan '88, on Wolf Catalogue no: **120 409**

**SHAKE YOUR MONEYMAKER (James, Homesick and Snooky Prior)**
Tracks: / Boogy fool / Crying shame / Work with me Annie / After you there won't be nobody else / Bobby's rock / I believe my time ain't long / Tin Pan Alley / Shake your moneymaker.
**Album:** Released Dec '84, on Krazy Kat by Interstate Music. Catalogue no: **KK 790**

## James, Skip

**1931**
Tracks: / Devil got my woman / Cypress Grove blues / Cherry ball blues / Illinois blues / Four o'clock blues / Hard luck child / Hard time killin' floor blues / Yola my blues away / Jesus is a mighty good leader / Be ready when he comes / Drunken spree / I'm so glad / Special rider

blues / How long buck / Little cow and calf is gonna die blues / What am I to do blues / 22-20 blues / If you haven't any hay get on down the road.
**Album:** on Matchbox (Bluesmaster) by Saydisc Records. Catalogue no: **MSE 207**

**COMPLETE 1931 SESSIONS**
**Album:** Released May '86, on Yazoo (USA) by Shanachie Records (USA). Catalogue no: **L 1072**

**I'M SO GLAD**
**2 LP Set:** Released May '78, on Vanguard by Start Records Ltd.. Catalogue no: **VPD 20001**

**LIVE AT 2ND. FRET, PHILADELPHIA 1966**
**Album:** Released Apr '88, on Document Catalogue no: **DLP 523**

**TODAY**
**CD:** Released Aug '89, on Start by Start Records Ltd.. Catalogue no: **VMCD 7310**
**Cass:** Released Aug '89, on Start by Start Records Ltd.. Catalogue no: **VMTC 6310**
**Album:** Released Aug '89, on Start by Start Records Ltd.. Catalogue no: **VMLP 5310**

## Jansens, Huub

**AMAZING JAZZBAND**
**Album:** Released '88, on Timeless by Timeless Records. Catalogue no: **TTD 536**

## Jarreau, Al

**Biographical details:** Jarreau, Al This American singer, who hails from Milwaukee, first came to prominence in the jazz field in the early Seventies. Since then he has gradually built up a larger and larger following, retaining his jazz base but also exploring areas of soul, MoR and pop. From a technical standpoint, he is certainly one of the world's finest singers; his range and precision are outstanding.
Because Jarreau's climb to fame has been steady rather than dramatic, he has never quite become the major household name that might have been expected of a man of his calibre. He reached his commercial peak in 1981 with the US Top 20 pop success of his single *We're In This Love Together* and the LP *Breakin' Away*. He followed this in 1983 with the *Jarreau* album (titled *Trouble In Paradise* in the States), which yielded the beautiful single *Mornin'* - this delicately evocative rendition reached No.21 on the US singles chart and became his biggest UK hit, climbing to No.28. His silky smooth singing has consolidated his status on both sides of the Atlantic during the mid-Eighties with regular concerts. The 1985 LP *In London* quickly penetrated the Top 10 of the American jazz charts, thus proving that Jarreau has lost none of his original following. After all, he has a degree in psychology, so he should be able to suss what the public wants. (Bob Macdonald 11/1185).

**AIN'T NO SUNSHINE**
Tracks: / Ain't no sunshine / Lean on me / Use me / Kissing my love / Grandma's hands / You / Lonely town / Lonely street / Same love that made me laugh, The.
**Cass:** Released May '88, on Street Life by Mainline Records. Catalogue no: **216 2233**
**CD:** Released Jun '88, on Blue Moon (1) by Magnum Music Group. Catalogue no: **CDBML 1011**
**Album:** Released '84, on Blue Moon (1) by Magnum Music Group. Catalogue no: **BMLP 1011**
**Album:** Released May '88, on Street Life by Mainline Records. Catalogue no: **226 2233**

**AL JARREAU**
**Cass:** Released Aug '84, on DISC AZ (France) by Musidisc Records (France). Catalogue no: **C 467**
**Album:** Released Aug '84, on DISC AZ (France) by Musidisc Records (France). Catalogue no: **AZ 2467**

**ALL FLY HOME**
Tracks: / Thinkin' about it too / I'm home / Brite 'n' sunny babe / I do / Fly / Wait a little while / She's leaving home / All / Dock of the bay, The.
**Album:** Released '77, on Warner Bros. by WEA Records. Deleted '82. Catalogue no: **K 56546**

**ALL FLY HOME/THIS TIME**
**Cass set:** Released Nov '83, on WEA (International) by WEA Records. Catalogue no: **923948 4**

**ALL OR NOTHING AT ALL**
Tracks: / All or nothing at all.
**7" Single:** Released Apr '89, on WEA by WEA Records. Deleted Jan '90. Catalogue no: **U 7663**
**CD Single:** Released Apr '89, on WEA by WEA Records. Deleted Jan '90. Catalogue no: **U 7663CD**
**12" Single:** Released Apr '89, on WEA by WEA Records. Deleted Jan '90. Catalogue no: **U 7663T**

**BOOGIE DOWN**
Tracks: / Boogie down / Our love.
**7" Single:** Released Sep '83, on WEA by WEA Records. Deleted '86. Catalogue no: **U 9814**
**12" Single:** Released Sep '83, on WEA by WEA Records. Deleted '86. Catalogue no: **I 9814 T**

**BREAKIN' AWAY**
Tracks: / Closer to your love / My old friend / We're in this love together / Easy / Our love / Breakin' away / Roof garden / Blue rondo a la turk / Teach me tonight.
**Album:** Released Aug '81, on Warner Bros. by WEA Records. Catalogue no: **K 56917**
**CD:** Released '83, on Warner Bros. by WEA Records. Catalogue no: **256 917**
**Cass:** Released Aug '81, on Warner Bros. by WEA Records. Catalogue no: **K4 56917**

**CLOSER TO YOUR LOVE**
Tracks: / Closer to your love / Love is real.
**7" Single:** Released Nov '81, on WEA by WEA Records. Catalogue no: **K 17876**
**12" Single:** Released Nov '81, on WEA by WEA Records. Catalogue no: **K 17876T**

**GLOW**
Tracks: / Rainbow in your eyes / Your song / Agua de beber / Have you seen the child / Hold on me / Fire and rain / Somebody's watching you / Milwaukee glow.
**Album:** Released Jul '77, on Reprise (USA) Catalogue no: **K 54073**

**HEARTS HORIZON**
Tracks: / All or nothing at all / So good / All of my love / Pleasure over pain / Yo jeans / Way to your heart / One way / 10 K HI / I must have been a fool / More love / Killer love / Hearts horizon.
**Album:** Released Nov '88, on Warner Bros. by WEA Records. Catalogue no: **WX 230**
**Cass:** Released Nov '88, on Warner Bros. by WEA Records. Catalogue no: **WX 230 C**
**CD:** Released Nov '88, on Warner Bros. by WEA Records. Catalogue no: **255975 2**

**HIGH CRIME**
Tracks: / Raging waters / Imagination / Murphy's law / Tell me / After all / High crime / Let's pretend / Sticky wicket / Love speaks louder than words / Falling.
**Album:** Released Nov '84, on WEA by WEA Records. Catalogue no: **250807 1**
**Cass:** Released Nov '84, on WEA by WEA Records. Catalogue no: **250807 4**
**CD:** Released Jan '85, on WEA by WEA Records. Catalogue no: **250807 2**

**IN LONDON**
Tracks: / Raging waters / Black and blues / I will be here for you / Let's pretend / High crime / Roof garden / Teach me tonight / We're in this love together.
**CD:** Released Nov '85, on WEA by WEA Records. Catalogue no: **252369 2**
**Cass:** Released Nov '85, on WEA by WEA Records. Catalogue no: **252369 4**
**Album:** Released Nov '85, on WEA by WEA Records. Catalogue no: **252369 1**

**IN LONDON (VIDEO)**
**Beta:** Released Jun '86, on WEA by WEA Records. Catalogue no: **252233 5**
**VHS:** Released Jun '86, on WEA by WEA Records. Catalogue no: **252233 3**

**JARREAU**
Tracks: / Mornin' / Boogie down / I will be here for you / Save me / Step by step / Black and blues / Trouble in paradise / Not like this / Love is waiting.
**Cass:** Released Apr '83, on WEA (International) by WEA Records. Catalogue no: **U 00702**
**CD:** Released Jan '84, on WEA by WEA Records. Catalogue no: **U 00702**
**Album:** Released Apr '83, on WEA (International) by WEA Records. Catalogue no: **U 0070**

**JAZZ SINGER, THE**
**Album:** Released '88, on Masters (Holland) Catalogue no: **MA 18128**
**Cass:** Released Dec '88, on Masters (Holland) Catalogue no: **MAMC 9181285**

**L IS FOR LOVER**
Tracks: / Tell me what I gotta do / Says / Pleasure / Golden girl / Across the midnight sky / No ordinary romance / L is for lover / Real tight.
**Cass:** Released Oct '86, on WEA (International) by WEA Records. Catalogue no: **253080 4**
**CD:** Released Oct '86, on WEA by WEA Records. Catalogue no: **253080 2**
**Album:** Released Oct '86, on WEA by WEA Records. Catalogue no: **253080 1**

**L IS FOR LOVER (SINGLE)**
Tracks: / L is for lover.
**12" Single:** Released Oct '86, on WEA (International) by WEA Records. Deleted Jun '87. Catalogue no: **U 8612T**
**7" Single:** Released Oct '86, on WEA (International) by WEA Records. Deleted Jun '87. Catalogue no: **U 8612**

**LET'S PRETEND**
Tracks: / Let's pretend / I keep calling.
**12" Single:** Released Nov '84, on Warner Bros. by WEA Records. Deleted Nov '87. Catalogue no: **W 9257T**
**7" Single:** Released Nov '84, on Warner Bros. by WEA Records. Deleted Nov '87. Catalogue no: **W 9257**

**LET'S PRETEND (LIVE)**
Tracks: / Let's pretend (live).
**7" Single:** Released Sep '85, on Warner Bros. by WEA Records. Catalogue no: **U 8911**
**12" Single:** Released Sep '85, on Warner Bros. by WEA Records. Catalogue no: **U 8911 T**

**LOOK TO THE RAINBOW (LIVE)**
Tracks: / Letter perfect / Rainbow in your eyes / One good turn / Could you believe / Burst in with the dawn / Better than anything / So long girl / Look to the rainbow / You don't see me / Take five / Loving you / We got by.
**2 LP Set:** Released May '77, on Warner Bros. by WEA Records. Catalogue no: **K 66059**

**LOVE IS WAITING**
Tracks: / Love is waiting / Christmas song / Blue rondo a la Turk.
**12" Single:** Released Dec '83, on WEA by WEA Records. Deleted Dec '86. Catalogue no: **U 9744T**
**7" Single:** Released Dec '83, on WEA by WEA Records. Deleted Dec '86. Catalogue no: **U 9744**

**MANIFESTO**
**Cass:** Released '88, on Masters (Holland) Catalogue no: **MAMC 9181285**
**Album:** Released '88, on Masters (Holland) Catalogue no: **MA 181285**

**MASQUERADE IS OVER, THE**
Tracks: / My favourite things / Stockholm sweetnin' / Sleeping bee / Masquerade is over, The / Sophisticated lady / Joey / Come rain or come shine / One note samba.
Note: Outstanding album recorded in 1973 in Los Angeles immediately prior to the artist signing with Warner Brothers. The material on the album is excellent and features a number of jazz influenced compositions. (Blue Moon 1989).
**Cass:** Released Jun '83, on Happy Bird (Germany) Catalogue no: **MB 990136**
**CD:** Released 17 Nov '89, on Blue Moon (1) by Magnum Music Group. Catalogue no: **CDBM 079**
**Album:** Released 17 Nov '89, on Blue Moon (1) by Magnum Music Group. Catalogue no: **BMLP 079**
**Album:** Released Jun '83, on Happy Bird (Germany) Catalogue no: **B 90136**

**MOONLIGHTING**
Tracks: / Moonlighting / Golden girl (LP version).
**12" Single:** Released Feb '87, on WEA (International) by WEA Records. Deleted Jul '88. Catalogue no: **U 8407 T**
**7" Single:** Released Feb '87, on WEA (International) by WEA Records. Catalogue no: **U 8407**

**MORNIN'**
Tracks: / Mornin' / Not like this / Roof garden.
**7" Single:** Released May '83, on WEA by WEA Records. Catalogue no: **U 9929**
**12" Single:** Released Apr '83, on WEA (International) by WEA Records. Catalogue no: **U 9929 T**

**OUR LOVE**
Tracks: / Our love / Roof garden.
**7" Single:** Released Feb '82, on Warner Bros. by WEA Records. Deleted '85. Catalogue no: **K17907**

**RAGING WATERS**
Tracks: / Raging waters / Too hot.
**7" Single:** Released Apr '85, on Warner Bros. by WEA Records. Catalogue no: **W 9145**
**12" Single:** Released Apr '85, on Warner Bros. by WEA Records. Catalogue no: **W 9154T**

**REPLAY OF AL JARREAU**
**Album:** Released Feb '85, on Sierra by Sierra Records. Catalogue no: **FEDB 5003**
**Cass:** Released Feb '85, on Sierra by Sierra Records. Catalogue no: **CFEDB 5003**

**SINGS BILL WITHERS**
Tracks: / Ain't no sunshine / Lean on me / Use me / Missing my love / Grandma's hands / You / Lonely town, lonely street / That same love that made me laugh.
**Album:** Released Apr '87, on Topline by Charly Records. Catalogue no: **TOP 173**
**Cass:** Released Apr '87, on Topline by Charly Records. Catalogue no: **KTOP 173**

**SO GOOD**
Tracks: / So good / Pleasure over pain / Mornin' (12" only).
**12" Single:** Released Dec '88, on WEA (International) by WEA Records. Catalogue no: **W 7664T**
**7" Single:** Released Dec '88, on WEA (International) by WEA Records. Catalogue no: **W 7664**

**SPIRITS AND FEELINGS**
Tracks: / Ain't no sunshine / Lean on me / Use me / Kissing my love / Grandma's hands / You / Lonely town, lonely street / Same love that made me laugh, The.
**Album:** Released May '84, on Happy Bird (Germany) Catalogue no: **B 90168**

**TELL ME WHAT I GOTTA DO**
Tracks: / Tell me what I gotta do / Roof garden.
**7" Single:** Released Apr '87, on WEA (International) by WEA Records. Deleted Jan '88. Catalogue no: **U 8523**
**12" Single:** Released Nov '86, on WEA (International) by WEA Records. Deleted Jan '88. Catalogue no: **U 8523T**

**THIS TIME**
Tracks: / Never givin' up / Gimme what you got / This time / Your sweet love / Alonzo / Spain / Distracted / Love is real / Change your mind.
**Album:** Released Jun '80, on WEA by WEA Records. Catalogue no: **K 56804**

**TROUBLE IN PARADISE**
Tracks: / Trouble in paradise / Save me.
**12" Single:** Released Jul '83, on WEA (International) by WEA Records. Catalogue no: **U 9871 T**
**7" Single:** Released Jul '83, on WEA (International) by WEA Records. Catalogue no: **U 9871**

**WE GOT BY**
Tracks: / Spirit / We got by / Susan's song / You don't see me / Lock all the gates / Raggedy Ann / Letter perfect / Sweet potato pie / Aladdin's lamp.
**Album:** Released Jun '77, on Reprise (USA) Catalogue no: **K 54045**

**WE'RE IN THIS LOVE TOGETHER**
Tracks: / We're in this love together / Easy.
**7" Single:** Released Sep '81, on Warner Bros. by WEA Records. Deleted '84. Catalogue no: **K 17849**
**12" Single:** Released Sep '81, on Warner Bros. by WEA Records. Deleted '84. Catalogue no: **K 17849T**

**YOU**
**Cass:** Released Oct '85, on Platinum (W.Germany) Catalogue no: **PMC 19**
**Album:** Released Oct '85, on Platinum (W.Germany) Catalogue no: **PLP 19**

## Jarrett, Keith

**ARBOUR ZENA**
Tracks: / Dunes / Solara march / Mirrors.
Note: Keith Jarrett (piano), Jan Garbarek (tenor and soprano saxes), Charlie Haden (bass), with members of the Stuttgart Radio Symphony Orchestra conducted by Miaden Gutesha.
**Album:** Released Aug '85, on ECM Catalogue no: **ECM 1070**
**CD:** Released Aug '85, on ECM Catalogue no: **825 592-2**

**BACKHAND**
**Album:** Released Mar '83, on Jasmine

by Hasmick Promotions. Deleted Feb '88. Catalogue no: **JAS 67**

**BELONGING**
Tracks: / Spiral dance / Blossom / Long as you know you're living yours / Belonging / Windup, The / Solstice.
**Album:** Released Nov '88, on ECM Catalogue no: **ECM 1050**
**Cass:** Released Oct '88, on ECM Catalogue no: **310 1050**
**CD:** Released Jun '86, on ECM Catalogue no: **829 115 2**

**BEST OF KEITH JARRETT**
Tracks: / Blackberry winter / Introduction / Yaqui Indian folk song / Roads travelled, roads veiled / Fantasm / Byablue / Treasure island / De drums / Silence.
**Album:** Released Jan '79, on Impulse by Impulse Records. Deleted Jan '84. Catalogue no: **IMPL 8054**

**BOOK OF WAYS**
**2 LP Set:** Released Sep '87, on ECM Catalogue no: **ECM 1344**
**CD Set:** Released Oct '87, on ECM Catalogue no: **831 396-2**

**BOP-BE**
Tracks: / Mushi mushi / Silence / Pyramids moving / Gotta get some sleep / Pocket full of cherry / Blackberry winter / Bop be.
**Album:** Released Jun '82, on Jasmine by Hasmick Promotions. Deleted Feb '88. Catalogue no: **JAS 29**
**Cass:** Released Jun '82, on Jasmine by Hasmick Promotions. Catalogue no: **JAS C29**

**CELESTIAL HAWK**
**Cass:** Released Jul '85, on ECM Catalogue no: **7200 188**
**CD:** Released Aug '88, on ECM Catalogue no: **829 370 2**
**Album:** Released Aug '88, on ECM Catalogue no: **ECM 1175**

**CHANGES**
Tracks: / Flying / Prism (In digital stereo).
Note: Keith Jarrett (piano), Gary Peacock (bass), Jack De Johnette (drums).
**Album:** Released Nov '88, on ECM Catalogue no: **ECM 1276**
**CD:** Released Oct '84, on ECM Catalogue no: **817 436-2**

**CONCERTS**
**CD:** Released Aug '88, on ECM Catalogue no: **827 286-2**
**Album:** Released Oct '82, on ECM Catalogue no: **ECM 1227**
**LP Set:** Released Nov '88, on ECM Catalogue no: **ECM 1227/29**

**DARK INTERVALS**
Tracks: / Opening / Hymn / Americana / Entrance / Parallels / Fire dance / Ritual prayer / Recitative.
Note: Solo piano performances recorded in Tokyo during April 1987 & featuring eleven improvised compositions by Jarrett. This follows his highly acclaimed recordings of J.S.Bach's "Well Tempered Klavier".
**Album:** Released Oct '88, on ECM Catalogue no: **ECM 1379**
**CD:** Released Oct '88, on ECM Catalogue no: **837 342-2**

**EYES OF THE HEART**
Tracks: / Eyes of the heart (part one) / Eyes of the heart (part two) / Encore (A-B-C).
Note: Keith Jarrett (piano, soprano sax, osi drums, tambourine), Dewey Redman (tenor sax, tambourine, maracas), Charlie Haden (bass), Paul Motian (drums, percussion).
**CD:** Released Oct '85, on ECM Catalogue no: **825 476-2**
**2 LP Set:** Released Oct '85, on ECM Catalogue no: **ECM 1150**

**FACING YOU**
Tracks: / In front / Ritooria / Lalene / My lady: my child / Landscape for future earth / Starbright / Vapallia / Semblence.
**CD:** Released Dec '85, on ECM Catalogue no: **827 132-2**
**Album:** Released Nov '88, on ECM Catalogue no: **ECM 1017**

**FORT YAWUH**
Tracks: / If the misfits wear it / Fort Yawuh / De drums / Still life, still life.
**Album:** Released Jun '82, on Jasmine by Hasmick Promotions. Catalogue no: **JAS 23**
**Cass:** Released Jun '82, on Jasmine by Hasmick Promotions. Catalogue no: **JAS C23**

**HYMNS / SPHERES**
**2 LP Set:** Released Nov '88, on ECM Catalogue no: **ECM 1086**

**IN THE LIGHT**
Note: With Ralph Towner and the strings of the Sudfunk Symphony Orchestra.
**2 LP Set:** Released Nov '88, on ECM Catalogue no: **ECM 1033**
**CD Set:** Released Jul '88, on ECM Catalogue no: **835 011-2**

**INVOCATIONS: THE MOTH & THE FLAME**
Tracks: / Invocations 1st-7th / Moth and the flame part 1-v, The.
**CD Set:** Released Oct '85, on ECM Catalogue no: **825 473-2**
**2 LP Set:** Released Oct '85, on ECM Catalogue no: **ECM 1201**

**JUDGEMENT, THE**
Tracks: / Gypsy moth / Toll road / Pardon my rags / Pre judgement atmosphere / El juicio / Piece for Ornette (lv) / Piece for Ornette (sv).
**Album:** on Atlantic by WEA Records. Catalogue no: **K 50154**

**KOLN CONCERT, THE**
**CD:** Released '83, on ECM Catalogue no: **810 067-2**
**2 LP Set:** Released Nov '88, on ECM Catalogue no: **ECM 1064**
**Cass:** Released Oct '88, on ECM Catalogue no: **354 106 4**

**LUMINESSENCE (Jarrett, Keith / Jan Garbarek)**
Note: Music for string orchestra and saxophone. Composed by Keith Jarrett. Saxophone imporovisation by Jan Garbarek. Strings of the Sudfunk Symphony Orchestra Stuttgart. Recorded April 1974.
**CD:** Released Sep '89, on ECM Catalogue no: **839307 2**
**Album:** Released Nov '88, on ECM Catalogue no: **ECM 1049**

**MY SONG**
Tracks: / Questar / My song / Tabarka / Mandela / Journey home, The.
**Cass:** Released Oct '88, on ECM Catalogue no: **310 1115**
**CD:** Released '84, on ECM Catalogue no: **821 406-2**
**Album:** Released Nov '88, on ECM Catalogue no: **ECM 1115**

**MYSTERIES**
Tracks: / Rotation / Everything that lives laments / Flame / Mysteries.
**CD:** Released Jan '90, on MCA (Impulse Jazz) Catalogue no: **MCAD 33113**

**NUDE ANTS**
Tracks: / Chant of the soil / Innocence / Processional / Oasis / New dance / Sunshine song.
**CD Set:** Released Jun '86, on ECM Catalogue no: **829 119 2**
**2 LP Set:** Released Jun '86, on ECM Catalogue no: **ECM 1171**

**PERSONAL MOUNTAINS (Jarrett, Keith & Belonging)**
Tracks: / Personal mountains / Oasis / Prism / Innocence.
Note: Personal Mountains is released to celebrate ECM's 20th anniversary. This milestone in the development of Keith Jarrett and producer, Manfred Eicher was recorded live in Tokyo during April 1979. It features Jarrett's European Quartet 'Belonging'; Jan Galbarek, Palle Danielsson, Jon Christensen, a group initiated by Eicher himself and recognised as one of the all time great jazz quartets. These recordings are issued for the first time. Personnel: Keith Jarret (piano & percussion), Jan Garbarek (tenor & soprano sax), Palle Danielsson (bass), Jon Christensen (drums). CD contains one bonus track.
**CD:** Released Apr '89, on Mew Catalogue no: **837 361-2**
**Cass:** Released Apr '89, on Mew Catalogue no: **837 361-4**
**Album:** Released Apr '89, on Mew Catalogue no: **ECM 1382**

**RUTA AND DAITYA**
Note: A duo album with Jack DeJohnette.
**Album:** Released Oct '88, on ECM Catalogue no: **ECM 1021**
**CD:** Released Oct '88, on ECM Catalogue no: **829 388-2**

**SACRED HYMNS OF G.I. GURDJIEFF**
Tracks: / Reading of sacred books / Prayer & despair / Religious ceremony / Hymn / Orthodox hymn from Asia minor

/ Hymn for Good Friday / Hymn for Easter Thursday / Hymn to the endless creator / Hymn from a great temple / Story of the resurrection of Christ, The / Holy affirming, holy denying, holy reconciling / Easter night procession / Meditation.
**Album:** Released Jun '86, on ECM Catalogue no: **ECM 1174**
**CD:** Released Jun '86, on ECM Catalogue no: **829 122 2**

**SOLO CONCERTS - BREMEN / LAUSANNE**
Note: Bremen-July 12, 1973 & Lausanne March 20, 1973.s
**LP Set:** Released Jul '86, on ECM Catalogue no: **ECM 1035**
**CD Set:** Released Jul '86, on ECM Catalogue no: **827 747-2**

**SPHERES**
Tracks: / Spheres - 1st Movement / Spheres - 4th Movement / Spheres - 7th Movement / Spheres - 9th Movement.
**Album:** Released Nov '88, on ECM Catalogue no: **ECM 1302**
**CD:** Released Jul '86, on ECM Catalogue no: **827 463-2**

**SPIRITS (Volumes 1 & 2)**
**CD Set:** Released Oct '86, on ECM Catalogue no: **829 467 2**
**2 LP Set:** Released Oct '86, on ECM Catalogue no: **ECM 1333**

**STAIRCASE**
Tracks: / Staircase (part 1) / Staircase (part 2) / Staircase (part 3) / Hourglass (part 1) / Hourglass (part 2) / Sundial (part 1) / Sundial (part 2) / Sundial (part 3) / Sand (part 1) / Sand (part 2) / Sand (part 3).
**CD Set:** Released Dec '85, on ECM Catalogue no: **827 337-2**
**2 LP Set:** Released Dec '85, on ECM Catalogue no: **ECM 1090**

**STANDARDS 2 (VIDEO)**
**VHS:** Released Feb '90, on Verve Catalogue no: **CFV 10242**

**STANDARDS LIVE**
Tracks: / Stella by starlight / Wrong blues, The / Falling in love with love / Too young to go steady / Way you look tonight / Old country, The.
Note: This new album captures a stunning live performance of this highly celebrated trio in Paris during 1985. It includes such noteworthy compositions as 'Stella by Starlight' and 'The Way You Look Tonight' among others. Standards live, once again proves the subtle interplay of the trio which has often been compared to the legendary Bill Evans Trio. It throws new light on well known compositions from the 'Great American Songbook'. Personnel: Keith Jarrett
**Album:** Released Feb '86, on ECM Catalogue no: **ECM 1317**
**CD:** Released Feb '86, on ECM Catalogue no: **827 827-2**

**STANDARDS, VOL 1**
Tracks: / Meaning of the blues / All the things you are / It never entered my mind / Masquerade is over, The / God bless the child.
Note: Keith Jarrett (piano), Gary Peacock (bass), Jack De Johnette (drums).
**Cass:** Released Dec '86, on Blue Note by EMI Records. Deleted Jun '89. Catalogue no: **TCBT 85130**
**Album:** Released Sep '83, on ECM Catalogue no: **ECM 1255**
**Cass:** Released Jun '84, on ECM Catalogue no: **310 1255**
**Cass:** Released Oct '88, on ECM Catalogue no: **811 966-4**
**CD:** Released Aug '88, on ECM Catalogue no: **811 966 2**

**STANDARDS, VOL 2**
Tracks: / So tender / Moon and sand / In love in vain / Never let me go / If I should lose you / I fall in love too easily.
Note: Keith Jarrett (piano), Gary Peacock (bass), Jack De Johnette (drums).
**CD:** Released May '85, on ECM Catalogue no: **825 015-2**
**Album:** Released Nov '88, on ECM Catalogue no: **ECM 1289**

**STILL LIVE (Jarrett, Keith Trio)**
Tracks: / My funny valentine / Autumn leaves / When I fall in love / Song is you, The / Come rain or come shine / Late lament / You and the night and the music / Some day my prince will come / I remember Clifford.
Note: "Keith Jarrett and his highly acclaimed trio recorded live in Munich, July 1986, as part of the Munich 'Klaviersommer'. The standards are used as a frame from which the improvisations can expand. The end result is a beautifully melodic, spontaneous double album. With Gary Peacock, Jack DeJohnette." (IMS Records, May 1988.)
**CD Set:** Released May '88, on ECM Catalogue no: **835 008-2**
**2 LP Set:** Released May '88, on ECM Catalogue no: **ECM 1360**

**SUN BEAR CONCERTS**
**LP Set:** Released Nov '88, on ECM Catalogue no: **ECM 1100**

**SURVIVOR'S SUITE**
**Cass:** Released Jul '85, on ECM Catalogue no: **7104651**
**CD:** Released Dec '85, on ECM Catalogue no: **827 131-2**
**Album:** Released '85, on ECM Catalogue no: **ECM 1085**

**TREASURE ISLAND**
**Album:** Released May '89, on MCA (Import) by MCA Records. Catalogue no: **MCA 39106**
**CD:** Released May '89, on MCA (Import) by MCA Records. Catalogue no: **MCAD 39106**

**WELL TEMPERED CLAVIER BOOK, THE**
**Cass:** Released Jun '89, on ECM Catalogue no: **835 246 4**
**2 LP Set:** Released Nov '88, on ECM Catalogue no: **ECM 1362**
**CD Set:** Released Nov '88, on ECM Catalogue no: **835 246 2**

**WORKS: KEITH JARRETT**
Tracks: / Belonging / Journey home, The / As long as you know you are living yours / Wind up / Country / My song / Solstice / Spiral dance.
**Cass:** Released Nov '83, on ECM Catalogue no: **3100 388**
**Album:** Released Jun '89, on ECM Catalogue no: **825 425-1**
**CD:** Released Jun '89, on ECM Catalogue no: **825 425-2**

## Jarrett, Keith Trio

**CHANGELESS**
Tracks: / Dancing / Endless / Lifeline / Ecstacy.
**CD:** Released Oct '89, on ECM Catalogue no: **839 618 2**
**Cass:** Released Oct '89, on ECM Catalogue no: **839 618 4**
**Album:** Released Oct '89, on ECM Catalogue no: **ECM 1392**

## Jason, David

**CREATIVE RAGTIME VOL 6 (Jason,David and Neville Dickie)**
**Album:** Released Apr '76, on Euphonic Catalogue no: **ESR 1206**

## Jaspar, Bobby

**AT RONNIE SCOTT'S, 1962 (Jaspar, Bobby Quartet)**
Tracks: / Be like Bud / Our delight / Darn that dream / Pent-up house / Oleo / Sonnymoon for two (on CD only) / Like someone in love (on CD only) / Stella by starlight (on CD only).
Note: With Rene Thomas (guitar), Bobby Jaspar (tenor sax & flute), Benoit Quersin (bass) and Daniel Humair (drums). Recorded live during 1962. Available for the first time on CD in November '89 and featuring three additional tracks. Over 76 minutes playing time.
**CD:** Released Nov '89, on Mole Catalogue no: **CDMOLE 11**
**Album:** Released '87, on Mole Catalogue no: **MOLE 11**

**BLOSSOM DEARIE (April in Paris)**
**Album:** Released Feb '88, on Fresh Sounds (Spain) by Fresh Sounds Records (Spain). Catalogue no: **FS 213**

**BOBBY JASPAR**
**Album:** Released Feb '88, on Fresh Sounds (Spain) by Fresh Sounds Records (Spain). Catalogue no: **FS 158**

**BOBBY JASPAR QUINTET**
**Album:** Released Feb '88, on Fresh Sounds (Spain) by Fresh Sounds Records (Spain). Catalogue no: **FS 169**

**MEMORY OF DICK (DICK TWARDZIK)**
Note: Personnel: Bobby Jaspar (tenor sax and flute), Sacha Distel (guitar), Rene Urtreger (piano), Benoit. Recorded Paris 1955.
**CD:** Released Feb '89, on Polygram (France) by PolyGram UK Ltd. Catalogue no: **837 208-2**

**NEW YORK 1956**
**Album:** Released Oct '86, on Ace by Ace Records. Catalogue no: **SW 8413**

**PHENIL ISOPROPIL AMINE**
Note: Bobby Jaspar (flute), Michel Hausser (vibes, xylophone), Paul

Rovere (bass), Kenny Clarke (drums), Humberto Canto (percussion), Sadi Lallemand (vibes), Jimmy Merritt (bass). Containing two previously unreleased tracks. Recorded Paris, 1958.
**CD:** Released Feb '89, on Polygram (France) by PolyGram UK Ltd. Catalogue no: **837 207-2**

## Jazz...

**JAZZ - IT'S A WONDERFUL SOUND (Various artists)**
Tracks: / It's a wonderful world: *Various artists* / Smoke rings: *Various artists* / Undecided: *Various artists* / Rose of Washington Square: *Various artists* / Sweet Lorraine: *Various artists* / Rose room: *Various artists*.
Note: Warren Vache Jnr (trumpet), Clarence Hutchenrider (clarinet), George Masso (trombone), Dick Welstood (piano), Dawes Thompson (guitar), Warren Vache (bass), Johnny Blowers (drums).
**Album:** Released Apr '79, on Starfire (USA) Deleted '83. Catalogue no: **QSR 0478**

**JAZZ LEGENDS (Various artists)**
**CD:** Released Jun '88, on Spectrum (1) Catalogue no: **U 4023**
**Cass set:** Released Jun '88, on Spectrum (1) Catalogue no: **M 10194**

**JAZZ LIFE (Various artists)**
Tracks: / R & R: *Various artists* / Black cat: *Various artists* / Lord, Lord, am I ever gonna know?: *Various artists* / Vassarlean: *Various artists* / Oh yeah, oh yeah: *Various artists*.
Note: Artists include: Charles Mingus, Eric Dolphy, Lucky Thompson, Booker Ervin, Max Roach, Booker Little, Kenny Dorham, Kenny Clarke, Tommy Flanagan, Roy Eldridge, Benny Bailey, Jimmy Knepper, Ted Curson, Julian Priester, Cecil Payne.
**Album:** Released Dec '86, on Candid Catalogue no: **LP 9019**

**JAZZ LIVE & RARE (Various artists)**
Note: The first Esquire concert featuring Art Tatum, Coleman Hawkins, Billie Holiday etc. Recorded January 1944. Mono.
**CD:** Released '86, on Delta (1) by Delta Records. Catalogue no: **11 043**

**JAZZ MASTERS (Various artists)**
**2 LP Set:** Released Oct '88, on Vogue by Vogue Records. Catalogue no: **416039**

**JAZZ ME BLUES - THE CHICAGO (Various artists)**
Tracks: / Jazz me blues: *Various artists* (Composer (Tom Delaney)) / There'll be some changes made: *Various artists* (Composer (W. Benton Overstreet/Billy Higgins) / Copenhagen: *Various artists* (Composer (Charles Davis/Frank Melrose)) / Trying to stop me crying: *Various artists* (Composer (Ray Biondi/C.J. Miskelly/Jack Lazier) / Bugle call rag: *Various artists* (Composer (Jack Pettis / Elmer Schoebel/Billy Meyers) / Downright disgusted: *Various artists* (Composer (Terry Shand/Joe Mammone) / Milenberg joys: *Various artists* (Composer (Naces/Jelly Roll Morton/Walter Melrose)) / Wailin' blues: *Various artists* (Composer (Ted Lewis/Lester Melrose)) / Baby won't you please come home?: *Various artists* (Composer (Clarence Williams/Charles Warfield)) / Tillie's downtown now: *Various artists* (Composer (Bud Freeman)) / Fare thee well: *Various artists* (Composer (Peck Kelly/Ray Mayer/Joe Mannone)) / My daddy rocks me (with one steady rock): *Various artists* / Prince of wails: *Various artists* (Composer (Elmer Schoebel)) / I've found a new baby: *Various artists* (Composer (Spencer Williams/Jack Palmer)) / Oh Susannah, dust off that old pianna: *Various artists* (Composer (Caeser/Lerner/Marks)) / Isn't there a little love (down in your heart for me)?: *Various artists* (Composer (Joe Mannone)) / Barrel house stomp: *Various artists* (Composer (Frank Melrose)) / I've found a new baby: *Various artists* (Composer (Spencer Williams/Jack Palmer)).
**Album:** Released Mar '87, on Affinity by Charly Records. Catalogue no: **AFS 1026**

**JAZZ MEETING IN HOLLAND (Various artists)**
Note: Artista include:Bud Freeman,J.McPartland,Ted Easton.
**Album:** Released Jun '86, on Circle (USA) by Jazzology Records (USA). Catalogue no: **CLP 10**

**JAZZ MONTEREY (1958-1980) (Various artists)**
**2 LP Set:** Released Jan '85, on Palo Alto Catalogue no: **PA 8080-2**

**JAZZ OFF THE AIR, VOL. 1 (Various artists)**
Tracks: / Ornithology: *Junior Jazz and Wnez* / Hot house: *Junior Jazz and Wnez* / Allen's alley: *Junior Jazz and Wnez* / Lover: *Junior Jazz and Wnez* / High on an open mike: *Junior Jazz and Wnez* / Sweet Georgia Brown: *Junior Jazz and Wnez*.
**Album:** Released '83, on Spotlite by Spotlite Records. Catalogue no: **SPJ 144**

**JAZZ SPECTACULAR (Various artists)**
**Album:** Released '84, on CBS by CBS Records. Catalogue no: **CBS 32413**
**Cass:** Released '84, on CBS by CBS Records. Catalogue no: **40 32413**

**JAZZ STREET (Various artists)**
**CD:** Released May '87, on CBS by CBS Records. Deleted Jan '89. Catalogue no: **450 377 2**

## Jazz '80

**JAZZ '80 (Various artists)**
Tracks: / Modus operandi: *Terry, Clark* / In a mellow tone: *Basie, Count* / Rockin' in rhythm: *Barber, Chris* / Eros Hotel: *Fame, Georgie* / Interfusion: *Scott, Ronnie* / It's a sin to tell a lie: *Melly, George* / Manteca: *Gillespie, Dizzy* / Everyday: *Williams, Joe* / Dykes on bikes: *National Youth Jazz Orchestra* / Milenberg joys: *Ball, Kenny* / Pata pata: *Osibisa* / I heard you've been around: *Bilk, Acker* / Baby won't you please come home?: *McRae, Carmen* / Moten swing: *Basie, Count.*
**Cass set:** Released May '83, on Vogue Jazz (France) by Vogue Records. Catalogue no: **ZC VJD 571**
**2 LP Set:** Released May '83, on Vogue Jazz (France) by Vogue Records. Catalogue no: **VJD 571**

## Jazz And...

**JAZZ AND CINEMA (Various artists)**
**Album:** Released Aug '84, on CBS (import) by CBS Records. Deleted Aug '87. Catalogue no: **21109**
**Cass:** Released Aug '84, on CBS (import) by CBS Records. Deleted Nov '87. Catalogue no: **4021109**

**JAZZ AND COUNTRY IN THE MOVIES (Film soundtrack) (Various artists)**
Tracks: / Pourin' whiskey blues: *Labelle, Patti* / Low down dirty shame: *Labelle, Patti & Larry Riles* / Cotton-eyed Joe: *Watson, Doc & Merle* / Ida Red: *Barnes, Roosevelt* / Faded love: *Barnes, Roosevelt* / Lovesick blues: *Barnes, Roosevelt* / Down home blues: *Barnes, Roosevelt* / Every time she goes by: *Oxford Community Choir* / I want to go home: *Oxford Community Choir* / Liberty: *Oxford Community Choir.*
Note: Blues and country music from the films A Soldier's Story, Places in the Heart and Mississippi Blues.
**Album:** Released Aug '85, on SPI Milan (France) Catalogue no: **ACH 030**

**JAZZ AND REG (Various artists)**
**Cass set:** Released 7 Nov '87, on Warwick by Warwick Records. Catalogue no: **WW 6034**

## Jazz Artists Guild

**JAZZ LIFE, THE**
**CD:** Released May '86, on Candid Catalogue no: **CCD 9019**
**Album:** Released May '86, on Candid Catalogue no: **CS 9019**

## Jazz At The...

**JAZZ AT THE PHIL-HAPPY REUNION (Various artists)**
**Album:** Released Apr '87, on Pablo Jazz (USA) by Pablo Records (USA). Catalogue no: **2620 117**

**JAZZ AT THE OPERA HOUSE (Various artists)**
**Cass:** Released Jul '83, on CBS by CBS Records. Catalogue no: **40 88622**
**Album:** Released Jul '83, on CBS by CBS Records. Catalogue no: **CBS 88622**

**JAZZ AT THE SANTA MONICA CIVIC (Various artists)**
Tracks: / Basie power: *Basie, Count & His Orchestra* / Meetin', The: *Basie, Count & His Orchestra* / Blues in Hoss's flat: *Basie, Count & His Orchestra* / Good time blues: *Basie, Count & His Orchestra* / In a mellow tone: *Jazz At The Philharmonic All Stars* / Loose walk: *Jazz At The Philharmonic All Stars* / Makin'

whoopee: *Jazz At The Philharmonic All Stars* / If I had you: *Jazz At The Philharmonic All Stars* / She's funny that way: *Jazz At The Philharmonic All Stars* / Blue and sentimental;: *Jazz At The Philharmonic All Stars* / I surrender, dear: *Jazz At The Philharmonic All Stars* / 5400 north: *Jazz At The Philharmonic All Stars* / You are my sunshine: *Peterson, Oscar & Ray Brown* / Shiny stockings: *Fitzgerald, Ella/County Basie Orchestra/Tommy Flanagan Trio* / You've got a friend: *Fitzgerald, Ella/County Basie Orchestra/Tommy Flanagan Trio* / What's going on?: *Fitzgerald, Ella/County Basie Orchestra/Tommy Flanagan Trio* / Spring can really hang you up the most: *Fitzgerald, Ella/County Basie Orchestra/Tommy Flanagan Trio* / Madalena: *Fitzgerald, Ella/County Basie Orchestra/Tommy Flanagan Trio* / Too darn hot: *Fitzgerald, Ella/County Basie Orchestra/Tommy Flanagan Trio* / It's alright with me: *Fitzgerald, Ella/County Basie Orchestra/Tommy Flanagan Trio* / Sandford and Son theme: *Fitzgerald, Ella/County Basie Orchestra/Tommy Flanagan Trio* / I can't stop loving you: *Fitzgerald, Ella/County Basie Orchestra/Tommy Flanagan Trio* / Finale: *Fitzgerald, Ella/County Basie/JATP All Stars.*
Note: Artists: Count Basie, Ella Fitzgerald, Oscar Peterson, Tommy Flanagan, Jazz at the Philharmonic All Stars.
**CD Set:** Released Jan '89, on JVC/Fantasy Catalogue no: **VDJ 25001-3**
**CD Set:** Released Jun '87, on Pablo Jazz (USA) by Pablo Records (USA). Catalogue no: **CD 20011/D**
**LP Set:** Released '82, on Pablo Jazz (USA) by Pablo Records (USA). Catalogue no: **2625 701**

## Jazz At The Philharmonic

**AT THE MONTREUX JAZZ FESTIVAL, 1975 (Jazz At The Philharmonic All Stars)**
Tracks: / For you / Autumn leaves / If I had you / I never knew.
Note: Featuring Benny Carter, Zoot Sims, Roy Eldridge, Clark Terry, Joe Pass, Peter Betts, Bobby Durham, Tommy Flanagan.
**Album:** Released '82, on Pablo Jazz (USA) by Pablo Records (USA). Catalogue no: **231 0748**
**Cass:** Released '82, on Pablo Jazz (USA) by Pablo Records (USA). Catalogue no: **K10 748**

**EXCITING BATTLE, STOCKHOLM, '55 (Jazz At The Philharmonic All Stars)**
Tracks: / Little David / Ow / Sticks / Man I love, The / I'll never be the same / Skylark / My old flame / Birks.
**Album:** Released '82, on Pablo Jazz (USA) by Pablo Records (USA). Catalogue no: **231 0713**
**Cass:** Released '82, on Pablo Jazz (USA) by Pablo Records (USA). Catalogue no: **K10 713**

**JAZZ AT THE PHILHARMONIC 1983 (Various artists)**
Tracks: / Lucky so and so: *Various artists* / I may be wrong: *Various artists* / Smoke gets in your eyes: *Various artists* / Stompin' at The Savoy: *Various artists* / Time after time: *Various artists* / Secret love: *Various artists* / It could happen to you: *Various artists* / Slow drag: *Various artists.*
**Album:** Released Jul '83, on Pablo Jazz (USA) by Pablo Records (USA). Catalogue no: **2310 882**

**JAZZ AT THE PHILHARMONIC : HARTFORD 1953 (Various artists)**
Tracks: / Cottontail: *Various artists* / Airmail special: *Various artists* / Swinging on a star: *Various artists* / Man I love, The: *Various artists* / Seven come eleven: *Various artists* / D.B. blues: *Various artists* / I cover the waterfront: *Various artists* / Up-'n'-Adam: *Various artists.*
Note: Recorded at a 1953 concert at Hartford's Bushnell Memorial Auditorium, this album features one of the best JATP line-ups: Charlie Shavers, Roy Eldridge (trumpets), Bill Harris (trombone), Lester Young, Ben Webster, Flip Phillips (tenor saxes), Benny Carter, Willie Smith (alto saxes), Oscar Peterson (piano), Herb Ellis (guitar), Ray Brown (bass), Gene Krupa, J.C. Heardman (drums).
**Album:** Released Mar '85, on Pablo Jazz (USA) by Pablo Records (USA). Catalogue no: **230 8240**
**Cass:** Released Mar '85, on Pablo Jazz (USA) by Pablo Records (USA). Catalogue no: **K 08240**

**LIVE AT THE NICHIGEKI THEATRE, TOKYO (Jazz At The Philharmonic All Stars)**
Tracks: / Tokyo blues / Up / Ballad medley (the nearness of you) / Someone to watch over me / Flamingo / I surrender dear / Sweet and lovely / Stardust / Embraceable you / That old black magic / Sushi blues / Alone together / Swingin' 'til the girls come home / Indiana / Cocktails for two / Don't be that way / Stompin' / At the savoy / On the sunny side of the street / Body and soul / Why don't you do right / Lady be good / I got it bad and that ain't good / How high the moon / My funny valentine / Smooth sailing / Frim fram sauce / Perdido.
**Cass set:** Released '82, on Pablo Jazz (USA) by Pablo Records (USA). Catalogue no: **K 20 104**
**2 LP Set:** Released '82, on Pablo Jazz (USA) by Pablo Records (USA). Catalogue no: **262 0104**

## Jazz Band Ball

**JAZZ BAND BALL (Various artists)**
Tracks: / Alexander's ragtime band: *Phillips, Sid And His Band* / Sensation rag: *Randell, Freddy And His Band* / Crazy rhythm: *Daniel's, Joe Jazz Band* / Farewell blues: *Randall, Freddy & His Band* / Chicago: *Daniels, Joe Jazz Group* / Mamma don't allow: *Phillips, Sid And His Band* / Won't you come home Bill Bailey: *Randell, Freddy And His Band* / On Sunday I go sailing: *Richford's, Doug London Jazzmen With Nat Gonella* / Who walks in when I walk out?: *Saints Jazz Band* / Heatwave: *Lyttelton, Humphrey & His Band* / Tiger rag: *Phillips, Sid & His Band* / St. Louis blues: *Daniel's, Joe Jazz Band* / Clarinet marmalade: *Phillips, Sid And His Band* / Bad penny blues: *Lyttelton, Humphrey* / Yip-I-addy-I-ay: *Richford's, Doug London Jazzmen With Nat Gonella* / Sunday: *Randell, Freddy And His Band* / Marie: *Daniel's, Joe Jazz Band* / P.T.Q. rag: *Lyttelton, Humphrey & His Band* / Pete Kelly's blues: *Phillips, Sid And His Band* / Lily of the valley: *Crane River Jazz Band* / I wish I could shimmy like my sister Kate: *Daniel's, Joe Jazz Band* / Muskrat ramble: *Phillips, Sid & His Band* / Someday, sweetheart: *Randell, Freddy And His Band* / Susie: *Daniels, Joe Jazz Group* / Little brown jug: *Daniels, Joe Jazz Group* / Pasadena: *Phillips, Sid & His Band* / Avalon: *Daniel's, Joe Jazz Band* / Hey lawdy papa: *Saints Jazz Band.*
**2 LP Set:** Released Nov '88, on MFP by EMI Records. Catalogue no: **DL 1137**
**Cass:** Released Nov '88, on MFP by EMI Records. Catalogue no: **TCDL 1137**

**JAZZ BAND BALL VOL.12 (Various artists)**
**Album:** Released Jan '83, on Swaggie (Australia) Catalogue no: **S 1398**

## Jazz Best

**JAZZ BEST (Various artists)**
Tracks: / Girl from Ipanema: *Gilberto, Astrud & Stan Getz* / St. Louis blues: *Ellington, Duke* / Sweet Lorraine: *Various artists* / Born to be blue: *Montgomery, Wes* / Georgia on my mind: *Peterson, Oscar Trio* / Summertime: *Fitzgerald, Ella & Louis Armstrong* / Desafinado: *Getz, Stan* / People: *Peterson, Oscar Trio* / Misty: *Fitzgerald, Ella* / Basin Street blues: *Smith, Jimmy (USA)* / My funny valentine: *Webster, Ben* / Lady sings the blues: *Holiday, Billie.*
**Album:** Released May '88, on Music Power Catalogue no: **33012**
**CD:** Released May '88, on Black Tulip Catalogue no: **263 629 2**
**Cass:** Released May '88, on Music Power Catalogue no: **63012**
**Album:** Released Apr '84, on Verve Catalogue no: **2367 406**

**JAZZ BEST, VOL 2 (Various artists)**
Tracks: / Shadow of your mind: *Gilberto, Astrud* / Honeysuckle rose: *Wilson, Teddy (dup)* / Insensatez: *Jobim, Antonio Carlos* / In a mellow tone: *Various artists* / Foggy day, A: *Fitzgerald, Ella & Louis Armstrong* / Line for Lyons: *Desmond, Paul* / Mr. Paganini: *Fitzgerald, Ella* / Walk on by: *Getz, Stan* / Tequila: *Montgomery, Wes* / Way down yonder in New Orleans: *Crosby, Bing & Louis Armstrong* / Makin' whoopee: *Webster, Ben* / Stormy weather: *Holiday, Billie.*
**Cass:** Released Jul '84, on Verve (Holland) Catalogue no: **3115 125**
**Album:** Released Jul '84, on Verve (Hol-

land) Catalogue no: **2367 416**

## Jazz City Presents

**JAZZ CITY PRESENTS (Various artists)**
**Album:** Released Feb '88, on Fresh Sounds (Spain) by Fresh Sounds Records (Spain). Catalogue no: **FS 205**

## Jazz Classics...

**JAZZ CLASSICS (Various artists)**
Tracks: / It's a sin to tell a lie: *Various artists* / Potato head blues: *Various artists* / Ostrich walk: *Various artists* / Riverboat shuffle: *Various artists* / Georgia on my mind: *Various artists* / Struttin' with some bar-b-q: *Various artists* / Creole jazz: *Various artists* / I'm gonna sit right down and write myself a letter: *Various artists* / Bourbon st.parade: *Various artists* / Snag it: *Various artists* / Sweet Georgia Brown: *Various artists* / Sophisticated lady: *Various artists* / This can't be love: *Various artists* / I can't get started with you: *Various artists* / After you've gone: *Various artists* / Old grey bonnet: *Various artists* / Old rugged cross, The: *Various artists* / There will never be another you: *Various artists* / Ain't misbehavin': *Various artists* / Woodchoppers ball: *Various artists.*
**Cass set:** Released Feb '90, on Kaz by Kaz Records. Catalogue no: **KAZMC 11**
**2 LP Set:** Released Feb '90, on Kaz by Kaz Records. Catalogue no: **KAZLP 11**
**CD:** Released Feb '90, on Kaz by Kaz Records. Catalogue no: **KAZCD 11**

**JAZZ CLASSICS IN DIGITAL STEREO (Hot violins) (Various artists)**
Tracks: / Wild cat: *Various artists* / Mama Mockingbird: *Various artists* / Boodle am shake: *Various artists* / My syncopated melody man: *Various artists* / Manhattan rag: *Various artists* / Nagasaki: *Various artists* / Ain't misbehavin: *Various artists* / Limehouse blues: *Various artists* / Calling all keys: *Various artists* / Nothing but notes: *Various artists* / I got rhythm: *Various artists* / Onyx club spree: *Various artists* / Bill street blues: *Various artists* / Serenade for a wealthy widow: *Various artists* / Honeysuckle rose: *Various artists* / Fiddle blues: *Various artists.*
**CD:** Released Jun '88, on BBC by BBC Records & Tapes. Catalogue no: **BBC CD 680**
**Cass:** Released Jun '88, on BBC by BBC Records & Tapes. Catalogue no: **ZCF 680**
**Album:** Released Jun '88, on BBC by BBC Records & Tapes. Catalogue no: **REB 680**

**JAZZ CLASSICS OF NEW ORLEANS (Various artists)**
**CD:** Released Oct '88, on Vogue by Vogue Records. Catalogue no: **VGCD 670 021**
**2 LP Set:** Released Oct '88, on Vogue by Vogue Records. Catalogue no: **400439**

**JAZZ CLASSICS, VOL.1 (New Orleans) (Various artists) (See panel below)**
**Album:** Released '79, on Blue Note by EMI Records. Deleted '84. Catalogue no: **BNS 40001**
**CD:** Released Jun '86, on BBC by BBC Records & Tapes. Catalogue no: **BBC CD 588**
**Album:** Released Feb '86, on BBC by BBC Records & Tapes. Catalogue no: **REB 588**
**Cass:** Released Feb '86, on BBC by BBC Records & Tapes. Catalogue no: **ZCF 588**

**JAZZ CLASSICS, VOL.2 (Various artists)**
**Album:** Released '79, on Blue Note by EMI Records. Deleted '84. Catalogue no: **BNS 40002**
**Album:** Released Sep '84, on Blue Note by EMI Records. Catalogue no: **LP 1202**
**CD:** Released Jun '86, on BBC by BBC Records & Tapes. Catalogue no: **BBC CD 589**
**Cass:** Released Jun '86, on BBC by BBC Records & Tapes. Catalogue no: **ZCF 589**
**Album:** Released Jun '86, on BBC by BBC Records & Tapes. Catalogue no: **REB 589**

**JAZZ CLASSICS, VOL.3 (Various artists)**
**CD:** Released Jun '86, on BBC by BBC Records & Tapes. Catalogue no: **BBC CD 590**
**Cass:** Released Jun '86, on BBC by BBC Records & Tapes. Catalogue no: **ZCF 590**
**Album:** Released Jun '86, on BBC by BBC Records & Tapes. Catalogue no: **REB 590**

**JAZZ CLASSICS, VOL.5 (Armstrong, Louis)**
Note: Features Louis Armstrong's Hot Five and Hot Seven, Johny Dodds, Earl Hinesand Jack Teagarden
**CD:** Released Jun '86, on BBC by BBC Records & Tapes. Catalogue no: **BBC CD 597**
**Cass:** Released Aug '86, on BBC by BBC Records & Tapes. Catalogue no: **ZCF 597**
**Album:** Released Aug '86, on BBC by BBC Records & Tapes. Catalogue no: **REB 597**

**JAZZ CLASSICS, VOL.6 (Waller, Fats)**
Note: Original 78's digitally remastered and stereo enhanced.This entirely new technique has received universal critical acclaim.
**CD:** Released Aug '86, on BBC by BBC Records & Tapes. Catalogue no: **BBC CD 598**
**Cass:** Released Aug '86, on BBC by BBC Records & Tapes. Catalogue no: **ZCF 598**
**Album:** Released Aug '86, on BBC by BBC Records & Tapes. Catalogue no: **REB 598**

**JAZZ CLASSICS, VOL.7 (Beiderbecke, Bix)**
**CD:** Released Aug '86, on BBC by BBC Records & Tapes. Catalogue no: **BBC CD 601**
**Album:** Released Aug '86, on BBC by BBC Records & Tapes. Catalogue no: **REB 601**

**Jazz Classics - Vol.1 New Orleans (BBC)**

**Cass:** Released Aug '86, on BBC by BBC Records & Tapes. Catalogue no: **ZCF 601**

### JAZZ CLASSICS, VOL.9 (Dodds, Johnny)
**Cass:** Released Oct '86, on BBC by BBC Records & Tapes. Catalogue no: **ZCF 603**
**CD:** Released Jun '86, on BBC by BBC Records & Tapes. Catalogue no: **BBC CD 603**
**Album:** Released Oct '86, on BBC by BBC Records & Tapes. Catalogue no: **REB 603**

### JAZZ CLASSICS, VOL.10 (Morton, Jelly Roll)
**CD:** Released Oct '86, on BBC by BBC Records & Tapes. Catalogue no: **BBC CD 604**
**Cass:** Released Oct '86, on BBC by BBC Records & Tapes. Catalogue no: **ZCF 604**
**Album:** Released Oct '86, on BBC by BBC Records & Tapes. Catalogue no: **REB 604**

### JAZZ CLASSICS, VOL.11 (Ellington, Duke)
Tracks: / Jubilee stomp / Blues with a feeling / Hop head / What can a poor fellow do / Chicago stompdown / Black beauty / Hot and bothered / Misty morning / Mooche, The / Paducah / East St. Louis toodle-oo / Creole love call / Fast and furious / Solitude / Stompy Jones / Live and love tonight.
**Album:** Released Oct '87, on BBC by BBC Records & Tapes. Catalogue no: **REB 643**
**CD:** Released Oct '87, on BBC by BBC Records & Tapes. Catalogue no: **BBC CD 643**
**Cass:** Released Oct '87, on BBC by BBC Records & Tapes. Catalogue no: **ZCF 643**

### JAZZ CLASSICS, VOL.12 (Venuti, Joe & Eddie Lang)
Tracks: / Stringing the blues / Bugle call rag / Four string Joe / Krazy kat / Sensation / My baby came home / Wild dog / Church street sobbin' blues / Shivery stomp / Running ragged / Hot heels / Put and take / Oh Peter / Beale street blues / Vibraphonia / Eddie's twister.
**Cass:** on BBC by BBC Records & Tapes. Catalogue no: **ZCF 644**
**CD:** Released Oct '87, on BBC by BBC Records & Tapes. Catalogue no: **BBC CD 644**
**Album:** Released Oct '87, on BBC by BBC Records & Tapes. Catalogue no: **REB 644**

## Jazz Club...

### JAZZ CLUB (Various artists)
Tracks: / Take the 'A' train: *Fitzgerald, Ella* / No more blues: *Gillespie, Dizzy* / Long, long summer: *Gillespie, Dizzy* / Buh's bossa: *Blakey, Art* / Moanin': *Blakey, Art* / G'won train: *Smith, Jimmy (USA)* / Southern suite: *Hayes, Tubby* / Manha de carnival: *Getz, Stan* / Lullaby of Birdland: *Vaughan, Sarah.*
**Cass:** Released Aug '84, on Club by Phonogram Ltd. Catalogue no: **JABBC 3**
**Album:** Released Aug '84, on Club by Phonogram Ltd. Catalogue no: **JABB 3**

### JAZZ CLUB 2 (Various artists)
Tracks: / Mack the knife: *Fitzgerald, Ella* / Tribute to Brownie: *Adderley, Cannonball* / 'Bout to wail: *Gillespie, Dizzy* / All of me: *Washington, Dinah* / Yeh yeh: *Hendricks, Jon* / Shulie a bop: *Vaughan, Sarah* / Jordu: *Brown, Clifford* / Sackful of soul: *Kirk, Roland* / T.V. is the thing: *Washington, Dinah* / Pint of bitter: *Hayes, Tubby.*
**Cass:** Released May '85, on Club by Phonogram Ltd. Catalogue no: **JABBC 7**
**Album:** Released May '85, on Club by Phonogram Ltd. Catalogue no: **JABB 7**

### JAZZ CLUB - ALTO SAX (Various artists)
Tracks: / Now's the time: *Parker, Charlie* / Sleepin' bee, A: *Pepper, Art* / Porky: *Adderley, Cannonball* / C-Jam blues: *Mariano, Charlie* / Blues greasy: *Stitt, Sonny* / Blues for bird: *Konitz, Lee* / Kicks wings: *Shank, Bud* / Yesterdays: *Woods, Phil* / Funky blues: *Parker/Hodges/Carter* / Standstill: *Desmond, Paul* / Confirmation: *McLean, Jackie* / Futurity: *Gryce, Gigi.*
**CD:** Released Nov '89, on Hanover by Polydor Ltd. Catalogue no: **840 036 2**
**Cass:** Released Nov '89, on Hanover by Polydor Ltd. Catalogue no: **840 036 4**
**Album:** Released Nov '89, on Hanover by Polydor Ltd. Catalogue no: **840 036 1**

### JAZZ CLUB - BASS (Various artists)
Tracks: / Blue horizon, The (take 1): *Wayne, Chuck* / Prayer for passive: *Mingus, Charles* / Blues in the closet: *Pettiford, Oscar* / How high the moon: *Safranski, Eddie* / If I were a bell: *Mitchell, Red* / Stompin' at the Savoy: *Carter, Ron* / Muses for Richard Davis: *Davis, Richard* / Northwest passage: *Jackson, Chubby* / Solo for unaccompanied bass: *Brown, Ray* / Golden striker: *Heath, Percy* / Little beaver: *Chambers, Paul* / Tribute to Brownie: *Jones, Sam* / Younger: *Hiels-Henning-Orsted-Pedersen* / Foreign fun: *Pastorius, Jaco.*
**Cass:** Released Nov '89, on Hanover by Polydor Ltd. Catalogue no: **840 037 4**
**Album:** Released Nov '89, on Hanover by Polydor Ltd. Catalogue no: **840 037 1**
**CD:** Released Nov '89, on Hanover by Polydor Ltd. Catalogue no: **840 037 2**

### JAZZ CLUB - BIG BANDS (Various artists)
**Cass:** Released Jun '89, on Hanover by Polydor Ltd. Catalogue no: **840 030 4**
**Album:** Released Jun '89, on Hanover by Polydor Ltd. Catalogue no: **840 030 1**
**CD:** Released Jun '89, on Hanover by Polydor Ltd. Catalogue no: **840 030 2**

### JAZZ CLUB - DRUMS (Various artists)
**CD:** Released Jun '89, on Hanover by Polydor Ltd. Catalogue no: **840 033 2**
**Cass:** Released Jun '89, on Hanover by Polydor Ltd. Catalogue no: **840 033 4**
**Album:** Released Jun '89, on Hanover by Polydor Ltd. Catalogue no: **840 033 1**

### JAZZ CLUB - GUITAR (Various artists)
Tracks: / Conception: *Wayne, Chuck* / Patti cake: *Ellis, Herb* / Nobody else but me: *Raney, Jimmy* / Downstairs: *Burrell, Kenny* / Samba triste: *Powell, Baden* / O Pato: *Byrd, Charlie* / Blues for Django: *Coryell, Larry & Philip Catherine* / Interlude, Take 1: *Bauer, Billy* / Heat wave: *Kessel, Barney* / You came along: *Farlow, Tal* / Li darling: *Pass, Joe* / Song for my father: *Benson, George* / Extrapolation: *McLaughlin, John.*
**Cass:** Released Nov '89, on Hanover by Polydor Ltd. Catalogue no: **840 035 4**
**Album:** Released Nov '89, on Hanover by Polydor Ltd. Catalogue no: **840 035 1**
**CD:** Released Nov '89, on Hanover by Polydor Ltd. Catalogue no: **840 035 2**

### JAZZ CLUB - PIANO (Various artists)
**Cass:** Released Jun '89, on Hanover by Polydor Ltd. Catalogue no: **840 032 4**
**Album:** Released Jun '89, on Hanover by Polydor Ltd. Catalogue no: **840 032 1**
**CD:** Released Jun '89, on Hanover by Polydor Ltd. Catalogue no: **840 032 2**

### JAZZ CLUB - TENOR SAX (Various artists)
**CD:** Released Jun '89, on Hanover by Polydor Ltd. Catalogue no: **840 031 2**
**Cass:** Released Jun '89, on Hanover by Polydor Ltd. Catalogue no: **840 031 4**
**Album:** Released Jun '89, on Hanover by Polydor Ltd. Catalogue no: **840 031 1**

### JAZZ CLUB - TROMBONE (Various artists)
Tracks: / Bill, not Phil: *Harris, Bill* / How are things in ...: *Winding, Kai* / Adam's in the apple: *Knepper, Jimmy* / Cat meets Chick: *Green, Urbie* / Blues melba: *Liston/Green/Grey/Powell* / Song is you, The: *Rosolino, Frank* / Trombone suite: *Maangelsdorff/Hamton* / Yesterday: *Johnson, J.J.* / Christmas eve: *Liston/Cleveland/Rehak* / He ain't got rhythm: *Brookmeyer, Bob* / Our love is here: *Cleveland, Jimmy* / Chang, chang, chang: *Fuller, Curtis* / Tonk: *Moncur, Grachan III.*
**CD:** Released Nov '89, on Hanover by Polydor Ltd. Catalogue no: **840 040 2**
**Cass:** Released Nov '89, on Hanover by Polydor Ltd. Catalogue no: **840 040 4**
**Album:** Released Nov '89, on Hanover by Polydor Ltd. Catalogue no: **840 040 1**

### JAZZ CLUB - TRUMPET (Various artists)
**CD:** Released Nov '89, on Hanover by Polydor Ltd. Catalogue no: **840 038 2**
**Album:** Released Nov '89, on Hanover by Polydor Ltd. Catalogue no: **840 038 1**
**Cass:** Released Nov '89, on Hanover by Polydor Ltd. Catalogue no: **840 038 4**

### JAZZ CLUB - VIBRAPHONE (Various artists)
**Album:** Released Jun '89, on Hanover by Polydor Ltd. Catalogue no: **840 034 1**
**Cass:** Released Jun '89, on Hanover by Polydor Ltd. Catalogue no: **840 034 4**

**CD:** Released Jun '89, on Hanover by Polydor Ltd. Catalogue no: **840 034 2**

**JAZZ CLUB - VIOLIN (Various artists)**
**CD:** Released Nov '89, on Hanover by Polydor Ltd. Catalogue no: **840 039 2**
**Cass:** Released Nov '89, on Hanover by Polydor Ltd. Catalogue no: **840 039 4**
**Album:** Released Nov '89, on Hanover by Polydor Ltd. Catalogue no: **840 039 1**

**JAZZ CLUB - VOCAL (Various artists)**
**Album:** Released Jun '89, on Hanover by Polydor Ltd. Catalogue no: **840 029 1**
**Cass:** Released Jun '89, on Hanover by Polydor Ltd. Catalogue no: **840 029 4**
**CD:** Released Jun '89, on Hanover by Polydor Ltd. Catalogue no: **840 029 2**

## Jazz Collection

**JAZZ COLLECTION (Various artists)**
Tracks: / When the saints go marching in: *Various artists* / At the woodchoppers' ball: *Herman, Woody* / Take the 'A' train: *Ellington, Duke* / Stardust: *Dorsey, Tommy & Frank Sinatra* / In the mood: *Various artists* / Begin the beguine: *Shaw, Artie* / Stompin' at the Savoy: *Goodman, Benny* / Laura: *James, Harry* / Monday date: *Hines, Earl* / Ain't misbehavin': *Waller, Fats* / Swanee: *Jolson, Al* / Minnie the moocher: *Calloway, Cab* / Lover man: *Holiday, Billie* / Sophisticated lady: *Fitzgerald, Ella* / Embraceable you: *Vaughan, Sarah* / Misty: *Garner, Erroll* / Take five: *Brubeck, Dave* / Autumn leaves: *Evans, Bill* / Blue Monk: *Monk, Thelonious* / Theme: *Davis, Miles.*
**Cass:** Released Jul '86, on Deja Vu Catalogue no: **DVMC 2052**
**Album:** Released Jul '86, on Deja Vu Catalogue no: **DVLP 2052**

## Jazz Couriers

**LAST WORD**
Tracks: / If this isn't love / Easy to love / Whisper not / Autumn leaves / Too close for comfort / Yesterdays / Love walked in.
**Album:** Released Dec '83, on Jasmine by Hasmick Promotions. Deleted Jun '87. Catalogue no: **JASM 2024**

**THEME, THE**
Tracks: / Through the night roared the overland express / On a misty night / Plebus / Reunion / Oh my / Foggy day, A / Royal Ascot / Cheek to cheek.
**Album:** Released Feb '83, on Jasmine by Hasmick Promotions. Deleted Jun '87. Catalogue no: **JASM 2004**

## Jazz Dance...

**JAZZ DANCE (Various artists)**
Tracks: / It's only a paper moon: *Various artists* / Jumpin' at the woodside: *Various artists* / Sweet and lovely: *Various artists* / Waltz I blew for you, The: *Various artists* / Sing, sing, sing: *Various artists* / Bundle o' funk: *Various artists* / Nature boy: *Various artists* / World is waiting for the sunrise, The: *Various artists* / Jitterbug waltz: *Various artists* / Take the 'A' train: *Various artists.*
**Cass:** Released Feb '87, on Atlantis by Charly Records. Catalogue no: **KATS 8**
**Album:** Released Dec '85, on Pablo Jazz (USA) by Pablo Records (USA). Catalogue no: **231 0890**

**JAZZ DANCE 1 (CD) (Various artists)**
Tracks: / Triple threat: *Kirk, Roland* ( (Composed: Kirk)*) / Hold it: *Doggett, Bill* ( (Composed: Scott\Butler)**) / Love me or leave me: *Simone, Nina* ( (Composed: Kahn\Donaldson)***) / Another one: *Pettiford, Oscar* ( (Composed: Jones)***) / My baby just cares for me: *Simone, Nina* ( (Composed: Kahn\Donaldson)***) / Fever: *John, Little Willie* ( (Composed: Davenport\Cooley)**) / Kidney stew: *Vinson, Eddie* ( (Composed: Vinson)***) / Tippin: *Various artists* ( (Composed: Byrd)***) / Boom boom: *Various artists* ( (Composed: Hooker)*) / Kinda dukish: *Various artists* / Roof garden: *Various artists* ( (Composed: Jarrow\Canning\Graydon)****) / Terrible T: *Morgan, Lee* ( (Composed: Morgan)*) / Right down front: *Blakey, Art.*
Note: Jazz Dj's may come and go but their music and scene they created will always remain. After all who will forget the likes of Paul Murphy, the Sol y Sombre on Friday nights, Andy McConnell's Saturday Night Fish Fry warehouse parties. Baz's Scala Jazz/Latin all-nighters and Take 5 team of Andy and Baz Fe Jazz are among the gigs and the people that helped the jazz scene. Probably everyone bar a few will remember - but in the words of Miles Davis 'So what'. This album is a collection of Jazz and Rhythm and blues club classics that captures the atmosphere, moods and attitudes of London's Jazz scene in the early eighties. The music of the small basement nightclubs and the illegal warehouse parties packed solid all night with young hipsters wearing period 50's and 60's clothes, dancing to real jazz and blues music. The music of a new underground scene which belonged only to those who were prepared to make the effort to seek and find good music without it being commercialised. Those days are gone, maybe for the best, as jazz has taken a new direction. More young people are now discovering jazz and jazz orientated music is fresh, exciting and danceable as it has been and always will be ... (Charly Records)
**CD:** Released Apr '87, on Charly by Charly Records. Catalogue no: **CDCHARLY 86**
**Album:** Released Jan '85, on Atlantis by Charly Records. Catalogue no: **ATS 8**
**Cass:** Released Jan '85, on Atlantis by Charly Records. Catalogue no: **TCATS 8**

**JAZZ DANCE 2 (Do it like you feel it) (Various artists)**
Tracks: / Do it like you feel it: *Green, Bunky* / Back talk: *Donaldson, Lou* / Hot Bossa: *Burrell, Kenny* / Wade in the water: *Lewis, Ramsey* / Summertime: *Moody, James* / Mas que nada: *Brown,Odell & The Organizers* / On Broadway: *Jacquet, Illinois* / Blackfoot: *Jacquet, Illinois* / Night in Tunisia: *Clark,Buck Sound* / Song for my father: *Bryant, Ray.*
Note: Including Bunky Green and Buck Clark.
**Cass:** Released Oct '87, on Chess by Vogue Records. Catalogue no: **ARCK 7504**
**Album:** Released Oct '87, on Chess by Vogue Records. Catalogue no: **ARC 504**

**JAZZ DANCE 5: IMPULSIVE (Various artists)**
Tracks: / I got my mojo working: *Various artists* / Spellbinder: *Various artists* / Hanky Panky: *Various artists* / Critics choice: *Various artists* / Cloud burst: *Various artists* / Oo oo bossa nova, The: *Various artists* / Alfie's theme differently: *Various artists* / Mas que nada: *Various artists* / Hard work: *Various artists* / Caravan: *Various artists* / See you later: *Various artists* / Guarachi guaro: *Various artists.*
**Cass:** Released Sep '88, on Affinity by Charly Records. Catalogue no: **TCAFF 190**
**Album:** Released Jul '88, on Affinity by Charly Records. Catalogue no: **AFF 190**

## Jazz Defektors

**JAZZ DEFEKTORS**
**CD:** Released Mar '88, on Factory (1) by Factory Records. Catalogue no: **FACD 205**
**Cass:** Released 27 Feb '88, on Factory (1) by Factory Records. Catalogue no: **FACT 205C**

## Jazz Doctors

**DOCTOR JAZZ**
**Album:** Released '88, on Storyville by Storyville Records AB. Catalogue no: **SLP 409**

**INTENSIVE CARE**
**Album:** Released '88, on Cadillac by Cadillac Music. Catalogue no: **SGC 1011**

## Jazz Erotica

**JAZZ EROTICA**
**Album:** Released Oct '87, on Fresh Sounds (Spain) by Fresh Sounds Records (Spain). Catalogue no: **FS 96**

## Jazz Et Cinema

**JAZZ ET CINEMA (Various artists)**
Tracks: / Singin' in the rain: *Various artists* / All that jazz: *Various artists* / Laura: *Various artists* / On Green Dolphin Street: *Various artists* / Girl talk: *Various artists* / Cheek to Cheek: *Various artists* / Somewhere: *Various artists* / Trolley song, The: *Various artists* / Way you look tonight: *Various artists* / Whistle while you work: *Various artists* / People: *Various artists* / Autumn leaves: *Various artists* / Stormy weather: *Various artists* / Who's afraid of the big bad wolf: *Various artists.*

**Album:** Released Jul '86, on CBS by CBS Records. Deleted Jun '88. Catalogue no: **CBS 21109**
**Cass:** Released Jul '86, on CBS by CBS Records. Deleted Nov '87. Catalogue no: **40 21109**

## Jazz Festival...

**JAZZ FESTIVAL, JAZZ (Various artists)**
**Album:** Released '88, on Queen Catalogue no: **QUEEN 044**

## Jazz Fiddlers

**BRAG**
**Album:** Released May '87, on Wam Catalogue no: **WAM/O No.6**

## Jazz For...

**JAZZ FOR ABSOLUTE BEGINNERS (Various artists)**
**Cass:** Released '86, on RCA by BMG Records (UK). Catalogue no: **NK 89874**
**Album:** Released '86, on RCA by BMG Records (UK). Catalogue no: **NL 89874**
**CD:** Released '86, on RCA by BMG Records (UK). Deleted May '89. Catalogue no: **PD 89874**
**CD:** Released Apr '89, on Bluebird (2) by BMG Records (UK). Catalogue no: **ND 90210**

**JAZZ FOR YOU - HOT, HEAVY & BLUE (Various artists)**
Tracks: / Bird song: *Parker, Charlie* / Blue lament: *Parker, Charlie* / It's a sin to tell a lie: *Parker, Charlie* / Cool bird: *Parker, Charlie* / All of me: *Holiday, Billie* / My man: *Holiday, Billie* / They can't take that away from me: *Holiday, Billie* / Lover come back to me: *Holiday, Billie* / Jammin' with Herbie: *Hancock, Herbie* / Hot and heavy: *Hancock, Herbie* / Cycles: *Hancock, Herbie* / Hot piano: *Hancock, Herbie* / Lover's theme: *Davis, Miles* / Cool blues: *Davis, Miles* / Love for sale: *Benson, George* / Masquerade is over, The: *Benson, George* / There will never be another you: *Benson, George.*
**Cass set:** Released Mar '85, on Cambra by Cambra Records. Deleted '88. Catalogue no: **CRT 5144**
**2 LP Set:** Released Mar '85, on Cambra by Cambra Records. Deleted '88. Catalogue no: **CR 5144**

## Jazz From...

**JAZZ FROM ST LOUIS, 1924-1926 (Various artists)**
Tracks: / Pleasure mad: *Creath, Chas Jazz O Maniacs* / Market Street blues: *Creath, Chas Jazz O Maniacs* / I woke up cold in hand: *Creath, Chas Jazz O Maniacs* / King Porter stomp: *Creath, Chas Jazz O Maniacs* / Every man that wears bell bottom britches: *Creath, Chas Jazz O Maniacs* / My daddy rocks me: *Creath, Chas Jazz O Maniacs* / Market Street stomp: *Creath, Chas Jazz O Maniacs* / Won't don't blues: *Creath, Chas Jazz O Maniacs* / Grandpa's spells: *Creath, Chas Jazz O Maniacs* / Frankie and Johnny: *Marable, Fate Society Syncopaters* / Pianoflage: *Marable, Fate Society Syncopaters* / Compton Avenue blues: *Washington, Benny Six Aces* / Soap suds: *St Louis Levee Band.*
**Album:** Released Jan '83, on Swaggie (Australia) Catalogue no: **810**

**JAZZ FROM THE GOLDEN ERA (Various artists)**
**Album:** Released Apr '79, on VJM (Vintage Jazz Music) by Vintage Jazz Music Society(VJM). Catalogue no: **VLP 52**

**JAZZ FROM THE USSR (Various artists)**
**CD:** on Mobile Fidelity Sound Lab(USA) by Mobile Fidelity Records (USA). Catalogue no: **MFCD 890**

**JAZZ FROM NEW YORK 1928-29 (Various)**
**Album:** Released '88, on Swaggie (Australia) Catalogue no: **S 1299**

## Jazz Gala '80

**JAZZ GALA '80 (Various artists)**
Tracks: / Sonny's blues: *Various artists* / Five hundred miles high: *Various artists* / Here's that rainy day: *Various artists* / Time after time: *Various artists* / Christmas song, The: *Various artists* / I'm here for you: *Various artists* / Magic spell: *Various artists* / Rhapsody in blue: *Various artists* / Hits medley: *Various artists* / Lady Day: *Various artists* / Autumn leaves: *Various artists* / Billie's bounce: *Various artists.*
Note: Featuring Stan Getz, Paul Horn, Mike Garson, Joe Farrell, Gayle Moran, Sugar Blue, Patrick Artero.
**2 LP Set:** Released Sep '83, on Kingdom Jazz by Kingdom Records. Catalogue no: **GATE 7009-10**

## Jazz Giants

**JAZZ GIANTS PLAY LOVE SONGS (Various artists)**
**Cass set:** Released Feb '85, on Cambra by Cambra Records. Deleted '88. Catalogue no: **CRT 027**
**2 LP Set:** Released Feb '85, on Cambra by Cambra Records. Deleted '88. Catalogue no: **CR 027**

## Jazz Gillum

**JAZZ GILLUM 1938-47**
Tracks: / It sure had a kick / Maybe you'll love me too / Tell me, mama / Little woman / 5 feet 4 / What a gal / Water pipe blues / She belongs to me / Boar hog blues / You are doing me wrong / You're tearing my playhouse down / I couldn't help it / Talking to myself / Muddy pond blues / War time blues / Blues what am.
**Album:** Released Jan '86, on Travelin' Man by Interstate Music. Catalogue no: **TM 808**

## Jazz Gold

**JAZZ GOLD (Various artists)**
**LP Set:** Released Nov '80, on Effects Gold by Ronco. Catalogue no: **EGS 4 5006**
**Cass set:** Released '80, on Effects Gold by Ronco. Catalogue no: **EC/EGS 4 5006**

## Jazz Group Akhangelsk

**PILGRIMS**
**2 LP Set:** Released Jun '89, on Leo by Leo Records. Catalogue no: **LR 412/413**

## Jazz Guitar...

**JAZZ GUITAR (Various artists)**
**LP Set:** Released '88, on Joker (USA) by Lifetime Records (USA). Catalogue no: **C 76/6 BOX 6**

**JAZZ GUITAR ALBUM (Burrell, Christian, Montgomery & other artists) (Various artists)**
**2 LP Set:** Released Jan '76, on Verve Catalogue no: **2683 065**

## Jazz Guitar Anthology

**JAZZ GUITAR ANTHOLOGY, VOL.1 (Various artists)**
**Cass:** Released '88, on Joker (USA) by Lifetime Records (USA). Catalogue no: **MC 4023**
**Album:** Released '88, on Joker (USA) by Lifetime Records (USA). Catalogue no: **SM 4023**

**JAZZ GUITAR ANTHOLOGY, VOL.2 (Various artists)**
**Album:** Released '88, on Joker (USA) by Lifetime Records (USA). Catalogue no: **SM 4024**
**Cass:** Released '88, on Joker (USA) by Lifetime Records (USA). Catalogue no: **MC 4024**

**JAZZ GUITAR ANTHOLOGY, VOL.3 (Various artists)**
**Cass:** Released '88, on Joker (USA) by Lifetime Records (USA). Catalogue no: **MC 4025**
**Album:** Released '88, on Joker (USA) by Lifetime Records (USA). Catalogue no: **SM 4025**

**JAZZ GUITAR ANTHOLOGY, VOL.4**
**Album:** Released '88, on Joker (USA) by Lifetime Records (USA). Catalogue no: **SM 4026**

**JAZZ GUITAR ANTHOLOGY, VOL.5**
**Album:** Released '88, on Joker (USA) by Lifetime Records (USA). Catalogue no: **SM 4027**

**JAZZ GUITAR ANTHOLOGY, VOL.6**
**Album:** Released '88, on Joker (USA) by Lifetime Records (USA). Catalogue no: **SM 4028**

## Jazz Hall Of Fame

**JAZZ HALL OF FAME (Various artists)**
**Album:** Released May '82, on Decca by Decca International. Catalogue no: **TAB 43**

## Jazz Highlights...

**JAZZ HIGHLIGHTS OF THE 1920'S - (Various artists)**
**Album:** Released Jun '88, on Bandstand Catalogue no: **BS 7127**
**Cass:** Released Jun '88, on Bandstand Catalogue no: **BS 7127C**

**JAZZ HIGHLIGHTS OF THE 1930'S - (Various artists)**
Tracks: / Prisoner's song: *Various artists* / Non-stop flight: *Various artists* / In a mist: *Various artists* / T'aint what you do (it's the way that you do it): *Various artists* / High society: *Various artists* / Rehearsal: *Various artists* / Let's stop the clock: *Various artists* / Pussy willow: *Various artists* / Losers weepers: *Various artists* / Southpaw serenade: *Various artists* / Jumpin' Jehosaphat: *Various artists* / It's sand, man!: *Various artists.*
Note: With Artie Shaw, Harry James, Duke Ellington, Jimmie Lunceford, Count Basie, Bunny Berigan, Larry Clinton, Tommy Dorsey, Benny Goodman, Jimmy Dorsey, Bob Crosby.
**Cass:** Released Jun '88, on Bandstand Catalogue no: **BS 7128C**
**Album:** Released Jun '88, on Bandstand Catalogue no: **BS 7128**

## Jazz & Hot..

**JAZZ & HOT DANCE AFTER THE NAZIS 1946-49 (Trummer Jazz)**
**Album:** Released Sep '86, on Harlequin by Interstate Music. Catalogue no: **HQ 2052**

**JAZZ & HOT DANCE IN ARGENTINA (Various artists)**
**Album:** Released '89, on Harlequin by Interstate Music. Catalogue no: **HQ 2010**

**JAZZ & HOT DANCE IN AUSTRALIA 1925-50 (Jazz & hot dance vol.12) (Various artists)**
**Album:** Released Sep '85, on Harlequin by Interstate Music. Catalogue no: **HQ 2021**

**JAZZ & HOT DANCE IN AUSTRIA 1926 - 44 (Jazz & hot dance vol.5) (Various artists)**
**Album:** Released '88, on Harlequin by Interstate Music. Catalogue no: **HQ 2014**

**JAZZ & HOT DANCE IN BELGIUM 1910-52 (Various artists)**
**Album:** Released Sep '87, on Harlequin by Interstate Music. Catalogue no: **HQ 2027**

**JAZZ & HOT DANCE IN CANADA 1916-49 (Jazz & hot dance vol.14) (Various artists)**
**Album:** Released May '86, on Harlequin by Interstate Music. Catalogue no: **HQ 2023**

**JAZZ & HOT DANCE IN CUBA 1909-53 (Jazz & hot dance vol.16) (Various artists)**
**Album:** Released Jun '86, on Harlequin by Interstate Music. Catalogue no: **HQ 2025**

**JAZZ & HOT DANCE IN CZECHOSLOVAKIA 1910-46 (Jazz & hot dance vol.10) (Various artists)**
**Album:** Released Jul '85, on Harlequin by Interstate Music. Catalogue no: **HQ 2019**

**JAZZ & HOT DANCE IN DENMARK 1909-53 (Jazz & hot dance vol.15) (Various artists)**
Note: Artists: Lumbye, Cornelius & Schmidt, Waldemar Elberg, Otto Lington, Kat Julian,Erik Tuxen, Benny Carter / Ewans, Anker Skjoldborg, Roger Henrichsen, Leon Abbey, Svend Asmussen, Valaida Snow, Kordt Sisters, Harlem Kidies, Peter Rasmussen, Adrian Bentzen. MONO
**Album:** Released Jun '86, on Harlequin by Interstate Music. Catalogue no: **HQ 2024**

**JAZZ & HOT DANCE IN FINLAND 1929-50 (Jazz & hot dance vol.8) (Various artists)**
Tracks: / Finnish rhapsody: *Various artists* / I'll remember you: *Various artists* / My baby: *Various artists* / Jungle song: *Various artists* / You can't stop me: *Various artists* / Jeeper's creepers: *Various artists* / As long as I live: *Various artists* / Sweet Sue: *Various artists* / Full scale of swing: *Various artists* / 100 swing: *Various artists* / St. Louis blues: *Various artists* / Nain nain: *Various artists* / Is you is or is you ain't my baby: *Various artists* / My serenade: *Various artists* / Blue: *Various artists* / Star dust: *Various artists.*
**Album:** Released Apr '85, on Harlequin by Interstate Music. Catalogue no: **HQ 2017**

**JAZZ / HOT DANCE & DOO WACKA - DOO FROM GERMANY VOL. 1 - 1924 (Hyde, Alex)**
**Album:** Released Nov '85, on Harlequin by Interstate Music. Catalogue no: **HQ 2033**

**JAZZ & HOT DANCE FROM GERMANY VOL.2 - 1925 (Hyde, Alex)**
Tracks: / Shine / San / Pleasure mad / No-one knows what it's all about / How I love that girl / Counting the hours / Sioux City Sue / Oh Peter / Alabamy bound / Farewell blues / Copenjagen / Glorida / Craving / Tessie / Ukulele lady / Happy four.
**Album:** Released Nov '85, on Harlequin by Interstate Music. Catalogue no: **HQ 2034**

**JAZZ & HOT DANCE IN HAWAII**
Tracks: / Andrew Aiona / Brown cats of rhythm / Black devils, The / Wailana grass shack boys / Tau Moe's tropical stars.
**Album:** Released Sep '89, on Harlequin by Interstate Music. Catalogue no: **HQ 2070**

**JAZZ & HOT DANCE IN HUNGARY 1912 - 49 (Various artists)**
**Album:** Released '88, on Harlequin by Interstate Music. Catalogue no: **HQ 2015**

**JAZZ & HOT DANCE IN INDIA 1926-44 (Jazz & hor dance vol.4) (Various artists)**
**Album:** Released Feb '85, on Harlequin by Interstate Music. Catalogue no: **HQ 2013**

**JAZZ & HOT DANCE IN MARTINIQUE 1929-1950 (Jazz & hot dance vol.9) (Various artists)**
**Album:** Released Jul '85, on Harlequin by Interstate Music. Catalogue no: **HQ 2018**

**JAZZ & HOT DANCE IN NETHERLANDS 1 (Jazz & hot dance vol.13) (Various artists)**
**Album:** Released '88, on Harlequin by Interstate Music. Catalogue no: **HQ 2022**

**JAZZ & HOT DANCE IN NORWAY 1920-46 (Jazz & hot dance vol.20) (Various artists)**
Tracks: / Chatterbox: *Orpheum Duo* / New peasant jazz: *Oslo Jazzband* / Just let y'rself go: *Hauger, Kristian* / Little bit of humour: *Vieth, Willie* / Caravan: *Hauger, Kristian* / Cocktail: *Funny Boys* / Nobody's sweetheart: *Valier, Freddie* / Nagasaki: *Aagard, Cecil* / Oslo jump: *Sonstevold, Gunnar* / I'm coming Virginia: *Oslo Swingklubb* / Rhythm is our business: *String Swing* / St. Louis blues: *Ork, Rowlands* / Mester Jacob: *Ottersen, Frank* / Rythm fever: *Syversen, Rolf* / Bob's lullaby: *Muntre, Syv* / Gotta be this or that: *Various artists.*
**Album:** Released Nov '87, on Harlequin by Interstate Music. Catalogue no: **HQ 2029**

**JAZZ & HOT DANCE IN RUSSIA 1910 - 50 (Volume 3) (Various artists)**
**Album:** Released '88, on Harlequin by Interstate Music. Catalogue no: **HQ 2012**

**JAZZ & HOT DANCE IN SOUTH AFRICA (Jazz & hot dance vol.11) (Various artists)**
**Album:** Released '88, on Harlequin by Interstate Music. Catalogue no: **HQ 2020**

**JAZZ & HOT DANCE IN SPAIN (Jazz & hot dance vol.17) (Various artists)**
Tracks: / Alabama jubilee: *Fusly, Nic* / Demons charleston: *Demons Jazz* / Blake's blues: *Chocolate Kiddies* / Es una dama de...: *Demon Tetto De Hot* / Ritz hotel: *Bernard Hilda* / Loca por el hot: *Katia Morlands Hot 5* / Eres la mas guapa: *Katia Morlands Hot 5* / Hello ma...: *Martin De La Rosa* / Tuxedo Junction: *Orch Gran Casino* / Kuky: *Adolfo Araco* / Bum bam bum: *Ribera, Sigfredo* / Estoy contenta: *Katia Morlands Hot 5* / Rhythm at the club: *Vives, Ramon* / Red bank boogie: *Ribalta, Jose* / Parece mentira: *Quinteto Saratoga* / Byas jump: *Don Byas All Stars.*
**Album:** Released Jan '87, on Harlequin by Interstate Music. Catalogue no: **HQ 2026**

**JAZZ & HOT DANCE IN SWITZERLAND 1921 (Jazz & hot dance vol.2) (Various artists)**
**Album:** Released '88, on Harlequin by Interstate Music. Catalogue no: **HQ 2011**

**JAZZ & HOT DANCE IN THAILAND 1956-67 (Jazz & hot dance vol.19) (Various artists)**

**Album:** Released Sep '87, on Harlequin by Interstate Music. Catalogue no: **HQ 2028**

**JAZZ & HOT DANCE IN TRINIDAD 1912 - 13 (Various artists)**
**Album:** Released '88, on Harlequin by Interstate Music. Catalogue no: **HQ 2016**

## Jazz In...

**JAZZ IN HARLEM (1926-31) (Various artists)**
**Album:** Released Apr '79, on Arcadia Catalogue no: **ARCADIA 2008**

**JAZZ IN REVOLUTION (Big Bands in the 1940's) (Various artists)**
Tracks: / A-la bridges: *Leonard, Harlan and His Rockets* / Dameron stomp: *Leonard, Harlan and His Rockets* / Saint, The: *Wilson, Gerald And His Orchestra* / Elevation: *Lawrence, Elliot & His Orchestra* / Five o' clock shadow: *Lawrence, Elliot & His Orchestra* / Good jelly blues: *Eckstine, Billy & His Orchestra* / Mingus fingers: *Hampton, Lionel & His Orchestra* / Donna Lee: *Thornhill, Claude & His Orchestra* / Perdido: *Webster, Ben Quartet* / Zonky: *Six men & a girl* / Tea for two: *Mooney, Joe Quartet* / I can't get up the nerve: *Mooney, Joe Quartet* / Mellow mood: *Marmarosa, Dodo Trio* / Royal roost: *Clarke, Kenny & His 52nd Street* / Chase, The: *Gordon, Dexter, Wardell Gray Quartet.*
Note: Recorded in Mono.
**Album:** Released Mar '87, on New World (USA) by New World Records (USA). CAtalogue no: **NW 284**

**JAZZ IN THE THIRTIES (Various artists)**
**2 LP Set:** Released '88, on DRG (USA) by DRG Records (USA) Catalogue no: **SW 8457/8**
**CD Set:** Released '88, on DRG (USA) by DRG Records (USA) Catalogue no: **CDSW 8457/8**

**JAZZ IN THE THIRTIES (1933-35) (Various artists)**
**2 LP Set:** Released Apr '76, on Retrospect by EMI Records. Catalogue no: **SHB 39**

## Jazz Incorporated

**WALKIN' ON**
Tracks: / Walkin' on / Poinciana / Milestones / Lazy bird / Painter's blues / Day the stranger felt at home, The / Nica's tempo / Rebus.
**Album:** Released Jun '86, on Dragon by Dragon Records. Catalogue no: **DRLP 37**

## Jazz Juice

**JAZZ JUICE (Various artists)**
**Album:** Released Sep '84, on DM Streetsounds Catalogue no: **MUSIC 1**
**Album:** Released Nov '85, on DM Streetsounds Catalogue no: **SOUND 1**
**Cass:** Released Nov '85, on DM Streetsounds Catalogue no: **ZCSND 1**

**JAZZ JUICE 2 (Various artists)**
Note: Artists include:John Hendricks,Dianne Schuur,Pat Longo,Marcos Valle,Dirty Dozen Brass Band, Last Poets,Carmen McCrae, Oscar Brown jnr,Wood Herman Orchestra.
**Cass:** Released Jun '86, on DM Streetsounds Catalogue no: **ZCSND 4**
**Album:** Released Jun '86, on DM Streetsounds Catalogue no: **SOUND 4**

**JAZZ JUICE 3 (Various artists)**
**Cass:** Released Sep '86, on DM Streetsounds Catalogue no: **ZCSND 5**
**Album:** Released Sep '86, on DM Streetsounds Catalogue no: **SOUND 5**

**JAZZ JUICE 4 (Various artists)**
**Cass:** Released Dec '86, on DM Streetsounds Catalogue no: **ZCSND 6**
**Album:** Released Dec '86, on DM Streetsounds Catalogue no: **SOUND 6**

**JAZZ JUICE 5 (Various artists)**
**Album:** Released Jul '87, on DM Streetsounds Catalogue no: **SOUND 8**
**Cass:** Released Jul '87, on DM Streetsounds Catalogue no: **ZCSND 8**

**JAZZ JUICE 6 (Various artists)**
**Cass:** Released Oct '87, on DM Streetsounds Catalogue no: **ZCSND 9**
**Album:** Released Oct '87, on DM Streetsounds Catalogue no: **SOUND 9**
**CD:** Released Oct '87, on DM Streetsounds Catalogue no: **CDSND 9**

**JAZZ JUICE 8 (Various artists)**
Tracks: / My favourite things: *Coltrane, John* / Sugar: *Kirk, Roland* / Samba de Orfeu: *Mann, Herbie* / Dance with me: *McFerrin, Bobby* / Gators groove: *Jackson, Willis* / New York afternoon: *Cole, Richie* / Last nite: *Mar Keys* / Braun blek blu: *dom um romao.*
**Album:** Released Jun '88, on DM Streetsounds Catalogue no: **SOUND 11**
**CD:** Released Jun '88, on DM Streetsounds Catalogue no: **CDSND 11**
**Cass:** Released Jun '88, on DM Streetsounds Catalogue no: **ZCSND 11**

## Jazz Live & Rare

**JAZZ LIVE & RARE VOL, 1-5 (Various artists)**
Note: Featuring Tatum, Hawkins, Teagarden, Norvo, Armstrong, Wilson, Bigard, Hampton, Eldridge, Pettiford, Holiday, Catlett, Bailey, Hodges.
**LP Set:** Released Sep '87, on Jazz Line by BMG Records (UK). Catalogue no: **JAZZLINE 95 810-14**

## Jazz Meeting

**JAZZ MEETING VOL. 1**
**Album:** Released '88, on Four Leaf Clover Catalogue no: **FLC 5019**

## Jazz Message

**JAZZ MESSAGE 1956-1965 (Blue Note anniversary collection vol. 2) (Various artists)**
Tracks: / Blue train: *Coltrane, John* / Appointment in Ghana: *McLean, Jackie* / Autumn leaves: *Adderley, Cannonball & Miles Davis* / Cheese cake: *Gordon, Dexter* / Mosaic: *Blakey, Art\Jazz Messengers* / Speak no evil: *Shorter, Wayne* / Maiden voyage: *Hancock, Herbie* / Little B's poem: *Hutcherson, Bobby* / Moontrane, The: *Young, Larry.*
**2 LP Set:** Released Jul '89, on Blue Note by EMI Records. Catalogue no: **BST2 92468**
**CD:** Released Jul '89, on Blue Note by EMI Records. Catalogue no: **CDB1 92468**
**Cass:** Released Jul '89, on Blue Note by EMI Records. Catalogue no: **TCBST2 92468**
**CD:** Released Jul '89, on Blue Note by EMI Records. Catalogue no: **CDBST 92468**
**CD:** Released Jul '89, on Blue Note by EMI Records. Catalogue no: **CDP 792 468 2**

## Jazz Messengers

**NIGHT AT CAFE BOHEMIA WITH THE JAZZ MESSENGERS VOL. 1**
Tracks: / Soft winds / Theme / Minor's holiday / Alone together / Prince Albert / Ladybird / What's new? / Decifering the message.
**CD:** Released Aug '87, on EMI-Manhattan by EMI Records. Catalogue no: **CDP 746 814 2**

## Jazz Nouville Orleans

**JAZZ TIME VOL.15**
**Album:** Released '88, on Vogue (France) by Vogue Records. Catalogue no: **502715**

## Jazz O'Maniacs

**HAVE YOU EVER FELT THAT WAY?**
**Album:** Released '88, on Stomp Off (USA) Catalogue no: **SOS 1046**

**JAZZ O'MANIACS-VOLUME 2**
**Album:** Released Jun '86, on Stomp Off (USA) Catalogue no: **SOS 1071**

## Jazz On ...

**JAZZ ON A SUMMERS DAY (Various artists)**
Note: A documentary by Bert Stern of Newport Jazz Festival way back in 1958, featuring music varying from Louis Armstrong to R & B rocker Chuck Berry. 1958 production. Running time: 85 mins.
**VHS:** Released Oct '86, on Virgin Vision by Virgin Records. Catalogue no: **VVD 170**

**JAZZ ON VERVE VOL.1 (Various artists)**
Tracks: / Nobody knows: *Various artists* / Honeysuckle rose: *Various artists* / Perdido: *Hodges, Johnny & Earl Hinds* / Airmail special: *Hampton, Lionel* / Summertime: *Fitzgerald, Ella* / Sing, sing, sing: *Krupa, Gene* / Top hat, white tie and tails: *Astaire, Fred* / Cottontail: *Webster, Ben* / April in paris: *Basie, Count.*
**Album:** Released Nov '84, on Verve (France) Catalogue no: **8337794**

**JAZZ ON VERVE VOL.2 (Various artists)**
**Album:** Released Nov '87, on Verve (France) Catalogue no: **8337801**

## Jazz Panorama ...

**JAZZ PANORAMA (Various artists)**
Note: Sarah Vaughan / Teddy Buckner / Fats Waller / Coleman Hawkins etc.
**CD:** Released Oct '87, on Vogue by Vogue Records. Catalogue no: **VG 670 012**

**JAZZ PANORAMA OF THE TWENTIES - VOL. 2 (Charleston era, The) (Various artists)**
**Album:** Released Apr '81, on Joker (USA) by Lifetime Records (USA). Catalogue no: **SM 3126**

## Jazz Piano ...

**JAZZ PIANO 2 (Various artists)**
**LP Set:** Released Nov '84, on RCA (France) by BMG Records (France). Catalogue no: **NL 89272**

**JAZZ PIANO ANTHOLOGY (Various artists)**
Tracks: / Sounds of Africa: *Various artists* / Keep out of the grass: *Various artists* / Muscle shoals blues: *Various artists* / Bear trap blues: *Various artists* / In a mist: *Various artists* / Honeysuckle rose: *Various artists* / 57 Varieties: *Various artists* / World is waiting for the sunrise, The: *Various artists* / Tiger rag: *Various artists* / Liza: *Various artists* / Boogie woogie prayer: *Various artists* / Little joe from chicago: *Various artists* / I didn't know what time it was: *Various artists* / For Miss Black: *Various artists* / Way back blues: *Various artists* / Yearning for love: *Various artists* / Round midnight: *Various artists* / Thelonious: *Various artists* / Back home again: *Various artists* / Polka Dots and Moonbeams: *Various artists* / In your own sweet way: *Various artists* / Silver: *Various artists* / Silver blue: *Various artists* / Billy boy: *Various artists* / Pawn ticket: *Various artists* / Splendid splinter: *Various artists* / Port of call: *Various artists.*
Note: From 1 to 15:Historical recordings transcriptions of the originals on 78rpm. 2 LP set.
**2 LP Set:** Released Jul '86, on CBS-Jazz Anthology(USA) by CBS Records (USA). Catalogue no: **S 2VL 1006**

**JAZZ PIANO QUARTET (Jazz Piano Quartet)**
**Album:** Released Feb '85, on RCA (France) by BMG Records (France). Catalogue no: **NL 89368**

## Jazz Potpourri

**JAZZ POTPOURRI 2 (20 collector items 1925-1933) (Various artists)**
Tracks: / Find me at the Greasy Spoon: *Grant, Coot/Kid Wesley Wilson* / Tack Annie: *Oliver, King Dixie Syncopators* / Rhythmic dream, A: *Henderson, Fletcher* / Endurance stomp: *Cobb, Junie C.* / I can't give you anything but love: *Ellington, Duke* / West End blues: *Oliver, King & his Orchestra* / My good man Sam: *Oliver, King & his Orchestra* / After you've gone: *Nichols, Red/his Five Pennies* / Is that religion: *Calloway, Cab* / Honeysuckle rose: *Trumbauer, Frank & His Orchestra* / Strange as it seems: *Hall, Adelaide* / I'll never be the same: *Hall, Adelaide* / You gave me everything but love: *Hall, Adelaide* / This time it's love: *Hall, Adelaide* / Just so you'll remember: *Wiley, Lee* / Trust me for a hamburger: *Washboard Rhythm Boys* / Mama don't allow it: *Jaxon, Frankie 'Half Pint'* / Spank it: *Jaxon, Frankie 'Half Pint'* / Mortgage blues part I: *Jaxon, Frankie 'Half Pint'* / Mortgage blues part II: *Jaxon, Frankie 'Half Pint'*.
Note: Artists include Oliver/Henderson / Ellington/Nichols/Calloway.
**Album:** Released Sep '87, on Meritt (USA) Catalogue no: **MERITT 24**

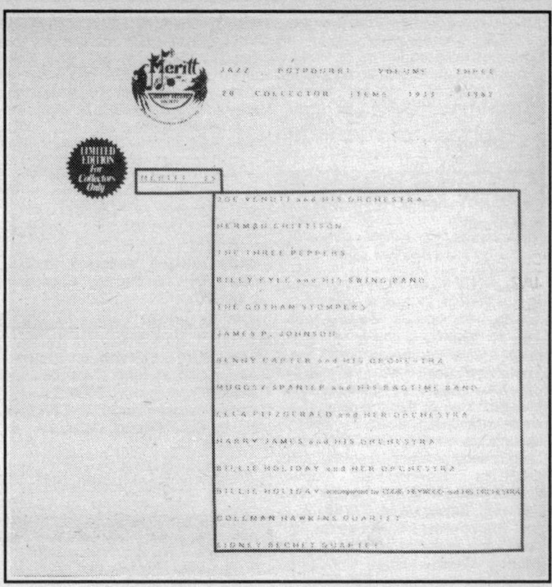

**Jazz Pot Pourri - Jazz Pot Pourri Vol.3 (Meritt)**

**JAZZ POTPOURRI 3 (20 collector items 1933-1947) (Various artists) (See panel above)**
Tracks: / Everybody shuffle: *Venuti, Joe & Orchestra* / You gave me everything but love: *Chittison, Herman* / Sheik of Araby, The: *Three Peppers* / Margie: *Kyle, Billy* / Did anyone ever tell you: *Gotham Stompers* / If dreams come true: *Johnson, James P.* / Shuffleberg shuffle: *Carter, Benny* / Shuffleberg shuffle (3rd try): *Carter, Benny* / Vagabond dreams: *Carter, Benny* / Love's got me down: *Carter, Benny* / More than you know: *Carter, Benny* / More than you know (2nd try): *Carter, Benny* / Relaxin' at the Touro: *Spanier, Muggsy & His Ragtime Band* / Untitled instrumental: *Fitzgerald, Ella & Her Orchestra* / Secrets in the moonlight: *James, Harry & His Orchestra* / It's the same old story: *Holiday, Billie & Her Orchestra* / Am I blue?: *Holiday, Billie* / Cattin' at the Keynote: *Hawkins, Coleman Quartet* / Buddy Bolden: *Bechet, Sidney Quartet* / Song of songs: *Bechet, Sidney Quartet.*
Note: Artists include Venuti/Chittison/Johnson/Carter/Spanier/Fitzgerald.
**Album:** Released Sep '87, on Meritt (USA) Catalogue no: **MERITT 25**

## Jazz Reactivation

**JAZZ REACTIVATION (Various artists)**
Tracks: / Confirmation: *Parker, Charlie & Dizzy Gillespie* / Kaba's blues: *Hampton, Lionel* / Boptura: *Ventura, Charlie* / Things ain't what they used to be: *Hodges, Johnny* / I got rhythm: *Wilson, Teddy (dup)* / It don't mean a thing: *Armstrong, Louis/Duke Ellington* / I cover the waterfront: *Brown, Clifford* / How high the moon: *Reinhardt, Django* / On Green Dolphin Street: *Powell, Bud* / Rat race: *Basie, Count* / Petite Fleur: *Bechet, Sidney* / Viva Gordo (long live Fats): *Richards, Johnny* / New blues up and down: *Ammons, Gene & Sonny Stitt* / Keep on keepin' on: *Herman, Woody* / Soft winds: *Burrell, Kenny* / Mission to Moscow: *Goodman, Benny* / 55th & state: *Sims, John Haley 'Zoot'* / Shaw 'nuff: *Red Rodney* / Off minor: *Monk, Thelonious* / Lester leaps in: *Jacquet, Illinois.*
**Cass set:** Released Oct '84, on Jazz Reactivation Catalogue no: **ZCJRS 6901**
**2 LP Set:** Released Oct '84, on Jazz Reactivation Catalogue no: **JRSD 6901**

## Jazz Renegades

**DO IT THE HARD WAY**

Tracks: / Do the hard way / Blues on the beach / Do the hard way(version).
**12" Single:** Released Jun '89, on Urban by Polydor Ltd. Deleted Dec '89. Catalogue no: **URBX 41**
**7" Single:** Released Jun '89, on Urban by Polydor Ltd. Deleted Dec '89. Catalogue no: **URB 41**

**FREEDOM SAMBA**
Note: Debut Polydor release from ex Style Council drummer Steve White's new band. Steve also provides rhythmic backing for the increasingly successful James Taylor Quartet. The Jazz Renegades are an integral part of the flourishing 'New Jazz' phenomenon currently happening in Britain and Europe. The single 'Do it the hard way' features lead vocals by Sarah-Jane Morris - already famous for her number one with the Communards' 'Don't leave me this way'. Most of the tracks are penned by sax player Alan Barnes, but the band also covers tracks such as Sonny Rollin' 'Mambo bounce' and Freddie Hubbard's 'A pec a sec'. (Polydor Records, July 1989)
**CD:** Released Jul '89, on Polydor by Polydor Ltd. Catalogue no: **839 651 2**
**Cass:** Released Jul '89, on Polydor by Polydor Ltd. Catalogue no: **839 651 4**
**Album:** Released Jul '89, on Polydor by Polydor Ltd. Catalogue no: **839 651 1**

**PLAYING FOR REAL**
**Album:** Released Nov '88, on Acid Jazz by Acid Jazz Records. Catalogue no: **JAZID 006**

**SUMMER TO REMEMBER, A**
**Album:** Released Jun '88, on Re-Elect The President Catalogue no: **KENNEDY 2**
**CD:** Released Jun '88, on Re-Elect The President Catalogue no: **CARTER 2**

## Jazz Sampler

**JAZZ CASSETTE SAMPLER (Various artists)**
Note: Nine tracks & 58 minutes taken from the new series and only avaliable on cassette. *(Count Basie Orchestra)*, *(Phil Woods)*, *(Carmen MacRae)*, *(Randy Brecker)*, *(Eddy Gomez)*, *(Benny Wallace)*, *(Great Jazz Trio)*, *(McCoy Tyner)* & *(Kazumbi Watanabe)*. (Denon 10/88)
**Cass:** Released Oct '88, on Denon Catalogue no: **CC 20**

**JAZZ SAMPLER (Compact/Walkman jazz) (Various artists)**
Note: Tracks by Elain Elias, Uncle Festive, Luis Conte, Bob Berg, The Ritz, Jim Hall trio, Benny Golson, Bennie Wallace, Steve Khan and Rob Mounsey.
**CD:** Released Jul '87, on Verve Catalogue no: **831 376 2**
**Cass:** Released Jun '87, on Verve Catalogue no: **831 376 4**

**JAZZ SAMPLER (2) (Various artists)**
**CD:** Released Oct '88, on Denon Catalogue no: **GES 9167**

**JAZZ SAMPLER VOL 4 (Various artists)**
Tracks: / C jam blues: *Ellington, Duke* / Ligia: *Getz, Stan* / Two bass hit: *Davis, Miles & John Coltrane* / One never knows...: *Holiday, Billie* / Good bait: *Gillespie, Dizzy* / Old yazoo: *Boswell Sisters* / Cornet chop suey: *Armstrong, Louis* / Take the 'A' train: *Roche/Ellington* / Thelonious: *Monk, Thelonious* / Things ain't what they used to be: *Various artists.*
**Cass:** Released 14 Aug '88, on CBS (import) by CBS Records. Catalogue no: **4608264**
**Album:** Released 14 Aug '88, on CBS (import) by CBS Records. Catalogue no: **4608261**

**JAZZ SAMPLER VOL.5 (Various artists)**
**Album:** Released May '89, on CBS (import) by CBS Records. Catalogue no: **463 335 1**
**Cass:** Released May '89, on CBS (import) by CBS Records. Catalogue no: **463 335 4**
**CD:** Released May '89, on CBS (import) by CBS Records. Catalogue no: **463 335 2**

## Jazz Singers

**JAZZ SINGERS (Various artists)**
**CD:** Released May '89, on Onn Catalogue no: **ONN 26**

## Jazz Sounds Of The...

**JAZZ SOUNDS OF THE TWENTIES (Blues singers) (Various artists)**
**Album:** Released Jan '83, on Swaggie (Australia) Catalogue no: **S 1240**
**Album:** Released Jan '83, on Swaggie (Australia) Catalogue no: **S 1254**

## Jazz Studio

**JAZZ STUDIO VOL. 1 (Various artists)**
**Album:** Released Sep '83, on Jasmine by Hasmick Promotions. Deleted Feb '88. Catalogue no: **JASM 1022**

**JAZZ STUDIO VOL. 2 (Various artists)**
Tracks: / Laura: *Jazz Studio Two* / Here come the lions: *Jazz Studio Two* / Paicheck: *Jazz Studio Two* / Graas point: *Jazz Studio Two* / Darn that dream: *Jazz Studio Two* / Do it again: *Jazz Studio Two.*
**Album:** Released Dec '83, on Jasmine by Hasmick Promotions. Deleted Feb '88. Catalogue no: **JASM 1029**

## Jazz Today

**JAZZ TODAY VOL.1 (Various artists)**
Tracks: / Sunday in New York: *Cole, Richie* / O.T.V.O.G.: *Rollins, Sonny* / Scrapple from the apple: *Morgan, Frank Quartet* / If dreams come true: *White, Carla* / Movin' on: *McGriff, Jimmy* / Vicki: *Crawford, Hank* / Underground express: *Campbell, Kerry* / Samba for Isabelle: *Habian, Cliff* / Toc de bola: *Azymuth* / Jacaranda: *Roditi, Claudio.*
**Album:** Released 2 May '89, on BGP by Ace Records. Catalogue no: **BGP 1026**

## Jazz Warriors

**OUT OF MANY ONE PEOPLE**
Tracks: / Warriors / In reference to our forefathers fathers dreams / Minor groove / St. Maurice (of Aragon) / Many pauses.
Note: Live album from Britain's influential all-black jazz big band. Features: Courtney Pine, Philip Bent, Ray Carless & Cleveland Watkiss.
**Cass:** Released Aug '87, on Antilles / New Directions by Island Records. Catalogue no: **ANC 8712**
**Album:** Released Aug '87, on Antilles / New Directions by Island Records. Catalogue no: **AN 8712**
**CD:** Released Aug '87, on Antilles / New Directions by Island Records. Catalogue no: **ANCD 8712**

## Jazz Women

**JAZZ WOMEN (Feminist retrospective, A) (Various artists)**
**2 LP Set:** Released Apr '81, on Stash (USA) Catalogue no: **ST 109**

## Jazz Workshop

**ARRANGERS, THE - RCA VICTOR JAZZ WORKSHOP (Various artists)**
Tracks: / Blues for Pablo: *McKusick, Hal* / Jambangle: *McKusick, Hal* / Miss Clara: *McKusick, Hal* / Day John Brown was hanged, The: *McKusick, Hal* / Lydian lullaby: *McKusick, Hal* / Honeysuckle rose: *Carisi, John* / Springsville: *Carisi, John* / Israel: *Carisi, John* / Lestorian mode: *Carisi, John* / Barry's tune: *Carisi, John* / How about you: *Carisi, John* / Hip's: *Carisi, John* / Vera Cruz: *Levitt, Rod Orchestra* / Holler no.3: *Levitt, Rod Orchestra* / Morning in Montevideo: *Levitt, Rod Orchestra* / Green up: *Levitt, Rod Orchestra* / Mr. Barrelhouse: *Levitt, Rod Orchestra.*
**CD:** Released Apr '89, on Bluebird (2) by BMG Records (UK). Catalogue no: **ND 86471**
**Album:** Released Apr '89, on Bluebird (2) by BMG Records (UK). Catalogue no: **NL 86471**
**Cass:** Released Apr '89, on Bluebird (2) by BMG Records (UK). Catalogue no: **NK 86471**

## Jazztet

**MOMENT TO MOMENT**
Note: With Art Farmer and Benny Golson.
**CD:** Released '86, on Soul Note Catalogue no: **SN 1066**

**VOICES ALL**
Note: With Art Farmer and Benny Golson.
**CD:** Released '86, on Toshiba-EMI (Japan) Catalogue no: **TEC 201**

## Jefferson, Blind Lemon

**BLACK SNAKE MOAN**
**Album:** Released Apr '81, on Joker (USA) by Lifetime Records (USA). Catalogue no: **SM 3103**

**BLIND LEMON JEFFERSON VOL.1**
**Album:** Released Oct '88, on Roots (Germany) Catalogue no: **RL 301**

**BLIND LEMON JEFFERSON VOL.2**
**Album:** Released Oct '88, on Roots (Germany) Catalogue no: **RL 306**

**BLIND LEMON JEFFERSON VOL.3**
**Album:** Released Oct '88, on Roots (Germany) Catalogue no: **RL 331**

**BLIND LEMON JEFFERSON / SON HOUSE (Jefferson, Blind Lemon & Son House)**
Tracks: / My black mama / Preachin' the blues / Dry spell blues / Delta blues / Wartime blues / Weary dog blues / Gone dead on you blues / One dime blues / Lemon's cannonball moan / Eagle eyed mama / Dynamite blues.
**Album:** Released 11 Apr '87, on Blue Moon (1) by Magnum Music Group. Catalogue no: **BMLP 1037**

**COLLECTION: BLIND LEMON (20 blues greats)**
Tracks: / Hangman's blues / Chock house blues / Prison cell blues / Jack o' diamonds / Broke and hungry / Matchbox blues / Rising high water blues / Lemon's worried blues / Mean jumper blues / Shuckin' sugar blues / Easy rider blues / Teddy bear blues / Piney Woods money mama / Lonesome house blues / Low down mojo blues / Sunshine special / Bad luck blues / Lock step blues / Bootin' me 'bout / Black horse blues.
**Cass:** Released Aug '86, on Deja Vu Catalogue no: **DVMC 2073**
**Album:** Released Aug '86, on Deja Vu Catalogue no: **DVLP 2073**

**KING OF THE COUNTRY BLUES**
**2 LP Set:** Released Feb '85, on Yazoo (USA) by Shanachie Records (USA). Catalogue no: **L 1069**

**MASTER OF THE BLUES**
Tracks: / 'Lectric chair blues / How long how long blues / D.B. blues / Maltese Cat Blues / Fence breakin' yellin' blues / Cat Man Blues / Booger Rooger Blues / Black Snake Dream Blues / Where Shall I Be / Chinch Bug Blues / Deceitful Brownskin Woman / Rambler Blues.
**Album:** Released May '89, on Blue Moon (1) by Magnum Music Group. Catalogue no: **BMLP 1.050**

**REMAINING TITLES, THE**
**Album:** Released Apr '84, on Matchbox by Flyright Records. Catalogue no: **MSE 1001**

## Jefferson, Carter

**RISE OF ATLANTIS, THE**
Note: With Terumasa Hino/Victor Lewis.
**Album:** Released Sep '86, on Timeless (Import) by Timeless Records. Catalogue no: **SJP 126**

## Jefferson, Eddie

**BODY AND SOUL**
Tracks: / See if you can get to that / Body and Soul / Mercy mercy mercy / So What / There I go, There I go again / Psychedelic Sally.
**Album:** Released Mar '88, on Prestige Catalogue no: **PR 7619**
**Cass:** Released Mar '88, on Prestige Deleted Jan '90. Catalogue no: **PRC 7619**

**HIPPER THAN YOU**
Tracks: / So what / Moody's mood for love / Sister Sadie / It's only a paper moon / TD's boogie / Now's the time / Body and soul / Workshop / Sherry / Baby girl / Memphis / Honeysuckle Rose / Preacher, The / Night train / NJR (I'm gone) / I got the blues / Silly little Cynthia / Red's new dream.
**CD:** Released '89, on Zu Zazz by Zu Zazz Records. Catalogue no: **CDZ 2015**

**LIVELIEST**
**Album:** Released Apr '81, on Muse by Black & Blue Records. Catalogue no: **MR 5127**

**STILL ON THE PLANET**
**Album:** Released Apr '81, on Muse by Black & Blue Records. Catalogue no: **MR 5063**

**THERE I GO AGAIN**
Tracks: / Old shoes / Strictly instrumental / Workshop / I got the blues / Disappointed / Take the 'A' train / Night in Tunisia / Parker's mood / Billie's bounce / Soft and furry / Things are getting better / Letter from home / Body and soul / Now's the time / So what? / Filthy McNasty / Mercy, mercy, mercy / There I go, there I go again / Yardbird suite / Come along with me / Baby girl / Dexter digs in.
**Album:** Released May '84, on Prestige (USA) by Fantasy Inc (USA). Catalogue no: **OJCD 503**

**THINGS ARE GETTING BETTER**
Tracks: / Bitches brew / Things are getting better / Freedom jazz dance / Night in Tunisia / 'Trane's blues / I just got back in town / Billie's bounce / Thank you.
Note: Eddie Jefferson, vocal; Joe Newman, trumpet; Billy Mitchell, tenor sax, flute, bass clarinet; Mickey Turner, piano; Sam Jones, bass; Eddie Gladden, drums. Recorded 5 March 1974.
**Album:** Released Apr '81, on Muse by Black & Blue Records. Catalogue no: **MR 5043**

## Jefferson, Thomas

**IF I COULD BE WITH YOU (Jefferson, Thomas & His Dixieland Band)**
**Album:** Released Apr '79, on Nola Catalogue no: **NOLA LP 10**

**INTERNATIONAL NOR JB**
**Album:** Released '88, on Storyville by Storyville Records AB. Catalogue no: **SLP 254**

**NEW ORLEANS AT MIDNIGHT**
**Album:** Released '89, on GHB by Jazzology Records (USA). Catalogue no: **GHB 129**

**THOMAS JEFFERSON & HIS DIXIELAND ALL STARS (Featuring Sammy Rimington)**
**Cass:** Released May '87, on Nola Catalogue no: **TC 010**

## Jenkins, Gus

**COLD LOVE**
**Album:** Released '88, on Diving Duck (Holland) Catalogue no: **DD 4309**

## Jenkins, John

**JENKINS, JORDAN & TIMMONS (Jenkins, John & Clifford Jordan & Bobby Timmons)**
**Album:** Released Jan '87, on Original Jazz Classics (USA) by Fantasy Inc (USA). Catalogue no: **OJC 251**

## Jenkins, Leroy

**GEORGE LEWIS**
**Album:** Released Jul '78, on Black Saint (Italy) Catalogue no: **BSR 0016**

**LEGEND OF AL GLATSON, THE**
Tracks: / Al Glatson / Brax Stone / Albert Ayler / Tuesday child / What goes around comes around.
**Album:** Released Apr '79, on Black Saint (Italy) Catalogue no: **BSR 0022**

**REVOLUTIONARY ENSEMBLE**
Tracks: / Vietnam 1 / Vietnam 2.
**Album:** Released Jan '82, on Enja (Germany) by Enja Records (West Germany). Catalogue no: **ENJA 3003**

**SOLO CONCERT**
**Album:** Released May '78, on India Navigation Catalogue no: **IN 1028**

**URBAN BLUES**
Tracks: / Static in the attic / Looking for the blues / Come on home baby / Why can't I fly / O W Frederick / No banks river / Through the ages / Jehova.
**Album:** Released May '85, on Black Saint (Italy) Catalogue no: **BSR 0083**

## Jennings, Bill

**BILLY IN THE LIONS DEN (Jennings, Bill & Leo Parker Quintet)**
Tracks: / Picadilly Circus / May 1 / Billy in the lions den / Sweet and Lovely / There will never be another you / Stuffy / Just You Just Me / Down To Earth / What'll I Do / Fine and Dandy / Get Hot / Solitude.
**Album:** Released Jun '88, on Swingtime by Contact Records (Denmark). Catalogue no: **ST 1025**

## Jensen, Theis

**DANISH JAZZ: VOL 3**
**Album:** Released Jul '82, on Storyville by Storyville Records AB. Catalogue no: **SLP 412**

## Jericho Alley

**JERICHO ALLEY BLUES FLASH, VOL. 1 (Various artists)**
**Album:** Released Apr '89, on Diving Duck (Holland) Catalogue no: **DD 4312**

**JERICHO ALLEY BLUES FLASH, VOL. 2 (Various artists)**
**Album:** Released Apr '89, on Diving Duck (Holland) Catalogue no: **DD 4313**

## Jerome, Henry

**1950/52**
**Album:** Released Mar '84, on Circle (USA) by Jazzology Records (USA). Catalogue no: **CLP 51**

## Jerome, Jerry Trio

**JERRY JEROME TRIO**
**Album:** Released Jun '86, on Vantage (USA) by LRJ Records (USA). Catalogue no: **LP 503**

## Jive At Five

**JIVE AT FIVE (Various artists)**
Tracks: / Every tub: *Basie, Count & Orchestra* / Melancholy: *Dodds, Johnny* / What is this thing: *Johnson, James P.* / What is this thing: *Becket, Sidney* / Pardon me pretty baby: *Carter, Benny* / I know that you know: *Noone, Jimmie* / I've found a new baby: *Goodman Sextet, Benny* / Body and soul: *Hawkins, Coleman* / I double dare you / Passion flower: *Hodges, Johnny* / Three blind mice: *Chicago Loopers* / Love me tonight: *Hines, Earl "Fatha"* / Bugle call rag: *Chocolate Dandies* / Wolverine blues: *Baby Dodds Trio* / Slippin' around: *Red & Miffs Stompers* / Pitter panther patter: *Ellington, Duke/Jimmy Blanton* / Jive at five: *Basie, Count & Orchestra.*
**Album:** Released Feb '87, on New World (USA) by New World Records (USA). Catalogue no: **NW 274**

## Jive Bombers

**BAD BOY**
**Album:** Released Mar '85, on Savoy Jazz (USA) by Malaco Records (USA). Catalogue no: **SJL 1150**

**THOSE BLOODSHOT EYES**
Tracks: / Those bloodshot eyes / You don't feel that good.
**7" Single:** Released Aug '81, on Meantime by Meantime Records. Catalogue no: **MEAN 3**

## Johansen, Henrik

**DANISH JAZZ VOL 4**
**Album:** Released Jul '82, on Storyville by Storyville Records AB. Catalogue no: **SLP 413**

## Johansson, Ake

**ENCORE (Johansson, Ake Trio)**
**Album:** Released Oct '88, on Dragon by Dragon Records. Catalogue no: **DRLP 159**

**LIVE AT NEFERTITI**
Tracks: / Synkopen 1 Umea / Lamesha / My shining hour / Tribute to Bud, A / Komner / New / Waiting / Igrottan / Igen.
**Album:** Released Jul '83, on Dragon by Dragon Records. Catalogue no: **DRLP 42**

## Johansson, Lasse

**KING PORTER STOMP**
Tracks: / Wild man blues / Mint julep / Buddy Bolden blues / Freakish / Seattle hunch / Cannonball blues / Kansas City stomp / Dead man blues / Mr. Jelly Lord / Sidewalk blues / Midnight momma / King Porter stomp / Chicago breakdown / Dixie knows / Jelly roll blues / Milenburg joys / Big foot ham / Sweet Peter / Grandpa's spells.
**Album:** Released Nov '80, on Kicking Mule by Sonet Records. Catalogue no: **SNKF 169**

## Johnson, Bessie

**BESSIE JOHNSON, 1928-29**
**Album:** Released '88, on Herwin by Shanachie Records (USA). Catalogue no: **HERWIN 202**
**Album:** Released Dec '88, on Herwin by Shanachie Records (USA). Catalogue no: **HER 202**

## Johnson, Blind Willie

**PRAISE GOD I'M SATISFIED**
**Album:** Released Dec '88, on Yazoo (USA) by Shanachie Records (USA). Catalogue no: **L 1058**

## Johnson, Bunk

**1942 (Johnson, Bunk Jazz Band)**
Tracks: / Big chief battle axe / Dusty rag / Franklin Street blues / Thriller rag / Sobbin' blues / Sobbin blues No 2 / When I leave the world behind / Sometimes my burden is so hard to bear / Blues bells goodbye / Yaaka hula hickey dula / Weary blues.
**Album:** Released Aug '82, on Commodore Class Catalogue no: **AG6 24547**

**BUNK JOHNSON BRASS & DANCE BAND**
**Album:** Released Jul '81, on Storyville by Storyville Records AB. Catalogue no: **SLP 670 202**

**BUNK JOHNSON & HIS BAND (Johnson, Bunk & His Band)**
**Album:** Released Apr '79, on Nola Catalogue no: **NOLA LP 3**

**BUNK JOHNSON & HIS BAND 1947 (Johnson, Bunk & His Band)**
**Cass:** Released May '87, on Nola Catalogue no: **TC 003**

**BUNK JOHNSON & HIS SUPERIOR JAZZ BAND**
Tracks: / Panama / Down by the riverside / Storyville blues / Ballin' the jack / Make me a pallet on the floor / Yes Lord I'm crippled / Weary blues / Moose march / Bunk's blues / Bunk Johnson talking.
Note: Johnson, one of the earliest and most influential New Orleans trumpeters, made these, some of his first recordings, in 1942. The album includes a nine-minute interview.
**Album:** Released Dec '81, on Contemporary (Import) Catalogue no: **1012 048**

**BUNK JOHNSON & LU WATTERS (Johnson, Bunk & Lu Watters)**
Tracks: / Georgia camp meeting / Irish black bottom / Original Jelly Roll blues / Smokey mokes / Maple leaf rag / Memphis blues / Black and white rag / Muscrat ramble / Careless love / 2.19 blues / Girls go crazy, The / When I move to the sky / Ace in the hole / Ory's Creole trombone / Nobody's fault but mine / Down by the riverside.
Note: Bunk Johnson, who died in 1949, is now recognised as one of the most important of New Orleans trumpeters. His recordings were few, but he worked with such musicians as Louis Armstrong, Buddy Bolden and Sydney Bechet. Artists on this album include Bunk Johnson (trumpet), Lu Watters, Bob Scobey (cornets), Turk Murphy (trombone), Ellis Horne (clarinet), Burt Bales, Wally Rose (pianos), Dick Lammi (tuba), Pat Patton, Clancy Hayes, Russ Bennett (banjos), Squire Girsbank (bass), Bill Dart (drums). Recorded in San Francisco, 1941-44.
**Album:** Released May '83, on Contemporary (Import) Catalogue no: **1012 024**

**BUNK JOHNSONS'S NEW ORLEANS JAZZBAND (Johnson, Bunk & His New Orleans Jazz Band)**
**Album:** Released '88, on Cadillac by Cadillac Music. Catalogue no: **SGC 12112**

**DOWN ON THE DELTA (Johnson, Bunk Band, Kid Rena's Band, Celestin's Original)**
Tracks: / Tiger rag / Weary blues / Make me a pallet on the floor / Careless love / When the saints go marching in / Oh, didn't he ramble / Li'l Liza Jane / High society / Panama / Gettysburg march / Milenburg joys / Lowdown blues / Clarinet marmalade / Get it right.
Note: Full Group name: Bunk Johnson's Jazz Band/Kid Rena's Delta Jazz Band/Celestin's Original Tuxedo Orchestra.
**Album:** Released Jul '87, on Esquire by Titan Int. Prod.. Catalogue no: **ESQ 331**

**NEW ORLEANS LEGENDS (Johnson, Bunk & Kid Ory)**
**Album:** Released Dec '79, on Joker (USA) by Lifetime Records (USA). Catalogue no: **SM 3095**

**NEW ORLEANS VOL.5 (1945-46)**
Tracks: / I wish I could shimmy like my Sister Kate / Just a closer walk with thee / Snag it / One sweet letter from you / When the saints go marching in / High society / Darktown strutters' ball / I can't escape from you / Franklin Street blues.
**Album:** Released '87, on RCA (France) by BMG Records (France). Catalogue no: **PM 42048**

**NEW YORK 1945 (Johnson, Bunk & His New Orleans Jazz Band)**
Note: With G.Lewis
**Album:** Released Sep '86, on Folklyric (USA) by Arhoolie Records (USA). Catalogue no: **FL 9047**

**PURIST ISSUES, THE**
**Album:** Released Apr '79, on Nola Catalogue no: **NOLA LP 6**

**SPICY ADVICE (Johnson, Bunk & His Band)**
**Album:** Released Jun '86, on GHB by Jazzology Records (USA). Catalogue no: **GHB 101**

**Frank Johnson - Dixieland Jazz (Swaggie)**

## Johnson, Frank

**DIXIELAND JAZZ (With his friends) 1954-56 (See panel above)**

Tracks: / Wocka the fish / Sweet patootie / Tea garden rag / When the saints go marching in / Steal away blues / Let's get together / Got no place to go / Silver bell's march / St.Louis blues / Dill pickles rag / Down South / Tiger rag / Tickle rag, The / Over in the glory land.

Note: Apart from the fact that my mother was frightened by an itinerant cornet player during the halcyon days of the Great Depression I don't know that there were any real musical influences in my life. Therefore, playing jazz, the trumpet, et al. was something of a fortuitous accident, rather like the tracks on this record. The Johnson band was never really formed as such, but was more like Topsy - it just growed. The reality was a collection of free wheeling individuals who got together, had a ball and were paid for it. If this sounds like an ideal situation, believe me it was. And this was reflected in our music which was truly good time jazz. We got so many kicks that like the libidinous lady of illfame, even if we didn't get paid, we still did it for fun. All of which brings me to the tracks of this record. The venue for the 'A' sides was a quaint edifice, long since vanished, designed by the builder of the Ruins of Anthens and nearly as old. Set in rustic charm by the banks of the Yarra and the terminus for river boat trips it was well known to a generation of jazzmen. Originally called the Hawthorn Tea Gardens, we re-christened it the Heathorn Spew Gardens and it was to there that we hid ourselves hence, on a sunny Sunday afternoon, to cut a few sides for our own pleasure. It's important to note this, because, if the whole session was a little rough around the edges, under the circumstances, it could have been a helluva bit rougher. We revived that fine old Australian custom a nine gallon keg of beer for the occasion. Subtract two non imbibers from a seven piece band, add an engineer plus a couple of jazz dags and you've made certain that every one gets a drink. Also on the technical side, the piano was a bit of a mess, but towards the end of the day so were we, so I don't suppose it matters that much. Doubling on goblet and equipment was Bill Armstrong, now the owner of a huge recording studio and a large overdraft, who had allowed himself to be talked into being an accessory before and after the fact. And thus armed we launched ourselves into the fray. I'd like to be able to say that everything went off without a hitch, but alas it wasn't to be so. What with the day trippers wandering in from the river boats to see what the commotion was about, Wocka telling outrageous stories and jokes, Bill Armstrong doing the occasional jig, stories and jokes, the odd sip to steady the nerves etc., it became less like a recording date and more like Old Home Week. So it was quite a surprise when the records turned out more of a success than we expected.

Made interesting by the inclusion of the occasional original number plus some little recorded tunes, some of the material was released and one tune *Sweet patootie*, an old Sidney Bechet opus, actually started to escalate in the direction of that all time low in music 'The Hit Parade'. However, the day was saved when some eagle eyed executive (may he rot in North Balwyn for ever) sensed the dirty, filthy, sexual innuendos lurking in the wretched depraved lyrics and *Sweet patootie* a la Johnson was banned henceforth from the unsullied pure steam wireless. The 'A' sides plus the 'B' track *Tea garden rag*, a virtuoso composition of that little known genius of the seven ounce glass, Frank Gow, made up the material of the first side of this album and are very typical of the Johnson band after Geoff Kitchen and Geoff Bland left it and before the tragedy of Warwick Dyer's untimely death. The 'C' tracks on side two were dreamed up as a high water mark in popular jazz music and once again Bill Armstrong was present at the scene of the crime. After releasing a phenomenally popular Frisco Joe record (actually Graeme Bell plus Smacka Fitzgibbon recorded in a country pub at Darnum) the idea of a roaring jazz band including the likes of Graeme Bell, Frank Traynor, Geoff Kitchen, etc. plus Smacka seemed a wow of an idea. I was thrown in like a sack of spuds to make up the all star content, and, working on the principle that if one trumpet was good, two must be twice as good, Bob Barnard also got a berth. After a lengthy rehearsal of what seemed like 10 minutes to familiarise the group with the various tunes, and also to give it a chance to actually play together, a feat never before attempted, we cut the sides.

The session was a great success, the covers were groovy, the disc jockeys promised to play it, and we have three minutes silence to observe the whole deal of taking off like a cast iron balloon. I still don't know what went wrong, but as the weeks rolled into months and the sales soared to eleven (mostly to close relatives of the band) it became obvious that the year of the Great Australian Jazz Revival was definitely not 1956. Although Bill did his brass and I'm not even sure whether I got paid, latter day listening makes me realise it was more than worth while. I will now pen a few words about the Graham Coyle solos - A few words - actually I wasn't present when they were cut and this is my first exposure (to the piano sides you fool) but they are marvellous early Coyle uncoiling, and in Ragtime furthermore. Worth a lolly from the end jar in any mans language - whatever that means. Nothing else to say except: Buy a dozen copies and keep Nevill Sherburn in a manner to which he's never been accustomed. (Frank Johnson, May 1973)

**Album:** Released Jan '83, on Swaggie (Australia) Catalogue no: **S 1325**

**FRANK JOHNSON AND HIS FABULOUS 1951-55**

**Album:** Released Jan '83, on Swaggie (Australia) Catalogue no: **S 1319**

**FRANK JOHNSON AND HIS FABULOUS DIXIELANDERS 1949-50**
**Album:** Released '88, on Swaggie (Australia) Catalogue no: **S 1414**

**FRANK JOHNSON AND HIS FABULOUS DIXIELANDERS**
Note: Vocals: Warwick Dyer / Frank Johnson
**Cass:** Released Jun '87, on Swaggie (Australia) Catalogue no: **S 1412**

## Johnson, Herman

**LOUISIANA COUNTRY BLUES (Johnson, Herman E.)**
**Album:** Released May '81, on Arhoolie (USA) by Arhoolie Records (USA). Catalogue no: **ARHOOLIE 1060**

## Johnson, J. J.

**FOR RECORDINGS SEE UNDER JOHNSON , JAY JAY**

## Johnson, James P.

**AIN'TCHA GOT MUSIC**
Note: Previously unissued solos and band sides featuring Tommy Dorsey, Harry Carney, B.Hackett etc.
**Album:** Released Nov '86, on Pumpkin Catalogue no: **PUMPKIN 117**

**FATHER OF THE STRIDE PIANO**
**Album:** Released Jul '88, on Sounds Catalogue no: **SOUNDS 1204**

**FEELIN' BLUE**
Tracks: / All that I had is gone / Snowy morning blues / Chicago blues / Mournful tho'ts / Riffs / Feelin' blue / Put your mind right on it / Fare thee honey blues / You don't understand / You've got to be modernistic / Crying for the Carolines / What is this thing called love / Jingles / Go Harlem / Just a crazy song.
**Cass:** Released Oct '86, on Halcyon (USA) by Submarine Records. Catalogue no: **CHDL 107**
**Album:** Released Feb '87, on Halcyon (USA) by Submarine Records. Catalogue no: **HDL 107**

**FROM RAGTIME TO JAZZ (Piano solos)**
**Album:** Released May '85, on CBS (import) by CBS Records. Catalogue no: **85387**
**Album:** Released Jan '87, on CBS by CBS Records. Catalogue no: **CBS 85387**

**HARLEM STRIDE PIANO SOLOS**
**Album:** Released Jan '83, on Swaggie (Australia) Catalogue no: **S1211**

**IT TAKES LOVE**
**Album:** Released Apr '81, on Kings Of Jazz Catalogue no: **KLJ 20008**

**JAMES P. JOHNSON 1928-31**
Note: With Louisiana Sugar Babes 1928/Jimmy Johnson & Orch 1928-31/Jimmy Jonson & Band 1929/Jimmy Johnson & Clarence Williams 1930.
**Album:** Released Jun '87, on Swaggie (Australia) Catalogue no: **S 849**

**JAMES P. JOHNSON & PERRY (Johnson, James P & Perry Bradford)**
**Album:** Released Apr '79, on Arcadia Catalogue no: **ARCADIA 2009**

**SYMPHONIC JAZZ OF JAMES P JOHNSON**
**CD:** Released Jan '89, on Music Masters by Music Masters Records. Catalogue no: **MMD 60066 A**

**WATCH ME GO**
**Album:** Released '89, on I.A.J.R.C (USA) by Vintage Jazz Music Society(VJM). Catalogue no: **IAJRC 52**

## Johnson, Jay Jay

**CONCEPTS IN BLUE**
Tracks: / Blue nun / Nermus / Village blues / Azure / Coming home / Concepts in blue / Mohawk.
**Album:** Released '82, on Pablo Jazz (USA) by Pablo Records (USA). Catalogue no: **2312 123**
**Cass:** Released '82, on Pablo Jazz (USA) by Pablo Records (USA). Catalogue no: **K 12 123**

**EMINENT, THE, VOL. 1**
Tracks: / Capri (alt. take) / Capri / Lover man / Turnpike / Turnpike (alt. take) / Sketch 1 / Get happy / Get happy (alt. take) / Jay / Old devil moon / It's you or no one / Too marvellous for words / Coffee pot / It could happen to you.
**CD:** Released Jul '89, on Blue Note by EMI Records. Catalogue no: **CDP 781 505 2**
**CD:** Released Jul '89, on Blue Note by EMI Records. Catalogue no: **BNZ 148**
**Album:** Released Jul '89, on Blue Note by EMI Records. Catalogue no: **B1 81505**
**Album:** Released Sep '84, on Blue Note by EMI Records. Catalogue no: **BLP 1505**

**EMINENT, THE, VOL.2**
Tracks: / Daylie double / Pennies from Heaven / You're mine you / Portrait of Jennie / Turnpike / It could happen to you / Groovin' / Time after time / Viscocity / Capri.
**Album:** Released Sep '84, on Blue Note by EMI Records. Catalogue no: **BLP 1506**
**Album:** Released Jul '89, on Blue Note by EMI Records. Deleted Jan '90. Catalogue no: **B1 81506**
**CD:** Released Jul '89, on Blue Note by EMI Records. Deleted Jan '90. Catalogue no: **CDP 781 506 2**
**CD:** Released Jul '89, on Blue Note by EMI Records. Deleted Jan '90. Catalogue no: **BNZ 149**
**Album:** Released Sep '84, on Pablo Jazz (USA) by Pablo Records (USA). Catalogue no: **2310 911**
**CD:** Released Sep '84, on Verve Catalogue no: **831 272-2**

**GREAT KAI AND J.J. (Johnson, J.J. & Kai Winding)**
Tracks: / This could be the start of something big / Georgia on my mind / Blue Monk / Judy / Alone together / Side by side / I concentrate on you / Picnic, Theme from / Trixie / Going, going, gone / Just for a thrill.
**Cass:** Released Oct '85, on MCA by MCA Records. Deleted Dec '89. Catalogue no: **ASC 1**
**Cass:** Released Jun '82, on Jasmine by Hasmick Promotions. Catalogue no: **JAS C7**
**Album:** Released Jun '82, on Jasmine by Hasmick Promotions. Deleted Feb '88. Catalogue no: **JAS 7**
**Album:** Released Oct '85, on MCA by MCA Records. Deleted Dec '89. Catalogue no: **AS 1**
**CD:** Released Jun '82, on MCA by MCA Records. Deleted Dec '89. Catalogue no: **2546 342**

**J.J.**
Tracks: / Swing spring / Bemsha swing / El camino real / Stolen moments / Train samba / So what? / Stratusphunk / My little suede shoes / Winter's waif.
**Album:** Released '83, on RCA (France) by BMG Records (France). Catalogue no: **PL 43530**

**LIVE: J.J.JOHNSON**
Tracks: / Decision / Overdrive / Jay's original / It's all right with me / Undecided / Overdrive / Angel eyes / Bag's groove.
Note: First two tracks: J.J. Johnson (trombone), Nat Adderley (trumpet), Tommy Flanagan (piano), Wilbur Little (bass), Albert Heath (drums). Final six tracks: J.J. Johnson (trombone), Bobby Jasper (tenor sax), Tommy Flanagan (piano), Wilbur Little (bass), Elvin Jones (drums).
**Album:** Released Apr '81, on Queendisc (Italy) Catalogue no: **QU 046**

**MAD BE-BOP**
**Album:** Released Mar '85, on Savoy Jazz (USA) by Malaco Records (USA). Catalogue no: **SJL 2232**

**OVERDRIVE (Johnson, Jay Jay, Quintet)**
Tracks: / Naptown USA / It might as well be spring / Tumbling tumbleweeds / Angel eyes / I should care / Solar / Overdrive / Undeçided / Never let me go / Chasin' the bird cube steak.
**Album:** Released 7 Nov '87, on Affinity by Charly Records. Catalogue no: **AFF 177**

**SAY WHEN (Johnson, J.J. & His Big Hands)**
Tracks: / My little suede shoes / Stratusphunk / So what / Bemsha swing / Stolen moments / Swing spring / El camino real / Say when / Ballade / Space walk / Little Dave / In walked Horace / Euro (take 1) / Euro (take 2) / Short cake.
**CD:** Released Jun '88, on Bluebird (2) by BMG Records (UK). Catalogue no: **ND 86277**

**THINGS ARE GETTING BETTER ALL THE TIME (Johnson, J.J. & Al Grey)**
Tracks: / Soft winds / Let me see / Softly as in a morning sunrise / It's only a paper moon / Boy meets horn / Things ain't what they used to be / Things are getting better all the time / Doncha hear me callin' to ya.
Note: Kenny Baron (piano), Ray Brown

( bass), Mickey Roker(drums). Recorded 1983.
**CD:** Released '88, on Pablo Jazz (USA) by Pablo Records (USA). Catalogue no: **311 260**
**Cass:** Released May '84, on Pablo Jazz (USA) by Pablo Records (USA). Catalogue no: **K 12 141**
**Album:** Released May '84, on Pablo Jazz (USA) by Pablo Records (USA). Catalogue no: **231 3141**
**Album:** Released May '84, on Pablo Jazz (USA) by Pablo Records (USA). Catalogue no: **2312 141**

**TOTAL J.J. JOHNSON, THE**
**Album:** Released Feb '85, on RCA (France) by BMG Records (France). Catalogue no: **NL 89367**

**TROMBONE BY THREE (Johnson, J J, Kai Winding, Bennie Green)**
Tracks: / Fox hunt / Elysee / Opus V / Hilo / Night on bop mountain, A / Broadway / Sid's bounce / Waterworks / Green junction / Flowing river / Whirl-a-licks / Pennies from Heaven.
**Album:** Released Jun '86, on Original Jazz Classics (USA) by Fantasy Inc (USA). Catalogue no: **OJC 091**

**TROMBONE MASTER, THE**
**Album:** Released May '89, on CBS (import) by CBS Records. Catalogue no: **463 340 1**
**CD:** Released May '89, on CBS (import) by CBS Records. Catalogue no: **463 340 2**
**Cass:** Released May '89, on CBS (import) by CBS Records. Catalogue no: **463 340 4**

**WE'LL BE TOGETHER AGAIN (Johnson, J J & Joe Pass)**
Tracks: / Wabe / We'll be together again / Naked as a jaybird / Blue bossa / Limehouse blues / How long has this been going on / Buds blues / Nature boy / Solar / When lights are low.
Note: Full details under Joe Pass.
**Album:** Released May '85, on Pablo Jazz (USA) by Pablo Records (USA). Catalogue no: **2310911**

**YOKOHAMA CONCERT, THE (Johnson, J.J. & Nat Adderley)**
Tracks: / Horace / Cyclops / Why not? / It happens / Work song / Walkin' / Jivin' / Lament / Humming / Melodee.
**2 LP Set:** Released '82, on Pablo Jazz (USA) by Pablo Records (USA). Catalogue no: **262 0109**
**Cass set:** Released '82, on Pablo Jazz (USA) by Pablo Records (USA). Catalogue no: **K 20 109**

## Johnson, Jimmy

**HEAP SEE**
**Album:** Released Jan '85, on Blue Phoenix by Black & Blue Records. Catalogue no: **33720**

**I DIDN'T GIVE A DAMN IF WHITES BOUGHT IT, VOL. 2**
Tracks: / Pepper's hangout / Looking for my baby / Pretty baby / High heel sneakers / When my first wife quit me.
**Album:** Released Oct '84, on Red Lightnin' by Red Lightning Records. Deleted Jun '89. Catalogue no: **RL 051**

**JOHNSON'S WHACKS**
**Album:** Released Dec '88, on Delmark (USA) by Delmark Records (USA). Catalogue no: **DL 644**

**NORTH/SOUTH (Johnson, Jimmy Band)**
**Album:** Released Dec '88, on Delmark (USA) by Delmark Records (USA). Catalogue no: **DL 647**

## Johnson, Lonnie

**1927-32 HISTORICAL RECORDINGS VOL. 2**
**Album:** Released Jun '88, on Matchbox by Flyright Records. Catalogue no: **MSE 1013**

**BLUES BY**
Tracks: / Don't ever love / No love for sale / There's no love / I don't hurt anymore / She devil / One-sided love affair / Big leg woman / There must be a way / She's drunk again / Blues 'round my door / You don't move me / You will need me.
**Album:** Released May '84, on Original Blues Classics (USA) by Fantasy Inc (USA). Catalogue no: **OBC 502**

**BLUES FOR EVERYBODY (Johnson, Lonnie & Blind Joe Davis)**
**Album:** Released '88, on Oldie Blues Catalogue no: **OL 2819**

**BLUES OF LONNIE JOHNSON, THE 1937-8**
**Album:** Released Jan '83, on Swaggie (Australia) Catalogue no: **S 1225**

**IT FEELS SO GOOD**
**Album:** Released Apr '81, on Queendisc (Italy) Catalogue no: **QU 043**

**LONNIE JOHNSON (Johnson, Lonnie / Victoria Spivey)**
**Album:** Released Jan '88, on OBC Catalogue no: **OBC 518**

**LONNIE JOHNSON: 1926-40**
**Album:** Released '89, on Blues Document Catalogue no: **BD 2064**

**LONNIE JOHNSON: 1926-42**
**Album:** Released Feb '88, on Document Catalogue no: **DLP 546**

**LONNIE JOHNSON VOL 1 (1926-28)**
Tracks: / When I was lovin' / Changed my mind blues / Sun to sun blues / Bed of sand / Lonesome jail blues / No good blues / Newport blues / Love story blues / Woman changed my life / Lonnie's got the blues / You drove a good man away / Ball & chain blues / To do this you got to know / Superstitious blues / Cotton patch blues / Black bird blues / Unkind mama / Backwater blues / Crowing rooster blues.
Note: There has been no blues singer to compare with Lonnie Johnson for diversity of experience and breadth of respect. As a recording artists he was one of the most popular of blues men, making a vast number of discs. His importance as a blues artist is without question, not only as a singer and guitarist, but also as an influence on his contempories.
**Album:** Released Feb '86, on Matchbox by Flyright Records. Catalogue no: **MSE 1006**

**ORIGINATOR OF MODERN GUITAR BLUES**
**Album:** Released Aug '87, on Blues Boy (Sweden) Catalogue no: **BB 300**

**TOMORROW NIGHT**
**Album:** Released Jul '88, on Bellaphon Catalogue no: **BID 8019**
**Cass set:** Released Mar '88, on Gusto (USA) by Gusto Records (USA). Catalogue no: **GD 5039**

## Johnson, Merline

**YAS YAS GIRL, THE**
**Album:** Released '89, on Document Catalogue no: **DLP 562**
**Album:** Released Jul '88, on Best Of Blues (USA) by Blue Island Records (USA). Catalogue no: **BOB 8**

## Johnson, Ossie

**BIT OF THE BLUES**
**Album:** Released Feb '88, on Fresh Sounds (Spain) by Fresh Sounds Records (Spain). Catalogue no: **FS 116**

## Johnson, Pete

**BLOWIN' THE FAMILY JEWELS**
**Album:** Released Mar '89, on Blue Shadow Catalogue no: **4704**

**KING OF BOOGIE BOOGIE**
**Album:** Released Sep '87, on Giants of Jazz by Hasmick Promotions. Catalogue no: **LPJT 17**

**PETE JOHNSON 1938-47**
Note: Featuring Albert Ammons, Joe Turner, Jack Teagarden, Benny Goodman, Hot Lips Page.
**Album:** Released Dec '88, on Document Catalogue no: **DLP 535**

**PETE JOHNSON VOL 1 (Master of the blues & boogie woogie)**
**Album:** Released Sep '79, on Oldie Blues Catalogue no: **OL 2801**

**PETE JOHNSON VOL 2 (Master of the blues & boogie woogie)**
**Album:** Released '88, on Oldie Blues Catalogue no: **OL 2806**

**PETE JOHNSON VOL 3 (Master of blues and boogie woogie)**
**Album:** Released '88, on Oldie Blues Catalogue no: **OL 2823**

## Johnson, Robert

**COLLECTION: ROBERT JOHNSON**
Tracks: / Rambling on my mind / Crossroads blues / Phonograph blues / Terraplane blues / I believe I'll dust my broom / Me and the Devil blues / Love in vain /

Travelling riverside blues / 32-20 blues / Little queen of spades / They're red hot / Come on in my kitchen / Preaching blues / Kind hearted woman blues / Walkin' blues / When you got a good friend / Last fair deal gone down / Stones in my passway / If I had possession over Judgement Day / Stop breakin' down blues.
**Album:** Released Nov '85, on Deja Vu Catalogue no: **DVLP 2050**
**Cass:** Released Nov '85, on Deja Vu Catalogue no: **DVMC 2050**

**DELTA BLUES, VOLUME 1**
**Cass:** Released Apr '90, on Aldabra Catalogue no: **ALB 1001 MC**
**Album:** Released Sep '89, on Aldabra Catalogue no: **ALB 1001**
**CD:** Released Sep '89, on Aldabra Catalogue no: **ALB 1001CD**

**DELTA BLUES, VOLUME 2**
**Cass:** Released Apr '90, on Aldabra Catalogue no: **ALB 1002 MC**
**CD:** Released Sep '89, on Aldabra Catalogue no: **ALB 1002CD**
**Album:** Released Sep '89, on Aldabra Catalogue no: **ALB 1002**

**KING OF THE DELTA BLUES**
Tracks: / Crossroads blues / Terraplane blues / Come to my kitchen / Walkin' blues / Last fair deal gone down / 32-20 Blues / Kind hearted woman blues / If I had possession over judgement day / Preaching blues / When you got a good friend / Rambling on my mind / Stones in my passway / Travelling riverside blues / Milkcow's calf blues / Me and the devil blues / Hellhound on my trail / Kind hearted woman blues / I believe I'll dust my broom / Sweet home chicago / Rambling on my mind / Phonograph blues / They're red hot / Dead shrimp blues / Preachin' blues / I'm a steady rollin' man from four till late / Little queen of spades / Malted milk / Drunken hearted man / Stop breakin' doen blues / Honeymoon blues / Love in vain.
**Cass:** Released Jun '85, on CBS (Blue Diamond) by CBS Records. Catalogue no: **40 22190**
**Album:** Released Jun '85, on CBS (Blue Diamond) by CBS Records. Catalogue no: **CBS 22190**

**MEMPHIS DEMOS**
Tracks: / I'll be waiting / Claudette / Burning love / Wish upon a star / Jimmy Dean's back / Shaking it down / Better love / Deep love.
**Album:** Released Aug '80, on Ensign by Ensign Records. Deleted '85. Catalogue no: **ENRJ 12**

**ROOTS OF ROBERT JOHNSON**
**Album:** Released Oct '88, on Yazoo (USA) by Shanachie Records (USA). Catalogue no: **L 1073**

**TERRY**
Tracks: / Terry / Tell me about it Slim.
**7" Single:** Released Feb '79, on Ensign by Ensign Records. Deleted '82. Catalogue no: **ENY 20**

**WISH UPON A STAR**
Tracks: / Wish upon a star / Guide my energy.
**7" Single:** Released May '79, on Ensign by Ensign Records. Deleted '82. Catalogue no: **ENY 25**

## Johnson, Tommy

**COMPLETE RECORDINGS 1928-30**
**Album:** Released '88, on Wolf Catalogue no: **WSE 104**

**SLEEPY JOHN ESTES 1928-30**
**Album:** Released Feb '89, on Bluetime (Denmark) by Contact Records (Denmark). Catalogue no: **BT 2010**

## Jolly, Pete

**DUO, TRIO, QUARTET**
**Album:** Released Feb '88, on Fresh Sounds (Spain) by Fresh Sounds Records (Spain). Catalogue no: **FS 171**

**FIVE, THE**
**Album:** Released Feb '88, on Fresh Sounds (Spain) by Fresh Sounds Records (Spain). Catalogue no: **FS 5**

**JOLLY JUMPS IN**
Tracks: / Will you still be mine? / El yorke / Jolly jumps in / I've got you under my skin / I'm with you / Pete's meat / It might as well be spring / Why do I love you? / That's all / Jolly lodger / Before and after.
**Album:** Released '83, on RCA (France) by BMG Records (France). Catalogue no: **PM 43666**

## Jones, Curtis

**BLUES & TROUBLE**
**Album:** Released '88, on Oldie Blues Catalogue no: **OL 2824**

**CURTIS JONES IN LONDON**
Tracks: / Shake it baby / Syl-vous play blues / Young generation boogie / Skid Row / Honeydripper / Lonesome bedroom blues / You got good business / Alley bound blues / Curtis Jones boogie / Dusty my broom / Red river blues / Good woman blues / Please send me someone to love / Roll me over.
**Album:** Released Aug '85, on See For Miles by See For Miles Records. Catalogue no: **SEE 53**

**TROUBLE BLUES**
**Album:** Released Jan '88, on OBC Catalogue no: **OBC 515**

## Jones, Dill

**UP JUMPED YOUR LOVE**
**Album:** Released Apr '89, on Hep Jazz by Hep Records. Catalogue no: **HEP 2025**

## Jones, Elvin

**BROTHER JOHN**
**Album:** Released Jul '84, on Palo Alto Catalogue no: **PA 8039**

**DIFFERENT DRUMMER (VIDEO)**
**VHS:** Released '88, on Kay Jazz (video) by Kay Jazz. Catalogue no: **KJ 043**

**EARTH JONES**
**Album:** Released Jul '86, on Palo Alto Catalogue no: **PA 8016**
**Cass:** Released Jul '86, on Palo Alto Catalogue no: **PAC 8016**

**ELVIN JONES**
**Album:** Released Jan '87, on Original Jazz Classics (USA) by Fantasy Inc (USA). Catalogue no: **OJC 259**

**HEAVY SOUNDS (Jones, Elvin & Richard Davis)**
Tracks: / Raunchy Rita / Shiny stockings / M.E. / Summertime / Elvin's guitar blues / Here's that rainy day.
**CD:** Released Jan '90, on MCA (Impulse Jazz) Catalogue no: **MCAD 33114**

**JOHN COLTRANE MEMORIAL CONCERT**
**Album:** Released Jan '80, on PM Catalogue no: **PM 004**

**LIVE AT THE VILLAGE VANGUARD**
**Album:** Released Jan '82, on Enja (Germany) by Enja Records (West Germany). Catalogue no: **ENJA 2036**

**LIVE IN JAPAN 1978**
**CD:** Released Feb '90, on Storyville by Storyville Records AB. Catalogue no: **STCD 4153**

**MR THUNDER (Jones, Elvin Quartet)**
**Album:** Released Jul '78, on EWR Catalogue no: **WR 7501**

**ON THE MOUNTAIN**
**Album:** Released Jan '80, on PM Catalogue no: **PM 005**

**POLY CURRENTS**
Tracks: / Agenda / Agappe love / Mr. Jones / Yes / When.
Note: In the late sixties and early seventies, Elvin Jones led a series of remarkable pianoless small groups with a mini saxaphone section. This album features tenormen Joe Farrell and George Coleman and baritone saxophonist Pepper Adams. Guest artist Candido, the legendary conga drum master brings another dimension to Elvin's brilliant polyrhythmic drumming. Among the albums highlights are 'Mr.Jones' and Fred Tompkin's 'Yes'.
**Album:** Released Jul '89, on Blue Note by EMI Records. Catalogue no: **784 331 1**
**Album:** Released Jul '89, on Blue Note by EMI Records. Catalogue no: **BST 84331**
**CD:** Released Feb '89, on Blue Note by EMI Records. Catalogue no: **CDP 784 331 2**

**PUTTIN' IT ALL TOGETHER**
Tracks: / Reza / Sweet little Maia / Kei Ko's birthday march / Village Green / Jay-ree / For heavens sake / Ginger bread boy.
**CD:** Released Apr '88, on Blue Note by EMI Records. Catalogue no: **CDP 784 282 2**
**CD:** Released Apr '88, on Blue Note by EMI Records. Catalogue no: **BNZ 106**

**QUINTET REUNITED (Jones, Elvin & McCoy Tyner)**
**CD:** Released Oct '87, on Black Hawk (USA) by Blackhawk Records (USA). Catalogue no: **CDBKH 521**
**Album:** Released Oct '87, on Black Hawk (USA) by Blackhawk Records (USA). Catalogue no: **BKH 521**

**SKYSCRAPERS: VOL 1**
**Album:** Released Oct '79, on Honeydew Catalogue no: **HD 6602**

**SKYSCRAPERS: VOL 2**
**Album:** Released Oct '79, on Honeydew Catalogue no: **HD 6603**

**SKYSCRAPERS: VOL 3**
**Album:** Released Oct '79, on Honeydew Catalogue no: **HD 6605**

**SUMMIT MEETING**
**Album:** Released Jun '78, on Vanguard by Start Records Ltd.. Catalogue no: **VSD 79390**

**TOGETHER (Jones, Elvin with Oregon)**
Tracks: / Le vin / Lucifer's fall / Charango / Three step dance / Driven omens / Teeth / Brujo.
**Album:** Released Jan '77, on Vanguard by Start Records Ltd.. Catalogue no: **VSD 79377**

## Jones, Floyd

**FLOYD JONES & EDDIE TAYLOR (Jones, Floyd & Eddie Taylor)**
**Album:** Released May '86, on Testament Catalogue no: **T 2214**

## Jones, Hank

**ARIGATO**
**Album:** Released Apr '81, on Progressive (USA) by Jazzology Records (USA). Catalogue no: **PRO 7004**

**BOP REDUX**
**Album:** Released Apr '81, on Muse by Black & Blue Records. Catalogue no: **MR 5123**

**GROOVIN' HIGH**
**Album:** Released Apr '81, on Muse by Black & Blue Records. Catalogue no: **MR 5169**

**I'M ALL SMILES (Jones, Hank & Tommy Flanagan)**
Tracks: / Relaxin' at Camarillo / In a sentimental mood / Some day my prince will come / Afternoon in Paris / Au privave / I'm all smiles / Rockin' in rhythm / Con Alma.
Note: Virtuoso pianists playing duos at the 1983 Black Forest Jazz Festival.
**CD:** Released Aug '84, on MPS Jazz (Germany) Deleted Aug '87. Catalogue no: **817 863-2**
**Album:** Released Sep '84, on MPS Jazz (Germany) Catalogue no: **817 863-1**

**JAZZ TRIO, THE**
**Album:** Released Oct '85, on Savoy (France) Catalogue no: **WL 70526**

**JUST FOR FUN**
**Album:** Released '79, on Galaxy (1) by President Records. Deleted '84. Catalogue no: **GXY 5105**

**LAZY AFTERNOON**
**Cass:** Released '89, on Concord by Concord Jazz Records (USA). Catalogue no: **CJ 391C**
**CD:** Released '89, on Concord by Concord Jazz Records (USA). Catalogue no: **CCD 4391**

**MOREOVER (Jones, Hank/Eddie Gomez/Al Foster)**
**Album:** Released Oct '82, on Phonogram (France) Catalogue no: **6315 097**

**RELAXIN' AT CAMARILLO**
Note: Artists include: Hank Jones (Piano); Bobby Jaspen (Flute); Paul Chambers (Bass); Kenny Clarke (Drums).This was Jones' last album as a leader for Savoy. Containing the great "Moonlight Becomes You" and Charlie Parker's "Relaxin' At Camarillo" it's as fresh-sounding today as when it first rolled off the Savoy presses thirty years ago. Recorded New Jersey 1956
**Album:** Released Dec '85, on Savoy (France) Deleted May '89. Catalogue no: **WL 70504**

**SPIRIT OF 176, THE (Jones, Hank & George Shearing)**
**Album:** Released 12 Apr '89, on Concord by Concord Jazz Records (USA). Catalogue no: **CJ 371**
**Cass:** Released 12 Apr '89, on Concord by Concord Jazz Records (USA). Catalogue no: **CJ 371C**
**CD:** Released 12 Apr '89, on Concord by Concord Jazz Records (USA). Catalogue no: **CCD 4371**

**TIPTOE TAPDANCE**
**Album:** Released '79, on Galaxy (1) by President Records. Deleted '84. Catalogue no: **GXY 5108**

## Jones, Isham

**ISHAM JONES & HIS ORCHESTRA 1920-24**
**Album:** Released Apr '79, on Fountain by Retrieval Records. Catalogue no: **FG 404**

## Jones, Ivan "Boogaloo"

**BLACK WHIP**
Tracks: / Black whip / My love / Freak off / Daniel / Ballad of Mad dogs and Englishmen, The / Crank me up.
Note: Ivan Jones: guitar. Dave Hubbard: soprano & tenor saxophones. Sonny Phillips: electric piano. Ron Carter: bass & electric bass. Jimmy Johnson: percussion. Bud Kelly: drums and percussion. Recorded 25 July 1973 in New York.
**Album:** Released Feb '84, on Musicwise Catalogue no: **CA 671**

## Jones, Jo

**ESSENTIAL JO JONES, THE**
Tracks: / Shoeshine boy / Lover man / Georgia may / Caravan / Lincoln heights / Embraceable you / Satin doll / Little Susie / Spider Kelly's blues / Cubano chant / Splittin' / Sweet Lorraine / Bicycle for two / Ol' man river / Sometimes I'm happy.
**2 LP Set:** Released May '83, on Vogue Jazz (France) by Vogue Records. Catalogue no: **VJD 542**

**INTRODUCING THE GUITAR OF JOE BLUES**
Tracks: / Mindbender, The / There is a mountain / Games / Sticks and stones / Blues for bruce / Beat goes on, The / Call me / Right now.
**Album:** Released Nov '88, on Prestige Catalogue no: **PR 7557**

**JO JONES QUARTET (Jones, Jo Quartet & Ray Bryant)**
**Album:** Released Jun '88, on Fresh Sounds (Spain) by Fresh Sounds Records (Spain). Catalogue no: **FS 323**

**MAIN MAN, THE**
Tracks: / Goin' to Chicago / I want to be happy / Ad lib / Dark eyes / Metrical portions / Ol' man river.
**Cass:** Released '82, on Pablo Jazz (USA) by Pablo Records (USA). Catalogue no: **K10 799**
**Album:** Released '82, on Pablo Jazz (USA) by Pablo Records (USA). Catalogue no: **23 10799**

**OUR MAN PAPA JO**
Tracks: / Take the 'A' train / Stompin' at the Savoy / My last affair / Broadway / As time goes by / Wrap your troubles in dreams / Solitude / It don't mean a thing.
Note: Jimmy Oliver, sax; Hank Jones, piano; Major Holley, bass; Jo Jones, drums.
**Album:** Released Mar '82, on Denon Deleted '88. Catalogue no: **YX 7527**
**CD:** Released '88, on Denon Catalogue no: **C38-7047**

## Jones, Johnny

**JOHNNY JONES & BILLY BOY ARNOLD (Jones, Johnny & Billy Boy Arnold)**
Note: Rare, never-before-released tapes by the legendary master of Chicago blues piano. Johnny played on dozens of sessions with Elmore James, Magic Sam and others but this is his only LP. Recorded in casual club setting in 1963 and capturing his two-fisted piano and witty vocals, with Billy Boy Arnold guesting on harp. "One of the 10 best LPs of 1980." (New York Times).
**Album:** Released Feb '80, on Alligator (Sonet) by Alligator Records (USA). Catalogue no: **SNTF 821**

**PURPLE HAZE (Jones, Johnny & The King Casuals)**
Tracks: / Purple haze / Horsing around.
**7" Single:** Released Mar '87, on Cream Catalogue no: **CRM 5004**

## Jones, Jonah

**BUTTERFLIES IN THE RAIN (Jones, Jonah & His Swing Band)**

Note: Mono. 1944.
**Album:** Released Jan '87, on Circle (USA) by Jazzology Records (USA). Catalogue no: **CLP 83**

**HARLEM JUMP AND SWING (Jones, Jonah Sextet & Pete Brown Sextet)**
Tracks: / There will never be another you / I can't believe that you're in love with me / Used blues / Moonlight in Vermont / World is waiting for the sunrise, The / Tea for two / Delta blues / Beatle street blues / Down by the riverside / European blues / You're the cream in my coffee / Wrap your troubles in dreams.
**Album:** Released '83, on Affinity by Charly Records. Deleted May '88. Catalogue no: **AFF 96**

**IN PARIS 1954**
**Cass:** Released '88, on DRG (USA) by DRG Records (USA). Catalogue no: **SWC 8408**
**Album:** Released '88, on DRG (USA) by DRG Records (USA). Catalogue no: **SW 8408**

**JONAH JONES QUARTET/GLEN GRAY & THE CASALOMA ORCHESTRA (Jones, Jonah & Glen Gray)**
Tracks: / Baubles, bangles and beads / Echoes of Harlem / Two o'clock jump / I can't get started / Boy meets horn / Hot lips / After you've gone / West end blues / Ciribiribin / Tenderly / Sugar blues / Apollo jumps.
Note: On this album, two capitol stars of the 50's and 60's are teamed together to present a string of exciting Big Band arrangements, Jonah Jones, a trumpeter, made many good selling albums with his quartet,while arranger/conductor Glen Gray was leader of the house Capitol Orchestra during the 50's and 60's. Together they swing through tunes by favourite composers.
**Cass:** Released Feb '87, on Capitol by EMI Records. Deleted Jun '88. Catalogue no: **TCEMS 1185**
**Album:** Released Feb '87, on Capitol by EMI Records. Deleted Jun '89. Catalogue no: **EMS 1185**

**JONAH'S WAIL**
**Album:** Released Oct '88, on Vogue by Vogue Records. Catalogue no: **500075**

**JUMPING WITH A SHUFFLE**
Tracks: / Dream / You're driving me crazy / Lazy river / More than you know / Nine-twenty special / Entratter's blues / Misty / Great lie, The / On the sunny side of the street / One for my baby / Lonesome road / My Monday date.
**Album:** Released Mar '84, on Pathe Marconi (France) Catalogue no: **PM 154 771 1**

**SWING STREET SHOWCASE (Jones, Jonah & Hot Lips Page)**
**Album:** Released May '87, on Commodore Class Catalogue no: **AG6.25524**

## Jones, Oliver

**COOKIN' AT SWEET BASIL**
Tracks: / Hymn To a Friend / You Are Too Beautiful / Blue mountain / Young and Foolish / Take the 'A' Train / Pe gros bois blues / Fly Me To The Moon / Someone to watch over me.
**Album:** Released Aug '88, on Bold Reprieve by Bold Reprieve Records. Catalogue no: **BRMLP 020**
**CD:** Released Aug '88, on Bold Reprieve by Bold Reprieve Records. Catalogue no: **BRMCD 020**

**JAZZ & RIBS LIVE AT BIDDLE'S (Jones, Oliver Trio & Charles Biddle & Bernard Primeau)**
**Album:** Released Nov '87, on Justin Time (Canada) Catalogue no: **JUST 1**

**MANY MOODS OF..., THE**
**Album:** Released Nov '87, on Justin Time (Canada) Catalogue no: **JUST 3**

**SPEAK LOW SWING HARD**
**Album:** Released Aug '88, on Bold Reprieve by Bold Reprieve Records. Catalogue no: **BRMLP 019**
**CD:** Released Aug '88, on Bold Reprieve by Bold Reprieve Records. Catalogue no: **BRMCD 019**

## Jones, Paul

**Biographical details:** Jones, Paul This British singer and actor was born Paul Pond, but later decided that Jones was a more marketable surname. While studying at Oxford, he grew increasingly interested in rhythm and blues; at the end of 1962 he became actively involved in the UK's fast growing R&B scene by joining a combo called the Mann Hugg Blues Brothers. The group took their name from two of the constituent members, Manfred Mann and Mike Hugg; the band soon became known simply as Manfred Mann and Jones became a star. He sang lead on all their hits until mid 1966 at which time he quit to launch a solo career.
Sticking to the commercial pop formula of his old group, Jones started promisingly with *High Time* and *I've Been A Bad Bad Boy*, two songs written or co written by Mike Leander (later of Gary Glitter songwriting/production fame) which both cracked the UK Top 5. However, Paul's chart career then disintegrated because he grew far more interested in acting. In 1967 he starred in 'Privilege' a movie directed by Peter Watkins, which also provided Paul with a No.1 on the British EP charts. He then did another film, 'The Committee' followed shortly afterwards by a two year stage stint in the play 'Conduct Unbecoming'. His seventies exploits included a horror movie, much more theatre work (including the West End), a delightful cover version of The Ramones' *Sheena Is a Punk Rocker'*, plus numerous appearances on British television and radio where his affable charm and good looks were always welcomed.
At the end of the Seventies Paul decided to have some real fun and formed The Blues Band with a group of mates. Initially intended as a hobby, the Blues Band went down so well that they stayed together until 1983. Also during the early Eighties, Jones took part in the London stage productions 'Cats', 'Guys and Dolls', 'Beggar's Opera' and 'Pump Boys and Dinettes'. (Bob Macdonald 15/11/85).

**AMERICAN GUESTS, THE (Jones, Paul Rhythm & Blues Show)**
Note: With guests Phil Guy, Lowell Fulson, Louisiana Red.
**CD:** Released Apr '88, on JSP by JSP Records. Catalogue no: **JSP CD 210**

**AQUARIUS**
Tracks: / Aquarius.
**7" Single:** Released Feb '69, on Columbia by EMI Records. Deleted '72. Catalogue no: **DB 8534**

**HIGH TIME**
Tracks: / High time.
**7" Single:** Released Oct '66, on H.M.V. by EMI Records. Deleted '69. Catalogue no: **POP 1554**
**7" Single:** Released Aug '82, on Creole (Replay) by Creole Records. Catalogue no: **CR 181**

**HITS & BLUES**
Tracks: / High time / Sonny boy williamson / When my little girl is smiling / Not before time / Bony moronie / Thinkin' ain't bad for me / I can't hold on much longer / How sweet it is / Nosher burns / Little sadie / Along came jones / You have no idea / It's getting better / Aquarius.
**Album:** Released May '80, on One-Up by EMI Records. Deleted May '85. Catalogue no: **OU 2231**

**I'VE BEEN A BAD BAD BOY**
Tracks: / I've been a bad bad boy / High time.
**7" Single:** Released Jun '80, on H.M.V. by EMI Records. Deleted '83. Catalogue no: **POP 2004**
**7" Single:** Released Jan '67, on H.M.V. by EMI Records. Deleted '70. Catalogue no: **POP 1576**

**PAUL JONES R & B SHOW VOL. 2 (Various artists)**
**CD:** Released Oct '88, on JSP by JSP Records. Catalogue no: **JSP CD 221**

**THINKIN' AIN'T FOR ME**
Tracks: / Thinkin' ain't for me.
**7" Single:** Released Aug '67, on H.M.V. by EMI Records. Deleted '70. Catalogue no: **POP 1602**

## Jones, Philly Joe

**BLUES FOR DRACULA (Jones, Philly Joe Sextet)**
**Album:** Released Apr '86, on Original Jazz Classics (USA) by Fantasy Inc (USA). Catalogue no: **OJC 230**

**DAMERONIA**
Tracks: / Philly JJ / Soultrane / Sid's delight / On a misty night / Fountainbleau / Scene is clean, The.
Note: With Johnny Coles, Walter Davis, Larry Ridley, Pritt Woodman, Frank

Wess, Cecil Payne, Charles Davis. Recorded 28 June 1982.
**Album:** Released Feb '83, on Uptown (USA) Catalogue no: **UP 27 11**

### LOOK STOP LISTEN (Jones, Philly Joe & Dameronia)
Note: Featuring Johnny Griffin
**Album:** Released Nov '86, on Uptown (USA) Catalogue no: **UP 27 15**

### MEAN WHAT YOU SAY
Tracks: / Mean what you say / You tell me / DC / Farewell / Jim's jewel / Gretchen / Ugetsu.
**Album:** Released Jan '78, on Sonet by Sonet Records. Catalogue no: **SNTF 735**

### PHILLY MIGNON
**Album:** Released '79, on Galaxy (1) by President Records. Deleted '84. Catalogue no: **GXY 5112**

### 'ROUND MIDNIGHT
Tracks: / That's Earl's brother / It don't mean a thing / Round midnight / Percy.
Note: Dizzy Reece, trumpet; Ben Jedig, tenor sax; Larry Vuckovich, piano; Isla Echinger, bass; Philly Joe Jones, drums. Recorded live at Pesaro, Italy, 1966.
**Album:** Released Apr '81, on Lotus Catalogue no: **LPPS 111 15**

### TRAILWAY EXPRESS
Tracks: / Mo Jo / Gone gone gone / Baubles, bangles and beads / Here's that rainy day / Ladybird.
Note: Tracks include those listed above.
**Album:** Released Jan '85, on Black Lion Catalogue no: **BLP 30116**

## Jones, Quincy

**Biographical details:** Jones, Quincy This American producer, composer, keyboardist, arranger and conductor is arguably the most successful 'behind the scenes' musician in the history of the US industry.
Born in Chicago in 1933, Jones was an early friend of Ray Charles and gave encouragement to the blind multi-talented singer, who was of similar age to himself. After attending the Berkley School of Music in Boston, he became a trumpeter for Lionel Hampton's Big Band and then spent several years in Paris perfecting his composing, arranging and conducting skills. He returned to the States in the early Sixties and began working on records by a host of big names including the now famous Ray Charles. Jones was also associated with Frank Sinatra, Johnny Mathis, Tony Bennett, Count Basie, Brook Benton and Billy Eckstine. In 1963 Lesley Gore's sugary schoolgirl smash *It's My Party* gave Quincy Jones his first US No.1 single as a producer.
During the late sixties and early seventies, Jones concentrated his energies on scoring music for films and television. His output at this time was feverish, including some forty cinema soundtracks and 250 episodes of TV programmes, most of the latter being for 'Ironside'. Anyone requiring further evidence of the fact that he is a workaholic might like to know that during his career, he has recorded approximately forty albums under his own name.
During the Seventies Jones used his own LPs to achieve a fusion of his two favourite forms of music, jazz and soul. He became one of the prime protagonists of the new jazz funk genre and, in 1976 successfully launched the recording career of his proteges, The Brothers Johnson.
In the late Seventies Jones forged the most important link of his showbusiness career when he teamed up with Michael Jackson for the *Off The Wall* album. Brilliantly talented though they were individually, the combination of Jones and Jackson produced a magic that captured the imagination - and the money - of millions of record buyers around the world. *Off The Wall* released in August 1979 sold over eight million copies and made the 21 year old Jackson (already a veteran star) one of the hottest singers in the history of black music. The production was typical of Jones' slickness, sounding equally great on the radio and the dance floor - his distinctive sound transcended barriers of pop, soul, disco, jazz and easy listening. But *Off The Wall* was a mere dress rehearsal for Michael Jackson's second Quincy produced LP *Thriller* which was issued in December 1982. Fifteen months after release, *Thriller* became the world's top selling recording of all time. By mid 1985 global sales of the blockbusting album were estimated at 40 million.
In between *Off The Wall* and *Thriller* Jones produced George Benson's blockbusting *Give Me The Night* album and released the most acclaimed album of his own career, *The Dude*. The latter reached the Top 20 on both sides of the Atlantic during 1981 and featured the vocal talents of his favourite singer Patti Austin. Jones' other main vocal protege was James Ingram - Quincy himself has always realised that his own vocal talents are limited and has always therefore used guest singers on his own records, including such respected names as Ashford and Simpson, Chaka Khan and Luther Vandross.
Jones, who runs his own Qwest label, was the producer of USA For Africa's 1985 charity single *We Are The World*. When it hit No.1 in the States, Billboard magazine reported that it was his seventh chart-topper and the 22 years from Lesley Gore to USA For Africa gave him the longest span of No.1 productions in US chart history. Before the galaxy of stars entered A&M Studios in Hollywood to record *We Are The World*, Jones gave them each a letter, requesting them to 'check their egos at the door' - this demand summarised the status and respect he commands in the music industry. (Bob Macdonald 17/11/85).

### AI NO CORRIDA
Tracks: / Ai no corrida.
Note: Vocals by Dune
**12" Single:** Released Mar '81, on A&M by A&M Records. Deleted Mar '84. Catalogue no: **AMSX 8109**
**7" Single:** Released Apr '81, on A&M by A&M Records. Deleted '83. Catalogue no: **AMS 8109**

### BACK ON THE BLOCK
**Album:** Released Dec '89, on WEA by WEA Records. Catalogue no: **WX 313**
**CD:** Released Dec '89, on WEA by WEA Records. Catalogue no: **926 020 2**
**Cass:** Released Dec '89, on WEA by WEA Records. Catalogue no: **926 020 4**
**Cass:** Released Dec '89, on WEA by WEA Records. Catalogue no: **WX 313C**

### BEST, THE
Tracks: / Ai no corrida / Stuff like that / I heard that / You have to do it yourself / Love, I never had it so good / Betcha' wouldn't hurt me / Superstition / Razzamatazz / Dude, The / Is it love that we're missin' / One hundred ways / I'm gonna miss you in the morning / Body heat.
Note: Inc. Razzamatazz/Ai no corrida/Dude/Stuff like that/One hundred ways/Superstition.
**Cass:** Released Feb '82, on A&M by A&M Records. Deleted Feb '89. Catalogue no: **CAM 68542**
**CD:** Released Feb '85, on A&M by A&M Records. Deleted Feb '89. Catalogue no: **CDA 68542**
**Album:** Released Feb '82, on A&M by A&M Records. Deleted Feb '89. Catalogue no: **AMLH 68542**

### BETCHA WOULDN'T HURT ME
Tracks: / Betcha wouldn't hurt me.
**7" Single:** Released Aug '81, on A&M by A&M Records. Deleted '83. Catalogue no: **AMS 8157**

### BIRTH OF A BAND
**CD:** on Emarcy Catalogue no: **822 469-2**

### BOSSA NOVA
Tracks: / Soul bossa nova / Boogie bossa nova / Desafinado / Carnival / Se e tarde me pardoa / On the street where you live / Samba de una nota so / Lalo bossa nova / Serenta / Chega de saudade.
**Album:** Released Nov '83, on Mercury (USA) by PolyGram Rec.Inc.(USA). Catalogue no: **814 225 1**

### COMPACT HITS: QUINCY JONES
Tracks: / Razzamatazz / Stuff like that / Ai no corrida / Dude, The.
**CD Single:** Released Apr '88, on A&M by A&M Records. Deleted Apr '88. Catalogue no: **AMCD 908**

### DEADEND WALKING IN SPACE
**Cass:** Released Oct '85, on Platinum (W.Germany) Catalogue no: **PMC 1**
**Album:** Released Oct '85, on Platinum (W.Germany) Catalogue no: **PLP 1**

### DUDE, THE
Tracks: / Ai no corrida / Dude, The / Just one / Betcha wouldnt hurt me / Something special / Razzamatazz / One hundred ways / Valas / Turn on the action.
Note: Re-issue
**Cass:** Released Apr '86, on A&M by

A&M Records. Catalogue no: **CKM 63721**
**Album:** Released Apr '86, on A&M by A&M Records. Catalogue no: **AMLK 63721**
**CD:** Released '83, on A&M by A&M Records. Catalogue no: **CDA 63721**

**GO WEST, MAN**
**Album:** Released '88, on Jasmine by Hasmick Promotions. Catalogue no: **JASM 1048**
**Album:** Released Feb '88, on Fresh Sounds (Spain) by Fresh Sounds Records (Spain). Catalogue no: **FS 73**

**GREAT WIDE WORLD, THE**
Tracks: / Lester leaps in / Ghana / Caravan / Everybody's blues / Cherokee (Indian love song) / Air mail special / They say it's wonderful / Chant of the weed / I never have seen snow.
Note: Recorded 11/59. All star band sessions featuring Phil Woods, Lee Morgan, Art Farmer and many others
**Album:** Released Nov '81, on Mercury (USA) by PolyGram Rec.Inc.(USA). Catalogue no: **6336 705**
**CD:** Released Apr '85, on Emarcy Catalogue no: **822 470 2**

**I'LL BE GOOD TO YOU**
Tracks: / I'll be good to you / I'll be good to you (good for your soul mix).
**12" Single:** Released Jan '90, on WEA by WEA Records. Catalogue no: **W 2697T**
**CD Single:** Released Jan '90, on WEA by WEA Records. Catalogue no: **W 2697CD**
**7" Single:** Released Jan '90, on WEA by WEA Records. Catalogue no: **W 2697**

**JUST ONCE**
Tracks: / Just once / Turn on the action.
**7" Single:** Released Oct '81, on A&M by A&M Records. Catalogue no: **AMS 8178**

**LOVE AND PEACE**
**Album:** Released May '88, on Street Life by Mainline Records. Catalogue no: **226 2025**
**Cass:** Released May '88, on Street Life by Mainline Records. Catalogue no: **216 2025**

**MELLOW MADNESS**
Tracks: / Is it love that we're missin' / Paranoid / Mellow madness / Beautiful black girl / Listen (what it is) / Just a little taste of me / My cherie amour / Tryin' to find out about you / Cry baby / Bluesette.
**Album:** Released Aug '75, on A&M by A&M Records. Deleted '88. Catalogue no: **AMLH 64526**

**MUSIC IN MY LIFE**
Tracks: / Superstition / Getaway love theme / Anderson Tapes, Theme from / Cast your fate to the wind / What's going on / Guitar blues odyssey from roots to fruits / Summer in the City / Eye of love, The / You've got it bad girl / Brown ballad / Manteca / Tribute to Afro day dreaming / First time ever I saw your face, The.
**Cass:** Released Aug '83, on Hallmark by Pickwick Records. Deleted '88. Catalogue no: **HSC 3126**
**Album:** Released Aug '83, on Hallmark by Pickwick Records. Deleted '88. Catalogue no: **SHM 3126**

**ONE HUNDRED WAYS**
Tracks: / One hundred ways / Dude.
**7" Single:** Released Feb '82, on A&M by A&M Records. Deleted Feb '87. Catalogue no: **AMS 8207**

**QUINCY JONES**
**CD:** Released May '89, on Object Enterprises Catalogue no: **ONN 46**

**QUINCY JONES ALL STARS (Jones, Quincy All Stars)**
Note: With Art Farmer & Clifford Brown
**Album:** Released Jul '86, on Esquire by Titan Int. Prod.. Catalogue no: **ESQ 322**

**QUINCY JONES AND HIS ORCHESTRA (Jones, Quincy & His Orchestra)**
Tracks: / Bridge over troubled water / You've got it bad, girl / Gula matari / Ironside / Smackwater Jack / Anderson tapes / Oh happy day / Cast your fate to the wind.
**Album:** Released Jan '80, on MFP by EMI Records. Deleted Jan '85. Catalogue no: **MFP 50441**

**QUINTESSENCE, THE**
Tracks: / Quintessence / Robot portrait / Little Karen / Straight, no chaser / For Lena and Lennie / Hard sock dance / Invitation / Twitch.
**Album:** Released Oct '85, on Impulse by Impulse Records. Deleted Dec '89. Catalogue no: **AS 11**
**CD:** Released '87, on MCA by MCA Records. Deleted Dec '89. Catalogue no: **MCAD 5728**
**Cass:** Released '85, on MCA by MCA Records. Deleted Dec '89. Catalogue no: **ASC 11**
**Album:** Released Jan '85, on Jasmine by Hasmick Promotions. Deleted Feb '88. Catalogue no: **JAS 79**

**RAZZAMATAZZ**
Tracks: / Razzamatazz / Velas.
Note: Vocals by Patti Austin
**7" Single:** Released Jun '81, on A&M by A&M Records. Deleted '83. Catalogue no: **AMS 8140**
**12" Single:** Released Jun '81, on A&M by A&M Records. Deleted '83. Catalogue no: **AMSP 8140**

**SECRET GARDEN, THE**
Tracks: / Secret garden, The.
**12" Single:** Released Mar '90, on Qwest (USA) by Qwest Records (USA). Catalogue no: **W 9992T**
**7" Single:** Released Mar '90, on Qwest (USA) by Qwest Records (USA). Catalogue no: **W 9992**
**Cassingle:** Released Mar '90, on Qwest (USA) by Qwest Records (USA). Catalogue no: **W 9992C**
**CD Single:** Released Mar '90, on Qwest (USA) by Qwest Records (USA). Catalogue no: **W 9992CD**

**SMACKWATER JACK**
Tracks: / Smackwater Jack / Cast your fate to the wind / Ironside / What's going on / Anderson tapes, Theme from / Brown ballad / Hikky burr / Guitar blues odyssey from roots to fruits.
**Album:** Released '74, on A&M by A&M Records. Deleted '88. Catalogue no: **AMLS 63037**
**Cass:** Released '74, on A&M by A&M Records. Deleted '85. Catalogue no: **CAM 63037**

**SOUNDS...AND STUFF LIKE THAT**
Tracks: / Stuff like that / Love, I never had it so good / Superwoman / I'm gonna miss you in the morning / Love me by my name / Takin' it to the streets.
**CD:** Released 24 Jul '89, on A&M by A&M Records. Catalogue no: **CDA 3249**
**Album:** Released Jun '78, on A&M by A&M Records. Deleted '88. Catalogue no: **AMLH 64685**
**Cass:** Released Jun '78, on A&M by A&M Records. Deleted '88. Catalogue no: **CAM 64685**

**STRIKE UP THE BAND**
Tracks: / Baby elephant walk / Pink panther / Dreamsville / Soldier in the rain / Blues in the night / Take five / After hours / Desafinado / Cast your fate to the wind / Jive samba / Strike up the band / Dear old Stockholm / Gentle rain, The / Bossa nova USA.
Note: Compilation of tracks recorded between 1961-1964. All star line-up including Zoot Sims, Phil Woods, Clark Terry, Jim Hall, Roland Kirk, Gary Burton to name but a few.
**CD:** Released Feb '88, on Verve (USA) by Polydor Ltd. Catalogue no: **830 774-2**

**STUFF LIKE THAT**
Tracks: / Stuff like that.
Note: Vocals by Ashford & Simpson & Chaka Khan.,
**7" Single:** Released Jul '78, on A&M by A&M Records. Deleted '82. Catalogue no: **AMS 7367**

**STUFF LIKE THAT (OLD GOLD)**
Tracks: / Stuff like that / Ai no corrida.
**12" Single:** Released Jan '87, on Old Gold by Old Gold Records. Catalogue no: **OG 4012**

**TAKE FIVE**
Tracks: / Walk on the wild side / Bossa nova USA / Take five / Gravy waltz / Exodus / Back at the chicken shack / Watermelon man / Cast your fate to the wind.
**Album:** Released Aug '83, on Happy Bird (Germany) Catalogue no: **B 90115**
**Cass:** Released Aug '83, on Happy Bird (Germany) Catalogue no: **MB 990115**

**THIS IS HOW I FEEL**
Tracks: / Walkin' / Sleepin' bee / Sermonette / Stockholm sweetenin' / Evening in Paris / Boo's blues.
**Album:** Released Feb '84, on Jasmine by Hasmick Promotions. Catalogue no: **JASM 1035**

**WALKING IN SPACE**
Tracks: / Dead end / Walking in space / Killer Joe / Love and peace / I never told you / Oh happy day.
**CD:** Released 28 Nov '88, on A&M by A&M Records. Catalogue no: **CDA 0801**
**Album:** Released '74, on A&M by A&M Records. Deleted '88. Catalogue no: **AMLH 68050**

**WE HAD A BALL**
Tracks: / Birth of a band / Golden Boy theme / Soul serenade / Midnight sun will never set, The / Boy in the tree / Happy faces / Airmail special / Back at the chicken shack / Exodus / Everybody's blues / Eesom / I had a ball.
Note: Quincy Jones with his great Big Band, including trumpeters Dizzy Gillespie, Nat Adderley and Freddie Hubbard, Milt Jackson on vibes and drummer Art Blakey. Also featured are Zoot Sims, Eddie Lockjaw Davis and Joe Newman.
**Album:** Released Sep '84, on Philips (Timeless) by PolyGram UK Ltd. Catalogue no: **TIME 07**
**Cass:** Released Sep '84, on Philips (Timeless) by PolyGram UK Ltd. Catalogue no: **TIMEC 07**

## Jones, Richard M.

**FROM N.O. TO CHICA (Jones, Richard M, Willie Hightower, Frankie Franko)**
**Album:** Released Jul '86, on Collectors Items Catalogue no: **CI 001**

## Jones, Rodney

**ARTICULATION**
**Album:** Released Apr '81, on Timeless by Timeless Records. Catalogue no: **SJP 125**

**MY FUNNY ... (Jones, Rodney & Tommy Flanagen Quartet)**
**Album:** Released '88, on Timeless by Timeless Records. Catalogue no: **SJP 162**

## Jones, Sam

**BASSIST, THE**
Tracks: / Rhythm-a-ning / Lillie / Seascape / Tragic magic / Hymn of Scorpio / Bittersuite.
Note: Keith Copeland-drums, Kenny Baron-piano.
**Album:** Released Mar '79, on Interplay (USA) by Interplay Records (USA). Catalogue no: **IP-7720**
**Album:** Released Jun '83, on Discovery (USA) by Discovery Records (USA). Catalogue no: **DS 861**

**SOMETHING IN COMMON**
Tracks: / Every man is a King / For all we know / Blue silver / Something in common / Bolivia / Seven minds.
**Album:** Released Apr '81, on Muse by Black & Blue Records. Catalogue no: **MR 5149**

**SOMETHING NEW**
**Album:** Released Jun '79, on Interplay (USA) by Interplay Records (USA). Catalogue no: **IP-7726**

**TWELVE PIECE BAND - SOMETHING NEW**
**Album:** Released Nov '88, on Sea Breeze Catalogue no: **SB 2004**

**VISITATION**
**Cass:** Released Jul '88, on Steeplechase (USA) Catalogue no: **SCM 51097**
**CD:** Released Jul '88, on Steeplechase (USA) Catalogue no: **SCCD 31097**
**Album:** Released Jul '88, on Steeplechase (USA) Catalogue no: **SCS 1097**

## Jones, Spike

**BEST OF SPIKE JONES - VOL.2**
**Album:** Released '83, on RCA (Germany) Catalogue no: **26 21113**

**CAN'T STOP MURDERING**
**Album:** Released '83, on RCA (Germany) Catalogue no: **26 28001**

**GREATEST HITS: SPIKE JONES**
**Cass:** Released Jul '86, on Timeless Treasures Catalogue no: **818**

**I WENT TO YOUR WEDDING (Jones, Spike & His City Slickers)**
Tracks: / I went to your wedding / I haven't been home for three whole nights / Too young / Sheik of Araby, The / Three little fishes / Pop corn snack / Rhapsody from Hunger(y) / Clink clink another drink / Old MacDonald had a farm / I'm getting sentimental over you / Our hour / People are funnier than anybody.
**Album:** Released Nov '80, on RCA by BMG Records (UK). Deleted Nov '85. Catalogue no: **INTS 5052**
**Cass:** Released Nov '84, on RCA International by BMG Records (UK). Catalogue no: **NK 89310**
**Album:** Released '84, on RCA International by BMG Records (UK). Catalogue no: **NL 89310**

**KING OF CORN, THE**
Tracks: / People will say we're in love / G.I. haircut / It never rains in Sunny California / Wang wang blues / My little girl / Sound effects man, The / Ragtime cowboy Joe / Vamp, The / He broke my heart in three places / Besa me mucho / I'm goin' back to where I came from / Trolly song, The / Red wing / There's a fly on my music / Row row row / I wanna girl just like the girl who married dear old dad / Jingle bells.
**Cass:** Released Jul '89, on Jasmine by Hasmick Promotions. Catalogue no: **JASC 2527**
**Album:** Released Jul '89, on Jasmine by Hasmick Promotions. Catalogue no: **JASM 2527**

**MURDERS THEM ALL**
Tracks: / Liebestraum / Blue Danube, The / Flight of the bumble bee / None but the lonely heart / Rhapsody from Hunger(y) / William Tell / Carmen murdered / Dance of the hours / Glow worm / I kiss your hand madame / Love in bloom / Hotcha cornia / Black bottom / Hawiian war chant / I went to your wedding / I'm in the mood for love / That old black magic.
**Cass:** Released Jul '86, on RCA by BMG Records (UK). Deleted Nov '88. Catalogue no: **NK 89044**
**2 LP Set:** Released Jul '86, on RCA by BMG Records (UK). Deleted Nov '88. Catalogue no: **NL 89044**

**ON THE AIR (1943 and 1944) (Jones, Spike & His City Slickers)**
**Album:** Released May '84, on Sandy Hook (USA) Catalogue no: **SH 2073**

**RADIO RECORDINGS (Jones, Spike & His City Slickers)**
**Cass:** Released Jan '89, on Silva Screen by Silva Screen Records. Catalogue no: **CSH 2073**
**Album:** Released Jan '89, on Silva Screen by Silva Screen Records. Catalogue no: **SH 2073**

**RIOT SQUAD (Jones, Spike & City Slickers)**
**CD:** Released Mar '90, on Harlequin by Interstate Music. Catalogue no: **HQCD01**

**SPIKE JONES AND HIS CITY SLICKERS (Jones, Spike & His City Slickers)**
**Album:** Released Jun '88, on Jass Catalogue no: **JASS 2**
**Album:** Released '88, on Lotus Catalogue no: **LOP 14,103**

**SPIKE JONES MURDERS AGAIN**
**Album:** Released '83, on RCA (Germany) Catalogue no: **26 28019**

**SPIKE JONES VOLUME 1 (Standard transcription discs) (Jones, Steve)**
**Album:** Released Mar '86, on Harlequin by Interstate Music. Catalogue no: **HQ 2041**

**SPIKE JONES VOLUME 2**
Note: Part 2 of the 16" Standard transcription discs
**Album:** Released Nov '86, on Harlequin by Interstate Music. Catalogue no: **HQ 2042**

**SPIKE JONES VOLUME 3 (Who killed Chloe)**
Tracks: / Blacksmith song / Moo woo woo / Don't give the chair to Buster / Big bad Bill / That's what makes the world go round / Hey Mabel / And the great big saw came nearer / Now laugh / Chloe / Trailer Annie / Mary Lou / Barstool cowboy / Row, row, row / Toot toot tootsie / Siam / No no Nora.
**Album:** Released Apr '88, on Harlequin by Interstate Music. Catalogue no: **HQ 2054**

**THANK YOU MUSIC LOVERS**
Tracks: / Cocktails for two / William Tell / Chloe / My old flame / Glow worm / None but the lonely heart / Laura / Man on the flying trapeze, The / You always hurt the one you love / Der Fuehrer's face / Dance of the hours / Hawaiian war chant.
**Cass:** Released Oct '83, on Deja Vu Catalogue no: **NK 89057**
**Album:** Released Oct '83, on Deja Vu Catalogue no: **NL 89057**
**Album:** Released '79, on RCA Victor by BMG Records (UK). Deleted '84. Catalogue no: **LSA 3084**

**UNCOLLECTED, THE 1946 (Jones, Spike & his Other Orchestra)**
Tracks: / Laura / When Yuba plays the rumba on the tuba / I'll never be the same / Minka / I've got the world on a string / Spike rocks the Troc / Hardly ever amber / I only have eyes for you / Pico pick-up / Young man with a French horn / E-bob-o-lee-bob / Spike speaks (theme).
**Album:** Released Apr '86, on Hindsight (UK) by Michele International Records. Catalogue no: **HUK 185**

## Jones, Thad

**ECLIPSE**
**Album:** Released Nov '86, on Storyville by Storyville Records AB. Catalogue no: **SLP 4089**

**GREETINGS AND SALUTATIONS**
**Album:** Released '88, on Four Leaf Clover Catalogue no: **FLC 5001**

**LIVE: THAD JONES (Jones, Thad Eclipse)**
**Album:** Released Jun '81, on Metronome (Denmark) Catalogue no: **MLP 15669**

**MAGNIFICENT THAD JONES, THE**
Tracks: / April in Paris / Billie - doo / If I love again / If someone had told me / Thedia / I've got a crush on you / Something to remember you by.
**CD:** Released Sep '87, on Blue Note by EMI Records. Catalogue no: **CDP 746 814 2**
**CD:** Released Sep '87, on Blue Note by EMI Records. Catalogue no: **BNZ 53**

**THAD JONES AND AURA RULLY**
**Album:** Released '88, on Four Leaf Clover Catalogue no: **FLC 5020**

**THAD JONES ECLIPSE (Jones, Thad, Eclipse)**
**Album:** Released Jun '81, on Metronome (Denmark) Catalogue no: **MLP 15652**

**THAD JONES AND MEL LEWIS (Jones, Thad & Mel Lewis)**
Tracks: / Brasserie / Father / Sing / Ballade / For life / Little pixie.
**2 LP Set:** Released '79, on Blue Note by EMI Records. Deleted '84. Catalogue no: **BND 4004**
**Album:** Released Jul '82, on Jazz Reactivation Catalogue no: **JR 122**

**THAD JONES AND THE DANISH RADIO BIG BAND (Jones, Thad & The Danish Radio Big Band)**
**CD:** Released Feb '90, on Storyville by Storyville Records AB. Catalogue no: **STCD 4172**

## Joplin, Scott

**ELITE SYNCOPATION**
Tracks: / Elite syncopations / Country club / Paragon rag / Eugenia / Cleopha / Real slow rag, A / Scott Joplin's new rag / Leola / Lilly queen / Chrysanthemum / Heliotrope bouquet / Reflection rag.
**Album:** Released Apr '87, on Meteor by Magnum Music Group. Catalogue no: **MTLP 1008**
**CD:** Released Jan '88, on Biograph (USA) by Biograph Records (USA). Catalogue no: **BCD 102**

**ENTERTAINER, THE**
Tracks: / Elite syncopations / Chrysanthemum, The / Scott Joplin's new rag / Eugenia / Paragon rag / Euphonic sounds / Pineapple rag / Something doing / Original rags / Entertainer, The / Maple leaf rag / Sun flower slow drag / Stoptime rag / Reflection rag / Cleopha / Lily Queen / Heliotrope bouquet / Country club / Real slow rag, A / Leola.
**Album:** Released May '88, on Classic Jazz Masters Catalogue no: **22022**
**CD:** Released Feb '88, on Entertainers Catalogue no: **ENTCD 220**
**CD:** Released '88, on Giants of Jazz by Hasmick Promotions. Catalogue no: **GOJCD 0220**
**CD:** Released Feb '88, on Biograph (USA) by Biograph Records (USA). Catalogue no: **BCD 101**
**Cass:** Released May '88, on Classic Jazz Masters Catalogue no: **42022**

**ENTERTAINER, THE (METEOR)**
Tracks: / Entertainer, The / Easy winners / Pineapple rag / Solace / Gladiolus rag / Ragtime dance / Sugar cane / Crush collision march, The / Bethena / Combination march / A breeze from Alabama.
**Album:** Released '88, on Meteor by Magnum Music Group. Catalogue no: **MTLP 1006**

**HIS GREATEST HITS WITH RICHARD ZIMMERMAN**
**CD:** Released '87, on Bescol Catalogue no: **CD 46**

**JOPLIN BOUQUET, A (Ann Charters)**
**Album:** Released '74, on Sonet by Sonet Records. Catalogue no: **SNTF 631**

**JOPLIN RAGS**
**Album:** Released '88, on Joker (USA) by Lifetime Records (USA). Catalogue no: **SM 3909**
**Cass:** Released '88, on Joker (USA) by Lifetime Records (USA). Catalogue no: **MC 3909**

**KING OF RAGTIME**
**Album:** Released Sep '85, on Saar Giants Of Jazz (Italy) Catalogue no: **LPJT 28**
**Cass:** Released Sep '85, on Saar Giants Of Jazz (Italy) Catalogue no: **MCJT 28**

**RAGTIME**
**CD:** Released Oct '89, on Jazz Anthology by Musidisc Records (France). Catalogue no: **550112**

**RAGTIME KING (Piano roll solos, 1899 - 1914)**
Tracks: / Maple leaf rag / Sunflower slow drag / Entertainer, The / Something doing / Weeping willow rag / Fig leaf rag / Pineapple rag / Euphonic sounds / Stoptime rag / Scott Joplin's new rag / Magnetic rag.
**Album:** Released Apr '81, on Joker (USA) by Lifetime Records (USA). Catalogue no: **SM 3097**

**SCOTT JOPLIN COLLECTION (20 golden greats)**
Tracks: / Entertainer, The / Maple leaf rag / Favourite, The / Pineapple rag / Fig leaf rag / Cascades / Peacherine rag / Pleasant moments / Strenuous life, The / Weeping willow rag / Rose leaf rag / Combination march / Ragtime dance / Felicity rag / Country club rag / Elite syncopations / Swipesy / Magnetic rag / Nonpareil.
**Cass:** Released May '86, on Deja Vu Catalogue no: **DVMC 2060**
**CD:** Released Jun '88, on Deja Vu Catalogue no: **DVCD 2060**
**Album:** Released May '86, on Deja Vu Catalogue no: **DVLP 2060**

**SCOTT JOPLIN STORY, THE**
Tracks: / Entertainer, The / Pineapple rag / Ragtime dance / Sugar cane / Combination march / Felicity rag / Scott Joplin's new rag / Peacherine rag / Rose leaf rag / Silver rag, The / Stoptime rag / Sycamore, The / Swipesy / Original rags / Sunflower slow drag / Maple leaf rag / Cascades / Weeping willow rag / Magnetic rag / Paragon rag / Nonpareil / Search light.
**Cass:** Released May '89, on Deja Vu Catalogue no: **DVREMC 10**
**CD:** Released May '89, on Deja Vu Catalogue no: **DVRECD 10**

**SCOTT JOPLIN'S RAG**
**Album:** Released '88, on Joker (USA) by Lifetime Records (USA). Catalogue no: **SM 3909**

## Jordan, Clifford

**ADVENTURER**
**Album:** Released Apr '81, on Muse by Black & Blue Records. Catalogue no: **MR 5163**

**BLOWING IN FROM CHICAGO (Jordan, Clifford/John Gilmore)**
**Album:** Released Sep '84, on Blue Note by EMI Records. Catalogue no: **BLP 1579**

**CLIFFORD JORDAN (Featuring Junior Cook) (Jordan, Clifford Quartet)**
**Album:** Released '88, on Criss Cross Catalogue no: **CRISS 1011**

**NIGHT AT BOOMERS, A (Jordan, Clifford / C. Walton)**
**Album:** Released Jun '77, on Muse by Black & Blue Records. Catalogue no: **MR 5010**

**NIGHT OF THE MARK VII**
**Album:** Released Apr '81, on Muse by Black & Blue Records. Catalogue no: **MR 5076**

**ROYAL BALLADS (Jordan, Clifford Quartet)**
**Album:** Released Jul '87, on Criss Cross Catalogue no: **CRISS 1025**

## Jordan, Duke

**BLUE DUKE**
**Album:** Released Jun '84, on RCA (France) by BMG Records (France).

Catalogue no: **NL 70245**

**CONNECTIONS / LES LIAISONS DANGEREUSES**
**2 LP Set:** Released Sep '75, on Vogue by Vogue Records. Catalogue no: **VJD 513**

**DUKE JORDAN**
**Album:** Released Sep '79, on Jazz Legacy by Vogue Records. Catalogue no: **JL 98**

**DUKE'S ARTISTRY (Jordan, Duke Quartet)**
**CD:** Released Jul '88, on Steeplechase (USA) Catalogue no: **SCCD 31033**
**Album:** Released Jul '88, on Steeplechase (USA) Catalogue no: **SCS 1103**

**FLIGHT TO JORDAN**
Tracks: / Flight to Jordan / Starbrite / Squawkin' / Deacon Joe / Split quick / Si-Joya / Diamond stud / I should care.
**CD:** Released Aug '87, on Blue Note by EMI Records. Deleted Jun '89. Catalogue no: **CDP 746 824 2**
**CD:** Released Aug '87, on Blue Note by EMI Records. Deleted Jun '89. Catalogue no: **BNZ 54**
**Album:** Released Dec '84, on Blue Note by EMI Records. Catalogue no: **BST 84046**

**GREAT SESSIONS, THE (Jordan, Duke Trio)**
**Album:** Released Sep '81, on Steeplechase (USA) Catalogue no: **SCS 1150**

**JORDU**
**Album:** Released Nov '88, on Vogue by Vogue Records. Catalogue no: **500098**

**LES LIASONS DANGEREUSES (Jordan, Duke/Rouse, Charlie)**
Tracks: / No problem 1-3 / Jazz vendor / Subway Inn / Feeling of love 1 and 2.
**Album:** Released Jan '82, on Jazz Reactivation Catalogue no: **JR 106**

**LIVE IN JAPAN**
**Album:** Released Jul '88, on Steeplechase (USA) Catalogue no: **SCS 1063/4**

**MIDNIGHT MOONLIGHT**
**Album:** Released May '81, on Steeplechase (USA) Catalogue no: **SCS 1143**

**MURRAY HILL CAPER, THE**
Tracks: / Worthless / Lay out blues / Flight to Jordan / Lady Dingbat / Night and day / 32nd Street love / Cold Bordeaux blues / Paula / Glad I met Pat.
Note: Trio and quartet featuring Cecil Payne.
**Album:** Released '83, on Spotlite by Spotlite Records. Catalogue no: **SPJ DJ5**

**TIME ON MY HANDS (Jordan, Duke Trio)**
**CD:** Released Jul '88, on Steeplechase (USA) Catalogue no: **SCCD 31232**
**Album:** Released Jul '88, on Steeplechase (USA) Catalogue no: **SCS 1232**

## Jordan, Louis

**20 GOLDEN GREATS: LOUIS JORDAN LIVE**
Tracks: / Mean and evil blues / Infantry blues / How high the moon / Is you is or is you ain't my baby / Broke but happy / Drippy drippers, The / Married woman blues / Buzz me / On the sunny side of the street / Five guys named Moe / I like 'em fat like that / Daddy o / Let the good times roll / Bahama Joe / Safe, sane and single / Choo choo ch' boogie / That's why we can't agree / Texas and Pacific.
**Cass:** Released Mar '87, on Magic (1) by Submarine Records. Catalogue no: **CAWM 3**

**1944/5 (Jordan, Louis & His Tympany Five)**
**Album:** Released Jun '84, on Circle (USA) by Jazzology Records (USA). Catalogue no: **CLP 53**

**BEST OF LOUIS JORDAN**
Tracks: / Choo choo ch' boogie / Five guys named Moe / Is you is or is you ain't my baby / Buzz me / G.I. blues / Saturday night fish fry / Early in the morning / What's the use of getting sober / Ain't nobody here but us chickens / Let the good times roll / Reet petite and gone / Blue light boogie / Beware brother beware / School days / Beans and cornbread / Caldonia.
**Album:** Released Dec '81, on MCA by MCA Records. Catalogue no: **MCL 1631**
**Cass:** Released Dec '81, on MCA by MCA Records. Catalogue no: **MCLC 1631**

**CHOO CHOO CH' BOOGIE (Jordan, Louis & Chris Barber)**
Tracks: / Fifty cents / Man ain't a man, A / No chance blues / I'm going to move to the outskirts of town / Jazz lips / Don't worry / 'Bout the mule / Choo choo ch' boogie / I'm gonna shimmy like my sister Kate / Is you is or is you ain't my baby / Black and tan fantasy / Back home again in Indiana.
**Cass:** Released Apr '82, on MFP by EMI Records. Deleted '87. Catalogue no: **TCMFP 50557**
**Album:** Released May '76, on Black Lion Catalogue no: **BLP 30175**
**7" Single:** Released Jul '82, on Revival Catalogue no: **REV 6019**
**Album:** Released Apr '82, on MFP by EMI Records. Deleted '87. Catalogue no: **MFP 50557**

**COLE SLAW**
Tracks: / Pettin' and pokin' / I know what I've got / Don't burn the candle at both ends / Coleslaw / Push ka pee shee pie / Baby's gonna go bye bye / Heed my warning / Hungry man / You will always have a friend / Weak minded blues / Is my pop in there? / Time marches on / Oil well Texas / Azure te / Junco partner / Jordan for President.
**Album:** Released Aug '87, on Jukebox Lil (Sweden) Catalogue no: **JB 605**

**COLLATES**
**Cass:** Released '84, on Swing House by Submarine Records. Catalogue no: **CSWH 9**
**Album:** Released '84, on Swing House by Submarine Records. Catalogue no: **SWH 9**

**G.I. JIVE**
**Album:** Released Aug '87, on Jukebox Lil (Sweden) Catalogue no: **JB 602**

**GO BLOW YOUR HORN**
**Album:** Released '83, on EMI (France) by EMI Records. Catalogue no: **2C 068 64793**
**Album:** Released '88, on Pathe Marconi (France) Catalogue no: **PM 1546680**

**GOLDEN GREATS: LOUIS JORDAN**
Tracks: / Caldonia / Choo choo ch' boogie / Is you is or is you ain't my baby / Ain't nobody here but us chickens / Beware, brother, beware / What's the use of getting sober / Let the good times roll / Reet' Petite, and gone / Blue light boogie / School days / Beans and cornbread / Five guys named Moe / Buzz me / G.I. Jive / Saturday night fish fry / Early in the morning.
**Album:** Released Jul '85, Catalogue no: **MCM 5005**
**CD:** Released Dec '88, on MCA by MCA Records. Catalogue no: **DMCL 1734**
**Cass:** Released Jul '85, Catalogue no: **MCMC 5005**

**GOOD TIMES**
**Cass:** Released '84, on Swing House by Submarine Records. Catalogue no: **CSWH 14**
**Album:** Released '84, on Swing House by Submarine Records. Catalogue no: **SWH 14**

**GREAT RHYTHM AND BLUES, VOL 1**
Tracks: / Choo choo ch' boogie / Caldonia / Let the good times roll / I got the walkin' blues / Saturday night fish fry / Ain't nobody here but us chickens / Beans and cornbread / Outskirts of town / Helping hand / I'm a good thing.
**Album:** Released Jul '82, on Bulldog Records by President Records. Catalogue no: **BDL 1000**

**GREATEST HITS: LOUIS JORDAN & TYMPANY FIVE(Jordan, Louis & His Tympany Five)**
**CD:** Released '88, on Official by Official Records. Catalogue no: **OFF 80000**

**HOODOO MAN**
**Album:** Released Aug '86, on Swingtime by Contact Records (Denmark). Catalogue no: **ST 1011**

**I BELIEVE IN MUSIC**
**Album:** Released Dec '84, on Black & Blue (1) by Black & Blue Records. Catalogue no: **33559**

**JIVIN' 1956-58 VOLUME 1**
Tracks: / Big Bess / Ain't nobody here but us chickens / Choo choo ch' boogie / Knock me a kiss / Let the good times roll / Cladonia / Is you is or is you ain't my baby / Beware brother beware / Don't let the sun catch you crying / I'm gona move to the outskirts of town / Salt pork West Virginia / Ruin Joe / Early in the morning / Cat scratchin / Morning light / Fire / Rock doc / Ella Mae / I want to know / I've found my peace of mind.

**Album:** Released Mar '86, on Bear Family by Bear Family Records (Germany). Catalogue no: **BFX 15201**

**JIVIN' 1956-58 VOLUME 2**
Tracks: / Jamf, The / Saturday night fish fry / I never had a chance / Got my mojo working / Sunday / Sweet Lorraine / Slop, The / I hadn't anyone till you / Nearness of you, The / Because of you (previously unissued: original Mercury recording) / That's what true love can do / I don't want to set the world on fire / Day away from you, A / I cried for you / Man ain't a man, A / I've found my peace of mind / Sweet hunk of junk / I love you so / Wish I could make some money / Route 66.
Note: *=Tracks previously unisued :Original Mercury recordings
**Album:** Released Mar '86, on Bear Family by Bear Family Records (Germany). Catalogue no: **BFX 15207**

**JIVIN' WITH JORDAN (Jordan, Louis & His Tympany Five)**
Tracks: / At the swing cats ball / Doug the jitterbug / Honeysuckle rose / But I'll be back / You're my meat / June tenth jamboree / What's the use of getting sober / Five guys named Moe / Is you is or is you ain't my baby / Buzz me / Salt pork West Virginia / Reconversion blues / How long must I wait for you / That's chick's too young to fry / No sale / All for the love of Lil / Texas and Pacific / Reet, petite and gone / Sure had a wonderful time / Open the door, Richard / Barnyard boogie / Early in the morning / Daddy o / Onions / Psycho loco / Lemonade / Chartreuse / Fat Sam from Birmingham.
Note: Licensed from MCA Records Ltd. This cassette: P 1985 Charly Records Ltd C 1986 Charley Records Ltd Produced by Milt Gabler.Compiled by Joop Visser
**Cass:** Released Sep '87, on Charly by Charly Records. Catalogue no: **TCCDX 7**
**2 LP Set:** Released May '85, on Charly by Charly Records. Catalogue no: **CDX 7**

**JUMP & JIVE**
Tracks: / Let the good times roll / Ain't nobody here but us chickens / Take the ribbon from her hair / Hard head wife / I believe in music / St. Louis blues boogie.
**Album:** Released Mar '84, on JSP by JSP Records. Catalogue no: **JSP 1069**

**JUMPIN' STUFF (Jordan, Louis / Hot Lips Page/Don Byas)**
**Album:** Released Apr '81, on Rarities Catalogue no: **RARITIES 46**

**KNOCK ME OUT**
**Album:** Released Aug '86, on Swingtime by Contact Records (Denmark). Catalogue no: **ST 1012**

**LIVE JIVE (Jordan, Louis & His Tympany Five)**
Tracks: / Five guys named Moe / Buzz me / Knock me a kiss / Let the good times roll / I like em' fat like that / Choo choo ch' boogie / On the sunny side of the street / All for the love of Lil / Safe, sane and single / Broke but happy / Texas and Pacific / Drippy drippers, The / Don't let the sun catch you crying / How long must I wait for you / Daddy-O / Jumping at the Jubilee / Baby thats alright for you.
**Cass:** Released 10 Jul '89, on A Touch Of Magic by Submarine Records. Catalogue no: **CATOM 4**
**CD:** Released 10 Jul '89, on A Touch Of Magic by Submarine Records. Catalogue no: **DATOM 4**

**LOOK OUR SISTER**
Tracks: / Jack you're dead / Caldonia / My new ten gallon hat / Don't burn the candle at both ends / Chicky Mo, Craney Crow / We can't agree / Boogie in the barnyard / You're much too fat / Roamin' blues / Early in the morning / Look our sister / Jumpin' at the jubliee / Please don't cry / Down down down / Five guys named Moe.
**Album:** Released Jul '83, on Krazy Kat by Interstate Music. Catalogue no: **KK 7415**

**LOOK OUT (Jordan, Louis & His Tympany Five)**
Tracks: / Keep a knockin' / Sam Jones done snagged his britches / You run your mouth I'll run my business / Pinetop's boogie woogie / Boogie woogie came to town / Saxa woogie / I like 'em fat like that / Raided the house / Ain't that just like a woman / Jack you're dead / Boogie woogie blue plate / Look out / Pettin' and pokin' / Junco partner / House party / I want you to see my baby.
**Cass:** Released '85, on Charly R&B by Charly Records. Catalogue no: **TCCRB 1048**
**Album:** Released Aug '83, on Charly R&B by Charly Records. Catalogue no: **CRB 1048**

**LOUIS JORDAN & FRIENDS**
**Album:** Released Dec '84, on MCA by MCA Records. Deleted Apr '88. Catalogue no: **MCL 1807**
**Cass:** Released Dec '84, on MCA by MCA Records. Deleted Apr '88. Catalogue no: **MCLC 1807**

**LOUIS JORDAN & TYMPANY FIVE 1945-52 (Jordan, Louis & His Tympany Five)**
**Album:** Released Aug '88, on Star Performance Catalogue no: **SP 3001**

**MORE...1944-1945 (Jordan, Louis & His Tympany Five)**
**Album:** Released Jul '87, on Circle (USA) by Jazzology Records (USA). Catalogue no: **CLP 97**

**OUT OF PRINT (Jordan, Louis & His Tympany Five)**
Tracks: / Don' worry 'bout that mule / It's so easy / Why'd you do it baby / You know it too / You didn't want me baby / Man's best friend is a bed, A / Lollypop / Hog wash / Soon a baby, The / Inflation blues / 'Fore day blues / Swinging in a coconut tree / It's a great great pleasure / Teardrops from my eyes / Garmoochie / There must be a way.
**Album:** on Official by Official Records. Catalogue no: **OFF 6025**

**PRIME CUTS**
Tracks: / Choo choo ch' boogie / Let the good times roll / Five guys named Moe / Buzz me / All for the love of Lil / Safe, sane and single.
**Cass:** Released Oct '84, on Swing House by Submarine Records. Catalogue no: **CSWH 1**
**Album:** Released Oct '84, on Swing House by Submarine Records. Catalogue no: **SWH 1**

**REET PETITE & GONE**
Tracks: / Texas and Pacific / All for the love of Lil / Wham Sam / I know what you're puttin' down / Let the good times roll / Reet petite and gone / That chick's too young to fry / Ain't that just like a woman / If it's love you want / Caldonia / Honey Chile / Tillie / Buzz me.
**Album:** Released Mar '83, on Krazy Kat by Interstate Music. Catalogue no: **KK 7414**

**ROCK 'N' ROLL CALL**
Tracks: / It's been said / Whatever Lola wants (Lola gets) / Slo' smooth and easy / Bananas / Baby let's do it up / Chicken back / Baby you're just too much / Were can I go / Rock 'n' roll call / Man ain't a man, A* / Texas stew / Hard head.
Note: *= previously unreleased track Original RCA Victor/Vik Recordings
**Album:** Released Nov '86, on Bear Family by Bear Family Records (Germany). Catalogue no: **BFX 15257**

**SOMEBODY DONE HOODOOED THE HOODOO**
**Album:** Released Dec '86, on Jukebox Lil (Sweden) Catalogue no: **JB 619**

**V-DISCS, THE**
Tracks: / Is you is or is you ain't my baby? / Knock me a kiss / Outskirts of town / I've found a new baby / Five guys named Moe / Jumpin' at the Jubilee / You can't get that no more / End of my worry, The / How high am I? / Hey now, let's live / Deacon James / I like 'em fat like that / Bahama Joe / Nobody but me.
**Album:** on Official by Official Records. Catalogue no: **OFF 6061**

## Jordan, Sheila

**CROSSING, THE**
**Album:** Released Aug '86, on Black Hawk (USA) by Blackhawk Records (USA). Catalogue no: **BKH 50501**

**OLD TIME FEELING (Jordan, Sheila / Harvie Swartz)**
**Album:** Released Jan '84, on Palo Alto Catalogue no: **PA 8038**

**PORTAIT OF SHEILA JORDAN**
Tracks: / Falling in love with love / If you could see me now / Am I blue? / Dat dere / When the world was young / Let's face the music and dance / Laugh clown laugh / Who can I turn to now / Baltimore oriole / I'm a fool to want you / Hum drum blues / Willow weep for me.
**CD:** Released Jan '90, on Blue Note by EMI Records. Catalogue no: **CDP 789 002 2**
**CD:** Released Jan '90, on Blue Note by EMI Records. Catalogue no: **BNZ 230**

## Jordan, Stanley

**CORNUCOPIA**
Tracks: / Impressions / Willow weep for me / Autumn leaves / Still got the blues / Fundance (CD only.) / What's going on / Always know / Asteroids / Cornucopia.
**CD:** Released Mar '90, on Blue Note by EMI Records. Catalogue no: **CDP 792 356 2**
**Album:** Released Mar '90, on Blue Note by EMI Records. Catalogue no: **B1 923 56**
**Album:** Released Mar '90, on Blue Note by EMI Records. Catalogue no: **792 356 1**
**CD:** Released Mar '90, on Blue Note by EMI Records. Catalogue no: **CDB1 92356**

**ELEANOR RIGBY**
Tracks: / Eleanor Rigby / All the children.
**7" Single:** Released Oct '85, on Blue Note by EMI Records. Catalogue no: **BLUE 3**

**FLYING HOME**
Tracks: / Street talk / Tropical storm / When Julia smiles / Can't sit down / Stairway to heaven / Music's gonna change, The / Time is now / Flying home.
**Cass:** Released Oct '88, on EMI-Manhattan by EMI Records. Catalogue no: **TCMTL 1034**
**CD:** Released Oct '88, on EMI-Manhattan by EMI Records. Catalogue no: **CDMTL 1034**
**CD:** Released Oct '88, on EMI-Manhattan by EMI Records. Catalogue no: **CDP 748 682 2**
**Album:** Released Oct '88, on EMI-Manhattan by EMI Records. Catalogue no: **MTL 1034**

**MAGIC TOUCH**
Tracks: / Eleanor Rigby / Freddie Freeloader / Round midnight / All the children / Lady in my life, The / Angel / Fundance / Return expedition / Child is born, A.
**Cass:** Released Jun '85, on Blue Note by EMI Records. Deleted Jan '90. Catalogue no: **TCBT 85101**
**CD:** Released Jul '85, on Blue Note by EMI Records. Catalogue no: **CDP 746 092 2**
**CD:** Released Jul '85, on Blue Note by EMI Records. Catalogue no: **BNZ 55**
**Album:** Released Apr '85, on Blue Note by EMI Records. Catalogue no: **BT 85101**

**STANDARDS, VOL 1**
Tracks: / Sound of silence, The / Sunny / Georgia on my mind / Send one your love / Moon River / Guitar man / One bell less to answer / Because / My favourite things / Silent night.
**CD:** Released Apr '87, on Blue Note by EMI Records. Catalogue no: **BNZ 56**
**CD:** Released Apr '87, on Blue Note by EMI Records. Catalogue no: **CDP 746 333 2**
**Album:** Released Dec '86, on Blue Note by EMI Records. Deleted Nov '88. Catalogue no: **BT 85130**

## Jormin, Anders

**EIGHT PIECES**
**Album:** Released Apr '89, on Dragon by Dragon Records. Catalogue no: **DRLP 165**

## Jubilee To Gospel...

**JUBILEE TO GOSPEL (Black Religious music 1921-53) (Various artists)**
**Album:** Released '88, on JEMF (USA) by Arhoolie Records (USA). Catalogue no: **JEMF 108**

## Jug Bands

**JUG BANDS 1924-31 (Give me another jug)**
**Album:** Released Apr '79, on Whoopee by Whoopee Records. Catalogue no: **WP 102**

## Jug & Washboard Bands

**JUG, JOOK & WASHBOARD BANDS (Various artists)**
**Album:** Released '88, on Blues Classics(USA) by Arhoolie Records (USA). Catalogue no: **BC 2**

**JUG & WASHBOARD BANDS VOL.1 (Various artists)**
**Album:** Released '88, on Earl Archives Catalogue no: **BD 2023**

**JUG & WASHBOARD BANDS VOL.2 (Various artists)**
**Album:** Released '88, on Earl Archives Catalogue no: **BD 2024**

## Juicy Harmonica

**JUICY HARMONICA (Various artists)**
**Album:** Released '88, on Sundown by Magnum Music Group. Catalogue no: **CG 709-06**

## Juke Joint Blues

**JUKE JOINT BLUES (Various artists)**
**Album:** Released '88, on Blues Classics(USA) by Arhoolie Records (USA). Catalogue no: **BC 23**

## Just Blues

**JUST BLUES (Various artists)**
**2 LP Set:** Released Oct '88, on Vogue by Vogue Records. Catalogue no: **416037**

## Just Jazz Concert

**JUST JAZZ CONCERT VOL. 1 (Civic auditorium Pasadena 1947) (Various artists)**
**CD:** Released Oct '87, on Vogue by Vogue Records. Catalogue no: **VGCD 600126**

**JUST JAZZ CONCERT VOL 2 (Various artists)**
**CD:** Released Oct '88, on Vogue by Vogue Records. Catalogue no: **VGCD 600 163**

# K

The following information was taken from the Music Master database on 14th April, 1990.

## Kaminsky, Max

**ART FORD'S JAZZ PARTY (July 1958)**
Note: With Cutty Cutshall/Bud Freeman/Herb Hall/Stuff Smith/Johnny Rae/Johnny Guarnieri/Danny Barker/Vinnie Burke/George Wettling/Big Joe Turner. Tracks include: Dippermouth blues/Joe Turner blues/Sweet Giorgie Brown/Just one of those things/Exactly like you, etc..
**Album:** Released Oct '87, on Jazz Connoisseur by Spotlite Records. Catalogue no: **AFJP 3**

## Kamuca, Richie

**JAZZ EROTICA**
**Album:** Released Feb '88, on Fresh Sounds (Spain) by Fresh Sounds Records (Spain). Catalogue no: **FS 96**
**CD:** Released Feb '88, on Fresh Sounds (Spain) by Fresh Sounds Records (Spain). Catalogue no: **FSCD 500**

**RICHIE KAMUCA QUARTET (Kamuca, Richie Quartet)**
**Album:** Released Apr '88, on VSOP Catalogue no: **VSOP 17**

## Kansas City

**KANSAS CITY 5 & 6(1938) (Kansas City 5 & 6 with Lester Young)**
Tracks: / Way down yonder in New Orleans / Countless blues / Them there eyes / I want a little girl / Paging the devil / Laughing at life / Good morning blues / I know that you know / Love me or leave me.
**Album:** Released Dec '84, on Commodore Class Catalogue no: **AG6 24057**

**PRES & FRIENDS ('44) (Kansas City 6 with Lester Young)**
**Album:** Released Jan '85, on Commodore Class Catalogue no: **AG6 24292**

## Kansas Joe

**BEST OF KANSAS JOE - VOL.1 -**
Note: Mono
**Album:** Released Jan '87, on Earl Archives Catalogue no: **BD 603**

## Kaspersen, Jan

**BIZARRE BALLET (Kaspersen, Jan Quintet)**
**Album:** Released Jan '88, on Storyville by Storyville Records AB. Catalogue no: **SLP 1023**

## Kaye, Sammy

**ONE NIGHT STAND WITH SAMMY KAYE**
**Album:** Released May '84, on Joyce (USA) Catalogue no: **JOYCE 1122**

**PLAY 22 ORIGINAL BIG BAND RECORDINGS (Kaye, Sammy Orchestra)**
**Album:** Released Jun '84, on Hindsight Catalogue no: **HSR 402**

**SAMMY KAYE AND HIS ORCHESTRA, 1944-46 (Kaye, Sammy Orchestra)**
**Album:** Released '88, on Hindsight Catalogue no: **HSR 163**
**Album:** Released '88, on Hindsight Catalogue no: **HSR 158**

**SAMMY KAYE AND ORCHESTRA, VOL. 3 1944-48 (Kaye, Sammy Orchestra)**
**Album:** Released '88, on Hindsight Catalogue no: **HSR 207**

**SAMMY KAYE & HIS ORCH. (WITH CLYDE MCCOY & HIS ORCHESTRA) (Kaye, Sammy Orchestra)**
**Album:** Released Jul '87, on Circle (USA) by Jazzology Records (USA). Catalogue no: **CLP 93**

## Keane, Brian

**SNOWFALLS**
**Album:** Released '88, on Flying Fish (USA) by Flying Fish Records (USA). Catalogue no: **FF 452**
**CD:** Released Oct '89, on Flying Fish (USA) by Flying Fish Records (USA). Catalogue no: **FFK 70452**

## Keene Quintet, Bob

**BOB KEENE QUINTET**
**Album:** Released 7 Nov '87, on Fresh Sounds (Spain) by Fresh Sounds Records (Spain). Catalogue no: **FS 263**

## Keeper, Jimmy

**TELL HIM (Keeper, Jimmy Sextet)**
**Album:** Released Feb '89, on Affinity by Charly Records. Catalogue no: **AF 183**

## Kelly, George

**FINE & DANDY (Kelly, George, Paul Sealey Trio, Harlem Jazz & Blues Band)**
**Album:** Released '88, on Barron Catalogue no: **VLP 405**

**PLAYS THE MUSIC OF DON REDMAN**
**Album:** Released Mar '87, on Stash (USA) Catalogue no: **ST 240**

## Kelly, Hambone

**DOWN HOME JAZZBAND (Kelly, Hambone Favourites)**
**Album:** Released Jun '89, on Stomp Off (USA) Catalogue no: **SOS 1171**

## Kelly, Wynton

**BLUES ON PURPOSE**
**CD:** Released '88, on Xanadu Catalogue no: **FDC 5166**

**KELLY BLUE (Kelly, Wynton Trio & Sextet)**
**CD:** Released Apr '86, on JVC/Fantasy Deleted '88. Catalogue no: **VDJ 1509**
**CD:** Released '88, on Fantasy (import) by Fantasy Inc (USA). Catalogue no: **FCD 6331142**
**CD:** Released Apr '87, on Carrere (France) Catalogue no: **98916**

**LIVE IN BALTIMORE (Kelly, Wynton & George Coleman)**
Tracks: / Unit 7 / Surrey with the fringe on top / Mister P.C. / Here's that rainy day.
**2 LP Set:** Released Apr '84, on Affinity by Charly Records. Deleted May '88. Catalogue no: **AFFD 108**

**WRINKLES (Kelly, Wynton & Friends)**
Tracks: / Wrinkles / Autumn leaves / Temperance / Make the man love me / Joe's avenue / What know / Weird lullaby / Love, I've found you / June night.
Note: Licensed from Vee Jay Records. This compilation (P) 1986 Charly Records Ltd./ (C) 1986 Charly Records Ltd.
**Album:** Released May '86, on Affinity by Charly Records. Deleted May '88. Catalogue no: **AFF 151**

**WYNTON KELLY**
Note: With Kenny Byrrell, Paul Chambers and Philly Joe Jones.
**CD:** Released '86, on JVC/Fantasy Deleted '88. Catalogue no: **VDJ 1540**
**CD:** Released Apr '87, on Carrere (France) Catalogue no: **98913**

**WYNTON KELLY IN CONCERT (Kelly, Wynton & George Coleman)**
**Album:** Released Feb '81, on Affinity by Charly Records. Deleted '88. Catalogue no: **AFF 54**

**WYNTON KELLY WITH BURRELL/CHAMBERS/JONES**
**CD:** Released Apr '87, on Carrere (France) Catalogue no: **98913**

## Kemp, Hal

**1934: HAL KEMP (Kemp, Hal Orchestra)**
**Album:** Released Aug '88, on Circle (USA) by Jazzology Records (USA). Catalogue no: **CLP 25**

**HAL KEMP, VOL. 1, 1934**
Tracks: / When summer is gone / This is romance / Boo boo booo / I guess I'll

have to change my plans / I don't care / It's only a paper moon / Doin' the uptown lowdown / Everything I have is yours / Ain't cha glad / You've got me crying again / Puddin head Jones / Boulevard of broken dreams / Nuts about mutts / Suffle off to Buffalo / Swingy little thingy, A / Too many tears / Between the devil and the deep blue sea.
Note: We are proud to offer this, a first in a series by the wonderful Hal Kemp orchestra. The LP contains 2 complete 1934 broadcasts made for the Lavena cosmetic company, the primary ingredient of it's product being oatmeal! Harlow Wilcox (later of Fibber McGee & Molly fame) is the announcer. The band could not have performed better and featured vocalist Skinnay Ennis sounds great. Dave Dexter, Jr., did the liner notes based on both his personal knowledge of the Kemp band and several tapes that the original Kemp pianist/arranger, John Scott Trotter, made in the early 50's re his days with Kemp. Not to be missed. (Hindsight Catalogue - 1989)

**Album:** Released '88, on Hindsight Catalogue no: **HSR 143**
**Album:** Released Apr '80, on London Records by London Records Ltd. Deleted '85. Catalogue no: **HMA 5069**

**ON THE AIR 1940 (Kemp, Hal Orchestra)**
Tracks: / Indian summer / Blue moonlight / Would you mind? / Friendship / Alone together / I've got no strings / Night and day / Little red fox, The / When summer is gone / I've got my eyes on you / Why not / Claire de lune / I concentrate on you / Believing / In Dutch with the Dutchess / Speak your heart / Vamp, The.
**Album:** Released Feb '88, on Aircheck (USA) by Kiner Ents.(USA). Catalogue no: **AIRCHECK 38**

## Kennedy, Nigel

**PLAYS ELLINGTON & BARTOK**
Tracks: / Sonata for solo violin (Bartok) / Mainly black.
**Album:** Released Nov '86, on H.M.V. by EMI Records. Catalogue no: **EL 2705381**
**CD:** Released Jan '87, on Angel (1) by EMI Records. Catalogue no: **CDC 747 621 2**
**Album:** Released Nov '86, on H.M.V. by EMI Records. Catalogue no: **NIGEL 1**
**Cass:** Released Nov '86, on H.M.V. by EMI Records. Catalogue no: **TCNIGEL 1**
**Cass:** Released Nov '86, on H.M.V. by EMI Records. Catalogue no: **EL 2705384**

**STRAD JAZZ (Kennedy, Nigel & Peter Pettinger)**
Tracks: / Body and soul / Autumn leaves / Swing '39 / Isn't she lovely / Lover man / Girl from Ipanema.
**Album:** Released May '84, on Chandos by Chandos Records. Deleted Jan '89. Catalogue no: **LBRD 011**
**CD:** Released Nov '84, on Chandos by Chandos Records. Catalogue no: **CHAN 8350**
**Cass:** Released May '84, on Chandos by Chandos Records. Catalogue no: **LBTD 011**

**STRAD JAZZ (VIDEO)**
**VHS:** Released '88, on Channel 5 by Channel 5 Video. Catalogue no: **CTV 1002**

## Kenton, Stan

**7.5 ON THE RICHTER SCALE (Kenton, Stan & His Orchestra)**
Tracks: / Live and let die / Body and soul / Down and dirty / Country cousin / Two thousand / Zarathustra revisited / It's not easy bein' green / Speak softly love.
**Cass:** Released '87, on Creative World(USA) by GNP Crescendo Records (USA). Catalogue no: **STC 1070**
**Album:** Released '87, on Creative World(USA) by GNP Crescendo Records (USA). Catalogue no: **ST 1070**
**Album:** Released May '85, on Jasmine by Hasmick Promotions. Catalogue no: **JAS 201**

**1941 (Kenton, Stan & His Orchestra)**
Tracks: / Artistry in rhythm / Tempo di Joe / Night life / Marvin's mumble / I haven't got the heart / El choclo / Safari / Trumpet symphonette / Little jive is good for you / Prelude to nothing / Old black Joe / Flamingo / Take it from the oven / Balboa bash.
**Album:** Released Oct '79, on London Records by London Records Ltd. Deleted '84. Catalogue no: **HMP 5049**

**1941, VOL 2 (Kenton, Stan & His Orchestra)**
Tracks: / Congo clambake / Arkansas traveller / Shuffling the chords / Take sixteen / Opus in pastels / Reed rapture / Etude for saxophones / Tribute to a flattened fifth / Underneath the stars / Quit your shovin' / Let her go / Too soon / Hold back the dawn / Low bridge / Popocatapetl / Blue flare.
**Album:** Released Oct '79, on London Records by London Records Ltd. Deleted '84. Catalogue no: **HMP 5055**

**1944: STAN KENTON**
**Album:** Released '84, on Swing House by Submarine Records. Catalogue no: **SWH 26**
**Cass:** Released '84, on Swing House by Submarine Records. Catalogue no: **CSWH 26**

**1951 (Kenton, Stan & His Orchestra)**
**Album:** Released Sep '83, on First Heard by Submarine Records. Catalogue no: **FH 1004**

**1962,VOL.6 (Kenton, Stan & His Orchestra)**
**Album:** Released Mar '84, on Hindsight

Stan Kenton

Catalogue no: **HSR 195**

**JAZZ OFF THE AIR, VOL.2**
Tracks: / Perdido / Great lie, The / Stealin' apples / WMGM jump / Cherokee.
**Album:** Released '83, on Spotlite by Spotlite Records. Catalogue no: **SPJ 145**

**1943-44 (Kenton, Stan & His Orchestra)**
Tracks: / Ol' man river / Shoo shoo baby / Eager beaver / Liza / In a little Spanish town / Paper doll / Hit that jive jack / Goon came on / Begin the beguine / None but the lonely heart / I know that you know / I lost my sugar in Salt Lake City / Russian lullaby / Hour of parting / Lady in red / I got rhythm.
**Album:** Released Oct '79, on London Records by London Records Ltd. Deleted '84. Catalogue no: **HMP 5061**

**ADVENTURES IN BLUES, 1961**
Tracks: / Reuben's blues / Dragonwyck / Blue ghost / Exit stage left / Night at the gold nugget / Formula SK-32 / Aphrodisia / Fitz / Blues story, The.
**Album:** Released '85, on Creative World(USA) by GNP Crescendo Records (USA). Catalogue no: **ST 1012**

**ADVENTURES IN JAZZ**
Tracks: / Turtle talk / Stairway to the stars / Limehouse blues / Misty / Waltz of the prophets / Body and soul.
**Album:** Released '85, on Creative World(USA) by GNP Crescendo Records (USA). Catalogue no: **ST 1010**

**ADVENTURES IN STANDARDS, 1961**
Tracks: / Some enchanted evening / Begin the beguine / It's all right with me / Make someone happy / Old devil moon / Gigi / Come rain or come shine / Almost like being in love / Just in time / If I were a bell / Bewitched, bothered and bewildered / I've grown accustomed to her face.
**Album:** Released '85, on Creative World(USA) by GNP Crescendo Records (USA). Catalogue no: **ST 1025**

**ARTISTRY IN BOSSA NOVA, 1963**
Tracks: / Artistry in rhythm / Opus in chartreuse / Interlude / Kentonova / Eager beaver / Concerto to end all concertos / Brasilia / Painted rhythm / Opus in pastels / Jump for Joe / Loco nova / Artistry in bossa nova.
**Album:** Released '85, on Creative World(USA) by GNP Crescendo Records (USA). Catalogue no: **ST 1045**

**ARTISTRY IN RHYTHM**
Tracks: / Just a sittin' and a rockin' / Soothe me / Ain't no misery in me / Willow weep for me / Come back to Sorrento / Artistry in percussion / Safranski / Artistry in Bolero / Cocktails for two / Fantasy / Opus in pastels / Santa Lucia.
**Album:** Released '85, on Creative World(USA) by GNP Crescendo Records (USA). Catalogue no: **ST 1043**

**ARTISTRY IN TANGO**
**Album:** Released Mar '79, on Gramercy 5 by Gramercy 5 Records. Catalogue no: **GM 7704**

**ARTISTRY IN VOICES & BRASS**
Tracks: / Flame / Moon love / Painted rhythm / These wonderful things / Eager beaver / Daydreams in the night / Concerto of love / It's love / Night song.
**Album:** Released '85, on Creative World(USA) by GNP Crescendo Records (USA). Catalogue no: **ST 1038**

**AT THE HOLLYWOOD PALLADIUM, LIVE**
**Album:** Released '88, on Jazz Band by Flyright Records. Catalogue no: **EB 413**

**AT THE RENDEZVOUS VOL. 1**
**CD:** Released Mar '90, on Status Catalogue no: **STATUSCD 102**

**BALLAD STYLE OF STAN KENTON**
Note: A 12 track album featuring the famed style of Stan Kenton. Scored by the foremost exponent of the style, Kenton himself, the album displays his distinctive piano style cushioned by beautifully played brass and reed sections.[EMI release sheet, May 1987]
**Album:** Released May '87, on Capitol by EMI Records. Catalogue no: **EMS 1248**
**Album:** Released '87, on Creative World(USA) by GNP Crescendo Records (USA). Catalogue no: **ST 1068**
**Cass:** Released May '87, on Capitol by EMI Records. Deleted Jun '89. Catalogue no: **TCEMS 1248**

**BEST OF BRANT INN (Kenton, Stan & His Orchestra)**
Tracks: / Piano theme into the waltz of the prophets / Intermission riff / Reuben's blues / Genghis Khan / Begin the beguine / Artistry in Bolero / Eager beaver..... (Medley includes:- Eager Beaver, Opus in Chartreuse, Dynaflow, Jump for J).
**Album:** Released '84, on First Heard by Submarine Records. Catalogue no: **FH 45**
**Cass:** Released May '87, on First Heard by Submarine Records. Catalogue no: **CFH 45**

**BIRTHDAY IN BRITAIN (Kenton, Stan & His Orchestra)**
Tracks: / Happy birthday to you / Daily dance / Street of dreams / Of space and time / For better and for Worseter / No harmful side effects / Ambivalence / Blues between & betwixt.
**Album:** Released '87, on Creative World(USA) by GNP Crescendo Records (USA). Catalogue no: **ST 1065**
**Album:** Released May '85, on Jasmine by Hasmick Promotions. Catalogue no: **JAS 200**

**BY REQUEST VOL. 3 1943-1951 (Kenton, Stan & His Orchestra)**
**Album:** Released '87, on Creative World(USA) by GNP Crescendo Records (USA). Catalogue no: **ST 1062**

**BY REQUEST VOL. 4 1950-1952 (Kenton, Stan Orchestra & The Four Freshmen)**
**Album:** Released '87, on Creative World(USA) by GNP Crescendo Records (USA). Catalogue no: **ST 1064**

**BY REQUEST VOL. 5 1953-1960 (Kenton, Stan Orchestra & The Four Freshmen)**
**Album:** Released '87, on Creative World(USA) by GNP Crescendo Records (USA). Catalogue no: **ST 1066**

**BY REQUEST VOL. 6 1958-1962 (Kenton, Stan Orchestra & The Four Freshmen)**
**Album:** Released '87, on Creative World(USA) by GNP Crescendo Records (USA). Catalogue no: **ST 1069**

**CARNEGIE (Kenton, Stan & His Orchestra)**
**Album:** Released Apr '81, on First Heard by Submarine Records. Catalogue no: **FH 1006**

**CHRISTY YEARS, THE (1945-47) (Kenton, Stan & June Christy)**
Tracks: / It's been a long, long time / Shoo fly pie and apple pan dowdy / Rika Jika Jack / It's a pity to say goodnight / Don't want that man around / Across the valley from the Alamo / Curio City / I told ya I love ya, now get out / He was a good man as good men go / How high the moon.
**Album:** Released '85, on Creative World(USA) by GNP Crescendo Records (USA). Catalogue no: **ST 1035**

**CITY OF GLASS AND THIS MODERN WORLD, THE**
**Album:** Released '85, on Creative World(USA) by GNP Crescendo Records (USA). Catalogue no: **ST 1006**

**COLLECTION: STAN KENTON (20 golden greats)**
Tracks: / Artistry in rhythm / Tempo de Joe / Love turns winter to spring / Shuffling the chords / Marvin's mumble / Flamingo / Harlem folk dance / Trumpet symphonette / Arkansas traveller / Little jive is good for you, A / Underneath the stars / Take sixteen / Safari / Blue flare / Congo clambake / Artistry in boogie / There is no greater love / Salute / Dynaflow / Be easy, be tender.
**Album:** Released Jan '86, on Deja Vu Catalogue no: **DVLP 2087**
**Cass:** Released Jan '86, on Deja Vu Catalogue no: **DVMC 2087**

**COLLECTOR'S CHOICE**
**Album:** Released '85, on Creative World(USA) by GNP Crescendo Records (USA). Catalogue no: **ST 1027**

**CONCEPT ERA '56',THE**
**Album:** Released Sep '86, on Artistry Catalogue no: **AR 103**

**CONCEPT ERA VOL.2**
**Album:** Released Sep '86, on Artistry Catalogue no: **AR 106**

**CONCERT ENCORES**
**Album:** Released '84, on First Heard by Submarine Records. Catalogue no: **FH 40**

**Cass:** Released '84, on First Heard by Submarine Records. Catalogue no: **CFH 40**

### CONCERT IN PROGRESSIVE JAZZ, A
Tracks: / Lonely woman / Come rain or come shine / Cuban carnival / Monotony lament / Theme for Alto / Impressionism / Elegy for alto / This is my theme / Fugue for rhythm section / Introduction to a latin rhythm / Thermopolae.
**Album:** Released '85, on Creative World(USA) by GNP Crescendo Records (USA). Catalogue no: **ST 1037**

### CONTEMPORARY CONCEPTS
Tracks: / What's new / I've got you under my skin / Cherokee / Stompin' at the Savoy / Limelight.
**Album:** Released '85, on Creative World(USA) by GNP Crescendo Records (USA). Catalogue no: **ST 1003**

### CUBAN FIRE, 1956
**Album:** Released '85, on Creative World(USA) by GNP Crescendo Records (USA). Catalogue no: **ST 1008**

### DEFINITIVE KENTON,THE
**2 LP Set:** Released Sep '86, on Artistry Catalogue no: **AR 2 102**

### ENCORES
Tracks: / He's funny that way / Please be kind / Painted rhythm / Peg o' my heart / Ecuador / Capitol punishment / Lover / Chorale for brass / Piano and bongo / Abstraction / Journey to Brazil / Somnambulism.
**Album:** Released '85, on Creative World(USA) by GNP Crescendo Records (USA). Catalogue no: **ST 1034**

### EUROPE '53 PART 1
Tracks: / Young blood (Theme tune) / Collaboration / Love for sale / Walking shoes / Opus in pastels / Zoot / Twenty three degrees north - eighty two degrees west / Solitaire / Intermission riff / Lover man / In a lighter vein.
**Cass:** Released Nov '85, on First Heard by Submarine Records. Catalogue no: **CFH 49**
**Album:** Released Oct '84, on First Heard by Submarine Records. Catalogue no: **FH 49**

### EUROPE '53 PART 2
Tracks: / Portrait of a Count / Round Robin / Eager beaver / Frank speaking / Taboo / Taking a chance on love / I'll remember April / Great scot / My heart belongs to only you / How high the moon / Something cool / Concerto to end all concerto's.
**Album:** Released Nov '85, on First Heard by Submarine Records. Catalogue no: **FH 50**
**Cass:** Released Nov '85, on First Heard by Submarine Records. Catalogue no: **CFH 50**

### EXCITING STAN KENTON (Kenton, Stan Orchestra & The Four Freshmen)
**Album:** Released '88, on Creative World(USA) by GNP Crescendo Records (USA). Catalogue no: **ST 1080**

### FABULOUS ALUMNI OF STAN KENTON,
Tracks: / I want a grown-up man / Easy Street / Adios / I get a kick out of you / Thrill, The / Cellology.
Note: Covering the years 1945 - 1956, the album features five fine singers - Anita O'Day, June Christie, Jerri Winters, Chris Connor, Ann Richards - plus guest musicians such as Lee Konitz, Frank Rosolino and cellist Gregory Bemko.
**Album:** Released '85, on Creative World(USA) by GNP Crescendo Records (USA). Catalogue no: **ST 1028**

### FESTIVAL OF MODERN AMERICAN JAZZ
**CD:** Released Mar '90, on Status Catalogue no: **STATUSCD 101**

### FIRE, FURY AND FUN (Kenton, Stan Orchestra & The Four Freshmen)
**Album:** Released '87, on Creative World(USA) by GNP Crescendo Records (USA). Catalogue no: **ST 1073**
**Cass:** Released '87, on Creative World(USA) by GNP Crescendo Records (USA). Catalogue no: **STC 1073**

### FOUR FRESHMEN, THE
**CD:** Released Sep '87, on Jasmine by Hasmick Promotions. Deleted Jun '88. Catalogue no: **CO-STO 1059**

### HITS IN CONCERT (Kenton, Stan Orchestra & The Four Freshmen)
**Album:** Released '87, on Creative World(USA) by GNP Crescendo Records (USA). Catalogue no: **ST 1074**
**Cass:** Released '87, on Creative World(USA) by GNP Crescendo Records (USA). Catalogue no: **STC 1074**

### HOLLYWOOD BOWL, PART 1 (Kenton, Stan & June Christy)
**Album:** Released '84, on Submarine by Submarine Records. Catalogue no: **FH 52**
**CD:** Released '84, on Submarine by Submarine Records. Catalogue no: **CFH 52**

### HOLLYWOOD PALLADIUM CONCERTS
Tracks: / Theme & I know that you know / Gotta be getting / Eager beaver / Wish you're waiting / Poor butterfly / Artistry in rhythm / Begin the beguine / Tico tico / Tabby the cat / Man I love, The / Taboo / In a little Spanish town / Sargeant's mess / And her tears flowed like wine / Russian lullaby.
**Album:** Released '81, on Queendisc (Italy) Catalogue no: **SJP 054**

### IN NEW JERSEY
**CD:** Released Mar '90, on Status Catalogue no: **STATUSCD 104**

### INNOVATIONS IN MODERN MUSIC,
Tracks: / Trajectories / Theme for Sunday / Conflict / Incident in jazz / Lonesome road / Mirage / Solitaire / Cuban episode.
**Album:** Released '85, on Creative World(USA) by GNP Crescendo Records (USA). Catalogue no: **ST 1009**

### JAZZ COMPOSITIONS OF STAN KENTON (Kenton, Stan Orchestra & The Four Freshmen)
**Album:** Released '88, on Creative World(USA) by GNP Crescendo Records (USA). Catalogue no: **ST 1078**

### JOURNEY INTO CAPRICORN
**Album:** on Creative World(USA) by GNP Crescendo Records (USA). Catalogue no: **ST 1077**
**Album:** Released Jul '88, on Jasmine by Hasmick Promotions. Catalogue no: **JAS 205**

### KENTON '76
Tracks: / Time for a change / Send in the clowns / Tiburon / My funny valentine / Decoupage / Smith named Greg, A / Samba de haps.
Note: 1976 recording for Creative World.
**Album:** Released '88, on Creative World(USA) by GNP Crescendo Records (USA). Catalogue no: **ST 1076**
**Album:** Released Jun '88, on Jasmine by Hasmick Promotions. Catalogue no: **JAS 204**
**Cass:** Released '88, on Creative World(USA) by GNP Crescendo Records (USA). Catalogue no: **STC 1076**

### KENTON AT THE TROPICANA
Tracks: / Artistry in rhythm / Bernie's tune / Tuxedo Junction / Street scene / Puck's blues / I concentrate on you / End of a love affair, The / You and I and George / Sentimental riff / Random riff.
**Album:** Released '85, on Creative World(USA) by GNP Crescendo Records (USA). Catalogue no: **ST 1032**

### KENTON CONDUCTS THE JAZZ
Tracks: / Man / Lonely boy / Singing oyster, The / Dilemma / Three thoughts / New day, A / Woman.
**Album:** Released '85, on Creative World(USA) by GNP Crescendo Records (USA). Catalogue no: **ST 1022**

### KENTON ERA, THE (Reissued collectors set)
Tracks: / Prologue (side 1) (Spoken introduction by Stan, tracing development of his music to 1955.) / Balboa bandwagon (side 2) (The original band, at the Rendezvous Ballroom, Balboa, California, 1941.) / Growing pains (side 3) (The band develops its unique sound, 1944.) / Artistry in rhythm (From the Capitol Library, 1945/6.) / Progressive jazz (side 5) (The swinging big band of 1947/8.) / Innovations (side 6) (The Kenton Band augmented by strings and horns.) / Contemporary (side 7) (Music band playing in 1952/53.) / Epilogue (side 8) (Spoken summation of the album by Stan, plus closing theme.).
Note: Originally released in 1955, and intended as a retrospective collecion of music. Includes a four-page booklet listing all personnel, etc. and locations/dates recorded.
**LP Set:** Released '85, on Creative World(USA) by GNP Crescendo Records (USA). Catalogue no: **STD 1030**

**KENTON FAVOURITES**
**Cass:** Released Dec '88, on Capitol (Specials) Catalogue no: **4XL 9094**

**KENTON IN CONCERT**
Note: Live at the Albert Hall, London, 1956.
**2 LP Set:** Released Sep '86, on Artistry Catalogue no: **AR 2 100**

**KENTON IN STEREO**
Tracks: / Painted rhythm / Artistry in boogie / Minor riff / Collaboration / Intermission riff / Peanut vendor / Unison riff / Eager beaver / Lover / Artistry jumps / Concerto to end all concertos / Interlude.
**Album:** Released '85, on Creative World(USA) by GNP Crescendo Records (USA). Catalogue no: **ST 1004**

**KENTON LIVE IN EUROPE**
Tracks: / Lush Life / Love for Sale / Turtle talk / My Old Flame / Tattooed lady, The / I'm Glad There is You / Fire and Ice / Eager Beaver / Artistry in rhythm.
**CD:** Released Jan '86, on London Records by London Records Ltd. Catalogue no: **820 288-2**

**KENTON PRESENTS, 1950**
**Album:** Released '85, on Creative World(USA) by GNP Crescendo Records (USA). Catalogue no: **ST 1023**

**KENTON SHOWCASE, 1953-4**
Tracks: / Bags / Hav-a-hava-na / Solo for Buddy / Opener, The / Fearless Finlay / Theme & variations / In lighter vein / King fish / Theme of four values, A / Study for bass, A / Blues before and after / Bacante / This be / Egdon heath / Sweets / Dusk.
**Album:** Released '85, on Creative World(USA) by GNP Crescendo Records (USA). Catalogue no: **ST 1026**

**KENTON TOUCH, 1958**
Tracks: / Lush interlude / Salute / Monotony / Elegy for alto / Theme for Sunday / Ballads for drums / Minor riff / End of the world / Opus in chartreuse / Painted rhythm / Rose for David, A.
**Album:** Released '85, on Creative World(USA) by GNP Crescendo Records (USA). Catalogue no: **ST 1033**

**KENTON'S CHRISTMAS**
Tracks: / O come all ye faithful / Christmas medley / O Tannenbaum / Holly and the ivy, The / We three kings of Orient are / Good King Wenceslas / Twelve days of Christmas, The / Once in Royal David's city / God rest ye merry gentlemen / Angels we have / Heard on high / O holy night.
**Album:** Released '85, on Creative World(USA) by GNP Crescendo Records (USA). Catalogue no: **ST 1001**

**KENTON/WAGNER, 1964**
Tracks: / Ride of the Valkyries / Siegfried's funeral march / Prelude to Act 1 of Lohengrin / Prelude to Act 3 of Lohengrin / Prelude to Tristan and Isolde / Wedding march from Lohengrin / Pilgrims / Chorus from Tann Haeuser.
**Album:** Released '85, on Creative World(USA) by GNP Crescendo Records (USA). Catalogue no: **ST 1024**

**LIGHTER SIDE, THE**
Tracks: / And her tears flowed like wine / His feet too big for de bed / Down in Chihuahua / Spider and the fly, The / Tortillas and beans / Stardust boogie / And the bull walked around / Ole / A-ting-a-ling.
**Album:** Released '85, on Creative World(USA) by GNP Crescendo Records (USA). Catalogue no: **ST 1050**

**LIVE AT BILOXY VOL. 2**
**Cass:** Released Sep '89, on A Touch Of Magic by Submarine Records. Catalogue no: **CATOM 5**
**CD:** Released Sep '89, on A Touch Of Magic by Submarine Records. Catalogue no: **DATOM 5**
**Album:** Released Sep '89, on A Touch Of Magic by Submarine Records. Catalogue no: **ATOM 5**

**LIVE AT BRIGHAM YOUNG UNIVERSITY**
Tracks: / Malaga / Rhapsody in blue / Love story / Kaleidoscope / April fool / Step beyond, A / Hank's opener / Bogota / What are you doing the rest of your life? / Macumba suite.
**Album:** Released '85, on Creative World(USA) by GNP Crescendo Records (USA). Catalogue no: **ST 1039**

**LIVE AT BUTLER UNIVERSITY (Kenton, Stan Orchestra & The Four Freshmen)**
**2 LP Set:** Released '87, on Creative World(USA) by GNP Crescendo Records (USA). Catalogue no: **STD 1058**

**LIVE AT REDLANDS UNIVERSITY**
Tracks: / Here's that rainy day / MacArthur Park / Minor booze / Didn't we? / Terry talk / Tico tico / Granada / Chia-pas / More peanut vendor / Artistry in rhythm / Bon homme Richard / Tiare / Hey Jude.
Note: Tracks include: Here's that rainy day/A little minor booz/MacArthur Park/Artistry in rhythm, etc.
**2 LP Set:** Released '85, on Creative World(USA) by GNP Crescendo Records (USA). Catalogue no: **STD 1015**
**CD:** Released Oct '87, on Creative World(USA) by GNP Crescendo Records (USA). Catalogue no: **STCD 1015**

**LIVE AT REDLANDS UNIVERSITY (JASMINE) (Kenton, Stan & His Orchestra)**
**CD:** Released Sep '87, on Jasmine by Hasmick Promotions. Deleted Jun '88. Catalogue no: **CO-STO 1015**
**Album:** Released '85, on Jasmine by Hasmick Promotions. Catalogue no: **JAS 202**

**LIVE CONCERT (Kenton, Stan & His Orchestra)**
**Album:** Released Feb '88, on Fresh Sounds (Spain) by Fresh Sounds Records (Spain). Catalogue no: **FS 294**

**LIVE IN LONDON:STAN KENTON 1972**
**CD:** Released Aug '87, on London Records by London Records Ltd. Catalogue no: **820 466-2**

**LIVE IN NEW JERSEY**
**CD:** Released Mar '90, on Status Catalogue no: **JJCD28**

**LIVE: STAN KENTON**
**Album:** Released Aug '81, on Queendisc (Italy) Catalogue no: **QU 054**

**LUSH INTERLUDE, 1958**
Tracks: / Interlude / Collaboration / Opus in pastels / Theme for my lady, A / Artistry in bolero / Concerto to end all concertos (concerti, surely!) / Machito / Theme to the west / Lush waltz / Artistry in rhythm.
**Album:** on Creative World(USA) by GNP Crescendo Records (USA). Catalogue no: **ST 1005**

**MELLOPHONIUM MAGIC 1962 (Kenton, Stan Orchestra & The Four Freshmen)**
**CD:** Released Mar '90, on Status Catalogue no: **STATUSCD 103**

**NATIONAL ANTHEMS OF THE WORLD (Kenton, Stan Orchestra & The Four Freshmen)**
**2 LP Set:** Released '87, on Creative World(USA) by GNP Crescendo Records (USA). Catalogue no: **STD 1060**

**NEW CONCEPTS OF ARTISTRY IN RHYTHM (Kenton, Stan & His Orchestra)**
Tracks: / Twenty three degrees north - eighty two degrees west / Portrait of a count / Invention for a guitar and trumpet / My lady / Young blood / Frank speaking / Prologue (this is an orchestra) / Improvision / Taboo (CD only.) / Lonesome train (CD only.) / Swing house (CD only.) / You go to my head (CD only.).
**CD:** Released Apr '90, on Pacific Jazz by EMI Records. Catalogue no: **CDP 792 865 2**
**CD:** Released Apr '90, on Pacific Jazz by EMI Records. Catalogue no: **CZ 299**
**Album:** Released Jul '85, on Capitol by EMI Records. Deleted Jun '88. Catalogue no: **EG 2606031**
**Cass:** Released Jul '85, on Capitol by EMI Records. Catalogue no: **EG 2606034**
**Album:** Released '85, on Creative World(USA) by GNP Crescendo Records (USA). Catalogue no: **ST 1002**

**ON THE ROAD (Kenton, Stan & His Orchestra)**
**Album:** Released Sep '86, on Artistry Catalogue no: **AR 101**

**ONE NIGHT STAND WITH STAN KENTON**
**Album:** Released May '84, on Joyce (USA) Catalogue no: **JOYCE 1120**

**PAINTED RHYTHM**
Tracks: / Artistry in rhythm / Artistry Jumps / We'll Be Together / I don't want to be loved / Body and Soul / Painted Rhythm / Just sittin' & rockin' / It's Only A Paper Moon / Eager Beaver / That's the stuff gotta watch / Southern Scandal / I never thought I'd sing the blues.
**Album:** Released Jul '88, on Giants of Jazz by Hasmick Promotions. Catalogue no: **GOJ 1007**

**Cass:** Released 16 Sep '88, on Giants of Jazz by Hasmick Promotions. Catalogue no: **GOJC 1007**

**PORTRAITS ON STANDARDS, 1951-3**
Tracks: / Street of dreams / You and the night and the music / Reverie / I've got you under my skin / Autumn in New York / Lady in red / April in Paris / How high the moon? / Crazy rhythm / I got it bad and that ain't good / Baia / Under a blanket of blue.
**Album:** Released '85, on Creative World(USA) by GNP Crescendo Records (USA). Catalogue no: **ST 1042**

**PROGRESSIVE JAZZ**
**Album:** Released Apr '85, on Swing House by Submarine Records. Catalogue no: **SWH 18**
**Cass:** Released Apr '85, on Swing House by Submarine Records. Catalogue no: **CSWH 18**

**RENDEZVOUS WITH KENTON**
Tracks: / With the wind and the rain in your hair / Memories of you / These things you left me / Two shades of Autumn / They didn't believe me / Walkin' by the river / High on a windy hill / Love letters / I get along without you very well / Desiderata / This is no laughing matter / I see your face before me.
**Album:** Released Mar '84, on Pathe Marconi (France) Catalogue no: **PM 1547801**
**Cass:** Released Mar '84, on Pathe Marconi (France) Catalogue no: **PM 154 7804**
**Album:** Released '87, on Creative World(USA) by GNP Crescendo Records (USA). Catalogue no: **ST 1057**

**RETURN TO BILOXY (Kenton, Stan & His Orchestra)**
Tracks: / Theme and variations / Opus in Chatreuse / I've never been in love / Harlem nocturne / Ad lib blues / Tenderly / Peanut vendor, The / Don't take your love / Intermission riff / When I fall in love / Younger that springtime / Day by day / Don't get around much any more / They didn't believe me / High on a windy hill / When your lover has gone / That old feeling / On the street where you live / Stompin' at the Savoy.
**CD:** Released '89, on Magic (1) by Submarine Records. Catalogue no: **DAWE 35**
**Cass:** Released '89, on Magic (1) by Submarine Records. Catalogue no: **CAWE 35**
**Album:** Released '89, on Magic (1) by Submarine Records. Catalogue no: **AWE 35**

**ROAD SHOW I & II**
**2 LP Set:** Released May '89, on GNP Crescendo (USA) by GNP Crescendo Records (USA). Catalogue no: **STD 1019**
**CD Set:** Released '87, on Creative World(USA) by GNP Crescendo Records (USA). Catalogue no: **STCD 1019/20**

**ROAD SHOW, THE (VOL.1)**
Tracks: / Artistry in rhythm / Big chase, The / I want to be happy / It's a most unusual day / Midnight sun.
**Album:** Released '85, on Creative World(USA) by GNP Crescendo Records (USA). Catalogue no: **ST 1019**

**ROAD SHOW, THE (VOL.2)**
Tracks: / Love for sale / Stompin at the Savoy / My old flame / Artistry in rhythm / Kissing bug / Bewitched / How high the moon / Paper doll / Them there eyes / September song / Walking shoes.
**Album:** Released '85, on Creative World(USA) by GNP Crescendo Records (USA). Catalogue no: **ST 1020**

**ROMANTIC APPROACH, THE**
Tracks: / Your lover has gone / All the things you are / I'm glad there is you / Say it isn't so / Imagination / Sweet and lovely / Fools rush in / You're mine / You / Once in a while / Moonlight in Vermont / I understood / Oh / You crazy moon.
**Album:** Released '85, on Creative World(USA) by GNP Crescendo Records (USA). Catalogue no: **ST 1017**

**SKETCHES ON STANDARDS, 1953-4**
Tracks: / Sophisticated lady / Begin the beguine / Lover man / Pennies from Heaven / Dark eyes / Don't take your love from me / Over the rainbow / Fascinating rhythm / There's a small hotel / Shadow waltz / More love than your love / Malaguena.
**Album:** Released '85, on Creative World(USA) by GNP Crescendo Records (USA). Catalogue no: **ST 1041**

**SOLO**
**Album:** Released '87, on Creative World(USA) by GNP Crescendo Records (USA). Catalogue no: **ST 1071**

**SOME WOMEN I'VE KNOWN, 1944-5**
Tracks: / Are you livin' old man / Travellin' man / Soothe me / Four months / Three weeks / Two days / One hour blues / All about Ronnie / Jeepers creepers / All because of you / Softly / Black coffee / Don't worry 'bout me / Give me a song with a beautiful melody / Warm blue stream.
**Album:** Released '85, on Creative World(USA) by GNP Crescendo Records (USA). Catalogue no: **ST 1029**

**SOPHISTICATED APPROACH**
Tracks: / But beautiful / Darn that dream / It might as well be spring / Moonlight becomes you / How do I look in blue / You stepped out of a dream / How long has this been going on / Memories of lady / Time after time / Easy to love / My one and only love / Like someone in love.
**Album:** Released '85, on Creative World(USA) by GNP Crescendo Records (USA). Catalogue no: **ST 1018**

**SOUND OF 62**
Tracks: / My one and only love / Malaguena / Quizas quizas quizas / Mission train / Come on back / Twist number one / Between the Devil and the deep blue sea.
Note: Medley: I've Got The World On A String/Eager Beaver/Opus In Charteuse/Dynaflow/Jump For Joe into Tiger Raf into Theme
**Album:** Released '84, on First Heard by Submarine Records. Catalogue no: **FH 46**

**STAGE DOOR SWINGS (Kenton, Stan & His Orchestra)**
Tracks: / Lullaby of Broadway (From 'Gold diggers of 1935'.) / Party's over, The (From 'The bells are ringing') / Baubles, bangles and beads (From 'Kismet') / Every time we say goodbye (From 'Seven lively Arts') / Whatever Lola wants (Lola gets) (From 'Damn Yankees') / Bali ha'i (From 'South Pacific') / Hey there (From 'Pajama Game') / Younger than Springtime (From 'South Pacific') / On the street where you live (From 'My Fair Lady') / I love Paris (From 'Can-Can') / All at once you love her (From 'Pipe Dream') / I've never been in love before (From 'Guys And Dolls').
Note: Track 1 B.Feldman & Co/EMI Music Publ:/ Track 2 Startford Music Ltd./ Tracks 3,410,11: Chappell Music/ Tracks 5,7: CBS Songs Ltd./ Tracks6,8,9, Williamson Music/ Track 12,- Anglo Pic. Ltd: Tracks 1-6 Total Time 15.56/ Tracks 7-12 Total Time 15.48:
**Album:** Released Jul '86, on Capitol by EMI Records. Catalogue no: **EMS 1159**
**Cass:** Released Jun '86, on Capitol by EMI Records. Deleted Nov '88. Catalogue no: **TCEMS 1159**

**STAGE DOOR SWINGS, 1958**
Tracks: / Younger than Springtime / Party's over, The / On the street where you live / I love Paris / Lullaby of Broadway / Baubles, bangles and beads / Every time we say goodbye / Whatever Lola wants (Lola gets) / Bali ha'i / Hey there / I've never been in love before / All at once you love her.
**Album:** Released '85, on Creative World(USA) by GNP Crescendo Records (USA). Catalogue no: **ST 1044**

**STAN KENTON**
**Album:** Released '89, on Echo Jazz Catalogue no: **EJLP 05**
**Album:** Released Apr '79, on Bright Orange Catalogue no: **BO 705**
**Cass:** Released '89, on Echo Jazz Catalogue no: **EJMC 05**
**CD:** Released '89, on Echo Jazz Catalogue no: **EJCD 05**

**STAN KENTON AND HIS ORCHESTRA, 1945-47 (Kenton, Stan & His Orchestra)**
**Album:** Released '88, on Hindsight Catalogue no: **HSR 157**

**STAN KENTON AND ORCHESTRA LIVE (Kenton, Stan Orchestra & The Four Freshmen)**
Tracks: / Lasuerte de los tontos / I concentrate on you / Lullaby of Broadway, The / Nearness of you, The / Kingfish / Early autumn / Love for sale / My old flame / Yesterdays / Out of nowhere / Night we called it a day, The / Everything happens to me / There will never be

another you / So in love / With the wind and the rain in your hair / Big chase.
**CD:** Released 8 Apr '89, on Magic (1) by Submarine Records. Catalogue no: **DAWE 32**
**Album:** Released 8 Apr '89, on Magic (1) by Submarine Records. Catalogue no: **AWE 32**
**Cass:** Released 8 Apr '89, on Magic (1) by Submarine Records. Catalogue no: **CAWE 32**

**STAN KENTON CONDUCTS DEE BARTON**
Tracks: / Man / Lonely boy / Singing oyster, The / Dilemma / Three thoughts / New day, A / Woman.
**Album:** Released Apr '79, on Creative World(USA) by GNP Crescendo Records (USA). Catalogue no: **ST 1021**

**STAN KENTON CONDUCTS THE LOS ANGELES ORCHESTRA**
Album: Released '85, on Creative World(USA) by GNP Crescendo Records (USA). Catalogue no: **ST 1013**

**STAN KENTON & FRANK ROSOLINO (Kenton, Stan & Frank Rosolino)**
**VHS:** Released '88, on Kay Jazz (video) by Kay Jazz. Catalogue no: **KJ 069**

**STAN KENTON & HIS ORCHESTRA (VIDEO)(Kenton, Stan & His Orchestra)**
**VHS:** Released '88, on Kay Jazz (video) by Kay Jazz. Catalogue no: **KJ 047**

**STAN KENTON IN HI FI**
Tracks: / Artistry jumps / Interlude / Intermission riff / Minor riff / Collaboration / Painted rhythm / Southern scandal / Peanut vendor / Eager Beaver / Concero to end all concertos / Artistry in boogie / lover / Unison riff.
Note: Stan Kenton originally made recordings for Capitol Records in the 40's. This album highlighting the important segment of Stan Kenton's career during the postwar years, is made up of his original hits re-recorded in Hi-Fi in the mid 50's.Including the well known 'Peanut Vendor' tune.
**Cass:** Released Jan '86, on Capitol by EMI Records. Catalogue no: **TCEMS 1149**
**Album:** Released Jan '86, on Capitol by EMI Records. Catalogue no: **EMS 1149**

**STAN KENTON LIVE IN PARIS, 1953**
**Album:** Released '89, on Royal Jazz Catalogue no: **RJ 504**

**STAN KENTON & ORCHESTRA 1941 (Kenton, Stan & His Orchestra)**
Tracks: / Opening theme / Tempo de Joe / Night life / Marvin's mumble / I haven't got the heart / Elegy / Love turns winter to spring / El choclo / Safari / Trumpet symphonette / Little jive is good for you, A / Prelude to nothing / Old black Joe / Flamingo / Take it from the oven / Balboa bash / Closing theme.
Note: The original Kenton's Orchestra's earliest radio transcriptions, cut August and September '41 while the band was at Balboa's Rendezvous Ballroom, have been re-mastered for this unique collectors treasure. In the liner notes, music critic-historian Dave Dexter, Jr., reports Kenton's exclaiming to Jimmie Lunceford just before these sessions: "I have ideas you won't believe--wild revolutionary jazz. Good jazz!" Every selection is composed and/or arranged by Kenton, Joe Rizzo or Ralph Yaw, and on Yaw's "A little jive is good for you", Stan and trumpeter Earl Collier both sing! Stan narrates the opening and closing "Artistry in rhythm", and Jimmy Lyons introduces the numbers. (Hindsight Catalogue - 1989)
**Album:** Released '88, on Hindsight Catalogue no: **HSR 118**

**STAN KENTON PLAYS CHICAGO (Kenton, Stan Orchestra & The Four Freshmen)**
**Album:** Released '87, on Creative World(USA) by GNP Crescendo Records (USA). Catalogue no: **ST 1072**

**STAN KENTON, VOL. 2, 1941**
Tracks: / Quit your shovin' / Underneath the stars / Let her go / Hold back the dawn / Low bridge / Blue flare / Congo clambake / Arkansas traveller / Shuffling the chords / Suite for saxophones.
**Album:** Released '88, on Hindsight Catalogue no: **HSR 124**

**STAN KENTON, VOL 2 (1953-60)**
Tracks: / Creep, The / Lover man / Alone too long / Suddenly / Skoot / Opus in chartreuse / Spring is here / Opus in turquoise / Sophisticated samba / Lemon twist / Lazy afternoon / Carnival.
**Album:** Released '85, on Creative World(USA) by GNP Crescendo Records (USA). Catalogue no: **ST 1040**

**STAN KENTON, VOL. 4, 1944-45**
Tracks: / Man I love, The / Blues / Tico tico / Tabby the cat / Sargeant's mess / Elegie / Pizzicato / Conversin' with the brain / Blow Jack / Are you livin' old man / Baby won't you please come home / Fine fine deal / Blue skies / Got a penny, Jenny / Poor butterfly / St. Louis blues.
Note: This completes the MacGregor series of transcriptions and covers the period of the orchestra when Anita O'Day was in the process of leaving and June Christy just having joined the orchestra. As a result, one unusual vocal is Christy singing "Are you livin' old man" which O'Day recorded with the band for Capitol. By now the band's brass section has grown to nine and the sound fattened accordingly. The last 2 numbers on side two are from Palladium broadcasts; Karl George is featured on a long ballad arrangement (no double time, uptempo!) of "Poor butterfly". Contains numerous Stan Getz tenor solos. Kenton died just prior to the release of this album. Produced by Wally Heider. (Hindsight Catalogue - 1989)
**Album:** Released '88, on Hindsight Catalogue no: **HSR 147**

**STAN KENTON/JEAN TURNER, 1963 (Kenton, Stan & Jean Turner)**
Tracks: / Lot of livin' to do, A / Oh you crazy moon / Sleepy lagoon / Love is here to stay / Piel canela / It's a big wide wonderful world / Someone to watch over me / Love walked in / Daydreams / Quizas quizas quizas / You're the top.
**Album:** Released '85, on Creative World(USA) by GNP Crescendo Records (USA). Catalogue no: **ST 1046**

**STAN KENTON'S GREATEST HITS**
Tracks: / Artistry in rhythm / Tampico / Interlude / Eager beaver / September song / Unison riff / Lover / Painted rhythm / And her tears flowed like wine / Laura / Peanut vendor.
**Album:** Released Apr '83, on MFP by EMI Records. Deleted '87. Catalogue no: **MFP 5607**
**Cass:** Released Apr '83, on MFP by EMI Records. Deleted '87. Catalogue no: **TCMFP 5607**

**STANDARDS IN SILHOUETTE, 1959**
Tracks: / Meaning of the blues / I get along without you very well / Willow weep for me / When Sunny gets blue / Lonely woman / Django / Thrill is gone, The / Ill wind.
Note: Featuring solos by Rolf Ericson, Archie LeCoque, Don Sebesky, Charlie Mariano, Bill Trujillo. Arrangements by Bill Mathieu.
**Album:** Released '85, on Creative World(USA) by GNP Crescendo Records (USA). Catalogue no: **ST 1049**

**STREET OF DREAMS (Kenton, Stan Orchestra & The Four Freshmen)**
**Album:** Released '88, on Creative World(USA) by GNP Crescendo Records (USA). Catalogue no: **ST 1079**
**Cass:** Released '88, on Creative World(USA) by GNP Crescendo Records (USA). Catalogue no: **STC 1079**

**SUMMER OF 51**
**CD:** Released May '89, on Garland Catalogue no: **GRZ 006**

**TOGETHER AGAIN (Kenton, Stan & June Christy)**
Tracks: / It could happen to you / Carioca / Let there be love / Opus in chartreuse / Willow weep for me / One hundred years from today.
**Cass:** Released Oct '84, on First Heard by Submarine Records. Catalogue no: **CFH 42**
**Album:** Released Oct '84, on First Heard by Submarine Records. Catalogue no: **FH 42**

**UNCOLLECTED STAN KENTON & HIS ORCHESTRA (Kenton, Stan & His Orchestra)**
Tracks: / Ol' man river / Shoo shoo baby / Eager beaver / Liza / In a little Spanish town / Paper doll / Hit that jive, Jack / Goon came on, The / Begin the beguine / None but the lonely / I know that you know / Salt Lake City blues / Hour of parting / Russian lullaby / Lady in red / I got rhythm.
Note: This is the Kenton band that had, by this time, grown to 7 brass and added

vocalist Dolly Mitchell, thereafter to be replaced by Anita O'Day. 12 of the 16 selections are from MacGregor master discs, the last 2 selections on each side being from "live" broadcasts. Liner notes are by Dave Dexter, Jr., and are based on interviews with trombonist Harry Forbes, baritone saxist Bob Gioga and arranger Joe Rizzo. Joe Rizzo's arrangements on this album of "Old man river", "Paper doll", and "I got rhythm" bring out the best of Kenton. Produced by Wally Heider. (Hindsight Catalogue - 1989)
**Album:** Released May '79, on Hindsight (UK) by Michele International Records. Catalogue no: **HSR 136**

**UNCOLLECTED,THE**
**Album:** Released Apr '86, on Hindsight (UK) by Michele International Records. Catalogue no: **HUK 195**

**VIVA KENTON (Kenton, Stan Orchestra & The Four Freshmen)**
**Album:** Released '87, on Creative World(USA) by GNP Crescendo Records (USA). Catalogue no: **ST 1063**

**WEST SIDE STORY (Kenton, Stan & His Orchestra)**
Tracks: / Prologue / Something's coming / Maria / America / Tonight / Cool / I feel pretty / Gee officer Krupke / Taunting scene / Somewhere (finale).
**Album:** Released Mar '88, on Capitol by EMI Records. Deleted Nov '88. Catalogue no: **EMS 1285**
**Album:** Released '85, on Creative World(USA) by GNP Crescendo Records (USA). Catalogue no: **ST 1007**
**Cass:** Released Jul '85, on EMI by EMI Records. Deleted 31 Jul '88. Catalogue no: **TCEMS 1285**

## Keppard, Freddie

**1924: FREDDIE KEPPARD (Keppard, Freddie/Red Onion Jazz Babies/Louis Armstrong/Doc Cook). (see also: Armstrong, Louis)**
**Album:** Released Jan '83, on Swaggie (Australia) Catalogue no: **804**

**FREDDIE KEPPARD (Keppard, Freddie/Doc Cook/Erskine Tate)**
**Album:** Released '88, on Jazz Treasury Catalogue no: **JT 1002**

## Kerr, Bob Whoopee Band

**BLUES JAZZ BOOGIE & RAGS**
Tracks: / Pinetop's boogie woogie / Blueberry Hill / Pep / Someday you'll be sorry / Maple leaf rag / Good morning blues / Kitchen man / Blue Monday / Deadman blues / Crying for the Carolines / Cascades / Bi bist du shon.
**Album:** Released Jan '82, on Whoopee by Whoopee Records. Catalogue no: **WP 101**

**BOOTLEGGING LIVE**
Tracks: / Home in Pasedena / Cocktails for two / You're driving me crazy / Chloe / Overture to Carmen / Sweet Georgia Brown / Doctor Jazz / That certain party / I love my Chilli bon bon / Maple leaf rag / My pet / My blue Heaven.

**Barney Kessel**

**Cass:** Released Dec '87, on Whoopee by Whoopee Records. Catalogue no: **WB 111**

**HARD PRESSED**
Tracks: / Down on Jollity farm / I've got a feeling I'm falling / 5,000 year old rock (take 2) / Sheik of Araby, The / Nightingale sang in Berkeley Square, A / Blue room / Tap dance man / Mean to me / My sweetie went away / Little boy blue / Overture to Carmen.
**Album:** Released Jan '82, on Whoopee by Whoopee Records. Catalogue no: **WP 104**

**MUSICAL MAYHEM**
Tracks: / You always hurt the one you love / Spread a little happiness / Jollity farm / My sweetie went away / Riley's cowshed / Hard hearted Hannah / Whispering / I love my Chilli bon bon / Sweet Georgia Brown / Room with a view / That certain party / My blue Heaven / Sunday.
**Cass:** Released Dec '87, on Whoopee by Whoopee Records. Catalogue no: **WB 112**

**REMEMBER REMEMBER**
Tracks: / Remember remember / Pleasant.
**7" Single:** Released Oct '81, on Whoopee by Whoopee Records. Catalogue no: **WP 106 S**

**TAP DANCE MAN**
Tracks: / Tap dance man / 5000 year old rock.
**7" Single:** Released May '79, on Whoopee by Whoopee Records. Catalogue no: **WP 100**

**THINGS THAT GO BUMP IN THE NIGHT**
Tracks: / Your nobody's sweetheart now / Ukelele lady / Riley's cowshed / My girl's pussy / Pleasant pluckin' / Cuckoo waltz / Running wild / Remember remember / Ain't she sweet / Storytime / Shine / Overture to Carmen / Tiger rag.
**Album:** Released Jan '82, on Whoopee by Whoopee Records. Catalogue no: **WP 108**

**WHOOPEE BAND, THE**
Tracks: / Crazy / Honey pie / Whispering / Victoria and Albert / Moonbeam waltz / I want a girl / Doctor Jazz / When I think of you / Ain't she sweet / Button up your overcoat / Lady Madonna.
**Album:** Released Jan '82, on Whoopee by Whoopee Records. Catalogue no: **WP 102**

**WINCHESTER CATHEDRAL (Kerr's, Bob Whoopee Band)**
Tracks: / Winchester Cathedral / Bob's fool house (Acid humour).
**7" Single:** Released Nov '88, on Frontier by Frontier Records. Catalogue no: **FTR 2**

## Kessel, Barney

**ARTISTRY OF BARNEY KESSEL, THE**
**CD:** Released Apr '87, on Fantasy (import) by Fantasy Inc (USA). Deleted '88. Catalogue no: **FCD 60021**

**AUTUMN LEAVES**
**CD:** Released Jun '88, on Black Lion Catalogue no: **BLCD 760112**

**Album:** Released Jun '88, on Black Lion Catalogue no: **BLP 60112**

**BARNEY KESSEL & FRIENDS**
**CD:** Released Jul '88, on Concord Jazz by Concord Jazz Records (USA). Catalogue no: **CCD 6009**

**BLUE SOUL**
Tracks: / Shuffling / Frank Mills / On a clear day / Watch what happens / Quail bait / Blue soul / Stumblin' around / Comin' home.
**Album:** Released Sep '85, on Black Lion Catalogue no: **BLP 30161**

**EASY LIKE**
**CD:** Released Jan '89, on JVC/Fantasy Catalogue no: **VDJ 1625**

**EXPLORING THE SCENE (Kessel, Barney/Ray Brown/Shelly Manne)**
Tracks: / Little Susie / Duke, The / So what? / Misty / Doodlin' / Golden striker, The / Li'l darlin' / Blessing, The / This here.
Note: Barney Kessel, guitar; Ray Brown, bass; Shelly Manne, drums.
**Album:** on Contemporary (Import) Catalogue no: **1007 581**

**GREAT GUITARS AT CHARLIE'S, GEORGETOWN (Kessel, Barney/ Charlie Byrd/ Herb Ellis)**
Tracks: / Where or when / New Orleans / When the saints go marching in / Change partners / Opus one / Old folks / Get happy / Trouble in mind.
**CD:** Released Apr '83, on Concord Jazz by Concord Jazz Records (USA). Catalogue no: **CJC 209**
**Album:** Released Apr '83, on Concord Jazz by Concord Jazz Records (USA). Catalogue no: **CJ 209**

**GREAT GUITARS AT THE WINERY (Kessel, Barney/ Charlie Byrd/ Herb Ellis)**
**Album:** Released Nov '80, on Concord Jazz by Concord Jazz Records (USA). Catalogue no: **CJ 131**

**IN CONCERT**
**CD:** Released May '88, on Compact Collection Catalogue no: **15011**
**Album:** Released May '88, on Jazz Life Catalogue no: **26011**
**Cass:** Released May '88, on Jazz Life Catalogue no: **46011**

**JELLY BEANS (Kessel, Barney Trio)**
**Album:** Released Dec '81, on Concord by Concord Jazz Records (USA). Catalogue no: **CJ 164**

**JUST FRIENDS**
**Album:** Released Jul '88, on Sonet by Sonet Records. Catalogue no: **SNTF 685**

**KESSEL PLAYS STANDARDS**
**Album:** Released 2 May '89, on Contemporary by Ace Records. Catalogue no: **COP 045**

**LET'S COOK**
**Album:** Released Jun '86, on Contemporary (USA) Catalogue no: **COP 028**

**LIMEHOUSE BLUES (Kessel, Barney & Stephane Grappelli)**
Tracks: / It don't mean a thing / Out of nowhere / Tea for two / Limehouse blues / How high the moon / Willow, weep for me / Little star / Undecided.
**Album:** Released '83, on Black Lion Catalogue no: **BLP 30129**

**LIVE AT SOMETIME**
**CD:** Released Feb '90, on Storyville by Storyville Records AB. Catalogue no: **STCD 4157**

**PLAYS STANDARDS**
**CD:** Released Apr '87, on Carrere (France) Catalogue no: **98628**

**POLL WINNERS RIDE AGAIN, THE**
**CD:** Released May '87, on JVC/Fantasy Catalogue no: **VDJ 1563**

**POLL WINNERS, THE (Kessel, Barney/Ray Brown/Shelly Manne)**
**CD:** Released May '87, on JVC/Fantasy Deleted '88. Catalogue no: **VDJ 1557**

**SLOW BURN**
Tracks: / Slow burn / Just in time / Shadow of your smile / Recado bossa nova / Sweet baby / Who can I turn to / One mint julep.
**Album:** Released Jan '77, on Phil Spector Int. by Chrysalis Records. Deleted '81. Catalogue no: **2307 011**

**SOLO**
Tracks: / Brazil / What are you doing the rest of your life? / Happy little song / Everything happens to me / You are the sunshine of my life / Manha de carnaval / People / Jellybeans / Alfie.
**Album:** Released Oct '83, on Concord Jazz by Concord Jazz Records (USA). Catalogue no: **CJ 221**

**SPONTANEOUS COMBUSTION (Kessel, Barney & Monty Alexander Trio)**
**CD:** Released Jan '89, on JVC/Fantasy Catalogue no: **VDJ 1113**

**SUMMERTIME IN MONTREUX**
Tracks: / Laura / Yesterday / It's a blue world / Summertime / In the garden of love / Bridging the blues.
**Album:** Released Sep '85, on Black Lion Catalogue no: **BLP 30151**

**SWINGING EASY**
Tracks: / On a clear day / Look of love, The / Autumn leaves / You're the one for me / I will wait for you.
Note: Tracks include those listed above.
**Album:** Released Jan '85, on Black Lion Catalogue no: **BLP 30107**

**TO SWING OR NOT TO SWING**
Tracks: / Begin the blues / Louisiana / Happy feeling / Embraceable you / Wail Street / Indiana / Moten swing / Midnight sun / Contemporary blues / Don't blame me / Twelfth St. rag.
**CD:** Released May '87, on JVC/Fantasy Catalogue no: **VDJ 1554**
**Album:** Released Nov '83, on Contemporary (USA) Catalogue no: **1003 513**

**TWO-WAY CONVERSATION (Kessel, Barney & Red Mitchell)**
**Album:** Released Mar '75, on Sonet by Sonet Records. Catalogue no: **SNTF 681**

## Kicks

**KICKS Jazz dance 4 (Various artists)**
Tracks: / Mr. Kicks: *Brown, Oscar Jnr* / Green onions: *Santamaria, Mongo* / Hot fudge: *Doggett, Bill* / Capricious: *Mulligan, Gerry* / Caravan: *Lambert, Hendricks & Annie Ross* / So what: *Davis, Miles* / Eso beso: *Ames, Nancy* / Fever: *Greco, Buddy* / Latin America: *Walton, Cedar* / Down Santiago way: *Various artists* / Signifying monkey, The: *Brown, Oscar Jnr* / Comin' home baby: *Torme, Mel* / Watermelon man: *Mann, Herbie* / Why not: *Pike, Dave* / Get out of town: *Mulligan, Gerry* / Take five: *Brubeck, Dave* / La Bamba: *Santamaria, Mongo.*
**2 LP Set:** Released Oct '87, on Affinity by Charly Records. Catalogue no: **AFFD 180**

## King, Al

**ON MY WAY**
**Album:** Released '88, on Diving Duck (Holland) Catalogue no: **DD 4302**

## King, Albert

**ALBERT**
Tracks: / Guitar man / I'm ready / Ain't nothing you can do / I don't care what my baby do / Change of pace / My babe / Running out of steam / Rub my back / (Ain't it) a real good sign.
**Album:** Released Mar '88, on Charly R&B by Charly Records. Catalogue no: **CRB 1173**
**CD:** Released Mar '88, on Charly R&B by Charly Records. Catalogue no: **CDCHARLY 103**
**Cass:** Released Mar '88, on Charly R&B by Charly Records. Catalogue no: **TCCRB 1173**

**ALBERT LIVE**
Tracks: / Watermelon man / Don't burn down the bridge / Blues at sunrise / That's what the blues is all about / Stormy Monday / Kansas city / I'm gonna call you as soon as the sun goes down (King) / Matchbox holds my clothes / Jam in a flat / As the years go passing by / Overall junction / I'll play the blues for you.
**CD:** Released Nov '88, on Charly by Charly Records. Catalogue no: **CDCHARLY 136**
**2 LP Set:** Released Nov '88, on Charly by Charly Records. Catalogue no: **CDX 35**
**Cass:** Released '88, on Charly by Charly Records. Catalogue no: **TCCDX 35**

**BEST OF ALBERT KING (I'll play the blues for you)**
Note: Tracks include: Killing floor, Born under a bad sign, The sky is crying, Crosscut saw, etc. 17 Tracks. CD only.
**CD:** Released Apr '87, on London Records by London Records Ltd. Deleted '88. Catalogue no: **FCD 60005**
**CD:** Released Nov '87, on Stax by Fantasy Inc (USA). Catalogue no: **CDSX 007**
**Album:** Released Feb '89, on Stax by Fantasy Inc. Catalogue no: **SX 007**

**BLUES AT SUNRISE**
Tracks: / Don't burn the bridge (cause you might wanna come back... / For the love of a woman / I'll play the blues for you / Roadhouse blues / I believe to my soul / Blues at sunrise / Little brother (make a way).
**Album:** Released Nov '88, on Stax by Fantasy Inc (USA). Catalogue no: **SX 017**

**BORN UNDER A BAD SIGN**
**Album:** Released Jun '88, on Atlantic by WEA Records. Catalogue no: **SD7723**

**DOOR TO DOOR (King, Albert/Otis Rush)**
**Album:** Released Oct '88, on Vogue (France) by Vogue Records. Catalogue no: **515021**

**GREAT KING ALBERT**
**Cass:** Released May '88, on Tomato (USA) by Tomato Music Co. (USA). Catalogue no: **2696034**
**Album:** Released May '88, on Tomato (USA) by Tomato Music Co. (USA). Catalogue no: **2696031**
**CD:** Released May '88, on Tomato (USA) by Tomato Music Co. (USA). Catalogue no: **2696032**

**I'LL PLAY THE BLUES FOR YOU -**
Tracks: / Born under a bad sign / Answer to the laundromatt blues / You threw your love on me too strong / Crosscut saw / I'll play the blues for you Part 1 / Angel of mercy / Heart fixing business / Killing floor / Sky is crying, The / Going back to luka / (I think I'm) drowning on dry land Part 1 / That's what the blues is all about / Left hand woman (get right with me) / Driving wheel / Firing line (Available on CD only) / Don't burn the bridge (cause you might wanna come back... (Available on CD only) / Can't you see what you're doing to me (Available on CD only).
**CD:** Released Jan '90, on Stax by Fantasy Inc (USA). Catalogue no: **CDSX 007**
**Cass:** Released Mar '88, on Stax by Fantasy Inc (USA). Catalogue no: **SXC 007**
**Album:** Released Mar '88, on Stax by Fantasy Inc (USA). Catalogue no: **SX 007**

**KING ALBERT**
Tracks: / Love shock / You upset me baby / Chump chance / Let me rock you easy / Boot lace / Love mechanic / Call my job / Good time Charlie.
**Album:** Released Jul '88, on Charly R&B by Charly Records. Catalogue no: **CRB 1191**
**Cass:** Released Jul '88, on Charly R&B by Charly Records. Catalogue no: **TCCRB 1191**
**CD:** Released Jul '88, on Charly by Charly Records. Catalogue no: **CDCHARLY 120**

**LAST SESSION, THE**
Tracks: / Won't gimme no livin' / Cold in hand / Stop lying / All the way down / Tell me what true love is / Down the road I go / Sun gone down.
Note: This previously unreleased album will excite a lot of people. The tapes had apparently been sitting on a shelf for fifteen years, untouched and forgotten.The pairing of Albert King and John Mayall was an inspired one, King being the most influential guitar stylist of the modern blues era and Mayall being the chief conceptualist of the British revival of the 60's.Recorded August 1971. Personell: Albert King- Vocals, Lead Guitar\John Mayall- organ, piano,Harmonica,12 String Guitar\Larry Taylor-Bass\Ron Selico-Drums\Lee King-Rhythm Guitar\Kevin (last name unknown)-Organ, Piano\Clifford Solomon-Alto and tenor saxes\Ernie Watts-Tenor saxophone\Blue Mitchell-Trumpet
**Album:** Released Nov '86, on Stax by Fantasy Inc (USA). Catalogue no: **MPS 8534**

**LAUNDROMAT BLUES**
Tracks: / Born under a bad sign / Laundromat blues / I love Lucy / Crosscut saw / You sure drive a hard bargain / You're gonna need me / (When I lost my baby) I almost lost my mind / Overall junction / Oh pretty woman / Funk-shun / Hunter, The / Personal manager / Cold feet / Kansas city / Down don't bother me / As the years go passing by.
**Album:** Released Apr '84, on Edsel by Demon Records. Catalogue no: **ED 130**

**LIVE WIRE/BLUES POWER**
**Album:** Released Dec '88, on Stax by Fantasy Inc (USA). Catalogue no: **STX 4148**
**CD:** Released Nov '89, on Stax by Fantasy Inc (USA). Catalogue no: **CDSXE 022**
**CD:** Released '86, on Mobile Fidelity Sound Lab(USA) by Mobile Fidelity Records (USA). Catalogue no: **MFCD 838**
**Album:** Released Nov '89, on Stax by Fantasy Inc (USA). Catalogue no: **SXE 022**

**NEW ORLEANS HEAT**
Tracks: / Get out of My Life Woman / Born under a bad sign / Feeling / We all wanna boogie / Very thought of you (The) / I got the blues / I get evil / Angel of Mercy / Flat tire.
Note: Original Tomato recordings P 1978.
**Album:** on Charly R&B by Charly Records. Catalogue no: **CRB 1066**
**CD:** Released Jan '87, on Charly by Charly Records. Catalogue no: **CDCHARLY 49**
**Album:** Released Aug '87, on Ariola by BMG Records (UK). Catalogue no: **203.007**

**SAN FRANCISCO 83**
**Album:** Released Nov '83, on Fantasy by Ace Records. Catalogue no: **F 9627**
**Album:** Released Apr '84, on Carrere (France) Catalogue no: **68535**

**TRAVELLIN' TO CALIFORNIA**
**Album:** Released Jul '88, on Bellaphon Catalogue no: **BID 8016**

**TRUCKLOAD OF LOVIN'**
Tracks: / Cold women with warm hearts / Gonna make it somehow / Sensation, communication, together / I'm your mate / Truckload of lovin' / Hold hands with one another / Cadillac assembly line / Nobody wants a loser.
**Cass:** Released Apr '88, on Charly R&B by Charly Records. Catalogue no: **TCCRB 1180**
**Album:** Released Apr '88, on Charly R&B by Charly Records. Catalogue no: **CRB 1180**
**CD:** Released Apr '88, on Charly R&B by Charly Records. Catalogue no: **CDCHARLY 112**

**VINTAGE BLUES (King, Albert/Otis Rush)**
**CD:** Released May '89, on Charly by Charly Records. Catalogue no: **CDRED 9**

## King, B.B.

**Biographical details:** Riley B.King, better known to his fans as B.B.King the "Beale Street Blues Boy" was born in Itta Bena, Mississippi on September 16th 1925. In his early years he was influenced by musicians like T.Bone Walker and Elmore James, but in turn has himself influenced many guitarists. He started out working for his local radio but in 1947 made the move to a station in Memphis. In 1949 he made his first recording *Miss Martha King* and as a result of meeting Ike Turner obtained a contract with Modern Records and their RPM subsiduary. His first record on this label *Three o'clock blues* was an immediate No.1 hit in 1950. He gained fame as a versatile performer whose extensive appeal was the result of his capacity to adapt many different musical styles - jazz, rock, country and pop - to his own personal blues interpretation. He continues to attract multiform audiences to his numerous concert performances.

This American guitarist, vocalist and songwriter is often referred to as the King of Blues. He was born Riley B King in Itta Bena, Mississippi in 1925. He did not start to take the guitar seriously until he was eighteen. In the late Forties he worked as a disc jockey on a radio station WDIA in Memphis - it was here that he earned the nickname 'Blues boy', which got shortened to B.B. In terms of his subsequent dominance of and influence upon the blues scene, he certainly lived up to his nickname and surname. B.B's recording career began at the end of the Forties, and quickly blossomed withe the success of his first smash hit *Three o'clock blues*, which enjoyed an extended run at the top of the American rhythm-and-blues, chart in 1950. A host of further successes followed, included 1953's *Woke up this morning* classic. By the end of the Fifties he had chalked up almost twenty entries on the US R&B charts, although virtually none crossed over to the white-dominated pop listings. King's influence upon

B.B. King

the white rock market started to emerge during the Sixties, when such seminal players as Eric Clapton took note of his pioneering, potent guitar style. B.B's technique on tracks like *Every day I have the blues* and *Rock me baby* was heard and imitated by a mass of young upstarts including Jimmy Page and Larry Coryell. King virtually introduced the guitar to a whole generation of musicians and played a key role in its development in blues and rock. His vocal sound, which ranged from a rich thick tenor to an emotional falsetto, was mesmerising. His perpetual, workaholic concert schedule kept him on the road for most of each year, and his show was a must for anyone interested in professionalism, audience rapport and sheer classy coolness. Thanks largely to his influence on world conquering British rock performers, white Americans finally caught up with B.B.King in 1970, when his string laden *The thrill is gone* reached the US Top 20. Grateful for the wider audience he was now reaching, he continued to record and tour at an exacting rate throughout the Seventies and into the Eighties. His commitment to the blues was displayed by the fact that he was still going strong in 1985, the year of his 60th birthday. For all the respect which he has always commanded amongst the British music fraternity, B.B. has never reached the UK singles chart and did not penetrate the LP list until 1979, when *Take it home* crept to No.60. (Bob MacDonald, 24th Nov 1985).

**ACROSS THE TRACKS**
Tracks: / Let's do the boogie / Bad luck / When my heart beats like a hammer / Everyday I have the blues / Dark is the night (part 1) / Dark is the night (part 2) / Why I sing the blues / Troubles troubles troubles / I got a girl who lives up on the hill / Everything I do is wrong / Woman I love, The / Jump with you baby / Be careful with a fool / Talkin' the blues / Confessin' the blues / Crying won't help you.
Note: Tracks include: Let's do the boogie/Everyday/The Woman I love/Confession' the blues etc.
**Album:** Released 2 Nov '87, on Ace by Ace Records. Catalogue no: **CHD 230**

**AIN'T NOBODY HOME**
Tracks: / Ain't nobody home / Lay another log on the fire.
**CD Single:** Released 24 Jul '89, on MCA by MCA Records. Catalogue no: **DMCAT 1354**
**12" Single:** Released 24 Jul '89, on MCA by MCA Records. Catalogue no: **MCAT 1354**
**7" Single:** Released 24 Jul '89, on MCA by MCA Records. Catalogue no: **MCA 1354**

**AMBASSADOR OF THE BLUES**
Tracks: / Ambassador of the blues / You upset my baby / Sweet little angel / Three o'clock blues / Did you ever love a woman / B.B Blues / I can't lose / Five long years / Other night blues, The / I stay in the mood / Worst thing in my life / Pray for you.
**Album:** Released Feb '86, on Crown by Ace Records. Catalogue no: **GEM 001**
**Cass:** Released Feb '86, on Crown by Ace Records. Deleted '88. Catalogue no: **GEMC 001**

**B.B. BOOGIE**
Tracks: / It's my own fault baby / You've done lost your good thing now / B.B. boogie / New way of driving, A / Catfish blues / Long nights / That evil child / Sweet sixteen / Paying the cost to be boss / How blue can you get / Other night blues, The / Mr. Pawnbroker / Walkin' and cryin' / Letter, The / Everyday I have the blues.
**Album:** Released Oct '89, on Blue Moon (1) by Magnum Music Group. Catalogue no: **BMLP 076**
**CD:** Released Oct '89, on Blue Moon (1) by Magnum Music Group. Catalogue no: **CDBM 076**

**B.B. KING STORY VOL. 1**
**Album:** Released '88, on Joker (USA) by Lifetime Records (USA). Catalogue no: **SM 3726**
**Cass:** Released '88, on Joker (USA) by Lifetime Records (USA). Catalogue no: **MC 3726**

**B.B. KING STORY VOL. 2**
**Cass:** Released '88, on Joker (USA) by Lifetime Records (USA). Catalogue no: **MC 3727**
**Album:** Released '88, on Joker (USA) by Lifetime Records (USA). Catalogue no: **SM 3727**

**BEST OF B.B. KING**
Tracks: / Hummingbird / Cook county jail introduction / How blue can you get / Sweet sixteen / Ain't nobody home / Why I sing the blues / Thrill is gone, The / Nobody loves me but my mother / Caldonia.
**Cass:** Released Aug '81, on ABC Records by MCA Records. Catalogue no: **MCLC 1612**
**Album:** Released Jan '83, on Fame by EMI Records. Catalogue no: **FA 3055**
**Album:** Released Aug '81, on ABC Records by MCA Records. Catalogue no: **MCL 1612**
**Cass:** Released Jan '83, on Fame by EMI Records. Catalogue no: **TC FA 3055**
**CD:** Released Sep '87, on MCA by MCA Records. Catalogue no: **CMCAD 31040**

**BEST OF B.B. KING (ACE)**
Tracks: / Please love me / You upset me, baby / Everyday I have the blues / Bad luck / Three o'clock blues / Blind love / Woke up this morning / You know I love you / Sweet little angel / Ten long years / Did you ever love a woman? / Crying won't help you.
**Album:** Released Jun '81, on Ace by Ace Records. Catalogue no: **CH 30**

**BEST OF B.B. KING VOL 1**
Tracks: / You upset me baby / Everyday / Five long years / Sweet little angel / Beautician blues / Dust my broom / Three o'clock blues / Ain't that just like a woman / I'm King / Sweet sixteen / Whole lot of love / Mean ole Frisco / Please accept my love / Going down slow / Blues for me / You don't know / Early every morning / Blues at sunrise / Please love me.

**Cass:** Released Dec '86, on Ace by Ace Records. Catalogue no: **CHC 198**
**CD:** Released '89, on Ace by Ace Records. Catalogue no: **CDCH 908**
**CD:** Released Nov '86, on Ace by Ace Records. Deleted Jan '90. Catalogue no: **CDCH 198**
**Album:** Released Dec '86, on Ace by Ace Records. Catalogue no: **CH 198**

**BEST OF B.B. KING VOL 2**
Tracks: / Bad luck soul / Get out of here / Jungle / Sugar mama / Ten long years / Bad case of love / House rocker / Sneakin' around / Shut your mouth / Letter, The / I've got a right to love my baby / Woman I love, The / You done lost your good thing now / Did you ever love a woman / B.B. rock / Rock me baby / It's my own fault / You know I love you / Low rider / You're gonna miss me.
**Cass:** Released Jan '87, on Charly by Charly Records. Catalogue no: **CHC 199**
**Album:** Released Jan '87, on Charly by Charly Records. Catalogue no: **CH 199**
**CD:** Released Feb '87, on Charly by Charly Records. Catalogue no: **CDCHARLY 199**

**BEST OF THE MEMPHIS MASTERS**
Tracks: / Please love me / You upset me baby / Everyday I have the blues / Bad luck / 3 o'clock blues / Blind love / Woke up this morning / You know I love you / Sweet little angel / Ten long years / Did you ever love a woman / Cryin' won't help you / Pray for you / Other night blues, The / Mistreated woman / Questionnaire blues / B.B. blues / New way of driving, A / B.B.'s boogie / It's my own fault darling / Walkin' & cryin' / Fine looking woman / She don't love me no more / Shake it up and go.
**Cass:** Released Jan '85, on Ace by Ace Records. Catalogue no: **CHC 801**

**BIM BAM**
Tracks: / Bim bam / Shake holler and run.
**7" Single:** Released May '81, on Ace by Ace Records. Deleted Jun '88. Catalogue no: **NS 69**

**BLUES IS KING**
Tracks: / Waitin' on you / Gambler's blues / Tired of your jive / Night life / Buzz me / Sweet sixteen part 1 / Don't answer the door / Blind love / I know what you're puttin' down / Baby get lost / Gonna keep on loving you / Sweet sixteen part 2.
**Album:** Released Dec '87, on Fat Shadow Catalogue no: **JMI 800**
**Album:** Released Nov '87, on See For Miles by See For Miles Records. Catalogue no: **SEE 216**

**BLUES 'N' JAZZ**
Tracks: / Inflation blues / Broken heart / Sell my monkey / Heed my warning / Teardrops from my eyes / Rainbow riot / Darlin' you know I love you / Make love to me / I can't let you go.
**Cass:** Released Oct '87, on MCA by MCA Records. Catalogue no: **MCLC 1836**
**Album:** Released Jul '83, on MCA by MCA Records. Deleted Jul '88. Catalogue no: **MCF 3170**
**Album:** Released Jul '82, on Noir by Noir Records. Catalogue no: **LAT 1036**
**Album:** Released Oct '87, on MCA by MCA Records. Catalogue no: **MCL 1836**

**BLUES ON TOP OF BLUES**
Tracks: / Heartbreaker / Losing faith in you / Dance with me / That's wrong little mama / Having my say / I'm not wanted anymore / Worried dream / Paying the cost to be the boss / Until I found you / I'm gonna do what they do to me / Raining in my heart / Now that you've lost me.
**CD:** Released '89, on Beat Goes On by Andy's Records. Catalogue no: **BGOCD 69**
**Album:** Released '89, on Beat Goes On by Andy's Records. Catalogue no: **BGOLP 69**

**BLUES SESSION, A (King, B.B. & Friends)**
Note: With Paul Butterfield, Eric Clapton, Phil Collins, Dr.John, Etta James, Chaka Khan, Albert King, Gladys Knight, Billy Ocean and Stevie Ray Vaughan. Running time: 59 mins.
**VHS:** Released '88, on Video Collection by Video Collection. Catalogue no: **VC 4051**

**BLUES, THE**
**Album:** Released '88, on Masters (Holland) Catalogue no: **MA 30585**
**Cass:** Released '88, on Masters (Holland) Catalogue no: **MAMC 30585**

**COLLECTION: B.B. KING (20 blues greats)**
Tracks: / Help the poor / Everyday I have the blues / Woke up this morning / Worry worry / Sweet little angel / How blue can you get / You upset me baby / It's my own fault / Please love me / She don't love me no more / Three o'clock blues / Fine looking woman / Blind love / You know I love you / Ten long years / Mistreated woman / Shake it up and go / Sweet sixteen / You done lost your good thing now / Outside help.
**CD:** Released Sep '87, on Deja Vu Catalogue no: **DVCD 2031**
**Album:** Released Nov '85, on Deja Vu Catalogue no: **DVLP 2031**
**Cass:** Released Nov '85, on Deja Vu Catalogue no: **DVMC 2031**

**COMPLETELY LIVE AND WELL**
Tracks: / Don't answer the door / Just a little love / My mood / Sweet little angel / Please accept my love / I want you so bad / Friends / Get off my back woman / Lets get down to business / Why i sing the blues / So exited / No good / You're losin' me / What happened / Confessin' the blues / Key to my kingdom / Crying won't help you now / You're mean / Thrill is gone, The.
Note: Double Album.
**Cass:** Released Nov '86, on Charly by Charly Records. Catalogue no: **TCCDX 14**
**2 LP Set:** Released Nov '86, on Charly by Charly Records. Catalogue no: **CDX 14**

**COMPLETELY WELL**
Tracks: / So excited / No good / You're losin' me / What happened / Confessin' the blues / Key to my kingdom / Crying won't help you now / You're mean / Thrill is gone, The.
**CD:** Released Sep '87, on MCA by MCA Records. Catalogue no: **CMCAD 31039**

**DO THE BOOGIE (B.B.King's early 50's classics)**
Tracks: / Boogie woogie woman / Past day / I gotta find my baby / Woke up this morning (my baby's gone) / Please love me / Blind love / When my heart beats like a hammer / Whole lotta love / That ain't the way to do it / Everyday (I have the blues) / Let's do the boogie / Dark is the night part 1 / Dark is the night part 2 / Why I sing the blues / Everything I do is wrong / Woman I love, The / Jump with you baby / Troubles, troubles, troubles / Crying won't help you.
**CD:** Released Oct '88, on Ace by Ace Records. Catalogue no: **CDCH 916**

**GREATEST HITS: B B KING**
**Album:** Released May '88, on Music Power Catalogue no: **33003**
**Album:** Released Sep '87, on Lotus Catalogue no: **LOP 14 023**
**Cass:** Released May '88, on Music Power Catalogue no: **63003**

**GUESS WHO**
**Album:** Released '89, on Beat Goes On by Andy's Records. Catalogue no: **BGOLP 71**
**CD:** Released '89, on Beat Goes On by Andy's Records. Catalogue no: **BGOCD 71**

**HIS BEST : THE ELECTRIC KING**
**Album:** Released Oct '88, on Beat Goes On by Andy's Records. Catalogue no: **BGOLP 37**
**CD:** Released Oct '88, on Beat Goes On by Andy's Records. Catalogue no: **BGOCD 37**

**IN LONDON**
**Album:** Released Oct '88, on Beat Goes On by Andy's Records. Catalogue no: **BGOLP 42**

**IN THE MIDNIGHT HOUR**
Tracks: / In the midnight hour / Heed my warning.
**7" Single:** Released Sep '87, on MCA by MCA Records. Catalogue no: **MCA 1196**

**INCREDIBLE SOUL OF B.B. KING**
Tracks: / I got papers on you, baby / Tomorrow is another day / Fool too long, A / Come by here / Woman I love, The / My silent prayer / I love you so / Sweet thing / We can't make it / Treat me right / Time to say goodbye / I'm cracking up over you.
**Album:** Released Oct '83, on Musidisc by Musidisc Records (France). Catalogue no: **CV 1309**

**INDIANOLA MISSISSIPPI SEEDS**
Tracks: / Nobody loves me but my mother / You're still my woman / Ask me no questions / Until I'm dead and cold / King's special / Ain't gonna worry my life

anymore / Chains and things / Go underground / Hummingbird.
**Album:** Released May '88, on Castle Classics by Castle Communications Records. Catalogue no: **CLALP 141**
**Cass:** Released May '88, on Castle Classics by Castle Communications Records. Catalogue no: **CLAMC 141**
**CD:** Released '88, on Castle Classics by Castle Communications Records. Catalogue no: **CLACD 141**

**INTO THE NIGHT**
Tracks: / Into the night / Century city chase.
**12" Single:** Released May '85, on MCA by MCA Records. Deleted May '88. Catalogue no: **MCAT 947**
**7" Single:** Released May '85, on MCA by MCA Records. Deleted May '88. Catalogue no: **MCA 947**

**INTRODUCING B.B.KING**
Tracks: / Into the night / Better not look down / My Lucille / Caldonia / Sell my monkey / In the midnight hour / Thrill is gone, The / Broken heart / Victim, The / Sweet sixteen / Rock me baby.
**CD:** Released Apr '89, on MCA by MCA Records. Catalogue no: **DMCB 8001**
**Cass:** Released Nov '87, on MCA by MCA Records. Catalogue no: **MCBC 8001**
**Album:** Released Nov '87, on MCA by MCA Records. Catalogue no: **MCB 8001**

**KING OF THE BLUES**
**Album:** Released Feb '89, on MCA by MCA Records. Catalogue no: **MCG 6038**
**Cass:** Released Feb '89, on MCA by MCA Records. Catalogue no: **MCGC 6038**
**CD:** Released Feb '89, on MCA by MCA Records. Catalogue no: **DMCCG 6038**

**KING OF THE BLUES GUITAR**
Tracks: / Slidin' and glidin' / Blues with B. B. / King of guitar / Jump with B. B. / 38th Street blues / Feedin' the rock / Going South / Step it up.
**Album:** Released Nov '85, on Ace by Ace Records. Catalogue no: **CH 152**

**LEGEND IN MY TIME**
Tracks: / Legend in my time / Love me tender.
**7" Single:** Released Nov '82, on MCA by MCA Records. Deleted Nov '85. Catalogue no: **MCA 772**

**LIVE AT NICK'S**
Note: King of the blues, with Lucille in concert. Running time: 60 mins.
**VHS:** Released '87, on Castle Hendring Video by Castle Communications Records. Catalogue no: **HEN 2053 G**

**LIVE AT THE REGAL**
Tracks: / Everyday I have the blues / Sweet little angel / It's my own fault / How blue can you get / Please love me / You upset me baby / Worry, worry / Woke up this morning / You done lost your good thing now / Help the poor.
**Album:** Released Oct '83, on Ace by Ace Records. Catalogue no: **CH 86**
**CD:** Released Jun '88, on MCA (USA) by MCA Records (USA). Catalogue no: **31106**

**LIVE IN COOK COUNTY JAIL**
Tracks: / Everyday I have the blues / How blues can you get / Worry, worry / 3 o'clock blues / Darlin you know I love you / Sweet sixteen / Thrill is gone, The / Please accept my love.
**Album:** Released Oct '87, on MCA by MCA Records. Catalogue no: **IMCA 27005**
**CD:** Released Jun '88, on MCA (USA) by MCA Records (USA). Catalogue no: **31080**

**LIVE IN LONDON: B.B. KING**
Tracks: / Introduction / Everyday I have the blues / Night life / Love the life I'm living / When it all comes down / I've got a right to give up livin' / Encore.
**Cass:** Released Apr '84, on MCA by MCA Records. Catalogue no: **MCFC 3226**
**Album:** Released Apr '84, on MCA by MCA Records. Catalogue no: **MCF 3226**
**CD:** Released Oct '89, on Beat Goes On by Andy's Records. Catalogue no: **BGOCD 42**

**LIVE & WELL**
**CD:** Released Jun '88, on MCA (USA) by MCA Records (USA). Catalogue no: **31191**

**LOVE ME TENDER**
**Album:** Released Jun '82, on MCA by MCA Records. Deleted Jan '88. Catalogue no: **MCF 3139**

**LUCILLE**
**CD:** Released Feb '89, on Beat Goes On by Andy's Records. Catalogue no: **BGOCD 36**
**Album:** Released Feb '89, on Beat Goes On by Andy's Records. Catalogue no: **BGOLP 36**

**LUCILLE HAD A BABY**
Tracks: / You don't know / Shut your mouth / Early every morning / Ruby Lee / Don't you want a man like me / I stay in the mood / Can't we talk it over / Please remember me / Sweet little angel / Baby look at you / Lonely and blue / Trouble in mind / I want to get married / Love you baby / You upset me baby / I'm cracking up over you.
**Album:** Released 30 May '89, on Ace by Ace Records. Catalogue no: **CHD 271**

**MEMPHIS MASTERS, THE (Memphis Masters)**
Tracks: / Pray for you / Other night blues, The / Mistreated woman / Questionnaire blues / BB Blues / New way of driving, A / BB's boogie / It's my own fault darling / Walkin' and cryin' / Fine looking woman / She don't move me no more / Shake it up and go.
**Album:** Released Mar '82, on Ace by Ace Records. Catalogue no: **CH 50**

**MIDNIGHT BELIEVER**
Tracks: / When it all comes down / I just can't leave your love alone / Midnight believer / Hold on (I feel our love is changing) / Never make a move too soon / World full of strangers, A / Let me make you cry a little longer.
**Cass:** Released Jun '84, on MCA by MCA Records. Catalogue no: **MCLC 1802**
**Album:** Released Jun '84, on MCA by MCA Records. Catalogue no: **MCL 1802**

**NOW APPEARING AT OLE MISS**
Tracks: / Caldonia (blue theme) / Don't answer the door / You done lost your good thing now / I need love so bad / Nobody loves me but my mother / I got some outside help (I don't really need) / Darlin' you know I love you / When I'm wrong / Thrill is gone, The / Never make a move too soon / Three o'clock in the morning / Rock me baby / Guess who / I just can't leave your love alone.
Note: Double Album and Cassette.
**2 LP Set:** Released Feb '86, on MCA by MCA Records. Catalogue no: **MCDL 601**
**Cass:** Released Oct '87, on MCA by MCA Records. Catalogue no: **MCLDC 601**

**ONE NIGHTER BLUES**
Tracks: / She's dynamite / Low down dirty baby / I'm so glad / I gotta find my baby / Past day (didn't have to cry) / Bye bye baby / Highway bound / Boogie woogie woman / Please Love me / Blind love / Wake up this morning / When my heart beats like a hammer / Whole lot of love / That ain't the way to do it / Everything I do is wrong / Whole lotta meat.
Note: 16 tracks, 6 previously unissued and the remaining 10 very rare recordings from 1951-54.
**Album:** Released Apr '87, on Ace by Ace Records. Catalogue no: **CHD 201**

**ONE OF THOSE NIGHTS**
Tracks: / One of those nights / Since I met you baby.
**7" Single:** Released '82, on MCA by MCA Records. Deleted '87. Catalogue no: **MCA 788**

**RAREST B.B. KING**
Tracks: / Miss Martha King / My baby's gone / Hard working woman / Shake it up and go / Please hurry home / Woman I love, the / Everything I love is wrong / My sometime baby / When your baby packs up and goes / She's a mean woman / Someday, somewhere / Gotta find my baby / Why did you leave me / Love you baby / I need you so bad / Sugar mama.
**Album:** Released Aug '87, on Blues Boy (Sweden) Catalogue no: **BB 301**

**ROCK ME BABY**
Tracks: / Rock me, baby / Blue shadows / Worst thing in my life / Jungle / Eyesight to the blind / It's a mean world / I stay in the mood / I can hear my name / Got 'em bad / And like that.
**Album:** Released Oct '84, on Ace by Ace Records. Catalogue no: **CH 119**

**SIX SILVER STRINGS**
**Cass:** Released Sep '85, on MCA by MCA Records. Catalogue no: **MCFC 3281**
**CD:** Released Jun '88, on MCA (USA) by MCA Records (USA). Catalogue no: **5616**

**Album:** Released Sep '85, on MCA by MCA Records. Catalogue no: **MCF 3281**

**SPOTLIGHT ON LUCILLE**
Tracks: / Six silver strings / Big boss man / In the midnight hour / Into the night / My Lucille / Memory blues / My guitar sings the blues / Double trouble / Memory lane.

**Cass:** Released Sep '86, on Ace by Ace Records. Catalogue no: **CHC 187**

**STANDING ON THE EDGE OF LOVE**
Tracks: / Standing on the edge of love / Don't tell me nothing / Let yourself in for it (Extra track on 12" release only).

**12" Single:** Released Mar '87, on MCA by MCA Records. Catalogue no: **MCAT 1124**
**7" Single:** Released Mar '87, on MCA by MCA Records. Catalogue no: **MCA 1124**

**TAKE IT HOME**
Tracks: / Better not look down / Same old story / Happy birthday blues / I've always been lonely / Second hand woman / Tonight I'm gonna make you a star / Beginning of the end, The / Story everybody knows, A / Take it home.

**Cass:** Released Feb '84, on MCA by MCA Records. Catalogue no: **MCLC 1784**
**Album:** Released Aug '79, on MCA by MCA Records. Deleted Aug '84. Catalogue no: **MCF 3010**
**Album:** Released Feb '84, on MCA by MCA Records. Catalogue no: **MCL 1784**

**THERE MUST BE A BETTER WORLD**
**Album:** Released '81, on CBS by CBS Records. Deleted '86. Catalogue no: **MCF 3095**

**TOGETHER FOR THE FIRST TIME - (King, B.B. & Bobby Bland)**
Note: Historic live performance between blues giants B.B. King and Bobby Bland. Featuring some of their classic hits and blues standards. Recorded before a specially invited studio audience.
**Album:** Released Sep '89, on MCA (Import) by MCA Records. Catalogue no: **MCA 24160**
**CD:** Released Sep '89, on MCA (Import) by MCA Records. Catalogue no: **MCAD 24160**

## King, Freddie

**BONANZA OF INSTRUMENTALS**
Tracks: / Surf monkey / Low tide / Remington ride / King-a-ling / Manhole / Fish fair / Funnybone / Ploughed sailin' / Sad nite owl / Nickleplated / Freddie's midnite dream / Freeway 75 / Side tracked / Was out / Driving sideways / Untouchable glide.

**Album:** Released Dec '88, on Crosscut by Topic Records. Catalogue no: **CCR 1010**

**BURGLAR**
**Album:** Released Jun '88, on Polydor by Polydor Ltd. Catalogue no: **831 815-1**

**FREDDIE KING, 1934 - 1976**
**Album:** Released Jun '88, on Polydor by Polydor Ltd. Catalogue no: **831 817-1**
**CD:** Released May '88, on Polydor by Polydor Ltd. Deleted 30 Jun '89. Catalogue no: **831 817-2**

**FREDDIE KING**
**Album:** Released Jul '88, on Bellaphon Catalogue no: **BID 8012**

**GIVES YOU A BONANZA OF INSTRUMENTALS**
**Album:** Released Mar '90, on Crosscut by Topic Records. Catalogue no: **CCX1010**
**Album:** Released Nov '84, on Crosscut by Topic Records. Catalogue no: **CCR 1010**

**HIDEAWAY**
**Album:** Released Jul '88, on Bellaphon Catalogue no: **BID 8015**

**LARGER THAN LIFE**
**Album:** Released Jun '88, on Polydor by Polydor Ltd. Catalogue no: **831 816-1**

**LIVE IN ANTIBES 1974**
Tracks: / Going down the Highway / Woman across the river / It ain't nobody's business if I do / Let the good time roll / Big legged woman / Have you ever loved a woman / Hideaway.

**Album:** Released Jun '88, on France's Concert Catalogue no: **FC 111**
**CD:** Released Jun '88, on France's Concert Catalogue no: **FCD 111**

**LIVE IN NANCY 1975 VOL.1**
**Cass:** Released Jun '89, on France's Concert Catalogue no: **FCD 126**
**Album:** Released Jun '89, on France's Concert Catalogue no: **FC 126**

**ROCKIN' THE BLUES LIVE**
Tracks: / Hideaway / Big legged woman / Key to the highway / Mojo boogie / Wee baby blues / Meet me in the morning / Blues band shuffle.

**Album:** Released Oct '83, on Crosscut by Topic Records. Catalogue no: **CCR 1005**

**TAKIN' CARE OF BUSINESS**
Tracks: / I'm tore down / She put the wammee on me / Sen-sa-shun / Teardrops on your letter / Side tracked / Welfare, The (turns its back on you) / Stumble, The / Some day after a while (you'll be sorry) / Have you ever loved a woman / You know that you love me (but you never tell me so) / Hide away / I love the woman / San-ho-zay / Takin' care of business / High rise / You've got to love her with a feeling.
Note: An original King recording. Licensed from Gusto Records Inc., Nashville, Tennessee.
**Album:** Released Jul '85, on Charly R&B by Charly Records. Catalogue no: **CRB 1099**
**Cass:** Released Jul '85, on Charly R&B by Charly Records. Catalogue no: **TCCRB 1099**
**CD:** Released Oct '86, on Charly by Charly Records. Catalogue no: **CDCHARLY 30**

## King Of Drums

**KING OF DRUMS (Various artists)**
**Album:** Released Aug '84, on CBS (I love Jazz) by CBS Records. Catalogue no: **CBS 21113**
**Cass:** Released Aug '84, on CBS (I love Jazz) by CBS Records. Catalogue no: **40-21113**

## King, Peter

**BAD MEMORY**
Tracks: / Bad memory.

**12" Single:** Released Mar '86, on Fashion by Fashion Records. Catalogue no: **FAD 045**

**CRUSADE**
**Album:** Released Sep '89, on WEA by WEA Records. Catalogue no: **BYN 19**
**CD:** Released Sep '89, on WEA by WEA Records. Catalogue no: **K 2461172**
**Cass:** Released Sep '89, on WEA by WEA Records. Catalogue no: **BYNC 19**

**MY KIND OF COUNTRY**
**Album:** Released Dec '77, on Tank Catalogue no: **BSS 114**

**NITE LIFE**
Tracks: / Nite life.
**12" Single:** Released Sep '83, on 6 AM by 6 AM Records. Deleted '87. Catalogue no: **AM 12 704**
**7" Single:** Released Sep '83, on 6 AM by 6 AM Records. Deleted '87. Catalogue no: **AM 704**

**SOMETHING WICKED**
Tracks: / Something wicked / Young blood.
**7" Single:** Released May '86, on Spirit (1) by Spirit Records. Catalogue no: **FIRE 10**
**12" Single:** Released May '86, on Spirit (1) by Spirit Records. Catalogue no: **FIRET 10**

**STEP ON THE GAS**
Tracks: / Step on the gas / Ten comandments of M.C..
**12" Single:** Released May '85, on Fashion by Fashion Records. Catalogue no: **FAD 029**

## King, Peter Quartet

**BROTHER BERNARD**
Tracks: / Overjoyed / But beautiful / Dalin / Brother Bernard / Chatelet / Playing in the yard.
Note: This album features the saxophonist Peter King with his regular quartet and guests Alan Skidmore and Guy Barker. A must for all jazz buyers.
**Album:** Released Sep '88, on Miles Music by Miles Music Records. Catalogue no: **MM 076**

**EAST 34TH STREET**
**Album:** Released '83, on Spotlite by Spotlite Records. Catalogue no: **SPJ 524**

**HI FLY (King, Peter with Philippe Briand Trio)**
**Album:** Released Apr '88, on Spotlite by Spotlite Records. Catalogue no: **SPJ 527**

**NEW BEGINNING (King, Peter Quartet)**
Tracks: / Blues for S.J. / Dolphin dance. / Before the dawn / Dream dancing / Fourth emergence / New beginning / Three blonde mice / Gingerbread boy / Confirmation.
**Album:** Released '83, on Spotlite by Spotlite Records. Catalogue no: **SPJ 520**

**NINETY PERCENT OF ONE PERCENT**
Tracks: / Old folks / 3/4 peace / Eye of the hurricane / Gingerhead boy.
**Album:** Released '88, on Spotlite by Spotlite Records. Catalogue no: **SPJ 529**

## King Pleasure

**AIN'T NOBODY HERE BUT US (new jive version) (King Pleasure & The Biscuit Boys)**
Tracks: / Ain't nobody here but us chickens (new jive) / Chicken rhythm / All night long.
**7" Single:** Released 16 Jun '89, on Big Bear by Big Bear Records. Catalogue no: **BB 40**

**KING PLEASURE & ANNIE ROSS SING (King Pleasure & Annie Ross)**
Tracks: / Red top / Sometimes I'm happy / What can I say after I say I'm sorry / Parker's mood / Twisted / Time was right, The / Jumpin' with symphony sid / This is always / Don't get scared / I'm gone / Farmer's market / Annie's lament.
**Album:** Released May '88, on Prestige Catalogue no: **PR 7128**
**Cass:** Released May '88, on Prestige Deleted Jan '90. Catalogue no: **PRC 7128**

**KING PLEASURE & THE BISCUIT BOYS (King Pleasure & The Biscuit Boys)**
**Album:** Released Dec '88, on Big Bear by Big Bear Records. Catalogue no: **BEAR 30**

**THIS IS IT (King Pleasure & The Biscuit Boys)**
**CD:** Released Jan '90, on Big Bear by Big Bear Records. Catalogue no: **BEARCD 32**
**Cass:** Released Jan '90, on Big Bear by Big Bear Records. Catalogue no: **BEARMC 32**
**Album:** Released Jan '90, on Big Bear by Big Bear Records. Catalogue no: **BEAR 32**

## King, Saunders

**FIRST KING OF THE BLUES**
Tracks: / Summertime boogie part 1 / Summertime boogie part 2 / Lazy woman / Every night about midnight / Read the good book / I'm so worried / Get yourself another fool / I had a dream last night / Drop me a line / My close friend / Quit hanging around / Long long time / Quit hanging around (alternative version) / Going mad / Empty bed room blues / Summertime / Saunders King blues / What's the story morning glory.
**2 LP Set:** Released Oct '88, on Ace by Ace Records. Catalogue no: **CHD 248**

**WHAT'S YOUR STORY MORNING GLORY**
Tracks: / Swingin' / Why was I born / Write me a letter blues / What's your story, morning glory? / What's your story, morning glory? / S.K. groove / Something's worrying me / 2.00 a.m. hop / St. James infirmary blues / Little girl / Empty bedroom blues / Imagination / Stormy night / Stormy night blues / Read the good book / Misery blues / Danny boy / Going mad.
**Album:** Released Aug '87, on Blues Boy (Sweden) Catalogue no: **BB 303**

## King Soloman

**NON SUPPORT BLUES**
**Album:** Released '88, on Diving Duck (Holland) Catalogue no: **DD 4303**

## Kings Of Dixieland

**KINGS OF DIXIELAND 20 Great Dixieland jazz hits (Various artists)**
Tracks: / Washington post march: *Various artists* / Bill Bailey: *Various artists* / Thunder and blazes: *Various artists* / East side, West side: *Various artists* / Wait till the sun shines Nellie: *Various artists* / Daisy Bell: *Various artists* / Tell me your dream: *Various artists* / Careless love: *Various artists* / Ramblin' wreck from Georgia Tech: *Various artists* / Carry me back to old Virginny: *Various artists* / New Washington and Lee swing: *Various artists* / Ida: *Various artists* / Semper Fidelis: *Various artists* / Give my regards to Broadway: *Various artists* / Somebody stole my gal: *Various artists* / Merry widow blues: *Various artists* / Oh, dem golden slippers: *Various artists* / Goodnight ladies: *Various artists* / King fish blues: *Various artists* / Battle hymn of the republic: *Various artists* (Traditional words by Howe and Steffe).
**CD:** Released Jun '87, on Hermes by Nimbus Records. Catalogue no: **HRM 7004**

**KINGS OF DIXIELAND: VOL 1 (Various artists)**
**Album:** Released Apr '79, on Bright Orange Catalogue no: **BO 726**

**KINGS OF DIXIELAND: VOL 2 (Various artists)**
**Album:** Released Apr '79, on Bright Orange Catalogue no: **BO 727**

**KINGS OF DIXIELAND: VOL 3 (Various artists)**
**Album:** Released Apr '79, on Bright Orange Catalogue no: **BO 728**

**KINGS OF DIXIELAND: VOL 4 (Various artists)**
**Album:** Released Apr '79, on Bright Orange Catalogue no: **BO 729**

**KINGS OF DIXIELAND: VOL 5 (Various artists)**
**Album:** Released Apr '79, on Bright Orange Catalogue no: **BO 730**

**KINGS OF DIXIELAND: VOL 6 (Various artists)**
**Album:** Released Apr '79, on Bright Orange Catalogue no: **BO 731**

## Kings Of Ragtime Guitar

**KINGS OF RAGTIME GUITAR (Various artists)**
**Album:** Released Dec '88, on Yazoo (USA) by Shanachie Records (USA). Catalogue no: **L 1044**

## Kings Of Soul

**KINGS OF SOUL (Various artists)**
Note: Sam & Dave, Percy Sledge, Aretha Franklin, Ben E. King, Brook Benton, Fontella Bass, Barbara Mason.
**CD:** Released Oct '86, on Bridge (MCS Bridge) Catalogue no: **100 022**

## Kings Of Swing

**KINGS OF SWING (Various artists)**
Tracks: / I've heard that song before: *James, Harry Orchestra* / Willow weep for me: *Goodman, Benny* / Ultra: *James, Harry* / Oh lady be good: *Goodman, Benny* / All or nothing at all: *James, Harry* / Intermission riff: *Kenton, Stan* / Peanut vendor: *Kenton, Stan* / You make me love you: *James, Harry* / Take the 'A' train: *Kenton, Stan* / Satin doll: *James, Harry* / Don't be that way: *Goodman, Benny* / Two o'clock jump: *James, Harry*.
Note: Orchestras of Benny Goodman, Harry James, Les Brown, Bob Crosby, Charley Barnet, and Tex Beneke.
**CD:** Released Apr '87, on Bridge (MCS Bridge) Catalogue no: **100 017**
**Album:** Released Feb '82, on Elite (Decca) by Decca Records. Deleted '88. Catalogue no: **TAB 35**
**CD:** Released Jan '86, on Delta (1) by Delta Records. Catalogue no: **11 041**
**CD Set:** Released '88, on Delta (1) by Delta Records. Catalogue no: **19 900**

## Kings Of Blues

**KINGS OF THE BLUES (Various artists)**
Tracks: / Sweet little angel: *King, B.B.* / She moves me: *Watson, Johnny 'Guitar'* / I'll get along somehow: *Sims, Frankie Lee* / Blues serenade: *Turner, Babyface* / On my way back home: *Flash Terry* / Odds against me: *Hooker, John Lee* / Sitting here thinking: *Walker, T-Bone* / Problem child: *Dee, Mercy* / Lonesome old feeling: *Slim, Bumble Bee* / I tried: *Young Wolf* / Cotton picker: *Higgins, Chuck & The Melotones* / Wild hop: *Crayton, Pee Wee* / Worried about my baby: *Howlin' Wolf* / Tavern lounge boogie: *Burns, Eddie 'guitar'* / Believe I'll change towns: *Hogg, Smokey* / Too many rivers: *Fulsom, Lowell* / Yesterday: *Chenier, Clifton* / Lonesome dog blues: *Lightnin' Hopkins* / Hard times: *Fuller, Johnny* / Riding mighty high: *Dixon, Floyd* / Please find my baby: *James, Elmore*.

**Cass:** Released 31 Jul '89, on Ace by Ace Records. Catalogue no: **CHC 276**
**Album:** Released 31 Jul '89, on Ace by Ace Records. Catalogue no: **CH 276**
**CD:** Released 31 Jul '89, on Ace by Ace Records. Catalogue no: **CDCH 276**

**KINGS OF THE BLUES (BRIDGE) (Various artists)**
Note: Brownie McGhee, Big Joe Williams, Lonnie Johnson, Sonny Terry, Champion Jack Dupree etc.
**CD:** Released Jan '86, on Bridge (MCS Bridge) Catalogue no: **100 004**

**KINGS OF THE BLUES (SOUND) (Various artists)**
Tracks: / Blue monday: *Various artists* / Holy cow: *Various artists* / Dimples: *Various artists* / Honky tonk: *Various artists*
**CD:** Released Jan '89, on Sound by Target Records. Catalogue no: **2 - 804**

**KINGS OF THE BLUES (TOPLINE) (Various artists)**
**CD:** Released May '87, on Topline by Charly Records. Catalogue no: **CD CHARLY 520**
**Cass:** Released Aug '87, on Topline by Charly Records. Catalogue no: **KTOP 180**
**Album:** Released Aug '87, on Topline by Charly Records. Catalogue no: **TOP 180**

## Kings Of Memphis Town

**KINGS OF MEMPHIS TOWN (Various artists)**
**Album:** Released Oct '88, on Roots (Germany) Catalogue no: **RL 333**

## Kinsey, Tony

**THAMES SUITE (Kinsey,Tony Big Band)**
Tracks: / Sunbury seminar / Chertsey mead / Kingston reach / Henley ho / Hard times / Cockham Bridge / Beachy Head / Girl Friday.
**Album:** Released '83, on Spotlite by Spotlite Records. Catalogue no: **SPJ 504**

## Kirby, John

**1941: JOHN KIRBY (Kirby, John & His Orchestra)**
**Album:** Released Aug '88, on Circle (USA) by Jazzology Records (USA). Catalogue no: **CLP 14**

**BIGGEST LITTLE BAND IN THE LAND**
Note: Featuring Charlie Shavers, Buster Bailey
**Album:** Released Sep '87, on Giants of Jazz by Hasmick Promotions. Catalogue no: **LPJT 26**

**JOHN KIRBY**
Tracks: / Ida / Peanut vendor / Revolutionary etude / Blue fantasy / Same old story / Polonaise / Prelude for trumpet / Last night the nightingale woke me / I give you my word / Rustle of spring No.1 / Rehearsin' for a nervous breakdown / Echoes of Harlem.
**Album:** Released Jan '87, on Atlantis by Charly Records. Deleted May '88. Catalogue no: **ATS 6**
**Cass:** Released Dec '86, on Atlantis by Charly Records. Deleted May '88. Catalogue no: **TCATS 6**

**JOHN KIRBY 1939-41**
**Album:** Released '88, on Tax Catalogue no: **TAX 8016**

**JOHN KIRBY AND ORCHESTRA (With Maxine Sullivan) (Kirby, John & His Orchestra)**
**Album:** Released Jun '88, on Circle (USA) by Jazzology Records (USA). Catalogue no: **CLP 47**

**JOHN KIRBY & ONYX CLUB BOYS VOL. 2 (Kirby, John & Onyx Club Boys)**
**Album:** Released '88, on Collector's Classics Catalogue no: **12-3**

**JOHN KIRBY & ONYX CLUB BOYS VOL. 3 (Kirby, John & Onyx Club Boys)**
**Album:** Released '88, on Collector's Classics Catalogue no: **12-10**

**JOHN KIRBY & ONYX CLUB BOYS VOL. 4 (Kirby, John & Onyx Club Boys)**
**Album:** Released '88, on Collector's Classics Catalogue no: **12-11**

**MORE (Kirby, John & His Orchestra)**
**Album:** Released Aug '88, on Circle (USA) by Jazzology Records (USA). Catalogue no: **CLP 64**

## Kirk, Andy

**ALL OUT FOR HICKSVILLE**
**Album:** Released '88, on Hep Jazz by Hep Records. Catalogue no: **HEP 1007**

**ANDY KIRK AND CLOUDS OF JOY (Kirk, Andy/Clouds of Joy/June Richmond)**
**Album:** Released '88, on Hindsight Catalogue no: **HSR 227**

**ANDY KIRK AT TRIANNON, CLEVELAND (Kirk, Andy/Clouds of Joy/June Richmond)**
**Album:** Released '89, on Jazz Society Catalogue no: **AA 503**

**ANDY'S JIVE (Kirk, Andy / his orchestra)**
**Album:** Released Dec '84, on Swing House by Submarine Records. Catalogue no: **SWH 39**

**CLOUDY (Kirk, Andy/his Twelve Clouds of Joy)**
**Album:** Released May '84, on Hep Jazz by Hep Records. Catalogue no: **HEP 1002**

**WALKIN' AND SWINGIN' (Kirk, Andy / his Twelve Clouds of Joy)**
Tracks: / Mary's idea / Until the real thing comes along / Walkin' and swingin' / Lady who swings the band / Floyd's guitar blues / Lotta sax appeal / Ring dem bells / Twinklin' / Little Joe from Chicago / McGhee special / Moten swing / Wednesday night hop / Cloudy / Twelfth St. rag / Big Jim blues / 47th street live.
**Album:** Released Sep '83, on Affinity by Charly Records. Catalogue no: **AFS 1011**

## Kirk, Rahsaan Roland

**CASE OF THE THREE**
**CD:** Released '88, on Atlantic Jazz by WEA Records. Catalogue no: **K78 139 6**

**EARLY ROOTS**
**Album:** Released Jun '84, on Affinity by Charly Records. Catalogue no: **AFF 121**

**INFLATED TEAR, THE (Kirk, Roland)**
Tracks: / Black and crazy blues, The / Laugh for Rory, A / Many blessings / Fingers in the wind / Inflated tear, The / Creole love call / Handful of fives, A / Fly by night / Lovelieveliloqui.
**Album:** on Atlantic by WEA Records. Catalogue no: **K 50233**

**INTRODUCING ROLAND KIRK**
Tracks: / Call,The / Soul station / Our waltz / Our love is here to stay / Spirit girl / Jack the ripper.
Note: Featuring Ira Sullivan.
**Cass:** Released Aug '88, on Chess by Vogue Records. Catalogue no: **GCHK 78093**
**Album:** Released Aug '88, on Chess by Vogue Records. Catalogue no: **GCH 8093**

**KIRK'S WORKS**
Tracks: / Three for Dizzy / Makin' Whoopee / Funk underneath / Kirk's works / Doin' the sixty-eight / Too Late Now / Skater's Waltz.
**Cass:** Released Mar '88, on Prestige Deleted Jan '90. Catalogue no: **PRC 7210**
**Album:** Released Mar '88, on Prestige Catalogue no: **PR 7210**

**LIVE IN PARIS 1970**
Tracks: / Easy to love / My cherie amour / Inflated tear, The / Boogie man song / Love Madeline / Petite fleur / Three for the festival.
**Album:** Released Jun '88, on France's Concert Catalogue no: **FC 109**
**CD:** Released Jun '88, on France's Concert Catalogue no: **FCD 109**

**LIVE IN PARIS 1970 VOL. 2**
Tracks: / Sweet fire / Make me a pallet on the floor / Charlie Parker medley / Volunteer slavery / You did it, you did it / Satin doll.
**CD:** Released Jun '88, on France's Concert Catalogue no: **FCD 115**
**Album:** Released Jun '88, on France's Concert Catalogue no: **FC 115**

**NOW PLEASE DON'T YOU CRY**
Tracks: / Blue roll / Alfie / Why don't they know ? / Silverlization / Fall out / Don't you cry, beautiful Edith / Stomping ground / It's a grand night for singing.
Note: Roland Kirk, tenor sax, clarinet, manzello, stritch, flute, voice; Lonnie Smith, piano; Ronnie Boykins, bass; Grady Tate, drums. Recorded in 1968.
**Album:** Released Apr '83, on Verve

(USA) by Polydor Ltd. Catalogue no: **2304 519**

**Album:** Released Aug '89, on Polydor by Polydor Ltd. Catalogue no: **837 439 1**

## PREPARE TO DEAL WITH A MIRACLE

Tracks: / Salvation and reminiscing / Seasons / One mind winter summer / Ninth ghost / Celestial bliss / Saxophone miracle / Saxophone concerto / One breath beyond / Dance of revolution.

**Album:** on Atlantic by WEA Records. Catalogue no: **K 40508**

## PRE-RAHSAAN

Tracks: / Three for Dizzy / Makin' whoopee / Funk underneath / Kirk's work / Doin' the sixty-eight / Too late now / Skater's waltz / Parisian thoroughfare / Hazy Eve / Shine on me / Evidence / Memories of you / Teach me tonight.

**2 LP Set:** Released '79, on Prestige Deleted '84. Catalogue no: **PR 24080**

## SOULFUL SAXES (Kirk, Rahsaan Roland & Booker Ervin)

Tracks: / Roland's theme / Slow groove / Stormy weather / Nearness of you, The / A la carte / Easy living / Triple threat / Blue book, The / Git it / Little Jane / Book cooks, The / Largo / Poor butterfly.

Note: Note: Tracks 1-7 recorded New York City, 1956. Features James Madison (piano), Carl Pruitt (bass), Henry Duncan (drums).

Tracks 8-13 recorded New York City, 1960. Features Tommy Turrentine (trumpet), Booker Ervin (tenor sax), Zoot Sims (tenor sax), Tommy Flanagan (piano), George Tucker (bass), Dannie Richmond (drums).

Not content with releasing the recent *Saxophone syndicate* (CDAFF 754) Affinity welcome you herewith to another stunning saxists spectacular. Unlike the relatively conventional two-tenor tournaments on the earlier CD between Paul Quinichette and Charlie Rouse and between Red Holloway and Sonny Stitt, the sessions involved here both field a potential three piece front line, one including the tenors of Booker Ervin and Zoot Sims and the other featuring three saxophones, all of them played by Rahsaan Roland Kirk. The legendary Kirk still seems somewhat improbable to those never privileged to see him in the flesh, but the fact remains that playing three horns simultaneously and making them make sense was an integral part not just of an act, but of his musical interpretations. It was, or course, reserved by and large for theme standards which could be prepared beforehand, or to create climactic moments in a performance (rather like this use of a siren to underscore the release of tension). Already by the time of making the enclosed debut session at the age of 20, he had begun experimenting with three-part harmonies as heard in the theme statement of the original title-track *Triple threat* and the closing choruses of *A la carte*, both of theme 12-bar blues in G like some of his later variants such as *Three for the festival.*

*A la carte*, incidentally, appears to be closely based on Bill Doggett's hit *Honky tonk* recorded only five months previously for the same label (King Records); its tenor solo also quotes from the rather earlier Ruth Brown song *Mama, he treats your daughter mean* and constitutes about the only possible justification for the *New Grove Dictionary of jazz* describing this Kirk debut as 'a rhythm and blues album'. But surely one of the most important aspects, probably the most important aspect, of the Kirk phenomenon was his demonstration of how meaningless such categorisation can sometimes be. Jazz, blues, rhythm and blues, swing, bebop, trad, avant-garde, Latin and doubtless one or two other styles, all were grist to his mill. And, as well as his eventually explicit aim of exposing the continuity and unity of all these forms of 'black classical music', he did do by achieving a personal amalgam which was recognisably individual and indivisible.

Clearly he was already thinking along these lines when he came to make this early session, just a few short years after he had his famous dream about playing simultaneous saxophones which led directly to his discovery of the archaic stritch and manzello in an instrument shop. (It was in a later dream that he acquired the name 'Rahsaan' which although to the ear rather like a reversal of Sun Ra, was never to my knowledge given a translation). The alto-register stritch and the soprano sounding manzello are heard soloing respectively on *Slow groove* and *Roland's theme*, both also 12 bars with their themes played in two part harmony. And on two of the three remaining popular song standards, he found a way to realise another part of his dream and create not merely saxophone 'section' chords but two independent melodic lines at the same time; by 1970 and the album *Rahsaan Rahsaan* he had actually managed to achieve this feat absolutely live whereas in 1956 he had to be content with over dubbing (for the only time in his career, I think), beginning both *Stormy weather) and The nearness of you* with a tenor lead plus manzello improvisation and then switching roles for the second half of each piece.

Not much is known about Kirk's accompanists, with the exception of the bassist Carl Pruitt who worked with (among many others) Cootie Williams in the '40s, Earl Hines in the late 50s and Woody Herman in the 60s. Henry Duncan did play drums in Roland's touring group in the early 60s and made half an album with him at the time that Andrew Hill was his regular pianist. Butthe incisive James Madison, who has his solo on *Easy living* graced by a sax-section fill-in phrase (and immediately followed by a stritch quotation from *the boy next door*, is something of a mystery unless it's significant that, on the aforementioned 1970 Kirk album, he had a drummer by the name of James Madison. Happily, the same is not so true of the Booker Elvin Group heard here, with George Tucker who played bass on many 60s dates (including Eric Dolphy's debut album) and Stanley Turrentine's elder brother Tommy being perhaps the least renowned, albeit rather unjustly. The remainder of the rhythm section has the ever resourceful and sprightly Tommy Flanagan on piano and drummer Dannie Richmond, who had just become Booker's workmate again as Ervin replaced Yusef Lateef in the Charles Mingus group that was bound forthe Antibes Jazz Festival.

Very possibly it was the producer's idea to pair Ervin for this session (his debut under his own name) with the great, and at the time much better-known, swing to bop tenor of Zoot Sims who was shortly to make his own album for the same label, Bethlehem (with Tucker, Richmond and Dave McKenna, the results were reissued on Affinity CDCHARLY 59). One of the reasons the idea was such a success is that the wide contrast between the tenorists' styles is combined with a great compatibility of energy levels, (another reason may be that Zoot was also a somtime colleague and fan of Mingus, having known him from their mid-40s California days and subsequently recording with him not only on the 1962 Town Hall concert but also on an obscure Pepper Adams album that featured Mingus's compositions and in studio direction). Nowhere is their compatibility more evident than on the 10 1/2 minute album title track *The book cooks* which apart from taking separate solos, then 4s, 12s, 2s and collective improvisation. Whether this was also the producer's idea, or whether mutual appreciation and competition were the main reason, their exciting exchange continues with unflagging invention by both parties until the tape runs out.

By no coincidence, Elvin's like Kirk's was a session with a lot of blues material; in addition to *The book cooks*, there is the impressively slow *Blue book* and the irrepressible medium-temp *Git it*, on both of which Ervin comes storming in after a piano solo. This is the sort of deliberate contrast beloved of Mingus, and it certainly heightens the impact of Booker's unique wailing tone, often enhanced as well by his tense articulation and his selection of shouts, smear and falls on specific notes. Even such an innocent seeming popular standard as *Poor butterfly* is subjected to an intense treatment which is all of a piece with Booker's two other original, the 32-bar *Little Jane* and the 12 + 12 + 8 + 12 Largo, a supremely moody tenor solo with just the rhythm section. Ervin went on to make two further albums within the space of six months and several more in the remaining ten years of his life, all of them consistently emotive. Bookier died in 1970 aged 39, Rahsaan in 1977 aged

41, and both gave of themselves unremittingly in the cause of music. As far as I know, the only way you can hear them playing together is on the 1961 Mingus session which produced *Oh yeah* and half of *Tonight at noon*, where they comprised the sextet front line along with trombonist Jimmy Knepper (who incidently has his own concurrent release on Affinity CD AFF 756). But the musical links between them make it highly appropriate to hear them one after the other on this compact disc. (Brian Priestley, Author, Mingus: A critical biography, Quartet/Paladin)
**CD:** Released Nov '89, on Affinity by Charly Records. Catalogue no: **CDAFF 758**

**VIBRATION CONTINUES,THE**
Tracks: / Inflated tear, The (introduction and medley) / Water for Robeson and Williams / Volunteered slavery / I love you / Yes I do / Rahsaanica / Do nothin' 'til you hear from me / Ain't no sunshine / Tribute to John Coltrane, A / Three for the festival / Old rugged cross / Black and crazy blues, The / Portrait of those beautiful ladies / If I loved you / Creole love call / Seasons.
**Album:** Released Jul '78, on Atlantic by WEA Records. Catalogue no: **K 60133**

**VIBRATION SOCIETY**
**Album:** Released Nov '87, on Stash (USA) Catalogue no: **ST 261**

**WE FREE KINGS**
Tracks: / Three for the festival / Moon song / Sackful of soul / Haunted melody / Blues for Alice / We free kings / You did it, you did it / Some kind of love / My delight.
Note: Roland Kirk, tenor sax, manzello, stritch, flute; Richard Wyands, Hank Jones, piano; Art Davis, Wendell Marshall, bass; Charlie Persip, drums. First issued in 1961.
**Album:** Released Jun '83, on Mercury by Phonogram Ltd. Catalogue no: **6336 384**
**CD:** Released Nov '86, on Polydor by Polydor Ltd. Catalogue no: **826 455-2**

## Kitchen, Geoff

**JAZZ FOUNDATIONS**
**Album:** Released Jan '83, on Swaggie (Australia) Catalogue no: **S 1385**

## Knapp, James

**FIRST AVENUE**
**Album:** Released Jul '81, on ECM Catalogue no: **ECM 1194**

## Knepper, Jimmy

**CUNNINGBIRD**
**Album:** Released Jul '88, on Steeplechase (USA) Catalogue no: **SCS 1061**
**CD:** Released Jul '88, on Steeplechase (USA) Catalogue no: **SCCD 31061**

**DREAM DANCING (Knepper, Jimmy Quintet)**
**Album:** Released Jan '87, on Criss Cross Catalogue no: **CRISS 1024**

**I DREAM TOO MUCH (Knepper, Jimmy Sextet)**
**CD:** Released '86, on Soul Note Catalogue no: **SN 1092**

**IDOL OF THE FLIES**
Tracks: / Love letters / Ogling ogre / You stepped out of a dream / How high the moon / Gee baby / Ain't I good to you / Idol of the flies / Close as pages in a book / Avid admirer / Irresistible you.
**Album:** Released May '82, on Affinity by Charly Records. Deleted '88. Catalogue no: **AFF 89**

**MUTED JOYS**
Tracks: / Love letters / Ogling ogre / You stepped out of a dream / How high the moon / Gee baby, ain't I good to you / Idol of the flies / Close as pages in a book / Avid admirer / Irresistible you / Tell me / Brewery boys blues / Ecclusiastics / I thought about you / Home.
Note: The music of Jimmy Knepper is an intriguing combination of strength and subtlety. The strength is evident throughout the disc, drawn from widely separated segments of Knepper's career. It is also evident in his contributions to the work of Charles Mingus (the bandleader with whom his name is most closely associated), from the 1957 *Haitian fight song* on his first Mingus album *The clown* to his guest appearance on *Cumbia and jazz fusion* two decades later. Versatility can also be a sign of strength, the ability to blend with others' conceptions without losing one's own individuality being rarer (even within the jazz world) than you might think. But Knepper has worked successfully with big bands as different as Stan Kenton, Benny Goodman, Thad Jones & Mel Lewis and Gil Evans, recording with each of them. At other times he earned a living with more commercial bands such as Ralph Marterie and played for several years in Broadway pit orchestras. The Knepper solo style remained intact even between 1961 and 1976 when very little of it was being exposed in public or on record, surely another sign of strength.

It's fair to say, however, that for many listeners that musical strength is obscured by the subtlety of Jimmy's approach. Even in a shouting solo his tone is not the traditional jazz trombone sound, nor is it the dry and rather clipped tone of J.J. Johnson and his followers. Rather it's the emotive expression of ambiguous anxieties and muted joys (incidentally, he frequently manages to suggest an actual trombone mute while playing 'open' by his special use of embouchure and slide). Similarly his melodic style is not routine or predictable; above all, the convolutions of his lines betray his absorption of Charlie Parker's vocabularly. It was the impact of Parker that prompted Jimmy to help operate the portable disc-cutter of Dean Benedeti at Los Angeles's Hi De Ho Club and others, and later to tape Bird on 52nd Street, at St Nick's and at the famous *Apartment sessions.* There is also something in the combination of bebop phraseology, laid back legato phrasing and veiled articulation that suggests a similarity between Jimmy and Lee Konitz, with whose nonet he worked in the late 1970s. One further manifestation of Knepper's subtlety is his interest in composition and arranging. Although capable of creating complex scores such as the Roy Porter band's *Gassin' the wig,* it's most instructive to study the contents of the tracks reissued here. The many standard (and not so standard) popular songs are all interpreted with care and individuality, wit and (yes) subtlety, even though at first hearing they may seem simple and straightforward, they turn out to be more memorable than expected.
There is also considerable variety in the material, even between the two 12 bar blues in B-flat, *Brewery boy blues* and *Avid admirer.* While Jimmy's solo work is recognisably consistent despite the timespan, the 1979 theme is an exercise in punched out rhythmic figures, changing from chorus to chorus, whereas the earlier composition is a difficult but logical Parkeresque line, capable of being played as in the second chorus. (Coincidentally, though the exchange of fours in the last mentioned opus begins with a deliberate quotation, the tune of *Avid admirer's* answer, *Ogling ogre* is based on a phrase that turned up the following year in Ellington's *Mr. Gentle and Mr. Cool.* Compare the title-track of the 1979 album, *Tell me* with the equally lengthy structure of *Idol of the flies* (also elevated to title-track status on some re-issues); the model approach of both represents one way of harnessing the Mingus influence, which is of course specifically acknowledged in the later session's beautiful version of *Ecclusiastics*
Looking at some of the standards, note Jimmy's backings behind the tunes on, for instance the up tempo *Love letters* complete with verse (recorded about the same time as the pop gospel version by Ketty Lester and *You stepped out of a dream.* The trombone countermelodies are conceived with such freedom that it takes a while to realise that, like the piano figure on *How high the moon,* they are pre-arranged by Knepper. What is more, the same harmonic style is clearly at the root of the Dutch session's three-horn arrangement of *Home* the song, done in 1931 by Armstrong also with an allusion to *There's no place like home,* was originally co-written by an Amsterdam born composer, Peter Van Steedan These selections, of course, illustrate Jimmy's eye for unusual material. *I thought about you,* done here as a duet with pianist Nico Bunink, is perhaps best-known, being associated with Frank Sinatra and Miles Davis among others. But the same cannot be said of other items here such as the three by the group with Gene Roland: *Close as pages in a book* and *Irresistible you* (recorded by Charlie Parker)were 1940's musical comedy numbers while Don Redman's 1929 *Gee baby,* though now something of a mainstream jazz standard, was a unexpected choice for 'mod-

ernist' musicians in 1957. By then, however, Knepper had left the West Coast for New York (making the move at 29, just like Mingus) and began working with the bassist on other unexpected tunes such as *Flamingo* (from Tijuana Moods) and *Memories of you* (see Affinity CD CHARLY 19). Indeed it was Mingus who had recorded Jimmy's debut under his own name just a couple of months earlier, and who had introduced him to Lee Kraft of Bethlehem who produced the first album here. Not surprisingly Knepper booked one of his favourite drummers, fellow Mingus sideman Dannie Richmond, while the two pianists were also heard in Mingus's own Bethlehem sessions on the aforementioned CD. Trumpeter (and prominent arranger) Gene Roland was an old friend from Jimmy's West Coast days, and his vocal on *Gee baby* allows the leader to idulge in some rootsy, almost Vic Dickenson like backing.

By the time of the 1979 session, Knepper had become an internationally celebrated soloist, taking part in the first Mingus Dynasty concerts, touring as a single and recording regularly (more often, inevitably, for European than American labels). His colleagues on this set for the Dutch label Daybreak included Nico Bunink who, with the sole exception of Philip Catherine, was the only European musician ever to work and record with Mingus in the U.S.A. And the remaining performers' interpretation of Jimmy's specially prepared arrangments are easily equal to comparison with their American counterparts of 22 years before. Commenting on his own work here, Jimmy once told me, 'I slept about two hours and then drove from Belgium to Amsterdam, and I was kinda out on my feet when we did it. I was lucky to get through that day. But that's the way a musician's life goes; sometimes you have to do something when you're in no shape at all to do it'. Startling revelations indeed, for suffice it to say that I (and you I think) would never have suspected it. As always, Knepper plays up to his usual high standard and, as always, sounds like no one but himself.
**CD:** Released Nov '89, on Affinity by Charly Records. Catalogue no: **CDAFF 756**

**PRIMROSE PATH (Knepper, Jimmy & Bobby Wellins)**
**Album:** Released Jul '82, on Hep Jazz by Hep Records. Catalogue no: **HEP 2012**

**TELL ME (Knepper, Jimmy Sextet)**
Tracks: / Tell me / Brewery boys blues / Nearer my God / Ecclusiastics / I thought about you / Home / Tell me.
**Album:** Released 30 Apr '88, on Affinity by Charly Records. Catalogue no: **AFF 183**

## Knudsen, Mikkelborg

**HEART TO HEART (Knudsen, Mikkelborg)**
**Album:** Released '88, on Storyville by Storyville Records AB. Catalogue no: **SLP 4114**

## Koch, Merle

**MERLE KOCH'S POLITE JAZZ QUARTET**
**Album:** Released Aug '88, on Audiophile (USA) by Jazzology Records (USA). Catalogue no: **AP 126**

## Koller, Hans

**EARLY RECORDINGS OF HANS KOLLER 1942-50**
Tracks: / Harlem swing / Sioux city Sue / Stop / Prisoner's song / Hallo Tommy / Pipsi boogie / Nesty boogie / Dunkle schatten / Delphi / Air mail special / Amapola / Open the door Richard / Frankies boogie / Study in F / What's this / Bei mir bist du schon / Ray's idea.
**Album:** Released Jan '88, on Harlequin by Interstate Music. Catalogue no: **HQ 2066**

## Konitz, Lee

**BLEW see also under Space Jazz Trio (Konitz, Lee & Space Jazz Trio)**
**Album:** Released Mar '90, on Philology Catalogue no: **214W 26**

**CHICAGO 'N ALL THAT JAZZ**
Tracks: / My own best friend / Razzle dazzle / Loopin' de loop / Funny honey / Class / Me and my baby / Roxie / Ten per cent.
Note: Personnel: Lee Konitz - alto & soprano sax; LLoyd Michaels & Richard Gurwitz - trumpets; Barry Maur & Alan Raph - trombones; Don Palmer & Joe Farrell - tenor saxes; Dick Katz - piano & electric piano; Michael Longo - keyboard & synthesizer; George Davis - guitar; Major Holly - bass; Eddie Locke - drums; Ray Armand - percussion.
**CD:** Released '88, on Denon. Catalogue no: **C38 7971**
**CD:** Released Apr '89, on Denon. Catalogue no: **DC 8544**
**Cass:** Released Apr '89, on Denon. Catalogue no: **MC 7971**

**DOVE TAIL**
Tracks: / I want to be happy / Night has a thousand eyes, The / Counterpoint / Dovetail / Sweet Georgia Brown / Alone together / Cherokee / Penthouse serenade.
**Album:** Released Apr '84, on Sunnyside Jazz(USA) Catalogue no: **SSC 1003**

**FIGURE & SPIRIT (Konitz Lee Quintet)**
**Album:** Released Apr '81, on Progressive (USA) by Jazzology Records (USA). Catalogue no: **PRO 7003**

**FOUR KEYS (Konitz Lee/Matial Solal)**
**Album:** Released May '81, on MPS Jazz Catalogue no: **MPS 68 241**

**GLAD KONITZ (Live fron the Swedish tour 1983)**
**Album:** Released Jul '87, on Dragon by Dragon Records. Cat no: **DRLP 104**

**I CONCENTRATE ON YOU**
**Album:** Released Jul '88, on Steeplechase (USA) Catalogue no: **SCS 1018**
**CD:** Released Jul '88, on Steeplechase (USA) Catalogue no: **SCCD 31018**

**IDEAL SCENE**
**CD:** on Soul Note Catalogue no: **121119-2**

**IN RIO**
**Album:** Released Oct '89, on M.A. Catalogue no: **LPA 7391**
**CD:** Released Oct '89, on M.A. Catalogue no: **CDA 7392**
**Cass:** Released Oct '89, on M.A. Catalogue no: **MCA 7394**

**IN SWEDEN 1951/53**
**Album:** Released Jun '86, on Dragon by Dragon Records. Catalogue no: **DRLP 18**

**JAZZ AT STORYVILLE**
**Album:** Released Jun '88, on Black Lion. Catalogue no: **BLP 60901**
**CD:** Released Jun '88, on Black Lion. Catalogue no: **BLCD 760901**

**KONITZ MEETS MULLIGAN (Konitz, Lee & Gerry Mulligan)**
Tracks: / Too marvellous for words / Lover man / I'll remember April / These foolish things / All the things you are / Bernie's tune / Almost like being in love / Sextet / Broadway / I can't believe that you're in love with me / Lady be good / Lady be good (alt. take).
**CD:** Released Mar '89, on EMI-Manhattan by EMI Records. Catalogue no: **CZ 45**
**CD:** Released Jan '89, on Pacific Jazz by EMI Records. Catalogue no: **CDP 746 847 2**

**LEE KONITZ AND WARNE MARSH (Konitz, Lee & Warne Marsh)**
Tracks: / Topsy / There will never be another you / I can't get started / Donna Lee / Two not one / Don't squawk / Ronnie's line / Background music.
**Album:** on Atlantic by WEA Records. Catalogue no: **K 50298**

**LEE KONITZ DUETS, THE**
Note: With Jim Hall, Joe Henderson etc.
**CD:** Released May '87, on JVC/Fantasy Deleted '88. Catalogue no: **VDJ 1571**

**LEE KONITZ IN RIO**
**CD:** Released Oct '89, on M.A.Music Catalogue no: **A 737-2**
**Cass:** Released Oct '89, on M.A.Music Catalogue no: **A 737-4**
**Album:** Released Oct '89, on M.A.Music Catalogue no: **A 737-1**

**LEE PLAYS THE MUSIC OF LARS GULLIN (See under Sjoesten, Lars) (Konitz, Lee & Lars Sjoesten Octet)**
**Album:** Released Jun '86, on Dragon by Dragon Records. Catalogue no: **DRLP 66**

**LIVE AT LAREN**
Tracks: / April / Who you / Without a song / Moon dreams / Times lie / Matrix.
**Album:** Released May '85, on Soul Note Catalogue no: **SN 1069**

**CD:** Released '86, on Soul Note Catalogue no: **SNCD 1069**

**LONDON CONCERT 1976 (Konitz, Lee and others)**
**Album:** Released Apr '79, on Wave by Wave Records. Catalogue no: **WAVE LP 16**

**MOTION**
Tracks: / I remember you / All of me / Foolin' myself / You don't know what love is / You'd be so nice to come home to / Out of nowhere / I'll remember April / It's you or no one.
Note: Personnel: Lee Konitz - alto sax / Sonny Dallas - bass / Elvin Jones - drums.
**CD:** Released Jul '87, on Verve (USA) by Polydor Ltd. Catalogue no: **821 553-2**
**Album:** Released Oct '84, on Verve Catalogue no: **821 553-1**

**NONET, THE**
Tracks: / If dreams come true / Pretty girl is like a melody, A / Tea for two / Matrix / Times lie / Without a song / Nefertiti.
**Album:** Released Feb '78, on Pye International Catalogue no: **NSPL 28240**

**OLEO (Konitz, Lee Trio)**
**Album:** Released Jul '88, on Sonet by Sonet Records. Catalogue no: **SNTF 690**

**PYRAMID**
**Album:** Released Jul '78, on Improvising Artists Catalogue no: **IAI 37 38 45**

**ROUND & ROUND**
Tracks: / Round and round and round / Someday my prince will come / Luv / Nancy / Boo doo / Valse hot / Lover man / Bluesette / Giant steps.

**CD:** Released Nov '89, on Limelight Catalogue no: **820 804-2**
**Album:** Released '89, on Music Masters by Music Masters Records. Catalogue no: **CIJD 40167T**
**CD:** Released '89, on Music Masters by Music Masters Records. Catalogue no: **CIJD 60167M**

**SHADES OF KENTON (Konitz, Lee/Jiggs Whigham)**
**Cass:** Released Dec '88, on Hep Jazz by Hep Records. Catalogue no: **HEPTDK 002**

**SONGS OF THE STARS (Konitz, Lee & John Taylor)**
Note: Saxophonist Lee Konitz and pianist John Taylor improvise through fourteen titles which in turn compliment and mirror the 1989 Pirelli Calendar, for which this recording was specially commissioned. One doesn't have to own a calendar to enjoy the talent of these two superb musicians playing at their best (Jazz House, 1988).

**Album:** Released Nov '88, on Jazz House Catalogue no: **JHR 006**

**STEREOKONITZ**
**Album:** Released Oct '85, on RCA (France) by BMG Records (France). Catalogue no: **NL 70576**

**TIMESPAN (text book solos)**
**Album:** Released Dec '77, on Wave by Wave Records. Catalogue no: **WAVE LP 14**

**VERY COOL**
Tracks: / Sunflower / Stairway to the stars / Movin' around / Kary's trance / Crazy she calls me / Billie's bounce.
Note: Lee Konitz (alto sax), Don Ferrara (trumpet), Sal Mosca (piano), Peter Ind (bass), Shadow Wilson (drums). Recorded in New York, 12 May 1957.
**Album:** Released Nov '83, on Verve Catalogue no: **2304 344**

**WILD AS SPRINGTIME**
Tracks: / She's as wild as springtime / Hairy canary / Ez-thetic / Duende / Chopin Prelude No.20 / Spinning Waltz / Silly samba / Hi, Beck / Ko.
Note: Harold Danko - piano.
**Album:** Released Feb '87, on GFM Catalogue no: **GFM LP8002**

**YES YES NONET (Konitz, Lee Nonet)**
**Album:** Released Sep '79, on Steeplechase (USA) Catalogue no: **SCS 1119**

**YOUNG LEE**
**Album:** Released Nov '88, on Vogue by Vogue Records. Catalogue no: **500105**

## Korner, Alexis

**ALEXIS 1957 (with Cyril Davies)**
**Album:** Released Nov '84, on Krazy Kat by Interstate Music. Catalogue no: **KK 789**

**BEIRUT**
Tracks: / Beirut / Meanful.
**7" Single:** Released May '84, on Charisma by Virgin Records. Deleted '89. Catalogue no: **CB 412**

**BLUES INCORPORATED**
**CD:** Released Nov '89, on Line by Line Records (W.Germany). Catalogue no: **TACD9.00634**

**COLLECTION: ALEXIS KORNER**
Tracks: / Gospel ship / Captain America / Thief, The / Robert Johnson / Get off my cloud / Honky tonk women / Spoonful / Daytime song / Lend me some time / Hey pretty mama / Stump blues / I got my mojo working / Geneva / Wreck of the old '97 / Casey Jones / High heel sneakers / King BB / Juvenile delinquent.
**CD:** Released Sep '88, on Castle Collector Series by Castle Communications Records. Catalogue no: **CCSCD 192**
**Cass:** Released Sep '88, on Castle Collector Series by Castle Communications Records. Catalogue no: **CCSMC 192**
**2 LP Set:** Released Sep '88, on Castle Collector Series by Castle Communications Records. Catalogue no: **CCSLP 192**

**COLLECTION: ALEXIS KORNER**
Tracks: / She fooled me / Hoochie coochie man / Oh Lord don't let them drop that atom bomb on me / I got a woman / Corina Corina / Everday I have the blues / Operator / Rosie / Polly put the kettle on / I see it / You don't miss your water till your well runs dry / Mighty mighty spade and whitey / Lo and behold / Louisiana blues / Ooh wee baby / Rock

**Alexis Korner**

me baby / Sweet sympathy / Country shoes.
**CD:** Released '88, on Castle Collector Series by Castle Communications Records. Catalogue no: **CCSCD 150**
**Cass:** Released Sep '86, on Castle Collector Series by Castle Communications Records. Catalogue no: **CCSMC 150**
**2 LP Set:** Released Sep '86, on Castle Collector Series by Castle Communications Records. Catalogue no: **CCSLP 150**

**EAT A LITTLE RHYTHM AND BLUES**
**VHS:** Released '88, on BBC Video by BBC Video. Catalogue no: **BBCV/B 3011**

**HAMMER AND NAILS**
Tracks: / Honky tonk women / Louise / Hammer and nails / Santa Fe blues / How long blues / Roberta / Precious Lord / Honour the young man / And again / East St. Louis blues.
Note: "Original direct to disc live recording made in Germany and released in the U.K. for the first time." (Magnum Music Group, May 1988).
**Cass:** Released Jan '87, on Thunderbolt by Magnum Music Group. Catalogue no: **THBC 037**
**Album:** Released Jan '87, on Thunderbolt by Magnum Music Group. Catalogue no: **THBL 037**

**JUVENILE DELINQUENT**
Tracks: / Beirut / Mean fool / Spinx, The / Get off my cloud / King B.B. / Juvenile delinquent.
**Album:** Released Aug '88, on Charisma by Virgin Records. Catalogue no: **CHC 64**
**Cass:** Released Jun '84, on Charisma by Virgin Records. Deleted May '88. Catalogue no: **CASMC 1165**
**Album:** Released Jun '84, on Charisma by Virgin Records. Deleted '88. Catalogue no: **CAS 1165**

**LIVE IN PARIS: ALEXIS KORNER (Korner, Alexis with Colin Hogkinson)**
Tracks: / Blue monday / Key to the highway / Catcoke rag / Phonograph blues / Little bitty gal blues / Sweet home Chicago / Cherry red / I got my mojo working / Gospel ship / Geneva / Working in a coalmine / Flocking with you.
Note: Outstanding recording with Colin Hogkinson.
**CD:** Released Feb '88, on The CD Label by Magnum Music Group. Catalogue no: **CDTL 001**

**PROFILE: ALEXIS KORNER**
**Album:** Released May '81, on Teldec (1) by ASV (Academy Sound & Vision). Catalogue no: **6.24475**
**Cass:** Released Jun '81, on Teldec (1) by ASV (Academy Sound & Vision). Catalogue no: **CL4 24475**

**R & B FROM THE MARQUEE (Korner, Alexis & Blues Inc)**
Tracks: / Gotta move / Rain is such a lonesome sound / I got my brand on you / Spooky but nice / Keep your hands off / I wanna put a tiger in your tank / I got my mojo working / Finkles cafe / Hoochie coochie / Down town / How long, how long blues / I thought i heard that train whistle blow.
**Album:** Released Feb '84, on Ace Of Clubs by Decca Records. Catalogue no: **ACL 1130**

**TESTAMENT**
Tracks: / One scotch, one bourbon, one beer / Stump blues / Stream line train / My babe / 32-20 blues / High heel sneakers / Will the circle be unbroken / Mary open the door.
Note: Recordings from the legendary British rhythm and blues musician and vocalist together here with bassist Colin Hodgkinson. (Magnum Music May, 1988).
**CD:** Released '86, on Thunderbolt by Magnum Music Group. Catalogue no: **CDTB 2.026**
**Album:** Released Jun '85, on Thunderbolt by Magnum Music Group. Catalogue no: **THBL 2.026**
**Cass:** Released Jun '85, on Thunderbolt by Magnum Music Group. Catalogue no: **THBC 2.026**

## Krahmer, Carlo

**CARLO KRAHMER MEMORIAL ALBUM**
**Album:** Released Nov '77, on Esquire by Titan Int. Prod.. Catalogue no: **ESQ 306**

**CARLO KRAHMER'S CHICAGOANS (Krahmer, Carlo Chicagoans)**
**Album:** Released Jun '86, on Esquire by Titan Int. Prod.. Catalogue no: **ESQ 319**

## Kremer, Gidon

**EDITION LOCKENHAUS VOL'S. 1 & 2 (Kremer, Gidon & Valery Afanassiev)**
**CD Set:** Released Dec '85, on ECM Catalogue no: **827 024-2**
**2 LP Set:** Released Dec '85, on ECM Catalogue no: **ECM 1304**

**EDITION LOCKENHAUS VOL. 3 (Kremer, Gidon & Valery Afanassiev)**
**CD:** Released Aug '86, on ECM Catalogue no: **829 539 2**
**Album:** Released Aug '86, on ECM Catalogue no: **ECM 1328**

## Kress, Carl

**TWO GUITARS (Kress, Carl / George Barnes)**
**Album:** Released Apr '83, on Stash (USA) Catalogue no: **ST 222**

## Kriegal, Volker

**HOUSEBOAT**
**Album:** Released May '81, on MPS Jazz Catalogue no: **MPS 68 206**

**LONG DISTANCE**
**Album:** Released May '81, on MPS Jazz Catalogue no: **MPS 68 243**

**MISSING LINK**
**2 LP Set:** Released May '81, on MPS Jazz Catalogue no: **MPS 88 030**

**STAR EDITION**
**2 LP Set:** Released May '81, on MPS Jazz Catalogue no: **MPS 88 036**

## Krimsky, Katrina

**STELLA MALU (Krimsky, Katrina & Trevor Watts)**
**CD:** Released Jul '88, on ECM Catalogue no: **833 516-2**
**Album:** Released Dec '81, on ECM Catalogue no: **ECM 1199**

## Krog, Karin

**I REMEMBER YOU**
Tracks: / I remember you / Trane / Lester's happy / Moody's mood for love / It's you or no one / Loverman / Speak low / That old feeling.
**Album:** Released '83, on Spotlite by Spotlite Records. Catalogue no: **SPJ LP 22**

**SOME OTHER SPRING (Krog, Karin & Dexter Gordon)**
**Album:** Released May '86, on Storyville by Storyville Records AB. Catalogue no: **SLP 4045**

**SOMETHING BORROWED**
**CD:** Released Mar '90, on Meantime by Meantime Records. Catalogue no: **JJCD30**

**SOMETHING BORROWED, SOMETHING NEW**
Tracks: / Thrill is gone, The / Out of this world / If I should lose you / My foolish heart / Canto mai / I get a kick out of you / All blues / Meaning of the blues, The / This is new / Just one of those things / I'm beginning to see the light / Ev'rytime we say goodbye / Tivoli.
**CD:** Released Jan '90, on Meantime by Meantime Records. Catalogue no: **MR 2**

**SONG FOR YOU, A**
Tracks: / Song for you, A / Feeling too good today blues / Stardust / I won't dance / Child is born, A / I have the feeling I've been here before / I ain't here / Blue and sentimental / Sentimental and melancholy / Scandia skies / I was doing alright / Lush life / I've got the right to sing the blues.
**Album:** Released '82, on Phontastic (Sweden) Catalogue no: **PHONT 7512**
**Cass:** Released '82, on Phontastic (Sweden) Catalogue no: **PHONT 8512**

**SUCH WINTERS OF MEMORY (Krog, Karin/John Surman)**
**Album:** Released Sep '83, on ECM Catalogue no: **ECM 1254**

## Kronos Quartet

**KRONOS QUARTET**
Note: Featuring the music of Peter Sculthorpe, Aullis Sallinen, Philip Glass, Conlon Nancarrow and Jimi Hendrix.
**CD:** Released Jan '87, on Nonesuch Catalogue no: **979 111 2**
**Cass:** Released Jan '87, on Nonesuch (USA) by Nonesuch Records (USA). Catalogue no: **9791114**
**Album:** Released Jan '87, on Nonesuch (USA) by Nonesuch Records (USA).

Catalogue no: **9791111**

**MONK SUITE**
**CD:** Released Aug '88, on Polygram by PolyGram UK Ltd. Catalogue no: **LCD 1505**

**MUSIC BY BILL EVANS**
Tracks: / Waltz for Debbie / Very early / Nardis / Re: person I knew / Time remembered / Walking up / Turn out the stars / Five / Peace piece.
Note: Kronos Quartet is a young adventurous San Francisco-based ensemble with a swiftly growing international reputation. Formed in 1978, they specialize in contemporary composers such as John Cage, Terry Riley and Philip Glass. Of late their interest has been directed to the works of the great jazz composers. Their last album featured compositions by Thelonious Monk and Duke Ellington and this new album is dedicated to the music of Bill Evans. Kronos Quartet are joined on this recording by Eddie Gomez and Jim Hall. Gomez had along association with Bill Evans and is a natural choice for this project.
**Album:** Released Oct '86, on Line by Line Records (W.Germany). Catalogue no: **LLP 1510**
**Cass:** Released Oct '86, on Line by Line Records (W.Germany). Catalogue no: **LLP 51510**

**WHITE MAN SLEEPS**
Tracks: / White man sleeps no 1 / White man sleeps no 3 / White man sleeps no 5 / Scherzo holding your own / Pano da costa(Cloth from the coast) ( / Lonely woman / Amazing grace.
**CD:** Released Jul '88, on Nonesuch (USA) by Nonesuch Records (USA). Catalogue no: **979163 2**
**Album:** Released Sep '87, on Nonesuch (USA) by Nonesuch Records (USA). Catalogue no: **K 979163 1**
**Album:** Released Sep '87, on President by President Records. Catalogue no: **STLS 1087**
**Cass:** Released Sep '87, on Nonesuch (USA) by Nonesuch Records (USA). Catalogue no: **K 979163 4**

**WINTER WAS HARD**
Tracks: / Winter was hard / Fratres / Bella by barlight / Door is ajar, A / Half wolf dances mad in moonlight / Forbidden fruit / Quartet No 3.
**Album:** Released Oct '88, on Nonesuch Catalogue no: **979181 1**
**CD:** Released '88, on Nonesuch Catalogue no: **K 979181 2**
**Cass:** Released Oct '88, on Nonesuch Catalogue no: **979181 4**

## Krupa, Gene

**1938-1939**
Tracks: / Grandfather's clock / I know that you know / Fare thee well, Annie Laurie / Wire brush stomp / Bolero at the Savoy / Murdy purdy / Ta-ra-ra-boom-der-e / Never felt better, never had less / Apurksody / Do you wanna jump, children / Madam, swings it, The / Dracula.
**Album:** Released '87, on Joker (USA) by Lifetime Records (USA). Catalogue no: **SM 3236**
**Cass:** Released '87, on Joker (USA) by Lifetime Records (USA). Catalogue no: **MC 3236**

**ACE DRUMMER MAN (1943-47)**
**Album:** Released Aug '79, on Giants of Jazz by Hasmick Promotions. Catalogue no: **GOJ 1006**

**BLUE MOON 1944-46**
Tracks: / Blue moon / There's no you / I got it all over again lover / Wirebrush stomp no. 2 / Chickery chick / Leave us leap / Hop skip and jump / We'll gather lilacs / These foolish things / Limehouse blues / Man I love, The / Out of nowhere.
**Album:** Released Apr '81, on Hep Jazz by Hep Records. Catalogue no: **HEP 16**

**CHALLENGING THE CHALLENGER (Krupa, Gene Orchestra & Trio)**
**Album:** Released '88, on First Heard by Submarine Records. Catalogue no: **FH 35**

**DRUM BATTLE (Krupa, Gene & Buddy Rich)**
**Album:** Released Oct '76, on Verve Catalogue no: **2317 116**

**DRUM BOOGIE**
Tracks: / opus one / Leave us leap / Drum boogie / Body and soul / Boogie blues / Massachusetts / How high the moon / Tuxedo Junction / Dark eyes / That's what you think / Bolero at the Savoy / Lover.
Note: Mono.
**Album:** Released Sep '86, on Verve (USA) by Polydor Ltd. Catalogue no: **VSLP 345**
**Album:** Released '88, on Big Band Era Catalogue no: **20178**
**Cass:** Released May '88, on Big Band Era Catalogue no: **40178**

**DRUMMER MAN**
**CD:** Released '86, on Polydor by Polydor Ltd. Deleted Mar '88. Catalogue no: **827 843-2**
**Album:** Released '86, on Polydor by Polydor Ltd. Deleted Mar '88. Catalogue no: **827 843-1**
**Cass:** Released '86, on Polydor by Polydor Ltd. Deleted Mar '88. Catalogue no: **827 843-4**

**DRUMMIN' MAN (AFFINITY)**
Tracks: / Nagasaki / Jeepers creepers / Do you wanna jump children / Symphony in riffs / Drummin' man / Drumboogie / Let me off uptown / After you've gone (CD only) / Rockin' chair / Bolero at the Savoy / Massachusetts / Leave us leap / Dark eyes / Stompin' at the Savoy (CD only) / Opus one / Lover / How high the moon / Disc jockey jump / Calling Dr. Gillespie.
**CD:** Released Oct '87, on Charly by Charly Records. Catalogue no: **CDCHARLY 81**
**Album:** Released Oct '87, on Affinity by Charly Records. Catalogue no: **AFS 1042**

**DRUMMIN' MAN (CBS)**
Tracks: / Opus one / Drum boogie / Body and soul / Boogie blues / How high the moon / Massachusetts / Drummin' man / Tuxedo Junction / Leave us leap / Bolero at the Savoy / Dark eyes / That's what you think.
**Album:** Released Mar '83, on CBS Cameo by CBS Records. Deleted Aug '87. Catalogue no: **CBS 32262**
**CD:** Released Mar '83, on CBS Cameo by CBS Records. Deleted Aug '87. Catalogue no: **40-32262**

**EXCITING GENE KRUPA, THE**
**Album:** Released Oct '84, on Giants of Jazz by Hasmick Promotions. Catalogue no: **GOJ 1028**

**GENE KRUPA (Compact/Walkman jazz)**
Tracks: / Drummin' man / Swedish schnapps / Paradise / Just you, just me / Gene's solo flight / Disc jockey jump / 'S wonderful / Let me off uptown hipp-deebip / Imagination / Who's rhythm / Mulligan stew / Gene's blues.
**Cass:** Released Mar '88, on Verve Catalogue no: **833 286 4**
**CD:** Released Mar '88, on Verve Catalogue no: **833 286 2**

**GENE KRUPA & BUDDY RICH (Compact/Walkman jazz) (Krupa, Gene & Buddy Rich)**
Tracks: / King Porter stomp / Bernie's tune / It don't mean a thing (if it ain't got...) / Evolution / Sweethearts on parade / Jumpin' at the woodside / Buddy's blues / Duet.
**CD:** Released Aug '88, on Verve Catalogue no: **835 314-2**
**Cass:** Released 15 Aug '88, on Verve Catalogue no: **835 314-4**

**GENE KRUPA COLLECTION 20 golden greats**
Tracks: / Drum boogie / Drummin' man / How high the moon / Bolero at the Savoy / Boogie blues / Opus one / Tuxedo Junction / Leave us leap / That's what you think / Massachusetts / King Porter stomp / St. Louis blues / Stompin' at the Savoy / Alexander's ragtime band / Get happy / I've got the world on a string / Dark eyes / Caravan / I left my heart in San Francisco / Big noise from Winnetka.
**Cass:** Released Feb '87, on Deja Vu Catalogue no: **DVMC 2093**
**Album:** Released Feb '87, on Deja Vu Catalogue no: **DVLP 2093**

**GENE KRUPA & HIS MEN OF JAZZ**
**Cass:** Released Jan '88, on Starline (Jazz) Catalogue no: **SLC 61006**

**GENE KRUPA, LIONEL HAMPTON & (Krupa, Gene, Lionel Hampton & Teddy Wilson)**
**Album:** Released Mar '81, on Verve (Import) Catalogue no: **2304 482**

**GENE KRUPA ON THE AIR 1944-1946 (Krupa, Gene & His Orchestra)**
Tracks: / Futurama / It had to be you / Blue moon / Dear old Southland / Swingin on a star / I'll walk alone / You never say yes / Drum boogie / Liza / Hodge podge / How high the moon / Man I love,

The / Ten Rich Drive / Very thought of you, The.
**Album:** Released Feb '88, on Aircheck (USA) by Kiner Ents.(USA). Catalogue no: **AIRCHECK 35**

**GENE KRUPA ORCHESTRA (1941) (Krupa, Gene & His Orchestra)**
**Album:** Released Apr '81, on Jazz Live (Italy) Catalogue no: **BLJ 8002**

**GENE KRUPA ORCHESTRA & TRIO (Krupa, Gene Orchestra & Trio)**
**Album:** Released Oct '86, on Swing House by Submarine Records. Catalogue no: **SWH 40**

**GENE KRUPA PLUS (VIDEO)**
**VHS:** Released '88, on Kay Jazz (video) by Kay Jazz. Catalogue no: **KJ 079**

**GENE KRUPA - VOL.1**
**Album:** Released Aug '81, on Kings Of Jazz Catalogue no: **KLJ 20014**

**GENE KRUPA - VOL.1 (1935-8)**
**Album:** Released Apr '79, on Ajax (USA) Catalogue no: **AJAX 101**

**GENE KRUPA - VOL.2 (1938)**
**Album:** Released Apr '79, on Ajax (USA) Catalogue no: **AJAX 105**

**GENE KRUPA - VOL.3 (1938)**
**Album:** Released Apr '79, on Ajax (USA) Catalogue no: **AJAX 110**

**GENE KRUPA - VOL.4 (1939)**
**Album:** Released Apr '79, on Ajax (USA) Catalogue no: **AJAX 111**

**GENE KRUPA - VOL.5 (1939)**
**Album:** Released Apr '79, on Ajax (USA) Catalogue no: **AJAX 121**

**GENE KRUPA - VOL.6 (1939-40)**
**Album:** Released Apr '79, on Ajax (USA) Catalogue no: **AJAX 122**

**GENE KRUPA - VOL.7 (1940)**
**Album:** Released Apr '79, on Ajax (USA) Catalogue no: **AJAX 125**

**GENE KRUPA - VOL.8 (1940)**
**Album:** Released Apr '79, on Ajax (USA) Catalogue no: **AJAX 127**

**GENE KRUPA - VOL.9 (1940)**
**Album:** Released Apr '79, on Ajax (USA) Catalogue no: **AJAX 130**

**GENE KRUPA - VOL.10 (1940)**
**Album:** Released Apr '79, on Ajax (USA) Catalogue no: **AJAX 132**

**GENE KRUPA - VOL.11 (1940-1)**
**Album:** Released Apr '79, on Ajax (USA) Catalogue no: **AJAX 138**

**GENE KRUPA - VOL.12 (1941)**
**Album:** Released Apr '79, on Ajax (USA) Catalogue no: **AJAX 146**

**GENE KRUPA - VOL.13 (1941)**
**Album:** Released Apr '79, on Ajax (USA) Catalogue no: **AJAX 154**

**GENE KRUPA - VOL.14 (1941)**
**Album:** Released Apr '79, on Ajax (USA) Catalogue no: **AJAX 161**

**GENE'S BAND**
**Album:** Released '84, on First Heard by Submarine Records. Cat no: **FH 26**

**HISTORY OF JAZZ**
**Album:** Released Apr '81, on Joker (USA) by Lifetime Records (USA). Catalogue no: **SM 3230**

**KRUPA & RICH (Krupa, Gene & Buddy Rich)**
Tracks: / Buddy's blues & Bernie's tune / Gene's blues / Sweethearts on parade / I never knew.
**Album:** Released May '84, on Verve (USA) by Polydor Ltd. Catalogue no: **817 109-1**

**ORIGINAL DRUM BATTLE (Krupa, Gene & Buddy Rich)**
**Album:** Released Aug '81, on Verve (Import) Catalogue no: **2304 308**

**RADIO DISCS OF GENE KRUPA, THE**
**Album:** Released Jul '77, on Joyce Catalogue no: **JLP 2008**

**SUPERB PERFORMANCES (1945-1949) (Krupa, Gene & His Orchestra)**
**Album:** Released Jan '77, on First Heard by Submarine Records. Catalogue no: **FH 7**

**SWINGIN' GENE KRUPA QUARTET**
**Album:** Released Feb '89, on Sounds Great Catalogue no: **SG 1019**

**SWINGING BIG BANDS 1947-47, THE (Krupa, Gene & His Orchestra)**
**Album:** Released Apr '81, on Joker (USA) by Lifetime Records (USA). Catalogue no: **SM 3616**

**THAT DRUMMERS BAND (Krupa, Gene & His Orchestra)**
**Album:** Released '74, on S.O.S.(USA) Catalogue no: **LP 114**

**WHAT'S THIS (1946-1947) (Krupa, Gene & His Orchestra)**
**Album:** Released Jun '81, on Hep Jazz by Hep Records. Catalogue no: **HEP 26**

**WIRE BRUSH STOMP 1938 - 41 (Krupa, Gene & His Orchestra)**
**Album:** Released Jun '88, on Bandstand Catalogue no: **BS 7117**
**Cass:** Released Jun '88, on Bandstand Catalogue no: **BS 7117C**

## Kuhn, Joachim

**SPRING FEVER**
Tracks: / Lady Amber / Sunshine / Two whips / Spring fever / Morning / Mushroom / Equal evil / California woman.
**Album:** Released '77, on Atlantic by WEA Records. Deleted '82. Catalogue no: **K 50280**

## Kuniyoshi-Kuhn, Akemi

**HANDSCAPES**
**Album:** Released Jan '87, on Leo by Leo Records. Catalogue no: **LR 143**

## Kunz, Charlie

**Biographical details:** Of American nationality but based in Britain, this pianist began to build a reputation during his long mid-thirties residency at the Casani Club in London's Regent Street. A contemporary of singer Vera Lynn, his career blossomed during the forties. In January 1955 Kunz achieved a no.16 placing on Britain's recently inaugurated record charts with *Piano medley no.114* (Charlie was not a guy to deviate from an established formula) - this single contained a keyboard romp through some of 1954's biggest hits, namely those by Frankie Laine, Don Cornell, Doris Day, Kitty Kallen, Nat King Cole and the aforementioned Lynn. His discs might have fared better during the fifties, had they not faced such stiff competition from the other piano of Winifred Atwell. Working permanently within the middle of the road style of old school popular music, he chalked up a UK top 10 album in June 1969 with the Decca compilation LP *The world of Charlie Kunz*. (Bob Macdonald 85).

**AND THE CASANI CLUB BAND (Kunz, Charlie & The Casani Club Orchestra)**
**Cass set:** Released '88, on Ditto by Pickwick Records. Catalogue no: **DTO 10258**

**CHARLIE KUNZ & HIS CASANI CLUB ORCHESTRA (Kunz, Charlie & The Casani Club Orchestra)**
Tracks: / You gotta know how to dance / Star fell out of heaven, A / Let's sit this one out / Did you ever see a dream walking / Learn to croon / I'm putting all my eggs in one basket / On a steamer / Love is everywhere / Robins and roses / White cliffs of Dover, The / Have you forgotten so soon / Love is a dancing thing / Life begins when you're in love / Goodnight my love / I've got a feelin' you're foolin'.
**Album:** Released '83, on Decca by Decca International. Deleted '88. Catalogue no: **RFL 24**

**CLAP HANDS, HERE COMES CHARLIE**
Tracks: / Between 18th and 15th on Chestnut Street / Clap hands, here comes Charlie / March winds and April showers / Heart of gold / Red sails in the sunset / All alone in Vienna / Boo hoo / Cherokee / There's a small hotel / I believe in miracles / Crying my heart out for you / On then night of June 3rd / Harbour lights / Someone to care for / I'm in the mood for love / On the good ship lollipop / Did your mother come from Ireland? / Every night at eight / Swing time medley.
**Album:** Released Nov '83, on Recollections (Decca) by Decca Records. Catalogue no: **RFL 37**

**DANCE YOUR WAY THROUGH THE THIRTIES (Kunz, Charlie & The Casani Club Orchestra)**
Tracks: / Unless / There was an old woman / Learn to croon / Did my heart beat did I fall in love / Let's sit this one out / Did you ever see a dream walking / She fell for a feller from "Oopasala" / Dear stranger / When you're sixty / Moonstruck / By a waterfall / Roaming /

Doggone I've done it / Lazybones / Memories of hours spent with you / I raise my hat / On the good ship lollipop / There's no green grass round the old North Pole.
**Album:** Released May '87, on Joy by President Records. Catalogue no: **JOY 286**

**FOCUS ON CHARLIE KUNZ**
**Cass:** Released Oct '77, on Decca by Decca International. Deleted '88. Catalogue no: **KFOC2 8075**

**MUSIC FOR THE MILLIONS**
Tracks: / Medleys / Carousels / Show boat / Oklahoma / Rodger and heart / South american.
**Album:** Released Mar '83, on Philips (Import) by PolyGram UK Ltd. Catalogue no: **6495 109**
**Cass:** Released Mar '83, on Philips (Import) by PolyGram UK Ltd. Catalogue no: **7195 109**

**MUSIC GOES ROUND, THE**
Tracks: / When Irish eyes are smiling / Coming through the rye / Oh you beautiful doll / Yip I addy I ay / On Treasure Island / Thanks a million / Music goes round and around, The / I can't give you anything but love baby / Ain't she sweet / Auf wiedersehen my dear / Lost / Glory of love, The / Is it true what they say about dixie? / I ain't got nobody / If I had you / time on my hands / I'll see you again / Desert song, The / My hero / Can't we talk it over / Oh you beautiful doll / Dinah / Annie Laurie / Loch Lomond / Comin' through the rye / Auld lang syne / She shall have music / Alone at a table for two / Pink elephants / Merry widow walts, The / Love will find a way / Blue Danube, The / Some of these days / With a song in my heart / Night and day / What'll I do / Always / When you and I were seventeen / You are my lucky star / I've got a feelin' you're foolin' / She's funny that way / Sho shine boy / When I'm with you / Somebody stole my gal / Poor buterfly / After you've gone / Whispering / Some other time / Little bit independent, A / Goodnight sweetheart.
**Album:** Released Oct '89, on Conifer Happy Days by Conifer Records. Catalogue no: **CHD 162**
**CD:** Released Oct '89, on Conifer Happy Days by Conifer Records. Catalogue no: **CDHD 162**
**Cass:** Released Oct '89, on Conifer Happy Days by Conifer Records. Catalogue no: **MCHD 162**

**NO ONE BUT YOU**
Tracks: / My friend / I need you now / Birth of the blues / Whatever will be will be / Here in my heart / You belong to me / Kiss of fire / All my love / Mister Sandman / Softly / Under the bridge of Paris / Stars shine in your eyes / Because you're mine / Love is a many splendoured thing / Shifting whispering sands.
**Album:** Released Feb '81, on Decca by Decca International. Deleted '88. Catalogue no: **TAB 11**
**Cass:** Released Feb '81, on Decca by Decca International. Catalogue no: **KTBC 11**

**PIANO MEDLEY NO.114**
**7" Single:** Released Dec '54, on Decca by Decca International. Deleted '57. Catalogue no: **F 10419**

**PRETTY GIRL IS LIKE A MELODY, A**
Tracks: / Crying my heart out for you / Until tomorrow / Would you / Pretty girl is like a melody, A / Love is a dancing thing / Cheek to cheek / Misty islands of the highlands / Look up and laugh / Boo-hoo / All alone in Vienna / When my dreamboat comes home / Learn to croon / Lazybones / Did my heart beat? Did I fall in love / Dear stranger / Life is empty without you man of... / Monnstruck / Unless.
**CD:** Released Sep '88, on Burlington (nostalgia) by Counterpoint Distribution. Catalogue no: **2 BUR 010**
**Album:** Released Jun '88, on Burlington (nostalgia) by Counterpoint Distribution. Catalogue no: **BUR 010**
**Cass:** Released Jul '88, on Burlington (nostalgia) by Counterpoint Distribution. Catalogue no: **4BUR 010**

**WORLD OF...**
**Album:** Released Mar '69, on Decca by Decca International. Catalogue no: **SPA 15**
**Cass:** Released Feb '72, on Decca by Decca International. Catalogue no: **KCSP 15**

**WORLD OF... VOL. 3**
**Cass:** Released Aug '73, on Decca by Decca International. Catalogue no: **KCSP 194**

## Kustbandet

**KUSTBANDET (Coast line band)**
**Album:** Released Jul '82, on Kenneth Catalogue no: **KS 2051**

**NEW CALL OF THE FREAKS**
**Album:** Released Feb '89, on Stomp Off (USA) Catalogue no: **SOS 1178**

## Kweskin, Jim

**GREATEST HITS:KWESKIN, JIM & JUG BAND (Kweskin, Jim & The Jug Band)**
**CD:** Released Jun '89, on Start by Start Records Ltd.. Catalogue no: **VNP 7404**
**Album:** Released Jun '89, on Start by Start Records Ltd.. Catalogue no: **VNP 6404**

## Kyle, Billy

**FINISHING UP A DATE**
Note: With the Spencer Trio/Jim Mundy & his Swing Club 7/Kyle & Swing Clubland.
**Album:** Released '88, on Collectors Items Catalogue no: **CI 020**

## Kyser, Kay

**DANCE DATE (Kyser, Kay/his orchestra)**
**Album:** Released Jul '82, on Big Band Archives Catalogue no: **BBALP 1220**

**OL' PROFESSOR, THE 1935 - 42 (Kyser, Kay & His Orchestra)**
Tracks: / All God's chillun got rhythm / Mighty like a rose / Humpty Dumpty heart / Fresh as a daisy / Ish kabibble / Take your girlie to the movies / East side of Heaven / That sly old gentleman / Bad humour man, The / Zoot suite / When the roses bloom again / Egg a bread.
Note: With Ginny Sims, Harry Babbitt, Ish Kabibble, Sully Mason.
**Cass:** Released Jun '88, on Bandstand Catalogue no: **BS 7137C**
**Album:** Released Jun '88, on Bandstand Catalogue no: **BS 7137**

**SWINGING SIDE, THE (Kyser, Kay Orchestra)**
**Album:** Released Aug '89, on Golden Era by Delta Records. Catalogue no: **GELP 15052**

## Kyte, Sydney

**1931-1932 (Kyte, Sydney & his Piccadilly Hotel Band)**
Tracks: / Guilty / Close your eyes / Just once for all time / Yes, yes / Live, laugh & love / Tom Thumb's drum / Starlight serenade / There's nothing to good for my baby / "Bow Bells" selection / My bluebird's back again / Sweetheart / Let's drift away on Dreamers Bay / I'll make a happy landing / It's always goodbye / Whereever you are / I do like to see a game of football.
**Album:** Released Oct '80, on Retrospect by EMI Records. Catalogue no: **SH 387**

# L

The following information was taken from the Music Master database on 14th April, 1990.

## L.A. Four

**EXECUTIVE SUITE**
Tracks: / Blues wellington / Amazonia / You and I / Simple invention / Entr'Acte / My funny valentine / Chega de Saudade.
**Album:** Released Jun '83, on Concord Jazz by Concord Jazz Records (USA). Catalogue no: **CJ 215**
**Cass:** Released Jun '83, on Concord Jazz by Concord Jazz Records (USA). Catalogue no: **CJC 215**

**L.A. FOUR**
Tracks: / Dindi / Rainbows / Rondo es pressivo / Manteca / St. Thomas / Concierto de Aranjuez.
**CD:** Released Sep '86, on Concord Jazz by Concord Jazz Records (USA). Catalogue no: **CCD 4018**

**L.A. FOUR SCORES**
**CD:** Released Jul '88, on Concord Jazz by Concord Jazz Records (USA). Catalogue no: **CCD 6008**

**MONTAGE**
**Album:** Released Nov '81, on Concord Jazz by Concord Jazz Records (USA). Catalogue no: **CJ 156**

**PAVANE POUR UNE INFANTE DEFUNKT**
**CD:** Released '88, on Import (label unknown) Catalogue no: **35JD 2**

**ZACA**
**Album:** Released Nov '80, on Concord Jazz by Concord Jazz Records (USA). Catalogue no: **CJ 130**

## La Jazz Quintet

**LA JAZZ QUINTET**
**Album:** Released 10 Apr '87, on King (Japan) Catalogue no: **K 28P 6440**
**CD:** Released 10 Apr '87, on King (Japan) Catalogue no: **K32Y 6116**

## La Barbera, Pat

**PASS IT ON**
**Album:** Released Jan '80, on PM Catalogue no: **PM 009**

## La Beque, Katia

**AN AMERICAN IN PARIS (La Beque, Katia & Marielle)**
**Cass:** Released Sep '84, on H.M.V. by EMI Records. Deleted Feb '90. Catalogue no: **EJ 2701224**
**Album:** Released Sep '84, on H.M.V. by EMI Records. Deleted Feb '90. Catalogue no: **EJ 2701221**
**CD:** Released Sep '84, on H.M.V. by EMI Records. Deleted Mar '89. Catalogue no: **CDC 7470442**

**BARTOK CONCERTO (La Beque, Katia & Marielle)**
**Cass:** Released Jun '87, on H.M.V. by EMI Records. Deleted Feb '90. Catalogue no: **EL 2704184**
**Album:** Released Jun '87, on H.M.V. by EMI Records. Deleted Feb '90. Catalogue no: **EL 2704181**
**CD:** Released Jun '87, on H.M.V. by EMI Records. Catalogue no: **CDC 747 446 2**

**BERNSTEIN (La Beque, Katia & Marielle)**
**Album:** Released Sep '89, on CBS by CBS Records. Catalogue no: **45531**
**CD:** Released Sep '89, on CBS by CBS Records. Catalogue no: **CD 45531**
**Cass:** Released Sep '89, on CBS by CBS Records. Catalogue no: **40 45531**

**GERSHWIN SECOND RHAPSODY (Music for two pianos) (La Beque, Katia & Marielle)**
Tracks: / Second Rhapsody / I got rhythm / Variations / Two waltzes / Blue Monday / Two songs.
Note: Recorded in 1987 at Abbey Road Studios.
**CD:** Released Aug '88, on H.M.V. by EMI Records. Catalogue no: **CDC 749 7522**
**Album:** Released Aug '88, on H.M.V. by EMI Records. Deleted Feb '90. Catalogue no: **EL 7497521**
**Cass:** Released Aug '88, on H.M.V. by EMI Records. Deleted Feb '90. Catalogue no: **EL 7497524**

**GLAD RAGS (La Beque, Katia & Marielle)**
Tracks: / Rialto ripples / Honky tonk / Carolina shout / Entertainer, The / Antoinette / Magnetic rag / Maple leaf / Eite syncopations / Strenuous life / Stop time / Bethera / Entertainer, The / Maple leaf rag.
**CD:** Released Dec '84, on Angel (1) by EMI Records. Catalogue no: **CDC 7470932**
**Cass:** Released Mar '83, on EMI by EMI Records. Deleted Feb '90. Catalogue no: **TC-EMD 5541**
**Album:** Released Mar '83, on EMI by EMI Records. Deleted Jun '89. Catalogue no: **EMD 5541**

**REMINISCENCES DE DON JUAN (La Beque, Katia & Marielle)**
**CD:** Released Mar '88, on H.M.V. by EMI Records. Catalogue no: **CDC 749 303 2**

## Ladd's Black Aces

**LADD'S BLACK ACES 1921-2, VOL.1**
**Album:** Released Apr '79, on Fountain by Retrieval Records. Catalogue no: **FJ 102**

**LADD'S BLACK ACES 1922-3/1923-4 (Volumes 2 & 3)**
**2 LP Set:** Released Apr '79, on Fountain by Retrieval Records. Catalogue no: **FJ 111**

**LADD'S BLACK ACES VOL 2**
**Album:** on Fountain by Retrieval Records. Catalogue no: **FJ 106**

## Ladies Get The Blues

**LADIES GET THE BLUES (Various artists)**
Tracks: / Can't get even the blues no more: *McEntire, Reba* / Today all over again: *McEntire, Reba* / Someday when things are good: *Williams, Leona* / You take me for granted: *Williams, Leona* / Love at the five and dime: *Mattea, Kathy* / Walk the way the wind blows: *Mattea, Kathy* / For every inch I've laughed I've cried a mile: *Hensley, Teri* / Hard baby to rock: *Hensley, Teri* / Funny face: *Fargo, Donna* / Happiest girl in the whole USA: *Fargo, Donna*.
Note: "This thematically structured compilation showcases some of the strongest music released by Mercury Records in the 1980's." (IMS Records, May 1988.)
**Album:** Released May '88, on Mercury by Phonogram Ltd. Catalogue no: **834 199-1**
**Cass:** Released May '88, on Mercury by Phonogram Ltd. Catalogue no: **834 199-4**

**LADIES SING THE BLUES (Various artists)**
**2 LP Set:** Released Mar '85, on Savoy Jazz (USA) by Malaco Records (USA). Catalogue no: **SJL 2233**

**LADIES SING THE BLUES VOLUME 2 (Various artists)**
**Album:** Released Mar '85, on Savoy Jazz (USA) by Malaco Records (USA). Catalogue no: **SJL 2256**

## Ladies Of Swing

**LADIES OF SWING, THE (Various artists)**
Tracks: / Beyond the blue horizon: *Tilton, Martha* / Hundred from today, A: *Christie, June* / You and I passing by: *Lee, Peggy* / Maybe you'll be there: *Holiday, Billie* / I get along without you very well: *Clooney, Rosemary*.
Note: Including Peggy Lee, Rosemary Clooney & Billie Holliday.
**Cass:** Released Aug '89, on One For

The Road by One For The Road. Catalogue no: **CONE 1**

## Lagrene, Bireli

**Biographical details:** Bireli Lagrene is 18 years old, yet, already his extraordinary talents as a jazz guitarist have been duly noted throughout Europe. In the past three years Bireli has built a formidable reputation, appearing on television and at jazz festivals. During that time he has also released two albums, both of which featured prominently on the German Jazz charts. Bireli Lagrene, like Django Reinhardt, has a gypsy background. Django is his most obvious influence. There is however, more to his music than just imitation. He has adopted, for instance, elements of Brazilian music together with Bebop phrasing plus a little Wes Montgomery thrown in from time to time. He was born in Alsace, on the German / French border, on Sept 4th 1966. His father, Fiso was a famous guitarist in France during the Thirties, thus it was natural for Bireli to be introduced to the instrument from an early age. He first hit the limelight in 1978, winning a prize at a festival in Strasbourg. The following year he appeared at a gipsy festival in Darmstadt, a show that was televised throughout Germany. In 1980, he was invited to play with Stephane Grappelli and Nils Henning Orsted Pederson in Strasbourg. In that same year he recorded his first album called *Routes to Django*, which received rapturous applause from the critics. A second album was released and again it was met with critical acclaim. (Island Records, Feb 1984.).

### 15

Tracks: / Douce ambiance / Schwarze augen / Valse d'Alsace / Sweet Georgia Brown / Blues for Bireli / Mirage / Anduman / Solicarnosc / Micro / Autumn leaves / I can't give you anything but love.
Note: Recorded live at the Metropole, Berlin, 1982, aged 15. His second UK release.
**Album:** Released Aug '82, on Antilles/New Directions by Island Records. Catalogue no: **AN 1009**
**Cass:** Released Aug '82, on Antilles/New Directions by Island Records. Catalogue no: **ICT 1009**

### BIRELI SWING 81

Tracks: / B.L. / Swing valse / Djangology / Bireli hi gogoro / Lady be good / Thundering noise / September song / Schwarze augen / Carlos / Limehouse blues / Nuages / How high the moon.
**Album:** Released Jul '83, on Austrophon Diepholz(Germany) Catalogue no: **JP 1009**

### DOWN IN TOWN

Tracks: / Mitti / Berga / Melodie au Crepescule / Down in town / Paris / Reinsburgstrasse / Diminishing blackness / Rue de Pierre / Zum trotz / I can't get started.
**Cass:** Released Nov '83, on Antilles/New Directions by Island Records. Deleted '87. Catalogue no: **ICT 1010**
**Album:** Released Nov '83, on Antilles/New Directions by Island Records. Catalogue no: **AN 1010**

### FOREIGN AFFAIRS

Tracks: / Timothee / Josef / Rue de Pierre (part IV) (CD only.) / Jack Rabbit / Passing through the night / Rue de Pierre (part V) (CD only.) / Senegal / Rue de Pierre (part III) / St. Jean / I can't get started.
**Cass:** Released Jan '89, on Blue Note by EMI Records. Catalogue no: **TCB1 90967**
**CD:** Released Jan '89, on Blue Note by EMI Records. Catalogue no: **CDP 790 967 2**
**Album:** Released Jan '89, on Blue Note by EMI Records. Catalogue no: **B1 90967**

### INFERNO

Tracks: / Inferno / Rue de Pierre (part II) / Action / Rock it / Incertitude / Berga / Ballade / Hips.
**Cass:** Released Apr '88, on Blue Note by EMI Records. Deleted Oct '89. Catalogue no: **TCBLJ 48016**
**CD:** Released Apr '88, on EMI by EMI Records. Deleted Oct '89. Catalogue no: **CDBLJ 48016**
**Album:** Released Apr '88, on Blue Note by EMI Records. Deleted Aug '89. Catalogue no: **BLJ 48016**
**CD:** Released Apr '88, on EMI by EMI Records. Deleted Oct '89. Catalogue no: **CDP 748 016 2**

### LIVE

**CD:** Released Jun '88, on Inak Catalogue no: **INAK 8610CD**
**CD:** Released '88, on Inak Catalogue no: **INAK 865 CD**

### ROUTES TO DJANGO

Tracks: / Night and day / All of me / My melancholy baby.
**Album:** Released Apr '82, on Antilles/New Directions by Island Records. Catalogue no: **AN 1002**
**CD:** Released '86, on Polystar (Japan) Deleted '88. Catalogue no: **J33D 20009**
**CD:** Released '87, on Antilles/New Directions by Island Records. Deleted Jun '88. Catalogue no: **ANCD 1002**

## Lahm, David

### REAL JAZZ FOR THE FOLKS WHO FEEL JAZZ

**Album:** Released Jan '84, on Palo Alto Catalogue no: **PA 8027**

## Laibman, David

### CLASSICAL RAGTIME GUITAR, THE

**Album:** Released Aug '88, on Rounder (USA) by Rounder Records (USA). Catalogue no: **ROUNDER 3040**

## Laine, Cleo

**Biographical details:** Laine, Cleo This British singer has been a part of the UK music business for three decades. Using jazz as her base, she has also recorded and sung in various classical and middle of the road styles. Laine's crystal clear voice has assured her of a steady and lucrative career from the fifties through to the eighties. She has often recorded and performed with her husband, the saxophonist/clarinettist/orchestra leader John Dankworth.
Laine has penetrated the UK pop singles chart on only two occasions. *Let's Slip Away* peaked at No.42 in December 1960. *You'll Answer To Me*, a cover version of Patti Page's minor US hit, was a much bigger success for the British vocalist, reaching the UK No.5 position in 1961. On the British LP chart, Cleo's success was delayed until 1978, when the *Best of Friends* album, a collaboration with classical guitarist John Williams, reached No.18 and logged 22 listed weeks. Flautist James Galway was her partner on the 1980 LP. *Sometimes When We Touch*, which climbed to No.15 and spent 14 weeks on the chart. As a solo artist Laine reached No.68 in December 1978 with an album simply entitled *Cleo*. (Bob Macdonald 30/11/85).

### 16 GOLDEN CLASSICS

Tracks: / He was beautiful (With John Williams. A lyric version of 'Cavatina'.) / People / Aquarius / Somewhere / Killing me softly with his song (With John Williams.) / Send in the clowns / If (With John Williams.) / Don't cry for me Argentina / Just the way you are / Streets of London / When I need you / Let's have a quiet night in / Eleanor Rigby (With John Williams.) / I believe (when you fall in love) / You'll never walk alone / Feelings (With John Williams.).
Note: All tracks licensed from Sierra Records Ltd\Westminster Music Ltd. Design: Shoot that Tiger!; (c) 1986. Castle communications place, Unit 7, 271, Merton Road, London SW18 5JS
**Album:** Released Dec '86, on Unforgettable by Castle Communications Records. Catalogue no: **UNLP 008**
**Cass:** Released Dec '86, on Unforgettable by Castle Communications Records. Catalogue no: **UNMC 008**
**CD:** Released '86, on Unforgettable by Castle Communications Records. Catalogue no: **UNCD 08**

### AN EVENING WITH CLEO LAINE

**2 LP Set:** Released '88, on DRG (USA) by DRG Records (USA). Catalogue no: **MRS 608**

### BEAUTIFUL THING, A

Tracks: / All in love is fair / Skip a long Sam / Send in the clowns / Least you can do is the best you can, The / They needed each other / I loves you Porgy / Until it's time for you to go / Life is a wheel / Summer knows, The / Beautiful thing, A.
**Album:** Released '79, on RCA Victor by BMG Records (UK). Deleted '84. Catalogue no: **SF 8398**

### BEST FRIENDS (Laine, Cleo & John Williams)

Tracks: / Feelings / Time does fly / Killing me softly with his song / Before love went out of style / My day has started

with you / Wave / Eleanor Rigby / Wake my love / If / Charms / Sleep now / He was beautiful.
**Album:** Released Sep '81, on RCA by BMG Records (UK). Catalogue no: **RCALP 3016**
**Cass:** Released Dec '81, on Magenta Catalogue no: **ZCMTA 201**
**Cass:** Released Sep '81, on RCA by BMG Records (UK). Catalogue no: **RCAK 3016**
**Album:** Released Dec '81, on Magenta Catalogue no: **MTA 201**

**BEST OF FRIENDS (Laine, Cleo & John Williams)**
Tracks: / feelings / Time does fly / Killing me softly with his song / Before love went out of style / My day has started with you / Wave / Eleanor Rigby / Awake my love / If / Charms / Sleep now / He's so beautiful (Cavatina).
**Album:** Released Jan '78, on RCA by BMG Records (UK). Deleted Jan '83. Catalogue no: **RS 1094**
**Cass:** Released Jan '78, on RCA by BMG Records (UK). Deleted Jan '83. Catalogue no: **PK 11755**

**BORN ON A FRIDAY**
Tracks: / Come back to me / Colours ran, The / Sunday / Do you really want you / Birdsong (sambalaya) / Let me be the one / Living is easy / I think it's gonna rain today / Unlucky woman (born on a Friday) / Streets of London / Any place I hang my hat is home.
**Album:** Released '79, on RCA Victor by BMG Records (UK). Deleted '84. Catalogue no: **RS 1031**

**CLEO**
**2 LP Set:** Released Dec '78, on Arcade Deleted Dec '83. Catalogue no: **ADEP 37**

**CLEO AT CARNEGIE**
Tracks: / Any place (Medley.) / I'm shadowing you / Crazy rhythm / Primrose colour blue / We are the music makers / You spotted snakes / Methuselah / When I was one and twenty / Sing me no song / Triboro' fair / You've got to do what you've got to do / He was beautiful / Turkish delight / Never let me go / Hoagy Carmichael Medley (Georgia on my mind/Lazy bones/The nearness of you/I get along without yo) / I want to be happy.
**CD:** Released Apr '87, on DRG (USA) by DRG Records (USA). Catalogue no: **CDXP 2101**
**Cass set:** Released Apr '88, on DRG (USA) by DRG Records (USA). Catalogue no: **DARC 2C 2101**
**Cass set:** Released Jun '87, on RCA by BMG Records (UK). Deleted Jul '89. Catalogue no: **PK 71399**
**2 LP Set:** Released Jun '87, on RCA by BMG Records (UK). Deleted Jul '89. Catalogue no: **PL 71399**
**2 LP Set:** Released Apr '88, on DRG (USA) by DRG Records (USA). Catalogue no: **DARC 2 2101**

**CLEO CLOSE UP**
Tracks: / Keep the faith / We could be flying / Loving isn't easy / I saw the light / Sun, the moon and I, The / I believe (when you fall in love) / Lookin' for another pure love / There's something sad / Wish you were here (I do miss you) / That's how heartaches are made / Wondering what to write / Show and tell.
**Album:** Released '79, on RCA Victor by BMG Records (UK). Deleted '84. Catalogue no: **LPL1 5026**

**CLEO LAINE WITH JOHN DANKWORTH (Laine, Cleo & John Dankworth Orchestra)**
**Album:** Released '88, on DRG (USA) by DRG Records (USA). Catalogue no: **MRS 502**
**Cass:** Released '88, on DRG (USA) by DRG Records (USA). Catalogue no: **MRSC 502**

**CLEO LIVE AT CARNEGIE**
Tracks: / I know where I'm going / Music / Wish you were here (I do miss you) / Gimme a pig foot and a bottle of beer / You must believe in Spring / Perdido / Control yourself / Send in the clowns / Ridin' high / Bill / Big best shoes / Stop and smell the roses / Please don't talk about me when I'm gone.
Note: The 10th Anniversary Concert.
**Cass:** Released '79, on RCA by BMG Records (UK). Deleted '84. Catalogue no: **LPK1 5015**
**Album:** Released Sep '86, on Towerbell Catalogue no: **TOWDLP 18**
**Album:** Released '79, on RCA by BMG Records (UK). Deleted '84. Catalogue no: **LPL1 5015**
**Cass:** Released Sep '86, on Towerbell Catalogue no: **ZCTOWD 18**

**CLEO SINGS SONDHEIM**
Tracks: / Everybody says don't (from 'Anyone can whistle') / Losing my mind (from 'Follies') / Ah but underneath (from 'Follies') / I remember (from 'Evening primrose') / Liaisons (from 'A little night music') / You could drive a person crazy (from 'Company') / Not while I'm around (from 'Sweeney Todd') / Ladies who lunch, The (from 'Company') / Send in the clowns (from 'A little night music') / Little things you do together, The (from 'Company') / Anyone can whistle (from 'Anyone can whistle') / I'm calm (from 'A funny thing happened on the way to the Forum') / No one is alone (from 'Into the woods') / Miller's son, the (from 'A little night music') / Not a day goes by (from 'Merrily we roll along') / I'm still here (from 'Follies').
**Cass:** Released Apr '88, on Red Seal by RCA Records. Catalogue no: **RK 87702**
**CD:** Released Apr '88, on Red Seal by RCA Records. Catalogue no: **RD 87702**
**Album:** Released Apr '88, on Red Seal by RCA Records. Catalogue no: **RL 87702**

**CLEO'S CHOICE**
**Album:** Released '88, on GNP Crescendo (USA) by GNP Crescendo Records (USA). Catalogue no: **GNPS 9024**

**COLETTE**
**Cass:** Released Sep '80, on Evolution by Evolution Records. Catalogue no: **RSC 1006**
**Album:** Released Sep '80, on Evolution by Evolution Records. Catalogue no: **RSR 1006**

**ESSENTIAL COLLECTION, THE**
**CD:** Released May '87, on Sierra by Sierra Records. Catalogue no: **CDCL 1**

**GONNA GET THROUGH**
Tracks: / One more night / When I need you / Just the way you are / On and on / I believe you / Gonna get through / I'll have to say I love you in a song / Wish / Let's have a quiet night in / Merchant song.
**Album:** Released Apr '80, on RCA by BMG Records (UK). Deleted '85. Catalogue no: **PL 12926**

**HE WAS BEAUTIFUL**
Tracks: / He was beautiful / Unlucky woman / Streets of London / Jewel in the crown.
**7" EP:** Released Dec '79, on RCA by BMG Records (UK). Deleted '81. Catalogue no: **EPTC 8452**

**HOW, WHERE, WHEN (Laine, Cleo & James Galway)**
Tracks: / How, where, when / Drifting, dreaming.
**7" Single:** Released Apr '80, on RCA by BMG Records (UK). Deleted Apr '83. Catalogue no: **RB 5246**

**I AM A SONG**
Tracks: / I'm gonna sit right down and write myself ... / Early Autumn / Friendly persuasion / There is a time / Day when the world comes alive / I am a song / It might as well be Spring / Music / But not for me / Two part invention / Talk to me baby / Thieving boy / Hi-heel sneakers.
**Album:** Released '79, on RCA Victor by BMG Records (UK). Deleted '84. Catalogue no: **SF 8352**

**IN CONCERT AT THE CARNEGIE**
**Album:** Released Oct '85, on Sierra by Sierra Records. Catalogue no: **FEDD 1006**
**Cass:** Released Oct '85, on Sierra by Sierra Records. Catalogue no: **CFEDD 1006**

**IN RETROSPECT (Laine, Cleo & Johnny Dankworth)**
Tracks: / Mood indigo / Stormy weather / My one and only love / St. Louis blues / Lady sings the blues / Mean to me / I'll get by / Love is here to stay / Early autumn / T'aint what you do (it's the way that you do it) / Happiness is just a thing called Joe / Hit the road to dreamland.
**LP Set:** Released May '83, on Polydor (Germany) by Polydor Ltd. Catalogue no: **MRS 501**

**INCOMPARABLE CLEO LAINE, THE (Live at the Wavendon Festival)**
Tracks: / Eleanor Rigby / Song / You spotted snakes / If we lived on top of a mountain / Papaito / Happiness is just a thing called Joe / Control yourself / That certain feeling / Doctor David Mantle / To music / Go and catch a falling star / Lorelei / Perdido / It's a pity to say good-

night.
**Album:** Released Jul '80, on Black Lion Catalogue no: **BLM 51006**

## JAZZ FIRST (Laine, Cleo & Jean Luc Ponty)
**Cass:** Released Jul '86, on Timeless Treasures Catalogue no: **813**

## LET'S SLIP AWAY
Tracks: / Let's slip away.
**7" Single:** Released Dec '60, on Fontana by Phonogram Ltd. Deleted Dec '63. Catalogue no: **H 269**

## LIVE AT CARNEGIE HALL
Tracks: / I know where I'm going / Music / Wish you were here / Gimme a pigfoot and a bottle of beer / You must believe in spring / Perdido / Control yourself / Send in the clowns / Riding high / Bill / Big best shoes / Stop and smell the roses / Please don't talk about me when I'm gone / Blues in the night / How long? / Streets of London / London pride / Direction / Company / Miller's song, The / Broadway baby / Being alive / Born on a Friday / One alone / I've got the music in me / Fascinating rhythm / Jazzman / By Strauss / I gotta right to sing the blues / It don't mean a thing / Be a child.
**2 LP Set:** Released '82, on Magenta Catalogue no: **ICSD 2002**

## OFF THE RECORD WITH CLEO LAINE
**Cass:** Released Nov '84, on Sierra by Sierra Records. Catalogue no: **CFEDD 1003**
**Album:** Released Nov '84, on Sierra by Sierra Records. Catalogue no: **FEDD 1003**

## ONE MORE DAY
Tracks: / Driving home / All the skinny schoolgirls / Tomboy / First love half light / Goodbye friend / Over the moon / Shall we get married? / Settling down / One more day / Move / Lovers and friends / Year is gone, The.
**Album:** Released Feb '83, on Sepia Catalogue no: **RSR 1009**
**Cass:** Released Feb '83, on Sepia Catalogue no: **ZC RSR 1009**
**Album:** Released May '84, on DRG (USA) by DRG Records (USA). Deleted Jan '89. Catalogue no: **SL 5198**
**Cass:** Released May '84, on DRG (USA) by DRG Records (USA). Catalogue no: **SLC 5198**
**CD:** Released '88, on DRG (USA) by DRG Records (USA). Catalogue no: **CDSL 5198**

## ONE MORE DAY (SINGLE)
Tracks: / One more day / Over the moon.
**7" Single:** Released Apr '81, on Sepia Deleted '85. Catalogue no: **RSS 102**

## PLATINUM COLLECTION
Tracks: / He was beautiful / If / Let's have a quiet night in / Send in the clowns / Let me be the one / Summer knows, The / Streets of London / Loving isn't easy / Killing me softly with his song / Music / All in love is fair / I believe (when you fall in love) / When I need you / Don't cry for me Argentina / I think it's going to rain today / You'll never walk alone / Feelings / Wish you were here / Eleanor Rigby / Just the way you are / Gonna get through / Sunday / Unlucky woman (is born on a Friday) / Until it's time for you to go.
Note: John Williams (guitar) features on five tracks.
**Cass:** Released Oct '81, on Cube (Platinum collection) Catalogue no: **ZCPLT 1007**
**Album:** Released Nov '81, on Dakota Deleted Nov '86. Catalogue no: **PLAT 1007**

## PORTRAIT OF A SONG STYLIST
Tracks: / On a clear day / I could write a book / Look of love, The / Come rain or come shine / Fascinating rhythm / I can dream, can't I / I cover the waterfront / I'm a dreamer, aren't we all / I got it bad and that ain't good / Talk about me when I'm gone / They say it's wonderful / St Louis blues / Lady sings the blues / Stormy weather.
**Album:** Released Apr '89, on Masterpiece by Castle Communications Records. Catalogue no: **HARLP 107**
**CD:** Released Apr '89, on Masterpiece by Castle Communications Records. Catalogue no: **HARCD 107**
**Cass:** Released Apr '89, on Masterpiece by Castle Communications Records. Catalogue no: **HARMC 107**

## RETURN TO CARNEGIE
Tracks: / Blues in the night / How long / Streets of London / London pride / Direction / Company (medley) / Broadway baby / Being alive / Born on a Friday / One alone / I've got the music in me / Fascinating rhythm / Jazzman / By Strauss / I gotta right to sing the blues / It don't mean a thing if it ain't got that ... / Playoff (I've got the music in me) / Be a child.
**Album:** Released '79, on RCA Victor by BMG Records (UK). Deleted '84. Catalogue no: **PL 12407**
**Cass:** Released '79, on RCA Victor by BMG Records (UK). Deleted '84. Catalogue no: **PK 12407**

## SHAKESPEARE AND ALL THAT JAZZ (Featuring the music of John Dankworth)
Tracks: / If music be the food of love / O mistress mine / Duet of sonnets / Winter (love's labours lost) / My love is as a fever (sonnet 1477) / It was a lover and his lass / Dunsinane blues / Take all my loves (sonnet 40) / Blow, blow thou winter wind (as you like it) / Shall I compare thee (sonnet 18) / Witches, fair and foul / Fear no more (cymbeline) / Sigh no more, ladies / Complete works, The.
**Album:** Released Oct '88, on Affinity by Charly Records. Catalogue no: **AFF 196**
**Cass:** Released Oct '88, on Affinity by Charly Records. Catalogue no: **TCAFF 196**

## SOMETIMES WHEN WE TOUCH (Laine, Cleo & James Galway)
Tracks: / Drifting dreaming / Sometimes when we touch / Play it again Sam / Skylark / How, where, when? / Fluter's ball, The / Consuelo's love theme / Keep loving me / Anyone can whistle / Still was the night / Lo, hear the gentle lark / Like a sad song.
**Cass:** Released Nov '84, on RCA International by BMG Records (UK). Deleted Jul '89. Catalogue no: **NK 70007**
**Album:** Released Nov '84, on RCA International by BMG Records (UK). Deleted Jul '89. Catalogue no: **NL 70007**
**Album:** Released May '80, on RCA by BMG Records (UK). Deleted May '85. Catalogue no: **PL 25296**
**CD:** Released Jan '87, on RCA by BMG Records (UK). Catalogue no: **RD 83628**

## SPOTLIGHT ON CLEO LAINE (See panel over)
Tracks: / I want to be happy / I think of you / I can dream can't I / I've got my love to keep me warm / I've got it bad and that ain't good / I'm a dreamer, aren't we all / Popular song / I'm just wild about Harry / On a slow boat to China / Perdido / They say it's wonderful / If we lived on top of a mountain / Peel me a grape / Song without words / Fascinating rhythm / Oh, lady be good / Little boat / I cover the waterfront / Biding my time / Come rain or come shine / Lines to Ralph Hodgeson, Esquire / Ridin' high / Woman talk / I could write a book / Second time around, The / On a clear day / Complete works, The / Please don't talk about me when I'm gone.
**2 LP Set:** Released '74, on Phillips. Catalogue no: **6625 008**

## THAT OLD FEELING
Tracks: / That old feeling / Tenderly / I've got a crush on you / Once in a while / Imagination / It never entered my mind / Ain't misbehavin' / I didn't know about you / I never went away / It's not easy (to say I love you) / Alfie / I've got it bad and that ain't good / Every time we say goodbye / Embraceable you / My funny valentine / It happens quietly / He needs me / You're looking at me.
**CD:** Released Dec '86, on The Colours Series Catalogue no: **KNEWCD 101**
**CD:** Released Apr '87, on The Collection by Object Enterprises. Catalogue no: **OR 0003**

## THEMES
**Cass:** Released Oct '85, on Sierra by Sierra Records. Catalogue no: **FEDC 2000**

## THIS IS CLEO LAINE
Tracks: / Feel the warm / Make it with you / From both sides now / Somethings wrong / Traces / Can it be true / Slow motion / Stop and smell the roses / Rainy day man / Good bad but beautiful / Day by day / Prepare ye the way of the Lord / Don't talk now.
**Album:** Released '81, on EMI by EMI Records. Deleted '86. Catalogue no: **THIS 31**

## UNFORGETTABLE CLEO LAINE
Tracks: / Something's gotta give / Unforgettable / Big best shoes / All of you / Too late now / I'll remember April / Hand-

**Cleo Laine - Spotlight on Cleo Laine (Philips)**

me-down love / I'm putting all my eggs in one basket / Teach me tonight / Young at heart / Jeepers creepers / He needs me / Summer is a comin' in / April in Paris / I'm beginning to see the light / They were right.
Note: Sixteen tracks of early Cleo with John Dankworth and Dave Lindup arrangements.
(With the John Dankworth Orchestra.)

**Cass:** Released Mar '88, on PRT by Castle Communications Records. Catalogue no: **PYM 6028**
**Album:** Released Mar '88, on PRT by Castle Communications Records. Catalogue no: **PYL 6028**

**WOMAN TO WOMAN**
**Album:** Released Sep '89, on RCA by BMG Records (UK). Catalogue no: **RL 87999**
**Cass:** Released Sep '89, on RCA by BMG Records (UK). Catalogue no: **RK 87999**
**CD:** Released Sep '89, on RCA by BMG Records (UK). Catalogue no: **RD 87999**

**WORD SONGS**
Tracks: / All the world's a stage / If music be the food of love / You spotted snakes / Winter, when icicles hang by the wall / Fear no more the heat o' the sun / It was a lover and his lass / Sigh no more, ladies / Dunsinane blues / When that I was a little boy / Shall I compare thee to a summer's day / Blow, blow, thou winter wind / O mistress mine, where you are roaming / Take all my loves / My love is as a fever / Who is Sylvia / Compleat works / Our revels now are ended / Lines to Ralph Hodgson Esquire / Goe, and catche a falling starre / Bread and butter / Dr. David Mantle / Advice to a girl / O tell me the truth about love / In Tenebris 1 / Sun and fun / song / English teeth / Viva sweet love / Mungojerrie and rumpelteazer / Thieving boy / Sing me no song.
Note: Famous Philips recording of Cleo Laine singing the poetry of William ShakespeareT.S.Eliott, John Dunne, William Makepeace Thackeray, Spike Milligan, Sir John Betjeman, Thomas Hardy and others, set to music by John Dankworth. "Word Songs"was always one of the most popular sections of Cleo's concert repertoire and hasnot been available on album for some years. Over one hour of music.
Recorded January 1977 to February, '78.
Personnel: John Dankworth - soprano sax, alto sax, clarinet/Paul Hart - keyboard/Pete Morgan, Daryl Runswick - bass, bass guitar/Kenny Clare, Allan Ganley, Tony Kinsey - drums.
**2 LP Set:** Released '78, on RCA Red Seal by BMG Records (UK). Catalogue no: **RL 25176**
**Cass:** Released '78, on RCA Red Seal by BMG Records (UK). Catalogue no: **RK 25176**
**CD:** Released Apr '87, on Philips by Phonogram Ltd. Catalogue no: **8304612**

**YOU'LL ANSWER TO ME**
Tracks: / You'll answer to me.
**7" Single:** Released Sep '61, on Fontana by Phonogram Ltd. Deleted Sep '63. Catalogue no: **H 326**

**YOU'VE GOT TO DO WHAT YOU'VE GOT**
Tracks: / You've got to do what you've got to do / Our relationship.
**7" Single:** Released Oct '80, on Sepia Deleted Oct '83. Catalogue no: **RSS 101**

## Lake, Oliver

**CLEVONT FITZHUBERT (Lake, Oliver Quertet)**
**Album:** Released Jul '82, on Black Saint (Italy) Catalogue no: **BSR 0054**

**CONCERT A SPACE (Lake, Oliver & Joseph Bowie)**
**Album:** Released Apr '81, on Sackville by Spotlite Records. Catalogue no: **2010**

**HOLDING TOGETHER**
**Album:** Released Jul '78, on Black Saint (Italy) Catalogue no: **BSR 009**

**JUMP UP**
**Album:** Released May '83, on Gramavision Catalogue no: **GR 8106**

**OTHERSIDE**
Note: Saxophonist Oliver Lake is a member of not one but four ensembles each exploring different aspects of jazz music. World saxophone quartet for bebop, Jump Up for funk, Blue Star for free form improvisation and his own band, now a quintet on side one plus a specially assembled big band for side two. The quintet includes Oliver Lake (alto sax), Geri Allen (piano), Fred Hopkins (bass) and Andrew Cyrille (drums). The big band includes Oliver Lake (alto sax) Marty Ehrlich (reeds), John Stubblefield (reeds), Frank Lacy (trombone), Al Patterson (trombone), Michelle Rosewoman (piano).
**Album:** Released Feb '89, on Gramavision Catalogue no: **188 901 1**
**CD:** Released Feb '89, on Gramavision Catalogue no: **188901 2**
**Cass:** Released Feb '89, on Gramavision Catalogue no: **188901 4**

**PLUG IT (Lake,Oliver and Jump Up)**
Tracks: / Trickle down theory / Plug it / Tone clone / Breath of life / Go for it / Be the one / Stratosphere / No more wars.
**Album:** Released Dec '83, on Gramavision Catalogue no: **GR 8206**

## Lamarche, Susan

**SUSAN LAMARCHE & WALDOS GUTBUCKET SYNCOPATORS (Lamarche, Susan & Waldos Gutbucket)**
**Album:** Released '88, on Stomp Off (USA) Catalogue no: **SOS 1032**

## Lambert, Hendricks...

**Biographical details:** Singer and songwriter Jon Hendricks, born in 1921 in Ohio, formed Lambert, Hendricks and Ross in 1957 with Dave Lambert (1917-66) and Annie Ross (born in 1930 in Mitcham, Surrey). Ross was the hostess of the legendary London jazz club, Annie's Room in 1965-6 and is also a fine actress. Eddie Jefferson, King Pleasure and others had tried writing lyrics to jazz solos; Hendricks wrote words for Woody Herman's *Four brothers* and for the George Russell album *New York, New York* in 1959; Ross had written *Twisted* in 1952 based on a solo by Wardell Gray; the Lambert, Hendricks & Ross group were easily the most successful in this style: their Roulette album, *Sing a song of Basie* was a sensation in 1958. Hendricks was had a lower profile since those days but is always in demand as a lyricist and performer. (Donald Clarke, November 1989).

**AT NEWPORT '63 (Lambert/Hendricks/Bavan)**
**Album:** Released May '83, on RCA (France) by BMG Records (France). Catalogue no: **PL 3531**

**EVERYBODY'S BOPPIN' (Lambert, Hendricks & Annie Ross)**
**Cass:** Released '88, on CBS by CBS Records. Catalogue no: **465 199 4**
**Album:** Released '88, on CBS by CBS Records. Catalogue no: **465 199 1**
**CD:** Released '88, on CBS by CBS Records. Catalogue no: **465 199 2**

**HAVIN' A BALL AT THE VILLAGE GATE (Lambert/Hendricks/Bavan)**
**Album:** Released Oct '85, on RCA (France) by BMG Records (France). Catalogue no: **NL 89580**

**SING A SONG OF BASIE (Lambert, Hendricks & Annie Ross)**
Tracks: / Everyday / It's sand man / Two for the blues / One o'clock jump / Little pony / Down for double / Fiesta in blue / Down for the Count / Blues backstage / Avenue C.
**Album:** Released Jun '82, on Jasmine by Hasmick Promotions. Catalogue no: **JAS 6**
**Cass:** Released Jun '82, on Jasmine by Hasmick Promotions. Catalogue no: **JAS C6**

**SWINGERS, THE (Lambert, Hendricks & Annie Ross)**
Tracks: / Airegin / Babe's blues / Dark clouds / Jackie / Swingin' 'til the girls come home / Four / Little niles / Where / Now's the time / Love makes the world go round / Clap hands here comes Charley.
**CD:** Released Aug '88, on EMI-Manhattan by EMI Records. Catalogue no: **CZ 46**
**CD:** Released Aug '88, on EMI-Manhattan by EMI Records. Catalogue no: **CDP 746 849 2**
**Album:** Released Nov '84, on Affinity by Charly Records. Catalogue no: **AFF 131**

**SWINGIN' 'TIL THE GIRLS COME HOME (Lambert/Hendricks/Bavan)**
Tracks: / One o'clock jump / Cousin Mary / April in Paris / Feed me / Melba's blues / Dis hyunh / Swingin' 'til the girls come home / Gimme that wine / Watermelon man / Walkin' / Cloudburst / Jumpin' at The Woodside / It's sand, man! / Stops and goes blues.
Note: Recorded live.
**CD:** Released Apr '88, on Bluebird (2) by BMG Records (UK). Catalogue no: **ND 86282**

## Lamond, Don

**DON LAMOND & HIS BIG BAND**
Tracks: / Early Autumn / Four brothers / Apple honey / Apple valley / Home folks / Dear John / What am I here for? / Here's that rainy day / Yesterday I heard the rain / Cherie Amour / Uptight.
**Album:** Released Feb '83, on Progressive (USA) by Jazzology Records (USA). Catalogue no: **PRO 7067**

**EXTRAORDINARY (Lamond, Don & His Big Swing Band)**
**Album:** Released Apr '88, on Statiras (USA) by Statiras(USA) Records. Catalogue no: **SLP 8071**

## Lamont, Duncan

**BLUES IN THE NIGHT (Lamont, Duncan Quartet)**
Note: With Brian Dee, Mario Castronari, Allan Ganley.
**Album:** Released Jun '88, on LDC Catalogue no: **LDC 4001**

**SUMMER SOUNDS**
Tracks: / Girl from Ipanema / Quiet nights of quiet stars / Shadow of your smile / Call me / Felicidade / Destination love / Wave / My cherie amour / Mas que nada / Fool on the hill / Desafinado / Un homme et une femme / Meditation / How insensitive / Summer samba / Our day will come / Look of love, The / We've only just begun / Gentle one / Alone again.
**Cass:** Released May '86, on Hour Of Pleasure by EMI Records. Deleted Apr '90. Catalogue no: **HR 4181114**
**Cass:** Released May '86, on Hour Of Pleasure by EMI Records. Deleted Apr '90. Catalogue no: **HR 8111**

## Lan Doky, Niels

**DAYBREAK**
Tracks: / All or nothing at all / Why / Final decision / Jet lag / Natural / Daybreak.
**Album:** Released '88, on Storyville by Storyville Records AB. Catalogue no: **SLP 4160**
**CD:** Released '88, on Storyville by Storyville Records AB. Catalogue no: **STCD 4160**

**HERE OR THERE (Lan Doky, Niels Trio)**
Note: With Niels Henning O.P.\Alvin Queen
**CD:** Released Feb '89, on Storyville by Storyville Records AB. Catalogue no: **STCD 4117**
**Album:** Released Nov '86, on Storyville by Storyville Records AB. Catalogue no: **SLP 4117**

**TARGET, THE (Lan Doky, Niels Trio)**
**Album:** Released Jun '88, on Storyville by Storyville Records AB. Catalogue no: **SLP 4140**
**CD:** Released Feb '89, on Storyville by Storyville Records AB. Catalogue no: **STCD 4140**

**TRUTH, THE (Live at Montmartre) (Lan Doky, Niels Trio)**
**Album:** Released Jun '88, on Storyville by Storyville Records AB. Catalogue no: **SLP 4144**
**CD:** Released Feb '89, on Storyville by Storyville Records AB. Catalogue no: **STCD 4144**

## Landry, Art

**1924-1927 (Landry, Art & His Orchestra)**
**Cass:** Released Jul '86, on Emporium Cassettes Catalogue no: **049**

## Lane, Steve

**I'VE GOT FORD ENGINE 1969-72 (Lane, Steve/Southern Stompers)**
**Album:** Released May '74, on VJM (Vintage Jazz Music) by Vintage Jazz Music Society(VJM). Catalogue no: **LC 14S**

**JUST IMAGINE (Lane, Steve & Red Hot Peppers)**
**Cass:** Released Aug '89, on VJM (Vintage Jazz Music) by Vintage Jazz Music Society(VJM). Catalogue no: **VC 38**

**MOVIN' ON (Lane, Steve/Famous Southern Stompers)**
**Album:** Released Apr '79, on VJM (Vintage Jazz Music) by Vintage Jazz Music Society(VJM). Catalogue no: **SLC 31**

**STEVE LANE & HIS FAMOUS SOUTHERN STOMPERS (Lane, Steve/Famous Southern Stompers)**
**Album:** Released Dec '82, on Stomp Off (USA) Catalogue no: **SOS 1040**

**STEVE LANE IN CONCERT (Lane, Steve/Southern Stompers/Michele)**
**Album:** Released May '74, on VJM (Vintage Jazz Music) by Vintage Jazz Music Society(VJM). Catalogue no: **UNKNOWN**

**STEVE LANE & RED HOT PEPPERS (Lane, Steve & Red Hot Peppers)**
Tracks: / New Orleans shuffle / Was I drunk? / Barney / Lady love / Lazy / Bugle boy march / Give me a call / Heaven on earth / Alexander's ragtime band / St Philip St Breakdown / Careless love blues / Wild man blues / Sweet Georgia Brown / Sweet daddy.
**Album:** Released '88, on VJM (Vintage Jazz Music) by Vintage Jazz Music Society(VJM). Catalogue no: **LC 36**

**STEVE LANES SOUTHERN STOMPERS WITH MICHELE (Lane, Steve/Southern Stompers/Michele)**
Note: 1968/9. Tracks include: That's you baby/Blue baby/Brand new papa/Stop it Joe/Nobody knows you when you're down and out/Ugly child, etc. Cassette only.
**Cass:** Released Oct '87, on VJM (Vintage Jazz Music) by Vintage Jazz Music Society(VJM). Catalogue no: **AC 10**

**Eddie Lang - A Handful Of Riffs (ASV)**

**WEMBLEY WIGGLE (Lane, Steve/Southern Stompers)**
**Album:** Released May '74, on 77 by 77 Records. Catalogue no: **77 EU 12/3**

## Lang, Eddie

**EDDIE LANG & LONNIE JOHNSON**
**Album:** Released Jan '83, on Swaggie (Australia) Catalogue no: **S 1229**
**Album:** Released Jan '83, on Swaggie (Australia) Catalogue no: **S 1276**

**HANDFUL OF RIFFS, A (See panel above)**
Tracks: / Eddie's twister / April kisses / Prelude / Melody man's dream / Perfect / Rainbow / Add a little wiggle / Jeannine / I'll never be the same / Church street sobbin' blues / There'll be some changes made / Two tone stomp / Jet black blues / Blue blood blues / Bullfrog moan / Handful of riffs, A / Bugle call rag / Freeze and melt / Hot heels / Walking the dog / March of the hoodlums.
**Cass:** Released 1 May '89, on Living Era by Academy Sound & Vision Records. Catalogue no: **ZC AJA 5061**
**Album:** Released 1 May '89, on Living Era by Academy Sound & Vision Records. Catalogue no: **AJA 5061**
**CD:** Released 1 May '89, on Living Era by Academy Sound & Vision Records. Catalogue no: **CD AJA 5061**

**JAZZ GUITAR VIRTUOSO**
**Album:** Released Dec '88, on Yazoo (USA) by Shanachie Records (USA). Catalogue no: **L 1059**

**TROUBLES, TROUBLES (Lang, Eddie/Edgar Blanchard & The Gondoliers)**
**Cass:** Released '88, on Rounder (USA) by Rounder Records (USA). Catalogue no: **ROUNDER 2080C**
**Album:** Released '88, on Rounder (USA) by Rounder Records (USA). Catalogue no: **ROUNDER 2080**
**CD:** Released '88, on Rounder (USA) by Rounder Records (USA). Catalogue no: **CD 2080**

## Lanigiro Synkopating...

**LANIGIRO SYNKOPATING MELODY**
Tracks: / Happy days and lonely nights / Ice cream / Xashariana / Birmingham breakdown / Little old lady / It's the natural thing to do / September in the rain / St. Louis blues / Fifth avenue / Two dukes on a pier / Drummer boy / Tangerine / Sweet Georgia Brown / My melancholy baby / St. Louis blues / For me and my gal.
**Album:** Released Jul '88, on Harlequin by Interstate Music. Catalogue no: **HQ 2061**

## Lanphere, Don

**GO AGAIN (Various artists)**
**CD:** Released Feb '89, on Hep Jazz by Hep Records. Catalogue no: **HEPCD 2040**
**Album:** Released '88, on Hep Jazz by Hep Records. Catalogue no: **HEP 2040**

**INTO SOMEWHERE (Lanphere, Don Quintet)**
**Album:** Released '88, on Hep Jazz by Hep Records. Catalogue no: **HEP 2022**

**STOP**
**Album:** Released Mar '87, on Hep Jazz by Hep Records. Catalogue no: **HEP 2034**

## Lateef, Yusef

**ANGEL EYES**
**2 LP Set:** Released Mar '85, on Savoy Jazz (USA) by Malaco Records (USA). Catalogue no: **SJL 2238**

**CENTAUR & THE PHOENIX, THE**
Tracks: / Revelation / Apathy / Ev'ry lady / Centaur & the phoenix,The / Iqbal / Summer song / Philanthropist, The.
**Album:** Released Feb '88, on Riverside (USA) by Fantasy Inc (USA). Catalogue no: **RSLP 337**

**CONTEMPLATION**
Tracks: / Hazing / Rip de boom / Teef / I need you / Back yard / Sassy Ann.
**Album:** Released Sep '84, on Affinity by Charly Records. Deleted May '88. Catalogue no: **AFF 120**

**GOLDEN FLUTE, THE**
Tracks: / Road runner / Straighten up and fly right / Oasis / I don't stand a ghost of a chance with you / Exactly like you / Golden flute, The / Rosetta / Head hunters / Smart set, The.
**Album:** Released Mar '83, on Jasmine by Hasmick Promotions. Deleted Feb '88. Catalogue no: **JAS 63**

**GONG**
Tracks: / Prayer to the east / I got it bad / Eighty five forty (8540) / Twelfth street / Sounds of nature / Suelb / Lover man / Check blues / Gypsy arab / Night in Tunisia / Love dance / Sram / Endura / Delilah.
**2 LP Set:** Released Mar '85, on Savoy Jazz (USA) by Malaco Records (USA). Catalogue no: **SJL 2226**

**MORNING (Savoy sessions)**
Tracks: / Morning / O'blues / Ameena / Metaphor / Yusef's mood / Blues in space / G. Bouk / Polarity / Midday / Happyology / Space / Beginning, The / Beauregard.
**Album:** Released Mar '85, on Savoy Jazz (USA) by Malaco Records (USA). Catalogue no: **SJL 2205**

**SAX MASTERS**
**2 LP Set:** Released Jan '76, on Vogue by Vogue Records. Catalogue no: **VJD 512**

**YUSEF LATEEF**
Tracks: / Outside blues / Solid blues / Blues rocky / Dexterity / Trudy's delight / Introlude / Train stop / Big foot.
**Album:** Released Jan '82, on Jazz Reactivation Catalogue no: **JR 104**

## Latin Jazz

**LATIN JAZZ VOL.1 (Various artists)**
Tracks: / Nica's dream: *Burrell, Kenny* / Gunky: *Lytle, Johnny* / Mambo inn: *Tay-*

*lor, Billy Trio* / Caravan: *Pucho & His Latin Soul Brothers* / Sambop: *Adderley, Cannonball* / Baion baby: *Stitt, Sonny* / Tin tin deo: *Forrest, Jimmy* / Montuneando: *Santamaria, Mongo.*
**Album:** Released 28 Mar '89, on BGP by Ace Records. Catalogue no: **BGP 1023**

**LATIN JAZZ VOL.2 (Various artists)**
Tracks: / Ping pong: *Blakey, Art/Jazz Messengers* / Mau mau: *Farmer, Art Septet* / Manteca: *Garland, Red Trio* / Sea food wally: *Rodriguez, Willie* / Screamin': *McDuff, Brother Jack* / Fat man: *Montego Joe* / Mambo ricci: *Dolphy, Eric & Latin Jazz* / Chop sticks: *Braith, George.*
**Album:** Released Aug '89, on BGP by Ace Records. Catalogue no: **BGP 1027**

## Laughing In Rhythm

**LAUGHING IN RHYTHM (Various artists)**
**Album:** Released Apr '81, on Stash (USA) Catalogue no: **ST 116**

## Laurie, Cy

**CY LAURIE & LES JOWETT 1957 (Laurie, Cy & Les Jowett)**
Tracks: / Beale street blues / House in Harlem for sale / Jazz me blues / Ain't gonna give nobody none of my jelly roll / Mississippi mud / In a mist / Our Monday date / Louisiana / Footstpes in the sand / Spain / Gee baby ain't I good to you / It's tight like that / Reefer drag / Gatemouth / At the jazz band ball.
**Album:** Released Jul '82, on Flyright by Interstate Music. Catalogue no: **FLY 217**

**DELVING BACK WITH CY (Laurie, Cy quartet\band)**
Note: Cy Laurie quartet with Fred Hunt, Les jowett. Cy Laurie band with Al Fairweather
**Album:** Released Nov '86, on Esquire by Titan Int. Prod.. Catalogue no: **ESQ 324**

**SHADES OF CY**
Note: with Hugh Rainey/Peter Corrigan/Steve Nice.
**Album:** Released Mar '87, on Suntan Catalogue no: **S/12L/A1**

## Laury, Booker T.

**MEMPHIS PIANO JEWEL**
**Album:** Released '88, on Wolf Catalogue no: **120 912**

**ONE OF THE LAST MEMPHIS BLUES PIANO JEWELS**
**Album:** Released Aug '87, on Wolf Catalogue no: **W 120912**

## Laws, Ronnie

**Biographical details:** Laws, Ronnie This American saxophonist, flautist, singer, songwriter and producer was briefly a member of Earth Wind & Fire during the early Seventies, and used that band's jazz influences when launching his solo career in 1975. Ronnie is the younger brother of two other noted musicians, Hubert Laws and Eloise Laws. His first LP 1975's *Pressure Sensitive*, became the biggest selling debut album in the history of Blue Note Records; it was a smash on the Billboard jazz charts and reached No.73 on the US pop list. This, and Laws' other early albums were produced by Wayne Henderson of Crusaders fame.
Laws never quite lived up to the success of *Pressure Sensitive.* He began producing himself in 1980, continuing to release polished and well crafted jazz funk records which achieved respectable US chart positions. He finally made his chart debut in Britain with October 1981's *Solid Ground* LP - this was listed on the UK Top 100 Albums chart for one week, at No.100! (Bob Macdonald 4/12/85).

**ALL DAY RHYTHM**
Tracks: / Smoke house / Dreams I dream, The / All day rhythm / Rhythm of romance / Still / Junior boy / Nite life / Distant eyes / Arrival / Home dance.
**Album:** Released Dec '87, on CBS by CBS Records. Deleted 17 Apr '89. Catalogue no: **460592 1**
**CD:** Released Nov '87, on CBS by CBS Records. Catalogue no: **460592 2**
**Cass:** Released Dec '87, on CBS by CBS Records. Deleted 17 Apr '89. Catalogue no: **460592 4**

**ALL FOR YOU**
Tracks: / All for you / Let's keep it together.
**7" Single:** Released Feb '79, on United Artists by EMI Records. Deleted '82. Catalogue no: **UP 36481**
**12" Single:** Released Feb '79, on United Artists by EMI Records. Deleted '82. Catalogue no: **12 UP 36481**

**ALWAYS THERE**
Tracks: / Always there / Love is here / Goodtime ride.
**12" Single:** Released Mar '80, Deleted Mar '83. Catalogue no: **UP 36497**
**12" Single:** Released Mar '80, Deleted Mar '83. Catalogue no: **UP12-36497**

**CLASSIC MASTERS**
Tracks: / City girl / Always there / Love is here / Every generation / Paradise (you are) / Friends and strangers / In the groove / Stay awake / Saturday evening.
**CD:** Released Mar '88, on Capitol by EMI Records. Catalogue no: **BU 6**
**CD:** Released Mar '88, on Capitol by EMI Records. Catalogue no: **CDP 746 585 2**

**EVERY GENERATION**
**Album:** Released Feb '80, on United Artists by EMI Records. Deleted Jun '89. Catalogue no: **UAG 30289**

**EVERY GENERATION (SINGLE)**
Tracks: / Every generation / O.T.B.A. law.
**7" Single:** Released May '80, on United Artists by EMI Records. Deleted May '85. Catalogue no: **UP 626**
**12" Single:** Released May '80, on United Artists by EMI Records. Deleted May '85. Catalogue no: **12UP 626**

**FLAME**
Tracks: / All for you / These days / Flame / Living love / Love is here / Grace / Joy / Live your life away.
**Album:** Released Jan '79, on United Artists by EMI Records. Deleted Jan '84. Catalogue no: **UAG 30204**

**MIRROR TOWN**
Tracks: / Come to me / Misled / Tell me / Mirror town / Like a crazy man / Midnight side / Cold day / You have to be in love / Take a chance.
**Cass:** Released Oct '86, on CBS by CBS Records. Catalogue no: **450068 4**
**Album:** Released Oct '86, on CBS by CBS Records. Deleted Jun '88. Catalogue no: **450068 1**

**MR NICE GUY**
Tracks: / Can't save tomorrow / Mr. Nice Guy / In the groove / Third hour / You / Big stars / Rollin' / What does it take (to win your love) / Off and on again.
**Album:** Released Sep '83, on Capitol by EMI Records. Catalogue no: **ATAK 67**
**Cass:** Released Sep '83, on Capitol by EMI Records. Catalogue no: **TCATAK 67**
**Album:** Released Sep '83, on Capitol by EMI Records. Catalogue no: **EST400 1671**

**PRESSURE SENSITIVE (Laws, Ronnie & Pressure)**
Tracks: / Always there / Momma / Never be the same / Tell me something good / Nothing to lose / Tidal wave / Why do you laugh at me / Mis' Mary's place.
**CD:** Released May '87, on EMI-America by EMI Records. Deleted Jun '89. Catalogue no: **CDP 746 554 2**

**RONNIE LAWS**
Tracks: / City girl / Always there / Love is here / Every generation / Paradise (you are) / Friends and strangers / In the groove / Stay awake / Saturday evening.
**CD:** Released Apr '87, on Capitol by EMI Records. Catalogue no: **BU 6**

**SOLID GROUND**
Tracks: / Solid ground / Heavy on easy / Segue / There's a way / Stay awake / Your stuff / Just as you are / Summer fool / Good feelings.
**Album:** Released Oct '81, on Liberty by EMI Records. Deleted Oct '86. Catalogue no: **LBG 30336**

**STAY AWAKE**
Tracks: / Stay awake / Heavy on easy.
**12" Single:** Released Sep '81, on United Artists by EMI Records. Deleted '84. Catalogue no: **12UP 644**

**THERE'S A WAY**
Tracks: / There's a way / Your stuff / Always there.
**12" Single:** Released Jan '82, on United Artists by EMI Records. Deleted Jan '85. Catalogue no: **12 UP 648**
**7" Single:** Released Jan '82, on United Artists by EMI Records. Deleted Jan '85. Catalogue no: **UP 648**

**YOUNG CHILD**
Tracks: / Young child / Tomorrow.
**12" Single:** Released Feb '80, on United Artists by EMI Records. Deleted Feb

'85. Catalogue no: **12UP 619**
**7" Single:** Released Feb '80, on United Artists by EMI Records. Deleted Feb '85. Catalogue no: **UP 619**

## Lawson, Yank

### BEST OF JAZZ IN THE TROC
Tracks: / South Rampart Street parade / Vipers drag / Tin roof blues / Wolverine blues / Just a closer walk with Thee / Savoy blues / Summertime / After you've gone.
**Album:** Released Apr '81, on World Jazz Catalogue no: **WJLPS 14**

### EASY TO REMEMBER
**Album:** Released Feb '89, on Flyright by Interstate Music. Catalogue no: **FLY 208**

### LAWSON-HAGGART JAZZ BAND GO TO NEW ORLEANS (Lawson-Haggart Jazz Band)
**Album:** Released Jun '88, on Jazzology (USA) by Jazzology Records (USA). Catalogue no: **J 153**

### LIVE AT LOUISIANA JAZZCLUB 1979 (Lawson-Freeman-Davern-Sutton)
**Album:** Released May '88, on FDC Catalogue no: **FDC 3002**

### PLAYS COLE PORTER (see also Bob Haggart) (Lawson, Yank & Bob Haggart)
**Album:** Released Aug '75, on World Jazz Catalogue no: **WJLPS 6**

### PLAYS MOSTLY BLUES
Note: with Al Klink, G. Masso, B. Haggart etc.
**Album:** Released Feb '87, on Audiophile (USA) by Jazzology Records (USA). Catalogue no: **AP 221**

### SOMETHING OLD, SOMETHING NEW, SOMETHING BORROWED, SOMETHING BLUE (Lawson, Yank Jazzband)
**CD:** Released Apr '89, on Audiophile (USA) by Jazzology Records (USA). Catalogue no: **APCD 240**

### WORLD'S GREATEST DIXIE BAND (We want to be happy)
Tracks: / I want to be happy / Makin' whoopee / There will never be another you / Mean to me / S'wonderful / Lotus blossom / Blue room, The.
**Album:** Released Apr '79, on Jazz Connoisseur by Spotlite Records. Catalogue no: **JC 001**

### WORLDS GREATEST JAZZ BANDS (Lawson, Yank & Bob Haggart)
**Album:** Released '88, on Timeless by Timeless Records. Catalogue no: **TTD 533**

## Le Concert Arban

### LE RAGTIME DE SCOTT JOPLIN A CLAUDE BOLLING (Various artists)
Tracks: / Ragtime dance: *Various artists* / Junk man rag: *Various artists* / Bethena concert waltz: *Various artists* / Mississippi rag: *Various artists* / Golliwogg's cake-walk: *Various artists* / Easy winners: *Various artists* / Harlem rag: *Various artists* / Cascades, The: *Various artists* / Pleasant moments: *Various artists* / Lassus trombone: *Various artists* / Ragtime du paquebot: *Various artists* / Chevy chase: *Various artists* / Chantecler rag: *Various artists.*
**CD:** Released May '88, on Arion by Arion Records (France). Catalogue no: **ARN 64022**

## Leadbelly

### ALABAMA BOUND
Tracks: / Pick a bale of cotton / Whoa back buck / Midnight special / Alabama bound / Good morning blues / Red Cross store blues / Alberta / You can't lose-a me cholly / Gray goose / Stewball / Can't you line 'em / Rock Island line / Easy rider / New York city / Roberta / On my last go round.
**CD:** Released Jan '90, on Bluebird (2) by BMG Records (UK). Catalogue no: **ND 90321**
**Album:** Released Jan '90, on Bluebird (2) by BMG Records (UK). Catalogue no: **NL 90321**
**Cass:** Released Jan '90, on Bluebird (2) by BMG Records (UK). Catalogue no: **NK 90321**

### COLLECTION: LEADBELLY (20 blues greats)
Tracks: / Good morning blues / Goodnight, Irene / There is a man, going around taking names / On a Monday / Gallis pole, The / Bring a little water Silvie (medley) / Stewball / We shall be free / T B blues / John Hardy / Poor Howard (medley) / Outskirts of town / Blood done sign my name, The / Boll weevil / Jean Harlow / Little children's blues / National defence blues / Fiddler's dram / Keep your hands off her / Cow cow yicky yicky yeah.
Note: Bring me a little water, Silvy medley: Bring me a little water, Silvy/ Julie Ann Johnson/ Line whoa back, buck. Poor Howard medley: Poor Howard/ Green corn.
**Album:** Released Oct '86, on Deja Vu Catalogue no: **DVLP 2072**
**Cass:** Released Oct '86, on Deja Vu Catalogue no: **DVMC 2072**

### EARLY MORNING BLUES
Tracks: / I ain't going down / Went back to the mountains / Whoa back / Worried blues / You can't lose me Charlie / Boll weevil / Death letter blues parts 1 & 2 / Kansas city papa / Daddy I'm coming back to you / Shorty George / Yellow jacket / TB woman blues.
**Album:** Released Oct '87, on Blue Moon (1) by Magnum Music Group. Catalogue no: **BMLP 1038**

### GOOD MORNING BLUES
**Album:** Released Jun '88, on Bluetime (Denmark) by Contact Records (Denmark). Catalogue no: **BT 2011**

### HIS GUITAR, HIS VOICE & HIS PIANO
**Album:** Released Sep '84, on Pathe Marconi (France) Catalogue no: **2C 068 80701**

### LAST SESSIONS (VOLUME 1)
Tracks: / Grey goose / Red cross door blues / Ham 'n' eggs / Red river in the pines / You don't miss your water / Blind lemon / Leadbelly's dance / In the evening when the sun goes down / Diggin' my potatoes.
**Album:** Released Feb '87, on Spartan Catalogue no: **SMPC 5001**
**Cass:** Released Feb '87, on Spartan Catalogue no: **SPMC 5001**

### LEADBELLY
**Album:** Released '83, on EMI (France) by EMI Records. Catalogue no: **2C 068 80701**

### LEADBELLY 1935
Tracks: / Roberta (part 1) / Roberta (part 2) / Packin' trunk blues / C.C. rider / You can't lose me Charlie / New black snake moan / Alberta / Baby don't you love me no more / Death letter blues (part 1) / Death lettter blues (part 2) / Kansas City papa / Red river blues / My friend Blind Lemon / Mister Tom Hughes' town / Matchbox blues / Bull cow.
**Album:** Released 22 Apr '88, on Travelin' Man by Interstate Music. Catalogue no: **TM 810**

### LEADBELLY: 1934-46
**Album:** Released Feb '89, on Document Catalogue no: **DLP 544**

### LEGENDARY LEADBELLY
**Cass:** Released Jan '88, on Demand Performance Catalogue no: **DPC 405**

## Leading Ladies Of Jazz

### LEADING LADIES OF JAZZ (Various artists)
**Cass:** Released May '88, on Flash by Mainline Records. Catalogue no: **62004**
**Album:** Released May '88, on Flash by Mainline Records. Catalogue no: **32004**

## Lee, Peggy

**Biographical details:** Lee, Peggy This American singer, songwriter and film star was born Norma Egstrom in Jamestown, North Dakota. She began her professional career in 1938 at the age of 18, working in a Hollywood nightclub and singing with a big band. Her first big break occurred in 1941, when she joined Benny Goodman as a resident vocalist. After two years with the famous bandleader who was known as the King of Swing, she took temporary retirement from showbusiness in 1943 before commencing her own recording career.
Lee's first smash hit was *Manana*, which she co-wrote with guitarist/arranger/conductor Dave Barbour; this was one of America's biggest sellers of 1948. During the late Forties and early Fifties, when popular middle of the road singers were in their element, Lee established herself as a major star. She made her movie debut in 1951's 'Mr Music' with Bing Crosby and followed it with

Peggy Lee

further hit discs like *Lover* and *This Is a Very Special Day.* After turning in an acclaimed performance in the film 'Pete Kelly's Blues' (1955), she also helped to score the 1956 movie *The Lady and the Tramp.*
Peggy's rendition of the theme from the show *Mr Wonderful* (also '56) reached No.14 on the US charts and might have gone higher were it not for two other competing versions, which also made the Top 20; in Britain where she had no such competition, Lee climbed to No.5 with the song in 1957. Successfully holding her own in the face of the rock'n'roll phenomenon, she reached the Top 10 on both sides of the Atlantic with her inventive 1958 single *Fever.* In 1960 the singer enjoyed a big UK hit album with *Latin a la Lee.*
Lee faded from the record charts during the Sixties, save for a US No.11 hit with 1969's engaging and memorable *Is That All There Is.* She remained an active live performer, however, throughout the Seventies and into the Eighties. (Bob Macdonald 5/12/85).

**16 GOLDEN CLASSICS**
Tracks: / Mr. Wonderful / Lover / He needs me / Joey Joey Joey / Siamese cat song / He's a tramp / I didn't know what time it was / Let me go lover / Bouquet of blues / Johnny guitar / Straight ahead / It must be so (with the Mills brothers) / Black coffee / Love me or leave me / My heart belongs to daddy / I've got you under my skin / When the world was young / Easy living.
**Cass:** Released Dec '87, on Unforgettable by Castle Communications Records. Catalogue no: **UNMC 027**
**Album:** Released Dec '87, on Unforgettable by Castle Communications Records. Catalogue no: **UNLP 027**
**CD:** Released Dec '87, on Unforgettable by Castle Communications Records. Catalogue no: **UNCD 027**

**16 GREATEST HITS: PEGGY LEE**
**Album:** Released '83, on EMI (Holland) by EMI Records. Catalogue no: **5C 054 85001**

**ALL AGLOW AGAIN**
Tracks: / Fever / Where do I go from here? / Whee baby / My man / You deserve / Manana / Hallelujah, I love him so / You don't know / Louisville Lou / I'm lookin' out the window / It keeps you young / Let's call it a day.
**Cass:** Released Jul '85, on Capitol by EMI Records. Deleted Jun '88. Catalogue no: **EG 2606054**
**Album:** Released Jul '85, on Capitol by EMI Records. Deleted Jun '88. Catalogue no: **EG 2606051**

**BEAUTY AND THE BEAT (Lee, Peggy & George Shearing)**
Tracks: / Do I love you? / I lost my sugar in Salt Lake City / If dreams come true / All too soon / Mambo in Miami / Isn't it romantic? / Blue prelude / You came a long way from St Louis / Always true to you in my fashion / There'll be another Spring / Get out of town / Satin doll.
**Album:** Released Jun '60, on Capitol by EMI Records. Deleted Jun '65. Catalogue no: **T 1219**
Catalogue no: **OL 2820**

**BEST OF PEGGY LEE**
Tracks: / Lover / Apples, peaches and cherries / Love me or leave me / I don't know enough about you / He's a tramp / Mr. Wonderful / Black coffee / Siamese cat song / He needs me / My heart belongs to daddy / Where can I go without you? / Easy living / I didn't know what time it was / They can't take that away from me / Just one of those things / Love, you didn't do right by me.
**Cass:** Released Dec '81, on MCA by MCA Records. Catalogue no: **MCFC 1632**
**Cass:** Released Dec '81, on MCA by MCA Records. Catalogue no: **MCLC 1632**

**BEST OF PEGGY LEE (MFP)**
**Cass:** Released Apr '83, on MFP by EMI Records. Deleted '87. Catalogue no: **TCMFP 5605**
**Album:** Released Apr '83, on MFP by EMI Records. Deleted '87. Catalogue no: **MFP 5605**

**BEST OF PEGGY LEE Vol. 2**
**Album:** Released May '61, on Brunswick by Decca Records. Deleted May '66. Catalogue no: **LAT 8355**

**BLACK COFFEE**
Tracks: / Black coffee / I've got you under my skin / Easy living / My heart belongs to daddy / It ain't necessarily so / Gee baby ain't I good to you / Woman alone with the blues / I didn't know what time it was / When the world was young / Love me or leave me / You're my thrill / There's a small hotel.
**Album:** Released Oct '61, on Ace Of Hearts by Decca Records. Deleted Oct '66. Catalogue no: **AH 5**
**Album:** Released Aug '83, on Jasmine by Hasmick Promotions. Catalogue no: **JASM 1026**

**BLUES CROSS COUNTRY**
Tracks: / Basin Street blues / Kansas city / St. Louis blues.
**Album:** Released Oct '84, on Pathe Marconi (France) Catalogue no: **PM 1552941**
**Cass:** Released Oct '84, on Pathe Marconi (France) Catalogue no: **PM 1552944**

**CAPITOL YEARS, THE: PEGGY LEE (Best of...)**
Tracks: / Manana / Golden Earrings / It's a good day / Don't smoke in bed / Why don't you do right? / Fever / Folks who live on the hill, The / Hallelujah I love him so / I'm a woman / Doodlin' song, A / Big spender / So what's new / Shining sea, The / Alright, okay, you win / Is that all there is? / I'm gonna go fishin'.
Note: Original sound recordings made by Capitol records Inc. This compilation (P) 1988 EMI Records Ltd.
**Album:** Released 6 Jun '88, on Capitol by EMI Records. Catalogue no: **EMS 1294**
**CD:** Released 6 Jun '88, on Capitol by EMI Records. Deleted Aug '89. Catalogue no: **CZ 108**
**Cass:** Released 6 Jun '88, on Capitol by

EMI Records. Catalogue no: **TC EMS 1294**
**CD:** Released 6 Jun '88, on Capitol by EMI Records. Catalogue no: **CDP 790 552 2**
**CD:** Released 6 Jun '88, on Capitol by EMI Records. Catalogue no: **CDEMS 1294**

**CLOSE ENOUGH FOR LOVE**
Tracks: / Easy does it / You / Just one of those things.
**Album:** Released '88, on DRG (USA) by DRG Records (USA). Catalogue no: **SLC 5190**
**CD:** Released '88, on DRG (USA) by DRG Records (USA). Catalogue no: **CDSL 5190**

**DREAM STREET**
Tracks: / Street of dreams / What's new / Too late now / You're blase / It's alright with me / My old flame / Dancing on the ceiling / It never entered my mind / I don't know enough about you / Something i dreamed last night / Last night when we were young.
**Album:** Released '88, on Jasmine by Hasmick Promotions. Catalogue no: **JASM 1032**

**EASY LISTENING**
**Cass:** Released Apr '85, on Artistic by Submarine Records. Catalogue no: **CART 005**
**Album:** Released Apr '85, on Artistic by Submarine Records. Catalogue no: **ART 005**

**FABULOUS PEGGY LEE, THE**
Tracks: / You let my love get cold / Love you didn't do right by me / Oh no (please don't go) / Tavern, The / Wrong, wrong, wrong / Gypsy with fire in his shoes, The / Do I love you / Wrong Joe / Me / Johnny guitar / I belong to you / Autumn in Rome.
**Album:** Released '88, on Official by Official Records. Catalogue no: **OFF 12002**

**FEVER**
Tracks: / Fever.
**7" Single:** Released Jul '84, on EMI (Holland) by EMI Records. Catalogue no: **1A 006 81169**
**7" Single:** Released Apr '83, on EMI (France) by EMI Records. Catalogue no: **2C 008 83378**
**7" Single:** Released Feb '85, on EMI Golden 45's by EMI Records. Catalogue no: **G 4538**

**FEVER (2)**
Tracks: / Fever.
**7" Single:** Released Aug '58, on Capitol by EMI Records. Deleted Aug '61. Catalogue no: **CL 14902**

**FEVER AND OTHER HITS**
Tracks: / Fever / I'm a woman / Alright, okay, you win / Big spender / Hallelujah / I love him so / Alley cat song, The / Is that all there is? / Heart / Doodlin' song, A.
**Cass:** Released Dec '88, on Capitol (Specials) Catalogue no: **4XL 9095**

**GOLDEN GREATS: PEGGY LEE**
Tracks: / Lover / Mr. Wonderful / He's a tramp / Siamese cat song / He needs me / Apples, peaches and cherries / Love me or leave me / I don't know enough about you / Black coffee / My heart belongs to daddy / Where can I go without you / Easy living / I didn't know what time it was / They can't take that away from me / Just one of those things / Love you didn't do right by me.
**Album:** Released Jul '85, on MCA by MCA Records. Catalogue no: **MCM 5010**
**Cass:** Released Jul '85, on MCA by MCA Records. Catalogue no: **MCMC 5010**

**I DON'T WANT TO PLAY IN YOUR YARD**
Tracks: / I don't want to play in your yard / Black coffee.
**7" Single:** Released Jun '82, on MCA by MCA Records. Deleted Jun '85. Catalogue no: **MCA 782**

**I LIKE MEN!**
Tracks: / Charley, my boy / Good-for-nothin' Joe / I love to love / When a woman loves a man / I like men! / I'm just wild about Harry / My man / Bill / So in love / Jim / It's so nice to have a man around the house / Oh Johnny, oh Johnny, oh.
**Cass:** Released Mar '88, on Capitol by EMI Records. Catalogue no: **TCEMS 1287**
**Album:** Released Mar '88, on Capitol by EMI Records. Deleted Nov '88. Catalogue no: **EMS 1287**

**IF I COULD BE WITH YOU**
Note: with Benny Goodman, Tommy Dorsey
**Album:** Released Jan '88, on Sounds Rare Catalogue no: **SR 5008**
**Cass:** Released Oct '89, on Jasmine by Hasmick Promotions. Catalogue no: **JASMC 2534**

**IF YOU GO**
Tracks: / As time goes by / If you go / Oh love, hast thou forsaken me? / Say it isn't so / I wish I didn't love you so / Maybe it's because I love you too much / I'm gonna laugh you out of my life / I get along without you very well / I love your gypsy heart / When I was a child / Here's that rainy day / Smile.
Note: Quincy Jones conducts the orchestra.
**Album:** Released May '85, on Capitol by EMI Records. Catalogue no: **ED 2604121**
**Cass:** Released May '85, on Capitol by EMI Records. Catalogue no: **ED 2604124**

**IS THAT ALL THERE IS?**
Tracks: / Is that all there is?.
**7" Single:** Released Jul '84, on Capitol (import) Catalogue no: **1A 006 80182**

**I'VE HAD MY MOMENTS**
**Cass:** Released Jan '88, on Starline (Jazz) Catalogue no: **SLC 61008**

**JUMP FOR JOY**
Tracks: / Jump for joy / Back in your own back yard / When my sugar walks down the street / I hear music / Just in time / Old devil moon / What a little moonlight can do / Four or five times / Music music music / Cheek to cheek / Glory of love.
Note: Originally released in 1958, 12 excellent 'up' tracks. Lightheartedly backed by the legendary Nelson Riddle and his Orchestra. A swinging classic.
**Album:** Released Dec '85, on Capitol T (USA) Catalogue no: **T 979**

**LATIN A LA LEE**
Tracks: / Heart / On the street where you live / Till there was you / I am in love / Hey there / I could have danced all night / Surrey with the fringe on top / Party's over, The / Dance only with me / Wish you were here / C'est Magnifique / I enjoy being a girl.
**Cass:** Released Aug '88, on Capitol by EMI Records. Catalogue no: **TC EMS 1304**
**Album:** Released Jun '60, on Capitol by EMI Records. Deleted Jun '65. Catalogue no: **T 1290**
**Album:** Released Aug '88, on Capitol by EMI Records. Catalogue no: **EMS 1304**

**MAN I LOVE, THE**
Tracks: / Man I love, The / Please be kind / Happiness is just a thing called Joe / Just one way to say I love you / That's all / Something wonderful / He's my guy / Then I'll be tired of you / My heart stood still / If I should lose you / There is no greater love / Folks who live on the hill, The.
Note: The orchestra is conducted by Frank Sinatra.
**Album:** Released Apr '84, on Capitol by EMI Records. Catalogue no: **CAPS 2600051**
**Cass:** Released Apr '84, on Capitol by EMI Records. Deleted Jan '90. Catalogue no: **TCCAPS 2600054**

**MINK JAZZ**
**Cass:** Released Nov '89, on Memoir by Memoir Records. Catalogue no: **CMOIR 213**
**Album:** Released Nov '89, on Memoir by Memoir Records. Catalogue no: **MOIR 213**

**MISS PEGGY LEE SINGS THE BLUES**
Tracks: / See see rider / Basin Street blues / Squeeze me / You don't know / Fine and mellow / Baby please come home / Kansas City / Birmingham jail / Love me / Beale street blues / T'aint nobody's biz-ness if I do / God bless the child.
**CD:** Released Nov '89, on Limelight Catalogue no: **820 809-2**

**MISS WONDERFUL**
Tracks: / Mister wonderful / They can't take that away from me / Where flamingos fly / You've got to see mama every night / Come back, The / Take a little time to smile / I don't know enough about you / Joe sings Joey, Joey, Joey / Crazy in the heart / You oughta be mine / We laughed at love / That's alright honey.
**Album:** Released '89, on Official by Official Records. Catalogue no: **OFF 12013**

**MR. WONDERFUL**
Tracks: / Mr. Wonderful.
**7" Single:** Released May '57, on Brunswick by Decca Records. Deleted May '60. Catalogue no: **05671**

**PEGGY LEE & BENNY GOODMAN (Lee, Peggy & Benny Goodman)**
Tracks: / How long has this been going on / That did it, Marie / Elmer's tune / I threw a kiss in the ocean / We'll meet again / That's the way it goes / All I need is you / Not a care in the world / Full moon.
**Album:** Released May '84, on CBS Cameo by CBS Records. Catalogue no: **32417**

**PEGGY LEE COLLECTION (20 golden greats)**
Tracks: / I can't give you anything but love / I don't know enough about you / Stormy weather / Golden earrings / On the sunny side of the street / Somebody loves me / It's a good day / As long as I'm dreaming / You and I passing by / While we're young / It takes a long, long train / Lady from 29 palms / Manana / Why don't you do right? / Up a lazy river / Aintcha ever comin' back? / Hold me / When the red, red robin comes bob, bob, bobbin' along / Them there eyes.
**Cass:** Released Nov '85, on Deja Vu Catalogue no: **DVMC 2021**
**Album:** Released Nov '85, on Deja Vu Catalogue no: **DVLP 2021**

**PEGGY LEE SINGS THE BLUES**
Tracks: / See see rider / Basin Street blues / Beale Street / God bless the child / Kansas city.
**Cass:** Released Jan '89, on Music Masters by Music Masters Records. Catalogue no: **CIJD 20155 K**
**CD:** Released Jan '89, on Music Masters by Music Masters Records. Catalogue no: **CIJD 60155 F**
**Album:** Released Jan '89, on Music Masters by Music Masters Records. Catalogue no: **CIJD 40155 H**

**PERFECT LEE**
Tracks: / Baubles, bangles and beads / Ooh that kiss / That's alright honey / Street of dreams / Be anything / This is a very special day / When the world was young / I'm glad there is you / Where flamingos fly / You've got to see mamma every night / Moonflowers / Johnny Guitar / I don't want to play in your yard.
**CD:** Released Apr '89, on MCA by MCA Records. Catalogue no: **DMCL 1794**

**PETE KELLY'S BLUES (Lee, Peggy & Ella Fitzgerald)**
Tracks: / Oh, didn't he ramble? / Sugar (that sugar baby of mine) / Somebody loves me / I'm gonna meet my sweetie now / I never knew / Bye bye blackbird / What can I say, after I say I'm sorry? / Hard hearted Hannah / Ella hums the blues / He needs me / Sing a rainbow / Pete Kelly's blues.
**Album:** Released Sep '83, on Jasmine by Hasmick Promotions. Catalogue no: **JASM 1024**

**PRETTY EYES**
Tracks: / As you desire me / It could happen to you / Pretty eyes / Moments like this / Remind me / You fascinate me so / I wanna be loved / I'm walking through / I remember you / Too close for comfort / Fly me to the moon / Because I love him so.
Note: This album sets Peggy Lee against string and flute arrangements through a selection of warm, misty songs. Billy May leads the orchestra in some expert string arrangements- a refreshing change to his more familiar brass sound. Includes standards such as 'Too close for comfort' and 'Fly with me to the moon ', some- times lightly swung, sometimes reflective, but all sung in the incomparable Peggy Lee style.
**Cass:** Released May '86, on Capitol by EMI Records. Deleted Oct '89. Catalogue no: **TCEMS 1153**
**Album:** Released May '86, on Capitol by EMI Records. Deleted Oct '89. Catalogue no: **EMS 1153**

**QUINTESSENTIAL, THE**
Note: Running time: 60 mins.
**VHS:** Released May '89, on Castle Hendring Video by Castle Communications Records. Catalogue no: **HEN 2 149 G**

**RENDEZVOUS WITH PEGGY LEE**
Tracks: / Why don't you do right? / Them there eyes / Deed I do / I don't know enough about you / It's a good day / Golden earrings / I can't give you anything but love / Stormy weather / Don't smoke in bed / While we're young / Manana / Hold me.
**Album:** Released Mar '84, on Pathe Marconi (France) Catalogue no: **PM 154 773 1**
**Cass:** Released Mar '84, on Pathe Marconi (France) Catalogue no: **PM 154 773 4**

**SEA SHELLS**
Tracks: / Brown bird singing / I don't want to play in your yard / Maid with the flaxen hair / Wearing of the green, The / Chaconde / Chinese love poems / Riddle song / Golden wedding ring / Sea fever / Nine thorny thickets / Little old car / Greensleeves / Happy monks / White birch and the sycamore / Of such is the Kingdom of God.
**Album:** Released Oct '84, on Jasmine by Hasmick Promotions. Deleted Jun '87. Catalogue no: **JASM 1046**

**THINGS ARE SWINGIN'**
Tracks: / It's a wonderful world / Things are swinging / Alright, okay, you win / Ridin' high / It's been a long long time / Lullaby in rhythm / Alone together / I'm beginning to see the light / It's a good, good night / You're getting to be a habit with me / You're mine, you / Life is for living.
Note: One of Peggy Lee's most popular albums which has only been available for some time on import. This 5-star collection of swinging numbers includes 'Alright, okay you win', 'I'm beginning to see the light' and many more.
**Album:** Released Dec '85, on Capitol by EMI Records. Deleted Nov '88. Catalogue no: **EMS 1139**
**Cass:** Released Dec '85, on Capitol by EMI Records. Deleted Nov '88. Catalogue no: **TCEMS 1139**

**TILL THERE WAS YOU**
Tracks: / Till there was you.
**7" Single:** Released Mar '61, on Capitol by EMI Records. Deleted Mar '64. Catalogue no: **CL 15184**

**UNCOLLECTED**
**Album:** Released Sep '86, on Hindsight (UK) by Michele International Records. Catalogue no: **HUK 220**

**WHY DON'T YOU DO RIGHT?**
**CD:** Released Jan '88, on Entertainers Catalogue no: **ENTCD 239**

**WITH THE DAVID BARBOUR AND BILLY MAY BANDS 1948**
**Album:** Released Oct '86, on Hindsight (UK) by Michele International Records. Catalogue no: **HUK 220**

**YOU CAN DEPEND ON ME**
**Album:** Released Dec '87, on Glendale (USA) by Glendale Records (USA). Catalogue no: **GL 6023**

## Lee, Tony

**BRITISH JAZZ ARTISTS 1 (Lee, Tony, Trio)**
**Album:** Released May '80, on Lee Lambert by Lee Lambert Records. Catalogue no: **LYN 3416**

**BRITISH JAZZ ARTISTS 2 (Lee, Tony, Trio & Terry Smith)**
**Album:** Released May '77, on Lee Lambert by Lee Lambert Records. Catalogue no: **LAM 002**

**STREETS OF DREAMS**
Tracks: / Li'l darlin' / Loss of love / Street of dreams / Dick's mood / Love for sale / My funny valentine / Green Dolphin Street.
**Album:** Released May '80, on Lee Lambert by Lee Lambert Records. Catalogue no: **LAM 102**

**TONY LEE TRIO AND FRIENDS (Lee, Tony, Trio)**
Tracks: / Blue 'n' boogie / Body and soul / Tenderly / Leeward / If / Bluesology.
**Album:** Released Jul '79, on Pye Catalogue no: **N 104**

## Le Febvre, Gary

**GARY LE FEBVRE QUARTET (Le-Febvre, Gary Quartet)**
Tracks: / Some other time / Milestones / Windows.
Note: Gary Le Febvre-sax, Kei Akagi-piano, Frank Butler-drums, Leroy Vinnegar-bass.
**Album:** Released '88, on Discovery (USA) by Discovery Records (USA). Catalogue no: **DS 849**

## Legacy Of The Blues

**LEGACY OF THE BLUES (Various artists)**
Tracks: / Funky malaguena: *Eaglin, Snooks* / Found my baby gone: *Dupree, Champion Jack* / Wishy washy woman: *Young, Mighty Joe* / I'm a bluesman: *Bonner, Juke Boy* / Black gal you're sure looking warm: *Williams, Big Joe* / Long time gone: *Slim, Memphis* / Stary crown blues: *Shore, J D* / I'm going to have myself a ball: *Williams, Robert Pete* / Cannonball: *Boyd, Eddie* / She's so mellow: *Sunnyland Slim* / Please help poor me: *Hopkins, Lightnin'*.
**Album:** Released '82, on Sonet by Sonet Records. Catalogue no: **SNTX 1**

**LEGACY OF THE BLUES SAMPLER (Various artists)**
**Album:** Released May '89, on GNP Crescendo (USA) by GNP Crescendo Records (USA). Catalogue no: **GNPS 10010**
**2 LP Set:** Released May '89, on GNP Crescendo (USA) by GNP Crescendo Records (USA). Catalogue no: **GNPSX 10010**
**Cass:** Released May '89, on GNP Crescendo (USA) by GNP Crescendo Records (USA). Catalogue no: **GNP5 10010**

## Legendary...

**LEGENDARY BIG BANDS (Various artists)**
**Album:** Released Apr '82, on Ronco Catalogue no: **RTL 2047**

**LEGENDARY OLDIES (Various artists)**
**CD:** Released May '88, on Black Tulip Catalogue no: **263 630 2**

## Legendary Sessions

**LEGENDARY SESSIONS (Memphis style) (Various artists)**
**Album:** Released Oct '88, on Roots (Germany) Catalogue no: **RSE 2**
**Album:** Released Oct '88, on Roots (Germany) Catalogue no: **RSE 5**

## Legendary Speciality...

**LEGENDARY SPECIALTY MISSING MASTERS (Various artists)**
Tracks: / Oh babe: *Milton, Roy* / Wah-bop-sh-wah: *Twilighters* / Jump Jack jump: *Carr, Wynona* / Bouncin' the boogie: *Royal Kings* / Brand new baby: *Williams, Lester* / Hey fine mama: *Pierce, Henry* / Jelly bean: *Don & Dewey* / Let it lay: *Moore, Kenzie* / I've got my sights on someone new: *Jackson, Roddy* / Just to hold my hand: *Myles, Big Boy* / Bangin' the boogie: *Howard, Camille* / Rock & roll fever: *Monitors* / Ooh bop she bop: *Dukes* / Boogie woogie lou: *Liggins, Joe* / Check yourself baby: *Allen, Tony* / Goodbye baby goodbye: *Lowbry, Sonny*.
**Album:** Released Mar '84, on Sonet by Sonet Records. Catalogue no: **SNTF 5029**

## Legends Of Jazz

**LEGENDS OF JAZZ (Various artists)**
Note: With Barney Bigard, Louis Nelson, Alton Purnell, Joe Darensbourg.
**Album:** Released Jul '88, on Crescent Jazz Prods. Catalogue no: **CJP 2**

**LEGENDS OF JAZZ, THE**
**Album:** Released '88, on Blue Boy Catalogue no: **BB 1001**

## Legrand, Michel

**AFTER THE RAIN**
Tracks: / Nobody knows / I was born in love with you / After the rain / Pieces of dreams / Martina / Orson's theme.
**Album:** Released May '83, on Pablo Jazz (USA) by Pablo Records (USA). Catalogue no: **2312 139**
**Cass:** Released May '83, on Pablo Jazz (USA) by Pablo Records (USA). Catalogue no: **K12 139**

**CONCERT LEGRAND, THE**
Tracks: / Once upon a summer time / Saddest thing of all, The / You must believe in Spring / Wonder where I'll be tomorrow / Christine / Sweet gingerbread man / Love theme from 'Lady sings the blues' / Snowbird serenade / Fickle fingers / Petite musique d'amour / Pieces of dreams.
**Album:** Released '79, on RCA Victor by BMG Records (UK). Deleted '84. Catalogue no: **RS 1087**

**LEGRAND JAZZ**
**CD:** Released '86, on Philips (France) by PolyGram UK Ltd. Catalogue no: **830 074-2**

**MICHEL LEGRAND**
**Cass:** Released Oct '84, on Audio Fidelity(USA) by Audio Fidelity (USA). Catalogue no: **ZCGAS 730**

**MICHEL LEGRAND & THE LONDON SYMPHONY ORCHESTRA (Legrand, Michel & London Symphony Orchestra)**
Tracks: / Umbrellas of Cherbourg / Symphonic suite / Go / Between / Variations for two pianos and orchestra.
**Album:** Released '79, on CBS by CBS Records. Deleted '84. Catalogue no: **CBS 73886**

**PARIS WAS MADE FOR LOVERS**
**Cass:** Released Mar '90, on Prestige Catalogue no: **ZPREC 5001**
**Album:** Released Mar '90, on Prestige Catalogue no: **PREC 5001**
**CD:** Released Mar '90, on Prestige Catalogue no: **CDPC 5001**

## Leigh, Carol

**BLAME IT ON THE BLUES (Leigh, Carol/Bob Helm/Ray Skjelbred)**
**Album:** Released Jun '86, on GHB by Jazzology Records (USA). Catalogue no: **GHB 152**

**CAROL LEIGH-VOLUME 2 (Leigh, Carol & Jim Dapogny)**
**Album:** Released Jun '86, on Stomp Off (USA) Catalogue no: **SOS 1087**

**GO BACK WHERE YOU STAYED LAST NIGHT**
Note: Mono. With H.Smith/E.Carson
**Album:** Released Jun '86, on GHB by Jazzology Records (USA). Catalogue no: **GHB 167**

**IF YOU DON'T, I KNOW WHO (Leigh, Carol & Jim Dapogny)**
**Album:** Released '88, on Stomp Off (USA) Catalogue no: **SOS 1064**

**YOU'VE GOT TO GIVE ME SOME**
Note: With Hal Smith/Knocky Parker
**Album:** Released Jun '86, on GHB by Jazzology Records (USA). Catalogue no: **GHB 136**

## Leitch, Peter

**ON A MISTY NIGHT**
**Album:** Released Jul '87, on Criss Cross Catalogue no: **CRISS 1026**

**RED ZONE - GUITAR**
**Album:** Released Feb '88, on Reservoir Catalogue no: **RSR 103**
**CD:** Released Oct '89, on Reservoir Catalogue no: **RSRCD 103**

## Lemon, Brian

**OUR KIND OF MUSIC**
**Album:** Released '88, on Hep Jazz by Hep Records. Catalogue no: **HEP 2029**

## Lenoir, J.B.

**ALABAMA BLUES**
**Album:** Released '88, on L&R Catalogue no: **LR 42.001**

**CHESS MASTERS**
Tracks: / Natural man / Don't dog your woman / Let me die with the one I love / Carrie Lee / Mama whatabout your daughter / If I give my love to you / Five years / Don't tough my head / I've been down so long / What have I done / Eisenhower blues / Korea blues / Everybody wants to know / I'm in love / Mama your daughter's going to miss me / We can't go on this way / Give me one more shot / When I am drinking / J.B.'s rock / If you love me / Low down dirty shame / Man watch your woman / Mama / Sitting down thinking / Daddy talk to your son / I don't know / Good lookin' woman / Voodoo boogie.
**Album:** Released Jul '84, on Chess (PRT) Deleted '88. Catalogue no: **CXMD 4054**

**CHICAGO GOLDEN YEARS**
**2 LP Set:** Released Oct '88, on Vogue by Vogue Records. Catalogue no: **427003**

**DOWN IN MISSISSIPPI**
**Album:** Released '88, on L&R Catalogue no: **LR 42.012**

**FINE BLUES**
Tracks: / Deep in debt blues / My baby

told me / In the evening / Please don't go away / Fine girls / I lost my baby / Daddy talk to your son / She don't know / Back door / Lou Ella / Oh baby / Do what I say / Move to Kansas City / I been down so long / Mojo boogie / I don't care what nobody say / Oh baby.
**Album:** on Official by Official Records. Catalogue no: **OFF 6049**

**JOB RECORDINGS 1951/54**
**CD:** Released '89, on Flyright by Interstate Music. Catalogue no: **FLY CD 04**

**MOJO BOOGIE (Job series vol.2)**
**Album:** Released '88, on Flyright by Interstate Music. Catalogue no: **FLY 564**

**NATURAL MAN**
**Album:** Released Oct '86, on Chess (PRT) Deleted '88. Catalogue no: **BRP 2014**

**ONE OF THESE MORNINGS (Lenoir, J.B./Willie Dixon)**
**Album:** Released Sep '86, on JSP by JSP Records. Catalogue no: **JSP 1105**

## Leonhart, Jay

**SALAMANDER PIE**
**CD:** Released '86, on DMP Catalogue no: **CD 442**

**THERE'S GONNA BE TROUBLE**
Tracks: / Summers on the river / There's gonna be trouble / Ali Privaye / Life in the middle ages / Lonely rider / Jimmy don't go away / Confirmation / Couple from Duluth, The / Smile / I got the blues / Down in the south / Patience / Blues for Donna.
Note: Music composed by Charlie Parker (Atlantic Music Corp, BMI). Music composed by Jay Leonhart (Chancellor Music Ltd, BMI). Lyrics written by Jay Leonhart (Chancellor Music Ltd, BMI). Joe Beck-Guitar/Jay Leonhart-vocals, bass, acoustic guitar, synthesizer programming.
**Album:** Released Jan '87, on Sunnyside Jazz(USA) Catalogue no: **SSC 1006**

## Leroy, Baby Face

**BABY FACE LEROY & FLOYD JONES (Leroy, Baby Face & Floyd Jones)**
Tracks: / My head can't rest / Take a little walk / Boogy fool / Raisin' sand / Pet rabbit / Louella / Late hours at midnight / Blues is killin' me / Dark road / I lost a good woman / Skinny mama / Rising wind / On the road again / My head is turning grey / Where have you been so long / I can't feel good no more.
**Album:** Released Oct '86, on Flyright by Interstate Music. Catalogue no: **FLY 584**

## Leviev, Milcho

**BLUES FOR THE FISHERMAN (Leviev, Milcho, Quartet with Art Pepper)**
Note: With Art Pepper, Tony Dumas, Carl Burnett. Recorded live at Ronnie Scott's, London, in June 1980.
**Album:** Released Aug '80, on Mole Jazz by Mole Jazz Records. Catalogue no: **MOLE 1**
**CD:** Released May '87, on Mole Jazz by Mole Jazz Records. Catalogue no: **MOLECD 1**

**MUSIC FOR BIG BAND AND SYMPHONY ORCHESTRA**
Tracks: / Riff passacaglia / Blue adagio / Fast intermezzo / Fugue dithiramb / Waltz for Maurice / Issac's touchstone / Bulgarian boogie / Sad a little bit.
**Album:** Released Jun '83, on Trend (USA) by Trend Records (USA). Catalogue no: **TR 530**

**PLAYS THE MUSIC OF IRVING BERLIN**
Tracks: / What'll I do / Alexander's ragtime band / How deep is the ocean / Marie / Blue skies / Waiting at the end of the road / Soft lights and sweet music / Always / Cheek to cheek.
**Album:** Released Aug '83, on Discovery (USA) by Discovery Records (USA). Catalogue no: **DS 876**

**TRUE BLUES (Leviev, Milcho & Art Pepper)**
Note: Recorded live at Ronnie Scott's, London, in 1980.
**Album:** Released Jul '81, on Mole Jazz by Mole Jazz Records. Catalogue no: **MOLE 5**

## Levine, James

**HOMMAGE A SEVILLA (Various artists)**
**VHS:** Released Apr '90, on Deutsche Grammophon by PolyGram Classics. Catalogue no: **072 110 3**

**PLAYS SCOTT JOPLIN**
**Album:** Released '83, on RCA (Germany) Catalogue no: **RL 12243**

## Levine, Mike

**SMILEY AND ME**
Note: Well known for his tenure with Cal Tjader, pianist Levine is accompanied on drums by Smiley Winters.
**Album:** Released Jul '88, on Concord Jazz by Concord Jazz Records (USA). Catalogue no: **CJ 352**

## Levy, Stan

**STAN LEVY QUINTET (Levy, Stan Quintet)**
**Album:** Released Apr '88, on VSOP Catalogue no: **VSOP 41**

## Lewis, Father Al

**FATHER AL LEWIS AND LARS EDEGRAN'S NOR JAZZBAND (Lewis, Father Al/Lars Edegran's NOR Jazzband)**
**Album:** Released 8 Apr '89, on GHB by Jazzology Records (USA). Catalogue no: **GHB 245**

## Lewis, Furry

**BACK ON MY FEET AGAIN**
**Album:** Released Dec '87, on Prestige Catalogue no: **PRE 7810**

**BEALE STREET MESSAROUND (Various artists)**
**Album:** Released '88, Catalogue no: **ROUNDER 2006**

**DONE CHANGED MY MIND**
Tracks: / Baby you don't want me / Done changed my mind / Goin' to Kansas City / Judge Boushay blues / Casey Jones / This time tomorrow / I will turn your money green / Frankie and Johnny / Longing blues / Long tall gal blues.
**Album:** Released Oct '88, on Ace by Ace Records. Catalogue no: **CH 260**

**FURRY LEWIS IN HIS PRIME 1927-29**
**Album:** Released Dec '88, on Yazoo (USA) by Shanachie Records (USA). Catalogue no: **L 1050**

**MEMPHIS SESSIONS 1956-61 (Lewis, Furry/Will Shade)**
**Album:** Released '89, on Wolf Catalogue no: **120 920**

**REMAINING TITLES 1927-29**
**Album:** Released '88, on Wolf Catalogue no: **WSE 101**

## Lewis, George

**AT CLUB HANGOVER VOL 1**
**Album:** Released Jun '86, on Storyville. Catalogue no: **SLP 4055**

**AT CLUB HANGOVER VOL 3**
**Album:** Released May '86, on Storyville. Catalogue no: **SLP 4061**

**CITY OF A MILLION DREAMS**
**Album:** Released Oct '86, on GHB. Catalogue no: **GHB 10**

**FOR DANCERS ONLY**
**Album:** Released Jun '88, on GHB. Catalogue no: **GHB 37**

**FROM SAXOPHONE AND TROMBONE**
**Album:** Released Feb '81, on Incus. Catalogue no: **INCUS 35**

**GEORGE LEWIS AT CLUB HANGOVER**
**Album:** Released '88, on Storyville. Catalogue no: **SLP 251**

**GEORGE LEWIS AT CONGO SQUARE**
**Album:** Released Jun '88, on Jazzology (USA). Catalogue no: **JCE 27**

**GOERGE LEWIS AT HERBERT OTTO'S PARTY**
**Album:** Released Jun '88, on Jazzology (USA). Catalogue no: **JCE 24**

**GEORGE LEWIS AND HIS RAGTIME BAND**
**Album:** Released Jun '86, on Storyville. Catalogue no: **SLP 4049**

**GEORGE LEWIS IN CONCERT**
**Album:** Released May '86, on Storyville. Catalogue no: **SLP 4022**

**GEORGE LEWIS IN EUROPE, VOL 1: "PIED PIPER"**
Tracks: / Sister Kate / Old Nellie Grey / Mahogany Hall stomp / Chinatown, my Chinatown / Old man Mose / There's "yes, yes" in your eyes / Tin roof blues / Just a little while to stay here.
**Album:** Released Apr '81, on Rarities. Catalogue no: **RARITIES 47**

1957 - A Very Good Year
HISTORIC RECORDINGS OF KEN COLYER'S JAZZMEN & GEORGE LEWIS


George Lewis - Nineteen Fifty Seven - A Very Good Year (KC Records)

**GEORGE LEWIS AND PAPA BLUES VIKING JAZZ BAND**
**Album:** Released '88, on Jazz Unlimited. Catalogue no: **JU 1**

**GEORGE LEWIS AND THE EASY RIDERS JAZZ BAND**
**Album:** Released Jun '86, on GHB. Catalogue no: **GHB 29**

**HOMAGE TO CHARLES PARKER**
**Album:** Released Sep '79, on Black Saint (Italy). Catalogue no: **BSR 0029**

**IN JAPAN VOL 2**
**Album:** Released Jun '86, on GHB. Catalogue no: **GHB 15**

**NEW ORLEANS PARADE**
**Album:** Released '88, on Cadillac. Catalogue no: **SGC 12104**

**NINETEEN FIFTY SEVEN - A VERY GOOD YEAR (See panel above)**
Tracks: / Happy wanderer / Gatemouth / Working man blues / One sweet letter from you / Dusty rag / Joplin's sensation / Over the waves / Walking with the King / Corrine Corrine / Ice cream / Running wild.
**Album:** Released on Ken Colyer. Catalogue no: **KC 1**

**PERENNIAL GEORGE LEWIS, THE**
Tracks: / Ace in the hole / It's a long way to Tipperary / West End blues / Jambalaya / Mack the knife / Careless love.
**Album:** Released Jun '82, on Verve. Catalogue no: **2304 553**

**PIED PIPER, THE**
Tracks: / Chiri cheri bin / It's a long way to Tipperary / Savoy blues / Ice cream / Panama rag / Nobody knows the way I feel this morning / Who's sorry now / High society.
**Album:** Released Apr '81, on Rarities. Catalogue no: **RARITIES 54**

**PIED PIPER VOL 2, THE**
Tracks: / South Rampart Street parade / Bucket's got a hole, The / At a Georgia camp meeting / West End blues / That's a plenty / Lord, lord / Nobody know's the way I feel this morning / Hindustan.
**Album:** Released Apr '81, on Rarities.Catalogue no: **RARITIES 51**

**RAGTIME BAND**
Tracks: / Ice cream / Down by the riverside / Burgandy Street blues / Just a closer walk with thee / Panama / Doctor jazz / When the Saints go marching in / Lou-easy-an-i-a.
**Album:** Released Apr '81, on Joker (USA). Catalogue no: **SM 3072**

**WHEN THE SUN GOES DOWN**
Tracks: / Swanee river / In the evening when the sun goes down / Willie the weeper / Redwing / St Philip Street breakdown / Bourbon Street parade / Cheek to cheek / If I ever cease to love.
**Album:** Released Jun '89, on Ken Colyer. Catalogue no: **KC 3**

## Lewis, John

**BRIDGE GAME**
Tracks: / One at heart / Game demand, The / Two clubs / Little slam in diamonds,A / One spade (tears from children) / One diamond / Takeout double, The / Invitation to a slam, The / Preempt, The.
Note: Personnel:John Lewis-Piano/Joel Lester-Violin/Lois Martin-Viola/Scott Nickrenz- Viola/Howard Collins-Guitar/Marc Johnson-Bass. Composed by John Lewis (of the MJQ)"The Bridge Game" is a work based on J.S Bach "The Well-Tempered Clavier"Book 1.This is a beautiful example of how classical & jazz can be brought together naturally without sounding contrived.
**Cass:** Released Jun '86, on Philips (Europe) by PolyGram UK Ltd. Catalogue no: **826 698-4**
**Album:** Released Jun '86, on Philips (Europe) by PolyGram UK Ltd. Catalogue no: **826 698-1**
**CD:** Released Jun '86, on Philips (Holland) by PolyGram UK Ltd. Catalogue no: **826 698-2**

## Lewis, Johnny

**ALABAMA SLIDE GUITAR**
**Album:** Released May '81, on Arhoolie (USA) by Arhoolie Records (USA). Catalogue no: **ARHOOLIE 1055**

## Lewis, Meade Lux

**BARRELHOUSE PIANO**
**Album:** Released '88, on Storyville by Storyville Records AB. Catalogue no: **SLP 208**

**CHICAGO PIANO BLUES VOL.3**
**Album:** Released Dec '88, on Oldie Blues Catalogue no: **OL 2827**

**HONKY TONK PIANO**
**Cass:** Released May '88, on Classic Jazz Masters Catalogue no: **42026**
**Album:** Released May '88, on Classic Jazz Masters Catalogue no: **22026**

**JAZZ PIANO, THE (Lewis, Meade Lux/Albert Ammons and Pete Johnson)**
Tracks: / Dying mother blues / Roll me / Sweet patootie blues / Boogie woogie blues / Boogie woogie no.2.
**Album:** Released Apr '81, on Joker (USA) by Lifetime Records (USA). Catalogue no: **SM 3105**

**MEADE LUX LEWIS 1927-39**
Note: Also featuring Pete Johnson, Albert Ammons, Bob Robinson, George Hannah, Joe Turner, Benny Goodman
**Album:** Released '88, on Document Catalogue no: **DLP 534**

**MEADE LUX LEWIS 1939-54**
**Album:** Released Apr '89, on Blues Document Catalogue no: **BD 2031**

**MEADE LUX LEWIS VOL 1 (Tell your story)**
**Album:** Released '88, on Oldie Blues Catalogue no: **OL 2805**

**MEADE LUX LEWIS VOL 2 (Tell your story)**
**Album:** Released '88, on Oldie Blues

Catalogue no: **OL 2820**

## Lewis, Mel

**20 YEARS AT THE VILLAGE VANGUARD (Lewis, Mel and the Jazz Orchestra)**
Tracks: / All of me / Blue note / Butter / C-Jam blues / Dearly beloved / Interloper / Alone together / American express.
**Cass:** Released Jun '87, on Atlantic by WEA Records. Catalogue no: **781 655 4**
**Album:** Released Apr '87, on Atlantic by WEA Records. Catalogue no: **781 655 1**

**GOT' CHA (Lewis, Mel Septet)**
**Album:** Released Feb '88, on Fresh Sounds (Spain) by Fresh Sounds Records (Spain). Catalogue no: **FS 63**

**JAZZ AT THE SMITHSONIAN VOL.3 (Lewis, Mel & The Jazz Orchestra)**
Tracks: / One finger snap / Dolphin dance / Make me smile / Eye of the hurricane.
Note: When Mel Lewis teamed with cornettist, flugelhorn player and composer Thad Jones to form the Jazz Orchestra he already had ample big band experience. The son of a drummer, he had been playing professionally since the age of fifteen in bands like Ray Anthony's, Boyd Raeburn's and Tex Beneke's. This seventeen player concert chronicles the invigorating music from an orchestra that played an essential role in revitalizing the big band sound. Essential viewing for all jazz followers. Running time: 55 mins. (Parkfield Publishing)
**VHS:** Released Sep '89, on Parkfield Publishing Catalogue no: **MKJ 0005**

**MEL LEWIS LIVE**
**CD:** Released Dec '87, on Ina Catalogue no: **INAK 8611 CD**

**NATURALLY, PLAY THAD JONES (Lewis, Mel & The Jazz Orchestra)**
Tracks: / Cherry juice / Two as one / My centennial / 61st and Rich'id / Que pasa bossa o / Easy living.
**Album:** Released Sep '80, on Telarc Deleted Sep '85. Catalogue no: **10044**

## Lewis, Philip

**RHYTHM MANIACS SESSIONS 1929**
**Album:** Released '88, on Fountain by Retrieval Records. Catalogue no: **FG 412**
**Album:** Released Jul '87, on Fountain by Retrieval Records. Catalogue no: **FG 410**

## Lewis, Ramsey

**Biographical details:** Lewis, Ramsey, This American pianist was born in Chicago in 1935 and began studying the keyboards at the age of six. After an impressive childhood and adolescence, during which his prodigious talent won him scholarships and plaudits galore, he formed the Ramsey Lewis Trio in 1956. Working as a piano/bass/drums unit, the threesome spent a decade building their reputation in the field of jazz. Work included numerous gigs in nightclubs, sessions in the studio for other jazz artists, plus their own albums, the first of which was released in 1959.
The slow but steady rise of the Ramsey Lewis Trio reached its climax in 1965, when they cruised to fame on the US national pop chart with an atmospheric cover version of *The In Crowd*. This catchy song had already been a US No.13 hit for vocalist Dobie Gray earlier in the same year, but the undeterred Lewis released his bluesy jazzy instrumental rendition and watched it shoot to No.5. Realising he was onto a good thing, he recorded a version of the McCoys' current No.1 smash *Hang On Sloopy* and got to No.11. 1966 brought him a US No.29 hit with the Beatles' *A Hard Day's Night*, plus a No.19 success with *Wade In The Water*. The latter was a Lewis arrangement of an ancient slaves' song; it gave the pianist a rare and belated British hit in 1972, peaking at No.31.
Concentrating on albums rather than singles during the late Sixties and Seventies, Lewis continued to enjoy considerable commercial success by revamping well known and not so familiar material with his punchy piano panache. He retained a distinctive blend of jazz, blues, pop and soul influences in his work and never succumbed to the conveyor belt blandness of such remake merchants as James Last. Some of Ramsey's Seventies albums were produced by members and associates of Earth Wind & Fire. He was still going strong in the Eighties. (Bob Macdonald 7/12/85).

**BEST OF RAMSEY LEWIS**
Tracks: / Sun goddess / Skippin' / Caring for you / Spring high / All the way live / Tequila mockingbird / Hot dawgit / Funky serenity / Love notes / Brazilica.
**Album:** Released Oct '88, on Vogue (France) by Vogue Records. Catalogue no: **515022**
**Album:** Released Jan '82, on CBS by CBS Records. Deleted Jan '87. Catalogue no: **CBS 84911**

**CHANCE ENCOUNTER**
Tracks: / What's going on / Chance encounter / Up where we belong / Intimacy / Special place, A / Paradise / I can't wait / Just a little ditty.
**Album:** Released Jan '83, on CBS by CBS Records. Deleted Jan '88. Catalogue no: **CBS 25057**

**CLASSIC ENCOUNTER**
**Album:** Deleted 10 Jul '89. Catalogue no: **460 818-1**
**CD:** Deleted 10 Jul '89. Catalogue no: **460 818-2**
**Cass:** Deleted 10 Jul '89. Catalogue no: **460 818-4**

**FANTASY**
Tracks: / This ain't no fantasy / Ram jam / It's gonna change / Les ciefs de mon coeur / Victim of a broken heart / Slow dancin' / Never give up / Part of me / Quest.
**Album:** Released '86, on CBS by CBS Records. Catalogue no: **CBS 26688**

**GREATEST HITS**
**CD:** Released Feb '90, on MCA by MCA Records. Catalogue no: **CHD 6021**

**HANG ON RAMSEY (Lewis, Ramsey Trio)**
**Album:** Released May '66, on Chess by Vogue Records. Deleted May '71. Catalogue no: **CRL 4520**

**HIS GREATEST SIDES VOL.1**
Tracks: / High heel sneakers / Hang on sloopy / Dancing in the streets / Hard day's night, A / Something you've got / In crowd, The / Wade in the water / Soul man / Since you've been gone / One two three / Les fleurs / Uptight.
**Album:** Released Jun '84, on Chess by Vogue Records. Deleted Jun '89. Catalogue no: **CXMP 2051**
**Album:** Released Aug '86, on Chess by Vogue Records. Catalogue no: **GCH 8003**
**Cass:** Released Aug '86, on Chess by Vogue Records. Catalogue no: **GCHK 78003**

**IN CROWD**
Tracks: / In crowd / Hang on Sloopy / Wade in the water / Hard day's night.
**7" Single:** Released Jul '85, on Chess by Vogue Records. Deleted Jul '88. Catalogue no: **CHES 4006**

**'IN' CROWD, THE (Greatest hits)**
Tracks: / Hang on sloopy / 'In' crowd, The / Dancing in the street / Hi heel sneakers / Something you've got / Soul man / One two three / Since I fell for you / Wade in the water / Hard day's night / Upright / You been talking 'bout me baby / Since you've been gone / Les fleurs / Tennessee waltz / Felicidade (happiness) / Love theme Spartacus / Come Sunday.
**CD:** Released Oct '89, on Black Tulip Catalogue no: **2636462**
**CD:** Released 23 Feb '90, on MCA by MCA Records. Catalogue no: **CHD 6021**
**Cass:** Released Oct '89, on Black Tulip Catalogue no: **2636464**

**KEYS TO THE CITY**
Tracks: / Keys to the city / You're falling in love / 7-11 / Strangers / My love will lead you home / Melody of life / Shamballa / Love and understanding.
**Album:** Released May '87, on CBS by CBS Records. Catalogue no: **450870 1**
**Cass:** Released May '87, on CBS by CBS Records. Catalogue no: **450870 4**

**LEGACY**
Tracks: / Toccata / Adagio / Fugue / All the way love / I love to please you / Well, well, well / Moogin' on / Don't look back.
**Album:** Released Jan '79, on CBS by CBS Records. Deleted Jan '84. Catalogue no: **CBS 82964**

**LES FLEURS**
Tracks: / Super woman / House is not a home / Essence of love / Les fleurs /

Physical / With a gentle touch / Reasons.
**Album:** Released Sep '83, on CBS by CBS Records. Deleted Jan '88. Catalogue no: **CBS 25524**

**LIVE AT THE SAVOY**
Tracks: / Close your eyes and remember / Sassy stew / Callin' fallin' / Baby what you want me to do / You never know / Lynn / It's just called love / Wade in the water / Hang on Sloopy / In crowd.
**Album:** Released Apr '82, on CBS by CBS Records. Deleted Apr '87. Catalogue no: **CBS 85502**

**RAMSEY LEWIS**
Tracks: / Aquarius / Let the sun shine in / Wearin' it out / I just can't give you up / Every chance I get / Dancin' / I'll always dream about you / Intermezzo / Spanoletts / Don't cry for me Argentina.
**Album:** Released '79, on CBS by CBS Records. Deleted '84. Catalogue no: **CBS 83584**

**REUNION**
Tracks: / In crowd, The / (Song of) Delilah / Hello cello / Hang on sloopy / Wind, The / Carmen / Horizon.
**Cass:** Released Jan '84, on CBS by CBS Records. Catalogue no: **40 25804**
**Album:** Released Jan '84, on CBS by CBS Records. Catalogue no: **CBS 25804**

**ROUTES**
Tracks: / Whisper zone / High point / Tondelayo / Caribbean blue / Looking glass / Come back jack / Colors in space / Crystals 'n sequence / You are the reason / Hell on wheels.
**Album:** Released Oct '80, on CBS by CBS Records. Deleted Jan '88. Catalogue no: **CBS 84243**

**SOUND OF CHRISTMAS, THE (Lewis, Ramsey Trio)**
Tracks: / Merry Christmas baby / Winter wonderland / Santa Claus is coming to town / Christmas blues / Here comes Santa Claus / Sound of Christmas, The / Christmas song, The / God rest ye merry gentlemen / Sleigh ride / What are you doing New Year's Eve.
**Cass:** Released Jan '87, on Chess by Vogue Records. Catalogue no: **GCHK 8016**
**Album:** Released Jan '87, on Chess by Vogue Records. Catalogue no: **GCH 8016**

**SUN GODDESS**
**CD:** Released '88, on Columbia (USA) by CBS Records (USA). Catalogue no: **CK 331 94**

**THREE PIECE SUITE**
Tracks: / Lakeshore cowboy / Romance me / Will you / Love is / Michelle / Don't ever go away / So much more / Can't wait till summer / She's out of my life / Expansions.
**Album:** Released Jul '81, on CBS by CBS Records. Deleted '86. Catalogue no: **CBS 84980**

**UP WHERE WE BELONG**
Tracks: / Up where we belong / Chance encounter.
**7" Single:** Released Dec '82, on CBS by CBS Records. Deleted Dec '87. Catalogue no: **A 2946**

**WADE IN THE WATER**
Tracks: / Wade in the water / In crowd.
**7" Single:** Released Jun '81, on Chess by Vogue Records. Deleted Jun '84. Catalogue no: **CHES 101**
**7" Single:** Released Apr '72, on Chess by Vogue Records. Deleted Apr '75. Catalogue no: **6145 004**
**12" Single:** Released Jun '81, on Chess by Vogue Records. Deleted Jun '84. Catalogue no: **CHESL 101**

**WADE IN THE WATER (OLD GOLD) (Lewis, Ramsey Trio)**
Tracks: / Wade in the water / In crowd, The.
**7" Single:** Released Jan '89, on Old Gold by Old Gold Records. Catalogue no: **OG 9848**

## Lewis, Sabby

**BOSTON BOUNCE (Lewis, Sabby Orchestra & Quartet)**
**Album:** Released '88, on Phoenix (1) by Phoenix Records. Catalogue no: **PHOENIX 9**

**SABBY LEWIS ORCHESTRA & QUARTET, 1946 (Lewis, Sabby Orchestra & Quartet)**
Tracks: / Boston bounce / Edna / Bottoms up / Hangover / I can't give you anything but love / Minor mania / Embraceable you / Sweet Georgia Brown / I surrender, dear / Undecided.
Note: The quartet features the great tenor saxist Paul Gonsalves; the 13-piece band includes trumpeter Freddie Webster.
**Album:** Released Apr '81, on Phoenix (1) by Phoenix Records. Catalogue no: **LP 9**

## Lewis, Ted

**IS EVERYBODY HAPPY**
**Album:** Released Dec '86, on Halcyon (USA) by Submarine Records. Catalogue no: **HDL 109**

**JAZZ HOLIDAY, A (Lewis, Ted/his band)**
Tracks: / Jazz holiday, A / Shimme-shawabble / My mama's in town / Say, Arabella / Glad rag doll / Bugle call rag / Bam bam bammy shore / Where'd you get those eyes? / Milenberg joys / She's funny that way / Camel walk, The / Hello Montreal / New St Louis blues, The / That certain party / Some of these days / Darktown strutters' ball.
**Album:** Released 1 Mar '81, on Living Era by Academy Sound & Vision Records. Catalogue no: **AJA 5006**

**TED'S HIGHLIGHTS VOL. 1 (Lewis, Ted/his orchestra)**
**Album:** Released Jan '88, on Gaps Catalogue no: **GAPS 020**

**TEDS HIGHLIGHTS VOL. 3 (Lewis, Ted/his orchestra)**
**Album:** Released Jan '88, on Gaps Catalogue no: **GAPS 140**

**VINTAGE SHOW BIZ GREATS (also see Tucker, Sophie) (Lewis, Ted & Sophie Tucker)**
**Album:** Released Mar '84, on Folkways (USA) by Folkways Records (USA). Catalogue no: **RFS 603**

## Lewis, Vic

**IN CONCERT 1954 (Lewis, Vic & His Orchestra)**
**Album:** Released '88, on Hep Jazz by Hep Records. Catalogue no: **HEP 20**

**JAM SESSIONS Vol. 1(The war years)**
Tracks: / Yellow dog blues / Blues in E. / Johnny's idea / Wigmore jump / Wigmore blues / My blue Heaven / Someday, sweetheart / Ain't misbehavin' / Ja da / Tea for two.
Note: Mono recording.
**Album:** Released Jun '86, on Harlequin by Interstate Music. Catalogue no: **HQ 3008**

**JAM SESSIONS Vol. 2**
**Album:** Released Jun '86, on Harlequin by Interstate Music. Catalogue no: **HQ 3009**

**JAM SESSIONS Vol. 3**
**Album:** Released Jun '86, on Harlequin by Interstate Music. Catalogue no: **HQ 3010**

**JAM SESSIONS Vol. 4**
Tracks: / Soft winds / What's new / Blues / I found a new baby / Washboard blues / Woo woo / Stardust / Cottontail / Body and soul / Sweet Georgia Brown.
Note: With Buddy Featherstonhaugh RAF Rhythm club sextet -1943-1944. Mono recording,not issued HMV sides but previously unissued tracks from broad- casts.
**Album:** Released Nov '86, on Harlequin by Interstate Music. Catalogue no: **HQ 3011**

**JAM SESSIONS Vol. 5 (1938-46)**
Tracks: / I ain't got nobody / Shine on harvest moon / Stooge blues / Don't be angry / Blues part 1 (1943), The / Blues part 2 (1943), The / Squatty roo / Jazz me blues (1943) / Jazz me blues (1946) / NRC jump / Eager beaver / Sgt on a furlough / Honeysuckle rose.
**Album:** Released 11 Apr '87, on Harlequin by Interstate Music. Catalogue no: **HQ 3012**

**JAM SESSIONS Vol. 6 (1946-49)**
Tracks: / I like to riff / In love in vain / Smiles / You do / Making whoopee / Things we did last summer, The / Red top / Hep Boyd's / Body and soul / I wish I didn't love you / Pat's party / I never loved anyone / Bam bam / Don't smoke in bed / It might as well be swing.
**Album:** Released Apr '86, on Harlequin by Interstate Music. Catalogue no: **HQ 3013**

**MULLIGAN'S MUSIC (Lewis, Vic & His Orchestra)**
Note: Reissue of two Decca 10in LPs -- Mulligan's Music and At The Festival Hall, 1955 -- plus two unreleased tracks. Mulligan's Music features Tubby Hayes on tenor and baritone saxes.
**Album:** Released '87, on Mole Cata-

logue no: **MOLE 9**

**NEW YORK '38 (Lewis, Vic & his American Jazzmen)**
**Album:** Released Jan '86, on Esquire by Titan Int. Prod.. Catalogue no: **ESQ 313**

**PLAY BILL HOLMAN (Lewis, Vic West Coast All Stars)**
Tracks: / Oleo / Yeserdays / Sizzler before lunch / When I fall in love / Easter parade / As we speak / Sizzler after lunch.
**Cass:** Released Jan '90, on Mole Jazz by Mole Jazz Records. Catalogue no: **MOLECASS 14**
**CD:** Released Jan '90, on Mole Jazz by Mole Jazz Records. Catalogue no: **CDMOLE 14**

**PLAYS STAN KENTON 1948-54**
Tracks: / Stan Kenton speaks / Minor riff / Balbao bash / Concerto to end all concertos / Collaboration / Harlem holiday / I told ya I love ya, now get out / Metronome riff / Interlude / Rhythm incorporated / Intermission riff / Sweets / You'd be so nice to come home to / Bill's blues / Fearless fosdike.
**Album:** Released Apr '87, on Harlequin by Interstate Music. Catalogue no: **HQ 3014**

**VIC LEWIS BIG BANDS**
Tracks: / Triple threat / Loneliest monk, The / Conversation / Sunday girl / Apple piety / Intermission rif / Shorty.
Note: This CD has been specially released to celebrate Vic Lewis's 50th year in the entertainment business.
Recorded at two sessions during May 1984 and September 1985.
Featured soloists are Shorty Rogers, Bud Shank, Peter King and Jiggs Whigham playing compositions by Alan Ferguson, Bill Holman, Gerry Mulligan, Shorty Rogers and others.

**CD:** Released Sep '88, on Concept (1) Catalogue no: **VLCD 1**

**VIC LEWIS AND R.P.O.**
Tracks: / Don't cry for me Argentina / Theme from Mash / Serenade for strings / Coco / Always Madamoiselle / Hannie Caulder / 49th parallel / So much you loved me / Louise / Escape me never / Little Prince / My ship.
**Album:** Released Feb '77, on RCA by BMG Records (UK). Deleted '80. Catalogue no: **PL 25403**

## Lewis, Willie

**IN PARIS (1925-1937)**
**2 LP Set:** Released '88, on DRG (USA) by DRG Records (USA). Catalogue no: **SW 8400/01**

## Ley, Eggy

**COME AND GET IT (Ley, Eggy & Fiona Duncan)**
**Album:** Released Jun '87, on Veloce Catalogue no: **VELP 001**

**EGGY LEY'S HOTSHOTS**
**Album:** Released May '87, on Wam Catalogue no: **WAM/N No.1**
**Cass:** Released Feb '89, on Wam Catalogue no: **WAM R20TC LC 1415**

**EGGY LEY'S HOTSHOTS E.C.4 (Ley, Eggy Hotshots)**
**12" Single:** Released Aug '89, on Viaphon Catalogue no: **V 0508**

## Liebman, David

**DOIN' IT AGAIN (Liebman, David Quartet)**
Tracks: / Doin' it again / Lady Stardust / Cliff's vibes.
**Album:** Released Apr '81, on Timeless by Timeless Records. Catalogue no: **SJP 140**

**FORGOTTEN FANTASIES (Liebman, David & Richie Beirach)**
**Album:** Released Jul '76, on A&M by A&M Records. Deleted '88. Catalogue no: **AMLJ 709**

**HOMAGE TO COLTRANE**
**CD:** on Owl (France) Catalogue no: **LC 046**

**IF THEY ONLY KNEW**
Tracks: / If they and only knew / Capistrano / Moontide / Reunion / Autumn in New York / Move on some.
**Album:** Released '81, on Timeless by Timeless Records. Catalogue no: **SJP 151**

**LIGHT'N UP PLEASE**
**Album:** Released Apr '77, on Horizon by A&M Records. Catalogue no: **AMLJ 721**

**OPAL HEART, THE (Liebman, David Quartet)**
**Album:** Released Jan '82, on Enja (Germany) by Enja Records (West Germany). Catalogue no: **ENJA 3065**

**PENDULUM (Liebman, David Quartet)**
**Album:** Released May '81, on Artists House Catalogue no: **AH 8**

**QUEST**
**Album:** Released Jan '85, on Palo Alto Catalogue no: **PA 8061**
**Album:** Released Feb '84, on New Jazz (USA) by Fantasy Inc (USA). Catalogue no: **OJC 082**

**QUEST 2 (Liebman, David & Richie Beirach)**
**CD:** Released Feb '90, on Storyville by Storyville Records AB. Catalogue no: **STCD 4132**
**Album:** Released Feb '90, on Storyville by Storyville Records AB. Catalogue no: **SLP 4132**

**SWEET HANDS**
**Album:** on Horizon by A&M Records. Catalogue no: **AMLJ 702**

## Liggins, Jimmy

**I CAN'T STOP**
Tracks: / I can't stop it / Don't put me down / Troubles good-bye / Misery blues / That song is gone / Move out baby / Answer to teardrops blues / I want my baby for Christmas / Down and out blues / That's what's knocking / Lonely nights blues / Goin' down with the sun / Brown skin baby / Lover's prayer / Dark hour blues / I'll never let you go.
**Album:** Released Aug '87, on Route 66 (Sweden) Catalogue no: **KIX 18**

## Liggins, Joe

**DARKTOWN STRUTTERS' BALL, THE (Liggins, Joe & His Honey Drippers)**
Tracks: / Miss Betty's blues / Got your love in my heart / Caravan / I know my love is true / Got a right to cry / Walkin' / Tanya / Sugar lump / Darktown strutters' ball / Downhome blues / Breaking my heart / Sweet Georgia Brown / Blues,The / Loosiana / Spooks holiday / Daddy on my mind.
**Album:** Released Aug '81, on Jukebox Lil (Sweden) Catalogue no: **JB 601**

**GREAT RHYTHM & BLUES: VOL 6**
Tracks: / Honeydripper (part 1) / Honeydripper (part 2) / Pink champagne / Boom-chick-a-boogie / Goin' back to L.A. / I've got a right to cry / Tanya / Stinky / Brown angel.
**Album:** Released Jul '82, on Bulldog Records by President Records. Catalogue no: **BDL 1005**

**HONEYDRIPPER, THE (1945-49) (Liggins, Joe & His Honey Drippers)**
**Album:** Released Nov '88, on Jukebox Lil (Sweden) Catalogue no: **JB 622**

**JOE & JIMMY LIGGINS (Liggins, Joe & Jimmy)**
Tracks: / Honey dripper / Pink champagne / I've got a right to cry / Rhythm in the barnyard / Little Joe's boogie / So alone / Dripper's boogie / Saturday night boogie woogie man / Drunk / Homecoming blue / Nite life boogie / Tear drop blues / Cadillac boogie / Washboard special, The.
**Album:** Released '74, on Sonet by Sonet Records. Catalogue no: **SNTF 5020**

## Lightfoot, Papa George

**NATCHEZ TRACE**
Tracks: / My woman is tired of my lyin' / New mean old train / Love my baby / Goin' down that muddy road / Ah come on honey / I heard somebody cryin' / Take it witcha / Night time.
**Album:** Released Sep '84, on Crosscut by Topic Records. Catalogue no: **CCR 1001**

## Lightfoot, Terry

**1959-1968**
**CD:** Released Mar '90, on Philips by Phonogram Ltd. Catalogue no: **JJCD 31**

**AS TIME GOES BY**
Tracks: / Country cousin / Satin doll /

T'aint what you do (it's the way that you do it) / Lonesome / Chu' chu' boogie / Granpa's spells / Bloodshot eyes / Bra timing from Phomolong / Naw you has jazz / Back in the high life again / As time goes by / Skyliner.
**Album:** Released Mar '87, on PRT by Castle Communications Records. Catalogue no: **N 6564**
**Cass:** Released Mar '87, on PRT by Castle Communications Records. Catalogue no: **ZCN 6564**

**AT THE JAZZBAND BALL (Lightfoot, Terry & His Band)**
**CD:** Released Oct '88, on Bold Reprieve by Bold Reprieve Records. Catalogue no: **BRMCD 028**
**Album:** Released Oct '88, on Bold Reprieve by Bold Reprieve Records. Catalogue no: **BRMLP 028**

**CLEAR ROUND (Lightfoot, Terry & His Band)**
Tracks: / Tuxedo Junction / Mack the knife / Mardi gras / Plant life boogie / Rockin' in rhythm / That da da strain / Ragtime music / Jive at five / Nobody knows you (when you're down and out) / Drum boogie.
**Album:** Released Nov '81, on Plant Life Jazz by Plant Life Records. Catalogue no: **PLJ 003**

**KING KONG**
**Album:** Released Nov '61, on Columbia by EMI Records. Deleted Nov '64. Catalogue no: **SCD 2165**

**LONESOME (Lightfoot, Terry & His Band)**
Tracks: / Lonesome / Bloodshot eyes.
**7" Single:** Released Jan '87, on PRT by Castle Communications Records. Catalogue no: **PRT 7P 370**

**NEW ORLEANS JAZZMEN**
**CD:** Released Feb '90, on Hanover by Polydor Ltd. Catalogue no: **838 763 2**
**Album:** Released Feb '90, on Hanover by Polydor Ltd. Catalogue no: **838 763 1**

**TAVERN IN THE TOWN**
Tracks: / Tavern in the town.
**7" Single:** Released May '62, on Columbia by EMI Records. Deleted Jun '65. Catalogue no: **DB 4822**

**TERRY LIGHTFOOT IN CONCERT**
Tracks: / Rockin' in rhythm / West End blues / Sentimental journey / Black and tan / Sweet Georgia Brown / Summertime / Honeysuckle rose / Drum boogie / Honky tonk train / Tuxedo Junction / Joshua fit de battle of Jerico.
**2 LP Set:** Released May '79, on Black Lion Catalogue no: **BLPX 12143/4**

**TERRY LIGHTFOOT'S NEW ORLEANS JAZZMEN (The best of dixieland)**
**Album:** Released Jan '90, on Verve Catalogue no: **837 763 1**
**CD:** Released Jan '90, on Verve Catalogue no: **837 763 2**

**TRUE LOVE**
Tracks: / True love.
**7" Single:** Released Aug '61, on Columbia by EMI Records. Deleted Aug '64. Catalogue no: **DB 4696**

## Lightsey, Kirk

**EVERYTHING HAPPENS TO ME (Lightsey, Kirk Trio)**
**Cass:** Released Oct '86, on Timeless by Timeless Records. Catalogue no: **SJP 1176**

**FIRST AFFAIRS (Lightsey, Kirk Quartet)**
**Album:** Released '88, on Limetree Catalogue no: **MLP 0015**

**ISOTOPE (Lightsey, Kirk Trio)**
**Album:** Released '88, on Criss Cross Catalogue no: **CRISS 1003**

**KIRK 'N' MARCUS**
Tracks: / All my love / Loves I once knew / Windmill / Marcus' mates / Golden legacy / Lower bridge level.
**Album:** Released Jan '88, on Criss Cross Catalogue no: **CRISS 1030**

**LIGHTSEY 1 (Lightsey,Kirk Piano)**
Tracks: / Fee fi fo fum / Habiba / Trinkle tinkle / Moon ra / Fresh air / Wild flower / Never let me go.
Note: Kirk Lightsey on piano and flute.Recorded at Penthouse Recordings.
**Album:** Released Sep '86, on Sunnyside Jazz(USA) Catalogue no: **SSC 1002**

**LIGHTSEY 2**
**Album:** Released Apr '84, on Sunnyside Jazz(USA) Catalogue no: **SSC 1005**

**LIGHTSEY LIVE**
Tracks: / Pee Wee / Habiba / Trinkle tinkle / Spring is here / Fee fi fo fum / Just one of those things.
Note: Kirk Lightsey - piano.Recorded at the Baird Auditorium of the Smithsonian institution in Washington D.C on June 28 1985.
**CD:** Released Nov '86, on Sunnyside Jazz(USA) Catalogue no: **SSC 1014D**

**SHORTER BY TWO (Lightsey, Kirk/Harold Denko)**
**Album:** Released Apr '84, on Sunnyside Jazz(USA) Catalogue no: **SSC 1004**

## Lil' Ed

**CHICKEN, GRAVY & BISCUITS (Lil'ed & The Blues Imperials)**
**CD:** Released Mar '89, on Alligator (Sonet) by Alligator Records (USA). Catalogue no: **ALCD 4772**
**Album:** Released Mar '89, on Alligator (Sonet) by Alligator Records (USA). Catalogue no: **AL 4772**

**ROUGHHOUSIN' (Lil'ed & The Blues Imperials)**
**Album:** Released '89, on Sonet by Sonet Records. Catalogue no: **SNTF 966**

## Limehouse Jazzband

**RHYTHM IS OUR BUSINESS**
**Album:** Released '88, on Stomp Off (USA) Catalogue no: **SOS 1014**

## Lincoln, Abbey

**AFFAIR**
**Album:** Released Jan '85, on EMI (France) by EMI Records. Catalogue no: **LRP 3025**

**STRAIGHT AHEAD**
Tracks: / Straight ahead / When Malindy sings / In the red / Blue Monk / Left alone / African lady / Retribution.
Note: With Max Roach, Coleman Hawkins, Eric Dolphy, Mal Waldron, Booker Little, Julian Priester, Art Davis, Walter Benton.
**CD:** Released 16 Sep '88, on Candid Catalogue no: **CCD 9015**
**Album:** Released Jul '88, on Candid Catalogue no: **CS 9015**

**TALKING TO THE SUN**
**Album:** Released Nov '84, on Enja (Germany) by Enja Records (West Germany). Catalogue no: **ENJA 4060**

**THAT'S HIM**
Tracks: / Strong man / Happiness is just a thing called Joe / My man / Tender as a rose / That's him / Porgy / When a woman loves a man / Don't explain.
**Album:** Released Feb '84, on Riverside (USA) by Fantasy Inc (USA). Catalogue no: **OJC 085**

## Lincoln, Charley

**CHARLEY LINCOLN**
Tracks: / Jealous hearted blues / Hard luck blues / Mojoe blues / My wife drove me from my door / Country breakdown / Chain gang trouble / If it looks like jelly shakes like jelly it must be gelatine / Ugly papa / Jacksonville blues / Midnight weeping blues / Depot blues / Gamblin' Charley doodle hole blues / Mama don't rush me.
**Album:** Released Aug '83, on Matchbox by Flyright Records. Catalogue no: **MSE 212**

## Lindenstrand,Bo

**MY SHINING HOUR (Lindenstrand,Bo Quartet)**
**Album:** Released Aug '86, on Teldec (Germany) by ASV (Academy Sound & Vision). Catalogue no: **PHONT 7557**

## Linn, Ray

**CHICAGO JAZZ (Linn, Ray & The Chicago Stompers)**
Tracks: / Poor butterfly / Can't we be friends / Jeepers creepers / Royal Garden blues / Keepin' out of mischief now / Ain't misbehavin'.
Note: Ray Linn-trumpet, Henry Cuesta-clarinet & baritone sax, Eddie Miller-tenor sax, Bob Havens-trombone, Dave Frishberg-piano, Richard Maloof-string bass, Jack Davenport-drums.
**Album:** Released '88, on Trend (USA) by Trend Records (USA). Catalogue no: **TR 515**

**EMPTY SUIT BLUES (Linn, Ray & The Chicago Stompers)**
Tracks: / Memories of you / Stars fell on Alabama / What is there to say?.
Note: Mary-Ann McCall-vocals,; Gary Foster, Eddie Miller-sax; Bob Havens-trombone; Dave Frishberg-piano; Jim Hughart-bass; Dick Berk-drums.

**Album:** Released '88, on Discovery (USA) by Discovery Records (USA). Catalogue no: **DS 823**

## Lipscomb, Mance

### MANCE LIPSCOMB
**Cass:** Released '88, on Arhoolie (USA) by Arhoolie Records (USA). Catalogue no: **C 205**
**Album:** Released '88, on Collectable Issues Catalogue no: **C 5521**

### MANCE LIPSCOMB, VOL. 3
**Album:** Released '88, on Arhoolie (USA) by Arhoolie Records (USA). Catalogue no: **F 1026**

### MANCE LIPSCOMB VOL 4
**Album:** Released May '81, on Arhoolie (USA) by Arhoolie Records (USA). Catalogue no: **ARHOOLIE 1033**

### MANCE LIPSCOMB, VOL. 5
**Album:** Released '88, on Arhoolie (USA) by Arhoolie Records (USA). Catalogue no: **F 1049**

### MANCE LIPSCOMB, VOL. 6
**Album:** Released '88, on Arhoolie (USA) by Arhoolie Records (USA). Catalogue no: **F 1069**

### TEXAS BLUES
**Album:** Released May '81, on Arhoolie (USA) by Arhoolie Records (USA). Catalogue no: **ARHOOLIE 1049**

### TEXAS SONGSTER
**Album:** Released May '81, on Arhoolie (USA) by Arhoolie Records (USA). Catalogue no: **ARHOOLIE 1001**

### TEXAS SONGSTER VOL 2
**Album:** Released May '81, on Arhoolie (USA) by Arhoolie Records (USA). Catalogue no: **ARHOOLIE 1023**

### TEXAS SONGSTER VOL 3
**Album:** Released May '81, on Arhoolie (USA) by Arhoolie Records (USA). Catalogue no: **ARHOOLIE 1026**

### TEXAS SONGSTER VOL 6
**Album:** Released May '81, on Arhoolie (USA) by Arhoolie Records (USA). Catalogue no: **ARHOOLIE 1069**

### YOU'LL NEVER FIND ANOTHER
**Album:** Released May '81, on Arhoolie (USA) by Arhoolie Records (USA). Catalogue no: **ARHOOLIE 1077**

## Lipton, Sydney

### 1932-3 (Lipton, Sydney & his Orchestra)
**Album:** Released Sep '77, on Retrospect by EMI Records. Catalogue no: **SH 257**

### BEAUTIFUL MELODIES FROM AROUND THE WORLD
**Album:** Released Nov '85, on Horatio Nelson by Horatio Nelson Records & Tapes Ltd.. Catalogue no: **YU 101**
**Cass:** Released Nov '85, on Horatio Nelson by Horatio Nelson Records & Tapes Ltd.. Catalogue no: **CYU 101**

### DANCING AT THE GROSVENOR HOUSE (Lipton, Sydney & his Orchestra)
Tracks: / Elmer's tune / Tisket a tasket, A / All I do is dream of you / Goodnight my love / I saw stars / Chloe / I'm sitting on top of the world / Sunday / Candy / Cabin in the sky / That old feeling / Should I / Deep in the heart of Texas / Down yonder / Frenesi / I'm thinking of my blue eyes / Adios / Till the end of the world / Perfidia / Do I worry? / Petticoats of Portugal / Lisbon Antigua / My adobe hacienda / Cherry.
**Album:** Released Feb '85, on President by President Records. Catalogue no: **PLE 519**

### JUST DANCE (Lipton, Sydney & His Grosvenor House Orchestra)
Tracks: / Darkness on the delta / I've got an invitation to a dance / Why am I blue / Just a catchy little song / One night in Chinatown / Oh my goodness / Dinner music for a pack of hungry cannibals / Supposin' / Madame ah la marquise ah / Trusting my luck / Amoresque / It's a long way to your heart / Harlem / When a lady meets a gentleman down south / Reckless night on board an ocean liner / Souvenir of love / Just dance.
**Album:** Released Oct '82, on Decca by Decca International. Deleted Oct '87. Catalogue no: **RFL 22**

## Listen To Dr Jive

### LISTEN TO DR. JIVE (Various artists)
**Album:** Released Jan '84, on Krazy Kat by Interstate Music. Catalogue no: **KK 780**

## Listen To The Banned

### LISTEN TO THE BANNED (Various artists)
Tracks: / I've gone and lost my little yo yo: *Cotton, Billy* / With my little ukelele in my hand: *Formby, George (Junior)* / Guy what takes his time, A: *West, Mae* / She was only a postman's daughter, but...: *Durium Dance Band* / Nellie the nudist queen: *Ross & Sargent* / My private affair: *Davies, Dawn* / What's it: *Rodgers, Jimmie* / He hadn't up 'til yesterday: *Tucker, Sophie* / Winnie the worm: *Frankau, Ronald* / I'm a bear in a lady's boudoir: *Edwards, Cliff* / Everyone's got sex appeal for someone: *Frankau, Ronald/Monte Crick* / All poshed up with my daisies in my hand: *Higgins, Charlie* / Pu-leeze Mr. Hemingway: *Carlisle, Elsie* / Let's all be fairies: *Durium Dance Band* / I'm going to give it to Mary with love: *Edwards, Cliff* / Physician, The: *Lawrence, Gertrude* / No wonder she's a blushing bride: *Fowler, Art* / Flora McDonald: *Byng, Douglas* / Or anything else I've got: *Sutton, Randolph* / And so does he: *Davies, Dawn.*
**Cass:** Released 1 Sep '84, on Living Era by Academy Sound & Vision Records. Catalogue no: **ZC AJA 5030**
**CD:** Released Oct '88, on Living Era by Academy Sound & Vision Records. Catalogue no: **CD AJA 5030**
**Album:** Released 1 Sep '84, on Living Era by Academy Sound & Vision Records. Catalogue no: **AJA 5030**

## Little Milton

### ANNIE MAE'S CAFE
**Album:** Released Dec '86, on Malaco by Malaco Records (UK). Catalogue no: **MAL 008**

### CHICAGO GOLDEN YEARS
**2 LP Set:** Released Oct '88, on Vogue by Vogue Records. Catalogue no: **427013**

### HIS GREATEST HITS
Tracks: / Grits ain't groceries / I play dirty / Just a little bit / Who's cheating who / Losing hand / Blind man / More and more / If walls could talk / We're gonna make it / Baby I love you / Man loves two / So mean to me / Without my sweet baby / Feel so bad.
**Album:** Released Jan '87, on Chess by Vogue Records. Catalogue no: **GCH 8011**
**Cass:** Released Jan '87, on Chess by Vogue Records. Catalogue no: **GCHK 78011**

### HIS GREATEST SIDES VOL 1
Tracks: / Grits ain't groceries / I play dirty / Just a little bit / Who's cheating who / Losing hand / Blind man / More and more / If walls could talk / We're gonna make it / Baby I love you / Man loves two / So mean to me / Without my sweet baby / Feel so bad.
**Album:** Released Jul '84, on Chess (PRT) Deleted '88. Catalogue no: **CXMP 2053**

### HITTIN' THE BOOGIE (Memphis days 1953-54)
**Album:** Released '88, on Zu Zazz by Zu Zazz Records. Catalogue no: **Z 2007**

### I WILL SURVIVE
**Album:** Released '88, on Malaco by Malaco Records (UK). Catalogue no: **MAL 7427**

### LITTLE MILTON SINGS BIG BLUES
Tracks: / Feel so bad / Reconsider / Stormy monday / Woke up this morning / Hard luck blues / Please,please,please / Sweet sixteen / Fever / Sneakin' around / Don't decieve me / Have mercy baby / Part time love.
**Album:** Released Oct '87, on Chess by Vogue Records. Catalogue no: **GCH 8037**
**Cass:** Released Oct '87, on Chess by Vogue Records. Catalogue no: **GCHK 78037**

### MOVING TO THE COUNTRY
**CD:** Released '88, on Malaco by Malaco Records (UK). Catalogue no: **MALCD 7445**
**Cass:** Released Mar '89, on Malaco by Malaco Records (UK). Catalogue no: **MALC 7445**
**Album:** Released Dec '87, on Malaco by Malaco Records (UK). Catalogue no: **MAL 7445**

### PLAYING FOR KEEPS
**Album:** Released Dec '84, on Malaco by Malaco Records (UK). Catalogue no:

**MAL 7419**

### RAISE A LITTLE SAND

Tracks: / Homesick for my baby / Somebody told me / Lonesome for my baby / If you love me / Begging my baby / Let's boogie baby / Love at first sight / Hold me tight / I'm trying / Dead love / I found me a new love / Long distance operator / That will never do / My baby pleases me / Same old blues / I'm a lonely man.

**Album:** Released Sep '82, on Red Lightnin' by Red Lightning Records. Deleted Jun '89. Catalogue no: **RL 011**

### SAM'S BLUES

**Album:** Released Jun '76, on Charly by Charly Records. Catalogue no: **CR 30102**

### WE'RE GONNA MAKE IT

**CD:** Released Mar '90, on Roots Catalogue no: **RTS 33012**

**Cass:** Released May '87, on Chess by Vogue Records. Catalogue no: **GCHK 78028**

**Album:** Released Apr '87, on Chess by Vogue Records. Catalogue no: **GCH 8028**

## Little Ramblers

### LITTLE RAMBLERS 1924/5 VOL 1, THE

**Album:** Released Apr '79, on VJM (Vintage Jazz Music) by Vintage Jazz Music Society(VJM). Catalogue no: **VLP 28**

### LITTLE RAMBLERS 1925/6 VOL 2, THE

**Album:** Released Apr '79, on VJM (Vintage Jazz Music) by Vintage Jazz Music Society(VJM). Catalogue no: **VLP 29**

## Little Sonny

### NEW KING OF THE BLUES HARMONICA

Tracks: / Baby what you want me to do / Eli's pork chop / Hey little girl / Hot potato / Don't ask me no questions / Tomorrow's blues today / Back down yonder / Sad funk / Creeper return, The.

Note: Born Aaron Willis in 1932, Little Sonny is one of the great blues harmonica players to have come out of Detroit. This was his first album and mainly features his own compositions.

**Cass:** Released Nov '86, on Stax by Fantasy Inc (USA). Catalogue no: **MPS 58533**

**Album:** Released Nov '86, on Stax by Fantasy Inc (USA). Catalogue no: **MPS 8533**

## Little Walter

### BEST OF LITTLE WALTER

Tracks: / My babe / Sad hours / You're so fine / Last night / Blues with a feeling / Can't hold out much longer / Juke / Mean old world / Off the wall / You better watch yourself / Blue light / Tell me mama.

**Cass:** Released Apr '87, on Chess by Vogue Records. Catalogue no: **GCHK 78018**

**Album:** Released Apr '87, on Chess by Vogue Records. Catalogue no: **GCH 8018**

### BLUES WORLD OF LITTLE WALTER

**Album:** Released Dec '88, on Delmark (USA) by Delmark Records (USA). Catalogue no: **DL 648**

### BOSS BLUES HARMONICA

Tracks: / Juke / Can't hold out much longer / Mean old world / Sad hours / Tell me mama / Off the wall / Blues with a feeling / Too late / You're so fine / Last night / You better watch yourself / Blue light / My babe / Thunderbird / I got to go / Boom, boom out goes the lights / Flying saucer / It's too late brother / Teenage beat / Just a feeling / Shake dancer / Ah'w baby / Back track / Just your fool.

**CD:** Released Dec '86, on Vogue by Vogue Records. Catalogue no: **VGCD 600118**

**CD:** Released Aug '88, on Chess by Vogue Records. Catalogue no: **CDRED 4**

### CHESS MASTERS - LITTLE WALTER 1

Tracks: / Boogie / Don't have to hunt no more / Tonight with a fool / Quarter to twelve / Last boogie / Too late / Fast boogie / Lights out / Thunderbird / I got to go / Crazy for my baby / Who / It ain't right / Flying saucer / Just a feeling / Shake dancer / Ah'w baby / Confessin' the blues / Key to the highway / Back track / Blue and lonesome / Goin' down slow / I don't play / Just your fool.

**2 LP Set:** Released May '83, on Chess (USA) Catalogue no: **CXMD 4011**

**2 LP Set:** Released Apr '81, on Chess (PRT) Deleted '88. Catalogue no: **CXMD 4002**

### CHICAGO GOLDEN YEARS

**2 LP Set:** Released Oct '88, on Vogue by Vogue Records. Catalogue no: **427001**

### COLLECTION: LITTLE WALTER (20 blues greats)

Tracks: / Walter's blues / Going down slow / Blue mood / Lovin' you all the time / Rock bottom / I've had my fun / Mean old Frisco / Temperature / Flying saucer / Just you fool / Snake dancer / Too late / Mellow down easy / I don't play / Ah'w baby / Me and Piney Brown / I got to go / Thunderbird / One more chance with you / It's too late, brother.

**Cass:** Released Dec '87, on Deja Vu Catalogue no: **DVMC 2114**

**Album:** Released Dec '87, on Deja Vu Catalogue no: **DVLP 2114**

### CONFESSIN' THE BLUES

**Album:** Released Oct '86, on Chess (PRT) Deleted '88. Catalogue no: **BRP 2025**

### ON THE ROAD AGAIN

**Album:** Released '79, on Xtra Catalogue no: **XTRA 1133**

### QUARTER TO TWELVE

Tracks: / Quarter to twelve / Mellow down easy / Lights out / I hate to see you go / My baby is sweeter / Crazy mixed up world / Rocker / Oh baby / Blue midnight / It ain't right / Who / Back track / Everything gonna be alright / Crazy legs / Crazy for my baby / Toddle, The.

**Album:** Released Sep '82, on Red Lightnin' by Red Lightning Records. Deleted Jun '89. Catalogue no: **RL 002**

### THUNDERBIRD

Tracks: / Too late / Thunderbird / I got to go / One more chance with you / Flying saucer / It's too late brother / Just a good feeling / Teenage beat / Shake dancer / Temperature / I've had my fun / Ah'w baby / Rock bottom / Mean old Frisco.

**Album:** Released Sep '82, on Syndicate Chapter Deleted Jun '89. Catalogue no: **SC 004**

### WINDY CITY BLUES (Little Walter/Otis Rush)

Tracks: / It's hard for me to believe baby / May be the last time / I feel good / Otis' blues / Going down slow / Walter's blues / Lovin' you all the time / Blue mood.

Note: Recorded live in chicago. Top blues artists. Archive edition.

**Album:** Released Feb '86, on Blue Moon (1) by Magnum Music Group. Catalogue no: **BMLP 1028**

## Little Willie John

### FEVER

Tracks: / Fever / I'm stickin' with you baby / Do something for me / Love, life and money / Suffering with the blues / Dinner date / All around the world / Need your love so bad / Young girl / Letter from my darling / I've got to go cry / My nerves.

**Album:** Released '88, on Sing Catalogue no: **SING 564**

### FREE AT LAST

**Cass set:** Released Mar '88, on Gusto (USA) by Gusto Records (USA). Catalogue no: **GD 5034**

### LITTLE WILLIE JOHN

**CD:** on Gusto (USA) by Gusto Records (USA). Catalogue no: **CD 1034**

### SURE THINGS

**CD:** Released Mar '90, on King Catalogue no: **KCD 739**

## Littlefield, Little

### HOUSEPARTY

**Album:** Released '88, on Oldie Blues Catalogue no: **OL 8003**

### LITTLE WILLIE LITTLEFIELD PLAYS BOOGIE WOOGIE (July 1987)

**Album:** Released May '88, on Schubert Catalogue no: **SCH 100**

### LITTLE WILLIE LITTLEFIELD, VOL.1

Tracks: / Mello cats / Life of trouble / I like it / Moon is rising / Once was lucky / Ain't a better story told / Mean mean woman / Real fine mama / Nakite stomp / Lump in my throat.

**Album:** Released Dec '80, on Ace by Ace Records. Deleted Dec '85. Catalogue no: **CH 24**

### LITTLE WILLIE LITTLEFIELD VOL 2

Tracks: / Love me tonight / Blues at sunset / I'd like to see you / Cheerful baby / Hit the road / Rockin' chair mama

/ Trouble all around me / Tell me baby / Long about midnight / Train whistle blowing.
**Album:** Released Jun '81, on Ace by Ace Records. Deleted '86. Catalogue no: **CH 34**

## Littlejohn, Johnny

**CHICAGO BLUES STARS**
**Album:** Released May '81, on Arhoolie (USA) by Arhoolie Records (USA). Catalogue no: **ARHOOLIE 1043**

**SO CALLED FRIENDS**
**Album:** Released Oct '88, on Rooster (USA) Catalogue no: **R 2621**

**SULTANS OF THE SLIDE GUITAR**
**Album:** Released Sep '79, on Blues Ball Catalogue no: **2003**

## Live...

**LIVE AND DIRECT - VOL.2 (Various artists)**
**Cass:** Released Mar '83, on Hawkeye by Hawkeye Records. Catalogue no: **INC 5**
**Album:** Released Mar '83, on Hawkeye by Hawkeye Records. Catalogue no: **INT 5**

**LIVE AT NEWPORT (Various artists)**
Tracks: / Outside help: *Various artists* / Little red rooster: *Various artists* / Ball and chain: *Various artists* / Long distance call: *Various artists* / Where's my woman been: *Various artists* / Got my mojo working: *Various artists.*
**Album:** Released Jun '84, on Blue Moon (1) by Magnum Music Group. Catalogue no: **BMM 002**

**LIVE AT THE FESTIVAL**
**Album:** Released Feb '82, on Enja (Germany) by Enja Records (West Germany). Catalogue no: **ENJA 2030**

**LIVE AT THE HAIG, LOS ANGELES, 1952 (Various artists)**
**Album:** Released Apr '79, on Jamm Session Catalogue no: **JAMM SESSION 101**
**Album:** Released Apr '79, on Jamm Session Catalogue no: **JAMM SESSION 102**

**LIVE AT THE TRADEWINDS, INGLEWOOD 1952 (Various artists)**
**Album:** Released Apr '79, on Jamm Session Catalogue no: **JAMM SESSION 103**

**LIVE IN LONDON - VOL.1 (Various artists)**
Tracks: / Down to the doctors: *Mickey Jupp Band* / All night worker: *Red Beans & Rice* / Somebody's changed the lock: *Diz & The Doormen* / Bluebird two step: *Electric Bluebirds* / Square dancin' Momma: *Electric Bluebirds* / Shame shame shame: *Red Beans & Rice* / Whistlin' Joe: *Red Beans & Rice* / Five guys named Moe: *Chevalier Brothers* / Jumpin' at the woodside: *Chevalier Brothers* / Kansas city: *Mickey Jupp Band* / Call me the breeze: *Electric Bluebirds* / Messaround: *Diz & The Doormen.*
**Album:** Released Feb '84, on Ace by Ace Records. Deleted Jun '88. Catalogue no: **CH 91**

## Living Chicago Blues

**LIVING CHICAGO BLUES, VOL.1 (Various artists)**
Note: Includes Jimmy Johnson, one of the modern Chicago blues idiom's most impressive singer/guitarists, a progressive stylist combining technical expertise with soaring, gospel influenced vocals; Eddie Shaw & The Wolf Gang, former Howlin' Wolf band with the great Hubert Sumlin on guitar; and Left Hand Frank, a fun-loving, powerfully built guitarist playing some of the strongest, most distinctive vintage blues in Chicago. (Alligator catalogue 7/88)
**Album:** Released Feb '79, on Alligator (Sonet) by Alligator Records (USA). Catalogue no: **SNTF 784**

**LIVING CHICAGO BLUES, VOL.2 (Various artists)**
Note: Includes Carey Bell, a student of Little Walter, the genius whose classic 50's sounds revolutionised blues harmonica playing, has brought the art of Chicago blues harmonica up-to-date; Memphis Slim & The Teardrops, one of the city's hardest driving party bands; and Johnny 'Big Moose' Walker, whose two-fisted piano has sparked records by Elmore James, Son Seals and Earl Hooker. (Alligator catalogue 7/88)
**Album:** Released Feb '79, on Alligator (Sonet) by Alligator Records (USA). Catalogue no: **SNTF 785**

**LIVING CHICAGO BLUES, VOL.3 (Various artists)**
Note: Includes Lonnie Brooks, who was originally called 'Guitar Jr.' but changed his name when he came to Chicago and has played an important part in the city's living blues tradition; Pinetop Perkins, who was the senior member of the Muddy Waters band and is recognised as one of the world's premier piano men; and the Sons of the Blues, Chicago's best young bluesmen, featuring Billy Branch on harp and Laurie Bell on guitar.
**Album:** Released Feb '79, on Alligator (Sonet) by Alligator Records (USA). Catalogue no: **SNTF 786**

**LIVING CHICAGO BLUES, VOL.4 (Various artists)**
Tracks: / Hard times: *Reed, A.C. & The Spark Plugs* / She's fine: *Reed, A.C. & The Spark Plugs* / Moving out of the ghetto: *Reed, A.C. & The Spark Plugs* / Going to New York: *Reed, A.C. & The Spark Plugs* / Big leg woman: *Scotty & The Rib Tips* / Careless without love: *Scotty & The Rib Tips* / Road block: *Scotty & The Rib Tips* / Poison ivy: *Scotty & The Rib Tips* / I dare you: *Lee, Lovie & Carey Bell* / Nobody knows my troubles: *Lee, Lovie & Carey Bell* / Sweet little girl: *Lee, Lovie & Carey Bell* / Nap town: *Lee, Lovie & Carey Bell.*
Note: Includes A.C Reed, tenor sax player, singer and songwriter best known for his work on tour with the likes of Albert Collins, Buddy Guy and Son Seals; Scotty and the Red Tips, one of the Chicago South Side's top bar bands with guitarist Buddy Scott; and Lovie Lee, the hard rocking piano man, plus his stepson Carey Bell on harp. (Alligator catalogue 7/88)
**Album:** Released Jan '81, on Alligator (Sonet) by Alligator Records (USA). Catalogue no: **SNTF 840**

**LIVING CHICAGO BLUES, VOL.5 (Various artists)**
Tracks: / Drown in my own tears: *Various artists* / Crying for my baby: *Various artists* / I feel so bad: *Various artists* / Wish me well: *Various artists* / Blues for a real man: *Various artists* / Thirteen years in prison: *Various artists* / Country boy: *Various artists* / My life ain't the same: *Various artists* / You don't know: *Various artists* / Morning noon and night: *Various artists* / Two years: *Various artists.*
Note: Includes Lacy Gibson, a highly original and charismatic guitarist , formerly with Son Seals and playing here with Son's Band; Big Leon Brooks, whose deep voice and heavy harmonic tone hark back to the fifties- his style having been preserved by a long haitus from the music scene; and Andrew Brown, an energetic modern guitarist from Chicago's south suburbs, who has cut a number of regional hit 45's. (Alligator records 7/88)
**Album:** Released Jan '81, on Alligator (Sonet) by Alligator Records (USA). Catalogue no: **SNTF 841**

**LIVING CHICAGO BLUES, VOL.6 (Various artists)**
Tracks: / If I hadn't been high: *Detroit Junior* / Some nerve: *Detroit Junior* / Somebody to shack: *Detroit Junior* / I got money: *Detroit Junior* / Somebody have mercy: *Johnson, Luther "Guitar Junior"* / Got to have money: *Johnson, Luther "Guitar Junior"* / Just like mama said: *Johnson, Luther "Guitar Junior"* / Look what you've done: *Johnson, Luther "Guitar Junior"* / Going upstairs: *Embry, Queen Sylvia* / Blues this morning: *Embry, Queen Sylvia* / Tired of being pushed around: *Embry, Queen Sylvia* / Please let me stay: *Embry, Queen Sylvia.*
Note: Includes Detroit Junior, one of the blues' funniest songwriters and a fine piano player; Luther 'Guitar Junior' Johnson, carrying an the driving West Side tradition of Magic Sam; and Queen Sylvia Embry, Chicago's top new bluewoman, singing her own songs in a rich, gospel-tinged voice. (Alligator catalogue 7/88)
**Album:** Released Jan '81, on Alligator (Sonet) by Alligator Records (USA). Catalogue no: **SNTF 842**

## Living Country Blues...

**LIVING COUNTRY BLUES INTRODUCTION (Chatmon, Sam & Hammie Nixon)**
**2 LP Set:** Released '88, on L&R Catalogue no: **LR 42.030**

**LIVING COUNTRY BLUES USA VOL 1 (Various artists)**
Note: Featuring: Bowling Green John, Hea Wiggins.
**Album:** Released '88, on L&R Catalogue no: **LR 42.031**

**LIVING COUNTRY BLUES USA VOL 2 (Various artists)**
Note: Featuring: James Son Thomas & Sam Chatmon.
**Album:** Released '88, on L&R Catalogue no: **LR 42.032**

**LIVING COUNTRY BLUES USA VOL 3 (Various artists)**
Note: Featuring: Flora Molton & The Truth Band.
**Album:** Released '88, on L&R Catalogue no: **LR 42.033**

**LIVING COUNTRY BLUES USA VOL 4 (Various artists)**
Note: Featuring: Tennessee Blues, Hammie Nixon etc.
**Album:** Released '88, on L&R Catalogue no: **LR 42.034**

**LIVING COUNTRY BLUES USA VOL 5 (Various artists)**
Note: Featuring: Mississippi Blues.
**Album:** Released '88, on L&R Catalogue no: **LR 42.035**

**LIVING COUNTRY BLUES USA VOL 6 (The road is rough & rocky) (Various artists)**
Note: Featuring: Archie Edwards from Washington DC.
**Album:** Released '88, on L&R Catalogue no: **LR 42.036**

**LIVING COUNTRY BLUES USA VOL 7 (Various artists)**
Note: Featuring: Afro American blues.
**Album:** Released '88, on L&R Catalogue no: **LR 42.037**

**LIVING COUNTRY BLUES USA VOL 8 (Lonesome home blues) (Various artists)**
Note: Featuring: Guitar Slim & Guitar Frank.
**Album:** Released '88, on L&R Catalogue no: **LR 42.038**

**LIVING COUNTRY BLUES USA VOL 9 (Mississippi moan) (Various artists)**
Note: Featuring: Boogie Bill etc.
**Album:** Released '88, on L&R Catalogue no: **LR 42.039**

**LIVING COUNTRY BLUES USA VOL 10 (Country boogie) (Various artists)**
Note: Featuring: Lottie Murrell etc.
**Album:** Released '88, on L&R Catalogue no: **LR 42.040**

**LIVING COUNTRY BLUES USA VOL 11 (Country gospel rock) (Various artists)**
**Album:** Released '88, on L&R Catalogue no: **LR 42.041**

**LIVING COUNTRY BLUES USA VOL 12 (East Coast blues) (Various artists)**
**Album:** Released '88, on L&R Catalogue no: **LR 42.042**

**LIVING COUNTRY BLUES USA VOL 13 (More country gospel rock) (Various artists)**
**Album:** Released '88, on L&R Catalogue no: **LR 42.043**

**LIVING COUNTRY BLUES (Bottle up & go) (Various artists)**
**Album:** Released '88, on L&R Catalogue no: **LR 42.044**

## Living New Orleans Jazz

**LIVING NEW ORLEANS JAZZ 1973 various artists (Various artists)**
**Album:** Released Apr '79, on Smokey Mary Deleted '84. Catalogue no: **SMOKEY MARY 1973T**

**LIVING NEW ORLEANS JAZZ 1974 various artists (Various artists)**
**Album:** Released Apr '79, on Smokey Mary Deleted '84. Catalogue no: **SMOKEY MARY 1974P**

## Lloyd, Charles

**DREAM WEAVER (Lloyd, Charles Quartet)**
Tracks: / Autumn sequence / Autumn prelude / Autumn leaves / Meditation / Dervish dance / Bird flight / Love ship / Sombrero Sam.
**Album:** on Atlantic by WEA Records. Catalogue no: **K 50300**

**FISH OUT OF WATER (Lloyd, Charles Quartet)**
Tracks: / Fish out of water / Haghia Sophia / Dirge, The / Bharti / Eyes of love / Mirror.
**Cass:** Released Jan '90, on ECM Catalogue no: **841 088 4**
**Album:** Released Jan '90, on ECM Catalogue no: **ECM 1398**
**CD:** Released Jan '90, on ECM Catalogue no: **841 088 2**

**NIGHT IN COPENHAGEN, A**
Tracks: / Lotus land (To Thakur & Trane) / Lady Day / El encanto / Third floor Richard / Night blooming Jasmine.
**Album:** Released Jul '89, on Blue Note by EMI Records. Catalogue no: **BT 85104**
**Album:** Released Jul '89, on Blue Note by EMI Records. Catalogue no: **785 104 1**

## Lloyd, Frank Harmonica

**FRANK LLOYD HARMONICA**
**Album:** Released May '81, on Adelphi (1) Catalogue no: **AD 1023**

## Loaded Down With Blues

**LOADED DOWN WITH THE BLUES (Various artists)**
Tracks: / Loaded down: *Various artists* / Tight like that: *Various artists* / Nervous condition: *Various artists* / I'm gonna make you eat them words: *Various artists* / Moanin' and screamin' (parts 1 & 2): *Various artists* / Ain't broke, ain't hungry: *Various artists* / Early morning blues: *Various artists* / Way in the middle of the night: *Various artists* / Bad luck and trouble: *Various artists* / Somebody's doin' me wrong: *Various artists* / (If I only had a) chance for your love: *Various artists* / It's a thing you gotta face: *Various artists* / What is life?: *Various artists* / Fooler, The: *Various artists*.
Note: Boogie Jake/Polka Dot Slim/Edgar Blanchard etc.
**Album:** Released Dec '87, on Charly R&B by Charly Records. Catalogue no: **CRB 1170**
**Cass:** Released Oct '88, on Charly R&B by Charly Records. Catalogue no: **TCCRB 1170**

## Locke, Joe

**RESTLESS DREAMS (Locke, Joe-Phil Markowitz Quartet)**
Tracks: / Restless dreams / My foolish heart / Kahalid the warrior / May moon (Phil Markowitz) / You and I / Calypso nouveau.
Note: Joe Locke on vibes, Phil Markowitz on piano, Eddie Gomez on bass, Keith Copeland on drums. Recorded in 1983. This is a pretty, acoustic album which will appeal to New Age as well as jazz fans. There are two original tunes by Joe, two by Phil and ballads by Victor Young and Stevie Wonder.
**CD:** Released Mar '89, on Chief Catalogue no: **CHIEFCD 1**

## Lockwood, Didier

**1.2.3.4.**
Tracks: / Stormy day / Have to find a way / Aquamarine / Criss cross / Cleo / Badiya / Elephant blues / Precious day / Senorita / Ending to begin / Elektroperc / Ave Maria / Music is the way / Et c'est / Pour ca / Que la terre / Est arree.
**2 LP Set:** Released Jan '88, on JMS (France) Catalogue no: **JMS 041**

**NEW WORLD**
**Album:** Released Nov '84, on JMS (France) Catalogue no: **JMS 034**
**Album:** Released Jun '81, on MPS Jazz Catalogue no: **MPS 68 237**

## Lockwood, Robert Jnr.

**BLUES LIVE IN JAPAN**
**Album:** Released Apr '79, on Advent by Advent Records. Catalogue no: **ADVENT 2807**

**HANGIN' ON**
**Album:** Released '88, on Rounder (USA) by Rounder Records (USA). Catalogue no: **ROUNDER 2023**

**MR BLUES IS BACK TO STAY**
**Album:** Released '88, on Rounder (USA) by Rounder Records (USA). Catalogue no: **ROUNDER 2026**

**STEADY ROLLIN' MAN**
**Album:** Released Dec '88, on Delmark (USA) by Delmark Records (USA). Catalogue no: **DL 630**
**Album:** Released '74, on Delmark (USA) by Delmark Records (USA). Catalogue no: **DS 630**

## Loften, Cripple

**CLARENCE'S BLUES (Lofton, Cripple Clarence)**
**Album:** Released '88, on Oldie Blues Catalogue no: **OL 2817**

**CRIPPLE CLARENCE LOFTEN & WALTER DAVIS**
**Album:** Released Dec '88, on Yazoo (USA) by Shanachie Records (USA). Catalogue no: **L 1025**

## Loissier, Jacques

**JACQUES LOISSIER PLAYS BACH**
**Cass:** Released Dec '89, on Accord (France) by Musidisc Records (France). Catalogue no: **556602**
**CD:** Released Dec '89, on Accord (France) by Musidisc Records (France). Catalogue no: **556604**

## Lomax, Alan

**MURDERERS HOME AND BLUES IN THE MISSISSIPPI NIGHT**
Tracks: / Road song / No more my Lord / Katy left Memphis / Old Alabama / Black woman / Jumpin' lady / Whoa back / Prettiest train / Old dollar mamie / It makes a long time man feel bad / Rosie / Leave camp roller / Early in the morning / Tangle eyes blues / Stackerlee / Prison blues / Sometimes I wonder / Bye bye baby / Blues in the Mississippi night.
**Album:** Released Jun '83, on Vogue Jazz (France) by Vogue Records. Catalogue no: **VJD 515**

**TEXAS FOLK SONGS**
Tracks: / Rambling gambler / I'm bound to follow the longhorn cows / Lord Lovel / Rich old lady, The / Long summer days / Ain't no more cane on this brazis / All the pretty little horses / Billy Barlow / Wild rippling water, The / Rattlesnake / Sam Bass / Dying cowboy, The / God almighty drag / Eradie / Black Betty / My little John Henry.
**Album:** Released May '88, on Arion by Arion Records (France). Catalogue no: **ARN 33690**
**Cass:** Released May '88, on Arion by Arion Records (France). Catalogue no: **ARN 433690**

## Lombardo, Guy

**ALL-TIME FAVOURITES**
**Cass:** Released Dec '88, on Capitol (Specials) Catalogue no: **4XL 9030**

**GUY LOMBARDO AND ROYAL CANADIANS 1950 (Lombardo, Guy/his Royal Canadians)**
**Album:** Released '88, on Hindsight Catalogue no: **HSR 187**

**UNCOLLECTED, THE**
**Album:** Released Apr '86, on Hindsight (UK) by Michele International Records. Catalogue no: **HUK 187**

## London Community ...

**CONVERSION (London Community Gospel Choir)**
Tracks: / Conversion / May day song for North Oxford.
**7" Single:** Released Dec '87, on RAK by EMI Records. Catalogue no: **RAK 502**

**FEEL THE SPIRIT (London Community Gospel Choir)**
Tracks: / All to Jesus / O happy day.
Note: On this new album we find a collection of the Choir's own material plus other songs which they have featured in concerts around Europe. Once again their album catches the energy and excitement that is associated with Black Gospel music but, more importantly, expected whenever you listen to the London Community Gospel Choir.
**Album:** Released Sep '86, on Myrrh by Word Records (UK). Catalogue no: **MYR R 1221**
**Cass:** Released Sep '86, on Myrrh by Word Records (UK). Catalogue no: **MYR C 1221**

**FILL MY CUP (London Community Gospel Choir)**
Tracks: / Filly my cup / Over flow.
**7" Single:** Released Feb '84, on Island by Island Records. Deleted '87. Catalogue no: **IS 148**
**12" Single:** Released Feb '84, on Island by Island Records. Deleted '87. Catalogue no: **12IS 148**

**GIVE A CHILD A CHANCE (London Community Gospel Choir)**
Tracks: / Give a child a chance.
**7" Single:** Released Nov '89, on London Ocean & Coastal by London Ocean & Coastal. Catalogue no: **LOC 2**

**GOSPEL GREATS (London Community Gospel Choir)**
Tracks: / Sing low, sweet chariot / Precious Lord, amazing grace / Nobody knows the trouble I've seen / What a friend we have in Jesus / Kumbaya / Count your blessings / Love lifted me / When the saints go marching in / There is a green hill far away / Oh happy day / Old rugged cross.
**Album:** Released Oct '85, on MFP by EMI Records. Deleted Nov '88. Catalogue no: **MFP 5731**
**Cass:** Released Oct '85, on MFP by EMI Records. Catalogue no: **TC MFP 5731**
**Album:** Released Oct '85, on MFP by EMI Records. Deleted Nov '88. Catalogue no: **MFP 4 15731 1**
**Cass:** Released Oct '85, on MFP by EMI Records. Catalogue no: **MFP 4 15731 4**

**SING THE GOSPEL GREATS (London Community Gospel Choir)**
Tracks: / Swing low, sweet chariot / Precious Lord / Amazing grace / Nobody knows the trouble I've seen / What a friend we have in Jesus / Kumbaya / Count your blessings / Love lifted me / When the saints go marching in / There is a green hill far away / Oh happy day / Old rugged cross, The.
**Album:** Released Oct '85, on MFP by EMI Records. Catalogue no: **41 5731 1**
**Cass:** Released Oct '85, on MFP by EMI Records. Catalogue no: **41 5731 4**

## London Ragtime Orch.

**GRACE & BEAUTY (London Ragtime Orchestra)**
**Album:** Released Jun '88, on GHB by Jazzology Records (USA). Catalogue no: **GHB 199**

**LONDON RAGTIME ORCHESTRA (London Ragtime Orchestra)**
**Album:** Released Jun '86, on Stomp Off (USA) Catalogue no: **SOS 1081**

## Lonesome Road Blues

**LONESOME ROAD BLUES 15 years in the delta (Various artists)**
**Album:** Released Dec '88, on Yazoo (USA) by Shanachie Records (USA). Catalogue no: **L 1038**

## Lonesome Sundown

**See under Green, Cornelius**

**BEEN GONE TOO LONG**
Tracks: / They call me sundown / One more night / Louisiana lover man / Dealin' from the bottom / Midnight blues again / Just got to know / Black cat bone / I betcha / You don't miss your water / If ain't been to Houston.
Note: The down home blues of Louisiana has a sound all of it's own. Distinguished by it's rolling instrumental work and warm, lazy but most expressive vocals it conveys its message with the minimum of histrionics and the maximum of impact. There are few better performers who epitomise this style so well as Cornelius Green - or as he's better known - Lonesome Sundown. This album marked his welcome return to recording after a long haitus. (Alligator catalogue 7/88)
**Album:** Released Apr '80, on Alligator (Sonet) by Alligator Records (USA). Catalogue no: **SNTF 832**

**FROM L.A. TO L.A. (Lonesome Sundown & Phillip Walker)**
**Cass:** Released '88, on Rounder (USA) by Rounder Records (USA). Catalogue no: **ROUNDER 2037C**
**Album:** Released '88, on Rounder (USA) by Rounder Records (USA). Catalogue no: **ROUNDER 2037**

**IF ANYBODY ASKS YOU MY HOME AIN'T HERE His best**
Tracks: / If anybody asks you (my home ain't here) / Blues for my baby (Lonely lonely me) / Opelousas blues / Things have changed / My home is a prison / You know I love you / I never thought / You give me all kinds of misery / Lonesome whistle / If you see my baby / Learn to treat me better / I've got a broken heart baby / I found an angel / I'll still be loving you.
**Album:** Released '88, on Flyright by Interstate Music. Catalogue no: **FLY 617**

**LONESOME SUNDOWN**
**CD:** Released Mar '90, on Flyright by Interstate Music. Catalogue no: **FLYCD16**
**Album:** Released Dec '87, on Excello (USA) Catalogue no: **LP 8012**

**LONESOME WHISTLER**
Tracks: / Don't say a word / I stood by /

California blues / Lonely lonely me / Give it up / Gonna stick to you baby / Lonesome whistle / Leave my money / My home is a prison / Lost without love / Mojo man / Don't go.
**Album:** Released Oct '86, on Flyright by Interstate Music. Catalogue no: **FLY 587**

## Long, Johnny

**1941: JOHNNY LONG (Long, Johnny & His Orchestra)**
**Album:** Released Aug '88, on Circle (USA) by Jazzology Records (USA). Catalogue no: **CLP 56**

## Loose Tubes

**DELIGHTFUL PRECIPICE**
Tracks: / Sad Afrika / Delightful precipice / Shelley / Sosbun Brakk / Sunny / Hermeto's giant breakfast / Would I were.
**Cass:** Released Oct '86, on Loose Tubes by Loose Tubes Records. Catalogue no: **LTMC 03**
**Album:** Released Oct '86, on Loose Tubes by Loose Tubes Records. Catalogue no: **LTLP 003**

**LOOSE TUBES**
Tracks: / Eden express / Rowing boat delineation egg / Descarge / Descarge occuriencia / Yellow hill / Mister Zee / Arriving.
Note: Debut album from Loose Tubes - the dynamic 21 piece band currently taking the UK by storm. The guys are all dedicated musicians involved in a variety of projects; from session work with major recording artists to work with their individual bands. Together they pool their diverse resources and make Loose Tubes a highly original statement.
**Album:** Released Feb '86, on Loose Tubes by Loose Tubes Records. Catalogue no: **LTLP 001**

**OPEN LETTER**
Tracks: / Sweet Williams / Children's game / Blue / Sticklebacks / Excepting suites from strangers / Last word, The / A / Open letter to Dudu Pukwana / Shadow play (CD & cassette only) / Mo Mhutrnin Ban (CD & cassette only).
Note: This is the third album from Loose Tubes who are an exciting twenty one piece jazz group.This album has been produced by Teo Macero,the legendary producer known for his work with Miles Davis,Duke Ellington & Charles Mingus.
**CD:** Released 7 Mar '88, on Editions EG by E.G. Records. Catalogue no: **EEGCD 55**
**Cass:** Released 7 Mar '88, on Editions EG by E.G. Records. Catalogue no: **EGEDC 55**
**Album:** Released 7 Mar '88, on Editions EG by E.G. Records. Catalogue no: **EGED 55**

## Los Angeles Jazz Workshop

**SHOPWORK SHUFFLE (Los Angeles Jazz Workshop)**
Tracks: / Where have you gone / Angel eyes / Goodbye pork-pie hat / Mickey's revenge / Greazy rider.
**Album:** Released '88, on Am-Pm (USA) Catalogue no: **AM 16**

## Loss, Joe

**Biographical details:** This British bandleader was hailed as the most tenacious and longest-lasting person in his field when, in 1980, he celebrated his 50th year as an orchestra leader. He was never an innovative man, but his skill lay in his ability to adapt to the changing challenges of each new musical era. His band's function was to play the hits of the day for the benefit of radio listeners, record buyers and concert-goers. During the first half of the Sixties, Loss chalked up five hit singles on the UK pop charts. The classic *Wheels cha cha* reached No.21 in 1961, and logged an impressive total of 21 weeks on the Top 50. His other chart entries included *Sucu sucu*, the *Maigret* theme and *Must be Madison*. The fifth and final one was *March of the Mods*, which reached No.31 at the end of 1964 - this was the venerable bandleader's bow to one of Britain's leading youth cults of the era, although he probably had no wish to be associated with the beach hooliganism which sometimes tainted the Mods' reputation! In addition to the aforementioned singles, Loss also had two chart EP's and one chart album to his credit. (Bob MacDonald, 18th Dec 1985).

**50 BIG BAND FAVOURITES (Loss, Joe/Parnell, Jack)**
**Cass set:** Released Oct '84, on Trio by EMI Records. Deleted Oct '88. Catalogue no: **TR 4115305**
**Cass set:** Released Oct '84, on Trio by EMI Records. Deleted Oct '88. Catalogue no: **MFP 411 530 5**
**Cass set:** Released Oct '84, on Trio by EMI Records. Deleted Oct '88. Catalogue no: **TR 1530**

**50 FABULOUS YEARS**
Tracks: / Let's dance at the make believe ballroom / Begin the beguine / At the woodchopper's ball / In the mood / Amapola / Donkey serenade / Wheels cha-cha / Maigret / Must be Maidson / March of the mods / I'm looking over a four leaf clover / When the red, red robin comes bob, bob, bobbin' along / Applause / Congratulations.
**Cass:** Released Nov '80, on Note by EMI Records. Deleted Oct '89. Catalogue no: **TCNTS 217**
**Album:** Released Nov '80, on Note by EMI Records. Deleted Oct '89. Catalogue no: **NTS 217**

**ALL TIME PARTY HITS**
**Album:** Released Oct '71, on MFP by EMI Records. Deleted Oct '76. Catalogue no: **MFP 5227**

**AN HOUR OF SWING (Loss, Joe & His Orchestra)**
Tracks: / At the woodchopper's ball / I'm getting sentimental over you / Stompin' at the Savoy / You made me love you / One o'clock jump / Take the 'A' train / Skyliner / Solitude / Don't be that way / Song of India / Begin the beguine / Trumpet blues and cantabile / Girl from Ipanema / Desafinado / Killing me softly with his song / Sheik of Araby, The / Five foot two, eyes of blue / It had to be you / Anvil chorus / Perfidia.
**CD:** Released Sep '89, on Compacts For Pleasure by Music For Pleasure Records. Catalogue no: **CDB 792 190 2**
**Cass:** Released Mar '89, on Hour Of Pleasure by EMI Records. Catalogue no: **HR 8178**
**CD:** Released Sep '89, on Compacts For Pleasure by Music For Pleasure Records. Catalogue no: **CC 249**

**BEGIN THE BEGUINE (Loss, Joe & His Orchestra)**
Tracks: / Begin the beguine / Change partners / Maria Elena / Please be kind / Heart and soul / So rare / I know now / Cinderella (stay in my arms) / My prayer / Scene changes, The / In the chapel in the moonlight / Sweet Sue / Little Sir Echo / I never knew heaven could speak / Are you having any fun / Wish me luck (as you wave me goodbye).
**Album:** Released Mar '84, on Retrospect by EMI Records. Deleted '89. Catalogue no: **SH 430**

**BEST OF LATIN**
Tracks: / La cumparsita / Jealousy / wheels (Cha cha) / Tea for two (Cha cha) / Quando caliente el sol / Girl from Ipanema / Soul bossa nova / Best thing for you is me,The (Bossa nova) / Tequila / Spanish gypsy dance (Paso doble) / March of the Matadors (Paso doble) / Roberta (Rumba) / La bamba / Guantanamera / Brazil / Copacabana / Banda,A / Manolet (Merengue).
Note: Featuring the best of the tangos, the cha cha, the samba, the rumbas, the paso dobles etc. for ballroom dancing, including 3 tracks with vocals by Ross McManus father of Elvis Costello. This compilation, personally selected by Joe Loss could truly be described as 'The Best Of Latin'.
**Cass:** Released Dec '85, on EMI by EMI Records. Catalogue no: **EG 2607594**
**Album:** Released Nov '85, on EMI by EMI Records. Catalogue no: **EG 2607591**

**GOLDEN AGE OF JOE LOSS, THE**
Tracks: / Over my shoulder / Madame - ah la marquise - ah / Scene changes, The / Let's dance at the make believe ballroom / Sweet Sue / Boo hoo / So rare / Please be kind / I'm gonna lock my heart / Change partners / Latin quarter, The / Little Sir Echo / Boomps a daisy / Are you havin' any fun / At the woodchopper's ball / In the mood.
**Cass:** Released Apr '85, on Golden Age by EMI Records. Catalogue no: **GX 41 2529 4**
**Album:** Released Apr '85, on Golden Age by EMI Records. Catalogue no: **GX41 2529 1**

**HITS OF 1940, THE**
Tracks: / Are you having any fun? / Oh Johnny, Oh Johnny / Good morning

(From the film "Babes In Arms".) / Where and when (From the film "Babes In Arms".) / In the mood / It's a hap-hap-happy day / At the woodchoppers ball / Gaucho serenade / Let the people sing / When you wish upon a star (From the film "Pinocchio".) / You made me care (Vocal by Chick Henderson.) / Let the curtain come down / Woodpecker song / I've got my eyes on you (Vocal by Paula Green.) / Honky tonk train blues / I'll never smile again / Breeze and I, The (Vocal by Cyril Grantham.,) / I'm nobody's baby (Vocal by Paula Greene.) / Six lessons from Madame Le Zonga (Vocal by Paula Greene.) / All the things that you are (Vocal by Paula Greene.).
Note: Includes medley - Joe Loss At The Empire Edinburgh: Part 1; Let's dance at the make believe ballroom/In the mood/Punchinello (Joe Loss, The Orchestra and Monte Rey. Part 2; At the woodchoppers ball/A nightingale sang in Berkley Square/Post horn gallop (Joe Loss, The Orchestra, Paula Greene and Billy Burton). Part 3; Community singing - Ain't she sweet/Beer barrel polka/In ther quartermasters store/The music goes round (Dance orchestra with vocal) Part 4; Annie Laurie/The donkey serenade (Joe Loss, The orchestra/Monte Rey and The Loss Chords.
**Cass:** Released May '90, on Retrospect by EMI Records. Catalogue no: **TCSH 517**
**Album:** Released May '90, on Retrospect by EMI Records. Catalogue no: **SH 517**
**CD:** Released May '90, on Retrospect by EMI Records. Catalogue no: **CZ 294**
**Album:** Released May '90, on Retrospect by EMI Records. Catalogue no: **794 335 1**
**Cass:** Released May '90, on Retrospect by EMI Records. Catalogue no: **794 334 4**
**CD:** Released May '90, on Retrospect by EMI Records. Catalogue no: **CDP 794 334 2**

**IN A ROMANTIC MOOD (Loss, Joe, Big Band & Orchestra)**
Tracks: / Begin the beguine / Song from Moulin Rouge / Sugar blues / April in Portugal / Ciribiribin / Summer Place, A theme from / Oh mein papa / Stranger on the shore / Humoresque / Stardust / Everything's coming up roses / I left my heart in San Francisco / Belle of the ball / On the street where you live / Fascination / Sweetie / Wheels / Can't take my eyes off you / Swingin' samba / March of the matadors / A banda / Do you know the way to San Jose? / Tequila.
**CD:** Released Oct '87, on EMI by EMI Records. Deleted Aug '89. Catalogue no: **CZ 26**
**CD:** Released Oct '87, on EMI by EMI Records. Catalogue no: **CDP 746 930 2**
**Album:** Released Oct '87, on EMI by EMI Records. Deleted '88. Catalogue no: **EMS 1260**
**CD:** Released Oct '87, on EMI by EMI Records. Catalogue no: **CDEMS 1260**
**Cass:** Released Aug '88, on EMI by EMI Records. Catalogue no: **TCEMS 1260**

**IN THE MOOD WITH JOE (Loss, Joe & His Orchestra)**
Tracks: / In the mood / Daddy / That lovely weekend / Fur trapper's ball / You made me care / Five o'clock whistle / Fan it / For all that I care / Yeah man / Sweet little sweetheart / No mama no / Cornsilk / Six lessons from Madame La Zonga / Memories live longer than dreams / Cow cow boogie / If I should fall in love again / Amapola / Let the curtain come down.
**Album:** Released Nov '85, on President by President Records. Catalogue no: **PLE 522**
**Cass:** Released Nov '85, on President by President Records. Catalogue no: **TC-PLE 522**

**ISN'T IT HEAVENLY (Loss, Joe & his band)**
Tracks: / Smoke gets in your eyes / In other words we're through / When the new moon shines / I love you truly / Let's fall in love / La cucaracha / There's a ring around the Moon / For you madonna / Stars fell on Alabama / Soon / Tina / One morning in May / Isn't it heavenly / Don't forget(1933 version) / Ending with a kiss / General's fast asleep, The / Continental, The / Under a blanket of blue.
Note: Produced, Re-mastered, Compiled & Transferred by Colin Brown
**Album:** Released Jun '86, on Conifer Happy Days Catalogue no: **CHD 128**

**JOE LOSS PLAYS GLENN MILLER**
Tracks: / Moonlight Serenade / American patrol / At last / I've got a gal in Kalamazoo / Pennsylvania 6-5000 / Little brown jug / In the mood / Adios / Moonlight Cocktail / Jersey bounce / Tuxedo Junction / I know why / String of pearls / Serenade in blue / St. Louis blues / Chattanooga choo choo / Bugle call rag / Frenesi / Elmer's tune / My guy's come back.
**Cass:** Released May '86, on Hour Of Pleasure by EMI Records. Catalogue no: **HR 8116**
**CD:** Released Sep '88, on Compacts For Pleasure by Music For Pleasure Records. Catalogue no: **CC 229**
**Cass:** Released May '86, on Hour Of Pleasure by EMI Records. Catalogue no: **HR 4181164**
**CD:** Released Sep '88, on Compacts For Pleasure by Music For Pleasure Records. Deleted Aug '89. Catalogue no: **CDB 906532**

**LET'S DANCE AT THE MAKE-BELIEVE BALLROOM 1934-1940 (Loss, Joe Band)**
**2 LP Set:** Released Oct '77, on Retrospect by EMI Records. Catalogue no: **SHB 46**

**MAIGRET THEME**
Tracks: / Maigret theme.
**7" Single:** Released Mar '62, on H.M.V. by EMI Records. Deleted '65. Catalogue no: **POP 995**

**MARCH OF THE MODS (Loss, Joe Orchestra)**
Tracks: / March of the mods.
**7" Single:** Released Oct '64, on H.M.V. by EMI Records. Catalogue no: **POP 1351**

**MARCH OF THE MODS (FINJENKA)**
Tracks: / March of the mods (Finjenka dance) / Tango '65.
**7" Single:** Released Nov '89, on EMI by EMI Records. Catalogue no: **EM 122**
**7" Single:** Released Nov '89, on EMI by EMI Records. Catalogue no: **203 621 7**

**MUST BE MADISON**
Tracks: / Must be Madison.
**7" Single:** Released Nov '62, on H.M.V. by EMI Records. Deleted '65. Catalogue no: **POP 1075**

**NEW WORLD CHAMPIONSHIP BALLROOM DANCES (Loss, Joe & His Orchestra)**
Tracks: / Let's keep dancing / We make music / Woman in love / Even now / Deerhunter / Blue danube / YMCA / Chiquitita / In the navy / Summer nights / We don't talk anymore / Rivers of Babylon / Too much love / Madrid.
**Album:** Released Nov '75, on Columbia by EMI Records. Deleted '84. Catalogue no: **SCX 6625**

**OVER MY SHOULDER**
Tracks: / I've got my love to keep me warm / Head over heels in love / Caravan / I know now / Raindrops / Ev'rything you do / Boo hoo / For you madonna / At the balalaika / Over my shoulder / September in the rain / Toy trumpet, The / May I have the next romance with you / What will I tell my heart / When the poppies bloom again / When you've got a little springtime / Love bug will bite you, The / This years kisses.
**Album:** Released Jun '88, on Burlington (nostalgia) by Counterpoint Distribution. Catalogue no: **BUR 004**
**CD:** Released Sep '88, on Burlington (nostalgia) by Counterpoint Distribution. Catalogue no: **2 BUR 004**
**Cass:** Released Jul '88, on Burlington (nostalgia) by Counterpoint Distribution. Catalogue no: **4BUR 004**

**PARTY DANCE TIME (Loss, Joe & His Orchestra)**
Tracks: / Cole porter medley / Irving berlin medleys / In a little spanish town / Irish lullaby / When you and i were seventeen / Apple blossom time / exicali rose / Little sir echo.
**Album:** Released Mar '84, on Retrospect by EMI Records. Deleted Jan '90. Catalogue no: **SH 107 825 1**
**Cass:** Released Mar '84, on Retrospect by EMI Records. Deleted Jan '90. Catalogue no: **TCSH 107 859 4**

**PLAYS YOUR ALL TIME PARTY HITS (Loss, Joe & His Orchestra)**
**2 LP Set:** Released Sep '81, on MFP by EMI Records. Deleted Sep '86. Catalogue no: **MFP 1009**
**Cass set:** Released Sep '81, on MFP by EMI Records. Deleted Sep '86. Catalogue no: **TCMFP 1009**

**REMEMBER ME? (Loss, Joe & His Orchestra)**
Tracks: / There's a new world / Nice cup of tea, A / With plenty of money and you / Home town / Ramona / Diane / Charmaine / Felix kept on walking / Sheik of Araby, The / My blue Heaven / Remember me? / Lullaby of Broadway / Tiptoe through the tulips / If I had a talking picture of you / I double dare you / All by yourself in the moonlight / Horsey, keep your tail up / Poor little Angeline / You're an education / Cry, baby, cry / Penny serenade / You go to my head / Chestnut tree, The / And the angels sing / Boom (Why does my heart go-) / Oh, you crazy moon / Scatterbrain / Oh Johnny, oh Johnny oh.
Note: Compiled and transferred by Chris Ellis
**Cass:** Released Oct '86, on Retrospect by EMI Records. Deleted Nov '88. Catalogue no: **TC-SH 506**
**Album:** Released Sep '86, on Retrospect by EMI Records. Deleted Nov '88. Catalogue no: **SH 506**

**SUCU SUCU**
Tracks: / Sucu sucu.
**7" Single:** Released Oct '61, on H.M.V. by EMI Records. Deleted '64. Catalogue no: **POP 937**

**WHEELS CHA CHA (Loss, Joe Orchestra)**
Tracks: / Wheels cha cha.
**7" Single:** Released May '61, on H.M.V. by EMI Records. Catalogue no: **POP 880**

**WORLD CHAMPIONSHIP BALLROOM DANCES (Loss, Joe & His Orchestra)**
Tracks: / Dream / I only have eyes for you / Jealousy / Singin' in the rain / We make music / Toreando / Fascination / C-n't help falling in love / Brazil / Something tells me / Mama mia / Music to watch girls by / Cavatina / Forever and ever / Waltz is for dancing, A / Save your kisses for me / Don't it make my brown eyes blue / Till / Don't cry for me Argentina / Sunrise sunset / Mull of Kintyre / Spanish gypsy dance / Fernando / Tea for two / Copacabana / Rivers of Babylon / Guantanamera / Is this the way to Amarillo / What's happened to Broadway / I'd like to teach the world to sing / My resistance is low / How deep is your love.
**2 LP Set:** Released Mar '89, on MFP by EMI Records. Catalogue no: **DL 1146**
**Cass:** Released Mar '89, on MFP by EMI Records. Catalogue no: **TCDL 1146**

## Louis, 'Big' Joe

**BIG JOE LOUIS AND HIS BLUES KINGS (Louis, 'Big' Joe & His Blues Kings)**
Tracks: / What's the matter with you / Now she's gone / You can't live long / I cried last night / I think you need a shot / Bloody tears / Down home blues / Monkey motion / These young girls / Hey hey now baby / She felt too good / Mean old Frisco blues.
**Album:** Released 2 May '89, on Blue Horizon by Ace Records. Catalogue no: **BLUH 008**

## Louisiana ...

**LOUISIANA HIGH SCHOOL HOP (Various artists)**
**Album:** Released Jan '89, on Flyright by Interstate Music. Catalogue no: **FLY 616**

**LOUISIANA R & B (Various artists)**
Tracks: / Life problem: *Various artists* / Sick & tired: *Various artists* / Don't touch me, baby: *Various artists* / Humpty dumpty heart: *Various artists* / Crawl: *Various artists* / Shed so many tears: *Various artists* / I'm gonna have to pass: *Various artists* / I've been your fool: *Various artists* / Nobody knows: *Various artists* / Help me forget her: *Various artists* / My life is a lonely one: *Various artists* / Mexican shoeshine boy: *Various artists* / Let's stick together: *Various artists* / Drifting cloud: *Various artists.*
**Album:** Released Jul '83, on Red Pepper by Interstate Music. Catalogue no: **RP 702**

**LOUISIANA SOUTHERN SOUL Various artists (Various artists)**
**Album:** Released Jul '85, on Krazy Kat by Interstate Music. Catalogue no: **KK 791**

## Louisiana Blues

**BLUESSCENE USA**
**Album:** Released '88, on Storyville by Storyville Records AB. Catalogue no: **SLP 177**

**LOUISIANA BLUES (Various artists)**
**Album:** Released May '81, on Arhoolie (USA) by Arhoolie Records (USA). Catalogue no: **ARHOOLIE 1054**

## Louisiana (Film)

**LOUISIANA (Original soundtrack)**
**Album:** Released May '84, on CBS (import) by CBS Records. Catalogue no: **CBS 71127**
**Cass:** Released May '84, on CBS (import) by CBS Records. Catalogue no: **40 71127**

## Louisiana Red

**ANTI-NUCLEAR BLUES**
**Album:** Released '88, on L&R Catalogue no: **LR 42.045**

**BACK TO THE ROOTS September 1987**
**Album:** Released May '88, on Schubert Catalogue no: **SCH 101**

**BLUES FOR IDA B.**
Note: Last USA JSP session, Chicago.
**CD:** Released Jan '88, on JSP by JSP Records. Catalogue no: **JSP CD 209**

**BLUES FROM THE HEART**
Tracks: / Blues for Ida B / This little letter / Nothing but the blues / I wonder why / Grease me baby / Love me true / Love me mama.
**Album:** Released Jan '83, on JSP by JSP Records. Catalogue no: **JSP 1053**

**BLUES MAN**
Tracks: / Little boy / Nothing but a gypsy man / Chicken lickin' / Sittin' here looking / If I had a dollar / Sweet Elesse / Whole world / Ride on.
**Album:** Released Jun '84, on JSP by JSP Records. Catalogue no: **JSP 1073**

**BOY FROM BLACK BAYOU (Louisiana Red & His Chicago Friends)**
**Album:** Released '88, on L&R Catalogue no: **LR 42.055**

**HOT SAUCE**
Tracks: / Lightnin' bug / Alabama train / You're gonna need me, baby / Trouble all my days / Ride on, red, ride on / Whose ol' funky drawers is these / Wo-ho-ho baby / 'Let these' blues / Sometimes I wonder / Gonna move on down the line.
**Album:** Released Jul '87, on Red Lightnin' by Red Lightning Records. Catalogue no: **RL 071**
**Cass:** Released Jul '88, on Red Lightnin' by Red Lightning Records. Catalogue no: **CRL 0071**

**LOWDOWN BACK PORCH BLUES**
**Album:** Released Mar '84, on Vogue by Vogue Records. Catalogue no: **522 004**
**CD:** Released Jun '88, on Vogue by Vogue Records. Catalogue no: **VGCD 600184**

**MIDNIGHT RAMBLER**
**CD:** Released May '88, on Tomato (USA) by Tomato Music Co. (USA). Catalogue no: **269 607 2**

**MY LIFE WITH CAREY BELL (Louisiana Red & Carey Bell)**
**Album:** Released '88, on L&R Catalogue no: **LR 42.061**

**NEW YORK BLUES**
**Album:** Released '88, on L&R Catalogue no: **LR 42.002**

**REALITY BLUES**
**Album:** Released '88, on L&R Catalogue no: **LR 42.011**

**RED FUNK 'N' GREEN (Louisiana Red/Sugar Blue)**
**Album:** Released Apr '79, on Black Panther by Black Panther Records. Catalogue no: **BP 1001**

## Louisiana Repertory...

**HOT & SWEET SOUNDS OF LOST NEW ORLEANS (Louisiana Repertory Jazz Ensemble)**
**CD:** Released Jan '88, on Stomp Off (USA) Catalogue no: **SOSCD 1140**
**Album:** Released Jan '88, on Stomp Off (USA) Catalogue no: **SOS 1140**

**LIVE & WELL (Louisiana Repertory Jazz Ensemble)**
**Album:** Released '88, on Stomp Off (USA) Catalogue no: **SOS 1029**

**LOUISIANA REPERTORY JAZZ (Louisiana Repertory Jazz Ensemble)**
**Album:** Released '88, on Stomp Off (USA) Catalogue no: **SOS 1055**

## Louisiana Swamp Blues

**LOUISIANA SWAMP BLUES (Various artists)**
Tracks: / I'm a king bee: *Harpo, Slim* / I hope you come back home: *Guy, Buddy* / I'm warning you baby: *Lightning Slim* / Gonna stick to you baby: *Lonesome Sundown* / I'm a lover not a fighter: *Lazy Lester* / Sugar coated love: *Lazy Lester* / Baby baby: *Webster, Katie/Ashton Savoy* / Naggin': *Anderson, Jimmy* / Alimonia blues: *Johnson, Joe* / Mumblin' blues: *Garlow, Clarence* / Early in the morning: *Boogie Jake* / My baby walked out: *Hogan, Silas* / Baby left me this morning: *Smith, Whispering* / Hey Mattie: *Mr. Calhoun* / Early one morning: *Harris, Rambling Hi* / Wild cherry: *Washington, Leroy* / Hoodoo party: *Thomas, Tabby* / Midnight dream: *Gray, Henry* / Little queen bee: *Harpo, Slim*.
**CD:** Released 10 Jul '89, on Flyright by Interstate Music. Catalogue no: **FLYCD 09**

## Lou's Blues Revenue

**COME OUT AND PLAY**
**Cass:** Released Sep '88, on WRC Catalogue no: **ZCWIL 3006**
**Album:** Released Sep '88, on WRC Catalogue no: **WIL 3006**

## Loussier, Jacques

**FOCUS ON JACQUES LOUSSIER**
**2 LP Set:** Released Sep '75, on Decca by Decca International. Deleted '88. Catalogue no: **FOS R 5-6**

**JACQUES LOUSSIER (VIDEO)**
Note: Running time: 60 mins.
**VHS:** Released '88, on Channel 5 by Channel 5 Video. Catalogue no: **CFV 07662**

**KEEP LOVE ALIVE (Loussier, Jacques and Harry Secombe)**
Tracks: / Keep love alive / Whispering hope.
**7" Single:** Released Nov '82, on Starblend by Starblend Records. Catalogue no: **STAR 1**

**PAGAN MOON**
Tracks: / Night riders / Furies / Moonchild / Invaders / Phantom lady / Nocturnal sea / Enchantress / Dawn.
**Album:** Released Aug '82, on CBS by CBS Records. Deleted Jan '88. Catalogue no: **CBS 85850**

**PULSION**
Tracks: / Pulsion / Soupir / Distraction / Cafeine / Mozart / Ludwig / Murmure / Secousse.
**Album:** Released Jul '81, on CBS by CBS Records. Deleted '86. Catalogue no: **CBS 84994**
**Album:** Released Mar '80, on CBS by CBS Records. Deleted '85. Catalogue no: **CBS 84179**

## Love, Clayton

**COME ON HOME BLUES**
Tracks: / Blues come home / Big question, The / Chains of love / Worried life blues / Just like a woman / St. Louis blues / Tore up / Key to the highway.
**Album:** Released Sep '82, on Red Lightnin' by Red Lightning Records. Catalogue no: **RL 0029**

## Lowdown Memphis...

**LOWDOWN MEMPHIS HARMONICA JAM (1950-1955 recordings) (Various artists)**
**Album:** Released Apr '79, on Nighthawk by Nighthawk Records (USA). Catalogue no: **NH 103**

## Lowe, Mundell

**GUITAR MOODS**
Tracks: / Speak low / We'll be together again / Memories of you / Ill wind / You don't know what love is / I dream too much / June in January / I'll take romance / It's so peaceful in the country / Our waltz / I'm old fashioned / Goodbye.
**Album:** Released Feb '88, on Riverside (USA) by Fantasy Inc (USA). Catalogue no: **RLP 208**

**PORGY AND BESS (Lowe, Mundell Jazzmen)**
**Album:** Released '83, on RCA (France) by BMG Records (France). Catalogue no: **PL 43552**

**TV ACTION JAZZ (Lowe, Mundell All Stars)**
**Album:** Released Feb '88, on Fresh Sounds (Spain) by Fresh Sounds Records (Spain). Catalogue no: **FS 179**

## L&R Blues Sampler

**L AND R BLUES SAMPLER (Various artists)**
Note: Featuring: Louisiana Red, J.B.Lenoir, Eddie Taylor etc.
**Album:** Released '88, on L&R Catalogue no: **LR 42.006**

## Lucas, Matt

**RIDE THAT TRAIN TONIGHT (17 tracks recorded 1959-65 and 1970-75)**
Tracks: / Ooby dooby / Put me down / My heavenly angel / Water mocccasin / Maybellene / Tradin' kisses / No one like you / Turn on your lovelight / I'm movin' on / Motor city twine, The / Massage parlour blues / I'm so thankful / Zoo blues / You gotta love / Newspaper man blues / Peepin' Tom blues / I need your lovin'.
**Album:** Released Aug '83, on Charly by Charly Records. Catalogue no: **CR 30222**

## Lucraft, Howard

**SHOWCASE FOR MODERN JAZZ**
**Album:** Released Feb '88, on Fresh Sounds (Spain) by Fresh Sounds Records (Spain). Catalogue no: **FS 230**

## Lunceford, Jimmie

**1940: JIMMIE LUNCEFORD (Lunceford, Jimmie & Orchestra)**
**Album:** Released Aug '88, on Circle (USA) by Jazzology Records (USA). Catalogue no: **CLP 11**

**1944: JIMMIE LUNCEFORD (Lunceford, Jimmie & Orchestra)**
**Album:** Released Aug '88, on Circle (USA) by Jazzology Records (USA). Catalogue no: **CLP 92**

**COMPLETE, THE**
Note: 4 L.P. set.
**Album:** Released Jun '86, on CBS (import) by CBS Records. Catalogue no: **66421**

**FOR DANCERS ONLY (Lunceford, Jimmie & Orchestra)**
Tracks: / Close out / Margie / Sit back and relax / Jimmies, The / Four or five times / Call the police / Water faucet / Cement mixer / Them who has gets / Shut out / Jay Gee / I need a lift / Just once too often / One o'clock jump.
**Album:** on Official by Official Records. Catalogue no: **OFF 3043**

**GOLDEN SWING YEARS, (THE) (Lunceford, Jimmie/his orchestra)**
**Album:** Released Jul '81, on Storyville by Storyville Records AB. Catalogue no: **SLP 828**

**HARLEM SHOUT (Lunceford, Jimmie & Orchestra)**
**Album:** Released '88, on Hep Jazz by Hep Records. Catalogue no: **HEP 1022**

**JIMMIE LUNCEFORD AND HIS (1935-41) (Lunceford, Jimmie and Orchestra)**
Tracks: / Impromptu / By the river Sainte Marie (Vocal:Dan Grissom) / Stratosphere / Annie Laurie / Swanee River / Yard dog Mazurka / Hell's bells / Hi spook / Margie (Vocal: Johnny Young) / Pigeon walk / My blue Heaven / Siesta at the Fiesta.
**Album:** Released '86, on Jasmine by Hasmick Promotions. Deleted Feb '88. Catalogue no: **JASM 1023**
**Cass:** Released '82, on Jazz Bird Catalogue no: **ZCJAZ 2013**
**Album:** Released '82, on Jazz Bird Catalogue no: **JAZ 2013**

**JIMMIE LUNCEFORD & HIS ORCHESTRA (Lunceford, Jimmie and his orchestra)**
**CD:** Released '88, on Delta (1) by Delta Records. Catalogue no: **11 088**

**JIMMIE LUNCEFORD & LOUIS PRIMA (Lunceford, Jimmie/Prima, Louis)**
Tracks: / Jeep rhythm / Blues in the night / What to do / Are you kidding baby? / Meditation from Thais / Honeydripper / Robin Hood / Don't ever change / Angelina / St Louis blues / I wonder / Hitsum kitsum.
**Album:** Released Apr '79, on Aircheck (USA) by Kiner Ents.(USA). Catalogue no: **AIRCHECK 8**

**JIMMIE LUNCEFORD AND ORCHESTRA 1935-45**
Note: with Sy Oliver etc.
**Album:** Released Jan '88, on Swingfan Catalogue no: **SWINGFAN 1009**

**JIMMIE LUNCEFORD VOLUME 1**
**Album:** Released Aug '81, on Kings Of Jazz Catalogue no: **KLJ 20016**

**JIMMIE LUNCEFORD VOLUME 2 (Lunceford, Jimmie/his orchestra)**

Tracks: / Impromptu / By the river Sainte Marie / Stratosphere / Annie Laurie / Swanee river / Yard dog Mazurka / Hell's bells / Hi spook / Margie / Pigeon walk / My blue Heaven / Siesta at the fiesta.
**Album:** Released Mar '87, on Hep Jazz by Hep Records. Catalogue no: **HEP 1013**

**JIMMIE LUNCEFORD-VOLUME 1 1934 (Lunceford, Jimmie & Orchestra)**
Note: Mono.
**Album:** Released Nov '86, on Hep Jazz by Hep Records. Catalogue no: **HEP 1011**

**LITTLE JOHN (1945)**
**Album:** Released Dec '77, on First Heard by Submarine Records. Catalogue no: **FH 15**

**MASTERPIECES (Lunceford, Jimmie & Orchestra)**
Note: Featuring Trummy Young, Sy Oliver, Willie Smith, Paul Webster.
**Album:** Released Sep '87, on Giants of Jazz by Hasmick Promotions. Catalogue no: **LPJT 22**

**NO TITLE ON FILE (Lunceford, Jimmie Orchestra)**
**Album:** Released Apr '81, on Jazz Live (Italy) Catalogue no: **BLJ 8006**

**OH BOY (Lunceford, Jimmie and Orchestra)**
Tracks: / Miss Otis regrets (she's unable to lunch today / Because you're you / Chillun, get up / Shake your head (from side to side) / If I had rain / Rhythm in my nursery rhymes / Since my best gal turned me down / Charmaine / Babs / I'm nuts about screw music / Best things in life are free, The / On the beach at Bali-Bali / Oh boy / Melody man, The / Muddy water (A Mississippi moan) / You take the east,.. I'll take the south.
**Album:** Released Dec '87, on Conifer Happy Days Catalogue no: **CHD 132**
**Album:** Released '88, on Hep Jazz by Hep Records. Catalogue no: **HEP 1017**
**Cass:** Released Dec '87, on Conifer Happy Days by Conifer Records. Catalogue no: **MCHD 132**

**RUNNIN' A TEMPERATURE**
Tracks: / Runnin' a temperature / Bird of paradise / Mood indigo / My melancholy baby / Yard dog mazurka / Coquette / Harlem shout / Unsophisticated Sue / Knock me a kiss / Stratosphere / Hittin' the bottle / Black and tan fantasy / Love nest, The / Sleepy time gal / Runnin' wild / Sweet Sue / Avalon / Posin'.
**Cass:** Released Sep '86, on Affinity by Charly Records. Catalogue no: **TCAFS 1033**
**Album:** Released Oct '86, on Affinity by Charly Records. Catalogue no: **AFS 1033**

**STRICTLY LUNCEFORD (Big Band Bounce and Boogie) (Lunceford, Jimmie Orchestra)**
Tracks: / Strictly Lunceford / My blue Heaven / Organ grinder's swing / Rhythm is our business / Sophisticated lady / Four or five times / I'm gonna move to the outskirts of town / For dancers only / Twenty four robbers / Swanee river / Blue prelude / Blues in the night (parts 1 & 2) / Annie Laurie / Down by the old mill stream / Back door stuff (parts 1 & 2) / Margie / Siesta at the fiesta.
**Album:** Released Sep '83, on Affinity by Charly Records. Catalogue no: **AFS 1003**

**SWING GOES ON VOL. 7**
**Album:** Released '83, on EMI (Germany) by EMI Records. Catalogue no: **IC 054 52716**

**'TAIN'T WHAT YOU DO**
**Cass:** Released Sep '85, on Saar Giants Of Jazz (Italy) Catalogue no: **MCJT 22**
**Album:** Released Sep '85, on Saar Giants Of Jazz (Italy) Catalogue no: **LPJT 22**

**TAKIN' OFF WITH JIMMIE**
**Album:** Released '88, on Tax Catalogue no: **M 8003**

## Lundstrem, Oleg

**IN SWING TIME (Lundstrem, Oleg and His Orchestra)**
**CD:** Released '88, on Mobile Fidelity Sound Lab(USA) by Mobile Fidelity Records (USA). Catalogue no: **MFCD 881**

## Lusher, Don

**DON LUSHER BIG BAND (Lusher, Don Big Band)**
Tracks: / Cavatina / Blues in the night / D.L. blues / Georgia / Gospel singers / I loves you, Porgy / Send in the clowns / Stardust / Star wars / That's living / Toreador song.
**Album:** Released Aug '81, on Chandos by Chandos Records. Catalogue no: **BBR 1006**
**Cass:** Released Aug '81, on Chandos by Chandos Records. Catalogue no: **BBT 1006**

**DON LUSHER BIG BAND VOL. 1**
**CD:** Released May '89, on Horatio Nelson by Horatio Nelson Records & Tapes Ltd.. Catalogue no: **CDSIV 110**

**DON LUSHER COLLECTION**
**Album:** Released May '76, on One-Up by EMI Records. Catalogue no: **OU 2129**

**DON LUSHER WITH BRIGHOUSE & (Lusher, Don with Brighouse & Rastrick Band)**
**Album:** Released Jan '77, on Grosvenor by Grosvenor Records. Catalogue no: **GRS 1050**

**TRIBUTE TO THE GREAT BANDS VOL. 1 (Lusher, Don Big Band)**
Tracks: / Carnival / Benny rides again / Song of India / Cute / Wales '87 / Moonlight serenade / Woodchopper's ball / Boogie woogie / Love for sale / High and the mighty / Cotton tail / Tea for two.
**CD:** Released Feb '90, on Horatio Nelson by Horatio Nelson Records & Tapes Ltd.. Catalogue no: **CDSIV 1125**
**Album:** Released Feb '90, on Horatio Nelson by Horatio Nelson Records & Tapes Ltd.. Catalogue no: **SIV 1125**
**Cass:** Released Feb '90, on Horatio Nelson by Horatio Nelson Records & Tapes Ltd.. Catalogue no: **CSIV 1125**
**CD:** Released Feb '90, on Horatio Nelson by Horatio Nelson Records & Tapes Ltd.. Catalogue no: **CDSIV 110**
**Cass:** Released Feb '90, on Horatio Nelson by Horatio Nelson Records & Tapes Ltd.. Catalogue no: **CSIV 1114**
**Album:** Released Feb '90, on Horatio Nelson by Horatio Nelson Records & Tapes Ltd.. Catalogue no: **SIV 1114**
**Album:** Released Feb '90, on Horatio Nelson by Horatio Nelson Records & Tapes Ltd.. Catalogue no: **SIV 110**
**Cass:** Released Feb '90, on Horatio Nelson by Horatio Nelson Records & Tapes Ltd.. Catalogue no: **CSIV 110**
**CD:** Released Feb '90, on Horatio Nelson by Horatio Nelson Records & Tapes Ltd.. Catalogue no: **CDSIV 1114**

## Lutcher, Joe

**JOE JOE JUMP**
Tracks: / No name boogie / Strato cruiser / Be bop blues / Mo jo jump / How fine can you be / Shuffle boogie / Sunday blues / Title track / Lucy Lindy boogie / Hit the block / Sauterne special / I know you when / Bagdad bebop / Watch it gate / Walk in to my heart / Toodle-oo.
**Album:** Released Apr '82, on Charly R&B by Charly Records. Catalogue no: **CRB 1038**

## Lutcher, Nellie

**DITTO FROM ME TO YOU**
Tracks: / Ditto from me to you / I took a trip on the train / One I love belongs to somebody else, The / Humoresque / Pig-Latin song, The / Imagine you having eyes for me / Princess Poo-Poo-Ly has plenty papya / Say a little prayer for me / Baby please stop and think about me / Only you / I really couldn't love you / He sends me / That's how it goes / Mean to me / If I didn't love you like I do / St. Louis blues, The.
**Album:** Released Aug '87, on Jukebox Lil (Sweden) Catalogue no: **JB 1103**

**FOR YOU MY LOVE**
Tracks: / For you my love / He's a real gone guy.
**7" Single:** Released Apr '85, on Capitol by EMI Records. Deleted Apr '88. Catalogue no: **CL 351**
**12" Single:** Released Apr '85, on Capitol by EMI Records. Deleted Apr '88. Catalogue no: **12CL 351**

**MY NEW PAPAS GOT TO HAVE EVERYTHING**
Tracks: / Kinda' blue and low / There's another mule in your stall / Song is ended, The / Chi-chi-chi-Chicago / You better watch yourself / Reaching for the moon / Lake Charles boogie / Maid's prayer, A / My new papas got to have everything / Chicken ain't nothin' but a bird, A / I'll never get tired / Little Sally Water / Pa's not home, ma's upstairs / Whee baby! / Muchly verily / Please come back.
**Album:** Released Jan '85, on Jukebox Lil (Sweden) Catalogue no: **JB 1100**

**REAL GONE GAL**
Tracks: / He's a real gone guy / Fine brown frame / My new papa's got to have everything / My mother's eyes / There's another mule in your stall / I wish I was in Walla Walla / Pa's not home, ma's upstairs / For you my love / That'll just about knock me out / Hurry on down / Fine and mellow / Lake Charles boogie / Come and get it honey / Lutcher's leap / So nice to see you baby.
**Cass:** Released Mar '85, on Stateside by EMI Records. Deleted Jan '90. Catalogue no: **EG 2604794**
**Album:** Released Mar '85, on Stateside by EMI Records. Catalogue no: **EG 2604791**

## Luter, Claude

**BLUE CLARINET**
**Album:** Released '88, on Vogue (France) by Vogue Records. Catalogue no: **502612**

**JAZZ NOUVELLE ORLEANS**
**Album:** Released Oct '88, on Vogue (France) by Vogue Records. Catalogue no: **509007**

**JAZZ TIME VOL.2**
**Album:** Released '88, on Vogue (France) by Vogue Records. Catalogue no: **502702**

**LOUISIANA AND ME**
**Album:** Released '88, on Vogue (France) by Vogue Records. Catalogue no: **502610**

**PEARLS, THE**
**Album:** Released '88, on Vogue (France) by Vogue Records. Catalogue no: **502606**

**SAINT GERMAIN DES PRES**
**CD:** Released 10 Jul '89, on Vogue by Vogue Records. Catalogue no: **VGCD 670214**

**SURMALE**
**Album:** Released '88, on Vogue (France) by Vogue Records. Catalogue no: **502604**

## Lyons, Jimmy

**GIVE IT UP (Lyons, Jimmy Quintet)**
**CD:** Released '86, on Black Saint (Italy) Catalogue no: **BSR 0087**

**OTHER AFTERNOONS**
**Album:** Released Nov '79, on Affinity by Charly Records. Deleted '88. Catalogue no: **AFF 34**

## Lyttelton, Humphrey

**1960-1963**
**CD:** Released Mar '90 on Philips by Philipos Records. Catalogue no: **JJCD 32**

**BACK TO THE 60's (Lyttelton, Humphrey Band and Helen Shapiro)**
**CD:** Released '89 on Polydor by Polydor Ltd. Catalogue no: **8344582**

**BAD PENNY BLUES (SINGLE)**
Tracks: / Bad penny blues.
**7" Single:** Released '56 on Parlophone by EMI Records. Deleted '59. Catalogue no: **R 4184**

**BAD PENNY BLUES (THE BEST OF HUMPH 1949-1956**
Tracks: / Maple leaf rag / Irish black bottom / Careless love / Snake rag / Trouble in mind / Buddy's habit / Panama rag / On Treasure Island / Trog's blues / Hoppin' mad / Don't monkey with it / Take a note from the South / Jelly roll blues / Blue for Waterloo / Fish seller.
**Album:** Released Jan '83 on Cube by Cube Records. Catalogue no: **HI FLY 39**

**BEANO BOOGIE (Lyttelton, Humphrey and his Band)**
**Album:** Released Jul '89 on Calligraph by PRT. Catalogue no: **CLGLP 021**
**Cass:** Released Jul '89 on Calligraph by PRT. Catalogue no: **ZCLG 021**
**CD:** Released Jul '89 on Calligraph by PRT. Catalogue no: **CLGCD 021**

**BEST OF HUMPHREY LYTTELTON**
**Album:** Released Apr '80 pm Black Lion by Black Lion Records. Catalogue no: **BLM 51002**
**Cass:** Released Apr '80 on Black Lion by Black Lion Records. Catalogue no: **KBLM 51002**

**BUCK CLAYTON WITH HUMPHREY LYTTELTON Vol. 2 (See under Clayton, Buck)**

**DELVING BACK WITH HUMPH (Lyttelton, Humphrey and his Band)**
**Album:** Released Apr '79 on Esquire by Titan International Productions. Catalogue no: **ESQ 310**

**DOGGIN' AROUND**
**Album:** Released May '87 on Wam by Wam Records. Catalogue no: **WAM 007**

**ECHOES OF HARLEM**
Tracks: / Big / Echoes of Harlem / You can depend on me / Adagio for David / Scorpio swings again / Unbooted character, The / Lady of the lavender mist / Pennies from heaven / Ce mossieu qui parle.

**ECHOES OF THE DUKE ( Lyttelton, Humphrey and his Band, with Helen Shapiro)**
**Album:** Released Sep '85 on Calligraph by PRT. Catalogue no: **CLGLP 002**

**GIGS (Lyttelton, Humphrey and his Band)**
**Album:** Released Nov '87 on Calligraph by PRT. Catalogue no: **CLGLP 015**

**HUMPH AT THE CONWAY**
Tracks: / Texas moaner / Coal black shine / Last smile blues / Elephant stomp blues / My bucket's got a hole in it / I double dare you / That's the old man's blues / Feline stomp / St. James Infirmary / Memphis shake / Mo pas lemme cas.
**Album:** Released Mar '86 on Calligraph by PRT. Catalogue no: **CLGLP 006**

**HUMPH LIVE AT THE BULL'S HEAD (Lyttelton, Humphrey and his Band)**
Tracks: / Now that we're here, let's go / Echoes of Harlem / Doggin' around / Harbour front hangout / Miss Matilda / High society / Do nothing till you hear from me / Toot suite / Three little words / Caribana Queen.
**Album:** Released Nov '85 on Calligraph by PRT. Catalogue no: **CLGLP 005**

**IN CANADA**
**Album:** Released Jul '88 on Sackville by Spotlite Records. Catalogue no: **3033**

**IT SEEMS LIKE YESTERDAY (Lyttelton, Humphrey and his Band)**
Tracks: / Don't monkey with it / K. C. blues / Trog's blues / Blue blow blew...
**Cass:** Released Jun '86 on Calligraph by PRT. Catalogue no: **ZCLG 1**
**Album:** Released Jul '85 on Calligraph by PRT. Catalogue no: **CLGLP 001**

**KANSAS CITY WOMAN (See under Tate, Buddy) (Lyttelton, Humphrey and Buddy Tate)**

**LONG TALL TENOR (See under Tate, Buddy) (Lyttelton, Humphrey and Buddy Tate)**

**M AND B JAM SESSION, THE (Lyttelton, Humphrey and Various artists)**
Note: Features Roy Williams, Bruce Turner and others.
**Album:** Released Feb '87 on Big Bear by Big Bear Records. Catalogue no: **BEAR 26**

**ONE DAY I MET AN AFRICAN (Lyttelton, Humphrey and his Band)**
Tracks: / Ladyless and lachrymose / It's a thing / Blues in the afternoon / One day I met an African / Hop frog / Sally / Hot house / Sirrumph
**Album:** Released Sep '80 on Black Lion by Black Lion Records. Deleted Sep '80. Catalogue no: **BLP 12199**

**PARLOPHONE YEARS, THE**
**Cass:** Released Feb '89 on Doormouse by Dormouse Records. Catalogue no: **DMCD 21**
**Album:** Released Feb '89 on Doormouse by Dormouse Records. Catalogue no: **DMCD 21**

**SALUTE TO SATCHMO (See under Welsh, Alex)**

**SCATTERBRAINS**
Note: With Kenny Davern and Al Casey.
**Album:** Released '88 on Stomp Off (USA) by Stomp Off Records. Catalogue no: **SOS 1111**

**SIR HUMPH'S DELIGHT**
**Album:** Released Oct '79 on Black Lion by Black Lion Records. Catalogue no: **BLP 12188**

**SPREADING JOY**
Tracks: / Spreading joy / Tishomingo blues / Mabel's dream / Hundred years from today / Ugly duckling, The / Black and blue / Blues my naughty sweetie gives to me / East St. Louis toodle-oo / When your lover has gone / Honey-

suckle rose / James / If I could be with you / Fish seller.
**Album:** Released Feb '79 on Black Lion by Black Lion Records. Catalogue no: **BLP 12173**

**TAKE IT FROM THE TOP**
**Album:** Released '88 on Black Lion by Black Lion Records. Catalogue no: **BLP 12134**

**TRIBUTE TO HUMPH, A Vol. 1**
**Album:** Released Nov '87 on Dormouse by Dormouse Records. Catalogue no: **DM 1**

**TRIBUTE TO HUMPH, A Vol. 2**
**Album:** Released Nov '87 on Dormouse by Dormouse Records. Catalogue no: **DM 2**

**TRIBUTE TO HUMPH, A Vol. 3**
**Album:** Released Nov '87 on Dormouse by Dormouse Records. Catalogue no: **DM 3**

**TRIBUTE TO HUMPH, A Vol. 4**
**Album:** Released Nov '87 on Dormouse by Dormouse Records. Catalogue no: **DM 4**

**TRIBUTE TO HUMPH, A Vol. 5**
**Album:** Released Nov '87 on Dormouse by Dormouse Records. Catalogue no: **DM 12**

**TRIBUTE TO HUMPH, A Vol. 7**
**Album:** Released Nov '87 on Dormouse by Dormouse Records. Catalogue no: **DM 13**

**TRIBUTE TO HUMPH, A Vol. 8**
**Album:** Released Nov '87 on Dormouse by Dormouse Records. Catalogue no: **DM 14**

**WORLD OF BUDDY BOLDEN, THE (Lyttelton, Humphrey and Johnny Barnes)**
**Album:** Released Jan '87 on Calligraph by PRT. Catalogue no: **CLGLP 013**

## Lytton, Paul

**COLLECTIVE CALLS (Lytton, Paul and Evan Parker)**
**Album:** Released Nov '76, on Incus by Incus Records. Catalogue no: **INCUS 5**

**RA 1+2 H (Lytton, Paul with Evan Parker)**
**Album:** Released Jul '78, on Ring Catalogue no: **RING 01016**
**Album:** Released Jul '78, on Ring Catalogue no: **RING 01016**

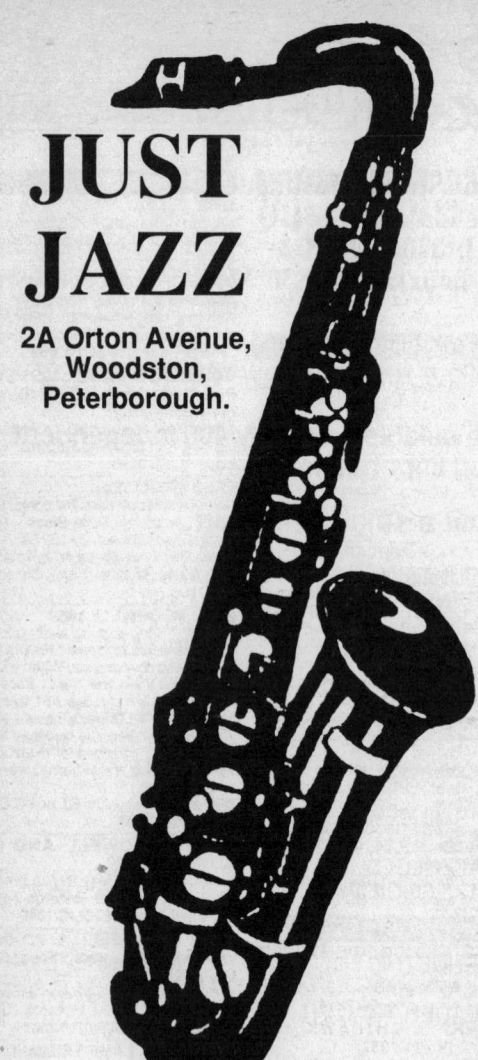

# M

The following information was taken from the Music Master database on 14th April, 1990.

## Mabon, Willie

**BLUES ROOTS VOL 16**
Tracks: / I don't know / Beggar on bandit / You're a fool / Monday woman / Willie's blues / Someday you gotta pay / Poison ivy / I'm mad at you / Lonely blues / I'm tired / He lied / Knock on wood / Why did it happen to me / Seventh son.
**Album:** Released '88, on Chess by Vogue Records. Catalogue no: **GCH 8099**

**CHESS MASTERS...WILLIE MABON**
Tracks: / I don't know / Beggar or bandit / You're a fool / Monday woman / Willie's blues / Someday you gotta pay / Poison ivy / I'm mad at you / Lonely blues / I'm tired / He lied / Knock on wood / Why did it happen to me / Seventh son.
**Album:** Released Mar '85, on Chess (PRT) Deleted '88. Catalogue no: **CXMP 2056**

**CHICAGO BLUES SESSION**
**Album:** Released '88, on L&R Catalogue no: **LR 42.003**

**COMEBACK, THE**
**Album:** Released Apr '79, on Big Bear by Big Bear Records. Deleted '88. Catalogue no: **BEAR 9**

**I'M THE FIXER**
**Album:** Released Oct '86, on Flyright by Interstate Music. Catalogue no: **FLY 580**

**SEVENTH SON, THE**
Tracks: / I don't know / I'm mad / You're a fool / I got to go / Late again / Poison ivy / Wow I feel good / Seventh son / Knock on wood / Worry blues / Night latch / Monday woman / Cruisin' / Would you baby / Say man / Come on baby / Lucinda / Got to let you go.
**Album:** Released Aug '87, on Crown Prince (Sweden) Catalogue no: **IG 402**

## McClean, Jackie

**CONSEQUENCE**
**Album:** Released Jun '80, on Liberty by EMI Records. Catalogue no: **LBR 1027**

**TIPPIN' THE SCALES**
Tracks: / Tippin' the scales / Rainy blues / Nursery blues / Nicely / Two for one / Cabin in the sky.
**CD:** Released Jun '89, on Blue Note by EMI Records. Catalogue no: **BNZ 198**
**CD:** Released Jun '89, on Blue Note by EMI Records. Catalogue no: **CDP 784 427 2**
**Album:** Released Jul '89, on Blue Note by EMI Records. Catalogue no: **BST 84427**

## McClennan, Tommy

**BLUEBIRD**
**Album:** Released Nov '77, on Black & White by Black & White Records. Catalogue no: **PM 24040**

**TOMMY MCCLENNAN**
**Album:** Released Oct '88, on Roots (Germany) Catalogue no: **RL 305**

## McCorkle, Susannah

**NO MORE BLUES**
**Cass:** Released 12 Apr '89, on Concord by Concord Jazz Records (USA). Catalogue no: **CJ 370C**
**Album:** Released 12 Apr '89, on Concord by Concord Jazz Records (USA). Catalogue no: **CJ 370**
**CD:** Released 12 Apr '89, on Concord by Concord Jazz Records (USA). Catalogue no: **CCD 4370**

**QUALITY OF MERCER, THE**
**Album:** Released Apr '79, on Black Lion Catalogue no: **BLP 12169**

**THERE WILL NEVER BE ANOTHER YOU (The music of Harry Warren)**
**Album:** Released Dec '76, on Retrospect by EMI Records. Catalogue no: **WRS 1001**

## McCoy, Kansas Joe

**KANSAS JOE MCCOY 1934-44**
**Album:** Released '87, on Best Of Blues (USA) by Blue Island Records (USA). Catalogue no: **BOB 6**

**KANSAS JOE MCCOY AND JOE WILLIAMS (McCoy, Kansas Joe & Joe Williams)**
**Album:** Released Apr '89, on Blues Document Catalogue no: **BD 2032**

## McCoy, Robert

**BLUES AND BOOGIE WOOGIE CLASSICS**
**Album:** Released Sep '79, on Oldie Blues Catalogue no: **OL 2814**

**ROBERT 'NIGHTHAWK' LEE MCCOY (Vol. 1 1937)**
**Album:** Released Jan '88, on Wolf Catalogue no: **WSE 120**
**Album:** Released Jan '88, on Wolf Catalogue no: **WSE 121**

## McCuy, Clyde

**SUGAR BLUES (McCuy, Clyde & His Orchestra)**
Note: Mono. 1951.
**Album:** Released Jan '87, on Circle (USA) by Jazzology Records (USA). Catalogue no: **CLP 82**
/ Ciaradh an fheasgair / Kyleakin ferry /

## McDowell, Fred

**1962**
**Album:** Released Dec '88, on Heritage by Interstate Music. Catalogue no: **HT 302**

**DOSE OF DOUBLE DYNAMITE, A (McDowell, Fred & Phil Guy)**
**Album:** Released Jan '86, on Red Lightnin' by Red Lightning Records. Deleted Jun '89. Catalogue no: **RL 063**

**DOUBLE DYNAMITE : MISSISSIPPI & CHICAGO BLUES (McDowell, Fred & Phil Guy)**
**Album:** Released Jun '86, on Red Lightnin' by Red Lightning Records. Catalogue no: **RL 0063**

**FRED MCDOWELL**
Note: Doubleplay cassette contains albums: Mississippi Delta Blues - 1021; Mississippi Blues vol. 2 - 1027.s
**Cass:** Released '88, on Arhoolie (USA) by Arhoolie Records (USA). Catalogue no: **C 202**

**FRED MCDOWELL 1959**
Tracks: / Been drinking water out of a log / Shake 'em on down / Freight train blues / Drop down mama / When you get home write me a few lines / Poor boy blues / Cool water blues / 61 highway blues / Fred McDowell's blues / Keep your lamp trimmed and burning / Soon one morning / You done tol' everybody / My mother died and left me / I wished I was in heaven.
**Album:** Released Jun '88, on KC Catalogue no: **KC 107**

**FRED MCDOWELL AND HIS BLUES BOYS**
**Album:** Released May '81, on Arhoolie (USA) by Arhoolie Records (USA). Catalogue no: **ARHOOLIE 1046**

**FRED MCDOWELL & JOHNNY WOODS (McDowell, Fred/John Dudley)**
**Album:** Released '88, on Rounder (USA) by Rounder Records (USA). Catalogue no: **ROUNDER 2007**

**KEEP YOUR LAMP TRIMMED**
**Album:** Released May '81, on Arhoolie (USA) by Arhoolie Records (USA). Catalogue no: **ARHOOLIE 1068**

**MCDOWELL, FRED**
**CD:** Released Mar '90, on Flyright by Interstate Music. Catalogue no: **FLYCD14**

**MISSISSIPPI DELTA BLUES**
**Album:** Released May '81, on Arhoolie (USA) by Arhoolie Records (USA). Catalogue no: **ARHOOLIE 1021**

**Album:** Released Jul '87, on Black Lion Catalogue no: **BLP 30140**

**MISSISSIPPI DELTA BLUES VOL 2**
**Album:** Released May '81, on Arhoolie (USA) by Arhoolie Records (USA). Catalogue no: **ARHOOLIE 1027**

**STANDING AT THE BURYING GROUND (see also Jo Ann Kelly)**
**Album:** Released Aug '84, on Red Lightnin' by Red Lightning Records. Deleted Jun '89. Catalogue no: **RL 053**

**WHEN I LAY MY BURDEN DOWN (McDowell, Fred/Furry Lewis)**
Tracks: / If you see my baby / John Henry / Louise / 61 highway / Big fat mamma / When I lay my burden down / Dankin farm / Casey Jones / Harry furry blues / Everyday in the week / Grieve my mind / Beale street blues.
Note: Bar Code: 5099882 234714
**Album:** Released 20 Feb '88, on Blue Moon (1) by Magnum Music Group. Catalogue no: **BMLP 1047**

## McDowell, Mississippi

**SHAKE 'EM ON DOWN**
**CD:** Released Mar '90, on Tomato (USA) by Tomato Music Co. (USA). Catalogue no: **JJCD36**

## McDuff, Jack

**HONEYDRIPPER,THE**
**Album:** Released Apr '86, on Original Jazz Classics (USA) by Fantasy Inc (USA). Catalogue no: **OJC 222**

## Macero, Teo

**IMPRESSIONS OF CHARLES MINGUS**
**Album:** Released Jun '84, on Palo Alto Catalogue no: **PA 8046**

## McFarland, Tom

**TRAVELLIN' WITH THE BLUES**
**Album:** Released May '81, on Arhoolie (USA) by Arhoolie Records (USA). Catalogue no: **ARHOOLIE 1079**

## McFerrin, Bobby

**BOBBY MCFERRIN**
Tracks: / Dance with me / Feline / You really got a hold on me / All feets can dance / Sightless bird / Peace / Jubilee / Hallucinations / Chicken.
**CD:** Released '89, on Elektra by Elektra Records (UK). Catalogue no: **960 023 2**
**Album:** Released Jun '82, on Elektra (Musician) by Elektra Records (USA). Catalogue no: **K 52387**

**DON'T WORRY BE HAPPY**
Tracks: / Don't worry be happy (LP version) / Simple pleasures / From me to you (CD single only.) / Don't worry be happy (7" version).
**CD Single:** Released Sep '88, on EMI-Manhattan by EMI Records. Deleted Jun '89. Catalogue no: **CDMT 56**
**7" Single:** Released Sep '88, on EMI-Manhattan by EMI Records. Catalogue no: **MT 56**
**12" Single:** Released Sep '88, on EMI-Manhattan by EMI Records. Deleted Oct '89. Catalogue no: **12MT 56**

**GOOD LOVIN'**
Tracks: / Good lovin' / There ya go.
**CD Single:** Released Jul '88, on EMI-Manhattan by EMI Records. Deleted Jun '89. Catalogue no: **CDMT 42**
**7" Single:** Released Jun '88, on EMI-Manhattan by EMI Records. Deleted Aug '89. Catalogue no: **MT 42**
**12" Single:** Released Jun '88, on EMI-Manhattan by EMI Records. Deleted Aug '89. Catalogue no: **12MT 42**

**SIMPLE PLEASURES**
Tracks: / Don't worry, be happy / All I want / Drive my car / Simple pleasures / Good lovin' / Come to me / Suzie Q / Drive / Them changes / Sunshine of your love.
Note: Producer/Arranger Linda Goldstein.
**Cass:** Released Apr '88, on EMI-Manhattan by EMI Records. Catalogue no: **TCMTL 1018**
**Album:** Released Apr '88, on EMI-Manhattan by EMI Records. Catalogue no: **MTL 1018**
**CD:** Released Apr '88, on EMI-Manhattan by EMI Records. Catalogue no: **CDP 748 059 2**
**CD:** Released Apr '88, on EMI-Manhattan by EMI Records. Catalogue no: **CDMTL 1018**

**SPONTANEOUS INVENTIONS**
Tracks: / Thinkin' about your body / Turtle shoes / From me to you / There ya go / Cara mia / Another night in Tunisia / Opportunity / Walkin' / I hear music / Beverly Hills blues / Manana Iguana.
**CD:** Released Dec '86, on Blue Note by EMI Records. Catalogue no: **CDP 746 298 2**
**Cass:** Released Jan '89, on Blue Note by EMI Records. Catalogue no: **TCBT 85110**
**CD:** Released Dec '86, on Blue Note by EMI Records. Deleted Aug '89. Catalogue no: **CDBT 85110**
**Album:** Released Aug '86, on Blue Note by EMI Records. Catalogue no: **BT 85110**
**CD:** Released Dec '86, on Blue Note by EMI Records. Catalogue no: **BNZ 57**

**SPONTANEOUS INVENTIONS (VIDEO)**
Tracks: / Scrapple from the apple / Honeysuckle rose / Bwee-Dop / Cara mia / Fascinating Rhythm / Itsy bitsy spider / Thinkin' about your body / Drive / Opportunity / I got the feelin' / Walkin' / Blackbird / Manna Iguana.
Note: Running time: 48 mins. Filmed at the Aquarius Theatre, Hollywood. Features 5 tracks from his album of the same name plus others.
**VHS:** Released Nov '86, on PMI by EMI Records. Deleted Aug '89. Catalogue no: **MVP 99 1145 2**

**THINKIN' ABOUT YOUR BODY (For Debs)**
Tracks: / Thinkin' about your body / From me to you.
**7" Single:** Released Dec '86, on EMI by EMI Records. Deleted Jul '87. Catalogue no: **BLUE 4**

**THINKIN' ABOUT YOUR BODY**
Tracks: / Thinkin' about your body / Don't worry be happy / From me to you(not 7") / Come to me (Only available on CD single.).
**CD Single:** Released Dec '88, on EMI-Manhattan by EMI Records. Catalogue no: **CDBLUE 6**
**12" Single:** Released Dec '88, on EMI-Manhattan by EMI Records. Deleted Oct '89. Catalogue no: **12BLUE 6**
**7" Single:** Released Dec '88, on EMI-Manhattan by EMI Records. Catalogue no: **BLUE 6**

**VOICE, THE**
Tracks: / Blackbird / El brujo / I feel good / I'm my own walkman / Music box.
Note: This album contains a medley which contains the following tracks, "Donna Lee","Big Top", "We're in the money", "I'm alone", "T.J.", "Take the A-train".
**CD:** Released '88, on Elektra (Musician) by Elektra Records (USA). Catalogue no: **960 366 2**
**Album:** Released Aug '84, on Elektra (Musician) by Elektra Records (USA). Catalogue no: **960661**

## McGarity,Lou

**DAVISON, OLIVER JACKSON ETC.**
**Album:** Released '88, on Storyville by Storyville Records AB. Catalogue no: **SLP 513**

**SOME LIKE IT HOT & SOME LIKE IT BLUE (McGarity,Lou Big 5 and 7)**
**Cass:** Released Jun '86, on Holmia Cassettes Catalogue no: **HM 02**

## McGhee, Brownie

**BEST OF BROWNIE MCGHEE**
**Album:** Released May '86, on Storyville by Storyville Records AB. Catalogue no: **SLP 4032**

**BROWNIE BLUES**
**Album:** Released Jun '84, on Prestige Catalogue no: **OBC 505**

**BROWNIE MCGHEE BLUES 1944-59**
**Album:** Released Sep '87, on Magpie by Interstate Music. Deleted '88. Catalogue no: **PY 1809**

**BROWNIE MCGHEE, SONNY TERRY & SVEND ERIK NORREGA (McGhee, Brownie, Sonny Terry, Svend Erik Norrega)**
**Album:** Released Jul '81, on Storyville by Storyville Records AB. Catalogue no: **SLP 4007**

**BROWNIE MCGHEE & SONNY TERRY 1940-41 (McGhee, Brownie/Sonny Terry/Jordan Webb)**
**Album:** Released Dec '88, on Document Catalogue no: **DLP 541**

**FACTS OF LIFE**
Note:
With Mark Hummel on harp
**Album:** Released Dec '88, on Blue

**Howard McGhee**

Rock-It (USA) by Blue Rock-It Records (USA). Catalogue no: **BR 104**

**I COULDN'T BELIEVE MY EYES (McGhee, Brownie & Sonny Terry With Earl Hooker)**
Tracks: / Black cat bone / Brownie's new blues / Poor man blues / Tell me why / My baby's so fine / You just usin' me for a convenience / Hole in the wall / Long way from home / Don't wait for me / I'm in love with you baby / Parcel post blues / When I was drinking / I couldn't believe my eyes / Life is a gamble / Don't mistreat me / Rock Island line.
Note:
All tracks produced by Ed Mitchell Original sound recordings made by ABC Bluesway/MCA Records Inc This compilation published 1987. See For Miles Records Ltd. Copyright 1987 See For Miles Miles Ltd A Colin Miles Compilation
**CD:** Released Feb '90, on See For Miles by See For Miles Records. Catalogue no: **SEECD 92**
**Album:** Released May '87, on See For Miles by See For Miles Records. Catalogue no: **SEE 92**

**LETS HAVE A BALL 1945-55 (McGhee, Brownie & his Buddies)**
**Album:** Released Jan '79, on Magpie by Interstate Music. Deleted '88. Catalogue no: **PY 1805**

**YOU HEAR ME TALKIN' (see Terry, Sonny) (McGhee, Brownie & Sonny Terry)**
Note: See under Terry, Sonny.
**Album:** Released Apr '81, on Muse by Black & Blue Records. Catalogue no: **MR 5131**

## McGhee, Howard

**COOKIN' TIME (McGhee,Howard Orchestra)**
Tracks: / Blues deundi / Round midnight / Cookin' time / Willow weep for me / On Green Dolphin Street / Highest mountain / Bless you / Summertime / Satin doll / Chronos.
**Album:** Released Apr '79, on Hep Jazz by Hep Records. Catalogue no: **HEP 2001**

**DUSTY BLUE**
Tracks: / Dusty blue / Sound of music, The / I concentrate on you / Sleep talk / Part avenue petite / Flyin'colours / With malice / Groovin' high / Cottage for sale.
Note: Licensed from Bethlehem Records.This compilation:(1986 Charly Records Ltd(c) 1986 Charly records.
**Album:** Released May '86, on Affinity by Charly Records. Catalogue no: **AFF 156**

**HERE COMES FREDDY (McGhee, Howard & Illinois Jacquet)**
Tracks: / Here comes Freddy / Suite for Dru / Deep in the hat / All soul / Stardust / Travel / Come Sunday / Yardbird suite.
**Album:** Released '76, on Sonet by Sonet Records. Catalogue no: **SNTF 714**

**HOME RUN (McGhee, Howard & Benny Bailey)**
**Album:** Released Jan '88, on Storyville by Storyville Records AB. Catalogue no: **SLP 4082**

**HOWARD MCGHEE JAZZ BROTHERS & CHARLIE ROUSE (McGhee, Howard Jazz Brothers & Charlie Rouse)**
**Album:** Released '88, on Storyville by Storyville Records AB. Catalogue no: **SLP 4077**

**LIVE AT EMERSON'S**
**Album:** Released Apr '81, on Zim (USA) Catalogue no: **ZMS 2006**

**MAGGIE**
Tracks: / Merri-Lee / Short life / Talk of the town / Bass C Jam / Bass C Jm (master) / Down home / Sweet & lovely / Fiesta / I'm in the mood for love / Belle from Bunnycock / Lip flip / Man I love, The / Last word, The / Royal Garden blues / Mood indigo / St. Louis blues / Twelfth Street / One o'clock jump / Stormy weather / Perdido / Man with a horn / Stompin' at the Savoy / Lady be good / Stardust / How high the moon / Don't blame me / Body and soul / Harvest time.
**Album:** Released Mar '85, on Savoy Jazz (USA) by Malaco Records (USA). Catalogue no: **SJL 2219**

**MAGGIE'S BACK IN TOWN**
Tracks: / Demon chase / Softly as in a morning sunrise / Maggie's back in town / Brownie speaks / Willow weep for me / Sunset eyes / Summertime.
**Album:** Released Dec '81, on Contemporary (Import) Catalogue no: **1007 596**
**Album:** Released Feb '89, on Fantasy by Ace Records. Catalogue no: **CIO 044**
**Album:** Released 27 Feb '89, on Contemporary by Ace Records. Catalogue no: **COP 044**

**SHADES OF BLUE**
Tracks: / Sharpe edge, The / Shades of blue / Cool / Day after, The / Topside / Arbee / Ill wind / My delight.
Note: With George Coleman, Junior Mance, George Tucker, Jimmy Cobb.
**Album:** Released Jul '87, on Black Lion Catalogue no: **BLP 30146**

**SHARP EDGE**
**CD:** Released Dec '88, on Black Lion Catalogue no: **BLCD 760110**
**Album:** Released Dec '88, on Black Lion Catalogue no: **BLP 60110**

**THAT BOP THING (McGhee, Howard Quintet)**
Tracks: / Get happy / Tahitian lullaby / Lover man / Lullaby of the leaves / You're teasing me / Transpicuous / Rifftide / Oo wee but I do / Don't blame me / Tweedles / I'll remember April.
**Album:** Released May '82, on Affinity by Charly Records. Deleted '88. Catalogue no: **AFF 94**

**TRUMPET AT TEMPO**
Tracks: / Trumpet at tempo / Thermodynamics / Up in Dodo's room / Dilated pupils / Midnight at Mintons / High wind in Hollywood / Night mist / Dorothy / Coolerini / Turnip blood / Surrender / Sleepwalker boogie / Stoptime blues / You.
Note: Musicians include Teddy Edwards, Dodo Marmarosa, Arvin Garri-

son, James Moody, Milt Jackson.
**Album:** Released '83, on Spotlite by Spotlite Records. Catalogue no: **SPJ 131**

**WISE IN TIME (McGhee, Howard & Teddy Edwards)**
**Album:** Released Nov '86, on Storyville by Storyville Records AB. Catalogue no: **SLP 4081**

**YOUNG AT HEART (McGhee, Howard & Teddy Edwards)**
Tracks: / Relaxing at Camarillo / Reflection / Blues in the closet / On a misty night / In walked Bud / Yardbird suite / Moose the Mooche.
**Album:** Released Sep '86, on Storyville by Storyville Records AB. Catalogue no: **SLP 4080**

## McGhee, Reverend F.W

**REVEREND F.W.MCGHEE**
**Album:** Released Oct '88, on Roots (Germany) Catalogue no: **RL 338**

## McGregor, Chris

**BLUE NOTES FOR JOHNNY**
Tracks: / Funk dem dudu to Erica / Eyomzi / Ntyilo Ntyilo / Blues for Nick / Monks & Mbizo / Ithi Gqi.
**Album:** Released Jan '88, on Ogun by Cadillac Music. Catalogue no: **OG 532**

**COUNTRY COOKING (McGregor, Chris/Brotherhood Of Breath)**
Tracks: / Country cooking / Bakwetha / Sweet as honey / You and me / Big G / Maxine / Dakar / Thunder in the mountains (Cassette only).

Note: "Stunning big band music from legendary South African-born jazz pianist McGregor and the recently re-formed Brotherhood of Breath. Produced by Joe Boyd, this is jazz music with a strong African influence." (Virgin Records, May 1988.)
**Album:** Released 31 May '88, on Venture (2) by Virgin Records. Catalogue no: **VE 17**
**CD:** Released 31 May '88, on Venture (2) by Virgin Records. Catalogue no: **CDVE 17**
**Cass:** Released 31 May '88, on Venture (2) by Virgin Records. Catalogue no: **TCVE 17**

**IN HIS GOOD TIME**
Tracks: / Call / Raincloud / Unnome / Yikiti / Mngqusho / In his good time / Bride / Ududu nombambula.
**2 LP Set:** Released Jun '79, on Blue Note by EMI Records. Catalogue no: **OG 521**

**PROCESSION**
**Album:** Released '78, on Ogun by Cadillac Music. Catalogue no: **OG 524**

## McGriff, Jimmy

**ALL ABOUT MY GIRL**
Tracks: / All about my girl.
**7" Single:** Released Apr '83, on EMI by EMI Records. Catalogue no: **2C 008 83376**

**BLUES FOR MR.JIMMY**
Tracks: / Bump de bump de bump / Discotheque U.S.A / Cash box / Blues for Joe / Blues for Mr.Jimmy / Dog (you dog), The / Sho' nuff / Turn blue / Party's over, The.

Note: One of the all-time great R 'n' B organ players.A re-issue of a much sought after collectors album.
**Cass:** Released Apr '86, on Stateside by EMI Records. Deleted 31 Jul '88. Catalogue no: **TCSSL 6005**
**Album:** Released Apr '86, on Stateside by EMI Records. Deleted Oct '89. Catalogue no: **SSL 6005**

**COUNTDOWN**
Tracks: / Countdown.
**Album:** Released Nov '83, on Milestone by Ace Records. Catalogue no: **M 9116**

**FLY DUDE**
**Album:** Released '87, on UNKNOWN Deleted Jun '89. Catalogue no: **PLEO 14**

**GEORGIA ON MY MIND**
Tracks: / Let's stay together / Shaft, Theme from / What's going on / Georgia on my mind / April in Paris / Everyday I have the blues / Yardbird suite / It's you I adore / Lonesome road / Mack the knife / There will never be another you / Canadian sunset / Mr. Lucky / Moonglow / Red sails in the sunset / Secret love.
**CD:** Released '88, on Denon Catalogue no: **DC-8513**
**Cass:** Released '88, on Denon Catalogue no: **MC 8513**

**I'VE GOT A WOMAN**
Tracks: / I've got a woman / All about my girl / Watermelon man.
**7" Single:** Released Nov '79, on United Artists by EMI Records. Deleted '82. Catalogue no: **UP 613**
**7" EP:** Released Oct '83, on Ensign by Ensign Records. Deleted Oct '86. Catalogue no: **ENS 6**

**LAST MINUTE, THE**
**Album:** Released Dec '83, on Sue by Island Records. Deleted '88. Catalogue no: **ENSUE 2**

**SOUL SURVIVORS (McGriff, Jimmy & Hank Crawford)**
Tracks: / Because of you / Frim fram sauce / Peeper, The / One mint julep / Second time around / After supper.

Note: Straight ahead Jazz/Blues playing from two master musicians who truely are soul Survivors.Both came through the 50s and 60s soul period.Crawford making a name for himself with the Ray Charles band and moving on to make countless recordingsfor Atlantic and CTI.McGriff following in the wake of fellow organist Jimmy Smi-th to emerge as one of the most popular organists of the period.His version of "I've got a woman" was a great favourite with the Mods.
This album has a great Blue Note sound about it.Not suprising when you see that the engineer was Rudy Van Gelder!
**Album:** Released Oct '86, on Milestone by Ace Records. Catalogue no: **M 9142**
**Cass:** Released Oct '86, on Milestone (USA) by Fantasy Inc (USA). Catalogue no: **5M 9142**

**STARTING FIVE, THE**
**Album:** Released Oct '87, on Milestone by Ace Records. Catalogue no: **MX 9148**

**STATE OF THE ART**
Tracks: / Headbender / Stormy weather / Cheesesteak / Don't ever doubt me / New wave blues / Slow gindin' / Hip hop be bop.

Note: Along with Jimmy Smith, Jack McDuff and Richard 'Groove' Holmes, Jimmy McGriff is one of the great Jazz/R&B organists to have emerged from the 60's period.
In 1962 he had a top twenty US hit with his instrumental version of Ray Charles' "I've Got A Woman"and won a huge following with UK mods thanks to 'MG Blues' and other free-wheeling singles issued by SUE Records which were jazzier than Booker T & the MG's.
This new album features material ranging from ballads to sythesized funk to classier jazz organ over a walking bass line.
**Album:** Released Feb '86, on Milestone by Ace Records. Catalogue no: **M 9135**

## Machito

**AFRO-CUBOP (Machito & His Orchestra)**
Tracks: / Howard's blues / Indianola / How high the moon / Cubop city / Boppin' the vibes / Mambo / Lament for the Congo / Reminiscing at twilight / Tanga / Lean on me / Hip hop be bop / In the beginning / Man made / Together again / Hip hop be bop (part 2) / Six simple synthesizers / Techno trax / Street clap / Heatstroke.
**Album:** Released '83, on Spotlite by Spotlite Records. Catalogue no: **SPJ 138**

**GREATEST HITS:MACHITO & HIS AFRO (Machito & His Afro Cuban**

**Salseros)**
Tracks: / Sopa de pichon / Sisi nono / Piniero tenia razon / Caso perdido / Noche de farra / El as de la rumba / Tibiri tabara / Quimbobo / Carambou / Adoracion / Asia Minor / La paella.
**CD:** Released Jun '88, on Caliente by Charly Records. Catalogue no: **CDCHARLY 126**
**Cass:** Released Sep '88, on Caliente by Charly Records. Catalogue no: **TCHOT 106**
**Album:** Released Jul '88, on Caliente by Charly Records. Catalogue no: **HOT 106**

**LATIN SOUL PLUS JAZZ (Machito & His Orchestra)**
Tracks: / Wild jungle / Congo mulence / Kenya / Oyeme / Holiday / Cannonology / Ring-a-levio / Renzy / Blues a la machito / Conversation / Tin tin deo / Minor rama.
**Album:** Released Nov '88, on Caliente by Charly Records. Catalogue no: **HOT 120**
**Cass:** Released Nov '88, on Caliente by Charly Records. Catalogue no: **TCHOT 120**
**CD:** Released Nov '88, on Caliente by Charly Records. Catalogue no: **CDCHARLY 120**

**LIVE AT NORTH SEA '82 (Machito & His Salsa Big Band)**
Note: Recorded July 1983, Holland. Personnel: Charl Syvarth (alto sax), Thomas Hamilton (alto sax), Glenn Stulpin (tenor sax), Scott Villiger (baritone sax), Jeff Davis (tpt), James Oats (tpt), Paul Spong (tpt), Alfredo Spong (tpt), Alfredo 'Chocolate' Armenteros (tpt), Ruben Rodrigues (bass), William Rodrigues (piano), Francisco Valdes Jnr (congas), Frank Grillo/Machito (vocals, maracas), Paula C. Grillo (vocals), Mario Grillo (timbales).
**Album:** Released '88, on Timeless by Timeless Records. Catalogue no: **SJP 168**
**Album:** Released Apr '83, on Timeless by Timeless Records. Catalogue no: **SJP 168**
**CD:** Released Jun '88, on Timeless by Timeless Records. Catalogue no: **CDSJP 168**

**MACHITO AT THE CRESCENDO**
**Album:** Released '88, on GNP Crescendo (USA) by GNP Crescendo Records (USA). Catalogue no: **GNPS 58**
**CD:** Released '88, on GNP Crescendo (USA) by GNP Crescendo Records (USA). Catalogue no: **GNPD 58**

**MACHITO & HIS SALSA BIG BAND (Machito & His Salsa Big Band)**
**Album:** Released '88, on Timeless by Timeless Records. Catalogue no: **SJP 183**
**CD:** Released Jun '88, on Timeless by Timeless Records. Catalogue no: **CDSJP 183**

**MUCHO MACHO MACHITO (Machito & His Afro Cuban Salseros)**
**Album:** Released '82, on Pablo Jazz (USA) by Pablo Records (USA). Catalogue no: **2625 712**
**Cass:** Released '82, on Pablo Jazz (USA) by Pablo Records (USA). Catalogue no: **K 25 712**

**SALSA BIG BAND 1982 (Machito & His Salsa Big Band)**
Tracks: / Elas de la rumba / Quimbobo / Piniero tenia razon / Caso perdido / Manicero / Sambia / Yerbero.
**CD:** Released '89, on Timeless by Timeless Records. Catalogue no: **CDSJP 161**
**Album:** Released Aug '85, on Timeless by Timeless Records. Catalogue no: **SJP 161**
**Cass:** Released Aug '85, on Timeless by Timeless Records. Catalogue no: **SJP 1161**

**WORLD'S GREATEST LATIN BAND**
**Album:** Released '88, on GNP Crescendo (USA) by GNP Crescendo Records (USA). Catalogue no: **GNPS 72**

## McIntyre, Hal

**ECSTACY**
**Album:** Released Aug '89, on Golden Era by Delta Records. Catalogue no: **GELP 15022**

**HAL MCINTYRE & HIS ORCHESTRA**
**Album:** Released Jul '77, on First Heard by Submarine Records. Catalogue no: **FH 13**

## McIntyre, Ken

**INTRODUCING THE VIBRATIONS (McIntyre, Ken, Sextet)**
**Album:** Released Aug '77, on Steeplechase (USA) Catalogue no: **SCS 1065**

**LOOKING AHEAD (McIntyre, Ken & Eric Dolphy)**
Tracks: / Lautir / Curtsy / Geo's tune / They all laughed / Head shakin'.
**Album:** Released Jan '87, on Original Jazz Classics (USA) by Fantasy Inc (USA). Catalogue no: **OJC 252**

## MacIntyre, Maurice

**FORCES & FEELINGS (MacIntyre, Maurice, Kalaparusha)**
**Album:** Released '74, on Delmark (USA) by Delmark Records (USA). Catalogue no: **DS 425**

**HUMILITY IN LIGHT OF CREATOR**
**Album:** Released '74, on Delmark (USA) by Delmark Records (USA). Catalogue no: **DS 419**

## McKenna, Dave

**CELEBRATION OF HOAGY CARMICHAEL**
Tracks: / Stardust / Riverboat shuffle / One morning in May / Moon country / Two sleepy people / Come easy, go easy love / Nearness of you, The / Lazybones / Sky lark / Georgia / Lazy river.
**Album:** Released Nov '83, on Concord Jazz by Concord Jazz Records (USA). Catalogue no: **CJ 227**

**DANCING IN THE DARK**
Tracks: / By myself / Shine on your shoes / I see your face before me / Alone together / Me / I guess I'll have to change my pains / You and the night and the music / Dancing in the dark / Something to remember you by / New sun in the sky / Oh but I do / Gal in calico, A.
Note: What better combination could be found? The two-fisted, swing piano styling of thegreat Dave McKenna and eleven beautiful selections from the prolific Tin Pan Alley composer, Arthur Schwartz.
**Cass:** Released Feb '86, on Concord Jazz by Concord Jazz Records (USA). Catalogue no: **CJC 292**
**Album:** Released Feb '86, on Concord Jazz by Concord Jazz Records (USA). Catalogue no: **CJ 292**

**DUAL PIANO JAZZ See under Overton, Hal (McKenna, Dave/Hal Overton)**
Tracks: / Keeping out of mischief / Dizzy atmosphere / Ruby my dear / Hi-fly / Monks mood / Baubles, bangles and beads / Dardanella.
**Album:** Released 12 Feb '88, on Fresh Sounds (Spain) by Fresh Sounds Records (Spain). Catalogue no: **FS 292**

**KEY MAN, THE**
Tracks: / Singing the blues / Yours is my heart, alone / Garden in the rain / Don't be blue / Golden earrings / Louisiana / London by night / I'll be your friend with pleasure / We'll meet again / Gypsy, The.
**Album:** Released Apr '85, on Concord Jazz by Concord Jazz Records (USA). Catalogue no: **CJ 261**

**LIVE AT MAYBECK RECITAL HALL**
Tracks: / Dream dancing / Detour ahead / Exactly like you / I'm glad there is you/I'm glad I waited for you / Knowledge medley / Teach me tonight / School days / An apple for the teacher / I didn't know about you / Knowledge medley (pt 2).
**CD:** Released Mar '90, on Concord by Concord Jazz Records (USA). Catalogue no: **CCD 4410**
**Cass:** Released Mar '90, on Concord by Concord Jazz Records (USA). Catalogue no: **CJ 410C**

**MY FRIEND THE PIANO**
Tracks: / Margie / Only trust your heart / Mean to me / Slowly / You're driving me crazy / Summer medley: guess I'll go back home this su / Indian summer / Baby, baby all the time / Always medley: It's always you / Always / This is always.
Note: Dave McKenna - piano.
**Album:** Released Feb '87, on Concord Jazz by Concord Jazz Records (USA). Catalogue no: **CJ 313**
**CD:** Released Jul '87, on Concord Jazz by Concord Jazz Records (USA). Catalogue no: **CCD 4313**

**NO HOLDS BARRED (McKenna Dave Swing Six)**
**Album:** Released Feb '79, on Famous Door (USA) by Famous Door Records (USA). Catalogue no: **HL 122**

**NO MORE OUZO FOR PUZO (McKenna, Dave Quartet)**
Tracks: / Look for the silver lining / Smile / For you, for me, for evermore / You and I / You brought a new kind of love to me / Talk of the town / Shake down the stars / Lonesome me / No more ouzo for Puzo / I keep going back to Joe's / Talk to me / Please don't talk about me when I'm gone.
**Cass:** Released Jan '89, on Concord by Concord Jazz Records (USA). Catalogue no: **CJ 365C**
**Album:** Released Jan '89, on Concord by Concord Jazz Records (USA). Catalogue no: **CJ 365**
**CD:** Released Jan '89, on Concord by Concord Jazz Records (USA). Catalogue no: **CCD 365**

**OIL AND VINEGAR**
**Album:** Released Oct '79, on Honeydew Catalogue no: **HD 6613**

**PIANO MOVER (McKenna Dave & Dick Johnson)**
**Album:** Released May '81, on Concord by Concord Jazz Records (USA). Catalogue no: **CJ 146**

**PLAYS THE MUSIC HARRY WARREN (McKenna Dave Trio)**
**Album:** Released Mar '82, on Concord Jazz by Concord Jazz Records (USA). Catalogue no: **CJ 177**

## McKinley,Ray

**BLUE SKIES**
**Album:** Released Jan '84, on First Heard by Submarine Records. Catalogue no: **FH 32**
**Cass:** Released Jan '84, on First Heard by Submarine Records. Catalogue no: **CFH 32**

**CLASS OF 49**
**Album:** Released Apr '81, on Hep Jazz by Hep Records. Catalogue no: **HEP 4**

**DOWN THE ROAD APIECE (McKinley,Ray & his Orchestra)**
Tracks: / I'm an old cowhand (Vocal by Ray McKinley) / You started something (Vocal by Jean Finley) / You came a long way from St. Louis (Vocal by Ray McKinley) / Stars fell on Alabama / What did I do (Vocal by Ray McKinley) / Mint julep / Blue skies (Vocal by Jean Finley & The Four Hormones) / On a slow boat to China (Vocal by Ray McKinley) / Hair of gold (Vocal by Ray McKinley) / Blue moon / Richest man in the cemetary (Vocal by Ray McKinley) / Down the road apiece (Vocal by Ray McKinley) / Red silk stockings and green perfume (Vocal by Ray McKinley).
Note: Radio Transcriptions
**Cass:** Released Jun '86, on Dance Band Days by Prism Leisure. Catalogue no: **DBDC 05**
**Album:** Released Jun '86, on Dance Band Days by Prism Leisure. Catalogue no: **DBD 05**

**GLENN MILLER STORY THE**
**Album:** Released Jan '83, on RCA (Germany) Catalogue no: **26 21108**

**HOWDY FRIENDS (McKinley,Ray & his Orchestra)**
Tracks: / Jug of wine, A / Day by day / Cyclops / Nobody but you.
**Album:** Released Jun '89, on Limited Edition Catalogue no: **LE 102**

**RAY MCKINLEY & HIS MAGICIANS (McKinley,Ray & his Orchestra)**
**Album:** Released Apr '79, on First Heard by Submarine Records. Catalogue no: **FH 11**

## McKinney's Cotton

**Biographical details:** See biographical note under Redman, Don..

**MCKINNEY'S COMPLETE COTTON 1929-1930**
**Album:** Released '83, on RCA (France) by BMG Records (France). Catalogue no: **PM 43258**
**Album:** Released '83, on RCA (France) by BMG Records (France). Catalogue no: **PM 42407**
**Album:** Released Mar '84, on RCA (France) by BMG Records (France). Catalogue no: **NL 89161**

## McKusick, Hal

**EAST COAST JAZZ (McKusick, Hal Quartet)**
**Album:** Released Feb '88, on Fresh Sounds (Spain) by Fresh Sounds Records (Spain). Catalogue no: **FS 209**

**JAZZ WORKSHOP**
Tracks: / Tommy Hawk / Lydian lullaby / Blues for Pablo / Just leave it alone / Miss Clara / Alto cumulus / Day John Brown was hanged, The / One score and eight horns ago / Ain't nothin' but a memory now / Jambangle / Blues train.
**Album:** Released Jan '83, on RCA (France) by BMG Records (France). Catalogue no: **PM 43637**

## McLaughlin, John

**ADVENTURES IN RADIOLAND**
Tracks: / Wait, The / Just ideas / Jozy / Half man, half cookie / Florianopolis / Gotta dance / Wall will fall, The / Reincarnation / Mitch match / 20th century limited.
Note: Brand new album from guitar John McLaughlin. Digitally recorded and featuring new self-penned compositions. John also produced the album. Knowing the reputation that McLaughlin has and the high esteem in which he is held through his workwith the Mahavishnu Orchestra and earlier with musicians of the calibre of MilesDavis etc this new album is bound to attract alot of media attention. Personnel: Jonas Hellborg - bass / Bill Evans - saxes / Danny Gottlieb - drums / MitchellForman - keyboards / John McLaughlin - guitars.
**Cass:** Released Jul '87, on Polygram by PolyGram UK Ltd. Catalogue no: **SOSMC 2020**
**CD:** Released Jul '87, on Polygram by PolyGram UK Ltd. Catalogue no: **SOSCD 2020**
**Album:** Released Jul '87, on Polygram by PolyGram UK Ltd. Catalogue no: **SOS 2020**

**BELO HORIZONTE**
Tracks: / Belo Horizonte / La Baleine / Very early / One melody / Stardust on your sleeve / Waltz for Katia / Zamfir / Manitas d'oro.
**Album:** Released Feb '82, on WEA by WEA Records. Deleted Feb '87. Catalogue no: **K 99185**

**BEST OF JOHN MCLAUGHLIN**
Tracks: / Love supreme, A / New York on my mind / Dark prince, The / La danse du bonheur / Friendship / Face to face / Unknown dissident, The / Lotus feet.
**Album:** Released Jan '81, on CBS by CBS Records. Catalogue no: **CBS 84455**

**BETWEEN NOTHING AND ETERNITY**
**CD:** Released '88, on CBS by CBS Records. Deleted Jan '89. Catalogue no: **CD 69046**
**Album:** Released Dec '88, on Beat Goes On by Andy's Records. Catalogue no: **BGOLP 31**

**BIRDS OF FIRE (McLaughlin, John & Mahavishnu Orchestra)**
Tracks: / Birds of fire / Miles beyond / Celestial terrestrial commuters / Sapphire bullers of pure love / Thousand Island park / Hope / One word / Sanctuary / Open country joy / Resolution.
**Album:** Released Mar '73, on CBS by CBS Records. Deleted Mar '78. Catalogue no: **CBS 65321**
**Cass:** Released Nov '83, on CBS by CBS Records. Catalogue no: **40 32280**
**CD:** Released Nov '83, on CBS by CBS Records. Deleted Jan '89. Catalogue no: **CD 65321**
**Album:** Released Nov '83, on CBS by CBS Records. Catalogue no: **CBS 32280**

**DEVOTION**
**Album:** Released Jul '87, on CBS by CBS Records. Catalogue no: **GL 65075**

**ELECTRIC DREAMS**
Tracks: / Guardian angels / Miles Davis / Electric dreams / Electric sighs / Love and understanding / Desire and the comforter / Singing earth / Dark prince / Unknown dissident.
**Album:** Released '79, on CBS by CBS Records. Deleted '84. Catalogue no: **CBS 83526**

**EXTRAPOLATION**
**Album:** Released '69, on Polydor by Polydor Ltd. Catalogue no: **2310 018**

**HANDFUL OF BEAUTY, A (McLaughlin, John & Shakti)**
**Album:** Released Mar '77, on CBS by CBS Records. Catalogue no: **CBS 81664**

**INNER MOUNTAIN FLAME (McLaughlin, Mahavishnu, John)**
**Album:** Released '74, on CBS by CBS Records. Catalogue no: **64 717**

**INNER WORLDS**
**Album:** Released '87, on CBS by CBS Records. Catalogue no: **69261**

**LIVE AT THE ROYAL FESTIVAL HALL**
**Cass:** Released 2 Apr '90, on Phonogram by Phonogram Ltd. Catalogue no: **834 426 4**
**CD:** Released 2 Apr '90, on Phonogram by Phonogram Ltd. Catalogue no: **834 426 2**
**Album:** Released 2 Apr '90, on Phonogram by Phonogram Ltd. Catalogue no: **834 426 1**

**MCLAUGHLIN, JOHN (WITH SHAKTI)**
**Album:** Released Jun '76, on CBS by CBS Records. Catalogue no: **CBS 81388**

**MUSIC SPOKEN HERE**
Tracks: / Aspan / Blues for LW / Translators / Honky tonk haven / Viene clareando / David / Negative ions / Brise de coeur / Loro.
**Album:** Released '82, on WEA by WEA Records. Catalogue no: **WEA 99254**

**MY GOAL'S BEYOND (McLaughlin, Mahavishnu, John)**
**Album:** on CBS by CBS Records. Catalogue no: **DGL 69014**

**NATURAL ELEMENTS (McLaughlin, John & Shakti)**
**Album:** Released Dec '77, on CBS by CBS Records. Catalogue no: **CBS 82329**

**PASSION GRACE AND FIRE (McLaughlin, John/Al Di Meola/Paco De Lucia)**
Tracks: / Aspen / Orient blues / Chiquito / Sichia / David / Passion, grace and fire.
**Album:** Released Jun '83, on Mercury by Phonogram Ltd. Catalogue no: **MERL 24**
**Cass:** Released Jun '83, on Mercury by Phonogram Ltd. Catalogue no: **MERLC 24**
**CD:** Released Jun '83, on Mercury by Phonogram Ltd. Catalogue no: **811 334 2**

**THUNDERBYRD**
**Album:** Released '87, on CBS by CBS Records. Catalogue no: **81883**

## McLean, Jackie

**Biographical details:** This American alto saxophonist and composer has been a jazz artist since the early Fifties, although his performing activities have been spasmodic. He was given early encouragement by a famous fellow alto saxman, the legendary Charlie Parker. Born in 1932, McLean made his first records under his own name in the mid-Fifties, his first great composition being *Little Melonae*. McLean was steadily building his reputation when drug difficulties began to affect him. During the Sixties his live work gradually diminished until, by the end of that decade, he hade ceased performing live altogether; he was barred from many New York clubs even after the problem eased. Nonetheless, he compensated for this in no uncertain terms - his 1962-67 period on the famed Blue Note label yielded what many critics consider to be his greatest disc output. The album *Let Freedom Ring* was particularly noteworthy.
The Seventies saw him return to occasional performing. He continued beheld in high esteem in jazz circles, although he never quite entered the very top league. Late in his career, McLean achieved his only entry into the UK pop charts - *Dr Jackyll and Mr Funk*, a single featuring the assistance of a vocal backup group, reached No.53. This was a surprising nod to the then fashionable disco scene (July 1979); by this time McLean was devoting much of his time to teaching activities and to the study and furtherance of Afro-American cultural ties. (Bob MacDonald, 14th January 1986).

**BLUESNIK**
Tracks: / Bluesnik / Goin' 'way blues / Drew's blues / Cool green / Blues function / Torchin' / Goin' 'way blues (alt. take) (CD only.) / Torchin' (alt. take) (CD only.).
**CD:** Released Aug '89, on Blue Note by EMI Records. Catalogue no: **CDP 784 067 2**
**CD:** Released Aug '89, on Blue Note by EMI Records. Catalogue no: **BNZ 225**
**Album:** Released Jan '85, on Blue Note by EMI Records. Deleted '87. Catalogue no: **BST 84067**

**CONNECTION, THE (McLean, Jackie & Freddie Redd)**
Tracks: / Who killed Cock Robin? / Wigglin' / Music forever / Time to smile / Theme for Sister Salvation / Jim Dunn's dilemma / O.D. (overdose).
**Album:** Released Sep '84, on Blue Note by EMI Records. Deleted '87. Catalogue no: **BST 84027**
**Album:** Released Oct '83, on Boplicity by Ace Records. Deleted '88. Catalogue no: **BOP 004**

**CONTOUR**
Tracks: / Foggy day / Keerplunk / Inding / Lights out / Up / Lorraine / Sentimental journey / Why was I borne / Contour.
**2 LP Set:** Released Apr '80, on Prestige Catalogue no: **PR 24076**

**DEMON'S DANCE**
Tracks: / Toyland / Boo Ann's grand / Sweet love of mine / Floogeh / Message from trane / Demon's dance.
Note: Producer/Arranger Francis Wolff. (P) 1987 EMI-Manhattan Records, a division of Capitol Records inc.
**CD:** Released May '88, on Blue Note by EMI Records. Catalogue no: **BNZ 61**
**CD:** Released May '88, on Blue Note by EMI Records. Catalogue no: **CDP 784 345 2**

**DOCTOR JACKYLL AND MISTER FUNK**
Tracks: / Doctor Jackyll and Mister Funk / On the slick side.
**7" Single:** Released Jul '79, on RCA by BMG Records (UK). Deleted '82. Catalogue no: **PB 1575**
**12" Single:** Released Jul '79, on RCA by BMG Records (UK). Deleted '82. Catalogue no: **PC 1575**

**FAT JAZZ**
Tracks: / Filide / Millies pad / Two sons / What good am I without you / Tune up.
**Album:** Released 12 Feb '88, on Fresh Sounds (Spain) by Fresh Sounds Records (Spain). Catalogue no: **FS 307**

**FRICKLE SONANCE,A**
**Album:** Released Sep '84, on Blue Note by EMI Records. Deleted '87. Catalogue no: **BST 84089**

**JACKIE MCLEAN & CO. (Various artists)**
Tracks: / Minor dream: *Various artists* / Mirage: *Various artists* / Beau Jack: *Various artists* / Help: *Various artists* / Flickers: *Various artists.*
**Album:** Released Feb '84, on Prestige (USA) by Fantasy Inc (USA). Catalogue no: **OJC 074**

**JACKIE MCLEAN ON MARS (VIDEO)**
**VHS:** Released '88, on Kay Jazz (video) by Kay Jazz. Catalogue no: **KJ 074**

**JACKIE'S BAG**
Tracks: / Quadrangle / Blues Inn / Fidel / Appointment in Ghana / Ballad for Doll, A / Isle of Java / Street singer / Melonae's dance / Medina.
**Album:** Released Jul '89, on Blue Note by EMI Records. Catalogue no: **BST 84051**
**CD:** Released Sep '87, on Blue Note by EMI Records. Deleted Feb '90. Catalogue no: **CDP 746 142 2**
**Album:** Released Jul '89, on Blue Note by EMI Records. Catalogue no: **784 051 1**
**CD:** Released Sep '87, on Blue Note by EMI Records. Catalogue no: **BNZ 59**

**LET FREEDOM RING**
Tracks: / Melody for Melonae / I'll keep loving you / Rene / Omega.
**Album:** Released Jul '89, on Blue Note by EMI Records. Catalogue no: **BST 84106**
**CD:** Released May '87, on Blue Note by EMI Records. Catalogue no: **BNZ 58**
**CD:** Released May '87, on Blue Note by EMI Records. Catalogue no: **CDP 746 527 2**

**LONG DRINK OF THE BLUES, A**
**Album:** Released Jan '87, on Original Jazz Classics (USA) by Fantasy Inc (USA). Catalogue no: **OJC 253**

**MCLEANS SCENE**
**Album:** Released Aug '84, on Prestige (USA) by Fantasy Inc (USA). Catalogue no: **OJC 098MONUMENTS**
Tracks: / Gotta get a piece of your soul / They all seem to disappear / Molimo / Monuments / Doctor Jackyll and Mister Funk / Long time lover / On the slick side.
**Album:** Released '79, on RCA by BMG Records (UK). Deleted '84. Catalogue no: **PL 13230**

**NEW AND OLD GOSPEL**
Tracks: / Lifeline / Offspring / Midway / Vernzone / Inevitable end / Old gospel / Strange as it seems.
**Album:** Released Jan '85, on Blue Note

by EMI Records. Deleted Jan '88. **Catalogue no: BST 84262**

**NEW SOIL**
Tracks: / Hip strut / Mince apprehension / Greasy / Sweet cakes / Davis cup / Formidable (CD only.).
**Album:** Released Apr '89, on Blue Note by EMI Records. Catalogue no: B1 **84013**
**CD:** Released Apr '89, on Blue Note by EMI Records. Catalogue no: **CDP 784 013 2**
**CD:** Released Apr '89, on Blue Note by EMI Records. Catalogue no: **BNZ 158**

**NEW YORK CALLING**
**Album:** Released Jul '88, on Steeplechase (USA) Catalogue no: **SCS 1023**
**CD:** Released Jul '88, on Steeplechase (USA) Catalogue no: **SCCD 31023**

**ONE STEP BEYOND**
Tracks: / Frankenstein / Blue rondo / Ghost town / Saturday and sunday / Saturday and sunday (alternate take).
**CD:** Released Sep '87, on Blue Note by EMI Records. Catalogue no: **BNZ 60**
**Album:** Released Sep '84, on Blue Note by EMI Records. Deleted '87. Catalogue no: **BST 84137**
**CD:** Released Sep '87, on Blue Note by EMI Records. Catalogue no: **CDP 746 821 2**

**SWING SWANG SWINGIN'**
Tracks: / What's new? / Let's face the music and dance / Stablemates / I remember you / I love you / I'll take romance / 116th and Lennox.
**Album:** Released Sep '83, on Boplicity by Ace Records. Deleted '88. Catalogue no: **BOP 002**

**TRIBUTE TO CHARLIE PARKER FROM**
**Album:** Released '83, on RCA (France) by BMG Records (France). Catalogue no: **PL 43560**

## McLellan,Tommy

**COTTON PATCH BLUES**
**Album:** Released Nov '84, on Travelin' Man by Interstate Music. Catalogue no: **TM 804**

## McNab, Ted

**BIG BAND SWING (McNab, Ted And Company)**
**Album:** Released Feb '88, on Fresh Sounds (Spain) by Fresh Sounds Records (Spain). Catalogue no: **FS 29**

## McNeil, John

**EMBARKATION**
**Album:** Released Apr '79, on Steeplechase (USA) Catalogue no: **SCS 1099**

**FAUN (McNeil, John Quintet)**
**Album:** Released Sep '79, on Steeplechase (USA) Catalogue no: **SCS 1117**

**THINGS WE DID LAST SUMMER**
**Album:** Released Jul '88, on Steeplechase (USA) Catalogue no: **SCS 1231**
**CD:** Released Jul '88, on Steeplechase (USA) Catalogue no: **SCCD 31231**

## Macon, Albert

**BLUES & BOOGIE FROM ALABAMA (Macon, Albert & Robert Thomas)**
**Album:** Released May '86, on Swing Master Catalogue no: **2105**

## McPartland, Jimmy

**ONE NIGHT STAND**
**Album:** Released Jan '87, on Jazzology (USA) by Jazzology Records (USA). Catalogue no: **J 137**

## McPartland, Marian

**AT HICKORY HOUSE**
**2 LP Set:** Released Mar '85, on Savoy Jazz (USA) by Malaco Records (USA). Catalogue no: **SJL 2248**

**JANUARY 6TH & 8TH 1964**
Tracks: / Y'know what I mean / Easy like / Hawk talk / Ida / Blues for Indian Jim / Don't panic / Magpie / So little time / Secret / Deep river / Warmin' up / Lonely.
**Album:** Released Oct '80, on From The Jazz Vault by Damont Audio Ltd.. Catalogue no: **JV 113**

**MUSIC OF LEONARD BERNSTEIN, THE**
**Cass:** Released May '85, on Bainbridge by Ducale S.p.A.. Catalogue no: **BT 41013**
**Album:** Released May '85, on Bainbridge by Ducale S.p.A.. Catalogue no: **BT 1013**

**PERSONAL CHOICE**
Tracks: / I hear a rhapsody / Meditation / In your own sweet way / Sleeping bee / I'm old fashioned / When the sun comes out / Tricotism / Melancholy mood.
**Album:** Released Mar '83, on Concord Jazz by Concord Jazz Records (USA). Catalogue no: **CJ 202**
**Cass:** Released Mar '83, on Concord Jazz by Concord Jazz Records (USA). Catalogue no: **CJC 202**
**CD:** Released Mar '87, on Concord Jazz by Concord Jazz Records (USA). Catalogue no: **CCD 4202**

**PLAYS THE MUSIC OF BILLY STRAYHORN**
Tracks: / Intimacy of the blues, The / Isfahan / Lotus blossom / Raincheck / Lush life / U.M.M.G. / Flower is a lovesome thing, A / Take the 'A' train / Daydream / After all.
**Cass:** Released Oct '87, on Concord Jazz by Concord Jazz Records (USA). Catalogue no: **CJC 326**
**CD:** Released Oct '87, on Concord Jazz by Concord Jazz Records (USA). Catalogue no: **CCD 4326**
**Album:** Released Oct '87, on Concord Jazz by Concord Jazz Records (USA). Catalogue no: **CJ 326**

**WILLOW CREEK AND OTHER BALLADS**
Tracks: / Without you / Things we did last summer, The / All in love is fair / Willow creek / Long ago and far away / Some day I'll find you / I saw stars / Blood count / I've got a crush on you / Summer song.
**Album:** Released Jul '85, on Concord Jazz by Concord Jazz Records (USA). Catalogue no: **CJ 272**
**Cass:** Released Jul '85, on Concord Jazz by Concord Jazz Records (USA). Catalogue no: **CJC 272**

## MacPherson, Fraser

**I DIDN'T KNOW ABOUT YOU (MacPherson, Fraser & Oliver Gannon)**
Tracks: / This heart of mine / Do nothing till you hear from me / Everything happens to me / All by myself / More I see you, The / Mean to me / I didn't know about you / Day by day / Nightingale sang in Berkeley Square, A / You go to my head / In a mellow tone.
**Album:** Released Jul '86, on Sackville by Spotlite Records. Catalogue no: **4009**

**JAZZ PROSE (MacPherson, Fraser Quintet)**
Tracks: / Darn that dream / It could happen to you / Happy man / All alone / On a slow boat to China / There is no greater love / I'll never be the same / You'd be so nice to come home to.
**Cass:** Released Jul '85, on Concord Jazz by Concord Jazz Records (USA). Catalogue no: **CJC 269**
**Album:** Released Jul '85, on Concord Jazz by Concord Jazz Records (USA). Catalogue no: **CJ 269**

## McRae, Carmen

**ALIVE**
**Album:** Released Mar '83, on Audio Fidelity(USA) by Audio Fidelity (USA). Deleted Mar '88. Catalogue no: **MRD 5001**

**ANY OLD TIME**
Tracks: / Tulip or turnip / Old devil moon / Have you met Miss Jones / Love me tender / I hear music / This is always / Body and soul / Prelude to a kiss / Mean to me / Any old time / It could happen to you / I'm glad there is you / Billie's blues.
Note: In this superb Denon recording, Carmen McRae sings, with her usual distinct style and expression, her own selection of no less than thirteen evergreens and famous jazz and pop numbers which form a comprehensive survey of her career. (Denon 10/88). Personnel: Carmen McRae (Vocal), Eric Gunnison (Piano), Scott Colley (Bass), John Collins (Guitar), Mark Pulice (Drums), Clifford Jordan (Tenor sax).
**CD:** Released Oct '88, on Denon Catalogue no: **CY 1216**
**Cass:** Released Oct '88, on Denon Catalogue no: **CC 13**

**CARMEN MCRAE**
**CD:** Released Jul '89, on Cleo Catalogue no: **CLCD 5009**
**Cass:** Released Oct '84, on Audio Fidelity(USA) by Audio Fidelity (USA). Catalogue no: **ZCGAS 750**

**CARMEN MCRAE LIVE**
**CD:** Released Sep '88, on Kingdom Jazz by Kingdom Records. Catalogue no: **CDGATE 7001**

**FINE AND MELLOW**
Tracks: / What can I say, after I say I'm

sorry? / Fine and mellow / These foolish things / Black and blue / One more chance / Until the real thing comes along / My handy man ain't handy no more / What is this thing called love? (Bonus track on CD only.).
Note: "Carmen McRae is at the top of her profession and Fine And Mellow is an apt description of this superlative performance recorded live at Birdland West, Long Beach, California. The vocals and accompaniment are perfection , with Carmen supported by an all-star quintet under the musical direction of Red Holloway. Carmen McRae, vocals; Red Holloway, alto, tenor saxes; John Clayton, bass; Paul Humphrey, drums; Jack McDuff, organ; Phil Upchurch, guitar." (IMS Records, May 1988.)
**Cass:** Released May '88, on Concord Jazz by Concord Jazz Records (USA). Catalogue no: **CJC 342**
**CD:** Released May '88, on Concord Jazz by Concord Jazz Records (USA). Catalogue no: **CCD 4342**
**Album:** Released May '88, on Concord Jazz by Concord Jazz Records (USA). Catalogue no: **CJ 342**

### HEATWAVE (McRae, Carmen/Cal Tjader)
Tracks: / Heatwave / All in the love is fair / Besame mucho / Evil ways / Do nothing till you hear from me / Love / Upside down / Visit / Speak low / Don't you worry 'bout a thing.
**Album:** Released Jul '82, on Concord Jazz by Concord Jazz Records (USA). Catalogue no: **CJ 189**
**CD:** Released '88, on Concord Jazz by Concord Jazz Records (USA). Catalogue no: **CCD 4189**

### INVITATION
Tracks: / Passing fancy / I guess I'll dress up for the blues / Never loved him anyhow / Invitation / As I love you / Moon ray / So nice to be wrong / go for you / Lo and behold / Come down to earth, Mr. Smith / You don't know me / It's like getting a donkey to gallop / How many stars have to shine? / Tonight he's out to break another heart / It's so much fun / Belonging to you.
**CD:** on Official by Official Records. Catalogue no: **OFF 83027**
**Album:** on Official by Official Records. Catalogue no: **OFF 3027**

### LIVE
Tracks: /. Black magic / Superwoman / New York state of mind / Underneath the apple tree / Thou swell / Send in the clowns / I just can't wait to see you / How long has this been going on / If I were a bell / My foolish heart / Secret love / I concentrate on you (CD only.).
**Cass:** Released '89, on Kingdom Jazz by Kingdom Records. Catalogue no: **CGATE 7001**
**Album:** Released Sep '83, on Kingdom Jazz by Kingdom Records. Catalogue no: **GATE 7001**
**CD:** Released '89, on Kingdom Jazz by Kingdom Records. Catalogue no: **CDGATE 7001**

### LIVE (VIDEO)
**VHS:** Released Feb '90, on Verve Catalogue no: **CFV10282**

### MISS MAGIC
**CD:** Released '86, on Dunhill Compact Classics (USA) Catalogue no: **DZS 021**

### RONNIE SCOTT'S PRESENTS CARMEN
**Album:** Released Jan '78, on Pye-Ronnie Scott Catalogue no: **NSPL 18543**

### TORCHY
Tracks: / Last night when we were young / Speak low / But beautiful / If you'd stay the way I dream about you / Midnight sun / We'll be together again / I'm a dreamer / Good morning heartache / Starry eyes / I don't stand a ghost of a chance with you.
**Album:** Released Nov '89, on Memoir by Memoir Records. Catalogue no: **MOIR 204**
**Cass:** Released Nov '89, on Memoir by Memoir Records. Catalogue no: **CMOIR 204**

### VELVET SOUL
Tracks: / Nice work if you can get it / It takes a whole lot of human feeling / I fall in love too easily / Hey John / Where are the words / Straighten up and fly right / Inside a silent tear / Imagination / Right to love, The / All the things you are / You're mine you / You and I / How could I settle for less / Good life / Sunshine of my life / Exactly like you / There will come a time / Masquerade.
**Cass:** Released Apr '89, on Denon Catalogue no: **MC 7970**
**CD:** Released '88, on Denon Catalogue no: **C38 7970**
**CD:** Released Apr '89, on Denon Catalogue no: **DC 8542**

### YOU'RE LOOKING AT ME
Tracks: / I'm an errand girl for rhythm / Beautiful moons ago / Frim fram sauce / Come i out of the rain / How does it feel / If I had you / I can't see for lookin' / Sweet Lorraine / You're lookin' at me / Just you just me.
**Album:** Released Apr '84, on Concord Jazz by Concord Jazz Records (USA). Catalogue no: **CJ 235**
**CD:** Released Sep '86, on Concord Jazz by Concord Jazz Records (USA). Catalogue no: **CCD 4235**

## McShann, Jay

### AFTER HOURS
**Album:** Released Jan '88, on Storyville by Storyville Records AB. Catalogue no: **SLP 4024**

### AIRMAIL SPECIAL
Note: With Neil Swainson, Terry Clarke.G
**Album:** Released Jun '88, on Sackville by Spotlite Records. Catalogue no: **3040**
**CD:** Released '88, on Sackville by Spotlite Records. Catalogue no: **SACKCD 3040**

### BAND THAT JUMPS THE BLUES, THE
Tracks: / Hot biscuits / Slow drag blues / Mr. Boogie / Buttermilk / Skid Row blues / Soft winds / No name boogie / Thinking about my baby / Geronimo / Twelve o'clock whistle / Mellodrag / Eatin' watermelon.
**Album:** Released Sep '85, on Black Lion Catalogue no: **BLP 30144**

### BIG BAND BOUNCE AND BOOGIE (see under Hootie's KC Blues)

### BLUES & BOOGIE (McShann, Jay & Sammy Price)
Tracks: / Hands off / Ain't nobody's business / St. Louis blues / You've been a good ol' wagon / Let the good times roll / St. James' infirmary blues / In the evening / Price is right, The / Blues for two pianos / Boogie for Jay and Sam / Everyday I have the blues.
**Album:** Released Apr '84, on Philips (Holland) by PolyGram UK Ltd. Catalogue no: **9198 203**
**Cass:** Released Apr '84, on Philips (Holland) by PolyGram UK Ltd. Catalogue no: **7298 203**

### CRAZY LEGS & FRIDAY STRUT (McShann, Jay & Buddy Tate)
**Album:** Released Apr '81, on Sackville by Spotlite Records. Catalogue no: **3011**

### EARLY BIRD (McShann, Jay and his Orchestra)
Tracks: / I found a new baby / Body and soul / Moten swing / Coquette / Lady be good / Blues / Honeysuckle rose / Cherokee / You say forward, I'll march / Lonely boy blues / Vine Street boogie / Jump the blues away / Bottle it / Sweet Georgia Brown / Wrap your troubles in dreams.
**Album:** Released '83, on Spotlite by Spotlite Records. Catalogue no: **SPJ 120**

### GOING TO KANSAS CITY (McShann, Jay & The All Stars)
**CD:** Released '88, on New World (USA) by New World Records (USA). Catalogue no: **NWCD 358**
**Album:** Released '88, on New World (USA) by New World Records (USA). Catalogue no: **NW 358**
**Album:** Released Jan '83, on Swaggie (Australia) Catalogue no: **S 1322**

### HOOTIE'S KC BLUES Big band bounce & boogie (McShann, Jay and his Orchestra)
Tracks: / Hootie blues / Red river blues / Confessin' the blues / Vine Street boogie / 'For day rider / Sepian bounce / Hold 'em Hootie / Swingmatism / Jumpin' blues / One woman's blues / Get me on your mind / Dexter blues / Hootie's ignorant oil / Lonely boy blues / So you won't jump / (New) confessin' the blues.
Note: When *Confessin' the blues* made it big in 1942, with a section of the American record buying public. It focused attention on the combined talents of the Jay McShann Orchestra, and its singer Walter Brown. To an appreciative audience stretching far and wide outside the 'Mid West', to which the popularity of both had been more or less confined in previous times. *Confessin'* also brough band and singer to New York - the focal point of so much important jazz activity at the time - where even those with pro-

**Jay McShann - Big Band Bounce and Boogie (Affinity)**

fessed comprehensive interest in the big band scene wondered where this 'new' dynamic, blues based outfit had been hiding itself. And when they heard Jay McShann laying down his own splended brand of blues-based jazz piano in live performance, the general reaction again was one of astonished delight. For the warm friendly, large framed man from Muskogee, Oklahoma, brought to the New York jazz scene an irresistible blend of admirable technique, eloquence, down home primitivism, not to mention an all-round maturity, that mad the New Yorkers realise comprehensively, what they'd been missing. All of which must, have seemed amusing and ironic to Jay, who had been pumping out his timeless piano playing - in jazz as well as blues venues - since at least the beginning of the 1930's.

He'd been fronting a variety of bands, too, of varying numbers. And many of the sidemen he brought with him to New York had worked with him for some time before and between them they had collected not inconsiderable experience outside the Jay McShann band.

Truth was of course, that McShann and Co, were from the Mid-West, a large area of North America that for years had had its own comprehensive volume of musicians and bands, many of whom had never ventured furhter north than Chicago. Kansas City was the home base for many Mid-Westerners. And Kansas City was where Jay McShann first established his own enviable reputation as a pianist of redoubtable abilities. Jay had graduated to KC - a legendary jazz spot for the many and famous cutting contests, involving locals and the touring greats - from Muskogee, via Tulsa, Arkansas City, and valuable ground work with bands like those of Al Denny (McShann was 15 when he joined this 12 piece Tulsa based outfit). Eddie Hill and His Bostonians (visiting Arizona, New Mexico), and Dee Prince Stewart. It was shortly after this latter gig, in 1937, that McShann put together his own seven piece combo to play the posh future events, amongst the sidemen were drummer Gus Johnson, bassist Gene Ramey, trumpeter Orville Minor, tenorist Bob Maband and saxist writer Willie Scott, together forming the nucleus of the first Jay McShann Orchestra. Some help in establishing Jay's reputation on a national basis came through a rave review, published in Down Beat magazine, and submitted by a young, jazz-keen writer for the Kansas City Journal Post. Dave Dexter Jr had first heard McShann live, playing solo piano, had been impressed and, as he write in his autobiography (Playback, Billboard Publications Inc). 'He had style, particularly with the blues, and was so likeable that I began a minor crusade to establish his name nationally'. And it was Dexter who persuaded the Decca record label's Jack Kapp to send his brother Dave to record the McShann outfit, in Dallas, Texas. (In actual fact, the McShann band had visited Chicago before this Dallas date. No recording contract had been signed at least 48 hours before the event, he would be violating union rules. The session was cancelled.)

The Dallas session was the breakthrough the band needed. A slightly larger ensemble had been assembled following a successful 4 and a half month long season at the Century Room, K.C. The most significant addition to the personnel that made the first historic recording date was a slim alto-saxophonist who'd worked occasionally with McShann - led bands previously. Charlie Parker, just a short period before becoming recognised as the arch-contributor to jazz' most significant revolution, already was turning heads around - especially those of fellow musicians: McShann apart, he was to become the most notable solo contributor to the various bands that Jay was to front between 1940 and thereafter. The inclusion of Walter Brown came only days before the first record date. The fascinating story of how McShann first heard liner note for Brown's *Confessin' the blues* (Affinity AFF 66). Briefly, an obviously impressed McShann asked Brown if he'd collaborate on some blues songs for the singer to perform at that Dallas session. It was important that McShann found a vocalist to sing the blues - even though Jay himself has been a fine vocalist, right from his early days. For Dave Kapp was interested only in recording blues - he didn't want any of the McShann Band jazz offerings: Which included a Parker' original known then as *What price love*, but which soon thereafter achieved classic status under the more personal title of *Yardbird suite*.

More irony came at the Dallas date insofar as the McShann big band was featured on only half the six tracks waxed on April 30, 1941. And the big selling, *Confessin' the blues* features Brown's nasally blues singing accompanied only by the McShann Ramey Johnson rhythm section. Brown's no nonsense approach is of course the focal point about *Confessin'* and the single most important contributor in helping to make this side a smash hit success. For the connoisseurs though, probably the most significant aspect *Confessin'*, is the superb piano playing, both in support of the singer, and even more in solo performance - the gorgeous intro, just reeeking of pure KC blues; remains a perfect model for demonstrating mood and tempo.

The rhythm section, minus Brown, is splendidly represented on two quick tempoed boogie blues numbers - *Vine Street boogie* and *Hold 'em Hootie* - Both featuring effortless, playing by McShann, each performance amply showing his controlled strength, something which, of course reamins a hallmark of his work today. The full band does get three chances to show its collective and individual strength. There's a marvellous relaxation about *Dexter blues*, (an obvious dedication to the writer, later record producer of the same name), with a short torrid plunger-mute outburst from Minor, and a delightfully understated piano contribution. And to show that, even at this stage, Parker was beginning to influence other players. John Jackson (the band's other altoist) takes a shapely solo on *Dexter*that contains several key elements of his colleague's more embryonic style (viz, tone, phraseology blues feel). But there is no doubt whatsoever who takes the superb alto solo near the end of *Swingmatism.* Absoloutely gorgeous - if all too short. *Hootie blues*, jointly written and arranged by McShann and Parker - and with lyrics by Brown, who takes one of his best vocals with the band - is the real gem of the session. Basically, a solid feature for Brown, it contains a miniature masterpiece in Parker's blues-drenched 12 bar solo. For those who took the trouble to really listen to the B side of *Confessin'*, it proved something of a watershed, both in Parker's own development as a soloist and as an individual declaration of the jazz revolution just around the corner.

Dave Kapp, pleased with how the first record date had gone, fixed a second, this time in Chicago. This was strictly a non-big band affair. In between times, McShann had added a guitarist, Leonard 'Lucky' Enois, to the overall lineup, and Enois participated at the Chicago session, along with the ususal rhythm section. Brown was featured more prominently than the last time. For one track, a trumpet (almost certainly Orville Minor) and one of the altoists, also put in an appearance. (No positive confirmation yet of another theory as to the exact lineup but the keen-eared Brian Priestley suggests close aural reference indicates the presence of a trombone in there with trumpet and alto. Very difficult to say for sure, as Brian readily agrees). The horns - two or three - have so little to do on *One woman's man*, that final indentification is hardly of great importance buy whether or not it's Jackson (who most discographers seem to think it is) or Parker who handles the brief obbligato support, remains unanswered in a definitive way. Anyway, the most important segments of the track are the singing - this is one of Walter Brown's very best recordings - and McShann's inspiring piano, especially behind the first vocal chorus. All but two of the octet of cuts emanating from that November '41 session are contained herein. Which is good news for the real collector, for it seems unlikely that too many individual tracks from this second session have appeared as part of previous British LP releases before this time. For some seeminly unexplained reason, Brown and the enlarged rhythm section cut another version of *Confession' the blues*. Some basic approach to the hit number as before. Same basic results - although if anything; both the vocal performance and McShann's fine intro are better than on the previous recording. This apart, there seems no real difference ... but why did Decca require a second *Confessin* especially so close to the making of the first? Of the remaining titles here, also from that late '41 date, *Red river blues* has even better Brown ('my woman she gotta mouth like a lighthouse on the sea') The singer manages to add extra conviction to *Fore day rider*, although it is Jay's expressive blues playing that takes second place to no-one and nothing else. Butperhaps the finest vocal instrumental number from the session is *Hootie's ignorant oil.* Opening with some lovely boogie blues, KC style from McShann the track never lets up, from start to finish. Johnson's drumming is inspiring throughout, with Ramey's rock steady bass in pivotal support. Brown too, really raises his game here, evidencing more personality in his singing. Again, though, it's McShann's spring heeled solo that cops honours. The final Decca session covered by this fine compilation took place in New York, after the band had arrived and had begun creating a favourable impression in the Big Apple. It is significant, if only for the fact that it marked the final occasion Charlie Parker would record commercially with the band (in this case, the full size big band). Parker had been worrying McShann by his erratic behaviour, caused mostly it seemed by his pre-occupation with drugs and booze. And it didn't appear to the leader that the altoist was too interested in the band anymore. But later, for Stanley Dance he remembered ('The World of Count Basie': Sidgwick and Jackson) Parker's contributions to his band with obvious gratitude and pride.

'I always say his peak was when he was with my band. He played more then: If anything, he lost when he got involved with the 'stuff' and got so far-out. No-one who heard it ever forgets the time we were broadcasting from the Savoy Ballroom and playing *Cherokee.* The engineer on that broadcast must have been a musician, because he told me to keep right on and we played right through the theme. Bird was straight then and he really had his chops.' Well Parker's final contributions to the McShann band's discography aren't half bad. For instance, he is relaxed and in full flight during McShann's fine *The jumpin' blues*, his beautifully logical solo cut off only by Brown's entry. Certainly, the band sounds inspired by Parker's playing.

His solo presence is much too short during *Sepian bounce*, but there's little doubt his story is the one that counts. Solo wise, that's all for Parker. But his influence on Jackson is emphasised strongly, again, by the latter's opening solo during *Lonely boy blues* (McShann is the only individual support for Al Hibbler's solid vocal on *Get me on your mind.* Jay McShann continued to lead his band until inducted into the US Forces in 1944, which virtually ended his career as a big band leader. Subsequently he fronted a variety of fine, jumpin' small combos, and in the last 20 years, he's worked mostly in a solo capacity - and quite splendidly too. His big band leading days didn't last too long. But he and his sidemen left an endelible impression on those who heard the Jay McShann orchestra in live performance, or at the least, heard them on the record. For the latter, especially we should be most grateful.... (Stan Britt, Jazz Link, 1983.)

**Album:** Released Sep '83, on Affinity by Charly Records. Catalogue no: **AFS 1006**

**JUST A LUCKY SO 'N' SO**

**Album:** Released Jul '88, on Sackville by Spotlite Records. Catalogue no: **3035**

**KANSAS CITY HUSTLE**

**Album:** Released Apr '81, on Sackville by Spotlite Records. Catalogue no: **3021**

**MAGICAL JAZZ (McShann, Jay/Burks, Martha)**

**Album:** Released Feb '89, on Jazz Mark Catalogue no: **JAZZ MARK 102**

**MAN FROM MUSKOGEE, THE**

Tracks: / Vine Street boogie / Staggers The / Yardbird waltz / My Chile / Confessin' the blues / Moten swing / Man from Muskogee, The / Blues for on old cat / I ain't mad at you / Do wah doo / Dexter blues.

**Album:** Released '86, on Affinity by Charly Records. Catalogue no: **AFF 147**

**Album:** Released Apr '81, on Sackville by Spotlite Records. Catalogue no: **3005**

**TRIBUTE TO FATS WALLER, A**

**Album:** Released Apr '81, on Sackville by Spotlite Records. Catalogue no: **3019**

**TUXEDO JUNCTION**

Tracks: / Tuxedo Junction / One sided love / Robbins nest / Froggy bottom / Gee baby ain't I good to you / Do nothing till you hear from me / Barrelhouse bolero.

**Album:** Released '81, on Sackville by Spotlite Records. Catalogue no: **3025**

**VINE STREET BOOGIE**

Tracks: / My chile / Hootie blues / Satin doll / I'm beginning to see the light / Vine Street boogie / Confessin' the blues / Yardbird waltz / Hooties ignorant oil.

**Album:** Released Sep '87, on Black Lion Catalogue no: **BLP 30169**

## McTell, Blind Willie

**BLIND WILLIE MCTELL, 1927-35**

**Album:** Released Dec '88, on Yazoo (USA) by Shanachie Records (USA). Catalogue no: **L 1037**

**BLIND WILLIE MCTELL, 1933-35**

**Album:** Released Oct '88, on Roots (Germany) Catalogue no: **RL 324**

**Album:** Released '88, on Document Catalogue no: **DLP 531**

**EARLY YEARS, THE 1927-33**

**Album:** Released Dec '88, on Yazoo (USA) by Shanachie Records (USA). Catalogue no: **YAZOO 1005**

**LAST SESSION**

**Album:** Released Jan '87, on OBC Catalogue no: **OBC 517**

**LEGENDARY LIBRARY OF CONGRESS 1940**

Tracks: / Chainey / Murderer's home / Kill it kid rag / I got to cross the river o' Jordan / Monologue / Old time reli-

gion, amen / Willie Fox / Dying crapshooter's blues / Amazing grace / Monologue / Medley / King Edward blues / Delia / Boll weevil / I got to cross the river o' Jordan.
**Album:** Released Oct '87, on Blue Moon (1) by Magnum Music Group. Catalogue no: **BMLP 1049**

**LOVE CHANGIN' BLUES**
Tracks: / Love changin' blues / Savannah mama / Talkin' to you mama / East St. Louis / Wee midnight hours / Pal of mine / Down home girl / Night watchman blues / Why did I make you cry / Kid man blues / Ludella.
**Album:** Released Jun '89, on Blue Moon (1) by Magnum Music Group. Catalogue no: **BMLP 1.073**

**REMAINING TITLES 1927-49**
**Album:** Released '88, on Wolf Catalogue no: **WSE 102**

## McVea, Jack

**1944-1947**
**Album:** Released Apr '81, on Solid Sender Catalogue no: **SOL 507**

**COME BLOW YOUR HORN**
Tracks: / Tryin' to tell ya / Ube dubie / You brought me heartaches / Tequila hop / Fishman / Fiddlesticks / Don't bruise the feeling / Chop chop boom / Cha cho hop / Nobody in mind / On the sunny side of the street / That'll be joyful / I owe everybody / Oh how i miss you tonight / Hoodoo you baby / I'll get along somehow.
**Album:** Released Aug '85, on Ace by Ace Records. Catalogue no: **CH 147**

**NEW DEAL (McVea, Jack Allstars)**
Tracks: / My business is C.O.D. / Play it over / Rainy day blues / F minor boogie / It never should have been this way / Jack's boogie / Baby make up your mind / Butch / Two timin' baby boogie / Evening / Fish for supper / New deal.
**Album:** Released Aug '89, on Jukebox Lil (Sweden) Catalogue no: **JB 625**

**NOTHIN' BUT JAZZ 1962 (McVea, Jack Quintet)**
Note: Re-issue of 1977 album. MONO.
**Album:** Released May '86, on Harlequin by Interstate Music. Catalogue no: **HQ 2046**

**OPEN THE DOOR RICHARD (McVea, Jack Allstars)**
Tracks: / Bartender boogie / Tarrant blues / O-Kay for baby / We're together again / Ooh mop / Don't blame me / Frisco blues / Don't let the sun catch you crying / Open the door Richard / Wine-o / Inflation blues / Groovin' boogie / No no you can't do dot mon / Jack Frost / Mumblin' blues / Keys in the mailbox, The.
**Album:** Released Jan '85, on Jukebox Lil (Sweden) Catalogue no: **JB 607**

**TWO TIMIN' BABY (McVea, Jack & His Door Openers)**
Tracks: / New worried life / Houseparty boogie / Listen baby blues / Silver symphony / Frantic boogie / Lonesome blues / Richard gets hitched / Bulgin' eyes / Jam boogie / Slowly goin' crazy blues / Groove juice / Blues with a feeling / Swing man / Fighting mama blues.
**Album:** Released May '86, on Jukebox Lil (Sweden) Catalogue no: **JB 612**

## Madame Tussaud

**ROCKIN' IN RHYTHM (Madame Tussaud's Dance Orchestra)**
Tracks: / Rockin' in rhythm / Black eyed Susan Brown / Jazz cocktail / My bluebird's singing the blues / Mood indigo / I raise my hat / Stevedore stomp / Roll up the carpet / Lightning / You're still in my heart / Wild goose chase / Sophisticated lady / Echoes of the jungle / Old man blues / We'll all go riding on a rainbow / Old fashioned sweethearts / Who walks in when I walk out? / You're gonna lose your gal.
**Album:** Released '86, on Fountain by Retrieval Records. Catalogue no: **FG 408**

## Maddocks, John

**GOOD VIBRATIONS (Maddocks, John & Jazz Maniacs)**
**Album:** Released Jan '78, on Folk Heritage by Folk Heritage Records. Catalogue no: **FHR 077**

**JUST GONE (Maddocks, John Jazzmen)**
Tracks: / Come back sweet papa / Blue turning grey over you / Just gone / St. Philips street / Breakdown / Flow gently sweet Afton / Black bottom stomp / Carry me back to old Virginny / Frog-I-more rag / Chimes blues / Norwegian wood / Blue blood blues / I can't dance.
**Album:** Released Jul '82, on Folk Heritage by Folk Heritage Records. Catalogue no: **FHR 091**

## Magadini, Pete

**BONES BLUES (Magadini,Pete,Quartet)**
**Album:** Released Apr '81, on Sackville by Spotlite Records. Catalogue no: **4004**

## Magic Sam

**BLACK MAGIC**
**Album:** Released Dec '88, on Delmark (USA) by Delmark Records (USA). Catalogue no: **DL 620**
**Album:** Released '74, on Delmark (USA) by Delmark Records (USA). Catalogue no: **DS 620**

**EASY BABY**
Note:
15 tracks, recorded 1957-1966, from Cobra, Chief & Crash Records. Although neither man achieved long lasting success in the late 1950's, Otis Rush and magic Sam were at the forefront of a 'new wave' of young Chicago bluesmen (the generation that also included Buddy Guy, Junior Wells, and Billy Boy Arnold).
Both men were forceful, intense singers and inventive guitar players and both during their all too brief periods of creativity, cut sides that would later be called 'classic' Chicag o blues of the era. Those sides are all here. N.B. Otis' and Sam's recordings have been reissued on albums before, in the late 60's and about five years ago, but never exactly in this form.
Previous issues have been mixtures of known recordings and alternative takes: these two albums are comprised soleyof the very best takes, the tracks that were originally issured.
**Album:** Released Oct '85, on Charly R&B by Charly Records. Catalogue no: **CRB 1108**

**LATE GREAT MAGIC SAM, THE**
**Album:** Released '88, on L&R Catalogue no: **LR 42.014**

**LEGACY, THE**
**Album:** Released '89, on Delmark (USA) by Delmark Records (USA). Catalogue no: **DL 651**

**LIVE AT THE ANN ARBOR BLUES 1963 & 1969**
**2 LP Set:** Released Dec '88, on Delmark (USA) by Delmark Records (USA). Catalogue no: **DL 645/646**

**MAGIC ROCKER Cobra 1957-8 (Magic Sam & Shaky Jake)**
**Album:** Released '88, on Flyright by Interstate Music. Catalogue no: **FLY 561**

**MAGIC TOUCH (Magic Sam & Shaky Jake)**
**Album:** Released '88, on Black Magic by Topic Records. Catalogue no: **BM 9003**

**WEST SIDE GUITAR**
**CD:** Released '89, on Flyright by Interstate Music. Catalogue no: **FLY CD 02**

**WEST SIDE SOUL (Magic Sam Blues Band)**
**Album:** Released May '84, on Delmark (USA) by Delmark Records (USA). Catalogue no: **DS 615**
**Album:** Released Dec '88, on Delmark (USA) by Delmark Records (USA). Catalogue no: **DL 615**

## Magic Slim

**SON OF A GUN (Magic Slim and the Teardrops)**
**Album:** Released Oct '88, on Rooster (USA) Catalogue no: **R 2618**

## Magnolia Jazz Band

**MAGNOLIA JAZZ BAND**
**Album:** Released '89, on GHB by Jazzology Records (USA). Catalogue no: **GHB 220**
**Album:** Released Jun '86, on Stomp Off (USA) Catalogue no: **SOS 1016**

**SHAKE THAT THING (Magnolia Jazz 5 & Jimmy Mazzy)**
**Album:** Released Nov '87, on Stomp Off (USA) Catalogue no: **SOS 1137**

## Magnusson, Bob

**REVELATION (Magnusson, Bob Quintet)**
Note:
Bob Magnusson-acoustic bass; Joe Farrell-tenor & soprano sax, flute; Bill Mays-acoustic & electric piano; John Guerin-drums; Jim Plank-percussion.

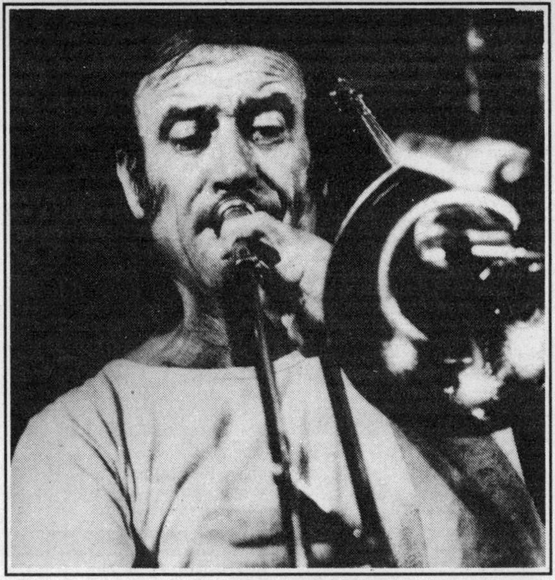

Albert Mangelsdorff

**CD:** Released Dec '86, on Discovery (USA) by Discovery Records (USA). Catalogue no: **DSCD 927**
**Album:** Released '88, on Discovery (USA) by Discovery Records (USA). Catalogue no: **DS 804**

**ROAD WORK AHEAD (Magnusson, Bob Quartet)**
Note: Bob Magnusson-bass, Peter Sprague-guitar, Bill Mays-piano, Jim Plank-drums & percussion.
**Album:** Released '88, on Discovery (USA) by Discovery Records (USA). Catalogue no: **DS 824**

**SONG FOR JANET LEE (Magnusson, Bob Quintet)**
Tracks: / Song for Janet Lee / Waltz you saved, The / Poet, The / When it comes to pass / Peace of mine / Double play (a pitcher's delight).
Note: Bob Magnusson-bass/Hubert Laws-flute/Bobby Shew-trumpet and flugelhorn/Peter Sprague-guitar/Billy Mintz-drums
**Album:** Released Nov '84, on Discovery (USA) by Discovery Records (USA). Catalogue no: **DS 912**
**CD:** Released Sep '86, on Discovery (USA) by Discovery Records (USA). Catalogue no: **DSCD 912**
**Cass:** Released '88, on Discovery (USA) by Discovery Records (USA). Catalogue no: **DSC 912**

**TWO GENERATIONS OF MUSIC (Magnusson, Bob Classical Jazz Chamber)**
Note: Compositions by Gordon Brisker and Daniel Magnusson. Bob Magnusson-bass, Daniel Magnusson-clarinet, Bill Mays-piano, Peter Sprague-guitar, Jim Plank-drums, percussion, mallets.
**Album:** Released '88, on Trend (USA) by Trend Records (USA). Catalogue no: **TR 537**
**Album:** Released '88, on Trend (USA) by Trend Records (USA). Catalogue no: **TR 528**

## Mahavishnu Orchestra

**Biographical details:** At the time of their greatest success, this jazz-rock fusion band consisted of guitarist/leader Mahavishnu John McLaughlin, Billy Cobham, Jerry Goodman, Jan Hammer and Rick Laird. John McLaughlin was born in Yorkshire, England, but emigrated to the US in 1968. The Mahavishnu monicker was given to him by his guru Sri Chimnoy, to whose philosophical and religious teachings he was devoted. McLaughlin was already a noted figure in jazz by the time he formed the Orchestra in 1971. The ensemble's finest hour was also their only UK chart entry *Birds of fire* reached No.20 on the British LP list in 1973. In that same year, he teamed up with fellow guru-inspired guitarist Carlos Santana for a duet LP entitled *Love, devotion, surrender*; the duo's album reached No.7 on the UK chart. McLaughlin, a highly influential jazz player who dazzlied audiences with his 100mph guitarist technique, disbanded the Orchestra in 1976 when he felt that it had fulfilled all that it could. Several crack musicians passed through the Orchestra - in addition to those listed above, these included Jean Luc Ponty and Narada Michael Walden. McLaughlin subsequently pursued various other projects, including membership of an acoustic Indian trio named Shakti plus solo albums and link-ups with other jazz and fusion stars. (Bob MacDonald, 16th Jan 1986).

**BEST OF THE MAHAVISHNU ORCHESTRA**
Tracks: / Birds of fire / Open country joy / Wings of Karma / Sister Andrea / Dance of Maya / Meeting of the spirits / Lila's dance / Be happy.
**Album:** Released Jun '80, on CBS by CBS Records. Deleted '85. Catalogue no: **CBS 4232**

**BIRDS OF FIRE**
Tracks: / Birds of fire / Miles beyond / Celestial terrestrial commuters / Thousand island park / Hope / One word / Sanctuary / Open country joy / Resolution.
**Album:** Released Mar '83, on CBS by CBS Records. Deleted Mar '88. Catalogue no: **CBS 32280**

**LOVE/DEVOTION SURRENDER**
**CD:** Released '88, on CBS by CBS Records. Deleted 17 Apr '89. Catalogue no: **CD 69037**

**MAHAVISHNU**
Tracks: / East side west side / Radio activity / Nostalgia / Nightriders / Clarendon hills / Jazz / Unbeliever, The / When blue turns gold.
**Album:** Released Jan '85, on WEA by WEA Records. Catalogue no: **251351 1**

## Makowicz, Adam

**CLASSIC JAZZ DUETS (Makowicz, Adam & George Mraz)**
**Album:** Released Nov '87, on Stash (USA) Catalogue no: **ST 216**

**INTERFACE (Makowicz, Adam Trio)**
**Album:** Released Jul '87, on Sonet by Sonet Records. Catalogue no: **SNTF 963**
**CD:** Released Jul '87, on Sonet by Sonet Records. Catalogue no: **SNTCD 963**

**NAME IS MAKOWICZ, THE (Makowicz, Adam & Phil Woods)**
**Album:** Released '88, on Sheffield Lab.(USA) by Sheffield Lab. Inc.(USA). Catalogue no: **LAB 21**
**CD:** Released '88, on Sheffield Lab.(USA) by Sheffield Lab. Inc.(USA). Catalogue no: **CD 21**

**SOLO**
**Album:** Released Jul '88, on Sonet by Sonet Records. Catalogue no: **SNTF 964**

## Malach, Bob

**SOME PEOPLE**
**Album:** Released Jun '81, on MPS Jazz Catalogue no: **MPS 68 258**

## Malfatti, Radu

**BRACKNELL BREAKDOWN (Malfatti, Radu/Harry Miller)**
**Album:** Released '88, on Ogun by Ca-

dillac Music. Catalogue no: **OG 320**

**FORMU**
Tracks: / Funf leichte stucke / Formu.
**Album:** Released Sep '86, on Nato Catalogue no: **NATO 175**

## Mance, Junior

**AT THE VILLAGE VANGUARD**
**CD:** Released Apr '87, on Carrere (France) Catalogue no: **98958**

**DEEP (Mance, Junior Trio)**
**Album:** Released Mar '82, on JSP by JSP Records. Catalogue no: **JSP 1013**

**FOR DANCERS ONLY (Mance, Junior & Martin Rivera)**
**Album:** Released Jul '88, on Sackville by Spotlite Records. Catalogue no: **3031**

**SMOKEY BLUES (Mance, Junior Trio)**
**CD:** Released Jul '88, on JSP by JSP Records. Catalogue no: **JSP CD 219**

**TENDER TOUCH OF..., THE (Mance, Junior & Martin Rivera Duo)**
**Album:** Released Apr '84, on Nilva (Switzerland) Catalogue no: **NQ 3405**

## Mangelsdorff, Albert

**ETERNAL RHYTHM**
**Album:** Released May '81, on MPS Jazz Catalogue no: **MPS 68 225**

**LIVE IN TOKYO**
**Album:** Released Jan '82, on Enja (Germany) by Enja Records (West Germany). Catalogue no: **ENJA 2006**

**SPONTANEOUS**
**Album:** Released Jan '82, on Enja (Germany) by Enja Records (West Germany). Catalogue no: **ENJA 2064**

**TRILOGUE-LIVE**
**Album:** Released Jun '81, on MPS Jazz Catalogue no: **MPS 68 175**

**WIDE POINT, THE (Mangelsdorff/Jones/Danielson)**
**Album:** Released May '81, on MPS Jazz Catalogue no: **MPS 68 071**

## Mangione, Chuck

**BEST OF CHUCK MANGIONE Compact/Walkman jazz**
**Cass:** Released '87, on Mercury by Phonogram Ltd. Catalogue no: **830 696 4**
**2 LP Set:** Released Jul '84, on Mercury (Holland) Catalogue no: **6672 019**
**CD:** Released '87, on Mercury by Phonogram Ltd. Catalogue no: **830 696 2**

**BEST OF CHUCK MANGIONE VOL 1**
**Album:** Released May '83, on Mercury (Import) Catalogue no: **9279 150**
**Cass:** Released May '83, on Mercury (Import) Catalogue no: **7159 150**

**CLASSICS:CHUCK MANGIONE**
**CD:** on A&M by A&M Records. Deleted Aug '88. Catalogue no: **CDA 2502**

**COMPACT JAZZ: CHUCK MANGIONE**
Tracks: / Land of make believe / As long as we're together.
**CD:** Released Jul '87, on Phonogram by Phonogram Ltd. Catalogue no: **831 696-2**
**Cass:** Released Jul '87, on Phonogram by Phonogram Ltd. Catalogue no: **831 696-4**

**EVENING OF MAGIC, AN**
Tracks: / Feels so good / XIth commandment / Chase the clouds away / Hill where the Lord hides / Doin' everything with you / Love the feelin' / I get crazy / Land of make believe / Hide and seek / Day after / Children of Sanchez / B'bye.
**2 LP Set:** Released '79, on A&M by A&M Records. Deleted '84. Catalogue no: **AMLM 66701**

**EYE OF THE VEILED TEMPTRESS**
Tracks: / That's nice / Eyes of the veiled temptress / Do you ever think about me / Open their eyes / Long hour soulful / Sweet butterfly / Freedom song.
**Album:** Released Jul '88, on CBS by CBS Records. Deleted Oct '89. Catalogue no: **461162 1**
**CD:** Released Jul '88, on CBS by CBS Records. Deleted Oct '89. Catalogue no: **461162 2**
**Cass:** Released Jul '88, on CBS by CBS Records. Deleted Oct '89. Catalogue no: **461162 4**

**FEELS SO GOOD**
Tracks: / Feels so good / Maui waui / Side Street, Theme from / Hide and seek / Last dance / XIth commandment, The.
**Album:** Released Apr '78, on A&M by A&M Records. Deleted '88. Catalogue no: **AMLH 64658**

**FUN AND GAMES**
Tracks: / Fun and games / Give it all you've got / Feels so good.
**7" Single:** Released May '80, on A&M by A&M Records. Deleted '83. Catalogue no: **AMSP 7522**

**GIVE IT ALL YOU'VE GOT**
Tracks: / Give it all you've got / B'bye.
**7" Single:** Released Feb '80, on A&M by A&M Records. Deleted '83. Catalogue no: **AMS 7508**

**JAZZ BROTHER**
Tracks: / Hey baby / Bag's groove / Night has a thousand eyes / Givin' the business / Wha's happ'nin' / Just you, just me / Old folks / Bassett sound / Recuerdo / Big foot / I had the craziest dream / Solar / Blues for Saandar / If ever I should leave you / Little prince.
**2 LP Set:** Released Jul '80, on Milestone by Ace Records. Deleted Jul '85. Catalogue no: **M 47042**

**JOURNEY TO A RAINBOW**
**Album:** Released Jul '83, on CBS by CBS Records. Catalogue no: **CBS 25435**
**Cass:** Released Jul '83, on CBS by CBS Records. Catalogue no: **40 25435**

**LAND OF MAKE BELIEVE**
Tracks: / Legend of the one eyed sailor / Lullaby for Nancy Carol / Carol / El gato triste / Gloria from mass of St Bernard / As long as we're together / Land of make believe.
Note: Jazz flugelhorn/trumpet star Chuck Mangione recorded live in concert with the Hamilton Philharmonic featuring Esther Satterfield with her superb rendition of the title track.
**CD:** Released Jul '85, on Phonogram (Import) Catalogue no: **822 538 2**

**LOVE NOTES**
Tracks: / Steppin' out / No problem / Memories of Scirocco / To the 80's / Love notes.
**Album:** Released Sep '82, on CBS by CBS Records. Deleted Jan '88. Catalogue no: **CBS 85879**

**SAVE TONIGHT FOR ME**
**CD:** Released May '87, on CBS by CBS Records. Deleted Jan '89. Catalogue no: **CD 26890**

**TARANTELLA**
Tracks: / Tarantella / Neopolitan tarantella / XIth Commandment suite / Legend of the one eyed sailor / Bellavia / Hill where the Lord hides / Lake placid fanfare / Things to come / Round midnight / Manteca / My one and only love / All blues.
**2 LP Set:** Released Jun '81, on A&M by A&M Records. Deleted '86. Catalogue no: **AMLM 66703**

## Manhattan Jazz Quintet

**AUTUMN LEAVES**
Tracks: / Jordu / Recado bossa nova / Confirmation / Autumn leaves / Mood piece.
Note: Following on from their award winning debut album, 'Autumn Leaves' is further proof that this group is one of the best to have emerged in recent years. Still strictly a studio band, their music is in the tradition of the hard bop tenor-trumpet quintets of the fifties and sixties, as heard on labels like Blue Note and Prestige. *Personnel:* Lew Soloff-trumpet/George Young-tenor sax/David Matthews-piano/Charnett Moffett-bass/Steve Gadd-drums.
**Album:** Released Jul '86, on King (Japan) Catalogue no: **K 28P 6350**

**FACE TO FACE**
**CD:** Released '89, on King Catalogue no: **292 E 6032**

**LIVE: MANHATTAN JAZZ QUINTET**
**2 LP Set:** Released Apr '87, on King (Japan) Catalogue no: **K 20P 6429**

**MANHATTAN JAZZ QUINTET**
Tracks: / Summertime / Rosario / Milestones / My favourite things / Airegin / Summer waltz.
Note: Straight ahead Be-bop album from five of New York's top sidemen lead by David Matthews. As well as two original compositions by David Matthews, one each from Miles Davis and Sonny Rollins, the selection also includes two popular standards 'Summertime' and 'My Favourite Things'. This album won Swing Journal's 1984 Gold Disk award in Japan. Personnel: Lew Soloff-trumpet/George Young-tenor sax/David Matthews-piano/Charnett Moffett-bass/Steve Gadd-drums.

**Album:** Released Jul '86, on King (Japan) Catalogue no: **K 28P 6313**

### MY FAVOURITE THINGS

**CD:** Released Sep '88, on Electric Bird Catalogue no: **K32Y 6210**
**Album:** Released Sep '88, on Electric Bird Catalogue no: **K 28P 6452**

### MY FUNNY VALENTINE

Tracks: / Mr. P.C. / Round midnight / On a clear day / New York state of mind / U blues.
Note: New album from this quintet, who's forte is updating the sound of the best jazz tunes from the 50's and 60's. On *My funny valentine* they take on three jazz standards, two tunes associated with pop singers Barbara Streisand and Billy Joel and one original blues number from pianist David Matthews. Personnel: Lew Sollof-trumpet/George Young-Tenor sax/David Matthews-piano/Eddie Gomez-bass/Steve Gadd-drums.
**CD:** Released Oct '87, on King (Japan) Catalogue no: **K32Y 6070**
**Album:** Released Jan '87, on King (Japan) Catalogue no: **K 28P 6410**

### PLAYS BLUE NOTE

Tracks: / Cleopatra's dream / Cool struttin' / Sweet love of mine / Dear old Stockholm / Wolf pack / Cheese cake / For Alfred / Moanin'.
Note: Recorded January 1988. Personnel: David Matthews (piano), Lew Soloff (tpt), George Young (tenor sax), and new members John Patitucci (bass), Dave Weckl (drums). Compositions associated with and inspired by the Blue Note label.
**CD:** Released Jun '89, on Paddlewheel/King Catalogue no: **K32Y 6230**
**Album:** Released Jun '89, on Paddlewheel/King Catalogue no: **K28P 6480**

## Manhattan Jazz Septet

### MANHATTAN JAZZ SEPTET

Tracks: / King Porter stomp / Never never land / Like listen / Since when / Love of my life / Rapid transit / Flute cocktail / At bat for K.C. / Do you know what it means to miss New Orleans / My shining hour / Thou svelt / There will never be another you.
**Album:** Released Jun '83, on Jasmine by Hasmick Promotions. Deleted Feb '88. Catalogue no: **JASM 1017**

## Manhattan Transfer

**Biographical details:** At the time of their greatest success this American vocal group consisted of Tim Hauser, Laurel Masse, Alan Paul and Janis Siegel. Formed in 1969, Manhattan Transfer have always been led by Hauser. Indeed, he was the only original member to stay the course after the dismal failure of the group's first album, 1971's *Jukin*. A re-shaped, re-styled Manhattan Transfer built up a cult following in New York, first in gay bars and then in more general nightclubs. When an LP called simply *Manhattan Transfer* was issued in 1975 most people were were under the impression that this second album was their first. It reached No 33 on the US chart and yielded a pair of successful singles: *Operator* reached No 22 in America and *Tuxedo Junction* climbed to No 24 in Britain as part of a Glenn Miller revival in the UK at the time. Man Tran's stock-in-trade was revivalism and chic nostalgia and it was the 40's that came most often under their microscope. With sleek professionalism the two-man/two-woman line-up developed a smooth vocal harmony sound and refined their stage act. But their commercial career was distinctly erratic. They were too middle-of-the-road to be a pop group yet too purist to be a cabaret act. Their enormous versatility was accompanied by a passion for accurate reproduction of a style or genre rather than Las Vegas-type mushiness. The quartet's chart career consisted of a series of pleasant one-offs. Manhattan Transfer's biggest British single, 1977's *Chanson D'Amour*, was a revamp of a '58 number; the remake reached the UK No 1 slot but failed to chart at all in America. Conversely, their biggest US success, *Boy From New York City*, reached No 7 in '81 but flopped in Britain where it had been recently rehashed by Darts. In 1980 Man Tran went electronic and ultra-modern with *Twilight Zone-Twilight Zone*. Four years later they jumped on the Michael Jackson bandwagon by recording Rod Temperton's song *Spice Of Life*. But their most accomplished piece of work was the aptly-named 1978 album *Pastiche*. (Bob MacDonald, January 1986.).

### BEST OF MANHATTAN TRANSFER

Tracks: / Tuxedo Junction / Boy from New York City / Twilight zone / Body and soul / Candy / Four brothers / Birdland / Gloria / Trickle trickle / Operator / Java jive / Nightingale sang in Berkeley Square, A.
**CD:** Released '83, on Atlantic by WEA Records. Catalogue no: **250841 2**

### BIRDLAND

Tracks: / Birdland / Wacky dust.
**7" Single:** Released '79, on Atlantic by WEA Records. Catalogue no: **K 11387**

### BODIES AND SOULS

Tracks: / Spice of life / This independence / Mystery / American pop / Soldier of fortune / Code of ethics / Malaise en malaise / Down south camp meeting / Why not / Goodbye love / Night that monk returned to heaven, The.
**Album:** Released Feb '84, on Atlantic by WEA Records. Deleted '86. Catalogue no: **780 104-1**
**Cass:** Released Feb '84, on Atlantic by WEA Records. Deleted Aug '87. Catalogue no: **780 104-4**
**CD:** Released Feb '84, on Atlantic by WEA Records. Deleted Aug '87. Catalogue no: **780 104-2**

### BOP DOO WOP

Tracks: / Unchained melody / Route 66 / My cat fell in the well / Duke of Dubuque / How high the moon / Baby come back to me / Safronia B / Heart's desire / That't the way it goes.
**Cass:** Released Feb '85, on Atlantic by WEA Records. Deleted Aug '87. Catalogue no: **781 233-4**
**Album:** Released Feb '85, on Atlantic by WEA Records. Deleted Aug '87. Catalogue no: **781 233-1**
**CD:** Released Feb '85, on Atlantic by WEA Records. Deleted Aug '87. Catalogue no: **781 233-2**

### BOY FROM NEW YORK CITY

Tracks: / Boy from New York City / World of confrontation.
**7" Single:** Released Apr '81, on WEA by WEA Records. Catalogue no: **K 11585**

### BRASIL

Tracks: / Soul food to go / Zoo blues / So you say / Capim / Metroplis / Hear the voices / Agua / Jungle pioneer, The / Notes from the underground.
**Cass:** Released Dec '87, on Atlantic by WEA Records. Catalogue no: **781 803-4**
**CD:** Released Dec '87, on Atlantic by WEA Records. Catalogue no: **781 803-2**
**Album:** Released Dec '87, on Atlantic by WEA Records. Catalogue no: **781 803-1**

### CHANSON D'AMOUR

Tracks: / Chanson d'amour / Popsicle toes.
**7" Single:** Released Jan '87, on Atlantic by WEA Records. Deleted '80. Catalogue no: **K 10886**

### CHANSON D'AMOUR (OLD GOLD)

Tracks: / Chanson d'amour / Walk in love.
**7" Single:** Released Sep '85, on Old Gold by Old Gold Records. Catalogue no: **OG 9547**

### CLAP YOUR HANDS

Tracks: / Clap your hands / Blue champagne.
**7" Single:** Released '79, on Atlantic by WEA Records. Deleted '82. Catalogue no: **K 10630**

### COMING OUT

Tracks: / Don't let go / Zindy Lou / Chanson d'amour / Helpless / Scotch and soda / Speak up mambo, The / Cuentame / Poinciana / S.O.S. / Popsicle toes / It wouldn't have made any difference / Thought of loving you, The.
**Cass:** Released Aug '76, on Atlantic by WEA Records. Catalogue no: **K4 50291**
**Album:** Released Aug '76, on Atlantic by WEA Records. Deleted Aug '87. Catalogue no: **K 50291**

### DON'T LET GO

Tracks: / Don't let go.
**7" Single:** Released May '77, on Atlantic by WEA Records. Deleted '80. Catalogue no: **K 10930**

### EXTENSIONS

Tracks: / Birdland / Wacky dust / Nothin' you can do about it / Coo coo u / Body and soul (Eddie and the bean) / Twilight zone (part 1) / Twilight zone (part 2) / Trickle trickle / Shaker song, The / Foreign affair.
**Cass:** Released Nov '79, on Atlantic by

WEA Records. Deleted Nov '84. Catalogue no: **K4 50674**
**Album:** Released Nov '79, on Atlantic by WEA Records. Deleted Nov '84. Catalogue no: **K 50674**

### FOREIGN AFFAIR
Tracks: / Foreign affair / Body and soul.
**7" Single:** Released Dec '79, on Atlantic by WEA Records. Deleted '81. Catalogue no: **K 11422**

### INDEPENDENCE
Tracks: / Independence / Night that monk returned to heaven.
**7" Single:** Released Oct '83, on Atlantic by WEA Records. Catalogue no: **A 9766**
**12" Single:** Released Oct '83, on Atlantic by WEA Records. Catalogue no: **A 9766 T**

### JE VOULAISE TE DIRE
Tracks: / Je voulaise te dire / On a little street in Singapore.
**7" Single:** Released Jan '78, on Atlantic by WEA Records. Deleted '81. Catalogue no: **K 11062**

### LIVE: MANHATTAN TRANSFER
Tracks: / Four brothers / Rambo / (You should) meet Benny Bailey / Airegin II / To you / Sing joy spring / Move / That's killer Joe / Duke of Dubuque, The / Gloria / On the boulevard / Shaker song, The / Ray's rockhouse.
**Cass:** Released '78, on Atlantic by WEA Records. Catalogue no: **K4 50540**
**Cass:** Released Jun '87, on Atlantic by WEA Records. Catalogue no: **781 723-4**
**CD:** Released Oct '87, on WEA by WEA Records. Catalogue no: **781 723-2**
**Album:** Released Jun '87, on Atlantic by WEA Records. Catalogue no: **781 723-1**
**Album:** Released '78, on Atlantic by WEA Records. Deleted Aug '87. Catalogue no: **K 50540**

### MANHATTAN TRANSFER
**CD:** Released Sep '89, on WEA by WEA Records. Catalogue no: **K 731 493 2**
**Album:** Released May '75, on Atlantic by WEA Records. Catalogue no: **K 50138**
**CD:** Released Nov '83, on WEA by WEA Records. Deleted Nov '88. Catalogue no: **250 841**
**CD:** Released '87, on Atlantic by WEA Records. Catalogue no: **781 493-2**

### MANHATTAN TRANSFER & GENE PISTILLI
**Album:** Released Jul '78, on MFP by EMI Records. Deleted '83. Catalogue no: **MFP 50387**

### MECCA FOR MODERNS
Tracks: / On the Boulevard / Boy from New York City / Smile again / Dead or alive / Spies in the night / Corner pocket / Confirmation / Kafka / Nightingale sang in Berkeley Square.
**Album:** Released Jun '81, on Atlantic by WEA Records. Deleted '86. Catalogue no: **K 50789**
**Cass:** Released May '81, on Atlantic by WEA Records. Catalogue no: **K4 50789**

### NIGHTINGALE SANG IN BERKELEY SQUARE
Tracks: / Nightingale sang in Berkeley Square, A / On the boulevard.
**7" Single:** Released Dec '81, on Atlantic by WEA Records. Catalogue no: **K 11685**

### NOTHING YOU CAN DO ABOUT IT
Tracks: / Nothing you can do about it / Wacky dust.
**7" Single:** Released Sep '80, on Atlantic by WEA Records. Deleted '83. Catalogue no: **K 11606**

### ON A LITTLE STREET IN SINGAPORE
Tracks: / On a little street in Singapore.
**7" Single:** Released May '78, on Atlantic by WEA Records. Deleted '81. Catalogue no: **K 11136**

### PASTICHE
Tracks: / Four brothers / Gal in Calico, A / Love for sale / Je voulais (te dire que je t'attends) / On a little street in Singapore / In a mellow tone / Walk in love / Who, what, when, where and why / It's not the spotlight / Pieces of dreams / Where did our love go.
**Cass:** Released Oct '82, on Atlantic by WEA Records. Catalogue no: **K4 60167**
**Album:** Released Feb '78, on Atlantic by WEA Records. Deleted Aug '87. Catalogue no: **K 50444**

### RAY'S ROCKHOUSE
Tracks: / Ray's rockhouse / Another night in Tunisia.
**12" Single:** Released Jul '85, on Atlantic by WEA Records. Deleted Jul '88. Catalogue no: **A 9533 T**
**7" Single:** Released Jul '85, on Atlantic by WEA Records. Deleted Jul '88. Catalogue no: **A 9533**

### SOUL FOOD TO GO
Tracks: / Soul food to go / Hear the voices.
**7" Single:** Released Jan '88, on Atlantic by WEA Records. Catalogue no: **A 9156**
**12" Single:** Released Jan '88, on Atlantic by WEA Records. Catalogue no: **A 9156 T**

### SPICE OF LIFE
Tracks: / Spice of life / Soldier of fortune / Wonderful dream.
**12" Single:** Released Jan '84, on Atlantic by WEA Records. Catalogue no: **A 9728 T**
**7" Single:** Released Jan '84, on Atlantic by WEA Records. Catalogue no: **A 9728**

### TUXEDO JUNCTION
Tracks: / Tuxedo Junction.
**7" Single:** Released Feb '76, on Atlantic by WEA Records. Deleted '79. Catalogue no: **K 10670**

### TWILIGHT ZONE - TWILIGHT TONE
Tracks: / Twilight zone - twilight tone / Body & soul.
**7" Single:** Released May '80, on Atlantic by WEA Records. Deleted '83. Catalogue no: **K 11476**

### VOCALESE
Tracks: / That's killer Joe / Rambo / Airegin / To you / Meet Benny Bailey / Another night in Tunisia / Ray's rockhouse / Blee blop blues / Oh yes, I remember Clifford / Sing joyspring / Move.
**Album:** Released Aug '85, on Atlantic by WEA Records. Catalogue no: **781 266-1**
**CD:** Released '88, on WEA by WEA Records. Catalogue no: **781 266-2**
**Cass:** Released Aug '85, on Atlantic by WEA Records. Catalogue no: **781 266-4**

### VOCALESE (VIDEO)
**VHS:** Released Jun '86, on Atlantic by WEA Records. Catalogue no: **252 412-3**
**Beta:** Released Jun '86, on Atlantic by WEA Records. Deleted Aug '87. Catalogue no: **252 412-5**

### WALK IN LOVE
Tracks: / Walk in love.
**7" Single:** Released Feb '78, on Atlantic by WEA Records. Deleted '81. Catalogue no: **K 11075**

### WANTED DEAD OR ALIVE
Tracks: / Wanted dead or alive / Smile again.
**7" Single:** Released Jul '81, on Atlantic by WEA Records. Deleted '84. Catalogue no: **K 11668**

### WHERE DID OUR LOVE GO
Tracks: / Where did our love go / Je voulais te dire (que je t'attends).
**7" Single:** Released Sep '78, on Atlantic by WEA Records. Deleted '81. Catalogue no: **K 11182**

### WHO WHAT WHEN WHERE WHY
Tracks: / Who, what, when, where and why.
**7" Single:** Released Dec '78, on Atlantic by WEA Records. Deleted '81. Catalogue no: **K 11233**

## Mann, Herbie

### AT THE VILLAGE GATE
**CD:** Released Jul '87, on Atlantic Jazz by WEA Records. Catalogue no: **781 350-2**

### BEND DOWN LOW
Tracks: / Bend down low / Cecilia.
**7" Single:** Released Aug '81, on Atlantic by WEA Records. Deleted Aug '84. Catalogue no: **K 11677**

### BIRD IN A SILVER CAGE
Tracks: / Bird in a silver cage / Aria / Fly, robin, fly / Birdwalk / Years of love / Piper, The.
**Album:** on Atlantic by WEA Records. Catalogue no: **K 50338**

### JISCO DAZZ
Tracks: / Jisco dazz / Waterbed / Highjack / Jisco dazz reprise.
**7" Single:** Released '79, on Warner Bros. by WEA Records. Deleted '82. Catalogue no: **LV 34**

### LONDON UNDERGROUND
Tracks: / Bitch / Something in the air / Layla / Spin ball / Mellow yellow / White shade of pale, A / Memphis spoon and dover sole / Paper sun / You never give me your money.
**Album:** on Atlantic by WEA Records. Catalogue no: **K 50032**

**MEMPHIS UNDERGROUND**
Tracks: / Memphis underground / New Orleans / Hold on I'm coming / Chain of fools / Battle hymn of the republic.
**CD:** Released '88, on Atlantic Jazz by WEA Records. Catalogue no: **K781 364 2**
**Album:** Released Jan '79, on Atlantic by WEA Records. Catalogue no: **K 40038**
**Album:** Released Jan '86, on Atlantic by WEA Records. Catalogue no: **K 50520**

**NIRVANA (Mann, Herbie & Bill Evans)**
Tracks: / Nirvana / Gymnopedie / I love you / Willow weep for me / Lover man / Cashmere.
**Album:** on Atlantic by WEA Records. Catalogue no: **K 50238**

**OPALESCENCE**
**Cass:** Released 12 Apr '89, on Gramavision Catalogue no: **139020 4**
**Album:** Released 12 Apr '89, on Gramavision Catalogue no: **139020 1**
**CD:** Released 12 Apr '89, on Gramavision Catalogue no: **139020 2**

**SUPERMAN**
Tracks: / Superman / Itagui.
**7" Single:** Released Jan '79, on Atlantic by WEA Records. Deleted '82. Catalogue no: **K 11237**

## Mann, Johnny Singers

**UP, UP AND AWAY**
Tracks: / Up, up and away.
**7" Single:** Released Jul '67, on Liberty by EMI Records. Deleted '70. Catalogue no: **LIB 55972**

## Manning, Sam

**BARBADOS BLUES (Manning, Sam & Wilmoth Houdini)**
**Album:** Released Jul '86, on Collectors Items Catalogue no: **CI 015**

## Manone, Wingy

**1947: WINGY MANONE (Manone, Wingy & Sidney Bechet)**
Note: MONO
**Album:** Released Jul '86, on Jazz Archives (USA) by Jazz Archives Inc.(USA). Catalogue no: **JA 29**

**WINGY MANONE & PAPA BUE'S VIKING JAZZ BAND (Manone, Wingy & Papa Bue's Viking Jazzband)**
Tracks: / When you're smiling / Up the country blues / Sister Kate.
**Album:** Released '88, on Storyville by Storyville Records AB. Catalogue no: **SLP 4066**

**WINGY MANONE & WILL BRADLEY (Manone, Wingy & Will Bradley)**
Tracks: / Jingle bells / Cryin' the boogie blues / Lightnin' boogie / Sugar Hill boogie woogie / O sole mio / Snake the blues away / That glory day / Bread and gravy / That's a gasser / Mr. Boogie Man.
Note: First four tracks by the Will Bradley Boogie Woogie Boys, recorded in 1943; rest by Wingy Manone, recorded 1944.
**Album:** Released Jul '82, on Harlequin by Interstate Music. Catalogue no: **HQ 2001**

**WINGY MANONE-VOLUME 4**
**Album:** Released Jul '84, on Little Gem (USA) Catalogue no: **LITTLE GEM 1073**

## Maria, Tania

**BRAZIL WITH MY SOUL**
**Album:** Released May '78, on Barclay (France) by Decca Records. Catalogue no: **90169**

**COME WITH ME**
Tracks: / Sangria / Embraceable you / Lost in Amazonia / Come with me / Sementes, graines & seeds / Nega / Euzinha / Its all over now.
**CD:** Released Jul '87, on Concord Jazz by Concord Jazz Records (USA). Catalogue no: **CCD 4200**
**Cass:** Released Mar '83, on Concord Jazz by Concord Jazz Records (USA). Catalogue no: **CJPC 200**
**Album:** Released Mar '83, on Concord Jazz by Concord Jazz Records (USA). Catalogue no: **CJP 200**

**DON'T GO**
Tracks: / Don't go / Made in New York.
**7" Single:** Released May '85, on Manhattan Records by President Records. Deleted May '88. Catalogue no: **MT 2**
**12" Single:** Released May '85, on Manhattan Records by President Records. Deleted May '88. Catalogue no: **12 MT 2**

**LADY FROM BRAZIL, THE**
Tracks: / Lady from Brazil, The / I should not call you / Tanoca vignette / Bronx / Just get up / Valeu / All gone love / It hurts so much.
**CD:** Released Feb '87, on EMI by EMI Records. Deleted Jun '89. Catalogue no: **CDP 746 425 2**

**LIVE: TANIA MARIA**
Tracks: / Mr. & Mrs. Gatoamante / Pingas da vida / Seu dia vai chegar / O que e amar / Carona.
**Cass:** Released Aug '83, on Musidisc by Musidisc Records (France). Catalogue no: **130 189**
**Album:** Released Aug '83, on Musidisc by Musidisc Records (France). Catalogue no: **ACV 13005**

**LOVE EXPLOSION**
Tracks: / Funky tambourine / It's all in my hands / You've got me feeling your love / Love explosion / Bela la bela / Rainbow of your love / Deep cove view / Pour toi.
**Album:** Released Jan '84, on Concord Picante by Concord Jazz Records (USA). Catalogue no: **CJP 230**
**CD:** Released Dec '86, on Concord Jazz by Concord Jazz Records (USA). Catalogue no: **CCD 4230**
**Cass:** Released Jan '84, on Concord Picante by Concord Jazz Records (USA). Catalogue no: **CJPC 230**

**MADE IN NEW YORK**
Tracks: / Don't go / E carnival / My space / I do love you / Made in New York / Together / Forock / Walking in the rain.
**Cass:** Released Apr '85, on EMI-Manhattan by EMI Records. Deleted Nov '88. Catalogue no: **EJ 2403214**
**Album:** Released Apr '85, on EMI-Manhattan by EMI Records. Deleted Nov '88. Catalogue no: **EJ 2403211**

**PIQUANT**
**Album:** Released May '81, on Concord Picante by Concord Jazz Records (USA). Catalogue no: **CJP 151**
**CD:** Released Jul '88, on Concord Jazz by Concord Jazz Records (USA). Catalogue no: **CCD 4151**

**REAL TANIA MARIA-WILD, THE**
Tracks: / Yatra - ta / A cama na varanda / Vem pra roda / Come with me / Funy tamborine / 2 a.m. / Sangria.
**CD:** Released Nov '86, on Concord Jazz by Concord Jazz Records (USA). Catalogue no: **CCD 4264**
**Cass:** Released Feb '85, on Concord Picante by Concord Jazz Records (USA). Catalogue no: **CJPC 264**
**Album:** Released Feb '85, on Concord Picante by Concord Jazz Records (USA). Catalogue no: **CJP 264**

**TAURUS**
**Album:** Released Mar '82, on Concord Jazz by Concord Jazz Records (USA). Catalogue no: **CJP 175**
**CD:** Released Oct '87, on Concord by Concord Jazz Records (USA). Catalogue no: **CCD 4175**
**Cass:** Released Mar '82, on Concord Jazz by Concord Jazz Records (USA). Catalogue no: **CJPC 175**

**VIA BRAZIL (VOLUME 1)**
**Album:** Released Jul '87, on Barclay (France) by Decca Records. Catalogue no: **80550**

## Mariano, Charlie

**ALTO SAX-FOR YOUNG MODERNS (Mariano, Charlie, Quartet)**
Tracks: / Johnny one note / Very thought of you, The / Smoke gets in your eyes / King for a day / Darn that dream / Floormat / Blues - traditional / I heard you cried last night.
**Album:** Released Oct '82, on Affinity by Charly Records. Deleted '88. Catalogue no: **AFF 99**

**CHARLIE MARIANO PLAYS**
**Album:** Released Feb '88, on Fresh Sounds (Spain) by Fresh Sounds Records (Spain). Catalogue no: **FS 260**

**IBERIAN WALTZ (Mariano Charlie & Sadao Watanabe)**
Tracks: / Iberian waltz / I thought about you / Palisades / Lament / You are my heart's delight.
Note: Personnel: Charlie Mariano, Sadao Watanabe, Masabumi Kikuchi, Masanaga Harada, Masahiko Togashi, Fumio Watanabe.
**CD:** Released '88, on Denon Catalogue no: **C38-7690**

**JYOTHI**
Tracks: / Voice solo (Ramamani,R.A.-Tamboura.Mani,T.A.S.-Mridangam.Rajagopal,R.A.-ghatam,morsi) / Vanda-

nam / Varshini / Saptarshi / Kartik / Bhajan.
**CD:** Released Aug '86, on ECM Catalogue no: **811 548 2**
**Album:** Released Nov '83, on ECM Catalogue no: **ECM 1256**

## Mark, Stan

**STAN MARK & HIS BIG NEW BAND (Mark, Stan & band)**
**Album:** Released '88, on Progressive Catalogue no: **PRO 7070**

## Markham, Pigmeat

**HERE COMES THE JUDGE**
Tracks: / Here comes the judge.
**7" Single:** Released Jul '68, on Chess by Vogue Records. Deleted '71. Catalogue no: **CRS 8077**

## Marmarosa, Dodo

**CHICAGO SESSIONS**
Tracks: / Mellow mood / Cottage for sale / April played the fiddle / Everything happens to me / On Green Dolphin Street / Why do I love you / I thought about you / Me and my shadow / Tracy's blues / You call it madness / Gone with the wind / Someday / Automation / Dodo's tune / Analysis / Only a rose.
**CD:** Released Sep '89, on Affinity by Charly Records. Catalogue no: **CDAFF 755**
**CD:** Released Dec '86, on Arco by Charly Records. Deleted May '88. Catalogue no: **ARCD 502**

**DODO'S DANCE**
Tracks: / Bopmatism (x2) / Dodo's dance (x2) / Trade winds (x2) / Dary departs (x3) / Cosmo Street (x2) / Tone paintings 1 & 2 / Deep purple / Tea for two.
**Album:** Released '83, on Spotlite by Spotlite Records. Catalogue no: **SPJ 128**

**EXPERIMENT IN BOP**
**Album:** Released Feb '89, on Raretone Catalogue no: **FC 5020**

**LIVE DODO, A**
Tracks: / C jam blues / Be bop / Deep purple / Rose room / How high the moon / Perdido / Great lie, The.
**Cass:** Released Oct '86, on Swing House by Submarine Records. Catalogue no: **CSWH 10**
**Album:** Released Oct '79, on Swing House by Submarine Records. Catalogue no: **SWH 10**

**PIANO MAN**
**Album:** Released Apr '81, on Phoenix (USA) by All Star Talent Inc.(USA). Catalogue no: **LP 20**

## Marocco, Frank

**JAZZ ACCORDION (Marocco, Frank & Ray Pizzi)**
Tracks: / Night and day / Easy living / Round midnight / I love you / Giant steps / Joy Spring.
**Album:** Released '88, on Discovery (USA) by Discovery Records (USA). Catalogue no: **DS 797**

**NEW COLORS (Marocco, Frank & Ray Pizzi)**
Tracks: / Night has a thousand eyes, The / You don't know what love is / I'm old fashioned / Jitterbug waltz / My one and only love / Artists spoken autograph / More friends / Into somewhere.
Note: Frank Marocco-accordion, Ray Pizzi-reeds.
**Album:** Released '88, on Trend (USA) by Trend Records (USA). Catalogue no: **TR 516**

**ROAD TO MAROCCO (Marocco, Frank Quintet)**
Tracks: / Spain / My Desiree / Baubles, bangles and beads / Sleeper / Ballad for Anne / Sweet gorgeous George / Brazilian waltz / Vision / Giddy girl / My ship.
Note: Frank Marocco & Kenny Kotwitz-accordions, Andy Simpkins-bass, Roy Anthony-guitar, Jeff Hamilton-drums.
**Album:** Released '84, on Discovery (USA) by Discovery Records (USA). Catalogue no: **DS 854**

**TRIO, THE (Marocco, Frank & Ray Pizzi)**
Tracks: / Home again / Reverie / All the things you are / One by one / Spring is here / One morning in May / Fiesta Ecaroh, La.
**Album:** Released '87, on Discovery (1) by Oryx Records. Catalogue no: **DS 838**

## Mars, Johnny

**BORN UNDER A BAD SIGN**
Tracks: / Born under a bad sign / Standing in line.
**Cass:** Released Oct '87, on Genie Catalogue no: **GENIE LC 2**
**7" Single:** Released Jul '84, on Lamborghini by Lamborghini Records. Catalogue no: **LSU 2**
**7" Single:** Released Oct '81, on Ace by Ace Records. Deleted Jun '88. Catalogue no: **NS 73**
**12" Single:** Released Jul '84, on Lamborghini by Lamborghini Records. Catalogue no: **12LSU 2**
**Album:** Released Oct '87, on Genie Catalogue no: **GENIE LP 2**

**HOT LIPS BOOGIE**
Tracks: / Hot lips boogie.
**7" Single:** on Sundance by Sundance Records. Catalogue no: **SUND 004**

**JOHNNY MARS WITH MIGHTY MARS (Mars, Johnny/Mighty Mars)**
**Album:** Released Jan '82, on JSP by JSP Records. Catalogue no: **JSP 1023**

**KING OF THE BLUES HARP**
Tracks: / Horses and places / Rocket 88 / Johnny's groove / Desert island / I'll go crazy / Imagination / Mighty Mars / Cash ain't nothing / If I had a woman.
**CD:** Released Jul '88, on JSP by JSP Records. Catalogue no: **JSP CD 217**
**Album:** Released Aug '85, on JSP by JSP Records. Catalogue no: **JSP 1089**

**LIFE ON MARS**
Tracks: / Born under a bad sign / Don't start me talking / Back door man / Steal away / Standing in line / Hot lips boogie / I can't take a jealous woman / Get on up / Desert island / Keep on swinging.
**Album:** Released Jul '84, on Lamborghini by Lamborghini Records. Catalogue no: **LSULP 2**

**OAKLAND BOOGIE, THE**
Tracks: / I've been down so long / Nine below zero / Rocket 88 / Call me / Love is a wonderful thing / Honey bee / Blue midnight / Cruisin' / If I had a woman / My dog can't bark.
**Album:** Released '82, on Big Bear by Big Bear Records. Deleted '88. Catalogue no: **BEAR 12**

## Marsala, Joe

**1944: JOE MARSALA (Marsala,Joe & his band)**
**Album:** Released Jun '86, on Jazzology (USA) by Jazzology Records (USA). Catalogue no: **J 106**

**JOE MARSALA 1942 (Marsala, Joe & His Orchestra with Adele Girard)**
Tracks: / I've got a gal in Kalamazoo / Lullaby of the rain / Can't get out of this mood / Blue skies / There are such things / Solid geometry for squares / Barrel roll / So nobody cares / Mr. Five by five / Lover / Be careful, it's my heart / Topsy.
**Album:** Released Apr '79, on Aircheck (USA) by Kiner Ents.(USA). Catalogue no: **AIRCHECK 14**

## Marsalis, Branford

**RANDOM ABSTRACT**
Tracks: / Yes and no / Crescent city / Broadway fools / Lonjellis / I thought about you / Lonely woman / Steep's theme.
**CD:** Released 22 Aug '88, on CBS by CBS Records. Catalogue no: **461 067 2**
**Cass:** Released 22 Aug '88, on CBS by CBS Records. Deleted Jan '90. Catalogue no: **461067 4**
**Album:** Released 22 Aug '88, on CBS by CBS Records. Deleted Jan '90. Catalogue no: **461067 1**

**RENAISSANCE**
Tracks: / Just one of those things / Lament / Peacocks, The / Love stone / Citadel / Wrath, The (structured burnout) / St. Thomas.
**Cass:** Released Nov '87, on CBS by CBS Records. Deleted 10 Jul '89. Catalogue no: **460 229-4**
**Album:** Released Nov '87, on CBS by CBS Records. Deleted Jan '90. Catalogue no: **460229 1**

**ROYAL GARDEN BLUES**
Tracks: / Swingin at the haven / Dienda / Strike up the band / Emanon / Royal Garden blues / Shadows / Wrath of Tain, The.
**CD:** Released Mar '87, on CBS by CBS Records. Catalogue no: **450 151 2**
**Album:** Released Nov '86, on CBS by CBS Records. Catalogue no: **450 151 1**
**Cass:** Released Nov '86, on CBS by CBS Records. Catalogue no: **450 151 4**

**SCENES IN THE CITY**
Tracks: / No backstage pass / Scenes in the city / Solstice / Waiting for Tain /

**Wynton Marsalis - Black Codes (CBS)**

No sidestepping / Parable.
**Album:** Released May '84, on CBS by CBS Records. Deleted Aug '87. Catalogue no: **CBS 25952**
**CD:** Released '88, on UNKNOWN Catalogue no: **35DP 172**

## STEEP

**VHS:** Released Oct '89, on CMV Enterprises (video) by CBS Records. Catalogue no: **490212**

## TRIO GP

Tracks: / Housed from Edward / Three little words / UMMG / Doxy / Stardust / Random abstract (Tain's rampage) / Nearness of you, The / Makin' whoopee / Gutbucket steepy / Makin' whoopee (reprise) / Peace.
**CD:** Released Jul '89, on CBS by CBS Records. Catalogue no: **465 134 2**
**Album:** Released Jul '89, on CBS by CBS Records. Catalogue no: **465 134 1**
**Cass:** Released Jul '89, on CBS by CBS Records. Catalogue no: **465 134 4**

# Marsalis, Wynton

## AMERICAN HERO, AN

Tracks: / One by one / My funny valentine / Round 'bout midnight / ETA / Time will tell / Blakey's theme.
Note: With Bobby Watson/Billy Pierce/Jimmy Williams/Charles Farnbrough/Art Blakey. Recorded 1980.
**CD:** Released Nov '86, on Kingdom Jazz by Kingdom Records. Catalogue no: **CDGATE 7018**
**Cass:** Released '89, on Kingdom Jazz by Kingdom Records. Catalogue no: **CGATE 7018**
**Album:** Released '86, on Kingdom Jazz by Kingdom Records. Catalogue no: **GATE 7018**

## BLACK CODES (from the underground) (See panel above)

Tracks: / Black codes / For wee folks / Delfeayo's dilemma / Phryzzian march / Aural oasis / Chambers of Tain / Blues.
Note: As the cover tells you, it all comes down to knowing and wanting to know. To study and experience, to rebellion against the bondage of ignorance. And no major art can subsist on luck or on natural talent that is never put to the head-slapping test of discipline. So there is never a point at which learning and knowing don't come together for the best expression of talent. The objective is mastery, which is always born of sophistication. In jazz, mastery has to do with an unavoidable velocity because the improvisor must work in a context where the moment is all, where the recipe for shape, continuity, and form has to be conceived, mixed, cooked, and served immediately. As with all art, the more you know, the more you can do. And when everything is focused by integrity, you hear the emotion of idealism boiling over the top, spanning moods from the bristling to the frail tenderness of a vulnerable lover's whisper. This recording has that scope of passion, and it is delivered with a gutbucket high-mindedness as intruiging, as it is exciting, as infectious as it is soothing.
With *Black codes*, Wynton Marsalis closes the door on high and low rabble ranting about his lacking a personal direction or the ability to express himself with entrancing emotion, already, his tone, his phrasing, the notes he chooses and the harmonies included in his songs detail the imposing growth of a unique artist. That his work and the colour of his music recall the contributions of seminal figures in jazz only means that he is part of a tradition, since the person who reminds the audience of no one has somehow managed to avoid the colossal problem of giving personal character to the essential particulars of an idiom.
He calls this album *Black codes (from the underground)* as a reference to the prohibitive 19th Century slave laws that emphasized depriving chattels of anything other than what was necessary to maintain their postions as talking working animals. But Marsalis isn't after whining or guilt-mongering; he is concerned with how those laws have evolved into contemporary trends and conceptions of both specific and universal implications. Marsalis sees the present problem as one in which too many have chosen to be no more than barometers of trends, not individuals making their own way and expanding the expression of human intricacy as they move. Just as Bill Cosby's television show decries the limitations of buffoon humour, opting for an artistry as down-home as it is universal, Marsalis wants to make music in keeping with the world-spirited joy and seriousness of Armstrong, Ellington, Parker, Monk, Coltrane, and the best of Davis, Coleman, Shorter, and Hancock. In his mind, the pressure of commercialism is another form of black codes, one that reduces all willing musicians to highly paid but low-grade plantation entertainers, regardless of race or idiom. The late Roland Kirk called it "volunteer slavery". Coming from the other side of the field, Marsalis is more interested in the statement than the payment.
The first obvious level of statement is the leader's development as a composer, each of the pieces is written differently, has its own mood, and reveals an individual emerging through the influences that are immediately obvious. "In every era you have composers who stand out and who set up directions. Ellington and Strayhorn tower over everybody, then you have Monk, then Wayne Shorter. Right now, it is easy to see that Wayne took the music in a fresh direction because of his organic conception of the interaction of melody, harmony, and rhythm. Some of the avant-garde composers wrote interesting lines, but I haven't been impressed by their harmonic ideas. Wayne Shorter knows harmony perfectly and, just like Monk, every note and every chord, every rhythm, every accent - each of them is there for a good reason."
Beyond the impressive skill exhibited in the odd structures of the writing, there are improvisations of such conscious order, fire, and rhythmic fluidity that the combination of individuality and continuity gives each piece the feeling of a whole because each musician so de-

cidedly uses what has been played before him as he makes his own statement, the compositions never stop and are always more than strings of so-called solos. Above it all, however, is the swing and the lyricism, the leader has never played this well on record. There is the clarion melancholy of his superbly controlled work on the title tune, the breezy relaxation of *Delfeayo's dilemma*, the puckish snarls of *Phryzzinian man*, the raw force and structure of *Chambers of tain*, and the sublime flutters of his ballads. Branford Marsalis, like his brother, has absorbed many ways of swinging, from shifting molten rhythms to the way he sweeps Lester Young's coolness and detached elegance into contemporary harmony on *Phryzzinian man*, moving from a superb variation on the brief interlude that introduces him into a creation that is absolutely melodic. Kenny Kirkland not only accompanies each horn with different colours, attacks, rhythms, and meters, but proves that there is no pianist under 40 in jazz who can swing harder, invent with more linear control, or execute such supple rhythms. Seventeen-year-old Charnett Moffett is shocking in his swing and his sound, never losing his place as Kirkland and Watts reorder the accents and superimpose other time signatures. Ron Carter, as usual, does an impeccable job in reinterpreting and developing the thematic structures and harmonic ideas presented in *Aural oasis*. Then there is Tain ("What's your name? Puddin' and tain, ask me again and I'll tell you the same."): Probably the Dean of the younger drummers. As the ballads show, he is already a master of cymbal timbre, and the swing he pulls off by periodically accenting his sock cymbal on the second half of two and four or effortlessly adjusting when other meters are introduced, prove him a man of remarkable instincts and attentiveness to detail. Most importantly, his playing is in the tradition of the hot heart of polyrhythm Elvin Jones perfected.

In all, this recording is a testament to the craft, integrity, and passion that idealism instigates. We are all lucky that such young musicians are playing jazz and handling its greatest demands with such an emotive sense of order. This is an eloquent attack on the contemporary definitions of black codes, which the leader explains with direct insight: "Black codes mean a lot of things. Anything that reduces potential, that pushes your taste down to an obvious, animal level. Anything that makes you think less significance is **more** enjoyable. Anything that keeps you on the surface, the way they depict women in rock videos - black codes. People gobble up junk food when they can afford something better - black codes. The argument that illiteracy is valid in a technological world - black codes. People who equate ignorance with soullfulness - definitely black codes. The overall quality of every true artist's work is a rebellion against black codes. That's the line I want to be in - and I definitely have plenty of examples." In fact, young Mr Marsalis, you are quite an example yourself. (Stanley Crouch)

**CD:** Released Nov '85, on CBS by CBS Records. Catalogue no: **CDCBS 26686**
**Cass:** Released Nov '85, on CBS by CBS Records. Catalogue no: **40 26686**
**Album:** Released Nov '85, on CBS by CBS Records. Catalogue no: **CBS 26686**

**BLUES AND SWING**
**VHS:** Released Oct '89, on CMV Enterprises (video) by CBS Records. Catalogue no: **490022**

**CARNAVAL (With Eastman Wind Ensemble)**
Tracks: / Variations on le carnaval de Venise / Grand Russian fantasia / Debutante, The / Believe me, if all those endearing young charms / Moto perpetuo / 'Tis the last rose of summer / Flight of the bumble bee / Napoli / Variations on a Neapolitan song / Fantasie brillante / Sometimes I feel like a motherless child / Valse brillante.
**Album:** Released Apr '87, on CBS by CBS Records. Catalogue no: **IM 42137**
**Cass:** Released Apr '87, on CBS by CBS Records. Catalogue no: **IMT 42137**
**CD:** Released Apr '87, on CBS by CBS Records. Catalogue no: **MK 42137**

**CRESCENT CITY CHRISTMAS CARD**
Tracks: / Carol of the bells / Silent night / Hark the herals angels sing / Little drummer boy / We three kings of orient are / Oh tannenbaum / Sleigh ride / Let it snow let it snow let it snow / God rest ye merry gentlemen / Winter wonderland / Jingle bells / O come all ye faithful / Twas the night before Christmas.
**Cass:** Released Dec '89, on CBS by CBS Records. Catalogue no: **4658794**
**CD:** Released Dec '89, on CBS by CBS Records. Catalogue no: **4658792**
**Album:** Released Dec '89, on CBS by CBS Records. Catalogue no: **4658791**

**FIRST RECORDINGS WITH ART BLAKEY**
Tracks: / Angel eyes / Bitter dose / Wheel within a wheel, A / Gipsy / Jody.
Note: Recorded 1980 with Art Blakey/Jimmy Williams/Ellis Mardsalis/Charles Fambrough/Billy Pierce. Tracks include: Angel eyes/Bitter dose/Jody/Wheel within a wheel/Gipsey.
**Cass:** Released '89, on Kingdom Jazz by Kingdom Records. Catalogue no: **CGATE 7013**
**Album:** Released Oct '87, on Kingdom Jazz by Kingdom Records. Catalogue no: **GATE 7013**
**CD:** Released Oct '87, on Kingdom Jazz by Kingdom Records. Catalogue no: **CDGATE 7013**

**HOT HOUSE FLOWERS**
Tracks: / Stardust / Lazy afternoon / For all we know / When you wish upon a star / Django / Melancholia / Hot house flowers / Confession.
**Album:** Released Nov '84, on CBS by CBS Records. Catalogue no: **CBS 26145**
**Cass:** Released Nov '84, on CBS by CBS Records. Catalogue no: **40 26145**
**CD:** Released Nov '84, on CBS by CBS Records. Catalogue no: **CD 26145**

**J MOOD**
Tracks: / J mood / Presence that lament brings / Insane asylum / Skain's domain / Melodique / After / Much later.
**Cass:** Released '88, on CBS by CBS Records. Catalogue no: **40 57068**
**CD:** Released '88, on CBS by CBS Records. Deleted Jan '89. Catalogue no: **CD 57068**

**LIVE AT BLUES ALLEY**
Tracks: / Knozz-Moe-King / Just friends / Juan / Cherokee / Delfeayo's dilemma / Chambers of Tain / Au privave / Do you know what it means to miss... / Skain's domain / Much later.
**Cass:** Released Jul '88, on CBS by CBS Records. Deleted Jan '90. Catalogue no: **461109 4**
**CD:** Released Jul '88, on CBS by CBS Records. Catalogue no: **461 109 2**
**Album:** Released Jul '88, on CBS by CBS Records. Deleted Jan '90. Catalogue no: **461109 1**

**MAJESTY OF THE BLUES, THE**
Tracks: / Majesty of the blues, The (Puheeman strut) / Hickory dickory dock / New Orleans function, The / Death of jazz, The / Premature autopsies (sermon) / Oh, but on the third day (happy feet blues).
**CD:** Released Jun '89, on CBS by CBS Records. Catalogue no: **465 129 2**
**Cass:** Released Jun '89, on CBS by CBS Records. Catalogue no: **465 129 4**
**Album:** Released Jun '89, on CBS by CBS Records. Catalogue no: **465 129 1**

**MARSALIS STANDARD TIME**
Tracks: / Caravan / April in Paris / Cherokee / Goodbye / New Orleans / Soon all will know / Foggy day in London town, A / Song is you, The / Memories of you / In the afterglow / Autumn leaves.
**Album:** Released Aug '87, on CBS by CBS Records. Deleted Jan '90. Catalogue no: **451039 1**
**CD:** Released Oct '87, on CBS by CBS Records. Catalogue no: **451 039 2**
**Cass:** Released Aug '87, on CBS by CBS Records. Catalogue no: **451039 4**

**THINK OF ONE**
Tracks: / Think of one / Knozz-Moe-King / Fuschia / My ideal / What is happening here (now) / Bell ringer / Later / Melancholia.
**CD:** Released Jul '83, on CBS by CBS Records. Deleted Jan '89. Catalogue no: **CD 25354**
**Cass:** Released Jul '83, on CBS by CBS Records. Deleted '87. Catalogue no: **40 25354**
**Album:** Released Jul '83, on CBS by CBS Records. Catalogue no: **CBS 25354**

**WYNTON MARSALIS**
**CD:** Released Jul '89, on Cleo Catalogue no: **CLCD 5014**
**CD:** Released '88, on CBS by CBS

Records. Deleted Jan '90. Catalogue no: **CD 85404**
**Album:** Released Feb '82, on CBS by CBS Records. Deleted Aug '87. Catalogue no: **CBS 85404**

## Marsh, Warne

**ALL MUSIC**
**Album:** Released Mar '79, on Nessa Deleted '83. Catalogue no: **N 7**

**ART OF IMPROVISING VOL 1**
Tracks: / Strike up the band / It's you or no one / Sub-conscious Lee / You stepped out of a dream / Scrapple from the apple / I'll remember April / Indiana / Lunar elevation / Song for you, A / How about you / Blues / I can't believe that you're in love wtih me / Indian summer / Half Nelson.
**Album:** Released Apr '81, on Revelation (USA) by Hit Record Entertainment Inc.(USA). Catalogue no: **REV 22**

**ART OF IMPROVISING VOL 2**
Tracks: / Sweet Georgia Brown / Out of nowhere / Fishin' around / Tangerine / Will you still be mine / What is this thing called love / You stepped out of a dream / Lennie's pennies / Yardbird.
**Album:** Released Apr '81, on Revelation (USA) by Hit Record Entertainment Inc.(USA). Catalogue no: **REV 27**

**BACK HOLME (Marsh, Warne Quartet & Quintet)**
**Album:** Released Jan '87, on Criss Cross Catalogue no: **CRISS 1023**

**HOW DEEP, HOW HIGH (Marsh, Warne Group)**
Tracks: / Hard way / Note worthy / Finishing touch / How deep how high / Background music / She's funny that way.
Note: Warne Marsh-sax, Sal Mosca-piano, Sam Jones-bass, Roy Haynes-drums.
**Album:** Released '88, on Discovery (USA) by Discovery Records (USA). Catalogue no: **DS 863**
**Album:** Released Jun '79, on Interplay (USA) by Interplay Records (USA). Catalogue no: **IP 7725**

**JAZZ FROM THE EAST VILLAGE**
**Album:** Released Apr '79, on Wave by Wave Records. Catalogue no: **WAVE LP 10**

**LIVE AT THE MONTMARTRE CLUB (Marsh, Warne\Lee Konitz Quintet)**
Note: Mono Production.
**Album:** Released Jun '86, on Storyville by Storyville Records AB. Catalogue no: **SLP 1020**
**Album:** Released Nov '86, on Storyville by Storyville Records AB. Catalogue no: **SLP 4026**

**MUSIC FOR PRANCING (Marsh, Warne Quartet & Quintet)**
**Album:** Released '88, on Criss Cross Catalogue no: **CRISS 1004**

**NE PLUS ULTRA**
Tracks: / You stepped out of a dream / Lennie's pennies / 317 E. 32nd / Subconscious Lee / Touch & go.
**Album:** Released Apr '81, on Revelation (USA) by Hit Record Entertainment Inc.(USA). Catalogue no: **REV 12**

**NEWLY WARNE**
**CD:** Released Feb '90, on Storyville by Storyville Records AB. Catalogue no: **STCD4162**

**NOTEWORTH (Marsh, Warne Group)**
**CD:** Released '88, on Discovery (USA) by Discovery Records (USA). Catalogue no: **DSCD 945**

**POSTHUMOUS**
**Album:** Released Apr '89, on Interplay (USA) by Interplay Records (USA). Catalogue no: **IP-8604**

**REPORT OF THE SYMPOSIUM ON RELAXED IMPROVISATION VOL.1 (Marsh, Warne/Clare Fischer/Gary Foster)**
Tracks: / It could happen to you / Bluesy rouge / In a mellow tone / Yesterdays.
**Album:** Released Apr '81, on Revelation (USA) by Hit Record Entertainment Inc.(USA). Catalogue no: **REV 17**

**TWO DAYS IN THE LIFE OF WARNE (STORYVILLE)**
**CD:** Released Feb '90, on Storyville by Storyville Records AB. Catalogue no: **STCD 4165**

**TWO DAYS IN THE LIFE OF WARNE**
**Album:** Released Nov '88, on Interplay (USA) by Interplay Records (USA). Catalogue no: **IP 8602**

**WARNE MARSH**
**Album:** Released Apr '79, on Wave by Wave Records. Catalogue no: **WAVE LP 6**

**WARNE MARSH & LEE KONITZ VOL 3 (Warne Marsh/ Lee Konitz)**
**Album:** Released Jun '86, on Storyville by Storyville Records AB. Catalogue no: **SLP 4096**

**WARNE MARSH AND SUSAN CHEN (Marsh, Warne & Susan Chen)**
**Album:** Released Nov '88, on Interplay (USA) by Interplay Records (USA). Catalogue no: **IP 8601**

**WARNE MARSH QUINTET (Marsh, Warne Quintet)**
**Album:** Released Jun '86, on Storyville by Storyville Records AB. Catalogue no: **SLP 1017**
**Album:** Released Nov '86, on Storyville by Storyville Records AB. Catalogue no: **SLP 4001**

**WARNE OUT**
**Album:** Released Sep '77, on Interplay (USA) by Interplay Records (USA). Catalogue no: **IP-7709**
**Album:** Released Sep '80, on Flyright by Interstate Music. Catalogue no: **FLY 212**

## Marshall, Eddie

**ALMANAC (See also under Bennie Maupin, Cecil McBee, Mike Nock)**
**Album:** Released Nov '87, on Improvising Artists Catalogue no: **IAI 373835**

**DANCE OF THE SUN (Hutcherson, Bobby / Eddie Marshall / Manny Boyd / George Cables)**
**Album:** Released Apr '81, on Timeless by Timeless Records. Catalogue no: **SJP 109**

## Marshall, Joy

**MORE I SEE YOU, THE**
Tracks: / More I see you, The.
**7" Single:** Released Jun '66, on Decca by Decca International. Deleted '69. Catalogue no: **F 12422**

## Martyn, Barry

**VINTAGE BARRY MARTYN**
**Album:** Released '88, on GHB by Jazzology Records (USA). Catalogue no: **GHB 75**

## Maryland Jazzband

**25 YEARS OF JAZZ**
**Album:** Released Dec '87, on GHB by Jazzology Records (USA). Catalogue no: **GHB 178**

## Masekela, Hugh

**AFRICAN BREEZE**
Tracks: / African breeze / Don't go lose it baby / Coal train.
**7" Single:** Released Oct '85, on Jive by Zomba Records. Deleted Jul '87. Catalogue no: **JIVE 100**
**12" Single:** Released Oct '85, on Jive by Zomba Records. Deleted Jul '87. Catalogue no: **JIVET 100**

**BRING HIM BACK HOME**
Tracks: / Serengeti / Bring him back home.
**12" Single:** Released Feb '87, on Atlantic by WEA Records. Deleted Jan '88. Catalogue no: **U 8466 T**
**7" Single:** Released Feb '87, on Atlantic by WEA Records. Deleted Jan '88. Catalogue no: **U 8466**

**DON'T GO LOSE IT BABY**
Tracks: / Don't go lose it baby / African breeze (Track on 1988 release only, not on 1984 release.).
**12" Single:** Released May '84, on Jive by Zomba Records. Catalogue no: **JIVET 64**
**7" Single:** Released May '88, on Jive by Zomba Records. Deleted '88. Catalogue no: **JIVE 173**
**7" Single:** Released May '84, on Jive by Zomba Records. Catalogue no: **JIVE 64**
**12" Single:** Released May '88, on Jive by Zomba Records. Deleted '88. Catalogue no: **JIVET 173**

**IF YOU DON'T KNOW ME BY NOW**
Tracks: / If you don't know me by now / Hold on.
**7" Single:** Released Mar '90, on Novus by BMG Records (UK). Catalogue no: **PB 43525**

**KE BALE**
Tracks: / Ke bale / Bird on the wing.
**7" Single:** Released 13 Jun '87, on Warner Bros. by WEA Records. Catalogue

no: **W 8311**
**12" Single:** Released 13 Jun '87, on Warner Bros. by WEA Records. Catalogue no: **W 8311T**

**LADY**
Tracks: / Lady / Ritual dancer.
**7" Single:** Released Apr '85, on Jive Africa by Zomba Records. Catalogue no: **JIVE 94**
**12" Single:** Released Apr '85, on Jive Africa by Zomba Records. Catalogue no: **JIVET 94**

**LIBERATION - THE BEST OF**
Tracks: / Don't go lose it baby / Rainmaker, the / Run no more / Lady / Joke of a life, The / Coal train / African breeze / It's raining / Grazing in the grass / Politician / Ritual dancer.
**Album:** Released Jun '88, on Jive by Zomba Records. Deleted Nov '89. Catalogue no: **HOP 222**
**CD:** Released Jun '88, on Jive by Zomba Records. Catalogue no: **CDHOP 222**
**Cass:** Released Jun '88, on Jive by Zomba Records. Deleted Nov '89. Catalogue no: **HOPC 222**

**NOTICE TO QUIT**
Note: A musical semi documentary of his country, South Africa, featuring the music of Jazz trumpeteer Hugh masekela, plus poetry and news footage. 1986 production . Running time: 52 mins.
**VHS:** Released Sep '86, on Castle Hendring Video by Castle Communications Records. Catalogue no: **HEN 2 036 G**

**PULA EA NA (IT'S RAINING)**
Tracks: / Pula ea na (it's raining) / Pula ea na (it's raining) (version).
**12" Single:** Released Nov '84, on Jive Africa by Zomba Records. Catalogue no: **JIVET 81**
**7" Single:** Released Nov '84, on Jive Africa by Zomba Records. Catalogue no: **JIVE 81**

**TECHNO-BUSH**
**Album:** Released Jun '84, on Jive Africa by Zomba Records. Deleted Nov '89. Catalogue no: **HIP 11**
**Cass:** Released Jun '84, on Jive Africa by Zomba Records. Deleted Nov '89. Catalogue no: **HIPC 11**

**TOMORROW (Masekela, Hugh, with Kalahari)**
Tracks: / Bring him back home / Mayibuyi / Ke bale / London fog / Everybody's standing up / Bird on the wing / Something for nothing / Serengeti.
**Cass:** Released Jan '87, on WEA by WEA Records. Catalogue no: **254573 4**
**Album:** Released Jan '87, on WEA by WEA Records. Catalogue no: **254573 1**
**CD:** Released Jan '87, on WEA by WEA Records. Catalogue no: **254573 2**

**UPTOWNSHIP**
Tracks: / Uptownship / If you don't know me by now / Now or never / Hold on / Ooo baby baby / Egoli / No woman, no cry / Emavungweni / Naledi.
**Cass:** Released Nov '89, on Novus by BMG Records (UK). Catalogue no: **PK 83070**
**CD:** Released Dec '89, on Novus by BMG Records (UK). Catalogue no: **PD 83070**
**Album:** Released Nov '89, on Novus by BMG Records (UK). Catalogue no: **PL 83070**

**WAITING FOR THE RAIN**
**Album:** Released May '85, on Jive by Zomba Records. Deleted Nov '89. Catalogue no: **HIP 25**
**Cass:** Released May '85, on Jive by Zomba Records. Deleted Nov '89. Catalogue no: **HIPC 25**

**WIMOWEH (THE LION NEVER SLEEPS)**
Tracks: / Wimoweh.
**12" Single:** Released Sep '84, on Jive Africa by Zomba Records. Catalogue no: **JIVET 76**
**7" Single:** Released Sep '84, on Jive Africa by Zomba Records. Catalogue no: **JIVE 76**

## Maslak, Keshavan

**BIG TIME (Maslak, Keshavan Quartet)**
Tracks: / Mr. Moffett / You'll love it / 2300 skiddoo / Big money cha, cha, cha / Big time / Big heart / You left your big shoe at my house.
**Album:** Released Feb '88, on Affinity by Charly Records. Catalogue no: **AFF 185**

**BLASTER MASTER (Maslak, Keshavan with Charles Moffett)**
Tracks: / Blast yo mama / Jizz and cocktails / Blaster master / Jim jizz bo / Judy jizz bo.
**Album:** Released May '85, on Black Saint (Italy) Catalogue no: **BSR 0079**

**HUMANPLEXITY**
**Album:** Released Sep '84, on Leo by Leo Records. Catalogue no: **LR 101**

**LOVED BY MILLIONS**
**Album:** Released Sep '84, on Leo by Leo Records. Catalogue no: **LR 105**

## Mason, Rod

**CARRY ME BACK**
**Album:** Released May '87, on Wam Catalogue no: **WAM/O No.8**

**COME BACK SWEET PAPA (Mason, Rod Hot Five)**
Tracks: / Last time, The / Melancholy blues / Papa de da da / Wild man blues / Georgia grind / Heebie jeebies / Perdido street blues / Potato head blues / Winnin' boy / Come back sweet papa / Sweet substitute / Do what Ory say / You made me love you.
**Album:** Released May '85, on Black Lion Catalogue no: **BLM 51102**

**GOOD COMPANIONS**
**Album:** Released '88, on Black Lion Catalogue no: **BLP 12145**

**GREAT HAVING YOU AROUND**
Tracks: / Down home rag / Great having you around / I want a big butter and egg man / Pennies from heaven / It's only a paper moon / There'll be some changes made / Memphis blues / Professor Foxley's manipulations / Sweet Lorraine / Way down yonder in New Orleans.
**Album:** Released Apr '79, on Black Lion Catalogue no: **BLP 12180**

**MEET ME WHERE THEY PLAY THE BLUES**
**Album:** Released Jun '78, on Black Lion Catalogue no: **BLP 12167**

**PEARLS, THE Jelly Roll Morton Interpretations (Mason, Rod Hot Seven)**
Tracks: / Pearls, The / Grandpa's spells / Don't you leave me here / King Porter stomp / Cannonball blues / Frog-I-more rag / Kansas City stomp / Dead man blues / Wolverine blues / My home in a southern town / Frenchman's, The / Original Jelly Roll blues.
**Album:** Released Jul '87, on Black Lion Catalogue no: **BLM 51114**

**ROD MASON (Mason, Rod/Beryl Bryden)**
**Album:** Released Feb '80, on Black Lion Catalogue no: **BLP 12194**

**ROD MASON'S HOT FIVE**
**Album:** Released Aug '89, on Timeless by Timeless Records. Catalogue no: **TTD 538**

**SAVANNAH ORCHESTRA AND HOT FIVE (Mason, Rod Hot Five)**
**2 LP Set:** Released May '89, on Timeless by Timeless Records. Catalogue no: **TTD 551**

## Massey, Cal

**BLUES TO COLTRANE**
Note: With Calvin Massey/Julius Watkins/Hugh Brodie/Patti Brown/Jimmy Garrison/G.T. Hogan. Tracks include: Blues to Coltrane/What's wrong/Bakai/These are soulful days/Father and son. Recorded 1961.
**CD:** Released Dec '87, on Candid Catalogue no: **CCD 9029**
**Album:** Released Jul '87, on Candid Catalogue no: **CS 9029**

## Masso, George

**DIALOGUE AT CONDON'S (Al Klink, Lou Stein, Jack Lesberg, Bobby Roseng (Masso, George Quintet)**
Tracks: / This can't be love / Man I love / Coquette / Mean to me / Tea for two / Let's get away from it all.
**Album:** Released May '81, on World Jazz Deleted '86. Catalogue no: **WJLPS 18**

## Massters, Joe

**JAZZ MASS BY MASSTERS, THE**
Note: Featuring the Mike Wofford Septet, with the Allan Davies 30 Voice Choir, Mike Wofford-piano, Bobby West-bass, John Guerin-drums, Jerry Williams-timpani, Gary Barone-trumpet, Harold Land-tenor sax, Anthony Ortega-alto sax.
**Album:** Released '88, on Discovery (USA) by Discovery Records (USA). Catalogue no: **DS 785**

## Master Jazz Piano

**MASTER JAZZ PIANO Vol. 3 (Various artists)**
**Album:** Released '88, on Swaggie (Australia) Catalogue no: **S 1337**

**MASTER JAZZ PIANO Vol. 4 (Various artists)**
**Album:** Released '88, on Swaggie (Australia) Catalogue no: **S 1363**

**MASTER JAZZ PIANO Vol. 6 (Various artists)**
**Album:** Released '88, on Swaggie (Australia) Catalogue no: **S 1387**

**MASTER JAZZ PIANO 1928-30 (Various artists)**
**Album:** Released '88, on Swaggie (Australia) Catalogue no: **S 1298**

## Master, Mark

**SILVER THREADS AMONG THE BLUES (Master's, Mark Jazz Composers Orchestra)**
**Album:** Released Nov '88, on Sea Breeze Catalogue no: **SB 2033**

## Masters Of The Blues

**MASTERS OF THE BLUES VOL. 5 (Various artists)**
**Album:** Released '88, on Collector's Classics Catalogue no: **CC 29**

**MASTERS OF THE BLUES VOL. 12 (Various artists)**
**Album:** Released '88, on Collector's Classics Catalogue no: **CC 38**

## Masters Of The Ragtime

**MASTERS OF THE RAGTIME GUITAR (Various artists)**
**Album:** Released Aug '77, on Kicking Mule by Sonet Records. Catalogue no: **SNKF 130**

## Mathews, Mat

**DAVISON, BUTTERFIELD, TATE, (Mathews, Mat & Friends)**
**Album:** Released Aug '88, on Jazzology (USA) by Jazzology Records (USA). Catalogue no: **AP 219**

**JUST LIKE THIS (Mathews, Mat(elect) & Roy Hansen (Acoustic))**
**Album:** Released '84, on Accordion Record Club by Accordion Record Club. Catalogue no: **MC 8174**

## Mathews, Tony

**ALIEN IN MY OWN HOME**
Tracks: / Too many people in my bed / Alien in my own home / (Coming with) loving on my mind / My life ain't nothing but a blues song / You send me / Warning (big danger ahead) / One hour ago / She rides in the fast lane / Who needs it / I'll tell you, I do.
**CD:** Released Oct '89, on S.D.E.G. Catalogue no: **SDE 4004CD**
**Cass:** Released Oct '89, on S.D.E.G. Catalogue no: **SDE 4004MC**
**Album:** Released Oct '89, on S.D.E.G. Catalogue no: **SDE 4004**
**Album:** Released Mar '90, on Sonet by Sonet Records. Catalogue no: **SNTF 1028**
**CD:** Released Mar '90, on Sonet by Sonet Records. Catalogue no: **SNTCD 1028**

**CONDITION BLUE**
Tracks: / I really got the blues today / White powder / Coming home to you / Uncle Joe / Lovely Linda / Ann Marie / Laid off / Let me know when you're comin' / Changes.
Note: Solo album featuring Ray Charles' gifted guitar player, Tony Mathews. Like "Brother Ray', Tony has created a personal blend of music from the elements of soul, gospel, jazz, rock, pop and funk, and fused them into something uniquely his own. 'Condition Blue' has the feel of T-Bone Walker's blues, the rich chords of gospel groups, the funky bounce of city streets, the fire and drive of Little Richard and Jackie Wilson, and the sophisticated technique of jazz. (Alligator catalogue 7/88)
**Album:** Released Jun '81, on Alligator (Sonet) by Alligator Records (USA). Catalogue no: **SNTF 866**

## Mathisen, Leo

**DANISH JAZZ, VOL 2**
**Album:** Released Jul '82, on Storyville by Storyville Records AB. Catalogue no: **SLP 411**

## Mauro, Turk

**HEAVYWEIGHT**
Tracks: / Cottontail / Old folks / Big sound from the east, The / You're my everything / Home / Jazz guys / East 121st Street.
**Album:** Released '81, on Phoenix (USA) by All Star Talent Inc.(USA). Catalogue no: **LP 1004**

**UNDERDOG, THE (Mauro, Turk/Al Cohn/Hugh Lawson/Bob Cranshaw)**
**Album:** Released Nov '86, on Storyville by Storyville Records AB. Catalogue no: **SLP 4076**

## May, Billy

**Biographical details:** This American orchestra leader, conductor and arranger was an important behind-the-scenes figure in the Los Angeles music scene during the forties and fifties. His imaginative arrangements graced the records of many artists on Capitol, the label for which he worked. His association with Frank Sinatra was particularly notable, as were his liaisons with Peggy Lee and Nat 'King' Cole. In 1956 May scored a one-off UK chart entry with the main title theme from *The Man With The Golden Arm*. This single reached no. 9 which compensated for the fact that in America he was beaten by a host of rival versions of the movie tune. Bob McDonald, June 1985.

**20 GOLDEN PIECES: BILLY MAY**
Tracks: / Come rain or come shine / Little green apples / It's getting baby / Baby I need your lovin' / Walk on by / Cherry cherry / Spanish harlem / Come back to me / Hold me / Blues in the night / Marrakesh express / Jackie / Soulful strut / Pepito / Pass me by / Soul coaxing / Stripper, The / Little games / Some of these days / Summer place, A (theme from).
**Cass:** Released Feb '82, on Bulldog Records by President Records. Catalogue no: **AJKL 2025**
**Album:** Released Nov '81, on Bulldog Records by President Records. Catalogue no: **BDL 2025**

**BACCHANALIA! (May, Billy & His Orchestra)**
Tracks: / Top hat, white tie and tails / Cocktails for two / You and the night and the music / Pick yourself up / Show me the way to go home / Little brown jug / Makin' whoopee / Bacchanalia / Let's put out the lights / Accent on youth / It's the natural thing to do.
**Cass:** Released Mar '85, on Capitol by EMI Records. Deleted Jul '87. Catalogue no: **ED 2604204**
**Album:** Released Mar '85, on Capitol by EMI Records. Deleted Jun '89. Catalogue no: **ED 2604201**

**BEST OF BILLY MAY**
**LP Set:** Released Jul '86, on Aerospace Catalogue no: **RA 1013**
**CD:** Released Nov '88, on Aerospace Catalogue no: **RA 1013CD**
**Cass set:** Released Jul '86, on Aerospace Catalogue no: **RA 1013C**

**BEST OF BILLY MAY AND HIS ORCHESTRA (May, Billy & His Orchestra)**
Tracks: / Bye bye blackbird / Fascinatin' rhythm / Preacher man / You're driving me crazy / Mad about the boy / In a Persian market.
**Album:** Released Apr '83, on MFP by EMI Records. Deleted '87. Catalogue no: **MFP 5609**
**Cass:** Released Apr '83, on MFP by EMI Records. Deleted '87. Catalogue no: **TCMFP 5609**

**BEST OF BILLY MAY, VOL. 2 (May, Billy & His Orchestra)**
**CD:** Released '89, on Aerospace Catalogue no: **RACD 1014**

**BILLY MAY'S BIG FAT BRASS**
Tracks: / Brassmen's holiday / Autumn leaves / Love is the thing / Ping pong / Moonlight becomes you / Pawn ticket / Solving the riddle / Invitation / Continental (You kiss while you're dancing), The / Return of the zombie / On a little street in Singapore / Joom jooms.
Note: A timely reissue of this Grammy award-winning album from the creative Billy May and his brass ensemble. As usual, each track contains the humourous musical expression always present in Billy May's arrangements - a brief description of each is outlined on the sleeve, along with personnels. A good selection of well known tracks including some May originals, using just brass - no reeds - a refreshing change incorporating plenty of swingy inventions for brass.
**Cass:** Released May '86, on Capitol by

EMI Records. Deleted Jun '88. Catalogue no: **TCEMS 1155**

**Album:** Released May '86, on Capitol by EMI Records. Deleted Aug '89. Catalogue no: **EMS 1155**

**BILLY MAY'S NAUGHTY OPERETTA (May, Billy & His Orchestra)**

Tracks: / Serenade from the student prince / Italian street song / Desert song, The / Rose Marie / I'll see you again / She didn't say yes / Vilia / Hugette waltz / Softly as in a morning sunrise / One kiss / March of the toys.

**Cass:** Released Feb '84, on Capitol by EMI Records. Deleted Jul '87. Catalogue no: **TC CAPS 2400154**

**Album:** Released Feb '84, on Capitol by EMI Records. Deleted Jul '87. Catalogue no: **CAPS 2400151**

**CAPITOL YEARS, THE: BILLY MAY (May, Billy & His Orchestra)**

Tracks: / Cute piece of property, A (Vocal:The Encores) / Memphis in June (Vocal:Johnny Mercer) / Lemon twist / What does it take to make you take to me (Vocal:Nat King Cole) / Good gravy (Vocal:The Encores) / Christropher Columbus / Belly up to the bar, boys (With Stan Kenton & Nelson Riddle) / Dixieland band / Oklahoma / Street of dreams / Breeze and I, The / Mean to me (Vocal:Nellie Lutcher) / High noon / What kind of fool am I? (Vocal:Vic Damone) / Floater, The / When I take my sugar to tea (Vocal:The Maytimers) / Song is you, The / Young at heart.

**Cass:** Released Dec '87, on Capitol by EMI Records. Catalogue no: **TC EMS 1275**

**Album:** Released Dec '87, on Capitol by EMI Records. Catalogue no: **EMS 1275**

**FANCY DANCIN'**

Tracks: / It happened in Monterey / Say isn't so / Star eyes / I'll never say 'never again' again / Stumbling / She reminds me of you / Songs of the wanderer / Azure / Bye bye blackbird / You turned the tables on me.

**Cass:** Released Mar '85, on Pathe Marconi (France) Catalogue no: **PM 1547784**

**Album:** Released Mar '85, on Pathe Marconi (France) Catalogue no: **PM 1547781**

**GIRLS AND BOYS ON BROADWAY, THE (May, Billy Big Band)**

**Album:** Released Feb '88, on Fresh Sounds (Spain) by Fresh Sounds Records (Spain). Catalogue no: **FS 1**

**I BELIEVE IN YOU**

**Album:** Released May '85, on Bainbridge by Ducale S.p.A.. Catalogue no: **BT 1001**

**Cass:** Released May '85, on Bainbridge by Ducale S.p.A.. Catalogue no: **BT 41001**

**MAIN TITLE THEME FROM MAN WITH THE GOLDEN ARM**

Tracks: / Man with the golden arm, Theme from.

**7" Single:** Released Apr '56, on Capitol by EMI Records. Deleted '59. Catalogue no: **CL 14551**

**MAY BE (May, Billy & His Orchestra)**

Tracks: / Conrail flyer / Blonde again / I'm back where I started from / Chloe's song / Too soon for June / Blue and all alone / These are the good old days / Once more won't hurt / Pretty plaything / Opportunity rag / Old Cayucas / I heard ya the first time.

**Album:** Released Sep '80, on Raphaele by Mozart Edition. Deleted Sep '85. Catalogue no: **RRS 101**

**SKYLINER**

**Album:** Released Nov '77, on Golden Hour Catalogue no: **GH 868**

**SORTA DIXIE (May, Billy & His Orchestra)**

**Album:** Released '87, on Creative World(USA) by GNP Crescendo Records (USA). Catalogue no: **ST 1054**

**SORTA MAY (May, Billy & His Orchestra)**

**Album:** Released Mar '79, on Capitol by EMI Records. Catalogue no: **M 562**

**SORTA MAY/SORTA DIXIE (May, Billy & His Orchestra)**

**CD:** Released '87, on Creative World(USA) by GNP Crescendo Records (USA). Catalogue no: **STCD 1051**

**Album:** Released May '89, on GNP Crescendo (USA) by GNP Crescendo Records (USA). Catalogue no: **STD 1051**

**SWING GOES ON VOL 8**

**Album:** Released '83, on EMI (Germany) by EMI Records. Catalogue no: **IC 054 52717**

**YOU MAY SWING**

Tracks: / You ain't makin' it / Jornal do Brasil / Silvery cloud / I don't know where I'm goin' / Sunset colours / Santa Lucia / Bouncin' runners / Second chance / You may swing / Novo amor / Fingers / Sooper sloop.

**Album:** Released Apr '85, on IMS by Polydor Ltd. Catalogue no: **ISST 118**

## Mayall, John

**Biographical details:** This British vocalist, guitarist, keyboards player, harmonica player and composer was one of the three vital catalysts of the UK's blues boom of the Sixties. The others were Graham Bond and Alexis Korner - between them, these three men fathered and nurtured a movement which produced many of Britain's leading rock and pop stars.

Born in 1933, Mayall learned piano and guitar during his teens. He grew up in Manchester. He did not become a full time professional until 1963, the year he reached the age of 30. Prior to that, he had a variety of occupations including two years' national service in the army, four years at Manchester's Regional College of Art and a job in the art studio of an advertising agency. Finally, Korner persuaded him that he could transform his passion for music into a full-time career provided he moved to London. This he did, and thus began an extraordinary saga.

From 1963 until 1970 John was the boss of John Mayall's Bluesbreakers, one of the most influential forces in the British music scene of the era. According to Pete Frame's invaluable book "Rock Family Trees", there were no less than fifteen different lineups of this band. Amongst the future stars who passed through the Bluesbreakers were John McVie (Fleetwood Mac), Hughie Flint (McGuinness Flint), Jack Bruce (Cream), Peter Green and Mick Fleetwood (both Fleetwood Mac), Aynsley Dunbar (various bands), Andy Fraser, (Free) and Mick Taylor (The Rolling Stones). But the most important of all was guitar wizard Eric Clapton, the ex-Yardbird whose performances in the Bluesbreakers led some fans to instigate a graffiti campaign proclaiming 'Clapton Is God'. Clapton's stint with the band gave Mayall his first hit album in 1966 - it was a truly remarkable achievement for a blues LP to reach the Top 10. This success paved the way for Clapton's future illustrious career.

John Mayall's Bluesbreakers enjoyed further UK Top 10 albums with *A Hard Road* and *Crusade* (both 1967), *Bare Wires* (1968) and *Empty Rooms* (1970). Because his singles were not hits, and because he made no concessions to the pop market, Mayall remained a cult figure rather than a pop star; but the music scene of the era might have looked very different without him.

He moved from London to California in 1970. The Bluesbreakers ceased to exist but, true to form, Mayall assembled a new American band with a host of never-ending personnel changes. He continued releasing albums through the Seventies, but his influence and success had waned.

Perhaps the two finest tracks of his career were *Hideaway* and *Steppin' Out* from the Eric Clapton period. Another great moment was *Stormy Monday*, which can be found on the *Looking Back* compilation. Bob McDonald, 25 January 1986.

**ARCHIVES TO THE 80'S**

**CD:** Released Mar '89, on Polydor by Polydor Ltd. Catalogue no: **837 127-2**

**BACK TO THE ROOTS**

**Album:** Released Jun '71, on Polydor by Polydor Ltd. Deleted Jun '76. Catalogue no: **2657 005**

**BARE WIRES (Mayall, John & The Bluesbreakers)**

Tracks: / Bare wires suite / Bare wires / Where did I belong / Start walking / Open a new door / Fire / I know now / Look in the mirror / I'm a stranger / No reply / Hartley quits / Killing time / She's too young / Sandy.

Note: "This gave John Mayall his highest

UK album listing position and also spent a very creditable 19 weeks on Uncle Sam's top 200 best sellers." June 1988, London.
**CD:** Released Jun '88, on London Records by London Records Ltd. Catalogue no: **820 538-2**
**Album:** Released Jul '68, on Decca by Decca International. Deleted Jul '73. Catalogue no: **SKL 4945**

**BEHIND THE IRON CURTAIN**
**Cass:** Released '88, on GNP Crescendo (USA) by GNP Crescendo Records (USA). Catalogue no: **GNP5 2184**
**Cass:** Released May '86, on PRT by Castle Communications Records. Catalogue no: **ZCNCP 709**
**Album:** Released May '86, on PRT by Castle Communications Records. Catalogue no: **NCP 709**
**Album:** Released '88, on GNP Crescendo (USA) by GNP Crescendo Records (USA). Catalogue no: **GNPS 2184**

**BEYOND THE TURNING POINT**
**Album:** Released '74, on Polydor by Polydor Ltd. Catalogue no: **2483 016**

**BLUES ALONE, THE**
Tracks: / Brand new start / Please don't tell / Down the line / Sonny boy blow / Marsha's mood / No more tears / Catch that train / Cancelling out / Harp man / Brown sugar / Broken wings / Don't kick me.
Note: "A typical diversion for the ever restless Mayall. A package of self penned songs, was committed in just one day in 1967 and features him playing nearly all instruments himself."
**CD:** Released Jun '88, on London Records by London Records Ltd. Catalogue no: **820 535-2**
**Album:** Released '67, on Ace Of Clubs by Decca Records. Catalogue no: **SCL 1243**

**BLUES FROM LAUREL CANYON**
Tracks: / Vacation / Walking on sunset / Laurel Canyon home / 2401 / Ready to ride / Medicine man / Somebody's acting like a child / Bear, The / Miss James / First time alone / Long gone midnight / Fly tomorrow.
Note: Yet another gem from Macclesfield's azure hued son makes a transfer to the silver marvel thanks to public demand. This album dates from 1968, and was made up of entirely of the revered leader's own compositions. Co-produced with his regular advocate, Mike Vernon, this release comes complete with original sleeve graphics, historical note and a period shot or two from the archives as the projected release of everything John taped for 'The Supreme Record Company' moves a step closer to reality. (Deram, August 1989)
**Album:** Released '68, on Decca by Decca International. Catalogue no: **SKL 4972**
**CD:** Released Jan '88, on Deram by Decca International. Catalogue no: **820 539-2**

**BLUESBREAKERS**
**Album:** Released '83, on Decca by Decca International. Catalogue no: **SKL 4804**
**CD:** Released Nov '88, on Decca by Decca International. Catalogue no: **800 086 2**

**BOTTOM LINE (SINGLE)**
Tracks: / Bottom line / Dreamboat.
**7" Single:** Released Jun '79, on DJM Deleted '82. Catalogue no: **DJS 10918**

**BOTTOM LINE**
Tracks: / Bottom line / Dreamboat / Desert flower / I'm gonna do it / Revival / Game of love / Celebration / Come with me.
**Album:** Released Apr '79, on DJM Deleted Apr '84. Catalogue no: **DJF 20556**

**CHICAGO LINE (Mayall, John & The Bluesbreakers)**
Tracks: / Chicago line / Gimme one more day / One life to live / Last time, The / Dream about the blues / Fascinatin' lover / Cold blooded woman / Dirty dozen, The / Tears came rollin' down / Life in the jungle.
**CD:** Released '89, on Charly by Charly Records. Catalogue no: **CDCHARLY 202**

**COLLECTION: JOHN MAYALL**
Tracks: / Key to love / Hideaway / Ramblin' on my mind / All your love / They call it stormy Monday / Hoochie coochie man / Crocodile walk / Crawling up a hill / Marsha's mood / Sonny boy blow / Looking back / Hard road, A / Super-natural, The / You don't love me / Leaping Christine / Suspicions, part 2 / Picture on the wall / Death of J. B. Lenoir, The / Sandy / Bear, The / Walking on sunset / Fly tomorrow.
**Cass:** Released Apr '86, on Castle Collector Series by Castle Communications Records. Catalogue no: **CCSMC 137**
**CD:** Released '86, on Castle Collector Series by Castle Communications Records. Catalogue no: **CCSCD 137**
**2 LP Set:** Released Apr '86, on Castle Collector Series by Castle Communications Records. Catalogue no: **CCSLP 137**

**CRUSADE (Mayall, John & The Bluesbreakers)**
Tracks: / Oh, pretty woman / Stand back baby / My time after awhile / Snowy wood / Man of stone / Tears in my eyes / Driving sideways / Death of J. B. Lenoir, The / I can't quit you baby / Streamline / Me and my woman / Checkin' up on my baby.
**Album:** Released '67, on Decca by Decca International. Deleted '88. Catalogue no: **SKL 4890**
**CD:** Released Jun '88, on London Records by London Records Ltd. Catalogue no: **820 537-2**

**DIARY OF A BAND VOL 1 (Mayall, John Bluesbreakers)**
**Album:** Released '68, on Decca by Decca International. Deleted '88. Catalogue no: **SKL 4918**

**DIARY OF A BAND VOL 2 (Mayall, John Bluesbreakers)**
**Album:** Released Mar '68, on Decca by Decca International. Deleted Mar '73. Catalogue no: **SKL 4919**

**EMPTY ROOMS**
**2 LP Set:** Released Apr '70, on Polydor by Polydor Ltd. Deleted Apr '75. Catalogue no: **583 580**
**2 LP Set:** Released Aug '74, on Polydor by Polydor Ltd. Catalogue no: **2683 039**

**GREATEST HITS: JOHN MAYALL**
**Cass:** Released Nov '80, on Polydor by Polydor Ltd. Catalogue no: **3578 483**
**2 LP Set:** Released Nov '80, on Polydor by Polydor Ltd. Catalogue no: **2664 436**

**HARD ROAD, A (Mayall,John Bluesbreakers)**
Tracks: / Hard road, A / It's over / You don't love me / Stumble, The / Another kinda love / Hit the highway / Leaping Christine / Dust my blues / There's always work / Same way, The / Supernatural, The / Top of the hill / Some day after a while (you'll be sorry) / Living alone.
**CD:** Released Dec '87, on London Records by London Records Ltd. Deleted 1 Mar '89. Catalogue no: **820 474-2**
**Album:** Released '67, on Decca by Decca International. Catalogue no: **SKL 4853**

**JAZZ BLUES FUSION**
**Album:** Released '74, on Polydor by Polydor Ltd. Deleted Mar '87. Catalogue no: **2425 103**

**JOHN LEE BOOGIE**
Tracks: / John Lee boogie / Why worry / Mama talk to your daughter.
**7" Single:** Released '82, on DJM Catalogue no: **DJS 10969**

**JOHN MAYALL PLAYS JOHN MAYALL**
Tracks: / Crawling up a hill (version 2) / I wanna teach you everything / When I'm gone / I need your love / Hoot owl, The / R & B time / Night train / Crocodile walk (version 1) / What's the matter with you / Doreen / Runaway / Heartache / Chicago line.
**CD:** Released Jun '88, on London Records by London Records Ltd. Catalogue no: **820 536-2**
**Album:** Released '65, on Decca by Decca International. Deleted '88. Catalogue no: **LK 46800**

**JOHN MAYALL STORY, THE VOL 1**
**Album:** Released Oct '83, on Rock Echoes by Decca Records. Catalogue no: **TAB 74**

**JOHN MAYALL STORY, THE, VOL 2**
Tracks: / Pretty woman / My time after a while / Death of JB Lenoir / Suspicions / Picture on the wall / Open a new door / No reply / Harely quits / Sandy / Walking on sunset / Medicine man / Somebody's acting like a child.
**Album:** Released Jan '84, on Rock Echoes by Decca Records. Deleted Jan '89. Catalogue no: **TAB 75**

**LAST EDITION**
Tracks: / Gasoline blues / Perfect peace / Going to take my time / Deep down feelings / Troubled times / Pusher man / One of the few / Love song / Little kitten / Crazy games.
**Album:** Released Jun '83, on Polydor by Polydor Ltd. Catalogue no: **2486 278**
**Cass:** Released Jun '83, on Polydor by Polydor Ltd. Catalogue no: **3186 104**

**LAST OF THE BRITISH BLUES, THE**
Tracks: / Tucson lady / Parchman farm / There's only now / Teaser, The / Hideaway / Bear, The / Lonely birthday / Lowdown blues / It must be there.
**Album:** Released Feb '82, on MCA by MCA Records. Catalogue no: **MCL 1643**
**Cass:** Released Feb '82, on MCA by MCA Records. Catalogue no: **MCLC 1643**

**LOOKING BACK (Mayall, John & The Bluesbreakers)**
**Album:** Released '69, on Decca by Decca International. Deleted '88. Catalogue no: **SKL 5010**
**CD:** Released Jan '89, on London by London Records Ltd. Catalogue no: **830 331 2**

**MOVING ON**
**Album:** Released Aug '85, on Polydor (Germany) by Polydor Ltd. Catalogue no: **2459 325**

**NIGHTRIDING: JOHN MAYALL**
Tracks: / Law must change, The / Saw mill gulch road / I'm gonna fight for you J.B. / So hard to share / California / Thoughts about Roxanne / Room to move.
**Album:** Released Jul '88, on Knight by Knight Records Ltd.. Catalogue no: **KNLP 10010**
**Cass:** Released Jul '88, on Knight by Knight Records Ltd.. Catalogue no: **KNMC 10010**
**CD:** Released '89, on Knight by Knight Records Ltd.. Catalogue no: **KNCD 10010**

**NO MORE INTERVIEWS**
Tracks: / Hard going up / Bigger slice of pie, A / Falling / Take me home tonight / Sweet honey bee / Stars in the night / Consideration / Gypsy lady / Wild new lover.
**Album:** Released '82, on DJM Catalogue no: **DJF 20564**

**NOTICE TO APPEAR**
**Album:** Released Feb '76, on ABC Records by MCA Records. Catalogue no: **ABCL 5142**

**POWER OF THE BLUES, THE**
**CD:** Released 23 Feb '90, on Decal by Charly Records. Catalogue no: **CDLIK 62**
**Album:** Released 23 Feb '90, on Decal by Charly Records. Catalogue no: **LIK 62**

**PRIMAL SOLOS**
Tracks: / Intro - Maudie / It hurts to be in love / Have you ever loved a woman / Bye bye bird / Hoochie coochie man / Intro - look at the girl / Wish you were mine / Start walking.
**CD:** Released Nov '88, on Decca by Decca International. Catalogue no: **820 320-2**
**Album:** Released Apr '83, on Decca by Decca International. Catalogue no: **TAB 66**
**Cass:** Released Apr '83, on Decca by Decca International. Deleted '88. Catalogue no: **KTBC 66**

**RAW BLUES**
**Album:** Released '67, on Ace Of Clubs by Decca Records. Catalogue no: **SCL 1220**

**ROADSHOW BLUES**
Tracks: / Why worry / Road show / Mama talk to your daughter / Big man / Lost and gone / Mexico City / John Lee Boogie / Reaching for a mountain / Baby what you want me to do.
**Album:** Released Jun '88, on Thunderbolt by Magnum Music Group. Catalogue no: **THBL 060**
**Album:** Released '82, on DJM Catalogue no: **DJF 20570**
**Cass:** Released '82, on DJM Catalogue no: **DJH 40570**
**CD:** Released Oct '88, on Thunderbolt by Magnum Music Group. Catalogue no: **CDTB 060**

**ROOM TO MOVE**
Tracks: / Room to move / Took the car / Crying / My pretty girl / Don't waste my time / Thinking of my woman / Plan your revoloution / Something new / Deep blue sea / Don't pick a flower.
**Album:** Released Apr '84, on IMS by Polydor Ltd. Catalogue no: **2486 041**

**SENSE OF PLACE, A (Mayall, John & The Bluesbreakers)**
**Cass:** Released Apr '90, on Island by Island Records. Catalogue no: **ICT 9958**
**CD:** Released Apr '90, on Island by Island Records. Catalogue no: **CID 9958**
**Album:** Released Apr '90, on Island by Island Records. Catalogue no: **ILPS 9958**

**SOME OF MY BEST FRIENDS ARE BLUES**
Tracks: / All your love / It ain't right / You don't love me / Dust my blues / Oh pretty woman / My time after awhile / I can't quit you baby / Double trouble / So many roads / All my life.
**Album:** Released Apr '86, on Decal by Charly Records. Catalogue no: **LIK 1**

**TURNING POINT**
**CD:** Released Aug '87, on Polydor by Polydor Ltd. Deleted Jan '89. Catalogue no: **823 305-2**
**Cass:** Released May '82, on Polydor by Polydor Ltd. Catalogue no: **3201 294**
**Album:** Released May '82, on Polydor by Polydor Ltd. Catalogue no: **2485 222**
**Album:** Released Nov '69, on Polydor by Polydor Ltd. Deleted Nov '74. Catalogue no: **583 571**

**USA UNION**
**Album:** Released Dec '70, on Polydor by Polydor Ltd. Deleted Dec '75. Catalogue no: **2425 020**

**WORLD OF JOHN MAYALL VOL 2**
**Album:** Released '71, on World Of Learning by World Of Learning Records. Catalogue no: **SPA 138**

## Maycock, George Trio

**GEORGE MAYCOCK TRIO**
**Album:** Released Jul '78, on Ring Catalogue no: **RING 01008**

## Mayerl, Billy

**KING OF SYNCOPATION**
**Album:** Released '73, on Retrospect by EMI Records. Catalogue no: **SH 189**

**MARIGOLD**
Tracks: / Marigold / Baby's birthday party / Sweet nothin's / Please handle with care / Here comes the bride medley / Honeysuckle / Three dances medley / Ace of clubs / Ace of hearts / Wedding of the painted doll, The / Jasmine / Hollyhock / Balloons, who'll buy my balloons? / Wake up and dream medley / Love lies medley / Mignonette / House that Jack built, The (medley) / Ace of diamonds / Ace of spades.
Note: Here comes the bride medley: I'll always remember/ I'm like a sailor/ High and low. Three dances medley: English dance/ Cricket dance/ Harmonica dance. Wake up and dream medley: Looking at you/ Let's do it/ Let's fall in love. Love lies medley: House on a hilltop/ You've made a difference to me/ I lift up my finger and say tweet tweet. House that Jack built medley: My heart is saying/ Thought never entered my head/ She's such a comfort to me.
**Album:** Released Aug '88, on Joy by President Records. Catalogue no: **JOYD 294**

**VERSATILITY OF BILLY MAYERL**
**2 LP Set:** Released May '82, on Flapper (USA) Deleted May '87. Catalogue no: **PAST 704/5**

## Mayfield, Percy

**HIT THE ROAD AGAIN**
**Album:** Released Nov '85, on Timeless by Timeless Records. Catalogue no: **SJP 170**

**MY HEART IS ALWAYS SINGING SAD SONGS**
Tracks: / I need love son bad / It's good to see you baby / Nightmare / Hunt is on / My heart / Lonesome highway / You don't exist no more / Bachelor blues / Proposal / Come home / One room country shack / Ain't gonna cry no more / Does anyone care for me / I dare you baby / Wasted dream / Big question.
**Album:** Released Nov '85, on Ace by Ace Records. Deleted Jun '88. Catalogue no: **CHD 153**

**PERCY MAYFIELD**
Tracks: / Life is suicide / Hunt is on, The / Hopeless / My heart is crying / Baby, you're rich / My blues / I dare you, baby / Memory pain / You are my future / Get way back / Advice (for men only) / Lonesome highway / Kiss tomorrow goodbye / Strange things happening / Ruthie Mae / Pease send me someone to love / Hit

the road, Jack / Prayin' for your return / What a fool I was / Lost love / Nightless lover / Cry baby / Lost mind / River's invitation, The / Big question, The / Wasted dream / Louisiana / Bachelor blues / Loose lips / You don't exist no more / Nightmare.
**Album:** Released Oct '89, on Ace by Ace Records. Catalogue no: **CHD 283**
**CD:** Released Oct '89, on Ace by Ace Records. Catalogue no: **CDCHD 283**

**VOICE WITHIN, THE**
Tracks: / How wrong can a good man be / Leary blues / Hunt is on, The / Hopeless / Two hearts are greater than one / Lonesome highway / I dare you, baby / How deep is the well / Lonely one, The / Bachelor blues, The / Sugar mama - peachy papa / Voice within, The / My heart / Are you out there / Bluest blues / Blues blues, The.
**Album:** Released Aug '87, on Route 66 (Sweden) Catalogue no: **KIX 22**

## Mazzy, Jimmy

**SHAKE IT DOWN (Mazzy, Jimmy and Eli Newberger)**
**Album:** Released Oct '86, on Stomp Off (USA) Catalogue no: **SOS 1109**

## Meet The Band Leaders

**MEET THE BAND LEADERS VOL. 1 (Various artists)**
Tracks: / One o'clock jump: *Basie, Count & His Orchestra* / This could be the start of something big: *Basie, Count & His Orchestra* / Git: *Basie, Count & His Orchestra* / I can't stop loving you: *Basie, Count & His Orchestra* / April in Paris: *Basie, Count & His Orchestra* / Big brother: *Basie, Count & His Orchestra* / Jumping at the woodside: *Basie, Count & His Orchestra* / One o'clock jump: *Basie, Count & His Orchestra* / Broadway: *Hampton, Lionel & His Orchestra* / Cute: *Hampton, Lionel & His Orchestra* / Hamp's boogie: *Hampton, Lionel & His Orchestra* / Airmail special: *Hampton, Lionel & His Orchestra* / Take the 'A' train: *Ellington, Duke/His Orchestra* / Rockin' in rhythm: *Ellington, Duke/His Orchestra* / Satin doll: *Ellington, Duke/His Orchestra* / Prowling cat: *Ellington, Duke/His Orchestra* / Do nothing til you hear from me: *Ellington, Duke/His Orchestra.*
Note: Featuring Count Basie, Lionel Hampton and Duke Ellington.
**VHS:** Released May '89, on Charly Video Catalogue no: **VIDJAM 1**

**MEET THE BAND LEADERS VOL. 2 (Various artists)**
Tracks: / Ciribiribin: *James, Harry & His Orchestra* / Shiny stockings: *James, Harry & His Orchestra* / Come rain or come shine: *James, Harry & His Orchestra* / Green onions: *James, Harry & His Orchestra* / I'm beginning to see the light: *James, Harry & His Orchestra* / Take the 'A' train: *James, Harry & His Orchestra* / That's all: *James, Harry & His Orchestra* / Caravan: *James, Harry & His Orchestra* / Rainbow kiss: *James, Harry & His Orchestra* / String of pearls: *McKinley, Ray & His Orchestra* / Rhapsody in blue: *McKinley, Ray & His Orchestra* / Little brown jug: *McKinley, Ray & His Orchestra* / Lazy river: *Zenter, Si & His Orchestra* / Sentimental journey: *Zenter, Si & His Orchestra* / Puddle jumpin': *Zenter, Si & His Orchestra* / Without a song: *Zenter, Si & His Orchestra* / Lazy river: *Zenter, Si & His Orchestra* / Just friends: *Marterie, Ralph & His Orchestra* / Little girl blue: *Marterie, Ralph & His Orchestra* / Tangerine: *Marterie, Ralph & His Orchestra.*
Note: Featuring Harry James, Ray McKinley, Si Zentner & Ralph Marterie.
**VHS:** Released May '89, on Charly Video Catalogue no: **VIDJAM 2**

**MEET THE BAND LEADERS VOL. 3 (Various artists)**
Tracks: / At last: *Beneke, Tex & His Orchestra* / Chattanooga choo choo: *Beneke, Tex & His Orchestra* / Moonlight cocktails: *Beneke, Tex & His Orchestra* / Hot Toddy': *Flanagan, Ralph Orchestra* / Medley: *Flanagan, Ralph Orchestra* / With a song in my heart: *Flanagan, Ralph Orchestra* / Where or when: *Flanagan, Ralph Orchestra* / Penthouse serenade: *Flanagan, Ralph Orchestra* / Heart of my heart: *Elgart, Les & Larry* / Skyliner: *Elgart, Les & Larry* / Harlem nocturne: *Elgart, Les & Larry* / Cherokee: *Elgart, Les & Larry* / So rare: *Elgart, Les & Larry* / Blues in the night: *Elgart, Les & Larry* / You made me love you: *Elgart, Les & Larry* / Song of India: *Elgart, Les & Larry* / It's delovely: *Elgart, Les & Larry* / Begin the beguine: *Elgart, Les & Larry* / Heart of my heart: *Elgart, Les & Larry* / Let it snow: *Monroe, Vaughn & Orchestra* / Take it Jackson: *Monroe, Vaughn & Orchestra* / Racing with the moon: *Monroe, Vaughn & Orchestra* / Cape cold clambake: *Monroe, Vaughn & Orchestra* / Ghost riders in the sky: *Monroe, Vaughn & Orchestra.*
Note: Featuring Tex Beneke, Ralph Flanagan, Les & Larry Elgart, Vaughn Monroe.
**VHS:** Released May '89, on Charly Video Catalogue no: **VIDJAM 3**

**MEET THE BAND LEADERS VOL. 4 (Various artists)**
Tracks: / Moonlight serenade: *Beneke, Tex & Miller Orchestra* / In the mood: *Beneke, Tex & Miller Orchestra* / Medley: *Beneke, Tex & Miller Orchestra* / Londonderry air: *Beneke, Tex & Miller Orchestra* / Five minutes more: *Beneke, Tex & Miller Orchestra* / Don't be that way: *Beneke, Tex & Miller Orchestra* / Serenade in blue: *Beneke, Tex & Miller Orchestra* / American Patrol: *Beneke, Tex & Miller Orchestra* / Woodchuck song: *Beneke, Tex & Miller Orchestra* / Boogie blues: *Krupa, Gene & His Orchestra* / Opus #145: *Krupa, Gene & His Orchestra* / Dark eyes: *Krupa, Gene & His Orchestra* / Up an atom: *Krupa, Gene & His Orchestra* / Call of the wild: *Wald, Jerry & His Orchestra* / Wonder when my baby's comin' home: *Wald, Jerry & His Orchestra* / Diga diga doo: *Wald, Jerry & His Orchestra* / Mad about him blues: *Wald, Jerry & His Orchestra* / Artistry in ryhthm: *Kenton, Stan & His Orchestra* / Down in chihuahua: *Kenton, Stan & His Orchestra* / Just a sittin' and a rockin': *Kenton, Stan & His Orchestra* / Concerto to end all concertos: *Kenton, Stan & His Orchestra* / Tampico: *Kenton, Stan & His Orchestra.*
Note: Featuring Tex Beneke, Gene Krupa, Jerry Wald and Stan Kenton.
**VHS:** Released May '89, on Charly Video Catalogue no: **VIDJAM 4**

**MEET THE BAND LEADERS VOL 5 (Various artists)**
Tracks: / Dipsy doodle: *Clinton, Larry & His Orchestra* / Love doesn't grow on trees: *Clinton, Larry & His Orchestra* / I fell up to heaven: *Clinton, Larry & His Orchestra* / Heart and soul: *Clinton, Larry & His Orchestra* / Contrasts: *Dorsey, Jimmy & His Orchestra* / Fingerbustin': *Dorsey, Jimmy & His Orchestra* / Rubber dolly: *Dorsey, Jimmy & His Orchestra* / Only a rose: *Dorsey, Jimmy & His Orchestra* / John silver: *Dorsey, Jimmy & His Orchestra* / St.Louis blues: *Nichols, Red & Orchestra* / Dixieland band: *Nichols, Red & Orchestra* / Everybody loves my baby: *Nichols, Red & Orchestra* / You can't pull the wool over my eyes: *Berigan, Bunny & His Orchestra* / Until today: *Berigan, Bunny & His Orchestra* / Tiger rag: *Berigan, Bunny & His Orchestra* / (untitled instrumental): *Hutton, Ina Ray & Her Melodears* / Truckin': *Hutton, Ina Ray & Her Melodears* / (untitled instrumental): *Hutton, Ina Ray & Her Melodears* / I'm 100% for you: *Hutton, Ina Ray & Her Melodears* / (untitled instrumental): *Hutton, Ina Ray & Her Melodears* / Medley: *Hutton, Ina Ray & Her Melodears* / Organ grinders swing/Stardust: *Hutton, Ina Ray & Her Melodears* / Doin' the Suzy Q: *Hutton, Ina Ray & Her Melodears* / Melody of swing: *Hutton, Ina Ray & Her Melodears.*
Note: Featuring Larry Clinton, Jimmy Dorsey, Red Nichols, Bunny Berigan & Ina Ray Hutton.
**VHS:** Released May '89, on Charly Video Catalogue no: **VIDJAM 5**

**MEET THE BAND LEADERS VOL. 6 (Various artists)**
Tracks: / Bubbles in the wine: *Welk, Lawrence* / I go for that: *Welk, Lawrence* / Ain't she sweet: *Welk, Lawrence* / Kinda lonesome: *Welk, Lawrence* / When paw was courtin' maw: *Welk, Lawrence* / Does your heart beat for me: *Morgan, Russ & His Orchestra* / Wabash blues: *Morgan, Russ & His Orchestra* / Us on a bus: *Morgan, Russ & His Orchestra* / Stella: *Morgan, Russ & His Orchestra* / Wang wang blues: *Morgan, Russ & His Orchestra* / Medley: *Morgan, Russ & His Orchestra* / Linger awhile: *Morgan, Russ & His Orchestra* / Stumbling: *Morgan, Russ & His Orchestra* / Never should have told you: *Morgan, Russ & His Orchestra* / Limehouse blues': *Morgan, Russ & His Orchestra* / Sweet moments: *Morgan, Russ & His Orchestra* / Old heart of mine: *Morgan, Russ & His Orchestra* / Holiday in Toyland: *Morgan, Russ & His Orchestra* / Am I proud: *Morgan, Russ & His Orches-*

*tra* / When summer is gone: *Kemp, Hal Orchestra* / You've got me cryin' again: *Kemp, Hal Orchestra* / I'm building up to an awful letdown: *Kemp, Hal Orchestra* / Bride comes home,The: *Kemp, Hal Orchestra* / Stop,look and listen: *Kemp, Hal Orchestra* / Ten little bottles: *Kemp, Hal Orchestra* / When summer is gone: *Kemp, Hal Orchestra* / Medley: *Garber, Jan & His Orchestra* / Louise: *Garber, Jan & His Orchestra* / Sing you sinners: *Garber, Jan & His Orchestra* / Just one more chance: *Garber, Jan & His Orchestra* / Please: *Garber, Jan & His Orchestra* / Did you ever see a dream walking: *Garber, Jan & His Orchestra* / Love in bloom: *Garber, Jan & His Orchestra* / Lookie lookie here comes cookie: *Garber, Jan & His Orchestra* / Melody from the sky: *Garber, Jan & His Orchestra* / Blue Hawaii: *Garber, Jan & His Orchestra* / Thanks for the memory: *Garber, Jan & His Orchestra.*
Note: Featuring Lawrence Welk, Russ Morgan, Hal Kemp & Jan Garber.
**VHS:** Released May '89, on Charly Video Catalogue no: **VIDJAM 6**

**MEET THE BAND LEADERS VOL. 7 (Various artists)**
Tracks: / Auld lang syne: *Lombardo, Guy/His Royal Canadians* / Sioux city Sue: *Lombardo, Guy/His Royal Canadians* / I need you know: *Lombardo, Guy/His Royal Canadians* / That old gang of mine: *Lombardo, Guy/His Royal Canadians* / Now is the hour: *Lombardo, Guy/His Royal Canadians* / Roaming in the gloaming: *Lombardo, Guy/His Royal Canadians* / On a slow boat to China: *Lombardo, Guy/His Royal Canadians* / Sweet Sue: *Lombardo, Guy/His Royal Canadians* / Frankie and Johnnie: *Lombardo, Guy/His Royal Canadians* / Humoresque: *Lombardo, Guy/His Royal Canadians* / St Louis blues: *Lombardo, Guy/His Royal Canadians* / Darktown strutters ball: *Lombardo, Guy/His Royal Canadians* / Toot toot tootsie: *Lombardo, Guy/His Royal Canadians* / Get out those old records: *Lombardo, Guy/His Royal Canadians* / Seems like old times: *Lombardo, Guy/His Royal Canadians* / Boo hoo: *Lombardo, Guy/His Royal Canadians* / Coquette: *Lombardo, Guy/His Royal Canadians* / Powder your face with sunshine: *Lombardo, Guy/His Royal Canadians* / Good night, good luck and God bless: *Lombardo, Guy/His Royal Canadians.*
Note: Featuring Guy Lombardo.

**MEET THE BAND LEADERS VOL. 8 (Various artists)**
Tracks: / Take the 'A' train: *Ellington, Duke/His Orchestra* / Afro bosso: *Ellington, Duke/His Orchestra* / Step in time: *Ellington, Duke/His Orchestra* / Supercalifragillisticexpialidocious: *Ellington, Duke/His Orchestra* / Fly me to the moon: *Ellington, Duke/His Orchestra* / Never on Sunday: *Ellington, Duke/His Orchestra* / Things ain't what they used to be: *Ellington, Duke/His Orchestra* / One o'clock jump: *Basie, Count & His Orchestra* / Shiny stockings: *Basie, Count & His Orchestra* / I needs to be be'd with: *Basie, Count & His Orchestra* / Shake rattle and roll: *Basie, Count & His Orchestra* / Blue for Ilean: *Basie, Count & His Orchestra* / Whirlybirds: *Basie, Count & His Orchestra* / Georgia on my mind: *Hampton, Lionel & His Orchestra* / Flying home: *Hampton, Lionel & His Orchestra.*
Note: Duke Ellington, Count Basie and Lionel Hampton.
**VHS:** Released Sep '89, on Charly Video Catalogue no: **VIDJAM 8**

**MEET THE BAND LEADERS VOL. 9 (Various artists)**
Tracks: / When summer is gone: *Kemp, Hal Orchestra* / In an 18th century drawing room: *Kemp, Hal Orchestra* / Vagabond blues: *Kemp, Hal Orchestra* / In the shade of the old apple tree: *Kemp, Hal Orchestra* / Swampfire: *Kemp, Hal Orchestra* / White star of Sigma Nu: *Long, Johnny & His Orchestra* / Shanty in old shanty town: *Long, Johnny & His Orchestra* / You made me love you: *Long, Johnny & His Orchestra* / September song: *Long, Johnny & His Orchestra* / My dear: *Garber, Jan & His Orchestra* / Medley: *Garber, Jan & His Orchestra* / Little white lies/We just couldn't say goodbye: *Garber, Jan & His Orchestra* / Till: *Garber, Jan & His Orchestra* / Love letters: *Garber, Jan & His Orchestra* / Java: *Garber, Jan & His Orchestra* / Sunset to sunrise: *Mooney, Art & Orchestra* / Satin doll: *Mooney, Art & Orchestra* / I'm looking over a four leaf clover: *Mooney, Art & Orchestra* / Memories of you: *Mooney, Art & Orchestra* / Sweet narcissus: *Mooney, Art & Orchestra* / I don't to meet anymore people: *Carle, Frankie & His Orchestra* / Carle meets Mozart: *Carle, Frankie & His Orchestra* / I'm the chick with the band: *Carle, Frankie & His Orchestra* / Carle meets Chopin: *Carle, Frankie & His Orchestra* / When you were sweet sixteen: *Carle, Frankie & His Orchestra* / La Paloma: *Carle, Frankie & His Orchestra.*
Note: Hal Kemp, Johnny Long, Frankie Carle, Jan Garber and Art Mooney.
**VHS:** Released Sep '89, on Charly Video Catalogue no: **VIDJAM 9**

**MEET THE BAND LEADERS VOL. 10 (Various artists)**
Tracks: / St.Louis blues: *McKinley, Ray & His Orchestra* / Big boy: *McKinley, Ray & His Orchestra* / Jive bomber: *McKinley, Ray & His Orchestra* / (untitled instrumental): *Stabile, Dick & His Orchestra* / Pack up your troubles in your old kit bag: *Stabile, Dick & His Orchestra* / Melody in F: *Stabile, Dick & His Orchestra* / You go to my head: *Stabile, Dick & His Orchestra* / Song of India: *Donahue, Sam & His Orchestra* / Opus #1: *Donahue, Sam & His Orchestra* / Dream: *Donahue, Sam & His Orchestra* / Boogie woogie: *Donahue, Sam & His Orchestra* / Artistry in rhythm: *Kenton, Stan & His Orchestra* / Limehouse blues: *Kenton, Stan & His Orchestra* / Reuben's blues: *Kenton, Stan & His Orchestra* / Malaguena: *Kenton, Stan & His Orchestra* / Intermission riff: *Kenton, Stan & His Orchestra* / Peanut vendor: *Kenton, Stan & His Orchestra.*
Note: Ray McKinley, Dick Stabile, Sam Donahue and Stan Kenton.
**VHS:** Released Sep '89, on Charly Video Catalogue no: **VIDJAM 10**

**MEET THE BAND LEADERS VOL. 11 (Various artists)**
Tracks: / One o'clock jump: *Basie, Count & His Orchestra* / Pleasingly plump: *Basie, Count & His Orchestra* / All of me: *Basie, Count & His Orchestra* / Corner pocket: *Basie, Count & His Orchestra* / Take the 'A' train: *Ellington, Duke/His Orchestra* / Cottontail: *Ellington, Duke/His Orchestra* / Medley: *Ellington, Duke/His Orchestra* / Caravan: *Ellington, Duke/His Orchestra* / I got it bad: *Ellington, Duke/His Orchestra* / Don't get around much anymore: *Ellington, Duke/His Orchestra* / Mood indigo: *Ellington, Duke/His Orchestra* / Beginning to see the light: *Ellington, Duke/His Orchestra* / Sophisticated lady: *Ellington, Duke/His Orchestra* / Banquet theme: *Ellington, Duke/His Orchestra* / Skillipop: *Ellington, Duke/His Orchestra* / Tuttie for cootie: *Ellington, Duke/His Orchestra* / Ciriribin: *James, Harry & His Orchestra* / Don't be that way: *James, Harry & His Orchestra* / Tuxedo junction: *James, Harry & His Orchestra* / Sunday morning: *James, Harry & His Orchestra* / Walk on the wild side: *James, Harry & His Orchestra* / Prelude to a kiss: *James, Harry & His Orchestra* / Two o'clock jump: *James, Harry & His Orchestra* / Rainbow kiss: *James, Harry & His Orchestra.*
Note: Count Basie, Duke Ellington and Harry James.
**VHS:** Released Sep '89, on Charly Video Catalogue no: **VIDJAM 11**

**MEET THE BAND LEADERS VOL. 12 (Various artists)**
Tracks: / Nightmare: *Shaw, Artie & his Orchestra* / Table d'hote: *Shaw, Artie & his Orchestra* / So help me: *Shaw, Artie & his Orchestra* / Shoot the likker to me: *Shaw, Artie & his Orchestra* / John boy: *Shaw, Artie & his Orchestra* / Two sleepy people: *Teagarden, Jack & His Orchestra* / Medley: *Teagarden, Jack & His Orchestra* / Washboard blues: *Teagarden, Jack & His Orchestra* / Lazy bones: *Teagarden, Jack & His Orchestra* / Small fry: *Teagarden, Jack & His Orchestra* / Rockin' chair: *Teagarden, Jack & His Orchestra* / That's right,I'm wrong: *Teagarden, Jack & His Orchestra* / Stardust: *Teagarden, Jack & His Orchestra* / Hotcha-razz-ma-tazz: *Calloway, Cab & His Orchestra* / Long about midnight: *Calloway, Cab & His Orchestra* / Jitterbug: *Calloway, Cab & His Orchestra* / Mood indigo: *Ellington, Duke/His Orchestra* / Sophisticated lady: *Ellington, Duke/His Orchestra* / It don't mean a thing: *Ellington, Duke/His Orchestra* / Don't get around much anymore: *Ellington, Duke/His Orchestra* / Ballerina: *Raeburn, Boyd & His Orchestra* / St.Louis blues: *Raeburn, Boyd & His Orchestra* / Temptation: *Raeburn, Boyd & His Orchestra.*

Note: Artie Shaw, Jack Teagarden, Cab Calloway, Duke Ellington, Boyd Raeburn.
**VHS:** Released Sep '89, on Charly Video Catalogue no: **VIDJAM 12**

**MEET THE BAND LEADERS VOL. 13 (Various artists)**
Tracks: / Cherokee: *Barnet, Charlie* / Andy's boogie: *Barnet, Charlie* / My old flame: *Barnet, Charlie* / Skyliner: *Barnet, Charlie* / Billboard march: *Brown, Les* / Time takes care of everything: *Brown, Les* / I've got the world on a string: *Brown, Les* / Etiquette blues: *Brown, Les* / Dance of renown: *Brown, Les* / Gianni-na mia: *Flanagan, Ralph* / Joshua: *Flanagan, Ralph* / Just one more chance: *Flanagan, Ralph* / Stars and stripes forever: *Flanagan, Ralph* / I don't worry 'bout stangers: *Flanagan, Ralph* / Margie: *Flanagan, Ralph.*
Note: Charlie Barnet, Les Brown, Ralph Flanagan and Tony Pastor.
**VHS:** Released Sep '89, on Charly Video Catalogue no: **VIDJAM 13**

**MEET THE BAND LEADERS VOL. 14 Meet the Dixieland bands (Various artists)**
Note: Jack Teagarden & His Sextet and the Bobcats (of Bob Crosby fame). Bobcats are:- Billy Butterfield, Matty Matlock, Eddie Miller, Bob Haggart, Nappy La Mare, Jess Stacy, Ray Bauduc and Warren Smith.
**VHS:** Released Sep '89, on Charly Video Catalogue no: **VIDJAM 14**

**MEET THE BAND LEADERS VOL. 15 Meet the small bands (Various artists)**
Note: Count Basie Sextet, Cab Calloway & His Cabaliers, The Four Freshmen and The George Shearing Quintet.
**VHS:** Released Sep '89, on Charly Video Catalogue no: **VIDJAM 15**

**MEET THE BAND LEADERS VOL. 16 Meet the singers (Various artists)**
Note: Nat King Cole, Sarah Vauhan and Herb Jeffries.
**VHS:** Released Sep '89, on Charly Video Catalogue no: **VIDJAM 16**

**MEET THE BAND LEADERS VOL. 17 (Various artists)**
Note: Duke Ellington and Lionel Hampton.
**VHS:** Released Sep '89, on Charly Video Catalogue no: **VIDJAM 17**

**MEET THE BAND LEADERS VOL. 18 Meet the singers (Various artists)**
Note: Peggy Lee, Mel Torme and June Christy.
**VHS:** Released Sep '89, on Charly Video Catalogue no: **VIDJAM 18**

**MEET THE BAND LEADERS VOL. 19 Meet the Dixieland bands (Various artists)**
Note: Firehouse Five Plus Two, Red Nichols & His Pennies and Pete Dailey & His Chicagoans.
**VHS:** Released Sep '89, on Charly Video Catalogue no: **VIDJAM 19**

**MEET THE BAND LEADERS VOL. 20 Unforgettable performances 1950-1952 (Various artists)**
Note: Bonnie Baker, Nat King Cole, Ginny Simms, Lionel Hampton, Connie Haines, Teresa Brewer, Connie Boswell.
**VHS:** Released Sep '89, on Charly Video Catalogue no: **VIDJAM 20**

## Meldonian, Dick

**IT'S A WONDERFUL WORLD (Meldonian, Dick Trio)**
**Album:** Released Nov '87, on Statiras (USA) by Statiras(USA) Records. Catalogue no: **SLP 8076**

**JERSEY SWING CONCERTS, THE**
Tracks: / Jump the blues away / You gotta try / In a mellow tone / Love for sale / I'll never say "never again" again / Three little words / Jeeps' blues / When you done went / Spring is here / Chicago.
**Album:** Released Apr '83, on Progressive (USA) by Jazzology Records (USA). Catalogue no: **PRO 7058**

**SOME OF THESE DAYS (Meldonian, Dick & Jersey Swingers)**
**Album:** Released Apr '81, on Progressive (USA) by Jazzology Records (USA). Catalogue no: **PRO 7033**

**SWING ALTERNATE (Meldonian, Dick & Orchestra)**
**CD:** Released Mar '90, on Circle Catalogue no: **CLCD 150**

**SWING GENE ROLAND (Meldonian, Dick & Jersey Swingers)**
**Album:** Released '89, on Circle Catalogue no: **CLP 150**

## Melly, George

**16 GOLDEN CLASSICS**
Tracks: / Mississippi mud / Hound dog / This train / Abdul Abulbul Amir / Mama don't allow it / Frankie and Johnny / Send me to the 'lectric chair / I'm a ding dong daddy / My canary has circles under his eyes / Heebie jeebies / Black bottom / Sporting life / Ma Rainey's black bottom / St. Louis blues / Spider crawl / Sent for you yesterday.
Note: Tracks 1 & 3 with Alex Welsh and his dixielanders; track 2 with Mick Mulligan's band & guests; 11 with Mick Mulligan & his band; 13 & 16 with mick Mulligan's band & guests. All tracks licensed from The Decca Record Co. Ltd. Design by Shoot That Tiger! (C) 1986 Castle communications Place, unit 7, 271, Merton Rd, London SW18 5JS. Bar Code 5\013428\920145
**Cass:** Released '87, on Unforgettable by Castle Communications Records. Catalogue no: **UNMC 014**
**Album:** Released Dec '86, on Unforgettable by Castle Communications Records. Catalogue no: **UNLP 014**

**AIN'T MISBEHAVIN (Melly, George & John Chilton's Feetwarmers)**
Tracks: / Ain't misbehavin / Squeeze me / I'm gonna sit right down / An awful lot my gal ain't got / Your feet's too big / My very good friend the milkman / Joint is jumpin' / It's a sin to tell a lie / Foolin' myself / Honeysuckle Rose / Blue, turning grey over you / Keepin' out of mischief now / I've got a feeling I'm falling.
**Album:** Released Mar '79, on Pye Deleted Nov '89. Catalogue no: **NSPL 18602**
**Cass:** Released Mar '79, on Pye Catalogue no: **ZCP 18602**
**Album:** Released '87, on PRT by Castle Communications Records. Catalogue no: **PYL 4**
**Cass:** Released '87, on PRT by Castle Communications Records. Catalogue no: **PYM 4**

**ANYTHING GOES (Melly, George & John Chilton's Feetwarmers)**
Tracks: / (Get your kicks on) Route 66 / September song / Maybe not at all / It had to be you / Wrap your troubles in dreams / Chicago / I've got what it takes / Then I'll be happy / Anything goes / Someday sweetheart / Life with you / Lock and key.
**Album:** Released 29 Aug '88, on PRT by Castle Communications Records. Catalogue no: **PYL 15**
**Cass:** Released Dec '89, on Castle Collector Series by Castle Communications Records. Catalogue no: **LLMK 3024**
**Album:** Released Dec '89, on Castle Collector Series by Castle Communications Records. Catalogue no: **LLM 3024**
**Cass:** Released 29 Aug '88, on PRT by Castle Communications Records. Catalogue no: **PYM 15**
**CD:** Released 29 Aug '88, on PRT by Castle Communications Records. Catalogue no: **PYC 15**
**CD:** Released Dec '89, on Castle Collector Series by Castle Communications Records. Catalogue no: **LLMCD 3024**

**HOMETOWN (Melly, George & John Chilton's Feetwarmers)**
Tracks: / Home town / I won't grow old / Sweet Georgia Brown / Boogie woogie man / I'm busy and you can't come in / It's de-lovely / My momma rocks me / Shakin' the blues away / Draggin my heart around / Don't get around much anymore / Thinking blues / Running wild.
**Album:** Released '86, on PRT by Castle Communications Records. Catalogue no: **UNKNOWN**

**HOMETOWN (SINGLE) (Melly, George & John Chilton's Feetwarmers)**
Tracks: / Hometown.
**7" Single:** Released Nov '86, on PRT by Castle Communications Records. Catalogue no: **7P 368**

**IT'S GEORGE (Melly, George & The Feetwarmers)**
Tracks: / I don't mean a thing / Waiter, the porter and the upstairs maid, The / Boogie woogie man / Gee baby ain't I good to you / Give her a little drop more / Food of love / Rosetta / Hard hearted Hannah / T'ain't no sin / Trouble in mind / Lulu's back in town / All the whores go

crazy.
**Album:** on Warner Bros. by WEA Records. Catalogue no: **K 56087**

**LET'S DO IT (Melly, George & John Chilton's Feetwarmers)**
Tracks: / Gonna catch you with your britches down / Let's do it / Lady wants some jazz, The / Backwater blues / Monday on, my Monday date / Fanny Brown / Downhearted blues / You're driving me crazy / Hundred years from today / Was I drunk? / T'aint what you do (it's the way that you do it) / On revival day.
**Album:** Released Sep '80, on Pye Deleted Jan '90. Catalogue no: **N 131**
**Cass:** Released '87, on PRT by Castle Communications Records. Catalogue no: **PYM 5**
**Album:** Released '87, on PRT by Castle Communications Records. Catalogue no: **PYL 5**
**Cass:** Released Sep '80, on PRT by Castle Communications Records. Deleted Jan '90. Catalogue no: **ZCN 131**

**LIKE SHERRY WINE (Melly, George & John Chilton's Feetwarmers)**
Tracks: / Wait till you see my baby do the Charleston / Baby won't you please come home? / You've got the right key but the wrong keyhole / Papa de da da / Way down yonder in New Orleans / Jerry the junker / Beale Street mama / Michigan water blues / Please don't mention your sign / I wanna hot dog for my roll / Dapper Dan / Empty bed blues.
**Cass:** Released Oct '81, on PRT by Castle Communications Records. Catalogue no: **ZCN 140**
**Album:** Released '87, on PRT by Castle Communications Records. Catalogue no: **PYL 6**
**Cass:** Released '87, on PRT by Castle Communications Records. Catalogue no: **PYM 6**
**Album:** Released Oct '81, on PRT by Castle Communications Records. Catalogue no: **N 140**

**MAKIN' WHOOPEE (SINGLE)**
Tracks: / Makin' whoopee / Everybody loves my baby.
**7" Single:** Released Apr '83, on PRT by Castle Communications Records. Deleted '86. Catalogue no: **7P 268**

**MAKIN' WHOOPEE (Melly, George & John Chilton'sa Feetwarmers)**
Tracks: / Goody goody / Sporting life / Makin' whoopee / Shake your can / Someday you'll be sorry / Everybody loves my baby / Watch the Birdie / I wish I could shimmy like my sister Kate / Yellow dog blues / I can't give you anything but love / Bye bye boogie.
**Cass:** Released '87, on PRT by Castle Communications Records. Catalogue no: **PYM 7**
**Album:** Released Mar '83, on PRT by Castle Communications Records. Catalogue no: **N 147**
**Album:** Released '87, on PRT by Castle Communications Records. Catalogue no: **PYL 7**
**Cass:** Released Mar '83, on PRT by Castle Communications Records. Catalogue no: **ZCN 147**

**MANY MOODS OF MELLY, THE (Melly, George & John Chilton's Feetwarmers)**
Tracks: / Masculine women, feminine men / It's the bluest kind of blues my baby sings / Nobody's sweetheart / Drunk again / Kitchen man / St. Louis blues / Do your duty / As time goes by / Black mountain blues / Give her a little drop more / Send me to the 'lectric chair / Happy feet.
**CD:** Released Oct '84, on PRT by Castle Communications Records. Catalogue no: **CDNSP 7778**
**Album:** Released Oct '84, on PRT by Castle Communications Records. Deleted Jan '90. Catalogue no: **N 6550**
**Cass:** Released '87, on PRT by Castle Communications Records. Catalogue no: **PYM 8**
**Album:** Released '87, on PRT by Castle Communications Records. Catalogue no: **PYL 8**
**Cass:** Released Oct '84, on PRT by Castle Communications Records. Deleted Jan '90. Catalogue no: **ZCN 6550**
**CD:** Released '87, on PRT by Castle Communications Records. Catalogue no: **PYC 8**

**MASCULINE WOMEN FEMININE MEN**
Tracks: / Masculine women feminine men / It's the bluest kind of blues.
**7" Single:** Released Oct '84, on PRT by Castle Communications Records. Catalogue no: **7P 318**

**MELLY IS AT IT AGAIN**
Tracks: / Milenberg joys / Animule ball / Marie Laveau / Jeepers creepers / When my ship comes in / Barrelhouse music / Punch and Judy / Punch drunk mama / Yonder comes the blues / Pennies from Heaven.
**Album:** Released Nov '76, on Reprise (USA) Catalogue no: **K 54084**

**MELLY SINGS HOAGY (Melly, George & John Chilton's Feetwarmers)**
**Album:** Released '87, on PRT by Castle Communications Records. Catalogue no: **PYL 3**
**Cass:** Released '87, on PRT by Castle Communications Records. Catalogue no: **PYM 3**
**Cass:** Released Mar '78, on Ronnie Scott Catalogue no: **ZCP 18557**
**Album:** Released Jul '89, on Pye Deleted Nov '89. Catalogue no: **NSPL 18557**

**NUTS (Melly, George & The Feetwarmers)**
Tracks: / Doctor Jazz / T'aint nobody's business if I do / Sugar / Sam Jones' blues / If you're a viper / There'll be some changes made / I want a little girl / Nuts / Nobody knows you / Viper mad.
**Album:** Released '88, on Warner Bros. by WEA Records. Catalogue no: **K 36005**
**Cass:** Released '88, on Warner Bros. by WEA Records. Catalogue no: **K4 46188**

**RUNNING WILD (Melly, George & John Chilton's Feetwarmers)**
**Album:** Released Nov '86, on PRT by Castle Communications Records. Catalogue no: **N 6562**
**CD:** Released '87, on PRT by Castle Communications Records. Catalogue no: **PYC 9**
**Cass:** Released '87, on PRT by Castle Communications Records. Catalogue no: **PYM 9**
**CD:** Released Nov '86, on PRT by Castle Communications Records. Catalogue no: **CDN 6562**
**Album:** Released '87, on PRT by Castle Communications Records. Catalogue no: **PYL 9**
**Cass:** Released Nov '86, on PRT by Castle Communications Records. Catalogue no: **ZCN 6562**

**SON OF NUTS**
Tracks: / Old fashioned love / I need a little sugar in my bowl / Good time George / Winnin' boy / Joint is jumpin', The / Buddy Bolden's blues / Heebie jeebies / Kitchen man / Roll 'em Pete / Young woman's blues / Show me the way to go home.
**Album:** Released May '73, on Warner Bros. by WEA Records. Catalogue no: **K 46269**
**Album:** on Warner Bros. by WEA Records. Catalogue no: **K 36006**

## Melvin, Brian

**NIGHT FOOD**
Tracks: / Ain't nothin' but a party / Don't forget the bass / Night food / Zen turtles / For Max / Poly wanna rhythm / Primalass / Warrior / Continuum.
**CD:** Released '88, on Timeless by Timeless Records. Catalogue no: **CDSJP 214**

## Memphis Blues

**MEMPHIS BLUES 1927-37 (Various artists)**
**Album:** Released Sep '87, on HK Catalogue no: **HK 4002**

**MEMPHIS BLUES (KRAZY KAT) (Various artists)**
Tracks: / Last time, The: *Various artists* / Cat squirrel: *Various artists* / That's all right: *Various artists* / Black snake boogie: *Various artists* / 44: *Various artists* / Outside friends: *Various artists* / Sittin' on top of the world: *Various artists* / High (but high): *Various artists* / Peg leg baby: *Various artists* / Ooowee baby: *Various artists* / Stay with me: *Various artists* / Baby I'm off that stuff: *Various artists* / All alone: *Various artists* / Blues jumped a rabbit: *Various artists* / Hello

pretty baby: *Various artists* / Phineas boogie: *Various artists* / Joint is jumping, The: *Various artists.*
Note: Artists include: Woodrow Adams, Doctor Ross, William Stewart, Kenneth Banks, Raymond Hill, Johnny O'Neal, Rufus Thomas, Eddie Snow, Sherman Johnson, Phineas Newborn
**Album:** Released '85, on Krazy Kat by Interstate Music. Catalogue no: **KK 7427**

**MEMPHIS BLUES (RCA) (Various artists)**
Tracks: / How long?: *Stokes, Frank* / 'T'ain't nobody's business if I do: *Stokes, Frank* (part 2) / It won't be long now: *Stokes, Frank* / Right now blues: *Stokes, Frank* / I'm wild about my lovin': *Jackson, Jim* / I'm gonna move to Louisiana: *Jackson, Jim* (parts 1 & 2) / This mornin' she was gone: *Jackson, Jim* / Casey Jones: *Lewis, Furry* (part 1) / Dry land blues: *Lewis, Furry* / I will turn your money green: *Lewis, Furry* / Mistreatin' mama: *Lewis, Furry* / Jailhouse blues: *Wilkins, Robert* / Rolling stone: *Wilkins, Robert* (parts 1 & 2) / I do blues: *Wilkins, Robert* / Sun brimmer blues: *Memphis Jug Band* / Snitchin' gambler blues: *Memphis Jug Band* / Peaches in the Springtime: *Memphis Jug Band* / Black woman is like a black snake, A: *Memphis Jug Band* / Dirty butter: *Wallace, Minnie* / Old folks started it, The: *Wallace, Minnie* / Won't you be kind to me?: *Hart, Hattie* / You wouldn't would you Papa?: *Hart, Hattie* / Big railroad blues: *Cannon's Jug Stompers* / Feather bed: *Cannon's Jug Stompers* / Viola Lee blues: *Cannon's Jug Stompers* / Bring it with you when you come: *Cannon's Jug Stompers* / I'm going back home: *McCoy & Johnson* / I never told a lie: *McCoy & Johnson* / Don't want no woman: *McCoy & Johnson* / Georgia skin: *McCoy & Johnson.*
**Cass:** Released May '84, on RCA by BMG Records (UK). Catalogue no: **NK 89276**
**2 LP Set:** Released May '84, on RCA by BMG Records (UK). Deleted Jul '89. Catalogue no: **NL 89276**

**MEMPHIS BLUES VOL.1 (Various artists)**
**Album:** Released Oct '88, on Roots (Germany) Catalogue no: **RL 323**

**MEMPHIS BLUES VOL.2 (Various artists)**
**Album:** Released Oct '88, on Roots (Germany) Catalogue no: **RL 329**

## Memphis Harmonica Kings

**MEMPHIS HARMONICA KINGS Various artists (Lewis, Noah/Beale Street Rounders/Jed Davenport)**
Tracks: / Chickaway special / Devil in the woodpile / Like I want to be / Ticket agent blues / New minglewood blues / Selling the jelly / Bad luck's my buddy / I'm sitting on top of the world / Talking 'bout yo-yo / How long how long blues / Cow cow blues / Beale Street breakdown / You ought to move out of town / Dirty dozen, The / Jug blues / Save me some / Piccolo blues.
**Album:** Released Nov '83, on Matchbox by Flyright Records. Catalogue no: **MSE 213**

## Memphis Jazz Festival

**MEMPHIS JAZZ FESTIVAL 1982 (Various artists)**
**Album:** Released Mar '84, on Jazzology (USA) by Jazzology Records (USA). Catalogue no: **J 134**

## Memphis Minnie

**HOT STUFF 1936-49**
**Album:** Released Sep '87, on Magpie by Interstate Music. Catalogue no: **PY 1806**

**IN MY GIRLISH DAYS**
Tracks: / She wouldn't give me none / Mr tango blues / I'm gonna bake my biscuits / What fault you find of me / I'm talking about you / Bumble bee / Fishin' blues / Kind treatment blues / Jailhouse trouble blues / Keep it to yourself / Dirty mother for you / Sylvester and his mule blues / You can't give it away / You wrecked my happy home.
**Album:** Released '88, on Travelin' Man by Interstate Music. Catalogue no: **TM 803**

**KEEP ON GOIN' 1933-41**
**Album:** Released '89, on Document Catalogue no: **DLP 559**

**MEMPHIS & DELTA-FIFTIES (Memphis & Delta)**
**Album:** Released '88, on Blues Classics(USA) by Arhoolie Records (USA). Catalogue no: **BC 15**

**MEMPHIS MINNIE 1934-1942**
**Cass:** Released '88, on Arhoolie (USA) by Arhoolie Records (USA). Catalogue no: **C 215**

**MEMPHIS MINNIE 1930-41**
**Album:** Released Aug '89, on Blues Document Catalogue no: **BD 2048**

**MEMPHIS MINNIE & KANSAS JOE (Memphis Minnie & Kansas Joe)**
**Album:** Released Oct '88, on Paltram Catalogue no: **PL 101**

**MEMPHIS MINNIE & KANSAS JOE, VOL. 2 (Memphis Minnie & Kansas Joe)**
**Album:** Released Oct '89, on Earl Archives Catalogue no: **BD 617**

**MEMPHIS MINNIE VOL.1**
**Album:** Released Dec '88, on Blues Classics(USA) by Arhoolie Records (USA). Catalogue no: **BC 1**

**MEMPHIS MINNIE VOL.2**
**Album:** Released '88, on Blues Classics(USA) by Arhoolie Records (USA). Catalogue no: **BC 13**

**MEMPHIS MINNIE, VOL. 1 1929/38 (Memphis Minnie / Blind John Davis / Black Bob)**
**Album:** Released Dec '88, on Earl Archives Catalogue no: **BD 608**

**QUEEN OF COUNTRY BLUES 1930-41**
**Album:** Released Jan '88, on Old Tramp Catalogue no: **OT 1207**

**WORLD OF TROUBLE**
**Album:** Released Dec '82, on Flyright by Interstate Music. Catalogue no: **FLY 585**

## Memphis Slim

**MEMPHIS BLUES - PARIS SESSIONS**
**CD:** Released Aug '89, on Stash (USA) Catalogue no: **STCD 11**

**MEMPHIS SLIM (Various artists)**
**Album:** Released '88, on Joker (USA) by Lifetime Records (USA). Catalogue no: **SM 3588**

## Menza, Don

**BALLADS (Menza, Don & Frank Strazzeri)**
**Album:** Released Feb '88, on Fresh Sounds (Spain) by Fresh Sounds Records (Spain). Catalogue no: **FS 281**

**HIP POCKET (LIVE AT CARMELOS)**
**Album:** Released Jan '84, on Palo Alto Catalogue no: **PA 8010**

## Menzies, Ian

**REUNION JAZZ REVIVAL (Menzies, Ian & His Clyde Valley Stompers)**
Tracks: / Maryland, my Maryland / Georgia on my mind / Pearly gates / That's my desire / Lady be good / Just a closer walk with thee / Mention my name.
**Album:** Released Jun '82, on Country House by BGS Productions Ltd. Catalogue no: **BGC 307**
**Cass:** Released Jun '82, on Country House by BGS Productions Ltd. Catalogue no: **KBGC 307**

## Mercer, Johnny

**AUDIO SCRAP BOOK**
Tracks: / Huggin' and chalkin' / Blue in the night / Gentle on my mind / Love is just around the corner / Java jive / Little lost dream / Slippin' around the corner / Shooby dooin' / Shake it but don't break it / Accentuate the positive / Little ol' tune / Spring spring spring / Dance of life, The / Them there eyes / I wanna be in love again.
**Album:** Released Jan '84, on Magic (1) by Submarine Records. Catalogue no: **AWE 5**
**Cass:** Released Jan '84, on Magic (1) by Submarine Records. Catalogue no: **CAWE 5**

**CAPITOL COLLECTORS SERIES, THE**
Tracks: / Strip polka / I lost my sugar in Salt Lake City / G.I. jive / Blues in the night / Ac-cent-tchu-ate the positive / Candy / I'm gonna see my baby / On the Atchison, Topeka & the Santa Fe / Sur-

prise party / Personality / My sugar is so refined / One for my baby (and one more for the road) / Zip-a-dee-doo-dah / Gal in calico, A / Winter wonderland / Moon faced, starry eyed / Sugar blues / Save the bones for Henry Jones ('cause Henry don't eat meat) / Glow worm / Baby, it's cold outside.
**CD:** Released Sep '89, on Capitol by EMI Records. Catalogue no: **CDP 792 125 2**
**CD:** Released Sep '89, on Capitol by EMI Records. Catalogue no: **CZ 232**

**DON'T FENCE ME IN (Mercer,Johnny & His Music Shop)**
**Cass:** Released Jun '86, on Dance Band Days by Prism Leisure. Catalogue no: **DBDC 04**
**Album:** Released Jun '86, on Dance Band Days by Prism Leisure. Catalogue no: **DBD 04**

**JOHNNY MERCER**
Tracks: / Jeepers creepers / St. Louis blues / Hear them bells.
Note: **Tracks include those listed above.**
**Album:** Released Jul '88, on Glendale (USA) by Glendale Records (USA). Catalogue no: **GLS 9005**

**MUSIC SHOP**
Tracks: / Music shop theme / Conversation while dancing / Day after forever, The / Steamboat Bill / Don't fence me in / Rain / Fare thee well to Harlem / Sweet Georgia Brown / It could happen to you / Tired teddy bear / Amor / Somebody loves me / Button up your overcoat / I'll be seeing you.
**Album:** Released Jan '84, on Artistic by Submarine Records. Catalogue no: **ART 002**
**Cass:** Released Jan '84, on Artistic by Submarine Records. Catalogue no: **CART 002**

## Mercer, Mabel

**ECHOES OF MY LIFE**
**2 LP Set:** Released Aug '88, on Audiophile (USA) by Jazzology Records (USA). Catalogue no: **AP 161/2**

## Mercury All Stars

**KID ORY 1944 (Mercury All Stars Jazz Combination)**
Tracks: / High society / Muskrat ramble / That - a - plenty / Panama rag / Jimmie's blues / Sugarfoot stomp / Savoy blues / Weary blues / Tiger rag / E flat blues / Didn't he ramble / Royal Garden blues.
**Album:** Released Oct '81, on Joy by President Records. Catalogue no: **JOY 264**

## Merrill, Helen

**GIL EVANS**
**CD:** Released Feb '90, on Emarcy Catalogue no: **834 205 2**

**HELEN MERRILL**
Tracks: / Don't Explain / You'd be so nice to come home to / What's new? / Falling in love with love / Yesterdays / Born to be blue / Wonderful.
**CD:** Released Jan '84, on Phonogram by Phonogram Ltd. Catalogue no: **814 643 2**

**MUSIC MAKERS (Merrill, Helen / Gordon Beck)**
**CD:** Released '88, on Owl (France) Catalogue no: **LC 044**

**RODGERS & HAMMERSTEIN ALBUM**
Tracks: / It might as well be spring / Hello young lovers / I have dreamed / People will say we're in love / Getting to know you / My lord and master / If I loved you / My favourite things / Sound of music, The.
Note: All songs written by: Richard Rogers & Oscar Hammerstein II.
**Album:** Released Apr '87, on DRG (USA) by DRG Records (USA). Deleted Jan '89. Catalogue no: **SL 5204**
**Cass:** Released Apr '87, on DRG (USA) by DRG Records (USA). Catalogue no: **SLC 5204**

**SHADE OF DIFFERENCE, A (FANTASY)**
Tracks: / Never will I marry / While we're young / Lonely woman / I should care / Lady must live, A / I want a little boy / Spring can really hang you up the most / My funny valentine / Lover come back to me / Where go you go? / Where do you go?.
**Cass:** Released Jun '86, on Fantasy (import) by Fantasy Inc (USA). Catalogue no: **LLP 51308**
**Album:** Released Jun '86, on Fantasy (import) by Fantasy Inc (USA). Catalogue no: **LLP 1308**

**SHADE OF DIFFERENCE, A (SPOTLITE)**
**Album:** Released Jan '83, on Spotlite by Spotlite Records. Catalogue no: **SPJ LP 12**

**SINGS COLE PORTER**
**CD:** Released Jan '89, on Silva Screen by Silva Screen Records. Catalogue no: **CDP 709**

**SINGS IRVING BERLIN**
**CD:** Released Jan '89, on Silva Screen by Silva Screen Records. Catalogue no: **CDP 710**

**SINGS JEROME KERN**
**Album:** Released Jan '89, on Silva Screen by Silva Screen Records. Catalogue no: **CDP 708**

**SINGS RODGERS & HAMMERSTEIN**
**CD:** Released Jan '89, on Silva Screen by Silva Screen Records. Catalogue no: **CDP 707**

**SOMETHING SPECIAL**
**Album:** Released Apr '79, on Inner City Catalogue no: **INNER CITY 1060**

**S'POSIN**
Note:
Mono production: with Gary Peacock Trio
**Album:** Released May '86, on Storyville by Storyville Records AB. Catalogue no: **SLP 1014**

## Merrin, Billy

**TROUBLES ARE LIKE BUBBLES 1932-1937 (Merrin, Billy & His Commanders)**
**Album:** Released Jun '89, on Reid Catalogue no: **RD 5**

## Messner, Johnny

**JOHNNY MESSNER AND HOTEL MCALPIN (Messner, Johnny/Hote McAlpin Orchestra)**
**Album:** Released '88, on Hindsight Catalogue no: **HSR 186**

## Metheny, Pat

**80-81**
Tracks: / Goin' ahead / Two folk songs / Bat / Turn around / Open / Pretty scattered / Everyday I thank you.
Note: Digital stereo.
**CD Set:** Released Sep '84, on ECM Catalogue no: **815 579 2**
**Cass set:** Released Oct '88, on ECM Catalogue no: **354 1180**
**2 LP Set:** Released Nov '88, on ECM Catalogue no: **ECM 1180**

**ABSOLUTELY LIVE**
**Cass:** Released Oct '85, on Platinum (W.Germany) Catalogue no: **PMC 17**
**Album:** Released Oct '85, on Platinum (W.Germany) Catalogue no: **PLP 17**

**AMERICAN GARAGE**
Tracks: / Heartland (Cross the) / Airstream / Search, The / American garage / Epic, The.
**Album:** Released Jan '80, on ECM Catalogue no: **ECM 1155**
**Cass:** Released Oct '88, on ECM Catalogue no: **310 1155**
**CD:** Released Dec '85, on ECM Catalogue no: **827 134-2**

**ARE YOU GOING WITH ME (Metheny, Pat Group)**
Tracks: / Are you going with me / Au lait.
**7" Single:** Released Jun '82, on ECM Catalogue no: **ECM 7 29999**

**AS FALLS WICHITA, SO FALLS WICHITA FALLS (Metheny, Pat & Lyle Mays)**
Tracks: / As falls Wichita, so falls Wichita Falls / September 15th / It's for you / Estupenda graca.
**Album:** Released Jun '81, on ECM Catalogue no: **ECM 1190**
**Cass:** Released Jul '85, on ECM Catalogue no: **7200189**
**CD:** Released Jul '85, on ECM Catalogue no: **821 416-2**

**BRIGHT SIZE LIFE**
Tracks: / Bright size life / Sirabhorn / Unity village / Missouri incompromised / Midwestern nights dream / Unquity road / Omaha celebration / Round trip-Broadway blues.
**CD:** Released Dec '86, on ECM Catalogue no: **827 133-2**
**Album:** Released Jan '76, on ECM Catalogue no: **ECM 1073**

**FIRST CIRCLE (Metheny, Pat Group)**
Tracks: / Forward march / Yolanda / You learn / First circle, The / If I could / Tell it all / End of the game, The / Mas alla (beyond) / Praise.
**Album:** Released Nov '84, on ECM Catalogue no: **ECM 1278**
**CD:** Released Nov '84, on ECM Catalogue no: **8233422**

**LIVE IN CONCERT (Metheny, Pat, Heath Bros, Dave Brubeck Quartet, B B King)**
Tracks: / Introduction / Move to the groove / Lover man / Blue rondo / Ol' Bill Basie / Thrill is gone, The / Guess who? / Pay in the cost to be the boss / Move to the groove / Lover man / Blue rondo / Ol' Bill Basie / Thrill is gone, The / Guess who / Payin' the cost to be the boss.
Note: Pat Metheny with the Heath Brothers, Dave Brubeck 4 & B.B. King.
**Album:** Released Jan '85, on Kingdom Jazz by Kingdom Records. Catalogue no: **GATE 7017**
**CD:** Released '86, on Kingdom Jazz by Kingdom Records. Catalogue no: **CDGATE 7017**
**Cass:** Released Jan '85, on Kingdom Jazz by Kingdom Records. Catalogue no: **CGATE 7017**

**LIVE: PAT METHENY (Metheny, Pat Group Travels)**
Tracks: / Are you going with me / Fields, the sky, The / Goodbye / Phase dance / Straight on red / Farmer's trust / Extradition / Goin' ahead / As falls wichita, so falls wichita falls / Travels / Song for bilbao / San Lorenzo.
**Album:** Released May '83, on ECM Catalogue no: **ECM 1252**

**NEW CHAUTAUQUA**
Tracks: / New chautauqua / Country poem / Long-ago child / Fallen star, A / Hermitage / Sueno con Mexico / Daybreak.
Note: Personnel: Pat Metheny - electric 6- and 12-string guitars, acoustic guitar, 15-string harp guitar, electric bass.
**CD:** Released Aug '85, on ECM Catalogue no: **825 471-2**
**Album:** Released May '79, on ECM Catalogue no: **ECM 1131**

**OFFRAMP**
Tracks: / Barcarolle / Are you going with me? / Au lait / Eighteen / Offramp / James / Bat, The (part 2).
Note: Digital stereo
**Cass:** Released Oct '88, on ECM Catalogue no: **310 1216**
**CD:** Released Sep '84, on ECM Catalogue no: **817 138-2**
**Album:** Released May '82, on ECM Catalogue no: **ECM 1216**

**PAT METHENY**
**CD:** Released Jul '89, on Cleo Catalogue no: **CLCD 5006**

**PAT METHENY GROUP (Metheny, Pat Group)**
**CD:** Released Aug '88, on ECM Catalogue no: **825 593-2**
**Album:** Released Jan '78, on ECM Catalogue no: **ECM 1114**

**REJOICING**
Tracks: / Lonely woman / Tears inside / Humpty dumpty / Blues for Pat / Rejoicing / Story from a stranger / Calling (the) / Waiting for an answer.
Note: Personnel: Pat Metheny - guitars; Charlie Haden - bass; Billy Higgins - drums.
**Album:** Released Jan '77, on ECM Catalogue no: **ECM 1097**
**CD:** Released Jun '84, on ECM Catalogue no: **817 795 2**
**Album:** Released Jun '84, on ECM Catalogue no: **ECM 1271**

**STILL LIFE (TALKING) (Metheny, Pat Group)**
Tracks: / Minuano / So may it secretly begin / Last train home / It's just talk / Third wind / Distance / In her family.
**Cass:** Released Jul '87, on Geffen by Geffen Records (USA). Catalogue no: **924145 4**
**CD:** Released Oct '87, on WEA by WEA Records. Catalogue no: **924145 2**
**Album:** Released Jul '87, on Geffen by Geffen Records (USA). Deleted Jan '90. Catalogue no: **924145 1**

**TRAVELS (Metheny, Pat Group)**
Tracks: / Are you going with me? / Fields, the sky, The / Goodbye / Phase dance / Straight on red / Farmer's trust / Extradition / Goin' ahead / As falls wichita, so falls wichita falls / Travels / Song for bilbao / San Lorenzo.
Note: Personnel: Pat Metheny - guitars, guitar synthesizer; Lly Mays - piano, sunthesizers, organ, autoharp, synclavier; Steve Rodby - accoustic and electric bass, bass synthesizer; Dan Gottlieb - drums; special guest Nana Vasconcelos - percussion, voice, berimbau.
**2 LP Set:** Released Nov '88, on ECM Catalogue no: **ECM 1252**
**CD Set:** Released Aug '86, on ECM Catalogue no: **810 622-2**

**WATERCOLOURS**
Tracks: / Watercolours / Icefire / Lakes / River Quay / Sute 1 - Florida Greeting song / 11 - Legend of the fountain / Sea song.
Note: Personnel: Pat Metheny - guitar, 12-string guitar, 15-string harp guitar; Lyle Mays - piano; Eberhard Weber - bass; Dan Gotlieb - drums.
**CD:** Released Feb '86, on ECM Catalogue no: **827 409-2**
**Album:** Released Nov '88, on ECM Catalogue no: **ECM 1097**

**WORKS II: PAT METHENY**
Tracks: / Uniquity Road / Unity village / Open / Story from a stranger / Oasis / Sirabhorn / Farmer's trust.
Note: Personnel: Pat Metheny, Jaco Pastorius, Charlie Haden, Jack DeJohnette, Dewey Redman, Mike Brecker, Eberhard Weber, Nana Vasconcelos, Lyle Mays.
**Album:** Released Jun '89, on ECM Catalogue no: **837 272-1**
**CD:** Released Jun '89, on ECM Catalogue no: **837 272-2**

**WORKS: PAT METHENY**
Tracks: / Sueno con Mexico / (Cross the ) heartland / Travels / James / It's for you / Everyday I thank you / Goin' ahead.
Note: Digital stereo. Personnel: Pat Metheny, Lyle Mays, Mark Egan, Nana Vasconcelos,Charlie Haden, Jack DeJohnette, Mike Brecker.
**Cass:** Released Nov '83, on ECM Catalogue no: **3100 389**
**CD:** Released Jun '89, on ECM Catalogue no: **823 270-2**
**Album:** Released Jun '89, on ECM Catalogue no: **823 270-1**

## Metronome All Star

**METRONOME ALL-STAR BANDS**
Tracks: / Honeysuckle rose / Blues / Blue Lou / Blue Lou (alt take 1) / Blue Lou (alt take 2) / Blues, The / Blues, The (alt take) / Bugle call band / One o'clock metronome all out / Overtime (alt take) / Victory ball / Victory ball (alt take).
**CD:** Released Nov '88, on Bluebird (2) by BMG Records (UK). Catalogue no: **ND 87636**

## Mezzrow, Mezz

**CLARINET MARMALADE**
**Album:** Released Oct '88, on Vogue by Vogue Records. Catalogue no: **500065**

**IN PARIS 1955**
**Album:** Released '88, on DRG (USA) by DRG Records (USA). Catalogue no: **SW 8409**

**MEZZ MEZZROW IN CONCERT Theatre Des Champs Elysees**
**CD:** Released Oct '88, on Vogue by Vogue Records. Catalogue no: **VGCD 600 190**

## Mezzrow-Bechet

**KING JAZZ VOL.1 (Mezzrow-Bechet Quintet & Septet)**
Note: With Sammy Price "Out of the Gallion".
**Album:** Released Oct '86, on Storyville by Storyville Records AB. Catalogue no: **SLP 6004**

**KING JAZZ VOL.2 (Mezzrow-Bechet Quintet & Septet)**
Note: Artists include: Sammy Price 'Gone Away Blues'.
**Album:** Released Oct '86, on Storyville by Storyville Records AB. Catalogue no: **SLP 6005**

**KING JAZZ VOL.3 (Mezzrow-Bechet Quintet & Septet)**
Note: Artists include Sammy Price 'Gone Away Blues'.
**Album:** Released Oct '86, on Storyville by Storyville Records AB. Catalogue no: **SLP 6006**

**KING JAZZ VOL.4 (Mezzrow-Bechet Quintet & Septet)**
Note: Artists include Sammy Price 'Revolutionary Blues'.
**Album:** Released Oct '86, on Storyville by Storyville Records AB. Catalogue no: **SLP 6007**

**KING JAZZ VOL.5 (Mezzrow-Bechet Quintet & Septet)**
Note: With Sammy Price.

Out of The Gallion - Mezzrow-Bechet (Storyville)

**Album:** Released Nov '86, on Storyville by Storyville Records AB. Catalogue no: **SLP 4115**

**MEZZROW / BECHET QUINTET / SEPTET (Mezzrow-Bechet Quintet & Septet)**
Note: Mono production
**Album:** Released May '86, on Storyville by Storyville Records AB. Catalogue no: **SLP 820/1**

**OUT OF THE GALLION (See panel above)**
Note: Mono production
**Album:** Released May '86, on Storyville by Storyville Records AB. Catalogue no: **SLP 837**

**REALLY THE BLUES (Mezzrow Bechet Quintet)**
**Album:** Released Jul '81, on Storyville by Storyville Records AB. Catalogue no: **SLP 137**

## Midland Youth Jazz Orch.

**STARBURST**
Tracks: / Decoupage / Clearway / Majella / Blue rondo a la turk / Starburst / I remember Clifford / Chiefs blues / 920 special / Soul squeeze.
**Album:** Released Jun '81, on Grosvenor by Grosvenor Records. Catalogue no: **GRS 1092**

## Midnight On Bourbon Street

**MIDNIGHT ON BOURBON STREET (Various artists)**
Tracks: / Sheik of Araby, The: *Various artists* / Temptation rag: *Various artists* / Eh la bas: *Various artists* / She's crying for me: *Various artists* / Li'l Liza Jane: *Various artists* / Corina Corina: *Various artists* / San: *Various artists* / Jazz it blues: *Various artists* / That's a plenty: *Various artists* / Won't you come home Bill Bailey: *Various artists* / On the sunny side of the street: *Various artists* / Mama don't allow it: *Various artists* / Pizza pie boogie: *Various artists.*
**Album:** Released May '87, on Rhapsody by President Records. Catalogue no: **RHA 6035**

## Midnite Follies

**JUNGLE NIGHTS IN HARLEM**
Tracks: / Shakin' the African / Jungle nights in Harlem / Happy as the day is long / Mooche, The / Okay baby / Alligator crawl / Blue skies / He's the viper / Kicking the gong around / Snake hips / Sophisticated lady / Ring dem bells / Truckin' / Black beauty / Let's do it / Stomp de luxe.
**Album:** Released Mar '81, on ASV (Academy Sound & Vision) by Academy Sound & Vision Records. Deleted Feb '89. Catalogue no: **ALA 3002**
**Cass:** Released Mar '81, on ASV (Academy Sound & Vision) by Academy Sound & Vision Records. Deleted Feb '89. Catalogue no: **ZC ALA 3002**

**KICKING THE GONG AROUND**
Tracks: / Kicking the gong around / Snake hips.
**7" Single:** Released Mar '81, on ASV (Academy Sound & Vision) by Academy Sound & Vision Records. Deleted Mar '84. Catalogue no: **ASV 102**

## Mighty Clouds Of Joy

**BEST OF THE MIGHTY CLOUDS OF JOY**
**Album:** Released Oct '87, on MCA (USA) by MCA Records (USA). Catalogue no: **MCA 28019**

**CATCHIN' ON**
**Album:** Released Jan '89, on Rejoice by Word Records (UK). Catalogue no: **REJ R 5013**
**Cass:** Released Jan '89, on Rejoice by Word Records (UK). Catalogue no: **REJ C 5013**

**CLOUDBURST**
Tracks: / Wings of faith / Glow love / Walk around heaven all day / Praise the Lord / I ain't no ways tired / I'll always stay with God / Showing each other love / Everybody ought to praise His Name / I made a step / I'll always stay with God.
**Cass:** Released May '82, on Myrrh by Word Records (UK). Catalogue no: **MC 1096**
**Album:** Released May '82, on Myrrh by Word Records (UK). Catalogue no: **MYR 1096**

**MIRACLE MAN**
Tracks: / Miracle man / He'll be there / You oughta been there / You are my happiness / Home of the lord, The / Help me to be strong / This world is not my home / Any good time at all / Jesus is the rock / Son of God / Build me a cabin in glory.
**Cass:** Released May '82, on Myrrh by Word Records (UK). Catalogue no: **MC 1118**
**Album:** Released May '82, on Myrrh by Word Records (UK). Catalogue no: **MYR 1118**

**NIGHT SONG**
Tracks: / I can't turn back no way / All that I am / Just keep on trusting God / You'll never walk alone.
**CD:** Released '1, on Rejoice by Word Records (UK). Catalogue no: **REJ D 5029**
**Cass:** Released '1, on Rejoice by Word Records (UK). Catalogue no: **REJ C 5029**
**Album:** Released '1, on Rejoice by Word Records (UK). Catalogue no: **REJ R 5029**

**SING & SHOUT**
**Cass:** Released May '84, on Myrrh by Word Records (UK). Catalogue no: **MC 1156**
**Album:** Released May '84, on Myrrh by Word Records (UK). Catalogue no: **MYR 1156**

**THEIR BEST**
**Cass:** Released May '88, on Supreme by Supreme Records. Catalogue no: **2651014**

**TRUTH IS THE POWER**
Tracks: / There's love in the world / That's what friends are made of / Music is my way of life / Truth will set you free / God is not dead / I'll keep my light in my window / Listen people / Like a child.
**Album:** Released May '82, on Myrrh by Word Records (UK). Catalogue no: **MYR**

**1111**
**Cass:** Released May '82, on Myrrh by Word Records (UK). Catalogue no: **MC 1111**

## Milder, Bjorn

**SWING PIANO MY WAY**
**Album:** Released Mar '87, on Kenneth Catalogue no: **KS 2048**

## Miles, Buddy

**LIVE: BUDDY MILES (Miles, Buddy & Carlos Santana)**
**Cass:** Released Sep '84, on CBS by CBS Records. Deleted '87. Catalogue no: **40 32271**
**Album:** Released Sep '84, on CBS by CBS Records. Catalogue no: **CBS 32271**

**SNEAK ATTACK (Miles, Buddy Regiment)**
Tracks: / Latin rock fusion / Can you hold me / Sunshine of your love / I've made up my mind / Working hard every day / Colossus / Let's make it together / Jazz fusion / Buddy Miles, live at CIM, Chino, Ca / Hold her tight / Dust in the wind / For your precious love.
**Album:** Released Oct '81, on Atlantic by WEA Records. Deleted Oct '86. Catalogue no: **K 60156**

## Miller, Eddie

**LAZY MOOD FOR TWO (Miller, Eddie & Lou Stein)**
Tracks: / I've got a crush on you / Lady be good / I got it bad / Dizzy fingers / Little girl blue / Coquette / Lazy mood / I'm gonna sit right down and write myself ... / Sophisticated lady / Diane / Bag balm boogie / Can't we be friends.
**Album:** Released Aug '79, on 77 by 77 Records. Catalogue no: **77S 59**

**LIVE AT MICHELE'S SILVER STOPE (Miller, Eddie/Merle Koch)**
**Album:** Released Aug '88, on Audiophile (USA) by Jazzology Records (USA). Catalogue no: **AP 135**

## Miller, Glenn

**Biographical details:** Born in Clarinda, Iowa, USA on Ist March 1904, Glenn Alton Miller first learned to play cornet and mandolin, only graduating to trombone so that he could play in the town band in Grant City, Missouri, to where the family had moved. His interest in arranging evolved in the early 1920's and he worked for Max Fischer and Ben Pollack before arranging freelance for Broadway shows. He joined the Dorsey Brothers Orchestra in 1934, leaving them after one year to work with, first, Ray Noble and then with Glen Gray and the Casa Loma Band. He formed his own band in 1937, cut some sides for Decca and began playing the ballrooms although not with much success. The band only really gained popularity in the latter half of 1938. On August 1st 1939 the band recorded it's biggest hit *In The Mood.* Miller made two films - "Sun Valley Serenade" and "Orchestra Wives". In 1942 he volunteered for the army, becoming Captain Glenn Miller and formed an all-star band, touring first the USA and then England in 1944. The plane carrying him to a concert in France was lost over the English Channel on December 15th 1944. No trace of the wreckage was ever found and Glenn Miller was declared missing, presumed dead, by the United States government.

Glenn Miller

This American orchestra leader, conductor, arranger and trombonist was one of the most famous and successful musical figures of the 20th century. He was born in Clarinda, Iowa in 1904, and grew up in Platts, Nebraska. He acquired his first trombone at the age of 13. Miller attended the University of Colorado from 1924 until 1926. The following nine years were spent working for various bandleaders of the era, such as Ben Pollack, Paul Ash, Red Nichols and Victor Young; he travelled across America during this period, working on both the East and West Coasts. In 1935 he teamed up with British bandleader Ray Noble, helping to organise Noble's new band when the latter arrived in America. This experience proved valuable when Miller began to set up his own ensemble in 1937.

After a few hiccups, Glenn Miller's orchestra got into gear in mid-1938. Success was not long in coming. After a series of one-nighters in the New York area, the ensemble gained some plum residencies. By 1941 Miller was the top bandleader in the world. Adhering to a 'popular' danceband format rather than the authentic jazz stance of such contemporaries as Duke Ellington, the Miller magic popularised a host of tunes - *Little Brown Jug, In The Mood, Tuxedo Junction* and *Moonlight Serenade* (which he composed himself, and used as his theme tune) became synonymous with his name. When Billboard magazine published the world's first ever record chart in July 1940, Miller had three tunes in the Top 10: *Imagination* (No. 3), *Fools Rush In* (No. 5) and *Pennsylvania 6-5000* (No. 7).

In 1942, while Glenn was at the peak of his career, the Second World War beckoned. During his time in the US Forces, first as Captain and later as a Major, he continued to be one of the most popular musical figures in the world; his role as a morale-booster enhanced his already high reputation. He was stationed in Britain in 1944. In December of that year, while his plane was en route from France to the UK amid thick fog, Major Miller perished as his craft disappeared over the English Channel; he was aged 40.

Ten years after his passing, a biographical movie entitled 'The Glenn Miller Story' was released by Universal Pictures, with James Stewart in the title role. Miller's music lived on, not only in this film but throughout ensuing decades. During the Sixties and Seventies, seven separate Glenn Miller albums registered on the British LP chart. In 1976, more than thirty years after his death, he became an unlikely recipient of a Top 20 placing on the UK singles chart when a brief but enjoyable Glenn Miller revival took place in British discos, thus introducing his music to a new generation. Bob MacDonald, 29 January 1986..

**20 CLASSIC TRACKS: GLENN MILLER**
Tracks: / String of pearls / It happened in sun valley / Deep purple / Sun valley jump / Red cavalry march / Tuxedo Junction / Bugle brown jug / I've got a gal in Kalamazoo / Pennsylvania 6 5000 / Little brown jug / Sunrise serenade / Serenade in blue / Moonlight serenade / Adios / American patrol / Anvil chorus / Chattanooga choo choo / Moonlight cocktail / Boomshot / In the mood.
**Cass:** Released Feb '87, on Arena Catalogue no: **ARAC 1006**
**Album:** Released Feb '87, on Arena Catalogue no: **ARA 1006**

**20 GREATEST HITS: GLENN MILLER**
**Cass:** Released Nov '84, on Astan (USA) Catalogue no: **40124**
**Album:** Released Nov '84, on Astan (USA) Catalogue no: **20124**

**21 GOLDEN GREATS LIVE**
Tracks: / Moonlight serenade / Caribbean clipper / Summertime / American patrol / Nearness of you, The / Anvil chorus / Tuxedo Junction / El capitan / Deep purple / In the mood / Anchors aweigh / I want to be happy / Snafu jump / I dream of you / Long ago and far away / St. Louis blues / My blue Heaven / Chattanooga choo choo / Rhapsody in blue / In the gloaming / Little brown jug.
**Cass:** Released Jul '87, on Magic (1) by Submarine Records. Catalogue no: **CAWM 1**

**40TH ANNIVERSARY ALBUM**
**Cass:** Released '84, on Magic (1) by Submarine Records. Catalogue no: **CAWE 11**
**Album:** Released '84, on Magic (1) by Submarine Records. Catalogue no: **AWE 11**

**1940: GLENN MILLER**
**Album:** Released Aug '85, on Magic (1) by Submarine Records. Catalogue no: **AWE 14**

**1943 BAND IN HI-FI, THE**
**Album:** Released Nov '86, on Soundcraft (USA) Catalogue no: **LP 1015**

**AMERICAN PATROL (Miller, Glenn & His Orchestra)**
Tracks: / Serenade in blue / Song of the volga boatmen / Moonlight cocktail / Anvil chorus / I've got a gal in Kalamazoo / Sunrise serenade / Under the double eagle / Danny boy / Chattanooga choo choo / American Patrol / Jeep jockey jump / Sanfu jump / Keep 'em flying / Lover / Little brown jug.
**Album:** Released Apr '86, on Castle Showcase by Castle Communications Records. Catalogue no: **SHLP 103**
**Cass:** Released Apr '86, on Castle Showcase by Castle Communications Records. Catalogue no: **SHTC 103**

**AMERICAN PATROL (SINGLE)**
Tracks: / American patrol.
**7" Single:** Released Mar '77, on RCA by BMG Records (UK). Deleted '79. Catalogue no: **PB 9031**

**AMERICAN RHAPSODY**
Tracks: / Rhapsody in blue / Symphony / El capitan / In the gloaming / Deep purple / Killarney I've got a heart filled with love / Moonlight serenade / Wabash blues / Oranges and lemons / Buckle down winsocki / Stealin apples / Red cavalry march.
**Album:** Released Jun '85, on Swing House by Submarine Records. Catalogue no: **SWH 11**
**Cass:** Released Jun '85, on Swing House by Submarine Records. Catalogue no: **CSWH 11**

**AMERICA'S NO.1 DANCE BAND (live 1940)**
**Album:** Released Jan '88, on Sounds Great Catalogue no: **SG 8018**

**AND THE ARMY AIR FORCE BAND**
Tracks: / Over there / Anvil chorus / Stardust / Song of the volga boatmen / Farewell blues / They are Yanks / My ideal / Mission to Moscow / Sun Valley jump / Tuxedo Junction / I'll be around / Poinciana / I hear you screaming / Jukebox Saturday night / My blue Heaven / St. Louis blues march / It must be jelly / Blues in my heart / Everybody loves my baby / Alexander's ragtime band / Stompin' at the Savoy / Deep purple / Don't be that way / I can't give you anything but love / Wang wang blues / Shoo shoo baby / Way you look tonight / Victory polka / There'll be a hot time in the town of Berlin / Flying home / Here we go again / Jeep jockey jump / Enlisted mens mess / Begin the beguine / In the mood / It's love love love / Eighteenth century drawing room / There are Yanks / Closing theme and announcements.
**Album:** Released '83, on RCA (France) by BMG Records (France). Catalogue no: **PM 43172**

**APRIL 3RD 1940 CHESTERFIELD SHOW CAFE / ROUGE**
**Album:** Released '88, on Jasmine by Hasmick Promotions. Catalogue no: **JASM 2520**
**Cass:** Released Jan '89, on Jasmine by Hasmick Promotions. Catalogue no: **JASMC 2520**

**ARMY AIR FORCE BAND 1943-44, THE**
Tracks: / St. Louis blues march / Peggy, the pin-up girl / Speak low / Tail-end Charlie / Anvil chorus / Oh what a beautiful morning / There are Yanks / Everybody loves my baby(but my baby loves nobody but me) / Enlisted men's mess / I'll be around / There'll be a hot time in the town of Berlin / People will say we're in love / Pearls on velvet / Poinciana / It must be jelly / Jeep jockey jump / Victory polka.
**CD:** Released Jun '88, on Bluebird (2) by BMG Records (UK). Catalogue no: **ND 86360**

**ARMY AIR FORCE BAND - COMPLETE VDISC SESSIONS**
**Album:** Released Feb '89, on Sounds Great Catalogue no: **SG 8013**

**ARMY AIRFORCE ORCHESTRA-JOHNNY DESMOND**
**Album:** Released Mar '90, on Jasmine by Hasmick Promotions. Catalogue no: **JASM 2532**

**AT MEADOWBROOK 1939 (Miller, Glenn Orchestra)**
Tracks: / Moonlight serenade (theme) / Little brown jug / Blue rain / Oh Johnny, oh Johnny oh / In an old dutch garden / Tiger rag / Love with a capital you / Bugle call rag / Blue moonlight / Indian summer / Why couldn't it last last night / This changing world / I just got a letter / On a little street in Singapore / Faithful to you / Farewell blues / Moonlight serenade (theme and fadeout).
**Album:** Released Sep '89, on Magic (1) by Submarine Records. Catalogue no: **AWE 34**
**Cass:** Released Sep '89, on Magic (1) by Submarine Records. Catalogue no: **CAWE 34**
**CD:** Released Sep '89, on Magic (1) by Submarine Records. Catalogue no: **DAWE 34**

**AT THE GLENN ISLAND CASINO**
**Cass:** Released '88, on Jasmine by Hasmick Promotions. Catalogue no: **JASMC 2517**
**Album:** Released '88, on Jasmine by Hasmick Promotions. Catalogue no: **JASM 2517**

**AT THE STEEL PIER IN 1941**
**Album:** Released May '84, on Ajaz (USA) Catalogue no: **AJAZ 316**

**AUTUMN SERENADE (Miller, Glenn & His Orchestra)**
**Album:** Released '84, on Magic (1) by Submarine Records. Catalogue no: **AWE 9**
**Cass:** Released '84, on Magic (1) by Submarine Records. Catalogue no: **CAWE 9**

**BBC NOVEMBER 1944**
**Album:** Released May '86, on Jasmine by Hasmick Promotions. Catalogue no: **JASM 2504**
**Cass:** Released May '86, on Jasmine by Hasmick Promotions. Catalogue no: **JASMC 2504**

**BEST OF GLENN MILLER (CBS) (Miller, Glenn & His Orchestra)**
Tracks: / In the mood / Sunrise serenade / String of pearls / Rhapsody in blue / American patrol / Little brown jug / Alice blue gown / Tuxedo Junction / Adios / My sentiment.
**Cass:** Released Aug '85, on CBS Cameo by CBS Records. Deleted Jan '89. Catalogue no: **40 32665**
**Album:** Released Aug '85, on CBS Cameo by CBS Records. Catalogue no: **CBS 32665**

**BEST OF GLENN MILLER (CREOLE)**
**Cass:** Released Jul '84, on Creole (Everest-Europa) by Creole Records. Catalogue no: **16-9**

**BEST OF GLENN MILLER (FLASHBACK) (Miller, Glenn & His Or-**

**chestra)**
Note: Tracks include In the mood, American Patrol, A String of pearls, Little Brown jug, etc
**Cass:** Released May '88, on Flashback by Mainline Records. Catalogue no: **64027**

**BEST OF GLENN MILLER (PICKWICK) (Miller, Glenn & His Orchestra)**
Tracks: / Nearness of you, The / Lamplighter's serenade, The / Nightingale sang in Berkeley Square, A / Fools rush in / Missouri waltz / Say si si / My blue Heaven / My melancholy baby / Alice blue gown / Faithful forever / Old black Joe / In the mood.
**Cass:** Released Jul '84, on Pickwick by Pickwick Records. Catalogue no: **CAM 475**
**Album:** Released Jul '84, on Pickwick by Pickwick Records. Catalogue no: **CDS 1165**

**BEST OF GLENN MILLER (RCA) (Miller, Glenn & His Orchestra)**
Tracks: / In the mood / Along the Sante Fe trail / Johnson rag / Sunrise serenade / Chattanooga choo choo / Anvil chorus / St. Louis blues march / Don't sit under the apple tree / Tuxedo Junction / Stairway to the stars / Jukebox Saturday night / Song of the volga boatmen.
**Cass:** Released '84, on RCA International by BMG Records (UK). Catalogue no: **NK 83871**
**Album:** Released '84, on RCA International by BMG Records (UK). Catalogue no: **NL 83871**

**BEST OF GLENN MILLER VOL.2 (RCA) (Miller, Glenn & His Orchestra)**
Tracks: / Moonlight serenade / Elmer's tune / String of pearls / Lamplighter's serenade, The / Who's sorry now? / I've got a gal in Kalamazoo / Moonlight cocktail / By the waters of Minnetonka / Serenade in blue / Glen island special / Take the 'A' train / American patrol.
**Album:** Released Aug '81, on RCA International by BMG Records (UK). Deleted '84. Catalogue no: **INTS 5091**
**Album:** Released '84, on RCA International by BMG Records (UK). Catalogue no: **NL 83809**
**Cass:** Released '84, on RCA International by BMG Records (UK). Catalogue no: **NK 83809**

**BIG BAND BASH**
**CD:** Released Mar '90, on Giants of Jazz by Hasmick Promotions. Catalogue no: **GOJCD53024**

**CARNEGIE HALL CONCERT (Miller, Glenn & His Orchestra)**
Tracks: / Moonlight serenade / Running wild / Sunrise serenade / Little brown jug / Stairway to the stars / To you / One o'clock jump / Londonderry air / Jumpin' jive / F.D.R. Jones / Hold tight, hold tight / In the mood / Bugle call rag.
**Album:** Released Feb '77, on Star Call by BMG Records (UK). Deleted '80. Catalogue no: **NL 42010**

**CHATANOOGA CHOO CHOO**
**Cass:** Released May '88, on Flashback by Mainline Records. Catalogue no: **64026**

**CHESTERFIELD SHOWS, 1941-42 (Miller, Glenn & His Orchestra)**
Tracks: / Sweet Eloise / I've got a gal in Kalamazoo / People like you and me / I don't want to walk without you / V for victory hop / Jingle bells / Story of a starry night / Nobody ever wants me / Sun Valley jump / Jersey bounce, The.
Note: Mono. Featuring Tex Beneke\Skip Nelson\Marion Hutton\The modernaires. 1942.
**Cass:** Released Sep '85, on Jasmine by Hasmick Promotions. Catalogue no: **JASMC 2501**
**Album:** Released May '84, on Soundcraft (USA) Catalogue no: **LP 1002**
**Album:** Released Sep '85, on Jasmine by Hasmick Promotions. Catalogue no: **JASM 2501**

**CHESTERFIELD SHOWS-CHICAGO 1940 Civic Theatre, Chicago (Miller, Glenn & His Orchestra)**
Tracks: / In my solitude / Rumba jumps, The / I'm stepping out with a memory tonight / Everybody loves my baby / Five o'clock whistle / Siren's song, The / Handful of stars, A / Love in bloom / Birth of the blues / Beat me daddy eight to the bar / Slumber song / Lights out / Hold me tight / Along the Santa Fe trail / Tiger rag.
**Album:** Released May '84, on Soundcraft (USA) Catalogue no: **LP 1012**

**CHESTERFIELD SHOWS-N.Y.C. 1940 Radio Playhouse, NYC (Miller, Glenn & His Orchestra)**
Tracks: / Woodpecker song, The / Sweet and lovely / Sierra Sue / Very thought of you, The / Blue evening / Tiger rag / Midnight on the Nile / Shadows on the sand / Fresh as a daisy / Yesterthoughts / Solid as a stone wall, Jackson / Isn't that just like love / I dreamt I dwelt in Harlem / Slumber song.
**Album:** Released May '84, on Soundcraft (USA) Catalogue no: **LP 1010**

**CHRISTMAS PROGRAMME**
Note: Mono. Vocals by Johnny Desmond
**Album:** Released Nov '86, on Soundcraft (USA) Catalogue no: **LP 1017**

**COLLECTION: GLENN MILLER**
**Cass:** Released Jan '85, on RCA (Germany) Catalogue no: **NK 45169**
**Cass:** Released '87, on Castle Collector Series by Castle Communications Records. Catalogue no: **CCSMC 185**
**Album:** Released Jan '85, on RCA (Germany) Catalogue no: **NL 45169**
**2 LP Set:** Released '88, on Castle Collector Series by Castle Communications Records. Catalogue no: **CCSLP 185**
**CD:** Released '88, on Castle Collector Series by Castle Communications Records. Catalogue no: **CCSCD 185**

**COMPLETE SUNSET SERENADE**
**Album:** Released May '86, on Jasmine by Hasmick Promotions. Catalogue no: **JASM 2505**

**DIAMOND SERIES: GLENN MILLER**
Tracks: / Anchors aweigh / My buddy / I got rhythm / I dream of Jeannie with the light-brown hair / Sleepy lagoon / Moonlight sonata / Vilia / Limehouse blues / On the Alamo / Intermezzo / Fanhat stomp / Chattanooga choo choo / Beautiful Ohio / Pavanne / Danny boy.
**CD:** Released Apr '88, on Diamond Series by RCA Records. Catalogue no: **CD 90115**

**EARLY YEARS - PARADISE**
Tracks: / Butcher boy / Don't wake up my heart / Cowboy from Brooklyn / My best wishes / I know that you know / On the sentimental side / On the Alamo / Dipsy doodle, The / Closing / Please come out of your dream / Poinciana / Running wild.
**Album:** Released May '84, on Soundcraft (USA) Catalogue no: **LP 1014**

**FOREVER**
Tracks: / Take the 'A' Train / Back to back / Stairway to the stars / One I love belongs to somebody else, The / Song of the volga boatmen / Little man who wasn't there, The / Who's sorry now? / Runnin' wild / I want to be happy / Ding dong the witch is dead / Over the rainbow / You stepped out of a dream / Bugle call rag / Story of a starry night / When Johnny comes marching home / Adios / Skylark / Say si si / On a little street in Singapore / Ciri-biri-bin / Jingle bells / Baby me / Nearness of you / Blueberry Hill / Frenesi / At last / Woodpecker song, The / I'll never smile again / Keep them flying / My prayer / Yours is my heart alone.
**Album:** Released Jul '86, on RCA by BMG Records (UK). Deleted Nov '88. Catalogue no: **NL 89214**
**Cass:** Released Jul '86, on RCA by BMG Records (UK). Deleted Nov '88. Catalogue no: **NK 89214**

**GENIUS OF GLENN MILLER, THE**
Tracks: / Moonlight serenade / Little brown jug / I got rhythm / Blue skies / Sliphorn jive / String of pearls / Don't sit under the apple tree / Song of the volga boatmen / Elmer's tune / My blue Heaven / American patrol / Sun Valley jump / Anvil chorus / King Porter stomp / Jukebox Saturday night / Farewell blues.
**CD:** Released Apr '88, on RCA by BMG Records (UK). Catalogue no: **ND 90090**

**GENIUS OF GLENN MILLER VOL 2**
Tracks: / St. Louis blues march / Tuxedo Junction / Chattanooga choo choo / Johnson rag / Spirit is willing, The / Running wild / Perfidia / Stairway to the stars / Tisket a tasket, A / Moon love / Carribbean clipper / Sweet Eloise / Nightingale sang in Berkeley Square, A / Over the rainbow / Yes, my darling daughter / Adios.
**CD:** Released Jun '88, on RCA by BMG Records (UK). Catalogue no: **ND 90205**

**GLENN MILLER Live, April - June**

**1940**
Note: Musicians include Tex Beneke, Marion Hutton and Ray Eberle with songs such as St Louis Blues (two versions), Rug Cutter's Swing, Conversation Piece, Slip Horn Jive, Boog It and Runnin' Wild.
**Album:** Released Apr '88, on Sounds Great Catalogue no: **SG 8012**
**Album:** Released Sep '87, on Giants of Jazz by Hasmick Promotions. Catalogue no: **LPJT 12**
**CD:** Released Apr '84, on RCA by BMG Records (UK). Catalogue no: **PD 89260**
**CD:** Released Apr '87, on The Collection by Object Enterprises. Catalogue no: **OR 0004**
**Album:** Released Jun '86, on Magic (1) by Submarine Records. Catalogue no: **AWE 22**

**GLENN MILLER (4 CD PACK)**
**CD Set:** Released Dec '87, on The Collection by Object Enterprises. Catalogue no: **OX 0005**

**GLENN MILLER, 1937 - 1942 (Miller, Glenn & His Orchestra)**
Tracks: / Wistful and blue / I got rhythm / Sunrise serenade / Moon love / Sold American / Glen Island special / In the mood / Johnson rag / Yes, my darling daughter / Sun Valley jump / Caribbean clipper / Here we go again.
**Album:** Released '81, on Joker (USA) by Lifetime Records (USA). Catalogue no: **SM 3060**
**Cass:** Released '81, on Joker (USA) by Lifetime Records (USA). Catalogue no: **MC 3060**

**GLENN MILLER 1940-42**
Tracks: / Theme...intro St.Louis blues / I close my eyes / Sing and be gay / How deep is the ocean (medley) / Here after / I've got no strings / Isn't it romantic... (medley) / She's funny that way / Breakfast for two / Morning after, The / I hear you screaming closing.
**Cass:** Released Apr '87, on Jasmine by Hasmick Promotions. Catalogue no: **JASMC 2506**
**Album:** Released Apr '87, on Jasmine by Hasmick Promotions. Catalogue no: **JASM 2506**

**GLENN MILLER 1941-1944**
**Cass:** Released '88, on Joker (USA) by Lifetime Records (USA). Catalogue no: **MC 4008**
**Album:** Released '88, on Joker (USA) by Lifetime Records (USA). Catalogue no: **SM 4008**

**GLENN MILLER AIR FORCE ORCHESTRA JUNE 10, 1944 (Miller, Glenn Army Air Force Orchestra)**
Tracks: / D-Day announcement / Flying home / Long ago and far away / My buddy / Now I know / Music makers / Farewell blues / Poinciana / Caribbean clipper / Songs my mother taught me / Eighteenth century drawing room / Blue orchids / There are Yanks.
**Album:** Released May '84, on Soundcraft (USA) Catalogue no: **LP 1004**
**Album:** Released May '84, on Soundcraft (USA) Catalogue no: **LP 1005**
**Album:** Released '88, on Jazz Band by Flyright Records. Catalogue no: **EB 412**

**GLENN MILLER AND....., THE**
**Album:** Released Oct '86, on Jazz Live (Italy) Catalogue no: **BLJ 8005**

**GLENN MILLER ARMY AIR FORCE (1943-44), THE**
Tracks: / Anvil chorus / Stormy weather / Jukebox Saturday night / Jeep jockey jump / All the things you are / Song of the volga boatmen / With my head in the clouds / I hear you screaming / Long ago and far away / Cherokee / Peggy and the pin-up girl / In the mood / Holiday for strings / String of pearls / Don't be that way.
**Album:** Released Apr '81, on Rarities Catalogue no: **RARITIES 63**

**GLENN MILLER COLLECTION (20 golden greats)**
Tracks: / In the mood / Moonlight serenade / Chattanooga choo choo / Pennsylvania 6 5000 / Danny boy / Indian summer / American patrol / Blueberry Hill / Little brown jug / Tuxedo Junction / Don't sit under the apple tree / I've got a gal in Kalamazoo / Serenade in blue / That old black magic / String of pearls / Moonlight cocktail / Pavanne / Woodpecker song, The / Johnson rag / Sunrise serenade.
**CD:** Released Jul '87, on Deja Vu Catalogue no: **DVCD 2010**
**Cass:** Released Aug '85, on Deja Vu Catalogue no: **DVMC 2010**
**Album:** Released Aug '85, on Deja Vu Catalogue no: **DVLP 2010**

**GLENN MILLER & HIS ARMY AIR 1944**
**Album:** Released Jun '86, on Soundcraft (USA) Catalogue no: **LP 1018**

**GLENN MILLER & HIS ORCHESTRA**
Tracks: / Butcher Boy / Don't wake up my heart / Cowboy from Brooklyn / My best wishes / I Know that you know / On the sentimental side / On the Alamo / Dipsy Doodle, The / Meadowbrook, The / Sold American / Please come out of your dream / Poinciana / Runnin' wild / Broadcast closing.
**Cass:** Released May '88, on Jasmine by Hasmick Promotions. Catalogue no: **JASMC 2511**
**Album:** Released May '88, on Jasmine by Hasmick Promotions. Catalogue no: **JASM 2511**

**GLENN MILLER IN CONCERT**
Tracks: / Moonlight serenade / Perfidia / Little brown jug / Bless you / One o'clock jump / Don't sit under the apple tree / Lady be good / My devotion / String of pearls / Fresh as a daisy / Flagwaver / Make believe / Blues / Under a blanket of blue / Twenty four robbers / My melancholy baby / Moon love / Stompin' at the Savoy / Blue moon / Chattanooga choo choo / It must be jelly / Hop / I guess I'll have to change my plans / Bugle call rag / Porter stomp / Introduction to a waltz / Down the count / Farewell blues.
**Cass set:** Released '86, on RCA by BMG Records (UK). Deleted May '89. Catalogue no: **NK 89216**
**Cass:** Released Jun '84, on RCA International by BMG Records (UK). Catalogue no: **NK 45153**
**Album:** Released Jun '84, on RCA by BMG Records (UK). Catalogue no: **NL 45153**
**2 LP Set:** Released '86, on RCA by BMG Records (UK). Deleted May '89. Catalogue no: **NL 89216**

**GLENN MILLER LEGEND, THE**
Tracks: / Moonlight serenade / Little brown jug / St. Louis blues march / Tuxedo Junction / Chattanooga choo choo / I got rhythm / Blue skies / Johnson rag / Spirit is willing, The / Running wild / Perfidia / Sliphorn jive / Stairway to the stars / Tisket a tasket, A / Moon love / Caribbean clipper / Sweet Eloise / My blue Heaven / Slow freight / Nightingale sang in Berkeley Square, A / In the mood / String of pearls / Pennsylvania 6-5000 / I know why / Anchors aweigh / One o'clock jump / Sunrise serenade / Don't sit under the apple tree / When Johnny comes marching home / Elmer's tune / Jukebox Saturday night / Song of the volga boatmen / Farewell blues / On a little street in Singapore / Under a blanket of blue / Hop, the / Lamplighter's serenade, The / And the angels sing / Fools rush in / Moonlight becomes you / American patrol / Stardust / Sun Valley jump / I've got a gal in Kalamazoo / Flying home / Here we goagain / Serenade in blue / Tiger rag / Hallelujah / My melancholy baby / I want to be happy / Boulder buff / Anvil chorus / I wanna hat with cherries / Say it / Yes, my darling daughter / Dearly beloved / King Porter stomp / Adios.
**CD:** Released Jan '87, on RCA by BMG Records (UK). Deleted Nov '88. Catalogue no: **PD 89713**

**GLENN MILLER LIVE (1939)**
Tracks: / Lady's in love with you, The / Wishing / Pavanne / And the angels sing / King Porter stomp / Moon is over a silver dollar, The / Sometime / Hold tight / Glenn Island special / Lamp is low, The / Jumpin' jive / My blue Heaven / Closing.
**Album:** Released Apr '87, on Jasmine by Hasmick Promotions. Catalogue no: **JASM 2507**
**Cass:** Released Apr '87, on Jasmine by Hasmick Promotions. Catalogue no: **JASMC 2507**

**GLENN MILLER: LIVE 1940**
**CD:** Released Feb '89, on Tax Catalogue no: **TAXCD 3704-2**

**GLENN MILLER ORCHESTRA (Miller, Glenn Orchestra)**
**Album:** Released '88, on Joker (USA) by Lifetime Records (USA). Catalogue no: **SM 3865**
**Album:** Released May '84, on Soundcraft (USA) Catalogue no: **LP 1007**

**GLENN MILLER ORCHESTRA, AUGUST 30, 1941 (Sunset Serenade & Chesterfield Broadcasts) (Miller, Glenn & His Orchestra)**
Tracks: / Here we go again / Cowboy

serenade, The / Booglie wooglie piggy, The / Georgia on my mind / It's great to be an American / Till reveille / Daddy / Things I love, The / Intermezzo / Moonlight cocktail / Jersey bounce, The / I left my heart at the stage door canteen / Keep 'em flying.
**Album:** Released May '85, on Jasmine by Hasmick Promotions. Catalogue no: **JASM 2500**
**Cass:** Released May '85, on Jasmine by Hasmick Promotions. Catalogue no: **JASMC 2500**
**Album:** Released May '84, on Soundcraft (USA) Catalogue no: **LP 1001**

## GLENN MILLER ORCHESTRA, DECEMBER 27, 1941
Tracks: / Here we go again / White cliffs of Dover, The / Jingle bells / Introduction to a waltz / This is no laughing matter / Oh so good / Tuxedo Junction / It's great to be an American / Chattanooga choo choo / Papa Niccolini / This time the dream's on me / Dear Arabella / Elmer's tune / Keep 'em flying.
**Album:** Released May '84, on Soundcraft (USA) Catalogue no: **LP 1006**

## GLENN MILLER ORCHESTRA, VOL. 1 (Miller, Glenn Orchestra)
**Album:** Released '89, on Echo Jazz Catalogue no: **EJLP 02**
**Cass:** Released '89, on Echo Jazz Catalogue no: **EJMC 02**
**CD:** Released '89, on Echo Jazz Catalogue no: **EJCD 02**

## GLENN MILLER ORCHESTRA, VOL 2 (Miller, Glenn Orchestra)
**Cass:** Released '89, on Echo Jazz Catalogue no: **EJMC 10**
**Album:** Released '89, on Echo Jazz Catalogue no: **EJLP 10**
**CD:** Released '89, on Echo Jazz Catalogue no: **EJCD 10**

## GLENN MILLER PLAYS SELECTIONS (Miller, Glenn & His Orchestra)
**Album:** Released Jan '61, on RCA by BMG Records (UK). Deleted Jan '66. Catalogue no: **RD 27068 0023**

## GLENN MILLER REUNION IN CONCERT
Note: Conductor: Billy May
**Cass:** Released '88, on GNP Crescendo (USA) by GNP Crescendo Records (USA). Catalogue no: **GNP5 76**
**CD:** Released Dec '85, on Vogue by Vogue Records. Catalogue no: **VG 600 087**
**Album:** Released '88, on GNP Crescendo (USA) by GNP Crescendo Records (USA). Catalogue no: **GNPS 76**
**CD:** Released '88, on GNP Crescendo (USA) by GNP Crescendo Records (USA). Catalogue no: **GNPD 76**

## GLENN MILLER SOUND, THE
**Cass:** Released Jan '85, on VFM Cassettes by VFM Cassettes. Catalogue no: **VCA 019**

## GLENN MILLER STORY, THE
Tracks: / Moonlight serenade / Little brown jug / Sunrise serenade / Beer barrel polka / Indian summer / Woodpecker song, The / Pennsylvania 6-5000 / Slumber song / Chattanooga choo choo / String of pearls / Don't sit under the apple tree / My blue Heaven / In the mood / Sun valley jump / Farewell blues / Tuxedo Junction / Blues in my heart / Begin the beguine / Anvil chorus / St. Louis blues march / Everybody loves my baby / Over there / Song of the volga boatmen / Enlisted men's mess / It must be jelly.
**Cass:** Released Jun '86, on Big Band Era Catalogue no: **40187**
**Cass:** Released May '89, on Deja Vu Catalogue no: **DVREMC 06**
**Album:** Released Jun '86, on Big Band Era Catalogue no: **20187**
**CD:** Released May '89, on Deja Vu Catalogue no: **DVRECD 06**
**CD:** Released Sep '87, on Big Band Era Catalogue no: **70187**

## GLENN MILLER STORY (VIDEO)
**VHS:** Released '88, on CIC Video Catalogue no: **VHR 1187**

## GLENN MILLER STORY: VOL.1
**Album:** Released '83, on RCA (Germany) Catalogue no: **26 21415**
**Cass:** Released Aug '85, on RCA by BMG Records (UK). Catalogue no: **NK 89005**
**Album:** Released Aug '85, on RCA by BMG Records (UK). Catalogue no: **NL 89005**
**Cass:** Released Sep '89, on Big Band Era Catalogue no: **260 171**

## GLENN MILLER STORY: VOL.2
Tracks: / Flyin' home / Sun valley jump / Solitude / Tisket a tasket, A / I got rhythm / Johnson rag / One o'clock jump / Here we go again / Under a blanket of blue / Rhapsody in blue / King Porter stomp / Hop, The.
**Album:** Released '83, on RCA (Germany) Catalogue no: **26 21424**
**Cass:** Released Aug '85, on RCA by BMG Records (UK). Deleted Jul '89. Catalogue no: **NK 89221**
**Album:** Released Aug '85, on RCA by BMG Records (UK). Deleted Jul '89. Catalogue no: **NL 89221**

## GLENN MILLER STORY: VOL.3
**Cass:** Released Aug '85, on RCA by BMG Records (UK). Catalogue no: **NK 89222**
**Album:** Released Aug '85, on RCA by BMG Records (UK). Deleted Jul '89. Catalogue no: **NL 89222**

## GLENN MILLER STORY: VOL.4
Tracks: / Slow freight / Booglie wooglie piggy / Kiss polka / Boulder buff / Sweeter than the sweetest / Moonlight cocktail / Rainbow rhapsody / It's always you / I guess I'll have to dream the rest / Chip off the old block / Lamplighter's serenade / I wanna hat with cherries / Everything I love.
**Album:** Released Aug '85, on RCA by BMG Records (UK). Deleted Jul '89. Catalogue no: **NL 89223**
**Cass:** Released Aug '85, on RCA by BMG Records (UK). Deleted Jul '89. Catalogue no: **NK 89223**

## GLENN MILLER & THE ARMY AIR FORCE BAND
Tracks: / Over there / Anvil chorus / Star dust / Song of the volga boatmen / Farewell blues / They are yanks / My ideal / Mission to Moscow / Sun valley jump / Tuxedo Junction / I'll be around / Poinciana / I hear you screaming / Jukebox Saturday night / My blue Heaven / St. Louis blues march / It must be jelly / Blues in my heart / Everybody loves my baby / Alexander's ragtime band / Stompin' at the savoy / Deep purple / Don't be that way / I can't give you anything but love / Wang wang blues / Shoo shoo baby / Way you look tonight / Victory polka / There'll be a hot time in the town of Berlin / Flying home / Here we go again / Jeep jockey jump / Enlisted men's mess / Begin the Beguine / In the mood.
**2 LP Set:** Released Sep '86, on Jazz Tribune by BMG Records (UK). Deleted Jul '89. Catalogue no: **NL 89767**
**2 LP Set:** Released '83, on RCA (France) by BMG Records (France). Catalogue no: **M 43172**
**Cass set:** Released Sep '86, on Jazz Tribune by BMG Records (UK). Deleted Nov '88. Catalogue no: **NK 89767**

## GLENN MILLER'S UPTOWN HALL GANG
**Album:** Released Apr '79, on Enquire Catalogue no: **ESQ 302**

## GLENN MILLER'S UPTOWN HALL GANG (Miller's, Glenn Uptown Hall Gang)
Note: Led by Mel Powell with Peanuts Hucko/Bernie Privin & Beryl Davis.
**Album:** Released Jun '86, on Esquire by Titan Int. Prod.. Catalogue no: **ESQ 316**

## GOLDEN HOUR OF GLENN MILLER
Tracks: / Moonlight serenade / American patrol / It happened in Sun Valley / I've got a gal in Kalamazoo / I know why and so do you / Measure for measure / In the mood / People like you and me / At last / Chattanooga choo choo / Sun Valley jump / Moonlight sonata / Boom shot / Bugle call rag / Spirit is willing, The / That's sabotage / You say the sweetest things / Serenade in blue.
**Album:** Released Oct '75, on Golden Hour Catalogue no: **GH 831**

## GOLDEN SERENADE (Miller, Glenn & AAF Band)
**Album:** Released '84, on Swing World by Submarine Records. Catalogue no: **SWS 1**
**Cass:** Released '84, on Swing World by Submarine Records. Catalogue no: **CSWS 1**

## GRAVACIOES INEDITAS
Tracks: / From one love to another / I know why / Rug cutters swing / Yesterday's gardenias / It happened in Sun Valley / When the roses bloom again / Stardust / You stepped out of a dream / Caribbean clipper / Song of the volga boatmen / Slumber song / Story of a

starry night.
**Cass:** Released Jan '84, on RCA (Brazil) Catalogue no: **770 4042**
**Album:** Released Jan '84, on RCA (Brazil) Catalogue no: **107 4042**

**GREATEST HITS: GLENN MILLER**
**CD:** Released Oct '88, on Fun (Holland) Catalogue no: **FUNCD 9022**
**Album:** Released May '88, on Music Power Catalogue no: **33009**
**Cass:** Released Oct '88, on Fun (Holland) Catalogue no: **FUNC 9022**
**Cass:** Released May '88, on Music Power Catalogue no: **63009**
**Album:** Released Oct '88, on Fun (Holland) Catalogue no: **FUN 9022**

**HALLELUJAH**
Tracks: / Hallelujah / Now we know / Irresistible you / Alouette / Tuxedo Junction / Way you look tonight / Kingport stomp / Wham.
**Cass:** Released '84, on Magic (1) by Submarine Records. Catalogue no: **CAWE 6**
**Album:** Released '84, on Magic (1) by Submarine Records. Catalogue no: **AWE 6**

**HERE WE GO AGAIN-VOL 2 1940-41**
**Album:** Released Jan '86, on Magic (1) by Submarine Records. Catalogue no: **AWE 17**

**HITS FROM THE GLENN MILLER STORY**
Tracks: / Moonlight serenade / American patrol / Pennsylvania 6 5000 / In the mood / I've got a gal in Kalamazoo / Boulder buff / Tuxedo Junction / St. Louis blues / String of pearls / Little brown jug / Farewell blues / King Porter stomp.
**Album:** Released May '76, on RCA by BMG Records (UK). Catalogue no: **LSA 3274**

**I SUSTAIN THE WINGS SHOWS**
**Cass:** Released Sep '85, on Jasmine by Hasmick Promotions. Catalogue no: **JASMC 2503**
**Album:** Released Sep '85, on Jasmine by Hasmick Promotions. Catalogue no: **JASM 2503**

**IN 1940**
**Cass:** Released Aug '85, on Magic (1) by Submarine Records. Catalogue no: **CAWE 14**

**IN HOLLYWOOD**
**Album:** Released '88, on Mercury by Phonogram Ltd. Deleted 28 Feb '90. Catalogue no: **826 635 1**
**CD:** Released Jan '87, on Phonogram by Phonogram Ltd. Deleted Mar '88. Catalogue no: **826 635 2**
**Cass:** Released '88, on Mercury by Phonogram Ltd. Deleted 28 Feb '90. Catalogue no: **826 635 4**

**IN THE DIGITAL MOOD (Miller, Glenn Orchestra)**
Tracks: / In the mood / Chattanooga choo choo / American Patrol / String of pearls / Little brown jug / I've got a gal in Kalamazoo / Tuxedo Junction / St. Louis blues march / Pennsylvania 6-5000 / Moonlight serenade.
**Cass:** Released Jun '84, on GRP by GRP Records (USA). Catalogue no: **GRPC 1002**
**CD:** Released Jun '84, on GRP by GRP Records (USA). Catalogue no: **GRPD 9502**
**Album:** Released Jun '84, on GRP by GRP Records (USA). Catalogue no: **GRPA 1002**

**IN THE MOOD (ASTAN)**
Tracks: / In the mood / Chattanooga choo choo / American patrol / St. Louis blues march / Pennsylvania 6-5000 / Jumpin' jive / Moonlight serenade / Don't sit under the apple tree / I've got a gal in Kalamazoo / Serenade in blue / I know why / String of pearls.
**Album:** Released Nov '84, on Astan (USA) Catalogue no: **20103**
**Cass:** Released Nov '84, on Astan (USA) Catalogue no: **40103**

**IN THE MOOD (CBS)**
**Album:** Released Jun '86, on CBS by CBS Records. Catalogue no: **545 75**
**Cass:** Released Jun '86, on CBS (import) by CBS Records. Catalogue no: **40 54575**

**IN THE MOOD (DGR)**
**CD:** Released '86, on DGR (Holland) Catalogue no: **DGC 1010**

**IN THE MOOD (FLASHBACK)**
**Cass:** Released May '88, on Flashback by Mainline Records. Catalogue no: **64024**

**IN THE MOOD (OLD GOLD) (Miller, Glenn & His Orchestra)**
Tracks: / In the mood / String of pearls.
**7" Single:** Released Jun '88, on Old Gold by Old Gold Records. Catalogue no: **OG 9602**

**IN THE MOOD (PATHE MARCONI)**
**Album:** Released Dec '84, on Pathe Marconi (France) Catalogue no: **2M 056 64872**
**Cass:** Released Dec '84, on Pathe Marconi (France) Catalogue no: **2M 256 64872**

**IN THE MOOD (SINGLE)**
Tracks: / In the mood.
**7" Single:** Released Jan '76, on RCA by BMG Records (UK). Catalogue no: **RCA 2644**

**IN THE MOOD (TOPLINE)**
**Cass:** Released '86, on Topline by Charly Records. Catalogue no: **KTOP 140**
**Album:** Released '86, on Topline by Charly Records. Catalogue no: **TOP 140**
**CD:** Released Sep '89, on Big Band Era Catalogue no: **260 177 2**

**IN THE MOOD (VOGUE)**
**CD:** Released 10 Jul '89, on Vogue by Vogue Records. Catalogue no: **VG 670203**

**JAZZ TIME VOL.12**
**Album:** Released '88, on Vogue (France) by Vogue Records. Catalogue no: **502712**

**KEEP 'EM FLYING**
**Cass:** Released '84, on Swing World by Submarine Records. Catalogue no: **CSWS 5**
**Album:** Released '84, on Swing World by Submarine Records. Catalogue no: **SWS 5**

**LEGEND LIVES ON, THE (Miller, Glenn Orchestra)**
**Album:** Released 10 Jul '89, on Knowle Catalogue no: **KNO 001**
**Cass:** Released 10 Jul '89, on Knowle Catalogue no: **CKNO 001**

**LEGEND, THE**
**Album:** Released Jun '86, on Dance Band Days by Prism Leisure. Catalogue no: **DBD 01**
**CD:** Released Oct '87, on Dance Band Days by Prism Leisure. Catalogue no: **DBCD 01**
**Cass:** Released Jun '86, on Dance Band Days by Prism Leisure. Catalogue no: **DBDC 01**

**LEGENDARY GLENN MILLER: VOL 1**
Tracks: / My reverie / By the waters of the Minnetonka / King Porter stomp / Shut eye / How I'd like to be with you in Bermuda / Cuckoo in the clock / Romance runs in the family / 'Neath the chestnut tree / And the angels sing / Moonlight serenade / Lady's in love with you, The / Wishing (will make it so) / Three little fishes / Sunrise serenade / Little brown jug.
**Album:** Released '79, on RCA Victor by BMG Records (UK). Deleted '84. Catalogue no: **LFM1 7500**

**LEGENDARY GLENN MILLER VOL 2**
Tracks: / My last goodbye / But it didn't mean a thing / Pavane / Runnin' wild / To you / Stairway to the stars / Blue evening / Lamp is low, The / Rendezvous time in Paree / We can live on love / Cinderella (stay in my arms) / Moon love / Guess I'll go back home / I'm sorry for myself / Back to back.
**Album:** Released '79, on RCA Victor by BMG Records (UK). Deleted '84. Catalogue no: **LFM1 7501**

**LEGENDARY GLENN MILLER: VOL 3**
Tracks: / Oh you crazy moon / Ain't cha comin' out / Day we meet again, The / Wanna hat with cherries / Sold American / Pagan love song / Ding dong, the witch is dead / Over the rainbow / Little man who wasn't there, The / Man with the mandolin, The / Starlit hour / Blue orchids / Glenn Island special / Love with a capitol 'you' / Baby me.
**Album:** Released '79, on RCA Victor by BMG Records (UK). Deleted '84. Catalogue no: **LFM1 7502**

**LEGENDARY GLENN MILLER: VOL 4**
Tracks: / In the mood / Wham, re-bop-boom-bam / Angel in a furnished room,

An / Twilight interlude / I want to be happy / Farewell blues / Who's sorry now / My isle of golden dreams / My prayer / Blue moonlight / Basket weaver man / Melancholy lullaby / Last night / Out of space / So many times.
**Album:** Released '79, on RCA Victor by BMG Records (UK). Deleted '84. Catalogue no: **LFM1 7593**

**LEGENDARY GLENN MILLER: VOL.5**
Tracks: / Blue rain / Can I help it? / I just got a letter / Bless you / Blue birds in the moonlight / Faithful forever / Speaking of heaven / (American idyll) Indian summer / It was written in the stars / Johnson rag / Ciri-biri-bin / Careless / Oh Johnny, oh Johnny / In an old Dutch garden / This changing world.
**Album:** Released '79, on RCA Victor by BMG Records (UK). Deleted '84. Catalogue no: **LFM1 7512**

**LEGENDARY GLENN MILLER: VOL.6**
Tracks: / On a little street in Singapore / Vagabond dreams / I beg your pardon / Faithful to you / It's a blue world / Oh what you said / Gaucho serenade / Sky fell down, The / When you wish upon a star / Give a little whistle / Missouri waltz / Beautiful Ohio / What's the matter with me / Say 'si si' / Rumba jumps, The.
**Album:** Released '79, on RCA Victor by BMG Records (UK). Deleted '84. Catalogue no: **LFM1 7513**

**LEGENDARY GLENN MILLER: VOL.7**
Tracks: / Stardust / My melancholy baby / Let's all sing together / Rug cutter's swing / Woodpecker song / Sweet potato piper / Too romantic / Tuxedo junction / Londonderry air / Imagination / Shake down the stars / I'll never smile again / Starlight and music / Polka dots and moonbeams / My my / Say it.
**Album:** Released '79, on RCA Victor by BMG Records (UK). Deleted '84. Catalogue no: **LFM1 7514**

**LEGENDARY GLENN MILLER: VOL.8**
Tracks: / Moments in the moonlight / Hear my song Violetta / Sierra Sue / Boog it / Yours is my heart alone / I'm stepping out with a memory tonight / Alice blue gown / Wonderful one / Devil may care / April played the fiddle / Fools rush in / I haven't time to be a millionare / Slow freight / Pennsylvania 6-5000 / Bugle call rag / Nearness of you, The.
**Album:** Released '79, on RCA Victor by BMG Records (UK). Deleted '84. Catalogue no: **LFM1 7515**

**LEGENDARY GLENN MILLER: VOL.9**
Tracks: / Mister Meadowlark / My blue heaven / When the swallows come back to Capistrano / Million dreams ago, A / Blueberry Hill / Cabana in Havana, A / Be happy / Angel child / Call of the canyon / Our love affair / Cross town / What's your story Mornin' Glory / Fifth Avenue / I wouldn't take a million / Handful of stars, A / Old Black Joe.
**Album:** Released '79, on RCA Victor by BMG Records (UK). Deleted '84. Catalogue no: **LFM1 7516**

**LEGENDARY GLENN MILLER: VOL.10**
Tracks: / Yesterthoughts / Falling leaves / Shadows on the sand / Goodbye little darling / Five o'clock whistle / Beat me daddy, eight to a bar / Ring telephone ring / Make believe ball room time / You've got me this way / Nightingale sang in Berkeley Square, A / I'd know you anywhere / Fresh as a daisy / Isn't that just like love / Along the Santa Fe trail / Do you know why / Somewhere / Yes my darling daughter.
**Album:** Released Mar '76, on RCA by BMG Records (UK). Catalogue no: **LSA 3237**

**LEGENDARY GLENN MILLER: VOL.11**
Tracks: / Stone's throw from heaven, A / Helpless / Long time no see / You are the one / Anvil chorus / Frenesi / Mem'ry of a rose, The / I do, do you / Chapel in the valley / Prairieland lullaby / Ida, sweet as apple cider / Song of the volga boatmen / One I love, The / You stepped out of a dream / I dreamt I dwelt in Harlem / Sun Valley jump.
**Album:** Released Mar '76, on RCA by BMG Records (UK). Catalogue no: **LSA 3238**

**LEGENDARY GLENN MILLER: VOL.12**
Tracks: / When that man is dead and gone / Spirit is willing, The / Little old church in England, The / Perfidia / It's always you / Spring will be so sad / Air minded executive / Below the equator / Boulder buff / Booglie wooglie piggy, The / Chattanooga choo choo / I know why / Don't cry cherie / Cradle song / Sweeter than the sweetest.
**Album:** Released Mar '76, on RCA by BMG Records (UK). Catalogue no: **LSA 3239**

**LEGENDARY GLENN MILLER: VOL.13**
Tracks: / I guess I'll have to dream the rest / Take the 'A' train / Peekaboo to you / Angels came through, The / Under blue Canadian skies / Cowboy serenade, The / You and I / Adios / It happened in Sun Valley / I'm thrilled / Kiss polka / Delilah / From one love to another / Elmer's tune.
**Album:** Released Mar '76, on RCA by BMG Records (UK). Catalogue no: **LSA 3240**

**LEGENDARY GLENN MILLER: VOL.14**
Tracks: / Says who, says you, says I / Orange blossom lane / Dear Arabella / Man in the moon, The / Ma ma maria / This time the dream's on me / Dreamville, Ohio / Papa Niccolini / Jingle bells / This is no laughing matter / Humpty Dumpty heart / Ev'rything I love / String of pearls / Baby mine / Long tall mama / Daydreaming.
**Album:** Released May '77, on RCA by BMG Records (UK). Catalogue no: **PL 42016**

**LEGENDARY GLENN MILLER: VOL.15**
Tracks: / Moonlight sonata / Slumber song / White cliffs of Dover, The / We're the couple in the castle / It happened in Hawaii / Moonlight cocktail / Happy in love / Fooled / Keep them flying / Chip off the old block / Story of a starry night / President's birthday ball, The / Angels of mercy / On the old assembly line / Let's have another cup of coffee / Skylark / Dear mom.
**Album:** Released May '77, on RCA by BMG Records (UK). Catalogue no: **PL 42017**

**LEGENDARY GLENN MILLER: VOL.16**
Tracks: / When the roses bloom again / Always in my heart / Sh it's a military secret / Don't sit under the apple tree / She'll always remember / Lamplighter's serenade, The / When Johnny comes marching home / American patrol / Soldier let me read your letter / Sleep song / Sweet Eloise / I've got a gal in Kalamazoo / Serenade in blue / At last / Lullaby of the rain / Knit one, purl one.
**Album:** Released May '77, on RCA by BMG Records (UK). Catalogue no: **PL 42018**

**LEGENDARY GLENN MILLER: VOL.17**
Tracks: / That's sabotage / Conchita, Marquita, Lolita, Pepita, Rosita, Juanita, Lopez / Hummingbird / Yesterdays gardenias / Dearly beloved / Moonlight mood / Caribbean clipper / Here we go again / That old black magic / Moonlight becomes you / Jukebox Saturday night / It must be jelly / I'm old fashioned / Pink cocktail for a blue lady / Rainbow rhapsody / Sleepy town train / Rhapsody in blue.
**Album:** Released May '77, on RCA by BMG Records (UK). Catalogue no: **PL 42019**

**LEGENDARY PERFORMER**
Tracks: / Moonlight serenade / Talk / Sunrise serenade / Little brown jug / Londonderry air / Tuxedo junction / My melancholy baby / Pennsylvania 6500 / So you're the one / Sentimental me / Song of the Volga boatmen / Jack and Jill / Take the A train / String of pearls, A / Stardust / Ev'rything I love / Tchaikovsky's piano concerto / Elmer's tune / Jingle bells / In the mood / Chattanooga choo choo / At last / Moonlight cocktail / I've got a gal in Kalamazoo / Juke box Saturday night.
**Cass:** Released Feb '76, on RCA Victor by BMG Records (UK). Deleted Feb '81. Catalogue no: **DPMK 1035**
**Album:** Released Feb '76, on RCA Victor by BMG Records (UK). Deleted Feb '81. Catalogue no: **DPM 2065**

**LEGENDARY PERFORMER VOL.2**
Tracks: / Make believe ballroom time / Don't sit under the apple tree / Lamplighters serenade, The / I've got a gal in Kalamazoo / Serenade in blue / Beethoven's moonlight sonata / Johnson rag

/ Blueberry Hill / Oh, you crazy moon / Chestnut tree ('neath the spreading chestnut) / Fools rush in (where angels fear to tread) / I guess I'll have to dream the rest.
**Album:** Released Feb '76, on RCA Victor by BMG Records (UK). Deleted Feb '81. Catalogue no: **CPL 11349**
**Cass:** Released '79, on RCA Victor by BMG Records (UK). Deleted '84. Catalogue no: **PK 12080**
**Album:** Released '79, on RCA Victor by BMG Records (UK). Deleted '84. Catalogue no: **PL 12080**

**LEGENDARY PERFORMER VOL. 3**
Tracks: / Over there / Stardust / I've got a heart filled with love for you / Londonderry air (medley) / Way you look tonight, The / Blue Danube waltz, The / Vict'ry polka / St. Louis blues march / Stormy weather / Mission to Moscow / Long ago and far away / Pistol packin' mama.
**Cass:** Released '79, on RCA Victor by BMG Records (UK). Deleted '84. Catalogue no: **PK 12495**
**Album:** Released '79, on RCA Victor by BMG Records (UK). Deleted '84. Catalogue no: **PL 12495**

**LEGENDARY, THE**
**Cass:** Released Mar '90, on Silva Screen by Silva Screen Records. Catalogue no: **MRT 40050**

**LIVE AT GLENN ISLAND CASINO (Summer, 1939) (Miller, Glenn & His Orchestra)**
Tracks: / Moonlight serenade (theme) / At sundown / Cinderella, stay in my arms / Slip horn jive / Ain't cha comin' out? / Lamp is low, The / My isle of golden dreams / We can live on love / By the waters of Minnetonka / Moonlove / King Porter stomp / I want my share of love / In the middle of a dream / Lady's in love with you, The / In the mood / Chestnut tree, The / Pagan love song / Moonlight serenade (theme and fadeout).
**Album:** Released Jun '88, on Magic (1) by Submarine Records. Catalogue no: **AWE 31**
**Cass:** Released Jun '88, on Magic (1) by Submarine Records. Catalogue no: **CAWE 31**
**CD:** Released Jun '88, on Magic (1) by Submarine Records. Catalogue no: **DAWE 31**

**LIVE AT MEADOWBROOK 1939 (Miller, Glenn Orchestra)**
**Album:** Released '88, on Soundcraft (USA) Catalogue no: **LP 1023**

**LIVE FROM GLENN ISLAND CASINO, JULY 24, 1939**
Tracks: / I want to be happy / Bless you / Little man who wasn't there, The / Oh you crazy moon / Baby me / My isle of golden dreams / Johnson rag / Faithful to you / I just got a letter / In an old Dutch garden / Tiger rag / Closing.
**Album:** Released May '84, on Soundcraft (USA) Catalogue no: **LP 1009**

**LIVE FROM THE CAFE ROUGE, NOVEMBER 1940 (Chesterfield show 1942) (Miller, Glenn & His Orchestra)**
Tracks: / Down for the count / Blueberry Hill / Long time no see baby / Shadows on the sand / Limehouse blues / Handful of stars / Cross town / Tiger rag / Something to remember you by / One dozen roses / Moonlight cocktail / Oh so good.
**Album:** Released May '84, on Soundcraft (USA) Catalogue no: **LP 1003**
**Album:** Released Sep '85, on Jasmine by Hasmick Promotions. Catalogue no: **JASM 2502**
**Cass:** Released Sep '85, on Jasmine by Hasmick Promotions. Catalogue no: **JASMC 2502**

**LIVE REMOTES-1938**
Note: Mono.
**Album:** Released Nov '86, on Soundcraft (USA) Catalogue no: **LP 1022**

**LOVE SONGS FROM THE FABULOUS FORTIES**
Tracks: / Fools rush in / Chattanooga choo choo / Sentimental me / My prayer / Chestnut tree, The / Everything i love / Stardust / Lamplighter's serenade, The / Don't sit under the apple tree / Moonlight cocktail / That old black magic / Serenade in blue / My melancholy baby / At last / I've got a gal in Kalamazoo / Stairway to the stars.
**Cass:** Released '88, on RCA/Camden by BMG Records (UK). Catalogue no: **CAM 1223**
**Album:** Released Jul '87, on RCA/Camden by BMG Records (UK). Catalogue no: **CDS 1223**

**MAGIC MOMENTS**
Tracks: / Elmer's tune / String of pearls / Moonlight cocktail / American patrol / I've got a gal in Kalamazoo / Jukebox Saturday night / Beautiful Ohio / Missouri waltz / Adios / Oh Johnny, oh Johnny oh / Moonlight serenade / Little brown jug / In the mood / Johnson rag / Stardust / Tuxedo Junction / Pennsylvania 65000 / Song of the volga boatmen / Chattanooga choo choo / Along the Santa Fe trail / Anvil chorus / St. Louis blues march / Don't sit under the apple tree / Stairway to the stars / Lamplighter's serenade, The / Who's sorry now / By the waters of Minnetonka / Serenade in blue / Take the 'A' train.
**Cass:** Released Jun '84, on RCA by BMG Records (UK). Catalogue no: **NK 89406**

**MEMORIAL, 1944-69**
Tracks: / Moonlight serenade / Sunrise serenade / Little brown jug / To you / Stairway to the stars / In the mood / My prayer / Johnson rag / Indian summer / Stardust / Tuxedo Junction / Londonderry air / Pennsylvania 65000 / Anvil chorus / Song of the volga boatmen / Perfidia / Chattanooga choo choo / Adios / Elmer's tune / String of pearls / Moonlight cocktail / Skylark / Don't sit under the apple tree / American patrol / At last / I've got a gal in Kalamazoo / Serenade in blue / Jukebox Saturday night / That old black magic / St. Louis blues march.
**Cass:** Released Apr '70, on RCA by BMG Records (UK). Deleted Apr '75. Catalogue no: **DPMK 1006**
**Cass:** Released '84, on RCA by BMG Records (UK). Catalogue no: **NK 86019**
**Album:** Released Apr '70, on RCA by BMG Records (UK). Deleted Apr '75. Catalogue no: **GM 1**
**Album:** Released '84, on RCA by BMG Records (UK). Catalogue no: **NL 86019**

**MEMORIAL FOR GLENN MILLER (Miller, Glenn Orchestra)**
**Cass:** Released Dec '89, on Accord (France) by Musidisc Records (France). Catalogue no: **402302**
**CD:** Released Dec '89, on Accord (France) by Musidisc Records (France). Catalogue no: **402304**

**MEMORIAL FOR GLENN MILLER VOL.3**
**CD:** Released Dec '86, on Accord (France) by Musidisc Records (France). Catalogue no: **139 218**
**CD:** Released '86, on Accord (France) by Musidisc Records (France). Catalogue no: **139 201**
**CD:** Released Dec '86, on Accord (France) by Musidisc Records (France). Catalogue no: **139 005**

**MILLER MAGIC (Miller, Glenn & His Orchestra)**
Tracks: / In the mood / Moonlight serenade / Chattanooga choo choo / Frenesi / Pennsylvania 6-5000 / Farewell blues / Don't sit under the apple tree / I've got a gal in Kalamazoo / Stardust / My blue Heaven / Bugle call rag / American patrol / St. Louis blues / Jukebox Saturday night / Boulder buff / Who's sorry now? / I want to be happy / At last / Lamplighter's serenade, The / Tuxedo Junction / Indian summer / Little brown jug / Perfidia / White cliffs of Dover, The / Take the 'A' train / King Porter stomp / Sunrise serenade / String of pearls.
**Cass set:** Released '83, on Cambra by Cambra Records. Deleted '88. Catalogue no: **CRT 083**
**2 LP Set:** Released '83, on Cambra by Cambra Records. Deleted '88. Catalogue no: **CR 083**

**MILLION DREAMS AGO, A 1939 - 41 (Miller, Glenn & His Orchestra)**
Tracks: / Million dreams ago, A / Pagan love song / Blue orchids / At sundown / In a sentimental mood / Deep purple / Jumpin' jive / Hour of parting / Daisy Mae / Crosstown / Swingin' at the seance / I dreamt I dwelt in Harlem.
Note: With Ray Eberle, Marion Hutton.
**Album:** Released Jun '88, on Bandstand Catalogue no: **BS 7136**
**Cass:** Released Jun '88, on Bandstand Catalogue no: **BS 7136C**
**CD:** Released Jun '88, on Bandstand Catalogue no: **BS 7136CD**

**MOONLIGHT SERENADE**
**CD:** Released Oct '88, on Vogue by Vogue Records. Catalogue no: **VGCD 670 203**
**Cass:** Released May '88, on Flashback by Mainline Records. Catalogue no: **64025**

**CD:** Released Jun '88, on Spectrum (1) Catalogue no: **U 4027**

**MOONLIGHT SERENADE (OLD GOLD)**
Tracks: / Moonlight serenade / Tuxedo Junction.
**7" Single:** Released Nov '86, on Old Gold by Old Gold Records. Catalogue no: **OG 9651**

**MOONLIGHT SERENADE (SINGLE)**
Tracks: / Moonlight serenade / Sunrise serenade.
**12" Single:** Released Jul '85, on MCA by MCA Records. Catalogue no: **MCAV 985**
**7" Single:** Released Jul '85, on MCA by MCA Records. Catalogue no: **MCA 985**
**7" Single:** Released Mar '54, on H.M.V. by EMI Records. Deleted '57. Catalogue no: **BD 5942**
**7" Single:** Released '80, on Lightning Catalogue no: **LR 1158**
**7" Single:** Released Jan '76, on RCA by BMG Records (UK). Deleted '79. Catalogue no: **RCA 2644**

**MOSTLY SWINGING**
Note: With pianist Mel Powell.
**Cass:** Released '82, on Nostalgia by Mainline Records. Catalogue no: **NOST 8601**
**Album:** Released '82, on Nostalgia by Mainline Records. Catalogue no: **NOST 7601**

**NEARNESS OF YOU (Miller, Glenn & His Orchestra)**
**Album:** Released Sep '69, on RCA International by BMG Records (UK). Deleted Sep '74. Catalogue no: **INTS 1019**

**NIGHT AND DAY (Miller, Glenn & His Orchestra)**
**Cass:** Released '88, on RCA/Camden by BMG Records (UK). Catalogue no: **CAM 1230**
**Album:** Released '88, on RCA/Camden by BMG Records (UK). Catalogue no: **CDS 1230**

**OH SO GOOD, 1940-42**
Note: Recorded 1940 to 1942. Tracks include: Oh so good/My my/High on a windy Hill/Song of the Volga boatmen/Bugle boogie/The gentleman needs a shave etc..
**Album:** Released Oct '87, on Magic (1) by Submarine Records. Catalogue no: **AWE 29**
**Cass:** Released Oct '87, on Magic (1) by Submarine Records. Catalogue no: **CAWE 29**

**ON THE AIR**
**Album:** Released Apr '81, on Queendisc (Italy) Catalogue no: **QU 047**
**Cass set:** Released Mar '86, on RCA by BMG Records (UK). Deleted Nov '88. Catalogue no: **NK 89714**
**LP Set:** Released Mar '86, on RCA by BMG Records (UK). Deleted Nov '88. Catalogue no: **NL 89714**

**ON THE AIR: VOLUME 1 (Miller, Glenn & His Orchestra)**
Tracks: / Moonlight seranade / King Porter stomp / Please come out of your dream / FDR Jones / One o'clock jump / Guess I'll go back home this summer / Wishing will make it so / By the waters of Minnetonka / Lady's in love with you, The / Rendezvous time in Paree / I'm sorry for myself / Cinderella / I want to be happy / My last goodbye / Little man who wasn't there, The / Dippermouth blues.
**Album:** Released Feb '88, on Aircheck (USA) by Kiner Ents.(USA). Catalogue no: **AIRCHECK 39**

**ON THE AIR: VOLUME 2 (Miller, Glenn & His Orchestra)**
Tracks: / Moonlight seranade / Rug cutters swing / I love you too much / I wanna hat with cherries / Sweet and low / Hallelujah! / Stardust / Five O'Clock whistle / Blueberry hill / Anchors aweigh / Oh so good! / Along the Santa Fe trail / You've got me this way / Helpless / Anvil chorus / Call of the canyon, The / On brave old army team / Slumber song.
**Album:** Released Feb '88, on Aircheck (USA) by Kiner Ents.(USA). Catalogue no: **AIRCHECK 40**

**ON THE CONTINENT**
Note: Mono. Directed by Ray McKinley
**Album:** Released Nov '86, on Soundcraft (USA) Catalogue no: **LP 1016**

**ORIGINAL RECORDINGS**
Tracks: / Moonlight serenade / Hallelujah / In a sentimental mood / Back to back / Jumpin' jive / In the mood / Chattanooga choo choo / Happy in love / Serenade in blue / Don't sit under the apple tree / Moonlight cocktail / Pennsylvania 6-5000.
**Cass:** Released Jun '85, on Meteor by Magnum Music Group. Catalogue no: **MTMC 015**
**Album:** Released Jun '85, on Meteor by Magnum Music Group. Catalogue no: **MTM 015**

**ORIGINAL RECORDINGS BY GLENN MILLER & HIS ORCHESTRA**
**Cass:** Released Apr '86, on RCA/Camden by BMG Records (UK). Deleted '88. Catalogue no: **CAM 1040**
**Cass:** Released '88, on Pickwick by Pickwick Records. Catalogue no: **CAM 409**
**Album:** Released Apr '86, on RCA/Camden by BMG Records (UK). Deleted '88. Catalogue no: **CDS 1040**

**ORIGINAL RECORDINGS, THE**
**Album:** Released '69, on RCA/Camden by BMG Records (UK). Catalogue no: **CDS 1004**

**ORIGINAL SESSIONS VOL.2**
Tracks: / Rhapsody in blue / Johnson rag / St louis blues / My prayer / Caribbean clipper / Anchors away / I've got a gal in Kalamazoo / Medley-my melancholy baby / Moon love / Stompin' at the savoy / Blue moon / Woodpecker song, The / Song of the volga boatmen / I know why / Lamplighter's serenade, The.
**Cass:** Released '87, on Meteor by Magnum Music Group. Catalogue no: **MTMC 015**
**Album:** Released Oct '85, on Meteor by Magnum Music Group. Catalogue no: **MTM 017**

**ORIGINAL SOUNDS OF THE SWING ERA**
**Album:** Released '83, on RCA (Germany) Catalogue no: **CL 05514**

**POPULAR RECORDINGS 1938-1942, (Miller, Glenn Orchestra)**
Tracks: / Moonlight serenade / King Porter stomp / And the angels sing / Lady's in love with you, The / Little brown jug / But it didn't mean a thing / Stairway to the stars / Pagan love song / Over the rainbow / We can live on love (we haven't got a pot) / Glenn island special / It's a blue world / Ain't cha comin' out? / Runnin' wild / Moon love / Farewell blues / Blue evening / Bluebirds in the moonlight / Sunrise serenade / In the mood / Indian summer / Rhumba jumps, The / Star dust / Polka dots and moonbeams / Tuxedo junction / April played the fiddle / Danny boy / Be happy / Nearness of you, The / My blue heaven / It's always you / Bugle call rag / Nightingale sang in Berkeley Square, A / Pennsylvania 6-5000 / Yes, my darling daughter / Anvil chorus (parts 1 & 2) / I know why (and so do you) / You stepped out of a dream / I dreamt I dwelt in Harlem / String of pearls, A / Perfidia / Sun Vally jump / Slumber song, The / Adios / Moonlight cocktail / Moonlight sonata / Chattanooga choo choo / At last / Don't sit under the apple tree / Rhapsody in blue / (I've got a gal in) Kalamazoo / Serenade in blue / Caribbean clipper / That old black magic / Juke box Saturday night / Moonlight becomes you / American patrol.
**CD Set:** Released Dec '89, on Bluebird (2) by BMG Records (UK). Catalogue no: **ND 90412**
**Cass set:** Released Dec '89, on Bluebird (2) by BMG Records (UK). Catalogue no: **NK 90412**
**LP Set:** Released Dec '89, on Bluebird (2) by BMG Records (UK). Catalogue no: **NL 90412**

**REAL GLENN MILLER AND HIS ORCHESTRA, THE play original music of 'The Glen Miller Story' (Miller, Glenn Orchestra)**
**Album:** Released Dec '71, on RCA International by BMG Records (UK). Deleted Dec '76. Catalogue no: **INTS 1157**

**REMEMBER GLENN Vol. 3**
**Album:** Released '88, on Joker (USA) by Lifetime Records (USA). Catalogue no: **SM 4042**
**Album:** Released '88, on Joker (USA) by Lifetime Records (USA). Catalogue no: **SM 4008**

**REUNION IN HI-FI (Miller, Glenn, Singers)**
Tracks: / I've got a gal in Kalamazoo / Serenade in blue / Chattanooga choo choo / Wham / Nightingale sang in Berkeley Square, A / Sweet Eloise / Elmer's tune / Moonlight cocktail / Don't sit under

the apple tree / Booglie wooglie piggy, The / Perfidia / I know why.
**Album:** Released Jun '83, on Jasmine by Hasmick Promotions. Catalogue no: **JASM 1015**
**Cass:** Released Jun '83, on Jasmine by Hasmick Promotions. Catalogue no: **JASMC 1015**

**REVIVAL ORCHESTRA**
**Album:** Released Oct '86, on Timeless by Timeless Records. Catalogue no: **JC 1104**

**RHAPSODY IN BLUE**
**Album:** Released Nov '84, on Astan (USA) Catalogue no: **20104**
**Cass:** Released Nov '84, on Astan (USA) Catalogue no: **40104**

**SALUTE TO TRINIDAD ARMY BASE NOVEMBER 3,1941**
Tracks: / Introduction / Dear Arabella / Till reveille / Chattanooga choo choo / Song of the volga boatmen / Keep em flying / One I love, The / In the mood / Closing / Sweeter than the sweetest / High on a windy hill.
**Album:** Released May '84, on Soundcraft (USA) Catalogue no: **LP 1011**

**SILVER SERENADE (Miller, Glenn & AAF Band)**
Tracks: / Poinciana / Serenade in blue / Easter parade / Paper doll / White Christmas / Spirit is willing, The / Silent night / Blue rain / Chattanooga choo choo / St. Louis blues march / My buddy / Body and soul / Songs my mother taught me / I'll never mention your name / I'll be home for Christmas / Here we go again.
**Album:** Released Nov '86, on Swing World by Submarine Records. Catalogue no: **SWS 2**
**Cass:** Released Nov '86, on Swing World by Submarine Records. Catalogue no: **CSWS 2**

**SLOW FREIGHT (Miller, Glenn Orchestra)**
Tracks: / American patrol / Slow freight / Nearness of you, The / Sanfu jump / And the Alamo / In the mood / St. Louis blues / I don't want to be loved / Devil may care / My blue heaven.
**Cass:** Released Aug '89, on One For The Road by One For The Road. Catalogue no: **CONE 4**

**SOUNDTRACK**
**Album:** Released Jul '85, on MCA by MCA Records. Deleted Jan '88. Catalogue no: **MCF 3273**
**Cass:** Released Jul '85, on MCA by MCA Records. Deleted Jan '88. Catalogue no: **MCFC 3273**

**STARDUST**
Tracks: / Down for the count / I wouldn't take a million / Be happy / Little brown jug / Sweet potato piper / On the Alamo / Say it / Stardust / Never took a lesson in my life / When the swallows come back to Capistrane / Can't yo' heah me callin' Caroline? / King Porter stomp / Story of a starry night / Sunrise serenade.
**Album:** Released Jan '87, on Magic (1) by Submarine Records. Catalogue no: **AWE 25**
**Cass:** Released Jan '87, on Magic (1) by Submarine Records. Catalogue no: **CAWE 25**

**STORY OF A MAN AND HIS MUSIC, THE**
**CD:** Released '86 on Delta (1) by Delta Records. Catalogue no: **11 017**

**STRING OF PEARLS**
Tracks: / String of pearls / Falling leaves / Caribbean clipper / Sun valley jump / My love for you / Lover / Seven-o-five / Little brown jug / Music makers / Jeep jockey jump.
**Album:** Released '88, on Big Band Era Catalogue no: **20126**
**Cass:** Released '88, on Big Band Era Catalogue no: **40126**
**Album:** Released '85, on Bulldog Records by President Records. Catalogue no: **BDL 1055**
**Album:** Released '85, on Astan (USA) Catalogue no: **F 20126**

**SWING AND SWEET (With Army Airforce Band)**
**Album:** Released Mar '90, on Nostalgia (USA) by Sonic Arts Corporation (USA). Catalogue no: **NOST 7651**

**SWINGING BIG BANDS, 1939-42**
**2 LP Set:** Released '79, on Joker (USA) by Lifetime Records (USA). Catalogue no: **SM 3766/2**

**SWINGING BIG BANDS, 1939-42: VOL. 1**
**Album:** Released Apr '81, on Joker (USA) by Lifetime Records (USA). Catalogue no: **SM 3617**

**SWINGING BIG BANDS, 1939-42: VOL.2**
**Album:** Released Apr '81, on Joker (USA) by Lifetime Records (USA). Catalogue no: **SM 3618**

**SWINGING BIG BANDS, 1939-42: VOL.3**
**Album:** Released Apr '81, on Joker (USA) by Lifetime Records (USA). Catalogue no: **SM 3619**

**SWINGING GLENN MILLER**
Tracks: / King Porter stomp / Little brown jug / Runnin' wild / Sliphorn jive / Solid American / Pagan love song / Glen Island special / In the mood / My blue heaven / What's your story, morning glory / I dreamed I dwelt in Harlem / Sun Valley jump / When that man is dead and gone / Spirit is willing / Take the A train / String of pearls / Wham / I want to be happy / My Isle of golden dreams / Johnson rag / Rug cutter's swing / Hallelujah / Slow freight / Bugle call rag / Swing low sweet chariot / Long tall mama / Keep 'em flying / Chip off the old block / Blues in the night / Here we go again / Sleepy town train.
**2 LP Set:** Released Apr '84, on RCA (France) by BMG Records (France). Deleted Nov '88. Catalogue no: **NL 89162**
**Cass set:** Released Apr '84, on RCA (France) by BMG Records (France). Deleted May '89. Catalogue no: **NK 89162**

**SWINGING SUPERSTAR ORCHESTRA, THE**
**Album:** Released Apr '81, on Up International Catalogue no: **LPUP 5007**

**THAT OLD MILLER MAGIC**
Tracks: / In the mood / Chattanooga choo choo / St. Louis Blues / Don't sit under the apple tree / Tuxedo Junction / Little brown jug / American patrol / When Johnny comes marching home / I've got a gal in Kalamazoo / Serenade in blue / That old black magic / King Porter stomp.
Note: This record has been compiled from master tapes made in the 1930's and 40's. Thesound quality therefore reflects the age of these recordings and recording tech-niques available at the time. This compilation (P) 1986 & (C) RCA Records Ltd. issued under exclusive licence to Music for Pleasure.
**Cass:** Released Sep '86, on MFP by EMI Records. Deleted Apr '90. Catalogue no: **TCMFP 5776**
**Album:** Released Sep '86, on MFP by EMI Records. Deleted Apr '90. Catalogue no: **MFP 5776**

**UNCLE SAM PRESENTS (Miller Direct Aatco, Capt.Glenn)**
**Album:** Released Apr '86, on Hep Jazz by Hep Records. Catalogue no: **HEP 32**

**UNFORGETTABLE GLENN MILLER, THE**
**Album:** Released Apr '77, on RCA Victor by BMG Records (UK). Deleted Apr '82. Catalogue no: **TVL 1**

**VERY BEST OF GLENN MILLER, THE**
Tracks: / Elmers tune / String of pearls / Moonlight cocktail / American patrol / I've got a gal in Kalamazoo / Jukebox Saturday night / Beautiful Ohio / Missouri waltz / Adios / Oh Johnny, oh Johnny oh / Moonlight serenade / Sunrise serenade / Little brown jug / In the mood / Johnson rag / Stardust / Tuxedo Junction / Pennsylvania 65000 / Song of the volga boatmen / Chattanooga choo choo.
**Album:** Released May '82, on RCA by BMG Records (UK). Deleted May '87. Catalogue no: **RCALP 3055**
**Cass:** Released '84, on RCA by BMG Records (UK). Catalogue no: **PK 89009**
**Album:** Released '84, on RCA by BMG Records (UK). Catalogue no: **PL 89009**

## Miller, Harry

**CHILDREN AT PLAY**
**Album:** Released '88, on Ogun by Cadillac Music. Catalogue no: **OL 200**

**IN CONFERENCE**
**Album:** Released Feb '79, on Ogun by Cadillac Music. Deleted Feb '84. Catalogue no: **OG 523**

## Miller, Herb

**MEMORIES OF GLENN MILLER (Miller, Herb & his Orchestra)**
Note: Tracks include: On a clear day/Boulder buff/Little Brown jug/The song that I sing/Danny boy/Stairway to

the stars, etc..
**Album:** Released Oct '87, on Avimus-Rim Catalogue no: **AVI 3**
**Cass:** Released Oct '87, on Avimus-Rim Catalogue no: **AVIC 3**

**MUSIC OF GLENN MILLER, THE (Miller, Herb & his Orchestra)**
Tracks: / Adios / American patrol / At last / Little brown jug / Chattanooga choo choo / I've got a gal in Kalamazoo / Moonlight serenade / Perfidia / Pennsylvania 6-5000 / String of pearls / Serenade in blue / St. Louis blues march / Boulder buff / Tuxedo Junction / In the mood.
Note: Tracks include: American patrol/At last/In the mood/String of pearls/Adios, etc..
**Album:** Released Sep '84, on Avimus-Rim Catalogue no: **AVI 1**

**REMEMBER GLENN MILLER (Miller, Herb & his Orchestra)**
**CD:** Released 5 Mar '90, on BBC by BBC Records & Tapes. Catalogue no: **CDPT 504**
**Cass:** Released 5 Mar '90, on BBC by BBC Records & Tapes. Catalogue no: **ZPRST 504**
**Album:** Released 5 Mar '90, on BBC by BBC Records & Tapes. Catalogue no: **PRST 504**

**TRIBUTE TO SWING**
Tracks: / Rhapsody in blue / Smoke gets in your eyes / Shine on harvest moon / Limelight / Time after time / Moon river.
Note: Tracks include those listed above.
**Cass:** Released Jun '83, on RIM Catalogue no: **RIMC 510**
**Album:** Released Jun '83, on Avimus-Rim Catalogue no: **AVI 2**

**TUXEDO JUNCTION (Miller, Herb & his Orchestra)**
Tracks: / Tuxedo Junction / Anchors aweigh / American patrol.
**7" Single:** Released Nov '81, on Miller Catalogue no: **MEP 001**

## Miller, Jay

**JAY MILLER STUDIO BAND 1961-63**
**Album:** Released Jul '85, on Flyright by Interstate Music. Catalogue no: **FLY 608**

## Miller, Luella

**COMPLETE RECORDINGS 1926-27 (Miller, Luella/Lonnie Johnson)**
**Album:** Released '88, on Wolf Catalogue no: **WSE 125**

## Miller, Marcus

**LOVIN' YOU**
Tracks: / Lovin' you / Suddenly.
**12" Single:** Released Apr '83, on Warner Bros. by WEA Records. Deleted Apr '86. Catalogue no: **W 0101T**

**MARCUS MILLER**
**Album:** Released Aug '84, on WEA (Import) by WEA Records. Catalogue no: **925074 1**

**SUDDENLY**
**Album:** Released Mar '83, on Asylum by WEA Records. Catalogue no: **K 123806**

**SUDDENLY (IMPORT)**
**Album:** Released Sep '89, on Warner Bros. by WEA Records. Catalogue no: **9238061**

## Millinder, Lucky

**APOLLO JUMP Big band bounce & boogie (Millinder, Lucky And His Orchestra)**
Tracks: / Apollo jump / Ride, red ride / That's all / Shipyard social function / Hurry, hurry / Shout, sister shout / Mason flyer / Slide Mr Trombone / There's good blues tonight / Let me off uptown / Rock me / Little John special / Who threw the whiskey in the well / Trouble in mind / Big fat mama / Rock Daniel / All the time / I want a tall skinny papa.
Note: New York and more specifically Harlem was the place where Lucky Millinder and his band scored it's greatest triumphs. He was an intensely swinging band presenting a potent mixture of jazz, blues and rhythm and blues. The dancers loved it. Millinder himself was not a musician, but he did not miss a trick and had developed ear for the kind of musicians he required. Just judge by these names that propelled into stardom from the millinder ranks: Shouters, Wynonie Harris and Sister Rosetta Thorpe, trumpeters Freddie Webster and Dizzy Gillespie, saxophonist Bull Moose Jackson, Sam 'the man' Taylor and Tab Smith, pianist Bill Doggett and Sir Charles Thompson and the list goes on. Commercially this album has a wide appeal outside the jazz market, because it contains a lot of virile jumbo and rhythm and blues, aside the fact that there are no other Lucky millinder albums on the market.
**Album:** Released Sep '83, on Affinity by Charly Records. Catalogue no: **AFS 1004**

**LET IT ROLL AGAIN**
Tracks: / Hey huss / How big can you get little men / We're gonna have to slap the dirty ... / I can't see for lookin' / Fightin' Doug MacArthur / Spider and the fly, The / Your heart belongs to me / My little baby / Let it roll again / Blues done got me (and gone), The / Georgia rose / Teardrops from my eyes / Don't hesitate too long / Right kind of lovin', The / Bongo boogie / Mr. Trumpet man.
**Album:** Released Nov '85, on Jukebox Lil (Sweden) Catalogue no: **JB 613**

**LUCKY MILLINDER & HIS ORCHESTRA**
**Album:** Released Sep '87, on Hindsight Catalogue no: **HSR 233**

**RAM-BUNK-SHUSH**
Tracks: / Ram-bunk-shush / Oh babe / Please open your heart / Silent George / I'm waiting just for you / No one else could be / It's been a long, long time / Please be careful / Loaded with love / When I gave you my love / Heavy sugar / Old spice / I'm here love / It's a sad, sad feeling / Owl / Goody good love.
**Album:** Released '88, on Sing Catalogue no: **SING 1163**

**SHORTY'S GOT TO GO**
Tracks: / Are you ready / Shorty's got to go / More more more / I know how to do it / Chew tobacco rag / I love you I love you I do / Lord knows I tried / Bacslider's ball / Darlin' / Baby, you've been wrong / Fare thee well Deacon Jones / Someday / Jumpin' Jack / Grapevine / Clap your hands / Who said Shorty wasn't coming back.
**Album:** Released Apr '85, on Jukebox Lil (Sweden) Catalogue no: **JB 609**

**STOMPIN' AT THE SAVOY 1943 - 44 (Millinder, Lucky & His Orchestra)**
Tracks: / Savoy / Down by the riverside / I'll get by / Is you is or is you ain't my baby / Chinatown, my Chinatown / After I say I'm sorry / Cherokee / Rhythm changes / Rock me / St. Louis breakdown / I want a tall skinny papa / Little John special.
Note: With Sister Rosetta Tharpe, Sam "The Man" Taylor, Judy Carol.
**Album:** Released Jun '88, on Bandstand Catalogue no: **BS 7134**
**Cass:** Released Jun '88, on Bandstand Catalogue no: **BS 7134C**

## Million Sellers...

**MILLION SELLERS 1930-1940 (Various artists)**
**2 LP Set:** Released '88, on Cambra by Cambra Records. Catalogue no: **CR 033**
**Cass set:** Released '88, on Cambra by Cambra Records. Catalogue no: **CRT 033**

**MILLION SELLERS OF THE 30'S AND Various artists (Various artists)**
Tracks: / Tiger rag: *Mills Brothers* / Bei mir bist du schon: *Andrews Sisters* / Tisket a tasket, A: *Fitzgerald, Ella* / Over the rainbow: *Garland, Judy* / At the woodchoppers' ball: *Herman, Woody & His Orchestra* / Green eyes: *Dorsey, Jimmy & His Orchestra* / Paper doll: *Mills Brothers* / Oklahoma: *Original stage cast* / Besame mucho: *Dorsey, Jimmy* / You'll never know: *Haymes, Dick & The Songspinners* / Rum and coca cola: *Andrews Sisters* / Swinging on a star: *Crosby, Bing* / Into each life some rain must fall: *Fitzgerald, Ella* / Begin the beguine: *Heywood, Eddie* / Don't fence me in: *Crosby, Bing* / Is you is or is you ain't my baby: *Jordan, Louis* / Little bird told me, A: *Knight, Evelyn & The Stardusters* / MacNamara's band: *Crosby, Bing & The Jesters* / To each his own: *Ink Spots* / Maybe you'll be there: *Jenkins, Gordon & Charles La Vere* / Beware, brother, beware: *Jordan, Louis* / Easter parade: *Lombardo, Guy* / Little white lies: *Haymes, Dick & Gordon Jenkins* / You always hurt the one you love: *Mills Brothers* / I can dream, can't I: *Andrews, Patti* / Cruising down the river: *Morgan, Russ.*
**Cass set:** Released '83, on Cambra by Cambra Records. Deleted '88. Catalogue no: **CRT 033**

**MILLION SELLERS OF THE 40'S**

**Mills Blue Rythm Band - Blue Rhythm 1930-31 (Hep Jazz)**

**(Various artists)**
Tracks: / In the mood: *Miller, Glenn* / Stardust: *Shaw, Artie* / On the sunny side of the street: *Dorsey, Tommy* / Blues in the night: *Shore, Dinah* / Little brown jug: *Miller, Glenn* / Begin the beguine: *Shaw, Artie* / There are such things: *Dorsey, Tommy & Frank Sinatra* / Chattanooga choo choo: *Miller, Glenn* / Tuxedo Junction: *Miller, Glenn* / Frenesi: *Shaw, Artie* / Boogie woogie: *Dorsey, Tommy* / Pennsylvania 6-5000: *Miller, Glenn* / Dance ballerina dance: *Miller, Glenn* / Marie: *Dorsey, Tommy* / Dancing in the dark: *Shaw, Artie* / I've got a gal in Kalamazoo: *Miller, Glenn.*
**Cass:** Released Oct '88, on MFP by EMI Records. Catalogue no: **TC-MFP 5844**
**Album:** Released Oct '88, on MFP by EMI Records. Catalogue no: **MFP 5844**

## Mills Blue Rhythm Band

**BLUE RHYTHM 1930-31 (See panel left)**
Tracks: / They satisfy / Please don't talk about me when I'm gone / Straddle the fence / Levee down low / Moanin' / Minnie the moocher / Blue Rhythm / Blue flame / Red devil / Stardust / (Poor) Minnie the moocher / Black and tan fantasy / Sugar blues / Low down on the bayou / Futuristic jungleism.
Note: Irving Mills, New York-born, in 1894, the son of first generation Jewish immigrants, worked as a song plugger in 1916, started his own highly successful publishing house, Mills Music Inc., in 1919, and although you will search in vain for a biography of him in any of the standard reference works he, ostensibly, was the leader of many bands on hundreds of sides, mostly by white groups, The Hotsy Totsy Gang, Merry Makers, Swingphonic Orchestra, Musical Clowns, Goody-goodtimers, etc., and the black blue rhythm band, which was also labelled the Blue Rhythm Boys, Baron Lee and the Blue Rhythm Band, Billy Banks and the Blue Rhythm Band, King Carter and his royal orchestra and Earl Jacksons Musical Champions. This album comprises their first fifteen tracks in chronological order, although some experts believe that the first two, *They satisfy* and *Please don't talk about me when I'm gone*, are in all probability one

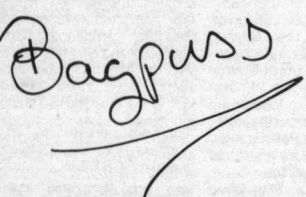

of the mainly white bands which recorded for the American Recording Company and the rather "commercial" nature of these would tend to support this contention. The rest, however, are fine examples of a gutsy, large black band of the thirties but, first, more information on the redoubtable Mills.

In addition to running his publishing company he managed many artists and bands inluding Duke Ellington, Cab Calloway and Jimmy Lunceford, and the titles on many of their records bear the attribution of Mills as co-composer, as in the case on several of the tracks here. As he published these compositions, took a part-composers cut and, very likely, a fee for fixing the session, he certainly waxed fat out of those in his thrall. He also "sung" on many a session and no doubt copped his might for vocalising as well. Mercifully, for he was no great shakes in the vocal department, he does not emote on this compilation although, to be truthful, those of those he booked for some tracks, Dick Robertson, Chick Bullock and Charlie Lawman, were not much better. Their inadequacies are fully compensated by the black George Morton on three sides. Mills was obviously and entrepreneurial buccaneer typical of the American entertainment scene (Joe Glaser, Louis Armstrong's manager, another case in point) during the twenties and thirties, and continued in business right up to his death in Palm Springs, California, on April 21st 1985. He was ninety-one.

There are many stories in print about this adroit wheeler and dealer, all showing him to be a very sharp man indeed. In his book "Trumpet on the wing", the New Orleans trumpeter Wingy Manone recalls that he signed a contract with Mills, showed it to clarrinetist Joe Marsala, who pointed out that it tied Manone for life. Failing to get a release from the contract, Manone and Marsala went to Mills, Marsala dressed and acted like a gangster. "This is my brother", said Manone. "He's gonna handle me. He's just blown in from Chicago where he works with the Capone mob." It scared Mills into returning that forever binding agreement. In the black newspaper Amsterdam News, November 17th 1936, a young Reverend Adam Clayton Powell wrote an article entitled "Sharecroppers" that addressed itself to the exploitation of black performers, particularly black orchestras, by their white managers. "The truth is that they are musical sharecroppers. Duke Ellington is a sharecropper... at the end of the year Massa Mill's cotton has been laid by and Duke is told that he owes hundred of thousands of dollars. Most of these conditions hold forth for the hi-de-ho master, Cab Calloway, now occupying the highest spot in the Rialto, his men earning under a hundred dollars a week... musical sharecroppers, that's all. Lunceford another example... they owed for their cabin, plot, mule and sorghum." The truth of these harsh words was borne out in the late thirties when Ellington examined his accounts in the Mill's office one morning, pored over them for an hour, got up, said "Thank you very much" to Mill's secretary, walked out and never did business with Mills again. Undoubtedly, the Mills Blue Rhythm Band were similarly exploited, but, financial jiggery-pokery aside, jazz enthusiasts have every reason to be pleased that Mills was so active in the recording studios and for us, over fifty-five years later, to enjoy this particular album, of a band that, while not in the same league as Duke Ellington, Fletcher Henderson and Count Basie, was a worthy outfit with many notable soloists.

Starting as drummer Willie Lynch's Orchestra in 1930 and accompanying Louis Armstrong on two recordings, *My sweet* and *I can't believe you're in love with me*, that year, they made over a hundred and thirty sides and lasted as a regular band with largely the same personnel for six years, trombonist Harry White and pianist Edgar Hayesthe coleaders. White, by the way, coined the phrase "jitterbug", to describe delerium tremens, but later became associated with the highly extrovert coloured dancers at the Savoy Ballroom, Harlem, and similar haunts. Leaving aside the first two tracks, *Straddle the fence* is a Cab Calloway, as is *Minnie the moocher*, two versions of which are on this compilation, the second called, for some reason, *Poor Minnie the moocher* with a different vocalist (George Morton, Dick Robertson the first) and arrangement, but the call and response from vocalist and ensemble routine very similar on both versions to Calloway's. Actually the first MBR version was recorded only six weeks after the Calloway, which took off as a big hit.

The band wrote many originals - all, of course, with the assistance of Mr Mills. *Moanin'* and *Futuristic jungleism* (what a delightful title), the former a little gem that compares with *Mood indigo* for its wistful plaintiveness, and the latter, in complete contrast, is uptempo, played with lustful vigour. Trumpeters Wardell "Preacher" Jones and Shelton "Scad" Hemphill wrote *Blue rhythm*, another tear-up theme and featuring an arresting solo by Edgar Hayes - without accompaniement and none needed. His powerful left hand compares with those of the great stride piano masters - James P Johnson, Fats Waller and Donald Lambert. He formed his own band in 1937 and in 1938 recorded the first version of *In the mood* (under that title), a year before Glenn Miller made the supersmash hit that by 1945 was to sell three million copies.

*Blue flame* I have seen attributed to saxophonist Cass McCord, but the information sheet here credits Perkins and, of course, I. Mills. It is unlikely that such a busy entrepreneur should have been so active as a composer, but, I believe, he did play an instument. Appropriately it was a fiddle. Whoever wrote it can be thanked for a gently lilting theme with two trombones achieving a fat, full section sound. *Low down on the Bayou* is a composition by the bands arranger, Nat Leslie - with the help of you-know-who. Unusually, the brass bass, expertly played by Hayes Alvis, later with Duke Ellington, is an integral part of the score. *Black and tan fancy* was recorded four times for different labels between 1927 and 1930 by Duke Ellington and the MBR version the first after Duke, following the pattern of the original and having the same brooding atmosphere. As *Minnie the moocher* was a hit for another band so was *Sugar blues*, a Clarence Williams tune. The hit record, selling a million copies, was by a white trumpeter, Clyde McCoy, specialising in a corny "wa wa" style. This MBR version is a million times superior to the McCoy. Hoagy Carmichael's *Stardust* (published, you will not be surprised to hear, by Mills Music Inc.) is given almost totally straight treatment, but with a tune like that, none the less enjoyable. The vocals by George Morton on the first *Minnie the moocher*, *Sugar blues* and *Futuristic jungleism* are a revelation. I had previously heard most of this album's tracks and having, of necessity, to research the band, Morton was a totally new name to me, but what a fine jazz singer he his. He has obviously heard his Louis and Red Allen and comes over as someone who should have graced many more records, but he didn't record before these sides and none after the last session with the band, on yet another version of *Minnie the moocher*, on Victor, on 26th June 1931. Nothing is known about him - a complete mystery. On *Futuristic jungleism* he can be heard making what became a familiar exhortation by band vocalists - Swing it, gate.

I gratefully acknowledge the help of Dave Carey, Alun Morgan and the excellent MBRB discography and solography in Storyville 108/9 by Frank Dutton, Nigel Haslewood, Martin Richards, Eric Townley, Peter Carr and John Hart. The general consensus of opinion in this was that the solo contributions are as follows: Eddie Anderson on trumpet, Henry Hicks on trombone, Cass McCord on tenor saxophone and clarinet, and Theodore "Ted" McCord on alto and baritone saxophones. Personally, I go along with Dave Carey in not being sure that Anderson is the only trumpet soloist, but if the honours are soley his he is surely one of the great underrated in jazz. He displays a full-bodied tone, searing attack, considerable range - and a debt to Red Allen - evidenced, particularly, on *Red devil* and *Sugar blues*, and if Hicks was the only trombone soloist, he too was much influenced - by Red's old sidekick in the Luis Russell Band, J.C. Higginbotham. Listen to those stabbing, Higgy-like phrases on *Red devil* and the second *Minnie the moocher*. I should also offer thanks to my stoic neighbours who were compelled to listen to the same tracksof this LP over and over

**Mills Blue Rhythm Band - Savage Rhythm (Hep Jazz)**

again in my vain attempt to identify the soloists and, no doubt, very thankful when I gave up. Jim Godbolt
**Album:** Released Sep '86, on Hep Jazz by Hep Records. Catalogue no: **HEP 1008**

## DOIN' THE NEW LOW DOWN 1928/29 (Mills, Irving & His Hotsy Totsy Gang)
**Album:** Released Mar '84, on Fountain by Retrieval Records. Catalogue no: **FJ 122**

## HIGH & DRY 1930-1 VOL. 3 (Mills, Irving & His Hotsy Totsy Gang)
**Album:** Released Jan '88, on Fountain by Retrieval Records. Catalogue no: **FJ 127**

## MILLS BLUE RHYTHM BAND, 1931 (Mills Music Masters, Blue Rhythm Boys, Blue Ribbon Boys) (Various artists)
**Album:** Released '88, on Classic Jazz Masters Catalogue no: **CJM 23**

## RHYTHM SPLASH
**Album:** Released '88, on Hep Jazz by Hep Records. Catalogue no: **HEP 1021**

## SAVAGE RHYTHM (See panel above)
Tracks: / Moanin' / Heebie jeebies / Minnie the moocher / Savage rhythm / I'm sorry I made you blue / Everytime I look at you / Snake hips / Scat song, The / Heat waves / Doin' the shake / Cabin in the cotton / Minnie the moocher's wedding day / Growl, The / Mighty sweet.
Note: Personnel: Wardell Jones, Shelton Hemphill, Ed Anderson (Trumpets); Harry White, Henry Hicks (trombones), Charlie Holmes (Clt.Alt.Sax), Ted McCord, Castor McCord (Clt.Ten. Saxes), Edgar Hayes (piano), Benny James (banjo, guitar), Hayes Alvis (St.Bs, Br, Bs), Willie Lynch (drums). Recorded in New York 1931/32. In my note for *Blue rhythm* by the Mills Blue Rhythm Band (HEP 1008) I wrote 'while not in the same league as Duke Ellington or Fletcher Henderson it was a worthy unit with many notable solists.' I should have added that it was certainly one of the finest half a dozen like bands and, at times, comparable to the carying Henderson orchestra. The Blue Rhythm Band started life as Willie Lynch's Orchestra in 1930, and was fronted by Louis Armstrong for six sides on the Okeh label in that year before they commenced recording in 1931 under Irving Mills' management. They were a regular unit until disbanding in 1937 and as the personnel changed little in their four years they developed a homogenity and style, particularly noticeable in the lusty brass, and in trumpeteer Eddy Anderson, trombonist Henry Hicks, reedman Cass McCord (especially on clarinet) and alto saxophonist Charlie Holmes they had solists of the first rank. Add to these attributes the tuneful compositions penned by the band, George Morton's highly rhythmical singing, a steady rhythm, and you have a combination of considerable value.

After their first stint with the American Record Company they moved to Victor, where on 19 June 1931 they cut another version of Harry White's *Moanin'*, this time with a vocal by the mysterious George Morton. Mysterious because he made no other records with this band and not a scrap of information can I find about him. The next two Victor items were not, unfortunately issued, and the band's following four titles for Columbia, recorded on 25th June 1931 under the name King Carter and His Royal Orchestra are not included in this collection. *Moanin'* is one of the loveliest recordings I know. I've said it once and I'll say it again, that as a composition it compares with Duke's *Mood indigo* and the band's treatment matches Duke's record of his classic. This version has the edge on the Brunswick recording on account of Morton's presence, his mixture of words and vocalese quite riveting. On this track the band became one of the first division, Anderson's poignant trumpet, and Cass McCord's 'woody' clarinet obligato to the vocal being truly outstanding. The band returned to the Victor studios on 26 June 1931 to make *Heebie jeebies* which sports some exultant brass and superbly constructed solos by Anderson and Hicks. Note the gently propulsive featherweight banjoy of Benny James. Listen how he switches to guitar on tracks where that instrument suits best. As the band was virtually owned by publisher/entrepeneur Irving Mills he moved the band from studio to studio, to enable them to record several times over number he published, *Minnie the moocher* being a case in point. *Minnie the moocher* is the bands' fourth stab at this number and I dare to disagree with the expert team of the Storyville magazine who put together an extensive discography and solography of the MBRB, that one of the two vocalists is George Morton. The other artist is undoubtedly Chuck Bullock. From the Victor Studios to Brunswick on 31 July 1931 for the next four sides. *Savage rhythm* (credited to Hoffman and Goodman) I have seen it attributed to Crawford Wethington on a German Brunswick EP is notable for a delightful chase between Henry Hicks and McCord demonstrating that he was an infinitely better clarinettist than he was a tenor saxophonist although no slouch on the latter instrument, *I'm sorry I made you blue* and *Everytime I look at you* are pretty numbers, played straight, but delightfully so. If all dance music of the thirties had been played with such charm and lilt my shelves would be stacked with Paul Whiteman, Guy Lombardo and Freddy Martin. There are occasional solo spots, a little of Shelton Hemphill's straight trumpet on the latter title, and Eddy Anderson concludes the treatment with Louis Armstrong's famous soaring coda. Edgar Hayes essays a few Ellington mannerisms. In contrast *Snake hips* is a lively tear-up with more of McCord's clarinet and effective use of the clarinet trio, a device long abandoned by big bands.

Side two finds the band back at the A.R.C. studios and *The scat song* is taken at a considerable lick with a tremendous solo by alto saxophonist Charlie Holmes. In the notes for HEP

1008 I studiously avoided mention of Holmes because according to the Storyville team of MBRB experts, Frank Duton, Nigel Haselwood, Martin Richards, Eric Townley, Peter Carr, and John Hart Holmes was not present on any of those tracks. However, Hep took the personnel notes from Rust's indispenable Jazz Records 1897-1942 and Holmes was listed, this no doubt causing a little perplexity amongst collectors, just one of those things. Mercifully the Storyville team agree with Rust in listing Holmes for this album but heavens, how like Johnny Hodges he sounds. His own man with Luis Russell, but here seemingly bent on emulating the Rabbit, not that this detracts from his flow of ideas and excellence of excecution. No wonder, years later, in 1951 when recordings by Al Sears were issued giving the name of Charlie Holmes as the altoist many were totally convinced that it was Hodges. It had been verified that Holmes was the man present on the date. This track comes to its natural finish, there is a pause of two beats and , suddenly a curious, seemingly rushed coda is tagged on. Note how tha bass playing of Hayes Alvis now picks his notes with great articulation instead of the less attractive bass slapping. *Heat waves* is an atmostpheric piece, in the same vein as Don Redman's *Chant of the weeds*, with growling brass and again good use of the clarinet trio. *Doin' the shake* is similar to *Moten swing* with Holmes again uncannily like Hodges, the banjoy again used very effectively, Hicks at his most Higgy like, Anderson stabbing out an urgent chorus and McCord's bubbling on tenor. Another version of *The scat song*; taken at a slower tempo, Charlie Holmes playing a lovely obligato to O Neil Spencer's vocal, Spencer replaced the band's original drummer and leader Willie Lynch. Again that very peculiar coda. *Cabin in the cotton* is one of those 'deep south' songs 'bout 'Ole Virginny and Piccaninnies' written by two white tunesmiths, Parish and Perkins. Joe Garland plays pretty clarinet and the vocal is by Billy Bands a Cab Calloway imitator - nuff said. *Minnie the moocher's wedding day* sports another Billy Banks vocal. Listen out for the superbly recorded bass of Hayes Alvis. On the album his progress can easily trace how he acquired a technique that led him into the Ellington ranks. *The growl* is very Ellingtonian in style, Hicks-Nanton, Holmes-Hodges, Jones-Miley, Hayes-Duke, not to mention the wah wah brass finale. *Mighty sweet* features more Banks, Garland's tenor, a pungent break by Holmes, Hick's trombone and a flourish from Holmes at the end. Overall a very satisfying collection from a band that should be much higher rated in jazz circles and if this, together with HEP 1008, helps achieve this desirable end then their issue will have been of considerable service to the jazz collector. I understand that there will be further MBRB issues and I, for one, look forward to them all. (Jim Godbolt 1987)

**Album:** Released Jan '87, on Hep Jazz by Hep Records. Catalogue no: **HEP 1015**

### SOME FUN 1929-30.VOL.2 (Mills, Irving & His Hotsy Totsy Gang)

Tracks: / Some fun / Can't we get together / Sweet Savannah Sue / Ain't misbehavin' / Doin' the new low down / Harvey ( (Two takes)) / March of the hoodlums / Stardust / Nobody's sweeheart / Manhattan rag / What kind of man is you? / My little honey and me / High and dry / Barbaric.

Note: Mono.

**Album:** Released Nov '86, on Fountain by Retrieval Records. Catalogue no: **FJ 123**

## Mills Brothers

**Biographical details:** Mills Brothers. The Mills Brothers were one of the leading close harmony vocal groups of the Thirties and Forties. John, Herbert, Harry and Donald were born in Piqua, Ohio, and started their career singing on a Cincinatti radio station. That was in 1930; over the following few years, the group became steady record sellers and made several film appearances. In 1934 their version of *Tiger Rag*, a 1917 Dixieland tune, made them internationally famous.

John died in 1935, and his place was taken by the group's father John Mills Sr. The group achieved their biggest success in 1942 with *Paper Doll*, a mammouth US No. 1; this was a surprise remake of a 1915 song. 1944 brought the Mills Brothers another American chart-topper with *You Always Hurt The One You Love*, a song successfully revived in the pop era by Connie Francis and Clarence 'Frogman' Henry. In 1948 the group scored a smash with their rendition of Hoagy Carmichael's *Lazy River*. Soon after the November 1952 inception of the British record charts, the Brothers reached the UK No. 10 position in January 1953 with their revival of the classic chestnut *Glow Worm*. Despite the onset of the rock 'n' roll era, they managed to hit the US Top 40 in 1957 with *Queen Of The Senior Prom* and in 1958 with *Get A Job*. They then disappeared from the charts, but made a surprise comeback in 1968 with their US No. 23 single *Cab Driver*.

Although their heyday was over by the time the rock era began in the mid-Fifties, the Mills Brothers' harmony singing had a considerable influence on the early development of pop and rock music, particularly the black rhythm and blues groups of the Fifties. The same could be said of the Brothers' contemporaroes, The Ink Spots. Henry Milles died in June 1982 at the age of 68. His father, John Sr., passed away in December 1967 at the age of 85. (Bob MacDonald, 30 January 1986.).

### 20 GREATEST HITS: MILLS BROTHERS

**Cass:** Released Dec '85, on Nostalgia (USA) by Sonic Arts Corporation (USA). Catalogue no: **42017**

**Album:** Released Dec '85, on Nostalgia by Mainline Records. Catalogue no: **N 22017**

### BEST OF THE MILLS BROTHERS (CREOLE)

Tracks: / Paper doll / You always hurt the one you love / Mr. Sandman / Across the valley from the Alamo / Glow worm / Autumn leaves / Till then.

Note: Tracks include those listed above.

**Cass:** Released Jul '84, on Creole (Everest-Europa) by Creole Records. Catalogue no: **16 11**

### BEST OF THE MILLS BROTHERS (EMI) (Featuring the Ink Spots)

**Album:** Released '88, on EMI (Holland) by EMI Records. Catalogue no: **1A 022 1583701**

**Cass:** Released '88, on EMI (Holland) by EMI Records. Catalogue no: **1A 222 1583704**

### BEST OF THE MILLS BROTHERS (MFP)

Tracks: / Paper doll / I'll be around / Lindy Lou / Cherry / Goodbye blues / Lazy river / You always hurt the one you love / Put another chair at the table / I guess I'll get the papers and go home / Till then / Glow worm / Say si si / Opus one / Please don't talk about me when I'm gone / I got her off my hands / Smack dab in the middle.

**Cass:** Released Apr '82, on MFP by EMI Records. Deleted '87. Catalogue no: **TCMFP 50560**

**Album:** Released Apr '82, on MFP by EMI Records. Deleted '87. Catalogue no: **MFP 50560**

### CHRONOLOGICAL, VOLUME 1

**CD:** Released Oct '88, on JSP by JSP Records. Catalogue no: **JSP CD 301**

### CHRONOLOGICAL, VOLUME 2

**CD:** Released Apr '89, on JSP by JSP Records. Catalogue no: **JSP CD 302**

**Album:** Released Jun '86, on JSP by JSP Records. Catalogue no: **JSP 1101**

### CHRONOLOGICAL, VOLUME 3

Note: with G.Lidberg, Robert Edman.

**Album:** Released Mar '87, on JSP by JSP Records. Catalogue no: **JSP 1109**

**CD:** Released 8 Apr '89, on JSP by JSP Records. Catalogue no: **JSPCD 303**

### CHRONOLOGICAL, VOLUME 4

**CD:** Released Oct '88, on JSP by JSP Records. Catalogue no: **JSP CD 304**

### FOUR BOYS AND A GUITAR

**Album:** Released '88, on GNP Crescendo (USA) by GNP Crescendo Records (USA). Catalogue no: **GNPS 9016**

**Cass:** Released '88, on GNP Crescendo (USA) by GNP Crescendo Records (USA). Catalogue no: **GNP5 9016**

### FROM THE BEGINNING VOL.1

**Album:** Released Feb '86, on JSP by JSP Records. Catalogue no: **JSP 1099**

**GLOW WORM**
Tracks: / Glow worm.
**7" Single:** Released Jan '53, on Brunswick by Decca Records. Deleted '56. Catalogue no: **05007**

**GOLDEN GREATS: MILLS BROTHERS**
Tracks: / Paper doll / Glow worm / Basin street blues / Nevertheless (I'm in love with you) / Till then / Cielito lindo / You always hurt the one you love / Across the valley from the Alamo / I'll be around / Rockin' chair swing / Be my life's companion / Put another chair at the table / I guess I'll get the papers and go home / Pennies from Heaven / When you were sweet sixteen / Someday you'll want me to want you / All myself / Opus one / Please don't talk about me when I'm gone / Lazy river.
Note: Another brand new collection in the 'Golden Greats' series, twenty classic hits from the legendary Mills Brothers who racked up millions of sales with such uni-que songs as 'Glow Worm','Paper Doll', 'Till Then','I'll Be Around', 'All By My-elf' and many others. This definitive collection is a superb tribute to one of America's foremost vocal groups of the 40's.
**Album:** Released Feb '86, on MCA by MCA Records. Catalogue no: **MCM 5030**

**GOODBYE BLUES**
Tracks: / Pennies from heaven / Limehouse blues / Lambeth walk / Lazy river.
**Album:** Released May '84, on MCA by MCA Records. Catalogue no: **MCL 1790**

**GREATEST HITS: MILLS BROTHERS**
Tracks: / Paper doll / Glow worm / Basin St. Blues / Till then / Nevertheless / Cielito Lindo / Lazy river / You always hurt the one you love / Across the alley from the Alamo / I'll be around / Rockin' chair / Be my life's companion.
**Album:** Released Feb '82, on MCA by MCA Records. Deleted Feb '87. Catalogue no: **MCL 1649**
**CD:** Released Jul '87, on MCA by MCA Records. Catalogue no: **CMCAD 31035**

**MILLS BROTHERS**
**CD:** Released May '89, on Object Enterprises Catalogue no: **ONN 23**
**Cass:** Released Aug '86, on Lotus Catalogue no: **LCS 14118**
**Album:** Released Aug '86, on Lotus Catalogue no: **LOP 14 118**

**MILLS BROTHERS & LOUIS (Mills Brothers & Louis Armstrong)**
**Album:** Released Sep '87, on Giants of Jazz by Hasmick Promotions. Catalogue no: **LPJT 49**

**MILLS BROTHERS VOL. 4**
**Album:** Released Jan '88, on JSP by JSP Records. Catalogue no: **JSP 1115**

**SWEETER THAN SUGAR**
Tracks: / Tiger rag / Old-fashioned love / Fiddlin' Joe / Smoke rings / I've found a new baby / Chinatown, my Chinatown / Lazybones / Diga diga doo / Nagasaki / Sweeter than sugar / Miss Otis regrets / Ida, sweet as apple cider / Rockin' chair / Some of these days / Sweet Georgia Brown / Nobody's sweetheart.
**Cass:** Released 1 Apr '85, on Living Era by Academy Sound & Vision Records. Catalogue no: **ZC AJA 5032**
**Album:** Released 1 Apr '85, on Living Era by Academy Sound & Vision Records. Catalogue no: **AJA 5032**
**CD:** Released Feb '87, on Living Era by Academy Sound & Vision Records. Catalogue no: **CD AJA 5032**

**SWING IS THE THING**
Tracks: / Swing is the thing / Lazybones / Solitude / London rhythm / Shoe shine boy / Rhythm saved the world / Old man of the mountain, The / Bugle call rag / How'm I doin' / Nagasaki / Organ grinder's song / My gal Sal / Ida sweet as apple cider / I've found a new baby / Put on your old gray bonnet / Baby won't you please come home / You rascal you / Nobody's sweetheart.
**Album:** Released Aug '82, on Decca by Decca International. Deleted '88. Catalogue no: **MOR 535**
**Album:** Released Jul '89, on Joy by President Records. Catalogue no: **JOY 297**
**Cass:** Released Aug '82, on Decca by Decca International. Deleted '88. Catalogue no: **KMORC 535**

**VERY BEST OF THE MILLS BROTHERS, THE**
**CD:** Released '86, on DGR (Holland) Catalogue no: **DGC 1002**

**VOLUME 1 1931-33**
**Album:** Released Nov '87, on Neovox by Neovox Records. Catalogue no: **NEO 918**

## Minerva Jazz Band

**PILE OF LOGS & STONE (CALLED HOME)**
**Album:** Released Oct '86, on Stomp Off (USA) Catalogue no: **SOS 1117**

## Mingus, Charles

**ABSTRACTIONS (Mingus, Charles Jazz Workshop)**
Tracks: / What is this thing called love / Minor intrusion / Stormy weather / Abstractions / Four hands / Thrice upon a theme / Spur of the moment.
**CD:** Released Sep '89, on Affinity by Charly Records. Catalogue no: **CDAFF 750**
**Album:** Released Apr '85, on Affinity by Charly Records. Catalogue no: **AFF 135**

**AH UM**
Tracks: / Better git it in your soul / Goodbye pork pie hat / Boogie stop shuffle / Self portrait in three colours / Open letter to Duke / Bird calls / Fables of Faubus / Pussy cat dues / Jelly roll.
**Cass:** Released May '83, on CBS by CBS Records. Deleted '87. Catalogue no: **40 21071**
**Album:** Released May '83, on CBS by CBS Records. Deleted '87. Catalogue no: **CBS 21071**

**ANTIBES FESTIVAL 1960 (see also under Dolphy, Eric) (Mingus, Charles & Eric Dolphy)**
**CD:** Released Mar '90, on Giants of Jazz by Hasmick Promotions. Catalogue no: **GOJCD53013**

**BLACK SAINT AND THE SINNER LADY, THE**
Tracks: / Solo dancer / Group and solo dancers / Single solos and group dance / Trio and group dancers / Group dancers freewoman / Duet solo dancers / Stop look and listen / Sinner Jim Whitney / Heart's beat and shades in physical embraces / Stop, look and sing songs of revolutions / Saint and sinner join in merriment on battle front / Group and solo dance of love / Pain & passioned revolt then / Farewell my beloved.
**Cass:** Released Dec '85, on MCA by MCA Records. Deleted Dec '89. Catalogue no: **ASC 35**
**Cass:** Released Jun '82, on Jasmine by Hasmick Promotions. Catalogue no: **JAS C13**
**CD:** Released '87, on MCA by MCA Records. Catalogue no: **MCAD 5649**
**Album:** Released Dec '85, on Impulse by Impulse Records. Catalogue no: **AS 35**
**Album:** Released Jun '82, on Jasmine by Hasmick Promotions. Deleted Feb '88. Catalogue no: **JAS 13**

**BLUES AND ROOTS**
Tracks: / Wednesday night prayer meeting / Crying blues / Moanin' / Tension / My Jelly Roll soul / E's flat ah's flat too.
**CD:** Released May '87, on Atlantic by WEA Records. Catalogue no: **781 336-2**
**Album:** Released Apr '87, on Atlantic by WEA Records. Catalogue no: **K 50232**

**CHANGES ONE**
Tracks: / Remember rockefeller at Attica / Sue's changes / Devil blues / Duke Ellington's sound of love.
**Album:** on Atlantic by WEA Records. Catalogue no: **K 50201**

**CHANGES TWO**
Tracks: / Free cell block F. tis Nazi USA / Orange was the colour of her dress / Then silk blue / Black bats and poles / Duke Ellington's sound of love / For Harry Carney.
**Album:** on Atlantic by WEA Records. Catalogue no: **K 50202**

**CHARLES MINGUS**
Tracks: / Better get hit (it) in your soul / Wednesday night prayer meeting / Prayer for passive resistance / I'll remember April / What love? / Folk forms.
**CD:** Released '89, on Giants of Jazz by

Hasmick Promotions. Catalogue no: **CD 0236**
**CD:** Released Jul '89, on Cleo Catalogue no: **CLCD 5005**

**CHARLES MINGUS PRESENTS CHARLES MINGUS**
**CD:** Released Aug '89, on Candid Catalogue no: **CCD 9005**
**Album:** Released Dec '85, on Candid Catalogue no: **CS 9005**

**CHARLES MINGUS WITH ORCHESTRA**
Tracks: / Man who never sleeps, The / O.P / Portrait.
Note: Personnel: Charles Mingus (Bass), Bobbie Jones (Tenor sax/clarinet), Eddie Preston (Trumpet), Masahiko Satoh (Piano), Toshiyuki Miyama & His New Herd.
**CD:** Released '88, on Denon Catalogue no: **CY-1388**

**COLLECTION: CHARLES MINGUS**
Tracks: / Pithecanthropus erectus / New York sketchbook / Orange was the colour of her dress / Duke Ellington medley / Duke's choice / Slippers / Nouroog / Epitaph, Part 1 / Epitaph, Part 2 / Clark in the dark / My search / Don't come back / Finale / From "Meditations on integration".
Note: Ellington medley: I've got it bad and that ain't good/ In a sentimental mood/ All too much/ Mood indigo/ Sophisticated lady/ Take the A train.
**Cass:** Released Aug '85, on Deja Vu Catalogue no: **DVMC 2038**

**CONNECTION**
Tracks: / I'll remember April / If I could be with you / Sweet and lovely / Shine on, harvest moon / Ladybird / I'm beginning to see the light / All the things you are / Yesterdays / Back home blues / I can't get started / Hamp's new blues / Summertime / Dizzy moods / Laura.
**Album:** Released Sep '79, on Vogue by Vogue Records. Catalogue no: **VJD 562**

**CUMBRIA & JAZZ FUSION**
Tracks: / Cumbia and jazz fusion / Music for Todo Modo.
**Album:** Released Jul '78, on Atlantic by WEA Records. Catalogue no: **K 50486**

**EAST COASTING (Mingus, Charlie Sextet)**
Tracks: / Memories of you / East coasting / West Coast ghost / Celia / Conversation / Fifty first street blues.
**Album:** Released May '82, on Affinity by Charly Records. Catalogue no: **AFF 86**

**FABLES OF FAUBUS VOL 2**
**Album:** Released Nov '82, on Ingo Catalogue no: **INGO 13**

**HIS FINAL WORK**
Tracks: / Just for laughs (part 1) / Peggy's blue skylight / Caroline Kiekki Mingus / Just for laughs (part 2) / Fables of Faubus / Duke Ellington's sound of love / Farewell farewell / So long Eric / Slop (CD only.) / It might as well be spring (CD only.).
Note: With Lionel Hampton/Dannie Richmond / Gerry Mulligan / Woody Shaw, etc.. Recorded 1977. Tracks include: Peggy's blue skylight / Fables of faubus / Caroline Keikki Mingus / Duke Ellingtons sound of love, etc..
**CD:** Released Oct '87, on Kingdom Jazz by Kingdom Records. Catalogue no: **CDGATE 7016**
**Album:** Released '84, on Kingdom Jazz by Kingdom Records. Catalogue no: **GATE 7016**
**Cass:** Released '89, on Kingdom Jazz by Kingdom Records. Catalogue no: **CGATE 7016**

**HOPE SO ERIC VOL 1 (Mingus, Charlie Orchestra with Eric Dolphy 1964)**
**Album:** Released Jul '82, on Ingo Catalogue no: **INGO 10**

**IMMORTAL CONCERTS (Jazz festival, Antibes, July 13, 1960) (Mingus, Charles & Eric Dolphy)**
Tracks: / Better git it in your soul / Wednesday night prayer meeting / Prayer for passive resistance / I'll remember April / What love? / Folk forms 1 / I'll remember April.
**CD:** Released Jul '88, on Entertainers Catalogue no: **ENTCD 236**
**CD:** Released '88, on Giants of Jazz by Hasmick Promotions. Catalogue no: **GOJCD 0236**

**IN BERLIN 1970 (Mingus, Charlie Sextet)**
**Album:** Released Mar '77, on Beppo Deleted '88. Catalogue no: **BEPPO 508**

**IN EUROPE**
**CD:** on Enja (Germany) by Enja Records (West Germany). Catalogue no: **ENJA 3077-38**

**JAZZ WORKSHOP**
**Album:** Released Feb '85, on Savoy (France) Deleted May '89. Catalogue no: **WL 70519**

**LIVE: CHARLIE MINGUS**
**Album:** Released May '79, on Affinity by Charly Records. Catalogue no: **AFF 19**

**LIVE IN CHATEAUVALLON 1972**
**Album:** Released '89, on France's Concert Catalogue no: **FC 135**
**CD:** Released '89, on France's Concert Catalogue no: **FCD 135**

**LIVE IN EUROPE (Mingus, Charlie Sextet)**
**Album:** Released Apr '81, on Unique Jazz by Spotlite Records. Catalogue no: **UJ 23**

**LIVE IN OSLO 1964**
**CD:** Released Jan '90, on Jazz-Up Catalogue no: **JU 307**

**LIVE IN PARIS 1964 VOL 2**
**CD:** Released Jun '88, on France's Concert Catalogue no: **FCD 110**
**Album:** Released Jun '88, on France's Concert Catalogue no: **FC 110**

**ME MYSELF AN EYE**
Tracks: / Three worlds of drums / Devil woman / Wednesday night prayer / Meeting / Carolyn 'Keki' Mingus.
**Album:** Released '77, on Atlantic by WEA Records. Deleted '82. Catalogue no: **K 50571**

**MEDITATION**
Tracks: / Peggy's blue skylight / Orange was the colour of her dress, then silk blue / Meditation for integration / Fables of Faubus.
**Album:** Released Jan '88, on Esoldun Catalogue no: **FC 102**
**CD:** Released Jan '88, on Esoldun Catalogue no: **FCD 102**

**MINGUS**
**Album:** Released Jun '86, on Candid Catalogue no: **CS 9021**
**CD:** Released Dec '87, on Candid Catalogue no: **CCD 9021**

**MINGUS AH UM**
Tracks: / Better git it in your soul / Goodbye pork pie hat / Boogie stop shuffle / Self portrait in three colours / Open letter to Duke / Bird calls / Fables of Faubus / Pussy cat dues / Jelly roll.
**Album:** Released 27 Feb '88, on CBS (import) by CBS Records. Catalogue no: **450 436 1**
**Cass:** Released 27 Feb '88, on CBS (import) by CBS Records. Catalogue no: **450 436 4**

**MINGUS AND DUKE**
**Album:** Released Jun '86, on Crusader Jazz Masterworks Catalogue no: **CJZ LP 10**

**MINGUS AT ANTIBES**
Tracks: / Wednesday night prayer meeting / Prayer for passive resistance / What love / I'll remember April / Folk forms 1 / Better git it in your soul.
**2 LP Set:** Released Dec '79, on Atlantic Jazz by WEA Records. Catalogue no: **SD 23001**

**MINGUS AT MONTEREY**
Tracks: / Duke Ellington medley / Orange was the colour of the dress, then blue / Meditations on integration.
**CD:** Released Jul '87, on JVC/Fantasy Deleted '88. Catalogue no: **VDJ 1572**
**2 LP Set:** Released Dec '81, on Prestige Catalogue no: **P 24100**

**MINGUS IN EUROPE VOL 1**
**Album:** Released Jan '82, on Enja (Germany) by Enja Records (West Germany). Catalogue no: **ENJA 3049**

**MINGUS IN EUROPE VOL 2**
**Album:** Released Jan '82, on Enja (Germany) by Enja Records (West Germany). Catalogue no: **ENJA 3077**

**MINGUS IN STUTTGART**
**2 LP Set:** Released Apr '81, on Unique Jazz by Spotlite Records. Catalogue no: **UJ 07/8**

**MINGUS IN STUTTGART VOL 2**
**Album:** Released Apr '81, on Unique Jazz by Spotlite Records. Catalogue no: **UJ 09**

**MINGUS, MINGUS, MINGUS, MINGUS, MINGUS**
Tracks: / II B.S. / I x love / Celia / Mood indigo.
**Album:** Released Jun '89, on MCA (Impulse Jazz) Catalogue no: **MCA 39119**

**Cass:** Released Aug '82, on Jasmine by Hasmick Promotions. Catalogue no: **JAS C36**
**CD:** Released Jun '89, on MCA (Impulse Jazz) Catalogue no: **MCAD 39119**
**Album:** Released Aug '82, on Jasmine by Hasmick Promotions. Deleted Feb '88. Catalogue no: **JAS 36**

**MINGUS OH YEAH**
Tracks: / Hog callin' blues / Devil woman / Wham bam thankyou ma'am / Ecclusiastics / Oh Lord don't let them drop that atomic bomb on me / Eat that chicken / Passions of a man.
**Album:** Released Jul '80, on Atlantic by WEA Records. Catalogue no: **K 40387**

**MINGUS PLAYS PIANO**
Tracks: / Myself when I am real / I can't get started / Body and soul / Roland Kirk's message / Memories of you / She's just Miss Popular hybrid / Orange was the colour of her dress, then silk blues / Meditations for Moses / Old portrait / I'm getting sentimental over you / Compositional theme story (Medley's, Anthems and Folklore.).
**Cass:** Released Sep '82, on Jasmine by Hasmick Promotions. Catalogue no: **JAS C49**
**Album:** Released Sep '82, on Jasmine by Hasmick Promotions. Catalogue no: **JAS 49**

**MINGUS QUINTET MEETS CAT ANDERSON**
**Album:** Released Apr '81, on Unique Jazz by Spotlite Records. Catalogue no: **UJ 20**

**MINGUS THREE**
**Album:** Released Feb '83, on Carosello Catalogue no: **JLP 1054**

**NEW TIJUANA MOODS**
Tracks: / Dizzy moods (2 takes) / Ysabel's table dance (2 takes) / Los mariachis (the street musicians) (2 takes) / Flamingo (2 takes) / Tijuana gift shop (2 takes).
**CD:** Released Jun '88, on Bluebird (2) by BMG Records (UK). Catalogue no: **ND 85644**
**Cass:** Released Jan '87, on RCA by BMG Records (UK). Deleted May '89. Catalogue no: **PK 85635**
**2 LP Set:** Released Jan '87, on RCA by BMG Records (UK). Deleted May '89. Catalogue no: **PL 85635**

**NEW YORK SKETCH BOOK**
Tracks: / Memories of you / East coasting / West Coast ghost / Celia / Conversation / Fifty first street blues / Scenes in the city / New York sketchbook.
Note: Track 1: Blake/Razaf. Tracks 2-9: Mingus. Including the complete 'East Coasting' session. Original Bethlehem Recordings.
**CD:** Released Jun '86, on Charly by Charly Records. Catalogue no: **CDCHARLY 19**

**NEWPORT REBELS (Mingus, Charles / Eric Dolphy / Roy Eldridge / Max Roach / Jo Jones)**
Tracks: / Mysterious blues / Cliff walk / Wrap your troubles in dreams / T'aint nobody's business if I do / Me and you.
**CD:** Released Apr '87, on Candid Catalogue no: **CCD 9022**
**Album:** Released Apr '87, on Candid Catalogue no: **CS 9022**

**PARKERIANA VOL 3**
**Album:** Released Nov '82, on Ingo Catalogue no: **INGO 15**

**PASSIONS OF A MAN**
Tracks: / Passions of a man / Pithecantropus erectus / Profile of Jackie / Reincarnation of a love bird / Haitian fight song / Wednesday night prayer meeting / Cryin' blues / Devil woman / Duke Ellington's sound of love / Better git hit in your soul / Sue's changes / Canon / Free cell block F 'tis Nazi USA / Goodbye pork pie hat / Mingus on Mingus / Wham bam thank you M'am / Passions of a woman loved / Tonight at noon.
**LP Set:** Released Sep '79, on Atlantic by WEA Records. Catalogue no: **SD3 600**

**PITHYCANTHROPUS ERECTUS**
**CD:** Released Dec '85, on Musidisc by Musidisc Records (France). Catalogue no: **139 216**
**CD:** Released '88, on Atlantic Jazz by WEA Records. Catalogue no: **K 781 456 2**

**PORTRAIT: CHARLES MINGUS**
Tracks: / So long eric / Playing with Eric / Meditation for a pair of wirecutters / So long Eric / She's funny that way / Embraceable you / I can't get started / Ghost of a chance / Old portrait / Cocktails for two.
**Album:** Released Oct '80, on Prestige Deleted Jan '88. Catalogue no: **PR 24092**

**PRE-BIRD**
Tracks: / Take the 'A' train / Prayer for passive resistance / Eclipse / Mingus fingus No.2 / Weird nightmare / Do nothing till you hear from me / Bemoanable / Half mast inhibition.
**Album:** Released Oct '83, on Philips (Holland) by PolyGram UK Ltd. Catalogue no: **6336 321**

**PRESENTS CHARLES MINGUS**
Note: Tracks include: Folk forms/Original faubus fables/What love/All the things you should be now.
**CD:** Released Nov '87, on Candid Catalogue no: **CCD 9005**

**REINCARNATION OF A LOVEBIRD**
Tracks: / Reincarnation of a lovebird (Take 1) / Wrap your troubles in dreams (take 4) / R & R (Take 1) / Body and soul (Take 2) / Bugs (Take 3).
**CD:** Released Jun '88, on Candid Catalogue no: **CCD 9026**
**Album:** Released Jun '88, on Candid Catalogue no: **CS 9026**

**REVISITED**
Tracks: / Take the 'A' train / Prayer for passive resistance / Eclipse / Mingus fingus (No.2) / Weird nightmare / Do nothing till you hear from me / Bemoanable lady / Half mast inhibition.
Note: Originally released in 1960 under the title "Pre-bird" this is one of the great Mingus large group recordings with all star line-up including Clark Terry and Marcus Belgrave trumpets, Slide Hampton and Jimmy Knepper, trombones, Eric Dolphy and Joe Farrell, saxes, Danny Richmond, drums, and others too numerous to list here. Apart from two "Ellingtonian" tracks all compositions are Mingus originals.
**Album:** Released Jul '81, on Polydor by Polydor Ltd. Catalogue no: **2478 146**
**CD:** Released Jun '86, on Verve (USA) by Polydor Ltd. Catalogue no: **826 496-2**

**RIGHT NOW: LIVE AT THE JAZZ**
**Album:** Released Apr '86, on Original Jazz Classics (USA) by Fantasy Inc (USA). Catalogue no: **OJC 237**

**SCENES IN THE CITY**
Tracks: / Scenes in the city / Nou roug / New York sketchbook / Duke's choice / Slippers.
Note: Recorded in 1957, with Clarence Shaw (trumpet), Jimmy Knepper (trombone), Shafi Hadi (tenor sax), Charles Mingus (bass), Dannie Richmond (drums).
**Album:** Released Nov '83, on Affinity by Charly Records. Catalogue no: **AFF 105**

**SHOES OF THE FISHERMANS WIFE**
Tracks: / Slop / Song with orange / Gunslinging bird / Things ain't what they used to be / Shoes of the fisherman's wife are... / Far wells, mill valley / Mood indigo.
**Album:** Released 22 Aug '88, on CBS (import) by CBS Records. Catalogue no: **4608221**
**Cass:** Released 22 Aug '88, on CBS (import) by CBS Records. Catalogue no: **4608224**

**STATEMENTS**
**Album:** Released Sep '87, on Lotus Catalogue no: **LOP 14 066**
**Album:** Released Apr '81, on Lotus Catalogue no: **LPPS 111 08**

**STRINGS AND KEYS**
**Album:** Released Jun '86, on Fantasy Inc (USA) by Fantasy Inc (USA). Catalogue no: **1902110**

**TIJUANA MOODS**
**Album:** Released Feb '87, on RCA by BMG Records (UK). Deleted May '89. Catalogue no: **PL 85635**
**Cass:** Released Feb '86, on RCA by BMG Records (UK). Deleted Nov '88. Catalogue no: **NK 89593**
**Album:** Released Feb '86, on RCA by BMG Records (UK). Deleted Nov '88. Catalogue no: **NL 89593**

**TOWN HALL CONCERT**
**CD:** Released Apr '87, on Carrere (France) Catalogue no: **98425**

**TRIO (Mingus, Charles Trio)**
**Album:** Released Feb '88, on Fresh Sounds (Spain) by Fresh Sounds Records (Spain). Catalogue no: **FS 279**

**WILD BASS, THE**
**Album:** Released Oct '88, on Vogue by Vogue Records. Catalogue no: **500081**

**YOUNG REBEL**
**Album:** Released Aug '86, on Swingtime by Contact Records (Denmark). Catalogue no: **ST 1010**

## Mingus Dynasty

**LIVE AT MONTREUX: MINGUS DYNASTY**
Tracks: / Haitian fight song / Consider me Oh Lord / Fables of Maubus / Ysabel's table dance / Sketch two / Better git hit in your soul.
**Album:** Released Mar '81, on Atlantic by WEA Records. Catalogue no: **K 99145**

**REINCARNATION**
**CD:** Released '86, on Soul Note Catalogue no: **SNCD 1042**

## Minstrels & Tunesmiths

**MINSTRELS & TUNESMITHS Roots of American music 1902-23 (Various artists)**
**Album:** Released '88, on JEMF (USA) by Arhoolie Records (USA). Catalogue no: **JEMF 109**

## Mintzer, Bob

**CAMOUFLAGE (Mintzer, Bob Big Band)**
**CD:** Released '86, on DMP Catalogue no: **CD 456**

**INCREDIBLE JOURNEY (Mintzer, Bob Big Band)**
**CD:** Released '86, on DMP Catalogue no: **CD 451**

**PAPA LIPS (Mintzer, Bob Horn Man Band)**
**CD:** Released '86, on Toshiba-EMI (Japan) Catalogue no: **TEC 2022**

## Mirage

**AVANT-GARDE AND THIRD-STREAM JAZZ**
Tracks: / Summer sequence (Ralph Burns) / Clothed woman (Duke Ellington) / Yesterdays (Jerome Kern & Otto Harbach) / Mirage (Pete Rugolo) / Eclipse (Charles Mingus) / Egdon Heath (Bill Russo) / Concerto for Billy the kid (George Russell) / Transformation (Gunther Schuller) / Piazza navona (John Lewis) / Laura (David Raksin & Johnny Mercer).
**Album:** Released Sep '86, on New World (USA) by New World Records (USA). Catalogue no: **NW 216**

## Misha Lobko Sextet

**RITUALS**
**Album:** Released 1 Mar '88, on Leo by Leo Records. Catalogue no: **LR 141**

## Mississippi...

**MISSISSIPPI COUNTRY BLUES VOL.1 (Various artists)**
Note: Featuring: Rob Johnson, Otto Virgial, Rob Lockwood.
**Album:** Released Apr '88, on Document Catalogue no: **DLP 519**
**Album:** Released Apr '88, on Document Catalogue no: **DLP 520**

**MISSISSIPPI DELTA BLUES (VOL.1) various artists (Various artists)**
**Album:** Released May '81, on Arhoolie (USA) by Arhoolie Records (USA). Catalogue no: **ARHOOLIE 1041**

**MISSISSIPPI DELTA BLUES (VOL.2) various artists (Various artists)**
**Album:** Released May '81, on Arhoolie (USA) by Arhoolie Records (USA). Catalogue no: **ARHOOLIE 1042**

**MISSISSIPPI GIRLS 1928-31 (Various artists)**
Note: Tracks by: Rosie Mae Moore, Mary Butler, Mattie Delaney, Geechie Wiley & Elvie Thomas.
**Album:** Released '88, on Earl Archives Catalogue no: **BD 2018**

**MISSISSIPPI LEGENDS Music of New Orleans (Mississippi Legends)**
**LP Set:** Released '83, on RCA (France) by BMG Records (France). Catalogue no: **FXM3 7242**

**UP & DOWN THE MISSISSIPPI (Various artists)**
**Album:** Released Oct '88, on Roots (Germany) Catalogue no: **RL 319**

## Mississippi Blues

**MISSISSIPPI BLUES (Various artists)**
**Album:** Released Sep '87, on HK Catalogue no: **HK 4001**

**MISSISSIPPI BLUES 1927-41 (Various artists)**
**Album:** Released Dec '88, on Yazoo (USA) by Shanachie Records (USA). Catalogue no: **L 1001**

**MISSISSIPPI BLUES GUITAR 1926-35 (Various artists)**
**Album:** Released '88, on Earl Archives Catalogue no: **BD 2014**

**MISSISSIPPI BLUES VOL.1 (Various artists)**
**Album:** Released Oct '88, on Roots (Germany) Catalogue no: **RL 302**

**MISSISSIPPI BLUES VOL.2 (Various artists)**
**Album:** Released Oct '88, on Roots (Germany) Catalogue no: **RL 303**

**MISSISSIPPI BLUES VOL.3 (Various artists)**
**Album:** Released Oct '88, on Roots (Germany) Catalogue no: **RL 314**

## Mississippi Moaners

**MISSISSIPPI MOANERS 1927-42 (Various artists)**
**Album:** Released Dec '88, on Yazoo (USA) by Shanachie Records (USA). Catalogue no: **L 1009**

## Mississippi Sheiks

**MISSISSIPPI SHEIKS VOL 1 (1930)**
**Album:** Released Sep '85, on Matchbox by Flyright Records. Catalogue no: **MSE 1005**

**MISSISSIPPI SHEIKS VOL. 2 1930-34**
**Album:** Released Feb '88, on Matchbox by Flyright Records. Catalogue no: **MSE 1012**

## Mister Charlie

**MISTER CHARLIES BLUES Old Timey anthology (Various artists)**
**Album:** Released Dec '88, on Yazoo (USA) by Shanachie Records (USA). Catalogue no: **L 1024**

## Mitchell, Bill

**VINTAGE PIANO VOL.3 (Mitchell, Bill/Paul Lingle)**
**Album:** Released Apr '79, on Euphonic Catalogue no: **ESR 1203**

## Mitchell, Billy

**FACES**
**Album:** Released Oct '87, on Optimism (Germany) Catalogue no: **VR 2501**
**Cass:** Released Oct '87, on Beserkley by Beserkley Records (USA). Catalogue no: **BZCA 1001**

**IN FOCUS**
**Album:** Released 12 Apr '89, on Optimism (Germany) Catalogue no: **OP 2502**
**CD:** Released 12 Apr '89, on Optimism (Germany) Catalogue no: **OPCD 2502**

## Mitchell, Blue

**CUP BEARERS, THE**
Tracks: / Turquoise / Why do I love you? / Dingbat blues / Capers / Cup bearers / How deep is the ocean? / Tiger Lily.
**Album:** Released Feb '88, on Riverside (USA) by Fantasy Inc (USA). Catalogue no: **RSLP 439**\

**GRAFFITI BLUES**
**Album:** Released Mar '83, on Audio Fidelity(USA) by Audio Fidelity (USA). Catalogue no: **MRL 5006**

**THING TO DO, THE**
Tracks: / Fungii mama / Mona's mood / Thing to do, The / Step lightly / Chick's tune.
Note: Trumpeter Mitchell's first album as leader, with Chick Corea, Junior Cooke, GeneTaylor, Al Foster.
**CD:** Released Mar '89, on Blue Note by EMI Records. Catalogue no: **BNZ 127**
**CD:** Released Mar '89, on Blue Note by EMI Records. Catalogue no: **CDP 784 178 2**
**Album:** Released Aug '89, on Blue Note by EMI Records. Catalogue no: **BST 84178**

## Mitchell, Grover

**GROVER MITCHELL & HIS ORCHESTRA (Mitchell, Grover & His Orchestra)**
**CD:** Released '88, on Stash (USA) Catalogue no: **STCD 9**

**TRUCKIN' WITH GROVER MITCHELL (Mitchell, Grover & His Orchestra)**
**Album:** Released '88, on Stash (USA) Catalogue no: **ST 277**

## Mitchell, Red

**BLUES FOR A CRUSHED SOUL**
**Album:** Released Jun '88, on Sonet by Sonet Records. Catalogue no: **SNTF 762**

**HOLIDAY (Various artists)**
**Album:** Released '88, on Phontastic (Sweden) Catalogue no: **PHONT 7548**

**JAM FOR YOUR BREAD**
Tracks: / Jam for your bread / Duff / You go to my head / Where or when / Ornithology / Section blues / East coast outpost / I'll never be the same / Will you still be mine.
**Album:** Released Oct '86, on Affinity by Charly Records. Deleted May '88. Catalogue no: **AFF 159**

**RED MITCHELL QUARTET (Mitchell, Red Quartet)**
Tracks: / Sandu / Paul's pal / Out of the blue / Scrapple from the apple.
Note: Tracks include those listed above.
**Album:** Released Dec '81, on Contemporary (USA) Catalogue no: **1007 538**

## Mitchell, Roscoe

**CONCERT TORONTO 4/5 OCT 1975**
**Album:** Released Apr '81, on Sackville by Spotlite Records. Catalogue no: **2009**

**CONGLIPTIONS**
**Album:** Released Mar '79, on Nessa Deleted '83. Catalogue no: **N 2**

**DUETS WITH ANTHONY BRAXTON**
**Album:** Released Apr '81, on Sackville by Spotlite Records. Catalogue no: **3016**

**MAZE, THE / S II EXAMPLES (L.R.G.)**
Note: A founder member of the Art Ensemble of Chicago, Mitchell is one of the most important composers in contemporary music. These legendary recordings, made in 1978 and originally a two-record set, now fill a CD at well over 70 minutes. LRG is a trio of Mitchell, Leo Smith and George Lewis, playing a total of 16 wind instruments among them. The Maze is an incredibly atmospheric piece for eight percussionists; S II Examples is a soprano sax solo by Mitchell. (Chief Records, June 1989)
**CD:** Released Jun '89, on Chief Catalogue no: **CHIEFCD 4**
**2 LP Set:** Released Mar '79, on Nessa Catalogue no: **N 14/15**

**MORE CUTOUTS (Mitchell, Roscoe / Hugh Ragin)**
**Album:** Released '88, on Cecma Catalogue no: **CECMA 1003**

**NONAAH**
**2 LP Set:** Released Mar '79, on Nessa Deleted '83. Catalogue no: **N 9/10**

**OLD/ QUARTET**
**Album:** Released Mar '79, on Nessa Deleted '83. Catalogue no: **N 5**

**ROSCOE MITCHELL SOLO SAXOPHONE**
**Album:** Released Jul '86, on Sackville by Spotlite Records. Catalogue no: **2006**

**SOUND**
**Album:** Released '74, on Delmark (USA) by Delmark Records (USA). Catalogue no: **DL 408**

## Mitchell, Sam

**BOTTLENECK & SLIDE GUITAR**
**Album:** Released Jan '78, on Kicking Mule by Sonet Records. Deleted '88. Catalogue no: **SNKF 121**
**Album:** Released Mar '89, on Kicking Mule by Sonet Records. Catalogue no: **KM 129**

**FOLLOW YOU DOWN**
**Album:** Released Feb '79, on Kicking Mule by Sonet Records. Catalogue no: **SNKF 146**

## Mitchell, Whitey

**WHITEY MITCHELL SEXTETTE (Mitchell, Whitey Sextette)**
**Album:** Released Feb '88, on Fresh Sounds (Spain) by Fresh Sounds Records (Spain). Catalogue no: **FS 72**

## Mobley, Hank

**ANOTHER WORKOUT**
Tracks: / Out of Joe's bag / I should care / Gettin' and jettin' / Hank's other soul / Hello young lovers / Three coins in the fountain.
**CD:** Released Jan '89, on Blue Note by EMI Records. Catalogue no: **CDP 784 431 2**
**CD:** Released Jan '89, on Blue Note by EMI Records. Catalogue no: **BNZ 130**
**Cass:** Released Sep '87, on Blue Note by EMI Records. Deleted Jun '88. Catalogue no: **4BN 84431**
**Album:** Released Jul '89, on Blue Note by EMI Records. Catalogue no: **BST 84431**

**DIPPIN'**
Tracks: / Dip, The / Recado bossa nova / Break through, The / Vamp, The / I see your face before me / Ballin.
**CD:** Released May '87, on Blue Note by EMI Records. Catalogue no: **BNZ 62**
**CD:** Released May '87, on Blue Note by EMI Records. Catalogue no: **CDP 746 511 2**

**FAR AWAY LANDS**
Tracks: / Dab of this and that / Far away lands / No argument / Hippity hop, The / Bossa for baby / Soul time.
**Album:** Released Apr '85, on Blue Note by EMI Records. Catalogue no: **BST 84425**
**CD:** Released Apr '89, on Blue Note by EMI Records. Catalogue no: **CDP 784 425 2**
**CD:** Released Apr '89, on Blue Note by EMI Records. Catalogue no: **BNZ 129**

**HANK MOBLEY QUINTET, THE**
Tracks: / Funk in deep freeze / Funk in deep freeze (alternate take) / Wham and they're off / Wham and they're off (alternate take) / Fin de l'affaire / Startin' from scratch / Stella-wise / Bass on balls.
**CD:** Released Aug '87, on Blue Note by EMI Records. Catalogue no: **CDP 746 816 2**
**CD:** Released Aug '87, on Blue Note by EMI Records. Catalogue no: **BNZ 65**

**HIGH VOLTAGE**
Tracks: / High voltage / Two and one / No more goodbyes / Advance notice / Bossa deluxe / Flirty gerty.
Note: Bolstering hisusual quintet format with a third horn,in this case Jackie McLean Mobley adds new colours and flavours to his writing and ensamble sound.TrumpeterBlue Mitchell Completes the front line.Aside from the funky title tune,there aresuch varied fare as the soulful 'Bossa Deluxe' and the beautiful ballad 'No moregoodbyes'.
**CD:** Released Apr '89, on Blue Note by EMI Records. Catalogue no: **BNZ 128**
**Album:** Released Jul '89, on Blue Note by EMI Records. Catalogue no: **BST 84273**
**CD:** Released Apr '89, on Blue Note by EMI Records. Catalogue no: **CDP 784 273 2**

**MONDAY NIGHT AT BIRDLAND**
**Album:** Released Mar '80, on Vogue by Vogue Records. Catalogue no: **VJD 565**

**NO ROOM FOR SQUARES**
Tracks: / No room for squares / Three way split / Me 'n' you / Carolyn / No room for squares (alt. take) (CD only.) / Comin' back (CD only.) / Carolyn (alt. take) (CD only.) / Syrup and biscuits (CD only.) / Up a step (LP only.) / Old world, new imports (LP only.).
**CD:** Released Jul '89, on Blue Note by EMI Records. Catalogue no: **BNZ 151**
**CD:** Released Jul '89, on Blue Note by EMI Records. Catalogue no: **CDP 784 149 2**
**Album:** Released Jul '89, on Blue Note by EMI Records. Catalogue no: **B1 84149**

**PECKIN' TIME**
Tracks: / High and flighty / High and flighty (alternate take) / Speak low / Speak low (alternate take) / Peckin' time / Stretchin' out / Stretchin' out (alt. take) / Git go blues.
**Album:** Released Jul '89, on Blue Note by EMI Records. Catalogue no: **B1 81574**
**CD:** Released Jun '89, on Blue Note by EMI Records. Catalogue no: **BNZ 170**
**Album:** Released Jul '89, on Blue Note by EMI Records. Catalogue no: **781 574 1**
**CD:** Released Jun '89, on Blue Note by EMI Records. Catalogue no: **CDP 781 574 2**

**ROLL CALL**
Tracks: / Roll call / My groove your move / Take your pick / Baptist beat, A / Baptist beat, A (alternate take) / More I see you, The / Breakdown, The.
**CD:** Released Aug '87, on Blue Note by EMI Records. Catalogue no: **CDP 746 823 2**
**CD:** Released Aug '87, on Blue Note by EMI Records. Catalogue no: **BNZ 64**

**SOUL STATION**
Tracks: / Remember / This I dig of you / Dig dis / Split feelin's / Soul station / If I should lose you.

**CD:** Released Apr '88, on Blue Note by EMI Records. Catalogue no: **BNZ 63**
**Album:** Released Feb '88, on Blue Note by EMI Records. Catalogue no: **BLJ 84031**
**CD:** Released Apr '88, on Blue Note by EMI Records. Catalogue no: **CDP 746 528 2**

**STRAIGHT NO FILTER**
Tracks: / Straight no filter / Chain reaction / Soft impression / Third time around (Not on CD.) / Hanks waltz (Not on CD.) / Feeling's good, The / Old world, new imports (CD only.) / Up a step (CD only.) / East of the village (CD only.) / Yes indeed (CD only.) / Good life, The (CD only.).
Note: Composed by Hank Mobley.Produced by CBS U Catalog Inc. / ASCAP.Original session produced by Alfred Lion.Produced for release by Michael Cuscana.
**CD:** Released Aug '89, on Blue Note by EMI Records. Catalogue no: **BNZ 153**
**Album:** Released Dec '86, on Blue Note by EMI Records. Catalogue no: **BST 84435**
**CD:** Released Aug '89, on Blue Note by EMI Records. Catalogue no: **CDP 784 435 2**

**TURNAROUND, THE**
Tracks: / Pat 'n' chat / Third time around (CD only.) / Hank's waltz (CD only.) / Turn around / Straight ahead / My sin / East of the village (LP only.) / Good life, The (LP only.).
**CD:** Released Aug '89, on Blue Note by EMI Records. Catalogue no: **BNZ 152**
**CD:** Released Aug '89, on Blue Note by EMI Records. Catalogue no: **CDP 784 186 2**
**Album:** Released Jul '89, on Blue Note by EMI Records. Catalogue no: **B1 84186**
**Album:** Released Jul '89, on Blue Note by EMI Records. Catalogue no: **784 186 1**

**WORKOUT**
Tracks: / Workout / Uh huh / Smokin' / Best things in life are free, The / Greasin' easy / Three coins in the fountain.
**Album:** Released Jul '89, on Blue Note by EMI Records. Catalogue no: **784 080 1**
**Album:** Released Jul '89, on Blue Note by EMI Records. Catalogue no: **B1 84080**
**Album:** Released Sep '84, on Blue Note by EMI Records. Deleted '87. Catalogue no: **BST 84080**
**CD:** Released '88, on Blue Note by EMI Records. Catalogue no: **BNZ 116**
**CD:** Released '88, on Blue Note by EMI Records. Catalogue no: **CDP 784 080 2**

## Modern Art Of Jazz

**MODERN ART OF JAZZ BY MAT MATTHEWS (Various artists)**
**Album:** Released Feb '88, on Fresh Sounds (Spain) by Fresh Sounds Records (Spain). Catalogue no: **FS 245**

## Modern Jazz

**MODERN JAZZ (Various artists)**
Note: Features Art Blakey, Gerry Mulligan and others.
**Album:** Released Oct '88, on Vogue (France) by Vogue Records. Catalogue no: **509171**

## Modern Jazz (Group)

**IN MY SLEEP**
Tracks: / In my sleep / Sheep B side.
**7" Single:** Released Feb '81, on Magnet by WEA Records. Deleted '84. Catalogue no: **MAG 185**

**IVORY TOWERS**
Tracks: / Ivory towers / I'm in reverse.
**7" Single:** Released May '81, on Magnet by WEA Records. Deleted May '84. Catalogue no: **MAG 201**

## Modern Jazz Piano

**MODERN JAZZ PIANO ALBUM**
Note: Artists include: Donald Bryd / Kenny Clarke / Max Roach / Herbie Nichols / etc..A classic double featuring legendary names recorded between 1946 - 1956 featuring.
**2 LP Set:** Released Dec '84, on Savoy (France) Deleted May '89. Catalogue no: **WL 70510**

## Modern Jazz Quartet

**Biographical details:** John Lewis (piano/arrangements), Milt Jackson (vibes), and Kenny Clarke (drums) met when they played together in the Dizzie Gillespie orchestra in the 1940's. They came together again in 1952, when Milt Jackson recorded an album under his own name (Percy Heath was the bass player). John Lewis was already recognised as an arranger and composer and was known for his personal, blues orientated piano interpretations. After the recording session Lewis accompanied Ella Fitzgerald on tour. On his return in 1954, realizing that the album had been a hit, Lewis reformed the quartet which gained recognition for a style in which each component improvised on a basic theme.Lewis, who had studied music at university, created a sound which rather than continuing in the black, American jazz tradition, was reminiscent of European, classical tones, subsequently percussionist Connie Kay replaced Kenny Clarke and the quartet went on to develop a very polished sound with attention to form and style tending to the baroque. In 1974, however, when Jackson decided to leave, the quartet broke up, not without having given a new dimension to jazz..

**ART OF MODERN JAZZ QUARTET: ATLANTIC YEARS**
Tracks: / Golden striker, The / Cortege / Bags groove / Cylinder, The / England's Carol / Lonely woman / Today (home) / Dijango / Sketch / Bluesology / Spanish steps / Concorde / Summertime / Fun / Ralph's new blues.
**Album:** Released '74, on Atlantic by WEA Records. Catalogue no: **K 60041**

**ARTISTRY IN JAZZ (Greatest hits)**
**CD:** Released May '87, on JVC/Fantasy Catalogue no: **VDJ 1592**

**AT BIRDLAND: MODERN JAZZ QUARTET**
**Album:** Released Apr '81, on Joker (USA) by Lifetime Records (USA). Catalogue no: **SM 3785**

**AT THE MUSIC INN WITH SONNY ROLLINS**
Tracks: / Oh Bess, oh where's my Bess / Fugue for Music Inn / Two degrees East, three degrees West / Serenade / Fun / Sun dance / Man that got away / Morning in Paris / God rest ye merry gentlemen (variation no. 1).
**Album:** Released Nov '80, on Atlantic by WEA Records. Catalogue no: **K 30026**

**AT THE OPERA HOUSE (Modern Jazz Quartet & Oscar Peterson Trio)**
Tracks: / Now's the time / Round midnight / D & E blues / Should I love you? / Big fat mama / Indiana / Joy spring / Elevation.
Note: Recorded in 1962.
**Album:** Released Oct '84, on Verve (USA) by Polydor Ltd. Catalogue no: **823 092-1**

**BEST OF MODERN JAZZ QUARTET, THE**
Tracks: / Valeria / Le cannet / Nature boy / Watergate blues / Connie's blues / Reunion blues / Echoes.
**Cass:** Released Jan '89, on Pablo Jazz (USA) by Pablo Records (USA). Catalogue no: **PEMC 003**
**CD:** Released Jan '89, on Pablo Jazz (USA) by Pablo Records (USA). Catalogue no: **CDPEM 003**
**Album:** Released Jan '89, on Pablo Jazz (USA) by Pablo Records (USA). Catalogue no: **PEM 003**

**BLUES ON BACH**
Tracks: / Regret / Blues in B flat / Rise up in the morning / Blues in A minor / Precious joy / Blues in C minor / Don't stop this train blues in H / Tears from the children.
**Album:** Released Oct '74, on Atlantic by WEA Records. Catalogue no: **K 50039**
**CD:** Released '88, on Atlantic Jazz by WEA Records. Catalogue no: **K78 139 32**

**COLLECTION: MODERN JAZZ QUARTET**
Tracks: / One bass hit / Queen's fancy, The / Now's the time / Django / D & E blues / Autumn in New York / Round about midnight / Delaunay's Dilemma / But not for me / Milano / La ronde suite (piano) / La ronde suite (bass) / La ronde suite (vibes) / La ronde suite (drums).
**CD:** Released Sep '87, on Deja Vu Catalogue no: **DVCD 2043**
**Cass:** Released Sep '87, on Deja Vu Catalogue no: **DVMC 2043**

**COMEDY**
Tracks: / Spanish steps / Columbine / Pulcinella / Pierrot / La cantarice / Har-

lequin / Piazza navona.
**Album:** Released May '81, on Atlantic by WEA Records. Deleted '86. Catalogue no: **K 50729**

**CONCORDE**
Tracks: / Ralph's New Blues / All of You / I'll Remember April / Gershwin melodies / Softly as in a morning sunrise / Concorde.
**Cass:** Released May '88, on Prestige Deleted Jan '90. Catalogue no: **PRC 7005**
**Album:** Released May '88, on Prestige Catalogue no: **PR 7005**
**CD:** Released '86, on Carrere (France) Catalogue no: **CA 98 427**

**DJANGO**
**CD:** Released '88, on Fantasy (import) by Fantasy Inc (USA). Catalogue no: **FCD 6307057**

**ECHOES**
**CD:** Released Jan '89, on JVC/Fantasy Catalogue no: **VDJ 28011**
**CD:** Released '88, on Pablo Jazz (USA) by Pablo Records (USA). Catalogue no: **131 124 1**
**Cass:** Released Sep '84, on Verve (USA) by Polydor Ltd. Catalogue no: **K12 142**
**Album:** Released Sep '84, on Verve (USA) by Polydor Ltd. Catalogue no: **2312 142**

**FOR ELLINGTON**
Tracks: / For Ellington / Jack the bear / Prelude to a kiss / It don't mean a thing / Koko / Maestro E.K.E. / Sepia panorama / Rockin' in rhythm.
**CD:** Released Sep '88, on WEA by WEA Records. Catalogue no: **790926 2**
**Cass:** Released Sep '88, on WEA by WEA Records. Catalogue no: **790926 4**
**Album:** Released Sep '88, on WEA by WEA Records. Catalogue no: **790926 1**

**IMMORTAL CONCERTS (Scandinavia, April 1960)**
Tracks: / Django / Bluesology / La ronde / I remember Clifford / Vendome / Odds against tomorrow / Pyramid / It don't mean a thing / Round midnight / Bag's Groove / I'll remember April / Skating in Central Park / I should care / Festival sketch.
**CD:** Released '88, on Giants of Jazz by Hasmick Promotions. Catalogue no: **GOJCD 0234**

**IN MEMORIAM**
Tracks: / In memoriam / First movement / Second movement / Jazz ostinato / Adagio from the guitar concerto / Converto de aranjuez.
**Album:** on Little David (USA) Catalogue no: **K 59650**

**LAST CONCERT, THE**
Tracks: / Softly as in a morning sunrise / Cylinder, The / Summertime / Trav'lin blues in a minor / One never knows / Bag's groove / Confirmation / Round midnight / Night in Tunisia / Golden striker, The / Skating in central park / Django / What's new.
**Album:** Released Jul '75, on Atlantic by WEA Records. Catalogue no: **K 60098**

**LESTER MEETS MILES (MJQ & Jack Teagarden All Stars)**
**Album:** Released Nov '86, on Unique Jazz by Spotlite Records. Catalogue no: **UJ 14**

**LIVE AT DONAUSCHINGEN, 1957, AND**
**Album:** Released Feb '83, on Ingo Catalogue no: **INGO 12**

**LIVE AT THE LIGHTHOUSE**
**CD:** Released '86, on Mobile Fidelity Sound Lab(USA) by Mobile Fidelity Records (USA). Catalogue no: **MFCD 827**

**LIVE IN MONTREUX**
**CD:** Released '88, on Pablo Jazz (USA) by Pablo Records (USA). Catalogue no: **J33J 20005**

**LONELY WOMAN**
Tracks: / Lonely woman / Animal dance / New York / Belkis / Why are you blue / Fugato / Lamb, leopard / Trieste.
**Album:** Released Aug '80, on Atlantic by WEA Records. Catalogue no: **K 50723**

**LONGING FOR THE CONTINENT**
Tracks: / Animal dance / Django / England's carol / Bluesology / Bag's groove / Sketch 3 / Ambiquite / Midsummer.
Note: Personnel: John Lewis (Piano), Milt Jackson (Vibraphone), Percy Heath (bass), Connie Kay, (Drums), and The Jazz Group De Paris conducted by Androe Holdeir.
**CD:** Released '88, on Denon Catalogue no: **C38-7678**
**Cass:** Released Apr '89, on Denon Catalogue no: **MC 7678**
**CD:** Released Apr '89, on Denon Catalogue no: **DC 8539**

**MODERN JAZZ QUARTET**
**Album:** Released Apr '87, on Crusader Jazz Masterworks Catalogue no: **CJZ LP 6**
**Cass:** Released Apr '87, on Crusader Jazz Masterworks Catalogue no: **CJZ MC 6**

**MODERN JAZZ QUARTET (Compact/Walkman jazz)**
Tracks: / Golden striker, The / On Green Dolphin Street / D & E / I'll remember April / Cortege / Now's the time / J.B. blues / Reunion blues / Round midnight / Three windows.
**CD:** Released 27 Feb '88, on Verve Catalogue no: **833 290-2**
**Album:** Released Sep '87, on Giants of Jazz by Hasmick Promotions. Catalogue no: **LPJT 56**
**Cass:** Released 27 Feb '88, on Verve Catalogue no: **833 290-4**
**Cass:** Released '88, on Joker (USA) by Lifetime Records (USA). Catalogue no: **MC 3785**
**Album:** Released '88, on Joker (USA) by Lifetime Records (USA). Catalogue no: **SM 3785**

**MODERN JAZZ QUARTET LIVE 1956**
**CD:** Released Oct '89, on Jazz Anthology by Musidisc Records (France). Catalogue no: **550062**

**MODERN JAZZ QUARTET (PRESTIGE)**
Tracks: / Concorde / Vendome / Milano / Gershwin medley / La ronde / Django / All the things you are / One bass hit / Autumn in New York / Queens fancy / I'll remember April / Softly as in a morning's sunrise / Delauney's dilemma / But not for me / La ronde suite / All of you / Rose of the Rio Grande / Ralph's new blues.
**Album:** Released '79, on Prestige Deleted '84. Catalogue no: **PR 24005**

**MORE FROM THE LAST CONCERT**
Tracks: / Really true blues / Tears from the children / Blues in H (B) / England's carol / Jasmine tree, The / In memoriam.
**Album:** Released '87, on Atlantic by WEA Records. Catalogue no: **K 50407**

**NO SUN FOR VENICE**
**CD:** Released '88, on Atlantic Jazz by WEA Records. Catalogue no: **K781 340 2**

**ODDS AGAINST TOMORROW**
Tracks: / Skating in Central Park / No happiness for Slater / Social call, A / Cue 9 (Judo) / Cold wind is blowing, A / Odds against tomorrow.
**CD:** Released Apr '90, on Blue Note by EMI Records. Catalogue no: **CDP 793 415 2**
**CD:** Released Apr '90, on Blue Note by EMI Records. Catalogue no: **BNZ 239**

**SAIT ON JAMAIS**
Tracks: / Golden striker, The / One never knows / Rose true / Cortege / Venice / Three windows.
**Album:** on Atlantic by WEA Records. Catalogue no: **K 50231**

**SCANDINAVIA APRIL 1960**
**CD:** Released Mar '90, on Giants of Jazz by Hasmick Promotions. Catalogue no: **GOJCD53012**

**SHERIFF, THE**
Tracks: / Natural affection / Donnie's theme / In a crowd / Carnival / Bachianas Brasillieras / Mean to me / Sheriff.
**Album:** Released Oct '80, on Atlantic by WEA Records. Catalogue no: **K 40285**

**THREE WINDOWS**
Tracks: / Three windows / Kansas City breaks / Encounter in Cagnes / Django / Day in Dubrovnik, A (first movement: afternoon) / Day in Dubrovnik, A (second movement: night) / Day in Dubrovnik, A (third movement: morning).
**Cass:** Released Jul '87, on WEA by WEA Records. Catalogue no: **254833 4**
**CD:** Released Oct '87, on WEA by WEA Records. Catalogue no: **254833 2**
**Album:** Released Jul '87, on WEA by WEA Records. Catalogue no: **254833 1**

**TOGETHER AGAIN**
**Cass:** Released Aug '85, on Pablo Jazz (USA) by Pablo Records (USA). Catalogue no: **K 8244**
**Album:** Released Aug '85, on Pablo Jazz (USA) by Pablo Records (USA). Catalogue no: **230 9244**

**TOPSY THIS ONE'S FOR BASIE**
Tracks: / Reunion blues / Nature boy / Topsy / D and E / Valeria / Milano / Le cannet.
Note: Second studio album for Pablo performances by Milt Jackson in a unique unaccompanied performance of Nature boy and John Lewis in a featured performance of a recomposed MJQ standard Milano. Also featured is a composition dedicated here to Count Basie d and d and one of the first tunes recorded by the MJQ. Peronnel: Milt Jackson- vibes/ John Lewis - piano/ Percy Heath- bass/ Connie Kay - drums.
**CD:** Released Sep '86, on Pablo Jazz (USA) by Pablo Records (USA). Catalogue no: **CD 231 0917**
**Cass:** Released Apr '86, on Pablo Jazz (USA) by Pablo Records (USA). Catalogue no: **K 10917**
**Album:** Released Apr '86, on Pablo Jazz (USA) by Pablo Records (USA). Catalogue no: **2310917**

## Modern Jazz Sextet

**MODERN JAZZ SEXTET**
Tracks: / Tour de force / Dizzy meets Sonny / Old folks / What's new / How deep is the ocean / Mean to me / Blues for bird.
**Album:** Released Nov '84, on Verve (USA) by Polydor Ltd. Catalogue no: **823 091-1**

## Modern Jazz Society

**CONCERT OF CONTEMPORARY MUSIC**
**Album:** Released Jan '85, on Verve (France) Catalogue no: **823 089-1**

## Modernaires

**1946-47**
**Album:** Released Jun '86, on Circle (USA) by Jazzology Records (USA). Catalogue no: **CLP 77**

**BEND (EP)**
Tracks: / Bend.
**7" Single:** Released Feb '82, on Illuminated Catalogue no: **ILL 8**
**12" Single:** Released Feb '82, on Illuminated Catalogue no: **ILL 812**

**LIFE IN OUR TIMES**
Tracks: / Life in our times.
**7" Single:** Released Nov '80, on Illuminated Catalogue no: **ILL 2**

**WE DID IT AGAIN**
Tracks: / We did it again / And again.
**7" Single:** Released Apr '81, on Illuminated Catalogue no: **ILL 4**

## Modernaires Orchestra

**TRIBUTE TO GLENN MILLER VOL. 1**
**CD:** Released Feb '89, on Ross by Ross Records. Catalogue no: **ROSSCD 6621-2**

**TRIBUTE TO GLENN MILLER VOL. 2**
**CD:** Released Feb '89, on Ross by Ross Records. Catalogue no: **ROSSCD 6622-2**

**TRIBUTE TO GLENN MILLER VOL. 3**
**CD:** Released Feb '89, on Ross by Ross Records. Catalogue no: **ROSSCD 6615-2**

## Moffett, Charles

**BEAUTY WITHIN**
Tracks: / Love never fails / Love never fails / Angela / My little one / Beauty within / Message, The / Eastwood.
**CD:** Released Jan '90, on Blue Note by EMI Records. Catalogue no: **CDP 791 650 2**
**Album:** Released Dec '89, on Blue Note by EMI Records. Catalogue no: **791 650 1**
**CD:** Released Jan '90, on Blue Note by EMI Records. Catalogue no: **CDB1 91650**
**Album:** Released Dec '89, on Blue Note by EMI Records. Catalogue no: **B1 91650**

**NET MAN**
Tracks: / Mizzom / Swing bass / One left over / Mona Lisa / Dance, The / Nett man / Softly as in a morning sunrise / For you.
**CD:** Released Oct '89, on Blue Note by EMI Records. Catalogue no: **CDP 746 993 2**
**CD:** Released Oct '89, on Blue Note by EMI Records. Catalogue no: **BNZ 214**
**Album:** Released Jan '88, on Blue Note by EMI Records. Catalogue no: **BLJ 46993**

## Mojo Jazzin Five

**MOJO JAZZIN FIVE**
**Album:** Released Jul '86, on Stomp Off (USA) Catalogue no: **SOS 1086**

## Mole, Miff

**MIFF MOLE'S MOLERS(1927)**
Tracks: / Alexander's ragtime band / Some sweet day / Hurricane / Davenport blues / Hot time in the old town tonight, A / Darktown strutters' ball / After you've gone / I ain't got nobody / One sweet letter from you / Fifty million frenchmen can't be wrong / Imagination / Feelin no pain / Original dixieland one-step / My gal Sal / Honolulu blues / New twister, The.
Note: This re-issue from one of the finest pioneers of hot jazz contains a good selection of the music which was urgently shipped to England in 1927 and released by Parlophone for the eager jazz enthusiasts. Miff was more or less responsible for the transition of the trombone's placing from a back instrument to one of the solo importance, with his virtuosity, creativity and range. Four of the tracks feature the inimitable Sophie Tucker three tug at the heart strings and one is a contemporary, wry social comment. The remainder are all by the same line up featuring Charles Elsworth Russell ( known as pee wee ).
**Album:** Released Jan '83, on Swaggie (Australia) Catalogue no: **S 1295**
**Cass:** Released Jul '86, on Retrospect by EMI Records. Catalogue no: **TC SH 503**
**Album:** Released Jul '86, on Retrospect by EMI Records. Deleted Nov '88. Catalogue no: **SH 503**

**MIFF MOLE'S MOLERS(1928-30) (Mole, Miff, Molers)**
**Album:** Released Jan '83, on Swaggie (Australia) Catalogue no: **S 1297**

## Monk, Thelonious

**1961 EUROPEAN TOUR, VOL 1**
Tracks: / I'm getting sentimental over you / Jackie-ing / Crepuscule with Nellie / Round midnight / Blue Monk.
Note: Recorded live at a concert in Berne, Switzerland. With Charlie Rouse, John Ore,Frankie Dunlop.
**Album:** Released '81, on Ingo Catalogue no: **INGO 5**

**1961 EUROPEAN TOUR, VOL 2**
Tracks: / Sweet Georgia Brown / Rhythm-a-ning epistrophy / Well you needn't / Blue Monk.
Note: With Charlie Rouse, John Ore, Frankie Dunlop.
**Album:** Released '82, on Ingo Catalogue no: **INGO 8**

**ALONE IN SAN FRANCISCO**
**CD:** Released Nov '86, on JVC/Fantasy Catalogue no: **VDJ 1549**
**CD:** Released Apr '87, on Carrere (France) Catalogue no: **98967**

**AND THE JAZZ GIANTS**
**CD:** Released Apr '87, on Fantasy (import) by Fantasy Inc (USA). Catalogue no: **FCD 60018**

**APRIL IN SPRING-LIVE**
Tracks: / Epistrophy / April in Paris / I'm getting sentimental over you / Just a gigolo / I mean you / Jackie-ing / Off minor / Rhythm-a-ning / Hackensack / Well you needn't.
**Album:** Released May '84, on Milestone by Ace Records. Catalogue no: **OJCD 508**
**Album:** Released Mar '82, on Milestone by Ace Records. Deleted Mar '87. Catalogue no: **M 47060**

**ARTISTRY IN JAZZ Greatest hits**
**CD:** Released May '87, on JVC/Fantasy Catalogue no: **VDJ 1589**

**BLUE MONK**
**Album:** Released Apr '86, on Crusader Catalogue no: **CJZ LP 8**

**BLUE SPHERE**
Tracks: / Tinkle tinkle / Crepuscule with Nellie / Darn that dream / Little rootie tootie / Nice work if you can get it / Melancholy baby / Jackie-ing / Blue Sphere.
**Album:** Released Jul '84, on Black Lion Catalogue no: **BLM 51501**

**BLUES FIVE SPOT**
**CD:** Released Apr '87, on Carrere (France) Catalogue no: **98162**
**CD:** Released Apr '87, on Carrere (France) Catalogue no: **98154**

**BRILLIANT CORNERS (Monk, Thelonious & Sonny Rollins)**
**CD:** Released Apr '87, on Carrere (France) Catalogue no: **98911**
**CD:** Released May '86, on JVC/Fantasy

**Thelonious Monk**

Catalogue no: **VDJ 1526**

**CLASSIC MONK**
**Album:** Released May '88, on Jazz Life Catalogue no: **2273252**
**Cass:** Released May '88, on Jazz Life Catalogue no: **2173252**
**CD:** Released May '88, on Jazz Life Catalogue no: **247 325 2**

**COLLECTION: THELONIOUS MONK**
Tracks: / Blue Monk / Nutty / Evidence / Epistrophy / Hackensack / Bemsha swing / I'm getting sentimental over you / Straight, no chaser / Pannonica / Epistrophy 2.
**Cass:** Released Aug '85, on Deja Vu Catalogue no: **DVMC 2040**

**COMPLETE GENIUS**
**2 LP Set:** Released '79, on Blue Note by EMI Records. Deleted '84. Catalogue no: **BND 4032**

**COMPOSER, THE**
**CD:** Released May '89, on CBS (import) by CBS Records. Catalogue no: **463 338 2**
**Cass:** Released May '89, on CBS (import) by CBS Records. Catalogue no: **463 338 4**
**Album:** Released May '89, on CBS (import) by CBS Records. Catalogue no: **463 338 1**

**CRISS-CROSS**
**Album:** Released Jan '87, on CBS by CBS Records. Catalogue no: **CBS 85691**

**EPISTROPHY**
**2 LP Set:** Released May '79, on Affinity by Charly Records. Catalogue no: **AFFD 26**

**EUROPEAN TOUR (Monk, Thelonious & Max Roach)**
Tracks: / Blue Monk / Light blue / Evidence / To Lady / Stop motion.
Note: Personnel (With Thelonius Monk): Thad Jones (Trumpet), Charlie Rouse (Tenor sax), Thelonius Monk (Piano), John Ore (Bass), Billy Higgins (drums). Personnel (With Max Roach): Tommy Turrentine (Trumpet), Julian Priester (Trombone), Stanley Turrentine (Tenor sax), Max Roach (Drums).
**CD:** Released Apr '89, on Denon Catalogue no: **DC 8536**
**CD:** Released '88, on Denon Catalogue no: **C38-7683**
**Cass:** Released Apr '89, on Denon Catalogue no: **MC 7683**

**EVIDENCE**
Tracks: / Rhythm-a-ning / Ruby My Dear / Bright Mississippi / Round About Midnight / Evidence / Jackie-ing / Stuffy / Blue Monk.
**Album:** Released Jan '88, on Esoldun Catalogue no: **FC 105**
**CD:** Released Jan '88, on Esoldun Catalogue no: **FCD 105**

**GENIUS OF MODERN MUSIC VOL.1**
Tracks: / Round midnight / Off minor / Ruby my dear / I mean you (Not on CD.) / April in Paris / In walked Bud / Thelonious / Epistrophy / Misterioso (Not on CD.) / Well you needn't / Introspection / Humph / Evonce (CD only.) / Evonce (alt. take) (CD only.) / Suburban eyes (alt. take) (CD only.) / Nice work if you can get it (CD only.) / Nice work if you can get it (alt. take) (CD only.) / Ruby my dear (alt. take) (CD only.) / Well you needn't (alt. take) (CD only.) / April in Paris (alt. take) (CD only.) / Monk's mood (CD only.) / Who knows (CD only.) / Who knows (alt. take) (CD only.).
**Album:** Released Jul '89, on Blue Note by EMI Records. Catalogue no: **781 510 1**
**Album:** Released Jul '89, on Blue Note by EMI Records. Catalogue no: **BST 81510**
**CD:** Released Apr '90, on Blue Note by EMI Records. Catalogue no: **BNZ 244**
**Album:** Released Aug '82, on Blue Note by EMI Records. Deleted Jan '88. Catalogue no: **BLP 1510**
**CD:** Released Apr '90, on Blue Note by EMI Records. Catalogue no: **CDP 781 510 2**
**Cass:** Released Apr '87, on Blue Note by EMI Records. Deleted Jan '88. Catalogue no: **4BN 81510**

**GENIUS OF MODERN MUSIC VOL.2**
Tracks: / Carolina moon / Hornin' in / Skippy / Let's cool one / Suburban eyes (Not on CD.) / Evonce (Not on CD.) / Straight no chaser / Four in one / Nice work if you can get it (Not on CD.) / Monk's mood (Not on CD.) / Who knows (Not on CD.) / Ask me now / Four in one (alt. take) (CD only.) / Criss cross (alt. take) (CD only.) / Eronel (CD only.) / Ask me now (alt. take) (CD only.) / Willow weep for me (CD only.) / Skippy (alt. take) (CD only.) / Hornin' in (alt. take) (CD only.) / Sixteen (first take) (CD only.) / Sixteen (second take) (CD only.) / I'll follow you (CD only.).
**Cass:** Released Aug '85, on Blue Note by EMI Records. Deleted Jun '88. Catalogue no: **4BN 81511**
**Album:** Released Aug '82, on Blue Note by EMI Records. Deleted Jan '88. Catalogue no: **BLP 1511**
**CD:** Released Apr '90, on Blue Note by EMI Records. Catalogue no: **CDP 781 511 2**
**Album:** Released Aug '85, on Blue Note by EMI Records. Catalogue no: **BST 81511**
**CD:** Released Apr '90, on Blue Note by EMI Records. Catalogue no: **BNZ 245**

**GREATEST HITS: THELONIUS MONK**
Tracks: / Well you needn't / Misterioso / Bemsha swing / Round midnight / Epistrophy / Ruby my dear / Crepuscule with Nellie / Blue monk / Straight, no chaser.
**Cass:** Released Jul '86, on CBS by CBS Records. Catalogue no: **40 21069**
**Album:** Released Jul '86, on CBS by CBS Records. Catalogue no: **CBS 21069**

**I MEAN YOU**
**Album:** Released Apr '84, on Carrere (France) Catalogue no: **65610**

**IN ACTION (Monk, Thelonious Quartet)**

**Thelonious Monk - Live in Stockholm**

**Album:** Released Aug '84, on Riverside (USA) by Fantasy Inc (USA). Catalogue no: **OJC 103**
**CD:** Released Apr '87, on Carrere (France) Catalogue no: **98914**

**IN JAPAN 1963 (Monk, Thelonious Quartet)**
**CD:** Released '86, on East Wind Catalogue no: **CDWIND 702**

**IT'S MONK'S TIME**
Tracks: / Lulu's back in town / Memories of you / Stuffy turkey / Brake's sake / Nice work if you can get it / Shuffle boil.
**Album:** Released Jul '87, on CBS by CBS Records. Deleted Jan '89. Catalogue no: **450868 1**
**Cass:** Released Jul '87, on CBS by CBS Records. Deleted Jan '89. Catalogue no: **450868 4**

**LIVE AT THE IT CLUB**
Tracks: / Blue Monk / Well you needn't / 'Round midnight / Rhythm-a-ning / Blues five spot / Bemsha swing.
**Album:** Released Oct '82, on CBS by CBS Records. Deleted Oct '87. Catalogue no: **CBS 88584**

**LIVE AT THE VILLAGE GATE**
**CD:** Released '88, on Xanadu Catalogue no: **FDC 5161**

**LIVE IN PARIS, 1964 VOL.1**
**CD:** Released '89, on France's Concert Catalogue no: **FCD 132**
**Album:** Released '89, on France's Concert Catalogue no: **FC 132**

**LIVE IN PARIS, 1964 VOL.2**
**CD:** Released '89, on France's Concert Catalogue no: **FCD 134**
**Album:** Released '89, on France's Concert Catalogue no: **FC 134**

**LIVE IN PARIS 1967**
Tracks: / Presentation A. Francis / Ruby my dear / We see / Epistrophy / Oska T / Evidence / Blue monk / Epistrophy (reprise).
**Album:** Released Jun '88, on France's Concert Catalogue no: **FC 113**
**CD:** Released Jun '88, on France's Concert Catalogue no: **FCD 113**

**LIVE IN STOCKHOLM (See panel above)**
**Album:** Released Sep '86, on Duke by Melodisc Records. Catalogue no: **D 1020**

**LIVE PERFORMANCES**
**Album:** Released Nov '88, on Musica Jazz Catalogue no: **2MJP 1063**

**LONDON COLLECTION, VOLUME 1**
Tracks: / Trinkle tinkle / Crepuscule with Nellie / Darn that dream / Little rootie tootie / Meet me tonight in dreamland / Nice work if you can get it / My melancholy baby / Jackie-ing / Loverman / Blue Sphere.
Note: Recorded in London, 15 November 1971.
**Album:** Released Jun '88, on Black Lion Catalogue no: **BLP 60101**
**CD:** Released Jun '88, on Black Lion Catalogue no: **BLCD 760101**

**LONDON COLLECTION, VOLUME 2**
**Album:** Released Feb '89, on Black Lion Catalogue no: **BLP 60116**

**MAN I LOVE, THE**
Tracks: / I mean you / Man I love, The / Ruby my dear / Little rootie tootie / Misterioso / Trinkle tinkle / Crepuscule with Nellie.
**Album:** Released Apr '85, on Black Lion Catalogue no: **BLP 30141**
**Cass:** Released Apr '85, on Black Lion Catalogue no: **BLP 30141C**

**MISTERIOSE**
**CD:** Released Apr '87, on Carrere (France) Catalogue no: **98915**

**MONK**
**Album:** Released Aug '84, on CBS (I love Jazz) by CBS Records. Catalogue no: **CBS 21117**

**MONK & BIRD (A tribute to Monk & Bird) (Monk, Thelonious & Charlie Parker)**
**Album:** Released Mar '79, on Tomato (USA) by Tomato Music Co. (USA). Catalogue no: **TOM 2-9002**

**MONK HIMSELF**
**CD:** Released Apr '87, on Carrere (France) Catalogue no: **98966**

**MONK ON RIVERSIDE**
Note: With Art Blakey, Paul Chambers, Kenny Clarke, John Coltrane, Ernie Herny, Oscar Pettiford, Max Roach, Sonny Rollins, Clarke Terry, Wilbur Ware.
**Album:** Released Jun '88, on Riverside (1) Catalogue no: **RIV 40047**

**MONK ON TOUR IN EUROPE**
Tracks: / Oska T / Epistrophy / Evidence / Blue monk / Monk's mood / We see aka Ganese / Hackensack / Lulu's back in town / I mean you / Round midnight.
**CD:** Released Jun '88, on Charly by Charly Records. Catalogue no: **CDCHARLY 122**
**2 LP Set:** Released Jun '88, on Affinity by Charly Records. Catalogue no: **AFFD 192**
**Cass:** Released Jun '88, on Affinity by Charly Records. Catalogue no: **TCAFFD 192**

**MONK WITH COLTRANE**
Tracks: / Ruby, my dear / Trinkle tinkle / Nutty / Well, you need'nt / Off minor / Epistrophy / Crepescule with Nellie / Abide with me / Monk's mood / Blues for tomorrow.
**2 LP Set:** Released Oct '80, on Milestone by Ace Records. Deleted Jan '88. Catalogue no: **M 47011**
**CD:** Released Apr '87, on Carrere (France) Catalogue no: **98912**

**MONK'S DREAM (Monk, Thelonious Quartet)**
Tracks: / Monk's dream / Body and soul / Bright Mississippi / Five spot blues / Bolivar blues / Just a gigolo / Bye ya / Sweet and lonely.
**Album:** Released Jan '87, on CBS by CBS Records. Catalogue no: **CBS 85682**
**Cass:** Released 27 Feb '88, on CBS (import) by CBS Records. Catalogue no: **4600654**
**Album:** Released 27 Feb '88, on CBS

**Thelonious Monk - Monk's Music (Riverside)**

(import) by CBS Records. Catalogue no: **4600651**

**MONK'S MUSIC (See panel above)**
Tracks: / Abide with me / Well you needn't / Ruby my dear / Epistrophy / Crepuscule with Nellie.
Note: Ray Copeland - trumpet, Gigi Grycee - alto sax, Coleman Hawkins and John Coltrane - tenor saxes, Thelonious Monk - piano, Wilbur Ware - bass, Art Blakey - drums. New York, June 26 1957.
**CD:** Released Apr '86, on JVC/Fantasy Catalogue no: **VDJ 1516**
**CD:** Released '88, on Fantasy (import) by Fantasy Inc (USA). Catalogue no: **FCD 642242**
**Album:** Released Feb '84, on Riverside (USA) by Fantasy Inc (USA). Catalogue no: **OJC 084**
**CD:** Released Apr '87, on Carrere (France) Catalogue no: **98948**

**MULLIGAN MEETS MONK (Monk, Thelonious & Gerry Mulligan)**
Tracks: / Round midnight / Rhythm-a-ning / Sweet and lonely / Decidedly / Straight, no chaser / I mean you.
**Album:** Released Feb '88, on Riverside (USA) by Fantasy Inc (USA). Catalogue no: **RSLP 247**

**PARIS CONCERT, THE**
Tracks: / Lulu's back in town / Just a gigolo / I am getting sentimental over you / Sweet and lovely / Off minor / Crepuscule with Nellie / Epistrophy.
**CD:** Released Oct '87, on Charly by Charly Records. Catalogue no: **CDCHARLY 74**

**PLAYS DUKE ELLINGTON**
Tracks: / It don't mean a thing (if it ain't...) / Sophisticated lady / I got it bad and that ain't good / Black and tan fantasy / Moon indigo / I let a song go out of my heart / Solitude / Caravan.
**CD:** Released Sep '89, on Riverside (USA) by Fantasy Inc (USA). Catalogue no: **CDRIVM 006**

**PORTRAIT OF AN ERMITE**
**Album:** Released Nov '88, on Vogue by Vogue Records. Catalogue no: **500104**

**RIVERSIDE TRIOS**
Tracks: / It don't mean a thing / Sophisticated lady / I got it bad / Black and tan fantasy / Mood indigo / I let a song go out of my heart / Solitude / Caravan / Liza / Memories of you / Honeysuckle Rose / Darn that dream / Tea for two / You are too beautiful / Just you, just me.
**Album:** Released Nov '80, on Milestone (USA) by Fantasy Inc (USA). Deleted Nov '85. Catalogue no: **M 47052**

**ROUND MIDNIGHT**
Tracks: / Round midnight / Off minor / Mysterioso / Criss cross / Hornin' in well / You needn't / Ruby my dear / Let's cool one / Straight, no chaser / Ask me now / Thelonious / Evidence / Epistrophy / Monk's dream / Little rootie tootie / Reflections / Blue monk / Let's call this / Bemesha swing / Rhythm-a-ning.
**CD:** Released '88, on Giants of Jazz by Hasmick Promotions. Catalogue no: **GOJCD 0222**
**Album:** Released Sep '85, on Saar Giants Of Jazz (Italy) Catalogue no: **LPJT 19**
**Cass:** Released Sep '85, on Saar Giants Of Jazz (Italy) Catalogue no: **MCJT 19**

**SOLO MONK**
**Album:** Released Apr '86, on Star Jazz (USA) by Charly Records. Catalogue no: **SJAZZ 8**
**Cass:** Released Apr '86, on Star Jazz (USA) by Charly Records. Catalogue no: **SJAZZC 8**

**SOMETHING IN BLUE**
**Album:** Released Jan '85, on Black Lion Catalogue no: **BLP 30119**
**Cass:** Released Jan '85, on Black Lion Catalogue no: **BLP 30119C**

**SPHERE (Monk, Thelonious Quartet)**
**Album:** Released May '79, on Affinity by Charly Records. Catalogue no: **AFF 20**

**THELONIOUS ALONE IN SAN FRANSISCO**
**Album:** Released Apr '86, on Original Jazz Classics (USA) by Fantasy Inc (USA). Catalogue no: **OJC 231**

**THELONIOUS HIMSELF**
Tracks: / April in paris / Ghost of a chance / Functional / I'm getting sentimal over you / I should care / All alone / Monk's mood / Round midnight.
**Album:** Released Jan '87, on Original Jazz Classics (USA) by Fantasy Inc (USA). Catalogue no: **OJC 254**
**CD:** Released Nov '86, on JVC/Fantasy Catalogue no: **VDJ 1537**

**THELONIOUS MONK**
**Album:** Released Apr '81, on Kings Of Jazz Catalogue no: **KLJ 20012**
**Album:** Released '88, on GNP Crescendo (USA) by GNP Crescendo Records (USA). Catalogue no: **GNPS 9009**
**Album:** Released Jul '82, on Jazz Reactivation Catalogue no: **JR 162**

**THELONIOUS MONK AND HERBIE NICHOLS (Monk, Thelonious & Herbie Nichols)**
Tracks: / Brake's sake / Gallop's gallop / Shuffle boil / Nica's tempo / Who's blues / 'S wonderful / 'S wonderful (alternative version) / Nichols & dimes / Nichols & dimes (alternative take) / My lady gingersnap / Good story blues.
**Album:** Released Oct '86, on RCA by BMG Records (UK). Deleted Nov '89. Catalogue no: **WL 70829**
**Cass:** Released Oct '86, on RCA by BMG Records (UK). Deleted May '89. Catalogue no: **WK 70829**

**THELONIOUS MONK AT TOWN HALL**
Tracks: / Thelonious / Friday The 13th / Monk's Mood / Little Rootie Tootie / Off Minor / Crepuscule with Nellie.
**Album:** Released Sep '88, on Riverside (USA) by Fantasy Inc (USA). Catalogue no: **RSLP 300**

**THELONIOUS MONK & JOHN COLTRANE (Monk, Thelonious & John Coltrane)**
**Album:** Released Jun '86, on CBS (import) by CBS Records. Catalogue no: **CBS 85682**
**CD:** Released Apr '86, on JVC/Fantasy

Catalogue no: **VDJ 1510**

**THELONIOUS MONK & JOHN COLTRANE (Monk, Thelonious & John Coltrane)**
**CD:** Released '88, on Fantasy (import) by Fantasy Inc (USA). Catalogue no: **FCD 634946**

**THELONIOUS MONK MEMORIAL ALBUM, THE**
Tracks: / 'Round midnight / I want to be happy / Bemsha swing / Black and tan fantasy / Brillant corners / I mean you / Jackie-ing / Little rootie tootie / Epistrophy / Ruby / My dear / Nutty / Let's cool one / I'm getting sentimental over you.
**Album:** Released Jun '82, on Milestone by Ace Records. Catalogue no: **M 47064**

**THELONIOUS MONK PLAYS DUKE ELLINGTON**
**Album:** Released Sep '88, on Riverside (1) Catalogue no: **RLP 201**
**CD:** Released Apr'87, on Carrere (France) Catalogue no: **98959**

**THELONIOUS MONK QUARTET & OCTET IN EUROPE**
**Album:** Released Apr '81, on Unique Jazz by Spotlite Records. Catalogue no: **UJ 12**

**THELONIOUS MONK TRIO (Monk, Thelonious Trio)**
**CD:** Released Jan '89, on JVC/Fantasy Catalogue no: **VDJ 1612**

**THELONIOUS MONK WITH GERRY MULLIGAN (Monk, Thelonious & Gerry Mulligan)**
**CD:** Released Apr '87, on Carrere (France) Catalogue no: **98917**

**UNDERGROUND**
**Cass:** Released 27 Feb '88, on CBS (import) by CBS Records. Catalogue no: **4600664**
**Album:** Released 27 Feb '88, on CBS (import) by CBS Records. Catalogue no: **4600661**

**UNIQUE, THE**
**CD:** Released May '87, on JVC/Fantasy Catalogue no: **VDJ 1528**
**CD:** Released Apr '87, on Carrere (France) Catalogue no: **98942**

## Monroe, Vaughn

**1943 (Monroe, Vaughn & Orchestra)**
**Album:** Released Dec '88, on Circle (USA) by Jazzology Records (USA). Catalogue no: **CLP 45**

**BEST OF VAUGHN MONROE (Monroe, Vaughn & Orchestra)**
Tracks: / Racing with the moon / There I go / My devotion / When the lights go on again / Trolley song, The / There, I've said it again / Let it snow, let it snow, let it snow / I wish I didn't love you so / Ballerina / You do / Cool water / Red roses for a blue lady / Riders in the sky / Someday you'll want me to want you / That lucky old sun / Mule train / Sound off (the duckworth chant) / On top of Old Smokey / They were doin' the mambo.
**Cass:** Released Oct '87, on RCA by BMG Records (UK). Catalogue no: **NK 90068**
**Album:** Released Oct '87, on RCA by BMG Records (UK). Catalogue no: **NL 90068**

**MONROE DOCTRINE, THE**
**Album:** Released Jul '82, on Swing Era (Import) Deleted '85. Catalogue no: **SELP 1014**

**MORE 1943 (Monroe, Vaughn & Orchestra)**
**Album:** Released Dec '87, on Circle (USA) by Jazzology Records (USA). Catalogue no: **CLP 116**

## Monsbourgh, Lazy Ade

**ADELAIDE COLLECTION - ALL**
**Album:** Released '88, on Swaggie (Australia) Catalogue no: **S 1417**

**RECORDER IN RAGTIME**
**Album:** Released '88, on Swaggie (Australia) Catalogue no: **S 1405**

**VINTAGE SELECTION (1950-70)**
**Album:** Released Jan '83, on Swaggie (Australia) Catalogue no: **S 1344**

**WILD LIFE (1956-70)**
**Album:** Released Jan '83, on Swaggie (Australia) Catalogue no: **S 1283**

## Montgomery, Buddy

**SO WHY NOT?**
**Album:** Released 12 Apr '89, on Landmark (USA) by Fantasy Inc (USA). Catalogue no: **LLP 1518**
**CD:** Released 12 Apr '89, on Landmark (USA) by Fantasy Inc (USA). Catalogue no: **LCD 15182**

**TIES OF LOVE**
**CD:** Released Aug '88, on Polygram by PolyGram UK Ltd. Catalogue no: **LCD 1512**

## Montgomery, Little

**1930-69**
**Album:** Released Jan '88, on Roots (Germany) Catalogue no: **RSE 3**

**CHICAGO, THE LIVING LEGEND**
**Album:** Released Jan '88, on OBC Catalogue no: **OBC 525**

**CHICAGO - THE LIVING LEGENDS**
Tracks: / Home again blues / Up the country blues / Saturday night function / Michigan water blues / Sweet daddy (your mam's done gone mad) / Prescription for the blues / 44 Vicksburg / Trouble in mind / Riverside boogie / Oh daddy blues / Somethin' keep worryin' me.
Note: As the sleeve says 'piano, vocal and band blues'. Cut at the 'Birdhouse Club' in Chicago in 1961 when Riverside records were putting together their 'Living Legends' series and by accident came across Montgomery. The 54 year old pianist was rehearsing with some younger players and regular side-kick Micke McKendrick on banjo when producer Chris Albertson caught them. Several days later he cut the band with cornet, clarinet and tenor along with banjo and singer Elaine McFarland. Apart from a bunch of tunes from Little Brother Montgomery they ran down Jelly Roll Morton's *Michigan Water Blues* and Ellington's *Saturday Night Function* done in real old style in fact the tone of the whole album is relaxed old time blues - refreshing. (Ace Records, August 1989)
**Album:** Released 29 Aug '89, on Ace by Ace Records. Catalogue no: **CH 263**

**DEEP SOUTH PIANO**
**Album:** Released Jan '88, on Storyville by Storyville Records AB. Catalogue no: **SLP 228**

**LITTLE BROTHER MONTGOMERY, 1960 (The piano blues unissued recordings, vol.1)**
**Album:** Released Oct '87, on Magpie by Interstate Music. Catalogue no: **PY 4451**

**LITTLE BROTHER MONTGOMERY, 1960 VOL.2**
**Album:** Released Mar '89, on Magpie by Interstate Music. Catalogue no: **PY 4452**

**LITTLE BROTHER MONTGOMERY & SUNNYLAND SLIM (Montgomery, Little Brother & Sunnyland Slim)**
**Album:** Released Sep '79, on 77 by 77 Records. Catalogue no: **77LA 12/21**

**TISHOMINGO BLUES**
**Album:** Released Mar '82, on JSP by JSP Records. Catalogue no: **JSP 1015**

## Montgomery, Marian

**I GOTTA RIGHT TO SING**
Tracks: / In the dark / Deed I do / Love dance / People will say we're in love / That old black magic / You came a long way from St. Louis / Mean to me / Ol' man river / Georgia on my mind / Yesterday's wine / I gotta right to sing the blues / He's my guy / Lady is a tramp, The.
Note: American born - but now English resident - Marian Montgomery although jazz-orientated, embraces a variety of musical styles, presenting them all in her own inimitable fashion. On this album recorded live at Ronnie Scott's Club in 1987, Marian shows her sympathy for what jazz musicians do and her instincts for making a song move.
**Album:** Released Nov '88, on Jazz House Catalogue no: **JHR 003**

**MARIAN MONTGOMERY ON STAGE**
Tracks: / Way I am, The / Oh Johnny / Don't it make my brown eyes blue? / Ain't no sunshine since you've gone / Rain sometimes / If I had my way / Seventeen / What's a lady like me doing in a joint like this? / Kansas City / It never entered my mind / If you could read my mind / There'll be some changes made / He's funny that way.
**Cass:** Released Apr '82, on Cube Cata-

logue no: **ZCFLY 29**
**Album:** Released Apr '82, on Cube Catalogue no: **HIFLY 29**

**PUTTIN' ON THE RITZ (Montgomery, Marian & Richard Rodney Bennett)**
**Album:** Released Feb '84, on Dakota Catalogue no: **HI FLY 40**
**Cass:** Released Feb '84, on Cube Catalogue no: **ZCFLY 40**

**SOMETIMES IN THE NIGHT**
Tracks: / Man I love, The / Somebody loves me / Just in time / People that you never get to love, The / My foolish heart / Maybe (if he knew me) / Tell me softly / You're the best love / I don't want to walk without you / But love (that's another game) / Very thought of you, The / You've come a long way from St Louis / Not funny / Tender trap, The / You are my lucky star / Sometimes in the night.
**Cass:** Released May '89, on C5 by C5 Records. Catalogue no: **C5K 532**
**Album:** Released May '89, on C5 by C5 Records. Catalogue no: **C5-532**
**CD:** Released May '89, on C5 by C5 Records. Catalogue no: **C5CD-532**

**SURPRISE SURPRISE (Montgomery, Marian & Richard Rodney Bennett)**
**Album:** Released Oct '81, on Cube Catalogue no: **HI FLY 24**
**Cass:** Released Oct '81, on Cube Catalogue no: **ZC FLY 24**

**TOWN AND COUNTRY (Montgomery, Marian & Richard Rodney Bennett)**
Tracks: / Do you know the way to San Jose? / Night owl / I'm always drunk in San Francisco / Let's go and live in the country / On Broadway / New York state of mind / Ballad of the sad young man / Any place I hang my hat is home / Summerhouse / Folks who live on the hill, The / Save the sunlight / Skylark / Eagle and me / Peaceful.
**Album:** Released Apr '82, on Cube Catalogue no: **HI FLY 28**
**Cass:** Released Apr '82, on Cube Catalogue no: **ZC FLY 28**

## Montgomery, Wes

**ARTISTRY IN JAZZ (Greatest hits)**
**CD:** Released May '87, on JVC/Fantasy Catalogue no: **VDJ 1590**

**BOSS GUITAR**
Tracks: / Besame mucho / Dearly beloved / Days of wine and roses / Trick bag / Canadian sunset / Fried pies / Breeze and i / For heavens sake.
**Album:** Released Jan '87, on Original Jazz Classics (USA) by Fantasy Inc (USA). Catalogue no: **OJC 261**
**CD:** Released Jan '89, on JVC/Fantasy Catalogue no: **VDJ 1620**

**BUMPIN'**
Tracks: / Tear it down / Con Alma / Quiet thing, A / Shadow of your smile / Mi cosa / Bumpin' / Here's that rainy day / Misty.
**CD:** Released Oct '84, on Verve Deleted Mar '88. Catalogue no: **821 985-2**

**CALIFORNIA DREAMING**
**CD:** on Verve Deleted Mar '88. Catalogue no: **827 842-2**

**COLLECTION: WES MONTGOMERY**
Tracks: / Starlight / Round midnight / Come rain or come shine / Mister Walker / Cariba / Here's that rainy day / Full house / Blue 'n' boogie / To Django / I've grown accustomed to her face / S.O.S..
**Cass:** Released Nov '85, on Deja Vu Catalogue no: **DVMC 2044**

**COMPACT JAZZ: WES MONTGOMERY**
**CD:** Released Jul '87, on Verve Deleted Jan '89. Catalogue no: **831 372-2**

**DOWN HERE ON THE GROUND**
Tracks: / Windsong / Georgia on my mind / Other man's grass, The / Up and at it / Goin' on to Detroit / I say a little prayer / When I look in your eyes / Know it all / Fox, The.
**CD:** Released 28 Nov '88, on A&M by A&M Records. Catalogue no: **CDA 0802**

**DYNAMIC DUO (Montgomery, Wes & Jimmy Smith)**
Tracks: / Down by the riverside / Night train / James and Wes / 13(Death march) / Baby, it's cold outside.
**CD:** Released Oct '84, on Verve Deleted Aug '87. Catalogue no: **821 577-2**
**CD:** Released '88, on Verve Catalogue no: **821 989 2**

**ENCORES**
Tracks: / Movin' along / Body and soul / Trick bag / Moanin' / Delilah / Blue Roz / If I should lose you / Tune up.
**Album:** Released May '84, on Milestone by Ace Records. Catalogue no: **OJC 3001**

**FULL HOUSE**
**CD:** Released Apr '86, on JVC/Fantasy Catalogue no: **VDJ 1508**
**Album:** Released Aug '84, on Riverside (USA) by Fantasy Inc (USA). Catalogue no: **OJC 106**
**CD:** Released '88, on Fantasy (import) by Fantasy Inc (USA). Catalogue no: **FCD 6329434**
**CD:** Released May '87, on JVC/Fantasy Deleted '88. Catalogue no: **VDJ 1508**

**GOIN' OUT OF MY HEAD**
Tracks: / O morro nao tem vez / Boss city / Chim chim cheree / Goin' out of my head / Naptown blues / Twisted blues / End of a love affair, The / It was a very good year / Golden earrings.
**CD:** Released Oct '85, on Polydor by Polydor Ltd. Deleted Mar '88. Catalogue no: **825 676-2**

**GREATEST HITS:WES MONTGOMERY**
**Album:** Released '74, on A&M by A&M Records. Deleted '88. Catalogue no: **AMLS 976**

**GROOVE BROTHERS**
Tracks: / D-natural blues / Lover man / June in January / Jeannine / Angel eyes / Beaux arts / Snowfall / Bock to bock / Groove yard / If I should lose you / Delirium / Just for now / Doujie / Heart strings / Remember.
**2 LP Set:** Released Apr '80, on Milestone by Ace Records. Deleted '85 Catalogue no: **M 47051**

**IMPRESSIONS**
Tracks: / 4 on 6 / Wes' rhythm / Impressions / To when.
**Album:** Released '78, on Affinity by Charly Records. Catalogue no: **AFF 13**

**INCREDIBLE JAZZ GUITAR**
**CD:** Released Nov '86, on JVC/Fantasy Catalogue no: **VDJ 1538**
**CD:** Released Apr '87, on Carrere (France) Deleted '88. Catalogue no: **98923**

**LIVE AT JORGIES AND MORE**
Note: Featuring Wes, Buddy and Monk Montgomery, Billy Hart, Elvin Bunn.
**Album:** Released Jan '83, on VGM (Import) Catalogue no: **VGM 0008**

**LIVE IN PARIS 1965**
**Album:** Released Jun '88, on France's Concert Catalogue no: **FC 108**
**CD:** Released Jun '88, on Esoldun Catalogue no: **FCD 108**

**MIDNIGHT GUITARIST**
Note: 1961 to 1965
**Album:** Released Jun '86, on Crusader Jazz Masterworks Catalogue no: **CJZ LP 9**

**MOVIN' ALONG**
Tracks: / Movin' along / Tune up / Ghost of a chance / Sandu / Body and soul / So do it / Says you.
**CD:** Released Apr '87, on Carrere (France) Catalogue no: **98951**
**Album:** Released Feb '84, on Riverside (USA) by Fantasy Inc (USA). Catalogue no: **OJC 089**

**MOVIN' WES**
Tracks: / West Coast blues / Caravan / Movin' Wes / Moca flor / Matchmaker matchmaker / Senza fine / Theodora / In and out / Born to be blue / People / Movin' Wes.
Note: Recorded in 1965. Tracks include those listed above.
**Cass:** Released '83, on Verve Deleted Mar '88. Catalogue no: **810 045-4**
**CD:** Released '83, on Verve Deleted Mar '88. Catalogue no: **810 045-2**
**Album:** Released '83, on Verve Deleted Mar '88. Catalogue no: **810 045-1**
**Album:** Released Aug '81, on Verve Catalogue no: **2304 377**

**PORTRAIT OF WES**
**CD:** Released Apr '87, on Carrere (France) Catalogue no: **98970**

**RECORDED LIVE AT JORGIES JAZZ CLUB**
Tracks: / All of you / Heartstrings / Summertime / Back to Bach.
Note: Wes Montgomery, guitar; Buddy Montgomery, piano, vibes; Monk Montgomery, bass; Billy Hart, drums. Recorded at Jorgies, St Louis, 19 August 1961.
**Album:** Released Apr '81, on VGM (Import) Catalogue no: **VGM 0001**

**ROUND MIDNIGHT**

Tracks: / 4 on 6 / Girl next door, The / Mr. Walker / Here's that rainy day / Round midnight / Impressions.

Note: Even during his lifetime jazz writers and musicians were hailing Wes Montgomery as the greatest guitarist since Charlie Christian. Since his death suddenly and unexpectedly following a heart attack in his Indianapolis home on June 15, 1968, the plaudits have increased and innumerable guitarists in and out of jazz now show the blanket influence of this singular man. Wes was born John Leslie Montgomery in Indianapolis, Indiana on March 6, 1925. An elder brother, Monk was destined to play bass while a younger Montgomery, Buddy was to take up piano and vibraharp in later years. All three were self-taught musicians and Wes left it late before he turned to the profession. He was 19 and newly married when he bought an amplifier and a guitar in the late war years. In those days he had already found an idol, Charlie Christian, the man who was to remain his inspiration for the rest of his life. 'He got me all messed up'. Wes told British guitarist Ike Isaacs (Crescendo magazine). 'I didn't play at all then - so he got me into it. I liked his sound and approach so well that I said I'll buy me a brand new guitar and amplifier, and I can do it - because he's probably playing on an old one. I though all you had to do was to get an instrument, put your hands on it, and it would come out right. I didn't know about the fundamentals or nothing. Using a plectrum lasted just a month. When I plugged in my amplifier to see what I was doing, the sound was too much even for my next door neighbours, so I took the back room in the house and started plucking with the fat part of my thumb. To this technique I added the trick of playing the melody line in two different registers at the same time, the octave thing. This made the sound even quieter'. And so one of jazz's most distinctive sounds came into being through a combination of naivety and good neighbourliness. Although Wes could not read music (and he never learned during his entire lifetime) he held down the guitar chair with the Lionel Hampton band from 1948 to 1950, at a time when Hamp's band contained men such as Charlie Mingus, Fats Navarro and Benny Bailey. Lionel let Wes keep his amplifier on when he was playing just rhythm, something he had never allowed any previous guitarist to do. In 1950 Montgomery went back to Indianapolis, leaving behind his band nickname 'The Rev' (an allusion to his teetotalism). And there he might have stayed, content to work with visiting jazzmen occasionally. There was a big concert scheduled for Indianapolis one night - Cannonball Adderley, Lennie Tristano, Count Basie, a bunch of great guys. I was playing an after-hours club - in fact I had three jobs. Well this was the only club open after hours and all the guys from the concert came down and we had a ball. Cannonball asked me if I'd like to record and naturally I said yes. So Orrin Keepnews from Riverside called me about three days later and said that Cannonball raved about me and although he didn't know me, I had a record date. That was the first record under my own name, the West Montgomery Trio.

Through his albums for Riverside, then Verve, Wes Montgomery achieved fame (he won the Down Beat Critics Poll (1960 and 1966-67 plus Down Beat Readers Poll for 1961, 1962, 1966 and 1967) but most of all he became the talk of the profession. Other musicians all wanted to hear him, to sit in with him and to play on his record dates. At the suggestion of Creed Taylor, then a and r man at Verve, he started making albums angled deliberately at a wider market starting with Movin' Wes in November, 1964. But away from the studios he was still working the clubs with a small group sometimes with a trio completed by Melvin Rhyne on organ and George Brown on drums at other times with local men. Then in the early part of 1965 he made what was to be his only trip to Europe playing concert club and festival gigs in London, Madrid, Brussels, Lugano, San Remo and Rotterdam. He brought with him an American rhythm section comprising reliable if peripatetic jazzmen, Memphis born Harold Mabern had worked with Lionel Hampton, Jay Jay Johnson and the Art Farmer-Benny Golson Jazztet while bass player Arther Harper had recorded with Jay Jay and Sonny Stitt, Jimmy Lovelace had been with the Roland Kirk Group, this was a trio which accompanied Wes at Ronnie Scott's and on a BBC TV Jazz 625 telerecording. (The trio however, was replaced by an all Dutch unit including drummer Han Bennink for Wes's stay at Rotterdam's B-14 club).

In Paris the all American quartet gave a concert and this is the first of two LP s from that engagement. The distinctive Montgomery tone is apparent from the first bar of his own *Four on six*. Wes played always with his thumb but told the late Ralph Gleason that 'in order to get a certain amount of speed you should use a pick. A lot of cats say you don't have to play fast but being able to play fast can cause you to phase better. But I didn't like the sound. I like the tone better with the thumb, the technique better with the pick. I couldn't have them both. In the light of the extended, beautifully developed solos which Wes played at the concert it is clear that his talents as a jazz soloist were not diminished at all by his decision to make LPs such as *Movin' Wes* and *Bumpin'*. The superb impressions is one of the finest and most concentrated examples of Wes digging in and sweeping audience and rhythm section along with him. Impressions uses the same harmonic base as Miles Davis's *So what* and was composed by the late John Coltrane. (Wes, Trane and Eric Dolphy shared a long gig at San Francisco's Jazz Workshop' club incidentally.)

Montgomery's own Mister Walker is a latterday version of a number which he included in his 1960 Riverside album *The incredible jazz guitar of Wes Montgomery*. Here his excellent rhythmic understanding enables him to push the rhythm section his way, giving them a series of lessons in the art of improvising propulsive riffs.

He also offers a gentle and quite beautiful reading of a Montgomery favourite, *The girl next door.* Wes's octave idea often cropped up on recorded solos by the late Django Reinhardt and while Montgomery obviously respected the work of the gypsy guitarist he was not an overt copyist. They rhythm section produces a gentle undulating backdrop for *Here's that rainy day*, a ballad which took on a fresh lease of life when both Frank Sinatra and Stan Getz recorded it. In this context Wes Montgomery was unbeatable, bridging the gap between the specialised jazz audience and the masses who simply enjoyed the tunefulness and pleasing tone. On *Round about midnight* the dramatic and mood provoking melody is presented by Wes before Johnny Griffin eases his way in at the beginning of the second chorus. Montgomery's delight at Griff's entry is obvious and it is not long before the two are making music together as if they were both members of the same regular group. This CD is an important addition to our recorded knowledge of this remarkable guitarist for it shows that despite the string laden albums aimed at the popular market, Wes Montgomery never lost his love for spontaneously improvised jazz. (Alun Morgan)

**CD:** Released Mar '86, on Charly by Charly Records. Catalogue no: **CDCHARLY 13**

**SILVER COLLECTION, THE**

Tracks: / If you could see me now / Impressions / Four on six / Unit 7 / Mellow mood / James and Wes / What's new / Misty / Portrait of Jennie / Here's that rainy day.

**CD:** Released Nov '84, on Verve Deleted Mar '88. Catalogue no: **823 448-2**

**SO MUCH GUITAR!**

**Album:** Released Apr '86, on Original Jazz Classics (USA) by Fantasy Inc (USA). Catalogue no: **OJC 233**

**CD:** Released '86, on Carrere (France) Catalogue no: **CA 98 924**

**SOLITUDE**

**Album:** Released May '79, on Affinity by Charly Records. Catalogue no: **AFF 18**

**TEQUILA**

**CD:** Released Aug '87, on Polydor by Polydor Ltd. Deleted 30 May '89. Catalogue no: **831 671 2**

**WES MONTGOMERY Compact/Walkman jazz**

**Cass:** Released Jun '87, on Verve Catalogue no: **831 372-4**

**CD:** Released Jun '87, on Verve Catalogue no: **831 372-2**

**WES MONTGOMERY PLAYS THE BLUES (Compact/Walkman jazz)**
Tracks: / Bumpin' on Sunset / California dreaming / Movin' Wes (part 1) / Golden earrings / Sunny / Shadow of your smile, The / OGD / Tequila / Caravan / Once I loved / Movin' Wes (part 2) / Here;s that rainy day / Goin' out of my head / How insensitive / What the world needs now is love.
**Cass:** Released 14 Aug '88, on Verve Catalogue no: **835 318-4**
**CD:** Released 14 Aug '88, on Verve Catalogue no: **835 318-2**

**WES MONTGOMERY TRIO, THE (Montgomery, Wes Trio)**
Tracks: / Round midnight / Yesterdays / End of a love affair, The / Whisper not / Ecaroh / Satin doll / Missile blues / Too late now / Jingles.
**Album:** Released Feb '88, on Riverside (USA) by Fantasy Inc (USA). Catalogue no: **RSLP 310**

## Montoliu, Tete

**CATALONIAN FOLKSONGS**
Tracks: / Cigales al ven / Canco de matinada / Manuel / Me embaix apeu / Una gitarra / Ruco / Cuin plan teniu, senor / La Amelia esta malalba / Els segadors.
Note: Solo piano
**Album:** Released Sep '86, on Timeless (Import) by Timeless Records. Catalogue no: **SJP 116**

**CATALONIAN NIGHTS VOL.1**
**Album:** Released Jun '81, on Steeplechase (USA) Catalogue no: **SCS 1148**

**LIVE AT THE KEYSTONE CORNER (Montoliu, Tete/Herbie Lewis / Billy Higgins)**
**Album:** Released Sep '86, on Timeless by Timeless Records. Catalogue no: **SJP 138**

**SECRET LOVE (Montoliu, Tete Trio)**
Tracks: / Secret love / Airegin / Confirmation / Four / Stella by starlight.
Note: With Sam Jones, bass; Billy Higgins, drums. Recorded live at Breda, Holland, 31 March and 1 April 1977.
**Album:** Released Apr '81, on Timeless by Timeless Records. Catalogue no: **SJP 111**

**SONGS FOR LOVE**
**Album:** Released Jan '82, on Enja (Germany) by Enja Records (West Germany). Catalogue no: **ENJA 2040**

**TALK ABOUT YOU**
**Album:** Released Apr '81, on Steeplechase (USA) Catalogue no: **SCS 1137**

**TETE!**
**Album:** on Steeplechase (USA) Deleted Jul '88. Catalogue no: **SCS 1029**
**CD:** Released Jul '88, on Steeplechase (USA) Catalogue no: **SCCD 31029**

**TOOTIE'S TEMPO**
**CD:** Released Jul '88, on Steeplechase (USA) Catalogue no: **SCCD 31108**

**Album:** Released Jul '88, on Steeplechase (USA) Catalogue no: **SCS 1108**

**YELLOW DOLPHIN STREET**
Tracks: / Yellow Dolphin Street / Come Sunday / I hate you / You've changed / Walse for Nicolien / Where are you? / Napoleon / If you could see me now.
Note: Recorded 28 February 1977.
**Album:** Released Sep '86, on Timeless by Timeless Records. Catalogue no: **SJP 107**

## Montreux 79

**MONTREUX 79 (Various artists)**
**Album:** Released Nov '80, on Rhapsody by President Records. Catalogue no: **RHAP 9**

## Montreux Summit

**MONTREUX SUMMIT 2 (various original jazz artists) (Various artists)**
**2 LP Set:** Released Sep '78, on CBS by CBS Records. Catalogue no: **CBS 88286**

**MONTREUX SUMMIT, VOL 1 (Various artists)**
Tracks: / Montreux summit: *Various artists* / Infant eyes: *Various artists* / Blues march: *Various artists* / Bahama mama: *Various artists* / Fried bananas: *Various artists* / Andromeda: *Various artists.*
Note: Recorded at the Montreux Jazz Festival, 1977, with, among others, Stan Getz, Dexter Gordon, Bob James, George Duke, Billy Cobham, Ralph MacDonald, Steve Khan, Janne Schaffer, Eric Gale, Woody Shaw, Alphonso Johnson, Benny Golson, Hubert Laws, Bobbi Humphrey, Thijs Van Leer, Maynard Ferguson.
**2 LP Set:** Released Jan '78, on CBS by CBS Records. Catalogue no: **CBS 88277**

## Montrose, J.R.

**AND A LITTLE PLEASURE (Montrose, J.R. & Tommy Flanagan)**
**Album:** Released Nov '86, on Uptown (USA) Catalogue no: **UP 27 06**

**IN ACTION**
Note: with Joe Abodeely Trio
**Album:** Released Jan '88, on Studio 4 Catalogue no: **SS 100**

## Moody, James

**BEBOP REVISITED, VOL 4 (Moody, James & Bennie Green)**
Tracks: / That's it / Mean to me / Date with Kate / Embraceable you / Big and little / 'S wonderful / Choice taste / Lesson in bopology / Loop-plu-e-du / Honeysuckle / Our very own / Lowland bounce / La vie en rose / Blues is green.
Note: With Ernie Royal, Ted Kelly, Raymond Fol, Wendell Marshall, Butch Ballard, Dave Burns, Bobby Tucker, Nelson Boyd, Jack Parker, Babs Gonzales, Bud Johnson, Jimmy Jones, John Collins, Tommy Potter, Roy Haynes. Recorded 1950.
**Album:** Released Jan '83, on Xanadu Catalogue no: **XAN 197**

**EASY LIVING**
Tracks: / Flutin' the blues / Birdland story, The / It could happen to you / I cover the waterfront / Body and soul / Breaking the blues / Parker's mood / Easy living / Boo's tune / Richard's blues / Great day / Search, The / Let's try / One never knows / Opalesque / Blues impromptu / Malice toward none.
Note: Moody on tenor and alto saxes and flute with, on the first album -- recorded in 1956 -- a small group including Johnny Coles (trumpet), William Shepherd (trombone) and Pee Wee Moore (baritone sax) and on the second -- recorded in 1963 -- a big band featuring Thad Jones and Johnny Coles (trumpets), Hubert Laws (flute), Jim Hall (guitar), Richard Davis (bass) and Mel Lewis (drums).
**2 LP Set:** Released Oct '84, on Chess Jazz by Vogue Records. Catalogue no: **CXJD 6702**
**Cass set:** Released Oct '84, on Chess Jazz by Vogue Records. Catalogue no: **ZCCJD 6702**

**FLUTE 'N' THE BLUES**
Tracks: / Flute'n' the blues / Birdland story / It could happen to you / I cover the waterfront / Body and soul / Breaking the blues / Parker's mood / Easy living / Boo's tune / Richard blues.
**Album:** on Chess by Vogue Records. Catalogue no: **GCH 8088**
**Cass:** Released '89, on Chess by Vogue Records. Catalogue no: **GCHK 8088**

**GREAT DAY, THE**
Tracks: / Great day / Search,The / Let's try / One never knows / Opalesque / Blues impromptu / Malice towards none.
**Cass:** Released Aug '88, on Chess by Vogue Records. Catalogue no: **GCHK 78090**
**Album:** Released Aug '88, on Chess by Vogue Records. Catalogue no: **GCH 8090**

**MOODY'S MOOD FOR LOVE**
**Album:** Released Jul '87, on Dragon by Dragon Records. Catalogue no: **DRLP 95**

**MOVING FORWARD**
Tracks: / Autumn leaves / Round midnight / Summer afternoon, A / November afternoon / Giant steps / What do you do / Cupbearers / Night has a thousand eyes, The / Moody's theme.
**Album:** Released Dec '88, on Novus by BMG Records (UK). Catalogue no: **PL 83026**
**CD:** Released Dec '88, on Novus by BMG Records (UK). Catalogue no: **PD 83026**

**SOMETHING SPECIAL**
Tracks: / Moody's mood update / I'm in the mood for love / Real feels good / Nubian fantasies / Transfer to Manhattan / More than you know / Inside lover / Shake, rattle and boogie (On compact disc only.).
**Album:** Released Oct '87, on RCA by BMG Records (UK). Catalogue no: **PL 83004**

**CD:** Released Oct '87, on RCA by BMG Records (UK). Catalogue no: **PD 83008**

**SWEET AND LOVELY**
Tracks: / My melancholy baby / Sweet and lovely / Con alma / Skippin' / Confirmation / My ideal / Get the booty / Rain (CD only.) / Get the booty (CD only.).
**Album:** Released 25 Sep '89, on Novus by BMG Records (UK). Catalogue no: **PL 83063**
**CD:** Released 25 Sep '89, on Novus by BMG Records (UK). Catalogue no: **PD 83063**
**Cass:** Released 25 Sep '89, on Novus by BMG Records (UK). Catalogue no: **PK 83063**

**TENOR CONTRASTS (Moody, James / Stan Getz)**
Tracks: / S'cool boy / Dear old Stockholm / I only have eyes for you / I'm getting sentimental over you / Prelude to a kiss / Night and day / Don't be afraid / Flamingo / Out of nowhere / These foolish things / I'm in the mood for bop / Flight of the bopple bee / Body and soul / I'm in the mood for love / Lester leaps in / Indiana / Esquire.
**Album:** Released '88, on Esquire by Titan Int. Prod.. Catalogue no: **ESQ 309**

## Mooney, Art

**1945-46 (Mooney, Art & Orchestra)**
**Album:** Released 10 Jul '89, on Circle Catalogue no: **CLP 134**

## Moore, Alex

**IN EUROPE**
**Album:** Released May '81, on Arhoolie (USA) by Arhoolie Records (USA). Catalogue no: **ARHOOLIE 1048**

**PIANO BLUES**
**Album:** Released May '81, on Arhoolie (USA) by Arhoolie Records (USA). Catalogue no: **ARHOOLIE 1008**

**WIGGLE TAIL**
**CD:** Released '88, on Rounder (USA) by Rounder Records (USA). Catalogue no: **CD 11559**
**Cass:** Released '88, on Rounder (USA) by Rounder Records (USA). Catalogue no: **ROUNDER 2091C**
**Album:** Released '88, on Rounder (USA) by Rounder Records (USA). Catalogue no: **ROUNDER 2091**

## Moore, Alice

**LONESOME WOMAN BLUES**
**Album:** Released Jul '88, on Agram Catalogue no: **AB 2013**

## Moore, Brew

**BREW MOORE QUINTET (Moore, Brew & Lars Sjosten Trio)**
**Album:** Released Aug '84, on Riverside (USA) by Fantasy Inc (USA). Catalogue no: **OJC 100**

**BREW'S STOCKHOLM DEW**
Tracks: / King Frederik's blues / Old folks / Ladislav / Batie / Brew's Stockholm Dew's.
**Album:** Released '74, on Sonet by Sonet Records. Catalogue no: **SNTF 624**

**Dudley Moore - At the Wavendon Festival (Black Lion)**

**DANISH BREW**
**Album:** Released '88, on Jazz Mark Catalogue no: **JAZZ MARK 1**
**Album:** Released Apr '83, on Jazz Mark Catalogue no: **101**

**NO MORE BREW**
**Album:** Released May '86, on Storyville by Storyville Records AB. Catalogue no: **SLP 4019**

## Moore, Dudley

**Biographical details:** British actor, comedian and pianist Moore first became famous via his long-lasting association with Peter Cook, though he had earlier been known as a fine jazz pianist and -- with Jonathan Miller, Alan Bennett and Cook -- as one of the four-strong cast of the seminal review Beyond The Fringe. It was with Cook that he first hit the British charts, peaking at No 18 in summer '65 with *Goodbye-ee.* Neither hit the singles chart again but Moore's skills as a serious pianist resurfaced on his two 1966 UK Top Twenty albums: *The Other Side of Dudley Moore* reached No 11 and *Genuine Dud* (credited to the Dudley Moore Trio) peaked at No 13. Pete 'n' Dud enjoyed a British LP chart entry together in May '66. The double act established themselves as one of Britain's most successful comedy teams, notably with their TV series 'Not Only But Also'. Later came their notorious Derek and Clive period: *Derek And Clive Live* reached No 12 and logged 25 weeks on the British LP chart in 1976 and the follow-up album, *Derek And Clive Come Again*, got to No 18. The diminutive Moore's burning desire for Hollywood stardom led to the duo splitting up. And he got what he wanted, becoming a major international star and a Hollywood sex symbol! His most notable triumph was the 1981 film 'Arthur', in which he starred with Liza Minelli and John Gielgud. Moore's skill on piano has led to collaborations with such musical heavyweights as John Williams (1973) and Cleo Laine (1982). (Bob MacDonald, February 1986.).

**AT THE WAVENDON FESTIVAL (See panel above)**
Tracks: / Should care,I / Two for the road / Chimes / Amalgam / Yesterdays / You'd be so nice to come home to / Cornfield / Waltz for Suzie / And the same to you / Horizon / Morning walk.
**Album:** Released '76, on Black Lion Catalogue no: **BLP12151**

**COVER STORY**
**VHS:** Released Sep '89, on Stylus Video by Stylus Music Records. Catalogue no: **UNKNOWN**

**DUDLEY DOWN UNDER**
Tracks: / Love walked in / Here's that rainy day / Prelude / Georgia on my mind / Young prince and young princess / Tricotism / Autumn in New York / Song for Suzy / Lover.
**Album:** Released Dec '81, on Dakota Catalogue no: **ICS 1003**
**Cass:** Released Dec '81, on Dakota Catalogue no: **ZCICS 1003**

**GENUINE DUD (Moore, Dudley Trio)**

**Album:** Released Jun '66, on Decca by Decca International. Deleted Jun '71. Catalogue no: **LK 4788**

**MUSIC OF DUDLEY MOORE**
Tracks: / Head first / Waltz for Suzy / Hello sailor / Rupert Street concerto / Madrigal / Mating cry / Thirty is a dangerous age, Cynthia / Italy / Bedazzled / Millionaire / Cornfield / Lillian Lust / Exactly like you / You'd be so nice to come home to / My blue Heaven / Poova nova / Sad one for George / Sooz blooz / Yesterdays / Straight life.
**2 LP Set:** Released Oct '81, on Cube Catalogue no: **TOOFA 14**
**Cass set:** Released Oct '91, on Cube Catalogue no: **ZCTOF 14**

**OTHER SIDE OF DUDLEY MOORE**
**Album:** Released Dec '65, on Decca by Decca International. Deleted Dec '70. Catalogue no: **LK 4732**

**SMILIN' THROUGH (Moore, Dudley/Cleo Laine)**
Tracks: / Smilin' through / Love me or leave me / I don't know why / When I take my sugar to tea / I'll be around / Strictly for the birds / Before love went out of style / Brown soft shoe / I can't give you anything but love / It's easy to remember / Play it again Sam / Be a child.
**Cass:** Released Nov '82, on CBS by CBS Records. Catalogue no: **40 25137**
**Album:** Released Nov '82, on CBS by CBS Records. Catalogue no: **CBS 25137**

**STRICTLY FOR THE BIRDS (Moore, Dudley/Cleo Laine)**
Tracks: / Strictly for the birds / Smiling through.
**7" Single:** Released Nov '82, on CBS by CBS Records. Catalogue no: **A 2947**

## Moore, Freddie

**GREAT FREDDIE MOORE & HOT JAZZ ORCHESTRA (Moore, Freddie & Hot Jazz Orchestra)**
Tracks: / I got it bad / Rockin' chair / Save it pretty mama / Rag alley blues / Blue turning grey / Snowball.
**Album:** Released 8 Apr '89, on New York Catalogue no: **J 001**

## Moore, Johnny B.

**CHICAGO BLUES SESSION 5 (Moore, Johnny B. & West Side All Stars)**
Note: Featuring Lester Davenport.
**Album:** Released Aug '87, on Wolf Catalogue no: **WOLF 120 851**

## Moore, Kid Prince

**COMPLETE RECORDINGS 1936-38 (Moore, Kid Prince/Shorty Bob Parker)**
**Album:** Released '88, on Wolf Catalogue no: **WSE 126**

## Moore, Ralph

**623 C STREET (Moore, Ralph Quartet)**
**Album:** Released Jul '87, on Criss Cross Catalogue no: **CRISS 1028**

**IMAGES: RALPH MOORE**
Tracks: / Freeway / Episode from a village dance / This I dig of you / Punjab / Enigma / Morning star / Blues for John / One second please.
Note: Recorded December 1988. Personnel: Ralph Moore (tenor sax), Terence Blanchard (tpt), Benny Green (piano), Peter Washington (bass), Kenney Washington (drums).
**CD:** Released Jun '89, on Landmark (USA) by Fantasy Inc (USA). Catalogue no: **LCD 15202**
**Album:** Released Jun '89, on Landmark (USA) by Fantasy Inc (USA). Catalogue no: **LLP 1520**

**ROUND TRIP**
**Album:** Released '88, on Reservoir Catalogue no: **RSR 104**
**CD:** Released Oct '89, on Reservoir Catalogue no: **RSRCD 104**

## Morath, Max

**PLAY THE BEST OF SCOTT JOPLIN**
**2 LP Set:** Released Jun '84, on Vanguard (France) by CBS Records. Catalogue no: **VSD 39**

## Moreno, Buddy

**1947: BUDDY MORENO (Moreno, Buddy & His Orchestra)**
**Album:** Released Aug '88, on Circle (USA) by Jazzology Records (USA). Catalogue no: **CLP 49**

## Morgan, Frank

**BEBOP LIVES (Morgan, Frank Quintet)**
**CD:** Released Jan '89, on JVC/Fantasy Catalogue no: **VDJ 1093**

**FRANK MORGAN**
**Album:** Released '88, on GNP Crescendo (USA) by GNP Crescendo Records (USA). Catalogue no: **GNPS 9041**

**MOOD INDIGO**
**CD:** Released Jan '90, on Antilles/New Directions by Island Records. Catalogue no: **ANCD 8748**
**Album:** Released Jan '90, on Antilles / New Directions by Island Records. Catalogue no: **AN 8748**
**Cass:** Released Jan '90, on Antilles / New Directions by Island Records. Catalogue no: **ANC 8748**

## Morgan, Jack

**DANCING IN THE DARK (Morgan, Jack/ Russ Morgan Orchestra)**
**Album:** Released May '89, on Russ Morgan Catalogue no: **RME 1005**

**REFLECTIONS OF DAD (Morgan, Jack/ Russ Morgan Orchestra)**
**Album:** Released May '89, on Russ Morgan Catalogue no: **RME 1004**

## Morgan, Lee

**BEST OF LEE MORGAN (Blue Note years)**
Tracks: / Ceora / Speedball / Night in Tunisia / Since I fell for you / Rumproller, The / I remember Clifford (CD only.) / Mr. Kenyatta (CD only.) / Cornbread (CD only.).
**Album:** Released Dec '88, on Blue Note by EMI Records. Catalogue no: **B1 91138**
**CD:** Released Dec '88, on Blue Note by EMI Records. Catalogue no: **CDP 791 138 2**
**CD:** Released Dec '88, on Blue Note by EMI Records. Catalogue no: **BNZ 144**

**CANDY**
Tracks: / Candy / Since I fell for you / C.T.A. / All the way / Who do you love / Personality / All at once you love her.
**CD:** Released Apr '87, on EMI-Manhattan by EMI Records. Catalogue no: **BNZ 67**
**CD:** Released Apr '87, on EMI-Manhattan by EMI Records. Catalogue no: **CDP 746 508 2**

**COOKER, THE**
Tracks: / Night in Tunisia / Heavy dipper / Just one of those things / Lover man / New-ma.
**Album:** Released Sep '84, on Blue Note by EMI Records. Deleted '87. Catalogue no: **BST 81578**

**CORNBREAD**
Tracks: / Cornbread / Our man Higgins / Ceora / Ill wind / Most like Lee.
**Album:** Released Jul '89, on Blue Note by EMI Records. Catalogue no: **B1 84222**
**CD:** Released Aug '88, on Blue Note by EMI Records. Catalogue no: **CDP 784 222 2**
**CD:** Released Apr '89, on Blue Note by EMI Records. Catalogue no: **BNZ 109**

**DELIGHTFULEE MORGAN**
Tracks: / Ca-lee-so / Zambia / Yesterday / Sunrise, sunset / Nite flite / Delightful deggie / Need I? (CD only.) / Filet of soul (CD only.) / Zambia (big band version) (CD only.) / Delightful deggie, The (Big band version) (CD only.).
**CD:** Released Aug '89, on Blue Note by EMI Records. Catalogue no: **BNZ 188**
**Album:** Released Jul '89, on Blue Note by EMI Records. Catalogue no: **BST 84243**
**CD:** Released Aug '89, on Blue Note by EMI Records. Catalogue no: **CDP 784 243 2**

**EXPOOBIDENT**
Tracks: / Expoobident / Easy living / Triple track / Fire / Just in time / Hearing / Lost and found.
**Album:** Released Apr '85, on Affinity by Charly Records. Deleted May '88. Catalogue no: **AFF 134**

**GIGOLO, THE**
Tracks: / Yes I can,no you can't / Trapped / Speedball / Gigolo, The / You go to my head.
Note: Both Lee Morgan and Wayne Shorter are in amazingly superb form for this quintet session with Harold Mabern, Bob Cranshaw and Billy Higgins. The material ranges from the progressive 'Yes I Can, No You Can't' to Lee's soulful, rapid 'Speedball' to his superb ballard playing on 'You Go To My

Head'. This is one if jazz's greatest trumpeters on peak form.
**CD:** Released Jul '89, on Blue Note by EMI Records. Catalogue no: **BNZ 199**
**Album:** Released Jul '89, on Blue Note by EMI Records. Catalogue no: **BST 84212**

### HERE'S LEE MORGAN
**Album:** Released Oct '85, on Affinity by Charly Records. Deleted May '88. Catalogue no: **AFF 143**

### INDESTRUCTIBLE LEE
Tracks: / Terrible 't' mogie / I'm a fool to want you / Running brook / Off spring / Bess / Expoobident / Easy living / Triple track / Fire / Just in time / Hearing, The / Lost and found.
**CD:** Released Jan '90, on Affinity by Charly Records. Catalogue no: **CDAFF 762**

### LEE MORGAN
**2 LP Set:** Released '88, on GNP Crescendo (USA) by GNP Crescendo Records (USA). Catalogue no: **GNPS 2.2074**

### LEE MORGAN VOLUME 3
Tracks: / Hasaan's dream / Domingo / I remember Clifford / Mesabi chant / Tiptoeing / Tip-toeing (alternate take) / With a song in my heart / With a song in my heart (alternate take) / Speak low / Speak low (alternate take) (From the musical 'One Touch Of Venus') / Come rain or come shine / Sonny's crib / Sonny's crib (alternate take) / News for Lulu.
**CD:** Released Sep '87, on Blue Note by EMI Records. Catalogue no: **CDP 746 817 2**
**CD:** Released Sep '87, on Blue Note by EMI Records. Catalogue no: **BNZ 68**

### ONE, TWO & FOUR (Morgan, Lee & John Coltrane)
Tracks: / Essie's dance / Doxy / I talk to the trees / Yesterdays / Oleo / Angel eyes / Suspended sentence / Minor strain / Bid for Sid / Exotica / One and four / Simple life.
**2 LP Set:** Released May '83, on Vogue Jazz (France) by Vogue Records. Catalogue no: **VJD 560**

### RAJAH, THE
Tracks: / Pilgrim's funny farm, A / Rajah, The / Is that so / Davisamba / What now my love / Once in a lifetime.
**Cass:** Released Sep '87, on Blue Note by EMI Records. Deleted Jun '88. Catalogue no: **4BN 84426**
**CD:** Released Mar '89, on Blue Note by EMI Records. Catalogue no: **BNZ 131**
**CD:** Released Feb '89, on Blue Note by EMI Records. Catalogue no: **CDP 784 426 2**
**Album:** Released Apr '85, on Blue Note by EMI Records. Catalogue no: **BST 84426**

### RUMPROLLER, THE
Tracks: / Rumproller, The / Desert moonlight / Eclipso / Edda / Lady, The / Venus de mildew.
Note: Produced by Alfred Lion.(P) 1986 Manhattan records,a divison of Capitol Records Inc. Lee Morgan's 'The Sidewinder' was the surprise hit of 1964 when it made the pop charts and crossed over into areas in which no jazz record had gone. Blue Note wasted no time getting Lee back into the studio with a similar band that included Sidewinder holdovers Joe Henderson and Billy Higgins for a follow-up date. This time,the funky title tune was penned by another Blue Note artist Andrew Hill. Other standouts on this recording are Lee's own 'Desert Moonlight' and the Wayne Shorter Balled 'Edda'.
**CD:** Released Aug '87, on Blue Note by EMI Records. Catalogue no: **BNZ 69**
**Album:** Released May '86, on Blue Note by EMI Records. Catalogue no: **BST 84199**
**CD:** Released Aug '87, on Blue Note by EMI Records. Catalogue no: **CDP 746 428 2**

### SEARCH FOR THE NEW LAND
Tracks: / Search for the new land / Joker, The / Mr. Kenyatta / Melancholee / Morgan the Pirate.
**CD:** Released May '89, on Blue Note by EMI Records. Catalogue no: **CDP 784 169 2**
**Album:** Released Aug '87, on Blue Note by EMI Records. Catalogue no: **BST 84169**
**CD:** Released May '89, on Blue Note by EMI Records. Catalogue no: **BNZ 172**

### SIDEWINDER
Tracks: / Sidewinder, The / Totem pole / Gary's notebook / Boy, what a night! / Hocus pocus.
**Album:** Released Aug '85, on Blue Note by EMI Records. Catalogue no: **BST 84157**
**Cass:** Released Aug '85, on Blue Note by EMI Records. Catalogue no: **TCBST 84157**
**CD:** Released Mar '87, on Blue Note by EMI Records. Catalogue no: **BNZ 66**
**CD:** Released Mar '87, on Blue Note by EMI Records. Catalogue no: **CDP 746 137 2**

### SONIC BOOM
Tracks: / Sneaky Pete / Mercenary / Sonic boom / Fathead / I'll never be the same / Mumbo jumbo.
**Album:** Released Jun '80, on Liberty by EMI Records. Catalogue no: **LBR 1020**

## Morgan, Russ

### BEST OF RUSS MORGAN
**Cass:** Released '88, on GNP Crescendo (USA) by GNP Crescendo Records (USA). Catalogue no: **GNP5 9015**
**Album:** Released '88, on GNP Crescendo (USA) by GNP Crescendo Records (USA). Catalogue no: **GNPS 9015**

### GOLDEN FAVOURITES (Morgan, Russ & His Orchestra)
Tracks: / Does your heart beat for me / Object of my affection, The / Do you ever think of me / Cruising down the river (Medley) / Linger awhile / Dogface soldier / Wang wang blues / So tired / Josephine / You're nobody till somebody loves you / Wabash blues / Johnson rag.
**Album:** Released Nov '89, on Memoir by Memoir Records. Catalogue no: **MOIR 207**
**Cass:** Released Nov '89, on Memoir by Memoir Records. Catalogue no: **CMOIR 207**

### MAGIC LINGERS ON, THE
**Album:** Released May '89, on Russ Morgan Catalogue no: **RME 1000**

### MUSIC IN THE MORGAN MANNER (Morgan, Russ & His Orchestra)
Note: 1938. Mono.
**Album:** Released Jan '87, on Circle (USA) by Jazzology Records (USA). Catalogue no: **CLP 87**

### ONE NIGHT STAND
**Album:** Released Jul '82, on Joyce Catalogue no: **JLP 1019**

### PLAY 22 ORIGINAL BIG BAND RECORDINGS (Morgan, Russ & His Orchestra)
**Album:** Released '88, on Hindsight Catalogue no: **HSR 404**

### RUSS MORGAN AND ORCHESTRA 1937-38 (Morgan, Russ & His Orchestra)
Tracks: / Does your heart beat for me / You must have been a beautiful baby / Moonlight and shadows / So help me / Boo hoo / What do you know about love / You got me / Room with a view / Could be / Say it with a kiss / To you / Moonlight serenade / I must see Annie tonight / Hurry home / I go for that / Goodnight, my beautiful / So long.
Note: This era is thought by many collectors to have been the finest period for the Morgan orchestra. Ray Austin and Morgan were doing most of the arranging, trumpet solos by Johnny McGee, and vocals by Morgan, Mert Curtis, etc. The liner notes were written by the author of The Big Band Almanac, Leo Walker, in cooperation with Russ Morgan's widow and vocalist Mert Curtis. Walker knew Morgan for over 25 years and the ups and downs of Morgan's career are chronicled in his liner notes. Produced by Wally Heider. (Hindsight Catalogue - 1989)
**Album:** Released '88, on Hindsight Catalogue no: **HSR 145**

## Morgan, Sam

### GET HAPPY BAND, THE
**Album:** Released Aug '84, on VJM (Vintage Jazz Music) by Vintage Jazz Music Society(VJM). Catalogue no: **VLP 32**

### KID HOWARD (Morgan, Sam Revisited)
**Album:** Released Jun '88, on Jazzology (USA) by Jazzology Records (USA). Catalogue no: **JCE 20**

## Morris, Chris

### CROSS MY PALM
Tracks: / Cross my palm / Something so right.
**7" Single:** Released Nov '83, on Tivoli by Tivoli Records. Catalogue no: **TIV 4**

### YOUNG WOMAN (Morris, Chris &

**Golden Eagle Jazz Band)**
**Album:** Released '88, on Stomp Off (USA) Catalogue no: **SOS 1100**

## Morris, Thomas

**GOIN' CRAZY WITH THE BLUES (Morris, Thomas & The Blues Singers)**
**Album:** Released Oct '89, on Fountain by Retrieval Records. Catalogue no: **FB 306**

**PAST JAZZ MASTER (1923)**
Tracks: / E flat blues, No 2 / Original Charleston strut / Lonesome journey blues / When the jazz band starts to play / Just blues, that's all / Bull blues / Those blues / Ceaucoupe de jazz / Achin' heart blues / Wild cat blues / Kansas City man blues / T'aint nobody's business if I do / New Orleans hop scop blues / Oh daddy blues / Old-fashioned love / House rent blues / Mean blues.
Note: With the Clarence Williams Blue Five.
**Album:** Released Jan '83, on Swaggie (Australia) Catalogue no: **805**

**THOMAS MORRIS AND 7 HOT BABIES (New Orleans Blue 5)**
**Album:** Released '88, on Collector's Classics Catalogue no: **CC 49**

**TOM MORRIS PAST JAZZ MASTERS & CLARENCE WILLIAMS (Morris, Tom Past Jazz Masters & Clarence Williams Blue Five)**
**Album:** Released Apr '79, on Fountain by Retrieval Records. Catalogue no: **FJ 113**

## Morrissey, Dick

**AFTER DARK**
Tracks: / I won't last a day without you / March on / They say it's wonderful / Pili-pili / Way we were, The / Running out of time / Lou Grant / Change partners.
Note: Digital stereo
**CD:** Released Oct '84, on Coda by Coda Records. Catalogue no: **CODA 2 CD**
**Album:** Released Mar '83, on Coda by Coda Records. Catalogue no: **CODA 2**

**CAPE WRATH (Morrissey, Dick & Jim Mullen)**
Tracks: / Lovely day / Cape Wrath / Bristol boogie / Return to Tooting Broadway / Soul eyes / Song for Carla / Dreams so real / Night song.
**Album:** Released Apr '79, on Harvest by EMI Records. Deleted Jan '88. Catalogue no: **SHSP 4098**

**LOVELY DAY (Morrissey, Dick & Jim Mullen)**
Tracks: / Lovely day / Night song.
**12" Single:** Released May '79, on Harvest by EMI Records. Deleted '82. Catalogue no: **12HAR 5182**

**RESURRECTION RITUAL (Morrissey, Dick Quartet)**
Tracks: / Resurrection ritual / Germina / Maestro, The / Lush life / Love dance / Star trek.
**Album:** Released Sep '88, on Miles Music by Miles Music Records. Catalogue no: **MM 077**

**SOULILOQUY**
Tracks: / Clouds 10, 33 / Lord Mayo / Angel / Soliloquy / East sunrise / Blue star Delhi / Red shoes.
**Album:** Released '88, on Coda by Coda Records. Catalogue no: **CODA 23**
**Album:** Released Feb '88, on Coda by Coda Records. Catalogue no: **8329401**
**Cass:** Released Feb '88, on Coda by Coda Records. Catalogue no: **8320404**
**Cass:** Released '88, on Coda by Coda Records. Catalogue no: **COCA 23**
**CD:** Released '88, on Coda by Coda Records. Catalogue no: **832 940 2**
**CD:** Released '88, on Coda by Coda Records. Catalogue no: **CODA 23 CD**

## Morrissey Mullen

**Biographical details:** Saxophonist Dick Morrissey and guitarist Jim Mullen are a jazz-funk duo who released their first album *Up* in 1977. Prior to this, both men had been gaining experience in various guises for a decade. Morrissey started out on the London jazz club circuit, principally the famous Ronnie Scott's Club. He played with many visiting jazz stars, toured with Cannonball Adderley, and became a session recording musician for such names as John Dankworth and Georgie Fame. He formed his own band If, who made a string of albums during the early Seventies. Mullen was based in Glasgow in the late Sixties, and moved his musical activities to London in the early Seventies. He played with Brian Auger, Vinegar Joe and Kokomo. It was while Dick was in New York with If and Jim was there working with the Average White Band and Herbie Mann, that the two guys met. Members of AWB guested on *Up*. The duo's second album *Cape wrath* was issued in 1979. As the Eighties dawned, Morrissey Mullen found themselves part of the UK's burgeoning jazz-funk scene. Attracting interest from disco audiences, they reached No.43 on the British LP chart with *Badness* (1981) and No.47 with *Life on the wire* (1982). The latter featured vocals by the up-and-coming Carol Kenyon who was acclaimed the following year for her work on Heaven 17's *Temptation*. Another acclaimed sessioner, Tessa Niles, sang on the duo's 1983 album *It's about time*; this LP contained the duo's tongue-in-cheek tribute to themselves, *Ol' sax and Captain Axe*. Also in 1983, Dick Morrissey (still an in demand session musician) released a solo LP entitled *After dark*; this was a more strictly jazz outing. (Bob MacDonald, 5th Feb 1986).

**BADNESS**
Tracks: / Do like you / Dragonfly / Blue tears / Stay awhile / Badness / Pass the music on / Slipstream.
Note: Digital Stereo
**CD:** Released Oct '84, on Beggars Banquet by Beggars Banquet Records. Deleted Aug '87. Catalogue no: **BEGA 27 CD**
**CD:** Released Jun '88, on Coda by Coda Records. Catalogue no: **CODA 24CD**
**Album:** Released Jun '88, on Coda by Coda Records. Catalogue no: **CODA 24**
**Album:** Released Jul '81, on Beggars Banquet by Beggars Banquet Records. Deleted Aug '87. Catalogue no: **BEGA 27**

**BLADE RUNNER**
Tracks: / Bladerunner / I pull the strings.
**7" Single:** Released Nov '82, on Beggars Banquet by Beggars Banquet Records. Deleted Jan '88. Catalogue no: **BEG 87**
**12" Single:** Released Nov '82, on Beggars Banquet by Beggars Banquet Records. Deleted Jan '88. Catalogue no: **BEG 87T**

**COME AND GET ME**
Tracks: / Come and get me.
**12" Single:** Released Feb '82, on Beggars Banquet by Beggars Banquet Records. Deleted Jan '88. Catalogue no: **BEG 73T**
**7" Single:** Released Feb '82, on Beggars Banquet by Beggars Banquet Records. Deleted Jan '88. Catalogue no: **BEG 73**

**HAPPY HOUR (Mullen, Morrissey)**
**Cass:** Released Dec '88, on Coda by Coda Records. Catalogue no: **COCA 29**
**2 LP Set:** Released Dec '88, on Coda by Coda Records. Catalogue no: **CODA 29**
**CD:** Released Dec '88, on Coda by Coda Records. Catalogue no: **COSA 29 CD**

**IT'S ABOUT TIME**
Tracks: / Stop and look around / It's about time / Ounce of bounce / So so fine / Ol' sax and Captain Axe / Bladerunner / Why does it always happen to me? / Do I do / Above the clouds.
Note: Digital Stereo
**CD:** Released Oct '84, on Beggars Banquet by Beggars Banquet Records. Deleted Aug '87. Catalogue no: **BEGA 44 CD**
**Album:** Released Mar '83, on Beggars Banquet by Beggars Banquet Records. Deleted Aug '87. Catalogue no: **BEGA 44**

**LIFE ON THE WIRE**
Tracks: / Life on the wire / Takin' time / Face of a child / Come and get me / Brazil nut / Ships that pass in the night / Making waves / Running out of time.
Note: Digital Stereo
**CD:** on Coda by Coda Records. Catalogue no: **CODA 27 CD**
**CD:** Released Oct '84, on Beggars Banquet by Beggars Banquet Records. Deleted Aug '87. Catalogue no: **BEGA 33 CD**
**Album:** Released Mar '82, on Beggars Banquet by Beggars Banquet Records. Deleted Aug '87. Catalogue no: **BEGA 33**

**LIFE ON THE WIRE (SINGLE)**
Tracks: / Life on the wire / Brazil nut.
**7" Single:** Released Apr '82, on Beggars Banquet by Beggars Banquet Rec-

**Jelly Roll Morton**

ords. Deleted Jan '88. Catalogue no: **BEG 75**

### LOVE DON'T LIVE HERE ANYMORE
Tracks: / Love don't live here anymore / Don't you worry.
**12" Single:** Released Jun '79, on Harvest by EMI Records. Deleted '82. Catalogue no: **12DIG 1001**

### OLD SAX AND CAPTAIN AXE
Tracks: / Ol' sax and Captain Axe / It's about time.
**7" Single:** Released Jul '83, on Beggars Banquet by Beggars Banquet Records. Deleted Jan '88. Catalogue no: **BEG 97**
**12" Single:** Released Jul '83, on Beggars Banquet by Beggars Banquet Records. Deleted Jan '88. Catalogue no: **BEG 97T**

### SO SO FINE
Tracks: / So so fine.
**7" Single:** Released Apr '83, on Beggars Banquet by Beggars Banquet Records. Deleted '88. Catalogue no: **EG 94**

### STAY AWHILE
Tracks: / Stay awhile.
**7" Single:** Released Sep '81, on Beggars Banquet by Beggars Banquet Records. Deleted Jan '88. Catalogue no: **BEG 63**
**12" Single:** Released Sep '81, on Beggars Banquet by Beggars Banquet Records. Deleted Jan '88. Catalogue no: **BEG 63T**

### THIS MUST BE THE PLACE
Tracks: / Tear for crystal, A / Mean time / This must be the place / With you / Southend Pier / Visions / All I want to do.
**Album:** Released May '84, on Coda by Coda Records. Catalogue no: **CODA 15**
**Cass:** Released May '84, on Coda by Coda Records. Catalogue no: **COCA 15**

## Morse, Ella Mae

### BARRELL HOUSE. BOOGIE AND THE BLUES
**Album:** Released Sep '84, on Pathe Marconi (France) Catalogue no: **PM 1546721**

### HITS OF ELLA MAE MORSE, THE
Tracks: / Cow cow boogie / Blacksmiths blues / I love you yes I do.
**Cass:** Released Oct '84, on Pathe Marconi (France) Catalogue no: **PM 1553044**
**Album:** Released Oct '84, on Pathe Marconi (France) Catalogue no: **PM 1553041**

### MORSE CODE, THE
Tracks: / Day in, day out / My funny valentine / Accentuate the positive / When my sugar walks down the street / Dream a little dream of me / Heart and soul / Jersey bounce / I can't get started / Baby, won't you please come home / You go to my head / Music, Maestro, please.
Note: Orchestra conducted by the brilliant Billy May, we have here an album torch blues to brisk up tempo. Released originally in 1957 and still sounding as fresh as today as then.
**Album:** Released Dec '85, on Capitol T (USA) Catalogue no: **T 898**

### SENSATIONAL
Tracks: / Mr. Memory maker / Put your arms around me honey / Livin' livin' livin' / Greyhound / Jump back / Tennessee saturday night / Sensational / Ain't that a shame / Razzle dazzle / Down in Mexico / Smake dab in the middle / I'm gone / T'aint what you do (it's the way that you do it) / Seventeen.
Note: A swing selection of tracks from "Ain't That a Shame" to "Tain't What you Do, It's the Way That You Do it", superbly delievered by one of the great ladies of the 40's and 50's.Along with her comparable contemporary, Nellie Lutcher, this lady enjoyed million selling successes in her era. Here she employs five different orchestras including the late Nelson Riddle's.
**Album:** Released Jan '86, on Capitol by EMI Records. Deleted Jul '87. Catalogue no: **EMS 1145**

## Morton, Jelly Roll

### 1926-39
**Album:** Released Sep '87, on Giants of Jazz by Hasmick Promotions. Catalogue no: **LPJT 23**

### BEST OF JELLY ROLL MORTON
**Album:** Released '83, on RCA (Germany) Catalogue no: **CL 43291**

### BLACK BOTTOM STOMP
**Cass:** Released Sep '85, on Saar Giants Of Jazz (Italy) Catalogue no: **MCJT 23**
**Album:** Released Sep '85, on Saar Giants Of Jazz (Italy) Catalogue no: **LPJT 23**

### CLIMAX RAG 1
**Cass:** Released Nov '84, on Astan (USA) Catalogue no: **40101**
**Album:** Released Nov '84, on Astan (USA) Catalogue no: **20101**

### COMPLETE JELLY ROLL MORTON 1 & 2 1926-27
Tracks: / Black bottom stomp / Smoke house blues / Chant, The / Sidewalk blues / Dead man blues / Steamboat stomp / Someday, sweetheart / Grandpa's spells / Original Jelly Roll blues / Doctor Jazz / Cannon ball blues / Hyena stomp / Billy goat stomp / Wild man blues / Jungle blues / Beale street / Pearls, The / Wolverine blues / Mister jelly roll.
**2 LP Set:** Released '83, on RCA (France) by BMG Records (France). Catalogue no: **PM 42405**
**2 LP Set:** Released Sep '86, on Jazz Tribune by BMG Records (UK). Deleted May '89. Catalogue no: **NL 89768**
**Cass set:** Released Sep '86, on Jazz Tribune by BMG Records (UK). Deleted May '89. Catalogue no: **NK 89768**

### COMPLETE JELLY ROLL MORTON 3 & 4 1927-29
Tracks: / Georgia swing / Wild man blues / Kansas City stomp / Shoes shiner's drag / Boogaboo / Shreveport stomp (1 & 2) / Mournful serenade / Red hot pepper stomp / Deep creek / Pep / Seattle hunch (1 & 2) / Frances / Freakish (1 & 2) / Burnin' the iceberg / Courthouse homp (1 & 2) / Pretty Lil (1 & 2) /

Sweet Aneta mine / New Orleans bump (1 & 2) / Down my way / Try me out / Tank town bump (1 & 2) / Sweet Peter (1 & 2).
**2 LP Set:** Released '83, on RCA (France) by BMG Records (France). Catalogue no: **PM 43170**
**2 LP Set:** Released Sep '86, on Jazz Tribune by BMG Records (UK). Deleted May '89. Catalogue no: **NL 89769**
**Cass set:** Released Sep '86, on Jazz Tribune by BMG Records (UK). Deleted May '89. Catalogue no: **NK 89769**

**COMPLETE JELLY ROLL MORTON 5 & 6 1929-1930**
Tracks: / Mississippi mildred / Mint julep / You oughta see my gal / Futuristic blues / Keep your business to yourself / She's got what I need / I hate a man like you / Don't tell me nothin' 'bout my man / Smilin' the blues away / Turtle twist / My little Dixie home / That's like it ought to be / Each day / If someone would only love me / That'll never do / I'm looking for a little bluebird / Little Lawrence / Harmony blues / Fussy Mabel / Ponchartrain / When they get lovin, they's gone / You done played out blues / Oil well / Load of coal / Jersey Joe.
**2 LP Set:** Released Jun '86, on Jazz Tribune by BMG Records (UK). Deleted May '89. Catalogue no: **NL 89757**
**2 LP Set:** Released '83, on RCA (France) by BMG Records (France). Catalogue no: **PM 43690**
**Cass set:** Released Jun '86, on Jazz Tribune by BMG Records (UK). Deleted May '89. Catalogue no: **NK 89757**

**COMPLETE JELLY ROLL MORTON 7 & 8 1930-1940**
Tracks: / Crazy chords / Primrose stomp / Big time woman / I'm her pappa she's my mama / New crawley blues / She saves her sweetest smile for me / Low gravy / Strokin' away / Blue blood blues / Mushmouth / Gambling Jack / Fickle fay creep / Oh, didn't he ramble / High society / I thought I heard Buddy Bolden say / Winin' boy blues / Climax rag / Don't you leave me here / West End blues / King Porter stomp.
**2 LP Set:** Released '83, on RCA (France) by BMG Records (France). Catalogue no: **PM 45372**
**Cass:** Released Jun '86, on Jazz Tribune by BMG Records (UK). Deleted May '89. Catalogue no: **NK 89748**
**Album:** Released Jun '86, on Jazz Tribune by BMG Records (UK). Deleted May '89. Catalogue no: **NL 89748**

**DOCTOR JAZZ**
Tracks: / Black bottom stomp / Chant / Sidewalk blues / Dead man blues / Original Jelly Roll blues / Doctor jazz / Wild man blues / Red hot pepper stomp / Jungle blues / Pearls / Kansas city stomp / Little Lawrence.
**Album:** Released Jul '86, on RCA by BMG Records (UK). Deleted Jul '89. Catalogue no: **CL 89808**
**Cass:** Released Jul '86, on RCA by BMG Records (UK). Deleted Jul '89. Catalogue no: **CK 89808**

**GENNET PIANO SOLOS, THE 1923-24**
Tracks: / King Porter stomp / New Orleans (Blues) / Joys (2 takes) / Grandpa's spells / Kansas City stomp / Wolverine blues / Pearls / Tia Juana / Shreveport stomp / Tom cat blues / Stratford hunch / Perfect rag.
**Album:** Released Jan '83, on Swaggie (Australia) Catalogue no: **801**

**HIS RED HOT PEPPERS & TRIOS (Morton, Jelly Roll & His Red Hot Peppers)**
**Album:** Released Apr '81, on Joker (USA) by Lifetime Records (USA). Catalogue no: **SM 3556**
**Album:** Released Apr '81, on Joker (USA) by Lifetime Records (USA). Catalogue no: **SM 3555**

**HIS RED HOT PEPPERS VOL.1 (Morton, Jelly Roll & His Red Hot Peppers)**
**Album:** Released Apr '81, on Joker (USA) by Lifetime Records (USA). Catalogue no: **SM 3550**

**HIS RED HOT PEPPERS VOL.2 (Morton, Jelly Roll & His Red Hot Peppers)**
**Album:** Released Apr '81, on Joker (USA) by Lifetime Records (USA). Catalogue no: **SM 3551**

**HIS RED HOT PEPPERS VOL.3 (Morton, Jelly Roll & His Red Hot Peppers)**
**Album:** Released Apr '81, on Joker (USA) by Lifetime Records (USA). Catalogue no: **SM 3552**

**HIS RED HOT PEPPERS VOL.4 (Morton, Jelly Roll & His Red Hot Peppers)**
**Album:** Released Apr '81, on Joker (USA) by Lifetime Records (USA). Catalogue no: **SM 3553**

**HIS RED HOT PEPPERS VOL.5 (Morton, Jelly Roll & His Red Hot Peppers)**
**Album:** Released Apr '81, on Joker (USA) by Lifetime Records (USA). Catalogue no: **SM 3554**

**I'M A WINNIN' BOY**
Tracks: / Honeysuckle rose / Melancholy baby / I'd do anything for you / I ain't got nobody / Pearls, The / Tiger rag / Trees / Winnin' boy blues / King Porter stomp.
**Album:** Released Oct '81, on Joy by President Records. Catalogue no: **JOY 265**

**INCOMPARABLE**
**Cass:** Released May '88, on Classic Jazz Masters Catalogue no: **42024**
**Album:** Released May '88, on Classic Jazz Masters Catalogue no: **22024**

**JAZZ CLASSICS IN DIGITAL STEREO**
Tracks: / Black bottom stomp / Chant (The) / Dead man blues / Grandpa's spells / Original Jelly Roll blues / Beale Street blues / Ham 'n' eggs / You need some loving / Kansas City stomp / Shoe shiner's drag / Deep creek / Pretty Lil / New Orleans bump / Ponchartrain / Blue blood blues / I'm alone without you.
**Cass:** Released Oct '86, on BBC by BBC Records & Tapes. Catalogue no: **ZCF 604**
**CD:** Released Oct '86, on BBC by BBC Records & Tapes. Catalogue no: **BBC CD 604**

**JELLY ROLL MORTON**
**Album:** Released '88, on Collector's Classics Catalogue no: **CC 7**
**Album:** Released '88, on Meritt (USA) Catalogue no: **MERITT 1**
**Album:** Released Apr '81, on Joker (USA) by Lifetime Records (USA). Catalogue no: **SM 3091**

**JELLY ROLL MORTON 1939**
**Album:** Released Dec '84, on Commodore Class Catalogue no: **AG6 24062**

**JELLY ROLL MORTON 1923/24**
Tracks: / King Porter stomp / New Orleans joys / Grandpa's spells / Kansas city stomp / Wolverine blues / Pearls / Tia Juana / Shreveport stomp / Frog-i-more rag / mamamita / Jelly roll blues / Big foot ham blues / My gal / Muddy water blues / Steady roll / Fish tail blues / High society / Weary blues / Tiger rag.
**Album:** Released Apr '81, on Milestone by Ace Records. Catalogue no: **M 47018**

**JELLY ROLL MORTON 1923-25**
**Album:** Released Apr '79, on Fountain by Retrieval Records. Catalogue no: **FJ 104**

**JELLY ROLL MORTON COLLECTION 20 golden greats**
Tracks: / Jelly Roll blues / King Porter stomp / London blues / New Orleans joys / Wolverine blues / Mr. Jelly Lord / Tank town bump / Wild man blues / Pep / Burning the iceberg / New Orleans bump / Shreveport stomp / Seattle hunch / Freakish / Red hot pepper stomp / Mississippi Mildred / My little Dixie home / Jersey Joe / Don't you leave me here / Crazy chords.
**Cass:** Released Jan '87, on Deja Vu Catalogue no: **DVMC 2084**
**Album:** Released Jan '87, on Deja Vu Catalogue no: **DVLP 2084**

**JELLY ROLL MORTON'S HOT SEVEN**
**Album:** Released May '87, on Commodore Class Catalogue no: **6.24546**

**KINGS OF NEW ORLEANS JAZZ (Morton, Jelly Roll & His Red Hot Peppers)**
Tracks: / Black bottom stomp / Chant, The / Smoke house blues / Steamboat stomp / Sidewalk blues / Dead man blues / Cannon ball blues / Grandpa's spells / Doctor Jazz / Original Jelly Roll blues / Jungle blues / Pearls, The / Beale Street blues / Kansas city stomp / Shoe shiner's drag / Georgia swing.
**Album:** Released Aug '81, on RCA In-

ternational by BMG Records (UK). Deleted Aug '86. Catalogue no: **INTS 5092**
**Cass:** Released Jun '81, on RCA International by BMG Records (UK). Catalogue no: **NK 89015**
**Album:** Released Jun '81, on RCA International by BMG Records (UK). Catalogue no: **NL 89015**

**LAST BAND DATES 1940**
Tracks: / Sweet substitute / Panama / Good old New York / Big lips blues / Why / Get the bucket / If you knew / Shake it / Dirty dirty dirty / Swinging the elks / Mama's got a baby / My home is in a southern town.
**Album:** Released Sep '82, on Commodore Class Catalogue no: **AG6 24546**

**LIBRARY OF CONGRESS RECORDINGS VOL. 1**
**Album:** Released Jan '83, on Swaggie (Australia) Catalogue no: **S 1311**

**LIBRARY OF CONGRESS RECORDINGS VOL. 2**
**Album:** Released Jan '83, on Swaggie (Australia) Catalogue no: **S 1312**
**Album:** Released Aug '87, on Classic Jazz Masters Catalogue no: **CJM 3**

**LIBRARY OF CONGRESS RECORDINGS VOL. 3**
**Album:** Released Jan '83, on Swaggie (Australia) Catalogue no: **S 1313**
**Album:** Released Aug '87, on Classic Jazz Masters Catalogue no: **CJM 4**

**LIBRARY OF CONGRESS RECORDINGS VOL. 4**
**Album:** Released Dec '86, on Classic Jazz Masters Catalogue no: **CJM 5**
**Album:** Released Jan '83, on Swaggie (Australia) Catalogue no: **S 1314**

**LIBRARY OF CONGRESS RECORDINGS VOL. 5**
**Album:** Released Jan '83, on Swaggie (Australia) Catalogue no: **S 1315**
**Album:** Released '88, on CJM by Wellard Dist.. Catalogue no: **CJM 6**

**LIBRARY OF CONGRESS RECORDINGS VOL. 6**
**Album:** Released Jan '83, on Swaggie (Australia) Catalogue no: **S 1316**
**Album:** Released Dec '86, on Classic Jazz Masters Catalogue no: **CJM 7**

**LIBRARY OF CONGRESS RECORDINGS VOL. 7**
Album: Released Jan '83, on Swaggie (Australia) Catalogue no: **S 1317**
**Album:** Released Dec '86, on Classic Jazz Masters Catalogue no: **CJM 8**

**LIBRARY OF CONGRESS RECORDINGS VOL. 8**
**Album:** Released Dec '86, on Classic Jazz Masters Catalogue no: **CJM 9**
**Album:** Released Jan '83, on Swaggie (Australia) Catalogue no: **S 1318**

**MISTER JELLY LORD (Morton, Jelly Roll & His New Orleans Rhythm Kings)**
Tracks: / Sobbin blues / Marguerite / Angry angry / Clarinet marmalade / Mister Jelly Lord / London blues / Milenberg joys / Mad.
**Album:** Released '74, on Rhapsody by President Records. Catalogue no: **RHA 6022**

**NEW ORLEANS JAZZ**
**Album:** Released May '88, on Classic Jazz Masters Catalogue no: **22027**
**Cass:** Released May '88, on Classic Jazz Masters Catalogue no: **42027**

**NEW ORLEANS JAZZMEN & TRIOS**
**CD:** Released '88, on Giants of Jazz by Hasmick Promotions. Catalogue no: **CD 530 18**

**NEW ORLEANS MEMORIES**
Tracks: / Sporting / House rag / Original rags / Crave, The / Naked dance / Mister Joe / King Porter stomp / Winin' boy blues / Don't you leave me here / Mamie's blues / Michigan water blues.
**CD:** Released May '87, on Commodore Class Catalogue no: **824 062**
**Album:** Released May '87, on Commodore Class Catalogue no: **AG6 24062**

**PEARLS, THE**
Tracks: / Black bottom stomp / Smokehouse blues / Chant, The / Sidewalk blues / Dead man blues / Steamboat stomp / Grandpa's spells / Original Jelly Roll blues / Doctor Jazz / Cannon ball blues / Pearls, The / Wolverine blues / Mr. Jelly Lord / Georgia swing / Kansas City stomp / Shreveport stomp / Mournful serenade / Red hot pepper stomp / Deep creek / Freakish / Tank town bump / I thought I heard Buddy Bolden say / Winin' boy blues.
**CD:** Released Nov '88, on Bluebird (2) by BMG Records (UK). Catalogue no: **ND 86588**

**PIANO BLUES & RAG 1924/25**
**CD:** Released Oct '89, on Jazz Anthology by Musidisc Records (France). Catalogue no: **550122**

**RARITIES VOL.1**
Tracks: / Big fat ham big fat ham / Muddy water blues / Mr. Jelly Roll / Mr. Jelly Roll (take 2) / Steady roll / Steady roll (take 2) / Fish tail blues / High Society / Weary blues / Tiger rag / King Porter, The / Tom cat / My gal / Wolverine blues / Mr. Jelly Lord.
**Album:** Released '74, on Rhapsody by President Records. Catalogue no: **RHA 6021**

**RARITIES VOL.2**
Note: Mono.
**Album:** Released Jun '86, on Rhapsody by President Records. Catalogue no: **RHA 6030**

**RED HOT PEPPERS, NEW ORLEANS JAZZMEN & TRIOS**
Tracks: / Oh, didn't he ramble? / West End blues / High society / I thought I heard Buddy Bolden say / Kansas city stomp / Shoe shiner's drag / Deep creek / Chant, The / Original Jelly Roll blues / Mr. Jelly Lord / Shreveport stomp / Turtle twist / Beale Street blues / Georgia swing / Wild man blues / Black bottom stomp / Grandpa's spells / Doctor Jazz / Cannon ball blues / Wolverine blues / Boogaboo / Winin' boy blues / Ballin' the jack.
**CD:** Released Jun '88, on Giants of Jazz by Hasmick Promotions. Catalogue no: **GOJCD 53018**

**SOLO PIANO SESSION 1924-1938**
Tracks: / Honky tonk music (2 takes) / Finger buster / Creepy feeling / Winnin' boy blues / Pep / Seattle hunch / Frances / Freakish / Pearls, The / Sweetheart o mine / Fat meat and greens / King Porter stomp / Thirty fifth street blues / Mamanita / Froggie Moore / London blues.
**Album:** Released Jan '83, on Swaggie (Australia) Catalogue no: **816**

**WEST END BLUES**
Tracks: / Oh didn't he ramble / Strokin' away / Blue blood blues / Mushmouth shuffle / Fickle fay creep / High society / Thought I heard Buddy Bolden say / Winnin' boy blues / Climax rag 1 / Don't you leave me here / West end blues / Ballin' the jack.
Note: Collectors Edition Series. Mono recording.
**Album:** Released Mar '86, on Meteor by Magnum Music Group. Catalogue no: **MTM 005**

## Mosby, Curtis

**CURTIS MOSBY BLUE BLOWERS**
**Album:** Released Apr '79, on VJM (Vintage Jazz Music) by Vintage Jazz Music Society(VJM). Catalogue no: **VLP 38**

## Moss, Danny

**DANNY MOSS & GEOFF SIMPINS VOL.2 (Moss, Danny & Geoff simpkins)**
**Album:** Released Jul '82, on Flyright by Interstate Music. Catalogue no: **FLY 218**

## Mosse, Sandy

**RELAXIN' WITH ... (Mosse, Sandy Quintet)**
**Album:** Released Feb '88, on Fresh Sounds (Spain) by Fresh Sounds Records (Spain). Catalogue no: **FS 66**

## Most, Sam

**FLUTE FLIGHT**
**Album:** Released Jul '82, on Xanadu Catalogue no: **XANADU 141**

**FLUTE TALK (Most, Sam & Joe Farrell)**
**Album:** Released '88, on Xanadu Catalogue no: **XAN 173**

**MOSTLY FLUTE (Various)**
**Album:** Released '88, on Xanadu Catalogue no: **XAN 133**

**PLAYS BIRD, MONK & MILES**
**Album:** Released 12 Feb '88, on Fresh Sounds (Spain) by Fresh Sounds Records (Spain). Catalogue no: **FS 305**

## Moten, Bennie

**BASIC BEGINNINGS**
Tracks: / Jones law blues, The / Small black / Rit dit ray / New Vine Street blues / Oh Eddie / That too, do blues / Count, The / Liza Lee / Somebody stole my gal / Now that I need you / Toby / Moten swing / Blue room, The / New Orleans /

**Bennie Moten - Kansas City Orchestra (Retrieval)**

Lafayette / Prince of Wales.
**Album:** Released Nov '89, on Bluebird (2) by BMG Records (UK). Catalogue no: **NL 90403**
**CD:** Released Nov '89, on Bluebird (2) by BMG Records (UK). Catalogue no: **ND 90403**
**Cass:** Released Nov '89, on Bluebird (2) by BMG Records (UK). Catalogue no: **NK 90403**

**BENNIE MOTEN'S KANSAS CITY ORCHESTRA (Moten, Bennie Kansas City Orchestra) (See panel above)**
Tracks: / Ill natured blues / Chattanooga blues / Evil mama blues / Elephant's wobble / Crawdad blues / Selma 'bama blues / Break o'day blues / Waco Texas blues / South / Vine Street blues / Tulsa blues / Goofy dust / Baby dear / She's sweeter than sugar / South Street blues / Sister honky tonk / As I like it / Things seem so blue to me / 18th Street strut / Kater Street rag.
Note: With Lammar Wright / Harry Cooper / Harlan Leonard / Woodie Walder / Sam Tall / Willie Hall. Tracks include: Ill natured blues / Chattanooga blues / As I like it / South / Tulsa blues / Kater Street rag, etc.. Bennie Moten was born in Kansas City on 13th November 1894. His mother was a pianist and he recieved tuition on this instrument. Early this century, the ragtime influence was strong, Sedalia, Missouri, being its centre, and it was here in 1899 that Scott Joplin met the music publisher John Stark and *Maple leaf rag* was published. This influence would have been strong with the young Moten while he was taking piano lessons, and this is very evident in his playing. Kansas City, by virtue of its location on the Missouri River and proximity to St. Louis, came under the influence of the musicians playing on the riverboats appearing there. It was also a railroad centre and musicians would come and go from the South-West. Consequently, the young KC musicians were subjected to a flow of new ideas which they absorbed into their own playing. Bennie Moten performed around Kansas City firstly on trumpet, but switched to piano, and in 1923 assembled a six piece dance band to fill a club vacancy. In September of that year they recorded for the Okeh company at St Louis. It would appear that the main purpose was to record Ada Brown and Mary Bradford, two fine strong voiced blues singers, whom the band was to accompany. Ada Brown's *Ill natured blues* is particularly fine, featuring a series of breaks by each instrumentalist, and her *Evil mama blues* has ensemble accompaniment and a band section between the two vocal periods. Mary Bradford's *Waco Texas blues* is accompanied by cornet and piano only but they complement her singing very effectively. Almost as a by-product of the session, it seems the band recorded two instrumental numbers - *Elephant's wobble* and *Crawdad blues*. The former number has good ensemble, followed by short trombone and cornet passages, some strange 'blue blowing' sounds (which Walder achieved using his clarinet mouthpiece), more fine ensemble playing and an apt cornet coda. The banjo seems far too loud, however, but no doubt this was popular at the time and in any case could have been due to difficulties in obtaining good balance on these early acoustic recordings. *Crawdad blues* follows the same formula and if one makes allowances for the period peculiarities of clarinet, banjo and freak noises, these are good sides with a splendid ensemble sense. The next recording session, also at St. Louis, took place over one year later, when a second trumpet player and a second reed man were added to the band. Five numbers were recorded and they all became Moten standards, to be re-recorded in the Victor era between 1927-1929. The music is an improvement on that of the first session: the clainet generally produces a better one, the banjoy is less obtrusive and the enlarged ensemble provides a more 'meaty' sound while retaining it's clarity. In these recordings, one sees the beginning of the band's shift away from the New Orleans tradition to a new direction, much as King Oliver was to do with his Dixie Syncopators.
South, later to become a juke box favourite in is Victor reincarnation, is mainly ensemble playing with short breaks by the two cornets and it moves easily with the fine rolling rhythm characteristic of the band. *Vine Street blues* is a typical instrumental blues with various solos punctuating the tight ensemble work. *Tulsa blues* is a haunting melody carried through most of the record with the clarinet maintaining a part clearly heard above the melody, but the short trombone solo is rather poor. *Goofy dust* is the pick of the bunch, featuring three choruses of Moten's ragtime-influenced piano. To my ears, this track reeks of nostalgia and period atmostphere. The ensemble playing is concise and breaks are heavily featured. *Baby dear* is another of Moten's attractive melodies and this version is better than the later Victor issue which suffers from rather banal lyrics. The third and final Okeh recording session took place six months later in Kansas city. A brass band had been added and the occupant of the banjo chair had changed. More interplay between the brass and reed sections can be observed and the rhythm section benefits from the foundation provided by the brass bass. According to Harlan Leonard, quoted by Ross Russell, there were no written arrangements, nor much preparation prior to arrival at the studios. The ragtme feeling, the blues, parade band influence and negro dancing requirements all appear in the music put down on this session. *She's sweeter than sugar* moves with a jaunty swaggering air, the brass and reeds play as sections and the whole has a tremendous life; even the period vocal is not unpleasant. *South Street blues* starts and ends with ensemble playing, between which solos are spaced, although Walder's clarinet tone leaves something to declare. *Sister honky tonk* is a spirited number featuring

Alphonse Mouzon

a wa wa trombone solo, while *As I like it* is played fairly straight without benefit of any breaks.
In *Things seem so blue to me* the band sounds as though it were on a parade with the brass section bouncing along. The next number, 18th Street Strut, is a simple repeated figure which, when enlarged upon by the cornet player, is reminicent of Dippermouth Blues. An extraordinary kazoo like episode is provided by Walder. The last track, *Kater Street rag*, finishes the session in great style. This is a Moten rag, the theme of which is introduced by the ensemble, followed by clarinet and alto breaks and 32-bar piano interlude leading into the final ensemble enriched with cornet and trombone breaks. The piece confirms Moten himself as being the premier solist during this period, although on record he is only featured on *Kater Street* and *Goofy dust*. It is interesting to observe the progress of the band from 1923 to 1925 during its Okeh recording life. The company allowed it to play its own material, which is nearly all credited either to 'Moten Hayes' or 'Bennie Moten's Kansas City Orchestra'. This remained firmly rooted in ragtime and blues, while the introduction of simple two cornet, two reed sections led to a move away from the N.O. ensemble conception towards what was to become known as Kansas City Style. Some of the numbers recorded were basically short repeated figures, pointing towards the riff style later to become fashionable. (Ray Batt)
**Cass:** Released Oct '87, on Fountain by Retrieval Records. Catalogue no: **CFJ 120**
**Album:** Released Oct '87, on Fountain by Retrieval Records. Catalogue no: **FJ 120**

**COMPLETE BENNIE 1/2 1926-28**
Tracks: / Thick lip stomp / Harmony City shuffle / Yazoo / White lightnin' blues / Muscle shoals blues / Missouri wobble / Sugar / Dear heart / New Tulsa blues / Baby dear / Twelfth St. rag / Pass out lightly / Ding dong blues / Moten stomp / Justrite / Slow motion / Tough breaks / It's hard to laugh or smile / Sad man blues / Kansas City breakdown / Trouble in mind / Hot water blues / Get low down blues.
**2 LP Set:** Released '83, on RCA (France) by BMG Records (France). Catalogue no: **PM 42410**

**COMPLETE BENNIE 3/4 1928-30**
Tracks: / She's no trouble / South / Terrific stomp / Let's get it / Kansas City squabble / Rite tite / Moten blues / That's what I'm talking about / That certain motion / It won't be long / When life seems so blue / Loose like a goose / Just say it's me / New goofy dust rag / Rumba negro / Jones law blues / Band box / Everyday blues / Boot it / Mary Lee / Rit-dit-ray / New Vine Street blues / Sweetheart of yesterday / Won't you be my baby.
**2 LP Set:** Released '83, on RCA (France) by BMG Records (France). Catalogue no: **PM 43693**

**MOTEN STOMP**
Tracks: / Thick lip stomp (track 1) / Harmony blues (track 2) / Kansas City shuffle (track 3) / Yazoo blues (track 4) / White lightnin' blues (track 5) / Muscle shoals blues (track 6) / Midnight mama (track 7) / Missouri wobble (track 8) / Sugar (track 9) / Dear heart (track 10) / New Tulsa blues (track 11) / Baby dear (track 12) / 12th Street rag (track 13) / Pass out lightly (track 14) / Ding-dong blues (track 15) / Moten stomp(track 16).
**Cass:** Released Oct '86, on Halcyon (USA) by Submarine Records. Catalogue no: **CHDL 108**
**Album:** Released Feb '87, on Halcyon (USA) by Submarine Records. Catalogue no: **HDL 108**

## Motian, Paul

**IT SHOULD'VE HAPPENED A LONG TIME AGO (Motian, Paul Trio)**
**Album:** Released Feb '85, on ECM Catalogue no: **ECM 1283**
**CD:** Released Apr '85, on ECM Catalogue no: **823 641-2**

**JACK OF CLUBS (Motian, Paul Quintet)**
**CD:** Released '86, on Soul Note Catalogue no: **SN 1124**

**MONK IN MOTIAN (Motian, Paul / Joe Lovano / Bill Frisell)**
**CD:** Released Feb '89, on JMT (Germany) Catalogue no: **824421-2**
**Album:** Released Feb '89, on JMT (Germany) Catalogue no: **834421-1**

**PSALM (Motian, Paul Band)**
**Album:** Released Jul '82, on ECM Catalogue no: **ECM 1222**

## Mouldy Five

**MOULDY FIVE-VOLUME 1**
**Album:** Released Jun '86, on GHB by Jazzology Records (USA). Catalogue no: **GHB 181**

## Moule,Ken

**AS TIME GOES BY**
**Album:** Released Sep '75, on BBC by BBC Records & Tapes. Deleted '88. Catalogue no: **REC 205**

**MIDNIGHT MUSIC (Moule,Ken and the Full Score Orchestra)**
**Album:** Released Apr '78, on BBC by BBC Records & Tapes. Deleted '88. Catalogue no: **REC 305**

## Mouzon, Alphonse

**BABY COME BACK**
**Album:** Released May '81, on MPS Jazz Catalogue no: **MPS 60 229**

**BACK TO JAZZ (Mouzon, Alphonse band)**
**Album:** Released Dec '86, on L&R Catalogue no: **LR 45.001**

**BEST OF ALPHONSE MOUZON**
**CD:** Released Nov '89, on Black Sun by Black Sun Records. Catalogue no: **CD 15005-2**

**DON'T WANT TO LOSE THIS FEELING**
Tracks: / Don't want to lose this feeling

/ Don't want to lose this feeling (part 2).
**7" Single:** Released Mar '82, on London Records by London Records Ltd. Deleted '86. Catalogue no: **LON 003**
**12" Single:** Released Mar '82, on London Records by London Records Ltd. Deleted '85. Catalogue no: **LONX 003**

**I'M GLAD THAT YOU'RE HERE**
Tracks: / I'm glad that you're here.
**7" Single:** Released Nov '81, on London by London Records Ltd. Deleted Nov '84. Catalogue no: **HL 10581**
**12" Single:** Released Nov '81, on London by London Records Ltd. Deleted Nov '84. Catalogue no: **HLX 10581**

**IN SEARCH OF A DREAM**
**Album:** Released May '81, on MPS Jazz Catalogue no: **MPS 68 192**

**MORNING SUN**
**Album:** Released Nov '81, on London Records by London Records Ltd. Catalogue no: **SH 8547**

**SKY IS THE LIMIT, THE**
**CD:** Released '88, on Polydor by Polydor Ltd. Catalogue no: **835 948 2**

**STEP INTO THE FUNK**
**Album:** Released Jul '82, on Polydor (Germany) by Polydor Ltd. Catalogue no: **1060 507**

## MPS Jazz...

**MPS JAZZ COLLECTION**
**CD:** Released '88, on Polydor by Polydor Ltd. Catalogue no: **821 018 2**

## Mr. B Detroit

**MR B DETROIT SPECIAL**
**Album:** Released '88, on Oldie Blues Catalogue no: **OL 8010**

## Mucho Calor

**MUCHO CALOR Presentation in latin jazz (Various artists)**
**Album:** Released Apr '88, on VSOP Catalogue no: **VSOP 47**

## Mullen, Jim

**THUMBS UP**
Tracks: / Blue Montreaux / Fall / As if you read my mind / Crepuscule / Thumbs up / Herbal scent / Friends / Beauty and the beast.
Note: Digital Stereo recording.
**CD:** Released Oct '84, on Coda by Coda Records. Catalogue no: **CODA 4CD**
**Album:** on Coda by Coda Records. Catalogue no: **CODA 4**

**UP (Mullen, Jim & Dick Morrissey)**
Tracks: / Footloose / Sing me softly of the blues / Everything must change / Philip Phuling / What a way to go / You'll know what I mean / Busted fender.
**Album:** Released Nov '81, on Embryo by Embryo Records. Deleted Aug '87. Catalogue no: **K 50835**

## Mulligan, Gerry

**'63 - THE CONCERT JAZZ BAND**
**Album:** Released Aug '89, on Verve Catalogue no: **837 438 1**

**AGE OF STEAM, THE**
Tracks: / One to ten in Ohio / K-4 pacific / Grand tour, The / Over the hill and out of the woods / Country beaver / Golden notebooks / Maytag.
**CD:** Released 24 Jul '89, on A&M by A&M Records. Catalogue no: **CDA 0804**
**CD:** Released 28 Nov '88, on A&M by A&M Records. Catalogue no: **CDA 0805**

**AT BIRDLAND NEW YORK 1960**
**CD:** Released Oct '89, on Jazz Anthology by Musidisc Records (France). Catalogue no: **550072**

**BEST OF GERRY MULLIGAN Compact/Walkman jazz**
Tracks: / Bernie's theme / Festive minor / This lady is a tramp / Blue at the roots / Sweet and lovely / Line for lyons / Demanton / Spring is sprung / Theme for joblim / Makin' whoopee / Westwood walk / Night lights.
**CD:** Released Jul '87, on Mercury by Phonogram Ltd. Catalogue no: **830 697-2**
**Cass:** Released May '87, on Mercury by Phonogram Ltd. Catalogue no: **830 697-4**

**BLUES IN TIME (Mulligan, Gerry & Paul Desmond)**
Tracks: / Blues in time / Body and soul / Stand still / Line for Lyons / Wintersong / Battle hymn of the republic / Fall out.
Note: The only collaboration between Mulligan (baritone sax) and Desmond (alto sax) on record. With Joe Benjamin (bass), Dave Bailey (drums). Recorded in New York, 1957, and produced by Norman Granz.
**Album:** Released Mar '84, on Verve (USA) by Polydor Ltd. Catalogue no: **2304 329**

**BY ALL MEANS**
**CD:** Released '88, on IMS by Polydor Ltd. Catalogue no: **GRPD 00950**

**CALIFORNIA CONCERTS VOL. 1 (Mulligan, Gerry & Chet Baker)**
Tracks: / Blues going up / Little girl blue / Piano blues / Yardbird suite / Blue for Tiny / Soft shoe / Makin' whoopee / Darn that dream / Onlet / Mark for Barksdale.
**CD:** Released Aug '88, on EMI-Manhattan by EMI Records. Catalogue no: **CDP 746 860 2**
**CD:** Released Aug '88, on EMI-Manhattan by EMI Records. Catalogue no: **CZ 65**

**CALIFORNIA CONCERTS VOL. 2**
Tracks: / Makin' whoopee / Nights at the turntable / Blues for Tiny / Frenesi / Limelite / People wil say we're in love / Western Union / I know, don't know why / Red door, The / Polka dots and moonbeams / I'll remember April / There will never be another you / It don't mean a thing / In a sentimental mood / Flamingo / Moon mist.
**CD:** Released Mar '89, on EMI-Manhattan by EMI Records. Catalogue no: **CZ 67**
**CD:** Released Jan '89, on Pacific Jazz by EMI Records. Catalogue no: **CDP 746 864 2**

**COLLECTION: GERRY MULLIGAN**
Tracks: / Jeru / Festive minor / I never knew / Rose room / Blue theme / Lady Chatterly's mother / Wee bit of bopita, A / My funny valentine / Chuggin' / Out of this world / Everything happens to me / Bernie's tune.
**Cass:** Released Nov '85, on Deja Vu Catalogue no: **DVMC 2045**

**COMPACT JAZZ: GERRY MULLIGAN**
Tracks: / Lady is a tramp, The / Westwood walk.
**CD:** Released Jul '87, on Phonogram by Phonogram Ltd. Catalogue no: **831 696-2**
**Cass:** Released Jul '87, on Phonogram by Phonogram Ltd. Catalogue no: **831 696-4**

**CONCERT IN JAZZ**
**Album:** Released May '83, on Verve (USA) by Polydor Ltd. Catalogue no: **2304 424**

**FABULOUS GERRY MULLIGAN QUARTET (Mulligan, Gerry Quartet)**
Tracks: / I may be wrong / Five brothers / Gold rush / Lullaby of the leaves / Makin' whoopee / Laura / Soft shoe / Nearness of you / Limelight / Come out wherever you are / Love me or leave me / Bernie's tune / Walking shoes / Moonlight in Vermont / Lady is a tramp, The / Bark for Barksdale.
**CD:** Released Feb '89, on Vogue by Vogue Records. Catalogue no: **VGCD 600028**
**2 LP Set:** Released Oct '74, on Vogue by Vogue Records. Catalogue no: **VJD 504**
**2 LP Set:** Released Oct '88, on Vogue by Vogue Records. Catalogue no: **400007**

**GERRY MULLIGAN**
**CD:** Released Jul '89, on Cleo Catalogue no: **CLCD 5020**
**Album:** Released Jul '82, on Jazz Reactivation Catalogue no: **JR 123**
**Album:** Released '81, on Kings Of Jazz Catalogue no: **KLJ 20021**

**GERRY MULLIGAN AND JIMMY (Mulligan, Gerry & Jimmy Witherspoon)**
Tracks: / Time's gettin' tougher than tough / How long blues / Corina Corina / C.C. rider / Roll 'em Pete / Everyday / Outskirts of town / Kansas city / Trouble in mind / St. Louis blues.
**Album:** Released '87, on Joker (USA) by Lifetime Records (USA). Catalogue no: **SM 3279**
**Cass:** Released '87, on Joker (USA) by Lifetime Records (USA). Catalogue no: **MC 3279**

**GERRY MULLIGAN IN CONCERT**
**CD:** Released May '85, on Roulette by Vogue Records. Catalogue no: **PRT 60028**

**GERRY MULLIGAN MEETS BEN WEBSTER (Mulligan, Gerry & Ben**

**Webster)**
Tracks: / Chelsea Bridge / Cat walk / Sunday / Who's got rhythm? / Tell me when / Go home.
Note: Gerry Mulligan, baritone sax; Ben Webster, tenor sax; Jimmy Rowles, piano; Leroy Vinnegar, bass; Mel Lewis, drums.
**Album:** Released Sep '60, on H.M.V. by EMI Records. Deleted Sep '65. Catalogue no: **CLP 1373**
**Album:** Released May '84, on Verve (USA) by Polydor Ltd. Catalogue no: **821 167-1**

**GERRY MULLIGAN MEETS JOHNNY HODGES (Mulligan, Gerry & Johnny Hodges)**
Tracks: / Bunny / What's the rush? / Back beat / What's it all about? / Eighteen carrots for Rabbit / Shady side.
Note: One of a series of collaborations between Mulligan (baritone sax) and other great saxists.
**Album:** Released Mar '82, on Verve (USA) by Polydor Ltd. Catalogue no: **2304 476**

**GERRY MULLIGAN QUARTET WITH CHET BAKER (Mulligan, Gerry & Chet Baker)**
**CD:** Released Aug '88, on Giants of Jazz by Hasmick Promotions. Catalogue no: **CD 53027**

**GERRY MULLIGAN-CHET BAKER**
**Album:** Released '88, on GNP Crescendo (USA) by GNP Crescendo Records (USA). Catalogue no: **GNPS 56**

**IMMORTAL CONCERTS**
Tracks: / I may be wrong / Gold rush / Makin' whoopee / Laura / Soft shoe / Nearness of you, The / Love me or leave me / Bernie's tune / Walking shoes / Five brothers / Lullaby of the leaves / Limelight / Come out wherever you are / Moonlight in Vermont / Lady is a tramp, The / Bark for Barksdale.
**CD:** Released Jun '88, on Giants of Jazz by Hasmick Promotions. Catalogue no: **GOJCD 53020**

**IN SWEDEN 1957**
**2 LP Set:** Released '88, on Jazz Information (Sweden) Catalogue no: **CAH 4003/4**

**JAZZ COMBO FROM 'I WANT TO LIVE' (Mulligan, Gerry & Shelly Manne)**
Tracks: / Black nightgown / I want to live, Theme from / Night watch, The / Frisco club / Barbara's theme / Life's a funny thing.
**Album:** Released Mar '88, on Affinity by Charly Records. Catalogue no: **AFF 188**

**JERU**
Tracks: / Get out of town / Here I'll stay / Inside impromptu / Blue boy / You've come home / Lonely town / Capricious.
**Cass:** Released Jul '86, on CBS by CBS Records. Deleted Nov '87. Catalogue no: **40 21135**
**Album:** Released Jul '86, on CBS by CBS Records. Catalogue no: **CBS 21135**

**LA MENACE (Film soundtrack)**
**2 LP Set:** Released Jul '83, on DRG (USA) by DRG Records (USA). Deleted Jan '89. Catalogue no: **MRS 506**

**LITTLE BIG HORN**
Tracks: / Under a star / Sun on stairs / Another kind of Sunday / Bright angel falls / I never was a young man / Little big horn.
Note: Gerry Mulligan, baritone sax; Michael Brecker, tenor sax; Dave Grusin, keyboards; Richard Tee, piano; Anthony Jackson, bass; Buddy Williams, drums.
**CD:** Released Sep '88, on GRP by GRP Records (USA). Catalogue no: **GRPD 9503**
**Album:** Released Sep '88, on GRP by GRP Records (USA). Catalogue no: **GRP 91003**

**LIVE IN STOCKHOLM, MAY 1957 (Mulligan, Gerry Quartet)**
Tracks: / Come out wherever you are / Birth of the blues / Moonlight in Vermont / Lullaby of the leaves / Open country / I can't get started / Frenesi / Baubles, bangles and beads / Yardbird suite.
Note: Gerry Mulligan, baritone sax; Bob Brookmeyer, valve trombone; Joe Benjamin, bass; Dave Bailey, drums.
**Album:** Released Apr '81, on Ingo Catalogue no: **INGO 3**

**LIVE IN STOCKHOLM, VOL 2 (Mulligan, Gerry Quartet)**
Tracks: / Walking shoes / My funny valentine / Blues at the roots / Bernie's tune / Lullaby of the leaves / Body and soul / All the things you are.
Note: Gerry Mulligan, baritone sax; Bob Brookmeyer, valve trombone; Joe Benjamin, bass; Dave Bailey, drums. Recorded 17 May 1957.
**Album:** Released '81, on Ingo Catalogue no: **INGO 6**

**MULLIGAN**
Tracks: / Jeru / Festive minor / Rose room / North Atlantic run / Taurus moon / Out back of the barn.
Note: Personnel: Gerry Mulligan (Baritone sax), Art Farmer (Trumpet), Bill Crow (Bass), Dave Bailey (Drums) and others.
**CD:** Released '88, on Denon Catalogue no: **C38-7682**
**CD:** Released Apr '89, on Denon Catalogue no: **DC 8537**
**Cass:** Released Apr '89, on Denon Catalogue no: **MC 7682**

**MULLIGAN - BAKER (CARNEGIE CONCERT, VOL. 1 & 2) (Mulligan, Gerry & Chet Baker)**
Tracks: / Carioca / Line for Lyons / Moonlight in Vermont / Bark for Barksdale / Turnstile / Lady is a tramp, The / My funny valentine / Funhouse / Ide's side / Round house / Kaper / Bweebida bobbida / Mullenium / Mulligan's two / Limelight / So easy / Go go / Bevan beeps / Rearin' back.
**CD:** Released May '84, on CBS by CBS Records. Deleted 17 Apr '89. Catalogue no: **450554 2**
**Album:** Released May '84, on Prestige (USA) by Fantasy Inc (USA). Catalogue no: **OJCD 504**

**MULLIGAN-BAKER (Mulligan, Gerry & Chet Baker)**
Tracks: / Carioca / Line for lYons / Moonlight in Vermont / Bark for Barksdale / Turnstile / Lady is a tramp / My funny valentine / Ide's side / Funhouse / Roundhouse / Kaper / Bweebida bobbida / Mullenium / Limelight / Go go / Mulligan's too / So easy / Bevan beeps / Rearin' bacl.
**2 LP Set:** Released Sep '79, on Prestige Deleted '84. Catalogue no: **PR 24016**

**MY FUNNY VALENTINE**
Tracks: / Catch as catch can / My funny valentine / Blueport / Utter chaos / What is there to say? / Just in time / News from Blueport / Festive minor.
**Album:** Released '84, on CBS by CBS Records. Catalogue no: **21102**
**Cass:** Released '84, on CBS by CBS Records. Deleted Aug '87. Catalogue no: **40 21102**

**NIGHT LIGHTS**
Tracks: / Morning of the carnival / Prelude in E minor / Night lights / Festive minor / Tell me when / In the wee small hours of the morning.
Note: With Art Farmer, Bob Brookmeyer, Jim Hall, Bill Crow, Dave Bailey. Recorded in New York, September 1963.
**Cass:** Released Dec '83, on Mercury Jazz Masters Catalogue no: **818 271 2**
**CD:** Released Aug '84, on Mercury Jazz Masters Catalogue no: **818 271 2**
**Album:** Released Dec '83, on Mercury Jazz Masters Catalogue no: **6336345**

**PARIS 1954 / L.A. 1953 (Mulligan, Gerry Quartet)**
**CD:** Released Jul '87, on Vogue by Vogue Records. Catalogue no: **VG 600 152**

**PLEYEL CONCERT**
Tracks: / I may be wrong / Gold rush / Makin' whoopee / Laura / Soft shoe / Nearness of you / Love me or leave me / Bernie's tune / Walking shoes / Moonlight in Vermont / Lady is a tramp, The / Bark for Barksdale.
**CD:** Released Jun '84, on Vogue by Vogue Records. Catalogue no: **VG 600 028**

**REUNION (Mulligan, Gerry & Chet Baker)**
Tracks: / When your lover has gone / Stardust / My heart belongs to daddy / Jersey bounce / Surrey with the fringe on top / Trav'lin' light / Trav'lin' light (alternate version) / Ornithology / People will say we're in love / Song is you, The / Gee baby ain't I good to you / Gee baby ain't I good to you (alternate versi / I got rhythm / All the things you are.
**CD:** Released Aug '88, on EMI-Manhattan by EMI Records. Catalogue no: **CZ 52**
**CD:** Released Aug '88, on EMI-Manhattan by EMI Records. Catalogue no: **CDP 746 857 2**

**SHADOW OF YOUR SMILE (Mulligan, Gerry Quartet)**

**CD:** Released Sep '89, on Moon by Moon Records (UK). Catalogue no: **MCD 003**

**Album:** Released Sep '89, on Moon by Moon Records (UK). Catalogue no: **MLP 003**

**SILVER COLLECTION, THE**

**CD:** on Verve Catalogue no: **827 436-2**

**SOFT LIGHTS AND SWEET MUSIC (Mulligan, Gerry & Scott Hamilton)**

Tracks: / Soft lights and sweet music / Gone / Do you know what I see? / I've just seen her / Noblesse / Ghosts / Port of Baltimore blues.

Note: Personnel: Gerry Mulligan : baritone sax / Scott Hamilton : tenor sax / Mike Renzi : piano / Jay Leonhart : bass / Grady Tate : drums.

**Cass:** Released Jul '86, on Concord Jazz by Concord Jazz Records (USA). Catalogue no: **CJC 300**

**Album:** Released Jul '86, on Concord Jazz by Concord Jazz Records (USA). Catalogue no: **CJ 300**

**CD:** Released Jan '87, on Concord Jazz by Concord Jazz Records (USA). Catalogue no: **CCD 4300**

**SUMMIT**

Tracks: / Twenty years ago / Close your eyes and listen / Years of solitude / Deus Xango / Twenty years after / Aire de Buenos Aires / Reminiscence / Summit.

Note: Recorded September, October 1974.

**Album:** Released Feb '83, on Carosello Catalogue no: **ORL 8588**

**WALK ON THE WATER (Mulligan, Gerry & His Orchestra)**

Tracks: / For an unfinished woman / Song for strayhorn / 42nd and Broadway / Angelica / Across the track blues / I'm getting sentimental over you.

**Album:** Released Mar '87, on DRG (USA) by DRG Records (USA). Deleted Jan '89. Catalogue no: **SL 5194**

**CD:** Released Mar '87, on DRG (USA) by DRG Records (USA). Deleted Jan '89. Catalogue no: **CDSL 5194**

**Cass:** Released Mar '87, on DRG (USA) by DRG Records (USA). Catalogue no: **SLC 5194**

**WHAT IS THERE TO SAY? (Mulligan, Gerry Quartet)**

Tracks: / What is there to say / Just in time / News from blueport / Festive minor / My funny valentine / As catch can / Blueport / Utter chaos.

**Album:** Released Sep '86, on Avan-Guard Catalogue no: **BVL 013**

## Mundy, Jimmy

**FIESTA IN BRASS (Mundy, Jimmy & Orchestra)**

**Album:** Released Aug '89, on Golden Era by Delta Records. Catalogue no: **GELP 15060**

## Murphy, Mark

**ARTISTRY OF MARK MURPHY, THE**

Tracks: / Odd child, The / I don't want to cry anymore / Moody's mood / Trilogy for kids / I remember Clifford / Autumn nocturne / Close enough for love / Long ago and far away.

**Album.** Released on Muse, Dec '82 by Black & Blue Records., Jazz Horizons, Celtic Music, Discovery. Catalogue no: **MR 5286.**

**Mark Murphy - Bop for Kerouac (Muse)**

**BOP FOR KEROUAC (see panel above)**

Tracks: / Be-bop lives (boplicity) / Good-bye pork pie hat / Parker's mood / You better go now / You've proven your point (bongo beep) / Bad and the beautiful / Down St Thomas way / Ballad of the sad young man.

**Cass.** Released on Muse (USA), Feb '87 by Muse Records (USA). Catalogue no: **MRC 5253.**

**CD.** Released on IMS, '88 by Polydor Ltd. Catalogue no: **MCD 5253.**

**BRAZIL SONG**

Tracks: / Desafinado / Two kites / Island, The / Bolero de sata / She / Someone to light up my life / Nothing will be as it was tomorrow / Outubro / bridges.

**Cass.** Released on Muse (USA), Feb '87 by Muse Records (USA). Catalogue no: **MRC 5297.**

**BRIDGING A GAP**

**Album.** Released on Muse, Apr '81 by Black & Blue Records., Jazz Horizons, Celtic Music, Discovery. Catalogue no: **MR 5009.**

**MARK 11**

**Album.** Released on Muse, Apr.'81 by Black & Blue Records., Jazz Horizons, Celtic Music, Discovery. Catalogue no: **MR 5041.**

**MARK MURPHY**

**Album.** Released on Muse, Apr '81 by Black & Blue Records. Catalogue no: **MR 5078.**

**MARK MURPHY SINGS DOROTHY FIELDS AND CY COLEMAN**

**Album.** Released Aug '88 on Audiophile (USA), by Jazzology Records (USA). Catalogue no: **AP 132.**

**SATISFACTION GUARANTEED**

**Album.** Released on Muse, Apr '81 by Black & Blue Records., Jazz Horizons, Celtic Music, Discovery. Catalogue no: **MR 5215.**

**SINGS NAT'S CHOICE VOLUMES 1 & 2**

Tracks: / Nature boy / Love letters / Oh you crazy moon / 'Tis autumn / I keep going back to Joe's / Tangerine / Lush life / Never let me go / These foolish things / Portrait of Jenny Ruby / For all we know / Maybe you'll be there / Blue gardenia / Don't let your eyes go shopping / More than you know / Look out for love / End of a love affair, The / Calypso blues / Serenata.

Note: Medleys include: Nature boy/calypso blues. Love letters/serenata

**CD.** Released on Muse (USA), Feb '87 by Muse Records (USA). Catalogue no: **MCD 6001.**

**SINGS THE NAT KING COLE SONGBOOK**

Tracks: / Nature boy / Calypso blues / Love letters / Serenata / Oh you crazy moon / 'Tis autumn / I keep going back to Joe's / Tangerine / Lush life / Until the real thing comes along / Baby, baby all the time / Never let me go / These foolish

things.
**Album**: Released Aug '86 on Black & Blues Catalogue no: **MR 5308**

**STOLEN MOMENTS**
**Album:** Released Apr '81 on Black & Blues Catalogue no: **MR 5012**

## Murphy, Turk

**CONCERT IN THE PARK (San Francisco Jazzband)**
**Cass:** Released '88, on Merry Makers Catalogue no: **C-MMRC 117**
**Album:** Released Jun '88, on Merry Makers Catalogue no: **MMRC 117**

**EARTHQUAKE MCGOON RECORDINGS (San Francisco Jazzband)**
**Cass:** Released '88, on Merry Makers Catalogue no: **C-MMRC 105**
**Album:** Released Jun '88, on Merry Makers Catalogue no: **MMRC 105**

**FAVOURITES (Murphy, Turk, Jazz Band)**
**CD:** Released Apr '87, on London Records by London Records Ltd. Catalogue no: **FCD 60011**

**LIVE AT EASY STREET VOL.1 (Murphy,Turk & His San Francisco Jazz Band)**
**Album:** Released Jun '79, on Dawn Club by Cadillac Music. Catalogue no: **DC 12015**

**LIVE AT EASY STREET VOL.2 (Murphy,Turk & His San Francisco Jazz Band)**
**Album:** Released Jun '79, on Dawn Club by Cadillac Music. Catalogue no: **DC 12018**

**LIVE AT EASY STREET VOL.3 (Murphy,Turk & His San Francisco Jazz Band)**
**Album:** Released Jun '79, on Dawn Club by Cadillac Music. Catalogue no: **DC 12019**

**SAN FRANCISCO JAZZ VOL 1 (Murphy, Turk, Jazz Band)**
**Album:** Released Jun '88, on Merry Makers Catalogue no: **MMRC 114**
**Cass:** Released '88, on Merry Makers Catalogue no: **C-MMRC 114**

**SAN FRANCISCO JAZZ VOL 2 (San Francisco Jazzband)**
**Cass:** Released '88, on Merry Makers Catalogue no: **C-MMRC 115**
**Album:** Released Jun '88, on Merry Makers Catalogue no: **MMRC 115**

**SAN FRANCISCO JAZZBAND & PAT YANKEE (San Francisco Jazzband)**
**Cass:** Released '88, on Merry Makers Catalogue no: **C-MMRC 106**
**Album:** Released Jun '88, on Merry Makers Catalogue no: **MMRC 106**

**SAN FRANCISCO MEMORIES (San Francisco Jazzband)**
**Cass:** Released '88, on Merry Makers Catalogue no: **C-MMRC 116**
**Album:** Released Jun '88, on Merry Makers Catalogue no: **MMRC 116**

**SEE'S CANDIES PRESENT SONGS OF CHRISTMAS (Murphy, Turk San Fransisco Jazz Band)**
**Album:** Released May '89, on Merry Makers Catalogue no: **SC 1001**

**SOUTHERN STOMPS (Murphy, Turk, Jazz Band)**
**Album:** Released '88, on Stomp Off (USA) Catalogue no: **SOS 1161**

**TURK AT CARNEGIE (Murphy, Turk, Jazz Band)**
Note: with Jim Cullum JB, Hot Antic JB
**Album:** Released Jan '88, on Stomp Off (USA) Catalogue no: **SOS 1155**

**TURK MURPHY IN CONCERT VOLUME 1. (Murphy,Turk & His San Francisco Jazz Band)**
**Album:** Released Jun '86, on GHB by Jazzology Records (USA). Catalogue no: **GHB 91**

**TURK MURPHY IN CONCERT VOLUME 2. (Murphy,Turk & His San Francisco Jazz Band)**
**Album:** Released Jun '86, on GHB by Jazzology Records (USA). Catalogue no: **GHB 92**

**TURK MURPHY IN CONCERT VOLUME 3. (Murphy,Turk & His San Francisco Jazz Band)**
**Album:** Released Jun '86, on GHB by Jazzology Records (USA). Catalogue no: **GHB 93**

## Murray, Arthur

**ARTHUR MURRAY SWINGS FOX TROTS (Murray, Arthur/Anthony, Ray & His Orchestra)**
Tracks: / Poor butterfly / Froggy day, A / On the sunny side of the street / This year's kisses / I can't beleive that you're in love with me / Can't get out of this mood / You stepped out of this dream / You're the cream in my coffee / I've never been in love before / Gang that sang heart of my heart / let's get lost / Love walked in.
Note: A different tempo from best selling artist Ray Anthony - famed for the dream dancing albums. Not to be confused with the LP "Fox Trots", this selection of well-known tunes has only been previously available in the UK as an abridged 10" version. Arrangements courtesy of one of the masters, Billy May, include "On The Sunny Side Of The Street", "You're The Cream In My Coffee" and "Love Walked In". Like the Stan Kenton album, this is perfect for dance enthusiasts and nostalgia listeners alike. [EMI release sheet, May 1987]
**Cass:** Released May '87, on Capitol by EMI Records. Deleted Jun '88. Catalogue no: **TCEMS 1247**
**Album:** Released May '87, on Capitol by EMI Records. Deleted Jun '89. Catalogue no: **EMS 1247**

## Murray, David

**Biographical details:** One of the best-selling artists on Black Saint, David Murray, born in Berkeley, California, in 1955, is a talented musician and composer, playing tenor and soprano sax and flute. His style favours Albert Ayler and he has played with Cecil Taylor, Don Cherry and Anthony Braxton. He names his major influences as Charlie Parker, Sonny Rollins, Albert Ayler, Ben Webster and Coleman Hawkins. (IMS, September 1985.).

**CHILDREN**
**CD:** Released '86, on Black Saint (Italy) Catalogue no: **BSR 0089**

**CONCEPTUAL SAXOPHONE**
**Album:** Released Jul '87, on Cadillac by Cadillac Music. Catalogue no: **SGC 1007**

**DAVID MURRAY**
**Album:** Released '88, on Cadillac by Cadillac Music. Catalogue no: **SGC 1007/8**

**FLOWERS FOR ALBERT**
**Album:** Released Jul '78, on India Navigation Catalogue no: **IN 1026**

**HEALERS, THE (Murray, David / Randy Weston)**
**CD:** on Black Saint (Italy) Catalogue no: **120118-2**

**HOME (Murray, David Octet)**
Tracks: / Home / Santa Barbara and Crenshaw / Follies / Choctaw blues / Last of the hipmen / 3-D family.
**CD:** Released Sep '85, on Black Saint (Italy) Catalogue no: **BSRCD 055**
**Album:** Released Apr '87, on Black Saint (Italy) Catalogue no: **BSR 0055**

**I WANT TO TALK ABOUT YOU (Murray, David Quartet)**
**CD:** Released Sep '89, on Black Saint (Italy) Catalogue no: **120105-2**
**Album:** Released Sep '89, on Black Saint (Italy) Catalogue no: **120105-1**

**INTERBOOGIEOLOGY (Various artists)**
**Album:** Released Jul '78, on Black Saint (Italy) Catalogue no: **BSR 0018**

**LET THE GREAT BIG WORLD KEEP TURNING**
Tracks: / Let the great big world keep turning / Let the great big world keep turning (Instrumental).
**7" Single:** Released Nov '85, on Pectcode Deleted '86. Catalogue no: **PECM 3**

**LIVE AT SWEET BASIL, VOL 1 (Murray, David Big Band)**
Tracks: / Lovers / Bechet's bounce / Silence / Duet for big band.
Note: David Murray, tenor sax, clarinet, bass; Olu Dara, cornet; Baikida Carroll, trumpet; Craig Harris, trombone; Bob Stewart, tuba; Vincent Chancey, French horn; Steve Coleman, alto, tenor saxes; John Purcell, alto sax, clarinet; Rod Williams, piano; Fred Hopkins, bass; Billy Higgins, percussion. Recorded at Sweet Basil, New York City, 24, 15, 26 August 1984. Conducted by Lawrence "Butch" Morris.
**Album:** Released May '85, on Black Saint (Italy) Catalogue no: **BSR 0085**
**CD:** Released '86, on Black Saint (Italy) Catalogue no: **BSRCD 085**

**LIVE AT SWEET BASIL VOL.2 (Murray, David Big Band)**
**CD:** Released '86, on Black Saint (Italy) Catalogue no: **BSR 0095**

**LONDON CONCERT, THE (Live at Collegiate Theatre)**
**2 LP Set:** Released Jul '87, on Cadillac by Cadillac Music. Catalogue no: **SGC 1008/9**

**LOW CLASS CONSPIRACY**
**Album:** Released May '81, on Adelphi (1) Catalogue no: **AD 5002**

**MING (Murray, David Octet)**
Tracks: / Fast life / Hill, The / Ming / Jasvan / Dewey's circle.
**CD:** Released Sep '85, on Black Saint (Italy) Catalogue no: **BSRCD 045**
**Album:** Released Sep '85, on Black Saint (Italy) Catalogue no: **BSR 0045**

**MORNING SONG (Murray, David Octet)**
Tracks: / Morning song / Body and soul / Light blue / Jitterbug waltz / Off season / Duet.
**CD:** Released Sep '85, on Black Saint (Italy) Catalogue no: **BSRCD 075**

**MURRAY'S STEPS (Murray, David Octet)**
**CD:** Released '86, on Black Saint (Italy) Catalogue no: **BSR 0065**

**ORGANIC SAXAPHONE**
**Album:** Released Jan '80, on Natural Organic (USA) Catalogue no: **PALM 31**

**PENTHOUSE JAZZ VOL.1**
**Album:** Released May '78, on Circle (USA) by Jazzology Records (USA). Catalogue no: **RK 1887/4**

**SOLO-LIVE, VOL. 1**
**Album:** Released '88, on Cecma Catalogue no: **CECMA 1001**

**SOLO-LIVE, VOL. 2**
**Album:** Released '88, on Cecma Catalogue no: **CECMA 1002**

**SOLOMON'S SONS (Murray, David & James Newton)**
**Album:** Released May '78, on Circle (USA) by Jazzology Records (USA). Catalogue no: **RK 16177/5**

**SUR-REAL SAXOPHONE**
**Album:** Released '78, on Horo Catalogue no: **HZ 09**

## Murray, Sunny

**AN EVEN BREAK**
**Album:** Released Aug '79, on Affinity by Charly Records. Deleted '88. Catalogue no: **AFF 30**

**APPLE CORES**
**Album:** Released Sep '79, on Philly Jazz (USA) Deleted '82. Catalogue no: **PJ 1004**

**LIVE AT MOERS FESTIVAL**
**Album:** Released Jan '80, on Moers Music Catalogue no: **MOERS 01054**

**SUNNY MURRAY**
**Album:** Released '88, on ESP Base Catalogue no: **ESP 1032**

## Music...

**MUSIC CITY SOUL (SUN RECORDINGS) (Various artists)**
**Album:** Released Jun '76, on Charly by Charly Records. Catalogue no: **CR 30107**

**MUSIC IMPROVISATION COMPANY (Various artists)**
**Album:** Released Feb '77, on Incus by Incus Records. Catalogue no: **INCUS 17**

**MUSIC TO REMEMBER (Various artists)**
**Cass:** Released Aug '84, on Ditto by Pickwick Records. Catalogue no: **DTO 10085**

**MUSIC YOU KNOW & LOVE (Various artists)**
**Cass:** Released Feb '83, on AIM (Budget Cassettes) Catalogue no: **AM 34**

## Music From...

**MUSIC FROM THE COTTON CLUB (Various artists)**
**Album:** Released Jun '86, on Big Band Era Catalogue no: **20186**
**CD:** Released May '88, on Big Band Era Catalogue no: **70186**
**Cass:** Released Jun '86, on Big Band Era Catalogue no: **40186**

**MUSIC FROM UTOPIA (Various artists)**
Tracks: / Old Fulham fertility: *Various artists* / Irden: *Various artists* / Gravity's angel: *Various artists* / East wind: *Various artists* / Naturliche liebe: *Various artists* / Constellation (part 1): *Various artists* / Kommunikation hipp-ipp: *Various artists* / Conditioning: *Various artists* / Speed display: *Various artists* / High on tech: *Various artists* / Eh-ei-joa: *Various artists* / Happy Grenada: *Various artists* / Expedition extra: *Various artists* / Cielouvert: *Various artists* / Ganna plasmid: *Various artists* / Silicon valley: *Various artists* / Interne 1: *Various artists* / Morgen und ein spaziergang: *Various artists* / Tique-taque: *Various artists* / Annabella: *Various artists* / Exotic defiler: *Various artists* / Later bagatelles 1 & 2: *Various artists* / Hotel reform: *Various artists* / Pujaparwata: *Various artists* / Selig, die-grerchtigkeit willen - tolgt werden: *Various artists.*
Note: A fascinating collection featuring artists such as Laurie Anderson, Yello and Howard Jones, to name but three. The theme is computers, futuristic holograms and a time beyond this century, expressed by various computer keyboard 'wizards'Side Four = Bob Moog's contribution to the Erdenklang Premiere.
**CD:** Released '88, on Teldec (1) by ASV (Academy Sound & Vision). Catalogue no: **8 261 76**
**Album:** Released Aug '85, on Erdenklang (Germany) Catalogue no: **628650 DW**
**Album:** Released Nov '85, on Teldec (1) by ASV (Academy Sound & Vision). Catalogue no: **6 28650**

## Music Goes Round...

**GOLDEN YEARS OF TIN PAN ALLEY, THE**
Tracks: / Stormy weather / How deep is the ocean / Heartaches / All of me / Blue moon / Ghost of a chance / Shoe shine boy / Music goes round and around, The / Untill the real thing comes along / When my dreamboat comes home / Once in a while / Undecided / Heart and soul / T'aint what you do (it's the way that you do it).
Note: Full title: The golden years of Tin Pan Alley 1930-1939.
**Album:** Released Sep '86, on New World (USA) by New World Records (USA). Catalogue no: **NW 248**

## Music On The Move

**MUSIC ON THE MOVE (20 BIG BAND & JAZZ GREATS (Various artists)**
**Album:** Released '84, on RCA by BMG Records (UK). Catalogue no: **NK 89330**
**Cass:** Released '81, on RCA International by BMG Records (UK). Deleted '84. Catalogue no: **INTK 9003**

## Musical Fun & Games

**MUSICAL FUN AND GAMES (Various artists)**
Tracks: / Childrens games: *Various artists* (MCPO/Batiz) / Sorcerer's apprentice, The: *Various artists* (MSSO/Batiz) / *Dolly Suite (Faure): Academy Of St.Martin In The Field & Neville Marriner* / Musical box, The (Liadov): *Various artists* (MCPO/Batiz) / Nutcracker suite: *Royal Philharmonic Orchestra* (cond. Batiz) / Pied piper, The (Mourant): *MacDonald, George / Northern Sinfonia of England* (cond. Steuart Bedford) / Themes for Narnia: *Robles, Marisa Ensemble / Christopher Hyde-Smith* / Scaramouche - Braziliera: *Johnson, Emma / Gordon Back.*
**Cass:** Released 1 Oct '89, on ASV (Academy Sound & Vision) by Academy Sound & Vision Records. Catalogue no: **ZC DCA 673**
**CD:** Released 1 Oct '89, on ASV (Academy Sound & Vision) by Academy Sound & Vision Records. Catalogue no: **CD DCA 673**
**Album:** Released 1 Oct '89, on ASV (Academy Sound & Vision) by Academy Sound & Vision Records. Catalogue no: **DCA 673**

## Musselwhite, Charlie

**ACE OF HARPS**
**CD:** Released Apr '90, on Sonet by Sonet Records. Catalogue no: **ALCD 4781**
**Album:** Released Apr '90, on Sonet by Sonet Records. Catalogue no: **AL 4781**

**CAMBRIDGE BLUES**
Tracks: / Miss Bessie / Big leg woman (with a short short mini skirt) / Key to the highway / Take a little walk with me / Up and down / Need my baby / Skinny

woman.
**Album:** Released Apr '88, on Blue Horizon by Ace Records. Catalogue no: **BLUH 005**

**CHARLIE MUSSELWHITE**
Note: Doubleplay cassette contains albums: Takin' My Time - 1056; Going Back Down South - 1074.
**Cass:** Released '88, on Arhoolie (USA) by Arhoolie Records (USA). Catalogue no: **C 203**

**CURTAIN CALL (Musselwhite, Charlie & The Dynatones)**
Tracks: / Curtain call blast off / Everybody needs somebody / I'm goin' home / Walk right in / This little voice / She used to be beautiful / Christo redemptor / Tick tock / Trouble no more.

**Album:** Released Nov '82, on Red Lightnin' by Red Lightning Records. Deleted Jun '89. Catalogue no: **RL 044**

**GOIN' BACK DOWN SOUTH**
**Album:** Released May '81, on Arhoolie (USA) by Arhoolie Records (USA). Catalogue no: **ARHOOLIE 1074**

**HARMONICA ACCORDING TO CHARLIE MUSSELWHITE, THE**
**Album:** Released Feb '79, on Kicking Mule by Sonet Records. Catalogue no: **SNKF 147**

**MELLOW DEE**
Tracks: / Hey Miss Bessie / Need my baby / I'll get a break / Peach orchard mama / Ask me nice / Come back baby / Coming home baby / Baby please don't go / Lotsa poppa / Steady on your trail / Can't you see what you're doing to me / Christo redemptor.
**Album:** Released Sep '86, on Crosscut by Topic Records. Catalogue no: **CCR 1013**
**CD:** Released Nov '88, on Crosscut by Topic Records. Catalogue no: **CCD 11013**

**MEMPHIS TENNESSEE**
Tracks: / She used to be beautiful / I got to go / Memphis Tennessee / One mint julep / Blues / Wolf, The / Temperature / Arkansas boogie / Willow weep for me / Trouble no more / Done somebody wrong.
**Album:** Released Nov '84, on Crosscut by Topic Records. Catalogue no: **CCR 1008**

**TAKIN' MY TIME**
**Album:** Released May '81, on Arhoolie (USA) by Arhoolie Records (USA). Catalogue no: **ARHOOLIE 1056**

**TELL ME WHERE HAVE ALL THE GOOD TIMES GONE**
**Album:** Released Dec '88, on Blue Rock-It (USA) by Blue Rock-It Records (USA). Catalogue no: **BR 103**

## Musso, Vido

**ONE NIGHT STAND**
**Album:** Released Jul '82, on Joyce Catalogue no: **JLP 1026**

## Mussolini, Romano

**JAZZ ALBUM**
**Album:** Released Apr '83, on Bang Bang (Import) Deleted '88. Catalogue no: **BBLP 8234**

## Mussulli, Boots

**LITTLE MAN**
**Album:** Released Jul '81, on Affinity by Charly Records. Deleted '88. Catalogue no: **AFF 67**

## Myles, Rayond A.

**NEW ORLEANS GOSPEL GENIUS**
**Album:** Released '87, on Great Southern (USA) by Flat Town Music Co.(USA). Catalogue no: **11021**
**Cass:** Released '87, on Great Southern (USA) by Flat Town Music Co.(USA). Catalogue no: **11021 TC**

# N

The following information was taken from the Music Master database on April 14th, 1990.

## Nakagawa, Masami

**PRELUDE FOR AUTUMN**
Note: Japan's No 1 flautist, renowned for his mastery of the instrument and his innovative jazz stylings, Nakagawa had worked with Gil Evans and Keith Jarrett.
**Cass:** Released Jul '88, on JVC Catalogue no: **JC 3304**
**CD:** Released Jul '88, on JVC Catalogue no: **JD 3304**

**TOUCH OF SPRING**
Note: Nakagawa creates an unconventional setting when he presents familiar classical themes in a contemporary jazz idiom.
**CD:** Released Oct '88, on JVC Catalogue no: **JD 3311**
**Cass:** Released Oct '88, on JVC Catalogue no: **JC 3311**

## Namyslowski, Zbigniew

**AIR CONDITION**
Tracks: / Speed limit / Convenient circumstances / Pretty dowseress / Play it to me / Dilemma / Ladderman / We'll have a nice day.
**Album:** Released Feb '82, on Affinity by Charly Records. Deleted '88. Catalogue no: **AFF 83**

## Nance, Ray

**RAY NANCE QUARTET & SEXTET (Nance, Ray-Quartet &Sextet)**
**Album:** Released Nov '86, on Unique Jazz by Spotlite Records. Catalogue no: **UJ 11**

## Napoleon,Phil

**1946-49 (Napoleon,Phil / Frank Signorelli)**
Tracks: / Alabama blues / Blue danube / Margie / Stationary woman / My man o'war / Save it pretty mama.
Note: Mono recording.
**Album:** Released Jun '86, on Harlequin by Interstate Music. Catalogue no: **HQ 2043**

**BAILEY'S LUCKY SEVEN**
Tracks: / How many times / Sweet Indiana home / Nobody lied / No wonder I'm lonesome / Tomorrow / Gee but I hate to go home alone / Tomorrow morning / Baby blue eyes / You know you belong to somebody else / Apple sauce / You're in Kentucky sure as you're born / Dear one / Won't you come back to my arms.
**Album:** Released May '83, on Queendisc (Italy) Catalogue no: **QU 059**

## Nash, Paul

**JAZZ COMPOSER'S ENSEMBLE, A**
**Album:** Released Apr '81, on Revelation (USA) by Hit Record Entertainment Inc.(USA). Catalogue no: **REV 32**

## Nashville Jazz...

**WHERE'S ELI (Nashville Jazz Machine (Big Band))**
Tracks: / Auralsynthes / Love song / Blue Bossa / Nashville connection, The.
**Album:** Released '88, on Am-Pm (USA) Catalogue no: **AM 14**

## Nasser, Jimmy

**EXPRESSLY ELLINGTON (Nasser, Jimmy Combo)**
**Album:** Released Jan '80, on Spotlite by Spotlite Records. Catalogue no: **PJLP 20**

## Nat West Jazz Band

**HOOKED ON DIXIE**
Tracks: / New Orleans / Fidgety feet / Onions / Chinatown.
**Album:** Released Jun '82, on Nat West Jazz Band Catalogue no: **NWJB 2**
**Cass:** Released Jun '82, on Nat West Jazz Band Catalogue no: **NWJBC 2**

**YOU CAN BANK ON US**
**Cass:** Released May '87, on Nat West Jazz Band Catalogue no: **NWJBC 3**
**Album:** Released May '87, on Nat West Jazz Band Catalogue no: **NWJB 3**

## Nathanson, Roy

**BROKEN NIGHT (Nathanson, Roy & Curtis Fowlkes & The Jazz Passengers)**
**Album:** Released Jun '87, on Crepescule (Les Disques du Crepescule) by Les Disques Du Crepuscule (Belgium). Catalogue no: **TWI 816**

**DERANGED & DECOMPOSED (Nathanson, Roy & Curtis Fowlkes & The Jazz Passengers)**
Note: Artists include Roy Nathan, Curtis Fowlkes & The Jazz Passengers.
**Album:** Released Oct '88, on Crepescule (Les Disques du Crepescule) by Les Disques Du Crepuscule (Belgium). Catalogue no: **TWI 846**
**CD:** Released '89, on Crepescule (Les Disques du Crepescule) by Les Disques Du Crepuscule (Belgium). Catalogue no: **TWI 8462**

## National Youth Jazz...

**11 PLUS (Live at LWT) (National Youth Jazz Orchestra)**
Tracks: / NYJO / Spaghetti junction / Good to be there / Marianne / Wait and see / 11 plus / Who-wray / Yesterday's blues today / Legs eleven / Threshing machine, The / Full house / NYJO reprise.
**Album:** Released '76, on RCA by BMG Records (UK). Catalogue no: **SF 8464**

**BORN AGAIN (National Youth Jazz Orchestra)**
Tracks: / Sweetheart of Sigmund Freud / Infinity promenade / I'm gonna go fishin' / Contours / Topsy / Short stop / Walk don't run / Viva Puente / Boar jibu / Manteca / Un poco loco / Jazz waltz.
**Cass:** Released '83, on N.Y.J.O. by National Youth Jazz Orchestra. Catalogue no: **ZCNYJ 004**

**CONCRETE COWS (National Youth Jazz Orchestra)**
Tracks: / Concrete cows / Dear John / John's jape / Airedale Sunset / Robbers of Vissenburg / Dialectics / Lady Di / Dynamo.
Note: New album from the world-famous NYJO with John Dankworth as soloist and composer on three main titles.
**Album:** Released Apr '86, on N.Y.J.O. by National Youth Jazz Orchestra. Catalogue no: **NYJ 006**

**FULL SCORE (National Youth Jazz Orchestra)**
Tracks: / Luton hoo / Waltz for Duke / Waiting for Morgan / London / Full score / Bud / Midnight newsroom / Lady can tell, A / Sea beaver, The.
**Album:** Released '85, on N.Y.J.O. by National Youth Jazz Orchestra. Catalogue no: **NYJ 005**
**Cass:** Released May '85, on N.Y.J.O. by National Youth Jazz Orchestra. Catalogue no: **ZCNYJ 05**
**Album:** Released May '85, on N.Y.J.O. by National Youth Jazz Orchestra. Catalogue no: **NYJ 05**

**IN CAMERA (National Youth Jazz Orchestra)**
Tracks: / Opening time / Legless in Garstang / Going for a burton / Ruddle's Rutland reflections / That old peculiar feeling / Fuggles fantastical fugue / Real ale real / Young's make me feel you so / Samuel Smith and his amazing dancing bear / Bitter from the woods / Drink Tolly only / Trip to Jerusalem.
**Album:** Released Feb '77, on N.Y.J.O. by National Youth Jazz Orchestra. Catalogue no: **PL 25036**

**LONDON (National Youth Jazz Orchestra)**
Tracks: / London / I wasn't looking for a love affair.
**7" Single:** Released Jul '85, on N.Y.J.O. by National Youth Jazz Orchestra. Catalogue no: **2NYJ**

**MARY ROSE (National Youth Jazz Orchestra)**
Tracks: / Eave-O / Early morning train / Dykes on bikes / Legend of the Mary Rose / Happy katz / Mary Rose / Nothing like a Thane / No flowers by request / Cop this / Cuban thing.
**Album:** Released Oct '79, on N.Y.J.O. by National Youth Jazz Orchestra. Catalogue no: **N 117**

**MARY ROSE (SINGLE) (National Youth Jazz Orchestra)**
Tracks: / Mary Rose / Legend of Mary Rose.
**7" Single:** Released Jun '79, on Pye Deleted '82. Catalogue no: **7P 104**

**NYJO DOWN UNDER (National Youth Jazz Orchestra)**
Tracks: / Australian opener / Okay with Jay / Schedule D / Barrio / Groover, The / Question time / Out of sight, out of mind / Blenkinsop's blues / As if I cared / Getting down to it / Gynaecology / To set before a queen / Cobwebs / Song to sing by, A / Amazing grace / Tubbs lives / Fox fur / Paying my tax.
**2 LP Set:** Released '80, on N.Y.J.O. by National Youth Jazz Orchestra. Catalogue no: **DNYJ 502**

**PLAYING TURKEY (National Youth Jazz Orchestra)**
Tracks: / Istanbul now / Jack of Hart's / Round Robin / Leaving here / And Henry guards the door / Looking back / Three for Tay / Turkish delight.
**Album:** Released '83, on N.Y.J.O. by National Youth Jazz Orchestra. Catalogue no: **NYJ 003**

**RETURN TRIP (National Youth Jazz Orchestra)**
Tracks: / Return trip / Velvet lady / Blue dolphin / Ballad for Brigitte / Morocco bound / Brahms arms, The / Li'l Jeannie / Gerryatrics / Cockpit / Seven of hearts / Get it right / Independence day celebration / Greasy spoon / Lift off / Tracy's trip / Maybe this time / Bones for Basie / Moon mood / Atropus / Go 'way from here.
**Album:** on RCA by BMG Records (UK). Catalogue no: **DPS 2072**

**SHERWOOD FOREST SUITE, THE (National Youth Jazz Orchestra)**
Tracks: / Fanfare for Robin / Robin's epitaph / Sherwood Forest / All clad in Lincoln green / Lincoln green / She is called Maid Marion / Maid Marion / Sheriff's song / Sheriff of Nottingham, The / Mrs. A'Dales's diary / Minstrel's lay, The / Serving the bishop / Bishop's move / Robin and Marion / Outlaws / Robin's epitaph - reprise / Last arrow, The.
**Album:** Released Jan '82, on N.Y.J.O. by National Youth Jazz Orchestra. Catalogue no: **NYJ 001**

**TO RUSSIA WITH JAZZ (National Youth Jazz Orchestra)**
Tracks: / Buffle off to shuffalo / Cruisin' / I wasn't looking for a love affair / Ballad for Bing / Y.H.B. / Blues two / Cannonball / With you in mind / Parkinson's law / Half man / Where is the music / Bristol cream / Home brew, The / Sneaky Pete / As long as there are summers / Summer sands / Black velvet / Girl can't grumble, A / Almost home / To Russia with jazz.
**2 LP Set:** Released '78, on N.Y.J.O. by National Youth Jazz Orchestra. Catalogue no: **DNYJ 501**

**WHY DON'T THEY WRITE SONGS LIKE THIS ANYMORE (SINGLE) (National Youth Jazz Orchestra)**
Tracks: / Why don't they write songs like this anymore.
**7" Single:** Released Aug '83, on SRT by SRT Records. Catalogue no: **NYJO SRTS 1**

**WHY DON'T THEY WRITE SONGS LIKE THIS ANYMORE (National Youth Jazz Orchestra)**
Tracks: Why don't they write songs like this anymore / I'll wait here / Too much, too soon / Don't try and argue with me / Girl can't grumble, A / Don't go to her / No flowers by request / Wait and see / Rich man / I said there'd be thunder / Accident prone.
**Album:** Released '82, on N.Y.J.O. by National Youth Jazz Orchestra. Catalogue no: **NYJ 002**

**WITH AN OPEN MIND (National Youth Jazz Orchestra)**
Tracks: / Cheese'n'Carrots / Revenge of the Amoebae / With an open mind / Rememberance for Jim / Aardvark / Syrup of Phiggs / Fly to me / Midnight oil / Going Dutch.
Note:
Released on occasion of the Band's 21st anniversary and featuring nine new compositions.
**Cass:** Released Oct '86, on N.Y.J.O. by National Youth Jazz Orchestra. Catalogue no: **ZNYJ 007**
**Album:** Released Oct '86, on N.Y.J.O. by National Youth Jazz Orchestra. Catalogue no: **NYJ 007**

## Navarro, Fats

**1946-49**
**Album:** Released Sep '87, on Giants of Jazz by Hasmick Promotions. Catalogue no: **LPJT 54**

**FABULOUS FATS NAVARRO VOL.1, THE**
Tracks: / Our delight / Squirrel, The / Chase, The / Wail (LP only.) / Bouncing with Bud (LP only.) / Double talk (LP only.) / Dameronia / Chase, The (alt. take) / Squirrel, The (alt. take) / Our delight (alt. take) / Dameronia (alt. take) / Sid's delight (CD only.) / Casbah (CD only.) / John's delight (CD only.) / What's new (CD only.) / Heaven's doors are wide open / Focus.
**Album:** Released Apr '83, on Blue Note by EMI Records. Deleted Jan '88. Catalogue no: **BLP 1531**
**CD:** Released Jul '89, on Blue Note by EMI Records. Catalogue no: **CDP 781 531 2**
**CD:** Released Jul '89, on Blue Note by EMI Records. Catalogue no: **BNZ 204**
**Album:** Released Jul '89, on Blue Note by EMI Records. Catalogue no: **BST 81531**

**FABULOUS FATS NAVARRO VOL.2, THE**
Tracks: / Ladybird - alternate master / Ladybird / Jarbero - alternate master / Jabero / Symphonette - alternate master / Symphonette / Double talk / Bouncing with Bud (LP only.) / Dance of the infidels (LP only.) / Skunk, The / Boperation / Skunk, The (78 Master) (CD only.) / Double talk (alt. take) (CD only.) / I think I'll go away (CD only.).
**Album:** Released Apr '83, on Blue Note by EMI Records. Deleted Jan '88. Catalogue no: **BLP 1532**
**Album:** Released Jul '89, on Blue Note by EMI Records. Catalogue no: **BST 81532**
**CD:** Released Jul '89, on Blue Note by EMI Records. Catalogue no: **CDP 781 532 2**
**CD:** Released Jul '89, on Blue Note by EMI Records. Catalogue no: **BNZ 205**

**FAT GIRL - THE SAVOY SESSION**
Tracks: / Boppin' a riff / Fat boy / Everything's cool / Webb city / Calling Dr. Jazz / Fracture / Maternity / Stealin' trash / Just a mystery / Red pepper / Spinal / Hollerin' and screamin' / Fat girl / Ice freezes / Eb pob / Goin' to Mintons / Bebop carroll, A / Tadd walk, The / Gone with the wind / That someone must be you / Nostalgia / Nostalgia (master) / Barry's bop / Barry's bop (master) / Bebop romp / Bebop romp (master) / Fat's blows.
**Album:** Released Mar '85, on Savoy Jazz (USA) by Malaco Records (USA). Catalogue no: **SJL 2216**

**FATS & TADD AT ROOST (1948) 1**
**Album:** Released Jun '76, on Beppo Deleted '88. Catalogue no: **BEP 505**

**FATS & TADD AT ROOST (1948) 2**
**Album:** Released Jun '76, on Beppo Deleted '88. Catalogue no: **BEP 506**

**SATURDAY NIGHT SWING (Navarro, Fats & Allen Eager)**
**Album:** Released Nov '76, on G.I. by Plastic Head Records. Deleted '87. Catalogue no: **GSS 2**

## Naylor, Oliver

**OLIVER NAYLOR'S SEVEN ACES**
**Album:** Released '88, on Fountain by Retrieval Records. Catalogue no: **FJ 103**

## Neely, Don

**HAPPY FEET (Royal Society Jazz Orchestra)**
**Album:** Released '88, on Merry Makers Catalogue no: **MMRC 110**

**JAZZ OF THE ROARING 20S Volume 2 (Royal Society Jazz Orchestra)**
**Album:** Released '88, on Merry Makers Catalogue no: **MMRC 109**
**Album:** Released '88, on Merry Makers Catalogue no: **MMRC 108**

**STARDUST (Royal Society Jazz Orchestra)**
**Album:** Released '88, on Merry Makers

Catalogue no: **MMRC 111**

## Nelson, Arnett

**WHEN THE MUSIC SOUNDS GOOD 1935-38**
**Album:** Released Sep '87, on Magpie by Interstate Music. Catalogue no: **PY 1803**

## Nelson, Louis

**APRIL IN NEW ORLEANS (Nelson, Louis & New Orleans Band)**
**Album:** Released Apr '89, on GHB by Jazzology Records (USA). Catalogue no: **GHB 241**

**EVERYBODY'S TALKING 'BOUT THE...**
**Album:** Released Jun '86, on GHB by Jazzology Records (USA). Catalogue no: **GHB 158**

**IN GERMANY WITH WHITE EAGLE (Nelson, Louis/Alton Purnell/Barry Martin)**
**Album:** Released Nov '88, on GHB by Jazzology Records (USA). Catalogue no: **GHB 204**

**LOUIS NELSON BIG FOUR VOL.1**
**Album:** Released Jul '87, on GHB by Jazzology Records (USA). Catalogue no: **GHB 25**

**LOUIS NELSON BIG FOUR VOL.2**
**Album:** Released Jul '87, on GHB by Jazzology Records (USA). Catalogue no: **GHB 26**

**LOUIS NELSON'S NEW ORLEANS BAND (Nelson, Louis & New Orleans Band)**
**Cass:** Released May '87, on Nola Catalogue no: **TC 007**
**Album:** Released Apr '79, on Nola Catalogue no: **NOLA LP 7**

**NEW ORLEANS ALL STARS**
**Album:** Released '89, on GHB by Jazzology Records (USA). Catalogue no: **GHB 241**

**NEW ORLEANS PORTRAITS VOL.3**
**Album:** Released Feb '90, on Storyville by Storyville Records AB. Catalogue no: **SLP 235**

**SKATER'S WALTZ (Nelson, Louis / Barry Martin's Serenaders)**
**Album:** Released Sep '86, on 504 Catalogue no: **LPS 2**
**Cass:** Released Sep '86, on 504 Catalogue no: **TCS 2**

## Nelson, Oliver

**BACK TALK (Nelson, Oliver/Lou Donaldson)**
Tracks: / Hobo flats / Post no bills / Bientot,A / Three plus one / Take me with you / Daylie's double / Teenie's blues / Laz-ie Kate / Tippin' in / L.D. blues / Days of wine and roses / Ignant oil / Rough house blues / Back talk / Huffin' and puffin'.
**2 LP Set:** Released '88, on Chess by Vogue Records. Catalogue no: **GCH 2-6032**

**BLUES AND THE ABSTRACT TRUTH**
Tracks: / Stolen moments / Hoe down / Cascades / Yearnin' / Butch and butch / Teenie's blues.
**Album:** Released Jul '82, on Jasmine by Hasmick Promotions. Deleted Jul '87. Catalogue no: **JAS 20**
**CD:** Released Apr '87, on MCA by MCA Records. Deleted Dec '89. Catalogue no: **MCAD 5659**

**HAPPENINGS (Nelson, Oliver / Hank Jones)**
Tracks: / Broadwalk samba / Winchester Cathedral / Mas que nada / Lullaby of jazzland / Jazztime USA / Cul de sac / Lou's good dues blues / Fugue tune / Spy with the cold nose, The / Funky but blues.
**Album:** Released Mar '83, on Jasmine by Hasmick Promotions. Deleted Feb '88. Catalogue no: **JAS 61**

**MEET OLIVER NELSON**
**Album:** Released Apr '86, on Original Jazz Classics (USA) by Fantasy Inc (USA). Catalogue no: **OJC 227**

**MORE BLUES AND THE ABSTRACT TRUTH**
Tracks: / Blues and the abstract truth / Blue o'mighty / Mr. Broadway / Midnight blue / Critics choice / One for Bob / Blues for Mr Broadway / Goin' to Chicago blues.
**CD:** Released May '89, on MCA by MCA Records. Catalogue no: **MCAD 5888**
**Cass:** Released Jun '82, on Jasmine by Hasmick Promotions. Catalogue no: **JAS C21**
**Album:** Released Jun '82, on Jasmine by Hasmick Promotions. Catalogue no: **JAS 21**

**OLIVER NELSON**
Tracks: / Empty ballroom blues / Duke's place / Echo's of Harlem / Disillusion blues / Yearning / Welcome to New York / Black, brown and beautiful / Rockin' in rhythm / Creole love call / Meditation / Mailman bring me no more blues / Skull session / It's glory.
**Cass:** Released Jul '89, on Bluebird (2) by BMG Records (UK). Catalogue no: **NK 86993**
**CD:** Released Jul '89, on Bluebird (2) by BMG Records (UK). Catalogue no: **ND 86993**
**Album:** Released Jul '89, on Bluebird (2) by BMG Records (UK). Catalogue no: **NL 86993**

**SCREAMIN' THE BLUES**
Tracks: / Screamin' the blues / March on, march on / Drive, The / Meetin' The / Three seconds / Alto-itis.
**Album:** Released Feb '84, on New Jazz (USA) by Fantasy Inc (USA). Catalogue no: **OJC 080**

**SOUL BATTLE (Nelson, Oliver / Jimmy Forrest / King Curtis)**
Tracks: / Blues at the Five Spot / Anacruses / In passing / Blues for.M.F / Perdido.
**Cass:** Released May '88, on Prestige Deleted Jan '90. Catalogue no: **PRC 7223**
**Album:** Released May '88, on Prestige Catalogue no: **PR 7223**

**STRAIGHT AHEAD (Nelson, Oliver / Eric Dolphy)**
**Album:** Released Aug '84, on New Jazz (USA) by Fantasy Inc (USA). Catalogue no: **OJC 099**

## Nelson, Ozzie

**1937: OZZIE NELSON (Nelson, Ozzie & His Orchestra)**
**Album:** Released Aug '88, on Circle (USA) by Jazzology Records (USA). Catalogue no: **CLP 27**

**OZZIE NELSON, 1940-42**
Tracks: / Jersey bounce / Moonlight cocktails / Everyone but me / Idaho / Somebody else is taking my place / Sir Walter's serenade / Breathless / Central Avenue shuffle / Tangerine / Autumn nocturne / Broad jump / I don't want to set the world on fire / Cuttin' classes / Strictly instrumental / Jersey jive / Texas jump.
Note: Although the Nelson Orchestra recorded more than a hundred 78's for various labels, most of the sixteen tunes on this LP, taken from radio transcriptions, were not among the commercial releases. The few duplications are in title only. Charts here, principally by Billy May and Larry Kramer, are different. *Cutting classes* and *Texas jump* are head arrangements - an unusual departure for this aggregation. Beiderbecke-influenced trumpeter Bo Ashford, the much admired baritone saxophonist Charlie Bubeck and pianists Paul Smith (then barely twenty years old) and Don Ferris are showcased on several numbers. With album annotator Dave Dexter, Jr. (Hindsight Catalogue - 1989).
**Album:** Released '88, on Hindsight Catalogue no: **HSR 107**

**OZZIE NELSON AND HIS ORCHESTRA (Nelson, Ozzie & His Orchestra)**
Tracks: / Jersey bounce / Moonlight cocktails / Everyone but me / Idaho / Somebody else is taking my place / Sir Walter's serenade / Breathless / Central Avenue shuffle / Tangerine / Autumn nocturne / Broad jump / I don't want to set the world on fire / Strictly instrumental / Cutting classes / Jersey jive / Texas jump.
**Album:** Released Feb '79, on London Records by London Records Ltd. Deleted Feb '84. Catalogue no: **HMP 5041**

**SATAN TAKES A HOLIDAY 1936 - 41 (Nelson, Ozzie & His Orchestra)**
**Album:** Released Jun '88, on Bandstand Catalogue no: **BS 7119**

**YOUNG AMERICA'S FAVORITE (Nelson, Ozzie & His Orchestra)**
Tracks: / Baby don't tell on me / Riff interlude / I'm looking for a guy who plays alto and barit / Do I love you? / It's a blue world / Alice blue gown / Leanin' on the old top rail / John's idea / Shake down

the stars / Poor girl / I've got my eyes on you / With the wind and the rain in your hair / Bee bezindt, A / Careless / Cherokee / All the things you are / Make believe dance land.
**Album:** Released Oct '86, on Aircheck (USA) by Kiner Ents.(USA). Catalogue no: **AIRCHECK 19**

## Nelson, Sonny Boy

**MISSISSIPPI MATILDA 1936**
**Album:** Released Jul '88, on Wolf Catalogue no: **WSE 128**

## Neptune, John Kaizan

**CIRCLE, THE**
Tracks: / Circle, The / Soul of the deep / Tokyo pace / Ryukyu / India indigo / Mountain mist / Spring breeze / Spirit lift / North of noplace / Musashi.
Note: All music composed and arranged by John Kaizan Neptune and performed by Mr Neptune (playing Shakuhachi) and his group.
**CD:** Released '88, on Denon Catalogue no: **C38-7770**

**JAZZEN Jazz & Zen**
Tracks: / Five directions / Water's edge, The / On a raft / Bamboo born / Can you feel the beat / Essence / Skip it / Todi / Foot notes / Zen forest.
Note: Personnel: John Kaizan Neptune - shakuhachi; Takao Naoi - guitar; Hitoshi Hamada - vibraphone/marimba; Yoshinori Nohmi - percussion; Yukihiro Takao - bass. All music composed and arranged by Mr Neptune.
**CD:** Released '88, on Denon Catalogue no: **CY-1570**

**TOKYOSPHERE**
Note: Master of the shakuhachi, the five hole Japanese bamboo flute. An innovative recording featuring co-performers who play traditional Japanese instruments.
**Cass:** Released 1 May '89, on JVC Catalogue no: **JC 3316**
**CD:** Released 1 May '89, on JVC Catalogue no: **JD 3316**

## Nestico, Sammy

**NIGHT FLIGHT (Nestico, Sammy Big Band)**
**CD:** Released Nov '88, on Sea Breeze Catalogue no: **CDSB 103**
**Album:** Released Nov '88, on Sea Breeze Catalogue no: **SBD 103**

## New Air

**LIVE AT MONTREAL INTERNATIONAL JAZZ FESTIVAL**
Tracks: / Sir Simpleton / Difda dance / Roll on / Tragedy on a Thursday afternoon / Number one.
Note: Trio fronted by flautist and sax man Henry Threadgill.
**Album:** Released May '85, on Black Saint (Italy) Catalogue no: **BSR 0084**

## New Black Eagle...

**NEW BLACK EAGLE JAZZ BAND (New Black Eagle Jazz Band)**
**Album:** Released Oct '86, on GHB by Jazzology Records (USA). Catalogue no: **GHB 59**

## New City Jazzmen

**ANOTHER MAN DONE GONE**
**Album:** Released Mar '79, on Flyright by Interstate Music. Catalogue no: **FLY 207**

**GOING TO TOWN**
**Album:** Released Aug '79, on Flyright by Interstate Music. Catalogue no: **FLY 203**

**TO BE COLLECTED**
**Album:** Released Mar '79, on Flyright by Interstate Music. Catalogue no: **FLY 206**

## New Delta Jazzmen '76

**NEW DELTA JAZZMEN, THE**
**Album:** Released Apr '79, on VJM (Vintage Jazz Music) by Vintage Jazz Music Society(VJM). Catalogue no: **SLC 28**

## New England...

**NEW ENGLAND TRADITIONAL FIDDLING 1926-1975 (Various artists)**
**Album:** Released '88, on JEMF (USA) by Arhoolie Records (USA). Catalogue no: **JEMF 105**

## New Era Jazz Band

**TIGHT LIKE THAT**
**Album:** Released '88, on Magic (1) by Submarine Records. Catalogue no: **AWE 2**

## New Lost City Ramblers

**20TH ANNIVERSARY CONCERT**
Tracks: / Old Joe Clark / Hot corn, cold corn / Barbara Allen / Freight train / Wreck of the old '97 / C & NW railroad blues / Did you ever see the devil / Keep on the sunny side / Soldier and the lady, The / Cold bottom strut / La cassine special / Give the fiddler a dram / Well may the world go / Medley.
**Album:** Released Feb '87, on Flying Fish (USA) by Flying Fish Records (USA). Catalogue no: **FF 090**

**TWENTY YEARS**
**Album:** Released May '79, on Flying Fish (USA) by Flying Fish Records (USA). Catalogue no: **FF 102**

## New Mayfair Dance

**HARMONY HEAVEN (New Mayfair Dance Orchestra)**
Tracks: / My Ohio home / All by yourself in the moonlight / Nobody's fault but your own / Good little, bad little you / My southern home / Do something / Deep hollow / Encore / I'm crazy about you / I'll be getting along / She's my slip of a girl / High society blues / We'll build a little world of our own / My heart is saying / Harmony heaven / Anytime's the time to fall in love / Sitting on a rainbow / Baby you've got the right idea / Your sunny disposition and mine / It must be you.
**Album:** Released Dec '83, on Saville by Conifer Records. Catalogue no: **SVL 162**

## New Mississippi Sheiks

**NEW MISSISSIPPI SHEIKS AND SAM CHATMON**
**Album:** Released '88, on Rounder (USA) by Rounder Records (USA). Catalogue no: **ROUNDER 2004**

## New Orleans...

**1925/26 (New Orleans Owls)**
**Album:** Released '74, on VJM (Vintage Jazz Music) by Vintage Jazz Music Society(VJM). Catalogue no: **VLP 21**

**ALGIERS STRUT (New Orleans Joymakers)**
**Album:** Released '74, on Sonet by Sonet Records. Catalogue no: **SNTF 662**

**AT PRESERVATION HALL (New Orleans Rascals of Osaka, Japan)**
**Album:** Released Sep '86, on Stomp Off (USA) Catalogue no: **SOS 1113**

**LOST DREAMS New Orleans vocal groups (Various artists)**
Tracks: / Drunk drunk drunk: *Kidds* / Why fool yourself: *Williams, Bernie* / Bluesy me: *Collis, Dave/Scubbs* / Lost dreams: *Dukes* / Sunny side of the street: *Bees* / Eternally yours: *Barons* / Cotton pickin' hands: *Dukes* / Later baby: *Matthews, Fat Man/4 kittens* / Boom boom: *New Orleans Vocal Groups* / Teardrop eyes: *Dukes* / Ain't gonna do it: *Pelicans* / Shake the dice: *Barons* / Darling please: *Bees* / Last ride, The: *Dukes*.
**Cass:** Released Apr '87, on Stateside by EMI Records. Deleted '88. Catalogue no: **TCSSL 6024**
**Album:** Released Apr '87, on Stateside by EMI Records. Deleted Jun '89. Catalogue no: **SSL 6024**

**MARCHING,RAGGING AND MOURNING. The music of New Orleans (Various artists)**
**Album:** Released Mar '90, on Stomp Off (USA) Catalogue no: **SOS1197**

**MODERN NEW ORLEANS MASTERS (Various artists)**
Note: With Irma Thomas, Johnny Adams, James Booker, Dirty Dozen Brass Band etc.
**CD:** Released '88, on Rounder (USA) by Rounder Records (USA). Catalogue no: **CD 11514**
**Cass:** Released Aug '88, on Rounder (USA) by Rounder Records (USA). Catalogue no: **ROUNDER 2072C**
**Album:** Released Aug '88, on Rounder (USA) by Rounder Records (USA). Catalogue no: **ROUNDER 2072**

**NEAR THE CROSS (New Orleans Gospel)**
**Album:** Released Apr '79, on Nola Catalogue no: **NOLA LP 11**

**NEW ORLEANS 1924-1925 (Various artists)**
Tracks: / Panama: *Droit, Johnny De & His New Orleans Jazz Orchestra* / Nobody knows blues: *Droit, Johnny De & His New Orleans Jazz Orchestra* / Southern woman blues: *Bolden, Lela* /

Seawall special blues: *Bolden, Lela* / Swing, The: *Droit, Johnny De & His New Orleans Jazz Orchestra* / Frankie and Johnny: *Fate Marable Society Syncopators* / Pianoflage: *Fate Marable Society Syncopators* / Black but sweet oh God: *Mack, Billy & Mary* / My heartbreakin' gal: *Mack, Billy & Mary* / Cross word mama: *Papalia, Russ & His Orchestra* / I never knew what a gal could do: *New Orleans Rhythm Kings* / Original Tuxedo rag: *Original Tuxedo Jazz Orchestra* / Careless love: *Original Tuxedo Jazz Orchestra* / Black rag: *Original Tuxedo Jazz Orchestra.*
**Album:** Released Apr '87, on Rhapsody by President Records. Catalogue no: **RHA 6033**

**NEW ORLEANS BANDS 1924-28 Various artists (Various artists)**
**Cass:** Released Jan '82, on Neovox by Neovox Records. Catalogue no: **NEO 769**

**NEW ORLEANS DAYS (Various artists)**
**2 LP Set:** Released Oct '88, on Vogue by Vogue Records. Catalogue no: **400034**

**NEW ORLEANS DIXIELAND EXPRESS (Various artists)**
Note: Artists include: Emile Christian/J.Capraro/Almerico
**Album:** Released Sep '86, on GHB by Jazzology Records (USA). Catalogue no: **GHB 133**

**NEW ORLEANS HORNS (Various artists)**
**2 LP Set:** Released Jul '87, on Document Catalogue no: **DOC 501/502**

**NEW ORLEANS IN THE TWENTIES (Various artists)**
**Album:** Released Mar '83, on VJM (Vintage Jazz Music) by Vintage Jazz Music Society(VJM). Catalogue no: **VLP 46**

**NEW ORLEANS MASTERS VOL.1 (Various artists)**
**Album:** Released '84, on Swing House by Submarine Records. Catalogue no: **SWH 42**
**Cass:** Released '84, on Swing House by Submarine Records. Catalogue no: **CSWH 42**

**NEW ORLEANS PARADE (New Orleans All Stars 1966)**
**Cass:** Released '88, on Dixieland Jubilee (USA) by GNP Crescendo Records (USA). Catalogue no: **DJC 518**
**Album:** Released '88, on Dixieland Jubilee (USA) by GNP Crescendo Records (USA). Catalogue no: **DJA 518**

**NEW ORLEANS RAGTIME ORCHESTRA (New Orleans Ragtime Orchestra)**
**Album:** Released Jun '88, on GHB by Jazzology Records (USA). Catalogue no: **GHB 210**
**Album:** Released '74, on Sonet by Sonet Records. Catalogue no: **SNTF 632**

**NEW ORLEANS RASCALS (New Orleans Rascals)**
**Album:** Released Jun '86, on Stomp Off (USA) Catalogue no: **SOS 1074**

**NEW ORLEANS RHYTHM & BLUES OFFICIAL ANNIVERSARY LP VOL.1 (Various artists)**
**Album:** Released Aug '85, on Sonet by Sonet Records. Catalogue no: **SNTF 937**

**NEW ORLEANS R'N'B 1949-67 (Various artists)**
**Album:** Released '88, on Krazy Kat by Interstate Music. Catalogue no: **KK 7403**

**NEW ORLEANS RYTHYM KINGS 1934/5 (New Orleans Rythym Kings 1934/5)**
Note: Wingy Manone/G. Brunies/N. Lamare/etc.
**Cass:** Released Jun '86, on Holmia Cassettes Catalogue no: **HM 07**

**NEW ORLEANS STOMP (Various artists)**
**Album:** Released Dec '84, on VJM (Vintage Jazz Music) by Vintage Jazz Music Society(VJM). Catalogue no: **VLP 35**

**NEW ORLEANS TEA PARTY (Various artists)**
**Album:** Released Apr '79, on Nola Catalogue no: **NOLA LP 18**

**NEW ORLEANS VOLUME 1 (Various artists)**
Tracks: / Eternity: *Various artists* / I want you: *Various artists* / Bouncing the boogie: *Various artists* / Do you really love me baby: *Various artists* / I need your love: *Various artists* / Say baby: *Various artists* / Heavy sugar: *Various artists* / I s everything alright: *Various artists* / Who's ben fooling you: *Various artists* / Hopeless love: *Various artists* / Mr. Bumps: *Various artists* / My dreams are in vain: *Various artists* / Got a gal in Nashville: *Various artists* / Long lost stranger: *Various artists* / Looked at the moon: *Various artists* / Preachin' & teachin': *Various artists.*
**Album:** Released May '86, on Ace by Ace Records. Catalogue no: **CH 165**

**NEW ORLEANS VOLUME 2 (Various artists)**
Note: Artists include: Lil Millet/Art Neville /Big Boy Myles/Robert Parker/Ernie K Doe /Etc.
**Album:** Released Oct '86, on Ace by Ace Records. Catalogue no: **CH 181**

**RECORDED 1923 (New Orleans Rhythm Kings)**
**Album:** Released Apr '81, on Joker (USA) by Lifetime Records (USA). Catalogue no: **SM 3092**

**TRIBUTE TO NEW ORLEANS (Various artists)**
**CD:** Released Mar '90, on Giants of Jazz by Hasmick Promotions. Catalogue no: **GOJCD53084**

**WAY DOWN YONDER (New Orleans All Stars 1966)**
**Album:** Released Apr '79, on Nola Catalogue no: **NOLA LP 2**

## New Orleans All Stars

**NEW ORLEANS ALL STARS IN CONCERT**
**Album:** Released '88, on Dixieland Jubilee (USA) by GNP Crescendo Records (USA). Catalogue no: **DJA 502**
**Cass:** Released '88, on Dixieland Jubilee (USA) by GNP Crescendo Records (USA). Catalogue no: **DJCD 502**

## New Orleans Gospel

**NEW ORLEANS GOSPEL QUARTETS 1947-56 (Various artists)**
**Album:** Released Jul '85, on Heritage by Interstate Music. Catalogue no: **HT 306**

## New Orleans Jazz

**AT THE KITTY HALLS**
**Album:** Released May '81, on Arhoolie (USA) by Arhoolie Records (USA). Catalogue no: **ARHOOLIE 1013**

**NEW ORLEANS JAZZ FESTIVAL (Various artists)**
Tracks: / Caledonia: *Various artists* / Brown skin girl: *Various artists* / Ice cream freezer: *Various artists* / Baby what you want me to do: *Various artists* / Breaks: *Various artists* / Paul Barbarin's second line: *Various artists* / Rock me mama: *Various artists* / Joie blonde: *Various artists* / Charleston rag: *Various artists* / Darktown strutters ball: *Various artists* / Themes from a movie: *Various artists* / Doxology: *Various artists.*
**Album:** Released Jun '80, on Sonet by Sonet Records. Catalogue no: **SNTF 812**

**NEW ORLEANS JAZZ FROM JIMMY RYANS (Various artists)**
**Album:** Released '88, on Vogue (France) by Vogue Records. Catalogue no: **502004**

**NEW ORLEANS JAZZ & HERITAGE Tenth anniversary (Various artists)**
**Album:** Released Mar '89, on Flying Fish (USA) by Flying Fish Records (USA). Catalogue no: **FF 099**

**NEW ORLEANS JAZZ PARTY (Various artists)**
Tracks: / Basin Street blues: *Various artists* / When the saints go marching in: *Various artists* / Buddy Bolden's blues: *Various artists* / Careless love: *Various artists* / Bucket's got a hole in it: *Various artists* / Blues: *Various artists* / High society: *Various artists* / Milenberg joys: *Various artists* / 2.19 blues: *Various artists* / Grandpa's spells: *Various artists* / Wolverine blues: *Various artists* / Armand hug interview: *Various artists* / Buzzards parade: *Various artists* / Bill Bailey: *Various artists* / Fidgety feet: *Various artists* / Closer walk with thee, A: *Various artists* / Saints, The: *Various artists.*
**Album:** Released Apr '81, on Rarities Catalogue no: **RARITIES 62**

**NEW ORLEANS JAZZ REVIVAL, VOL.1 (Various artists)**

**Album:** Released '88, on Swaggie (Australia) Catalogue no: **S 855**

**NEW ORLEANS JAZZ REVIVAL, VOL.2 (Various artists)**
**Album:** Released '88, on Swaggie (Australia) Catalogue no: **S 856**

**NEW ORLEANS JAZZ SERENADERS VOL.1 (New Orleans Jazz Serenaders)**
**Album:** Released Jul '87, on GHB by Jazzology Records (USA). Catalogue no: **GHB 221**

**NEW ORLEANS JAZZ SERENADERS VOL.2 (New Orleans Jazz Serenaders)**
**Album:** on GHB by Jazzology Records (USA). Catalogue no: **GHB 222**

**NEW ORLEANS JAZZ VOL.1 (Various artists)**
Note: With Bunk Johnson, George Lewis, Dink Johnson.
**Album:** Released '88, on Wolf Catalogue no: **WJS 1001**

**NEW ORLEANS JAZZ VOL.2 (Various artists)**
Note: With Wooden Joe Nicholas, Dink Johnson
**Album:** Released '88, on Wolf Catalogue no: **WJS 1002**

**OH DIDN'T HE RAMBLE (Various artists)**
**CD:** Released 10 Jul '89, on Vogue by Vogue Records. Catalogue no: **VGCD 670210**

**PUD BROWN'S TENOR FOR TWO**
**Album:** Released Jul '79, on Pud Brown Catalogue no: **LP 001**

## New Orleans Legends

**NEW ORLEANS LEGENDS Kid Ory, Joe Darensbourg, Singleton Palmer (Various artists)**
Tracks: / Didn't he ramble: *All Star Marching band* / Bourbon Street: *All Star Marching band* / Hindustan: *All Star Marching band* / Savoy blues: *Ory, Kid* / That's a plenty: *Ory, Kid* / Sugar foot: *Ory, Kid* / Tin roof blues: *Palmer, Singleton* / Sweet Georgia Brown: *Palmer, Singleton* / Careless love: *Palmer, Singleton* / Ballin' the Jack: *Palmer, Singleton* / Just a closer walk with thee: *Buckner, Teddy* / Chinatown: *Buckner, Teddy* / Yellow dog blues: *Darensbourg, Joe* / That da da strain: *Darensbourg, Joe* / Copenhagen: *Darensbourg, Joe* / Bogalusa Street: *New Orleans Heritage* / Fidgety feet: *New Orleans Heritage.*
Note: Ory/Buckner/S. Palmer etc.
**Cass:** Released Aug '88, on Vogue (France) by Vogue Records. Catalogue no: **829006**
**Album:** Released Aug '88, on Vogue (France) by Vogue Records. Catalogue no: **429006**
**CD:** Released Oct '87, on Vogue by Vogue Records. Catalogue no: **VGCD 600151**

## New Vaudeville Band

**Biographical details:** A deliberate and cheeky anachronism, the New Vaudeville Band revived a poular vocal and instrumental style of the Twenties and Thirties, and succesfully presented it to the totally different pop market of 1966-67. The Band's first and biggest hit *Winchester Cathedral* reached No.4 in America. *Peek a boo* and *Finchley Central* also cracked the British Top 20, but after *Green Street Green* had peaked at No.37 in August 1967, the Band's chart success finished altogether. But with the huge American success of *Winchester Cathedral* behind them, they were able to spend a year pumping out their quaint ditties of English geography at the Aladdin Hotel in Las Vegas. After returning to the UK, they moved into cabaret and adopted a more mainstream MoR approach. *Winchester Cathedral* and the other hits by the New Vaudeville Band were the brainchild of writer/producer Geoff Stephens, whose previous chart compostions included *The crying game* (Dave Berry) and *Tell me when* (The Applejacks). Using megaphones, he created the adeonoidal singing sound himself on *Winchester Cathedral* and used session musicians to record the instrumental track. When the single became a smash, a real group had to be formed for live performances. Being a behind-the-scenes man by nature, Stephens chose not to go out on the road; his place was taken by Alan Klein, who adopted the title 'Tristram, seventh Earl of Cricklewood'. But Stephens kept writing and producing the hits. The other recruited members of the New Vaudeville Band were Henry Harrison, Stan Heywood, Robert 'Pops' Kerr, Neil Korner, Hugh Watts and Mick Wilsher. Stephens continued churning out numerous pop hits for the likes of Herman's Hermits, The New Seekers and many others. (Bob MacDonald, 11th Feb 1988).

**6 TRACK HITS**
**7" EP:** Released Aug '84, on Scoop 33 by Pickwick Records. Catalogue no: **7SR 5044**
**Cass:** Released Aug '84, on Scoop 33 by Pickwick Records. Catalogue no: **7SC 5044**

**FINCHLEY CENTRAL**
Tracks: / Finchley central.
**7" Single:** Released May '67, on Fontana by Phonogram Ltd. Deleted '70. Catalogue no: **TF 784**

**GREEN STREET GREEN**
Tracks: / Green street green.
**7" Single:** Released Aug '67, on Fontana by Phonogram Ltd. Deleted '70. Catalogue no: **TF 853**

**LIVE VAUDEVILLE**
**Album:** Released Oct '77, on SRT by SRT Records. Catalogue no: **SRTXNV 77092**

**PEEK A BOO**
Tracks: / Peek-a-boo.
**7" Single:** Released Jan '67, on Fontana by Phonogram Ltd. Deleted '70. Catalogue no: **TF 784**

**TAP YOUR FEET**
Tracks: / Tap your feet / Peek-a-boo / Holiday Inn / Finchley Central / Green Street Green / Rosie / Shirl / Lili Marlene / Amy / Waiting for Wendy / Reflections / Whispering / So tired / Shine on harvest moon.
Note: The 27 tracks include those listed above.
**Cass set:** Released Apr '85, on Cambra by Cambra Records. Deleted '88. Catalogue no: **CRT 5148**
**2 LP Set:** Released Apr '85, on Cambra by Cambra Records. Deleted '88. Catalogue no: **CR 5148**

**WINCHESTER CATHEDRAL**
Tracks: / Winchester Cathedral.
**7" Single:** Released Sep '66, on Fontana by Phonogram Ltd. Deleted '69. Catalogue no: **TF 741**

**WINCHESTER CATHEDRAL (OLD GOLD)**
Tracks: / Winchester Cathedral / I was Kaiser Bill's Batman.
**7" Single:** Released Oct '88, on Old Gold by Old Gold Records. Catalogue no: **OG 9805**

## New York...

**NEW YORK JAZZ 1927-30 (Various artists)**
**Album:** Released Oct '88, on VJM (Vintage Jazz Music) by Vintage Jazz Music Society (VJM). Catalogue no: **VLP 41**

**NEW YORK NOTABLES (Various artists)**
**Album:** Released May '85, on Moonshine Catalogue no: **BLP 105**

**NEW YORK R 'N' B (Various artists)**
**Album:** Released Jul '79, on Magpie by Interstate Music. Deleted '88. Catalogue no: **PY 1817**

## New York Blues

**NEW YORK BLUES VOL.1 (Various artists)**
Tracks: / Shake baby shake: *Dupree, Champion Jack* / Daisy: *McGhee, Brownie* / Candied yams: *Brown, B & His Rockin' McVouts* / Drunk again: *Dupree, Champion Jack* / Doggin' my heart around: *Terry, Sonny* / My baby left me: *Brown, B & His Rockin' McVouts* / Number nine blues: *Dupree, Champion Jack* / Harmonica hop: *Terry, Sonny* / Fannie Mae is back: *Brown, B & His Rockin' McVouts* / Highway blues: *Dupree, Champion Jack* / Don't dog your woman: *McGhee, Brownie* / Stumbling block blues: *Dupree, Champion Jack* / Hardworking man: *Brown, B & His Rockin' McVouts* / Shim sham shammy: *Dupree, Champion Jack.*
**Album:** Released Jan '89, on Charly R&B by Charly Records. Catalogue no: **CRB 1207**

**NEW YORK BLUES VOL.2 (Various artists)**
Tracks: / Angel child: *Myers, Sammy* /

Little girl: *Myers, Sammy* / You don't have to go: *Myers, Sammy* / Sad sad lonesome day: *Myers, Sammy* / Rockin' with B: *Brown, B & His Rockin' McVouts* / Pleasure is all mine, The: *Long, Bobby* / I'm tired of it: *Doctor Horse* / I go into orbit: *Acey, Johnny*.
**Album:** Released Feb '89, on Charly R&B by Charly Records. Catalogue no: **CRB 1208**

## New York Grassroots...

**SACRED BLACK QUARTET TRADITION (New York Grassroots Gospel)**
**Album:** Released Aug '89, on Global Village Catalogue no: **GVM 206**

## New York Jazz Quartet

**BLUES FOR SARKA**
**Album:** Released Jan '82, on Enja (Germany) by Enja Records (West Germany). Catalogue no: **ENJA 3025**

**OASIS**
**Album:** Released Jan '82, on Enja (Germany) by Enja Records (West Germany). Catalogue no: **ENJA 3083**

**SONG OF BLACK NIGHT**
Tracks: / Song of the Black knight / Time for the dancers / After Paris / Romp in the woods somewhere / Estoril soul / Terezia.
**Album:** Released Aug '78, on Sonet by Sonet Records. Catalogue no: **SNTF 753**

**SURGE**
**Album:** Released Jan '82, on Enja (Germany) by Enja Records (West Germany). Catalogue no: **ENJA 2094**

## New York Quartet

**NEW YORK QUARTET & IMAMU AMIRI (New York Quartet/Imamu Amiri Baraka)**
**Album:** Released '73, on ESP by ESP Records. Catalogue no: **ESP 1004**

## New Zealand...

**AUSTRALIAN TOUR (New Zealand National Youth Jazz Band)**
Tracks: / Way out west / Loch Lomond / Comin' thru the rye / Choral and rock out / Waltzing Matilda / Ceramic city festival / Shadow of your smile / Strangers in the night / Shaft / Now is the hour / O my beloved father.
**Album:** Released Nov '79, on Viking (New Zealand) Catalogue no: **VP 430**

**BRASS TO GO (New Zealand Army Band)**
Tracks: / Fifth of Beethoven, A / Don't cry for me Argentina / Sweet gingerbread man / M A S H (Theme from the film) / Thingumy bob / After the lovin' / For to go / From Scotland with love / Hot toddy / Mah na mah na / Holly holy / Hustle, The / Homecoming / Jaws, Theme from / We love you superstar.
**Album:** Released Mar '78, on One-Up by EMI Records. Catalogue no: **OU 2206**

**ORIGINAL JAZZ COMPOSERS BY N.Z.S (New Zealand Jazz Orchestra)**
**Cass:** Released '84, on Kiwi-Pacific (New Zealand) Catalogue no: **TC SLC 174**
**Album:** Released '84, on Kiwi-Pacific (New Zealand) Catalogue no: **SLC 174**

## Newborn, Phineas Jr.

**FABULOUS PHINEAS**
Tracks: / Sugar Ray / What's new? / Forty-five degree angle / No moon at all / I'll remember April / Cherokee / Back home.
**Album:** Released Jan '83, on RCA (France) by BMG Records (France). Catalogue no: **PL 43163**

**HARLEM BLUES**
Note: With Ray Brown and Elvin Jones
**CD:** Released '86, on JVC/Fantasy Catalogue no: **VDJ 1558**

**HERE IS PHINEAS NEWBORN JR.**
Tracks: / Barbados / All the things you are / More I see you / Celia / Dahoud / Newport blues / I'm beginning to see the light / Afternoon in Paris.
**Album:** Released Feb '79, on Atlantic by WEA Records. Deleted Feb '84. Catalogue no: **K 50522**

**LOOK OUT - PHINEAS IS BACK**
Tracks: / Salt peanuts / Man I love, The / You are the sunshine of my life / Abber's song / Tamarind blues / Night in Tunisia / Sometimes I'm happy / Donald's dream.
**Album:** Released '82, on Pablo Jazz (USA) by Pablo Records (USA). Catalogue no: **231 0801**
**Cass:** Released '82, on Pablo Jazz (USA) by Pablo Records (USA). Catalogue no: **K10 801**

**NEWBORN PIANO**
Tracks: / Just in time / Blues theme / Chelsea Bridge / Star eyes / Caravan / It's alright with me / Golden earrings / I can't get started / Sweet and lovely / For all we know / Ain't misbehavin' / Take the 'A' train / Real gone guy / Undecided / Ivy League blues / Gee baby ain't I good to you / I've got the world on a string / Midnight sun never sets, The / Love and marriage / Give me the simple life.
**Album:** Released May '83, on Vogue Jazz (France) by Vogue Records. Catalogue no: **VJD 561**

**PIANO ARTISTRY: PHINEAS NEWBORN**
**CD:** Released '88, on Atlantic Jazz by WEA Records. Catalogue no: **K790 534 2**

**PLEASE SEND ME SOMEONE TO LOVE**
**CD:** Released Jan '89, on JVC/Fantasy Catalogue no: **VDJ 1628**

## Newman, Joe

**HANGIN' OUT (Newman, Joe & Joe Wilder)**
Tracks: / Midgets, The / Here's that rainy day / Duet / Battle hymn of the Republic / Secret love / You've changed / Lypso mania / He was too good to me.
Note: Joe Newman, trumpet; Joe Wilder, trumpet and flugelhorn; Hank Jones, piano; Rufus Reid, bass; Marvin Smith, drums.
**Album:** Released Feb '85, on Concord Jazz by Concord Jazz Records (USA). Catalogue no: **CJ 262**

**HAPPY CATS (Newman, Joe Sextet)**
Tracks: / Happy cats / Cocktails for two / Later for the happenings / Buttercup / Robbins nest / They can't take that away from me / Feather's nest / Mean to me / Between the Devil and the deep blue sea / Joe's tune / I never knew it.
**Album:** Released Feb '83, on Jasmine by Hasmick Promotions. Deleted Feb '88. Catalogue no: **JASM 1008**

**I FEEL LIKE A NEWMAN**
**Album:** Released Jun '88, on Black Lion Catalogue no: **BLP 60905**
**CD:** Released Jun '88, on Black Lion Catalogue no: **BLCD 760905**

**IN A MELLOW MOOD (Newman, Joe Quartet)**
**Album:** Released Aug '88, on Stash (USA) Catalogue no: **ST 219**

**IN SWEDEN**
**Album:** Released Aug '87, on Jazz Information (Sweden) Catalogue no: **CAH 4002**

**SHINY STOCKINGS**
**Album:** Released Oct '79, on Honeydew Catalogue no: **HD 6611**

**SIMILAR SOULS**
Tracks: / Bassing around / Mambo for Joe / Midnight fantasy / Oh Joe / O shay / Similar souls / Susette / 'Tater pie / Wolafunt's lament / Old devil moon / I'll get by / Out of nowhere / Speak low / Star eyes / Time / Baby, won't you please come home? / Lover man / Nancy / My old flame / You're my thrill / Travellin' light.
**2 LP Set:** Released May '83, on Vogue Jazz (France) by Vogue Records. Catalogue no: **VJD 563**

**WAY DOWN BLUES**
**Album:** Released Oct '79, on Honeydew Catalogue no: **HD 6612**

## Newport Jazz Festival

**BERN CONCERT '89**
Tracks: / I want to be happy / Jeep's blues / Just a gigolo (CD only.) / I'm just a lucky so and so / Johnny come lately / Blue and sentimental / In a sentimental mood (CD only.) / Jumpin' at the woodside.
**Cass:** Released Jan '90, on Concord by Concord Jazz Records (USA). Catalogue no: **CJ 401C**
**CD:** Released Jan '90, on Concord by Concord Jazz Records (USA). Catalogue no: **CCD 4401**

**EUROPEAN TOUR**
Tracks: / Tickle toe / Mood indigo / Love me or leave me / These foolish things / Take the 'A' train / Things ain't what they used to be / Through for the night.
Note: The Newport Jazz Festival All

Stars have spread music from the golden age of jazz around the globe. This concert, recorded live in Bern, Switzerland, features an extra musical guest, tenor saxophonist Al Cohn. Impresario George Wein and his spirited band swing from the very first note. George Wein, piano; Harold Ashby, Scott Hamilton, Al Cohn, tenor saxes; Oliver Jackson, drums; Slam Stewart, bass; Norris Turney, alto sax, clarinet; Warren Vache, cornet." (IMS Records, May 1988.)
**CD:** Released May '88, on Concord Jazz by Concord Jazz Records (USA). Catalogue no: **CCD 4343**
**Cass:** Released May '88, on Concord Jazz by Concord Jazz Records (USA). Catalogue no: **CJC 343**
**Album:** Released May '88, on Concord Jazz by Concord Jazz Records (USA). Catalogue no: **CJ 343**

**NEWPORT ALL STARS**
Tracks: / Take the 'A' train / These foolish things / My Monday date / Body and soul / Mean to me / I surrender, dear / Please don't talk about me when I'm gone / Pan Am blues.
Note: Ruby Braff, Buddy Tate, George Wein, Jack Lesberg, Don Lamond.
**Album:** Released Jan '85, on Black Lion Catalogue no: **BLP 30115**

**NEWPORT JAZZ FESTIVAL (Various artists)**
**2 LP Set:** Released '83, on CBS by CBS Records. Deleted '88. Catalogue no: **88605**

**NEWPORT JAZZ FESTIVAL ALL STARS**
Tracks: / Exactly like you / Centennial blues / I didn't know about you / Nobody knows you (when you're down and out) / Rosetta / Smiles / Jeep is jumpin' / Mooche, The / Body and soul / Man I love, The / What's new? / Struttin' with some barbecue / Moten swing.
Note: Scott Hamilton - tenor sax; Norris Turney - alto sax, clarinet; Warren Vache - cornet, flugelhorn; George Wein - piano; Slam Stewart - bass; Oliver Jackson - drums.
**2 LP Set:** Released Feb '85, on Concord Jazz by Concord Jazz Records (USA). Catalogue no: **CJ 260**
**CD:** Released Dec '87, on Concord Jazz by Concord Jazz Records (USA). Catalogue no: **CCD 4260**

**TRIBUTE TO CHARLIE PARKER (Various artists)**
Tracks: / Buzzy: *McGhee, Howard Sextet* / Now's the time: *McGhee, Howard Sextet* / Wee: *McGhee, Howard Sextet* / Embraceable you: *McClean, Jackie Quartet* / Old folks: *McClean, Jackie Quartet.*
**CD:** Released Nov '88, on Bluebird (2) by BMG Records (UK). Catalogue no: **ND 86457**

## Newton, Frankie

**AT THE ONYX CLUB 1937-39**
**Album:** Released Aug '87, on Tax Catalogue no: **M 8017**

## Nicholas, Albert

**ALBERT NICHOLAS QUARTET**
**Album:** Released '74, on Delmark (USA) by Delmark Records (USA). Catalogue no: **DL 207**

**ALBERT NICHOLAS & THE JOHN DEFFERARY JAZZTET (Nicholas, Albert & The John Defferary Jazztet)**
**Album:** Released '86, on GHB by Jazzology Records (USA). Catalogue no: **GHB 64**

**MEMORIAL**
**2 LP Set:** Released Oct '88, on Vogue by Vogue Records. Catalogue no: **400023**

**THIS IS JAZZ VOL.2**
**Album:** Released Feb '90, on Storyville by Storyville Records AB. Catalogue no: **SLP 4068**

**TRADITIONAL JAZZ 2**
Tracks: / Mo pas lemme ca / Memories of you / Les oignons / Embraceable you / How long how long blues / Please don't talk about me / Indiana / Lost hour blues / Rose room / Salee dame / I can't give you anything but love / Albert's blues.
**Album:** Released Dec '83, on IMS by Polydor Ltd. Catalogue no: **6459 214**

**TRIBUTE TO JELLY ROLL MORTON**
Note: with Art Hodes, Bobby Greene, Papa Bue.
**Album:** Released Jan '88, on Storyville by Storyville Records AB. Catalogue no: **SLP 4050**

## Nichols, Herbie

**BETHLEHEM SESSIONS**
Tracks: / Too close for comfort / Every cloud / Argumentative / Love, gloom, cash, love / Portrait of Ucha / Beyond recall / All the way / 45 degree angle / Infatuation eyes / S'crazy pad.
**CD:** Released Nov '89, on Affinity by Charly Records. Catalogue no: **CDAFF 759**

**HERBIE NICHOLS TRIO**
**Album:** Released Sep '84, on Blue Note by EMI Records. Catalogue no: **BLP 1519**

**OUT OF THE SHADOW**
Tracks: / Too close for comfort / Every cloud / Argumentative / Love, gloom, cash, love / Portrait of Ucha / Beyond recall / All the way / Forty-five degree angle / Infatuation eyes / S'crazy pad.
**Album:** Released May '82, on Affinity by Charly Records. Deleted '88. Catalogue no: **AFF 90**

## Nichols, Keith

**CHITTERLIN' STRUT**
**Album:** Released Jun '89, on Stomp Off (USA) Catalogue no: **SOS 1159**

**DOCTORS JAZZ (Nichols, Keith & Red Hot Syncopators)**
**Album:** Released Apr '88, on Stomp Off (USA) Catalogue no: **SOS 1135**

**SHAKIN' THE BLUES AWAY (Nichols, Keith Hot Six)**
**Album:** Released '88, on Stomp Off (USA) Catalogue no: **SOS 1063**

**WITH MOONLIGHT BROADCASTERS. see also under Moonlight Broadcasters (Nichols, Keith & Moonlight Broadcasters)**
**Album:** Released Mar '90, on Stomp Off (USA) Catalogue no: **SOS1193**

## Nichols, Red

**1925 - 1928 (Nichols, Red & Sam Lanin's Orchestra)**
**Album:** Released Apr '79, on Broadway (USA) Catalogue no: **BR 105**

**1936 (Nichols, Red & Orchestra)**
**Album:** Released Dec '87, on Circle (USA) by Jazzology Records (USA). Catalogue no: **CLP 110**

**1925-28**
**Album:** Released '88, on Fountain by Retrieval Records. Catalogue no: **FJ 110**

**CLASS OF 39 Radio transcriptions (Nichols, Red/his Five Pennies)**
**Album:** Released Apr '79, on Blue Lantern Catalogue no: **BLUE LANTERN 1000**

**FEELIN' NO PAIN**
Tracks: / Japanese Sandman / China boy / After you've gone / Sally, won't you come back? / Feelin' no pain / Wash board blues / Bugle call rag / Eccentric / Ida, sweet as apple cider / Smiles / Buddy's habits / Indiana / That's no bargain / Avalon / Boneyard shuffle / Riverboat shuffle / Sheik of Araby, The.
**Album:** Released Mar '87, on Affinity by Charly Records. Catalogue no: **AFS 1038**

**GREAT ORIGINAL PERFORMANCES Jazz classics in digital stereo) (Nichols, Red & Miff Mole)**
Tracks: / Darktown strutters' ball / Rhythm of the day / Hurricane / Someday, sweetheart / Wabash blues / Devonport blues / Shimme-sha-wabble / Hot time, A / Riverboat shuffle / Feelin' no pain / Original Dixieland / Honolulu blues / Harlem twist / Corina Corina.
Note: Red and Miff with the Five Pennies, The Charleston Chasers, The Molers and Ross Gorman's Orchestra
**Cass:** Released Jun '88, on BBC by BBC Records & Tapes. Catalogue no: **ZCF 664**
**CD:** Released Jun '88, on BBC by BBC Records & Tapes. Catalogue no: **BBC CD 664**
**Album:** Released Jun '88, on BBC by BBC Records & Tapes. Catalogue no: **REB 664**

**RED & BEN (Nichols, Red & Ben Pollack)**
**Album:** Released Apr '79, on Broadway (USA) Catalogue no: **BR 103**

**RED & MIFF, 1926-31 (Nichols, Red & Miff Mole)**
Tracks: / Jersey walk / Clap yo' hands / Wouldn't you / Just the same / Where the wild wild flowers grow / Tap tap / Let a

smile be your umbrella / Say yes today / Delirium / Davenport blues / Slippin' around / Feeling no pain / Sugar / Make my cot where the cot-cot-cotton grows / Harlem twist / Five pennies / That's where the south begins / I'm tickled pink / At last I'm happy / If you haven't got a girl.
**Album:** Released Jun '82, on Saville by Conifer Records. Catalogue no: **SVL 146**

**RED NICHOLS AND OTHER RADIO TRANSCRIPTIONS**
**Album:** Released '88, on Meritt (USA) Catalogue no: **MERITT 18**

**RED NICHOLS & HIS FIVE PENNIES (Nichols, Red/his Five Pennies)**
**Album:** Released Apr '88, on Swaggie (Australia) Catalogue no: **S 838**

**RED NICHOLS & THE FIVE PENNIES (Nichols, Red & The Five Pennies)**
**Album:** Released '88, on Jazzology (USA) by Jazzology Records (USA). Catalogue no: **J 90**

**RED NICHOLS & THE FIVE PENNIES, VOL 4 1928-29 (Nichols, Red & The Five Pennies)**
**Album:** Released Oct '89, on Swaggie (Australia) Catalogue no: **S 839**

**RED NICHOLS: VOL 2 (with Miff Mole, Jimmy Dorsey, Adrian Rollini,Pee Wee Russell)**
Tracks: / Five pennies / Mean dog blues / Riverboat shuffle / Eccentric / Ida / Feelin' no pain / Avalon / Japanese sandman / Nobody's sweetheart / My gal Sal / Poor butterfly / Can't you hear me?.
**Album:** Released Aug '79, on Classic Jazz Masters Catalogue no: **CJM 25**

**RED NICHOLS VOL. 3 1928**
**Album:** Released Aug '87, on Classic Jazz Masters Catalogue no: **CJM 27**

**RED NICHOLS-VOL.4**
**Album:** Released Oct '86, on Classic Jazz Masters Catalogue no: **CJM 28**

**RED NICHOLS-VOLUME 1**
**Album:** Released Sep '86, on Swaggie (Australia) Catalogue no: **S 836**

**RED NICHOLS-VOLUME 2**
**Album:** Released Sep '86, on Swaggie (Australia) Catalogue no: **S 837**

**RED NICHOLS-VOLUME 5**
**Album:** Released '88, on Classic Jazz Masters Catalogue no: **CJM 30**

**RHYTHM OF THE DAY (Nichols, Red/his Five Pennies)**
Tracks: / Rhythm of the day / Buddy's habits / Boneyard shuffle / Alexander's ragtime band / Alabama stomp / Hurricane / Cornfed / Mean dog blues / Riverboat shuffle / Eccentric / Feelin' no pain / Original Dixieland one-step / Honolulu blues / There'll come a time / Harlem twist / Alice blue gown / Corina Corina / Oh Peter, you're so nice / Waiting for the Evening Mail / Sweet Sue.
**Album:** Released 1 Dec '83, on Living Era by Academy Sound & Vision Records. Catalogue no: **AJA 5025**
**Cass:** Released 1 Dec '83, on Living Era by Academy Sound & Vision Records. Catalogue no: **ZC AJA 5025**
**CD:** Released Feb '87, on Living Era by Academy Sound & Vision Records. Catalogue no: **CD AJA 5025**

**SYNCOPATED CHAMBER MUSIC (Nichols, Red Five Pennies)**
**Album:** Released Jan '87, on Audiophile (USA) by Jazzology Records (USA). Catalogue no: **AP 201**
**Album:** Released Aug '88, on Audiophile (USA) by Jazzology Records (USA). Catalogue no: **AP 2**

## Nicols, Maggie

**DON'T ASSUME**
**Album:** Released Sep '87, on Leo by Leo Records. Catalogue no: **LR 145**

## Niehaus,Lennie

**OCTET,NO.2., THE**
**Album:** Released '88, on Boplicity by Ace Records. Catalogue no: **COP 017**

## Night At Birdland

**NIGHT AT BIRDLAND (Various artists)**
Tracks: / Walkin': *Various artists* / All the things you are: *Various artists* / Bag's groove: *Various artists* / There will never be another you: *Various artists* / It's you or no one: *Various artists* / Jamph: *Various artists* / Nutville: *Various artists* / Wee: *Various artists.*
**2 LP Set:** Released May '83, on Vogue Jazz (France) by Vogue Records. Catalogue no: **VJD 565**

## Nighthawk, Robert

**BLACK ANGEL BLUES**
Tracks: / Down the line / Handsome lover / My sweet lovin' woman / Sweet black angel / Anna Lee blues / Return mail blues / Sugar papa / She knows how to love a man / Good news / Six three O / Prison bound / Jackson town gal / Sorry my angel / Someday.
**Album:** Released '89, on Chess by Vogue Records. Catalogue no: **GCH 8108**

**LIVE ON MAXWELL STREET**
**Cass:** Released '88, on Rounder (USA) by Rounder Records (USA). Catalogue no: **ROUNDER 2022C**
**Album:** Released '88, on Rounder (USA) by Rounder Records (USA). Catalogue no: **ROUNDER 2022**

## Nimmons, Phil

**ATLANTIC SUITE**
**Album:** Released Jul '86, on Sackville by Spotlite Records. Catalogue no: **2008**

## Nineteen Fifties:

**1950'S: SINGERS (Various artists)**
Tracks: / Street of dreams: *Wiley, Lee* / Fine and mellow: *Holiday, Billie* / Easy to love: *Mathis, Johnny* / Hey! bartender, give...: *Williams, Joe* / Flying: *Gonzales, Babs/Griffin, Johnny* / Charleston: *Lambert, Hendricks & Annie Ross* / Mack the knife: *Various artists* / Russian lullaby: *Rushing, Jimmy* / There ain't no flies on...: *Hot Lips Page* / Take the 'A' train: *Elington, Duk* / Frenesi: *Carter, Betty.*
**Album:** Released Apr '88, on CBS (import) by CBS Records. Catalogue no: **4606081**

## Nineteen Forties

**1940'S - SINGERS (Various artists)**
Tracks: / (What did I do) wrong: *Waters, Ethel* / (I'll be glad): *Teagarden, Ted* / Old yazoo: *Boswell Sisters* / I'm crazy 'bout my baby: *Lewis, Ted* / Doin' what I please: *Redman, Don* / Frankie and Johnny: *Bullock, Chick* / Out where the blue begins / Rose of the Rio Grande: *Ellington, Duke* / Mama's gone: *Williams, Midge* / Blue again: *Armstrong, Louis* / Dinah: *Crosby, Bing & Mills Brothers* / River's taking care: *Boswell, Connie* / All my life: *Wilson, Teddy* / My old man: *Spirits Of Rhythm* / Chasin' shadows: *Prima, Louis* / Lover come back to me: *Bailey, Mildred* / Mean to me: *Wilson, Teddy.*
**Cass:** Released Apr '89, on CBS (import) by CBS Records. Catalogue no: **461095-4**
**CD:** Released Apr '89, on CBS (import) by CBS Records. Catalogue no: **461095-2**
**Album:** Released Apr '89, on CBS (import) by CBS Records. Catalogue no: **461095-1**

**1940'S SMALL GROUPS The New Directions (Various artists)**
Tracks: / Igor: *Various artists* / Four men on a horse: *Various artists* / Nero's conception: *Various artists* / Pam: *Various artists* / I surrender, dear (take 2): *Various artists* / Dark eyes: *Various artists* / Stompin' at the Savoy: *Various artists* / Limehouse blues: *Various artists* / Tuxedo Junction: *Various artists* / Steps: *Various artists* / Fan it: *Various artists* / Lost weekend: *Various artists* / I surrender, dear: *Various artists* / Someday, sweetheart: *Various artists* / Body and soul: *Various artists* / Three men on third: *Various artists* / Pagan love song: *Various artists.*
**Album:** Released Apr '89, on CBS (import) by CBS Records. Catalogue no: **461094-1**
**Cass:** Released Apr '89, on CBS (import) by CBS Records. Catalogue no: **461094-4**
**CD:** Released Apr '89, on CBS (import) by CBS Records. Catalogue no: **461094-2**

## Nineteen Forty Four...

**1944 REVISITED (Various artists)**
Note: Jim Robinson, S. Rimmington, B. Bissonnette.
**Album:** Released Mar '87, on GHB by Jazzology Records (USA). Catalogue no: **GHB 196**

## Nistico, Sal

**EAST OF ISAR (Nistico, Sal/Benny Bailey)**

**Album:** Released Oct '79, on Ego Catalogue no: **EGO 4010**

**JUST FOR FUN**
**Album:** Released Oct '79, on Ego Catalogue no: **EGO 4002**

**NEO/NISTICO**
**Album:** Released Dec '79, on Beehive (USA) Catalogue no: **BH 7006**

## Noble, Ray

**1930'S VOLUME 2, THE Complete COTY program (Noble, Ray & Joe Haymes)**
Tracks: / Very thought of you, The / Flowers for madame / Way down yonder in New Orleans / Koranga / I never had a chance / Danny boy / Night on the desert / Blue danube / In my country that means love / Two seats in the balcony / Honeysuckle rose / On the good ship lollipop / Nothin' ever happens when Gimbal hits the cymb / London on a rainy night / My melancholy baby / White star of Sigma Nu, The.
Note: Sidemen include Charlie Spivak, Pee Wee Erwin, Will Bradley, Glenn Miller, Johnny Mintz, Mike Doty, Milt Yaner, Bud Freeman, Nick Pisani, Fritz Prospero, Dan D'Andrea, Claude Thornhill, George Van Eps, Delmar Kaplan, Bill Harty with vocals by Al Bowlly
**Album:** Released Feb '88, on Aircheck (USA) by Kiner Ents.(USA). Catalogue no: **AIRCHECK 2**

**DINNER MUSIC (Noble, Ray & His Orchestra)**
**Album:** Released Jul '82, on Golden Era by Delta Records. Catalogue no: **GELP 15031**

**GOODNIGHT SWEETHEART (Noble, Ray & His Orchestra & Al Bowlly)**
**Cass:** Released Jun '88, on Joy by President Records. Catalogue no: **JOYTC 272**
**Album:** Released Apr '83, on Joy by President Records. Catalogue no: **JOYD 272**
**Album:** Released Jun '88, on Joy by President Records. Catalogue no: **JOY 272**

**HMV SESSIONS, THE (Noble, Ray Orchestra & Al Bowlly)**
Tracks: / Sweet and lovely / Over my shoulder / Close your eyes / When you've got a little springtime in your heart / Did you ever see a dream walking? / I can't get Mississippi off my mind / Remember me / Isle of Capri / Time on my hands / You ought to see Sally on Sunday / Guilty / One morning in May / I'll string along with you / Wanderer / Wagon wheels / You're driving me crazy / I'll be good because of you / Goodnight sweetheart.
Note: Recorded between 1930 and 1934.
**Cass:** Released Mar '84, on Retrospect by EMI Records. Deleted Nov '88. Catalogue no: **TCSH 107 822 4**
**Album:** Released Mar '84, on Retrospect by EMI Records. Deleted Nov '88. Catalogue no: **SH 107 822 1**

**NOTABLE NOBLE**
Tracks: / When the real thing comes your way / South sea rose / You've got to be modernistic / Crazy feel / Sweepin' the clouds away / I've got a feeling / Just imagine / It ain't no fault of mine / Tan-tan-tivvy-tally-ho / Mad about the boy / Blue Danube / Try a little tenderness / Chewing gum / I was in the mood / Sun is round the corner / Repeal the blues.
Note: Sixteen tracks from the 1929-34 repertoire.

**Cass:** Released Apr '85, on Retrospect by EMI Records. Catalogue no: **EG 2604594**
**Album:** Released Apr '85, on Retrospect by EMI Records. Catalogue no: **EG 2604591**
**Album:** Released May '82, on World by World Records. Deleted May '87. Catalogue no: **SH 429**

**OVER ON THE SUNNY SIDE (Noble, Ray & His Orchestra)**
**Album:** Released Apr '86, on Old Bean by Submarine Records. Catalogue no: **OLD 6**
**Cass:** Released Apr '86, on Old Bean by Submarine Records. Catalogue no: **COLD 6**

**RAY NOBLE & AL BOWLLY, NO.2 (Noble, Ray & His Orchestra)**
**Album:** Released Mar '79, on Monmouth Evergreen Catalogue no: **MES 7021**

**RAY NOBLE & AL BOWLLY, NO 1 (Noble, Ray & His Orchestra & Al Bowlly)**
Tracks: / Love is the sweetest thing / It's bad for me / You're mine, you / Hang out the stars in Indiana / Looking on the bright side of life / With all my love and kisses / I'm glad I waited / What more can I ask? / It's all forgotten now / Midnight, the stars and you / What now? / Love tales / This is romance / Remember me / Hustling and bustling for baby.
**Album:** Released Mar '79, on Monmouth Evergreen Catalogue no: **MES 6816**

**RAY NOBLE & AL BOWLLY, NO 6 (Noble, Ray & His Orchestra & Al Bowlly)**
Tracks: / Lady of Spain / This little piggie / On the other side of Lovers' Lane / Got a date with an angel / Twentieth Century blues / If you'll say yes, cherie / Oceans of time / Sailin' on the Robert E. Lee / Isle of Capri / You oughta be in pictures / Lazy day / Grinzing / You're driving me crazy.
**Album:** Released Mar '79, on Monmouth Evergreen Catalogue no: **MES 7056**

**RAY NOBLE ENCORES (Noble, Ray & His Orchestra)**
Tracks: / I'll be good because of you / You're twice as nice / Must it end like this? / Spin a little web of dreams / Can't we meet again? / Lady of Madrid / With love in my heart / Roll on, Mississippi, roll on / Japanese sandman / Tiger rag / Mad about the boy / Blue Danube / Evergreen (medley) / Happy ending.
Note: Recorded 1930-34.
**Album:** Released Mar '79, on Monmouth Evergreen Catalogue no: **MES 7070**

**RAY NOBLE ORCHESTRA 1935-6 (Noble, Ray & His Orchestra)**
**Album:** Released Jul '78, on London Records by London Records Ltd. Catalogue no: **HMG 5027**

**RAY NOBLE'S ENCORES, VOL.1 (Noble, Ray & His Orchestra)**
**Album:** Released May '79, on Monmouth Evergreen Catalogue no: **MES 6816**
**Album:** Released May '79, on Monmouth Evergreen Catalogue no: **MES 7021**

**RAY NOBLE'S ENCORES, VOL.3**
**Album:** Released May '79, on Monmouth Evergreen Catalogue no: **MES 7027**

**RAY NOBLE'S ENCORES, VOL.4 (Noble, Ray & His Orchestra)**
**Album:** Released May '79, on Monmouth Evergreen Catalogue no: **MES 7039**

**RAY NOBLE'S ENCORES, VOL.5 (Noble, Ray & His Orchestra)**
**Album:** Released May '79, on Monmouth Evergreen Catalogue no: **MES 7040**

**RAY NOBLE'S ENCORES, VOL.6 (Noble, Ray & His Orchestra)**
**Album:** Released May '79, on Monmouth Evergreen Catalogue no: **MES 7056**

**WE DANCED ALL NIGHT (Noble, Ray & His Orchestra)**
Tracks: / I've got my love to keep me warm / Easy to love / El relicario / Why stars come out at night / Chinatown, my Chinatown / Double trouble / Way down yonder in New Orleans / Soon / Touch of your lips, The / Dinah / I've got you under my skin / Allah holiday.
**Album:** Released Oct '84, on RCA by BMG Records (UK). Deleted '87. Catalogue no: **NL 89463**
**Cass:** Released Oct '84, on RCA by BMG Records (UK). Deleted '87. Catalogue no: **NK 89463**

## Nock, Mike

**IN OUT AND AROUND (Nock, Mike Quartet)**
Tracks: / Break time / Dark light / Shadows of forgotten / Gift, The / Hadrian's wall / In, out and around.
Note: Featuring: Mike Brecker/G. Mraz/Al Foster.
**Album:** Released Sep '86, on Timeless by Timeless Records. Catalogue no: **SJP 119**

**ONDAS**
Tracks: / Forgotten love / Ondas / Visionary / Land of the long white cloud / Doors.
Note: Personnel: Mike Nock - piano/Eddie Gomez - bass/Jon Christensen - drums.
**CD:** Released Aug '86, on ECM Catalogue no: **829 161 2**

**PIANO SOLOS**
Tracks: / Californian country song / Polyhedron / Fallen angel / Break time / Elsewhen / Enchanted garden / Soliloquy / Jacanori / Dolphin dance.
**Album:** Released Apr '81, on Timeless by Timeless Records. Catalogue no: **SJP 134**

**TALISMAN**
**Album:** Released Jan '82, on Enja (Germany) by Enja Records (West Germany). Catalogue no: **ENJA 3071**

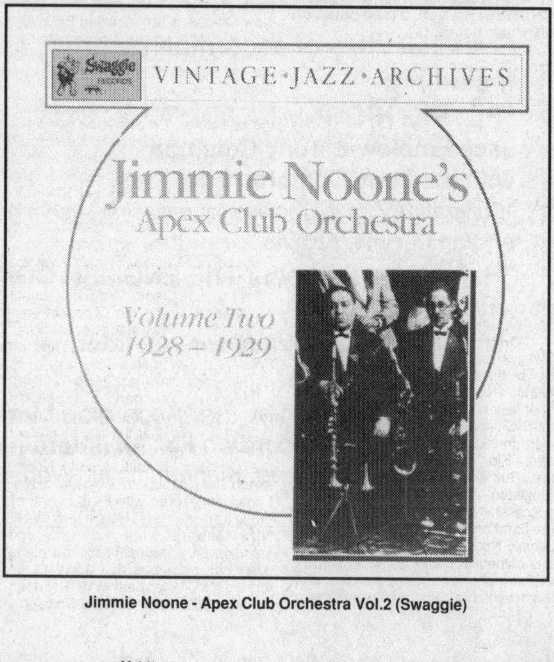

**Jimmie Noone - Apex Club Orchestra Vol.2 (Swaggie)**

## Noone, Jimmie

### APEX CLUB BLUES

Tracks: / Apex blues / New Orleans hop scop blues / Blues my naughty sweetie gives to me / Keystone blues / Four or five times / Bump it / Way down yonder in New Orleans / Every evening / My Monday date / I know that you know / Body and soul / Sweet Lorraine / Sweet Georgia Brown / King Joe / Sweet Joe / Oh Sister, ain't that hot?.

**Album:** Released Jun '86, on Affinity by Charly Records. Deleted '88. Catalogue no: **AFS 1023**

### JIMMIE NOONE 1931-40

Tracks: / I need lovin' / It's you / When it's sleepy time down South / Dixie Lee / Inka dinka doo / Delta bound / Like a little bit less / I'd do anything for you / Liza / Soon / Easy to remember / Rump it / Moody melody / They got my number now.

**Album:** Released Apr '81, on Queendisc (Italy) Catalogue no: **QU 014**

### JIMMIE NOONE (1936-41)

**Album:** Released Jan '83, on Swaggie (Australia) Catalogue no: **S 1226**

### JIMMIE NOONE, VOL.1 with Apex Club Orch., & with Stovepipe Johnson

Tracks: / I know that you know / Sweet Sue / Four or five times / Every evening / Ready for the river / Forever more / Oh sister / Ain't that hot / I ain't got nobody / Apex blues / Monday date / Blues.

**Album:** Released Aug '79, on Classic Jazz Masters Catalogue no: **CJM 29**

### JIMMIE NOONE'S APEX CLUB ORCHESTRA VOL.2 (see panel on previous page)

Tracks: / Sweet Lorraine / Sweet Lorraine (2) / Some rainy day / It's tight like that / It's tight like that (2) / Let's sow a wild oat / Let's sow a wild oat (2) / She's funny that way / St.Louis blues / Chicago rhythm / I got a misery / Wake up chill'un, wake up! / Love me or leave me / Love me or leave me (2) / Anything you want.

Note: The death of Jimmie Noone on 19th April 1944 four days before his 49th birthday was a loss for jazz, for after years of playing in obscure clubs and constant touring during the 1930's, one of the greatest New Orleans clarinet players was being discovered. Noone has already recorded with The Capitol Jazzmen in August 1943 (S 1406 - Swaggie) and early in 1944 was a member of the New Orleans All Stars put together by Orson Welles for his half hour weekly radio programme on the CBS Californian network. With Noone were musicians from his New Orleans past - Kid Ory, Mutt Carey, Buster Wilson, Bud Scott, Ed Garland and Zutty Singleton. The first broadcast was so successful that Orson Welles presented the band on a regular weekly basis but Jimmie Noone died at his home on the day of the fifth broadcast while shaving in preparation for his appearance. With this six volume chronological release of Jimmie Noone's Vocalion contract recordings we hope to fill a major gap in the recorded history of this famous New Orleans Jazzman. This album we present what little known of his movements in New Orleans and Chicago during the 1920's.

Jimmie Noone became interested in music at home in Cut Off, near New Orleans. At the age of 10 he began playing guitar, probably with the Sam Ross Orchestra but by the time he was 15 and the family had moved into New Orleans he had switched to clarinet, taking lessons from Lorenzo Tio Jr. Some writers perpetuate the myth that Noone was taught by Sidney Bechet but this hardly seems likely as Bechet was two years his junior. Tio was famous as a teacher and other well known clarinet players he taught were Barney Bigard, Albert Nicholas, Omer Simeon, Johnny Dodds, Emile Barnes, Albert Burbank, Louis Cottrell Jr, Wade Whaley and Sidney Bechet. Louis Nelson 'Big Eye' Delisle who studied with the Tios also had a strong stylistic influence on Jimmie Noone's early playing. Noone's first professional engagement was in 1912 with Freddy Keppard's Band in the Storyville district and eventually he worked permanently with Keppard (for about 12 months. In 1916 Jimmie Noone and cornet player Buddy Petit formed the Young Olympia Band which included trombonist Honore Dutrey. Noone about this time was also a member of the Tuxedo Brass Band which from 1910 to 1925 included many famous New Orleans musicians. In 1916 (some say 1914) Clarence Williams organised a vaudeville tour out of New Orleans which included Papa Celestin, cornet; Jimmie Noone, clarinet; Williams, piano; Johnny St. Cyr, banjo; John Lindsay, bass; and Armand J. Piron, violin, who was then Williams somewhat quarrelsome music publishing co-partner. It is said that Piron managed to break up the tour before it commenced. Jimmie Noone led a trio at the Pythian Temple Roof Gardens during the summer of 1916 and 1917 and played infrequently in Kid Ory's band with Joe 'King' Oliver at Pete Lala's in Storyville and also with Oscar 'Papa' Celestin's Orchestra. Freddy Keppard and bass player Bill Johnson had formed 'The Original Creole Orchestra' about 1912 which toured the Orpheum vaudeville circuit. They made appearances at the Grand Theatre in Chicago and the Winter Garden in New York City and were the first black jazz band to travel extensively. The band changed it's name in 1917 to the Original Creole Band and played at the Logan Square Theatre in Chicago before a final tour for the Orpheum Circuit. Jimmie Noone joined the Creoles in Chicago at the Logan and toured with them until they broke up in late 1917. Noone returned to New Orleans while Keppard and Johnson remained in Chicago. Accounts differ but it appears that Johnson reformed the Creoles early in 1918 to open the Royal Garden's Cafe on Chicago's South side. Buddy Petit declined to join them and King Oliver was engaged along with Jimmie Noone, Eddie Venson, trombone; Lottie Taylor, piano; and Paul Barbarin, drums. Oliver while with the Original Creoles doubled with Laurence Duhe's orchestra at Bill Bottom's Dreamland cafe. Noone also doubled while playing with the Creoles, leading his own small band at the Edelweiss with pianist Glover Compton.

When Oliver left the Original Creoles in mid 1920 to front Duhe's Dreamland Band Keppard replaced him. The actual demise of the Original Creole Band is unknown but was probably at the end of 1919. Both Noone and Keppard then jobbed around Chicago, including a stint at the Lorraine Club in a band with pianist Tony Jackson and drummer Jimmy Bertrand. Charles " Dock Cooke one of Chicago's successful orchestra leaders from 1918, employed Noone in mid 1920 and Noone was still with Cooke in mid 1922 when they opened at Harmon's Dreamland Casino. Cooke hired the best musicians including Freddy Keppard, Joe Poston, Jerome Pasquall, Clifford King, reeds; and Bill Newton, tuba; and the Cooke band began to rival Oliver's as one of the best in Chicago. Cooke's Dreamland engagement finished a mid-night which gave Jimmie Noone an opportunity to play after hours at various Chicago clubs. About mid 1923 he joined drummer singer Ollie Powell's group at the Midnite Club on Indiana Street. Te Powell Band with Noone and Glover Compton also appeared at various times at the Dreamland Cafe, Paradise Gardens, The Oriental and the Panama. Later Noone led a late night group at The Nest Club using Joe Poston reed man from the Cooke band, Bud Scott, banjo and pianist Walter Johnson. Tommy Ladnier also played with a Noone group in the 1920's which appears to be the Powell group that recorded Play that thing for Paramount in September 1923. Lee Collins then with King Oliver, recalled that in 1924 The Nest band included Freddy Keppard, Arthur Campbell, piano and Ollie Powell. While with Cooke, Jimmie Noone studied classical clarinet under Franz Schoepp(e), first clarinetist with Chicago Symphony, who taught at the Chicago Musical College, Schoepp also tutored Benny Goodman and Buster Bailey during the mid-1920's. The Nest situated at the corner of 35th and Prairie, was renovated in late 1926 to cater for a more up market clientele and renamed the Apex Club. Ollie Powell died soon after, Johnny Wells, another singer-drummer replaced Powell, and Noone assumed band leadership. Late in 1926 Noone left the security of the Doc Cooke band to concentrate on the Apex Club which had become the mecca for musicians from Louis Armstrong to the young white Chicagoans including Benny Goodman, Frank Teschemacher, Bud Freeman, Eddie Condon, Muggs Spanier, Mezz Mezzrow and Gene Krupa.

In 1927 Noone returned to the Cooke

Orchestra and for a while King Oliver's nephew Dave Nelson was a member of the Apex Club Orchestra. Earl Hines was engaged for a week in early 1928 to replace Walter Johnson as pianist at the Apex and in spite of inducements from Louis Armstrong and Zutty Singleton to reform their band he stayed until December 1928 just before opening at the Grand Terrace. At various times Noone also used musicians from Cooke's orchestra including George Mitchell, cornet and Bill Newton, tuba. In mid 1928 Joe Poston left Cooke and stayed with Noone until about April 1930. Through efforts of singer Red McKenzie, Vocalion put Noon under contract and the band recorded it's first session on 16 May 1928. The first releases were popular and monthly recording sessions followed. The sides are contained on volume one in this chronological series and there seems little doubt that the recordings feature the acutal Apex Club Group. Earl Hines departure from the Apex Club band seems to have been based on a misunderstanding between Hines and Noone. Hines recalled much later that there was some animosity on Noone's part about Hines popularity and although the owner allegedly offered Hines the Apex leadership and he was censured by the Musicians Union he claims he had no intention of accepting the job. This conflicts with the accepted opinion that Noone was a gentle friendly man. In December 1928, Bud Scott's place was filled by musical all rounder Junie Cobb and Earl Hines was replaced by Jerome Carrington for several weeks then by Alex Hill, who had arrived in Chicago about September 1928. Hill was in turn replaced by Zinky Cohn in mid 1929. The 1920's had been a success for Noone. The band at the Apex was extremely popular and the Vocalion records were selling well. But in the US a massive stock market crash was soon to change the fortunes of millions, including Jimmie Noone. (Bill Haesler, Feb 1986)
**Album:** Released Jan '86, on Swaggie (Australia) Catalogue no: **S 842**

**JIMMIE NOONE'S APEX CLUB ORCHESTRA VOL.3**
**Album:** Released Jan '86, on Swaggie (Australia) Catalogue no: **S 843**

**JIMMIE NOONE'S APEX CLUB ORCHESTRA VOL.4**
**Album:** Released Mar '87, on Swaggie (Australia) Catalogue no: **S 844**

**JIMMY NOONE: 1928-40**
**Album:** Released Feb '89, on Giants of Jazz by Hasmick Promotions. Catalogue no: **LPJT 75**
**Cass:** Released Feb '89, on Giants of Jazz by Hasmick Promotions. Catalogue no: **MCJT 75**

**JIMMY NOONE-VOL.1**
**Album:** Released Sep '86, on Swaggie (Australia) Catalogue no: **S 841**

**KINGS OF NEW ORLEANS (Noone, Jimmie & Bunk Johnson)**
**Cass:** Released '82, on Jazz Bird Catalogue no: **ZCJAZ 2018**
**Album:** Released Oct '86, on Avenue (USA) by Malaco Records (USA). Catalogue no: **1010**
**Album:** Released '82, on Jazz Bird Catalogue no: **JAZ 2018**

## Noone, Jimmie Jr

**JIMMY REMEMBERS JIMMIE**
Note: With John RT Davies
**Album:** Released Apr '88, on Stomp Off (USA) Catalogue no: **SOS 1121**

## Noren, Fredrik

**SNAKE, THE (Noren, Fredrik Band)**
**Album:** Released '88, on Phontastic (Sweden) Catalogue no: **PHONT 7551**

## Norfolk Jubilee

**1927-1938**
Tracks: / When the moon goes down / Moaning in the land / Wonder where the gambling man / When the train comes along / Believe in Jesus / Pure religion / Didn't it rain / No hiding place / Standing by the bedside / You got to live so God can use you / Way down in Egypt land / Jonah in the belly of a whale / Free at last / Jesus is making up my dying bed / Great changes to things I used to do / Beedle de beedle de bop bop.
**Album:** Released Jan '86, on Heritage by Interstate Music. Catalogue no: **HT 310**

## Norman, Gene

**GENE NORMAN'S JUST JAZZ CONCERTS**
Tracks: / Just you, just me / Perdido / Hot house / Groovin' high / Blue Lou / One o'clock jump / Lover / Body and soul / How high the moon / I got rhythm / Sweet Georgia Brown / C jam blues / Just bop / Yancey special / Swanee River boogie.
**LP Set:** Released Oct '80, on Vogue by Vogue Records. Catalogue no: **VJT 3003**

## Norris, Chuck

**LOS ANGELES FLASH, THE**
Tracks: / Los Angeles bounce / In the evening when the sun goes down / Shake, rattle and roll / Blues after hours / I know the blues / Chicken neck shuffle / See see rider / Everyday I have the blues / Honky tonk.
**Album:** Released Aug '87, on Stockholm (Sweden) Catalogue no: **RJ 201**

## Norris, Walter

**DRIFTING**
**Album:** Released Jan '82, on Enja (Germany) by Enja Records (West Germany). Catalogue no: **ENJA 2044**

**STEPPING ON CRACKS**
Tracks: / Stepping on cracks / Falling in love with love / Cherokee / Giant steps / Child is born, A.
**Album:** Released Nov '82, on Progressive (USA) by Jazzology Records (USA). Catalogue no: **PRO 7039**

**SYNCHRONICITY**
**Album:** Released Jan '82, on Enja (Germany) by Enja Records (West Germany). Catalogue no: **ENJA 3035**

**WINTER ROSE**
**Album:** Released Jan '82, on Enja (Germany) by Enja Records (West Germany). Catalogue no: **ENJA 3067**

## Norvo, Red

**1983 (Norvo, Red & His Orchestra)**
Note: With: Mildred Bailey/Terry Allen
**Album:** Released Jun '86, on Circle (USA) by Jazzology Records (USA). Catalogue no: **CLP 3**

**COLLECTIONS (Norvo, Red/Pepper, Art/Morello, Joe)**
**Album:** Released Feb '88, on Fresh Sounds (Spain) by Fresh Sounds Records (Spain). Catalogue no: **FS 224**

**JUST A MOOD**
Tracks: / Just a mood / Easy on the eye / Night is blue, The / Sunrise blues / Blue room / Blue moon / Serenade in blue / Blue Lou / Roses of Picardy / Rose room / Blue rose / Rose of the Rio Grande.
Note: Featuring small bands led by Norvo.
**CD:** Released Apr '88, on Bluebird (2) by BMG Records (UK). Catalogue no: **ND 86278**

**MISTER SWING**
**Album:** Released May '84, on Swing House by Submarine Records. Catalogue no: **SWH 16**

**NORVO - NATURALLY!**
Note: Red Norvo, Bob Drasnin, Jim Wyble, Buddy Clarke, Bill Douglas
**Album:** Released Apr '88, on VSOP Catalogue no: **VSOP 35**

**RED (Norvo, Red & His Orchestra)**
**Album:** Released '88, on Hep Jazz by Hep Records. Catalogue no: **HEP 1019**

**RED NORVO, CHARLES MINGO, TAL 1950-1 (Various artists)**
**Album:** Released '88, on Queen Catalogue no: **QUEEN 063**

**RED NORVO'S FABULOUS JAM SESSION**
Tracks: / Hallelujah - three takes / Congo blues - two excerpts, three complete takes / Slam slam blues - two takes.
Note: Featuring Charlie Parker, Dizzy Gillespie, Flip Phillips, Teddy Wilson.
**Album:** Released May '83, on Spotlite by Spotlite Records. Catalogue no: **SPJ 127**

**RED NORVO'S SWINGING BANDS**
Tracks: / Just you, just me / Which switch witch? / Bass on the bar room floor / NRC jump / Seven come eleven / Russian lullaby / Woody's tune / Seal it with a kiss / You ain't gonna bother me no more.
Note: Featuring Billie Holiday, Charlie Shavers, Teddy Wilson, Flip Phillips Peanuts Hucko. Recorded in the 1940's.
**Album:** Released Apr '81, on Rarities Catalogue no: **RARITIES 23**

**RED'S 'X' SESSIONS (Norvo, Red & His Orchestra)**
**Album:** Released Feb '88, on Fresh Sounds (Spain) by Fresh Sounds Records (Spain). Catalogue no: **FS 182**

**TOWN HALL CONCERT 1 (Norvo, Red & His Orchestra)**
**Album:** Released May '74, on London Records by London Records Ltd. Catalogue no: **HMC 5001**

## Now Creative Arts...

**NOW: CREATIVE ARTS JAZZ ENSEMBLE (Various artists)**
**Album:** Released May '81, on Arhoolie (USA) by Arhoolie Records (USA). Catalogue no: **ARHOOLIE 8002**

## Nucleus

**Biographical details:** At the time of their only UK chart entry, this British instrumental jazz-rock fusion band comprised Ian Carr, Jeff Clyne, Karl Jenkins, Jon Marshall, Brian Smith and Chris Spedding. Founded and led by trumpeter Carr, Nucleus were given a good launching by winning first prize at the Montreux International Festival in 1970. In that same year their debut album *Elastic Rock* reached No.46 on the British chart. The title was intended to signify the group's musical stance: rock should not adhere rigidly to its own form but should sometimes be prepared to merge with other styles. Along with Colosseum and Soft Machine, Nucleus were part of a wave of British jazz-rock bands whose members were drawn from both genres. Although Nucleus never returned to the British chart, they continued releasing albums on a regular basis from 1970 until 1980. Carr was the only constant factor in an often changing line-up and the outfit won considerable reputation for their highly improvised yet disciplined playing. Among their highlights were *We'll talk about it later*, the title track from their second LP (1970) and *Solar Plexus* (1971) which was the first rock record to be subsidised by the Arts Council -- there have veen very few such cases since. The final Nucleus album was *Awakening* (1980). Chris Spedding, who left Nucleus in '71, was one of Britain's most respected session guitarists of the 70's and enjoyed his own hit in '75 with *Motor Biking* (Bob MacDonald, February 1986.).

**NUCLEUS ELASTIC ROCK**
Tracks: / 1916 / Striation / Twisted track / Battle of the boogaloo / Personally, in my own opinion / Elastic rock / Taranaki / Creole blues / Speaking for myself / Persephones jive.
**Album:** Released Jul '70, on Vertigo by Phonogram Ltd. Deleted Jul '75. Catalogue no: **6360 006**
**Album:** Released May '89, on Beat Goes On by Andy's Records. Catalogue no: **BGOLP 47**

**WE'LL TALK ABOUT IT LATER**
**Album:** Released Jan '70, on Vertigo by Phonogram Ltd. Catalogue no: **6360 027**

# O

The following information was taken from the Music Master database on April 14th, 1990.

## Oakland Blues

**OAKLAND BLUES (Various artists)**
**Album:** Released May '81, on Arhoolie (USA) by Arhoolie Records (USA). Catalogue no: **ARHOOLIE 2008**

## O'Brien, Tim

**HARD YEAR BLUES**
**Album:** Released Mar '89, on Flying Fish (USA) by Flying Fish Records (USA). Catalogue no: **FF 319**

**TAKE ME BACK**
**Album:** Released Mar '89, on Sugar Hill (USA) Catalogue no: **SH 3766**

## O'Day, Anita

**ANITA O'DAY 1975**
**CD:** Released Feb '90, on Storyville by Storyville Records AB. Catalogue no: **STCD 4147**

**ANITA O'DAY 1949-50**
**Album:** Released Mar '90, on Tono Catalogue no: **TJ6003**

**ANITA O'DAY LIVE AT RONNIE SCOTTS**
**CD:** Released Dec '87, on Hendring Catalogue no: **HEN 6040 Y**
**CD:** Released Apr '87, on Hendring Catalogue no: **WHCD 005**

**ANITA O'DAY LIVE AT RONNIE SCOTTS (VIDEO)**
**VHS:** Released '88, on Castle Hendring Video by Castle Communications Records. Catalogue no: **HEN 2 040 G**

**ANITA SINGS THE MOST**
Tracks: / 'S wonderful / They can't take that away from me / Old devil moon / Love me or leave me / We'll be together again / Stella by starlight / Taking a chance on love / Them there eyes / I've got the world on a string / You turned the tables on me / Bewitched, bothered and bewildered.
Note: Anita O'Day singing eleven great standards with accompaniment from Oscar Peterson, Herb Ellis, Ray Brown and John Poole. Recorded January 1957 and digitally remastered directly from the original mono master tape.
**CD:** Released Oct '86, on Verve (USA) by Polydor Ltd. Catalogue no: **829 577-2**

**BIG BAND SESSIONS**
Tracks: / Up state / Night bird / Ballad of the sad young men / It had to be you / Hershey bar / Come rain or shine / Easy come, easy go / You're a clown / Don't explain / I hear music / Crazy he calls me / Ten cents a dance / Have you met Miss Jones / Get out of town / I get a kick out of you / Johnny one note.
**2 LP Set:** Released '79, on Verve Deleted '84. Catalogue no: **2632083**

**HIGH STANDARDS**
**Cass:** Released Jan '89, on DRG (USA) by DRG Records (USA). Catalogue no: **SLC 5209**
**Album:** Released Jan '89, on DRG (USA) by DRG Records (USA). Catalogue no: **SL 5209**
**CD:** Released Jan '89, on DRG (USA) by DRG Records (USA). Catalogue no: **CDSL 5209**

**LEGENDARY, THE (Vol. 2)**
**Album:** Released Dec '87, on Glendale (USA) by Glendale Records (USA). Catalogue no: **GLS 6001**

**MELLO DAY**
**Album:** Released '88, on GNP Crescendo (USA) by GNP Crescendo Records (USA). Catalogue no: **GNPS 2126**

**ONCE UPON A SUMMERTIME**
**Album:** Released Dec '87, on Glendale (USA) by Glendale Records (USA). Catalogue no: **GLS 6000**
**Cass:** Released '89, on Jasmine by Hasmick Promotions. Catalogue no: **JASMC 2531**
**Album:** Released '89, on Jasmine by Hasmick Promotions. Catalogue no: **JASM 2531**

**PICK YOURSELF UP**
Tracks: / Don't be that way / Let's face the music and dance / I never had a chance / Stompin' at the Savoy / Pick yourself up / Stars fell on Alabama / Sweet Georgia Brown / I won't dance / Man with a horn / I used to be color blind / There's a lull in my life / Let's begin.
**Album:** Released Dec '88, on Official by Official Records. Catalogue no: **OFF 3015**

**SINGS THE WINNERS**
Tracks: / Take the 'A' train / Tenderly / Night in Tunisia / Four / Early autumn / Four brothers / Sing, sing, sing / My funny valentine / Frenesi / Body and soul / What's your story, morning glory? / Peanut vendor.
**Album:** Released Mar '82, on Verve (USA) by Polydor Ltd. Catalogue no: **2304 255**

**TRAVELLIN' LIGHT**
Tracks: / Travellin' light / Moon looks down and laughs / God bless the child / If the moon turns green / I hear music / Lover come back to me / Crazy, he calls me / Miss Brown to you / Don't explain / Remember / Some other spring / What a little moonlight can do.
Note: Anita O'Day, vocals; Ben Webster, tenor sax; Don Fagerquist, trumpet; Jimmy Rowles, piano; Barney Kessel, guitar; Buddy Clarke, bass; Mel Lewis, drums. Recorded in 1961.
**Album:** Released Mar '83, on Verve (USA) by Polydor Ltd. Catalogue no: **2304 584**

**WAVE (Live at Ronnie Scott's)**
Tracks: / Wave / You'd be so nice to come home to / On Green Dolphin street / I can't get started / It don't mean a thing if it aint got that swin / Street of dreams,The / 'S wonderful / They can't take that away from me / Is you is or is you aint my baby / My funny valentine / I cried for you / Four brothers / Wave.
**Cass:** Released Feb '90, on Essential by Castle Communications Records. Catalogue no: **ESMMC 019**
**CD:** Released Feb '90, on Essential by Castle Communications Records. Catalogue no: **ESMCD 019**

## Odenhall, Staffan

**BIG EARS BIG BAND**
**Album:** Released Apr '89, on Dragon by Dragon Records. Catalogue no: **DRLP 144**

## Odetta

**ESSENTIAL, THE**
**Cass set:** Released Sep '89, on Start by Start Records Ltd.. Catalogue no: **MCCVSD 43/44**
**CD Set:** Released Sep '89, on Start by Start Records Ltd.. Catalogue no: **CDVCD 43/44**
**2 LP Set:** Released Sep '89, on Start by Start Records Ltd.. Catalogue no: **LPVSD 43/44**

**IT'S IMPOSSIBLE**
**Album:** Released '78, on Four Leaf Clover Catalogue no: **FLC 5007**

**ODETTA AND THE BLUES**
Tracks: / Hard, oh Lord / Believe I'll go / Oh papa / How long blues / Hogan's alley / Leavin' this mornin' / Oh, my babe / Yonder come the blues / Make me a pallet on the floor / Weeping willow blues / Go down sunshine / Nobody knows you (when you're down and out).
**Album:** Released Jun '84, on Prestige Catalogue no: **OBC 509**

## Okay Temiz Trio

**DERVISH SERVICE**
**CD:** Released Nov '89, on Sonet by Sonet Records. Catalogue no: **SNCD 1020**
**Album:** Released Nov '89, on Sonet by Sonet Records. Catalogue no: **SNTF 1020**

**TURKISH FOLK JAZZ**
Tracks: / Taksim / Introduction / Batum / Ulah-Balkan / Doktur / Kurt Havasi /

Madimak / Uskudar / Anadolu Havasi / Trabzon karsilamasi.
**Album:** Released '87, on Sonet by Sonet Records. Catalogue no: **SNTF 668**

## Old...

**OLD COUNTRY BLUES (Various artists)**
**Album:** Released Apr '79, on Flyright by Interstate Music. Catalogue no: **FLY 537**

## Old Time...

**OLD TIME BLUES VOL.1 (Various artists)**
Tracks: / Chicken hop: *Various artists* / Climbing on top of the hill: *Various artists* / Uncle Bud: *Various artists* / Slider: *Various artists* / She loves so easy: *Various artists* / I need a woman: *Various artists* / Confusing: *Various artists* / Crazy 'bout you baby: *Various artists* / Love's a disease: *Various artists* / Sweet sweet woman: *Various artists* / Reap what you sew: *Various artists* / Word out: *Various artists* / Sweet little girl: *Various artists* / Playboy: *Various artists* / Hard luck baby: *Various artists* / Let the doorbell ring: *Various artists.*
**Album:** Released Jun '86, on Ace by Ace Records. Deleted Jan '90. Catalogue no: **CH 180**

**OLD TIME JAZZ FOREVER (Various artists)**
**Album:** Released May '87, on Wam Catalogue no: **WAM/S No.455123**

**OLD TIME JAZZBAND**
Note: Reine Rimon with New Orleansians.
**Album:** Released Feb '87, on 504 Catalogue no: **504 LPS 15**

**REINE RIMON IN NEW ORLEANS**
**Album:** Released '88, on 504 Catalogue no: **LPS 15**

## Oliver, King

**1923 (Oliver, King & His Creole Jazz Band)**
**Album:** Released Jan '83, on Swaggie (Australia) Catalogue no: **S 1257**

**1923-30**
**Album:** Released Sep '87, on Giants of Jazz by Hasmick Promotions. Catalogue no: **LPJT 21**

**CHIMES BLUES**
**Album:** Released Sep '85, on Saar Giants Of Jazz (Italy) Catalogue no: **LPJT 21**
**Cass:** Released Sep '85, on Saar Giants Of Jazz (Italy) Catalogue no: **MCJT 21**

**CLASSIC JAZZ (Oliver, King & His Creole Jazz Band)**
**Album:** Released May '88, on Classic Jazz Masters Catalogue no: **22023**
**Cass:** Released May '88, on Classic Jazz Masters Catalogue no: **42023**

**CREOLE JAZZ BAND (Oliver, King & His Creole Jazz Band)**
Tracks: / Alligator hop / I'm going away to wear you off my mind / Froggie Moore / Snake rag / Chimes blues / Just gone / Canal street blues / Mandy Lee blues / Weather bird rag / Dippermouth blues / Krooked blues.
**Album:** Released '87, on Joker (USA) by Lifetime Records (USA). Catalogue no: **SM 3089**

**FAREWELL BLUES (1926-7)**
**Album:** Released Apr '81, on Joker (USA) by Lifetime Records (USA). Catalogue no: **SM 3809**

**FRANKIE & JOHNNY (1926-7)**
**Album:** Released Apr '81, on Joker (USA) by Lifetime Records (USA). Catalogue no: **SM 3811**

**GENNETT SIDES OF APRIL AND OCTOBER, 1923 (Oliver, King & His Creole Jazz Band)**
Tracks: / Just gone / Canal Street blues / Mandy Lee blues / I'm going away to wear you off my mind / Chimes blues / Weather bird rag / Dippermouth blues / Froggie Moore / Snake rag / Alligator hop / Zulus' ball / Working man blues / Krooked blues.
**Album:** Released Oct '81, on Rhapsody by President Records. Catalogue no: **RHA 6023**

**HOMETOWN BLUES**
Tracks: / Kiss me sweet / Construction gang / Home town blues / Sorrow valley blues / Empty bed blues (part 1) / Empty bed blues (part 2) / You're such a cruel papa to me / My diff'rent kind of man / My handy man / Organ grinder blues / I'm busy and you can't come in / Jeannine / In the bottle blues / What do you want me to do / Blue blood blues.
**Album:** Released Mar '87, on Rhapsody by President Records. Catalogue no: **RHA 6032**

**I'M CRAZY 'BOUT MY BABY**
**Album:** Released Apr '81, on Joker (USA) by Lifetime Records (USA). Catalogue no: **SM 3812**

**KING OLIVER 1929-30**
**Album:** Released Jan '88, on Family Catalogue no: **SFR DP 657**
**Album:** Released Oct '86, on Classic Jazz Masters Catalogue no: **CJM 19**

**KING OLIVER AND HIS ORCHESTRA (Oliver, King & his Orchestra)**
**2 LP Set:** Released '83, on RCA (France) by BMG Records (France). Catalogue no: **PM 42411**

**KING OLIVER COLLECTION (20 golden greats)**
Tracks: / Don't you think I love you? / Trumpet's prayer / Too late / My good man, Sam / New Orleans shout / Rhythm club stomp / Frankie and Johnny / Boogie woogie / Can I tell you ? / Olga / I'm lonesome, sweetheart / You're just my type / West End blues / Nelson stomp / I must have it / What you want me to do? / Mule face blues / Sweet like this / St. James' Infirmary / I can't stop loving you.
**Album:** Released Jan '87, on Deja Vu Catalogue no: **DVLP 2085**
**Cass:** Released Jan '87, on Deja Vu Catalogue no: **DVMC 2085**

**KING OLIVER & HIS DIXIE 1SYNCOPATORS 1926**
**Album:** Released '88, on Swaggie (Australia) Catalogue no: **S 821**

**KING OLIVER & HIS DIXIE 1SYNCOPATORS 1926-28**
**Album:** Released '88, on Swaggie (Australia) Catalogue no: **S 282**

**KING OLIVER & HIS DIXIE 1SYNCOPATORS 1926-28 VOL. 2**
**Album:** Released '88, on Swaggie (Australia) Catalogue no: **S 823**

**KING OLIVER & HIS ORCHESTRA 1929-30**
Tracks: / West end blues / I've got that thing / Call of the freaks, The / Trumpet's prayer / Freakish light blues / Can I tell you? / My good man Sam / What you want me to do / Sweet like this / Too late / I'm lonesome, sweetheart / I want you just myself / I can't stop loving you / Everybody does it in Hawaii / Frankie and Johnny / New Orleans shout / St. James Infirmary / I must have it / Rhythm club stomp / You're just my type / Edna / Boogie woogie / Mule face blues / Struggle bunny / Don't you think I love you / Olga / Shake it and break it / Stingaree blues / What's the use of living without you / You were only passing time with me / Nelson stomp / Stealing.
Note: Double album. Double cassette. Mono.
**Album:** Released Sep '86, on Jazz Tribune by BMG Records (UK). Deleted May '89. Catalogue no: **NL 89770**
**Cass:** Released Sep '86, on Jazz Tribune by BMG Records (UK). Deleted May '89. Catalogue no: **NK 89770**

**KING OLIVER VOL. 1 1928 & 31**
**Album:** Released '88, on CJM by Wellard Dist.. Catalogue no: **CJM 21**

**KING OLIVER'S CREOLE JAZZ BAND (1923)**
**Album:** Released Oct '88, on VJM (Vintage Jazz Music) by Vintage Jazz Music Society(VJM). Catalogue no: **VLP 49**

**OKEH SESSIONS,THE (Oliver, King & His Creole Jazz Band)**
Tracks: / Snake rag / My sweet lovin' man / High society rag / Sobbin' blues / Where did you stay last night / Dipper mouth blues / Jazzin' babies blues / Buddy's habits / Tears / I ain't gonna tell nobody / Room rent blues / Sweet baby doll / Working man blues / Mabel's dream.
**Cass:** Released Jun '85, on Retrospect by EMI Records. Deleted Nov '88. Catalogue no: **EG 2605794**

**Album:** Released Apr '80, on World by World Records. Deleted '85. Catalogue no: **SH 358**
**Album:** Released Jun '85, on Retrospect by EMI Records. Deleted Nov '88. Catalogue no: **EG 2605791**

**SNAG IT**
**Album:** Released Jan '88, on Family Catalogue no: **SFR DP 696**

**SNAG IT (1926-7)**
**Album:** Released Apr '81, on Joker (USA) by Lifetime Records (USA). Catalogue no: **SM 3808**

**SWEET LIKE THIS**
Tracks: / West end blues / I've got that thing / Call of the freaks, The / Trumpet's prayer / Freakish light blues / Can I tell you? / My good man Sam / What you want me to do? / Sweet like this / Too late / I'm lonesome sweetheart / I want you just myself / I can't stop loving you / New Orleans shout / Everybody does it in Hawaii / Frankie and Johnny / St. James' infirmary / When you're smiling.
**Album:** Released Feb '87, on Halcyon (USA) by Submarine Records. Catalogue no: **HDL 106**
**Cass:** Released Feb '87, on Halcyon (USA) by Submarine Records. Catalogue no: **CHDL 106**

**WEST END BLUES 1929**
**Album:** Released Apr '81, on Joker (USA) by Lifetime Records (USA). Catalogue no: **SM 3810**

## Oliver, Sy

**ANNE LAURIE**
**Album:** Released Oct '88, on Vogue by Vogue Records. Catalogue no: **500069**

**EASY WALKER**
**Album:** Released Oct '88, on Vogue by Vogue Records. Catalogue no: **500085**

**JULY 7TH 1960 & OCTOBER 18TH 1962**
Tracks: / I've been working on the railroad / I like you / Old time religion / Mixed doubles / Five flats furnished / Lazy / Easy walker / Oh them golden slippers / This is love / Blue tail fly, The / I'll fly away / Intermezzo / I found the one I love.
**Album:** Released Oct '80, on Jazz Vault Catalogue no: **JV 105**

**SENTIMENTAL SY**
Tracks: / On the sunny side of the street / Then I'll be happy / Stardust / Without a song / Yes indeed / Opus one / We'll git it / Chicago / East of the sun / Blue skies / For you / Swanee river.
**Album:** Released Oct '84, on Jasmine by Hasmick Promotions. Catalogue no: **JASM 1513**

## Olsson, Kvintetten

**LATT PA SNE (Also featuring The Olsson Quintet)**
Tracks: / Det ska vi sjunga / Fridolins darskap / Greensleeves / Om Beethoven / Inte ens en gra litne fagel / Vilse / Liten froken vid himlaporten / Balladen om herr Rosenbloms speleman / Yesterday / Sa lunka vi sa smaning om / Dixie / Per spelman / Trad fram du nattens gud / Varkonsert / Nu tror vi det kan vara tid.
**Album:** Released '82, on Phontastic (Sweden) Catalogue no: **PHONT 7524**

## Olympia Brass Band

**NOLA SINGLES ALBUM**
Note: with Jim Duggan, Lee Allen
**Cass:** Released Mar '87, on Nola Catalogue no: **TC 025**

**OLYMPIA BRASS BAND**
**Album:** Released Sep '79, on Nola Catalogue no: **NOLA LP 4**

**OLYMPIA BRASS BAND OF NEW ORLEANS, THE**
**Album:** Released Aug '88, on Audiophile (USA) by Jazzology Records (USA). Catalogue no: **AP 108**

## Omnibus Big Band

**MEMORIES OF YOU (Omnibus Big Band & Putte Wickman)**
**Album:** Released Jul '87, on Dragon by Dragon Records. Catalogue no: **DRLP 122**

## One Hundred Minutes

**100 MINUTES OF BIG BAND MEDLEYS (Various artists)**
**Cass:** Released Nov '85, on PRT by Castle Communications Records. Catalogue no: **ZCTON 8175**

**100 MINUTES OF BLUES (Various artists)**
**Cass:** Released Nov '83, on PRT (100 Minute Series) Catalogue no: **ZCTON 128**

**100 MINUTES OF TRAD JAZZ (Various artists)**
**Cass:** Released Nov '85, on PRT by Castle Communications Records. Catalogue no: **ZCTON 8172**

## One Night With...

**ONE NIGHT WITH BLUE NOTE VOL 1 (Various artists)**
Tracks: / Canterloupe island: *Various artists* / Recoda me: *Various artists* / Little B's room: *Various artists* / Bouquet: *Various artists* / Hat and beard: *Various artists.*
**Album:** Released Aug '85, on Blue Note by EMI Records. Deleted Jan '88. Catalogue no: **BT 85113**

**ONE NIGHT WITH BLUE NOTE VOL 2 (Various artists)**
Tracks: / Sweet and lovely: *Various artists* / Appointment in Ghana: *Various artists* / Passion dance: *Various artists* / Blues on the corner: *Various artists* / Pontos cantados: *Various artists* / Broadside: *Various artists.*
**Album:** Released Aug '85, on Blue Note by EMI Records. Deleted Jan '88. Catalogue no: **BT 85114**

**ONE NIGHT WITH BLUE NOTE VOL 3 (Various artists)**
Tracks: / Moanin': *Various artists* / Child is born: *Various artists* / Jumpin' blues: *Various artists* / Summertime: *Various artists* / I'm glad there is you: *Various artists* / Blues walk: *Various artists* / Getting setimnental over you: *Various artists.*
**Album:** Released Aug '85, on Blue Note by EMI Records. Deleted Jul '87. Catalogue no: **BT 85115**

**ONE NIGHT WITH BLUE NOTE VOL 4 (Various artists)**
Tracks: / Blessing: *Various artists* / Tone poem: *Various artists* / Lady lay: *Various artists* / El encanto: *Various artists* / How long: *Various artists* / Jumpin' jack: *Various artists* / When you wish upon a star: *Various artists.*
**Album:** Released Aug '85, on Blue Note by EMI Records. Deleted Jan '88. Catalogue no: **BT 85116**

## Ophelia Ragtime

**ECHOES FROM THE SNOWBALL CLUB**
**Album:** Released Sep '86, on Stomp Off (USA) Catalogue no: **SOS 1108**

## Organ Boogie Woogie

**ORGAN BOOGIE WOOGIE (Various artists)**
**Cass:** Released Aug '84, on CBS (I love Jazz) by CBS Records. Catalogue no: **40 21079**
**Album:** Released Aug '84, on CBS (I love Jazz) by CBS Records. Catalogue no: **CBS 21079**

## Original...

**ORIGINAL CLASSICS: DOO WOP HITS (Various artists)**
**Cass:** Released Oct '85, on Vogue by Vogue Records. Catalogue no: **722 020**
**Album:** Released Oct '85, on Vogue by Vogue Records. Catalogue no: **522 020**

**ORIGINAL RHYTHM'N'BLUES (Various artists)**
**Cass:** Released Oct '85, on Chess (France) by Vogue Records. Catalogue no: **722 017**
**Album:** Released Oct '85, on Chess (France) by Vogue Records. Catalogue no: **522 017**

**ORIGINAL SOUND OF THE TWENTIES (Various artists)**
Tracks: / Blue room: *Venuti, Joe & His Blue Four* / St. Louis blues: *Armstrong, Louis/his orchestra* / Varsity drag: *Hagan, Cass & His Park Central Hotel Orch.* / Alexander's ragtime band: *Lewis, Ted / his orchestra* / Black and blue: *Ethel Waters* / Am I blue: *Aunt Jemima (Tess Gardella)* / Bill: *Young, Victor* / Man I love, The: *Whiteman, Paul & His Orchestra* / Nobody's sweetheart: *Whiteman, Paul & His Orchestra* / Rhythm king: *Whiteman, Paul & Rhythm Boys* / Someone to watch over me: *Gershwin (Composer)* / Home on the range: *Sims, Lee* / Can't we be friends: *Various artists.*
Note: Mono.
**Cass:** Released Mar '86, on CBS by CBS Records. Deleted Aug '87. Catalogue no: **40 32741**
**Album:** Released Mar '86, on CBS by CBS Records. Deleted Aug '87. Catalogue no: **CBS 32741**

**ORIGINAL USA FOLK BLUES FESTIVAL (Various artists)**

**CD:** on Polydor by Polydor Ltd. Cata-

## Original 5 Blind Boys

**PRECIOUS MEMORIES**
**Album:** Released Jun '84, on MCA (USA) by MCA Records (USA). Catalogue no: **MCA 28002**

## Original Camelia

**ORIGINAL CAMELIA JAZZ BAND (Original Camelia Jazz Band)**
**Album:** Released Sep '86, on New Orleans Catalogue no: **NOR 7207**

## Original Dixieland...

**1943 (Original Dixieland Jazz Band)**
Note: Mono.
**Album:** Released Jun '86, on GHB by Jazzology Records (USA). Catalogue no: **GHB 100**

**DIXIELAND (Original Dixieland Stompers)**
Note: Including: When the saints go marching in, C.C.Rider, Tell it to the mountains etc.
**CD:** Released '86, on Delta (1) by Delta Records. Catalogue no: **11 012**

**NUMBER TWO BLUES (Original Dixieland Jazz Band)**
Note: with Johnny DeDroit.
**Album:** Released Jan '88, on Gaps Catalogue no: **GAPS 190**

**ORIGINAL DIXIELAND JAZZ BAND (Original Dixieland Jazz Band & Louisiana Five)**
**Album:** Released Apr '79, on Fountain by Retrieval Records. Catalogue no: **FJ 101**

**ORIGINAL DIXIELAND JAZZ BAND REVISITED (Original Dixieland Jazz Band)**
**Album:** Released Apr '79, on Rarities Catalogue no: **RARITIES 36**

**SENSATION (Original Dixieland Jazz Band)**
Tracks: / Livery stable blues / Sensation rag / Dixie jazz band one-step / That teasin' rag / Tiger rag / Bluein' the blues / Fidgety feet / Clarinet marmalade blues / Lazy daddy / At the Jazz Band Ball / Look at 'em doing it / Ostrich walk / Satanic blues / 'Lasses candy / Tell me / I've got my captain working for me now / Mammy o'mine / I've lost my heart in Dixieland / Margie / Singing the blues.
**CD:** Released Oct '88, on Living Era by Academy Sound & Vision Records. Catalogue no: **CD AJA 5023**
**Album:** Released 1 Jun '83, on Living Era by Academy Sound & Vision Records. Catalogue no: **AJA 5023**
**Cass:** Released 1 Jun '83, on Living Era by Academy Sound & Vision Records. Catalogue no: **ZC AJA 5023**

## Original Jazz Hounds

**ORIGINAL JAZZ HOUNDS & GULF COAST 7**
**Album:** Released Apr '79, on VJM (Vintage Jazz Music) by Vintage Jazz Music Society(VJM). Catalogue no: **VLP 45**

## Original Memphis..

**ORIGINAL MEMPHIS BLUES BROTHERS, THE (Various artists)**
Tracks: / Good lovin': *Bland, Bobby* / Dry up baby: *Bland, Bobby* / Crying all night long: *Bland, Bobby* / Drifting from town to town (take 1): *Bland, Bobby* / Drifting from town to town (take 2): *Bland, Bobby* / Love me baby: *Bland, Bobby & Junior Parker* / You're my angel: *Parker, Junior & the Blue Flames* / Bad women: *Parker, Junior & the Blue Flames* / Whole heap of mama: *Forrest, Earl* / I wronged a woman: *Forrest, Earl* / Sad and lonely: *Forrest, Earl* / Trouble and me: *Forrest, Earl* / I can't forgive you: *Forrest, Earl* / Rumpus romp: *Forrest, Earl* / Midnight hours journey: *Ace, Johnny* / I cried: *Ace, Johnny*.
**Album:** Released 2 May '89, on Ace by Ace Records. Catalogue no: **CHD 265**

## Original Ramblers

**ORIGINAL RAMBLERS (Theo Uden Masman)**
Note: featuring Coleman Hawkins.
**Album:** Released Jan '88, on R.F.C. Catalogue no: **RFC 100**

## Original Salty Dogs

**DOWN IN HONKY TONKY TOWN**
**Album:** Released Mar '87, on Stomp Off (USA) Catalogue no: **SOS 1115**

**RHYTHM KINGS ON THE RIGHT TRACK**
**Album:** Released Jun '88, on GHB by Jazzology Records (USA). Catalogue no: **GHB 62**

## Original Soul Stirrers

**DEVINE LOVE**
**Album:** Released '88, on Malaco Gospel by Malaco Records (UK). Catalogue no: **MAL 043 84**

**NOBODY'S CHILD**
**Album:** Released '88, on Malaco by Malaco Records (UK). Catalogue no: **MGS 4369**

## Ornberg, Tomas

**COME BACK, SWEET PAPA (Ornbergs, Tomas Blue Five)**
**Album:** Released '88, on Stomp Off (USA) Catalogue no: **SOS 1043**

## Orpheon Celesta

**LA GARE DE LYON**
**Album:** Released '88, on Stomp Off (USA) Catalogue no: **SOS 1083**

**ORPHEON CELESTA VOLUME 2**
**Album:** Released Jun '86, on Stomp Off (USA) Catalogue no: **SOS 1095**

## Ory, Kid

**1944 - 1945 (Ory, Kid & His Creole Jazz Band)**
Note: Mono.
**Album:** Released Oct '86, on Folklyric (USA) by Arhoolie Records (USA). Catalogue no: **FL 9008**

**1955 (Kid Ory's creole jazz band)**
Tracks: / Savoy blues / Good man is hard to find / Closer walk with thee / Shake that thing / Copenhagen / Royal garden blues / Mississippi mud / Tin roof blues / Indiana.
**Album:** Released '82, on Good Time Jazz(USA) by Fantasy Inc (USA). Catalogue no: **1012008**

**AT CLUB HANGOVER VOL. 6 (Ory, Kid & His Creole Jazz Band)**
**Album:** Released Jan '88, on Storyville by Storyville Records AB. Catalogue no: **SLP 4070**

**AT THE JAZZBAND BALL (Live in concert) (Ory, Kid & His Creole Jazz Band)**
Tracks: / Panama rag / At the jazz band ball / Peoria / Basin Street blues / St. James Infirmary blues / Wolverine blues / Savoy blues / Tin roof blues / That's a plenty / Aunt Hagar's blues.
**Album:** Released Jan '87, on Rhapsody by President Records. Catalogue no: **RHA 6034**

**ECHOES FROM NEW ORLEANS**
**CD:** Released Mar '90, on Giants of Jazz by Hasmick Promotions. Catalogue no: **GOJCD53037**
**CD:** Released Sep '88, on Giants of Jazz by Hasmick Promotions. Catalogue no: **CD 53037**

**GREATEST (Kid Ory's creole jazz band)**
Tracks: / South rampart street parade / Girls go crazy, The / How come you do me like you do / Four or five times / St. James infirmary / Bill Bailey / Milenberg joys / Creole song / Bucket's got a hole in it / Creole love call / Ballin' the jack / Aunt Hagar's blues.
**Album:** Released Jan '84, on Good Time Jazz(USA) by Fantasy Inc (USA). Deleted Jan '89. Catalogue no: **1012 045**

**KID ORY AT THE BEVERLY CAVERN (That's all, folks!)**
**Album:** Released Jul '88, on Sounds Catalogue no: **SOUNDS 1208**

**KID ORY & CREOLE BAND AT DIXIELAND JUBILEE (Ory, Kid & His Creole Jazz Band)**
**Album:** Released '88, on Dixieland Jubilee (USA) by GNP Crescendo Records (USA). Catalogue no: **DJA 519**

**KID ORY & CREOLE JAZZBAND (Ory, Kid & His Creole Jazz Band)**
Note: Featuring Don Ewell, Barney Kessell.
**Album:** Released Sep '87, on Giants of Jazz by Hasmick Promotions. Catalogue no: **LPJT 48**

**KID ORY FAVOURITES**
**CD:** Released Apr '87, on London Records by London Records Ltd. Catalogue no: **FCD 60009**

**KID ORY PLAYS THE BLUES**
Tracks: / Savoy blues / Snag it / Royal Garden blues / Yellow dog blues.
Note: Tracks include those listed above.
**Album:** Released Aug '83, on Storyville by Storyville Records AB. Catalogue no: **SLP 4064**

**KID ORY'S CREOLE BAND**
Tracks: / Original Dixieland one-step / I wish I were in Peoria / Careless love / Won't you come home Bill Bailey / St. James Infirmary / That's a plenty.
**Album:** Released '81, on Queendisc (Italy) Catalogue no: **QU 052**

**KID ORY'S CREOLE JAZZ BAND**
**Album:** Released Sep '81, on Good Time Jazz(USA) by Fantasy Inc (USA). Catalogue no: **1012 004**

**KID ORY'S CREOLE JAZZ BAND 1955**
Tracks: / Savoy blues / Good man is hard to find, A / Closer walk with thee, A / Shake that thing / Copenhagen / Royal Garden blues / Missipi mud / Tin roof blues / Indiana.
**Album:** Released Apr '82, on Contemporary (Import) Catalogue no: **1012 008**

**LIVE AT CLUB HANGOVER VOL.1 (Ory, Kid & His Creole Jazz Band)**
**Album:** Released Dec '86, on Dawn Club by Cadillac Music. Catalogue no: **DC 12013**

**LIVE AT CLUB HANGOVER VOL.2 (Ory, Kid & His Creole Jazz Band)**
**Album:** Released Jun '79, on Dawn Club by Cadillac Music. Catalogue no: **DC 12014**

**LIVE AT CLUB HANGOVER VOL.3 (Ory, Kid & His Creole Jazz Band)**
**Album:** Released Jun '79, on Dawn Club by Cadillac Music. Catalogue no: **DC 12016**

**LIVE AT CLUB HANGOVER VOL.4 (Ory, Kid & His Creole Jazz Band)**
**Album:** Released Jun '79, on Dawn Club by Cadillac Music. Catalogue no: **DC 12017**

**MERCURY THEATRE, L.A., BROADCASTS (Ory, Kid & Jimmy Noone)**
Tracks: / High Society / Muskrat ramble / That's a plenty / Panama rag / Sugar foot stomp / Jimmy's blues / Savoy blues / Weary blues / Kid Ory Creole Jazz Band blues.
**Album:** Released Apr '81, on Joker (USA) by Lifetime Records (USA). Catalogue no: **SM 3085**

**NEW ORLEANS (Ory, Kid & His Creole Jazz Band)**
Tracks: / Savoy blues / Creole song / Glory of love / Mahogany Hall stomp / Blues for Jimmy / At a Georgia camp meeting / Go back where you stayed last night / Yaaka hula hickey dula / Tiger rag / My bucket's got a hole in it / Eh la bas / Joshua fit de battle of Jerico / World's jazz crazy / Lawdy so am I / Farewell to Storyville / Creole bo bo / Bill Bailey, won't you please come home?.
**Cass:** Released May '83, on CBS by CBS Records. Catalogue no: **40 21061**
**Album:** Released May '83, on CBS by CBS Records. Deleted Aug '87. Catalogue no: **CBS 21061**

**NEW ORLEANS JUBILEE (Ory, Kid & His Creole Jazz Band)**
Tracks: / Fanfare / Maryland / Milenberg joys / Muskrat ramble / 12th street rag / Eh la bas / Blues for Jimmy Noone / St. Louis blues / Tiger rag.
**CD:** Released '86, on Vogue by Vogue Records. Catalogue no: **VGCD 600045**

**SONG OF THE WANDERER**
Tracks: / Song of the wanderer / Tailgate ramble / Mahogany Hall stomp / Baby won't you please come home? / St. Louis blues / Toot toot tootsie / Sheik of Araby, The / Tiger rag.
Note: Recorded in 1957.
**Album:** Released May '82, on Verve Catalogue no: **2304 542**

**THIS KID'S THE GREATEST (Ory, Kid & His Creole Jazz Band)**
Tracks: / South Rampart street parade / Girls go crazy, The / How come you do me like you do / Four or five times / St. James infirmary / Bill Bailey / Milneberg joys / Creole song / Bucket's got a hole in it / Creole love call / Ballin' the Jack / Aunt Hagar's blues.
**Album:** Released Nov '83, on Contemporary (Import) Catalogue no: **1012 045**

**WE'VE GOT RHYTHM (Ory, Kid & Red Allen)**
**Album:** Released Jun '81, on Verve (USA) by Polydor Ltd. Catalogue no: **2304 504**

## Osborne, Mike

**ALL NIGHT LONG (Osborne's, Mike Trio)**
**Album:** Released '88, on Ogun by Cadillac Music. Catalogue no: **OG 700**

**BORDER CROSSING**
**Album:** Released '88, on Ogun by Cadillac Music. Catalogue no: **OG 300**

**MARCEL'S MOUSE (Osborne, Mike Quintet)**
**Album:** Released '88, on Ogun by Cadillac Music. Catalogue no: **OG 810**

## Osborne, Will

**1936 (Osborne, Will & His Orchestra)**
**Album:** Released Mar '84, on Hindsight Catalogue no: **HSR 197**

**HALLELUJAH (Osborne, Will & His Orchestra)**
**Album:** Released Jul '82, on Golden Era by Delta Records. Catalogue no: **GELP 15035**

**WILL OSBORNE ON THE AIR (Osborne, Will & His Orchestra)**
Tracks: / Gentleman awaits, The / Charming little faker / Let there be love / Way back in 1939 AD / It was written in the stars / Tales from the Vienna Woods / Leanin' on the old top rail / Out of the mood / Little fox, The / Missouri scrambler / Imagination / Mr. Jackson Alexander Wolcott Brown / Too romantic / Bolero my dream / Tuxedo Junction.
**Album:** Released Feb '88, on Aircheck (USA) by Kiner Ents.(USA). Catalogue no: **AIRCHECK 37**

## Otis, Johnny

**Biographical details:** This American band leader, drummer, pianist, vibraphonist, songwriter and singer has often been described as the Godfather of Rhythm-and-Blues. This predominantly black music was championed by the white Otis, son of Greek immigrant parents. He was born in California in 1921, his real surname being Veliotes. Initially inspired by big band jazz, he built up his instrumental skills during his teens and twenties. After forming his own 16-piece swing ensemble, Otis chalked up his first national US hit in 1946 with *Harlem Nocturne*. After touring with such names as Nat King Cole, The Ink Spots and Louis Jordan, he arrived in Los Angeles in 1948 to open the city's first club devoted entirely to R&B. While running the Barrelhouse Club, he discovered two important talents: Little Esther, the 13-year-old prodigy who was later known as Esther Phillips, and the Robins, who evolved into the Coasters. As a duo, Little Esther and Johnny Otis achieved five Top 10 singles on the American R&B charts during 1950.

Also during the early Fifties, Otis pioneered the phenomenon that really made his name. He set in motion a multi-artist touring revue that was dubbed The Johnny Otis R&B Caravan; it was later called the Johnny Otis Show. This became the top showcase for rhythm-and-blues music during the Fifties. It gave a boost to the early careers of many of the genre's top artists including Johnny Ace, Hank Ballard, Etta James, Little Willie John, Sugar Pie De Santo, Big mama Thornton and Jackie Wilson. The success of the show paved the way for many later black music package tours, especially those by Tamla Motown.

During 1957-58 the Johnny Otis Show chalked up three substantial pop hits in its own right, two in Britain and one in America. *Ma, He's Making Eyes At Me*, a song that dated from 1921, surged to the UK No. 2 position; this featured vocals by Marie Adams and the Three Tons of Joy. Adams also sang on Otis' own song *Bye Bye Baby*, which peaked at No. 20 on the British chart. Another of Johnny's self-penned numbers, *Willie And The Hand Jive*, became a US No. 9 hit. *Willie* became Otis' best known track, and was successfully covered in Britain by Cliff Richard; the song was strongly influenced by Bo Diddley's eponymous anthem. All this pop success was a reflection of the fact that Otis had taken the new rock 'n' roll music on board.
Having made a huge contribution to R&B in the Fifties, the Sixties were a largely uninspiring period for Johnny Otis. After spending most of the decade as a backroom producer-arranger, he made an impressive comeback in 1969 with the *Cold Shot* LP. This fine album introduced the talents of his son Shuggie Otis, who carved out his own successful career as a blues guitarist. Johnny revived his revue for the Monterey Jazz Festival in 1970, featuring Esther Phillips and a host of other greats; a live

album, capturing the event, was released. After several more years on the road with renewed vigour, Otis faded from view during the mid-Seventies. But the shoe came back yet again in 1982. Bob MacDonald, 23 February 1986..

**BARRELHOUSE STOMP**
Tracks: / Omaha flash / Jeff-hi stomp / Miss Mitchell / Ultra-violet / Sgt. Barksdale / Love's nocturne / Barrelhouse stomp / Pay day blues / Hog jaws / Jelly roll, The / Happy new year baby / That's your last boogie / Alligator meat / Stardust / One nighter blues.
**Album:** Released Aug '87, on Jukebox Lil (Sweden) Catalogue no: **JB 611**
**Cass:** Released 11 Mar '88, on Jukebox Lil (Sweden) Catalogue no: **JB 611**

**BYE BYE BABY (Otis, Johnny Show)**
Tracks: / Bye bye baby.
**7" Single:** Released Jan '58, on Capitol by EMI Records. Deleted '61. Catalogue no: **CL 14817**

**GEE BABY (Otis, Johnny & Co.)**
Tracks: / Gee baby / Alimony boogie / My heart tells me / Crazy 'bout your cookin' / Square dance / New love / Baby baby blues / Voodoo / Call operator / Goomp blues / What's your name / Gypsy blues / Chittlin' switch / Brown skin butterball / Why don't you believe me / Wishing well.
**Album:** Released Aug '87, on Jukebox Lil (Sweden) Catalogue no: **JBLIL 617**
**Album:** Released Aug '87, on Jukebox Lil (Sweden) Catalogue no: **JB 617**

**GREAT RHYTHM AND BLUES, VOL 3**
Tracks: / Willie and the hand jive / Barrelhouse blues / Please don't leave me / Bad luck shadow / Fanny Mae / Signifying monkey, The / Harlem nocturne / Stack-a-lee / Don't start me to talkin' / Baby, I've got news for you / Country girl / Bye bye baby.
**Album:** Released Jul '82, on Bulldog Records by President Records. Catalogue no: **BDL 1002**

**INTO THE EIGHTIES**
Tracks: / Rock and roll wedding / Stand by me / Love (makes me do foolish things) / Hit that jive, jack rollin' / Do it again, baby / In the still of the night / Hide away / Will you love me tomorrow / Soothe me baby / When something is wrong with my baby / I found you / Fine and mellow / I'm gonna leave these women alone.
**Album:** Released May '86, on Charly R&B by Charly Records. Catalogue no: **CRB 1110**

**JOHNNY OTIS PRESENTS.... (Various artists)**
**Album:** Released Dec '88, on Ace by Ace Records. Catalogue no: **CH 88**

**JOHNNY OTIS SHOW, THE**
**Album:** Released '83, on Capitol (import) Catalogue no: **2C 068 86528**

**MA, HE'S MAKING EYES AT ME (Otis, Johnny Show / Marie Adams N/ Three Tons Of Joy)**
Tracks: / Ma, he's making eyes at me.
**7" Single:** Released Nov '57, on Capitol by EMI Records. Deleted '60. Catalogue no: **CL 14794**

**MA, HE'S MAKING EYES AT ME (OLD GOLD) (Otis, Johnny Show)**
Tracks: / Ma, he's making eyes at me / Fever.
**7" Single:** Released Apr '87, on Old Gold by Old Gold Records. Deleted Sep '89. Catalogue no: **OG 9720**

**NEW JOHNNY OTIS SHOW, THE**
Tracks: / Drinkin' wine spo-dee-o-dee / Every beat of my heart / Jonella and Jack / What else can I do? / Half steppin' woman / Why don't you do right? / Big time scoop / I never felt this way before / Don't deceive me / So fine.
Note: This album marked the return of Johnny Otis to recording after almost a decade. Otis, the man who, organised the first rock 'n' roll reviews in America, and discovered Etta James, Jackie Wilson, Esther Phillips and Hank Ballard, is featured along with his son Shuggie Otis on guitar, and a host of good-rockin' singers and players. Some great new Johnny Otis songs and beautiful guitar work. (Alligator catalogue 7/88)
**Album:** Released Feb '82, on Alligator (Sonet) by Alligator Records (USA). Catalogue no: **SNTF 878**

**ORIGINAL JOHNNY OTIS SHOW, THE**
**Album:** Released Mar '85, on Savoy Jazz (USA) by Malaco Records (USA). Catalogue no: **SJL 2230**

**ORIGINAL JOHNNY OTIS VOL 2, THE**
**Album:** Released Mar '85, on Savoy Jazz (USA) by Malaco Records (USA). Catalogue no: **SJL 2252**

**REASON WHY**
Tracks: / Reason why / Secret agent.
**7" Single:** Released Jun '83, on Sonet by Sonet Records. Catalogue no: **SON 2253**

**ROCK AND ROLL HIT PARADE**
**Album:** Released Oct '79, on Flyright by Interstate Music. Catalogue no: **FLY 550**

**ROCK'N'ROLL REVUE**
Tracks: / Shake it Lucy baby / Willie and the hand jive / Ring-a-ling-a-ling / Bye bye baby / Light still shines, The / Tell me so / Telephone baby / Mumblin' moise / Good golly / Ma, he's making eyes at me / Crazy country hop / Hum ding a ling / You just kissed me goodbye / In the dark / Can't you hear me callin' / Castin' my spell.
**Album:** Released Mar '82, on Charly R&B by Charly Records. Catalogue no: **CRB 1041**

## Out Of The Blue

**INSIDE TRACK**
Tracks: / Inside track / Cherry Pickens / Hot house / E force / Nathan Jones / Isolation / Elevation.
**CD:** Released Mar '87, on Blue Note by EMI Records. Catalogue no: **CDP 746 395 2**
**Album:** on Blue Note by EMI Records. Deleted Jun '88. Catalogue no: **BT 85128**
**CD:** Released Mar '87, on Blue Note by EMI Records. Catalogue no: **BNZ 72**

**LIVE AT MT.FUJI**
Tracks: / Parisian thoroughfare / Blue pearl / Nathan Jones / Elevation / OTB / Celia / Over the rainbow.
**CD:** Released Jan '88, on Blue Note by EMI Records. Deleted Jun '89. Catalogue no: **CDP 746 784 2**
**Album:** Released Jul '87, on Blue Note by EMI Records. Deleted Jun '89. Catalogue no: **BT 85141**
**CD:** Released Jan '88, on Blue Note by EMI Records. Deleted Jun '89. Catalogue no: **BNZ 73**

## Outside In ...

**OUTSIDE IN 1964-1989 (Blue Note 50th anniversary collection vol. 4) (Various artists)**
Tracks: / Out to lunch: *Dolphy, Eric* / Black fire: *Hill, Andrew* / Broad way blues: *Coleman, Ornette* / Passion dance: *Tyner, McCoy* / OTB / Life of the party: *Williams, Tony* / Calling Miss Khadija: *Hubbard, Freddie/Woody Shaw* / Song from the old country: *Pullen, Don & Adams, George Quartet* / Beatrice: *Henderson, Joe* / She did it again: *Petrucciani, Michel.*
**2 LP Set:** Released Jul '89, on Blue Note by EMI Records. Catalogue no: **BST2 92474**
**Cass:** Released Jul '89, on Blue Note by EMI Records. Catalogue no: **TCBST2 92474**
**CD:** Released Jul '89, on Blue Note by EMI Records. Catalogue no: **CDP 792 4742**
**CD:** Released Jul '89, on Blue Note by EMI Records. Catalogue no: **CDB1 92474**
**CD:** Released Jul '89, on Blue Note by EMI Records. Catalogue no: **CDBST2 92474**

## Overstreet, Rev Louis

**REV LOUIS OVERSTREET, HIS GUITAR AND CONGREGATION**
**Album:** Released May '81, on Arhoolie (USA) by Arhoolie Records (USA). Catalogue no: **ARHOOLIE 1014**

## Owens, Charles

**PLAYS THE MUSIC OF HARRY WARREN, VOL. 1 (Owens, Charles & The New York Ensemble)**
Tracks: / More I see you, The / I wish I knew / September in the rain / I only have eyes for you / Serenade in blue / You'll never know.
Note: Charles Owens-sax, Ray Brown-bass, George Cables-piano, Roy McCurdy-drums, Red Callender-bass tuba, James Newton-flute.
**Album:** Released '88, on Discovery (USA) by Discovery Records (USA). Catalogue no: **DS 811**

**TWO QUARTETS, THE**

Note: Side one: Charles Owens-tenor, Ted Saunders-piano, John Heard-bass, Carl Burnett-drums. Side two: Charles Owens-tenor, Dwight Dickerson-piano, Louis Spears-bass, Alex Acuna-drums.
**Cass:** Released '88, on Discovery (USA) by Discovery Records (USA). Catalogue no: **DSC 787**
**Album:** Released '88, on Discovery (USA) by Discovery Records (USA). Catalogue no: **DS 787**

## Oxley, Tony

**SECOND ALBUM**
**Album:** Released Nov '76, on Incus by Incus Records. Catalogue no: **INCUS 18**

**SONG FOR SOMEONE (see also D Bailey, E Parker) (Oxley, Tony, D Bailey, E Parker)**
**Album:** Released Nov '76, on Incus by Incus Records. Catalogue no: **INCUS 10**

**TONY OXLEY**
**Album:** Released Nov '76, on Incus by Incus Records. Catalogue no: **INCUS 8**

# P

The following information was taken from the Music Master database on April 14th, 1990.

## Pablo All Stars

### PABLO ALL STARS JAM

Tracks: / Cote d'azur / Pennies from Heaven / Samba de Orfeu / God bless the child.

**Album:** Released '82, on Pablo Jazz (USA) by Pablo Records (USA). Catalogue no: **2308 210**

**Cass:** Released '82, on Pablo Jazz (USA) by Pablo Records (USA). Catalogue no: **K 08 210**

## Pacific Coast ...

### PACIFIC COAST RAGTIME ORCHESTRA (Pacific Coast Ragtime Orchestra)

**Album:** Released Apr '89, on Circle Catalogue no: **CLP 137**

## Pacific Jazz

### PACIFIC JAZZ COLLECTION (Various artists)

Tracks: / St. Louis blues: *Evans, Gil* / King Porter stomp: *Evans, Gil* / Willow tree: *Evans, Gil* / Struttin' with some barbecue: *Evans, Gil* / Lester leaps in: *Evans, Gil* / Round midnight: *Evans, Gil* / Manteca: *Evans, Gil* / Bird feathers: *Evans, Gil* / Davenport blues: *Evans, Gil* / Straight no chaser: *Evans, Gil* / Ballad of the sad young men: *Evans, Gil* / Joy spring: *Evans, Gil* / Django: *Evans, Gil* / Chant of the weed: *Evans, Gil* / La Nevada (theme): *Evans, Gil* / Love me or leave me: *Lewis, John/Bill Perkins* / I can't get started: *Lewis, John/Bill Perkins* / Easy living: *Lewis, John/Bill Perkins* / 2 degrees east - 3 degrees west: *Lewis, John/Bill Perkins* / Skylark: *Lewis, John/Bill Perkins* / Almost like being in love: *Lewis, John/Bill Perkins* / Stompin' at the Savoy: *Hall, Jim* / Things ain't what they used to be: *Hall, Jim* / Thanks for the memory: *Hall, Jim* / Tangerine: *Hall, Jim* / Stella by starlight: *Hall, Jim* / 9.20 special: *Hall, Jim* / Deep in a dream: *Hall, Jim* / Look for the silver lining: *Hall, Jim* / Seven come eleven: *Hall, Jim* / Thing's ain't what they used to be (alt. take): *Hall, Jim* / Too close for comfort: *Hall, Jim* / To Mickey's memory: *Baker, Chet* / Slightly above moderate: *Baker, Chet* / Halema: *Baker, Chet* / Revelation: *Baker, Chet* / Something for Liza: *Baker, Chet* / Lucius Lu: *Baker, Chet* / Worrying the life out of me: *Baker, Chet* / Medium rock: *Baker, Chet* / I can't believe that you're in love with me: *Konitz, Lee & Gerry Mulligan* / Broadway: *Konitz, Lee & Gerry Mulligan* / Almost like being in love: *Konitz, Lee & Gerry Mulligan* / Sextet I: *Konitz, Lee & Gerry Mulligan* / Lady be good: *Konitz, Lee & Gerry Mulligan* / Too marvellous for words: *Konitz, Lee & Gerry Mulligan* / Lover man: *Konitz, Lee & Gerry Mulligan* / I'll remember April: *Konitz, Lee & Gerry Mulligan* / These foolish things: *Konitz, Lee & Gerry Mulligan* / All the things you are: *Konitz, Lee & Gerry Mulligan* / Bernies tune: *Konitz, Lee & Gerry Mulligan* (CD only.) / Lady be good (alt. take): *Konitz, Lee & Gerry Mulligan* (CD only.).

Note: Album & CD box sets containing 6 records: New bottle old wine - Gil Evans; Great jazz standards - Gil Evans; Grand encounter - John Lewis/Bill Perkins; Jazz guitar - Jim Hall; Chet Baker and crew - Chet Baker; Konitz meets Mullingan - Lee Konitz/Gerry Mulligan.

**CD Set:** Released Nov '89, on EMI-Manhattan by EMI Records. Catalogue no: **793 152 2**

**CD Set:** Released Nov '89, on EMI-Manhattan by EMI Records. Catalogue no: **CDWPX 1**

**LP Set:** Released Nov '89, on EMI-Manhattan by EMI Records. Catalogue no: **WPX 1**

**LP Set:** Released Nov '89, on EMI-Manhattan by EMI Records. Catalogue no: **793 152 1**

### PACIFIC JAZZ II COLLECTION (Various artists)

Tracks: / Four and one more: *Mulligan, Gerry* / Crazy day: *Mulligan, Gerry* / Turnstile: *Mulligan, Gerry* / Sextet: *Mulligan, Gerry* / Disc jockey jump: *Mulligan, Gerry* / Venus De Milo: *Mulligan, Gerry* / Revelation: *Mulligan, Gerry* / I may be wrong: *Mulligan, Gerry & Chet Baker* / Aren't you glad you're you: *Mulligan, Gerry & Chet Baker* / I'm beginning to see the light: *Mulligan, Gerry & Chet Baker* / Nearness of you, The: *Mulligan, Gerry & Chet Baker* / Makin' whoopee: *Mulligan, Gerry & Chet Baker* / Tea for two: *Mulligan, Gerry & Chet Baker* / Frenesi: *Mulligan, Gerry & Chet Baker* / Nights at the turntable: *Mulligan, Gerry & Chet Baker* / Lullaby of the leaves: *Mulligan, Gerry & Chet Baker* / Jeru: *Mulligan, Gerry & Chet Baker* / Cherry: *Mulligan, Gerry & Chet Baker* / Swing house: *Mulligan, Gerry & Chet Baker* / Bernie's tune: *Mulligan, Gerry & Chet Baker* / Freeway: *Mulligan, Gerry & Chet Baker* / Soft shoe: *Mulligan, Gerry & Chet Baker* / Walking shoes: *Mulligan, Gerry & Chet Baker* / Motel: *Mulligan, Gerry & Chet Baker* / Carson city stage: *Mulligan, Gerry & Chet Baker* / Festive minor: *Mulligan, Gerry & Chet Baker* / I never knew: *Shank, Bud* / All the things you are: *Shank, Bud* / Body and soul: *Shank, Bud* / Blue Lou: *Shank, Bud* / Thou swell: *Shank, Bud* / Tenderly: *Shank, Bud* / Over the rainbow: *Shank, Bud* / Long ago and far away: *Shank, Bud* / Arrowhead: *Brookmeyer, Bob* / Streetswingers: *Brookmeyer, Bob* / Hot buttered noodling: *Brookmeyer, Bob* / Musicale du jour: *Brookmeyer, Bob* / Raney day: *Brookmeyer, Bob* / Jupiter: *Brookmeyer, Bob* / Crutch for the crab, A: *Twardzik, Richard Trio* / Alburquerque social swim: *Twardzik, Richard Trio* / Bess you is my woman: *Twardzik, Richard Trio* / Round midnight: *Twardzik, Richard Trio* / I'll remember April: *Twardzik, Richard Trio* / Yellow tango: *Twardzik, Richard Trio* / Just one of those things: *Twardzik, Richard Trio* / You stepped out of a dream: *Freeman, Russ Trio* / Don't worry 'bout me: *Freeman, Russ Trio* / Rock's tops: *Freeman, Russ Trio* / Yesterdays Gardenias: *Freeman, Russ Trio* / At last: *Freeman, Russ Trio* / Backfield in motion: *Freeman, Russ Trio* / Eye opener, The: *Freeman, Russ Trio* / Laugh cry: *Freeman, Russ Trio* / Nice day: *Hamilton, Chico* / Funny valentine: *Hamilton, Chico* / Blue sands: *Hamilton, Chico* / I want to be happy: *Hamilton, Chico* / Spectacular: *Hamilton, Chico* / Walking carson blues: *Hamilton, Chico* / Buddy boo: *Hamilton, Chico* / Jonalah: *Hamilton, Chico* / Chrissie: *Hamilton, Chico* / Ghost, The: *Hamilton, Chico* / Santa Monica: *Hamilton, Chico* / Taking a chance on love: *Hamilton, Chico* / Squimp, The: *Hamilton, Chico* / Topsy: *Hamilton, Chico* / Drums west: *Hamilton, Chico* / Sleep: *Hamilton, Chico.*

Note: Six album, six cassette box set, three double CD set.

**LP Set:** Released Mar '89, on Capitol/Pacific Jazz by EMI Records. Catalogue no: **WPX 2**

**CD Set:** Released Mar '89, on Capitol/Pacific Jazz by EMI Records. Catalogue no: **CDS 791 611 2**

**CD Set:** Released Mar '89, on Capitol/Pacific Jazz by EMI Records. Catalogue no: **CDWPX 2**

**Cass set:** Released Mar '89, on Capitol/Pacific Jazz by EMI Records. Deleted Feb '90. Catalogue no: **TCWPX 2**

## Packin' Up My Blues

### PACKIN' UP MY BLUES (BLUES FROM THE DEEP SOUTH) (Various artists)

**Album:** Released Apr '79, on Muskadine by Topic Records. Catalogue no: **MUSKADINE 102**

## Page, Hot Lips

### HOT LIPS PAGE 1938-1940

Tracks: / Good old bosom bread / He's pulling his whiskers / Down on the levee / Old man Ben / I would do anything for you / I ain't got nobody / Porter's love song to a chambermaid, A / Gone with

the gin / Walk it to me / It won't be here long / Lafayette / South / Harlem rhumbain' the blues / No matter where you are.
**CD:** Released Dec '89, on Official by Official Records. Catalogue no: **OFF 43047**
**Album:** Released Dec '89, on Official by Official Records. Catalogue no: **OFF 3047**

**SWING STREET (Page, Hot Lips and His Orchestra with Jonah Jones & Orch.)**
**Album:** Released Feb '84, on Commodore Class Catalogue no: **AG6 25524**

## Paich, Marty

**Biographical details:** Paich is a pianist, arranger and bandleader, born in Oakland, California in 1925, best known for tasteful jazz-oriented arrangements in the 1950s for artists such as Mel Torme and Ella Fitzgerald on the Verve label, later Ray Charles, Sammy Davis Jr, Lena Horne, many others. Most of his own LPs were made in the second half of the 1950s, before lucrative studio work took over completely. (Donald Clarke 15.5.87).

**HOT PIANO**
**Album:** Released Apr '88, on VSOP Catalogue no: **VSOP 27**

**I GET A BOOT OUT OF YOU (Paich, Marty Big Band)**
Tracks: / It don't mean a thing / Love for sale / Violets for your furs / Things ain't what they used to be / Moanin'.
Note: Featuring Art Pepper, Jack Sheldon, Victor Feldman and Bill Hood.
**Cass:** Released '88, on Discovery (USA) by Discovery Records (USA). Catalogue no: **DSC 829**
**Album:** Released '88, on Discovery (USA) by Discovery Records (USA). Catalogue no: **DS 829**

**JAZZ CITY WORKSHOP**
**Album:** Released Feb '88, on Fresh Sounds (Spain) by Fresh Sounds Records (Spain). Catalogue no: **FS 235**

**MARTY PAICH OCTET (Paich, Marty Octet)**
**Album:** Released Dec '87, on Fresh Sounds (Spain) by Fresh Sounds Records (Spain). Catalogue no: **FS 287**

**NEW YORK SCENE, THE**
Tracks: / It's alright with me / I love Paris / Too close for comfort / Lazy afternoon.
Note: Featuring Art Pepper, Victor Feldman, Mel Lewis, Jimmy Guiffre, Bill Perkins, George Roberts, Vince De Rosa.
**Album:** Released Oct '82, on Discovery (USA) by Discovery Records (USA). Catalogue no: **DS 844**

**PICASSO OF BIG BAND JAZZ, THE**
**Album:** Released May '89, on Candid Catalogue no: **CS 9031**
**CD:** Released May '89, on Candid Catalogue no: **CCD 9031**

**WHAT'S NEW (Paich, Marty Big Band)**
Note: Marty Paich - piano; Mel Lewis - drums; Joe Mondragon - bass; Pete Candoll, Jack Sheldon - trumpets; Herbie Harper , Bob Enevoldsen - trombones; Vince De Rosa - French horn; Herb Geller, Bob Cooper, Marty Berman, Bill Perkins - saxes.
**Album:** Released '88, on Discovery (USA) by Discovery Records (USA). Catalogue no: **DS 857**

## Palm Beach Orchestra

**PLAY GLENN MILLER (BIG BAND VOLUME 1)**
**Cass:** Released Jan '83, on Bibi (Budget Cassettes) Catalogue no: **BBM 145**

## Pameijer, Pam

**JELLY ROLL MORTON - 100 YEARS Duet/Trio/Quartet**
**Album:** Released Nov '87, on Stomp Off (USA) Catalogue no: **SOS 1134**

**LONDON BLUES (Pameijer, Pam Trio)**
**Album:** Released Jun '89, on Stomp Off (USA) Catalogue no: **SOS 1172**

**PAM PAMEIJER AND HIS CLASSIC JAZZ ACES (Pameijer, Pam & His Classic Jazz Aces)**
**Album:** Released '89, on Stomp Off (USA) Catalogue no: **SOS 1194**

## Panorama Du Jazz

**HISTOIRE DES GEANTS DU JAZZ (Various artists)**
**CD:** Released Oct '88, on Vogue by Vogue Records. Catalogue no: **VGCD 670 052**

**LES GEANTS DU JAZZ**
**Album:** Released '88, on Vogue (France) by Vogue Records. Catalogue no: **504152**

## Paragon Brass Band

**LIVE ON THE STREETS OF ROUEN**
**Album:** Released Jun '86, on GHB by Jazzology Records (USA). Catalogue no: **GHB 87**

## Parenti's Liberty...

**MIDWAY DANCE ORCHESTRA & OTHERS, THE (Parenti's Liberty Syncopators)**
**Album:** Released Apr '79, on VJM (Vintage Jazz Music) by Vintage Jazz Music Society(VJM). Catalogue no: **VLP 34**

## Parenti,Tony

**FINAL BAR (Parenti, Tony & His Jazz Stars)**
**Album:** Released Jun '86, on Jazzology (USA) by Jazzology Records (USA). Catalogue no: **J 71**

## Parham, Tiny

**FROM THE LATE 1920'S (Parham, Tiny and His Musicians)**
**Album:** Released Oct '86, on Folklyric (USA) by Arhoolie Records (USA). Catalogue no: **FL 9028**

**TINY PARHAM & MUSICIANS VOL. 1 1928-29 (Parham, Tiny and His Musicians)**
**Album:** Released Jan '88, on Swaggie (Australia) Catalogue no: **S 831**

**TINY PARHAM VOL. 2**
**Album:** Released '88, on Collector's Classics Catalogue no: **CC 40**

Charlie Parker

## Paris, Jackie

### JACKIE PARIS
**Album:** Released Aug '88, on Audiophile (USA) by Jazzology Records (USA). Catalogue no: **AP 158**

## Park, John

### IF WINTER COMES
**Album:** Released Feb '89, on Jazz Mark Catalogue no: **JAZZ MARK 105**

## Parker, Charlie

**Biographical details:** Parker is the most influential jazz musician in history after Louis Armstrong, He was born in 1920 in Kansas City, Kansas. He played the alto saxophone (very occasionally tenor), led his own combo, endlessly and effortlessly composed every time he played. Nicknamed 'Yardbird' (for chicken), 'Bird' for short. He grew up across the river in Kansas City, Missouri, then a wide open town and an incubator of great jazzman; he practised on his horn until he could instantly modulate from any key to any other key, perhaps because he did not know that he needed only a few keys to play in a band. Influenced by local musicians Buster Smith and Lester Young, he played in the bands of Jay McShann, Earl Hines and Billy Eckstine; while playing *Cherokee* in a Harlem club, he began to improvise on the higher notes of the chords, creating a new melody on the old structure: he became a key creator of bebop, or bop; hence all of modern jazz. He died in 1955 in New York City, worn out by years of drug and alcohol abuse; within days the grafitti 'Bird Lives' appeared in the streets. His greatest recordings are on Savoy and Dial (now Spotlite). (Donald Clarke 15.5.87).

### 1947-1948
Tracks: / Koko / Hot house / I surrender, dear / Fine and dandy / Sunny side of the street / How deep is the ocean? / Tiger rag / 52nd Street theme / Lullaby in rhythm / Yardbird suite / Dee Dee's dance / Donna Lee / Everything I have is yours / Fats flats / Tea for two / Don't blame me / Groovin' high / Ornithology / Cheryl / Bird of paradise.
Note: Musicians include Dizzy Gillespie, Lennie Tristano, Fats Navarro, Al Haig, Ray Brown, Max Roach, Buddy Rich.
**2 LP Set:** Released Aug '83, on Musidisc by Musidisc Records (France). Catalogue no: **ALB 376**

### ALIVE & KICKIN' VOL 1
**Album:** Released Oct '88, on Vogue by Vogue Records. Catalogue no: **500204**

### ALIVE & KICKIN' VOL 2
**Album:** Released Oct '88, on Vogue by Vogue Records. Catalogue no: **500205**

### ALTERNATIVE MASTERS Vol. 1/2
**LP Set:** Released '88, on Dial (Holland) Catalogue no: **DIAL 904/905**

### ANTHOLOGY - CHARLIE PARKER
**LP Set:** Released Jun '84, on Musidisc by Musidisc Records (France). Catalogue no: **AM 008/9/10**

### ANTHROPOLOGY
Tracks: / Donna Lee / Everything I have is yours / Fats flats / Tea for two / Don't blame me / Groovin' high / Koko / Anthropology / Now's the time / Lady be good / Just you, just me.
**Album:** Released '83, on Spotlite by Spotlite Records. Catalogue no: **SPJ 108**

### APARTMENT SESSIONS
Tracks: / Little Willie leaps / All the things you are / Bernie's tune / Donna Lee / Out of nowhere / Half Nelson / Fine and dandy / Cherokee / Scrapple from the apple / Star eyes.
**Album:** Released '83, on Spotlite by Spotlite Records. Catalogue no: **SPJ 146**

### APEX OF BE BOP VOL 2
**Album:** Released Sep '87, on Giants of Jazz by Hasmick Promotions. Catalogue no: **LPJT 41**

### AT THE PERSHING BALLROOM
Tracks: / Indiana / I can't get started / Anthropology / Out of nowhere / Get happy / Hot house / Embraceable you / Body and soul / Cool blues / Stardust / All the things you are / Billie's bounce / Pennies from Heaven.
Note: Charlie Parker - alto saxophone; Bruz Freeman - drums; Von Freeman - tenor saxophone; George Freeman - guitar; Leroy Jackson - bass; Chris Anderson - piano. Recorded Chicago, Autumn 1950.
**Album:** Released Apr '81, on Zim (USA) Catalogue no: **ZM 1003**

### BALLADS AND BIRDLAND
Tracks: / Ornithology / 52nd street theme / How high the moon / Bewitched / Summertime / I cover the waterfront / Gone with the wind / Easy to love / Just friends / April in Paris.
**Album:** Released '88, on Zu Zazz by Zu Zazz Records. Catalogue no: **ZZ 1002**

### BAND THAT NEVER WAS, THE (Parker, Charlie & The Gene Roland Orchestra)
Tracks: / It's a wonderful world / Just you, just me / Stardust / 52nd Street theme / Dizzy atmosphere / My old flame (excerpt) / All the things you are / Half nelson / Big Foot.
Note: Strictly for collectors and modern jazz students: obscure wire recordings of the great altoist's working band from 1948 at the Three Deuces, plus rehearsal performances with the Roland band.
**Album:** Released '83, on Spotlite by Spotlite Records. Catalogue no: **SPJ 141**

### BIRD Film soundtrack
Tracks: / Lester leaps in / I can't believe that you're in love with me / Laura / All of me / This time the dream's on me / Koko / Cool blues / April in Paris / Now's the time / Ornithology / Parker's mood.
**Cass:** Released Nov '88, on Verve Catalogue no: **837 176-4**
**Album:** Released Nov '88, on Verve Catalogue no: **837 176-1**
**CD:** Released Nov '88, on CBS by CBS Records. Catalogue no: **461002 2**
**Cass:** Released Nov '88, on CBS by CBS Records. Catalogue no: **461002 4**
**Album:** Released Nov '88, on CBS by CBS Records. Catalogue no: **461002 1**
**CD:** Released Nov '88, on Verve Catalogue no: **837 176-2**
**CD:** Released 10 Jul '89, on Vogue by Vogue Records. Catalogue no: **VGCD 670220**

### BIRD 47
**CD:** Released Oct '88, on Vogue by Vogue Records. Catalogue no: **VGCD 600124**

### BIRD AT THE ROOST
**Album:** Released Mar '85, on Savoy Jazz (USA) by Malaco Records (USA). Catalogue no: **SJL 1108**

### BIRD FLIES DEEP Live performance
Tracks: / Groovin' high / Move / Ornithology / Out of nowhere / Hot house / How high the moon / Bebop / Scrapple from the apple / Street beat / Round midnight / Koko.
**Cass:** Released Apr '87, on Atlantis by Charly Records. Catalogue no: **TCATS 12**
**Album:** Released Apr '87, on Atlantis by Charly Records. Catalogue no: **ATS 12**

### BIRD IN PARIS
Tracks: / Scrapple from the apple / Out of nowhere / Barbados / 52nd Street theme / Salt peanuts / Allen's alley / Untitled blues / Ladybird.
Note: Paris live performances originally recorded by a portable disc cutting machine.
**Album:** Released '83, on Spotlite by Spotlite Records. Catalogue no: **SPJ 118**

### BIRD IS FREE
Tracks: / Rocker / Sly mongoose / Moose the mooche / Star eyes / This time the dream's on me / Cool blues / My little suede shoes / Lester leaps in / Laura.
**Album:** Released Feb '82, on Rhapsody by President Records. Catalogue no: **RHAP 7**

### BIRD MEETS BIRKS VOL.2
**Album:** Released 10 Jul '89, on Zu Zazz by Zu Zazz Records. Catalogue no: **ZZ 1003**

### BIRD ON TENOR 1943 (see panel on next page)
Tracks: / Sweet Georgia Brown / Three guesses / Boogie woogie / Embraceable you / Indiana / Sweet Georgia Brown (2) / Lover come back to me / Billie's bounce / Caravan / Drifting on a reed / Ornithology / Barbados / Cool blues.
Note: For a music whose life spans less than a century, jazz has an inordinate number of legends. Yet, every so often those legends give way to reality. In recent years, we have been let it on the after hours wizardry of Art Tatum; jam session glories by the likes of Hot Lips Page, Roy Eldridge, and Don Byas; a Benny Goodman practice date with Lester Young and Charlie Christian; the last and perhaps most spirited performance of Clifford Brown; and numerous hours of Duke Ellington - from major opuses

**Charlie Parker - Bird on tenor 1943 (Stash)**

like *Black brown and beige* to minor marvels such as his arrangement of *Monk's dream.* Those treasures, and others like them, were found in private collections, recorded on disc, wire, and tape - some professionals, others by amateurs. There is reason to believe that additional gaps in our knowledge of jazz's titans will be filled similarly. The perserverance of collectors has especially enriched the discography of Charlie Parker: performances we never expected to hear - and, in one instance, see - have been wrestled from the ether and brought to life. We now have his first broadcast with Jay McShann, concerts and club dates, and a kinescope of Parker on TV. With this album, one of the most remarkable jazz recordings ever released, another jazz legend bites the dust - to be reborn as endlessly fascinating reality. Here, at long last, are the fabled Redcross recordings. They are cause for celebration.

Jazz lovers have a penchant for speculating about the past, for jazz has never been adequately captured on records. What did the Original Creole Jazz Band or early editions of the Fletcher Henderson orchestra or Count Basie's Reno Club Band really sound like? We wonder and we imagine. The era, that stimulates the most fantasy, or course, is the incubation period of modern jazz. The reason is obvious. During the two years when bop was born, 1942-1944, a recording ban instigated by the American Federation of Musicians curtailed the making of records. As a result, the Earl Hines band of 1943, which included Parker and Gillespie, left no recordings, Billy Eckstine's band, which consolidated the modernist impulse for the first time, survives only on broadcasts made after Parker left. In short, there is no significance documentation of Parker's coming of musical age between July, 1942, when he last recorded with Jay McShann and September 1944, when he appeared on a Tiny Grimes Savoy session (which produced the tune *Red cross*). Indeed, the explosive impact of seminal bop performances such as *Shaw nuff, Salt peanuts, Ko ko* and *Now's the time* can be attributed in part to the fact that Parker's radical style appeared to be born fully formed. His workshop period had been totally obscured by the recording ban. Still, rumours surfaced of private recordings made during the period Parker worked with Hines. How those recordings were finally unearthed is a story in itself. Robert Redcross was born in Pittsburgh (the hometown of Hines and Eckstine) in 1913, and raised in Chicago from the age of six. He became interested in jazz at early age, in part because his parents worked at various clubs on the Southside, bringing him into daily contact with such musicians as King Oliver and Chippie Hill. An ardent record collector he soon discovered that there was a market for rare records - not least among musicians who no longer had copies of their own recordings. He turned a hobby into a business. In 1938, he bought a Silvertone disc recorder and took his passion another step: he recorded radio broadcasts and sessions he organized in his hotel room at Chicago's Savoy Hotel. He began with an old friend, Billy Eckstine, then a vocalist with the Hines band who was temporarily layed-off while the leader reformed his orchestra. Many of his recordings - which included Ellington, Cootie Williams, John Kirby, Fats Waller and others, were lost or stolen. But he managed to hold on to most of the Parker discs.

In February 1943, metal discs were impossible to get. As Redcross explained in the Gillespie book, some of his discs - Genuine Tru-Tone Records - were glass based, made with wax on top of the glass; and some were remnants or combinations of metal with wax. Eventually after many playings, the wax began to flake; the grooves were additionally worn by heavy needles. So six years after he made them, by which time Parker and Gillespie were among the most influential musicians in the world, Redcross wrapped them in the Chicago Tribune and put them on a shelf. Decades later, he offered to donate the discs to educational institutions, but incredibly, no one took him up on it. They gathered dust, became legendary. In the Koster-Bakker discography, Charlie Parker 1940-1955, published in 1974, an entry is listed for 1943, at the Ritz Hotel in Chicago: 'recorded for the American Red Cross ... unknown titles. Two years later, the discographers were able to correct the entry only slightly. 'Recorded by Mr Red Cross, valet of Billy Eckstine, not for the American Red Cross'. In 1979, the puzzle was solved with little fanfare, when Gillespie published his invaluable autobiography (written with Al Fraser), *To be or not to bop*, Bob Redcross, recording engineer and road manager, was interviewed at length. He spoke of 'recording in my hotel room' and went on to say that the fruits of his labors survived. 'See I got this bunch of 78s I refuse to get rid of. I just keep carrying them from one place to another, year to year. I was telling Diz I had some of those things that was made in the hotel room; I don't know if they will even play anymore ... These were made during the war, you know, back at the first part of the war when all metal had been conscripted for the defense effort.'

And still the recordings remained hidden. Red cross, who lives in Queens, New York and remains active in the jazz world, driving for Gillespie, Eckstine, and others, put them out of his mind. In 1981, while transporting a member of the Basie band, he met Phil Schaap, a New York disc-jockey, who took his number but never followed up. He did mention Redcross to a few collectors, however, including Don Manning, a Portland based DJ and veteran Parker enthusiast, who interviewed Redcross; as the result of a misunderstanding, he concluded that the discs had been stolen. Not until 1985, when Manning was in New York, and another Parker collector, the resolute Norman Saks, asked for an introduction to Redcross, did the recor-

dings finally come to light. Seated in Redcross's home, Saks remarked 'I understand your acetates were stolen'.
'Oh no' came the reply, 'I have them right here'. Redcross went into the attic and returned with a heavy bundle wraped in the Chicago Tribune for Sunday July 31, 1949 (the front page blares, Collision in Mid Air kills 16). Saks took the discs to a radio station to have them dubbed, and returned home to listen to music that no one had heard in 36 years. Soon they were the talk of collectors everywhere. A few months later, while researching a book on Parker, I visited Saks to hear them and other rare performances in his exhaustive collection of Birdlore. Toby Byron, my collaborator on the book, and I sat in Norman's basement with dropped jaws. I phoned a couple of people in the record business, suggesting they take whatever steps were necessary to release this material, but, much to my amazement, no one made the move until Will Friedwald of Stash called me on an entirely different matter. The five performances from 1943 are the most substantial of the surviving Redcross recordings with Parker. They exceed expectations, reclaiming - with surprising vivid fidelity (thanks to Redcross's original expertise and care and that of John R.T. Davies, who made the transfers) - a Charlie Parker historians thought was lost forever: here is the missing link between the young altoist who toured with McShann and the bold and brilliant innovator who changed the course of jazz. The music is doubly interesting because Parker plays tenor, as he did in the Hines Orchestra (the alto chair was filled). In 1943, he was still paying respects to Lester Young, but he was clearly becoming the agressive, tempo doubling, harmonically ingenious and technically awesome improvisor of 1945. Morever, the tenor underscores influences in his music, that are often ignored. The tendency to trace Parker's stylistic growth to Young overlooks the impact of the Coleman Hawkins school of saxophonists. Yet Parker learned much from Hawkins, whose *Body and soul* he quoted at least as late as *Moose the mooch*, as well as Leon 'Chu' Berry, one of his favourite musicians and the man he named his first son after, and Ben Webster, to whom he pays homage here.
The more you listen to these solos, the more you hear the past coming face to face with the future. Dizzy called an early bop classic *Things to come*. The Redcross recordings are roadmaps to those things. At the same time, they suggest autobiography.
Sweet Georgia Brown. This two sided disc, more than seven and a half minutes long, is a nakedly revealing joust by Bird and Diz (their first on record) accompanied by Oscar Pettiford's bass. It helps explain why each referred to the other as 'the other half of my heartbeat'. The disc fades up on the seventh bar of Gillespie's theme statement, followed by three Parker choruses, Dizzy comes back with eight bars of riffs and is so energized he threatens to overshoot the chorus, but resolves it just in time. Parker, more fluent this time, returns for five more, inspired by Pettiford's powerful walk and Dizzy's cheer, 'Come on Yard'. After three more by Gillespie, the two heartbeats converge. *Three guesses*. Redcross titled this one because it goes off in three directions. *Cotton tail, Mop mop* and *I got rhythm*.
There are other references as well, some almost subliminal. Bird begins alone, in a relaxed swing groove, strongly evoking Young; another sax harmonizes on the head, as does Billy Eckstine's trumpet. As he settles into *Rhythm* changes, Bird growls a bit, in the Webster manner, and follows through by quoting Webster's *Cotton tail* solo for the release. He begins the next chorus with a Lesorian gambit, but for the second eight bars switches to the *Mop mop* rhythmic lick that he recorded two years later as *Red Cross* (a typo for Redcross). Before the fade, he exchanges fours with Eckstine, using his last response to wave *Bye bye blackbird*. *Boogie woogie*. An identified friend dropped by and started things off with a Louis Armstrong impression. With Redcross on brushes, Birds comes in with the closing riff from Basie's *Boogie woogie* and continues to riff through the trumpet solo. Then he stomps off five blues choruses, quoting *London Bridges* in the second and a bop lick to be in the third. Parker and Eckstine counterpunch each other like section men working up a head arrangement, before settling into Gene Krupa's *Drum boogie*. *Embraceable you*. Here is the first of many Parker variations on Gershwin's melody. The pianist variations on Gershwin's melody. The pianist is Hazel Scott, and though you might not be able to tell from listening, she wasn't in Room 305 that day. On at least two occasions, Redcross recorded Parker playing along with anothre record. Parker's collaboration with the Benny Goodman's Quartet's *China boy* is lost, but we're lucky to have his revealing duet with a 1942 Scott performance.
He enters when she goes into time, and blends in seamlessly. Ever the gentleman, he tags along with her turnbacks and follows her rubato close, dressing his tone with a touch of Hawkins fuzz.
Indiana. Taken at a loping medium-tempo, this excerpt has a beautifully modulated chorus by Bird as well as half chorus of fours: his first exchange includes a bop figure that suggests 'Buzzy' in embryo. By 1945, Parker and Gillespie were recognized as the twin founders of a new movement in jazz; in December they made a fateful trip to Los Angeles to spread the word. By summer, Bird's drug abuse precipitated a breakdown that caused him to be incarcerated in Camarillo State Hospital for six months. His dial recordings and several private tapes of his work with Gillespie attest to the high spirits and great music with which the trip began. We could ask for no better evidence than the jam session Bob Redcross recorded in February at the home of a fan named Freddie James. Gillespie's book identifies bassist Red Callender and drummer Harold 'Doc' West, but not the pianist, who is barely audible, or the tenor saxophonist. According to Redcross, it was Don Byas, although he sounds a bit like Lucky Thompson (Bird's recording partner a few weeks later) to my ears. *Sweet Georgia Brown*. In some ways, this is the most exciting piece on the album, a blazing series of exchanges between the three winds, each at the top of his form. The recording begins with the last six bars of a tenor chorus, and proceeds through six choruses of unrelieved intensity. The solo breakdown is as follows: Bird (8 bars), Dizzy (8), tenor (16), Bird (16), Dizzy (16), tenor (8), Bird (8), Dizzy (8), Bird (8), Dizzy (8), tenor (8), Bird (8). For the fifth chorus, they riff in unison for 24 bars, leaving the last eight for Bird.
For the sixth, they go into a new riff for 12 bars, which leads to a hair raising four bar chase episode by Diz and Bird, before they all go out with an ensemble flourish. *Lover come back to me*. Recorded in two parts, this is a relatively cool Parker improvisation, followed by a brief episode in which Dizzy returns. The Hotel Diplomat recordings are from the collection of Don Manning, and the exact date and full personnel are not known. By now, Parker, although only thirty years old, was an elder statesman and much of the quoting he did was from his own past.

*Billie's bounce*. this famous blues in F, from Parker's first session as a leader, produces eight choruses and the oddest thing about them is that they refer twice (in choruses one and seven) to another blues. *Now's the time*, recorded at the same 1945 session. Bird also quotes hiw own *Ornithology* (second chorus) and the beguiling lick we heard in the third chorus of the Redcross *Boogie woogie* (fifth chorus). Parker's amateur recordists frequently turned off their machines during solos by other musicians. In this case, Miles got the gong, though we hear him in the concluding chase chorus with Parker. *Caravan*. One of the most bizarre and least satisfying curios in Birdlore is this excerpt of Parker playing Juan Tizol's theme as though he were imprisoned in it, while Roy Haynes beats a jungle rhythm. If he improvised it all, an abrupt edit destroyed any chance of our hearing it. *Drifting on a reed*. Fortunately, the recordist didn't edit this very fast five minute romp through Parker's 1947 B flat blues. Parker and Davis each stretch out for nine breathless choruses, while Haynes keeps them at attention with bass drum accents. This comprehensive survey ends, fittingly with one of Parker's last sessions, made toward the end of 1953, less than 18 months before his death. The occasion was a concert at the University of Oregon, and despite occasional flaws, the sound is of professional

quality - tape instead of disc. *Ornithology*. Parker's classic re-working of *How high the moon* (written with Little Benny Harris, another member of the Redcross recording circle), has a characteristically handsome Bird solo, accompanied by Jimmy Rowle's stirring chords. The tape fades down as soon as Chet Baker starts to play. *Barbados*. Probably the only reason we get all of Shelly Manne's fanciful drum solo is that it comes the beginning, taking the engineer by surprise. Baker doesn't fare as well. Bird, relaxed by the familiar territory of blues in F, struts through five choruses, and ends up swinging on a star. He thanks the audience for its applause. *Cool blues*. Another blues, this one in C, and the one Parker performed more than any other. Note an extra spin the ensemble places on the theme's held note. Once again, the tape fades down after Bird says 'thank you,' but it fades up for a long, series of trades that begin with Baker, Manne, and Bird, and then switches to Manne and the spry and witty Rowles. When Parker died in March, 1955, a minority of New York newspapers published obituaries and only one of them got his age right. Yet before he was buried, graffiti began to appear: Bird lives. He lives and he thrives as a constantly growing audience continues to savour genius. (Gary Giddins, October 1986)
**Album:** Released Jun '86, on Stash (USA) Catalogue no: **ST 260**

**BIRD ON VERVE, VOL 1**
Tracks: / Repetition / No noise / Mango mangue / Okie doke / Bird, The / Cardboard / Visa / Segment / Passport No. 1 / Passport No. 2 / Diverse / Just friends / Everything happens to me / April in Paris / Summertime / I didn't know what time it was / If I should lose you.
Note: Recorded between 1947 and 1953, this album features Parker in a range of moods and settings, from strings and Afro-Cuban rhythms to his own hard-bopping outfits, featuring Dizzy Gillespie, Thelonious Monk, Al Haig, Shelly Manne, Ray Brown, Max Roach, Buddy Rich.
**Album:** Released Mar '84, on Verve (USA) by Polydor Ltd. Catalogue no: **817 442-1**

**BIRD ON VERVE, VOL 2**
Tracks: / Star eyes / Blues / I'm in the mood for love / Mohawk / Melancholy baby / Leapfrog.
Note: The great alto saxist is backed by his orchestra on some tracks, by his quartet on others.
**Album:** Released Mar '84, on Verve (USA) by Polydor Ltd. Catalogue no: **817 443-1**

**BIRD ON VERVE, VOL 3**
Tracks: / Relaxin' with Lee / Dancing in the dark / Out of nowhere / Laura / East of the sun / They can't take that away from me / Easy to love / I'm in the mood for love / I'll remember April.
Note: Some of the tracks feature altoist Parker with strings, in its day quite an innovation.
**Album:** Released Mar '84, on Verve (USA) by Polydor Ltd. Catalogue no: **817 444-1**

**BIRD ON VERVE, VOL 4**
Tracks: / Repetition / What is this thing called love? / April in Paris / Easy to love / I'll remember April / Celebrity / Ballade / Cancion mambo 1 / Cancion mambo 2 / 6/8 jazz / Rhumba Abierta.
Note: The Bird flies high with his own quartet, with an orchestra and with strings.
**Album:** Released Mar '84, on Verve (USA) by Polydor Ltd. Catalogue no: **817 445-1**

**BIRD ON VERVE, VOL 5**
Tracks: / Au privave / She rote / K.C. blues / Star eyes / My little suede shoes / Un poquito de tu amor / Tico tico / Fiesta / Who do I love you? (three takes).
**Album:** Released Apr '84, on Verve (USA) by Polydor Ltd. Catalogue no: **817 446-1**

**BIRD ON VERVE, VOL 6**
Tracks: / Blues for Alice / Si si / Swedish schnapps / Back home blues / Lover man / Temptation / Lover / Autumn in New York / Stella by starlight / Mama Inez / La cucaracha / Estrellita / Begin the beguine / La paloma.
Note: Parker's alto soars with quintet, strings and orchestra.
**Album:** Released Apr '84, on Verve (USA) by Polydor Ltd. Catalogue no: **817 447-1**

**BIRD ON VERVE, VOL 7**
Tracks: / Night and day / Almost like being in love / I can't get started / What is this thing called love? / Song is you, The / Laird baird (blues for laird) / Cosmic rays (two takes) / In the still of the night / Old folks / If I love again / Chi chi (three takes).
Note: Tracks feature, variously, big band, orchestra and quartet as backing to Parker's incomparable alto.
**Album:** Released Apr '84, on Verve (USA) by Polydor Ltd. Catalogue no: **817 448-1**

**BIRD ON VERVE, VOL 8**
Tracks: / I remember you / Now's the time / Confirmation / I get a kick out of you / Just one of those things / My heart belongs to daddy / I've got you under my skin / Love for sale (two takes) / I love Paris (two takes).
Note: Small group bop with Parker's quartet and quintet.
**Album:** Released Apr '84, on Verve (USA) by Polydor Ltd. Catalogue no: **817 449-1**

**BIRD & PREZ CARNEGIE HALL 1949 (Parker, Charlie & Lester Young)**
**Album:** Released Apr '84, on Verve Deleted '87. Catalogue no: **LP VRV 5**

**BIRD SONG**
**Album:** Released Apr '86, on Star Jazz (USA) by Charly Records. Catalogue no: **SJAZZ 5**
**Cass:** Released Apr '86, on Star Jazz (USA) by Charly Records. Catalogue no: **SJAZZC 5**

**BIRD SYMBOLS**
Tracks: / Moose the mooche / Yardbird suite / Ornithology / Night in Tunisia / Bird's nest / Cool blues / Bird of paradise / Embraceable you / My old flame / Scrapple from the apple / Out of nowhere / Don't blame me.
**Album:** Released Nov '80, on Rhapsody by President Records. Catalogue no: **RHAP 5**

**BIRD, THE**
**Album:** Released Nov '84, on Astan (USA) Catalogue no: **20100**
**Cass:** Released Nov '84, on Astan (USA) Catalogue no: **40100**

**BIRD, THE SAVOY RECORDINGS, THE MASTER TAKES**
**Album:** Released Mar '85, on Savoy Jazz (USA) by Malaco Records (USA). Catalogue no: **SJL 2201**

**BIRD WITH STRINGS**
Tracks: / Easy to love / Jumping with Symphony Sid / Just friends / Everything happens to me / East of the sun / Laura / Dancing in the dark / What is this thing called love / Laura / They can't take that away from me.
**Album:** Released '79, on CBS by CBS Records. Deleted '84. Catalogue no: **CBS 82292**

**BIRD YOU NEVER HEARD, THE**
**CD:** Released May '89, on Stash (USA) Catalogue no: **STCD 10**
**Album:** Released May '89, on Stash (USA) Catalogue no: **ST 280**

**BIRDS EYES VOL. 1**
**Album:** Released '88, on Philology Catalogue no: **214W 5**

**BIRD'S EYES, VOL. 2 - PERSHING HOTEL 1949**
**Album:** Released Oct '88, on Philology Catalogue no: **214W 12**

**BIRD'S EYES VOL 4**
**Album:** Released Mar '90, on Philology Catalogue no: **214W 18**

**BIRD'S EYES VOL 5**
**Album:** Released Mar '90, on Philology Catalogue no: **214W 19**

**BIRD'S EYES VOL 6**
**Album:** Released Mar '90, on Philology Catalogue no: **214W29**

**BIRDS & FATS (Parker, Charlie Quintet)**
**Album:** Released Apr '81, on Jazz Live (Italy) Catalogue no: **BLJ 8029**

**BIRDS & FATS - VOL.2 (Parker, Charlie & Fats Navarro Quintet)**
**Album:** Released Apr '81, on Jazz Live (Italy) Catalogue no: **BLJ 8030**

**BIRD'S NIGHT: A CELEBRATION OF THE MUSIC OF CHARLIE PARKER (Various artists)**
**Album:** Released May '85, on Savoy Jazz (USA) by Malaco Records (USA). Catalogue no: **SJL 2257**

**BIRTH OF BE BOP 1944-47**
**Album:** Released Sep '87, on Giants of Jazz by Hasmick Promotions. Catalogue no: **LPJT 31**

**BOSS BIRD**
Tracks: / Swingmatism / Jumpin' blues, The / Red cross / Groovin' high / Now's

the time / Koko / Slim's jam / Lady be good / Moose the mooche / Yardbird suite / Ornithology / Night in Tunisia / Cool blues / Relaxin' at Camarilla / Hymn, The / Bird of paradise / Klactoveeseds-tene / Out of nowhere / Bluebird / Bird gets the worm / Barbados / Parker's mood / Bird, The / Segment / Just friends / Relaxin' with Lee / She rote / Star eyes / My little suede shoes / Laird laird / Cosmic rays / I remember you.
**Cass:** Released Oct '88, on Official by Official Records. Catalogue no: **OFF 43011-2**
**Album:** Released '88, on Official by Official Records. Catalogue no: **OFF 3011-2**
**CD:** Released Dec '88, on Official by Official Records. Catalogue no: **OFF 83011-2**

**CARNEGIE HALL, CHRISTMAS '49**
**CD:** Released '88, on Jass Catalogue no: **JASSCD 16**

**CHARLIE PARKER**
**Cass:** Released '84, on Audio Fidelity(USA) by Audio Fidelity (USA). Catalogue no: **ZCGAS 751**
**Album:** Released '88, on Queen Catalogue no: **QUEEN 002**
**Cass:** Released '88, on Joker (USA) by Lifetime Records (USA). Catalogue no: **MC 3288**
**Album:** Released '88, on Joker (USA) by Lifetime Records (USA). Catalogue no: **SM 3288**

**CHARLIE PARKER: 1949-52**
**Album:** Released Feb '89, on Giants of Jazz by Hasmick Promotions. Catalogue no: **LPJT 71**

**CHARLIE PARKER AT STORYVILLE**
Tracks: / Moose the mooche / I'll walk alone / Ornithology / Out of nowhere / Now's the time / Don't blame me / Dancing on the ceiling / Cool blues / Groovin' high.
Note: Previously unreleased recordings of the legendary sax player, recorded in two sessions for radio broadcast in 1953. Of all the great figures in jazz, Charlie 'Bird' Parker's work remains undoubtedly the most influential - his life the most written about.
**Album:** Released Jan '86, on Blue Note by EMI Records. Deleted Nov '88. Catalogue no: **BT 85108**

**CHARLIE PARKER COLLECTION**
**CD:** Released Oct '89, on Collection by K-Tel Records. Catalogue no: **OR 0063**
**CD:** Released Dec '87, on Deja Vu Catalogue no: **DVCD 2017**
**Cass:** Released Aug '85, on Deja Vu Catalogue no: **DVMC 2017**
**Album:** Released Aug '85, on Deja Vu Catalogue no: **DVLP 2017**

**CHARLIE PARKER & DIZZY GILLESPIE (Parker, Charlie & Dizzy Gillespie)**
Tracks: / Night in Tunisia / Confirmation / Groovin' high / Champ, The / They can't take that away from me / Good bait / I've got the bluest blues / Birks works.
**CD:** on Polydor by Polydor Ltd. Deleted Oct '88. Catalogue no: **831 133-2**
**Album:** Released Jun '84, on EMI (Europe) by EMI Records. Catalogue no: **2M 056 64847**
**Album:** Released Jul '89, on M & R Catalogue no: **JR 101**
**Cass:** Released Jun '84, on EMI (Europe) by EMI Records. Catalogue no: **2M 256 64847**
**CD:** Released Jul '89, on M & R Catalogue no: **JRCD 101**
**Cass:** Released Jul '89, on M & R Catalogue no: **JRC 101**

**CHARLIE PARKER IN SWEDEN**
Tracks: / Anthropology / Cheers / Lover man / Cool blues / Scrapple from the apple / Embraceable you / Star eyes / All the things you are / Strike up the band / How high the moon / Body and soul / Fine and dandy.
**2 LP Set:** Released '83, on Spotlite by Spotlite Records. Catalogue no: **SPJ 124/5**

**CHARLIE PARKER MEMORIAL CONCERT, THE (Dexter Gordon, Red Rodney)**
**CD:** Released Oct '88, on Vogue by Vogue Records. Catalogue no: **VGCD 600 188**

**CHARLIE PARKER & MILES DAVIS (Parker, Charlie & Miles Davis)**
**Cass:** Released Nov '84, on Chase Music (USA) by Chase Music Group (USA). Catalogue no: **SJAZC 7**
**Album:** Released Nov '84, on Chase Music (USA) by Chase Music Group (USA). Catalogue no: **SJAZZ 7**

**CHARLIE PARKER, MILES DAVIS & DIZZY GILLESPIE (Parker, Charlie/Miles Davis/Dizzy Gillespie)**
Tracks: / Bird feathers / Dewey square / Quasimodo / Crazeology / Bongo bop / Swing low sweet cadillac / My man / Klactoveesedstein / Dizzy atmosphere / Air conditioning.
**Album:** Released Jul '83, on Jazz Reactivation Catalogue no: **JR 124**

**CHARLIE PARKER (PRESTIGE)**
Tracks: / 52nd Street theme / Shaw 'nuff / Out of nowhere / Hot house / This time the dream's on me / Night in Tunisia, A / My old flame' / Way you look tonight, The / Chasin' the bird / Dizzy atmosphere / How high the moon / I didn't know what time it was / Ornithology / Embraceable you / Visa / I cover the waterfront / Scrapple from the apple / Star eyes / Theme / Confirmation / Smoke gets in your eyes / Now is the time.
**2 LP Set:** Released '79, on Prestige Deleted '84. Catalogue no: **PR 24009**

**CHARLIE PARKER, VOL 1**
Tracks: / Moose the mooche / Yardbird suite / Ornithology / Night in Tunisia / Bird's nest / Blowtop blues / I didn't know what time it was / Embraceable you / Bird of paradise / My old flame / Scrapple from the apple / Out of nowhere / Don't blame me / April in Paris.
**Album:** Released Oct '88, on Joker (USA) by Lifetime Records (USA). Catalogue no: **SM 3866**
**Album:** Released Jan '82, on Jazz Reactivation Catalogue no: **JR 116**

**CHARLIE PARKER, VOL 2**
Tracks: / Rocker / Sly mongoose / Moose the mooche / Star eyes / Just friends / Summertime / This time the dream's on me / Cool blues / My little suede shoes / Lester leaps in / Laura.
**Album:** on Jazz Reactivation Catalogue no: **JR 139**

**CHARLIE PARKER WITH THE ORCHESTRA**
Tracks: / Fine and dandy / These foolish things / Light green / Thou swell / Willis / Don't blame me / Something to remember you by / Blue room / Round house.
**Album:** Released Mar '82, on Elektra (Musician) by Elektra Records (USA). Catalogue no: **K 52359**

**CHOICE BIRD**
**Cass:** Released '82, on Jazz Bird Catalogue no: **ZCJAZ 2008**
**Album:** Released '82, on Jazz Bird Catalogue no: **JAZ 2008**

**COLE PORTER SONGBOOK**
**Album:** Released '87, on Polydor by Polydor Ltd. Catalogue no: **8232501**
**Album:** Released Aug '85, on Verve Catalogue no: **VRV 10**
**Cass:** Released '87, on Polydor by Polydor Ltd. Catalogue no: **8232504**

**COMPLETE CHARLIE PARKER ON VERVE, THE**
**CD:** Released Dec '88, on Polydor by Polydor Ltd. Catalogue no: **837 141-2**

**COMPLETE ROYAL ROOST**
Tracks: / Fifty second street theme / Ko Ko / Groovin' high / Big boot / Ornithology / Slow boat to China / Hot house / Salt peanuts / Chasin' the bird / Out of nowhere / How high the moon / Half Nelson / White Christmas / Little Willie leaps / Be bop / East of the sun / Cheryl.
**Album:** Released '87, on RCA by BMG Records (UK). Deleted Nov '89. Catalogue no: **WL 70541**
**Album:** Released Oct '86, on RCA by BMG Records (UK). Deleted Nov '89. Catalogue no: **WL 70831**
**Cass:** Released '87, on RCA by BMG Records (UK). Deleted Nov '89. Catalogue no: **WK 70541**
**Album:** Released Jan '87, on RCA by BMG Records (UK). Catalogue no: **WL 70825**
**Cass:** Released Oct '86, on RCA by BMG Records (UK). Deleted Nov '89. Catalogue no: **WK 70831**
**Cass set:** Released Jan '87, on RCA by BMG Records (UK). Deleted Nov '89. Catalogue no: **WK 70825**

**COMPLETE SAVOY SESSIONS**
**Album:** Released Mar '85, on Savoy Jazz (USA) by Malaco Records (USA). Catalogue no: **SJL 5500**

**COMPLETE SAVOY SESSIONS 1**
Tracks: / Tiny's tempo / I'll always love you just the same / Romance without finance / Red cross / Billie's bounce / Warming up a riff.
**Album:** Released Feb '85, on Savoy (France) Deleted Nov '89. Catalogue no: **WL 70520**

**Cass:** Released Feb '85, on RCA by BMG Records (UK). Catalogue no: **WK 70520**

**COMPLETE SAVOY SESSIONS 2**
Tracks: / Billie's bounce / Now's the time / Thriving / Meandering / Koko / Flat foot floogie / Dizzy's boogie / Poppity pop / Slim's jam.
**Album:** Released Oct '85, on RCA by BMG Records (UK). Deleted Nov '89. Catalogue no: **WL 70527**
**Cass:** Released Oct '85, on RCA by BMG Records (UK). Catalogue no: **WK 70527**

**COMPLETE SAVOY SESSIONS 3**
Tracks: / Donna Lee / Chasing the bird / Cheryl / Buzzy / Milestones / Little Wilie leaps.
**Cass:** Released Nov '85, on RCA by BMG Records (UK). Deleted Nov '89. Catalogue no: **WK 705 48**
**Album:** Released Nov '85, on RCA by BMG Records (UK). Deleted Nov '89. Catalogue no: **WL 705 48**

**COMPLETE SAVOY SESSIONS 4**
Tracks: / Half Nelson / Sippin' at bells / Another hair-do / Bluebird / Klaunstance / Bird gets the worm / Barbados / Ah leu cha / Constellation.
**Album:** Released Jul '86, on RCA by BMG Records (UK). Deleted Nov '89. Catalogue no: **WL 70813**
**Cass:** Released Jul '86, on RCA by BMG Records (UK). Deleted Nov '89. Catalogue no: **WK 70813**

**COMPLETE SAVOY SESSIONS 5 (1948)**
Tracks: / Parker's mood (takes 3 & 4) / Parker's mood (take 5) / Perhaps (take 1) / Perhaps (takes 2 & 3) / Perhaps (takes 4, 5, & 6) / Perhaps (take 7) / Marmaduke (takes 1, 2, & 3) / Marmaduke (takes 4 & 5) / Marmaduke (takes 6, 7, 8 & 9) / Marmaduke (takes 10, 11, & 12) / Steeplechase (takes 1 & 2) / Merry go round (take 1) / Merry go round (take 2) / Parker's mood (takes 1 & 2).
**Cass:** Released Jan '87, on RCA by BMG Records (UK). Deleted Nov '89. Catalogue no: **WK 70832**
**Album:** Released Jan '87, on RCA by BMG Records (UK). Deleted Nov '89. Catalogue no: **WL 70832**

**COOL BLUES**
**Album:** Released Apr '81, on Jazz Live (Italy) Catalogue no: **BLJ 8014**

**DIAL MASTERS 1 (BOX SET)**
**LP Set:** Released '88, on Spotlite by Spotlite Records. Catalogue no: **SPJBOX 6**

**DIAL MASTERS VOL.1**
Tracks: / Diggin' for Diz / Moose the mooche (three takes) / Yardbird suite (two takes) / Ornithology (three takes) / Famous alto break, The / Night in Tunisia (two takes) / Max making wax / Lover man / Gypsy, The / Bebop.
Note: The first of six volumes - presented in strict chronological order - of all known takes of these classics recorded by alto saxophonist Parker, one of the greatest and most influential figures in the history of jazz. All six are available as a box set but they can be bought separately. Featured musicians include Miles Davis, Dizzy Gillespie, Howard McGhee, Lucky Thompson, Dodo Marmarosa, Barney Kessell, Erroll Garner, Wardell Gray, Duke Jordan, J.J. Johnson, Max Roach...
**Album:** Released '83, on Spotlite by Spotlite Records. Catalogue no: **SPJ 101**

**DIAL MASTERS VOL.2**
Tracks: / This is always (two takes) / Dark shadows (four takes) / Bird's nest (three takes) / Cool blues (four takes).
Note: Featuring pianist Erroll Garner and singer Earl Coleman.
**Album:** Released '83, on Spotlite by Spotlite Records. Catalogue no: **SPJ 102**

**DIAL MASTERS VOL.3**
Tracks: / Relaxin' at Camarillo / Cheers / Carvin' the bird / Home cooking (three takes).
Note: Sidesmen include Howard McGhee, Wardell Gray, Dodo Marmarosa, Barney Kessell.
**Album:** Released '83, on Spotlite by Spotlite Records. Catalogue no: **SPJ 103**

**DIAL MASTERS VOL.4**
Tracks: / Dexterity (two takes) / Bongo bop / Deway Square (three takes) / Hymn (two takes) / Bird of paradise (three takes) / Embraceable you (two takes).
Note: Featuring Miles Davis, Duke Jordan, Tommy Potter, Max Roach.
**Album:** Released '83, on Spotlite by Spotlite Records. Catalogue no: **SPJ 104**

**DIAL MASTERS VOL.5**
Tracks: / Bird feathers / Klactoveesedstein (two takes) / Scrapple from the apple / My old flame / Out of nowhere (three tapes) / Don't blame me / Moose the mooche / Dark shadows / Hallelujah.
**Album:** Released '83, on Spotlite by Spotlite Records. Catalogue no: **SPJ 105**

**DIAL MASTERS VOL.6**
Tracks: / Drifting on a reed (three takes) / Quasimodo (two takes) / Charlie's wig (three takes) / Bongo beep / Crazeology (two excerpts) / How deep is the ocean? (two takes).
Note: Trombonist J.J. Johnson guests.
**Album:** Released '83, on Spotlite by Spotlite Records. Catalogue no: **SPJ 106**

**DIAL MATERIAL VOL.1**
**Album:** Released Apr '81, on Up International Catalogue no: **LPUP 5156**

**DIAL MATERIAL VOL.2**
**Album:** Released Apr '81, on Up International Catalogue no: **LPUP 5157**

**DIAL MATERIAL VOL.3**
**Album:** Released Apr '81, on Up International Catalogue no: **LPUP 5158**

**ENCORES**
**Album:** Released Mar '85, on Savoy Jazz (USA) by Malaco Records (USA). Catalogue no: **SJL 1107**

**ENCORES VOL.2**
**Album:** Released Mar '85, on Savoy Jazz (USA) by Malaco Records (USA). Catalogue no: **SJL 1129**

**EVERY BIT OF IT**
Tracks: / Seven-eleven / Do nothing till you hear from me / Don't blame me / Perdido / Nightcap / Saturday night / Floogie boo / St. Louis blues / What's the matter now? / I want every bit of it / That's the blues / G.I. blues / 4F blues / Dream of you / Seventh Avenue / Sorta kinda / Oh, oh, my, my / What more can a woman do? / I'd rather have a memory than a dream / Mean to me / Taking off / If I had you / 20th century blues / Street beat / Dizzy boogie (two takes) / Flat foot floogie / Poppity pop / Slim's jam.
Note: This album collates the 1945 recordings of alto saxophonist Parker, earlier found dotted about on countless records. Featuring singer Sarah Vaughan - on *Mean to me* - the Cootie Williams Orchestra, the Clyde Hart All Stars, the Sir Charles All Stars, with Dexter Gordon, and the Slim Gaillard Orchestra.
**2 LP Set:** Released '83, on Spotlite by Spotlite Records. Catalogue no: **SPJ 150D**

**FABULOUS BIRD BLOWS, THE Modern Jazz Collectors series**
**LP Set:** Released '88, on Dial (Holland) Catalogue no: **DIAL LP 901**

**FRAGMENTS**
**Album:** Released Sep '84, on Audio Fidelity(USA) by Audio Fidelity (USA). Catalogue no: **CP 508**

**FROM DIZZY TO MILES**
**CD:** Released Mar '90, on Giants of Jazz by Hasmick Promotions. Catalogue no: **GOJCD53052**

**GREATEST DIAL CUTS**
**Album:** Released '88, on Spotlite by Spotlite Records. Catalogue no: **JU6-7333**

**GREATEST HITS: CHARLIE PARKER**
**Cass:** Released Dec '88, on Masters (Holland) Catalogue no: **MAMC 925983**
**Album:** Released '88, on Masters (Holland) Catalogue no: **MA 25983**

**HAPPY BIRD, THE**
Tracks: / Happy bird blues / I'll remember April / Scrapple from the apple / I may be wrong.
**Album:** Released Mar '81, on Rhapsody by President Records. Deleted '86. Catalogue no: **RHAP 6**

**HEAVENLY HORNS**
Tracks: / Ornithology / Night in Tunisia / Birds nest / Long time / Pure delight / Blue lament / It's a sin to tell a lie / Dance time.
**Album:** Released Jun '80, on Manhattan Records by President Records. Deleted '85. Catalogue no: **MAN 5016**

**IN SWEDEN 1950**
**Album:** Released Feb '90, on Storyville by Storyville Records AB. Catalogue no: **SLP 4031**
**Album:** Released Jun '86, on Storyville

by Storyville Records AB. Catalogue no: **SLP 1007**
**CD:** Released Feb '90, on Storyville by Storyville Records AB. Catalogue no: **STCD 4031**
**CD:** Released Oct '87, on Storyville by Storyville Records AB. Catalogue no: **STCD 4031**

**IT HAPPENED ONE NIGHT (Parker, Charlie / Dizzy Gillespie / Ella Fitzgrald)**
**Album:** Released Apr '81, on Natural Organic (USA) Catalogue no: **NAT:ORG:7000**

**JAZZ TIME VOL.4**
**Album:** Released '88, on Vogue (France) by Vogue Records. Catalogue no: **502704**

**LEGENDARY DIAL MASTERS. VOL 1**
**CD:** Released Mar '90, on Stash (USA) Catalogue no: **STCD23**

**LEGENDARY DIAL MASTERS. VOL 2**
**CD:** Released Mar '90, on Stash (USA) Catalogue no: **SRCD25**

**LIVE AT BIRDLAND**
**Album:** Released '88, on Vogue by Vogue Records. Catalogue no: **VG 500905**

**LIVE AT THE CAFE SOCIETY**
**Album:** Released Sep '84, on Audio Fidelity(USA) by Audio Fidelity (USA). Catalogue no: **CP 509**

**LIVE AT THE ROCKLAND PALACE**
**Album:** Released Aug '84, on Audio Fidelity(USA) by Audio Fidelity (USA). Catalogue no: **CP 502**
**Cass:** Released Aug '84, on Audio Fidelity(USA) by Audio Fidelity (USA). Catalogue no: **ZCCP 502**

**LIVE IN LOS ANGELES 1947**
**CD:** Released Oct '89, on Jazz Anthology by Musidisc Records (France). Catalogue no: **550082**

**LULLABY IN RHYTHM**
Tracks: / Koko / I surrender, dear / Fine and dandy / Sunny side of the street / How deep is the ocean? / Tiger rag / 52nd Street theme / Lullaby in rhythm / Yardbird suite / Dee Dee's dance.
Note: The Bands of Bonds broadcasts featuring Dizzy Gillespie (trumpet), Lennie Tristano (piano) and Max Roach (drums).
**Album:** Released '83, on Spotlite by Spotlite Records. Catalogue no: **SPJ 107**

**MAGNIFICENT BIRD**
Tracks: / I can't get started / Lover man / They can't take that away from me / Laird baird / Old folks / I'm in the mood for love / April in Paris / I get a kick out of you / Au privave / An oscar for treadwell / Ballade / Cosmic rays.
**Album:** Released Sep '85, on Meteor by Magnum Music Group. Catalogue no: **MTM 013**

**MASTERWORKS 1946-47**
Tracks: / Bird of paradise / Embraceable you / Crazeology / Dewey square / My old flame / Relaxin' at Camarillo / Hymn / Klactoveesedstein / Don't blame me / Scrapple from the apple / Quasimodo / Dexterity / Night in Tunisia / Ornithology / Lover man / Yardbird suite / Moose the mooche / Gypsy, The / Bebop / Bird's nest / Out of nowhere / Cheers.
**CD:** Released '88, on Giants of Jazz by Hasmick Promotions. Catalogue no: **GOJCD 0217**
**CD:** Released Feb '88, on Entertainers Catalogue no: **ENTCD 217**

**MEMORIAL 1920-1955**
**Album:** Released Oct '88, on Vogue by Vogue Records. Catalogue no: **500 753**

**MOVE (Parker, Charlie/Fats Navarro/Bud Powell)**
**Album:** Released Apr '81, on Kings Of Jazz Catalogue no: **KLJ 20010**

**NEW BIRD**
**Album:** Released Apr '81, on Phoenix (USA) by All Star Talent Inc.(USA). Catalogue no: **LP 10**

**NEW BIRD, VOL 2**
**Album:** Released Apr '81, on Phoenix (USA) by All Star Talent Inc.(USA). Catalogue no: **LP 12**

**NOW'S THE TIME**
Tracks: / Song is you, The / Laird baird / Kim / Cosmic rays / Chi chi / I remember you / Now's the time / Confirmation.
**Album:** Released May '82, on Verve Catalogue no: **2304 095**
**CD:** Released May '82, on Verve Deleted Mar '88. Catalogue no: **825 671-2**

**ONCE THERE WAS BIRD**
Tracks: / Hallelujah (two takes) / Get happy (two takes) / Slam slam blues (two takes) / Congo blues (five takes).
**Album:** Released Nov '80, on Rhapsody by President Records. Catalogue no: **RHAP 4**

**ONE NIGHT IN CHICAGO**
**Album:** Released Mar '85, on Savoy Jazz (USA) by Malaco Records (USA). Catalogue no: **SJL 1132**

**ORNITHOLOGY**
**Album:** Released 21 Jul '89, on Jazz & Jazz Catalogue no: **JJ 610**
**CD:** Released 21 Jul '89, on Jazz & Jazz Catalogue no: **CDJJ 610**

**PARKER STREET**
Tracks: / Bird of paradise / Embraceable you / Bird song / Cool bird / Inside out / Soul time / Blue diamond / Soul interlude.
**Album:** Released Aug '80, on Manhattan Records by President Records. Catalogue no: **MAN 5026**

**QUARTET, QUINTET & SEXTET**
Note: Featuring Miles Davis, JJ Johnston, John Lewis.
**Album:** Released Sep '87, on Giants of Jazz by Hasmick Promotions. Catalogue no: **LPJT 60**

**RARE BIRD**
**CD:** Released Mar '90, on Stash (USA) Catalogue no: **STCD21**
**CD Set:** Released Jan '89, on Rare Catalogue no: **RARECD 04/05**

**SAVOY MASTER TAKES**
Tracks: / Tinyms tempo / Red cross / Warming up a riff / Billie's bounce / Now's the time / Thriving on a riff / Koko / Donna Lee / Chasin' the bird / Milestones / Little willie leaps / Half Nelson / Sippin' at bells / Another hair-do / Bluebird / Klaunstance / Bird gets the worm / Barbados / Ah-leu cha / Constellation / Parker's mood / Perhaps / Marmaduke / Steeplechase / Merry-go-round.
**CD:** Released Mar '86, on RCA by BMG Records (UK). Deleted Nov '89. Catalogue no: **ZD 707 37**

**SESSIONS LIVE, VOL.1**
**Album:** Released '88, on Zeta Catalogue no: **ZET 703**

**SESSIONS LIVE, VOL.2**
**Album:** Released '88, on Zeta Catalogue no: **ZET 712**

**SIMPLY CHARLIE**
Tracks: / Moose the mooch / Yardbird suite / My old flame / Charlie's theme / Train stop / Big foot / Blue soul / Delight.
**Album:** Released Jun '80, on Manhattan Records by President Records. Deleted '85. Catalogue no: **MAN 5017**

**TOP BOX, VOLS. 1-3**
Tracks: / Three guesses / Boogie woogie / Embraceable you / Indiana / Sweet Georgia Brown / Lover come back to me / Night in Tunisia / Dizzy atmosphere / Groovin' high / Confirmation / Ko ko / Barbados.
Note: Boxed set of 3 CDs in three parts (vols. 1-9). Each set contains a booklet giving full details of recordings and personnel. Live recordings made between 1943 and 1950 and presented in chronological order. Over 3 hours playing time.
**CD Set:** Released '89, on Jazz-Up Catalogue no: **JUTB 3001**

**TOP BOX, VOLS. 4-6**
Tracks: / Dizzy atmosphere / April in Paris / Move / 52nd Street theme / Street beat, The / Out of nowhere / Little Willie leaps / I'll remember April / Ornithology.
Note: Boxed set of 3 CDs. Part of complete set (vols. 1-9). Over 3 hours playing time. Each set contains a booklet giving full details of recordings and personnel. Live recordings made between 1943 and 1950 and presented here in chronological order.
**CD Set:** Released '89, on Jazz-Up Catalogue no: **JUTB 3004**

**TOP BOX, VOLS. 7-9**
Tracks: / Anthropology / Scrapple from the apple / Embraceable you / Star eyes / Cool blues / All the things you are / Strike up the band / How high the moon / Body and soul / Fine and dandy.
Note: Box set of 3 CDs. Part of complete set of 9 volumes. Each set contains a booklet giving full details of recordings and personnel. Live recordings made between 1943 and 1950 presented in chronological order. Over 2 hours and 50 mins playing time.
**CD Set:** Released '89, on Jazz-Up Catalogue no: **JUTB 3007**

**TOP BOX, VOLS. 10-12**

**CD Set:** Released Mar '90, on Jazz-Up Catalogue no: **JUTB 3010**

**TOP BOX, VOLS. 13-15**
**CD Set:** Released Mar '90, on Jazz-Up Catalogue no: **JUTB 3013**

**TOP BOX, VOLS. 16-18**
**CD Set:** Released Mar '90, on Jazz-Up Catalogue no: **JUTB 3016**

**TRIUMPH OF CHARLIE PARKER**
**CD:** Released 30 Jan '89, on Milan Catalogue no: **CDCH 380**

**TROIS GEANTS DU JAZZ (Parker, Charlie/Miles Davis/Dizzy Gillespie)**
**2 LP Set:** Released Oct '88, on Vogue (France) by Vogue Records. Catalogue no: **400008**

**YARDBIRD - DC - 53**
**Album:** Released Apr '83, on VGM (Import) Catalogue no: **VGM 0009**

**YARDBIRD IN LOTUS LAND**
Tracks: / Shaw 'nuff / Groovin' high / Dizzy atmosphere / Salt peanuts / Tea for two / Body and soul / Cherokee / Ornithology / Anthropology / Billie's bounce / Blue 'n' boogie / All the things you are.
Note: The only known recordings of the legendary Parker-Gillespie Bebop Six along with other fascinating 1946 West Coast performances featuring, among others, Miles Davies, Benny Carter, Al Haig, Willie Smith, Milt Jackson and Joe Albany.
**Album:** Released '83, on Spotlite by Spotlite Records. Catalogue no: **SPJ 123**

## Parker, Evan

**AT THE UNITY THEATRE (Parker, Evan & Paul Lytton)**
**Album:** Released Nov '76, on Incus by Incus Records. Catalogue no: **INCUS 14**

**COLLECTIVE CALLS (URBAN) (Parker, Evan & Paul Lytton)**
**Album:** Released Nov '76, on Incus by Incus Records. Catalogue no: **INCUS 5**

**SAXOPHONE SOLOS**
**Album:** Released Nov '76, on Incus by Incus Records. Catalogue no: **INCUS 19**

**SECOND EVAN PARKER SOLO A1**
**Album:** Released '78, on Incus by Incus Records. Catalogue no: **INCUS 27**

**TOPOGRAPHY OF THE LUNGS (Parker, Evan & Derek Bailey)**
**Album:** Released Nov '76, on Incus by Incus Records. Catalogue no: **INCUS 1**

## Parker, Johnny

**BOOGIE WOOGIE**
**Album:** Released Dec '86, on Dawn Club by Cadillac Music. Catalogue no: **DC 33 003**

**JOHNNY PARKER TRIO (Parker, Johnny Trio)**
**Album:** Released May '79, on Dawn Club by Cadillac Music. Catalogue no: **DCS 33 003**

**JOHNNY PARKER'S BOOGIE WOOGIE**
**Album:** Released May '84, on Dawn (USA) by Biograph Records (USA). Catalogue no: **CLUB 33003**

## Parker, Junior

**Biographical details:** Junior was born Herman Parker in 1932 in Clarksdale, Mississippi; he died of a brain tumour in 1971 in Blue Island, Illinois. Also called Little Junior Parker, he sang R & B and played harmonica, recorded on Modern and Sun in 1952-3 in Memphis, toured with Bobby 'Blue' Bland and Johnny Ace, recorded for Duke in Houston Texas; also for Mercury, United Artists and Capitol. His big R & B hits were all on Duke 1957-62, but he was one of those who first came to public attention during the wonderful heyday of Sun: he wrote *Mystery train*, Elvis Presley's first number one hit (in the country chart in 1955). (Donald Clarke 15.5.87).

**I WANNA RAMBLE (Parker, Junior & The Blue Flames)**
Tracks: / I wanna ramble / Please baby blues / Dirty friend blues / Can't understand / Sittin', drinkin' and thinkin' / Driving me mad / I'm tender / Pretty baby / Sweet home Chicago / Long years / Can you tell me, baby? / Backtracking / There better be no feet / Mother-in-law blues / That's alright.
**Album:** Released Feb '82, on Ace by Ace Records. Deleted Jun '88. Catalogue no: **CH 42**

**JUNIOR PARKER EP**
Tracks: / Love my baby / Mystery train / Feelin' good / Fussin' and fightin' blues.
**7" EP:** Released Feb '77, on Charly by Charly Records. Deleted '81. Catalogue no: **CEP 104**

**LEGENDARY SUN PERFORMERS (Parker, Junior & Billy 'Red' Love)**
Tracks: / Feelin' good / Mystery train / Love my baby / Fussin' and fightin' blues / Sittin' at the window / Sittin' at the bar / Sittin', drinkin' and thinkin' / Feel so bad / Gee I wish / Hearts bread boogie / News is all around town, The / Blues leave me alone / If you want to make me happy / There's no use / Early in the morning / Dream, A.
**Album:** Released '77, on Charly by Charly Records. Catalogue no: **CR 30135**

**MEMPHIS BLUES BROTHERS (Parker, Junior & Bobby Bland)**
Tracks: / Good lovin' / Drifting from town to town takes 1 & 2 / Dry up baby / Crying all night long / Love me baby / You're my angel / Bad women, bad whiskey / Whole heap of mama / I wronged to a woman / I can't forgive you / Sad and lonely / Rumpus romp / Trouble and me / I cried / Midnight hours journey.
**Album:** Released 10 Jul '89, on Ace by Ace Records. Catalogue no: **CHAD 265**

## Parker, Knocky

**Biographical details:** John W Parker (1918-86) was a good pianist in trad jazz, and it is particularly interesting that he came to jazz from the Western Swing genre. Born in Texas, he played with the Light Crust Doughboys in the late '30's, a western band sponsored on the radio by a flour company, and whose first leader had been the great Bob Wills. After WWII Parker switched to jazz, working with New Orleans greats such as Zutty Singleton, Omer Simeon and Albert Nicholas, as well as the Minnesota revivalist cornettist Doc Evans. Parker was also an English teacher and a lecturer on jazz. (Donald Clarke, November 1989).

**EIGHT ON EIGHTY-EIGHT - VOL.15**
**Album:** Released Apr '79, on Euphonic Catalogue no: **ESR 1215**

**FROM CAKEWALK TO RAGTIME**
Note: With:Bill Coffman/R.Rhodes. Mono recording.
**Album:** Released Jun '86, on Jazzology (USA) by Jazzology Records (USA). Catalogue no: **JCE 81**

**TEXAS JAZZ VOL.4 Smokey & The BearKats (Parker, Knocky & Smokey Montgomery)**
**Album:** Released Dec '87, on Circle (USA) by Jazzology Records (USA). Catalogue no: **CLP 10004**

**TEXAS SWING - AND THE BLUES (Parker, Knocky & Smokey Montgomery)**
**Album:** Released Dec '87, on Circle (USA) by Jazzology Records (USA). Catalogue no: **CLP 10003**

**TEXAS SWING - BOOGIE WOOGIE (Parker, Knocky & Smokey Montgomery)**
**Album:** Released Dec '87, on Circle (USA) by Jazzology Records (USA). Catalogue no: **CLP 10002**

**TEXAS SWING - THE BARRELHOUSE (Parker, Knocky & Smokey Montgomery)**
**Album:** Released Dec '87, on Circle (USA) by Jazzology Records (USA). Catalogue no: **CLP 10001**

## Parker, Leo

**BACK TO BACK BARITONES (Parker, Leo/Sax Gill)**
Tracks: / Woody / Rolling with Parker / Leo leaps in (2) / Solitude / Rolling with Parker (2) / Leo leaps in / Leo leaps in (3) / Crisco jump / That's the groovy thing / Shortnin' bread / Off beat jump / Mel's jump / Bullfrog bounce / Dancer's delight.
**Album:** Released 22 Apr '88, on Krazy Kat by Interstate Music. Catalogue no: **KK 829**

**LET ME TELL YOU 'BOUT IT**
Tracks: / Glad lad / Blue Leo / Let me tell you 'bout it / VI / Parker's pals / Low Brown / Low Brown (Long version) / TCTB / Lion's roar, The.
**CD:** Released Apr '90, on Blue Note by EMI Records. Catalogue no: **CDP 784 087 2**
**CD:** Released Apr '90, on Blue Note by EMI Records. Catalogue no: **BNZ 241**
**Album:** Released Sep '84, on Blue Note by EMI Records. Deleted '87. Catalogue no: **BST 84087**

**ROLLIN' WITH LEO**
Tracks: / Lion's roar, The / Bad girl / Rollin' with Leo / Music hall beat / Jumpin' Leo / Stuffy (This track is taken from the 'Mainstream' album from the boxed set.) / Talkin' the blues / Mad lad returns / Daphne.
**Album:** Released Aug '86, on Blue Note by EMI Records. Catalogue no: **BST 84095**
**CD:** Released Apr '89, on Blue Note by EMI Records. Catalogue no: **CDP 784 095 2**
**CD:** Released Apr '89, on Blue Note by EMI Records. Catalogue no: **BNZ 132**

## Parker, Robert

**Biographical details:** Alto saxist, singer and songwriter Robert Parker was born in New Orleans in 1930 and began a career as a sax session player on the city's rhythm-and-blues scene in 1949. As one of the most reliable studio musicians, he played with numerous R & B notables over the years, being heard on discs by such as Irma Thomas, Joe Tex, Professor Longhair and Ernie K-Doe. Despite several tries Parker had just one successful record in his own right -- *Barefootin'*, a self-penned dance-floor belter, reached No 7 on the US pop charts in '66 and peaked at No 24 in the UK. (Bob MacDonald, February 1986.).

**BAREFOOTIN'**
Tracks: / Barefootin' / Duke of earl / Let's go baby (where the action is) / Hiccup, The (on 12" only.).
**12" Single:** Released Jul '87, on Charly by Charly Records. Catalogue no: **CYZ 121**
**7" Single:** Released Aug '84, on Creole (Replay) by Creole Records. Catalogue no: **CR 218**
**7" Single:** Released Jul '87, on Charly by Charly Records. Catalogue no: **CYZ 7121**
**7" Single:** Released Aug '86, on Important Catalogue no: **TAN 12**
**7" Single:** Released Jul '80, on Charly by Charly Records. Deleted '87. Catalogue no: **CTD 123**

**BAREFOOTIN' (1966 SINGLE)**
Tracks: / Barefootin'.
**7" Single:** Released Aug '66, on Island by Island Records. Deleted '69. Catalogue no: **WI 286**

**BAREFOOTIN' (1977 SINGLE)**
Tracks: / Barefootin' / I caught you in a lie.
**7" Single:** Released Jan '77, on Contempo Deleted '80. Catalogue no: **CS 9010**

**GET TA STEPPIN'**
Tracks: / Barefootin' / Let's go baby (where the action is) / Little bit of something, A / Sneaking Sally thru the alley / Better luck in the summertime / You see me / Give me the country side of life / Get right down / Get ta steppin / Hiccup, The / Hot and cold / Skinny dippin' / I like what you do to me / Disco doctor.
**Cass:** Released Sep '87, on Charly R&B by Charly Records. Catalogue no: **TCCRB 1174**
**Album:** Released Sep '87, on Charly R&B by Charly Records. Catalogue no: **CRB 1174**

## Parlan, Horace

**Biographical details:** Horace Parlan was born in 1931 in Philadelphia; the fine jazz pianist was discovered by Charles Mingus and came to fame playing and recording with him in the late 1950s; he has also recorded with the Lockjaw Davis-Johnny Griffon quintet, Booker Ervin, Tubby Hayes, Slide Hampton, Dexter Gordon, Roland Kirk and others. Nearly all his own albums are trio sets; his seven Blue Note LPs were recorded 1960-63; from 1973 he recorded in Europe. (Donald Clarke)..

**BLUE PARLAN (Parlen, Horace Trio)**
**Album:** Released Sep '79, on Steeplechase (USA) Catalogue no: **SCS 1124**

**HAPPY FRAME OF MIND**
Tracks: / Home is Africa / Tune for Richard, A / Back from the gig / Dexi / Kucheza blues / Happy frame of mind.
Note: In the late fifties and sixties Horace Parlan was not only a frequent Blue Note recording artists, but also one of the label's busiest 'house' pianists, recording with Lou Donaldson, Stanley Turrentine, Dexter Gordon, and many others. This sextet with tenor saxophonist Booker Ervin and guitarist Grant Green offers a brilliant selection of tunes including Ronnie Boykin's "Home is Africa" and Randy Westons' "Kucheza Blues"
**Album:** Released Jul '89, on Blue Note by EMI Records. Catalogue no: **BST 84134**
**CD:** Released Mar '89, on Blue Note by EMI Records. Catalogue no: **BNZ 133**
**CD:** Released Mar '89, on Blue Note by EMI Records. Catalogue no: **CDP 784 134 2**

**JOE VAN ENKHUIZEN MEETS THE RHYTHM SECTION**
**CD:** Released '88, on Timeless by Timeless Records. Catalogue no: **CDJSP**
**Album:** Released '88, on Timeless by Timeless Records. Catalogue no: **SJP 249**

**MUSICALLY YOURS**
**Album:** Released May '81, on Steeplechase (USA) Catalogue no: **SCS 1141**

**PANNONICA (Parlen, Horace Trio)**
**Album:** Released Feb '85, on Enja (Germany) by Enja Records (West Germany). Catalogue no: **ENJA 4076**

**TROUBLE IN MIND (Parlan, Horace & Archie Shepp)**
**Album:** Released Sep '81, on Steeplechase (USA) Catalogue no: **SCS 1139**

**US THREE**
**Album:** Released Sep '84, on Blue Note by EMI Records. Catalogue no: **BLP 4037**

## Parnell, Jack

**BIG BAND STEREO SPECTACULAR (Parnell, Jack & His Orchestra/Joe Loss & His Orchestra)**
Tracks: / Skyliner / Peanut vendor / Swingin' shepherd blues / In a sentimental mood / I've got a gal in Kalamazoo /

**Pasadena Roof Orchestra - C'mon Along and Listen (Conifer)**

Sing, sing, sing / South Rampart Street parade / Opus one / Li'l darlin' / American patrol / Mood indigo / On the sunny side of the street / Satin doll / Hot toddy / Trumpet blues and cantabile / Take the 'A' train / Tuxedo Junction / Skin deep / Darktown poker club / St. Louis blues march / Blues in the night / Manhattan spiritual / Big noise from Winnetka / Caravan / Tristeza / Viramundo / Carnival / Deixa isso pra la / Brazil.
**2 LP Set:** Released Sep '81, on MFP by EMI Records. Deleted Sep '86. Catalogue no: **MFP 1007**
**Cass set:** Released Sep '81, on MFP by EMI Records. Deleted Sep '86. Catalogue no: **TCMFP 1007**

**MEMORIES**
Tracks: / Memories / Stardust / Touch of your lips, The / Shadow of your smile / I can't get started / Very thought of you, The / Serenade / I'll never smile again / Yesterdays / I had the craziest dream / Serenata / All the things you are / Remember / Way we were, The / Laura / Street of dreams.
**Album:** Released Jan '89, on Berkeley Catalogue no: **MEM 1**
**CD:** Released Jan '89, on Berkeley Catalogue no: **2MEM 1**
**Cass:** Released Jan '89, on Berkeley Catalogue no: **4MEM 1**

## Pasadena Roof Orchestra

**16 GREATEST HITS: PASADENA ROOF ORCHESTRA**
**Album:** Released '88, on Fun by Balaclava Records. Catalogue no: **FUN 9034**
**Cass:** Released Dec '88, on Fun by Balaclava Records. Catalogue no: **FUNC 9034**

**ANTHOLOGY - PASADENA ROOF ORCHESTRA**
**Album:** Released Apr '78, on Transatlantic by Transatlantic Records. Catalogue no: **MTRA 2009**

**C'MON ALONG AND LISTEN (See panel on previous page)**
Tracks: / Don't be that way / Honey pie / I'm on the crest of a wave / Duke steps out / Show must go on / She's a latin from Manhattan / Josephine Baker / Introducing Josephine Charleston / What is this thing called love / Sing, sing, sing / As time goes by / Skokiaan / Lullaby of Broadway.
Note: Arr.by Keith Nichols. Produced by Rolf Enoch.
**Album:** Released May '86, on Conifer Catalogue no: **CFRC 516**
**Cass:** Released May '86, on Conifer Catalogue no: **MCFRC 516**

**COLLECTION: PASADENA ROOF ORCHESTRA**
Tracks: / It don't mean a thing / Bye bye blackbird / Black bottom / Charleston / Temptation rag / Blue skies / What is this thing called love? / Lullaby of Broadway / Nobody's sweetheart / You're the cream in my coffee / Singing in the rain / Top hat, white tie and tails / I won't dance / Cheek to cheek / Three little words / Stormy weather / Don't be that way / I'll see you again / Pasedena / Georgia / Whispering / Paddlin' Madelin' home / Varsity drag / Here's to the next time.
**CD:** Released Jul '88, on Castle Collector Series by Castle Communications Records. Catalogue no: **CCSCD 189**
**2 LP Set:** Released Jul '88, on Castle Collector Series by Castle Communications Records. Catalogue no: **CCSLP 189**
**Cass:** Released '87, on Castle Collector Series by Castle Communications Records. Catalogue no: **CCSMC 189**

**EVERYTHIN' STOPS FOR TEA**
Tracks: / Lullaby of Broadway / As time goes by / Varsity drag / Charleston / Pasadena / Three little words / Cheek to cheek / Holding hands / Sing, sing, sing / Stormy weather / Black bottom / Top hat / I won't dance / Singing in the rain.
**Cass set:** Released Apr '84, on Cambra by Cambra Records. Deleted '88. Catalogue no: **CRT 135**
**2 LP Set:** Released Apr '84, on Cambra by Cambra Records. Deleted '88. Catalogue no: **CR 135**

**FIFTEEN YEARS ON**
Tracks: / I can't dance / Yes yes (my baby says yes) / You took advantage of me / Varsity drag / Very thought of you, The / Casa loma stomp / Pasadena / Lambeth walk / Solitude / I heard / Don't bring Lulu (Part of a 20's medley) / Ain't she sweet (Part of a 20's medley) / Five foot two, eyes of blue (Part of a 20's medley) / Charleston (Part of a 20's medley) / Here's to the next time.
Note: *Ain't she sweet* on CD only.
**CD:** Released May '87, on Pasadena Roof Orchestra by Pasadena Roof Orchestra Records. Catalogue no: **825 649-2**
**Cass:** Released Mar '85, on Pasadena Roof Orchestra by Pasadena Roof Orchestra Records. Catalogue no: **ARCT 1018**
**Album:** Released Mar '85, on Pasadena Roof Orchestra by Pasadena Roof Orchestra Records. Catalogue no: **ARC 1018**

**GOOD NEWS**
Tracks: / Good news / Vo do do de o blues / Stormy weather / My canary has circles under his eyes / Choo-choo / Three little words / Home / Everything stops for tea / Pasadena / Sugarfoot stomp / Sing Holly, Go whistle, hey hey / Georgia / That's my weakness now / King's horses, The / Mooche, The / Here's to the next time.
Note: Limited edition.
**Album:** Released Jul '87, on Transatlantic by Transatlantic Records. Catalogue no: **TRA 301**

**HAPPY FEET**
Tracks: / Happy feet / Nightingale sang in Berkeley Square, A / I got rhythm / Georgia on my mind / Cotton Club stomp / I'm crazy 'bout my baby / When it's sleepy time down South / Oh Donna Clara / Makin' wickey wackey down in waikiki / Just squeeze me / Bei mir bist du schon.
Note: Re-release of 1987 album but available on CD for the first time.
**Album:** Released Feb '88, on Pasadena Roof Orchestra by Pasadena Roof Orchestra Records. Catalogue no: **PROOF 1**
**Cass:** Released Feb '88, on Pasadena Roof Orchestra by Pasadena Roof Orchestra Records. Catalogue no: **TCPRO 1**
**CD:** Released Feb '88, on Pasadena Roof Orchestra by Pasadena Roof Orchestra Records. Catalogue no: **CDPRO 1**

**ISN'T IT ROMANTIC**
Tracks: / Isn't it romantic / I won't dance / I've told every little star / Cheek to cheek / Hey Miss Moonlight / Singing in the rain / Whispering / I'll see you again / Dream a little dream of me / Creole love call / Soft shoe shuffle blues / Sunday.
**Album:** Released Jul '87, on Transatlantic by Transatlantic Records. Catalogue no: **TRA 335**

**NIGHT OUT**
**Album:** Released Apr '79, on CBS by CBS Records. Catalogue no: **CBS 83220**
**Cass:** Released Apr '79, on CBS by CBS Records. Catalogue no: **40 83220**

**ON TOUR**
Tracks: / Black bottom / Top hat white tie and tails / East St. Louis toodle-oo / Mississippi mud / Blue skies / Ball and chain / It don't mean a thing / Bye bye blackbird / Clarinet marmalade / Meadow lark / Temptation rag / Nagasaki / Pasadena.
**Album:** Released Jul '87, on Transatlantic by Transatlantic Records. Catalogue no: **TRA 314**

**PASADENA ROOF ORCHESTRA, THE**
**Cass set:** Released '88, on Ditto by Pickwick Records. Catalogue no: **DTO 10253**
**Album:** Released Jul '87, on Transatlantic by Transatlantic Records. Catalogue no: **TRA 286**
**Cass:** Released 7 Nov '87, on Transatlantic by Transatlantic Records. Catalogue no: **TRAC 314**
**CD:** Released May '87, on Pasadena Roof Orchestra by Pasadena Roof Orchestra Records. Catalogue no: **821 745-2**

**PUTTIN' ON THE RITZ**
Tracks: / Young and healthy / I've found a new baby / Mean to me / You're never fully dressed without a smile / Am Sonntag will mein susser mit segein gehn / Going Hollywood / Hooray for Hollywood / There's a rainbow round my shoulder / Isn't this a lovely day / Puttin' on the Ritz / Keep young and beautiful / Little orphan Annie / Yes sir, that's my baby.
**Album:** Released Feb '83, on Spot by Pickwick Records. Catalogue no: **SPR 8528**
**Cass:** Released Feb '83, on Spot by Pickwick Records. Catalogue no: **SPC 8528**

**STEPPING OUT**
Tracks: / Who walks in? / My melancholy baby / How 'm doin? / Creole love call / Sahara / Skirts / Pennies from

heaven / Latin from Manhattan / Business in 'F' / I can't get started / Louisiana / Golden wedding / I only have eyes for you / Minnie the moocher / Stepping out / Pasadena.
**Cass:** Released Jan '90, on Pasadena Roof Orchestra by Pasadena Roof Orchestra Records. Catalogue no: **TCPRO 2**
**CD:** Released Jan '90, on Pasadena Roof Orchestra by Pasadena Roof Orchestra Records. Catalogue no: **CDPRO 2**
**Album:** Released Jan '90, on Pasadena Roof Orchestra by Pasadena Roof Orchestra Records. Catalogue no: **PROOF 2**

**TALKING PICTURE, A**
**Cass:** Released Jun '78, on CBS by CBS Records. Catalogue no: **40 82751**

**TOP HAT, WHITE TIE AND TAILS**
**Cass set:** Released '88, on Ditto by Pickwick Records. Catalogue no: **DTO 10220**

**WAY WE GET IT TOGETHER**
Tracks: / Way we get it together.
**7" Single:** Released May '82, on T. E. R. by That's Entertainment Records. Catalogue no: **TER 002 EP**

## Pass, Joe

**Biographical details:** Joe Pass was born Joseph Anthony Passalaqua in New Brunswick, New Jersey in 1929. He played guitar for bandleader Tony Pastor while still in his teens; after beating a drug problem in the early 1960s he recorded for Pacific Jazz records in California 1963-7 and soon became the most influential jazz guitarist since Wes Montgomery, for the sheer beauty of his technique. He played with George Shearing in the mid-'60s and many others; he also recorded in Europe and has been associated with Norman Granz's Pablo label since 1973, becoming world-famous as a sideman on albums with Oscar Peterson, Count Basie, Ella Fitzgerald, Duke Ellington and many others, also making nearly 20 albums of his own, including solo sets *Virtuoso* (series 1973-c.80), *Live at Montreux* 1977, *I Remember Charlie Parker* and *Live At Long Beach City College*; duets with bassist Niels-Henning Orsted Pederson are *Chops*, *Northsea Nights*, *Digital III At Montreaux* (1978-79). *Checkmate* is a 1981 duet with pianist Jimmy Rowles. (Donald Clarke 15.5.87).

Joe Pass

**AT THE MONTREUX JAZZ FESTIVAL**
Tracks: / You are the sunshine of my life / Very thought of you, The / Nobs / Lil' darlin' / Blues for Nina / How long has this been going on? / More than you know / Grete / Nuages / I'm glad there is you / Willow weep for me.
**Album:** Released '82, on Pablo Jazz (USA) by Pablo Records (USA). Catalogue no: **2310 752**

**BEST OF JOE PASS**
Tracks: / Foxy chick and a cool cat, A / How high the moon? / What are you doing the rest of your life? / Que que ha? / Summertime / Blues for Alican / Satin doll / On Green Dolphin Street.
**Album:** Released Oct '84, on Pablo Jazz (USA) by Pablo Records (USA). Catalogue no: **2310 893**

**BLUES FOR FRED**
Tracks: / Cheek to cheek / Night and day / Blues for Fred / Oh lady be good / Foggy day, A / Be myself / They can't take that away from me / Dancing in the dark / I concentrate on you / Way you look tonight.
**Album:** Released Jan '89, on Pablo Jazz (USA) by Pablo Records (USA). Catalogue no: **PAB 005**

**CHECKMATE (Pass, Joe/Jimmy Rowles)**
Tracks: / What's your story, morning glory? / So rare / As long as I live / Marquita / Stardust / We'll be together again / Can't we be friends? / Deed I do / 'Tis autumn / God bless the child.
**Album:** Released '82, on Pablo Jazz (USA) by Pablo Records (USA). Catalogue no: **D 2310 865**
**CD:** Released May '86, on Pablo Jazz (USA) by Pablo Records (USA). Catalogue no: **CD 311 22**
**CD:** Released '88, on Pablo Jazz (USA) by Pablo Records (USA). Catalogue no: **103 112 2**
**Cass:** Released '82, on Pablo Jazz (USA) by Pablo Records (USA). Catalogue no: **K10 865**

**CHOPS (Pass, Joe and Niels Pederson)**
Tracks: / Have you met Miss Jones? / Oleo / Lover man / Five pound blues / Come rain or come shine / Quiet nights / Tricrotism / Old folks / Yardbird suite / Your own sweet way.
**Cass:** Released '82, on Pablo Jazz (USA) by Pablo Records (USA). Catalogue no: **K10 830**
**Album:** Released '82, on Pablo Jazz (USA) by Pablo Records (USA). Catalogue no: **2310 830**

**COMPLETE 'CATCH ME' SESSIONS**
Tracks: / Catch me / You stepped out of a dream / No cover, no minimum / Just friends / Walkin' up / Summertime / But beautiful / Falling in love with love / Mood indigo / Days of wine and roses.
**Album:** Released Oct '80, on United Artists by EMI Records. Deleted Jan '88. Catalogue no: **LBR 1035**

**EXIMIOUS (Pass, Joe Trio)**
**CD:** Released Apr '87, on Pablo Jazz (USA) by Pablo Records (USA). Catalogue no: **CD 231 0877**

**FITZGERALD AND PASS...AGAIN (see Fitzgerald, Ella) (Pass, Joe & Ella Fitzgerald)**
**Album:** Released '82, on Pablo Jazz (USA) by Pablo Records (USA). Catalogue no: **2310 772**
**Cass:** Released '82, on Pablo Jazz (USA) by Pablo Records (USA). Catalogue no: **K10 772**

**I REMEMBER CHARLIE PARKER**
Tracks: / Just friends / Easy to love / Summertime / April in Paris / Everything happens to me / Laura / They can't take that away from me / I didn't know what time it was / If I should lose you / Out of

nowhere (concept 1) / Out of nowhere (concept 2).
**Album:** Released '82, on Pablo Jazz (USA) by Pablo Records (USA). Catalogue no: **2312 109**
**Cass:** Released '82, on Pablo Jazz (USA) by Pablo Records (USA). Catalogue no: **K 12 109**

**INTERCONTINENTAL**
Tracks: / Chloe / Meditation / I cover the waterfront / I love you / Stompin' at the Savoy / Watch what happens / Joe's blues / El gento / Ode to Billy Joe / Lil' darlin'.
**Album:** Released Oct '85, on Memoir by Memoir Records. Catalogue no: **MOIR 105**
**Cass:** Released Nov '89, on Memoir by Memoir Records. Catalogue no: **CMOIR 105**

**IRA, GEORGE, & JOE**
Tracks: / Bidin' my time / How long has this been going on? / Soon / Lady be good / But not for me / Foggy day, A / It ain't necessarily so / Love is here to stay / 'S wonderful / Nice work if you can get it / Embraceable you.
**Cass:** Released Jul '82, on Pablo Jazz (USA) by Pablo Records (USA). Catalogue no: **K 12133**
**Album:** Released Jul '82, on Pablo Jazz (USA) by Pablo Records (USA). Catalogue no: **2312 133**

**JOE PASS**
Tracks: / Blues for Yano San / Blues for Sitges / Blues for Val / Wait till you see her / She's funny that way / Blues for Martin / Masquerade.
**Cass:** Released '82, on Pablo Jazz (USA) by Pablo Records (USA). Catalogue no: **K 08 212**
**Album:** Released '82, on Pablo Jazz (USA) by Pablo Records (USA). Catalogue no: **2308 212**

**LIVE AT DONTE'S (Pass, Joe Trio)**
Tracks: / What have they done to my song? / You stepped out of a dream / Time for love, A / Donte's inferno / You are the sunshine of my life / Secret love / Sweet Georgia Brown / Stompin' at the Savoy / Darn that dream / Milestones / Lullaby of the leaves / What are you doing the rest of your life? / Blues for Pam.
**CD:** Released Apr '87, on Pablo Jazz (USA) by Pablo Records (USA). Catalogue no: **CD 262 0114**
**Cass:** Released '82, on Pablo Jazz (USA) by Pablo Records (USA). Catalogue no: **2620 114**

**LIVE AT LONG BEACH COLLEGE**
Tracks: / Wave / Blues in G / All the things you are / Round midnight / Here's that rainy day / Duke Ellington's sophisticated lady melange / Blues dues / Bluesette / Honeysuckle rose.
**Cass:** Released Sep '84, on Pablo Jazz (USA) by Pablo Records (USA). Catalogue no: **K 08 2239**
**Album:** Released Sep '84, on Pablo Jazz (USA) by Pablo Records (USA). Catalogue no: **230 8239**
**CD:** Released Apr '87, on Pablo Jazz (USA) by Pablo Records (USA). Catalogue no: **CD 230 8239**

**LIVING LEGENDS, THE (Pass, Joe & Robert Conti)**
Tracks: / Hello young lovers / Stella by starlight / Little girl blue / My romance / Nuages.
Note: Joe Pass, Robert Conti-guitar.
**Album:** Released '88, on Discovery (USA) by Discovery Records (USA). Catalogue no: **DS 906**

**LOVES GERSHWIN**
**CD:** Released May '86, on Pablo Jazz (USA) by Pablo Records (USA). Catalogue no: **CD 231 2133**

**NORTHSEA NIGHTS (Pass, Joe and Niels Pederson)**
Tracks: / If I were a bell / 'Round about midnight / How deep is the ocean? / Stella by starlight / I can't get started / Blues for the Hague.
**Cass:** Released '82, on Pablo Jazz (USA) by Pablo Records (USA). Catalogue no: **K 08 221**
**Album:** Released '82, on Pablo Jazz (USA) by Pablo Records (USA). Catalogue no: **2308 221**

**PORTRAITS OF DUKE ELLINGTON**
Tracks: / Satin doll / I let a song go out of my heart / Sophisticated lady / I got it bad / In a mellow tone / Solitude / Don't get around much anymore / Do nothing till you hear from me / Caravan.
**CD:** Released May '86, on Pablo Jazz (USA) by Pablo Records (USA). Catalogue no: **CD 20027**
**Album:** Released '82, on Pablo Jazz (USA) by Pablo Records (USA). Catalogue no: **231 0716**
**Cass:** Released '82, on Pablo Jazz (USA) by Pablo Records (USA). Catalogue no: **K10 716**

**QUADRANT**
Tracks: / Concorde / Joe's tune / Lady be good / Ray's tune / Grooveyard / Man I love / Blues for the stone.
**Album:** Released Nov '79, on Pablo Jazz (USA) by Pablo Records (USA). Deleted '84. Catalogue no: **2310837**

**STONE JAZZ, THE**
Tracks: / Play with fire / 19th nervous breakdown / I am waiting / Lady Jane / Not fade away / Mothers little helper / I can't get no satisfaction / Paint it black / What a shame / As tears go by / Stone jazz.
**Album:** Released Nov '89, on Memoir by Memoir Records. Catalogue no: **MOIR 505**
**Cass:** Released Nov '89, on Memoir by Memoir Records. Catalogue no: **CMOIR 505**

**TAKE LOVE EASY (Pass, Joe & Ella Fitzgerald)**
**Cass:** Released '82, on Pablo Jazz (USA) by Pablo Records (USA). Catalogue no: **K10 702**
**Album:** Released '82, on Pablo Jazz (USA) by Pablo Records (USA). Catalogue no: **231 0702**

**TUDO BEM! (Pass, Joe and Paulingo Da Costa)**
**Cass:** Released '82, on Pablo Jazz (USA) by Pablo Records (USA). Catalogue no: **K10 824**
**Album:** Released '82, on Pablo Jazz (USA) by Pablo Records (USA). Catalogue no: **231 0824**

**VIRTUOSO**
Tracks: / Night and day / Stella by starlight / Here's that rainy day / My old flame / How high the moon / Cherokee / Sweet Lorraine / Have you met Miss Jones? / Round midnight / All the things you are / Blues for Alican / Song is you, The.
**CD:** Released '88, on Pablo Jazz (USA) by Pablo Records (USA). Catalogue no: **131 121 5**
**Cass:** Released '82, on Pablo Jazz (USA) by Pablo Records (USA). Catalogue no: **K10 708**
**Album:** Released '82, on Pablo Jazz (USA) by Pablo Records (USA). Catalogue no: **231 0708**

**VIRTUOSO NO.2**
Tracks: / Giant steps / Five hundred miles / Grooveyard / Misty / Joy spring / Blues for O. P. / On Green Dolphin Street / Windows / Blues for Basie / Feelings / If / Limehouse blues.
**Cass:** Released '82, on Pablo Jazz (USA) by Pablo Records (USA). Catalogue no: **K10 788**
**Album:** Released '82, on Pablo Jazz (USA) by Pablo Records (USA). Catalogue no: **231 0788**

**VIRTUOSO NO.3**
Tracks: / Off beat / Trinidad / Nina's blues / Sevenths / Ninth / Dissonance / Minor detail / Pablo de Lucia / Sultry / Passanova / Pasta blues / Dissonance no. 2.
**Album:** Released '82, on Pablo Jazz (USA) by Pablo Records (USA). Catalogue no: **231 0805**
**Cass:** Released '82, on Pablo Jazz (USA) by Pablo Records (USA). Catalogue no: **K10 805**

**VIRTUOSO NO.4**
Tracks: / Lush life / Indian summer / Autumn leaves / Yesterdays / Come Sunday / Lover man (oh where can you be) / Come rain or come shine / My shining hour / I'll remember April / Some day my prince will come / Acoustic blues / Now's the time / I can't get started / It's a wonderful world / Man I love, The / Nearness of you, The / Limehouse blues / Easy living.
**Album:** Released May '83, on Pablo Jazz (USA) by Pablo Records (USA). Catalogue no: **2640 102**
**Cass:** Released May '83, on Pablo Jazz (USA) by Pablo Records (USA). Catalogue no: **K40 102**

**WE'LL BE TOGETHER AGAIN (Pass, Joe/J J Johnson)**
Tracks: / Wave / We'll be together again / Naked as a jaybird / Blue bossa / Limehouse blues / How long has this been going on? / Bud's blues / Nature boy / Solar / When lights are low.
**Album:** Released Mar '85, on Pablo Jazz (USA) by Pablo Records (USA). Catalogue no: **231 0911**
**Cass:** Released Mar '85, on Pablo Jazz (USA) by Pablo Records (USA). Cata-

logue no: **K10 911**
**CD:** Released Apr '87, on Pablo Jazz (USA) by Pablo Records (USA). Catalogue no: **CD 231 0911**

**WHITESTONE**
Tracks: / Light in your eyes / Shuffle city / Estate / Daquilo que eu sei / Whitestone / Lovin' eyes / Amancer / I can't help it / Tarde / Fleeting moments.
Note: Personnel includes: John Pisano-rhythm guitar/ Don Grusin-keyboards/ Harvey Mason-drums/ Abraham Laboriel & Nathan East-bass/ Paulinho Da Costa-percussion/ Armando Compean-vocalist on'Lovin'Eyes'.
**Cass:** Released Aug '85, on Pablo Jazz (USA) by Pablo Records (USA). Catalogue no: **K10 912**
**Album:** Released Aug '85, on Pablo Jazz (USA) by Pablo Records (USA). Catalogue no: **2310 912**
**CD:** Released Apr '86, on Pablo Jazz (USA) by Pablo Records (USA). Catalogue no: **2310 912**

## Pastor, Guy

**ITS MAGIC**
**CD:** Released Feb '89, on USA by Charly Records. Catalogue no: **USACD 584**

**THIS IS IT**
Tracks: / Just the way you are / Chicago / it goes like it goes.
Note: Featuring Guy Pastor-vocals, Mike Garson-keyboards, Abraham Laboreil-bass, Alex Acuna-drums, Sue Raney and Morgana King-vocals.
**Album:** Released '88, on Discovery (USA) by Discovery Records (USA). Catalogue no: **DS 918**

## Pastor, Tony

**Biographical details:** Tony Pastor (1907-69) was born Antonio Pestritto in Middletown, Connecticut; the tenor saxist and novelty vocalist became a star with Artie Shaw (his zany vocal on *Indian Lova Call* was on the other side of Shaw's giant hit *Begin the Beguine* in 1938). He formed his own band and had more than a dozen top 20 hits in the '40s, keeping the band going until 1959; later he had a night club act with sons Guy, John, Tony Jr. (Donald Clarke 15.5.87).

**1944-1947: TONY PASTOR (Pastor, Tony & His Orchestra)**
**Album:** Released Aug '88, on Circle (USA) by Jazzology Records (USA). Catalogue no: **CLP 31**

**CONFESSIN' 1940 - 49 (Pastor, Tony & His Orchestra)**
**Cass:** Released Jun '88, on Bandstand Catalogue no: **BS 7114C**
**Album:** Released Jun '88, on Bandstand Catalogue no: **BS 7114**

**LET'S DANCE WITH T.P. (Pastor, Tony & His Orchestra)**
**Album:** Released Feb '88, on Fresh Sounds (Spain) by Fresh Sounds Records (Spain). Catalogue no: **FS 131**

**LIVE: TONY PASTOR AND ORCHESTRA 1947 (Pastor, Tony & His Orchestra)**
**Album:** Released '88, on Fanfare by Captain Billy's Music. Catalogue no: **LP 42-142**

**MR. PASTOR GOES TO TOWN**
Tracks: / Funiculi funicula / Hollywood bowl / Mr. Pastor goes to town / Deed I do / Don't worry 'bout strangers / King Porter stomp / That's good enough for me / Paradiddle Joe / 'S wonderful / Dancing room only / Swinging on a star / I learned a lesson.
**Album:** Released '84, on Swing House by Submarine Records. Catalogue no: **SWH 36**

**RADIO DISCS OF ...LATE 1940'S,**
**Album:** Released Jul '82, on Joyce Catalogue no: **JLP 2001**

**WITH ROSEMARY AND BETTY CLOONEY 1942-47 (Pastor, Tony & His Orchestra)**
**Album:** Released 10 Jul '89, on Circle Catalogue no: **CLP 121**

## Pastorius, Jaco

**Biographical details:** Jaco Pastorius was born John Francis in Morristown, Pennsylvania in 1951; he played electric bass in local bands in Fort Lauderdale, Florida, also backing visiting stars such as the Supremes, the Temptations and Nancy Wilson; he soaked up country music and the music of the Carribean. With his enormous technical skill he has helped to redefine the bass in modern popular music. As a member of Weather Report he played on all their best albums; his first solo album was recorded for Epic in '73, and the other two for Warner Brothers. He has also recorded with Ira Sullivan, Paul Bley, Joni Mitchell, Pat Metheny, and others. (Donald Clarke 15.5.87).

**JACO PASTORIOUS**
**CD:** Released '88, on CBS by CBS Records. Deleted Jan '90. Catalogue no: **CD 81453**

**JAZZ STREET (Pastorius, Jaco / Brian Melvin)**
Tracks: / No clack / Miles modes / Wedding waltz / Drums of Yadzarah / Jazz Street / May day / Out of the night.
Note: Recorded Oct-Nov 1986. Personnel: Jaco Pastorius (bass), Brian Melvin (drums), Rick Smith (saxes), Jan Davis (piano), Paul Monsavi (gtr), Keith Jones (bass), Bill Keaney (percussion).
**CD:** Released Jun '89, on Timeless by Timeless Records. Catalogue no: **CDSJP 258**
**Album:** Released Jun '89, on Timeless by Timeless Records. Catalogue no: **SJP 258**

**WORD OF MOUTH**
Tracks: / Crisis / Three views of X secret / Liberty city / Chromatic fantasy / Blackbird / Word of mouth / John and Mary.
**Album:** Released Aug '81, on Warner Bros. by WEA Records. Deleted Aug '86. Catalogue no: **K 56897**

## Patitucci, John

**JOHN PATITUCCI**
Tracks: / Growing / Wind spirit / Searching, finding / Baja bajo / Change of seasons / Our family / Peace and quiet time / Crestline / Zaragoza / Then and now (Bonus track on CD only.) / Killeen (Bonus track on CD only.) / View, The (Bonus track on CD only.).
Note: "Stepping out of the Chick Corea Elektric Band comes bass player John Patitucci in what us clearly the most impressive debut of a bassist since the late Jaco Pastorious came on the scene. A rising star who has swept over the jazz world in the past several years, John Patitucci moved from playing with Freddie Hubbard, David Sanborn and the Crusaders to become a highly visible and integral part of the Chick Corea Elektric Band. With Michael Brecker, Chick Corea, Peter Erskine, Dave Weckl, Vinnie Colaiuta." (IMS Records, May 1988.)
**Cass:** Released May '88, on GRP by GRP Records (USA). Catalogue no: **GRPM 91049**
**CD:** Released 21 Mar '88, on GRP by GRP Records (USA). Catalogue no: **GRPD 9560**
**Album:** Released May '88, on GRP by GRP Records (USA). Catalogue no: **GRP 91049**

**ON THE CORNER**
**CD:** Released 20 Mar '89, on GRP by GRP Records (USA). Catalogue no: **D 9583**
**Cass:** Released 12 Apr '89, on GRP by GRP Records (USA). Catalogue no: **GRP 95834**
**Cass:** Released 20 Mar '89, on GRP by GRP Records (USA). Catalogue no: **C 9583**
**Album:** Released 12 Apr '89, on GRP by GRP Records (USA). Catalogue no: **GRP 95831**
**CD:** Released 12 Apr '89, on GRP by GRP Records (USA). Catalogue no: **GRP 95832**
**Album:** Released 20 Mar '89, on GRP by GRP Records (USA). Catalogue no: **A 9583**

## Patterson, Ottilie

**BACK IN THE OLD DAYS (Patterson, Ottilie with Chris Barber)**
Tracks: / There'll be a hot time in the old town tonight / Lordy Lord / Basin Street blues / T'aint what you do / Bad spell blues / Squeeze me.
**Album:** Released Apr '88, on Chris Barber Collection Catalogue no: **CBJBLP 4001**
**Cass:** Released Apr '88, on Chris Barber Collection Catalogue no: **ZCBJB 4001**
**CD:** Released Apr '88, on Chris Barber Collection Catalogue no: **CBJBCD 4001**

**CARELESS LOVE**
Tracks: / Careless love / Georgia grind.
**7" Single:** Released Nov '82, on Fat Hen by Fat Hen Records. Catalogue no: **FM 001**

**MADAME BLUES AND DOCTOR JAZZ (Patterson, Ottilie with Chris Barber)**
Tracks: / Georgia grind / There'll be a hot time in the old town tonight / Baby, won't you please come home / Stumbling block / I'm a salty dog / I'm a salty

dog / Doctor Jazz / A.U..
**Album:** Released Jul '84, on Black Lion Catalogue no: **BLM 51101**

## Patton, Charlie

**CHARLIE PATTON**
**2 LP Set:** Released Oct '88, on Yazoo (USA) by Shanachie Records (USA). Catalogue no: **L 1020**

**FOUNDER OF DELTA BLUES**
**2 LP Set:** Released Dec '88, on Yazoo (USA) by Shanachie Records (USA). Catalogue no: **L 1020**

**REMAINING TITLES 1929-34**
**Album:** Released '88, on Wolf Catalogue no: **WSE 103**

## Patton, John

**BLUE JOHN**
Tracks: / Hot sauce / Bermuda clay house / Dem dirty dues / Country girl / Nicety / Blue John.
**CD:** Released Oct '89, on Blue Note by EMI Records. Catalogue no: **CDP 784 143 2**
**CD:** Released Oct '89, on Blue Note by EMI Records. Catalogue no: **BNZ 226**
**Album:** Released Jul '89, on Blue Note by EMI Records. Catalogue no: **BST 84143**

**SOUL CONNECTION**
**Album:** Released Apr '84, on Nilva (Switzerland) Catalogue no: **NQ 3406**

## Patton, Sims

**PATTON, SIMS & BERTHA LEE (Patton, Sims & Bertha Lee)**
**Album:** Released Dec '88, on Herwin by Shanachie Records (USA). Catalogue no: **HER 213**

## Paul, Les

**Biographical details:** Les Paul was born Lester Polfus in Waukesha, Wisconsin in 1915; he has done more for the electric guitar than anyone else except Charlie Christian, with whom he was sometimes compared. He began playing on the radio in Wisconsin, then Chicago; he played country music as Hot Rod Red and Rhubarb Red; formed a jazz-oriented Les Paul Trio in 1936 and led it for nearly a decade ( a few tracks now on Guitar Genius on Charly). He also recorded with Bing Crosby and the Andrews Sisters on the American Decca label; by the time he toured with Jazz At The Philharmonic in the late '40s he was building his own guitars; he took the first solid-body electric guitar to Gibson in 1946, and the Les Paul model became one of the most famous guitars in the world. *Lover/Brazil* '48 was a two-sided hit on Capitol, overdubbed until it sounded like six guitars; he broke his right elbow in a car crash and had it reset at an angle so he could still play; the instrumental hits continued through 1953, including *Nola* (a piano novelty from 1919) with Paul playing both electric and Spanish guitars. Meanwhile he met country singer Mary Ford (born Colleen Summers in 1928; they married in 1949, seperated in 1963 and she died in 1977). Les Paul and Mary Ford were among the biggest hitmakers of the early '50s in the USA; 28 hits 1950-57 three at no. 2, *How high the moon* and *Vaya con dios* at no.1, the latter for 11 weeks in 1953. Les Paul's Capitol recordings used technology that was ahead of its time, most recorded in his own studio using an 8-track desk of his design, both his guitar and her voice overdubbed, and they stand up very well today. He retired to his work bench except for the album in 1968, but became active again in the mid-'70s, performing and promoting his guitars for Gibson; he moved full circle back to country picking, recording with his old friend Chet Atkins, winning a Grammy for *Chester And Lester* in 1977, followed by *Guitar monsters* '78. He was featured in a TV documentary, The Wizard of Waukesha, in 1980. (Donald Clarke 15.5.87).

**16 ORIGINAL HITS (Paul, Les & Mary Ford)**
**Cass:** Released 7 Nov '87, on Timeless Treasures Catalogue no: **MC 1630**

**ALL TIME GREATEST HITS (Paul, Les & Mary Ford)**
Tracks: / How high the moon / Jazz me blues / I'm sitting on top of the world / Nola / Bye bye blues / Chicken reel / Jealous / Lover / Little Rock getaway / I'm forever blowing bubbles / Goofus / St. Louis blues / La Rosita / World is waiting for the sunrise, The / Carioca / Vaya con Dios / Johnny is the boy for me / Walkin' and whistlin' blues / Tiger rag / Lady of Spain / Mockin' bird hill / Whispering / Tico tico / Meet Mr Callaghan / Mr. Sandman / Tennessee waltz / I'm a fool to care / 12th Street rag / Falling in love with love / Best things in life are free, The.
**Album:** Released Jan '83, on EMI (Holland) by EMI Records. Catalogue no: **5C 134 53027/28**

**ALL-TIME HITS (Paul, Les & Mary Ford)**
**Cass:** Released Dec '88, on Capitol (Specials) Catalogue no: **4XL 9101**

**CAPITOL YEARS, THE: LES PAUL & Best of (Paul, Les & Mary Ford)**
Tracks: / Whispering / World is waiting for the sunrise, The / Lover / Mockin' bird hill / Nola / That old feeling / Little Rock getaway / Bye bye blues / Twelfth St. rag / I'm sitting on top of the world / Chicken reel / How high the moon / Walkin' and whistlin' blues / How deep is the ocean / Tico tico / Vaya con dios.
**Album:** Released Jan '89, on Capitol by EMI Records. Catalogue no: **EMS 1309**
**CD:** Released Jan '89, on Capitol by EMI Records. Catalogue no: **CDP 791 299 2**
**Cass:** Released Jan '89, on Capitol by EMI Records. Catalogue no: **TCEMS 1309**

**FEEDBACK (1944-1945) (Paul, Les & His Trio)**
Note: Mono
**Album:** Released Dec '86, on Circle (USA) by Jazzology Records (USA). Catalogue no: **CLP 67**

**HOW HIGH THE MOON (Paul, Les & Mary Ford)**
Tracks: / How high the moon / Vaya con Dios.
**10" Single:** Released Feb '83, on Capitol by EMI Records. Deleted '88. Catalogue no: **10CL 282**
**7" Single:** Released Feb '83, on Capitol by EMI Records. Deleted '88. Catalogue no: **CL 282**

**LES PAUL & MARY FORD (EMI) (Paul, Les & Mary Ford)**
Tracks: / Mississippi blues / Carry me on / Je t'aime la vie / La ballade du chien loup.
**Album:** Released '88, on EMI (Holland) by EMI Records. Catalogue no: **1A 022 58099**
**Cass:** Released '88, on EMI (Holland) by EMI Records. Catalogue no: **1A 222 58099**

**LES PAUL & MARY FORD (Paul, Les & Mary Ford)**
Tracks: / Three little words / I can't give you anything but love / Vaya con Dios / Just one more chance / Carioca / In the good old Summertime / Moon of Manakoora, The / Lover / How high the moon / I'm confessin' / Bye bye blues / Whispering / Lonesome road / Don'cha hear them bells / How deep is the ocean / World is waiting for the sunrise, The.
**Album:** Released Sep '87, on Entertainers Catalogue no: **ENT LP 13014**
**Cass:** Released '88, on Entertainers Catalogue no: **ENT MC 13014**

**NEW SOUND VOLUME II, THE (Paul, Les & Mary Ford)**
Tracks: / In the good old summertime / Three little words / Lonesome road / Chicken reel / I'm confessin' / Carioca / I can't give you anything but love / Just one more chance / I'm forever blowing bubbles / Moon of Manakoora / Don'cha hear them bells / La rosita.
Note: Here we bring you the nostalgic 'New Sound' of the 50's by the duo who enjoyed million selling hits in their era. As ever, the album features the multi-track vocal and guitar effects which the couple pioneered and which are so popular today.
**Album:** Released Dec '85, on Capitol by EMI Records. Deleted Jan '88. Catalogue no: **EMS 1138**
**Cass:** Released Dec '85, on Capitol by EMI Records. Deleted Jul '87. Catalogue no: **TCEMS 1138**

**VAYA CON DIOS (Paul, Les & Mary Ford)**
Tracks: / Vaya con dios.
**7" Single:** Released Nov '53, on Capitol by EMI Records. Deleted '56. Catalogue no: **CL 13943**

**VERY BEST OF LES PAUL AND MARY (Paul, Les & Mary Ford)**
Tracks: / How high the moon / I'm sitting on top of the world / I'm forever blowing bubbles / Nola / Bye bye blues / Chicken reel / Jealous / Lover / Little rock getaway / Goofus / Jazz me blues / St. Louis blues / La Rosita / World is waiting for the sunrise, The / Carioca / Vaya Con Dios.
**Album:** Released Apr '83, on MFP by

EMI Records. Deleted '87. Catalogue no: **MFP 5604**
**Cass:** Released Apr '83, on MFP by EMI Records. Deleted '87. Catalogue no: **TCMFP 5604**

## Payne, Cecil

**Biographical details:** Payne, a jazz baritone saxophonist, was born in 1922 in Brooklyn, New York; also plays alto sax and flute. Baritone players are relatively few, and Payne is one of the best. He has been recording since 1946, toured with the Dizzy Gillespie big band in 1947-8; he acted and played in The Connection in 1961, a play about drugs with incidental music; among albums he has played on are Tadd Dameron's lovely *Fontainebleau* '56 and John Coltrane's darkly beautiful *Dakar* '57 (with Coltrane, Pepper Adams also on baritone, and rhythm: no brass). Nine albums of his own, five with Duke Jordan on piano, include *Brookfield andante* '66, made in Manchester with a UK rhythm section. (Donald Clarke 15.5.87).

**BIRD GETS THE WORM**
**Album:** Released Apr '81, on Muse by Black & Blue Records. Catalogue no: **MR 5061**

**BRIGHT MOMENTS**
Tracks: / Violets for your furs / Skylark / Lover man / Equinoxe / Disorder at the border / Bright moments / Solar / Speak low.
Note: Bariton sax star Payne is joined by trombonist Curtis Fuller.
**Album:** Released '83, on Spotlite by Spotlite Records. Catalogue no: **SPJ LP21**

**BROOKFIELD ANDANTE**
Tracks: / Opener, The / Sterling place / Brookfield andante / Azoff blues.
Note: Baritone man Payne recorded live with piano, bass and drums.
**Album:** Released '83, on Spotlite by Spotlite Records. Catalogue no: **CP 2**

**CONNECTION, THE (Payne, Cecil/Clark Terry & Bennie Green)**
Tracks: / Stop and listen / Born again blues / Dear people / Kenny's one / Sister Carol / Mighty fine wine / It's your life.
**Album:** Released Jan '82, on Jazz Reactivation Catalogue no: **JR 105**

## Payne, Freda

**Biographical details:** A fine jazz and soul singer, Freda Payne was born in Detroit in 1945. She will always be famous for her huge 1970 hit *Band of gold*. Earlier she had sung with Quincy Jones and Duke Ellington. After her success on Holland-Dozier-Holland's Invictus label she reverted to jazz, hosted a USA TV show and remained popular in clubs. (Donald Clarke, May 1987.).

**BAND OF GOLD**
Tracks: / Band of gold / Easiest way to fall.
**7" Single:** Released Jan '81, on Champagne by unknown. Deleted Jan '84. Catalogue no: **VAT 301**
**7" Single:** Released Sep '70, on Invictus Deleted '73. Catalogue no: **INV 502**
**7" Single:** Released Jun '89, Catalogue no: **HGH 451**
**12" Single:** Released Jan '81, on Champagne by unknown. Deleted Jan '84. Catalogue no: **VATS 301**

**BANDS OF GOLD**
**Album:** Released Apr '84, on HDH (Holland/Dozier/Holland) by Demon Records. Catalogue no: **HDH LP 002**

**BAND OF GOLD (SINGLE)**
**7" Single:** Released Mar '84, on HDH (Holland/Dozier/Holland) by Demon Records. Catalogue no: **HDH 451**

**CHERISH WHAT IS DEAR TO YOU**
Tracks: / Cherish what is dear to you.
**7" Single:** Released Mar '71, on Invictus Deleted '74. Catalogue no: **INV 509**

**DEEPER AND DEEPER The best of ...**
Tracks: / Unhooked generation / I left some dreams back there / Rock me in the cradle of love / Cherish what is dear to you / Mama's gone / Bring the boys home / You brought the joy / I'm not getting any better / You've got to love somebody / Road we didn't take, The / He's my life / Band of gold / Deeper and deeper / Easiest way to fall, The / Now is the time to say goodbye / Just a woman / Through the memory of my mind / World don't owe you a thing, The / Suddenly it's yesterday / How can I live without my life / Odds and ends / You're the only bargain I've got.
**CD:** Released Aug '89, on HDH (Holland/Dozier/Holland) by Demon Records. Catalogue no: **HDH CD 005**
**Album:** Released Jul '89, on HDH (Holland/Dozier/Holland) by Demon Records. Catalogue no: **HDH LP 005**

**DEEPER & DEEPER**
Tracks: / Deeper and deeper.
**7" Single:** Released Nov '70, on Invictus Deleted '73. Catalogue no: **INV 505**

**GREATEST HITS: FREDA PAYNE**
**Cass:** Released Oct '88, on BR Music/BR Music (Holland) by BR Music Records. Catalogue no: **BRMC 62**
**Album:** Released Oct '88, on BR Music/BR Music (Holland) by BR Music Records. Catalogue no: **BRLP 62**

**IN MOTION**
Tracks: / In motion.
**7" Single:** Released Nov '82, on Buddah by Buddah Records Inc.(USA). Deleted Nov '85. Catalogue no: **BDS 498**

**LOVE MAGNET**
Tracks: / Love magnet / Bring back the joy.
**7" Single:** Released Jan '78, on Capitol by EMI Records. Deleted '81. Catalogue no: **CL 15959**

## Payne, Jack

**GOLDEN AGE OF JACK PAYNE THE**
**Album:** Released Jul '85, on Golden Age by EMI Records. Catalogue no: **41 2535 4**

**I'LL STRING ALONG WITH YOU**
Tracks: / This'll make you whistle / My song for you / Tina / I'll string along with you / Little valley in the mountains / Over my shoulder / Guilty / Isle of Capri / Close your eyes / Until the real thing comes along / Nun-yuff and sun-yuff / Juba, The / Organ grinder's swing / Shadows on the pavement / When your hair has turned to silver / When it's Springtime in the Rockies / Just imagine / Sunny days.
**CD:** Released Sep '88, on Burlington (nostalgia) by Counterpoint Distribution. Catalogue no: **2 BUR 008**
**Cass:** Released Jul '88, on Burlington (nostalgia) by Counterpoint Distribution. Catalogue no: **4BUR 008**
**Album:** Released Jun '88, on Burlington (nostalgia) by Counterpoint Distribution. Catalogue no: **BUR 008**

**IMPERIAL DAYS, THE**
Tracks: / Smile and sing your cares away / Paradise / Love is the sweetest thing / Was that the human thing to do? / Good morning Mr. Sun / Love me tonight / Lullaby of the leaves / By the sycamore tree / Good evening / Auf wiedersehen my dear / While we danced at the Mardi Gras / I'll do my best to make you happy / Wanderer / She didn't say yes / Ooh that kiss / Where the blue of the night.
**Album:** Released Aug '83, on Joy by President Records. Deleted Aug '88. Catalogue no: **D 273**
**Album:** Released Jun '88, on Joy by President Records. Catalogue no: **JOY 273**
**Cass:** Released Jun '88, on Joy by President Records. Catalogue no: **JOYTC 273**

**JACK PAYNE**
**Album:** Released '70, on Retrospect by EMI Records. Catalogue no: **SH 143**

**RADIO NIGHTS, 1928-31 (Payne, Jack & His BBC Dance Orchestra)**
Tracks: / Radio nights / I've got a feeling I'm falling / Anything you say / If I could be with you one hour tonight / Old Italian love song / I'm crazy over you / Sweet Sue / Moonlight saving time / Down by the old front gate / Here comes Emily Brown / My baby just cares for me / Make yourself a happiness pie / You're driving me crazy / Dicky bird told me so / She's my slip of a girl / Exactly like you / Haven't I? / Haven't heard a single word from baby / Look in her eyes / I like a little girl like that.
**Album:** Released Apr '83, on Saville by Conifer Records. Catalogue no: **SVL 152**
**Cass:** Released Jan '86, on Saville by Conifer Records. Catalogue no: **CSVL 152**

**RHYTHMATITIS**
Tracks: / Yes sir, that's my baby / Sally's come back / Out of the dawn / Sweet Sue / Little dicky bird told me so, A / I faw down an' go boom / Blondy / When it's Springtime in the Rockies / Moochi, The / My baby just cares for me / If I could be with you (one hour tonight) / Lady of Spain / River stay 'way from my door / Miss

Elizabeth Brown / Lazy day / When the moon comes over the mountain / Rhythmatitis / Guilty / Love letters in the sand / Hot coffee.
**Album:** Released Jul '86, on Retrospect by EMI Records. Deleted 31 Jul '88. Catalogue no: **SH 508**
**Cass:** Released Jul '86, on Retrospect by EMI Records. Deleted 31 Jul '88. Catalogue no: **TC SH 508**

## Peacock, Annette

**Biographical details:** Singer, composer and multi-instrumentalist Peacock moved from jazz to jazz-rock to free form, always from a position of feminist integrity. She eloped, at 19, with bassist Gary Peacock, met Paul Bley and succeeded Carla Bley as his chief composer. Bley's 1967 trio album, *Ballads*, used her themes entirely and helped to set the style of the new ECM label. He has recorded about 35 of her songs and they were among the first to use synthesisers in jazz-fusion, in concert with Hans Bennink and others. She also invented a way to sing through the synth. Peacock's own debut LP, *Revenge*, released in 1972, was made with Bley's trio. Three albums on Aura included jazz-rock jams with Bill Bruford and she sessioned on Bruford's Feels Good To Me in '78. The first LP for her own Ironic label that year was Sky-skating, live concert recordings on which she played all the instruments, acoustic, electric, synth and percussion. In 1987 she toured Europe and performed with Karlheinz Stockhausen. (Donald Clarke, May 1987.).

**ABSTRACT CONTACT**
**Album:** Released Jun '88, on Ironic by Ironic Records. Catalogue no: **IRONIC 5**
**CD:** Released Aug '88, on Ironic by Ironic Records. Catalogue no: **IRONIC 5CD**

**BEEN IN THE STREETS TOO LONG**
Tracks: / Been in the streets too long / So hard, it hurts / Song to seperate, A / Half broken / Safe inside the fantasy / Pillow lined prison / No winning, no losing.
**Album:** Released May '83, on Ironic by Ironic Records. Catalogue no: **IRONIC 3**

**I HAVE NO FEELINGS**
Tracks: / Nothing ever was, anyway / Butterflie / I'm not perfect / I have no feelings / Cynic,The / Carousel / You've left me / Sincereless / Freefall / This almost spring / Feeling's free, The / Personal revolution, A / Not enough.
Note: Annette's third album on Ironic records, the previous two were *SkySkating* and *Been in the streets too long* both of which sold well. Annette is one of todays leading contemporary music composers/ musicians with a large cult following, *I have no feelings* is something of an event and will be eagerly received by critics and fans alike. Personnel: Anette Peacock - all music and words, all vocals and instruments, arrangements and programming; Roger Turner - percussion and paiste cymbals/Benjamin Allen - sound/ Alfrede Benje - cover painting
**CD:** Released Feb '86, on Ironic by Ironic Records. Catalogue no: **IRONIC 4CD**
**Album:** Released Feb '86, on Ironic by Ironic Records. Catalogue no: **IRONIC 4**

**I'M THE ONE**
Tracks: / I'm the one / Seven days / Pony / Been and gone / Blood / One way / Love me tender / Gesture without plot / Did you hear me mommy.
**Cass:** Released Jul '86, on RCA by BMG Records (UK). Deleted Jul '89. Catalogue no: **NK 89900**
**Album:** Released Jul '86, on RCA by BMG Records (UK). Deleted Jul '89. Catalogue no: **NL 89900**

**LOVE'S OUT TO LUNCH**
Tracks: / Love's out to lunch / Rubber hunger.
**7" Single:** Released Nov '82, on Aura Records by Aura Records. Deleted '88. Catalogue no: **AUS 113**

**PERFECT RELEASE**
Tracks: / Love's out to lunch / Solar systems / American sport / Loss of consiousness / Rubber hunger / Succubus / Survival.
**Album:** Released Oct '79, on Aura Records by Aura Records. Catalogue no: **AUL 707**

**SKY-SKATING**
**Album:** Released May '82, on Ironic by Ironic Records. Catalogue no: **IRONIC 2**
**CD:** Released Jul '89, on Ironic by Ironic Records. Catalogue no: **IRONIC 2CD**

**SKY-SKATING (SINGLE)**
**7" Single:** Released Dec '81, on Ironic by Ironic Records. Catalogue no: **IRONIC 1**

**X-DREAMS**
Tracks: / My mama never taught me how to cook / Real and defined androgens / Dear Bela / This feeling within' / Too much in the skies / Don't be cruel / Questions.
**Album:** Released Jul '79, on Aura Records by Aura Records. Catalogue no: **AUL 702**
**Album:** Released Mar '88, on Line by Line Records (W.Germany). Catalogue no: **LIL 400490**

## Peacock, Gary

**Biographical details:** Peacock is one of the best and most influential modern jazz bassists, born in Barley, Idaho in 1935. He played and toured with Bill Evans and Paul Bley, pianists well-known for hiring fine bassists; he also worked with George Russell, Don Cherry, Miles Davis and many others. He's made many fine albums as a sideman as well as several of his own, mostly on ECM. (Donald Clarke 15.5.87).

**DECEMBER POEMS**
**Album:** Released Mar '79, on ECM Catalogue no: **ECM 1119**

**GUAMBA**
Tracks: / Guamba / Requiem / Celina / Thyme time / Lila / Introending / Gardenia.
**Album:** Released Sep '87, on ECM Catalogue no: **ECM 1352**
**CD:** Released Oct '87, on ECM Catalogue no: **833 039 2**

**SHIFT IN THE WIND**
Tracks: / So green / Fractions / Last first / Shift in the wind centers / Caverns beneath the zoth / Valentine.
**Album:** Released Apr '81, on ECM Catalogue no: **ECM 1165**
**CD:** Released Aug '86, on ECM Catalogue no: **820 159-2**

**TALES OF... (Peacock, Gary, K. Jarrett & J. DeJohnette)**
**Album:** Released Aug '77, on ECM Catalogue no: **ECM 1101**

**TALES OF ANOTHER**
Tracks: / Vignette / Tone field / Major / Trilogy / Trilogy (II) / Trilogy (III).
**Cass:** Released Jul '85, on ECM Catalogue no: **7104659**
**CD:** Released Feb '86, on ECM Catalogue no: **827 418-2**

**VOICES FROM THE PAST - PARADIGM**
**Album:** Released May '82, on ECM Catalogue no: **ECM 1210**

## Pearce-Pickering

**1975-76 (Pearce-Pickering Barrelhouse Jazz Band)**
**Album:** Released Jan '83, on Swaggie (Australia) Catalogue no: **2LP 001**

**BARRELHOUSE JB**
**Album:** Released '88, on Swaggie (Australia) Catalogue no: **S 1404**

**FLANAGAN'S SHENANIGANS (1971-72) (Pearce-Pickering Ragtime Five)**
**Album:** Released Jan '83, on Swaggie (Australia) Catalogue no: **S 1309**

**RED HOT & BLUE (Pearce-Pickering Barrelhouse Jazz Band)**
**Album:** Released Sep '87, on Candle Catalogue no: **CFPS 122**

**TIN LIZZIE DAYS (1970-71) (Pearce-Pickering Ragtime Five)**
**Album:** Released Jan '83, on Swaggie (Australia) Catalogue no: **S 1293**

## Pearson, Duke

**WAHOO**
Tracks: / Amanda / Bedouin / Farewell Machelle / Wahoo / E.S.P. (extra sensory perception) / Fly, little bird fly.
**CD:** Released Mar '89, on Blue Note by EMI Records. Catalogue no: **CDP 784 191 2**
**CD:** Released Mar '89, on Blue Note by EMI Records. Catalogue no: **BNZ 134**
**Album:** Released Jul '89, on Blue Note by EMI Records. Catalogue no: **BST 84191**

## Pedersen, Niels

**CHOPS (Pedersen, Niels & Joe Pass)**
**Cass:** Released '82, on Pablo Jazz (USA) by Pablo Records (USA). Catalogue no: **K10 830**
**Album:** Released '82, on Pablo Jazz (USA) by Pablo Records (USA). Cata-

logue no: **231 0830**

**ETERNAL TRAVELLER, THE**
Tracks: / Moto perpetu / En elefant kom marcherende / Jeg gik ud en sommerdag / Det haver sa nyeligen regnet / His hvor vejen slar en bugt / Jeg ved en Laerkerede / Sig manen langsomt haever / Dawn / Eternal traveller / Skul gammel venskab / Rejn forgo / Moto perpetuo.
Note: Niels-Henning Orsted Pedersen - bass. Ole Kock Hansen - piano. Lennant Gruvstedt - drums. Recorded November 1984.
**Cass:** Released Aug '85, on Pablo Jazz (USA) by Pablo Records (USA). Catalogue no: **K10 910**
**Album:** Released Aug '85, on Pablo Jazz (USA) by Pablo Records (USA). Catalogue no: **2310 910**

**VIKING, THE**
Tracks: / Puzzle, The / My funny valentine / Marie / Nuages / Air power / Dancing girls / September start / Little train / Stella by starlight / I fall in love too easily.
Note: Niels Henning Orsted Pederson - bass. Philip Catherine - guitar. Recorded 1983.
**Album:** Released Oct '84, on Pablo Jazz (USA) by Pablo Records (USA). Catalogue no: **2310 894**
**CD:** Released Apr '87, on Pablo Jazz (USA) by Pablo Records (USA). Catalogue no: **CD 231 0894**

## Pell, Chris Orchestra

**50 HIT SOUNDS OF BIG BANDS**
**2 LP Set:** Released May '77, on Pickwick by Pickwick Records. Catalogue no: **50DA 310**

**BIG BAND FAVOURITES**
Tracks: / Songs of India / I could write a book / Sophisticated lady / And the angels sing / It's been a long long time / Christopher Columbus / Jersey bounce / Just a gigolo / Yesterdays / I let a song go out of my heart / I concentrate on you / Green eyes.
**Cass set:** Released Jul '82, on Ditto by Pickwick Records. Catalogue no: **DTO 10033**

## Pell, Dave

**PLAYS AGAIN (Pell, Dave Quartet)**
**Album:** Released Feb '88, on Fresh Sounds (Spain) by Fresh Sounds Records (Spain). Catalogue no: **FS 49**

**PLAYS IRVING BERLIN (Pell, Dave Octet)**
**Album:** Released Feb '88, on Fresh Sounds (Spain) by Fresh Sounds Records (Spain). Catalogue no: **FS 174**

**PREZ CONFERENCE**
Tracks: / I never knew / Sometimes I'm happy / Lester leaps in / Jumpin' with symphony Sid / Jumpin' at the Woodside / One o'clock jump / Just you, just me / Lester leaps again / Taxi war dance / Jump Lester jump.
**Album:** Released Mar '79, on Pye Deleted '84. Catalogue no: **NSPL 28274**

**PREZ & JOE (Pell, Dave/Joe Williams)**
Tracks: / Oh lady be good / Getting some fun out of life / You can depend on me / Fooling with myself / Boogie woogie / How high the moon / If I could be with you / If dreams come true / Easy living / When you're smiling.
**Cass:** Released Jan '88, on GNP Crescendo (USA) by GNP Crescendo Records (USA). Catalogue no: **GNP5 2124**
**CD:** Released Jan '88, on GNP Crescendo (USA) by GNP Crescendo Records (USA). Catalogue no: **GNPD 2124**
**Album:** Released Feb '80, on Pye Deleted '85. Catalogue no: **N 5006**
**Album:** Released Jan '88, on GNP Crescendo (USA) by GNP Crescendo Records (USA). Catalogue no: **GNPS 2124**

## Pelletier, Jean-Claude

**HAMMOND ORGAN-SLOW DANCE & BLUES**
**Album:** Released '88, on Vogue by Vogue Records. Catalogue no: **VG SLVLX 677**

## Pennies From Heaven

**LOVE IS GOOD FOR ANYTHING**
Tracks: / Love is good for anything that ails you / Life is just a bowl of cherries.
**7" Single:** Released Jun '82, on Warner Bros. by WEA Records. Catalogue no: **K 17963**

**MORE PENNIES FROM HEAVEN (Various artists)**
**Album:** Released May '78, on Retrospect by EMI Records. Catalogue no: **SH 276**

**PENNIES FROM HEAVEN (48 original recordings featured in the BBC TV series) (Various artists)**
**CD Set:** Released Feb '90, on BBC by BBC Records & Tapes. Catalogue no: **BBC CD 2008**
**CD:** Released May '89, on Object Enterprises Catalogue no: **ONN 18**
**LP Set:** Released Feb '90, on BBC by BBC Records & Tapes. Catalogue no: **REF 768**
**2 LP Set:** Released May '78, on Decca by Decca International. Deleted '88. Catalogue no: **DDV 5007/8**
**Cass set:** Released Feb '90, on BBC by BBC Records & Tapes. Catalogue no: **ZCD 768**
**2 LP Set:** Released Sep '82, on RCA by BMG Records (UK). Deleted Jan '88. Catalogue no: **K 66109**

**PENNIES FROM HEAVEN (BBC SERIES) (Various artists)**
**CD Set:** Released Mar '90, on BBC by BBC Records & Tapes. Catalogue no: **JJCD53**

**PENNIES FROM HEAVEN (GOLDEN AGE) (Various artists)**
Tracks: / Roll along, prairie moon: *Various artists* / Seeing is believing: *Various artists* / You rascal you: *Various artists* / You and the night and the music: *Various artists* / Yes yes (my baby says yes): *Various artists* / Love is good for anything that ails you: *Various artists* / We'll make hay while the sun shines: *Various artists* / It's got to be love: *Various artists* / Pop, goes your heart: *Various artists* / Painting the clouds with sunshine: *Various artists* / Moon got in my eyes: *Various artists* / Haunting me: *Various artists* / Roll along, covered wagon: *Various artists* / I like to go back in the evening: *Various artists* / Says my heart: *Various artists* / Pennies from Heaven: *Various artists.*
Note: Sixteen tracks from the orchestras of Harry Roy, Lew Stone, Ambrose, Roy Fox, Jack Hylton, Carroll Gibbons and Jack Jackson.
**Album:** Released Jul '83, on Golden Age by EMI Records. Catalogue no: **GX 41 2501**
**Cass:** Released Jul '83, on Golden Age by EMI Records. Catalogue no: **TC GX 2501**

**PENNIES FROM HEAVEN (VIDEO) (Various artists)**
Note: Cert: 15.
**VHS:** Released Jun '89, on MGM/UA (Video) by MGM/UA Video. Catalogue no: **SMV 10147**

## Pepper, Art

**Biographical details:** One of the most highly regarded of West Coast modern jazzmen, Pepper was born in California in 1925 and died in 1981. He played alto sax -- occasionally tenor and clarinet -- and composed many fine tunes. His most famous album (some say his best) is *Art Pepper Meets The Rhythm Section*, made in Los Angeles in 1957, with Miles Davis' rhythm section of the time, pianist Red Garland, bassist Paul Chambers and drummer Philly Joe Jones: Pepper later wrote that he was a mess when the session was arranged and hadn't even practised for months, but he certainly rose to the challenge. In 1960 he made *Gettin' Together*, with another Davis rhythm section -- Chambers, drummer Jimmy Cobb, pianist Wynton Kelly and trumpeter Conte Candoli guesting on two tracks -- but then made no records at all between 1960 and 1973. He led a harrowing life, including several jail terms, because of heroin addiction, but came back after a long stay at the Synanon rehabilitation centre to make many more beautiful records before he died. His wife Laurie helped him to write *Straight Life* ('79), a brutally honest book and one of the best-ever jazz autobuigraphies. (Donald Clarke, May 1987.).

**AMONG FRIENDS**
**CD:** Released Feb '90, on Storyville by Storyville Records AB. Catalogue no: **STCD 4167**
**Album:** Released '88, on Flyright by Interstate Music. Catalogue no: **FLY 211**
**Album:** Released Jan '79, on Interplay (USA) by Interplay Records (USA). Catalogue no: **IP-7718**

**AMONG FRIENDS (IMPORT)**
Tracks: / What is this thing called love / 'Round about midnight / What's new / I'll remember April.
Note: Featuring Bob Magnusson-bass, Russ Freeman-piano, Frank Butler-drums.
**Cass:** Released '88, on Discovery (USA) by Discovery Records (USA). Catalogue no: **DSC 837**

**Album:** Released '88, on Discovery (USA) by Discovery Records (USA). Catalogue no: **DS 837**
**CD:** Released '88, on Discovery (USA) by Discovery Records (USA). Catalogue no: **DSCD 837**

**ART OF PEPPER, THE (Complete Art Pepper Aladdin recordings vol. III)**
Tracks: / Holiday flight / Too close for comfort / Long ago and far away / Begin the beguine / I can't believe that you're in love with me / Webb city / Summertime / Fascinating rhythm / Body and soul / Without a song / Breeze and I, The / Surf ride.
**CD:** Released Nov '88, on Blue Note by EMI Records. Catalogue no: **BNZ 120**
**Album:** Released Apr '88, on VSOP Catalogue no: **VSOP 30**
**CD:** Released Nov '88, on Blue Note by EMI Records. Catalogue no: **CDP 746 853 2**

**ART OF PEPPER VOL 2, THE**
Note: Features Art Pepper, Carl Perkins, Ben Tucker, Chuck Flores
**Album:** Released Apr '88, on VSOP Catalogue no: **VSOP 33**

**ART PEPPER MEETS THE RHYTHM SECTION**
Tracks: / You'd be so nice to come home to / Red pepper blues / Imagination / Waltz me blues / Straight life / Jazz me blues / Tin tin deo / Star eyes / Birk's works.
**CD:** Released Feb '89, on Contemporary by Ace Records. Catalogue no: **CDCOP 004**
**CD:** Released Jan '89, on JVC/Fantasy Catalogue no: **VDJ 1556**
**Album:** Released Feb '89, on Contemporary by Ace Records. Deleted '88. Catalogue no: **COP 004**

**ART PEPPER WITH WARNE MARSH (Pepper, Art/Warne Marsh)**
**CD:** Released May '87, on JVC/Fantasy Deleted '88. Catalogue no: **VDJ 1577**

**ARTISTRY IN JAZZ (Greatest hits)**
**CD:** Released May '87, on JVC/Fantasy Catalogue no: **VDJ 1593**

**AT THE VILLAGE VANGUARD VOL 4**
**CD:** Released '86, on Carrere (France) Catalogue no: **CA 98 627**

**BALLADS BY FOUR**
**CD:** Released Nov '86, on Fantasy (import) by Fantasy Inc (USA). Catalogue no: **FCD 6065133**

**COLLECTION: ART PEPPER**
Tracks: / Deep purple / Chili pepper / Art's oregano / Way you look tonight / Thyme time / Cinnamon / Nutmeg / Suzy the poodle / Straight life / What's new? / Everything happens to me / Tickle toe / Salute / Be easy, be tender / Dynaflow / Harlem folk dance / Unison riff.
**Album:** Released Jan '87, on Deja Vu Catalogue no: **DVLP 2094**
**Cass:** Released Jan '87, on Deja Vu Catalogue no: **DVMC 2094**

**COMPLETE ART PEPPER ALADDIN RECORDINGS VOL. 1**
Tracks: / Pepper returns / Broadway / You go to my head / Angel wings / Funny blues / Five more / Minority / Patricia / Mambo de la pinta / Walkin' out blues / Pepper steak / You're driving me crazy / Tenor blooz / Yardbird suite / Straight life.
**CD:** Released Dec '89, on Blue Note by EMI Records. Catalogue no: **CDP 746 863 2**
**CD:** Released Dec '89, on Blue Note by EMI Records. Catalogue no: **BNZ 215**

**DISCOVERIES (Pepper, Art/7 others)**
Tracks: / Chilli pepper / Susie the poodle / Everything happens to me / Tickle toe / Nutmeg / Cinnamon / What's new / Thyme time / Straight life / Art's oregano / Way you look tonight.
Note: Other artists: Russ Freman(piano) Bob Whitlock (bass) Bobby White (drums) Jack Montrose (tenor sax) Claude Williamson (piano) Monte Ludwig (bass) Larry Bunker (drums)
**Album:** Released Dec '85, on Savoy (France) Deleted May '89. Catalogue no: **WL 70507**

**DISCOVERIES, THE SAVOY SESSIONS**
**Album:** Released Mar '85, on Savoy Jazz (USA) by Malaco Records (USA). Catalogue no: **SJL 2217**

**FRIDAY NIGHT AT THE VILLAGE VANGUARD**
**Album:** Released Jul '81, on Contemporary (Import) Catalogue no: **1007 643**

**GETTIN' TOGETHER (Pepper, Art & Conte Candoli)**
**CD:** Released May '87, on JVC/Fantasy Deleted '88. Catalogue no: **VDJ 1579**
**Album:** Released '88, on Contemporary by Ace Records. Catalogue no: **COP 023**

**GOIN' HOME**
Note: With George Cables-piano
**CD:** Released '86, on JVC/Fantasy Catalogue no: **VDP 9**

**INTENSITY**
Tracks: / I can't believe that you're in love with me / I love you / Come rain or come shine / Long ago and far away / Gone with the wind / I wished on the moon / Too close for comfort.
**CD:** Released Jul '87, on JVC/Fantasy Catalogue no: **VDJ 1581**
**Album:** Released Feb '89, on Contemporary by Ace Records. Catalogue no: **COP 010**

**LANDSCAPE**
Tracks: / True blues / Sometime / Avalon / Over the rainbow / Straight life / Landscape.
**Album:** on Galaxy (1) by President Records. Catalogue no: **GXY 5128**

**LIVE AT SONTE'S VOL 1**
**Album:** Released Feb '88, on Fresh Sounds (Spain) by Fresh Sounds Records (Spain). Catalogue no: **FS 309**

**LIVING LEGEND**
Tracks: / Orphelia / Here's that rainy day / What Laurie likes / Mr. Yohe / Lost life / Samba mom-mom.
**Album:** Released Jan '86, on Contemporary by Ace Records. Catalogue no: **COP 014**
**CD:** Released May '87, on JVC/Fantasy Catalogue no: **VDJ 1582**

**MEMORIAL COLLECTION VOL 1**
**CD:** Released Feb '90, on Storyville by Storyville Records AB. Catalogue no: **STCD 4128**

**MEMORIAL COLLECTION VOL 2**
**CD:** Released Feb '90, on Storyville by Storyville Records AB. Catalogue no: **STCD 4129**

**MEMORIAL COLLECTION VOL 3**
**CD:** Released Feb '90, on Storyville by Storyville Records AB. Catalogue no: **STCD 4130**

**MEMORIAL COLLECTION VOL 4**
**CD:** Released Feb '90, on Storyville by Storyville Records AB. Catalogue no: **STCD 4146**

**MODERN ART**
**Album:** Released Feb '88, on Fresh Sounds (Spain) by Fresh Sounds Records (Spain). Catalogue no: **FS 223**
**CD:** Released Nov '88, on Blue Note by EMI Records. Catalogue no: **BNZ 119**
**CD:** Released Nov '88, on Blue Note by EMI Records. Catalogue no: **CDP 746 848 2**

**MODERN JAZZ CLASSICS (Pepper, Art + Eleven)**
**CD:** Released Oct '86, on Mobile Fidelity Sound Lab(USA) by Mobile Fidelity Records (USA). Catalogue no: **MFCD 805**
**CD:** Released May '87, on JVC/Fantasy Catalogue no: **VDJ 1578**

**MORE FOR LES**
**Album:** Released '88, on Boplicity by Ace Records. Catalogue no: **COP 025**
**Album:** Released Jun '86, on Contemporary (USA) Catalogue no: **COP 025**

**NIGHT AT THE SURF CLUB, A - VOL. 1**
**CD:** Released '88, on Xanadu Catalogue no: **FDC 5153**

**NIGHT AT THE SURF CLUB, A - VOL. 2**
**CD:** Released '88, on Xanadu Catalogue no: **FDC 5154**

**NO LIMIT**
**Album:** Released 2 May '89, on Contemporary by Ace Records. Catalogue no: **COP 019**
**CD:** Released May '87, on JVC/Fantasy Catalogue no: **VDJ 1584**
**CD:** Released 2 May '89, on Contemporary by Ace Records. Catalogue no: **CDCOP 019**

**OMEGA ALPHA**
Tracks: / Surf ride / Body and soul / Too close for comfort / Summertime / Fascinating rhythm / Begin the beguine / Webb city.
**Album:** Released Mar '81, on Liberty by EMI Records. Deleted Jul '87. Catalogue no: **LBR 1039**

**ONE SEPTEMBER AFTERNOON**
Tracks: / Mr. Big falls his J.G. hand / Close to you alone / There will never be

another you / Melolev / Goodbye, again / Brazil.
**Album:** Released '82, on Galaxy (1) by President Records. Catalogue no: **GYX 5141**

**PLUS ELEVEN**
Tracks: / Move / Groovin' high / Opus de funk / Shaw nuff / Round midnight / Four brothers / Bernie's tune / Walkin' shoes / Airegin / Anthropology / Walkin' / Donna lee.
**Album:** Released May '89, on Contemporary by Ace Records. Catalogue no: **COP 007**
**CD:** Released May '89, on Contemporary by Ace Records. Catalogue no: **CDCOP 007**

**POPO (Pepper, Art & Shorty Rogers)**
**Album:** Released Jul '82, on Xanadu Catalogue no: **XANADU 148**

**REDISCOVERIES**
Tracks: / Chili pepper (take 3) / Suzy the poodle (take 3) / Everything happens to me (take 2) / Nutmeg (take 6) / Cinnamon / What's new / Thyme time / Straight line / Art's oregano / Chili pepper (take 5) / Suzy the poodle (take 5) / Everything happens to me (take 3) / Everything happens to me (take 6) / Nutmeg (take 7).
**Album:** Released Nov '86, on RCA by BMG Records (UK). Deleted Nov '89. Catalogue no: **WL 70828**
**Cass:** Released Nov '86, on RCA by BMG Records (UK). Catalogue no: **WK 70828**

**ROADGAME**
Tracks: / Roadgame / Road waltz / When you're smiling / Everything happens to me.
**Album:** Released Aug '82, on Galaxy (1) by President Records. Catalogue no: **GXY 5142**

**SATURDAY NIGHT AT THE VILLAGE VANGUARD**
**Album:** Released Dec '81, on Contemporary (Import) Catalogue no: **1007 644**

**SMACK UP**
Tracks: / Smack up / Las guevas de Mario / Bit of basic / How can you lose / Maybe next year / Tears inside.
**Album:** Released Nov '86, on Contemporary (USA) Catalogue no: **COP 031**

**STRAIGHT LIFE**
Tracks: / Chili pepper / Cinnamon / Tickle toe / Suzy the poodle / Everything happens to me / Nutmeg / Deep purple / What's new / Thyme time / Art's oregano / Way you look tonight / Straight life.
**CD:** Released '86, on Carrere (France) Catalogue no: **CA 98 175**
**Album:** Released Jan '80, on Galaxy (1) by President Records. Catalogue no: **GXY 5127**
**CD:** Released Jan '87, on RCA by BMG Records (UK). Deleted Nov '89. Catalogue no: **ZD 70820**

**TODAY**
Tracks: / Miss you / Mambo koyama / Lover come back to me / Patricia / These foolish things / Chris's blues.
**Album:** Released May '84, on Original Jazz Classics (USA) by Fantasy Inc (USA). Catalogue no: **OJC 3002**

**TRIP, THE**
Tracks: / Trip / Song for Richard / Sweet love of mine / Junior cat / Summer knows / Red car.
**CD:** Released May '87, on JVC/Fantasy Catalogue no: **VDJ 1583**
**Album:** Released Nov '86, on Contemporary (USA) Catalogue no: **COP 032**

**WAY IT WAS, THE**
Tracks: / I can't believe that you're in love / All the things you are / What's new / Tickle toe / Man I love, The / Autumn leaves / Way you look tonight.
Note: Side one of this album is a previously unissued session that Art Pepper recordedin 1957 with Warne Marse on tenor. Side two is three outtakes from the sessions that have ended up on the three previous Contemporary Pepper albums.
**Album:** Released 2 May '89, on Contemporary by Ace Records. Catalogue no: **COP 041**

**WINTER MOON**
Tracks: / Our song / Here's that rainy day / That's love / Winter moon / When the sun comes out / Blues in the night / Prisoner, The (love theme from 'Eyes of Laura Mars').
**CD:** Released '88, on Fantasy (import) by Fantasy Inc (USA). Catalogue no: **CA 802 981 62**
**Album:** Released Aug '81, on Galaxy (1) by President Records. Deleted Aug '86. Catalogue no: **GCY 5140**
**CD:** Released Nov '86, on Fantasy (import) by Fantasy Inc (USA). Catalogue no: **FCD 6155140**

## Perkins, Bill

**Biographical details:** West Coast jazz reedman Perkins was born in San Francisco in 1924. He played with Stan Kenton and Woody Herman in the 1950's, worked as a recording engineer at World Pacific Records, then in studios, and later played with Supersax during its first year. In jazz he played mostly tenor sax in the 50's, later occasionally baritone, flute, bass clarinet and soprano sax. He has spent most of his time in lucrative Hollywood studio work, making only two or three albums between 1958 and 1968, but still has many fans. (Donald Clarke, May 1987.).

**BILL PERKINS QUARTET with Claude Williamson (Perkins, Bill Quartet)**
**Album:** Released Jun '88, on Fresh Sounds (Spain) by Fresh Sounds Records (Spain). Catalogue no: **FS 321**

**CONFLUENCE (Perkins, Bill & Adams, Pepper)**
**Album:** Released Mar '79, on Interplay (USA) by Interplay Records (USA). Catalogue no: **IP-7721**

**MANY WAYS TO GO (Perkins, Bill Quartet)**
**Album:** Released Jul '88, on Sea Breeze Catalogue no: **SB 2006**

**PEPPER ADAMS**
**Album:** Released '88, on Flyright by Interstate Music. Catalogue no: **FLY 214**

**REMEMBRANCE OF DINO'S**
**Album:** Released '88, on Interplay (USA) by Interplay Records (USA). Catalogue no: **IP 8606**

**THE FRONT LINE (Perkins, Bill & Adams, Pepper)**
**CD:** Released Feb '90, on Storyville by Storyville Records AB. Catalogue no: **STCD 4166**

**WEST COAST CONFERENCE (Perkins, Bill/Paul Chambers/Philly Joe Jones)**
**Album:** Released Jan '81, on Affinity by Charly Records. Deleted '88. Catalogue no: **AFF 56**

## Perkins, Carl (jazz)

**Biographical details:** Jazz pianist Carl Perkins was born in Indiana in 1928: his life was shortened by drug addiction and he died aged only 30. He was a very fine and influential post-bop West Coast musician. His left hand was slightly handicapped by polio and compensating for this may partly account for his heavier blues feeling than that of most other modern jazz pianists. He played with an early edition of the famous Max Roach-Clifford Brown Quintet and was a key member of the Curtis Counce Quintet. He played and recorded with Harols Land - his tune *Grooveyard* on a 1958 Land LP became a modern jazz standard - but only made three or four albums - now highly prized - as leader. (Donald Clarke, May 1987.).

**INTRODUCING....**
Tracks: / Way cross town / You don't know what love is / Lady is a tramp, The / Marblehead / Woodyn you / Westside / Just friends / It could happen to you / Lilacs in the rain / Carl's blues.
**Album:** Released 2 May '89, on Boplicity by Ace Records. Catalogue no: **BOP 008**

## Perkins, Pinetop

**AFTER HOURS**
**CD:** Released Mar '90, on Blind Pig (USA) by Blind Pig Records (USA). Catalogue no: **JJCD38**
**Album:** Released Feb '89, on Blind Pig (USA) by Blind Pig Records (USA). Catalogue no: **BP 3088**

**BOOGIE WOOGIE KING**
**CD:** Released '86, on Black & Blue (1) by Black & Blue Records. Catalogue no: **233 520**

**CHICAGO BOOGIE BLUES PIANO MAN**
**Album:** Released Sep '86, on JSP by JSP Records. Catalogue no: **JSP 1107**

## Persip, Charlie

**SUPERBAND (Persip, Charlie & Gerry McFurns)**
**Album:** Released '81, on Stash (USA) Catalogue no: **ST 209**

## Persson, Bent

**LOUIS ARMSTRONG 50 HOT**

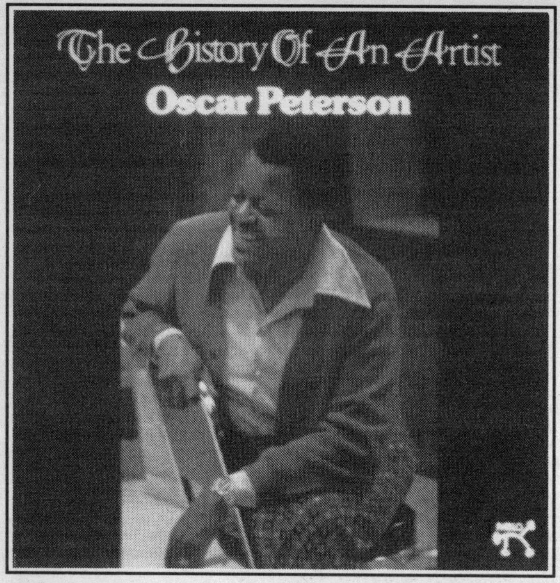


**Oscar Peterson - History of an artist (Pablo Jazz)**

**CORNET CHORUS 1**
**Album:** Released '88, on Kenneth Catalogue no: **KS 2044**

**LOUIS ARMSTRONG 50 HOT CORNET CHORUS 2**
**Album:** Released '88, on Kenneth Catalogue no: **KS 2045**

## Peruna Jazzmen

**DOCTOR JAZZ**
**Album:** Released Feb '90, on Storyville by Storyville Records AB. Catalogue no: **SLP 438**

**PERUNA JAZZMEN VOL.2**
Note: Track details not advised
**Album:** Released Jun '86, on Stomp Off (USA) Catalogue no: **SOS 1020**

**PERUNA JAZZMEN VOL.3**
Note: Tracks not advised
**Album:** Released Jun '86, on Stomp Off (USA) Catalogue no: **SOS 1105**

## Petersen, Pete

**JAZZ JOURNEY (Petersen, Pete & Collection Jazz Orchestra)**
**Album:** Released Feb '89, on Pausa by Ducale S.p.A.. Catalogue no: **PAUSA 7163**

**PLAYIN' IN THE PARK (Petersen, Pete & Collection Jazz Orchestra)**
**CD:** Released Aug '89, on CMJ Catalogue no: **CMD 8109**
**Album:** Released Feb '89, on Pausa by Ducale S.p.A.. Catalogue no: **PAUSA 7191**

**STRAIGHT AHEAD (Petersen, Pete & Collection Jazz Orchestra)**
**Cass:** Released '88, on Chase Music (USA) by Chase Music Group (USA). Catalogue no: **CMMC 8020**
**CD:** Released '88, on Chase Music (USA) by Chase Music Group (USA). Catalogue no: **CMCD 8020**
**Album:** Released '88, on Chase Music (USA) by Chase Music Group (USA). Catalogue no: **CM 8020**

**TEXAS STATE OF MIND (Petersen, Pete & Collection Jazz Orchestra)**
**Album:** Released Feb '89, on Pausa by Ducale S.p.A.. Catalogue no: **PAUSA 7143**

## Peters, Mike

**DJANGO'S MUSIC (Peters, Mike/Bob Wilberg/Birelli Lagrene)**
Note: Track details not advised
**Album:** Released Dec '85, on Stash (USA) Catalogue no: **ST 253**

## Peterson, Marvin

**ANGELS OF ATLANTA, THE (Peterson, Marvin 'Hannibal')**
**Album:** Released Jan '82, on Enja (Germany) by Enja Records (West Germany). Catalogue no: **ENJA 3085**

**HANNIBAL IN ANTIBES (Peterson, Marvin 'Hannibal')**
**Album:** Released Jan '82, on Enja (Germany) by Enja Records (West Germany). Catalogue no: **ENJA 3011**

**POEM SONG (Peterson, Marvin 'Hannibal')**
**Album:** Released Jul '83, on Mole Catalogue no: **MOLE 6**

## Peterson, Oscar

**Biographical details:** One of the most popular of all jazz musicians, Peterson was born in Montreal in 1925. From 1945 he recorded in Canada for RCA, and in 1949 he came to Carnegie Hall

**Marvin 'Hannibal' Peterson**

with Norman Granz's Jazz At The Philharmonic: he has been associated with Granz on the Verve and Pablo labels ever since, except for a period on European MPS in the mid-1970's when Granz was "retired". He led a trio with Ray Brown on bass and Irving Ashby, succeeded by Barney Kessell, then Herb Ellis, on guitar. In 1958 the guitar was replaced by drummer Ed Thigpen, in turn replaced in 1965 by Louis Hayes. Sam Jones took over from Brown on bass. Peterson occasionally sang, notably on *With Respect To Nat* in 1965, very much in Nat Cole's style. He is a serious, hardworking man, intent on doing a good job and raising the level of proficiency in jazz piano to that expected in classical music, influenced by -- and inspired by -- the great Art Tatum. Apart from scores of LPs with others he has made more than 60 of his own. (Donald Clarke, May 1987.).

**ACTION**
**Album:** Released May '81, on MPS Jazz Catalogue no: **MPS 68 073**

**AN EVENING AT THE HOLLYWOOD BOWL (Peterson, Oscar & Ella Fitzgerald)**
**2 LP Set:** Released '82, on IMS by Polydor Ltd. Catalogue no: **2610058**

**ANOTHER DAY (Peterson, Oscar Trio)**
Tracks: / Blues for Martha / I'm old fashioned / All the things you are / Too close for comfort / Jamfs are coming, The / It never entered my mind / Carolina shout.
Note: Recorded November 1970
**Album:** Released May '81, on MPS Jazz Catalogue no: **MPS 68 083**
**CD:** Released May '87, on MPS Jazz Catalogue no: **821 848-2**

**AT THE MONTREUX JAZZ FESTIVAL, 1975 (Peterson, Oscar Big Six)**
Tracks: / Au privave / Here's that rainy day / Poor butterfly / Reunion blues.
**Cass:** Released '82, on Pablo Jazz (USA) by Pablo Records (USA). Catalogue no: **K10 747**
**Album:** Released '82, on Pablo Jazz (USA) by Pablo Records (USA). Catalogue no: **231 0747**

**AT THE STRATFORD SHAKESPEARIAN FESTIVAL (Oscar Peterson Trio)**
Tracks: / Falling in love with love / How about you / Flamingo / Swinging on a star / Noreen's nocturne / Gypsy in my soul / How high the moon / Love you madly / 52nd Street theme.
**Album:** Released '82, on Verve Catalogue no: **2304223**

**BEST OF OSCAR PETERSON Compact/Walkman jazz**
**Cass:** Released May '87, on Mercury by Phonogram Ltd. Catalogue no: **830 698-4**
**CD:** Released May '87, on Mercury by Phonogram Ltd. Catalogue no: **830 698-2**

**BIG SIX AT MONTREUX**
Tracks: / Au privave / Here's that rainy day / Poor butterfly / Reunion blues.
Note: Personnel: Oscar Peterson - piano; Milt Jackson - vibes; Joe Pass - guitar; Toots Thilemans - harmonica; Niels Pederson - bass; Louis Bellson - drums.
**CD:** Released Apr '86, on Pablo Jazz (USA) by Pablo Records (USA). Catalogue no: **J33J 20050**

**BUSTIN' OUT WITH THE ALL STAR BAND**
**CD:** Released Oct '86, on Polydor by Polydor Ltd. Deleted Jul '88. Catalogue no: **821 986-2**

**CARIOCA**
Tracks: / Carioca / Samba sensitive / Amanha / Meditation / Mas que nada / Samba de Orfeu / Manha de carnaval / Soulville samba / How insensitive.
Note: Recorded around 1953, with Barney Kessel - guitar; Ray Brown - bass; Alvin Stoller - drums.
**Cass:** Released Jun '83, on Happy Bird (Germany) Catalogue no: **MB 990110**
**Album:** Released Jun '83, on Happy Bird (Germany) Catalogue no: **B 90110**

**COLE PORTER SONGBOOK**
**CD:** Released Nov '86, on Polydor by Polydor Ltd. Deleted Jan '89. Catalogue no: **821 987-2**

**COLLECTION: OSCAR PETERSON**
Tracks: / How high the moon / Falling in love with love / Sometimes I'm happy / Big fat mamma / Should I love you so? / Swinging on a star / Love you madly / In the wee small hours of the morning / I've never been in love before / Joy spring / Gypsy in my soul.
**Cass:** Released Nov '85, on Deja Vu Catalogue no: **DVMC 2041**

**COMPACT JAZZ: OSCAR PETERSON**
Tracks: / Let's fall in love / Mack the knife.
**Cass:** Released Jul '87, on Phonogram by Phonogram Ltd. Catalogue no: **831 698-4**
**CD:** Released Jul '87, on Phonogram by Phonogram Ltd. Catalogue no: **831 698-2**

**DIGITAL AT MONTREUX**
Tracks: / Old folks / Soft winds / Indiana / That's all / Younger than Springtime / Caravan / Rockin' in rhythm / C jam blues / Solitude / Satin doll / Caravan (reprise) / On the trail.
Note: Recorded July 1979.
**CD:** Released May '86, on Pablo Jazz (USA) by Pablo Records (USA). Catalogue no: **CD 20014**
**Album:** Released Apr '81, on Pablo Jazz (USA) by Pablo Records (USA). Catalogue no: **D 230 8224**
**Cass:** Released '82, on Pablo Jazz (USA) by Pablo Records (USA). Catalogue no: **K 08 224**

**'EXTRAORDINARY' CANADIAN CONCERT (Peterson, Oscar & Ray Brown)**
**Album:** Released Nov '87, on Can-Am (USA) Catalogue no: **CA 1400**

**FIORELLO (Peterson, Oscar Trio)**
Tracks: / When did I fall in love? / Little tin box / Home again / 'Til tomorrow / Politics and poker / Gentleman Jimmy / Unfair / On the side of the Angela / Where do I go from here?.
Note: Peterson - piano; Ray Brown - bass; Ed Thigpen - drums. Music from the Broadway musical by Jerry Beck and Sheldon Harnick.
**Album:** Released Jun '84, on Verve (France) Catalogue no: **8171 081**

**FREEDOM SONG (Peterson, Oscar Big 4)**
Tracks: / 'Round midnight / Watch what happens / For debby / Easy living / Move / Hymn to freedom / Fallen warrior / Sweet lorraine / You look good to me / Now's the time / Future child / Mississauga rattler / Nigerian market place / Emily / Tenderly / Nightchild / Cakewalk.
**Album:** Released Mar '83, on Pablo Jazz (USA) by Pablo Records (USA). Catalogue no: **2640 101**
**Cass:** Released Mar '83, on Pablo Jazz (USA) by Pablo Records (USA). Catalogue no: **K 40 101**

**GEORGE GERSHWIN SONGBOOK**
Tracks: / Man I love, The / Fascinating rhythm / It ain't necessarily so / Somebody loves me / Strike up the band / I've got a crush on you / I was doin' alright / 'S wonderful / Lady be good / I got rhythm / Foggy day, A / Love walked in.
**Album:** Released '88, on Polydor by Polydor Ltd. Deleted 30 Jun '89. Catalogue no: **823 249-1**

**GIANTS, THE (Peterson, Oscar/Ray Brown/Joe Pass)**
Tracks: / Riff blues / Who cares? / Jobim / Blues for Dennis / Sunny / Getting sentimental over you / Caravan / Eyes of love.
Note: Oscar Peterson - piano; Joe Pass - guitar; Ray Brown - bass.
**Album:** Released '82, on Pablo Jazz (USA) by Pablo Records (USA). Catalogue no: **231 0796**
**Cass:** Released '82, on Pablo Jazz (USA) by Pablo Records (USA). Catalogue no: **K10 796**

**GIRL TALK**
**Album:** Released May '81, on MPS Jazz Catalogue no: **MPS 68 074**

**GOOD LIFE, THE**
**Cass:** Released Dec '84, on Pablo Jazz (USA) by Pablo Records (USA). Catalogue no: **K 8241**
**CD:** Released Apr '87, on Pablo Jazz (USA) by Pablo Records (USA). Catalogue no: **CD 230 8241**
**Album:** Released Dec '84, on Pablo Jazz (USA) by Pablo Records (USA). Catalogue no: **230 8241**

**GREAT CONNECTION (Peterson, Oscar Trio)**
Tracks: / Younger than Springtime / Where do we go from here / Smile / Soft winds / Just squeeze me / On the trail / Wheatland.
Note: Recorded October 1971

**CD:** Released May '87, on MPS Jazz (Germany) Catalogue no: **821 851-2**
**Album:** Released May '81, on MPS Jazz Catalogue no: **MPS 68 086**

**HELLO HERBIE (Peterson, Oscar & Herb Ellis)**
**Album:** Released May '81, on MPS Jazz Catalogue no: **MPS 68 080**

**HISTORY OF AN ARTIST**
Tracks: / R.B. blues / I wished on the moon / You can depend on me / This is where it's at / Okie blues / I want to be happy / Texas blues / Main stem / Don't get around much anymore / Swamp fire / In a sentimental mood / Greasy blues / Sweety blues / Gay's blues / Good life / Richard's round / Lady of the lavender mist.
**2 LP Set:** Released '82, on Pablo Jazz (USA) by Pablo Records (USA). Catalogue no: **262 5702**
**Cass set:** Released '82, on Pablo Jazz (USA) by Pablo Records (USA). Catalogue no: **K 25 702**

**HISTORY OF AN ARTIST VOL.2**
Tracks: / Wes' tune / Reunion blues / When your lover has gone / Five o'clock whistle / Old folks / Ma, he's making eyes at me / Tenderly.
Note: With Barney Kessel, Joe Pass, Herb Ellis (guitars), Ray Brown, Niels Pedersen, Sam Jones, George Mraz (basses), Bobby Durham (drums). Recorded in 1972 and 1973.
**Album:** Released Oct '84, on Pablo Jazz (USA) by Pablo Records (USA). Catalogue no: **2310 895**
**CD:** Released Apr '87, on Pablo Jazz (USA) by Pablo Records (USA). Catalogue no: **CD 231 0895**

**IF YOU COULD SEE ME NOW**
Tracks: / Weird blues / If I should lose you / On Danish shore / L'Impossible / If you could see me now / Limehouse blues.
**Cass:** Released Jul '86, on Pablo Jazz (USA) by Pablo Records (USA). Catalogue no: **K10 918**
**Album:** Released Jul '86, on Pablo Jazz (USA) by Pablo Records (USA). Catalogue no: **231 0918**
**CD:** Released Feb '87, on Pablo Jazz (USA) by Pablo Records (USA). Catalogue no: **CD 231 0918**

**IN RUSSIA**
Tracks: / I've got it bad and that ain't good / I concentrate on you / Hogtown blues / Place St Henri / On Green Dolphin Street / You stepped out of a dream / Wave / On the trail / Take the 'A' train / Summertime / Just friends / Do you know what it means to miss New Orleans? / I loves you, Porgy / Georgia on my mind / Li'l darlin' / Watch what happens / Hallelujah trail / Someone to watch over me.
**Cass set:** Released '82, on Pablo Jazz (USA) by Pablo Records (USA). Catalogue no: **K 25 711**
**2 LP Set:** Released '82, on Pablo Jazz (USA) by Pablo Records (USA). Catalogue no: **262 5711**

**JAZZ PORTRAIT OF FRANK SINATRA, A**
Tracks: / You make me feel so young / Come dance with me / Learnin' the blues / Witchcraft / Tender trap, The / Saturday night is the loneliest night of the week / Just in time / It happened in Monterey / I get a kick out of you / All of me / Birth of the blues / How about you.
**CD:** Released Sep '85, on Verve Deleted Jan '89. Catalogue no: **825 769-2**

**JOUSTS (Peterson, Oscar & The Trumpet Kings)**
Tracks: / Danish pastry / Crazy rhythm / Stella by starlight / Satin doll / Oakland blues / There is no greater love / Summertime / Makin' whoopee / Trust in me.
**Cass:** Released '82, on Pablo Jazz (USA) by Pablo Records (USA). Catalogue no: **K10 817**
**Album:** Released '82, on Pablo Jazz (USA) by Pablo Records (USA). Catalogue no: **231 0817**

**LIVE AT THE NORTH SEA JAZZ FESTIVAL, 1980**
Tracks: / Caravan / Straight, no chaser / Like someone in love / There is no you / You stepped out of a dream / City lights / I'm old fashioned / Time for love, A / Bluesology / Goodbye / No greater love.
Note: With Joe Pass, Toots Thielemans, Neils Pedersen.
**Cass set:** Released '82, on Pablo Jazz (USA) by Pablo Records (USA). Catalogue no: **K 20 115**
**2 LP Set:** Released '82, on Pablo Jazz (USA) by Pablo Records (USA). Catalogue no: **262 0115**

**LONDON CONCERT, THE (Peterson, Oscar/John Heard/Louis Bellson)**
Tracks: / It's a wonderful world / People / Ain't misbehavin' / Jitterbug waltz / Pennies from Heaven / I get along without you very well / Sweet Georgia Brown / Falling in love with love / Hogtown blues / Emily / Satin doll / I got it bad and that ain't good / Do nothing till you hear from me / C jam blues / Lush life / Take the 'A' train / Caravan / Cute.
**Cass set:** Released '82, on Pablo Jazz (USA) by Pablo Records (USA). Catalogue no: **K 20 111**
**2 LP Set:** Released '82, on Pablo Jazz (USA) by Pablo Records (USA). Catalogue no: **2620 111**

**LOUIS ARMSTRONG MEETS OSCAR PETERSON The Silver Collection (Peterson, Oscar & Louis Armstrong)**
**CD:** on Verve Catalogue no: **825 713-2**

**MASTERS OF JAZZ**
**Album:** Released '83, on RCA (Germany) Catalogue no: **CL 42265**

**MEETS DIZZY GILLESPIE**
Tracks: / Caravan / Mozambique / Autumn leaves / Close your eyes / Blues for bird / Dizzy atmosphere / Alone together / Cone alma.
Note: Personnel: Oscar Peterson/Dizzy Gillespie
**CD:** Released Jul '86, on Pablo Jazz (USA) by Pablo Records (USA). Catalogue no: **J33J 20015**

**MELLOW MOOD**
**Album:** Released May '81, on MPS Jazz Catalogue no: **MPS 68 077**

**MOTIONS AND EMOTIONS**
Tracks: / Sally's tomato / Sunny / By the time I get to Phoenix / Wanderin' / This guy's in love with you / Wave / Dreamsville / Yesterday / Eleanor Rigby / Ode to Billy Joe.
**Album:** Released Sep '84, on MPS Jazz (Germany) Catalogue no: **821 289-1**
**Album:** Released May '81, on MPS Jazz Catalogue no: **MPS 68 079**

**MY FAVOURITE INSTRUMENT**
**Album:** Released May '81, on MPS Jazz Catalogue no: **MPS 68 076**

**NIGERIAN MARKETPLACE (Peterson, Oscar Trio)**
Tracks: / Nigerian marketplace / Au privave / Nancy with the laughing face / Misty / Waltz for Debbie / Cakewalk / You look good to me.
**Album:** Released '82, on Pablo Jazz (USA) by Pablo Records (USA). Catalogue no: **D 2308 231**
**CD:** Released '88, on Pablo Jazz (USA) by Pablo Records (USA). Catalogue no: **103 112 2**
**Cass:** Released '82, on Pablo Jazz (USA) by Pablo Records (USA). Catalogue no: **K 08231**

**NIGHT CHILD (Peterson, Oscar Quartet)**
Tracks: / Solar winds / Dancin' feet / Soliloquy / Night child / Charlie / Teenager.
**Cass:** Released '82, on Pablo Jazz (USA) by Pablo Records (USA). Catalogue no: **K 12 108**
**Album:** Released '82, on Pablo Jazz (USA) by Pablo Records (USA). Catalogue no: **231 2108**

**NIGHT RIDER (Peterson, Oscar & Count Basie)**
**Cass:** Released '82, on Pablo Jazz (USA) by Pablo Records (USA). Catalogue no: **K10 843**
**Album:** Released '82, on Pablo Jazz (USA) by Pablo Records (USA). Catalogue no: **231 0843**

**NIGHT TRAIN**
Tracks: / Night Train / C jam blues / Georgia on my mind / Bag's groove / Moten swing / Easy does it / Honeydripper / Things ain't what they used to be / I got it bad and that ain't good / Band call / Hymn to freedom.
**Album:** Released 17 Apr '89, on Polydor by Polydor Ltd. Deleted Dec '89. Catalogue no: **821 724-1**
**Cass:** Released 17 Apr '89, on Polydor by Polydor Ltd. Catalogue no: **821 724-4**
**CD:** Released Sep '84, on Verve Catalogue no: **821 724-2**

**OSCAR PETERSON (Peterson, Oscar Trio)**
Tracks: / Royology / Love for sale / Tenderly / Swingin' on a star / Marshmallow moon / Should I / Heatwave / You go to my head / Surrey with the fringe on top / Continental, The.
Note: With Herb Ellis - guitar; Ray Brown - bass. Recorded 15 September 1955 and 17 July 1957.

**Album:** Released '81, on Kings Of Jazz Catalogue no: **KLJ 20022**

**OSCAR PETERSON AND CLARK TERRY (Peterson, Oscar & Clark Terry)**
Tracks: / On a slow boat to China / But beautiful / Shaw 'nuff / Satin doll / Chops / Makin' whoopee / No flugel blues / Mack the knife.
**Album:** Released '82, on Pablo Jazz (USA) by Pablo Records (USA). Catalogue no: **231 0742**
**Cass:** Released '82, on Pablo Jazz (USA) by Pablo Records (USA). Catalogue no: **K10 742**

**OSCAR PETERSON AND DIZZY GILLESPIE (Peterson, Oscar & Dizzy Gillespie)**
Tracks: / Caravan / Mozambique / Autumn leaves / Close your eyes / Blues for Bird / Dizzy atmosphere / Alone together / Con Alma.
**Album:** Released '82, on Pablo Jazz (USA) by Pablo Records (USA). Catalogue no: **231 0740**
**Cass:** Released '82, on Pablo Jazz (USA) by Pablo Records (USA). Catalogue no: **K10 740**

**OSCAR PETERSON AND HARRY EDISON (Peterson, Oscar & Harry Edison)**
Tracks: / Easy living / Days of wine and roses / Gee baby ain't I good to you / Basie / Mean to me / Signify / Willow weep for me / Man I love, The / You go to my head.
**Cass:** Released '82, on Pablo Jazz (USA) by Pablo Records (USA). Catalogue no: **K10 741**
**Album:** Released '82, on Pablo Jazz (USA) by Pablo Records (USA). Catalogue no: **231 0741**

**OSCAR PETERSON AND JON FADDIS (Peterson, Oscar & Jon Faddis)**
Tracks: / Things ain't what they used to be / Autumn leaves / Take the 'A' train / Blues for Birks / Summertime / Lester leaps in.
**Cass:** Released '82, on Pablo Jazz (USA) by Pablo Records (USA). Catalogue no: **K10 743**
**Album:** Released '82, on Pablo Jazz (USA) by Pablo Records (USA). Catalogue no: **231 0743**

**OSCAR PETERSON AND ROY ELDRIDGE (Peterson, Oscar & Roy Eldridge)**
Tracks: / Little Jazz / She's funny that way / Way you look tonight / Sunday / Bad hat blues / Between the Devil and the deep blue sea / Blues for Chu.
**Album:** Released '82, on Pablo Jazz (USA) by Pablo Records (USA). Catalogue no: **231 0739**
**Cass:** Released '82, on Pablo Jazz (USA) by Pablo Records (USA). Catalogue no: **K10 739**

**OSCAR PETERSON AND THE BASSISTS**
Tracks: / No greater love / You look good to me / People / Reunion blues / Teach me tonight / Sweet Georgia Brown / Soft winds.
**Cass:** Released '82, on Pablo Jazz (USA) by Pablo Records (USA). Catalogue no: **K 08 213**
**Album:** Released '82, on Pablo Jazz (USA) by Pablo Records (USA). Catalogue no: **2308 213**

**OSCAR PETERSON IN CONCERT**
Tracks: / Bag's groove / I've got the world on a string / Daahoud / Gai / Sweet Georgia Brown / Tenderly / C jam blues / Pompton turnpike / Seven come eleven / Love for sale / Lollobrigida / Swingin' 'til the girls come home / Nuages / Avalon / Come to the Mardi Gras / Baby, baby all the time / Easy does it / Sunday / Falling in love with love / Noreen's nocturne / Gypsy in my soul / Flamingo / Love you madly / 52nd Street theme.
Note: With Barney Kessell and Herb Ellis (guitars) and Ray Brown (bass).
**2 LP Set:** Released Jan '76, on Verve Catalogue no: **2683 063**
**Album:** Released Apr '84, on Polydor (Holland) by Polydor Ltd. Catalogue no: **1635 206**

**OSCAR PETERSON JAM**
Tracks: / Ali and Frazier / If I were a bell / Things ain't what they used to be / Just in time.
**Album:** Released '82, on Pablo Jazz (USA) by Pablo Records (USA). Catalogue no: **2308 208**
**Cass:** Released '82, on Pablo Jazz (USA) by Pablo Records (USA). Catalogue no: **K 08 208**

**OSCAR PETERSON PLAYS JAZZ Compact/Walkman jazz**
Tracks: / Swingin' 'til the girls come home / Con Alma / Joy Spring / I remember Clifford / Love you madly / Bag's groove / When lights are low / Waltz for Debbie / 52nd Street theme.
**Album:** Released 27 Feb '88, on Verve Catalogue no: **833 283-4**
**CD:** Released Mar '88, on Verve Catalogue no: **833 283-2**

**OSCAR PETERSON & STEPHANE GRAPPELLI (Peterson, Oscar & Stephane Grappelli Quartet)**
Tracks: / Them there eyes / Blues for musidisc / Making whoopee / Thou swell / Walkin' my baby back home / Autumn leaves / Looking at you / Folks who live on the hill, The / I won't dance / Time after time / My one and only love / My heart stood still / Flamingo / If I had you / Let's fall in love.
Note: With Niels Pedersen and Kenny Clarke.
**2 LP Set:** Released Apr '84, on Musidisc by Musidisc Records (France). Catalogue no: **ALB 329**

**OSCAR PETERSON TRIO IN TOKYO (Peterson, Oscar Trio)**
**CD Set:** Released Jan '89, on JVC/Fantasy Catalogue no: **VDJ 25008-9**

**OSCAR PETERSON TRIO WITH CLARK TERRY (Peterson, Oscar Trio & Clark Terry)**
Tracks: / Brotherhood of man / Jim / Blues for Smedley / Roundalay / Mumbles / Mack the knife / They didn't believe me / Squeaky's blues / I want a little girl / Incoherent blues.
**Album:** Released Dec '83, on Mercury Jazz Masters Catalogue no: **6336 342**
**CD:** Released Jun '85, on Emarcy Catalogue no: **8188402**

**PARIS CONCERT, THE (Peterson, Oscar/Joe Pass/Niels Pedersen)**
Tracks: / Please don't talk about me when I'm gone / Who can I turn to? / Benny's bugle / Soft winds / Goodbye / Place St. Henri / Manha de carnaval / If / Ornithology / Blue Lou / How long has this been going on? / Gentle tears / Lover man / Samba de Orfeu / Donna Lee / Sweet Georgia Brown.
**2 LP Set:** Released '82, on Pablo Jazz (USA) by Pablo Records (USA). Catalogue no: **262 0112**
**Cass set:** Released '82, on Pablo Jazz (USA) by Pablo Records (USA). Catalogue no: **K 20 112**

**PLUS ONE-CLARK TERRY (Peterson, Oscar Trio)**
Tracks: / Jim / Blues for Smedley / Roundalay / Mumbles / Mack the knife / They didn't believe me / Squeaky's blues / I want a little girl / Incoherent blues.
Note: Emarcy productions recorded in August 1964.
Personnel: Oscar Peterson-piano/Ray Brown-bass/Thigpen-drums/lark Terry-trumpet, flugelhorn, vocal
**CD:** Released Apr '85, on Emarcy Catalogue no: **818 840 2**

**PORGY AND BESS (Peterson, Oscar & Joe Pass)**
Tracks: / Summertime / Bess, you is my woman now / My man's gone now / It ain't necessarily so / I got plenty o' nuttin' / Oh, Bess, oh where's my Bess? / I loves you, Porgy / They pass by singin' / There's a boat that's leaving shortly for New York / Strawberry woman.
**Album:** Released '82, on Pablo Jazz (USA) by Pablo Records (USA). Catalogue no: **231 0779**
**Album:** Released Jun '86, on Pablo Jazz (USA) by Pablo Records (USA). Catalogue no: **J33J 20052**
**Cass:** Released '82, on Pablo Jazz (USA) by Pablo Records (USA). Catalogue no: **K10 779**

**REUNION BLUES (Peterson, Oscar & Milt Jackson)**
Tracks: / Satisfaction / Dream of you / Some day my prince will come / Time for love, A / Reunion blues / When I fall in love / Red top.
**Album:** Released May '81, on MPS Jazz Catalogue no: **MPS 68 087**
**CD:** Released Jul '84, on Verve Deleted Mar '88. Catalogue no: **817 490-2**

**ROMANCE**
Tracks: / I'm glad there is you / Polka dots and moonbeams / One for my baby / I hear music / Autumn in New York / I can't give you anything but love / Spring is here / These foolish things / From this moment on / Things we did last summer, The / Too marvellous for words / But not for me.
**Album:** Released Mar '82, on Polydor by Polydor Ltd. Catalogue no: **2304 473**

**ROYAL WEDDING SUITE, A**
Tracks: / Announcement / London gets ready / When summer comes / It's on / Heraldry / Royal honeymoon / Lady Di's waltz / Let the world sing / Empty cathedral.
**Album:** Released '82, on Pablo Jazz (USA) by Pablo Records (USA). Catalogue no: **231 2129**
**Cass:** Released '82, on Pablo Jazz (USA) by Pablo Records (USA). Catalogue no: **K 12 129**

**SALLE PLEYE, A (Peterson, Oscar & Joe Pass)**
**Cass:** Released '82, on Pablo Jazz (USA) by Pablo Records (USA). Catalogue no: **K 25 705**
**Album:** Released '82, on Pablo Jazz (USA) by Pablo Records (USA). Catalogue no: **262 5705**

**SATCH AND JOSH (Peterson, Oscar & Count Basie)**
Tracks: / Bun's blues / These foolish things / R.B. burning / Exactly like you / Jumpin' at The Woodside / Louis B. / Lester leaps in / Big stockings / S and J blues.
**Cass:** Released '82, on Pablo Jazz (USA) by Pablo Records (USA). Catalogue no: **K10 722**
**Album:** Released '82, on Pablo Jazz (USA) by Pablo Records (USA). Catalogue no: **231 0722**

**SATCH AND JOSH AGAIN (Peterson, Oscar & Count Basie)**
Tracks: / Roots / Red wagon / Home run / Sweethearts on parade / Li'l darlin' / Time is right / Cherry / Lester leaps in / She's funny that way / Lady Fitz.
**Album:** Released '82, on Pablo Jazz (USA) by Pablo Records (USA). Catalogue no: **231 0802**
**Cass:** Released '82, on Pablo Jazz (USA) by Pablo Records (USA). Catalogue no: **K10 802**

**SILENT PARTNER**
Tracks: / Theme for Celine / Happy hour / Party time USA / Elliot (the silent partner) / Theme for Susannah / Blues for Chris (the fox).
**Album:** Released '82, on Pablo Jazz (USA) by Pablo Records (USA). Catalogue no: **231 2103**
**Cass:** Released '82, on Pablo Jazz (USA) by Pablo Records (USA). Catalogue no: **K 12 103**

**SILVER COLLECTION, THE**
Tracks: / My foolish heart / Round midnight / Some day my prince will come / Come Sunday / Nightingale / My ship / Sleeping bee / Portrait of Jennie / Goodbye / Con alma / Maidens of Cadiz / My heart stood still / Woody 'n' you.
**CD:** Released Nov '84, on Verve Catalogue no: **823 447-2**

**SKOL (Peterson, Oscar/Stephane Grappelli/Joe Pass)**
Tracks: / Nuages / How about you? / Someone to watch over me / Makin' whoopee / That's all / Skol blues.
Note: Oscar Peterson, piano; Stephane Grappelli, violin; Joe Pass, guitar; Niels Pedersen, bass, Mickey Roker, drums.

**Oscar Peterson - Swing the great standards (Verve)**

**Cass:** Released Sep '82, on Pablo Jazz (USA) by Pablo Records (USA). Catalogue no: **K08 232**
**Album:** Released Sep '82, on Pablo Jazz (USA) by Pablo Records (USA). Catalogue no: **230 8232**

**SOMETHING WARM**
Tracks: / There is no greater love / I remember Clifford / Autumn leaves / Blues for Big Scotia / Swamp fire / I love you.
**Album:** Released Aug '80, on Verve Deleted '85. Catalogue no: **2352 195**

**SWING THE GREAT STANDARDS (Peterson, Oscar Trio)**
Tracks: / Surrey with the fringe on top / Serenade in blue / Pick yourself up / You're a sweetheart / Foggy day, A / It's alright with me / Stormy weather / Lady is a tramp, The / Great day / Between the devil and the deep blue sea / They all laughed / Night and day / I won't dance / Song is ended, The / Blue moon / I feel a song coming on.
**Album:** Released Jun '88, on Memoir by Memoir Records. Catalogue no: **MOIR 130**
**Cass:** Released Nov '89, on Memoir by Memoir Records. Catalogue no: **CMOIR 130**

**THIS IS OSCAR PETERSON, VOL.1**
Tracks: / I got rhythm / Louise / My blue heaven / Sheik of Araby, The / Flying home / C jam blues, The / If I could be with you one hour tonight / Humoresque / Blue moon / In a little Spanish town / Time on my hands / China boy / Runnin' wild / Sweet Lorraine / Honeydripper / East of the sun.
**Album:** on Official by Official Records. Catalogue no: **OFF 3037**

**THIS IS OSCAR PETERSON, VOL.2**
Tracks: / Back home again in Indiana / Margie / I surrender dear / I don't stand a ghost of a chance with you / Oscar's boogie / Smiles / Stairway to the stars / Poor butterfly / Oop-bop sh-bam / Sweet Georgia Brown / Sleepy time gal / Rockin' in rhythm / Fine and dandy / My heart stood still / Somebody loves me / At sundown.
**Album:** on Official by Official Records. Catalogue no: **OFF 3039**

**TIMEKEEPERS**
**CD:** Released '88, on Pablo Jazz (USA) by Pablo Records (USA). Catalogue no: **131 124 3**

**TRACKS**
**Album:** Released May '81, on MPS Jazz Catalogue no: **MPS 68 084**

**TRAVELLIN' ON**
**Album:** Released '81, on MPS Jazz Catalogue no: **MPS 68 078**

**TRIBUTE TO MY FRIENDS, A**
Tracks: / Blueberry Hill / Sometimes I'm happy / Stuffy / Birk's works / Cottontail / Lover man / Tisket a tasket, A / Rockin' chair / Now's the time.
Note: Peterson plays tunes connected with Louis Armstrong, Lester Young, Coleman Hawkins, Dizzy Gillespie, Ben Webster, Billie Holiday, Ella Fitzgerald, Roy Eldridge and Charlie Parker.
**CD:** Released '88, on Pablo Jazz (USA) by Pablo Records (USA). Catalogue no: **311 249**

**Album:** Released May '84, on Pablo Jazz (USA) by Pablo Records (USA). Catalogue no: **231 0902**
**Cass:** Released May '84, on Pablo Jazz (USA) by Pablo Records (USA). Catalogue no: **K10 902**

**TRIO IN TRANSITION**
Tracks: / Children's tune / Younger than springtime / Misty / Django / Shadow of your smile / Shelley's world / Let's fall in love / Blues etude / Smudge / Autumn leaves / Moanin' / Lover's romance / L'impossible / If i were a bell / Stella by starlight / I know you oh so well / Bossa beguine.
**2 LP Set:** Released Oct '83, on Mercury (USA) by PolyGram Rec.Inc.(USA). Catalogue no: **6641 577**

**TRIO LIVE FROM CHICAGO, THE**
**Album:** Released Sep '84, on Verve (USA) by Polydor Ltd. Catalogue no: **2304 194**
**Cass:** Released Sep '84, on Verve (USA) by Polydor Ltd. Catalogue no: **823 008-4**

**TRIO, THE**
Tracks: / Blues etude / Chicago blues / Easy listening blues / Come Sunday / Secret love.
Note: Personnel: Oscar Peterson/Niels Pedersen/Joe Pass
**CD:** Released Feb '87, on Polydor by Polydor Ltd. Deleted Jul '88. Catalogue no: **823 008 2**
**CD:** Released Jul '86, on Pablo Jazz (USA) by Pablo Records (USA). Catalogue no: **J33J 20049**
**Album:** Released '82, on Pablo Jazz (USA) by Pablo Records (USA). Catalogue no: **2310 701**
**Cass:** Released '82, on Pablo Jazz (USA) by Pablo Records (USA). Catalogue no: **K10 701**

**TRISTEZA ON PIANO**
Tracks: / Tristeza / Nightingale / Porgy / Triste / You stepped out of a dream / Watch what happens / Down here on the ground / Fly me to the moon.
**Album:** Released May '81, on MPS Jazz Catalogue no: **MPS 68 081**
**CD:** Released May '84, on Pablo Jazz (USA) by Pablo Records (USA). Deleted Mar '88. Catalogue no: **817 489-2**

**TRUMPET SUMMIT MEETS THE OSCAR PETERSON BIG FOUR (Peterson, Oscar Big 4)**
Tracks: / Daahoud / Chicken wings / Just friends / Champ.
**Cass:** Released '82, on Pablo Jazz (USA) by Pablo Records (USA). Catalogue no: **K 12 114**
**Album:** Released '82, on Pablo Jazz (USA) by Pablo Records (USA). Catalogue no: **231 2114**

**TWO OF THE FEW (Peterson, Oscar & Milt Jackson)**
**Album:** Released May '83, on Pablo Jazz (USA) by Pablo Records (USA). Catalogue no: **2310 881**
**Cass:** Released May '83, on Pablo Jazz (USA) by Pablo Records (USA). Catalogue no: **K10 881**

**VOCAL STYLING OF OSCAR PETERSON**
Tracks: / I'm glad there is you / Polka dots and moonbeams / One for my baby / I hear music / Autumn in New York / I can't give you anything but love / These foolish things / From this moment on / Things we did last summer / Too marvellous for words / But not for me / Spring is here.
**Album:** Released Jan '77, on Verve Deleted '81. Catalogue no: **2352 169**

**WALKING ON THE LINE**
**Album:** Released May '81, on MPS Jazz Catalogue no: **MPS 68 082**

**WAY I REALLY PLAY, THE**
**Album:** Released May '81, on MPS Jazz Catalogue no: **MPS 68 075**

**WE GET REQUESTS**
Tracks: / Quiet nights of quiet stars / Days of wine and roses / My one and only love / People / Have you met Miss Jones / You look good to me / Girl from Ipanema / D & E blues / Time and again / Goodbye JD.
**CD:** Released '83, on Verve Deleted Jul '88. Catalogue no: **810 047-2**
**Cass:** Released '87, on Verve Catalogue no: **311 204-4**
**Album:** Released '83, on Verve Deleted Oct '89. Catalogue no: **2352 065**

**WEST SIDE STORY**
Tracks: / Something's coming / Somewhere / Jet song / Tonight / Maria / I feel pretty / Reprise.
**CD:** Released Oct '84, on Verve Deleted Mar '88. Catalogue no: **821 575-2**

**YESSIR THAT'S MY BABY (Peterson, Oscar & Count Basie)**
Note: See also under Count basie.
**Cass:** Released Dec '86, on Pablo Jazz (USA) by Pablo Records (USA). Catalogue no: **K10 923**
**Album:** Released Dec '86, on Pablo Jazz (USA) by Pablo Records (USA). Catalogue no: **231 0923**
**CD:** Released Apr '87, on Pablo Jazz (USA) by Pablo Records (USA). Catalogue no: **CD 231 0923**

## Peterson, Ralph

**RALPH PETERSON**
**CD:** Released May '89, on Blue Note by EMI Records. Catalogue no: **791 730 2**

**V (Peterson, Ralph Quintet)**
Tracks: / Enemy within / Monief / Short end of the stick, The / Soweto 6 / Viola's dance / Bebopskerony.
**CD:** Released May '89, on Blue Note by EMI Records. Catalogue no: **CDP 791 730 2**
**Album:** Released Jul '89, on Blue Note by EMI Records. Catalogue no: **791 730 1**
**Album:** Released Jul '89, on Blue Note by EMI Records. Catalogue no: **B1 91730**

## Petrucciani, Michel

**Biographical details:** Jazz pianist Michel Petrucciani, who was born in 1962 in Orange, France, suffers from calcium deficiency osteogenesis imperfecta ("glass bones"), is about three feet tall and has to be carried to the piano. As a child he was encouraged by seeing Duke Ellington on television. While still a teenager he played with touring jazz musicians in France and he soon became an international star. He was influenced by Bill Evans and Lennie Tristano. His composing and playing have already become noticeably more original and thoughtful and he is still a young man. He released 11 albums between 1980-87 and also recorded with the Charles Lloyd Quartet. (Donald Clarke, May 1987.).

**100 HEARTS**
Tracks: / Turn around / Three forgotten magic words / Silence / St. Thomas / Potpourri / Very early / Some day my prince will come / Child is born, A / 100 hearts.
**CD:** Released Jan '90, on Concord by Concord Jazz Records (USA). Catalogue no: **CCD 43001**
**Album:** Released Apr '84, on George Wein Collection(USA) by Concord Jazz Records (USA). Catalogue no: **GW 3001**

**LIVE AT THE VILLAGE VANGUARD**
**Album:** Released May '85, on George Wein Collection(USA) by Concord Jazz Records (USA). Catalogue no: **GW 3006**

**LIVE: MICHEL PETRUCCIANI**
**CD:** Released '88, on Concord by Concord Jazz Records (USA). Catalogue no: **CCD 43006**

**MICHEL PLAYS PETRUCCIANI**
Tracks: / She did it again / One for us / Sahara / 13th / Mr. K. J. / One night at Ken and Jessica's / It's a dance / La champagne / Brazilian suite.
**CD:** Released Jan '89, on Blue Note by EMI Records. Catalogue no: **CDP 748 679 2**
**Album:** Released Jul '89, on Blue Note by EMI Records. Catalogue no: **B1 48679**
**CD:** Released Jan '89, on Blue Note by EMI Records. Catalogue no: **BNZ 108**

**MUSIC**
Tracks: / Looking up / Memories of Paris / My bebop tune / Brazillian suite No. 2 / Bite / Lullaby / O nana oye / Play me / Happy birthday Mr. K (CD only.) / Thinking of Wayne (CD only.).
**Album:** Released Jan '90, on Blue Note by EMI Records. Catalogue no: **B1 92563**
**CD:** Released Jan '90, on Blue Note by EMI Records. Catalogue no: **792 563 2**
**CD:** Released Jan '90, on Blue Note by EMI Records. Catalogue no: **CDB1 92563**
**Album:** Released Jan '90, on Blue Note by EMI Records. Catalogue no: **792 563 1**

**PIANISM**
Tracks: / Prayer, The / Our tune / Face's face / Night and day / Here's that rainy day / Regina.
**Album:** Released Jul '89, on Blue Note by EMI Records. Catalogue no: **BT 85124**
**CD:** Released Nov '89, on Blue Note by

EMI Records. Catalogue no: **CDP 746 295 2**
**CD:** Released Nov '89, on Blue Note by EMI Records. Catalogue no: **BNZ 216**
**Album:** Released Jul '89, on Blue Note by EMI Records. Catalogue no: **785 124 1**

**POWER OF THREE**
Tracks: / Limbo / Careful / Morning blues / Waltz new / Beautiful love / In a sentimental mood / Bimini.
Note: At the age of 23, Michel Petrucciani is already well on his way to becoming a major force in jazz piano. With this album, recorded live at the 1986 Montreaux Jazz Festival in Switzerland, Michel has taken a giant step forward. This recording took place midway through a European tour by Petrucciani and the legendary jazz guitarist Jim Hall. By Montreaux, they had developed a deep empathy and a wonderful programme of Hall originals and standard tunes. In Montreaux, they intersected with a very special guest: saxophonist Wayne Shorter. The three had previously met on the tour trail in Toronto and Copenhagen to prepare for this night. Shorter joins the duo for his own *Limbo* made famous by Miles Davis, Jim Hall's "SRO", a powerful calypso dedicated to Sonny Rollins and Michel's soulful *Morning blues*. It was a special night indeed and it was captured by Blue Note Records.
**Album:** Released Mar '87, on Blue Note by EMI Records. Catalogue no: **BT 85133**
**CD:** Released Sep '87, on Blue Note by EMI Records. Catalogue no: **CDP 746 427 2**
**CD:** Released Sep '87, on Blue Note by EMI Records. Catalogue no: **BNZ 74**

**TRIO RECORDING**
**CD:** Released '88, on Owl Catalogue no: **OWL LC025**
**Album:** Released '88, on Owl Catalogue no: **OWL L025**

## Pettiford, Oscar

**Biographical details:** With his extraordinarily accurate tone and unfailing time, Oscar Pettiford was the most influential jazz bassist between Jimmy Blanton and Charles Mingus - and he was the first bass man to take up the cello as a second instrument. He was born in Oklahoma in 1922, grew up in Minnesota and died in Copenhagen in 1960. He played in the family band - 10 brothers and sisters were all musicians - before leaving Minnesota with the Charlie Barnet Band. He played, with Coleman Hawkins, on some of the first bop records, and with Duke Ellington (1945-48) and Woody Herman (1949). He later settled in Europe. (Donald Clarke, May 1987.).

**BLUES BROTHERS**
**Album:** Released Apr '85, on Black Lion Catalogue no: **BLP 30135**

**BOHEMIA AFTER DARK**
Tracks: / Another one / Minor seventh heaven / Stardust / Bohemia after dark / Oscalypso / Scorpio / Don't squawk / Kamman's a comin'.
**Album:** Released Apr '84, on Affinity by Charly Records. Catalogue no: **AFF 117**

**IN HI-FI**
Tracks: / Nican's tempo / Deep passion / Sunrise sunset / Perdido / Two french fries / Pendulum at Falcon's Lair / Gentle art of love / Not so sleepy / Speculation / Smoke signal.
**Album:** Released Feb '84, on Jasmine by Hasmick Promotions. Deleted Feb '88. Catalogue no: **JASM 1034**

**JAZZ ON THE AIR Volume 6 (Pettiford, Oscar & His Birdland Big Band)**
Tracks: / Theme / Aw c'mon / Nica's tempo / Seventh heaven / Perdido / Two french fries / He's my guy / Smoke signals / I remember Clifford / Not so sleepy.
**Album:** Released '88, on Spotlite by Spotlite Records. Catalogue no: **SPJ 153**

**LEGENDARY OSCAR PETTIFORD, THE**
Note: With Hans Koller/Attila Koller/Jimmy Pratt. Tracks include: Cohn's limit/The gentle art of love/All the things you are/Vienna blues/Oscars blues/Stardust/Blues in the closet. 1959.
**Album:** Released Sep '85, on Black Lion Catalogue no: **BLP 30185**

**MONTMARTRE BLUES**
**Album:** Released Feb '89, on Black Lion Catalogue no: **BLP 60124**

**OSCAR RIDES AGAIN (Pettiford, Oscar-Quintet & Nonet)**
Tracks: / Sextet / Golden touch / Cable car / Trictatism / Edge of love / Oscar rides again / Jack the bear / Tamalpais / Swing t'll the girls come home / Mood indigo / Chuckles / Time on my hands.
**Album:** Released Sep '86, on Affinity by Charly Records. Catalogue no: **AFF 160**

**VIENNA BLUES - THE COMPLETE SESSION**
Tracks: / Cohn's limit / Gentle art of love, The / All the things you are / Stalag 414 / Vienna blues / Oscar's blues / Stardust / There will never be another you / Blues in the closet.
Note: Recorded at Mastertone Studios, Vienna, 9 January 1959, 12 January 1959.
**CD:** Released Jun '88, on Black Lion Catalogue no: **BLCD 760104**
**Album:** Released Jun '88, on Black Lion Catalogue no: **BLP 60104**

## Pettis, Alabama Jr

**CHICAGO BLUES SESSION 4 (Pettis, Alabama Jr & Teardrops)**
Note: Complete artists: Alabama Jr Pettis & The Teardrops with Magic Slim & John Primer.
**Album:** Released Aug '87, on Wolf Catalogue no: **WOLF 120 850**

## Phillips, Barre

**CALL ME WHEN YOU GET THERE**
Tracks: / Grants pass / Craggy slope / Amos crowns / Barn / Pittmans rock / Highway 37 / Winslow cavern / Riverbend / Brewestertown.
**Album:** Released Feb '84, on ECM Catalogue no: **ECM 1257**

**MOUNTAINSCAPES**
**Album:** Released Sep '76, on ECM Catalogue no: **ECM 1076**

**MUSIC BY**
**Album:** Released May '81, on ECM Catalogue no: **ECM 1178**

**THREE DAY MOON**
**Album:** Released '78, on ECM Catalogue no: **ECM 1123**

## Phillips, Esther

**Biographical details:** Born Esther May Jones, this American blues, jazz and soul singer was discovered at the age of 13 by musician and entrepreneur Johnny Otis. Billed as Little Esther, she enjoyed a run of Top 10 collaborations with Otis on the US rhythm and blues charts during the following year (1950). An occasional visitor to the US pop charts, Phillips reached No. 8 in 1962 with *Release me* (a country and western song that was later turned into an even bigger hit by Engelbert Humperdinck) and climbed to No. 20 in America and No. 6 in Britain with 1975's *What a difference a day made.* She died in August 1984 at the age of 48. Bob MacDonald, 5 March 1986..

**CAPRICORN PRINCESS**
Tracks: / Magic's in the air / I haven't got anything better to do / Boy, I really tied one on / Candy / Beautiful friendship / Higher and higher / All the way down / Dream.
**Album:** Released Feb '77, on Kudu Deleted '80. Catalogue no: **KU 31**

**COMPLETE SAVOY RECORDINGS (Phillips, Little Esther)**
**2 LP Set:** Released Jan '87, on Savoy Jazz (USA) by Malaco Records (USA). Catalogue no: **SJL 2258**
**Album:** Released Mar '85, on Savoy Jazz (USA) by Malaco Records (USA). Catalogue no: **SJL 2258**

**CONFESSIN' THE BLUES**
Tracks: / I'm gettin' 'long alright / I wonder / Confessin' the blues / Romance in the dark / C.C. Rider / Cherry red / In the evenin' / I love Paris / It could happen to you / Bye bye blackbird / Blow top blues / Jelly jelly blues / Long John blues.
**Album:** Released Feb '79, on Atlantic by WEA Records. Deleted Feb '84. Catalogue no: **K 50521**

**ESTHER PHILLIPS**
Tracks: / What a difference a day made / Home is where the hatred is / Use me / I feel the same / I've never found a man (to love me like you do) / Boy I really tried one on / One night affair / From a whisper to a scream / Justified / Living alone / Candy.
**Album:** Released Apr '78, on Kudu Catalogue no: **SKU 001**

**GOOD BLACK IS HARD TO CRACK**
**Album:** Released Apr '81, on Mercury by Phonogram Ltd. Catalogue no: **SRM**

14005

**HERE'S ESTHER-ARE YOU READY**
Tracks: / Mr. Melody / Philadelphia freedom / I hope you'll be very unhappy without me / Love makes a woman / Our day will come / Bedtime stories / Oo oop oo oop / I'll close my eyes.
**Album:** Released Sep '79, on Mercury by Phonogram Ltd. Catalogue no: **9100 065**

**WAY TO SAY GOODBYE, A**
Tracks: / It's all in the game / Mama said / Going in circles / Nowhere to run / We are through / Fa fa fa fa fa (sad song) / Mr. Bojangles / Shake this off / Way to say goodbye, A.
**CD:** Released Feb '87, on Muse (USA) by Muse Records (USA). Catalogue no: **MCD 5302**
**Cass:** Released Feb '87, on Muse (USA) by Muse Records (USA). Catalogue no: **MRC 5302**

**WHAT A DIFFERENCE A DAY MAKES**
Tracks: / One night affair / What a difference a day makes / Hurtin' house / Oh papa / Turn around, look at me.
**CD:** Released '88, on CBS by CBS Records. Deleted Jan '89. Catalogue no: **450465-2**
**Cass:** Released Jul '85, on CTI (Musidisc France) by Polydor Ltd. Catalogue no: **CTK 9523**
**Album:** Released Jul '85, on CTI (Musidisc France) by Polydor Ltd. Catalogue no: **CTI 9023**

**WHAT A DIFFERENCE A DAY MAKES**
Tracks: / What a difference a day made.
**7" Single:** Released Oct '75, on Kudu Deleted '78. Catalogue no: **KUDU 925**

## Phillips, Flip

**FLIP PHILLIPS & SCOT HAMILTON (Phillips, Flip & Scot Hamilton)**
**CD:** Released Dec '87, on Concord Jazz by Concord Jazz Records (USA). Catalogue no: **CCD 4334**

**MELODY FROM THE SKY, A**
Tracks: / Melody from the sky, A / Stompin' at the Savoy / Sweet and lovely / Swingin' for Popsie / Bob's belief / Why shouldn't I? / Lover come back to me / Popolloma / Skyscraper / 1-2-3-4 jump / More than you know / Without Woody.
**Cass:** Released '86, on Doctor Jazz (USA) by CBS Records (USA). Catalogue no: **ZCAS 806**
**Album:** Released '86, on Doctor Jazz (USA) by CBS Records (USA). Catalogue no: **ASLP 806**

**REAL SWINGER, A**
Tracks: / Hashimoto's blues / Vol vistu gailey star / It was a very good year / Cottontail / Poor butterfly / I want to be happy / Tricotism / September song / Symphony / I got a right to sing the blues / Christian scientist.
Note: Personel: Flip Phillips (tenor sax & bass clarinet), Howard Alden (guitar), Wayne Wright (rhythm guitar), Dick Hyman (piano), Jack Lesberg (bass), Charles 'Butch' Miles (drums).
**Cass:** Released Oct '88, on Concord Jazz by Concord Jazz Records (USA). Catalogue no: **CJ 358 C**
**CD:** Released Oct '88, on Concord Jazz by Concord Jazz Records (USA). Catalogue no: **CCD 4358**
**Album:** Released Oct '88, on Concord Jazz by Concord Jazz Records (USA). Catalogue no: **CJ 358**

**SWINGING WITH FLIP (Phillips, Flip & Orchestra)**
**Album:** Released Dec '88, on Syndicate Chapter Catalogue no: **SC 1019**
**Album:** Released Nov '87, on Swingtime by Contact Records (Denmark). Catalogue no: **824**
**Album:** Released Jun '88, on Swingtime by Contact Records (Denmark). Catalogue no: **ST 1019**

## Phillips, Sonny

**I CONCENTRATE ON YOU**
**Album:** Released '88, on Muse by Black & Blue Records. Catalogue no: **MR 5157**

**MY BLACK FLOWER**
**Album:** Released '88, on Muse by Black & Blue Records. Catalogue no: **MR 5118**

## Phontastic Dixieland

**DIXIE DISC (From Basin Street to Louisiana)**
**Album:** Released '82, on Phontastic (Sweden) Catalogue no: **PHONT 7523**

## Piano Blues

**PIANO BLUES LEGENDS (Various artists)**
Tracks: / P L bounce: *Various artists* / Seasick and waterbound: *Various artists* / With you on my mind: *Various artists* / Mother Fuyer: *Various artists* / Going down slow: *Various artists* / St. Louis blues: *Various artists* / T 99: *Various artists* / Bloodstains on the wall: *Various artists* / Why should I cry: *Various artists* / Blues ain't nothing but a botheration: *Various artists* / I got a gal: *Various artists.*
**Album:** Released Jun '83, on JSP by JSP Records. Catalogue no: **JSP 1056**

**PIANO BLUES VOL.1 The Twenties 1923-30 (Various artists)**
Note: Clay Custer, L.C. Prigett, Jack Ranger etc.
**Album:** Released Sep '87, on Document Catalogue no: **DLP 513**

**PIANO BLUES, VOL.1: PARAMOUNT Whip it to a jelly (Various artists)**
**Album:** Released Sep '77, on Magpie by Interstate Music. Catalogue no: **PY 4401**

**PIANO BLUES VOL.2 The Thirties 1930-39 (Various artists)**
Note: Bob Robinson, Jesse James, Pigmeat Henry etc.
**Album:** Released Sep '87, on Document Catalogue no: **DLP 514**

**PIANO BLUES, VOL.2: BRUNSWICK Nothing but a worried mind (Various artists)**
**Album:** Released '88, on Magpie by Interstate Music. Catalogue no: **PY 4402**

**PIANO BLUES, VOL.3: VOCALION Shake your wicked knees (Various artists)**
**Album:** Released '88, on Magpie by Interstate Music. Catalogue no: **PY 4403**

**PIANO BLUES, VOL.4: THE THOMAS FAMILY Give it to me good Mr.Hersal (Various artists)**
**Album:** Released '88, on Magpie by Interstate Music. Catalogue no: **PY 4404**

**PIANO BLUES, VOL.5: POSTSCRIPT 1927-33 Hot box on my mind (Various artists)**
**Album:** Released Jul '78, on Magpie by Interstate Music. Catalogue no: **PY 4405**

**PIANO BLUES, VOL.6: WALTER ROLAND 1933-35 Take your big legs off (Various artists)**
**Album:** Released '88, on Magpie by Interstate Music. Catalogue no: **PY 4406**

**PIANO BLUES, VOL.7: LEROY CARR 1930-35 Don't cry when I'm gone (Various artists)**
**Album:** Released '88, on Magpie by Interstate Music. Catalogue no: **PY 4407**

**PIANO BLUES, VOL.8: TEXAS SEAPORT 1934-37 Stomp the grinder down (Various artists)**
**Album:** Released Jan '79, on Magpie by Interstate Music. Catalogue no: **PY 4408**

**PIANO BLUES, VOL.9: LOFTON/NOBLE 1935-6 What's the use of gettin' sober (Various artists)**
**Album:** Released Feb '79, on Magpie by Interstate Music. Catalogue no: **PY 4409**

**PIANO BLUES, VOL.10: TERRITORY BLUES 1934-41 That's where I was born (Various artists)**
**Album:** Released Apr '79, on Magpie by Interstate Music. Catalogue no: **PY 4410**

**PIANO BLUES, VOL.11: TEXAS SANTA FE 1934-37 There's a train leavin' Houston (Various artists)**
**Album:** Released '88, on Magpie by Interstate Music. Catalogue no: **PY 4411**

**PIANO BLUES, VOL.12: BIG FOUR 1933-41 Will you satisfy my mind (Various artists)**
**Album:** Released Oct '79, on Magpie by Interstate Music. Deleted '88. Catalogue no: **PY 4412**

**PIANO BLUES, VOL.13: CENTRAL HIGHWAY 1933-41 Pull up your dress babe (Various artists)**
**Album:** Released '88, on Magpie by Interstate Music. Catalogue no: **PY 4413**

**PIANO BLUES, VOL.14: THE Play it for me (Various artists)**
**Album:** Released '88, on Magpie by

Interstate Music. Catalogue no: **PY 4414**

**PIANO BLUES, VOL.15: DALLAS 1927-29 (Elm Street's paved in brass) (Various artists)**
**Album:** Released '88, on Magpie by Interstate Music. Catalogue no: **PY 4415**

**PIANO BLUES, VOL.16: CHARLIE SPAND 1929-31 (Soon this morning) (Various artists)**
**Album:** Released '88, on Magpie by Interstate Music. Catalogue no: **PY 4416**

**PIANO BLUES, VOL.17: PARAMOUNT, VOL.2 1927-32 (Raised in the alley) (Various artists)**
**Album:** Released Jul '82, on Magpie by Interstate Music. Catalogue no: **PY 4417**

**PIANO BLUES, VOL.18: ROOSEVELT SKYES / LEE GREEN 1 (The way I feel) (Sykes, Roosevelt & Lee Green)**
**Album:** Released '88, on Magpie by Interstate Music. Catalogue no: **PY 4418**

**PIANO BLUES, VOL.19: BARRELHOUSE WOMEN 1925-33 (Play it with your mama) (Various artists)**
**Album:** Released '88, on Magpie by Interstate Music. Catalogue no: **PY 4419**

**PIANO BLUES, VOL.20: BARRELHOUSE YEARS 1928-33 (Some piano player, I'll tell you that) (Various artists)**
**Album:** Released '88, on Magpie by Interstate Music. Catalogue no: **PY 4420**

**PIANO BLUES, VOL.21: UNISSUED BOOGIE 1938-45 (Jump for joy) (Various artists)**
**Album:** Released Jul '84, on Magpie by Interstate Music. Catalogue no: **PY 4421**

## Piano Boogie

**PIANO BOOGIE & THE BLUES (Various artists)**
Tracks: / If things don't get better: *Various artists* / G.R. boogie: *Various artists* / You ain't had no blues: *Various artists* / Boogie express: *Various artists* / Mr. Black man: *Various artists* / Blues boogie: *Various artists* / G.R. blues: *Various artists* / Rhapsody boogie: *Various artists* / Canal Street boogie woogie: *Various artists* / It was so good: *Various artists* / Hen house boogie: *Various artists* / Don't stop now: *Various artists* / Chocolate: *Various artists* / Man shortage blues: *Various artists* / Honky tonk train blues: *Various artists*.
Note: Featuring: Willie 'The Lion' Smith, Al Casey, Gene Rodgers, Deryck Sampson, Beverley White.
**Album:** Released '88, on Krazy Kat by Interstate Music. Catalogue no: **KK 802**

## Piano Jazz

**PIANO JAZZ (Boogie woogie pianists 1928-30) (Various artists)**
**Album:** Released Jan '83, on Swaggie (Australia) Catalogue no: **S 1326**

## Piano Legends

**PIANO LEGENDS (Various artists)**
**Album:** Released May '88, on Jazz Life Catalogue no: **2673051**
**Cass:** Released May '88, on Jazz Life Catalogue no: **2673054**
**CD:** Released May '88, on Jazz Life Catalogue no: **267 305 2**

**PIANO LEGENDS (VIDEO) (Various artists)**
**VHS:** Released '88, on Kay Jazz (video) by Kay Jazz. Catalogue no: **KJ 071**

## Piano Portraits

**PIANO PORTRAITS VOL.3 (Swingin' for joy) (Various artists)**
Tracks: / Swingin' for joy: *Various artists* / Mississippi moan: *Various artists* / Rosetta: *Various artists* / Boogie woogie Maxine: *Various artists* / Yancey special: *Various artists* / Jingles: *Various artists* / When a woman loves a man: *Various artists* / Three litle words: *Various artists* / Sheik of Araby, The: *Various artists* / Twinklin': *Various artists* / Just you, just me: *Various artists* / Oh Red: *Various artists* / Boogie woogie cocktail: *Various artists* / (I don' stand a) ghost of a chance (with you): *Various artists* / If I were a bell: *Various artists* / Blues for Django: *Various artists*.
**Album:** Released Apr '87, on Affinity by Charly Records. Catalogue no: **AFS 1035**

**PIANO PORTRAITS, VOLUME 1 (Various artists)**
Tracks: / You've got to be modernistic: *Various artists* / Pearls, The: *Various artists* / Early morning blues: *Various artists* / Kacyee feeling: *Various artists* / Time square blues: *Various artists* / Passionette: *Various artists* / Nobody knows you (when you're down and out): *Various artists* / Beautiful love: *Various artists* / I've got my love to keep me warm: *Various artists* / I'm sober now: *Various artists* / King Porter stomp: *Various artists* / What is this thing called love: *Various artists* / Hot and bothered: *Various artists* / Mr. Freddie blues: *Various artists* / Morning air: *Various artists* / Dive bomber: *Various artists*.
**Album:** Released Apr '86, on Affinity by Charly Records. Catalogue no: **AFS 1022**

**PIANO PORTRAITS VOLUME 2 (Rockin' in rhythm) (Various artists)**
Note: Artists:Pete Johnson,Mary Lou Williams,Johnny Guarnieri,Slim Gaillard,Cleo Brown,Count Basie,Ralph Sutton w.Eddie Condon's Band,Art Tatum. MONO.
**Album:** Released Jul '86, on Affinity by Charly Records. Catalogue no: **AFS 1028**

## Piano Red

**Biographical details:** Born William Lee Perryman, one of 16 children, in Hampton, Georgia, in 1911, blues pianist and singer Piano Red died in 1985 in Atlanta. His brother Rufus -- known as Speckled Red -- was also a bluesman. Both got their nicknames because they were Albino Negroes. Piano Red recorded with Blind Willie McTell in 1936 and with RCA in 1950: his two-sided hit *Rockin' With Red/Red's Boogie* sold a million in 1950-51 and is one of those discs sometimes called the first rock 'n' roll record. After the success of *Dr Feelgood* on Okeh he changed the name of his act to Dr Feelgood & The Interns and toured the college circuit. He was Piano Red again by the early 70's. (Donald Clarke, May 1987.).

**AIN'T GOIN' TO BE YOUR LOW DOWN DOG NO MORE**
Note: Tracks include: I've got my fingers crossed/Everyday I have the blues/It's a sin to tell a lie/Corrine Corrina/Do she love me/Boogie time, etc. Recorded 1974.
**Album:** Released Jul '87, on Black Lion Catalogue no: **BLP 30162**

**DOCTOR FEELGOOD**
Tracks: / Sloppy drunk / Blues, blues, blues / Pinetop's boogie / Doin' it / When things go wrong with you / Doctor Feelgood / Red's boogie / Dupree blues / Just another world goin' round / Whisky / You 'got the thing on me / Goodbye.
**Album:** Released May '79, on Black Lion Catalogue no: **BLP 30171**

**DOCTOR FEELGOOD ALONE**
**Album:** Released May '81, on Arhoolie (USA) by Arhoolie Records (USA). Catalogue no: **ARHOOLIE 1064**

**DOCTOR FEELGOOD - JUMPING TO THE BOOGIE**
**Album:** Released '88, on Oldie Blues Catalogue no: **OL 2821**

**ORIGINAL DR. FEELGOOD, THE**
**Album:** Released May '86, on JSP by JSP Records. Catalogue no: **JSP 1100**

## Piano Slim

**MEAN WOMAN BLUES**
**Album:** Released May '86, on Swing Master Catalogue no: **2103**

## Piano & Swing

**PIANO AND SWING (1935-1938)**
**Album:** Released Sep '84, on Pathe Marconi (France) Catalogue no: **PM 1552561**

## Pianola Roll

**KITTEN ON THE KEYS**
Tracks: / Bye bye blackbird / Thora / Miss Annabelle Lee / For me and my gal / Stars and stripes forever / Sweet genevieve / J'en ai marre / Alexander's ragtime band / I want to be happy / Doll dance / Moon river / Lovable & sweet / Me and Jane in a plane / Kitten on the keys / Stealing / Tippy canoe / Among my souvenirs / More we are together / Three o'clock in the morning.
Note: 54 minutes
**CD:** Released Mar '87, on Saydisc by Amon Ra Records. Catalogue no: **CD-SDL 355**
**Album:** Released Jun '86, on Saydisc by Amon Ra Records. Catalogue no: **SDL 355**
**Cass:** Released Jun '86, on Saydisc by Amon Ra Records. Catalogue no: **CSDL 355**

**PIANOLA JAZZ**
Tracks: / Skip along / Maple leaf rag / Blame it on the blues / For me and my gal / Aunt Hagar's blues / I'll dance till de sun breaks through / Rose of Washing-

ton Square / Georgia camp meeting / Stumbling / French trot / Alabama dream / Creole belles / Old-fashioned girl.
Note: 42 minutes. Early ragtime and jazz from 65 & 88 note pianola rolls from 1895 to the 1920s.
**Album:** Released Jun '82, on Saydisc by Amon Ra Records. Deleted '86. Catalogue no: **SDL 117**
**Cass:** Released Jun '82, on Saydisc by Amon Ra Records. Deleted '89. Catalogue no: **CSDL 117**

**PIANOLA RAGTIME (Piano rolls 1895-1916)**
Tracks: / Temptation rag / Ragtime skedaddle / Wabash blues / 1915 rag / Grizzly bear rag / Walhalla (two step craze) / Florida rag / Coon band contest / Smokey mokes / Tickled to death / Buzzer rag / Panama rag / Bow wow blues / Ragtime Oriole.
**Cass:** Released Nov '82, on Saydisc by Amon Ra Records. Deleted '89. Catalogue no: **CSDL 132**
**Album:** Released Nov '82, on Saydisc by Amon Ra Records. Deleted '86. Catalogue no: **SDL 132**

## Piccadilly Hotel Bands

**PICCADILLY REVELS BANDS**
**Album:** Released Aug '77, on Retrospect by EMI Records. Catalogue no: **SH 250**

## Piccadilly Nights

**PICCADILLY NIGHTS (British dance bands of the 1920's) (Various artists)**
Tracks: / That girl over there: *Various bands* / Swing on the gait: *Various bands* / It's a million to one you're in love: *Various bands* / What'll you do?: *Various bands* / Make my cot where the cot-cot-cotton grows: *Various bands* / How long has this been going on?: *Various bands* / Miss Annabelle Lee: *Various bands* / Lila: *Various bands* / That's my weakness now: *Various bands* / Sunny skies: *Various bands* / Matilda Matilda: *Various bands* / Saskatchewan: *Various bands* / There's a blue ridge round my heart Virginia: *Various bands* / 'S wonderful: *Various bands* / Crazy rhythm: *Various bands* / I'm a one man girl: *Various bands* / Spread a little happiness: *Various bands* / Out of the dawn: *Various bands* / Ida (sweet as apple cider): *Various bands* / I don't know why I do it but I do: *Various bands.*
Note: Bands include Billy Cotton's London Savannah Band, Alfredo's New Princes Orchestra, Jack Harris & his Band, Percival Mackey & his Orchestra, Harry Hudson & his Melody Men
**Cass:** Released Mar '87, on Halcyon (USA) by Submarine Records. Catalogue no: **CHAL 17**
**Album:** Released Mar '86, on Halcyon (USA) by Submarine Records. Catalogue no: **HAL 17**

## Pierce, Billie & De De

**BILLIE & DE DE PIERCE**
**Album:** Released Jun '88, on Jazzology (USA) by Jazzology Records (USA). Catalogue no: **JCE 25**

**NEW ORLEANS MUSIC**
**Album:** Released May '81, on Arhoolie (USA) by Arhoolie Records (USA). Catalogue no: **ARHOOLIE 2016**

## Pike, Dave

**DAVE PIKE AND CHARLES MCPHERSON See also McPherson, Charles (Pike, Dave / Charles McPherson)**
Tracks: / Scrapple from the apple / Off minor / Piano trio medley / Embraceable you / Up jumped Spring / Big foot.
Note: Recorded November 1988 Holland. Personnel: Dave Pike (vibes), Charles McPherson (alto sax), Rein de Graaff (piano), Koos Serierse (bass), Eric Ineke (drums).
**Album:** Released Jun '89, on Timeless by Timeless Records. Catalogue no: **SJP 302**
**CD:** Released Jun '89, on Timeless by Timeless Records. Catalogue no: **CDSJP 302**

**DAVE PIKE,VIBES WITH CEDAR**
**Album:** Released Jul '86, on Criss Cross Catalogue no: **XX 1021**

**LET THE MINSTRELS PLAY ON**
**Album:** Released Apr '81, on Muse by Black & Blue Records. Catalogue no: **MR 5203**

**MOON BIRD**
**Album:** Released '88, on Muse by Black & Blue Records. Catalogue no: **MR 5261**

**PIKE'S GROOVE (Pike, Dave / Cedar Walton Trio)**
**Album:** Released Jan '87, on Criss Cross Catalogue no: **CRISS 1021**

**TIMES OUT OF MIND**
**Album:** Released Apr '81, on Muse by Black & Blue Records. Catalogue no: **MR 5092**

## Pine, Courtney

**Biographical details:** The various activities of Courtney Pine -- born in London in 1964 -- are the most encouraging development in British jazz in a long time. The press refers to the hype surrounding him, but the press itself is responsible: Pine is a serious man ("I'm not going to spend my life playing *Stella By Starlight* in some wine bar") with enough talent to make any hype superfluous. He formed the Brixton-based big band Jazz Warriors, featuring black British musicians of all ages, many of whom had been stuck in reggae bands but who are now playing gloriously exciting original music. Pine's first album was a strong debut, showing the influences of John Coltgrane and Wayne Shorter. Future albums will all be exciting and they will all be different. (Donald Clarke, May 1987.)

**CHILDREN OF THE GHETTO**
Tracks: / Children of the ghetto / E.F.P. / When, where, how and why (Available on 12" version only.) / E.S.P. / Courtney Pine talks to Robert Elms (Part 1).
**Cassingle:** Released Nov '86, on Island by Island Records. Deleted Jul '87. Catalogue no: **CIS 301**
**7" Single:** Released Oct '86, on Island by Island Records. Catalogue no: **IS 301**
**12" Single:** Released Oct '86, on Island by Island Records. Deleted Jul '87. Catalogue no: **12IS 301**

**DESTINY'S SONG & THE IMAGE OF PURSUANCE**
Tracks: / Beyond the thought of my last reckoning / In pursuance / Vision, The / Guardian of the flame / Round midnight / Sacrifice / Prismic omnipotence / Alone / Raggamuffin's tale, A / Mark of the time.
Note: Courtney's first UK album on Antilles. Produced by Delfeayo Marsalis, younger brother of American jazz luminaries Wynton & Branford.
**CD:** Released 23 Jan '88, on Antilles/New Directions by Island Records. Catalogue no: **ANCD 8725**
**Album:** Released Jan '88, on Antilles/New Directions by Island Records. Catalogue no: **AN 8725**
**Cass:** Released Jan '88, on Antilles/New Directions by Island Records. Catalogue no: **ANC 8725**

**HIT OR MISS**
Tracks: / Hit or miss / Children of the night / Songs from our underground (part 1) (12" only).
Note: Theme from BBC TV's Juke Box Jury.
**12" Single:** Released Mar '90, on Antilles/New Directions by Island Records. Catalogue no: **12ANN 11**
**7" Single:** Released Mar '90, on Antilles/New Directions by Island Records. Catalogue no: **ANN 11**

**JOURNEY TO THE URGE WITHIN**
Tracks: / Mis-interpret / I believe / Peace / Delores St. S.F / As we would say / Children of the ghetto / When, where, how and why / C.G.C. / Seen / Sunday song.
**CD:** Released Oct '86, on Island by Island Records. Catalogue no: **CID 9846**
**Album:** Released Oct '86, on Island by Island Records. Catalogue no: **ILPS 9846**
**Cass:** Released Oct '86, on Island by Island Records. Catalogue no: **ICT 9846**

**ONLY FOR ONE NIGHT**
**CD:** Released '89, on Antilles/New Directions by Island Records. Catalogue no: **ANNCD 4**

**SACRIFICE**
Tracks: / Sacrifice / Mark of the time.
**10" Single:** Released Mar '88, on Antilles/New Directions by Island Records. Catalogue no: **10 ANN 3**

**TRADITIONS BECKONING**
Tracks: / Traditions beckoning.
**10" Single:** Released 12 Sep '88, on Antilles/New Directions by Island Records. Deleted Apr '89. Catalogue no: **10 ANN 4**
**7" Single:** Released 12 Sep '88, on Antilles/New Directions by Island Records. Deleted Apr '89. Catalogue no: **ANN 4**

**VISION'S TALE, THE**
Tracks: / Introduction / In a mellow tone / Just you, just me / Raggamuffin's

stance, A / No greater love / Skylark / I'm an old cowhand from the Rio Grande / God bless the child / And then (a warrior's tale) / Our descendants' descendants / CP's theme.
**Cass:** Released Aug '89, on Antilles/New Directions by Island Records. Catalogue no: **ANC 8746**
**Album:** Released Aug '89, on Antilles/New Directions by Island Records. Catalogue no: **AN 8746**
**CD:** Released Aug '89, on Antilles/New Directions by Island Records. Catalogue no: **ANCD 8746**

## Pinski Zoo

**RARE BREEDS**
Note: This quartet have been at the forefront of British contempory music since the launch of their first album *Introduce me to the doctor* in 1982. They have received every imaginable critical accolade in Britain and Europe and their latest album *Rare Breeds* (re-released through New Note) was voted top British group album of 1988 in the WIRE critics poll. In Pinski Zoo's music the avant-garde meets super heavy funk. Personnel: Jan Kopinski (tenor, soprano & alto sax), Steve Illiffe (keyboards), Karl Wesley Bingham (electric bass), Tim Bullock (drums and percussion).
**Album:** Released Feb '89, on M.M.P. Catalogue no: **PINS 006**
**CD:** Released Sep '89, on JCR Catalogue no: **JCRCD 903**

**SWEET AUTOMATIC**
Tracks: / Sweet automatic (acid mix) / New lunacy.
**7" Single:** Released Jan '89, on JCR Catalogue no: **JCR 901**

## Pioneers Of French Jazz

**PIONEERS OF FRENCH JAZZ 1906-31 (Various artists)**
**Album:** Released Sep '84, on Pathe Marconi (France) Catalogue no: **PM 1552551**

## Pioneers Of The Jazz ...

**PIONEERS OF THE JAZZ GUITAR (Various artists)**
**Album:** Released Dec '88, on Yazoo (USA) by Shanachie Records (USA). Catalogue no: **L 1057**

## Pipe, Spoon, Pot & Jug

**PIPE, SPOON, POT & JUG 14 (jazz vocals) (Various artists)**
**Album:** Released Apr '81, on Stash (USA) Catalogue no: **ST 102**

## Pizza Express

**PIZZA EXPRESS (Various artists)**
Note: Al Cohn, Don Harper, Denny Wright, Len Skeat, Martin Drew.
**Album:** Released Aug '88, on Pizza Express by Pizza Express Records. Catalogue no: **PE 5505**

**PIZZA EXPRESS ALL STAR JAZZ BAND (Various artists)**
Note: Digby Fairweather, Brian Lemon, Dave Shepherd, Len Skeat
**Album:** Released Aug '88, on Pizza Express by Pizza Express Records. Catalogue no: **PE 5506**

## Pizzarelli, Bucky

**2 X 7 = PIZZARELLI**
**Album:** Released Apr '81, on Stash (USA) Catalogue no: **ST 207**

**BUCKY PLAYS BIX**
**CD Set:** Released Apr '89, on Audiophile (USA) by Jazzology Records (USA). Catalogue no: **DAPCD 238**
**Album:** Released Mar '79, on Monmouth Evergreen Catalogue no: **MES 7066**

**BUCKY'S BUNCH**
**Album:** Released Mar '79, on Monmouth Evergreen Catalogue no: **MES 7082**

**CAFE PIERRE TRIO, THE**
**Album:** Released Jan '87, on Retrospect by EMI Records. Catalogue no: **MES 7093**

**GREEN GUITAR BLUES**
**Album:** Released Mar '79, on Monmouth Evergreen Catalogue no: **MES 7047**

**LOVE SONGS: BUCKY PIZZARELLI**
**Album:** Released Aug '88, on Stash (USA) Catalogue no: **ST 213**

**SOLO FLIGHT - UNACCOMPANIED**
**Album:** Released Jan '88, on Stash (USA) Catalogue no: **ST 263**

**SWINGING SEVENS (Pizzarelli,Bucky & John)**
**Album:** Released '86, on Stash (USA) Catalogue no: **ST 239**

## Pizzarelli, John

**HIT THAT JIVE, JACK! (Pizzarelli, John Jr)**
**Album:** Released Jan '88, on Stash (USA) Catalogue no: **ST 256**

**I LIKE JERSEY BEST**
Note: Special CD-only 63-minute compilation.
**CD:** Released Aug '87, on Stash (USA) Catalogue no: **STCD 1**

**I'M HIP (Pizzarelli, John & Bucky Pizzarelli Trio)**
**Album:** Released Nov '87, on Stash (USA) Catalogue no: **ST 226**

**SING SING SING See also under Eddie Daniels (Pizzarelli, John Jr)**
**Album:** Released Nov '87, on Stash (USA) Catalogue no: **ST 267**

## Pizzi, Ray

**ESPRESSIVO**
Tracks: / In a sentimental mood / 'Round about midnight / Spinnes / Ode to a toad / In and out / Killer Kowalski / Ballad for jazz bassoon / Espressivo.
Note: Ray Pizzi-saxes, flute and bassoon; John Chiodini-guitar; Dave Periato-bass; Jeff Hamilton-drums.
**Album:** Released '88, on Discovery (USA) by Discovery Records (USA). Catalogue no: **DS 853**

**LOVE LETTER, THE**
Tracks: / Buzzard's bay / Aicia / My funny Valentine.
Note: Ray Pizzi-tenor & soprano sax, flute & bassoon; Art Johnson-electric guitar & mandolin; Frank Zottoli-piano; Dave Edelstein-bass; Ralph Humphrey-drums and percussion.
**Album:** Released '88, on Discovery (USA) by Discovery Records (USA). Catalogue no: **DS 801**

## Playboy Jazz Festival

**PLAYBOY JAZZ FESTIVAL (Various artists)**
**2 LP Set:** Released Apr '84, on Elektra by Elektra Records (UK). Catalogue no: **960298 1**

## Polite, Nick

**NICK POLITE'S JAZZMEN (Melbourne NOR jazzband)**
**Album:** Released '88, on Swaggie (Australia) Catalogue no: **S 1332**

## Pollack, Ben

**BEN POLLACK & HIS ORCHESTRA (Pollack, Ben & His Orchestra)**
**Album:** Released Apr '79, on VJM (Vintage Jazz Music) by Vintage Jazz Music Society(VJM). Catalogue no: **VLP 43**

**FUTURISTIC RHYTHM 1928-1929 (Pollack, Ben & His Park Central Orchestra)**
Tracks: / Futuristic rhythm / Buy buy for baby / She's one sweet show girl / Then came the dawn / Sentimental baby / Let's sit and talk about you / Louisa / Wait till you see ma cherie / My kinda love / On with the dance / In the hush of the night / Won't cha / Bashful baby / Where the sweet forget-me-nots remember / Song of the blues / True blue Lou / Sweetheart / You've made me happy today / From now on / Keep your undershirt on.
**Album:** Released Apr '83, on Saville by Conifer Records. Catalogue no: **SVL 154**
**Cass:** Released '88, on Halcyon (USA) by Submarine Records. Catalogue no: **CHDL 117**
**Album:** Released '88, on Halcyon (USA) by Submarine Records. Catalogue no: **HDL 117**

## Pomeroy, Herb

**LIFE IS A MANY SPLENDORED GIG (Pomeroy, Herb Orchestra)**
**Album:** Released Feb '88, on Fresh Sounds (Spain) by Fresh Sounds Records (Spain). Catalogue no: **FS 85**

## Ponty, Jean-Luc

**Biographical details:** Jean-Luc Ponty was born in 1942 in Normandy, France. He took time off from school to practice several hours a day on the violin, played as a teenager in the Lamoureaux Symphony Orchestra, turned to jazz, then jazz-rock. He used an amplifier from the beggining and soon explored the electronic possibilities of the sound. He played in the Mahavishnu Orchestra with John McLaughlin, also with Frank Zappa and George Duke, as well as making his own albums. (Donald Clarke 15.5.87).

**AURORA**
Tracks: / Is once enough / Renaissance / Aurora (part 1) / Aurora (part 2) / Passenger of the dark / Lost forest / Between you and me / Waking dream.
**Album:** on Atlantic by WEA Records. Catalogue no: **K 50228**

**BEACH GIRL**
Tracks: / Beach girl / Somerset Drive.
**7" Single:** Released Jan '80, on Atlantic by WEA Records. Deleted Jan '83. Catalogue no: **K 11430**

**CIVILIZED EVIL**
Tracks: / Demagomania / In case we survive / Forms of life / Peace crusaders / Happy robots / Shape up your mind / Good guys bad guys / Once a blue planet.
**Album:** Released Mar '81, on Atlantic by WEA Records. Deleted '86. Catalogue no: **K 50744**

**COSMIC MESSENGER**
Tracks: / Cosmic messenger / Art of happiness / Don't let the world pass you by / I only feel good with you / Puppets' dance / Fake paradise / Ethereal mood / Egocentric molecules.
**Album:** Released Feb '79, on Atlantic Jazz by WEA Records. Deleted Feb '84. Catalogue no: **K 50505**
**CD:** Released '88, on Atlantic Jazz by WEA Records. Catalogue no: **K781 550 2**

**DEMAGOMANIA**
Tracks: / Demagomania / Happy robots.
**7" Single:** Released Jan '81, on Atlantic by WEA Records. Deleted Jan '84. Catalogue no: **K 11643**

**ENIGMATIC OCEAN**
Tracks: / Overture / Trans love express, The / Mirage / Enigmatic ocean (parts 1 & 2) / Nostalgic lady / Struggle of the turtle to the sea parts 1,2,3.
**Album:** Released Aug '87, on Atlantic by WEA Records. Catalogue no: **K 50409**

**FABLES**
Tracks: / Infinite pursuit / Elephants in love / Radioactive legacy / Cats tales / Perpetual rondo.
**Cass:** Released Jan '86, on Atlantic by WEA Records. Catalogue no: **781 276-4**
**Album:** Released Jan '86, on Atlantic by WEA Records. Catalogue no: **781 276-1**
**CD:** Released Oct '87, on WEA by WEA Records. Catalogue no: **781 276-2**

**GIFT OF TIME, THE**
Tracks: / Prologue / New resolutions / Faith in you / No more doubts / Between sea and sky / Metamorphosis / Introspective / Perceptions / Gift of time, The.
**CD:** Released May '88, on CBS by CBS Records. Deleted Jan '90. Catalogue no: **460436 2**
**Album:** Released Nov '87, on CBS by CBS Records. Deleted Oct '89. Catalogue no: **460436 1**
**Cass:** Released Nov '87, on CBS by CBS Records. Catalogue no: **460436 4**

**IMAGINARY VOYAGE**
Tracks: / New country / Gardens of Babylon / Wandering on the milky way / Once upon a dream / Tarantula / Imaginary voyage part 1 / Imaginary voyage part II.
**Album:** Released '87, on Atlantic by WEA Records. Catalogue no: **K 50317**

**INDIVIDUAL CHOICE**
Tracks: / Computer incantations for world peace / Far from the beaten paths / In spiritual love / Eulogy to Oscar Romero / Nostalgia / In spite of all / Individual choice.
**Album:** Released Apr '84, on Polydor by Polydor Ltd. Deleted '85. Catalogue no: **POLD 5138**
**CD:** Released Apr '84, on Polydor by Polydor Ltd. Deleted Mar '88. Catalogue no: **817 189-2**

**JAZZ FIRST (Ponty, Jean-Luc/Cleo Laine)**
Tracks: / King Kong / Idiot bastard son / Twenty small cigars / How would you like to have a head like that / America drinks and goes home.
**Cass:** Released Sep '86, on EMI (Italy) by EMI Records. Catalogue no: **3C 254 91651**
**Cass:** Released Jul '86, on Timeless Treasures Catalogue no: **813**
**Album:** Released Sep '86, on EMI (Italy) by EMI Records. Catalogue no: **3C 054 91651**

**JEAN-LUC PONTY & STEPHANE GRAPPELLI Compact/Walkman jazz (Ponty, Jean-Luc/Stephane Grappelli)**
Tracks: / Pent-up house / La chanson de rue / Carole's garden / Undecided / Sweet Lorraine / Cat coach / Summit soul / Flamingo / Sunday walk / Swing guitars / Tangerine.
**Cass:** Released 15 Aug '88, on MPS Jazz Catalogue no: **835 320-4**
**CD:** Released Aug '88, on MPS Jazz Deleted Dec '89. Catalogue no: **835 320-2**

**KING KONG**
Tracks: / King Kong / Idiot bastard son / Twenty small cigars / Music for electric violin and low budget orchestra / America drinks and goes home.
**Cass:** Released Aug '87, on Liberty by EMI Records. Deleted Jun '89. Catalogue no: **TCATAK 102**
**Cass:** Released '88, on EMI (Italy) by EMI Records. Catalogue no: **3C254 91651**
**Album:** Released Aug '87, on Liberty by EMI Records. Catalogue no: **EMS 1254**
**Album:** Released '88, on EMI (Italy) by EMI Records. Catalogue no: **3C054 91651**
**Cass:** Released Aug '87, on Liberty by EMI Records. Deleted Jun '89. Catalogue no: **TCEMS 1254**
**Album:** Released Aug '87, on Liberty by EMI Records. Deleted Aug '89. Catalogue no: **ATAK 102**

**MYSTICAL ADVENTURES**
Tracks: / Mystical adventures / Rhythms of hope / As / Final truth / Jig.
**Album:** Released Mar '82, on Atlantic by WEA Records. Deleted Mar '87. Catalogue no: **K 50872**

**OPEN MIND**
**Album:** Released Nov '84, on Polydor by Polydor Ltd. Deleted '85. Catalogue no: **823 581-1**
**Album:** Released Dec '84, on Polydor by Polydor Ltd. Catalogue no: **823 581 1**
**CD:** Released Nov '84, on Polydor by Polydor Ltd. Deleted Mar '88. Catalogue no: **823 581-2**
**CD:** Released Nov '84, on Polydor by Polydor Ltd. Catalogue no: **823 581 2**
**Cass:** Released Nov '84, on Polydor by Polydor Ltd. Catalogue no: **823 581-4**

**SONATA EROTICA**
Tracks: / Preludio / Pizzicato con fuoco e con echo / Con sensualito appassionato / Accelerando rallentando.
**Album:** Released May '85, on Affinity by Charly Records. Deleted May '88. Catalogue no: **AFF 133**
**Album:** Released Sep '79, on Atmosphere by E.S.S.P.. Catalogue no: **IRI 5008**

**UPON THE WINGS OF MUSIC**
Tracks: / Upon the wings of music / Question with no answer / Now I know / Polyfolk dance / Waving memories / Echoes of the future / Bowing bowing / Fight for life.
**Album:** Released Aug '75, on Atlantic by WEA Records. Catalogue no: **K 50149**

## Porcino, Al

**IN OBLIVION**
**Album:** Released Feb '89, on Jazz Mark Catalogue no: **JAZZ MARK 106**

## Porter, Cole

**Biographical details:** Cole Porter (1891-1964) is the greatest of all the songwriters of the Golden Age of the musical show tune, and the only one who wrote both music and witty, appropriate lyrics. He studied law and music at Harvard, served in the French army as an American citizen in WW1, married a wealthy woman and spent the 1920s in Paris. He returned to the USA in the early '30s, but never got Paris out of his blood or out of his songs. To name just one among many hit shows and films: **Anything Goes** in 1934 included hit songs *Anything Goes*, *I Get A Kick Out Of You*, *All Through The Night*, *You're the Top*: he had a hit record that year with the latter, accompanying himself on the piano. *Don't Force Me In*, written as a send-up, became the best Hollywood cowboy song of all, because he could not write bad lyrics. Both legs were shattered in 1937 when a horse fell on him; he was an invalid for the rest of his life. his last hit was *True Love* from the film **High Society**, with Bing Crosby and Grace Kelly. (Donald Clarke 15.5.87)..

**ANYTHING GOES (Various artists)**
Tracks: / Anything goes overture: *Vari-*

*ous artists* / I get a kick out of you: *Various artists* / Bon voyage: *Various artists* / All through the night: *Various artists* / There'll always be a lady fair: *Various artists* / Where are the men: *Various artists* / You're the top: *Various artists* / You're the top (Encore): *Various artists* / There'll always be a lady fair (reprise): *Various artists* / Anything goes: *Various artists* / Anything goes finale: *Various artists* / Entr'acte: *Various artists* / Public enemy No. 1: *Various artists* / What a joy to be young: *Various artists* / Blow, Gabriel, blow: *Various artists* / Be like the bluebird: *Various artists* / Buddie beware: *Various artists* / Gypsy in me, The: *Various artists* / Finale ultimo: *Various artists* / There's no cure like travel: *Various artists* / Kate the great: *Various artists* / Waltz down the aisle: *Various artists.*
Note: Kim Criswell (Reno Sweeney); Chris Groenendaal (Billy Crocker); Frederica Von Stade (Hope Harcourt); Jack Gilford (Moonface Martin); London Symphony Orchestra; Ambrosian Chorus conducted by John McGlinn.
**Album:** Released Oct '89, on EMI by EMI Records. Catalogue no: **EL 7498481**
**CD:** Released Oct '89, on EMI by EMI Records. Catalogue no: **CDC 749 848 2**
**Cass:** Released Oct '89, on EMI by EMI Records. Catalogue no: **EL 7498484**

**IN LONDON**
**2 LP Set:** Released Sep '74, on Retrospect by EMI Records. Catalogue no: **SHB 26**

**MEYER DAVIS PLAYS COLE PORTER**
**Album:** Released Mar '79, on Monmouth Evergreen Catalogue no: **MES 6813**

**SONG IS...COLE PORTER (Various artists)**
Tracks: / Just one of those things: *Various artists* / Anything goes: *Various artists* / I'm in love again: *Various artists* / I get a kick out of you: *Various artists* / How could we be wrong?: *Various artists* / Miss Otis regrets: *Various artists* / Lady fair: *Various artists* / I'm a gigolo: *Various artists* / Let's do it: *Various artists* / Night & day: *Various artists* / They all fall in love: *Various artists* / You're the top: *Various artists* / Love for sale: *Various artists* / All through the night: *Various artists* (7) / Be like the bluebird: *Various artists* / Experiment: *Various artists* / Thank you so much, Mrs Lowsborough: *Various artists* / Goodbye: *Various artists* / What is this thing called love: *Various artists.*
Note: Artists include: Cole Porter, Richard Himber/his Ritz-Carlton orch, Ben Bernie/his Hotel Roosevelt orch, Ethel Merman, Al Bowlly, Douglas Byng, the Anything Goes Foursome, Bing Crosby, Fred Astaire, Jack Hylton/his orch, Libby Holman, Ambrose/his orch, Gertrude Lawrence, Leo Reisman/his orch.
**Cass:** Released 1 Feb '87, on Living Era by Academy Sound & Vision Records. Catalogue no: **ZC AJA 5044**

**Position Alpha - Mote Monsunen (Dragon)**

**Album:** Released 1 Feb '87, on Living Era by Academy Sound & Vision Records. Catalogue no: **AJA 5044**

## Position Alpha

**MOTE MONSUNEN (See panel above)**
Tracks: / Calle schewens vals / Mote I Monsunen / Kinesika muren / Nocturne
**Album:** Released Apr '89, on Dragon Catalogue no: **DRLP 149**

## Potts, Bill

**555 FEET HIGH (Potts, Bill Big Band)**
**Album:** Released Feb '89, on Jazz Mark Catalogue no: **JAZZ MARK 107**

## Powell, Bud

**Biographical details:** Bud Powell (1924-66) is one of the most influential pianists in jazz history, and easily the most important in the bop era of 1945-50. He was influenced by Teddy Wilson, Nat King Cole, but especially by Art Tatum and Billy Kyle (1914-66, an urbane and underrated stylist who played with the John Kirby Sextet in the '40s, then found a secure gig with Louis Armstrong's All Stars from 1953 until his death). Powell was part of the birth of modern jazz in New York City, his technique and harmonic ideas astonishing everyone. He played with the Cootie Williams band in the mid-'40s: after a gig with Williams in Philadelphia,he was badly beaten by law enforcement officers and taken to Bellevue mental hospital in New York. He lived and breathed music, and was later given shock treatment to make him 'normal'. His best records are on Blue Note and Verve from the late '40s-early '50s were a low point, when he was often heavily tranquilised (RCA records not currently available in the UK); he moved to Paris in 1959, played with Kenny Clarke and Pierre Michelot in a famous rhythm section (e.g. on Dexters Gordon's Blue note album *Our Man In Paris*, 1963). The character played by Gordon in the film *Round Midnight* (1986) is based on Powell. (Donald Clarke 15.5.87)..

**ALTERNATE TAKES**
Tracks: / Bouncing with Bud / Wail / Dance of the infidels / Reets and I / Collard greens and black-eyed peas / Blue pearl / John's abbey / Comin' up / Like someone in love / Our love is here to stay.
**Album:** Released Jul '89, on Blue Note by EMI Records. Catalogue no: **BST 84430**

**AMAZING BUD POWELL, VOL 1**
Tracks: / Un poco loco (first take) / Un poco loco (second take) / Dance of the infidels / 52nd Street theme / It could happen to you (LP only.) / Night in Tunisia (LP only.) / Wail / Ornithology / Bouncing with Bud / Parisian thoroughfare (LP only.) / Bouncing with Bud (alt. take) (CD only.) / Bouncing with Bud (alt. take 2) (CD only.) / Wail (alt. take) (CD only.) / Dance of the infidels (alt. take) (CD only.) / You go to my head (CD only.) / Ornithology (alt. master) (CD only.) / Un poco loco (alt. take 2) (CD only.) / Over the rainbow (CD only.).

**CD:** Released Jul '89, on Blue Note by EMI Records. Deleted Jan '90. Catalogue no: **CDP 781 503 2**
**Album:** Released Aug '82, on Blue Note by EMI Records. Deleted Jan '88. Catalogue no: **BLP 1503**
**CD:** Released Jul '89, on Blue Note by EMI Records. Deleted Jan '90. Catalogue no: **BNZ 206**
**Album:** Released May '85, on Blue Note by EMI Records. Deleted '88. Catalogue no: **BST 81503**

## AMAZING BUD POWELL, VOL 2

Tracks: / Reets and I / Autumn in New York / I want to be happy / It could happen to you / Sure thing / Polka dots and moonbeams / Glass enclosure / Collard greens and black-eyed peas / Over the rainbow (LP only.) / Audrey / You go to my head (LP only.) / Ornithology (LP only.) / Night in Tunisia, A (CD only.) / Night in Tunisia, A (alt. master) (CD only.) / It could happen to you (alt. master) (CD only.) / Reets and I (alt. take) (CD only.) / Parisian thoroughfare (CD only.) / Collard greens and black-eyed peast (alt. take) (CD only.).
Note: This album was recorded at three Bud Powell Trio dates of the late 'forties and early 'fifties. Musicians include Roy Haynes, Max Roach and George Duvivier.
**Album:** Released '79, on Blue Note by EMI Records. Deleted '84. Catalogue no: **BNS 40006**
**CD:** Released Jul '89, on Blue Note by EMI Records. Catalogue no: **CDP 781 504 2**
**Album:** Released Aug '82, on Blue Note by EMI Records. Deleted Jan '88. Catalogue no: **BLP 1504**
**CD:** Released Jul '89, on Blue Note by EMI Records. Catalogue no: **BNZ 207**
**Album:** Released Jul '89, on Blue Note by EMI Records. Catalogue no: **BST 81504**

## AMAZING BUD POWELL, VOL 3

Tracks: / Some soul / Blue pearl / Frantic fancies / Bud on Bach / Keepin' in the groove / Idaho / Don't blame me / Moose the mooche / Blue pearl (alt. take).
Note: For his first full length Blue Note album, Bud Powell uses his regular drummer, Art Taylor and Miles Davis' bassist, Paul Chambers. They play several unique Powell originals including the lovely 'Blue Pearl'. On the second half of the session, virtuoso trombonist, Curtis Fuller joins them for three extended jazz standards including a rousing 'Moose The Mooche'. One of this disc's highlights is the astonishing and self explanatory solo piano performance 'Bud on Bach'.
**Album:** Released Nov '84, on Blue Note by EMI Records. Catalogue no: **BST 81571**
**Cass:** Released Apr '87, on Blue Note by EMI Records. Deleted Jun '89. Catalogue no: **4BN 81571**
**CD:** Released Jun '89, on Blue Note by EMI Records. Catalogue no: **CDP 781 571 2**
**CD:** Released Jun '89, on Blue Note by EMI Records. Catalogue no: **BNZ 173**

## AT THE BLUE NOTE CAFE PARIS 1961

**Album:** Released Apr '81, on ESP by ESP Records. Catalogue no: **ESP 1066**

## AT THE GOLDEN CIRCLE VOL 4

**Album:** Released Apr '81, on Steeplechase (USA) Catalogue no: **SCC 6014**

## AUTUMN SESSION 1953

**Album:** Released Apr '83, on Base Deleted '88. Catalogue no: **BASE 3035**

## BEST OF BUD POWELL

Tracks: / Bouncing with Bud / 52nd Street theme (CD only.) / Un poco loco / Parisian thoroughfare / Collard greens and black-eyed peas / Glass enclosure / Reets and I (CD only.) / Blue pearl / Bud on Bach / John's abbey / Monopoly / Buster rides again (CD only.) / Scene changes, The / Cleopatra's dream / Like someone in love (CD only.).
**Album:** Released Feb '90, on Blue Note by EMI Records. Catalogue no: **B1 93204**
**CD:** Released Feb '90, on Blue Note by EMI Records. Catalogue no: **CDP 793 204 2**
**CD:** Released Feb '90, on Blue Note by EMI Records. Catalogue no: **BNZ 234**
**Album:** Released Feb '90, on Blue Note by EMI Records. Catalogue no: **793 204 1**

## BEST YEARS, THE

**2 LP Set:** Released Oct '88, on Vogue by Vogue Records. Catalogue no: **421010**

## BOUNCING WITH BUD (Powell, Bud Trio)

**Album:** Released Nov '86, on Storyville by Storyville Records AB. Catalogue no: **SLP 4113**

## BUD POWELL

**Album:** Released Jan '81, on Kings Of Jazz Catalogue no: **KLJ 20019**
**Album:** Released 10 Jul '89, on Black Lion Catalogue no: **BLP 60135**

## BUD POWELL & THELONIOUS MONK (Powell, Bud & Thelonious Monk)

**CD:** Released Feb '89, on Vogue by Vogue Records. Catalogue no: **VGCD 600101**

## BUD POWELL TRIO PLAYS, THE (Powell, Bud Trio)

Tracks: / I'll remember April / Indiana / Somebody loves me / I should care / Bud's bubble / Off minor / Nice work if you can get it / Everything happens to me / Embraceable you / Burt covers Bud / My heart stood still / You'd be so nice to come home to / Bag's groove / My devotion / Stellar by starlight / Woody'n you.
**Album:** Released Feb '90, on Roulette (EMI) by EMI Records. Catalogue no: **ROU 1011**
**CD:** Released Feb '90, on Roulette (EMI) by EMI Records. Catalogue no: **CDP 793 902 2**
**CD:** Released Feb '90, on Roulette (EMI) by EMI Records. Catalogue no: **CDROU 1011**
**Album:** Released Feb '90, on Roulette (EMI) by EMI Records. Catalogue no: **793 902 1**

## COMPLETE ESSEN JAZZ FESTIVAL CONCERT, THE

Tracks: / Shaw 'nuff / Blues in the closet / Willow weep for me / John's abbey / Salt peanuts / All the things you are / Just you, just me / Yesterdays / Stuffy.
Note: Recorded 2 April 1960.
**CD:** Released Jul '88, on Black Lion Catalogue no: **BLCD 760105**
**Album:** Released Jul '88, on Black Lion Catalogue no: **BLP 760105**

## ESSENTIAL JAZZ FESTIVAL, THE

**Album:** Released 6 Jan '89, on Black Lion Catalogue no: **BLP 60107**
**CD:** Released 6 Jan '89, on Black Lion Catalogue no: **BLCD 60107**

## GENIUS OF BUD POWELL

Tracks: / Tempus fugit / Celia / Cherokee / I'll keep loving you / Strictly confidential / All God's chillun got rhythm / So sorry please / Get happy / Sometimes I'm happy / Sweet Georgia Brown / Yesterdays / April in Paris / Body and soul / Tea for two / Hallelujah / Parisian thoroughfare / Oblivion / Dusk at Saudi / Hallucinations / Fruit / Last time I saw Paris / Just one of those things / Nightingale sang in Berkeley Square.
**2 LP Set:** Released '79, on Verve Deleted '84. Catalogue no: **2532051**

## GENIUS OF BUD POWELL THE

Tracks: / Parisienne thororfare / Oblivion / Dusk in sandi / Hallucinations / Fruit / Tea for two / Hallelujah / Last time i saw paris / Just one of those things / Nightingale sang in berkeley square.
**Album:** Released Feb '84, on Verve (France) Catalogue no: **2304 112**

## GENIUS OF..., THE

Note: Featuring Dexter Gordon, Max Roach, Charlie Parker, Miles Davis, Buddy Rich.
**Album:** Released Sep '87, on Giants of Jazz by Hasmick Promotions. Catalogue no: **LPJT 44**

## IN EUROPE

Note: With Kenny Clarke, Johnny Griffin and P Michelot.
**Album:** Released Jun '86, on Duke by Melodisc Records. Catalogue no: **D 1012**

## IN PARIS (Powell, Bud Trio)

Tracks: / How high the moon / Body and soul / Satin doll / Jor-Du / I can't get started.
Note: Bud Powell-piano, Gilbert Rovere-bass, Carl Donnell "Kansas" Fields-drums.
**Album:** Released '88, on Discovery (USA) by Discovery Records (USA). Catalogue no: **DS 830**

## INVISIBLE CAGE, THE

Tracks: / Blues for Bouffemont / Little Willie leaps / My old flame / Moose the mooche / In the mood for a classic / Like someone in love / Una noche con Francis / Relaxin' at Camarillo.

**Album:** Released Jan '85, on Black Lion Catalogue no: **BLP 30120**

**JAZZ GIANT**
**Album:** Released Jun '89, on Verve Catalogue no: **829 937-1**

**LIVE AT BIRDLAND**
**Album:** Released Apr '81, on Queen-disc (Italy) Catalogue no: **QU 024**

**ORNITHOLOGY**
Note: 'Ornithology' Trio Performances from Birdland 1953
**Album:** Released Apr '81, on Jazz Live (Italy) Catalogue no: **BLJ 8034**
**Album:** Released Oct '86, on Jazz Live (Italy) Catalogue no: **BLJ 034**

**PARIS-NEW YORK**
Tracks: / Someone to watch over me.
**CD:** Released May '85, on Vogue by Vogue Records. Catalogue no: **VGCD 600046**

**PORTRAIT OF THELONIOUS**
Tracks: / Off minor / There will never be another you / Ruby / My dear / No name blues / Thelonious / Monk's mood / I ain't fooling / Squattyroo.
**Album:** Released Mar '81, on Jazz Odyssey Catalogue no: **CBS 54301**

**RETURN OF BUD POWELL**
**Album:** Released Oct '87, on Fresh Sounds (Spain) by Fresh Sounds Records (Spain). Catalogue no: **FS 226**

**SALT PEANUTS**
**CD:** Released Aug '89, on Black Lion Catalogue no: **BLCD7 60121**
**Album:** Released Feb '89, on Black Lion Catalogue no: **BLP 60121**

**SCENE CHANGES, THE**
Tracks: / Cleopatra's dream / Duid deed / Down with it / Danceland / Borderick / Crossin' the channel / Gettin' there / Scene changes, The / Comin' up (alternate take).
Note: All titles: Composed by Bud Powell. Published by Planetary Nom (Ldn) Ltd.
**CD:** Released Apr '87, on Blue Note by EMI Records. Catalogue no: **BNZ 75**
**CD:** Released Apr '87, on Blue Note by EMI Records. Catalogue no: **CDP 746 529 2**

**SHAW NUFF**
**CD:** Released '88, on Xanadu Catalogue no: **FDC 5167**

**SPRING SESSIONS 1953**
**Album:** Released Apr '83, on Base Deleted '88. Catalogue no: **BASE 3033**

**SUMMER SESSIONS 1953**
**Album:** Released Apr '83, on Base Deleted '88. Catalogue no: **BASE 3034**

**SWINGIN WITH BUD**
**Album:** Released Jan '83, on RCA (France) by BMG Records (France). Catalogue no: **PM 45137**

**TIME WAITS**
Tracks: / Buster rides again / Sub city / Time waits / Marmalade / Monopoly / John's abbey / Dry soul / Sub city (alternate take) / John's abbey (alternate take).
**CD:** Released Aug '87, on Blue Note by EMI Records. Catalogue no: **CDP 746 820 2**
**CD:** Released Aug '87, on Blue Note by EMI Records. Catalogue no: **BNZ 76**

**TIME WAS (Powell, Bud Trio)**
Tracks: / There will never be another you / They didn't believe me / I cover the waterfront / Time was / Topsy turvy / Elegy / Coscrane / Jump city / Blues for Bessie / Salt peanuts / Swedish pastry / Shaw 'nuff / Midway / Oblivion / Get it / Another dozen / She / Birdland blues.
**CD:** Released Apr '88, on Bluebird (2) by BMG Records (UK). Catalogue no: **ND 86367**

## Powell, Mel

**Biographical details:** Mel Powell was born in New York in 1923. The pianist, arranger, composer, teacher joined Benny Goodman in 1941, wrote hits like *Mission To Moscow* for him, also worked with Glenn Miller in England in 1943, then quit film and studio work to study composition at Yale with Paul Hindemith. He won five *Downbeat* polls, and his deperture to the groves of academe was a great loss to jazz. He occasionally played with Goodman again late '40s, '50s concentrated on composition, incl. electronic music. He taught at Queens College NYC, then Yale 1954-69, then at California Institute of Arts in Valencia from 1969. He jammed on the SS Norway's Floating Jazz Festival out of Miami in 1986 with Ruby Braff, Mel Lewis, Bob Wilber and others; Wilber said 'It's like he never stopped playing-it's all there.' Here's hoping some new jazz records will result. (Donald Clarke 15.5.87)..

**BOUQUET (Powell, Mel Trio)**
Tracks: / Quin and sonic / If dreams come true / Cross your heart / Avalon / Borderline / Makin' whoopee / What's new / Thigamagic / You're my thrill / Button up your overcoat / Don-que-de / Bouquet / Ain't she sweet / Take me in your arms / California here I come.
**Album:** Released May '83, on Vogue Jazz (France) by Vogue Records. Catalogue no: **VJD 572**

**PIANO FORTE (Powell, Mel & His Uptown Hall Gang)**
**Album:** Released May '86, on Nostalgia by Mainline Records. Catalogue no: **NOST 7649**

**WORLD IS WAITING 1942-46 (Powell, Mel & Joe Buskin)**
**Album:** Released Sep '82, on Commodore Class Catalogue no: **AG6 24963**

## Praeger, Lou

**DANCING CLOSE TOGETHER**
**Album:** Released '88, on Joy by President Records. Catalogue no: **JOY 245**

**ON THE SUNNY SIDE OF THE STREET (Praeger, Lou & His Orchestra)**
Tracks: / Peg o' my heart / Bring on my drums / Until / There's no one but you / Sophisticated lady / Don't be a baby baby / First day of summer, The / First floor jump / I want to learn to dance / I'm comin' a courtin' / Doggin' around / Two can dream as cheaply as one / Shoemaker's serenade, The / Third floor jump / Good, good, good / Saturday night is the loneliest night of the week / Carolina / On the sunny side of the street.
**Album:** Released Jan '83, on President by President Records. Catalogue no: **PLE 500**
**Cass:** Released Jan '83, on President by President Records. Catalogue no: **TC-PLE 500**

## Prestige All-Stars

**ROOTS**
Note: Artists include: Pepper Adams, Tommy Flanagan, E. Jones, etc.
**Album:** Released Jun '86, on Original Jazz Classics (USA) by Fantasy Inc (USA). Catalogue no: **OJC 062**

## Prestige Blues

**PRESTIGE BLUES SWINGERS (Various artists)**
**Album:** Released Jun '86, on Fantasy Inc (USA) by Fantasy Inc (USA). Catalogue no: **1902117**

## Prestige Jazz Sampler

**PRESTIGE JAZZ SAMPLER (Various artists)**
**Cass:** Released Mar '88, on Riverside (USA) by Fantasy Inc (USA). Catalogue no: **RIVMC 002**
**Album:** Released Mar '88, on Riverside (USA) by Fantasy Inc (USA). Catalogue no: **RIVM 002**
**CD:** Released Mar '88, on Riverside (USA) by Fantasy Inc (USA). Catalogue no: **CDRIVM 002**

## Previn, Andre

**Biographical details:** Born in Berlin in 1929, Andre Previn was a child prodigy on the piano but was kicked out of the Berlin Conservatory in 1938 because he was Jewish, whereupon the family immediately left the country for Los Angeles. He thought jazz was "men in funny hats playing in a hotel band" until he heard an Art Tatum record, and at the age of 16 he played jazz piano on a film soundtrack for pianist Jose Iturbi (who couldn't) and also orchestrated the scene. From then on he had parallel successful careers in the Hollywood studios and as a jazz pianist, until he turned to classical conducting. He composed a 40-minute sequence for Gene Kelly's ballet film Invitation To The Dance in 1954, which won an award, and scored many films until 1971, including the above-average musical It's Always Fair Weather in '55 (songs by Adolphe Green, Berry Comden), receiving Oscars for Gigi (Alan Jay Lerner, Frederick Lowe), in '58, Porgy and Bess (Gershwin), '59, Irma La Douce (themes by studio composers), '63 and My Fair Lady (Lerner and Lowe), '64. He later wrote a Broadway show, Coco, with Lerner. He also collaborated on film songs with his then wife, Dory Previn, and they also recorded together. Meanwhile he had made about 60 LPs in various combinations, mostly piano trios, many under his own name. With drummer Shelley Manne and bassist Leroy Vinnegar he made a jazz version of the songs from My Fair Lady which was a hit LP credited to Shelley Manne & Friends: they started the fad for jazzing up Broadway shows and released several albums on Contemporary, some under Manne and some under Previn. He later recorded for CBS/USA (including a remake of My Fair Lady) and had five hit albums in the American chart between '59 and '64, some with orchestras. Deciding that he really wanted to be in classical music he became one of the world's top conductors as well as a well-known composer. His first classical recording included Benjamin Britten's Sinfonia De Requiem, prompting Britten's reaction "Who is this fellow Andre Previn? That's the best performance I've ever heard." He conducted the Houston Symphony Orchestra '67-'69, the London Symphony Orchestra '69-'79 -- becoming the most popular conductor in England -- and succeeded William Steinberg as conductor of the Pittsburgh Symphony Orchestra in '76. In the 80's he occasionally returned to popular music , recording a duo album with Ella Fitzgerald and two LPs with violinist Itzhak Perlman : a set of Scott Joplin rags, then *A different kind of blues* ,making the US album chart again after more than 15 years. With Tom Stoppard he wrote the musical play Every Good Boy Deserves Favour, about a Soviet insane asylum: both men are banned from the USSR. (Donald Clarke, May 1987.).

**DIFFERENT KIND OF BLUES, A**
Tracks: / Look at him go / Little face / Who reads reviews / Night thoughts / Different kind of blues, A / Chocolate apricot / Five of us / Make up your mind.
**Cass:** Released Oct '80, on H.M.V. by EMI Records. Catalogue no: **TC ASK 3965**
**Album:** Released Oct '80, on H.M.V. by EMI Records. Catalogue no: **ASD 3965**

**EASY WINNERS (Previn, Andre / Itzhak Perlman)**
Tracks: / Ragtime dance / Bethena / Easy winners / Magnetic rag / Strenuous life / Entertainer, The / Elite syncopations / Solace / Pineapple rag / Sugarcane rag.
**CD:** Released May '86, on Angel (1) by EMI Records. Catalogue no: **CDC 747 170-2**

**GENIUS OF ANDRE PREVIN, THE**
Tracks: / Ain't misbehavin' / Honeysuckle rose / Black and blue / I've got a feeling / Oh, you sweet thing / That's where the west begins / Fatstuff / Stealin' apples.
**Cass:** Released Jul '84, on Allegience Catalogue no: **ZCALB 2311**
**Album:** Released Jul '84, on Allegience Catalogue no: **ALEB 2311**

**GIGI**
Tracks: / Parisians / I remember it well / A toujours / It's a bore / Aunt Alicia's march / Thank heaven for little girls / Gigi / She is not thinking of me.
Album: Released Sep '82, on Contemporary (Import) Catalogue no: **1007 548**

**Andre Previn - Sound Stage (CBS)**

**IT'S A BREEZE (Previn, Andre / Itzhak Perlman)**
Tracks: / It's a breeze / Rain in my head / Catgut your tongue / It's about time / Quiet diddling / Tune for Heather / Bowing and scraping / Red bar.
**Album:** Released Oct '81, on EMI by EMI Records. Deleted Oct '86. Catalogue no: **EMD 5537**

**MACK THE KNIFE & OTHER KURT WEILL SONGS (Previn, Andre & JJ Johnson)**
**Album:** Released Sep '81, on CBS by CBS Records. Deleted Sep '86. Catalogue no: **CBS 61352**

**PAL JOEY**
**Album:** Released Dec '81, on Contemporary Jazz Catalogue no: **1007 543**

**PLAYS FATS WALLER**
**Cass:** Released Feb '82, on Orchid Music Catalogue no: **ORC 014**

**PREVIN AT SUNSET**
Tracks: / I got it bad and that ain't good / Body and soul / Sunset in blue / All the things you are / Something to live for / Good enough to keep / That old blue magic / Blue skies / I found a new baby / Variations on a theme / Mulholland Drive.
**Album:** Released Jan '85, on Black Lion Catalogue no: **BLP 30121**

**PREVIN PLAYS GERSHWIN (Previn, Andre / London Symphony Orchestra)**
Tracks: / Rhapsody in blue / Concerto in F / American in Paris, An.
**CD:** Released '88, on H.M.V. by EMI Records. Catalogue no: **CDC 7471612**
**Album:** Released '88, on H.M.V. by EMI Records. Catalogue no: **EG 2908491**
**Cass:** Released '88, on H.M.V. by EMI Records. Catalogue no: **EG 2908494**

**SOUND STAGE (Under The Direction Of Johnny Williams) (See panel above)**
Tracks: / You oughta be in pictures / Way you look tonight,The / Zip-a-dee-doo-dah / Swinging on a star / Only have eyes for you,I / Around the world / Someday my prince will come / There will never be another you / When you wish upon a star / Stella by starlight / Summertime / That old black magic.
**Album:** Released '64, on CBS by CBS Records. Deleted '69. Catalogue no: **BPG 62394**

**WEST SIDE STORY (Previn, Andre & His Pals)**
**CD:** Released Jan '89, on JVC/Fantasy Catalogue no: **VDJ 1626**
**CD:** Released 2 May '89, on Contemporary by Ace Records. Catalogue no: **CDCOP 046**
**Album:** Released 2 May '89, on Contemporary by Ace Records. Catalogue no: **COP 046**

## Prevost, Eddie

**NOW HERE THIS THEN (Prevost, Eddie Band)**

**Album:** Released '83, on Spotlite by Spotlite Records. Catalogue no: **SPJ 505**

## Price, Sam

### DO YOU DIG MY JIVE
Tracks: / Nasty but nice / Cow cow blues / How 'bout that mess / Blow Katy blow / Teed-up / Eiffel Boogie / Blue rhythm stomp / Oh lawdt mama / Lead me daddy straight to the bear / I know how to do it / Pigalle blues.
**Album:** Released Aug '87, on Whiskey, Women & Song (Sweden) Catalogue no: **KM 704**

### PLAY IT AGAIN SAM
Tracks: / After hours at the Copley bar / Room 509 / Trouble in mind / 509 boogie / Empty bed blues / Do your duty / Box car shorty's return / Back bay bounce / Ain't nobody's business if I do / Bean town boogie / Movin' that thing / Good old wagon / Back water blues.
**Album:** Released Jan '85, on Whiskey, Women & Song (Sweden) Catalogue no: **KM 702**

### RIB JOINT
**2 LP Set:** Released Mar '85, on Savoy Jazz (USA) by Malaco Records (USA). Catalogue no: **SJL 2240**

### SINGING WITH SAMMY
**Album:** Released Aug '86, on Bluetime (Denmark) by Contact Records (Denmark). Catalogue no: **BT 2002**

## Price, Sammy

### BARRELHOUSE & BLUES
**Album:** Released Apr '85, on Black Lion Catalogue no: **BLP 30130**

### BLUE & BOOGIE
**Album:** Released Nov '88, on Vogue by Vogue Records. Catalogue no: **500103**

### BLUES ON MY MIND
**Album:** Released Aug '78, on Black Lion Catalogue no: **BLP 30201**

### BOOGIE WOOGIE TWINS, THE (Price, Sammy & Torben Plys Peterson)
**Album:** Released Feb '90, on Storyville by Storyville Records AB. Catalogue no: **SLP 278**

### COPENHAGEN BOOGIE (Price, Sammy With Fessor's Big City Band)
**Album:** Released Jan '88, on Storyville by Storyville Records AB. Catalogue no: **SLP 266**

### ORIGINAL PIANO SOLO
**Album:** Released Apr '81, on Joker (USA) by Lifetime Records (USA). Catalogue no: **SM 3538**

### ROCKIN' BOOGIE
**Album:** Released Jan '85, on Black & Blue (1) by Black & Blue Records. Catalogue no: **BB 33560**

### SAMMY PRICE AND HIS BLUESICIANS (Price, Sammy and His Bluesicians)
**Album:** Released Aug '88, on Circle (USA) by Jazzology Records (USA). Catalogue no: **CLP 73**

### SAMMY PRICE PIANO SOLOS
Tracks: / In a mezz / Those mellow blues / Gully loves blues / Cow cow blues / 133rd street boogie / I finally gotcha / Boogin' with Mezz / Callin' 'em home / Step down, step up / Shakin' loose / Boogin' with Big Sid.
**Album:** Released Apr '81, on Joker (USA) by Lifetime Records (USA). Catalogue no: **SM 3075**

### SWEET SUBSTITUTE
**Album:** Released Jul '86, on Sackville by Spotlite Records. Catalogue no: **3024**

## Prima, Louis

**Biographical details:** Trumpeter, novelty vocalist and bandleader Prima was born in New Orleans in 1910 and died there in 1978. He wrote *Sing, Sing, Sing,* interpolated by Benny Goodman in 1937 with *Christopher Columbus* for one of the biggest hits of the era. Other well-known compositions included *It's The Rhythm In Me* and *Sunday Kind Of Love.* His own hits were an entertaining, almost nonsensical mixture of jivespeak and Neapolitan slang with solid trumpet playing, including *Robin Hood, Bellbottom Trousers, Civilization* and *Oh Babe* (1944-50). He married his fourth wife, Keely Smith, in 1952, signed to Capitol with a combo featuring Sam Butera on tenor sax and soon became a hot attraction in Las Vegas. Smith sang in a straight jazz style, poker-faced with a Tonto haircut, while Prima perpetrated his familiar ebullient nonsense. Their interpolation of *I Ain't Got Nobody / Just A Gigolo* was a hit on EP (copied by David Lee Roth for a single hit in '85) and *That Old Black Magic* and *I've Got You Under My Skin* also charted. They made films in 1959, switched to the Dot label and had more hits, including Prima's version of *Wonderful By Night.* The marriage failed. Smith had a successful vocal career while Prima worked in Vegas and provided the voice for the cartoon orangutan in the '69 Disney film The Jungle Book. He fell into a coma in 1975 and lingered for three years in a nursing home before his death. (Donald Clarke, May 1987.).

### ANGELINA
Tracks: / Oh Marie / Hey boy hey girl / Pennies from heaven / San Fernando Valley / Do a little business on the side / Kentucky / That's how much I love you / Stella by starlight / Buona sera / Angelina / Lip, The / Sleepy time gal / Bacci goldo / It takes time / Roses in the rain / Chinatown.
**Album:** Released Sep '89, on Big Band Era Catalogue no: **20180**
**Cass:** Released Sep '89, on Big Band Era Catalogue no: **40183**

### BEST OF LOUIS PRIMA
Tracks: / Buona sera / Angelina / Oh Marie / Hey boy.
**Cass:** Released '86, on MFP (Holland) by EMI Records. Catalogue no: **1A 222 8158**
**Album:** Released '86, on MFP (Holland) by EMI Records. Catalogue no: **1A 022 8158**

### BUONA SERA
**CD:** Released Sep '87, on Entertainers Deleted '88. Catalogue no: **ENT CD 216**
**Cass:** Released '88, on Entertainers Catalogue no: **ENT MC 13026**

### BUONA SERA (SINGLE)
Tracks: / Buona Sera.
**7" Single:** Released Feb '58, on Capitol by EMI Records. Deleted '61. Catalogue no: **CL 14841**
**7" Single:** Released Jul '84, on EMI (Holland) by EMI Records. Catalogue no: **1A 006 80935**

### CALL OF THE WILDEST, THE
Tracks: / When you're smiling / Sheik of Araby, The / Autumn leaves / I've got the world on a string / Blow red blow / Pump song, The / Pennies from heaven / Birth of the blues, The / Closest to the bone.
**Cass:** Released Jul '89, on Jasmine by Hasmick Promotions. Catalogue no: **JASC 306**
**Album:** Released Jul '89, on Jasmine by Hasmick Promotions. Catalogue no: **JAS 306**

### HEY BOY, HEY GIRL (Prima, Louis and Keely Smith)
Tracks: / Hey boy, hey girl / Banana split for my baby, A / You are my love / Fever / Oh Marie / Lazy river / Nitey-nite / When the saints go marching in / Autumn leaves.
**Album:** Released Nov '85, on Capitol T (USA) Catalogue no: **T 1160**

### JUMP, JIVE AN' WAIL
Tracks: / Jump, jive and wail / Oh Marie / You rascal you (I'll be glad when you're dead) / Buona sera / I've got the world on a string / Fee fie foo / Gigolo / I ain't got nobody / Pennies from Heaven / Angelinda / Zooma zooma / Don't worry bout me / I'm in the mood for love / Them there eyes / Honeysuckle rose.
**Cass:** Released Sep '86, on Charly R&B by Charly Records. Catalogue no: **TCCRB 1116**
**Album:** Released Apr '86, on Charly R&B by Charly Records. Catalogue no: **CRB 1116**

### JUST A GIGOLO 1945 - 50 (Prima, Louis & His Orchestra)
**Album:** Released Jun '88, on Bandstand Catalogue no: **BS 7139**
**Cass:** Released Jun '88, on Bandstand Catalogue no: **BS 7139C**

### JUST A GIGOLO (SINGLE) (Prima, Louis & His Orchestra)
**7" Single:** Released Apr '83, on EMI (France) by EMI Records. Catalogue no: **2C 008 81166**

### LIVE FROM LAS VEGAS (See panel on next page)
Tracks: / Oh Marie / Buona sera / Imagination / I love Paris / Up jumped the rabbit / Georgia on my mind / I want you to be my baby / Baby won't you please come home / When the saint's go marching' in / Cold cold heart / Robin Hood / Going to Kansas City / Goody goody / Tiger rag / Night train / That old black

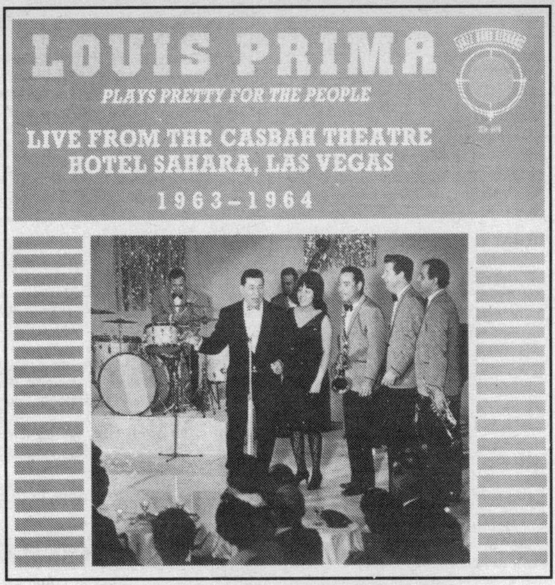


**Louis Prima - Live from Las Vegas (Jazz Band)**

magic / Sing sing sing.

Note: You may have known that Louis Prima wrote the Benny Goodman swing classic *Sing sing sing*, you may have even known that he was married five times; but I bet you didn't know he was the inventor of *Gleeby rhythm...* Impressed? Thought you would be. That song was one of Louis Prima's first hits, cut in 1941 for the Varsity label; however Gleeby Rhythm was born long before 1941 ... in 1910 in fact when Louis Prima was born in New Orleans. Influenced by N.O. jazz Prima formed his own band in school and in 1932 joined Red Nicholl's band for a spell. In 1933 he headed for New York forming a band called Louis Prima and his New Orleans Gang, which was almost self descriptive as they played New Orleans style jazz tinged with scat and a little Italian heptalk.

After appearing in a number of short films in Hollywood, Prima settled out West permanently and in 1936 wrote *Sing sing sing*, which Benny Goodman was to take a national popularity a year later. By 1940 Prima had begun to adapt to swing, but still kept his own sound ... he called it *Gleeby rhythm*. Throughout the 1940s he ploughed through record companies almost as fast as he went through wives. Although he didn't have many hits his reputation for hard work and an energetic stage show ensured him regular bookings; by 1954 he was pulling 10,000 dollars a week at the Vegas Sahara. Prima's popularity was based on the nature of his music - a mix of swing, jazz, boogie woogie, R&B, Italian machismo and a dash of salciousness represented for example in his number in praise of large women, *The bigger the figure*. It is impossible to describe Prima's music but his song *Jump jive and wail* and his own publicity describing the act as 'the wildest' will give some idea (as will listening to this record). Besides pulling the crowds during '54 he pulled his fourth wife, Keely Smith, a 21 year old singer from Virginia. She became a star of the show alongside his hard rocking band The Witnesses led by tenor sax man Sam Butera, believed by many to have been the best white R&B sax man ever.

By the late '50s 'The Wildest' had become almost resident in Las Vegas and he hit again with tunes like *Oh Marie, That old black magic* and *Buena sera* (much loved during the contemporary British trad boom). He had naturally by now added a dash of rock'n'roll to the show making the description even more difficult. The Smith-Prima-Butera triumvirate kept the crowds and the dollars rolling in until 1961, when Keely aplit. The relationship had begun to go wrong, supposedly when Louis caught Keely in the dressing room with a Vegas dealer, the result ... a black eye for the dealer and a visit from the born squad for the album's producers if we print the details in full ... Not one to give up, Louis hired a young singer, Gia Mione, and as you would expect, married her in 1965. Which is just about the time these remarkable recordings were made. They feature the show live at the Casbah Theatre in the Hotel Sahara and are taken from rare radio broadcasts from 1963 and New Years Eve 1964, and they show Prima at his 'wildest'. It's all there - R&B with *Night train* and *Kansas City*, a great version of Hank Williams' *Cold cold heart*, the hits *Buona sera, Marie* and *Old black magic*, old fashioned goodtime music on *Up jumped the rabbit* and his alma mater *Sing sing sing*. He continued to play Vegas and again achieved international fame taking the vocals of King Louis the orang-utan in the Disney classic cartoon *The jungle book*. Sad to say but the part will probably be better remembered than his jumping music of the 50s and 60s. In 1975 Louis Prima, 'the wildest', the master of jump, jive and wail, inventor of Gleeby Rhythm, entered hospital to have a brain tumour removed, sadly he slipped into a coma and almost three years later 'The Wildest' and "The Gleebs" headed for that big casino in the sky. Meanwhile we mortals will have to be prepared to listen to mere recordings. So roll back the carpet, turn up the volume and grab an earful of Louis Prima, Gia Mione, Sam Butera and the Witnesses ... The Wildest. (Tony Burke, Editor 'Blues and rhythm', Stockport 1987)

**Album:** Released '88, on Jazz Band by Flyright Records. Catalogue no: **EB 406**

**LOUIS PRIMA AND KEELY SMITH (Prima, Louis & Keely Smith)**

**Album:** Released Nov '87, on Entertainers Deleted '88. Catalogue no: **ENT LP 13026**

**LOUIS PRIMA WITH KEELY SMITH GREATEST HITS**

**Cass:** Released Dec '88, on Capitol (Specials) Catalogue no: **4XL 9277**

**PLAYS PRETTY FOR THE PEOPLE (Prima, Louis / his big Band)**

**Album:** Released Dec '87, on Materiali Sonori Catalogue no: **MASO 120003**

**Album:** Released Dec '87, on Hindsight Catalogue no: **EB 406**

**Album:** Released Jul '82, on Golden Era by Delta Records. Catalogue no: **GELP 15055**

**REMEMBER**

**Album:** Released Apr '85, on Magic (1) by Submarine Records. Catalogue no: **AWE 12**

**STRICTLY PRIMA (Prima, Louis with Sam Butera & The Witnesses)**

Tracks: / If you were the only girl in the world / Judy / 5 months, 2 weeks, 2 days / That's my home / Sing, sing, sing / Gotta see baby tonight / Felicia no capacia / Moonglow / Bourbon Street blues.

Note: A collectors album, featuring Louis Prima with Sam Butera and the Witnesses bringing you an excellent selection of tracks in a style heralding their succesful US nightclub act of the 60's.

**Album:** Released Jan '86, on Capitol by EMI Records. Catalogue no: **EMS 12135**

**Cass:** Released Dec '85, on Capitol by EMI Records. Deleted Jan '88. Catalogue no: **TCEMS 1135**

**Album:** Released Dec '85, on Capitol by EMI Records. Deleted Nov '88. Catalogue no: **EMS 1135**

**WILDEST SHOW AT TAHOE, THE (Prima, Louis and Keely Smith)**
**Cass:** Released Oct '84, on Pathe Marconi (France) Catalogue no: **PM 155 299-4**
**Album:** Released Oct '84, on Pathe Marconi (France) Catalogue no: **PM 155 299-1**

**WILDEST, THE**
Tracks: / Just a gigolo / I ain't got nobody / Nothing's too good for my baby / Lips / Body and soul / Five months, two weeks, two days / Basin street blues / When it's sleepy time down South / Jump, jive and wail / Buona sera / Night train / You rascal you.
**Cass:** Released Oct '87, on Jasmine by Hasmick Promotions. Catalogue no: **JAS C300**
**Album:** Released Jan '85, on Pathe Marconi (France) Catalogue no: **2C 062 80271**
**Album:** Released Oct '87, on Jasmine by Hasmick Promotions. Catalogue no: **JAS 300**
**Cass:** Released Jan '85, on Pathe Marconi (France) Catalogue no: **2C 244 80271**

## Prison Work Songs

**PRISON WORK SONGS (Various artists)**
**Album:** Released May '81, on Arhoolie (USA) by Arhoolie Records (USA). Catalogue no: **ARHOOLIE 2012**

## Probert, George

**INCREDIBLE, THE**
**Album:** Released Jun '88, on GHB by Jazzology Records (USA). Catalogue no: **GHB 70**

## Professor Longhair

**Biographical details:** Legendary pianist and songwriter Professor Longhair, aka Fess, was born Henry Roeland "Roy" Byrd in 1918 in Bogalusa, Louisiana, and died in 1980. He was the master of New Orleans rock 'n' roll and undoubtedly the biggest influence on Huey "Piano" Smith, Fats Domino and Mac Rebbenack (Dr John). His innovatory style included rumba and Spanish tinges and he was described by Allen Toussaint as "the Bach of rock 'n' roll". He played in Dave Bartholomew's combo in 1949 and formed his own outfit called the Four Hairs. He recorded for Federal and Atlantic as well as local labels between 1949 and 1954, but like so many blacks in those days he never saw much income from his records even though one of them was widely played during the Mardi Gras for many years. His best-known tune was *Big Chief*, because it was covered by Dr John. Before he died Professor Longhair was rediscovered, played at jazz festivals and made more albums. (Donald Clarke, May 1987.).

**COMPLETE LONDON CONCERT, THE**
Tracks: / Mess around / Hey now baby / Whole lot of lovin' / Go to the Mardi Gras / Baldhead / Tipitna / Big chief / Every day I have the blues / Hey little girl / Rockin' pneumonia.
Note: Recorded 1978.
**CD:** Released Jul '87, on JSP by JSP Records. Catalogue no: **JSP CD 202**

**CRAWFISH FIESTA**
Note: With this excellent album, the Alligator catalogue begins moving further afield than Chicago, starting in New Orleans, Louisiana with thw legendary pianist Professor Longhair. His students and admirers included James Booker, Fats Domino, Earl King, The Neville Brothers and Dr. John. Alan Toussaint once called Longhair, 'The Bach of Rock', probably because he played the piano like he'd invented it. 'A masterpiece' ("Village Beast", Alligator catalogue 7/88)
**Album:** Released Jun '80, on Alligator (Sonet) by Alligator Records (USA). Catalogue no: **SNTF 830**

**HOUSEPARTY NEW ORLEANS STYLE The lost sessions 1971-72**
Tracks: / No buts and maybes / Gone so long / She walked right in / Thank you pretty baby / 501 boogie / Tipitina / Gonna leave this town / Cabbagehead / Hey little girl / Big chief / Cherry pie / Junco partner / Everyday I have the blues / 'G' jam / Doctor Professor Longhair.
Note: Previously unreleased studio recordings.
**CD:** Released '87, on Rounder (USA) by Rounder Records (USA). Catalogue no: **CD 2057**
**Cass:** Released '88, on Rounder (USA) by Rounder Records (USA). Catalogue no: **ROUNDER 2057C**
**Album:** Released May '87, on Rounder Europa (USA) Catalogue no: **REU 1022**
**Album:** Released '88, on Rounder (USA) by Rounder Records (USA). Catalogue no: **ROUNDER 2057**

**LIVE ON THE QUEEN MARY**
Tracks: / Tell me pretty baby / Mess around / Everyday I have the blues / Tipitina / I'm movin' on / Mardi Gras in New Orleans / Cry to me / Gone so long / Stagger Lee.
Note: The greatest New Orleans piano player ever - the man who influenced them all from Fats Domino and Dr.John to Allen Toussaint. This album, recorded by Paul McCartney in 1978 features 'Fess' running through hits such as 'Tipitina' and 'Mardi Gras In New Orleans'. With the increase in popularity of New Orleans music via visits by Dr.John and the Neville Brothers, this makes a timely re-issue.
**Album:** Released Mar '86, on Stateside by EMI Records. Deleted Jun '89. Catalogue no: **SSL 6004**
**Cass:** Released Mar '86, on Stateside by EMI Records. Deleted Aug '89. Catalogue no: **TCSSL 6004**

**LONDON CONCERT, THE**
**Album:** Released Mar '84, on JSP by JSP Records. Catalogue no: **JSP 1025**

**MARDI GRAS IN NEW ORLEANS**
Tracks: / Mardi Gras in New Orleans / Tipitina / She walks right in / Mess around / Gone so long / Big chief / Hey little girl / Yancey's mixture / Well alright / Everyday I have the blues / Rockin' with Fes / Pinetop's boogie woogie.
**Album:** Released Dec '82, on Krazy Kat by Interstate Music. Catalogue no: **KK 7408**
**Album:** Released Jan '87, on Nighthawk by Nighthawk Records (USA). Catalogue no: **NH 108**

**NEW ORLEANS PIANO**
**Album:** Released Jan '88, on Atlantic by WEA Records. Catalogue no: **SD 7225**

## Progressive Records

**PROGRESSIVE RECORDS ALL STAR (Various artists)**
**Album:** Released Nov '82, on Progressive (USA) by Jazzology Records (USA). Catalogue no: **PRO 7017**
**Album:** Released Sep '79, on Progressive (USA) by Jazzology Records (USA). Catalogue no: **PRO 7015**

## Pryor, Snooky

**SNOOKY**
**Album:** Released Oct '87, on Blind Pig (USA) by Blind Pig Records (USA). Catalogue no: **BP-2387**

**SNOOKY PRYOR**
**Album:** Released Sep '87, on Magpie by Interstate Music. Deleted '88. Catalogue no: **PY 1813**

**SNOOKY PRYOR & MOODY JONES Job series vol.3 (Pryor, Snooky & Moody Jones)**
**Album:** Released '88, on Flyright by Interstate Music. Catalogue no: **FLY 565**

## Prysock, Arthur

**ALL MY LIFE**
Tracks: / All my life.
**7" Single:** Released Jun '77, on Polydor by Polydor Ltd. Deleted '78. Catalogue no: **2121 323**

**ROCKIN' GOOD WAY, A**
Tracks: / Baby (you've got what it takes) / I want to thank you, girl / Bloodshot eyes / Teach me tonight / Every morning baby / Passing strangers / Next time you see me / Rockin' good way, A.
Note: One of America's great vocalists, warm-voiced and in the Billy Eckstine and Brook Benton mould. During his long career, spanning more than 35 years, he recorded many fine albums, some of which were issued on Verve, including one with Count Basie.
**Album:** Released Feb '86, on Milestone by Ace Records. Catalogue no: **M 9139**

**ROCK'N'ROLL**
Tracks: / Jump, Red jump / Happy feet / Blow your horn / Little Jamie / Zonked / Rock 'n' roll / Zip / Fat's place / Alright, okay you win / That's the groovy thing / Jumbo / Hand clappin'.

**Album:** Released '88, on Official by Official Records. Catalogue no: **OFF 6017**

## Prysock, Red

### CRYIN' MY HEART OUT

**Album:** Released Aug '87, on Saxophonograph (Sweden) Catalogue no: **BP 502**

## Puente, Tito

**Biographical details:** Known as The King -- El Ray -- Puente, bandleader, virtuoso timbales player and multi-instrumentalist, composer, arranger and producer, has been a star in the New York Puerto Rican community for decades. Born in New York in 1923, he intended to be a dancer but tore a tendon in a cycling accident. He met bandleader Charlie Spivac in the US Navy in World War II, learned big band arranging and composition and later studied at Julliard under the GI Bill. After working with bands he formed his own outfit in 1947 and was one of the leaders of the big band mambo style and later the cha cha cha craze during the 50's. He recorded for Tico, RCA and other labels. Some of his original tunes were covered note-for-note by Santana in the late 60's. The number of albums made by Puente and the number of prominent Latin artists he has recorded with are largely uncountable but they include the Fania All Stars, who have appeared in London. Since 1979 he has toured with smaller groups, first known as the Latin Percussion Jazz Ensemble (LPJE), now as the Latin Ensemble. They recorded live at the Montreux Jazz Festival in 1980 and for the Concord Jazz label in the USA -- two LPs have won Grammies. (Donald Clarke, May 1987.).

### AZUQUITA CE MAGNIFIQUE

**Album:** Released Mar '89, on Sterns by Sterns African Records Centre. Catalogue no: **JMTS 1440**

### BEST OF THE SIXTIES (Puente, Tito & His Orchestra)

Tracks: / Vete pa' la luna / Fat mama / Ay carino / Ran kan kan / Fancy feet / Babarabatoro / Cuando calienta el sol / T.P's shing a ling / Caramelos / Noro morales, A / Azukiki.

**Cass:** Released Aug '88, on Caliente by Charly Records. Catalogue no: **TCHOT 105**

**Album:** Released Jul '88, on Caliente by Charly Records. Catalogue no: **HOT 105**

**CD:** Released Aug '88, on Caliente by Charly Records. Catalogue no: **CDCHARLY 125**

### DANCEMANIA 80'S

**Album:** Released Mar '89, on Sterns by Sterns African Records Centre. Catalogue no: **JMTS 1439**

### EL REY (Puente, Tito & His Latin Ensemble)

Tracks: / Oye como va / Autumn leaves / Ran kan kan / Rainfall / Giant steps / Linda Chicana / Medley: Stella by starlight / Delirio / Equinoxe / El rey del timbal.

Note: Tito Puente and his Latin Ensemble.

**Cass:** Released Oct '84, on Concord Picante by Concord Jazz Records (USA). Catalogue no: **CJPC 250**

**Album:** Released Oct '84, on Concord Picante by Concord Jazz Records (USA). Catalogue no: **CJP 250**

**CD:** Released Jan '87, on Concord Jazz by Concord Jazz Records (USA). Catalogue no: **CCD 4250**

### GOZA MI TIMBAL

Tracks: / Airegin / Cha cha cha / Pent up house / Picadillo a lo Puente / All blues / Ode to Cachao / Straight, no chaser / Lambada timbales.

**Cass:** Released Jan '90, on Concord Picante by Concord Jazz Records (USA). Catalogue no: **CJP 399C**

**CD:** Released Jan '90, on Concord Picante by Concord Jazz Records (USA). Catalogue no: **CCD 4399**

### MAMBO DIABLO (Puente, Tito & His Latin Ensemble)

Tracks: / Mambo diablo / Take five / Lush life / Pick yourself up / Lullaby of Birdland / No pienses asi / China / Eastern joy dance.

**CD:** Released Sep '86, on Concord Jazz by Concord Jazz Records (USA). Catalogue no: **CCD 4283**

**Album:** Released Dec '85, on Concord Jazz by Concord Jazz Records (USA). Catalogue no: **CJP 283**

### ON BROADWAY (Puente, Tito & His Latin Ensemble)

Tracks: / T.P.'s special / Sophisticated lady / Bluesette / Soul song / On Broadway / Maria Cervantes / Jo je ti / First light.

**Album:** Released Apr '83, on Concord Jazz by Concord Jazz Records (USA). Catalogue no: **CJP 207**

**Cass:** Released Apr '83, on Concord Jazz by Concord Jazz Records (USA). Catalogue no: **CJPC 207**

**CD:** Released Sep '88, on Concord by Concord Jazz Records (USA). Catalogue no: **CCD 4193**

**CD:** Released Jul '88, on Concord Jazz by Concord Jazz Records (USA). Catalogue no: **CCD 4207**

### PUENTE IN PERCUSSION

**Album:** Released Mar '89, on Sterns by Sterns African Records Centre. Catalogue no: **JMTS 1422**

### PUENTE NOW

**Cass:** Released '88, on GNP Crescendo (USA) by GNP Crescendo Records (USA). Catalogue no: **GNP5 2048**

**Album:** Released Aug '84, on Vogue by Vogue Records. Catalogue no: **516 002**

**Album:** Released '88, on GNP Crescendo (USA) by GNP Crescendo Records (USA). Catalogue no: **GNPS 2048**

### SALSA MEETS JAZZ

Note: The sixth album from the King of Latin Music featuring himself on vibes and timbales, Tito is supported by his eight piece latin ensemble plus special guest altoist Phil Woods. (New Note, August 1988)

**CD:** Released Sep '88, on Concord by Concord Jazz Records (USA). Catalogue no: **CCD 4354**

**Cass:** Released Sep '88, on Concord by Concord Jazz Records (USA). Catalogue no: **CJP 354 C**

**Album:** Released Sep '88, on Concord by Concord Jazz Records (USA). Catalogue no: **CJP 354**

### SALSA, SALSA! (Puente, Tito & His Orchestra)

**CD:** Released Dec '88, on World Records by EMI Records. Catalogue no: **WWCD 04**

### SENSATION

Tracks: / Fiesta a la king / Guajira for cal / Round Midnight / Que sensacion / Jordu / Cantigo en la distancia / Morning / Spain.

Note: Tito Puente - timbales, vibes, percussion; Sonny Bravo - piano; Jimmy Frisaura - valve trombone, trumpet, flugelhorn; Ray Gonzalez - Flugelhorn; Jose Madera - congas, percussion; Madero Rivera - tenor & soprano saxaphone, alto flute, piccolo; Bobby Rodriguez - bass; Johnny Dandy Rodriquez - bongos, percussion; Terry Gibbs - vibes (special guest).

**CD:** Released Apr '87, on Jazz (USA) by Concord Jazz Records (USA). Catalogue no: **CCD 4301**

**Cass:** Released Aug '86, on Concord Jazz by Concord Jazz Records (USA). Catalogue no: **CJPC 301**

**Album:** Released Aug '86, on Concord Jazz by Concord Jazz Records (USA). Catalogue no: **CJP 301**

### UN POCO LOCO (Puente, Tito & His Latin Ensemble)

Tracks: / Un poco loco / Swinging shepherd blues (goes Latin) / Alma con alma / El timbalon / Chang / Machito forever / Prelude to a kiss / Killer Joe / Triton.

**CD:** Released Oct '87, on Concord Jazz by Concord Jazz Records (USA). Catalogue no: **CCD 4329**

**Cass:** Released Oct '87, on Concord Jazz by Concord Jazz Records (USA). Catalogue no: **CJPC 329**

**Album:** Released Oct '87, on Concord Jazz by Concord Jazz Records (USA). Catalogue no: **CJP 329**

## Pukwana, Dudu

**Biographical details:** Born in Port Elizabeth, South Africa, in 1938, Pukwana plays alto and soprano saxes and is a prolific composer. He won a prize as best jazz saxophonist at the Jonannesburg Jazz Festival in 1962. Pianist Chris MacGregor formed the Blue Notes from musicians at the festival and the illegal, interracial group came to Europe in 1964. Pukwana settled in London. He has played everything from reggae to free jazz (with drummer Hans Bennink on an album in '78) and he has sessioned with John Dyani, the Incredible String Band and Keith Tippett's Centipede. There were LPs with the Blue Notes, with MacGregor's big band

Brotherhood of Breath and with Pukwana's own groups Assagai and Spear. With Hugh Masakela and Jonas Gwangwa he toured and recorded as African Explosion and he played on Masakela's 1972 album *Home Is Where The Music Is*. He formed the combo Zila in '78: its driving, Africa-inspired jazz/dance music is always popular. (Donald Clarke, May 1987.).

**IN THE TOWNSHIPS (Pukwana, Dudu & Spear)**
Tracks: / Baloyi / Ezilalini / Zukude / Sonia / Angel Nemali / Nobomyu / Sekela khuluma.
Note: The welcome re-release of the 70's jazz classic featuring Dudu Pukwana and Spear. Township jazz at its best.
**CD:** Released '87, on Earthworks (Virgin) by Earthworks/ Virgin Records. Catalogue no: **CDEWV 5**
**Cass:** Released Oct '87, on Earthworks (Virgin) by Earthworks/ Virgin Records. Catalogue no: **TCEWV 5**
**Album:** Released Oct '87, on Earthworks (Virgin) by Earthworks/ Virgin Records. Catalogue no: **EWV 5**

**LIFE IN BRACKNELL & WILLISAU (Pukwana, Dudu & Zila)**
Tracks: / Hug pine / Mahlomole / Lafente (Ntabeni - In the mountains) / Baqanga / Freely / Funk them up to Erika / Ziyekeleni(Let them be) / Big (pine)apple / Zama khwalo (try again).
**Album:** Released Feb '84, on Jika Catalogue no: **ZL 2**

**RADEBE-THEY SHOOT TO KILL (Pukwana, Dudu & John Stevens)**
Tracks: / Mbizo Radebe Pt. 1 / Mbizo Radebe Pt.2.
**Album:** Released Aug '87, on Affinity by Charly Records. Catalogue no: **AFF 179**

**ZILA 86 (Pukwana, Dudu & Zila)**
Tracks: / Madodana(the young ones) / Hamba (Go away) / Mra / Khali / Harare / Nonceba (merciful) / Nompongo / Let's get together / August one.
**Album:** Released Aug '86, on Jika Catalogue no: **ZL 3**

## Pullen, Don

**Biographical details:** A fine jazz pianist who first came to wide fame playing and recording with Charles Mingus in the mid-70's on Atlantic, Pullen was born in Roanoak, Virginia, in 1944. His first jazz recordings were also the first for bassist Eddie Gomez and avant garde percussionist Milford Graves in a quartet with Reedman Giuseppe Logan on ESP in 1964. He has recorded extensively with Graves and with the co-led George Adams-Don Pullen Quintet. Pullen's new quintet in 1985 had Olu Dara on trumpet, Donald Harrison on alto sax, Fred Hopkins on bass and Bobby Battle on drums. They made *The Sixth Sense on Black Saint*. (Donald Clarke).

**BREAKTHROUGH (Pullen, Don & Adams, George Quartet)**
Tracks: / Mr. Smoothie / Just foolin' around / Song from the old country / We've been here all the time / Time for sobriety, A.
**Album:** Released Jul '89, on Blue Note by EMI Records. Catalogue no: **BT 85122**

**CAPRICORN RISING**
**Album:** Released Jul '78, on Black Saint (Italy) Catalogue no: **BSR 004**

**DON PULLEN PLAYS MONK**
**Album:** Released Apr '76, on King (Japan) Catalogue no: **K 28P 6368**

**HEALING FORCE**
**Album:** Released Mar '77, on Black Saint (Italy) Catalogue no: **BSR 0010**

**LIFE LINE (Pullen, Don Quartet)**
**Cass:** Released Oct '86, on Timeless by Timeless Records. Catalogue no: **SJP 1154**

**MONTREUX CONCERT**
**Album:** Released Jul '78, on Atlantic by WEA Records. Catalogue no: **K 50499**

**NEW BEGINNINGS**
Tracks: / Jana's delight / Once upon a time / Warriors / New beginnings / At the Cafe Centrale / Reap the whirlwind / Silence-death (CD only.).
**Album:** Released Oct '89, on Blue Note by EMI Records. Catalogue no: **B1 91785**
**Album:** Released Oct '89, on Blue Note by EMI Records. Catalogue no: **791 785 1**
**CD:** Released Oct '89, on Blue Note by EMI Records. Catalogue no: **CDP 791 785 2**

**RESOLUTION (Pullen, Don / H. Bluiett)**
**Album:** Released Jul '78, on Black Saint (Italy) Catalogue no: **BSR 0014**

**SIXTH SENSE, THE (Pullen, Don Quintet)**
**CD:** Released '86, on Black Saint (Italy) Catalogue no: **BSR 0088**

**SOLO PIANO ALBUM**
**Album:** Released Jul '86, on Sackville by Spotlite Records. Catalogue no: **3008**

**SONG EVERLASTING (Pullen, Don & Adams, George Quartet)**
Tracks: / Another reason to celebrate (Extra track on CD only) / Sunwatchers / Serenade for Sarah / 1529 Gunn Street / Warm up / Sing me a song everlasting.
**CD:** Released Sep '87, on Blue Note by EMI Records. Deleted Aug '89. Catalogue no: **BNZ 77**
**Album:** Released Nov '88, on Blue Note by EMI Records. Catalogue no: **BLJ 46907**
**CD:** Released Sep '87, on Blue Note by EMI Records. Deleted Aug '89. Catalogue no: **CDBLJ 46907**
**CD:** Released Sep '87, on Blue Note by EMI Records. Deleted Aug '89. Catalogue no: **CDP 746 907 2**
**Album:** Released Aug '87, on Blue Note by EMI Records. Deleted Nov '88. Catalogue no: **BT 85143**

**WARRIORS**
**Album:** Released Jul '78, on Black Saint (Italy) Catalogue no: **BSR 0019**

## Puma, Joe

**SHINING HOUR**
Note: Featuring Hod O'Brien, Red Mitchell.
**Album:** Released Sep '87, on Reservoir Catalogue no: **RSR 102**

## Punch & Handy

**CALIFORNIA CRUSADERS, VOL. 2**
**Album:** Released '88, on GHB by Jazzology Records (USA). Catalogue no: **GHB 192**

**CALIFORNIA CRUSADERS, VOL. 3**
**Album:** Released '88, on GHB by Jazzology Records (USA). Catalogue no: **GHB 193**

## Punch, Kid

**CAPTAIN JOHN HANDY 1960**
**Album:** Released Jun '88, on Jazzology (USA) by Jazzology Records (USA). Catalogue no: **JCE 12**

## Purim, Flora

**500 MILES HIGH**
Tracks: / O cantador / Bridge / 500 miles high / Craro E canels / Baia / Un / Jive talk.
**Album:** Released Oct '80, on Milestone by Ace Records. Deleted '85. Catalogue no: **M 9070**

**HUMBLE PEOPLE (Purim, Flora & Airto)**
Tracks: / 20 years blue / Move it on up / Jogral / Bad jive / Humble people / Nvula ieza / Humbiumbi / Jungle cry / New flora / Shoulder (Ombro).
**Cass:** Released Sep '85, on George Wein Collection(USA) by Concord Jazz Records (USA). Catalogue no: **GWC 3007**
**Album:** Released Sep '85, on George Wein Collection(USA) by Concord Jazz Records (USA). Catalogue no: **GW 3007**

**LOVE REBORN**
**CD:** Released Nov '86, on Fantasy (import) by Fantasy Inc (USA). Catalogue no: **FCD 6209095**

**MAGICIANS, THE (Purim, Flora & Airto)**
Tracks: / Sweet baby blues / Garimpo / Esquinas / Bird of paradise / Magicians, The / Jennifer / Jump / Two minutes of peace / Love reborn.
Note: Frequent visitors to the UK,Flora Purim & husband Airto Moreira,with a programmeof unique & exciting latin-American pop music.Anchored by Latin,Bossa Nova and African dance rhythms,steeped in Brazilian blues & richly textured with synthesisers.Supported by 20 musicians including the very special guests,Kenny Loggins & George Duke.
**CD:** Released Nov '86, on Crosscut by Topic Records. Catalogue no: **CCD 45001**
**Cass:** Released Nov '86, on Crosscut by Topic Records. Catalogue no: **CRC 5001**

**Album:** Released Nov '86, on Crosscut by Topic Records. Catalogue no: **CCR 5001**

**MIDNIGHT SUN, THE**
Tracks: / Angel eyes / Light as a feather / Midnight sun, The / Nothing will be as it was / Las olas / Flora nova / A Esperanca / Good morning heartache / Bodas de prata.
Note: "The new album 'The Midnight Sun' is a stunning collection of jazz ballads, recorded and produced by her husband Airto Moreira featuring musicians including George Duke and Itchy Fingers." (Virgin Records, July 1988).
**Cass:** Released 13 Jun '88, on Venture (2) by Virgin Records. Catalogue no: **TCVE 21**
**Album:** Released Jul '88, on Venture (2) by Virgin Records. Catalogue no: **VE 21**
**CD:** Released Jul '88, on Venture (2) by Virgin Records. Catalogue no: **CDVE 21**

**MILESTONE MEMORIES**
Tracks: / Moon Dreams / Vera Cruz / Windows / Cravo E Canela / What Can I Say? / Casa Forte / Samba Michel / Open your eyes you can fly / Overture.
**CD:** Released 25 Apr '88, on BGP by Ace Records. Catalogue no: **CDBGP 1008**
**Cass:** Released 25 Apr '88, on BGP by Ace Records. Deleted '89. Catalogue no: **BGPC 1008**
**Album:** Released 25 Apr '88, on BGP by Ace Records. Catalogue no: **BGP 1008**

**SUN IS OUT, THE (Purim, Flora & Airto Moreira)**
Tracks: / Samba do cantor / Viver de arnor / Sun is out, The / Asas do imaginacao / Midday sun / Hope / Pablo sereno / Lua Flora / Forever friends / Olivia.
**Album:** Released Jan '89, on Crossover Catalogue no: **CR 5003**
**CD:** Released Jan '89, on Crossover Catalogue no: **CCD 45003**
**Cass:** Released Jan '89, on Crossover Catalogue no: **CR 5003C**

## Purnell, Alton

**ALTON PURNELL - LIVE**
**Album:** Released Feb '89, on CSA by CSA Records. Catalogue no: **CLPS 1018**

**ALTON PURNELL MEETS HOULIND**
Tracks: / Four or five times / I'll always be in love with you / Little coquette / Lady be good / Exactly like you / Runnin' wild / Melancholy blues / Altons blues.
**Cass:** Released '88, on Nathan Catalogue no: **MC 101**

## Pyne, Mick

**ALONE TOGETHER (Piano/cornet duets)**
**Album:** Released '83, on Spotlite by Spotlite Records. Catalogue no: **SPJ 506**

**LITTLE BLUE, A (Pyne, Mick Quartet)**
Tracks: / Another nice mess / Space in time / Di's waltz / Red zinger / Little blue, A / Nothing less than love.
Note: Features Don Weller on tenor saxophone, Ron Mathewson on bass, and Mick Pyne, piano.
**Album:** Released Apr '88, on Miles Music by Miles Music Records. Catalogue no: **MM 073**

**MICK PYNE QUARTET (Pyne, Mick Quartet)**
Note: With Don Weller/Ron Mathewson/Martin Taylor.
**Album:** Released Jan '88, on Miles Music by Miles Music Records. Catalogue no: **MM 003**

**ONCE IN A WHILE (Pyne, Mike & Humphrey Littleton)**
**Album:** Released Jun '78, on Black Lion Catalogue no: **BLP 12149**

# Q

The following information was taken from the Music Master database on April 14th, 1990.

## Quebec, Ike

**Biographical details:** Ike Quebec was born in 1918 in New Jersey and died in NYC in 1963. He turned pro on piano in 1942, then debuted on tenor sax and was a master of the late swing era style, also influenced by bop: *Mop Mop* with Kenny Clarke, recorded by Coleman Hawkins at one of the first bop record sessions He made juke box hits for Blue Note in the late 1940s 'swingette' small-group style, *Harlem* being one of the biggest hits the label ever had. In the 1950s he suffered through very hard times for jazz, and also from a drug habit; but he came back to Blue Note to make a beautiful series of albums in the late '50s-early '60s before he died of cancer. *Blue And Sentimental* has been a popular album ever since it was made; Quebec plays piano on two tracks. *Easy Living* is even more fun, with Stanley Turrentine on second tenor, Bennie Green on trombone, Milt Clark on piano; it has never been released until now in its original format. Digitally remastered by EMI, these albums sound as fresh as the day they were made. (Donald Clarke).

### BLUE AND SENTIMENTAL

Tracks: / Blue and sentimental / Minor impulse / Don't take your love from me / Blues for Charlie / Like / Count every star / That old black magic (CD only.) / It's all right with me (CD only.).

**CD:** Released May '89, on Blue Note by EMI Records. Catalogue no: **BNZ 174**

**CD:** Released May '89, on Blue Note by EMI Records. Catalogue no: **CDP 784 098 2**

**Album:** Released Mar '86, on Blue Note by EMI Records. Catalogue no: **BST 84098**

**Cass:** Released Mar '86, on Blue Note by EMI Records. Deleted Jun '89. Catalogue no: **TCBST 84098**

### EASY LIVING

Tracks: / See see rider / Congo lament / Que's pill / I've got a crush on you / Nancy (with the laughing face) / Easy living / B.G's groove two (On CD only) / I.Q. shuffle (On CD only).

**Album:** Released Aug '87, on Blue Note by EMI Records. Catalogue no: **BST 84103**

**CD:** Released Sep '87, on Blue Note by EMI Records. Catalogue no: **BNZ 78**

**CD:** Released Sep '87, on Blue Note by EMI Records. Catalogue no: **CDP 746 846 2**

## Queen City...

### EVERYBODYS RAG (Queen City Ragtime Ensemble)

**Album:** Released Apr '88, on Stomp Off (USA) Catalogue no: **SOS 1138**

## Quillian, Rufus

### RUFUS & BEN QUILLIAN 1929-31 (Quillian, Rufus & Ben)

**Album:** Released Jan '88, on Matchbox by Flyright Records. Catalogue no: **MSE 217**

## Quinichette, Paul

### KID FROM DENVER, THE

**Album:** Released '89, on Meteor by Magnum Music Group. Catalogue no: **MTLP 021**

**Album:** Released 7 Nov '87, on Fresh Sounds (Spain) by Fresh Sounds Records (Spain). Catalogue no: **FS 265**

### ON THE SUNNY SIDE

Tracks: / Blue dots / Circles / On the sunny side of the street / Cool-lypso.

**Album:** Released May '84, on RCA by BMG Records (UK). Deleted Jan '89. Catalogue no: **OJC 076**

# R

The following information was taken from the Music Master database on 14th April, 1990.

## Rabin, Oscar

**ESPECIALLY FOR YOU (Rabin, Oscar & His Band)**
Tracks: / I let a song go out of my heart / Proud of you / Especially for you / Sing my heart / At the woodchoppers ball / They say / Could be / I fall in love with you every day / Wrappin' it up / Begin the beguine / This time it's real / Ain't cha comin' out? / I hear a dream / I understand / Exactly like you / Where the blue begins / Starlight serenade / We'll go smiling along.
**Album:** Released Nov '81, on Decca by Decca International. Deleted Nov '86. Catalogue no: **RFL 15**

**TRY A LITTLE TENDERNESS**
Tracks: / It's gonna be you / Moon song / Try a little tenderness / Morning, noon and night / Shadows on the swanee / Shadow waltz / Rockabye moon / Rambling down the lane together / Horses carry tails / I can't remember / Pettin' in the park / Wear a great big smile / Hiawatha's lullaby / This is the rhythm for me / Willow weep for me / Two little windows / Waltzing in a dream / Hyde Park corner.
**Cass:** Released Dec '88, on Burlington Records by Plant Life Records. Catalogue no: **4 BUR 017**
**Album:** Released Dec '88, on Burlington Records by Plant Life Records. Catalogue no: **BUR 017**

## Rachell, Yank

**BLUES MANDOLIN MAN**
**Album:** Released '88, on Blind Pig (USA) by Blind Pig Records (USA). Catalogue no: **BP-1986**

**CHICAGO STYLE**
**Album:** Released Mar '90, on Delmark (USA) by Delmark Records (USA). Catalogue no: **DS 649**
**Album:** Released Dec '88, on Delmark (USA) by Delmark Records (USA). Catalogue no: **DL 649**

**COMPLETE RECORDINGS 1934-38**
**Album:** Released Dec '88, on Wolf Catalogue no: **WSE 106**

**COMPLETE RECORDINGS 1938-41**
**Album:** Released Dec '88, on Wolf Catalogue no: **WSE 107**

**Radio Leicester Big Band - .........and friends (RLBB)**

**YANK RACHELL'S TENNESSEE JUG BUSTERS (Rachell, Yank and his Tennessee Jug Busters)**
**Album:** Released Dec '88, on Delmark (USA) by Delmark Records (USA). Catalogue no: **DL 608**

## Radio Leicester

**RADIO LEICESTER BIG BAND AND FRIENDS (Radio Leicester Big Band) (see panel below)**
Tracks: / Take the 'A' train / Senorita blues / Twin town trip / Back to the barracks / Feels so good / Big dipper / Cute / Lucky for some / Bone free / Teddy the toad / More than Frolesworth.
**Album:** Released Aug '85, on RLBB Catalogue no: **RLBB 103**

## Raeburn, Boyd

**Biographical details:** Boyd Raeburn was born in 1913 in South Dakota; he died in Indiana in 1966. He was a saxophonist and a bandleader who began leading in college. He played a straight 'sweet' style until he came to NYC in 1944 and built a new jazz-orientated band, entering the history books: from 1944 to 1947 his and Woody Herman's bands were the ones full of young white boppers. Dizzy Gillespie, Budd Johnson and Tadd Dameron were among those who wrote for the band; it was formed during the musicians' union recording ban, then recorded for obscure labels; in 1944 the band's book of arrangements was destroyed by fire and Duke Ellington helped with arrangments and money. Raeburn disbanded in 1947 and re-formed in late 1948, during another recording ban. He left music in the late 1950s..

**1943 - 1948 (Raeburn, Boyd & His Musicians)**
**Album:** Released Jul '77, on First Heard by Submarine Records. Catalogue no: **FH 8**

**EXPERIMENTS IN BIG BAND JAZZ (Raeburn, Boyd Orchestra)**
Tracks: / Night in Tunisia / Summertime / Prisoner of love / Out of nowhere / Blue prelude / This heart of mine.
Note: Featuring Dizzy Gillespie, Johnny Bothwell.
**Album:** Released '88, on Musicraft (USA) by Discovery Records (USA). Catalogue no: **MVS 505**

**GEP BOYDS (Raeburn, Boyd & His Orchestra)**
**Album:** Released Jul '82, on Golden Era by Delta Records. Catalogue no: **GELP 15014**

**JEWELS**
**2 LP Set:** Released Mar '85, on Savoy Jazz (USA) by Malaco Records (USA). Catalogue no: **SJL 2250**

**MEMPHIS IN JUNE**
**Album:** Released Apr '81, on Hep Jazz by Hep Records. Catalogue no: **HEP 22**

**MORE 1944-45 (Raeburn, Boyd Orchestra)**
**Album:** Released Dec '87, on Circle (USA) by Jazzology Records (USA). Catalogue no: **CLP 113**

**ON THE AIR VOLUME 1 (Raeburn, Boyd Orchestra)**
Tracks: / Tonsillectomy / Picnic in the wintertime / Rip Van Winkle / Yerxa / Night in Tunisia / Eagle flies / Boyd meets Stravinsky / Tone poem in four movements.
**Album:** Released Apr '81, on Hep Jazz by Hep Records. Catalogue no: **HEP 1**

**ON THE AIR VOLUME 2 (Raeburn, Boyd Orchestra)**
Tracks: / Boyd meets Stravinsky / Where you at / Tea for two / Caravan / High tide / Bagdad / Hep Boyds / Boyds nest / There's no you / Duck waddle / Two spoons / St. Louis blues / How high the moon / Begin the beguine / Tonsillectomy.
**Album:** Released Apr '81, on Hep Jazz by Hep Records. Catalogue no: **HEP 3**

**RHYTHMS BY RAEBURN (Raeburn, Boyd & His Orchestra)**
Tracks: / There must be a way / Night in Tunisia / He's home for a little while / Boyd meets girl / If I loved you / Hep Boyd's / Out of this world / Bagdad / Stranger in town / There's no you / Who started love? / How deep is the ocean / Blue moon.
**Album:** Released Jan '78, on Aircheck (USA) by Kiner Ents.(USA). Catalogue no: **AIRCHECK 20**

## Raeburn, Ray

**1944: BOYD RAEBURN (Raeburn, Ray & His Orchestra)**
**Album:** Released Aug '88, on Circle (USA) by Jazzology Records (USA). Catalogue no: **CLP 22**

## Ragtime Banjo Commission

**RAGTIME BANJO COMMISSION, THE**
**Album:** Released Jul '87, on GHB by Jazzology Records (USA). Catalogue no: **GHB 154**

## Ragtime Blues Guitar

**RAGTIME BLUES GUITAR (1928-30) (Various artists)**
Tracks: / One way gal: *Moore, William* / Ragtime crazy: *Moore, William* / Midnight blues: *Moore, William* / Ragtime millionaire: *Moore, William* / Tillie Lee: *Moore, William* / Barbershop rag: *Moore, William* / Old country rock: *Moore, William* / Raggin' the blues: *Moore, William* / Brownie blues: *Gay, Tarter* / Unknown blues: *Gay, Tarter* / Jamestown exposition: *Baylesse Rose* / Black dog blues: *Baylesse Rose* / Original blues: *Baylesse Rose* / Frisco blues: *Baylesse Rose* / Dupree blues: *Walker, Willie* / Sould Caroline rag: *Walker, Willie.*
**Album:** Released Nov '82, on Matchbox (Bluesmaster) by Saydisc Records. Catalogue no: **MSE 204**

## Ragtime Collection

**RAGTIME COLLECTION (20 original greats, 1906-1930) (Various artists)**
Tracks: / Buffalo rag: *Various artists* / Dill pickle rag: *Various artists* / At a Georgia camp meeting: *Various artists* / Black and white rag: *Various artists* / Temptation rag: *Various artists* / Alexander's ragtime band: *Various artists* / Ragtime drummer: *Various artists* / Hungarian rag: *Various artists* / You're here and I'm here: *Various artists* / Desecration rag: *Various artists* / Ragging the scale: *Various artists* / Bullfrog blues: *Various artists* / Dixie jass band one-step: *Various artists* (Track title is correct: ie Dixie jass...) / Slippery Hank: *Various artists* / Yah-de-dah: *Various artists* / Laughing rag: *Various artists* / Ross juba: *Various artists* / Waiting for the Evening Mail: *Various artists* / I wonder where my baby is tonight: *Various artists* / Maple leaf rag: *Various artists.*
**Album:** Released Dec '87, on Deja Vu Catalogue no: **DVLP 2120**
**Cass:** Released Dec '87, on Deja Vu Catalogue no: **DVMC 2120**

## Ragtime Guitar

**(See under Contemporary Ragtime Guitar)**

## Ragtime Memories

**RAGTIME MEMORIES (Various artists)**
**Album:** Released Mar '83, on VJM (Vintage Jazz Music) by Vintage Jazz Music Society(VJM). Catalogue no: **VLP 51**

## Rainey, Ma

**Biographical details:** Ma Rainey was born Gertrude Pridgett in 1886 in Columbus, Ohio; she died there in 1939. She is perhaps the most famous female blues singer after Bessie Smith. Born into a family of minstrel troupers; they formed a song and dance team and worked throughout the South, sometimes with Bessie. Ma and Bessie began recording the same year and brought to the blues the authentic sound of the black working-class South at a time when the newly discovered genre was in danger of being 'citified'. Ma made about 90 sides for Paramount 1923-29; she recorded the best known version of the trad. *See See Rider* (aka *Easy Rider*, a sexually satisfying partner). (Donald Clarke)..

**COMPLETE RECORDINGS - VOL.1 (1923-1924)**
**Album:** Released Aug '79, on VJM (Vintage Jazz Music) by Vintage Jazz Music Society(VJM). Catalogue no: **VLP 81**

**COMPLETE RECORDINGS (August 1924 - July 1925)**
Tracks: / Shave 'em dry / Farewell Daddy blues / Booze and blues / Toad frog blues / Jealous hearted blues / See see rider blues / Jelly bean blues / Countin' the blues (Takes 2 and 3.) / Cell bound blues / Army camp harmony blues / Explaining the blues (Takes 1 and 2.) / Louisiana hoo doo blues / Goodbye daddy blues / Rough and tumble blues / Night time blues.
**Album:** Released Jul '86, on VJM (Vintage Jazz Music) by Vintage Jazz Music Society(VJM). Catalogue no: **VLP 82**

**MA RAINEY'S BLACK BOTTOM**
Tracks: / Ma rainey's black bottom / Don't fish in my sea / Booze and blues / Farewell daddy blues / Oh papa blues / Blues oh blues / Shave 'em dry / Lucky rock blues / Screetch owl blues / Georgia cake walk / Sleep talking blues / Yonder come the blues.
**Album:** Released May '86, on Yazoo (USA) by Shanachie Records (USA). Catalogue no: **L 1071**
**Album:** Released Feb '87, on Yazoo (USA) by Shanachie Records (USA). Catalogue no: **YAZOO 1071**

**OH MY BABE BLUES**
Tracks: / Jealousy blues / Shave 'em dry / Oh my babe blues / Soon this morning / Farewell daddy blues / Don't fish in my sea / Countin' the blues / Sissy blues / Jog camp blues / Hustlin' blues / Ma and pa poorhouse blues / Big feeling blues.
**Album:** Released Dec '87, on Blue Moon (1) by Magnum Music Group. Catalogue no: **BMLP 1048**

**PARAMOUNT SESSIONS**
**Album:** Released Aug '88, on Black Swan by Island Records. Catalogue no: **WCH 12001**

## Ramblin' Thomas

**RAMBLIN' THOMAS (1928-32)**
Tracks: / So lonesome / Hard to rule woman blues / Lock and key blues / Sawmill moan / No baby blues / Ramblin' mind blues / No job blues / Back gnawing blues / Jig head blues / Hard Dallas blues / Ramblin' man / Poor boy blues / Good time blues / New way of living blues / Ground hog blues / Shake it gal.
**Album:** Released Nov '83, on Matchbox by Flyright Records. Catalogue no: **MSE 215**

## Ramirez, Louie

**TRIBUTE TO CAL TJADER**
Tracks: / Latin blues / Milestones / It could happen to you / Mambo for Cal / Soul sauce / Lullaby of Birdland / El titere / Noche de salsa.
Note: Latin jazz with Ramirez on vibes.
**Album:** Released Jun '88, on BGP by Ace Records. Catalogue no: **BGP 1013**

## Rampal, Jean Pierre

**FASCINATIN' RAMPAL**
Tracks: / I got rhythm / Fascinating rhythm / Someone to watch over me /

Nice work if you can get it / Man I love / Liza / Porgy and Bess medley / Foggy day / American in Paris / Preludes.
**Album:** Released Sep '85, Catalogue no: **FM 39059**
**CD:** Released Feb '86, on CBS by CBS Records. Catalogue no: **MK 39700**

**SCOTT JOPLIN**
Tracks: / Maple leaf rag / Elite syncopations / Bathena / Combination march / Entertainer, The / Cascades / Cleopha / Ragtime dance / Chrysanthemum / Favourite ragtime two step / Original rags / Harmony club waltz / Great crush' collision march.
**Cass:** Released May '83, on CBS by CBS Records. Catalogue no: **40 73865**
**Album:** Released May '83, on CBS by CBS Records. Deleted Jun '88. Catalogue no: **CBS 73865**

**SUITE FOR FLUTE AND JAZZ PIANO**
**Album:** on CBS by CBS Records. Catalogue no: **CBS 73900**

## Randall, Freddy

**FREDDY RANDALL AND HIS BAND (Randall, Freddy & His Band)**
**Album:** Released Jun '86, on Dormouse Catalogue no: **DM 5**

**SOMETHING BORROWED, SOMETHING BLUE**
Tracks: / Struttin' with some barbecue / Ain't misbehavin' / Birth of the blues / Something old, something new / Blues my naughty sweetie gives to me / Moonglow / Love is just around the corner / Lonesome road / Something new / She's funny that way / Keepin' out of mischief now / Limehouse blues.
**Album:** Released Apr '78, on Alamo Deleted '88. Catalogue no: **AJ 4503**

## Randi, Don

**NEW BABY (Randi, Don & The Quest Jazz Sextet)**
**Album:** Released Oct '82, on Sheffield Lab.(USA) by Sheffield Lab. Inc.(USA). Catalogue no: **LAB 12**

## Raney, Doug

**GUITAR, GUITAR, GUITAR**
**Album:** Released Jul '88, on Steeplechase (USA) Catalogue no: **SCS 1212**
**CD:** Released Jul '88, on Steeplechase (USA) Catalogue no: **SCCD 31212**

**MEETING THE TENORS (Raney, Doug Sextet)**
**Album:** Released '88, on Criss Cross Catalogue no: **CRISS 1006**

## Raney, Jimmy

**COMPLETE... IN TOKYO**
**CD:** Released '88, on Xanadu Catalogue no: **FDC 5157**

**IN THREE ATTITUDES**
**Album:** Released '88, on Jasmine by Hasmick Promotions. Catalogue no: **JASM 1049**

**JIMMY RANEY TRIO (Raney, Jimmy Trio)**
Note: Artists include: Tommy Flanagan/George Mraz.
**Album:** Released Jul '86, on Criss Cross Catalogue no: **XX 1019**

**MASTER (Raney, Jimmy & Kirk Lightsey)**
**Album:** Released '88, on Criss Cross Catalogue no: **CRISS 1009**

**RANEY 1981**
**Album:** Released '88, on Criss Cross Catalogue no: **CRISS 1001**

**STOLEN MOMENTS (Raney, Jimmy and the Doug Raney Quartet)**
**Album:** Released Jul '88, on Steeplechase (USA) Catalogue no: **SCS 1118**
**CD:** Released Jul '88, on Steeplechase (USA) Catalogue no: **SCCD 31118**

**TRES CHOUETTE**
**CD:** Released Oct '88, on Vogue by Vogue Records. Catalogue no: **VGCD 600 181**

**TWO GUITARS (See Burrell, Kenny) (Raney, Jimmy and Kenny Burrell)**
**CD:** Released Apr '87, on Carrere (France) Catalogue no: **98444**

**TWO JIMS AND A ZOOT**
**CD:** Released '88, on Mobile Fidelity Sound Lab(USA) by Mobile Fidelity Records (USA). Catalogue no: **MFCD 833**

**VISITS PARIS**
**Album:** Released Feb '88, on Fresh Sounds (Spain) by Fresh Sounds Records (Spain). Catalogue no: **FS 282**

**WISTARIA (Raney, Jimmy Trio)**
**Album:** Released '88, on Criss Cross Catalogue no: **CRISS 1019**

## Rare Blues

**RARE BLUES (Various artists)**
Tracks: / Good morning little schoolgirl: *Ross, Dr.Isiah* / Alberta: *Maxwell Street Jimmy* / I ain't got nobody: *Williams, Big Joe* / Preachin' the blues: *House, Son* / I wish I was in heaven sitting down: *Wilkins, Rev Robert* / Pleadin' blues: *Little Brother Montgomery* / Lend me your love: *Sunnyland Slim* / Two trains running: *Maxwell Street Jimmy* / Whistling pines: *Williams, Big Joe* / Oh Lord I want you to help me: *Wilkins, Rev Robert.*
**Album:** Released Mar '81, on Sonet by Sonet Records. Catalogue no: **SNTF 853**

## Rare Blues Girls...

**RARE BLUES GIRLS FROM KING (Various artists)**
Tracks: / He's gone: *Ellis, Dorothy* / Grandpa can boogie too: *Greenwood, Lil* / Portrait of a faded love: *Young, Helen* / Please be good to me: *Hampton, Aletra* / Climb the wall: *Hunter, Fluffy* / You're gonna suffer baby: *Champion, Mickey* / I need you now: *McLawler, Sarah* / I dreamed the blues: *Carr, Valerie* / No more in life: *Anderson, Mildred* / Undecided: *Abernathy, Marion* / I'm on the outside lookin' in: *Garvin, Flo* / Let me keep you warm: *Garvin, Flo* / You can't have me now: *Lester, Lorraine* / It's a sad, sad feeling: *Ryan, Cathy* / Slowly going out of your mind: *Ellis, Dorothy* / Please be true: *Ellis, Dorothy* / Sugar pie: *Ellis, Dorothy.*
Note: With Sugar Pie, Valerie Carr, Mildred Anderson, Marion Abernathy.
**Album:** Released Aug '88, on Sing Catalogue no: **SING 1159**

## Rare Paramount...

**RARE PARAMOUNT COUNTRY BLUES 1926-29 (Various artists)**
**Album:** Released Aug '89, on Blues Document Catalogue no: **BD 2041**

## Rasmussen, Peter

**DANISH JAZZ VOL.5 1943 -44**
**Album:** Released Jul '82, on Storyville by Storyville Records AB. Catalogue no: **SLP 414**

## Raw Blues

**RAW BLUES**
**CD:** Released Oct '87, on London Records by London Records Ltd. Deleted 1 Mar '89. Catalogue no: **820 479-2**

## Real Ale & Thunder

**AT VESPERS**
Tracks: / Battle hymn of the republic / His eye is on the sparrow / Bye & bye / Old rugged cross, The / Royal telephone / Down by the riverside / What a friend we have in Jesus / Take my hand, precious Lord / Amazing grace / Just a closer walk with thee / Swing low - sweet chariot / Peace in the valley / When the saints go marching in.
**Album:** Released Apr '85, on Halcyon (USA) by Submarine Records. Catalogue no: **HAL 22**

## Real Sounds

**HARARE**
**Album:** Released May '86, on Zimbabwe Catalogue no: **ZML 1015**

**REAL SOUND OF JAZZ, THE (Various artists)**
**Album:** Released '88, on Pumpkin Catalogue no: **PUMPKIN 116**

**WALK FOR THE WORLD**
Tracks: / Walk for the world / Dynamos vs Tornadoes (On 12" only).
Note: Guests: Desmond Dekker & The London Community Gospel Choir
**12" Single:** Released 23 May '87, on Cooking Vinyl by Cooking Vinyl Records. Deleted '89. Catalogue no: **FRY 003T**
**7" Single:** Released 23 May '87, on Cooking Vinyl by Cooking Vinyl Records. Deleted '89. Catalogue no: **FRY 003**

**WENDE ZAKO (Various artists)**
**Cass:** Released '88, on Rounder (USA) by Rounder Records (USA). Catalogue no: **ROUNDER 5029C**
**Album:** Released Jun '87, on Cooking Vinyl by Cooking Vinyl Records. Catalogue no: **COOK 004**

**Album:** Released '88, on Rounder (USA) by Rounder Records (USA). Catalogue no: **ROUNDER 5029**
**CD:** Released Apr '88, on Cooking Vinyl by Cooking Vinyl Records. Catalogue no: **COOKCD 004**
**CD:** Released '88, on Rounder (USA) by Rounder Records (USA). Catalogue no: **CD 5029**
**Cass:** Released Jun '87, on Cooking Vinyl by Cooking Vinyl Records. Catalogue no: **COOKC 004**

## Rebirth Jazz Band

**FEEL LIKE FUNKIN' IT UP**
**CD:** Released Mar '90, on Rounder (USA) by Rounder Records (USA). Catalogue no: **JJCD41**

**HERE TO STAY**
**Cass:** Released '88, on Arhoolie (USA) by Arhoolie Records (USA). Catalogue no: **C 1092**

**REBIRTH JAZZ BAND OF NEW ORLEANS**
**Album:** Released Mar '85, on Arhoolie (USA) by Arhoolie Records (USA). Catalogue no: **F 1092**

## Red Onion Jazz Babies

**RED ONION JAZZ BABIES AND COOK'S DREAMLAND ORCHESTRA**
**Album:** Released Apr '79, on Fountain by Retrieval Records. Catalogue no: **FJ 107**

## Red Onions & Ottilie

**RED ONIONS AND OTTILIE**
**Album:** Released Jun '86, on Stomp Off (USA) Catalogue no: **SOS 1090**

## Red, Piano 'C'

**FLAT FOOT BOOGIE (Red, Piano 'C' & His Chicago Blues Band)**
**Album:** Released Dec '88, on Tramp Catalogue no: **9901**

## Red Rodney

**3 R'S, THE (Red Rodney/Richie Cole/Ricky Ford)**
**Album:** Released Dec '82, on Muse by Black & Blue Records. Catalogue no: **MR 5290**

**BIRD LIVES**
**Album:** Released May '81, on Muse by Black & Blue Records. Catalogue no: **MR 5034**

**HOME FREE**
**Album:** Released May '81, on Muse by Black & Blue Records. Catalogue no: **MR 5135**

**LIVE AT THE VILLAGE VANGUARD (featuring Ira Sullivan)**
**Album:** Released May '81, on Muse by Black & Blue Records. Catalogue no: **MR 5209**

**MODERN MUSIC FROM CHICAGO (Red Rodney Quintet)**
**Album:** Released Jun '86, on Original Jazz Classics (USA) by Fantasy Inc (USA). Catalogue no: **OJC 048**

**RED GIANT**
**CD:** on Steeplechase (USA) Catalogue no: **SCCD 31233**

**RED RODNEY**
Tracks: / Shaw 'nuff / Red hot and blue / I remember / 5709 / Two by two / Whirlwind / Jordu / Shelley.
**Album:** Released Jul '82, on Jazz Reactivation Catalogue no: **JR 158**

**RED RODNEY WITH THE BEBOP PRESERVATION SOCIETY**
Tracks: / Merry-go-round / March of Ides / Tenderly / Sid's delight / Blue to boogie / Seven dials / Esmerelda / If you could see me now.
Note: Veteran bop trumpeter Red Rodney with a two-trumpets and alto frontline backed by piano, bass and drums.
**Album:** Released '83, on Spotlite by Spotlite Records. Catalogue no: **SPJ LP7**

**RED TORNADO**
**Album:** Released May '81, on Muse by Black & Blue Records. Catalogue no: **MR 5088**

**RED,WHITE AND BLUES**
**Album:** Released Apr '81, on Muse by Black & Blue Records. Catalogue no: **MR 5111**

**SOCIETY RED**
**CD:** Released Feb '89, on Music Mecca by Ambia Music ApS. Catalogue no: **MECCACD 1003-2**

**SUPERBOP**
**Album:** Released Apr '81, on Muse by Black & Blue Records. Catalogue no: **MR 5046**

**YARD'S PAD**
Tracks: / Yard's pad / Red hot / Informality / S.A.S. / Here at last / Fourth of March / Don't remember April.
**Album:** Released Mar '87, on Sonet by Sonet Records. Catalogue no: **SNTF 698**

## Red Roseland...

**HANDFUL OF KEITH (Red Roseland Cornpickers & Keith Nichols)**
**Album:** Released Nov '87, on Stomp Off (USA) Catalogue no: **SOS 1133**

**RED HOT BAND (Red Roseland Cornpickers & Keith Nichols)**
**Album:** Released Jan '88, on Stomp Off (USA) Catalogue no: **SOS 1153**

**RED ROSELAND CORNPICKERS-VOL.1 (Red Roseland Cornpickers)**
**Album:** Released Jul '86, on Stomp Off (USA) Catalogue no: **SOS 1101**

**RED ROSELAND CORNPICKERS-VOL. 2 (Red Roseland Cornpickers)**
**Album:** Released Jun '86, on Stomp Off (USA) Catalogue no: **SOS 1102**

## Red, Sonny

**OUT OF THE BLUE**
**Album:** Released Sep '84, on Blue Note by EMI Records. Catalogue no: **BLP 4032**

## Red, Tampa

**BOTTLENECK GUITAR 1928-37**
**Album:** Released Dec '88, on Yazoo (USA) by Shanachie Records (USA). Catalogue no: **L 1039**

**CRAZY WITH THE BLUES**
**Album:** Released '88, on Oldie Blues Catalogue no: **OL 8001**

**DON'T TAMPA WITH THE BLUES**
**Album:** Released Jan '88, on OBC Catalogue no: **OBC 516**

**GUITAR WIZARD, THE 1935-42**
**Album:** Released Dec '88, on Old Tramp Catalogue no: **OT 1201**

**GUITAR WIZARD, THE 1935-53**
**Album:** Released Jul '87, on Blues Classics(USA) by Arhoolie Records (USA). Catalogue no: **BC 25**

**KEEP ON JUMPING 1946-52**
**Album:** Released Sep '87, on Wolf Catalogue no: **WBJ 001**

**MIDNIGHT BLUES**
**Album:** Released Oct '87, on Bluetime (Denmark) by Contact Records (Denmark). Catalogue no: **BT 2003**

**TAMPA RED 1928-41**
**Album:** Released Sep '87, on Earl Archives Catalogue no: **BD 2001**

**TAMPA RED WITH JOHNNY JONES**
Tracks: / It's a brand new boogie / Corrine blues / New bad luck blues / Come on if you're coming / Poor stranger blues / Sure enough I do / Put your money where your mouth is / Looka there looka there / Sugar baby / New deal blues / I'll never let you go / Don't blame Shorty for that / Too late, too late / 1950 blues / I'm gonna put you down / Got a mind to leave this town.
**Album:** Released May '83, on Krazy Kat by Interstate Music. Catalogue no: **KK 7411**

**YOU CAN'T GET THAT STUFF NO MORE**
**Album:** Released Sep '79, on Oldie Blues Catalogue no: **OL 2816**

## Redd, Freddie

**STRAIGHT AHEAD**
**Album:** Released Sep '79, on Interplay (USA) by Interplay Records (USA). Catalogue no: **IP 7715**

**UNDER PARIS SKIES**
**Album:** Released Jul '77, on Futura (Swing Imports) Catalogue no: **SWING 03**

## Redman, Dewey

**Biographical details:** Dewey Redman was born in 1931 in Fort Worth, Texas; he plays mainly tenor and alto saxes: the master of his instruments, he can play 'inside' or 'outside' and uses ethnic elements including the Arabian double-reed musette. He played in a high school marching band with Ornette Coleman and later played in Coleman's epoch making combos in the the early 1970's. He also recorded with Charlie Haden's

Liberation Music Orchestra, Carla Bley, Roswell Rudd, Keith Jarrett and with Haden, Don Cherry and Ed Blackwell in the quartet 'Old and New Dreams' on ECM, as well as his own albums. (Doanld Clarke 21.5.88).

**IN WILLISAU (Redman, Dewey and Ed Blackwell)**
Tracks: / Willisee / We hope / F I / Communication / S 126 T.
Note: Dewey Redman - tenor saxophone, musette. Ed Blackwell - drums. Recorded 31st August 1980 at Willisau '80 Jazz Festival.
**Album:** Released May '85, on Black Saint (Italy) Catalogue no: **BSR 0093**

**STRUGGLE CONTINUES, THE (Redman,Dewey Quartet)**
Note: Dewey Redman - tenor saxophone. Charles Eubanks - piano. Mark Helias - bass. Ed Blackwell - drums.
**Album:** Released Mar '83, on ECM Catalogue no: **ECM 1225**

## Redman, Don

**Biographical details:** Donald Mathem Redman was born in 1900; he died in 1964 in New York City. He is one of the great unsung heroes of popular music; though less well-known now than other bandleaders, he was as reponsible as anyone for inventing big band jazz. He was conservatory-trained and could play any wind instrument by the age of 12; he played saxophone as a teenager on a Louis Armstrong record and joined Fletcher Henderson's band as an arranger as well as a vocalist and reedman. Inspired by a year long stay by Armstrong in his band, as well by such Henderson sidemen as Coleman Hawkins, he took the dance-band style of Jean Goldkette and Paul Whiteman and invented jazz writing for the big band, not only writing separate parts for reed and brass choirs, leaving room for hot solos, but putting sections in opposition: he solved the problems of the new style showing everyone else how to do it and writing virtually all of Henderson's arrangements as it became the band to beat. In 1927 he was hired by the white Goldkette Cotton Pickers, and turned it into one of the most popular bands in the country. Hoagy Carmichael was an admirer; legend has it that Redman gave Carmichael advice and may have helped write the lovely introduction to *Stardust*: he was certainly among the first to record it, two years before it had lyrics, on a freelance recording session billed as the Chocolate Dandies (the band was effectively the Cotton Pickers). He formed his own band in 1931 and was the first black bandleader to have his own radio show; he was a great teacher and his often difficult arrangements were admired by other musicians. He made many of the most charming records of the decade; he invented the 'swing choir', in which a pop song was played straight by a soloist as the band chanted a 'hip' paraphase of the lyrics, a device used on many hits of the period. He freelanced in the 1940's writing arrangements such as *Just an Old Manuscript* for Count Basie; he became Pearl Bailey's music director and played a policeman in Harold Arlen's musical *House of Flowers* in 1954. He was a little guy with a modest personality; his slyly intimate, half-conversational vocals always had a humorous element in them, as on his own *Gee Baby, Ain't I Good to You?*. His other best-known tune is *Cherry*. (Also see under listing for *McKinney's Cotton Pickers*.) (Donald Clarke 21.5.88).

**1932-1936 REDMAN'S RED BOOK (Redman, Don & His Orchestra)**
**Album:** Released Dec '86, on Collectors Must Catalogue no: **M 8002**

**DOIN' THE NEW LOWDOWN (Redman, Don & His Orchestra)**
**Album:** Released Dec '84, on Hep Jazz by Hep Records. Catalogue no: **HEP 1004**

**DON REDMAN**
**Album:** Released Jul '82, on Jazz Reactivation Catalogue no: **JR 160**

**DON REDMAN ALL-STARS, THE**
**Album:** Released Oct '88, on Vogue by Vogue Records. Catalogue no: **500066**

**DON REDMAN VOL.3 (Redman, Don & His Orchestra)**
**Album:** Released '88, on Hep Me Catalogue no: **HEP 1026**

**D.R. ALL STARS VOL 1**
**Album:** Released Mar '90, Catalogue no: **VG JL 66**

**D.R. ALLSTARS VOL 2**
**Album:** Released Mar '90, Catalogue no: **VG JL 82**

**JULY 22ND AND 26TH,1957 (Redman,Don, and His All Stars)**
Tracks: / Last night in town / To the river / Ballad 'n' bounce / Dreamy melody / Christmas in the valley / Ain't gonna get fooled again / Donnybrook / Peetni petite / My dream of yesterday / Free and easy / Coffee light / Echoing.
**Album:** Released Oct '80, on From The Jazz Vault by Damont Audio Ltd.. Catalogue no: **JV 112**

**SHAKIN' THE AFRICAN (Redman, Don & his Orchestra)**
**Album:** Released Sep '86, on Hep Jazz by Hep Records. Catalogue no: **HEP 1001**

**SMOKE RINGS**
**Album:** Released May '88, on Nostalgia by Mainline Records. Catalogue no: **NOST 7641**

## Reece, Dizzy

**Biographical details:** Reece, Dizzy was born Alphonso Son Reece in 1931 in Kingston, Jamaica; the jazz trumpeter began on baritone horn at 11, went to Europe in 1948, to London in 1954, to the USA in 1959. He recorded in England with Ronnie Scott, Tubby Hayes and others and made LP's on Blue Note and many other labels. A post-bop stylist with a unique voice, admired by Dizzy Gillespie: played in Gillespie Big band in 1968 and the Paris Reunion Band in 1985; also albums by Duke Jordan, many others. (Donald Clarke 21.5.88).

**BLOWIN' AWAY (Reece, Dizzy & Ted Curson)**
**Album:** Released Aug '79, on Interplay (USA) by Interplay Records (USA). Catalogue no: **IP 7716**

**MANHATTAN PROJECT**
**Album:** Released Dec '79, on Beehive (USA) Catalogue no: **BGH 7001**

**MOOSE THE MOOCHE**
Tracks: / Stella by starlight / Walkin' / All the things you are.
Note: Dizzy Reece & Ted Curson - trumpets, Sam Jones - bass, Roy Haynes - drums, Claude Williamson - piano.
**Album:** Released '88, on Discovery (USA) by Discovery Records (USA). Catalogue no: **DS 839**

**POSSESSION, EXORCISM, PEACE**
**Album:** Released Oct '79, on Honeydew Catalogue no: **HD 6619**

**PROGRESS REPORT**
Tracks: / Now / Basie line / Gipsy, The / Scrapple from the apple / Rivera / Chorous / You came along from out of nowhere / Momentum.
**Album:** Released Mar '83, on Jasmine by Hasmick Promotions. Deleted Jun '87. Catalogue no: **JASM 2013**

## Reed, Jimmy

**Biographical details:** Jimmy Reed was born Mathis James Reed in 1925 in Mississippi; he suffered from epilepsy from the mid-'50's and died in his sleep in 1976 in California, but not before becoming a much-loved and influential blues singer and songwriter; he also played guitar and harmonica.
He signed with Vee-Jay in Chicago and had 13 influential R&B hits 1956-61 (including 12 crossovers to the pop Hot 100); *Baby what you want me to do* was covered by Elvis Presley, and *Honest I do* by Aretha Franklin and the Rolling Stones. Vee-Jay went broke; Reed came back to the R&B chart in 1966 on Exodus with *Knocking at your door*.
His laid-back style avoided the menace and dread of some other bluesmen, he was one of the first to use a neck mount so that he could play mouth harp and guitar at the same time. His wife Mary Lee 'Mama' Reed wrote many of his songs.
(Donald Clarke 21.5.88).

**12 GREATEST HITS**
Tracks: / Sun is shining, The / Honest I do / Down in Virginia / Baby what you want me to do / Found love / Hush hush / Bright lights big city / Close together / Big boss man / Aw shucks / Good lover / Shame shame shame.
**Album:** Released May '87, on Topline by Charly Records. Catalogue no: **TOP 174**
**Cass:** Released May '87, on Topline by Charly Records. Catalogue no: **KTOP 174**

**BEST OF JIMMY REED**
**2 LP Set:** Released May '89, on GNP Crescendo (USA) by GNP Crescendo Records (USA). Catalogue no: **GNPS 2-10006**
**Cass set:** Released May '89, on GNP Crescendo (USA) by GNP Crescendo Records (USA). Catalogue no: **GNP5 2-10006**
**CD:** Released Jan '88, on GNP Crescendo (USA) by GNP Crescendo Records (USA). Catalogue no: **GNPD-10006**

**BIG BOSS BLUES**
Tracks: / You don't have to go / I ain't got you / Ain't that loving you baby / Can't stand to see you go / You got me dizzy / Honest I do / Down in Virginia / I'm gonna get my baby / I wanna be loved / Going to New York / Take out some insurance / Baby what you want me to do / Hush hush / Found love / Big boss man / I'm a love you / Bright lights, big city / Aw shucks / Good lover / Too much / I'll change my style / Shame shame shame.
**CD:** Released Mar '86, on Charly by Charly Records. Catalogue no: **CDCHARLY 3**

**BOOGIE IN THE DARK**
Tracks: / Honest I do / Oh John / Go on to school / Boogie in the dark / I'm nervous / Caress me baby / My baby's so sweet / Little rain / I was so young / Shame shame shame.
Note: "Compilation album of material for the legendary blues artist and influential musician." (Magnum Music Group, May 1988).
**Album:** Released Feb '84, on Blue Moon (1) by Magnum Music Group. Catalogue no: **BMM 001**

**COLD CHILLS 1967-1970**
Tracks: / My baby told me / Just can't sleep at night / If the four winds don't change / I'll be home one day / Honey, it's time for love / Why can't I come in? / Tribute to a friend / Poor country boy / Texas is so doggone big / Cold chills / Somebody help me / Don't cry / Crazy 'bout that miniskirt.
**Album:** Released Jan '85, on Krazy Kat by Interstate Music. Catalogue no: **KK 786**

**FUNKY FUNKY SOUL (Reed, Jimmy & Screamin' Jay Hawkins)**
Tracks: / Hard walkin' Hannah / Cry before I go / Can't stand to leave / Big legged woman / Funky funky soul / Africa gone funky / Ashes / I need you / Sweet Ginny.
**Album:** Released Jun '81, on Manhattan Records by President Records. Deleted '86. Catalogue no: **MAN 5041**

**GOT ME DIZZY**
Tracks: / I'm a love you / Hush hush / Take out some insurance / I wanna be loved / Caress me baby / Boogie in the dark / I'll change my style / When you're doin' alright / You got me dizzy / Come love / Meet me / Odds and ends / Can't stand to see you go / Going by the river / You don't have to go / Crazy love.
**Album:** Released Jun '88, on Charly R&B by Charly Records. Catalogue no: **CRB 1028**

**HIGH AND LONESOME**
**Album:** Released Mar '81, on Charly R&B by Charly Records. Catalogue no: **CRB 1013**

**HONEST I DO**
**Cass:** Released '88, on Masters (Holland) Catalogue no: **CLMC 9281283**
**Album:** Released '88, on Masters (Holland) Catalogue no: **CL 281283**

**I'M THE MAN (DOWN THERE)**
Tracks: / I found my baby / Roll and rhumba / Shoot my baby / Come on baby / Rockin' with Reed / When you left me / State street boogie / Signals of love / I'm the man down there / Tell me you love me / Let's get together / Looking for you baby / Don't think I'm through / When girls do it / Left handed woman / New leaf, A.
**Album:** Released Jun '85, on Charly R&B by Charly Records. Catalogue no: **CRB 1082**

**JIMMY REED**
**CD:** Released Mar '90, on Flyright by Interstate Music. Catalogue no: **FLYCD15**

**RIDE 'EM ON DOWN (Reed, Jimmy and Eddie Taylor)**
Tracks: / Ride 'em on down / Bad boy / E.T. blues / Big town playboy / Don't knock at my door / You'll always have a home / I'm gonna love you / Looking for trouble / Find my baby / Stroll out west / I'm sitting here / Do you want me to cry / Jimmy's boogie / High and lonesome / I'm gonna ruin you / My first plea / Honey don't let me go / Honey where you going / My bitter seed / Ends and odds / String to your heart / You in that sack / I wanna be loved / You got me waiting.
**CD:** Released Mar '89, on Charly by Charly Records. Catalogue no: **CDCHARLY 171**

**ROCKIN' WITH REED**
Tracks: / I found my baby / Shoot my baby / Roll & rhumba / You upset my mind / Pretty thing / Rockin' with Reed / She don't want me no more / Come on baby / I don't go for that / When you left me / Do the thing / Little rain / Signals of love / Sun is shining, The / Caress me baby / Laughing at the blues / Baby what's wrong / Left handed woman / I'm going upside your head.
**CD:** Released Apr '87, on Charly by Charly Records. Catalogue no: **CDCHARLY 61**

**SHAME SHAME SHAME (SINGLE)**
Tracks: / Shame shame shame / Big boss man.
**7" Single:** Released Sep '64, on Stateside by EMI Records. Deleted '67. Catalogue no: **SS 330**
**7" Single:** Released Jul '80, on Charly by Charly Records. Deleted '87. Catalogue no: **CTD 105**

**SHAME SHAME SHAME VOLUME 1**
Tracks: / If you don't want me, baby / I'm leaving / When I woke up / I got to keep rolling / High yellow good lovin' / Cry before I go / Shame shame shame / Life is funny / Run here to me, baby / Two in love / Down at the grocery store / Big legged woman.
**Album:** Released Jan '84, on Krazy Kat by Interstate Music. Catalogue no: **KK 781**

**UPSIDE YOUR HEAD**
Tracks: / Shame shame shame / I'm gonna get my baby / I ain't got you / Ain't that loving you, baby? / Down the road / Bright lights / Big city / Too much / Big boss man / I'm goin' upside your head / Goo lover / Honest I do / Down in Virginia / Aw Shucks / Hush your mouth / Found love / Baby, what you want me to do? / Going to New York.
**Album:** Released '85, on Charly R&B by Charly Records. Catalogue no: **CRB 1003**
**Cass:** Released '85, on Charly R&B by Charly Records. Catalogue no: **TCCRB 1003**

## Reefer Madness

**REEFER MADNESS**
Tracks: / Bea foote weed / Cocaine / Willie the chimney sweeper / Reefer head woman / Cow cow Davenport / Mess is here, The / Pipe dream blues / Willie the weeper / Cocaine blues / Save the roach for me / Muggles / Kokey Joe / Sendin' the vipers / Viper's drag / Vipers dream / Chant of the weed / Blue reefer blues.
**Album:** Released Apr '81, on Stash (USA) Catalogue no: **ST 119**

## Reefer Songs

**REEFER SONGS (Various artists)**
**CD:** Released Jul '89, on Jass Catalogue no: **CD 501**
**Album:** Released Apr '81, on Stash (USA) Catalogue no: **ST 100**
**Cass:** Released Mar '85, on Stash (USA) Catalogue no: **STAC 100**

## Reese, Della

**Biographical details:** Della Reese was born Della Reese Taliaferro in 1932 in Detroit; she is a pop/soul singer with a big beautiful voice. She began in her teens as a gospel singer with the Mahalia Jackson troupe. She recorded for Jubilee, had a number 12 USA hit *And that reminds me* in 1957, further Hot 100 entry with *Sermontette* (a Cannonball Adderley tune with words by Jon Hendricks); she switched to RCA and had more pop hits. She was said to be Martha Reeve's favourite singer, and has remained popular in clubs. (Donald Clarke 21.5.88).

**CLASSIC DELLA**
Tracks: / Story of a starry night / These are the things I love / If you are but a dream / My reverie / Take my heart / Stranger in Paradise / Gone / Serenade / Moon love / Softly my love / Till the end of time / Don't you know?.
**Cass:** Released Oct '80, on RCA International by BMG Records (UK). Deleted '85. Catalogue no: **INTK 5046**

**Album:** Released Oct '80, on RCA International by BMG Records (UK). Deleted '85. Catalogue no: **INTS 5046**

**DELLA**
Tracks: / Lady is a tramp, The / If I could be with you one hour tonight / Let's get away from it all / Thou swell / You're driving me crazy / Goody goody / And the angels sing / Baby won't you please come home? / I'm beginning to see the light / I'll get by / Blue skies / Someday.
**Cass:** Released Oct '83, on Deja Vu Deleted Jul '89. Catalogue no: **NK 89054**
**Album:** Released Oct '83, on Deja Vu Deleted Jul '89. Catalogue no: **NL 89054**

**DELLA BY STARLIGHT**
Tracks: / Touch of your lips / He was too good to me / That old feeling / I had the craziest dream / I wish I knew / Lamplight / How did he look ? / More than you know / These follish things / Deep in a dream / Enbraceable you / Two sleeepy people.
**Album:** Released Sep '82, on RCA by BMG Records (UK). Deleted Jan '88. Catalogue no: **INTS 5194**

**DELLA DELLA CHA-CHA-CHA**
Tracks: / Diamonds are a girl's best friend / Come on...a my house / Why don't you do right / My heart belongs to daddy / Let's do it / Whatever Lola wants (Lola gets) / Daddy / Tea for two / Always true to you in my fashion / It's so nice to have a man around the house / There's a small hotel / Love for sale.
**Album:** Released Jun '87, on RCA by BMG Records (UK). Deleted Jul '89. Catalogue no: **NL 90039**
**Cass:** Released Jun '87, on RCA by BMG Records (UK). Deleted Jul '89. Catalogue no: **NK 90039**

**I LIKE IT LIKE DAT**
Tracks: / Travellin' light / If it's the last thing I do / T'aint nobody's business if I do / Ev'ry evening blues / Stranger on earth / I ain't ready for that / Fool that I am / If I ever get to heaven / Drinking again / Man with a horn / In the dark / Nobody knows the way I feel this morning.
**Album:** Released Mar '84, on Jasmine by Hasmick Promotions. Catalogue no: **JASM 1504**

**SURE LIKE LOVIN' YOU**
Tracks: / When I fall in love / That's all / Come rain or come shine / Love me tender / Touch me again / Morning comes too soon / Air that I breathe, The / Wrapped up in the comfort of you / Two together / Sure like lovin' you / It's over now.
**Album:** Released May '85, on President by President Records. Catalogue no: **PRCV 126**

**THREE GREAT GIRLS (Reese, Della, Ann Margret and Kitty Kallen)**
Tracks: / How lovely to be a woman / I'm in the mood for love / Begin the beguine / Misty / What is there to say / When a woman loves a man / Best is yet to come, The / I really don't want to know / It amazes me / True / I hadn't anyone till you / I get the blues when it rains.
**Cass:** Released Aug '88, on RCA by BMG Records (UK). Catalogue no: **NK 89455**
**Album:** Released Aug '88, on RCA by BMG Records (UK). Catalogue no: **NL 89455**

## Reeves, Dianne

**Biographical details:** Dianne Reeves was born in 1956 in Detroit. She is a jazz singer with a lovely contalto voice and a range of 3.5 octaves. She grew up in Denver, was discovered at 17 by Clarke Terry and sang with his band; moved to Los Angeles and worked with Sergio Mendez, Harry Belafonte and others; she was a sensation at a Monterey Jazz Festival backed by Tito Puente. After two LP's on Palo Alto she made her Blue Note debut in 1987. (Donald Clarke 21.5.88).

**BETTER DAYS**
Tracks: / Better days (Exta track on 12" version only.) / Better days (re-mix) / That's all.
Note: * extra track on 12" version.
**7" Single:** Released May '88, on Blue Note by EMI Records. Deleted Nov '88. Catalogue no: **BLUE 5**
**12" Single:** Released May '88, on Blue Note by EMI Records. Deleted Nov '88. Catalogue no: **12BLUE 5**

**DIANNE REEVES**
Tracks: / Sky islands / I'm OK / Better days / Harvest time / Chan's song / Yesterdays / I got it bad and that ain't good / That's all.
**CD:** Released Aug '88, on EMI by EMI Records. Deleted Jan '89. Catalogue no: **CDP 746 906 2**
**Cass:** Released Dec '87, on Blue Note by EMI Records. Catalogue no: **TC BLJ 46906**
**Album:** Released Dec '87, on Blue Note by EMI Records. Catalogue no: **BLJ 46906**
**CD:** Released Aug '88, on EMI by EMI Records. Deleted Jan '89. Catalogue no: **CDBLJ 46906**

**FOR EVERY HEART**
**Album:** Released Jan '85, on Palo Alto Catalogue no: **PA 203**

**NEVER TOO FAR**
Tracks: / Hello, haven't I seen you before / Never too far / Come in / How long / Eyes on the prize / Bring me joy / Fumilayo / More to love (than making love) / We belong together / Company.
**Cass:** Released Jan '90, on EMI-America by EMI Records. Catalogue no: **TCDIANNE 1**
**Album:** Released Jan '90, on EMI-America by EMI Records. Catalogue no: **DIANNE 1**
**Album:** Released Jan '90, on EMI-America by EMI Records. Catalogue no: **792 401 1**
**CD:** Released Jan '90, on EMI-America by EMI Records. Catalogue no: **CDDIANNE 1**
**CD:** Released Jan '90, on EMI-America by EMI Records. Catalogue no: **CDP 792 401 2**
**Cass:** Released Jan '90, on EMI-America by EMI Records. Catalogue no: **792 401 4**

**NEVER TOO FAR (SINGLE)**
Tracks: / Never too far (Not on 12".) / Never too far (LP version) (Not on 7".) / Eyes on the prize (Not on CD single.) / Eyes on the prize (LP version) (CD single only.) / Sky islands (12" only.) / Sky islands (LP version) (CD single only.).
**CD Single:** Released May '90, on EMI-America by EMI Records. Catalogue no: **203 847 2**
**CD Single:** Released May '90, on EMI-America by EMI Records. Catalogue no: **CDMT 82**
**12" Single:** Released May '90, on EMI-America by EMI Records. Catalogue no: **12MT 82**
**7" Single:** Released May '90, on EMI-America by EMI Records. Catalogue no: **203 847 7**
**12" Single:** Released May '90, on EMI-America by EMI Records. Catalogue no: **203 847 6**
**7" Single:** Released May '90, on EMI-America by EMI Records. Catalogue no: **MT 82**

**WELCOME TO MY LOVE**
**Cass:** Released Jul '86, on Palo Alto Catalogue no: **PAC 8026**
**Album:** Released Jan '84, on Palo Alto Catalogue no: **PA 8026**

## Reflexionen

**REFLEXIONEN (Various artists)**
**Album:** Released '88, on Timeless by Timeless Records. Catalogue no: **SFP 199**

**REFLEXIONEN LIVE**
**Album:** Released '88, on Timeless by Timeless Records. Catalogue no: **SFP 264**

## Rehak, Frank

**JAZZVILLE VOL. 2 (Rehak, Frank Sextet and the Alex Smith Quintet)**
**Album:** Released Feb '88, on Fresh Sounds (Spain) by Fresh Sounds Records (Spain). Catalogue no: **FS 283**

## Reichman, Joe

**PAGLIACCI OF THE PIANO (Reichman, Joe & His Orchestra)**
Note: Mono. 1941-1942.
**Album:** Released Jan '87, on Circle (USA) by Jazzology Records (USA). Catalogue no: **CLP 84**

## Reinhardt, Django

**Biographical details:** Django Reinhardt was born Jean Baptiste Reinhardt in 1910 in Belgium; he died in 1953 in Fontainebleau, France. The great guitarist was the first European musician to influence USA jazz. He wandered in Belgium and France as a gypsy playing guitar, violin, banjo; his hand was partially paralysed in a fire in his caravan in 1928 and he developed a new technique to ovecome it. He was already an adult

professional musician when he discovered jazz, immediately understood it and incorporated it into the gypsy guitar tradition, influenced by Eddie Lang; he worked with singer Jean Sablon, playing Lang to Sablon's Bing Crosby; then formed the quintet of the Hot Club of France in 1934 with Stephane Grappelli on violin (then spelt Grappelly), brother Joseph Reinhardt and Roger Chaput, guitars, Louis Vola on bass (other musicians passing through were guitarists Pierre Ferret, Eugene Vees; basses Emmanuel Soudieux, Roger Grasset). They make more than 200 sides and became internationally famous, not only on account of Django's technique and swing but his lyricism and lyrical interplay with the violin.
He recorded with Voleman Hawkins, Benny Carter and Dicky Wells, Rex Stewart and Barney Bigard in the late '30's (compiled on Prestige in USA, Giants of Jazz in Italy); the quintet recorded in London 1938-9. During the war he became a superstar, people whistling his lovely *Nuages* in the street: Grappelli was in England; Django experimented with a big band, formed a quintet with clarinettist Hubert Rostaing; during the occupation of the nazis outlawed jazz and murdered half a million gypsies: a gypsy jazz musician was twice an outlaw; Django not only survived but lived well (the ban on jazz didn't work too well either).
The quintet was recreated on record in 1946 in London with Jack Llewellyn and Alan Hodgkiss on guitars, Coleridge Goode on bass. During the war Django had worked on 'serious' music (a mass for organ, a symphony, etc); some of this music was used in a film soundtrack in 1946; late that year he went to USA to tour with Duke Ellington: due to his tendency to wander off, the tour was not a success.
He began to play electric guitar and was influenced by bop, which may not have been congenial with his personal lyricism.
He died of a stroke. His compositions included *Love's melody, Improvisation, Belleville, others with Grappelli, H.Q.C. Strut, Daphne, Souvenirs, Stomping at Decca, My Sweet, Djangology, Appel Direct, Nocturne* and many more. An 8 disc box Django on Affinity '87 has 144 tracks, good examples of everything he did. His heirs include Birelli Lagrene, Fapy Lafertin in Belgium, Elios Ferre and the brothers Boulou in Paris.
(Donald Clarke 21.5.88).

**50TH ANNIVERSARY CONCERT (Reinhardt, Django & Stephane Grappelli)**
Tracks: / I saw stars / Confessin' / Dinah / Tiger rag / Lady be good / Lily Belle May June / Sweet Sue / Continental / Simplement / Fumee aux yeux / Cocktails for two / Blue drag / Swanee river / Ton doux sourire / Ultra fox / Si j'avais ete.
**Album:** Released Oct '84, on Vogue by Vogue Records. Catalogue no: **VJD 6950**

**ATC BAND AND DUKE ELLINGTON**
**CD:** Released 10 Jul '89, on Vogue by Vogue Records. Catalogue no: **VGCD 600197**

**AVEC STEPHANE GRAPPELLI ET H. ROSTAING**
**Album:** Released Oct '88, on Vogue by Vogue Records. Catalogue no: **500 813**

**CLUB ST GERMAIN (February 1951)**
**Album:** Released '88, on Honeysuckle Rose (USA) Catalogue no: **HR 5003**

**CRAZY RHYTHM**
Tracks: / How high the moon / Fine and dandy / Yesterdays / Lover / Apple honey / Manoir de mes reves / Dream of you / Crazy rhythm.
**Cass:** Released '86, on Topline by Charly Records. Catalogue no: **KTOP 128**
**Album:** Released '86, on Topline by Charly Records. Catalogue no: **TOP 128**

**DJANGO**
Tracks: / Lady be good / Dinah / Confessin' / I saw stars / Tiger rag / Continental / Blue drag / Sweet sue / Sunshine of your smile / Nuages / Swanee river / Night and day / September song / Testament / Brazil / Manoir de mes reves / Blues for ike / Insensiblement / Gypsy with a song.
**Cass:** Released Jun '85, on CBS (Blue Diamond) by CBS Records. Deleted Aug '87. Catalogue no: **40 22186**
**CD:** Released Apr '86, on JVC/Fantasy Catalogue no: **VDJ 1515**
**Album:** Released Jun '86, on Original Jazz Classics (USA) by Fantasy Inc (USA). Catalogue no: **OJC 057**
**Album:** Released Jun '85, on CBS (Blue Diamond) by CBS Records. Deleted '87. Catalogue no: **CBS 22186**

**DJANGO - 1934**
**Album:** Released '88, on GNP Crescendo (USA) by GNP Crescendo Records (USA). Catalogue no: **GNPS 9031**

**DJANGO - 1935**
**Cass:** Released '88, on GNP Crescendo (USA) by GNP Crescendo Records (USA). Catalogue no: **GNP5 9023**
**Album:** Released '88, on GNP Crescendo (USA) by GNP Crescendo Records (USA). Catalogue no: **GNPS 9023**

**DJANGO - 1937-39**
**Album:** Released Jan '88, on Swaggie (Australia) Catalogue no: **S 1400**

**DJANGO - 1943-50**
**Album:** Released Jan '88, on Swaggie (Australia) Catalogue no: **S 1401**

**DJANGO ET COMPAGNIE**
**Album:** Released Oct '82, on Polydor (France) by Polydor Ltd. Catalogue no: **2489 188**

**DJANGO REINHARDT**
**CD:** Released '85, on EMI by EMI Records. Deleted Jan '90. Catalogue no: **CDP 748 451 2**

**DJANGO REINHARDT, 1934-53**
Note: With the Hotclub Quintette, featuring Coleman Hawkins & Rex Stewart.
**Album:** Released May '88, on Musica Jazz Catalogue no: **2MJP 1052**

**DJANGO REINHARDT (1936-37)**
**Album:** Released Jan '83, on Swaggie (Australia) Catalogue no: **S 1399**

**DJANGO REINHARDT 1910-1953**
Tracks: / Stardust / From you / Rendezvous sous la pluie / I'se a muggin' / After you're gone / Georgia on my mind / In the still of the night / Charlston / Solitude / Ain't misbehavin' / Mystery Pacific / Honeysuckle Rose / Hangin' around Boudon / St. Louis blues / Daphne / Bill Coleman blues / Minor swing / Viper's dream / Taj Mahal / Montmartre / Nuages / Swing 42 / Manoir de mes reves / Djangology / Echoes of France (La Marseillaise).
**CD:** Released Sep '88, on EMI-Manhattan by EMI Records. Catalogue no: **CDP 790 560 2**
**CD:** Released Sep '88, on EMI-Manhattan by EMI Records. Catalogue no: **CZ 135**

**DJANGO REINHARDT AU CLUB**
**Album:** Released '88, on Vogue (France) by Vogue Records. Catalogue no: **502011**

**DJANGO REINHARDT BOX SET, THE**
Tracks: / I'se a muggin' / I can't give you anything but love / Oriental shuffle / After you've gone / Are you in the mood? / Limehouse blues / Nagasaki / Swing guitars / Georgia on my mind / Shine / In the still of the night / Sweet chorus / Exactly like you / Charleston / You're driving me crazy / Tears / Solitude / Hot lips / Ain't misbehavin' / Rose room / Body and soul / When day is done / Runnin' wild / Chicago / Liebestraum No 3 / Miss Annabelle Lee / Little love, a little kiss, A / Mystery Pacific / In a sentimental mood / Sheik of Araby, The / Improvisation / Parfum / Alabamy bound / Crazy rhythm / Honeysuckle rose / Out of nowhere / Sweet Georgia Brown / Bugle call rag / Between the Devil and the deep blue sea / I got rhythm / Sweet Sue / Hangin' around Boudon / Japanese sandman / St. Louis blues / Bouncin' around / Eddie's blues / Lady be good / Dinah / Daphne / You took advantage of me / I've found a new baby / I ain't got nobody / Baby, won't you please come home? / Big boy blues / Bill Coleman blues / Somebody loves me / I can't believe that you're in love with me / Concerto in D Minor - first movement / Fiddle blues / Swingin' with Django / Paramount stomp / Bolero de Django / Mabel / My serenade / You rascal you / Stephen's blues / Sugar / Tea for two / Blues / Easy going / College stomp / Harlem swing / It had to be you / I'm coming, Virginia / Farewell blues / Blue light blues / Montmartre / Low cotton / Finesse / I know that you know / Solid old man / Stockholm / Younger generation, The / I'll see you in my dreams / Echoes of Spain / Naguine / At Jimmy's bar / Rhythme futur / Begin the beguine / Indecision / Swing 41 / Nuages / Pour

vous (exactly like you) / Fantaisie sur une dance Norvegienne / Vendredi 13 / Liebesfreud / Petit mesonges (Little white lies) / Les yeux noirs / Swing de Paris / Oiseaux des isles / All of me / Belleville / Lentement, Mademoiselle / Douce ambiance / Manoir de mes reves / Oui / Fleur d'ennui / Blues Clair / Improvisation no.3 (part 1) / Improvisation no.3 (part 2) / If dreams come true / Stompin' at the Savoy / Hallelujah / How high the moon / Djangology / Coquette / Django's tiger / Embraceable you / Echoes of France (La Marseillaise) / R-vingt-six / Lover man / Blue Lou / Swing dynamique / Festival 48 / Brick top / Time on my hands / Blue skies.
**LP Set:** Released Dec '81, on World Records by EMI Records. Catalogue no: **ALBUM 64**
**Cass set:** Released Dec '81, on World Records by EMI Records. Catalogue no: **CASSETTE 64**
**Cass set:** Released Jan '85, on Pathe Marconi (France) Catalogue no: **PM 1728839**
**LP Set:** Released '87, on Charly by Charly Records. Catalogue no: **BOX 107**
**LP Set:** Released Jan '85, on Pathe Marconi (France) Catalogue no: **PM 1728833**

**DJANGO REINHARDT COLLECTION (20 GOLDEN GREATS)**
**CD:** Released Oct '89, on Collection by K-Tel Records. Catalogue no: **OR 0062**
**Cass:** Released '86, on Deja Vu Catalogue no: **DVMC 2067**
**CD:** Released Jun '88, on Deja Vu Catalogue no: **DVCD 2067**
**Album:** Released '86, on Deja Vu Catalogue no: **DVLP 2067**

**DJANGO REINHARDT COLLECTION, Vol. 2**
**CD:** Released Oct '89, on Collection by K-Tel Records. Catalogue no: **OR 0074**

**DJANGO REINHARDT AND QUINTET OF HOT CLUB OF FRANCE Vol. 1 (Reinhardt, Django & Quintet of Hot Club of France)**
**Album:** Released Jan '83, on Swaggie (Australia) Catalogue no: **S 1305**
**Album:** Released Jan '83, on Swaggie (Australia) Catalogue no: **S 1306**
**Album:** Released Jan '83, on Swaggie (Australia) Catalogue no: **S 1389**

**DJANGO REINHARDT, VOL 1**
Tracks: / Daphne / Tears / Dinah / Tiger rag / Them there eyes / Improvisation / Uptown blues / Clair de Lune / Lentement Mademoiselle / Melodie au Crepuscule / How high the moon / Manoir de mes Reves / Danse nuptiale / I can't give you anything but love.
**Album:** Released Jan '82, on Jazz Reactivation Catalogue no: **JR 119**

**DJANGO REINHARDT WITH STEPHANE GRAPPELLI (Reinhardt, Django & Stephane Grappelli)**
**Album:** Released Jan '83, on Swaggie (Australia) Catalogue no: **S 1371**

**DJANGO REINHARDT AND THE QUINTET OF THE HOT CLUB OF FRANCE**
**Album:** Released Jan '85, on Musidisc by Musidisc Records (France). Catalogue no: **ALB 322**

**DJANGO REINHARDT AND STEPHANE GRAPPELLI (Reinhardt, Django and Stephane Grappelli)**
**CD:** Released Dec '86, on Vogue by Vogue Records. Catalogue no: **VG 600 121**

**DJANGO RHYTHM**
**Album:** Released Jan '83, on Swaggie (Australia) Catalogue no: **S 1251**

**DJANGO SWING**
**Album:** Released Jan '83, on Swaggie (Australia) Catalogue no: **S 1252**

**DJANGO AND THE QUINTET OF THE HOT CLUB OF FRANCE (Reinhardt, Django & Quintet of Hot Club of France (1936-37))**
**Album:** Released '88, on GNP Crescendo (USA) by GNP Crescendo Records (USA). Catalogue no: **GNPS 9019**

**DJANGOLOGY**
Tracks: / After you've gone / Limehouse blues / Nagasaki / Honeysuckle rose / Crazy rhythm / Out of nowhere / Chicago / Georgia on my mind / Shine / Sweet Georgia Brown / Bugle call rag / Between the devil and the deep blue sea / Exactly like you / Charleston / You're driving me crazy / Farewell blues / I got rhythm / I know that you know / Ain't misbehavin' / Rose room / Japanese sandman / Swing guitars / Minor swing / Nuages.

Note: Featuring Coleman Hawkins, Benny Carter, Dicky Wells.
**Album:** Released Sep '87, on Giants of Jazz by Hasmick Promotions. Catalogue no: **LPJT 8**
**CD:** Released '88, on Giants of Jazz by Hasmick Promotions. Catalogue no: **GOJCD 0219**

**DJANGOLOGY 49**
Tracks: / World is waiting for the sunrise, The / Hallelujah / I'll never be the same / Honeysuckle rose / All the things you are / Djangology / Daphne / Beyond the sea (le mer) / Lover man / Marie / Minor swing / Ou est tu mon amour / Swing 42 / After you've gone / I got rhythm / I saw stars / Heavy artillery (artillerie lourde) / It's only a paper moon / Bricktop.
**CD:** Released Apr '90, on RCA by BMG Records (UK). Catalogue no: **ND 90448**
**Cass:** Released Apr '90, on RCA by BMG Records (UK). Catalogue no: **NK 90448**
**Album:** Released Apr '90, on RCA by BMG Records (UK). Catalogue no: **NL 90448**

**DJANGOLOGY, VOL 1**
**Album:** Released '83, on EMI (France) by EMI Records. Catalogue no: **2C 054 16001**

**DJANGOLOGY, VOL 2**
**Album:** Released '83, on EMI (France) by EMI Records. Catalogue no: **2C 054 16002**

**DJANGOLOGY, VOL 3**
**Album:** Released '83, on EMI (France) by EMI Records. Catalogue no: **2C 054 16003**

**DJANGOLOGY, VOL 4**
**Album:** Released '83, on EMI (France) by EMI Records. Catalogue no: **2C 054 16004**

**DJANGOLOGY, VOL 5**
**Album:** Released '83, on EMI (France) by EMI Records. Catalogue no: **2C 054 16005**

**DJANGOLOGY, VOL 6**
**Album:** Released '83, on EMI (France) by EMI Records. Catalogue no: **2C 054 16006**

**DJANGOLOGY, VOL 7**
**Album:** Released '83, on EMI (France) by EMI Records. Catalogue no: **2C 054 16007**

**DJANGOLOGY, VOL 8**
**Album:** Released '83, on EMI (France) by EMI Records. Catalogue no: **2C 054 16008**

**DJANGOLOGY, VOL 9**
**Album:** Released '83, on EMI (France) by EMI Records. Catalogue no: **2C 054 16009**

**DJANGOLOGY, VOL 10**
**Album:** Released '83, on EMI (France) by EMI Records. Catalogue no: **2C 054 16010**

**DJANGOLOGY, VOL 11**
**Album:** Released '83, on EMI (France) by EMI Records. Catalogue no: **2C 054 16011**

**DJANGOLOGY, VOL 12**
**Album:** Released '83, on EMI (France) by EMI Records. Catalogue no: **2C 054 16012**

**DJANGOLOGY, VOL 13**
**Album:** Released '83, on EMI (France) by EMI Records. Catalogue no: **2C 054 16013**

**DJANGOLOGY, VOL 14**
**Album:** Released '83, on EMI (France) by EMI Records. Catalogue no: **2C 054 16014**

**DJANGOLOGY, VOL 15**
**Album:** Released '83, on EMI (France) by EMI Records. Catalogue no: **2C 054 16015**

**DJANGOLOGY, VOL 16**
**Album:** Released '83, on EMI (France) by EMI Records. Catalogue no: **2C 054 16016**

**DJANGOLOGY, VOL 17**
**Album:** Released '83, on EMI (France) by EMI Records. Catalogue no: **2C 054 16017**

**DJANGOLOGY, VOL 18**
**Album:** Released '83, on EMI (France) by EMI Records. Catalogue no: **2C 054 16018**

**DJANGOLOGY, VOL 19**
**Album:** Released '83, on EMI (France)

by EMI Records. Catalogue no: **2C 054 16019**

**DJANGOLOGY, VOL 20**
**Album:** Released '83, on EMI (France) by EMI Records. Catalogue no: **2C 054 16020**

**DJANGOLOGY / USA (Reinhardt, Django & Quintet of Hot Club of France (1936-37))**
**CD Set:** Released Jan '89, on DRG (USA) by DRG Records (USA). Catalogue no: **CDSW 8421/8422**

**DJANGOLOGY / USA, VOL 2 (Reinhardt,Django & Quintet of Hot Club of France (1936-37))**
**CD Set:** Released Jan '89, on DRG (USA) by DRG Records (USA). Catalogue no: **CDSW 8424/8425**

**DJANGOLOGY / USA VOLS 1-7 (Reinhardt, Django & The Quintet of the Hot Club of France)**
**LP Set:** Released Aug '88, on DRG (USA) by DRG Records (USA). Catalogue no: **SW 8420/26**

**DJANGO'S CASTLE**
Tracks: / Minor swing / Manoir de mes reve (Django's castle) / Saw star (I) / Nuages / Swing guitars / Artillerie lourde / Djangology / Daphne / After you've gone / Swing 42 / Bricktop / Honeysuckle rose.
**Album:** Released '86, on RCA by BMG Records (UK). Deleted Jul '89. Catalogue no: **CL 70907**
**Cass:** Released '86, on RCA by BMG Records (UK). Deleted Jul '89. Catalogue no: **CK 70907**

**DOUBLE ALBUM**
Tracks: / Ma reguliere / Par correspondance / Rosetta / Limehouse blues / Nagasaki / Charleston / Runnin' wild / Improvisation / Honeysuckle rose / Eddie's blues / Bill Coleman blues / Minors swing.
**Album:** Released Jun '87, on Pathe Marconi (France) Catalogue no: **1568023**
**Cass:** Released Jun '87, on Pathe Marconi (France) Catalogue no: **1568029**

**ENREGISTREMENTS ORIGINAUX**
Tracks: / Improvisation / Honeysuckle rose / Eddie's blues (Eddie South Blues.) / Bill Coleman blues / Minor's swing / Swingin' with Django / Christmas swing / I got rhythm / Younger generation / Tears / Swing 41 / Nuages / Les yeux noirs / La cigale et la fourmi / Belleville / Welcome (2e partie) / Ol' man river / Sweet Georgia Brown / Just a gigolo / Manoir de mes reves.
**CD:** Released Apr '87, on Pathe Marconi (France) Catalogue no: **746 501 2**

**ET LE QUINTETTE DU 'HOT CLUB DE FRANCE**
Tracks: / Ma reguliere / Par correspondance / Rossetta / Limehouse blues / Nagasaki / Charleston / Runnin' wild / Improvisation / Honeysuckle rose / Eddie's blues / Bill Coleman blues / Swingin' with Django / Minor's swing / Bolero / Christmas swing / I got rhythm / Younger generation / Tears / Swing 41 / Nuages / Les yeux noirs / La cigale et la fourmi / Belleville / Welcome / Ol' man river / Just a Gigolo / Manoir de mes reves.
**Album:** Released Dec '86, on Pathe Marconi (France) Catalogue no: **1568023**

**GOLDEN AGE OF DJANGO REINHARDT**
Tracks: / Nuages / Sweet Sue / Limehouse blues / Place de Broukere / Black eyes / Daphne / Mabel / Djangology / Swing '41 / Swing '42.
**Album:** Released Jul '83, on Golden Age by EMI Records. Catalogue no: **GX 2506**
**Cass:** Released Jul '83, on Golden Age by EMI Records. Catalogue no: **TC-GX 2506**

**I GOT RHYTHM**
Tracks: / I got rhythm / Crazy rhythm / My melancholy baby / Jeepers creepers / Sweet Georgia Brown / Honeysuckle rose / Liza / Nauges / Nuits de saint germain de press / Just one of those things / I cover the waterfront / I wonder where my baby is tonight.
Note: Collectors Edition series. Top session musicians.
**Album:** Released '86, on Meteor by Magnum Music Group. Catalogue no: **MTM 012**

**IMMORTAL DJANGO REINHARDT**
**Album:** Released '88, on GNP Crescendo (USA) by GNP Crescendo Records (USA). Catalogue no: **GNPS 9038**

**INDISPENSABLE DJANGO REINHARDT**
Tracks: / Minor swing / Beyond the sea / World is waiting for the sunrise, The / Django's castle / Dream of you / Menilmontant / It's only a paper moon / I saw stars / Nuages / Swing guitars / All the things you are / Tisket a tasket, A / September song / Heavy artillery (Artillerie lourde) / Improvisation / Djangology / Daphne / I'll never be the same / Marie / Jersey bounce / I surrender dear / Hallelujah / Anniversary song / After you've gone / Swing 42 / Stormy weather / Brick top / Lover man / I got rhythm / Honeysuckle rose / St. Louis blues.
**2 LP Set:** Released '83, on RCA (France) by BMG Records (France). Catalogue no: **PM 45362**
**Cass:** Released '86, on Jazz Tribune by BMG Records (UK). Deleted May '89. Catalogue no: **NK 70929**
**2 LP Set:** Released '86, on Jazz Tribune by BMG Records (UK). Deleted Nov '88. Catalogue no: **NL 70929**

**INEDITS VOL.1**
**Album:** Released '88, on Vogue (France) by Vogue Records. Catalogue no: **502010**

**INEDITS VOL 2**
**Album:** Released Jan '85, on Vogue by Vogue Records. Catalogue no: **VOGUE 502011**

**JAZZ TIME VOL.13**
**Album:** Released '88, on Vogue (France) by Vogue Records. Catalogue no: **502713**

**LA GRANDE PARADE**
**2 LP Set:** Released Oct '88, on Vogue by Vogue Records. Catalogue no: **400005**

**LE DISQUE D'OR**
**Album:** Released Oct '88, on Vogue (France) by Vogue Records. Catalogue no: **509031**

**LE DOUBLE DISQUE D'OR**
**2 LP Set:** Released Oct '88, on Vogue by Vogue Records. Catalogue no: **416003**

**LEGENDARY DJANGO REINHARDT**
**Album:** Released '88, on GNP Crescendo (USA) by GNP Crescendo Records (USA). Catalogue no: **GNPS 9039**

**LERE PUBLICATION**
**2 LP Set:** Released Oct '88, on Vogue by Vogue Records. Catalogue no: **406505**

**L'INOUBLIABLE**
**LP Set:** Released Oct '88, on Vogue by Vogue Records. Catalogue no: **000315**

**MASTERS OF JAZZ**
**Album:** Released '83, on RCA (Germany) Catalogue no: **CL 42342**

**NUAGES**
**Album:** Released Nov '88, on Vogue by Vogue Records. Catalogue no: **500100**
**Album:** Released Nov '84, on Astan (USA) Catalogue no: **20102**
**CD:** Released 10 Jul '89, on Vogue by Vogue Records. Catalogue no: **VG 670205**
**Cass:** Released Nov '84, on Astan (USA) Catalogue no: **40102**

**PARIS 1945' DJANGO REINHARDT**
Tracks: / If dreams come true / Stompin' at the Savoy / Hallelujah / How high the moon / Hommage a Fats Waller / Hommage a Debussy / After you've gone / Shoemaker's apron / China boy / Sugar / Don't blame me / Poor Miss Black.
**Album:** Released Dec '86, on Avan-Guard Catalogue no: **BVL 046**

**PARISIAN SWING**
**Album:** Released '88, on GNP Crescendo (USA) by GNP Crescendo Records (USA). Catalogue no: **GNPS 9002**

**RHYTHM IS OUR BUSINESS (Reinhardt, Django & Stephane Grappelli)**
Tracks: / Jeepers creepers / Sweet Sue / Noel brings the swing / Jive bomber / Dinah / Chasing shadows / Some of these days / Believe it, beloved / Clouds / Japanese sandman / Twelfth year / Au revoir / Stardust / Avalon / Swing '39 / I never knew.
Note: Recorded in Paris and London between 1935 and 1943.
**Album:** Released Nov '82, on Rock Echoes by Decca Records. Catalogue no: **TAB 55**
**Cass:** Released Nov '82, on Rock Echoes by Decca Records. Catalogue no: **KTBC 55**

**ROME 1949 Vol. 1 (Reinhardt, Django/Stephane Grappelli)**
**Album:** Released '88, on Swaggie (Australia) Catalogue no: **S 1390**

**ROME 1949 Vol. 2**
**Album:** Released '88, on Swaggie (Australia) Catalogue no: **S 1391**

**ROME SESSIONS, 1949-50: VOL 1**
Tracks: / Waiting for the sunrise / Hallelujah / I'll never be the same / Honeysuckle rose / All the things you are / Daphne / La mer / Lover man / Marie / Anniversary song / Stormy weather / Russian songs medley / Jersey bounce / Sophisticated lady / Dream of you / Darktown strutters' ball / Royal Garden blues (With Stephane Grappelli and Andre Ekyan.).
Note: With Stephane Grappelli, Andre Ekyan.
**CD:** Released Oct '87, on RCA by BMG Records (UK). Deleted Jul '89. Catalogue no: **PD 71297**

**ROME SESSIONS, 1949-50: VOL 2**
Tracks: / Minor swing / Ou es tu, mon amour? / Swing '42 / I surrender, dear / After you've gone / I got rhythm / I saw stars / Artillerie lourde / It's only a paper moon / Bricktop / Improvisation / Menilmontant / Swing guitars / Nuages / Tisket a tasket, A / Manoir de mes reves / September song / St. Louis blues.
Note: With Stephane Grappelli, Andre Ekyan.
**CD:** Released Oct '87, on RCA by BMG Records (UK). Deleted Jul '89. Catalogue no: **PD 71298**

**RHYTHM FUTURE (Radio Sessions - 1947)**
**Album:** Released Oct '88, on Vogue by Vogue Records. Catalogue no: **500108**

**SAME (Reinhardt, Django/Stephane Grappelli)**
**Cass:** Released Feb '85, on Decca by Decca International. Catalogue no: **KACC 1158**

**SOUVENIRS (Reinhardt, Django and Stephane Grappelli)**
Tracks: / Honeysuckle Rose / Night and day / Sweet Georgia Brown / Souvenirs / My sweet / Liza (all the clouds will roll away) / Stomping at Decca / Love's melody / Daphne / Lambeth walk / Nuages / H.C.Q. Strut / Man I love, The / Improvisation no.2 / Undecided / Please be kind / Nocturne / I've got my love to keep me warm / Louise / Don't worry 'bout me.
Note: Over 55 minutes of brilliance from the celebrated jazz guitarist Django Reinhardt, his violin-playing colleague Stephane Grappelli and their Quintet Of The Hot Club Of France.
Twenty recordings drawn from various Decca sessions of 1938, '39 and '46 many original compositions from the masters mingle freely with interpretaions from the songbooks of such as Cole Porter, George and Ira Gershwin and Irving Berlin.
Former Oscar Rabin vocalist Beryl Davis adds her contributions.
**CD:** Released Jun '88, on London Records. by London Records Ltd. Catalogue no: **829 591 2**
**CD:** Released Jun '88, on London Records by London Records Ltd. Catalogue no: **820 591-2**

**STRUTTIN' OUT (Reinhardt, Django & Stephane Grappelli)**
Tracks: / HCQ strut / Nuages / It don't mean a thing / I wonder where my baby is tonight / It was so beautiful / Them there eyes / Limehouse blues / Some of these days / Appel direct / I've found a new baby / Undecided / Improvisation no.2 / I've got my love to keep me warm / Chasing shadows / Swing '39 / If I had you / Don't worry 'bout me / My sweet / Duke and Dukie / Believe it, beloved / China boy / I've had my moments / Ultra fox / Del Salle / St. Louis blues / Nocturne / Songe d'automne / Moonglow / Just one of those things / Black and white / Sweet Georgia Brown / It had to be you / Daphne / Lambeth walk / Night and day / Liza.
**2 LP Set:** Released Jul '84, on Decca by Decca International. Deleted '88. Catalogue no: **DPA 3098**

**SWING FROM PARIS (Reinhardt, Django and Stephane Grappelli)**
Tracks: / Miss Annabelle Lee / Chasing shadows / Stomping at Decca / Solitude / ppel direct / J'attendrai / After you've gone / Nagasaki / Night and day / Avalon / Runnin' wild / Djangology / Shine / Sweet chorus / Them there eyes / Some of these days / If I had you / Three little words / Little love, a little kiss, A / Swing from Paris.
**CD:** Released '89, on Conifer Happy Days by Conifer Records. Catalogue no: **CDHD 165**
**Cass:** Released '89, on Conifer Happy Days by Conifer Records. Catalogue no: **MCHD 165**
**Album:** Released '89, on Conifer Happy Days by Conifer Records. Catalogue no: **CHD 165**

**SWINGING WITH DJANGO**
**Album:** Released Jan '83, on Swaggie (Australia) Catalogue no: **S 1370**

**TOGETHER (Reinhardt, Django, Stephane Grappelli and Eddie South)**
**Cass:** Released Dec '84, on Pathe Marconi (France) Catalogue no: **2M 256 78140**
**Album:** Released Dec '84, on Pathe Marconi (France) Catalogue no: **2M 056 78140**

**VERSATILE GIANT, THE**
**Album:** Released Oct '88, on Vogue by Vogue Records. Catalogue no: **500064**

## Reiser, Harry

**BANJO CRACKERJAX 1922-30**
**Album:** Released Dec '88, on Yazoo (USA) by Shanachie Records (USA). Catalogue no: **YAZOO 1048**

**BANJO VIRTUOSO Vol. 2**
**Album:** Released Jan '88, on Broadway (USA) Catalogue no: **BR 152**

## Reisman, Joe

**PARTY NIGHT AT JOE'S (Reisman, Joe & His Orchestra)**
**Album:** Released Feb '88, on Fresh Sounds (Spain) by Fresh Sounds Records (Spain). Catalogue no: **FS 180**

## Remue, Charles

**CHARLES REMUE & THE NEW STOMPER ORCHESTRA 1927**
**Album:** Released Apr '79, on Fountain by Retrieval Records. Catalogue no: **FG 401**

## Renaud, Henri, Et Son

**NEW SOUND AT THE 'BEOUF SUR LE TOIT**
**Album:** Released 7 Nov '87, on Fresh Sounds (Spain) by Fresh Sounds Records (Spain). Catalogue no: **FS 262**

## Rendell, Don

**EARTH MUSIC**
Tracks: / Genesis jump / Meridian mango / Land lovers / Seven sea rock / Blues tones / Tenor firma / Strata dance / Ground finale.
**Album:** Released '83, on Spotlite by Spotlite Records. Catalogue no: **SPJ 515**

**JUST MUSIC (Rendell, Don & Barbara Thompson)**
Tracks: / Wensleydale suite / Well, make it up / Sands of time / Blues for Adolphe Sax / Penta gone / Gab and Ben / Out of my window / Mina impact.
Note: Don Rendell, soprano, tenor saxes, clarinet, flute; Barbara Thompson, soprano, tenor saxes, flute; Pete Lemer, piano, electric piano; Steve Cook, bass, bass guitar; Laurie Allan, drums.
**Album:** Released '83, on Spotlite by Spotlite Records. Catalogue no: **SPJ 502**

**LIVE AT THE AVGARDE GALLERY (Rendell, Don & Joe Palin Trio)**
Tracks: / On the way / Euphrates / I can't get started / Antibes / Summer song.
Note: Don Rendell, soprano, tenor saxes, flute; Joe Palin, piano; Ian Taylor, bass; Gordon Beckett, drums. Pete Martin guests on trumpet and flugelhorn.
**Album:** Released '83, on Spotlite by Spotlite Records. Catalogue no: **SPJ 501**

**SET 2 (Rendell, Don Five)**
Tracks: / Becclesology / Devon dance / Waltz / It could've happened to you / Unicorn.
Note: Don Rendell, Alan Wakeman, reeds, flute; Pete Saberton, piano, electric piano; Paul Bridge, bass; Trevor Tompkins, drums.
**Album:** Released '33, on Spotlite by Spotlite Records. Catalogue no: **SPJ 516**

**TIME PRESENCE (Rendell, Don Quartet)**
Tracks: / Time presence.
**7" Single:** Released May '89, on DR

Catalogue no: **DR 101**

## Return of Jazz for Absolute..

**RETURN OF JAZZ FOR ABSOLUTE BEGINNERS (Various artists)**
Tracks: / Your feet's too big: *Waller, Fats & his Rhythm* / Boogie woogie man: *Ammons, Albert & Pete Johnson* / Conga brava: *Ellington, Duke* / Pick-a-rib (part 1): *Goodman, Benny Quintet* / Subtle slough: *Stewart, Rex* / Whoa babe: *Hampton, Lionel* / I got it bad (and that ain't good): *Ellington, Duke* (Featuring Ivy Anderson.) / Scat song, The: *Calloway, Cab/his Cotton Club Orchestra* / Rock it for me: *Page, Hot Lips* / Bach goes to town: *Goodman, Benny & His Orchestra* / Crawl, The: *Allen, Henry 'Red'* / Riffin' at the 24th Street: *Jacquet, Illinois* / Night in Tunisia: *Gillespie, Dizzy* / Solitude: *Various artists.*
**Album:** Released Jan '87, on RCA by BMG Records (UK). Catalogue no: **NL 89964**
**Cass:** Released Jan '87, on RCA by BMG Records (UK). Catalogue no: **NK 89964**

**RETURN OF MARTIN GUERRE (Original Soundtrack) (Various artists)**
Note: 2 scores by Michel Portal and Georges Delerue.

**Album:** Released '88, on DRG (USA) by DRG Records (USA). Catalogue no: **SL 9514**
**Cass:** Released '88, on DRG (USA) by DRG Records (USA). Catalogue no: **SLC 9514**

**RETURN OF ROCKAPHILLY (Various artists)**
Tracks: / Sixteen cats: *Wellington, Rusty* / Rock with me baby: *Coleman, Ray* / Rockin' jamboree: *Raye, Michael & Judy Shaye* / Wee willy waterdilly: *Keefer Sisters* / Jukebox cannonball: *Rogers, Jesse* / Go man go get gone: *Zario, Rex* / Rockin' in the nursery: *Starr, Sally* / I gotta go: *Rex, Al* / Jumpin' Jackie: *Lee, Jacky* / Buzz buzz buzz: *Satellites* / Philadelphia baby: *Hatcher, Ray* / Bitter tears: *Tanner Bros* / Bulldoggin' the steel: *Nastos, Nick* / I ain't a movin' on no more: *Wellington, Rusty* / Jump, jump honey: *Wellington, Rusty* / Rock chicken rock: *Coleman, Ray* / ABC rock: *Starr, Sally* / I'm rockin': *Coleman, Ray* / Toodle oo bamboo: *Coleman, Ray.*
**Album:** Released Sep '84, on Rollercoaster by Rollercoaster Records. Deleted '88. Catalogue no: **ROLL 2004**

**RETURN OF SUPERBAD (Various artists)**
**Cass:** Released Sep '88, on K-Tel by K-Tel Records. Catalogue no: **CE 2421**
**Album:** Released Sep '88, on K-Tel by K-Tel Records. Catalogue no: **NE 1421**
**CD:** Released Sep '88, on K-Tel by K-Tel Records. Catalogue no: **NCD 3421**

**RETURN OF THE BEAT MENACE (Various artists)**
**Album:** Released Mar '89, on Cheep Catalogue no: **CHEEP 006**

**RETURN OF THE JEDI (Various artists)**
**Cass:** Released Jul '83, on Disneyland by Disneyland-Vista Records (USA). Catalogue no: **D 155DC**
**CD:** Released May '83, on RSO (USA) by Polydor Ltd. Deleted Mar '88. Catalogue no: **811 767-2**
**Album:** Released Jul '83, on Disneyland by Disneyland-Vista Records (USA). Catalogue no: **D 455**
**Album:** Released May '83, on Polydor by Poiydor Ltd. Catalogue no: **POLD 5105**
**Cass:** Released May '83, on Polydor by Polydor Ltd. Catalogue no: **POLDC 5105**
**Cass:** Released Jul '83, on Disneyland by Disneyland-Vista Records (USA). Catalogue no: **D 160DC**
**Album:** Released Jul '83, on Disneyland by Disneyland-Vista Records (USA). Catalogue no: **D 460**

**RETURN OF THE LIVING DEAD (Film soundtrack) (Various artists)**
Tracks: / Surfin' dead: *Cramps* / Partytime (zombie version): *45 Grave* / Nothing for you: *Tsol* / Eyes without a face: *Flesh Eaters* / Burn the flames: *Erickson, Roky* / Dead beat dance: *Damned* / Take a walk: *Tall Boys* / Love under will: *Jet Black Berries* / Tonight (we'll make love until we die): *SSQ* / Trash's theme: *SSQ.*
**CD:** Released Jun '88, on Big Beat by Ace Records. Catalogue no: **CDWIK 38**
**LP Pic:** Released '88, on New Rose (1) by New Rose Records. Catalogue no: **ROSE 66P**
**Album:** Released Jun '85, on Big Beat by Ace Records. Catalogue no: **WIK 38**
**Cass:** Released Jun '85, on Big Beat by Ace Records. Catalogue no: **WIKC 38**

**RETURN OF THE LIVING DEAD (PART 2) (Various artists)**
Tracks: / Space hopper: *Cope, Julian* / I'm the man: *Anthrax* / Monster mash: *Big O* / AD 1: *Anthrax* / Dead return: *Robinson, J Peter* / High priest of love: *Mindwarp, Zodiac* / Big band boy: *Mantronix* / Alone in the night: *Leatherwolf* / Flesh to flesh: *Lamont.*
**Album:** Released 13 Feb '89, on Island by Island Records. Catalogue no: **ISTA 17**
**Cass:** Released 13 Feb '89, on Island by Island Records. Catalogue no: **ICT 17**
**CD:** Released 13 Feb '89, on Island by Island Records. Catalogue no: **CIDST 17**

**RETURN OF THE SOLDIER (Original soundtrack) (Various artists)**
**Album:** Released Apr '83, on T. E. R. by That's Entertainment Records. Catalogue no: **TER 1036**

## Rey, Alvino

**Biographical details:** Rey, Alvino was born in 1911 in California. The bandleader began as a guitarist, sideman in many bands, including Horace Heidt 1934-9, changed his name, formed his own band and took the popular King Sisters vocal group from Heidt (including his wife Louise). Rey gained respect for guitar work, often playing Hawaiian steel guitar in a non-corny manner; his opening theme *Blue Rey* was unique for a multiple-voice gimmick.
He played one-night gigs across USA; formed an excellent new band in 1942 using arrangements by Ray Conniff, Johnny Mandel, Billy May and Neal Hefti, but suffered a recording ban (musician's union strike).
The band had 10 brass; six saxes at one time including Al Cohn, Zoot Sims, Herbie Steward (later 3/4 of Woody Herman's famous 'Four Brothers'); He carried on with smaller line-ups to mid '60's with the King Family Show on TV. Documented on several albums on Hindsight label. (Donald Clarke 21.5.88).

**1946 (Rey, Alvino & His Orchestra)**
Tracks: / How high the moon / Bumble boogie / From the land of the sky blue water / You've got me crying again / April in Paris / Yesterdays / Dardanella / Hey frantic, relax / Stocking horse / Sheik of Araby / Just you, just me / Between the devil and the deep blue sea / Should I / Russian lullaby / High octane / Blue Lou.
**Album:** Released Oct '79, on London Records by London Records Ltd. Deleted '84. Catalogue no: **HMP 5057**

**1940/1 - VOL.3 (Rey, Alvino & His Orchestra)**
**Album:** Released Mar '84, on Hindsight Catalogue no: **HSR 196**

**ALVINO REY AND ORCHESTRA 1946 (Rey, Alvino & His Orchestra)**
Tracks: / How high the moon / Bumble boogie / Land of the sky blue water / You've got me crying again / April in Paris / Yesterdays / Dardanella / Stocking horse / Sheik of Araby / Just you, just me / Between the devil and the deep blue sea / Should I / Russuan lullaby / Hey frantic, relax / High octane / Blue Lou.

Note: Guitarist Alvino Rey's first postwar band--19 strong--boasted an almost unbelievable roster of talent. Herbie Stewart, Al Cohn, Zoot Sims, Hal McCuisick, John Gruey, Bud Estes, Dean Kincaide, Jimmy Wise, Dave Bowman, Bob Swift, Sam Levine, Bob McReynolds, Johnny Mandel, Stan Fishelson, Jack Gerheim, Russ Granger, Roger Ellick, Chuck Peterson, Frank Nelson, Joe Mondragon, Eddie Robertson, Rocco Coluccio (Rocky Cole). Don Lammond and Jimmy Pratt are on this album, taken from two radio transcription dates. Dave Dexter, Jr. interviewed Rey and his wife Louise (of the King Sisters) for the comprehensive liner notes. (Hindsight Catalogue - 1989)
**Album:** Released '88, on Hindsight Catalogue no: **HSR 121**

**BIG BAND SOUNDS (Dance With Me)**
**Album:** Released May '89, on Alysa Records Catalogue no: **R 1000**

**Buddy Rich - Buddy Rich '47 - '48 (HEP)**

## Rhythm Makers

**RHYTHM MAKERS OF BUENOS AIRES 1938-1948 (Unissued titles)**
**Album:** Released Mar '89, on Harlequin by Interstate Music. Catalogue no: **HQ 2064**

## Rhythm Plus One

**RHYTHM PLUS ONE**
**Album:** Released Feb '88, on Fresh Sounds (Spain) by Fresh Sounds Records (Spain). Catalogue no: **FS 24**

## Rhythm Rascals

**CROWN JEWELS 1935-1936**
Tracks: / Temptation rag / Tiger rag / Nobodys sweetheart / Bugle call rag / Music goes round and around, The / Talking it over / Dinah / My sweetie went away / I'm tickled to death I'm me / When a lady meets a gentleman down south / Keep smilin' / Wah hoo!.
**Album:** Released Apr '88, on Harlequin by Interstate Music. Catalogue no: **HQ 3017**

## Rice, Rev. D.C.

**REV. D.C. RICE AND CONGREGATION**
**Album:** Released Dec '88, on Herwin by Shanachie Records (USA). Catalogue no: **HER 212**

**TRADITIONAL JAZZ & SANCTIFIED**
**Album:** Released '88, on Herwin by Shanachie Records (USA). Catalogue no: **HERWIN 212**

## Rich, Buddy

**Biographical details:** Drummer and bandleader Buddy Rich was born in 1917 in Brooklyn; he died in 1987. He was a child prodigy, working with his parents on stage at 18 months, soon known as Baby Traps. He was one of the best white drummers of the Swing Era, playing in the bands of Bunny Berigan, Harry James, Artie Shaw and Tommy Dorsey. Opinionated and with a flint-hard intelligence, he did not get along with Dorsey (nor with Frank Sinatra, though somehow they remained friends). After military sevice he rejoined Dorsey, then formed his own first band in 1945-7; he played with Norman Granz's touring Jazz at the Philharmonic, with Les Brown, Charlie Ventura and others; during the '50's he played with James and Dorsey again, led combos and was also a good singer; he contemplated giving up playing for singing and acting but always came back to music; he had his first heart attack in 1959 and came back with a keep fit regiment, acquiring a black belt in karate. He worked for James again from 1961 and formed his own big band in 1966; some thought he was crazy trying to run a big band, but he was a demanding boss, a hard worker and had international success with a brilliant band; his albums made the pop charts in the USA in the late '60's. He led a small group in 1974 but re-formed a band in 1975; after heart by-pass surgery in 1983 he ignored the doctors and was back at work in two months. his personality and flashy showmanship saw to it that many of his fans were the kind of people who talk through the music on the bandstand, but musicians were in awe of his skill. (Donald Clarke 21.5.88).

**47/48 (See adjacent panel)**
Tracks: / I've got news for you / Man could be such a wonderful thing, A / Good bait / Budella / Just you and me / I believe / What is this thing called love? / Little white lies / You go to my head / Queer Street / That's rich / Fine and dandy / I may be wrong / Robbins' nest.
Note: The swing era was notable for the emergence, among other things, of the star sideman. Very often the popularity of the sideman outstripped that of his employer and there were plenty of backers ready to set up new bands to meet the almost insatiable demand of the late thirties and early forties. Many of the new leaders did hit the jackpot, but after the war any sideman going out on his own could only be sure of glory, as the promoters and public taste had gone elsewhere. Buddy Rich had been a star attraction with various bands since 1938, and was now anxious to get started. But there was an obstacle in the form of a contract with Tommy Dorsey-the shrewdest boss of them all - and he was understandably keen to hold on to his pollwinning drummer. However, after some slanging and union wrangling TD relented, and with the famous Sinatra loan the Buddy Rich band was born. It went into rehearsal in November 1945 before opeing at the Terrace Room, Newark, N.J. From the outset the drummer was determined to follow a progressive policy, as was evident from the roster of contributing arrangers - Turk van Lake, Tad Dameron, Neal Hefti, Billy Moore jun and two ex-Boyd Raeburn writers came in as regular staffmen - Eddie Finckle and Johnny Mandel. Actually Fincle arrived via another dummer leader and it was charts like *Leave us leap* which had pointed Krupa into the modern era. The band had some forceful solists in tenormen George Berg and Mickey Rich who blew in the Ventura vein, and two other Raeburn refugees - Tommy Allison and Earl Swope. Stylistically the band was something of a hybrid, sometimes roaring like the first herd, other times using the swooping counterpoint of Raeburn, and the potent influence of Basie, Lunceford and Gillespie never far away.
The orchestra toured fairly successfully for about a year and then suddenly in January 1947 Rich called it a day and went out as a soloist with JATP. But within' weeks he was back in New York with Eddie Finckle putting it together again around a nucleus of the old band plus Allen Eager whose Lestorian sound and endless invention was the outstanding solo voice. The ensemble sound had become distinctly cooler anticipating the send herd and at times even evoking a Thornhill sound. Al Cohn later replaced Eager, and the Swope brothers followed each other in and out

of the trombone section throughout the year. Then around October yet another link with the Raeburn era appeared in the formidable talent of George Handy who took over the piano spot from Harvey Leonard. he may also have done some writing for the band but details of this possibility are hard to find. Details of the band's progress through 1948 are also hard to come by other than the inclusion of Terry Gibbs on vibes, and Jimmy Giuffre came in a chief arranger. Conterporary music publications carried stories that Rich had decided to bend to commercial pressures and play more ballads, but apart from the frequently muted brass and generously featured vibes the jazz content remained high.

The music on this disc covers the period from the reformed 1947 orchestra to the edition which appeared at the Hollywood Palladium in the summer of 1948.
The first three tracks are V-disc performances, two of which, *Good bait* and *I've got new* have never been issued before. There are solo spots from Allen Eager on *I believe* and *Just you*, while *What is this thing* contains some Thornhill-like moments and fine muted trumpet from the late Tommy Allison. The second side has selections from Palladium engagement with solos from an unusually restrained Terry Gibbs and a stand-out Jimmy Munday arrangement of Basie's *Queer Street*.
As a bonus there are two combo tracks with some crackling Shavers trumpet and Ella scatting on one, and an engaging vocal duo of Rich and Ella at a 1947 WNEW Swing Session. These performances are proof of the drummer's earlier search for a band style of his own, and if he just failed in this, he succeeded in leaving some memorable attempts. (Alastair Robertson)
**Album:** Released Apr '81, on Hep Jazz by Hep Records. Catalogue no: **HEP 12**

**AT RONNIE SCOTT'S (Rich, Buddy & His Orchestra)**
Tracks: / Moments notice / St. Mark's Square / Little train / Time being / Word / Dancing men / In a mellow tone / Two bass hit.
**Album:** Released Jul '80, on RCA by BMG Records (UK). Deleted Jul '85. Catalogue no: **INTS 5012**

**BACK TO BACK (Rich, Buddy & Gene Krupa)**
**Cass set:** Released '88, on Ditto by Pickwick Records. Catalogue no: **DTO 10222**

**BUDDY AND SOUL**
**Album:** Released '89, on Beat Goes On by Andy's Records. Catalogue no: **BGOLP 23**

**BUDDY RICH**
**CD:** Released Jul '89, on Cleo Catalogue no: **CLCD 5010**
**Cass:** Released 27 Feb '88, on Verve Catalogue no: **833 295-4**
**CD:** Released Mar '88, on Verve Catalogue no: **833 295-2**

**BUDDY RICH AT RONNIE SCOTT'S**
Tracks: / Moments notice / St. Marks Square (a special day) / Little train / Time being / Milestones / Word, The / Dancing men / In a mellow tone / Two bass hit.
**Cass:** Released May '84, on RCA by BMG Records (UK). Deleted Jul '89. Catalogue no: **NK 89339**
**Album:** Released May '84, on RCA by BMG Records (UK). Deleted Jul '89. Catalogue no: **NL 89339**

**BUDDY RICH BAND (Rich, Buddy Band)**
Tracks: / Never can say goodbye / Fantasy / Listen here goes funky / Slo-funk / Good news / Beulah witch.
**Album:** Released Jul '87, on MCA (Import) by MCA Records. Deleted Jan '88. Catalogue no: **IMCA 853**
**Cass:** Released Jul '87, on MCA (Import) by MCA Records. Deleted Jan '88. Catalogue no: **IMCAC 5853**
**CD:** Released Jun '88, on MCA (USA) by MCA Records (USA). Catalogue no: **31151**

**BUDDY RICH COLLECTION**
**CD:** Released Oct '89, on Collection by K-Tel Records. Catalogue no: **OR 0080**

**BUDDY RICH AND HIS GREATEST BAND (1946-47)**
**Album:** Released Jul '77, on First Heard by Submarine Records. Catalogue no: **FH 5**

**BUDDY RICH AND HIS ORCHESTRA (Rich, Buddy & His Orchestra)**
**Album:** Released Apr '81, on MCA by MCA Records. Catalogue no: **MCF 3101**

**BUDDY RICH PLAYS AND PLAYS AND PLAYS**
Tracks: / Ya gotta try / Time out / 'Round midnight / Tales of Rhoda rat / No jive / Lush life / Party time / Kong / Mickey Mouse mambo.
**Album:** Released '79, on RCA by BMG Records (UK). Deleted '84. Catalogue no: **PL 12273**

**COOL BREEZE**
Tracks: / Cool breeze / Carioca / Four rich brothers / Sunday kind of love, A / What is this thing called love? / Nellie's nightmare / Handicap / Mind my business / I cover the waterfront / Poor little rich kid / Goof and I, The / Let's blow / Poon Tang / Rags to Riches.
**Album:** Released May '88, on Big Band Era Catalogue no: **20128**
**Album:** Released Mar '85, on Astan (USA) Catalogue no: **F 20128**
**Cass:** Released May '88, on Big Band Era Catalogue no: **40128**

**EASE ON DOWN THE ROAD (Rich, Buddy Big Band)**
Tracks: / Time check / Backwoods sideman / Nuttville / Playhouse / Senator Sam / Big Mac / Three day sucker / Ease on down the road / Tommy (medley) / Pieces of dreams / Lush life / Nik-nik / Layin' it down.
**CD:** Released '88, on Denon Catalogue no: **DC-8511**
**Cass:** Released '88, on Denon Catalogue no: **MC 8511**

**EXCITING BUDDY RICH JAZZ**
**Album:** Released May '83, on RCA (Germany) Catalogue no: **CL 42786**

**GREAT MOMENTS - 1946**
**Album:** Released Jul '82, on Golden Era by Delta Records. Catalogue no: **GELP 15021**

**IN LONDON**
Tracks: / Moment's notice / Love story / Time being / That's enough / Dancing men / Milestones / In a mellow tone / St. Mark's Square / Two bass hit.
**Album:** Released May '83, on RCA (France) by BMG Records (France). Catalogue no: **PL 43695**

**JAZZ OFF THE AIR VOL. 5 (Cinch, The) (Rich, Buddy Quintet)**
Tracks: / Four / If I were a bell / In a prescribed manner / Cinch, The / I don't wanna be kissed / Everyday / Our delight.
Note: Live performances from Birdland, featuring Sonny Criss, Ola Hannson, Kenny Drew, Phil Leshin and Buddy Rich.
**Album:** Released May '83, on Spotlite by Spotlite Records. Catalogue no: **SPJ 149**

**KEEP THE CUSTOMER SATISFIED (Rich, Buddy Big Band)**
Tracks: / Keep the customer satisfied / Long days journey / Midnight cowboy / He quit me man / Everybody's talkin' / Tears and joys / Celebration.
**Album:** Released Oct '86, on Liberty by EMI Records. Deleted Aug '89. Catalogue no: **EMS 1187**
**Cass:** Released Oct '86, on Liberty by EMI Records. Deleted Aug '89. Catalogue no: **TCEMS 1187**

**LIONEL HAMPTON PRESENTS BUDDY RICH (Rich, Buddy & Lionel Hampton)**
Tracks: / Moment's notice / Giant steps / Buddy's Cherokee / Take the 'A' train / I'll never be the same / Latin silk / Buddy's rock (CD only.) / My funny valentine (CD only.).
Note: With Lionel Hampton / Steve Marcus / Barry Kiener / Candido and others.
**Cass:** Released '89, on Kingdom Jazz by Kingdom Records. Catalogue no: **CGATE 7011**
**Album:** Released Sep '83, on Kingdom Jazz by Kingdom Records. Catalogue no: **GATE 7011**
**CD:** Released Jun '87, on Kingdom Jazz by Kingdom Records. Catalogue no: **CDGATE 7011**

**MAN FROM PLANET JAZZ, THE**
Tracks: / Beulah witch / Grand concourse / Blues a la 88 / Saturday night / Slow funk / Good news.
**Album:** Released Jan '81, on PRT by Castle Communications Records. Deleted '85. Catalogue no: **NSLP 18620**

**RICH AND FAMOUS**
Tracks: / Red snapper / Time will tell / Ballad of the matador / Dancing man /

Cottontain / One and only love / Manhattan-the city / Manhattan-central park.
**Cass:** Released Nov '86, on Meteor by Magnum Music Group. Catalogue no: **MTC 004**
**Album:** Released Nov '86, on Meteor by Magnum Music Group. Catalogue no: **MTLP 004**

**RICH RIOT (Rich, Buddy & His Orchestra)**
Tracks: / Theme quiet riot / Day by day / Nellie's nightmare / Great moments / Daily double / Just a sittin and a rockin / Rags to riches / Goof and I, The / Man could be such a wonderful thing, A / Little handicap, A.
**Cass:** Released May '87, on First Heard by Submarine Records. Catalogue no: **CFH 27**
**Album:** Released May '87, on First Heard by Submarine Records. Catalogue no: **FH 27**

**THIS ONE'S FOR BASIE**
Tracks: / Blue and sentimental / Down for double / Jump for me / Blues for Basie / Jumpin' at the woodside / Ain't it the truth / Shorty George / 9.20 Special.
**CD:** Released Nov '86, on Polydor by Polydor Ltd. Deleted Jul '88. Catalogue no: **817 788-2**

**TIME BEING: THE AMAZING BUDDY RICH**
Tracks: / Paul's tune / Chelsea Bridge / Straight, no chaser / Dancing men / Little train / Two bass hit / Time being / Best coast / Space shuffle / Sassy strut.
**CD:** Released Apr '88, on Bluebird (2) by BMG Records (UK). Catalogue no: **ND 86459**

**TOGETHER AGAIN - FOR THE FIRST TIME (Rich, Buddy & Mel Torme)**
Tracks: / When I found you / Here's that rainy day / Blues in the night / Bluesette / You are the sunshine of my life / I won't last a day without you / Oh lady be good.
**Album:** on RCA by BMG Records (UK). Catalogue no: **PL 25178**

**TUFF DUDE**
Tracks: / Donna Lee / Chameleon / Second Avenue blue / Jumpin' at the woodside / Sierra lonely / Nica's dream / Billie's bounce.
Note: Personnel: Buddy Rich (drums), Sonny Fortune (alto / soprano saxes), Sal Nastico (tenor sax), Kenny Barron & Mike Abene (piano), Jack Wilkins (guitar), Anthony Jackson (bass), Jimmy Maeulen (percussion).
**CD:** Released '88, on Denon Catalogue no: **C38-7972**
**CD:** Released Apr '89, on Denon Catalogue no: **DC 8543**
**Cass:** Released Apr '89, on Denon Catalogue no: **MC 7972**

## Richards, Johnny

**AIJALON (Richards, Johnny & His Orchestra)**
Tracks: / Waltz anyone? / For all we know / Dimples / Band aide / Turn about / Burrito borracho / Long ago and far away / Aijalon.
Note: All-star band with Maynard Ferguson, Charlie Mariano, Richie Kamuca, Ronnie Lang, Bill Holman, Stu Williamson, Buddy Childers, Pete Candolini, Shorty Rogers, Vince De Rosa, John Cave, Frank Rosolino, Stan Levey, and Lou Singer.
**Album:** Released '88, on Discovery (USA) by Discovery Records (USA). Catalogue no: **DS 895**

**AQUI HABLA ESPANOL**
Tracks: / Long live fats / Nothing more / Brass hat / Silver blue / Little apple / Perfume jungle / I go / Fort outside Mexico city / Spanish drink.
**Album:** Released Jul '82, on Jazz Reactivation Catalogue no: **JR 148**

**ARRANGER'S TOUCH, THE**
Tracks: / Get me to the church on time / On the street where you live / I could have danced all night / Wouldn't it be loverly? / Show me / Rain in Spain, The / I've grown accustomed to her face / With a little bit of luck / Omo ado / Kele kele / La pecadora / Ochun / Oluo anu / Ofo.
**Cass set:** Released May '83, on Vogue Jazz (France) by Vogue Records. Catalogue no: **ZC VJD 566**
**2 LP Set:** Released May '83, on Vogue Jazz (France) by Vogue Records. Catalogue no: **VJD 566**

**JE VOUS ADORE (Richards, Johnny & His Orchestra)**
Tracks: / Concerto to end all concertos, Theme from the / What is there to say / How are things in Glocca Morra / This time / No moon at all.
**Album:** Released '88, on Discovery (USA) by Discovery Records (USA). Catalogue no: **DS 915**

**MY FAIR LADY - MY WAY (Richards, Johnny & His Orchestra)**
**Album:** Released Feb '88, on Fresh Sounds (Spain) by Fresh Sounds Records (Spain). Catalogue no: **FS 304**

**NO SQUARES ALLOWED**
**Album:** Released Aug '89, on Golden Era by Delta Records. Catalogue no: **GELP 15047**

**SOMETHING ELSE (Richards, Johnny & His Orchestra)**
Tracks: / Waltz anyone? / For all we know / Dimples / Band aside / Turn about / Burrito Borracho / Long ago & far away / Aijalon.
Note: Mono recording.
**Album:** Released Jul '86, on Affinity by Charly Records. Catalogue no: **AFF 155**

**WALK SOFTLY - RUN WILD (Richards, Johnny & His Orchestra)**
Tracks: / Walk softly / Way you look tonight / Laura / Sunday's child / Alone together / You go to my head / Run wild / Tempest on the Charles / Three cornered hat / Yemaya.
**Album:** Released May '83, on Jasmine by Hasmick Promotions. Deleted Feb '88. Catalogue no: **JASM 1500**

**WIDE RANGE (Richards, Johnny & Orchestra)**
**Album:** Released '87, on Creative World(USA) by GNP Crescendo Records (USA). Catalogue no: **ST 1052**

## Richards, Red

**I'M SHOOTING HIGH (Richards, Red & George Kelly Quintet)**
**Album:** Released Jun '88, on Sackville by Spotlite Records. Catalogue no: **2017**

## Richards, Trevor

**NEW ORLEANS TRIO (Richards, Trevor & Louis Nelson)**
**Album:** Released '88, on Wam Catalogue no: **WAMO NO.11**

## Richmond, Dannie

**Biographical details:** Danny Richmond was born in 1935 in New York; he played tenor sax as a teenager, joined the Charles Mingus Workshop in 1956 and Mingus's drummer of choice for the rest of his life: 'He's a musician, not just a timekeeper, one of the most versatile and creative drummers I've ever heard.' He played on virtually every Mingus record; between Mingus dates he recorded with Chet Baker on Riverside, Jimmy Knepper on Bethlehem, also worked with Mark-Almond band (LP on CBS), Joe Cocker, Elton John, soul singer Johnny Taylor; gave drum clinics when not on tour, published a method book in Germany in 1965; played with Chico Freeman quartet in 1980. His versatility is still under-recognised; inspired by Philly Joe Jones and Max Roach, he himself should be far better known. He has mostly carried on working with other Mingus alumni: and the George Adams/Don Pullen quintet for other albums, as well as his own. (Donald Clarke 21.5.88).

**LAST MINGUS BAND PLAYS CHARLES MINGUS**
Tracks: / Fabour is fabous / Goodbye pork pye / Nostalgia in times square / Noddin' your head blues / Duke Ellington's sound of love / Wee.
**Album:** Released Jan '81, on Timeless by Timeless Records. Catalogue no: **SJP 148**

## Richmond Jazz Festival

**JAZZ AT THE RICHMOND JAZZ FESTIVAL (Various artists)**
**Album:** Released Apr '79, on Wave by Wave Records. Catalogue no: **WAVE LP 5**

## Ricotti, Frank

**BEIDERBECKE COLLECTION, THE (Ricotti, Frank All Stars)**
Note: Leon Bix Beiderbecke was born in Davenport, Iowa on 10 March 1903 started playing cornet whilst at college there leading a group called The Wolverines. His lyrical turn of phrase was soon recognised and by 1926 he was the featured cornet soloist with the Jean Goldkette Band - a year later he was invited to join the famous Paul Whiteman Orchestra. Many of his famous recordings were made during his stay with Whiteman, Bix being a leader member

of various small groups drawn from the larger orchestra which also included such musicians as Frankie Trumbauer (C-mel, sax), Jimmy Dorsey (cl. & alto sax) and Eddie Lang (gtr.). The young Bing Crosby was often called upon to sing the vocal refrain.
When Bix Beiderbecke died in 1931 he was already a legend, for he had crammed so much living into his twenty-eight years. Since his death the Bix stories have been polished, refurbished and expanded to the point where it is often difficult to tell fact from fiction. For many, his music will always be linked with America's Jazz Age, as much a part of the era as the novels of F. Scott Fitzgerald, the racoon skin coats and the Stutz Bearcats cars.
But jazz lovers adore Bix for what he was, the creator of beautiful solos which shimmered above the often turgid, top heavy supporting bands and broke through the surface noise of old 78 rpm. records. Those who heard him in the flesh were moved to describe Bix's unique cornet sound with almost poetic imagery. Ralph Berton, a writer whose brother played drums with Beiderbecke, said the notes came out 'like shooting bullets at a bell' while guitarist Eddie Condon claimed his solos 'sounded like a girl saying yes'. For this album Frank Ricotti has skillfully composed and arranged the music to capture the atmosphere and the instrumental voicings of those Twenties recordings by Bix and his colleagues, while Kenny Baker plays the solo passages with flair, taste and precision, the very qualities which have earned him, a truly international reputation in the world of music. Bix would have appreciated the care and attention to detail. (Dormouse)
**CD:** Released Dec '88, on Dormouse Catalogue no: **DMCD 20**
**Cass:** Released Dec '88, on Dormouse Catalogue no: **DMC 20**
**Album:** Released Dec '88, on Dormouse Catalogue no: **DM 20**

## Rifkin, Joshua

**Biographical details:** Joshua Rifkin was born in 1944 in New York. He arranged and conducted the Judy Collins album *Wildflowers* on Elektra, her biggest hit (a USA number 5 in 1968, with top 10 single *Both sides now*; also *The Baroque Beatles book* in 1965 on Elektra, variations on Beatle songs with the 'Baroque Ensemble of the Mersyside Kammermusikgesellschaft'.
He was instrumental in ragtime revival with three LPs of *Piano Rags* by Scott Joplin, which began coming out in 1970, winning many awards, and were the biggest selling records in *Nonesuch's* history; more recently he made a digital remake for *EMI*.
He conducts Bach on L'Oiseau-Lyre/Florilegium mid '80s. (Donald Clarke 21.5.88).

**DIGITAL RAGTIME (Rifkin, Joshua and the Southland Stingers)**
Tracks: / Digital ragtime / Wall Street rag.
**CD:** Released '88, on Angel (1) by EMI Records. Catalogue no: **CDC 747 199 2**

**SCOTT JOPLIN - DIGITAL RAGTIME**
Tracks: / Maple leaf rag / Entertainer / Easy winners / Gladiolus rag / Pineapple rag / Heliotrope bouquet / Paragon rag / Solace / Magnetic rag.
**CD:** Released May '81, on EMI by EMI Records. Catalogue no: **TCEMD 5534**
**Album:** Released Jun '80, on EMI by EMI Records. Deleted Feb '90. Catalogue no: **EMD 5534**
**Cass:** Released May '81, on EMI by EMI Records. Catalogue no: **TCCEMD 5534**

## Riggs, Chuck

**LIVE HOT JAZZ (See under Davern, Kenny) (Riggs, Chuck and Kenny Davern)**
**Album:** Released Nov '87, on Statiras (USA) by Statiras(USA) Records. Catalogue no: **SLP 8077**

## Riley, Howard

**FOR FOUR ON TWO TWO**
Tracks: / Pedal points / Four four on two two / Somethings / Activate / Unfold.
**Album:** Released Feb '84, on Affinity by Charly Records. Catalogue no: **AFF 110**

**IN FOCUS (Riley Howard and Keith Tippett)**
**Album:** Released May '85, on Affinity by Charly Records. Deleted '88. Catalogue no: **AFF 137**

**INTERWINE (MUSIC OF 2 PIANOS)**
**Album:** Released Aug '77, on Mosaic by Mosaic Records (UK). Catalogue no: **GCM 771**

**OTHER SIDE, THE (SOLO PIANO)**
Tracks: / Agitate / Yesterday's friends / Deflection / Furthest point, The / Trajectory / Returning.
**Album:** Released Jan '83, on Spotlite by Spotlite Records. Catalogue no: **SPJ 511**

**SHAPED**
**Album:** Released Apr '88, on Mosaic by Mosaic Records (UK). Catalogue no: **GCM 781**

**SYNOPSIS**
**Album:** Released Nov '76, on Incus by Incus Records. Catalogue no: **INCUS 13**

**TORONTO CONCERT**
**Album:** Released Mar '79, on Vinyl by Charly Records. Deleted '89. Catalogue no: **VS 112**

## Riley, Teddy

**HONKY TONK TOWN (Riley, Teddy Band)**
**Cass:** Released May '87, on Nola Catalogue no: **TC 021**

**HONKY TONK TOWN '79**
**Album:** Released Jul '82, on Nola Catalogue no: **NOLA LP 21**
**Cass:** Released Sep '86, on 504 Catalogue no: **NOLATCS 21**
**Album:** Released Sep '86, on 504 Catalogue no: **LPS 3**

**MY FANTASY (IMPORT)**
Tracks: / My fantasy.
**12" Single:** Released Jul '89, on Motown by BMG Records (UK). Catalogue no: **MOT 4643**

## Rimmington, Sammy

**EXCITING SAX, THE OF SAMMY RIMMINGTON**
**Album:** Released Aug '88, on Progressive Catalogue no: **PRO 7077**

**GEORGE LEWIS CLASSICS**
**Album:** Released Mar '87, on GHB by Jazzology Records (USA). Catalogue no: **GHB 94**

**IN TOWN WITH SAM LEE**
**Album:** Released Jun '88, on GHB by Jazzology Records (USA). Catalogue no: **GHB 213**

**NEW ORLEANS SESSION WITH SAMMY RIMMINGTON**
**Album:** Released '89, on GHB by Jazzology Records (USA). Catalogue no: **GHB 209**

**ONLY A LOOK**
**Album:** Released May '79, on Dawn Club by Cadillac Music. Catalogue no: **DC 12027**

**REED ALL ABOUT IT (Rimmington, Sammy and Ian Wheeler Band)**
Tracks: / J / My darling / Am I to blame / Once in a while / Something is gonna give way / Shoeshine boy / Decatur street / Hymn to freedom / Save your sorrows.
**Album:** Released Sep '79, on Hefty Jazz Catalogue no: **HJ 104**

**SAMMY RIMMINGTON AND BARRY MARTYN (Rimmington, Sammy & Barry Martyn)**
**Album:** Released '89, on GHB by Jazzology Records (USA). Catalogue no: **GHB 214**

**SAMMY RIMMINGTON AND NOR QUARTET(Rimmington, Sammy and Nor Quartet)**
**Album:** Released '88, on Music Mecca by Ambia Music ApS. Catalogue no: **ML 114**

## Risky Blues

**RISKY BLUES (Various artists)**
Tracks: / Big 10-inch record: *Jackson, Bull Moose* / It ain't the meat: *Swallows* / Annie had a baby: *Midnighters* / Wasn't that good?: *Harris, Wynonie* / Don't stop Dan: *Checkers* / Lovin' machine: *Harris, Wynonie* / Silent George: *Millinder, Lucky* / Sixty minute man: *Dominoes* / Somethin's gone wrong with my lovin' machine: *Henry, Robert* / Walkin' blues: *Powell, Jesse & Fluffy Hunter* / Keep on churnin' (till the butter comes): *Harris, Wynonie* / I want a bow-legged woman: *Jackson, Bull Moose* / Rocket 69: *Rhodes, Todd* / Mountain oysters: *Davis, Eddie 'Lockjaw'*.
**Album:** Released Jul '88, on Bellaphon Catalogue no: **BID 8026**

## Ritenour, Lee

**Biographical details:** Guitarist Lee Ritenour, born in Hollywood in 1952, also plays banjo, mandolin and other instruments.
He became an ace studio musician and seven of his easy-listening albums, fusing Latin, jazz and soul, charted in America between 1977 and 1984. (Donald Clarke, February 1988.).

**AMERICAN FLYERS (Original soundtrack) (Ritenour, Lee & Greg Mathieson)**
Tracks: / American flyers / Travelling music / Brand new day / Gone ridin' / Bad moon rising / Brothers theme (part 1) / 'J' factor, The / American flyers, Theme from / Breakaway / Brothers theme (part 2) / Treadmill / Epilogue (third race).
**Album:** Released Jan '87, on GRP by GRP Records (USA). Catalogue no: **GRPA 2001**
**Cass:** Released Nov '86, on GRP by GRP Records (USA). Catalogue no: **GRPC 2001**

**BANDED TOGETHER**
Tracks: / Operator / Other love / Sunset drivers / Mandela / Amaretto / Rit variations II / Be good to me / I'm not responsible / Shadow dancing / Heavenly bodies.
**Album:** Released Jul '84, on Elektra by Elektra Records (UK). Deleted Jul '89. Catalogue no: **9603581**

**CAPTAIN'S JOURNEY, THE**
Tracks: / Captains journey, The (part 1) / Captains journey, The (part 2) - The storm / Morning glory / Sugarloaf express / Matchmakers / What do you want / That's enough for me / Etude.
**Album:** Released '77, on Elektra by Elektra Records (UK). Deleted '82. Catalogue no: **K 52094**

**COLOR RIT**
**Cass:** Released Nov '89, on GRP by GRP Records (USA). Catalogue no: **GRP 95942**
**CD:** Released Nov '89, on GRP by GRP Records (USA). Catalogue no: **GRP 95944**
**Album:** Released Nov '89, on GRP by GRP Records (USA). Catalogue no: **GRP 95941**

**EARTH RUN**
Tracks: / Soaring / Earth run / If I'm dreamin' (don't wake me) / Watercolours / Sauce, The / Butterfly / Sanctuary / Water from the moon.
Note: Lee Ritenour's first solo album for GRP since his highly successful collaborative venture, *Harlequin* with Dave Grusin. *Earth Run* is marked by the immense virtuosity and intense eclectic range of composition and arrangements that has made *Captain Fingers* one of the world's most renowned guitarists. Dave Grusin- keyboards / Larry Wilaiams and Don Grusin - synthesizers / Harvey Mason - drums / Tom Scott - lyrican / Abraham Laboriel - bass; the cast goes on and on including on the only track *If I'm Dreamin (Don't Wake Me)*, vocals by Phil Perry, Maurice White and Tommy Funderburk.
**Cass:** Released Aug '86, on GRP by GRP Records (USA). Catalogue no: **GRPM 91021**
**Album:** Released Aug '86, on GRP by GRP Records (USA). Catalogue no: **GRP 91021**
**CD:** Released Aug '86, on GRP by GRP Records (USA). Catalogue no: **GRPD 9538**

**FEEL THE NIGHT**
Tracks: / Feel the night / Market place / Wicked wine / French roast / You make me feel like dancing / Midnight lady / Uh oh.
**Album:** Released '77, on Elektra by Elektra Records (UK). Deleted '82. Catalogue no: **K 52141**

**FESTIVAL**
Note: This album is a celebration of contemporary jazz, r&b, funk & irrepressible Brazilian rhythms. All-star support is given by Bob James, Dave Grusin, Marcus Miller, Omar Hakim, Ernie Watts, Jao Bosco, Paulinho DaCosta & Brazilian vocalist Caetano Veloso.
**CD:** Released Oct '88, on GRP by GRP Records (USA). Catalogue no: **GRPD 9570-2**
**Album:** Released Oct '88, on GRP by GRP Records (USA). Catalogue no: **GRPA 9570-1**
**Cass:** Released Oct '88, on GRP by GRP Records (USA). Catalogue no: **GRPM 9570-4**

**FRIENDSHIP**
**Album:** Released Nov '79, on JVC Catalogue no: **VIDC 3**

**GENTLE THOUGHTS**
**Album:** Released Apr '78, on JVC Catalogue no: **VID CIE**

**IS IT YOU?**
Tracks: / Is it you.
**12" Single:** Released Jun '81, on Asylum by WEA Records. Catalogue no: **K 12540T**
**7" Single:** Released Jun '81, on Asylum by WEA Records. Catalogue no: **K 12540**

**LIVE AT THE RECORD PLANT (VIDEO) (Ritenour, Lee & Dave Grusin)**
**VHS:** Released Feb '90, on Verve Catalogue no: **CFV 10252**

**MR. BRIEFCASE**
Tracks: / Mr. Briefcase / Sugarloaf Express.
**12" Single:** Released Apr '81, on Asylum by WEA Records. Catalogue no: **K 12525T**
**7" Single:** Released Apr '81, on Asylum by WEA Records. Catalogue no: **K 12525**

**ON THE LINE**
Tracks: / Rit variations / Starbright / Pedestrian / Dolphin dreams / California roll / Heavenly bodies / On the line / Tush.
**CD:** Released Sep '88, on GRP by GRP Records (USA). Catalogue no: **GRD 9525**
**Album:** Released Apr '84, on Elektra (Musician) by Elektra Records (USA). Deleted Apr '88. Catalogue no: **960 310 1**

**PORTRAIT: LEE RITENOUR**
Tracks: / Route 17 (Available on CD only) / Portrait / Asa / Windmill / G-rit / White water / Turn the heat up / Children's games / Run away / Shades in the shade.
**CD:** Released Oct '87, on GRP by GRP Records (USA). Catalogue no: **GRD 9553**
**Cass:** Released Oct '87, on GRP by GRP Records (USA). Catalogue no: **GRPM 91042**
**Album:** Released Oct '87, on GRP by GRP Records (USA). Catalogue no: **GRP 91042**

**RIO**
Tracks: / Rainbow / San Juan sunset / Rio funk / It happens every day / Ipanema sol / Simplicidad / Little bit of this and a little bit of that, A.
**Album:** Released Sep '85, on GRP by GRP Records (USA). Catalogue no: **GRP 91017**
**Cass:** Released 1 Jun '85, on GRP by GRP Records (USA). Catalogue no: **C 1017**
**CD:** Released Sep '85, on GRP by GRP Records (USA). Catalogue no: **GRD 9524**

**RIT**
Tracks: / Mr. Briefcase / Tell me pretty lies / No sympathy / Is it you? / Dream walk / Countdown / Good question / On the slow glide.
**Album:** Released Apr '81, on Asylum by WEA Records. Catalogue no: **K 52273**

**RIT 2**
Tracks: / Cross my heart / Voices / Dreamwalkin' / Keep it alive / Malibu / Tied up / Road runner / Promises, promises / On the Boardwalk / Fantasy.
**Album:** Released Feb '83, on Elektra by Elektra Records (UK). Deleted Feb '88. Catalogue no: **E 0186**

**SUGARLOAF EXPRESS (Ritenour, Lee & Kazumi Watanbe)**
Tracks: / Sugarloaf express / Gentle afternoon / Jennifer Anne's samba / Beginning song.
**7" Single:** Released Jul '84, on Elite Records by Elite Records. Deleted '86. Catalogue no: **4PLAY 101**
**12" Single:** Released Oct '82, on Elite (Inner City) Catalogue no: **4PLAY 101**

## Riverboat Shuffle

**RIVERBOAT SHUFFLE (Various artists)**
**Album:** Released '88, on Black Lion-Intercord Catalogue no: **INT 155 003**
**2 LP Set:** Released '82, on Black Lion-Intercord Catalogue no: **INT 157 003**

## Rivers, Sam

**Biographical details:** Sam Rivers was born in 1930 in Oklahoma; his father was a gospel singer. The tenor saxophonist also plays other instruments; he attended Boston Conservatory and soon had a high reputation among musicians due to local gigs with Herb Pomeroy, Jaki Byard, Gigi Gryce; he worked with Miles Davis in 1964 and later played and recorded with Cecil Taylor in the late 1970s. He opened Studio RivBea in 1971 in Manhattan with his wife Bea, played there with his own group and many guests. He has recorded on Blue Note, Impulse, Improvising Artists and many other labels, a highly rated composer/leader in modern jazz. (Donald Clarke)..

**DIMENSIONS AND EXTENSIONS**
Tracks: / Precis / Paean / Effusive melange / Involution / Afflatus / Helix.
**Album:** Released Jul '89, on Blue Note by EMI Records. Catalogue no: **BST 84261**
**CD:** Released Mar '89, on Blue Note by EMI Records. Catalogue no: **BNZ 135**
**CD:** Released Feb '89, on Blue Note by EMI Records. Catalogue no: **CDP 784 261 2**

**FUCHSIA SWING SONG**
**Album:** Released Jul '89, on Blue Note by EMI Records. Catalogue no: **BST 84284**

**RIVERS AND HOLLAND Vol. 2 (Rivers, Sam & Dave Holland)**
**Album:** Released Jul '78, on Improvising Artists Catalogue no: **IAI 373848**

**STREAMS**
Note: Recorded live, at the 1973 Montreux Jazz Festival. Personnel: Sam Rivers (sax), Cecil McBee (bass), Norman Conners (drums).
**CD:** Released Jun '89, on MCA (Impulse Jazz) Catalogue no: **MCAD 39120**
**Album:** Released Jun '89, on MCA (Impulse Jazz) Catalogue no: **MCA 39120**

**TUBA TRIO Vol. 1**
**Album:** Released May '78, on Circle (USA) by Jazzology Records (USA). Catalogue no: **RK 2976/1**

**TUBA TRIO Vol. 2**
**Album:** Released May '78, on Circle (USA) by Jazzology Records (USA). Catalogue no: **RK 2976/2**

**WAVES**
Tracks: / Shockwaves / Torch / Pulse / Flux / Surge.
**Album:** Released Mar '88, on Affinity by Charly Records. Catalogue no: **AFF 186**

## Riverside Jazz Sampler

**RIVERSIDE JAZZ SAMPLER (Various artists)**
Tracks: / Scramble: *Gaylor, Bean and Norris* / Stix' trix: *Various artists* / Last time I saw..., The: *Various artists* / Centaur and the...: *Various artists* / Carol: *Various artists* / Nearness of you, the: *Various artists* / Work song: *Various artists* / Think deep: *Various artists* / Wild rice: *Various artists* / We'll be together: *Various artists* / Groovin' high: *Various artists* / Why do I love you: *Various artists.*
**Cass:** Released May '88, on Riverside (USA) by Fantasy Inc (USA). Catalogue no: **RIVMC 001**
**CD:** Released 25 Apr '88, on Riverside (USA) by Fantasy Inc (USA). Catalogue no: **CDRIVM 001**
**Album:** Released Feb '88, on Riverside (USA) by Fantasy Inc (USA). Catalogue no: **RIVM 001**

## Riverside Jazz Band

**30 YEARS ON**
**Album:** Released '88, on Burlington Records by Plant Life Records. Catalogue no: **BURL 025**

**IN AT THE DEEP END**
**Album:** Released Oct '86, on Burlington Records by Plant Life Records. Deleted '88. Catalogue no: **BURL 016**

## Roach, Max

**Biographical details:** One of the all-time greatest jazz drummers, Max Roach, born in 1929, was a key figure in the development of modern jazz in the 1940's as a regular drummer with Charlie Parker. Later he led, co-led and played in countless groups and had an important association with brilliant, tragically short-lived trumpeter Clifford Brown. (IMS, August 1985.)
Max Roach was born in North Carolina in 1924. The drummer, composer and leader was one of the founding fathers of bop, influenced by Kenny Clarke, and became one of the outstanding percussionists of all time. he was partners with Charles Mingus in their debut label, and played at the famous Massey Hall concert with Mingus, Bud Powell, Charlie Parker, Dizzy Gillespie in 1953. From 1954 he co-lead a quintet with Clifford Brown wich was probably the most influential of it's time; after Brown's death he carried on with Kenny Dorham and Sonny Rollins. He has made a great many records, among the most famous the *Freedom Now Suite* on Candid c.1960 (aka *We Insist-Freedom Now!*) with singer Abbey Lincoln (they were married 1962-70). She also appears on *Max Roach-Again*, made live in Paris 1960-3 *Historic Concerts* on soul note is a duo with Cecil Taylor, made live in NYC in 1979, he was involved since 1972 with the percussion ensemble M'Boom: LPs Re: *Percussion* '73 on baystate, *M'Boom* '79 on CBS and *Collage* '84 on soul note, with remarkably consistant personnel incl. Ray Mantilla, Joe Chambers, Freddie Waits, up to six more on marimba, xylophone, tympani, woodblocks, orchestral bells, gongs etc. He taught at Yale, other schools; is professor of music at U of Mass at Amherst; he has been an influence in turn on Elvin Jones,many others. (Donald Clarke 4.2.88).

**BIRTH AND REBIRTH (Roach, Max & Anthony Braxton)**
**CD:** Released '86, on Black Saint (Italy) Catalogue no: **BSR 0024**

**CONVERSATIONS**
Tracks: / Speak brother speak / Variation, A / You stepped out of a dream / Filide / It's you or no one / Jodies cha cha / Deeds, not words / Larry Larne / Conversations.
**Album:** Released Dec '81, on Milestone by Ace Records. Catalogue no: **M 47061**

**DAAHOUD (Roach, Max & Clifford Brown)**
**CD:** Released '88, on Mobile Fidelity Sound Lab(USA) by Mobile Fidelity Records (USA). Catalogue no: **MFCD 826**

**DRUMMIN' THE BLUES (Roach Max/Stan Levy)**
**Album:** Released Jan '85, on EMI (France) by EMI Records. Catalogue no: **LRP H3064**

**DRUMS UNLIMITED**
Tracks: / Drum also waltzes / Nommo / Drums unlimited / St. Louis blues / For big Sid / In the red.
**Album:** Released Feb '79, on Atlantic by WEA Records. Deleted Feb '84. Catalogue no: **K 50519**

**EASY WINNERS (Roach, Max Double Quartet)**
Tracks: / Bird says / Sis / Little booker / Easy winners.
**CD:** Released '86, on Soul Note Catalogue no: **SN 1109**

**FREEDOM NOW SUITE**
**Album:** Released Oct '79, on Amigo Catalogue no: **AMLP 810**

**GRAZ CONCERT 1963 (see also Rollins, Sonny Trio) (Roach, Max Quintet & Sonny Rollins Trio)**
**Album:** Released Apr '79, on Jazz Connoisseur by Spotlite Records. Catalogue no: **JC 108**

**HISTORIC CONCERTS (see also Taylor, Cecil) (Roach, Max & Cecil Taylor)**
**Album:** Released May '85, on Soul Note Catalogue no: **SN 1100**

**IN THE BEGINNING (Roach, Max & Clifford Brown)**
**Album:** Released '88, on Vogue by Vogue Records. Catalogue no: **VG 500097**

**IN THE LIGHT (Roach, Max Quartet)**
**CD:** Released '86, on Soul Note Catalogue no: **SNCD 1053**

**IT'S TIME**
**Cass:** Released Oct '85, on Impulse by Impulse Records. Deleted Dec '89. Catalogue no: **ASC 16**
**Album:** Released Oct '85, on Impulse by Impulse Records. Deleted Dec '89. Catalogue no: **AS 16**

**LONG AS YOU'RE LIVING**
**Album:** Released Nov '84, on Enja (Germany) by Enja Records (West Germany). Catalogue no: **ENJA 4074**

**MAX ROACH AGAIN**
**2 LP Set:** Released Aug '79, on Affinity by Charly Records. Deleted '88. Catalogue no: **AFFD 32**

**MAX ROACH COLLECTION**
Tracks: / Now's the time / Donna Lee / S'il vous plait / Stop motion / To Lady /

Drum variations.
**Cass:** Released Jun '88, on Deja Vu Catalogue no: **DVMC 2127**
**Album:** Released Jun '88, on Deja Vu Catalogue no: **DVLP 2127**

**MAX ROACH IN CONCERT (Roach, Max and Clifford Brown)**
Tracks: / Jor-du / I can't get started / I get a kick out of you / Parisian thoroughfare / All God's chillun got rhythm / Tenderly / Sunset eyes / Clifford's axe.
**CD:** Released Jan '86, on Vogue by Vogue Records. Catalogue no: **VG 600 032**

**PICTURES IN A FRAME (Roach, Max Quartet)**
**CD:** Released '86, on Soul Note Catalogue no: **SNCD 1003**

**SCOTT FREE**
Tracks: / Scott free (part 1) / Scott free (part II).
**Album:** Released Aug '85, on Soul Note Catalogue no: **SN 1103**
**CD:** Released '86, on Soul Note Catalogue no: **SNCD 1103**

**SOUNDS AS A ROACH (Roach, Max & Abbey Lincoln)**
**Album:** Released Sep '86, on Lotus Catalogue no: **LPPS 111 17**

**SURVIVORS**
Tracks: / Survivors / Third eye, The / Billy the kid / Jasme / Drum also waltzes,The / Sassy Max (self portrait) / Smoke that thunders,The.
Note: Recorded 19th-21st October 1984 at Vanguard Studios, New York. Personnel: Max Roach - multiple percussion set / String Quartet - Guillermo Figueroa - 1st violin / Donald Bauch - 2nd violin / Louise Schulman - viola / Chrustopher Finckel - cello.
**Album:** Released May '85, on Soul Note Catalogue no: **SN 1093**
**CD:** Released May '85, on Soul Note Catalogue no: **SNCD 1093**

**WE INSIST (Freedom Now Suite)**
Tracks: / Driva' man / Freedom day / Triptych (With: Prayer/Protest/Peace.) / All Africa / Tears for Johannesburg.
Note: With Coleman Hawkins/Abbey Lincoln.
**Album:** Released Jul '87, on Candid Catalogue no: **CS 9002**
**CD:** Released Sep '87, on Candid Catalogue no: **CCD 9002**

## Roaring 20's

**ROARING 20'S, THE (Various artists)**
Tracks: / If you knew Susie: *Shilkret, Jack and His Orchestra(Billy Murray vocal)* (78rpm record; 15 May 1925) / Sheik of Araby, The: *Pianola Roll* (1922) / I'm tellin' the birds, tellin' the bees: *Smith, Jack ('Whispering')* (78rpm record; 1 December 1926) / That's my weakness now: *Pianola Roll* (1928) / Canadian capers: *Biese, Paul Trio* (78 rpm record; 18 July 1921) / Rose Marie: *Pianola Roll* (1925) / Collette: *Whiteman, Paul & His Orchestra* (78rpm record 15 June 1927 vocal Jack Fulton/Charles Gaylord/Austin Young) / Where the lazy daisies grow: *Pianola Roll* (1924) / Ain't misbehavin': *Hylton, Jack/his orchestra/Sam Browne)* (78rpm record; 18 September 1929) / My inspiration is you: *Pianola Roll* (1928) / Wedding of the painted doll, The: *Pianola Roll* (1929) / Don't bring Lulu: *Garber, Jan & His Orchestra* (78rpm record; 5 May 1925) / Always: *Pianola Roll* (1925) / Where, oh where do I live?: *Douglas, Fred/orchestra* (78rpm record; October 1927) / Birth of the blues: *Pianola Roll* (1927) / I miss my Swiss: *Golden Gate Orchestra (Arthur Fields vocal)* (78rpm record; 2 July 1925) / Ain't she sweet?: *Pianola Roll* (1927) / Hello, Swanee, hello: *Syncopated Four* (78rpm record; May 1927) / Ramona: *Pianola Roll* (1928) / Charleston (78rpm record; 7 July 1925).
Note: 61 minutes
**Album:** Released Nov '84, on Saydisc by Amon Ra Records. Catalogue no: **SDL 344**
**Cass:** Released Nov '84, on Saydisc by Amon Ra Records. Catalogue no: **CSDL 344**
**CD:** Released Feb '89, on Saydisc by Amon Ra Records. Catalogue no: **CD-SDL 344**

## Roaring Seven Jazz Band

**ROARING SEVEN JAZZ BAND**
**Album:** Released Jun '86, on Stomp Off (USA) Catalogue no: **SOS 1019**

## Roberts, David Thomas

**BOYS IN AUTUMN**
Tracks: / Boys in autumn / Wrong side of the tracks.
**7" Single:** Released Mar '83, on WEA by WEA Records. Catalogue no: **K 72021**

**EARLY FOLK RAGS**
**Album:** Released '88, on Stomp Off (USA) Catalogue no: **SOS 1021**

**RAGS**
**Album:** Released Jun '86, on Stomp Off (USA) Catalogue no: **SOS 1132**

**THROUGH THE BOTTOM LANDS**
**Album:** Released '88, on Stomp Off (USA) Catalogue no: **SOS 1072**

## Robichaux, Joe

**1933 (Robichaux, Joe And His New Orleans Boys)**
**Album:** Released Dec '86, on Classic Jazz Masters Catalogue no: **CJM 37**

**COMPLETE J. ROBICHAUX, THE**
**2 LP Set:** Released Nov '88, on Blu-Disc (USA) Catalogue no: **T 1007/8**

**JOE ROBECHAUX AND HIS NEW ORLEANS BOYS**
**Album:** Released Dec '86, on Folklyric (USA) by Arhoolie Records (USA). Catalogue no: **FL 9032**

## Robinson, Banjo Ikey

**1929-35 - BLUES, SKIFFLE AND JAZZ**
**Album:** Released Jul '87, on Document Catalogue no: **DOC 509**

## Robinson, Fenton

**BLUES IN PROGRESS**
**Album:** Released Aug '84, on Black Magic by Topic Records. Catalogue no: **BM 9005**

**I HEAR SOME BLUES DOWNSTAIRS**
Tracks: / I hear some blues downstairs / Just a little bit / West side baby / I'm so tired / I wish for you / Tell me what's the reason / Going west / Killing floor / As the years go passing by.
**Album:** Released '87, on Sonet by Sonet Records. Catalogue no: **SNTF 712**

**MELLOW FELLOW**
Tracks: / Somebody loan me a dime / Little turch / Leave you in the arms (of your other man) / Let me come on home / She's a wiggler / Laughin cryin blues / I wanna ooh / I fell in love one time / Sky is crying, The / Getaway / Sideman / Mellow fellow.
**Album:** Released Jan '87, on Charly R&B by Charly Records. Catalogue no: **CRB 1131**

**SOMEBODY LOAN ME A DIME**
Tracks: / Somebody loan me a dime / Getaway / Directly from my heart / Going to a chicago / You say you're leaving / Checking on my woman / You don't know what love is / I've changed / Country girl / Gotta wake up / Texas flood.
**Album:** Released Aug '76, on Sonet by Sonet Records. Catalogue no: **SNTF 686**

## Robinson, Jim

**JIM ROBINSON WITH....**
**Album:** Released Apr '79, on Smokey Mary Deleted '84. Catalogue no: **SMOKEY MARY 197J**

## Robinson, L.C.

**UPS AND DOWNS**
**Album:** Released May '81, on Arhoolie (USA) by Arhoolie Records (USA). Catalogue no: **ARHOOLIE 1062**

## Robinson, Spike

**GERSHWIN COLLECTION**
**CD:** Released Feb '89, on Hep Jazz by Hep Records. Catalogue no: **HEPCD 2042**
**Album:** Released '88, on Hep Jazz by Hep Records. Catalogue no: **HEP 2042**

**JUSA BIT O' BLUES (Robinson, Spike and the Harry Edison Quintet)**
Tracks: / One I love, The / Autumn leaves / Elaine / Just in time / 'Tis autumn / Slow boat to China / Jusa bit o' blues / Stars fell on Alabama / Time after time.
**CD:** Released '88, on Capri Catalogue no: **CD 74012-2**

**MUSIC OF HARRY WARREN (Robinson, Spike Quartet)**
Tracks: / This is always / This heart of mine / More I see you, The / Chattanooga choo choo / Cheerful little earful /

Jimmy Rogers

I only have eyes for you / Lulu's back in town / I wish I knew.
Note: Spike Robinson - sax, Victor Feldman - piano, Ray Brown - bass, John Guerin - drums.
**Album:** Released Jun '83, on Discovery (USA) by Discovery Records (USA). Catalogue no: **DS 870**
**CD:** Released '88, on Discovery (USA) by Discovery Records (USA). Catalogue no: **DSCD 937**

**SPIKE ROBINSON AND LOUIS STEWART (Robinson, Spike & Louis Stewart)**
**CD:** Released Oct '89, on Hep Jazz by Hep Records. Catalogue no: **HEPCD 2045**

**SPIKE ROBINSON AND TOMMY POLLARD'S DOWNBEAT FIVE, WITH VICTOR FELDMAN**
**Album:** Released Jun '86, on Esquire by Titan Int. Prod.. Catalogue no: **ESQ 318**

## Robinson, Sugar Chile

**Biographical details:** Robinson, Sugar Chile was born Frank Robinson in 1940 in Detroit. He played the piano and sang; he was a child prodigy who made his first record at the age of six. He played at a party for President Truman, appeared on TV, had hits on Capitol and slipped into obscurity in the early 1950s. (Donald Clarke 4.2.88).

**GO BOY GO**
**Album:** Released Dec '84, on Oldie Blues Catalogue no: **OL 2828**

**JUNIOR JUMP**
Tracks: / Go boy go / Say little girl / Bases were loaded / Sticks and stones / Whop whop / Yancey special / I'll eat my spinach / Caldonia / Numbers boogie / Frustration boogie / Lazy boys boogie / Bounding ball boogie / After school blues / Christmas boogie.
**Album:** Released Jun '86, on Charly R&B by Charly Records. Catalogue no: **CRB 1126**

## Robinson's Jacinto...

**ROBINSON'S JACINTO BALLROOM (Robinson's Jacinto Ballroom Orchestra)**
**Album:** Released Jun '86, on GHB by Jazzology Records (USA). Catalogue no: **GHB 28**

## Roche, Betty

**SOPHISTICATED LADIES (Roche, Betty & Marilyn Moore)**
Tracks: / Take the 'A' train / Something to live for / In a mellow tone / Time after time / Go away blues / Can't help lovin' that man / Route 66 / All my life / I just got the message, baby / All too soon / You don't love me no more / September in the rain / I'm just a lucky so and so / Ill wind / If love is trouble / Is you is or is you ain't my baby / Born to blow the blues / Lover come back to me / You're driving me crazy / Trav'lin' all alone / I cried for you / Leavin' town / Trouble is a man / I got rhythm.
**CD:** Released Jan '90, on Affinity by Charly Records. Catalogue no: **CDAFF 763**

**TAKE THE 'A' TRAIN**
Tracks: / Take the 'A' train / Something to live for / In a mellow tone / Time after time / Go away blues / Can't help lovin' dat man / Route 66 / All my life / I just got the message, baby / All too soon / You don't love me no more / September in the rain.
**Album:** Released Jul '87, on Affinity by Charly Records. Catalogue no: **AFF 175**

## Rodger, Mart

**GIVE US A STOMPER KID (Rodger, Mart & Manchester Jazz)**
Tracks: / Copenhagen / I can't say / Georgia on my mind / Dusty rag / Bogalusa strut / Papa dip / Saturday night function / Sweet Sue just you / Wild man blues / Fidgety feet.
**Album:** Released Jun '88, on Bowstone Catalogue no: **OWSLP 2601**

**I BELIEVE IN RAINBOWS (Rodger, Mart & Manchester Jazz)**
Tracks: / I believe in rainbows / I'll be loving you always.
**7" Single:** Released Jun '88, on Bowstone Catalogue no: **OWS 201**

**JAZZ CLUB SESSION, A (Rodger, Mart & Manchester Jazz)**
**VHS:** Released Mar '90, on Bowstone Catalogue no: **OWSV251**

**JAZZ TALE OF TWO CITIES (Rodger, Mart & Manchester Jazz)**
**Album:** Released Apr '89, on GHB by Jazzology Records (USA). Catalogue no: **GHB 224**

## Rogers, Billie

**ONE NIGHT STAND...WOMENS LIB IN 1944**
**Album:** Released Jul '82, on Joyce Catalogue no: **JLP 1018**

## Rogers, Jimmy

**CHESS MASTERS**
Tracks: / Left me with a broken heart / Blues all day long / Today today blues / World's in a tangle, The / She loves another man / Hard working man / Chance to love / My little machine / Mistreated baby / What's the matter? / You're the one / If it ain't me / One kiss / I can't believe / What have I done? / My baby don't love me any more / Crying shame / Give love another chance / This has never been / Rock this house / My last meal / You don't know / Can't keep from worrying.
**2 LP Set:** Released Jun '88 on Chess. Catalogue no: **GCH 2-6027**
**Cass Set:** Released on Jun '88 on Chess. Catalogue no: **GCHK 2-2067**

**CHESS MASTERS: JIMMY ROGERS**
Tracks: / Chance to love / Mistreated baby / What's the matter / My little machine / Crying shame / Left with a broken heart / Today today blues / She loves another man / World is a tangle / Hard working man / You're the one / Money, marbles and chalk / Luedella / Act like you love me / Back door friend / last time / I used to have a woman / Sloppy drunk/ Blues leave me alone / Out on the road

/ Goin' away / That's all right / Chicago bound / Walking by myself.
**2 LP Set:** Released Apr '82, on Chess (USA). Catalogue no: **CXMD 4008**

**CHICAGO BAND**
**Album:** Released '88 on Blues Rock Project. Catalogue no: **BRP 2027**

**CHICAGO BLUES**
**Album:** Released Jan '82, on JSP. Catalogue no: **JSP 1008**

**CHICAGO GOLDEN YEARS**
**Album:** Released Oct '88, on Vogue. Catalogue no: **42701**

**DIRTY DOZEN**
Tracks: / Take a walk / You're sweet / Mean red spider / Fishing in my pond / Crazy woman blues / Information, please / Dirty dozens / Oh baby / Honky tonk / One-room country shack / Cleo's gone / Baby please.
**Album:** Released on Jun '85, on JSP. Catalogue no: **JSP 1090**

**FEELIN' GOOD**
**Album:** Released May '84, on Murray Brothers. Catalogue no: **MB 1006**

**LIVE: JIMMY ROGERS**
Tracks: / Sloppy drunk / I can't keep from worrying / Frank's blues / Linda Lu / Blues for Freddy / That's alright / Brown skin woman.
**Album:** Released Mar '82, on JSP. Catalogue no: **JSP 1043**

## Rogers, Shorty

**Biographical details:** Shorty Rogers was born Milton Michael Rajonsky in 1924 in Massachusetts.
The trumpeter, bandleader, arranger and composer was popular in the 1950's, and reissues show that his work hasn't dated: he is a swing era musician who was influenced in his writing by bop, and his all-star West-coast small-group sides from the early '50s, as well as the work on Atlantic c.1955 (the *Martians Go Home* period) still sounds very good indeed.
His big-band work was directly influenced by Count Basie. He toured the UK in 1982 with National Youth Jazz Orchestra.
(Donald Clarke 4.2.88)..

**BACK AGAIN- LIVE AT THE CONCORDE**
Tracks: / Shorty / Deep roots / Down home / Evolving / Full circle / Lift off / Warm valley / My romance.
**Album:** Released Feb '85, on Concept (1) Catalogue no: **VL 1**

**BLUES EXPRESS**
**Album:** Released Feb '85, on RCA (France) by BMG Records (France). Catalogue no: **NL 89502**

**CLICKIN' WITH CLAX**
Tracks: / Toyland / Adam in New York / I dig Ed / Clickin' with Clax / Put the goodies on / Our song / Pete's meat / Mike's peak.
**Album:** Released '77, on Atlantic by WEA Records. Deleted '82. Catalogue no: **K 50481**

**COLLABORATION (Rogers,Shorty and Andre Previn)**
**Album:** Released Nov '84, on RCA (France) by BMG Records (France). Catalogue no: **NL 89308**

**GREATEST HITS: SHORTY ROGERS**
Tracks: / Short stop / Blues for Brando / Goof and I, The / Sweetheart of Sigmund Freud / Gigi... / Martian's lullaby / Doggin' around / Morpo / Bunny / Blues express / Tickle toe / Red dog play.
**Cass:** Released Jul '86, on RCA by BMG Records (UK). Deleted May '89. Catalogue no: **CK 89807**
**Album:** Released Jul '86, on RCA by BMG Records (UK). Deleted May '89. Catalogue no: **CL 89807**

**JAZZ WALTZ (Rogers, Shorty Big Band)**
Tracks: / Greensleeves / Witchcraft / Taste of honey, A.
Note: Featuring Bud Shank, Paul Horn, Bill Hood, Bob Cooper, Mel Lewis, Milt Bernhart, Harry Betts, Emil Richards.
**Album:** Released Oct '82, on Discovery (USA) by Discovery Records (USA). Catalogue no: **DS 843**

**LIVE FROM THE RENDEZVOUS BALLROOM 1953 (Rogers,Shorty Big Band)**
**Album:** Released Apr '81, on Scarecrow Catalogue no: **SC 801**

**MARLON BRANDO: THE WILD ONE (EP) (Film soundtrack)**
Tracks: / Chino / Blues for Brando / Wild one / Windswept.
**12" Single:** Released 1 Jun '89, on Bear Family by Bear Family Records (Germany). Catalogue no: **BFE 15349**

**MARTIANS STAY AT HOME**
Tracks: / Loaded / Martians stay home / Lady in red / Amber leaves / Bill / Barbaro / Peals / 12th Street rag / Easy.
**Album:** Released Jun '80, on Atlantic by WEA Records. Catalogue no: **K 50714**

**MODERN SOUNDS (Rogers, Shorty and Gerry Mulligan)**
Tracks: / Popo / Didi / Four others / Over the rainbow / Apropos / Sam and the lady / Westwood walk / Ballad, A / Walking shoes / Rocker / Taking a chance on love / Flash / Simbah / Ontet.
Note: Side one: Shorty Rogers & His Giants; Side two: The Gerry Mulligan Tentette.
**Cass:** Released Aug '86, on Affinity by Charly Records. Catalogue no: **TCAFF 158**
**Album:** Released Aug '86, on Affinity by Charly Records. Catalogue no: **AFF 158**

**POPO (Rogers, Shorty & Art Pepper)**
**Album:** Released Jul '82, on Xanadu Catalogue no: **XANADU 148**

**RETURN TO RIO (Rogers, Shorty & His Giants)**
**Cass:** Released '88, on Discovery (USA) by Discovery Records (USA). Catalogue no: **DSC 899**
**Album:** Released Apr '84, on Discovery (USA) by Discovery Records (USA). Catalogue no: **DS 899**

**SHORT STOPS (Rogers, Shorty with His Orchestra & The Giants)**
Tracks: / Powder puff / Pesky serpent, The / Bunny / Pirouette / Morpo / Diablo's dance / Mambo del crow / Indian club / Coop de graas / Infinity promenade / Short stop / Boar jibu / Contours / Tale of an African lobster / Chiquito loco / Sweetheart of Sigmund Freud / Blues for Brando / Chino / Wild one / Windswept / Topsy / Basie eyes / It's sand, man / Doggin' around / Jump for me / Over and out / Down for double / Swingin' the blues / H & J / Tickle toe / Taps Miller / Walk, don't run.
**Album:** Released Sep '87, on RCA by BMG Records (UK). Catalogue no: **NL 85917**
**CD:** Released Sep '87, on RCA by BMG Records (UK). Catalogue no: **NK 85917**
**CD:** Released Apr '89, on Bluebird (2) by BMG Records (UK). Catalogue no: **ND 90209**

**SHORTY ROGERS AND HIS GIANTS Vol. 1 (Rogers, Shorty & His Giants)**
**Album:** Released '83, on RCA (France) by BMG Records (France). Catalogue no: **PM 43549**

**WEST COAST JAZZ**
Tracks: / Isn't it romantic? / Tricky diddler / Oh play that thing / Not really the blues / Martians go home / My heart stood still / Michele's meditation / That's what I'm talking about.
**Album:** Released Jul '76, on Atlantic by WEA Records. Catalogue no: **ATL 50247**

**WHEREVER THE FIVE WINDS BLOW (Rogers, Shorty Quintet)**
**Album:** Released Feb '88, on Fresh Sounds (Spain) by Fresh Sounds Records (Spain). Catalogue no: **FS 19**

**YESTERDAY, TODAY AND FOREVER**
Tracks: / Budo / Blood count / Yesterday, today and forever / T.N.T / Wagon wheels / Lotus bud / Have you hugged a Martian today?.
Note: Shorty Rogers, trumpet and flugelhorn; Bud Shank, flute and alto saxophone; George Cables, piano; Bob Magnusson, bass; Roy McCurdy, drums.
**Album:** Released Oct '83, on Concord Jazz by Concord Jazz Records (USA). Catalogue no: **CJ 223**

## Rollini, Adrian

**1938-40**
**Album:** Released Aug '87, on Tax Catalogue no: **M 8036**

## Rollins, Sonny

**Biographical details:** Sonny Rollins was born Theodore Walter Rollins in 1929 in NYC; he was the most influential tenor saxophonist between Coleman Hawkins and John Coltrane; his influence continues and may in the end be as great as theirs. His tone is uncompromising, his harmonic ideas unique; he can do more with the bare bones of a tune than can some composers with an entire orchestra: the way he improvises on the melody rather than jumping around in the chords means that he cannot hide from the musically literate listener; he walks a tightrope, skill and ideas always fully in view, and has been described as extending the possibilities of the solo more than anyone since Louis Armstrong.

He first recorded in 1948 and became a solo voice to watch on Prestege in the early '50s. He also worked with Miles Davis, Thelonious Monk, others; Davis's LP *Collectors Items* on Prestege has '53 tracks with both Rollins and Charlie Parker on tenor (as 'Charlie Chan').

The Prestege LP *Tenor Madness* (1956) has both Rollins and Coltrane on it. He joined Clifford Brown--Max Roach quintet in 1955-7, has led his own combos ever since, with sabbitcals late '50s, late '60s. *Way Out West* ('57) is a trio with Ray Brown and Shelley Manne, was a landmark LP, with famous sleeve photo of Rollins with cowboy hat in the desert; also *Sonny Rollins And The Contemporary Leaders* ('58) with Manne, Hampton Hawes, Barry Kessel, Leroy Vinnegar on bass, Victor Feldman playing vibes on one track; *Alternate Takes* from both dates releesed '86 on LP, tracks added to CD editions (on Contemprary) of the original LPs. Sabbaticals were times of examination and woodshedding as well as dissatisfaction with the jazz scene; he practiced late '50s on the Williamsburg Bridge over the East River. He came back from sabbatical on RCA with epochal *The Bridge* '62, pianoless quartet with young Jim Hall on guitar; other quartet tracks with Hall compiled in a 2-disc Bluebird set.

He also recorded for Blue Note, Riverside, Impulse; after his next layoff he went with Milestone for another long series of fine albums from 1972.

His best-known tunes are *Oleo* and *Airegin*; he wrote the film score for *Alfie* 1966 including *Alfie's Tune* (not the Bacharach-David title song).

He was awarded a Guggenheim Fellowship in 1972; his concerto for Saxaphone and Orchestra was premiered in Japan in 1986, featured in film *Saxophone Colossus*.

(Donald Clarke 4.2.88).

**ALFIE**
**CD:** Released May '89, on MCA (Import) by MCA Records. Catalogue no: **MCAD 39107**
**Album:** Released May '89, on MCA (Import) by MCA Records. Catalogue no: **MCA 39107**
**Cass:** Released May '89, on MCA (Import) by MCA Records. Catalogue no: **MCAC 39107**

**ALTERNATE TAKES**
Tracks: / I'm an old cowhand / Come, gone / Way out west / Song is you / You / I've found a new baby.
**Album:** Released 2 May '89, on Contemporary by Ace Records. Catalogue no: **COP 034**

**ALTERNATIVE ROLLINS, THE (With Herbie Hancock, Ron Carter, Jim Hall and others)**
Tracks: / Now is the time / Django / Fifty second street theme / I remember Clifford / St. Thomas / Afternoon in Paris / Trav'lin' light / Winter in wonderland / Four / When you wish upon a star.
**2 LP Set:** Released '83, on RCA (France) by BMG Records (France). Catalogue no: **PL 43268**

**ARTISTRY IN JAZZ (Greatest Hits)**
**CD:** Released May '87, on JVC/Fantasy Catalogue no: **VDJ 1588**

**BEST OF SONNY ROLLINS**
Tracks: / Decision / Poor butterfly / Why don't I (CD only.) / Misterioso / Tune up / How are things in Glocca Morra / Sonnymoon for two / Softly as in a morning sunrise (CD only.) / Striver's row (CD only.).
**Album:** Released Feb '90, on Blue Note by EMI Records. Catalogue no: **793 203 1**
**CD:** Released Feb '90, on Blue Note by EMI Records. Catalogue no: **CDP 793 203 2**
**Album:** Released Feb '90, on Blue Note by EMI Records. Catalogue no: **B1 93203**
**CD:** Released Feb '90, on Blue Note by EMI Records. Catalogue no: **BNZ 235**

**BRASS AND TRIO**
Tracks: / Who cares / Love is a simple thing / Grand street / Far out east / What's my name? / If you were the only girl in the world / Manhattan / Body and soul.
**CD:** Released Apr '84, on Verve Deleted Mar '88. Catalogue no: **815 056-2**
**Album:** Released Apr '83, on Verve (USA) by Polydor Ltd. Catalogue no: **2304 192**

**CONTEMPORARY LEADERS (Rollins, Sonny and Barney Kessel)**
**CD:** Released May '87, on JVC/Fantasy Deleted '88. Catalogue no: **VDJ 1552**
**Album:** Released May '89, on Contemporary by Ace Records. Catalogue no: **COP 018**
**CD:** Released Jul '87, on Contemporary by Ace Records. Deleted '88. Catalogue no: **CDCOP 018**

**DANCING IN THE DARK**
Tracks: / Just Once / O T Y O G / Promise, The / I'll String Along With You / Allison.
**Album:** Released Sep '88, on Milestone by Ace Records. Catalogue no: **MX 9155**
**Cass:** Released '88, on Milestone by Ace Records. Deleted Jan '90. Catalogue no: **MXC 9155**

**DON'T STOP THE CARNIVAL**
Tracks: / Don't stop the carnival / Silver city / Autumn nocturne / Camel / Nobody else but me / Non cents / Child's prayer / President Hayes / Sais.
**2 LP Set:** Released '79, on RCA by BMG Records (UK). Deleted '84. Catalogue no: **M 55005**

**EAST BROADWAY RUN DOWN**
Tracks: / East Broadway run down / Blessings in diguise / We kiss in a shadow.
**Album:** Released Mar '83, on Jasmine by Hasmick Promotions. Catalogue no: **JAS 69**

**ESSENTIAL, THE**
**CD:** Released Apr '87, on Fantasy (import) by Fantasy Inc (USA). Catalogue no: **FCD 60020**

**FALLING IN LOVE WITH JAZZ**
**CD:** Released Apr '90, on Milestone by Ace Records. Catalogue no: **CDMX 9179**

**FIRST RECORDINGS 1957**
**CD:** Released Oct '89, on Jazz Anthology by Musidisc Records (France). Catalogue no: **550142**

**FREEDOM SUITE**
Tracks: / Some day I'll find you / Till there was you / Will you still be mine / Shadow waltz.
**CD:** Released Apr '86, on JVC/Fantasy Catalogue no: **VDJ 1520**
**Album:** Released Sep '88, on Riverside (USA) by Fantasy Inc (USA). Catalogue no: **RLP 258**
**Cass:** Released Sep '88, on Riverside (USA) by Fantasy Inc (USA). Deleted Jan '90. Catalogue no: **RLPC 258**

**HARLEM BOYS**
Tracks: / Harlem boys / My ideal.
**12" Single:** Released Dec '79, on Milestone by Ace Records. Deleted '82. Catalogue no: **MRC 100**

**IN EUROPE 1963 Vol. 1**
Tracks: / On Green Dolphin Street / Introduction / Without a song / Oleo / Sonny's tune / Sonny's tune (second version).
Note: Live recording made in and around Paris during January 1963. 56 minutes playing time.
**CD:** Released Nov '89, on Jazz-Up Catalogue no: **JU 313**

**IN EUROPE 1963 Vol. 2**
Tracks: / 52nd Street / On Green Dolphin Street / Solitude / Without a song.
Note: Live recording made in and around Paris during January 1963. 58 minutes playing time.
**CD:** Released Nov '89, on Jazz-Up Catalogue no: **JU 314**

**IN SWEDEN 1959**
Tracks: / Another me, another you / I've told every little star / Stay as good as you are / Oleo / It don't mean a thing / Paul's pal / Love letters.
**Album:** Released Jul '83, on Ingo Catalogue no: **INGO 9**

**ISLAND LADY**
**Album:** Released Apr '81, on Lotus Catalogue no: **LPPS 111 07**

**LIVE AT GREENWICH VILLAGE**
**CD:** Released Jan '89, on Giants of Jazz by Hasmick Promotions. Catalogue no: **CD 530 44**

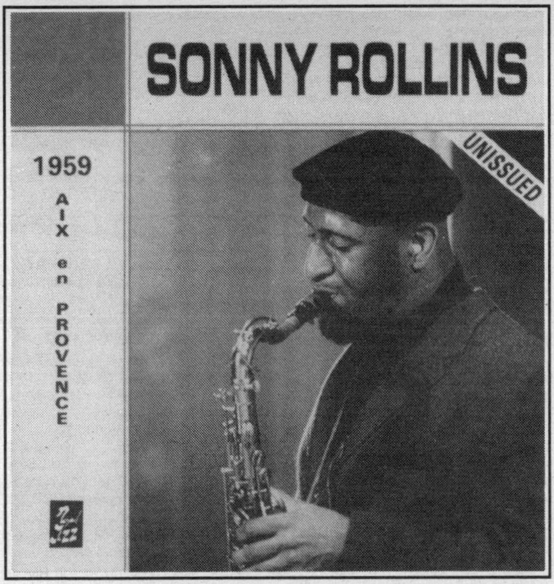


Sonny Rollins - Live in Aix en Provence 1959 (Royal Jazz)

**LIVE IN AIX EN PROVENCE 1959 (See panel above)**
Tracks: / Woddin' you / But not for me / Lady bird.
Note: Recorded at Aix en Provence, France, March 11th, 1959. Sonny Rollins - tenor saxophone, Henry Grimes - bass, Kenny Clarke - drums.

**CD:** Released '89, on Royal Jazz Catalogue no: **RJ 502**

**LIVE IN EUROPE**
**Album:** Released Apr '81, on Unique Jazz by Spotlite Records. Catalogue no: **UJ 22**

**LIVE IN JAPAN**
**Album:** Released Apr '78, on G.I. by Plastic Head Records. Deleted '87. Catalogue no: **GSS 4**

**LOVE AT FIRST SIGHT**
Tracks: / Little lulu / Dream that we fell out of / Strode rode / Very thought of you, The / Caress / Double feature.
**Album:** Released Jan '81, on Milestone by Ace Records. Catalogue no: **M 9098**

**MASTERS OF JAZZ**
**Album:** Released '83, on RCA (Germany) Catalogue no: **CL 42874**

**NEWK'S TIME**
Tracks: / Tune up / Asiatic races / Wonderful wonderful / Surrey with the fringe on top / Blues for Philly Joe / Namely you.
**Album:** Released Sep '84, on Blue Note by EMI Records. Deleted '87. Catalogue no: **BST 84001**
**Album:** Released '79, on Blue Note by EMI Records. Deleted '84. Catalogue no: **BNS 40011**
**CD:** Released Apr '90, on Blue Note by EMI Records. Catalogue no: **BNZ 238**
**CD:** Released Apr '90, on Blue Note by EMI Records. Catalogue no: **CDP 784 001 2**

**NIGHT AT THE VILLAGE VANGUARD**
Tracks: / Old devil moon / Sonnymoon for two / Night in Tunisia / Softly as in a morning sunrise / Strivers Row / I can't get started.
**Cass:** Released Apr '87, on Blue Note by EMI Records. Deleted Jun '89. Catalogue no: **4BN 81581**
**Album:** Released Apr '87, on Blue Note by EMI Records. Catalogue no: **BST 81581**

**NIGHT AT THE VILLAGE VANGUARD Vol. 1**
Tracks: / Night in Tunisia / I've got you under my skin / Softly as in a morning sunrise / Four / Woody 'n' you / Old devil moon.
Note: Tenor saxophonist Sonny Rollins was at the height of his considerable creative powers in the mid-fifties.
This daring session is one of the finest examples from the period. Here Rollins takes the bandstand with only Wilbur Ware's bass and Elvin Jones' drumsbehind, Two of his best known compositions 'Striver's Row' and 'Sonnymoon For Two' made their debut here.
Rollins' interpretations of standard have been his trademark andhis performances of 'Old Devil Moon' and 'Softly As In A Morning Sunrise' on this set are masterful.
**CD:** Released May '87, on EMI-Manhattan by EMI Records. Catalogue no: **CDP 746 517 2**
**Album:** Released '79, on Blue Note by EMI Records. Deleted '84. Catalogue no: **BNS 40010**
**CD:** Released May '87, on EMI-Manhattan by EMI Records. Catalogue no: **BNZ 79**

**NIGHT AT THE VILLAGE VANGUARD Vol. 2**
**CD:** Released Apr '88, on Blue Note by EMI Records. Catalogue no: **CDP 746 518 2**
**CD:** Released Apr '88, on Blue Note by EMI Records. Catalogue no: **BNZ 81**

**NO PROBLEM**
Tracks: / No problem / Here you come again / Jo Jo / Coconut bread / Penny saved / Illusions / Joyous lake.
**Album:** Released Jul '82, on Milestone by Ace Records. Catalogue no: **M 9104**

**ON IMPULSE**
Tracks: / On Green Dolphin Street / Everything happens to me / Hold 'em Joe / Blue room / Three little words.
**CD:** Released Feb '87, on Impulse by Impulse Records. Deleted Dec '89. Catalogue no: **MCAD 5655**
**Cass:** Released Jun '82, on Jasmine by Hasmick Promotions. Catalogue no: **JAS C2**
**Album:** Released Jun '82, on Jasmine by Hasmick Promotions. Catalogue no: **JAS 2**

**PLUS ELEVEN**
**CD:** Released Jul '87, on Boplicity by Ace Records. Deleted '88. Catalogue no: **CDBOP 007**

**QUARTET, THE**
Tracks: / God bless the child / John S. / You do something to me / Where are you / Without a song / Bridge, The / If ever I would leave you / Brownskin girl / Don't stop the carnival / Night has a thousand eyes, The / My ship / Love letters / Long ago (and far away) (Featuring Jim Hall, guitar.).
**Cass:** Released Feb '87, on RCA by BMG Records (UK). Deleted May '89. Catalogue no: **PK 85634**
**Album:** Released Feb '87, on RCA by BMG Records (UK). Deleted May '89. Catalogue no: **PL 85634**

**QUARTETS (FEATURING JIM HALL)**
Tracks: / God bless the child / John S / You do something to me / Where are you? / Without a song / Bridge, The / If ever I would leave you / Night has a thousand eyes, The.
**CD:** Released Apr '88, on Bluebird (2) by BMG Records (UK). Catalogue no: **ND 85643**

**ROLLINS PLAYS FOR BIRD (Rollins, Sonny Quintet)**
**Album:** Released Apr '86, on Original Jazz Classics (USA) by Fantasy Inc (USA). Catalogue no: **OJC 214**

**SAXOPHONE COLOSSUS**
**CD:** Released Apr '86, on JVC/Fantasy Catalogue no: **VDJ 1501**
**CD:** Released Apr '87, on Carrere (France) Catalogue no: **98429**

**SAXOPHONE COLOSSUS AND MORE**
Tracks: / Moritat / Blue seven / Strode rode / St. Thomas / You don't know what love is / Kids know / House I live in, The / I've grown accustomed to her face / Star eyes / I feel a song comin' on / Pent up house / Kiss and run.
**2 LP Set:** Released '79, on Prestige Deleted '84. Catalogue no: **PR 24050**

**SAXOPHONE COLOSSUS (VIDEO)**
**VHS:** Released '88, on Virgin Vision by Virgin Records. Catalogue no: **VVD 350**

**SOLO ALBUM, THE**
Tracks: / Soloscope (Part 1) / Sonny Rollins' tenor saxophone / Soloscope (Part 2).
Note: Sonny Rollins has been a major force in jazz since 1957 when he won the Down Beat critics poll as New Star. One critic wrote "No other jazzman approaches him in sustaining the creativity and aesthetic balance of solo work ... Rollins has performed entire concerts by himself in brilliant style as if he were accompanied by a huge orchestra". This new album was recorded live in New York on 19th July, 1985 and features a Sonny Rollins original extended composition entitled *Soloscope.*
**Album:** Released Feb '86, on Milestone by Ace Records. Catalogue no: **M 9137**
**CD:** Released '86, on JVC/Fantasy Catalogue no: **VDJ 1021**
**CD:** Released May '87, on Carrere (France) Catalogue no: **98172**

**SONNY ROLLINS (Prestige Years, Vol. 1 - 1949-53)**
Tracks: / Elysee (alternate take) / Elysee / Opus 5 / Hi-lo (alternate take) / Foxhunt, The / Morpheus / Down / Blue room / Whispering / I know / My old flame / It's only a paper moon / Time on my hands / Mambo bounce / This love of mine / Shadrack / Slow boat to China / Scoops / Newk's fadeaway / Compulsion / Serent's tooth / Serpent's tooth (alternate take) / Round midnight / In a sentimental mood / Stopper, The / Almost like being in love / No more / Let's call this / Think of one / Think of one (alternate take) / Friday the 13th.
Note: With Art Blakey, Kenny Clarke, Miles Davis, Kenny Dorham, Roy Haynes, Percy Heath, Milt Jackson, J.J. Johnson, Philly Joe Jones, John Lewis, Jackie McLean, Thelonious Monk, Charlie Parker , Max Roach and others.
**Album:** Released Jun '88, on Prestige Catalogue no: **PRE 4001**

**SONNY ROLLINS (Prestige Years, Vol. 2 - 1954-56)**
Tracks: / Soft shoe / Confab in tempo / I'll take romance / Airegin / Oleo / But not for me / But not for me (alternate take) / Doxy / Movin' out / Swingin' for Bumsy / Silk 'n' satin / Solid / I want to be happy / Way you look tonight / More than you know / There's no business like show business / Paradox / Raincheck / There are such things / It's all right with me / In your own sweet way / No line / Weird blues / I feel a song coming on / Pent-up house / Valse hot / Kiss and run / Count your blessings.
Note: With Art Blakey, Clifford Brown, Paul Chambers, Kenny Clarke, Miles Davis, Kenny Dorham, Art Farmer, Tommy Flanagan, Percy Heath, Elmo Hope, Thelonious Monk, Max Roach, Horace Silver, Art Taylor and others.
**Album:** Released Jun '88, on Prestige Catalogue no: **PRE 4002**

**SONNY ROLLINS (Prestige Years, Vol. 3 - 1956)**
Tracks: / My reverie / Most beautiful girl in the world, The / Paul's pal / When your lover has gone / Tenor madness / You don't know what love is / St. Thomas / Strode rode / Blue seven / Moritat / I've grown accustomed to her face / Kids know / House I live in, The / Bird medley / I remember you / Melancholy baby / Old folks / They can't take that away from me / Just friends / My little suede shoes / Star eyes / B swift / My ideal / Sonny boy / Two different worlds / Ee-ah / B quick.
Note: With Paul Chambers, Earl Coleman, John Coltrane, Kenny Dorham, Kenny Drew, Tommy Flanagan, Red Garland, Philly Joe Jones, Wade Legge, George Morrow, Max Roach, Doug Watkins.
**Album:** Released Jun '88, on Prestige Catalogue no: **PRE 4003**

**SONNY ROLLINS AND THAD JONES (Rollins, Sonny & Thad Jones Quintets)**
**Album:** Released '88, on Zeta Catalogue no: **ZET 704**

**SONNY ROLLINS (IN EUROPE)**
**Album:** Released '81, on Unique Jazz by Spotlite Records. Catalogue no: **UJ 29**

**SONNY ROLLINS IN STOCKHOLM 1959**
**Album:** Released '88, on Dragon by Dragon Records. Catalogue no: **DRLP 73**

**SONNY ROLLINS LIVE (VIDEO)**
**VHS:** Released '88, on Kay Jazz (video) by Kay Jazz. Catalogue no: **KJ 011**

**SONNY ROLLINS PLUS FOUR (Rollins, Sonny and Clifford Brown)**
**CD:** Released '86, on JVC/Fantasy Catalogue no: **VDJ 1524**
**Album:** Released Jan '87, on Original Jazz Classics (USA) by Fantasy Inc (USA). Catalogue no: **OJC 243**

**SONNY ROLLINS QUINTET AND THAD JONES AND HIS ORCHESTRA**
**Album:** Released 7 Nov '87, on Fresh Sounds (Spain) by Fresh Sounds Records (Spain). Catalogue no: **FS 261**

**SONNY ROLLINS AND THE CONTEMPORARY PLUS**
**CD:** Released Jun '87, on Contemporary by Ace Records. Catalogue no: **CDCOP 078**

**SONNY ROLLINS VOL.1**
Tracks: / Decision / Bluesnote / How are things in Glocca Morra / Plain Jane / Sonnysphere.
**Cass:** Released Mar '86, on Blue Note by EMI Records. Catalogue no: **TCBST 81542**
**CD:** Released Jan '89, on Blue Note by EMI Records. Catalogue no: **BNZ 114**
**CD:** Released Jan '89, on Blue Note by EMI Records. Catalogue no: **CDP 781 542 2**
**Album:** Released Aug '82, on Blue Note by EMI Records. Deleted Jan '88. Catalogue no: **BLP 1542**
**Album:** Released Jul '89, on Blue Note by EMI Records. Catalogue no: **BST 81542**

**SONNY ROLLINS VOL.2**
Tracks: / Why don't I / Wail march / Misterioso / Reflections / You stepped out of a dream / Poor butterfly.
**CD:** Released Feb '89, on Blue Note by EMI Records. Catalogue no: **BNZ 80**
**CD:** Released Feb '89, on Blue Note by EMI Records. Catalogue no: **CDP 781 558 2**
**Album:** Released Aug '82, on Blue Note by EMI Records. Deleted Jan '88. Catalogue no: **BLP 1558**
**Album:** Released Aug '85, on Blue Note by EMI Records. Catalogue no: **BST 81558**
**Cass:** Released Aug '85, on Blue Note by EMI Records. Deleted Jun '89. Catalogue no: **4BN 81558**

**SOUND OF SONNY, THE**
Tracks: / Last time I saw Paris, The / Toot toot tootsie / Dearly beloved / Cutie / Mangoes / Just in time / What is there to say / Every time we say goodbye / It could happen to you.
**Album:** Released Feb '88, on Riverside (USA) by Fantasy Inc (USA). Catalogue no: **RLP 241**

**STUTTGART 1963 CONCERT**
**Album:** Released Jul '81, on Jazz Connoisseur by Spotlite Records. Catalogue no: **JC 106**

**SUNNY DAYS, STARRY NIGHTS**
Tracks: / Mava mava / I'm old fashioned / Wynton / Tell me you love me / I'll see you again / Kilauea.
Note: Personnel: Sonny Rollins-tenor sax/Clifton Anderson-trombone/Mark Soskin-keyboards/Russel Blake-electric bass/Tommy Campbell-drums.
**CD:** Released Apr '87, on Carrere (France) Catalogue no: **98152**
**CD:** Released Jan '87, on Fantasy (import) by Fantasy Inc (USA). Deleted '88. Catalogue no: **FCD 6049122**

**TENOR MADNESS**
**CD:** Released May '87, on JVC/Fantasy Catalogue no: **VDJ 1514**

**TOUR DE FORCE**
**Album:** Released Aug '84, on Prestige (USA) by Fantasy Inc (USA). Catalogue no: **OJC 095**

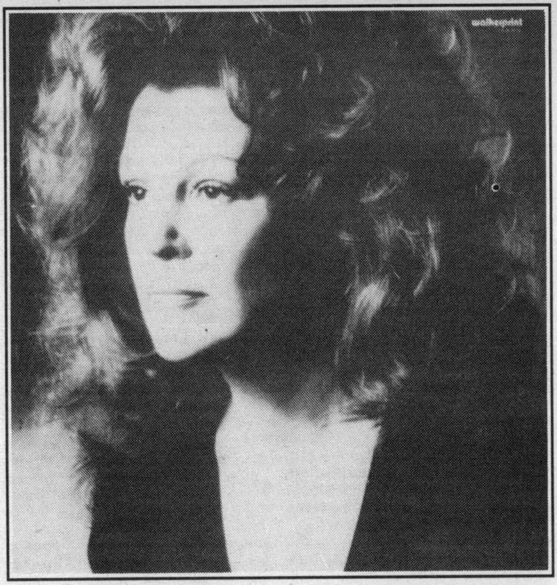

**Annie Ross**

**WAY OUT WEST**
Tracks: / I'm an old cowhand / Solitude / Come gone / Wagon wheels / There is no greater love / Way out west.

**CD:** Released 6 Mar '89, on Contemporary by Ace Records. Catalogue no: **CDCOP 006**
**CD:** Released Apr '87, on Carrere (France) Catalogue no: **98600**
**CD:** Released May '87, on JVC/Fantasy Catalogue no: **VDJ 1551**
**Album:** Released Feb '89, on Contemporary by Ace Records. Catalogue no: **COP 006**
**CD:** Released '86, on Mobile Fidelity Sound Lab(USA) by Mobile Fidelity Records (USA). Catalogue no: **MFCD 801**

**WITH ELVIN JONES AND WILBUR WARE (See also Jones, Elvin & Ware, Wilbur)**
**CD:** Released Mar '90, on Giants of Jazz by Hasmick Promotions. Catalogue no: **GOJCD53044**

**WORKTIME**
**CD:** Released Jan '89, on JVC/Fantasy Catalogue no: **VDJ 1607**

## Romano, Joe

**AND FINALLY ROMANO**
Tracks: / Chance It / Love Nest, The / Dance of the Infidels / U.M.M.G. / Joe Cheeze / Daydreams / Like blues.
**Album:** Released 25 Mar '88, on Fresh Sounds (Spain) by Fresh Sounds Records (Spain). Catalogue no: **FS 311**

## Romantic Clarinet For...

**ROMANTIC CLARINET FOR LOVERS (Various artists)**
Tracks: / Stranger on the shore: *Bilk, Acker* / Sentimental journey: *Bilk, Acker* / Alley cat: *Bilk, Acker* / I left my heart in San Francisco: *Bilk, Acker* / Let's put out the lights: *Bilk, Acker* / Here's that rainy day: *Morks, Jan* / You don't know how much you can suffer: *Morks, Jan* / Forbidden games: *Morks, Jan* / LO.V.E.: *Morks, Jan* / Love walked in: *Mullings, Gerry* / Night lights: *Mullings, Gerry* / I'll walk alone: *Mullings, Gerry* / Easy living: *Semple, Archie* / Last spring that old feeling: *Semple, Archie* / Memories of you: *Nicholas, Albert* / Lonesome: *Sunshine, Monty*.
**CD:** Released '84, on Phonogram (Import) Catalogue no: **818 272 2**

## Romantic Guitar For...

**ROMANTIC GUITAR FOR LOVERS (Various artists)**
Tracks: / Your song: *Souer, Piet* / Once upon a time in the west: *Souer, Piet* / Do you know where you're going to?: *Souer, Piet* (Theme from Mahogany) / If: *Souer, Piet* / How insensitive: *Souer, Piet* / Alone at last: *Kershaw, Martin* / Emmanuelle: *Goya, Francis* / Don't cry for me Argentina: *Goya, Francis* / Aranjuez mon amour: *Nieuwerf, Peter* / Sing along junk: *Nieuwerf, Peter* / Summertime: *Steenhuis, Wout* / Body and soul: *Steenhuis, Wout* / Autumn leaves: *Steenhuis, Wout* / I sing to the moon: *Overgaauw, Win* / Who can I turn to?: *Overgaauw, Win* / Here there and everywhere: *Blonker*.
**CD:** Released '84, on Phonogram (Import) Catalogue no: **814 458 2**

## Romantic Sax For...

**ROMANTIC SAX FOR LOVERS (Various artists)**
Tracks: / Three times a lady: *Van Mechelen, Clous* / Don't it make my brown eyes blue: *Van Mechelen, Clous* / You needed me: *Van Mechelen, Clous* / When I need you: *Van Mechelen, Clous* / Shadow of your smile: *Mulligan, Gerry* / Second time around: *Mulligan, Gerry* / P.S. I love you: *Mulligan, Gerry* / Solitude: *Webster, Ben* / Woman in love: *Katsaros, George* / Abrazame: *Katsaros, George* / Are you lonesome tonight?: *Moss, Andre* / Broken promises: *Austin, Sil* / My man: *Morks, Jan* / Once I loved: *Verbeke, Harry* / Yesterdays: *Schilperoort, Peter* / If: *Noordijk, Piet* / Harlem Nocturne: *Austen, Sil* / How insensitive: *Doldinger, Klaus*.
**CD:** Released Nov '85, on Polydor International by Polydor Ltd. Catalogue no: **816 185-2**

## Roots Of..

**ROOTS OF AMERICA'S MUSIC (Various artists)**
**2 LP Set:** Released May '81, on Arhoolie (USA) by Arhoolie Records (USA). Deleted '88. Catalogue no: **ARHOOLIE 2001-2**

**ROOTS OF THE BLUES (Various artists)**
Tracks: / Louisiana: *Ratcliff, Henry* / Field song from Senegal: *Bakari Badji* / Po' boy blues: *Dudley, John* / Katie left Memphis: *Tangle Eye* / Berta berta: *Miller, Leyroy & A Group Of Prisoners* / Old original blues: *McDowell, Fred and Miles Pratcher* / Jim and John: *Young, Ed & Lonnie Young* / Emmaline, take your time: *Askew, Alec* / Buttermilk: *Pratcher, Miles & Bob* / Mama Lucy: *Gary, Leroy* / I'm gonna live, anyhow till I die: *Pratcher, Miles & Bob* / No more my lord: *Tangle Eye & A Group Of Prisoners* / Lining hymn and prayer: *Rev' Crenshaw & Congregation* / Death comes a creepin' in my room: *McDowell, Fred* / Church house moan: *Congregation Of New Brown's Chapel* / Beggin the blues: *Jones, Bessie* / Rolled and tumbled: *Hemphill, Rose & Fred McDowell* / Goin' down to the races: *McDowell, Fred, Miles Pratcher and Fannie Davis* / You gotta cut that out: *Forest City Joe*.
**Album:** Released Mar '87, on New World (USA) by New World Records (USA). Catalogue no: **NW 252**

## Rosengarden, Bobby

**BY REQUEST (See also under Higgins, Eddie and Hinton, Milt)**
**Album:** Released Nov '87, on Statiras (USA) by Statiras(USA) Records. Catalogue no: **SLP 8079**
**Cass:** Released '88, on Statiras (USA) by Statiras(USA) Records. Catalogue no: **SC 8079**

## Rosengren, Bernt

**SUMMIT MEETING (See also Sandstrom, Nisse) (Rosengren, Bernt & Nisse Sandstrom Quintet)**
**Album:** Released May '86, on Phontastic (Sweden) Catalogue no: **PHONT 7560**

**TENTET - LIVE!**
**Album:** Released '88, on Dragon by Dragon Records. Catalogue no: **DRLP 55**

## Rosolino, Frank

**CONNECTION**
Tracks: / I may be wrong / Things we did last summer / Frieda / Doxy / My de luxe / Flamingo.
**Album:** Released '84, on Affinity by Charly Records. Deleted '89. Catalogue no: **AFF 111**

**FRANK ROSOLINO QUINTET (Rosolino, Frank Quintet)**
**Album:** Released Apr '88, on VSOP Catalogue no: **VSOP 16**

**FRANK ROSOLINO SEXTET (Rosolino, Frank Sextet)**
**Album:** Released Apr '81, on Affinity by Charly Records. Catalogue no: **AFF 61**

**FRANKLY SPEAKING (Roslino, Frank Quintet)**
Tracks: / Frenesi / Rhythm rascals / Moonlight in Vermont / Missus, The / There's no you / Our delight / Now I lay me down (to dream of you) / Taps miller / Slan / Stairway to the stars / King fish.
**Album:** Released Dec '81, on Affinity by Charly Records. Deleted '88. Catalogue no: **AFF 69**

**THINKING ABOUT YOU**
Note: Artists also include: Ed Bickert / Don Thompson / T.Clarke.
**Album:** Released Jul '86, on Sackville by Spotlite Records. Catalogue no: **2014**

## Ross, Annie

**ANNIE ROSS SINGS A SONG WITH GERRY MULLIGAN (Ross, Annie / Gerry Mulligan)**
Tracks: / I feel pretty / I've grown accustomed to your face / All of you / Give me the simple life / This is always (alternative version) / It don't mean a thing / Lady's in love with you, The / You turned the tables on me / I've grown accustomed to your face (alternative version) / This is always / My old flame / This time the dream's on me / Let there be love / Between the devil and the deep blue sea / How about you? / I guess I'll have to change my plan.
**CD:** Released Aug '88, on EMI-Manhattan by EMI Records. Catalogue no: **CZ 48**
**CD:** Released Aug '88, on EMI-Manhattan by EMI Records. Catalogue no: **CDP 746 852 2**
**Album:** Released Feb '88, on Fresh Sounds (Spain) by Fresh Sounds Records (Spain). Catalogue no: **FS 27**

**GASSER, A (Ross, Annie & Zoot Sims)**
Tracks: / I'm just a lucky so and so / You're nearer / I'm nobody's baby / Lucky day / Invitation to the blues / You're driving me crazy / Invitation to the blues (instrumental) / Everything I've got / I didn't know about you / I was doing all right / You took advantage of me / I don't want to cry anymore / Bones for Zoot / Funky old bones / Brushes.
**CD:** Released Jan '89, on Pacific Jazz by EMI Records. Catalogue no: **CZ 49**
**CD:** Released Jan '89, on Pacific Jazz by EMI Records. Catalogue no: **CDP 746 854 2**

**IN HOAGLAND 81 (Ross, Annie & Georgie Fame)**
**Album:** Released Sep '81, on Bald Eagle Catalogue no: **BELP 181**

**LIKE SOMEONE IN LOVE (Ross, Annie / Johnny Spence & His Orchestra)**
Tracks: / Lot of livin' to do, A / Let me love you / All the things you are / I'm gonna go fishin' / Like someone in love / Limehouse blues / Handful of songs / All of you / Fly me to the moon / Nature boy / What's new / Love for sale.
**Album:** Released Jul '83, on Bulldog Records by President Records. Catalogue no: **BDL 1049**

**SINGS A HANDFULL OF SONGS**
**Album:** Released Feb '88, on Fresh Sounds (Spain) by Fresh Sounds Records (Spain). Catalogue no: **FS 221**

## Ross, Doctor Isiah

**CAT SQUIRREL**
Tracks: / Cat squirrel.
**7" Single:** Released Mar '84, on Northwood by Northwood Records. Catalogue no: **NW 45 004**

**HARMONICA BOSS**
**Album:** Released Oct '86, on Big Bear by Big Bear Records. Deleted '88. Catalogue no: **BRP 2013**

**HARMONICA MAN, THE**
Tracks: / Boogie disease No.2 / Baby please don't go / Harmonica boogie / Decoration day / How much more long / Don't worry 'bout the bear / That's alright mama / Blue in the night / Do the boogie woogie / Rockin' after midnight / Ethel Mae / San Francisco breakdown.
**Album:** Released '82, on Big Bear by Big Bear Records. Deleted '88. Catalogue no: **BEAR 2**

**HIS FIRST RECORDINGS**
**Album:** Released May '81, on Arhoolie (USA) by Arhoolie Records (USA). Catalogue no: **ARHOOLIE 1065**

**JIVIN' THE BLUES**
**Album:** Released Sep '79, on Big Bear by Big Bear Records. Deleted '88. Catalogue no: **BEAR 15**

**ONE MAN BAND**
Tracks: / Doctor Ross's rock / My little woman / Mama's blues / Thirty two twenty / Chicago breakdown / Good morning little schoolgirl / Hobo blues / Fox chase, The / Going down slow / Boogie woogie, The.
**Album:** Released Jul '81, on Sonet by Sonet Records. Catalogue no: **SNTF 862**

## Round Midnight

**ROUND MIDNIGHT (Film Soundtrack) (Various artists)**
Tracks: / Round midnight: *Various artists* / Body and soul: *Various artists* / Berangere's nightmare: *Various artists* / Fair weather: *Various artists* / Una noche con Francis: *Various artists* / Peacocks, The: *Various artists* / How long has this been going on?: *Various artists* / Rhythm a ning: *Various artists* / Still time: *Various artists* / Minuit aux champselysees: *Various artists* / Chan's song: *Various artists* / Now's the time: *Various artists* / Autumn in New York: *Various artists* / Encore: *Various artists* / April in Paris: *Various artists* / Parisienne thorotare: *Various artists.*
Note: Dexter Gordon, Miles Davis, John Coltrane, Charlie Parker, Bud Powell, Lester Young, Billie Holliday, Coleman Hawkins, Thelonious Monk, Buddy Rich, Red Garland, Ray Brown, Kenny Drew, Oscar Peterson, Herb Ellis, Henry Edison, Art Blakey, Al Haig, Barney Kessel, Max Roach, Jimmy Rowles, Charlie Rouse, Ben Webster.
**Album:** Released Sep '87, on Lotus Catalogue no: **LOP 14 124**
**Album:** Released Nov '86, on CBS by CBS Records. Catalogue no: **450079 1**
**Album:** Released Nov '88, on CBS by CBS Records. Deleted Jan '90. Catalogue no: **CBS 70300**
**CD:** Released Nov '88, on CBS by CBS Records. Catalogue no: **CD 70300**
**Cass:** Released Nov '86, on CBS by CBS Records. Catalogue no: **450079 4**
**Cass:** Released Sep '87, on Lotus Catalogue no: **LCS 14124**

**ROUND MIDNIGHT (SINGLE)**
Tracks: / Round midnight.
**12" Single:** Released Jul '87, on Music Of Life by Music Of Life Records. Catalogue no: **NOTE 9**

## Rouse, Charlie

**Biographical details:** Charlie Rouse was born in 1924 in Washington DC. The tenor saxist was a member of Thelonious Monk's quartet 1959-74. Critics who earlier failed to understand Monk also tended to underrate Rouse, whose sly high spirits are always recognisable and entertaining. Rouse worked with Mal Waldron in the early 1980s, then in the cooperative band Sphere, with Buster Williams on bass, Kenny Barron on piano, Ben Ridley on drums; he has made several solo albums. (Donald Clarke 4.2.88)..

**CHASE IS ON, THE (Rouse, Charlie / Paul Quinichette)**
Tracks: / Chase is on, The / When the blues come on / This can't be love / Last time for love / You're cheating yourself / Knittin' / Tender trap, The / Things I love,

The.
**Album:** Released Jul '86, on Affinity by Charly Records. Deleted May '88. Catalogue no: **AFF 154**
**Cass:** Released Jul '86, on Affinity by Charly Records. Deleted '88. Catalogue no: **TCAFF 154**

**EPISTROPHY**
Tracks: / Nutty / Blue monk / Epistrophy / Ruby, my dear / 'Round midnight.
Note: Recorded 10 October 1988 at a Thelonious Monk Birthday Tribute, San Francisco. Personnel: Charlie Rouse (tenor sax), Don Cherry (tpt), Buddy Montgomery (vibes), George Cables (piano), Jeff Chambers (bass), Ralph Penland (drums).
**Album:** Released Jun '89, on Landmark (USA) by Fantasy Inc (USA). Catalogue no: **LLP 1521**
**CD:** Released Jun '89, on Landmark (USA) by Fantasy Inc (USA). Catalogue no: **LCD 15212**

**MOMENTS NOTICE (Rouse, Charlie Quartet)**
**Album:** Released Nov '86, on Storyville by Storyville Records AB. Catalogue no: **SLP 4079**

**PLAYIN' IN THE YARD (Rouse, Charlie & Stan Tracey)**
Tracks: / Playin' in the yard / In a sentimental mood / I've found a new baby / Li'l ol' Pottsville / Li'l Sherrie / Wee.
**Album:** Released Mar '88, on Steam Catalogue no: **SJ 116**

**SOCIAL CALL (Rouse, Charlie / Red Rodney)**
**Album:** Released '88, on Uptown (USA) Catalogue no: **UP 27.18**

## Rowles, Jimmy

**Biographical details:** Jimmy Rowles was born in 1918 in Wahinton DC. A pianist with an amazing memory, he is said to be a favorite of every singer he has accompanied including Peggy Lee, Julie London, Billy Holiday, Carmen McRae, Sarah Vaughan, others. He has done a lot of studio work, including the boogie-woogie calliope on Henry Mancini's *Elephant Walk*, and has a uniquely witty solo style. He has always been highly regarded by other musicians; Jess Stacey (who himself has many fans) said that it still made him laugh that Benny Goodman (who often didn't get along with people) fired Rowles in 1942 to rehire Stacey. (Donald Clarke 4.2.88)..

**FIORELLE UPTOWN/ MARY SUNSHINE**
**Album:** Released 7 Nov '87, on Fresh Sounds (Spain) by Fresh Sounds Records (Spain). Catalogue no: **FS 267**

**ISFAHAN**
Tracks: / Marjo / Black butterfly / It might as well be spring / How deep is the ocean / Voices deep within me / Yesterdays / Button up your overcoat / This is a night for love / Isfahan.
**Album:** Released Jan '79, on Sonet by Sonet Records. Catalogue no: **SNTF 790**

**LET'S GET ACQUAINTED WITH JAZZ (Rowles, Jimmy Sextet)**
**Album:** Released Apr '88, on VSOP Catalogue no: **VSOP 11**

**LOOKING BACK (Rowles, Jimmy & Stacy)**
**CD:** Released Mar '90, on delos Catalogue no: **DE 4009**

**MUSIC'S THE ONLY THING ON MY MIND (Rowles, Jimmy & George Mraz)**
**Album:** Released '89, on Audiophile (USA) by Jazzology Records (USA). Catalogue no: **AP 188**
**Album:** Released '81, on Progressive (USA) by Jazzology Records (USA). Catalogue no: **PRO 7009**

**WE COULD MAKE SUCH BEAUTIFUL MUSIC**
**CD:** Released '88, on Xanadu Catalogue no: **FDC 5152**

**WEATHER IN A JAZZ VANE (Rowles, Jimmy Septet)**
**Album:** Released Apr '88, on VSOP Catalogue no: **VSOP 48**

## Roy, Alvin

**JAZZ IN PARK ROYAL (Roy, Alvin Star Sound)**
**Album:** Released May '81, on Zodiac by Delta Records. Catalogue no: **ZR 1012**

## Roy, Harry

**ARE YOU LISTENING? (Roy, Harry & His Orchestra)**
**2 LP Set:** Released Nov '73, on Retrospect by EMI Records. Catalogue no: **SH 187/8**

**BUGLE CALL RAG (Roy, Harry & His Orchestra)**
Tracks: / Bugle call rag / It had to be you / Darktown strutter's ball / I've found a new baby / You made a plaything out of my heart / Blues in mayfair / Guilty / Cuban moonlight / Lover man / Leicester square rag / Imaginez / Temptation rag / Old gal's got that new look / Park Lane blues / You're my baby / Canadian capers / After you get what you want, you don't want it / Picadilly rag.
**Album:** Released May '82, on Decca by Decca International. Deleted Jan '88. Catalogue no: **RFL 20**

**EVERYBODY'S SWINGIN' IT NOW (Roy, Harry & His Tiger Ragamuffins)**
Tracks: / Jazz me blues / You gotta know how to dance / Someday, sweetheart / Everybody's swingin' it now / Hot lips / Jealous / Whispering / Poor butterfly / Ev'ry time I look at you / Swing / Scat singers, The / Shine / That's a plenty / Eeny meeny miney mo / Memories of you / Rain / Goodbye blues / I heard a song in a taxi / I'm a ding dong daddy / Farewell blues / You rascal you / Muddy waters / Bugle call rag / Tiger rag / St. Louis blues.
**Cass:** Released 1 Oct '87, on Living Era by Academy Sound & Vision Records. Catalogue no: **ZC AJA 5050**
**Album:** Released 1 Oct '87, on Living Era by Academy Sound & Vision Records. Catalogue no: **AJA 5050**

**GOLDEN AGE OF HARRY ROY AND HIS ORCHESTRA (Roy, Harry & His Orchestra)**
Tracks: / Bugle call rag / Roy rag, The (Roy) / Alexander's ragtime band / Canadian capers / She had to go and lose it at the Astor / Emaline / Mood indigo / Jubilation rag / Tiger rag / Somebody stole my gal / Twelfth St. rag / Nobody's sweetheart / Porcupine rag / Temptation rag / What a difference a day made / Heatwave.
**Album:** Released Jul '83, on Golden Age by EMI Records. Catalogue no: **GX 2508**
**Cass:** Released Jul '83, on Golden Age by EMI Records. Catalogue no: **TC GX 2508**

**HARRY ROY AND HIS ORCHESTRA (Roy, Harry & His Orchestra)**
Tracks: / Truckin' on down / No moon,no stars, just you / London on a rainy night / Troublesome trumpet / Smoke gets in your eyes / Beat o'my heart (The) / Gertie the girl with the gong / Object of my affection, The / Cowboy in Manhatten / Let's have a jubilee / Louisiana lullaby / We're gonna have smooth sailing / Love and a dime / Words are in my heart, The / My hat's on the side of my head / Was in the mood (I) / Hurricane Harry / Stars over Devon / You've got me crying again / Swingly little thingy.
Note: Produced and transfered by Colin Brown. Mono
**Cass:** Released '86, on Old Bean by Submarine Records. Catalogue no: **COLD 8**
**Album:** Released '86, on Old Bean by Submarine Records. Catalogue no: **OLD 8**

**HOT-CHA-MA-CHA-CHA (Roy, Harry & His Orchestra)**
Tracks: / Rock and roll / There's a new day coming / Twelfth Street rag (Bowman) / When a St. Louis woman comes down to New Orleans / Stay out of the south / Canadian capers / Roy rag, The (Roy) / Let's call it a day / Troublesome trumpet / Eadie was a lady / Bugle call rag / Mama dont want no rice and peas or coconut oil / Lover / Build a little home / My pet / Black panther.
**Cass:** Released 1 Sep '86, on Living Era by Academy Sound & Vision Records. Catalogue no: **ZC AJA 5035**
**Album:** Released 1 Sep '86, on Living Era by Academy Sound & Vision Records. Catalogue no: **AJA 5035**

**LET'S SWING IT**
Tracks: / Let's swing it / There's a small hotel / Life is empty without love / Cubalero, The / Remember me / Sentimental fool / Here comes the sandman / Goodnight my love / There's that look in your eyes again / Speaking of the weather / I feel like a feather in the breeze / With plenty of money and you / Love bug will bite you, The / Lookin'

around corners for you / What will I tell my heart / Let's put our heads together / Boo-hoo / All's fair in love and war.
**Album:** Released Dec '88, on Burlington Records by Plant Life Records. Catalogue no: **BUR 013**
**Cass:** Released Dec '88, on Burlington Records by Plant Life Records. Catalogue no: **4 BUR 013**

**MAYFAIR NIGHTS (Roy, Harry & His Orchestra)**
Tracks: / There's a new day comin' / Lou'siana lullaby / Build a little home / Keep young and beautiful / Lonely feet / Beat o' my heart / Ridin' around in the rain / When you climb those golden stairs / Ill wind (you're blowin' me no good) / Dreamy serenade / Like taking candy from a baby / Say it / Casa Loma stomp / What are you going to do (when love comes)? / La cucaracha / Stay as sweet as you are / Continental, The / Love is just around the corner / June in January / Rock and roll.
**Album:** Released Jul '88, on Saville by Conifer Records. Catalogue no: **SVL 171**

**MILENBERG JOYS**
**Album:** on Harlequin by Interstate Music. Catalogue no: **HQ 3022**

**RAGGIN' THE RAGS (Roy, Harry & The Hotcha Boys)**
Tracks: / Tiger rag / Leave it to Eddie / Harry's rag / Leicester Square rag / Love is / Uncle Wilbur / Sweet Georgia Brown / 12th street rag.
**Album:** Released Nov '82, on Joy by President Records. Catalogue no: **JOY 131**

**THERE GOES THAT SONG AGAIN (Roy, Harry & His Band)**
Tracks: / Drummer boy / That's the moon, my son / Missouri scrambler / My heart tells me / Pennsylvania polka / Infatuation / You are my sunshine / There goes that song again / Kindergarten conga / Two pairs of shoes / You're wrong / Tzigane swing / I've got a gal in Kalmazoo / Sweetheart it's you / Victory roll rag / Our back street is Broadway / Sailor with the navy blue eyes, The / Swinging with Rig.
**Cass:** Released '84, on President by President Records. Catalogue no: **TC-PLE 501**
**Album:** Released '83, on President by President Records. Catalogue no: **PLE 501**

**TRUCKIN' ON DOWN (Roy, Harry & His Orchestra)**
Tracks: / What a little moonlight can do / I wish I were twins / Jungle fever / Dr. Heckle and Mr.Jibe / Valentina rumba / Easter parade / You and the night and the music / Blue moon / Stars over Devon / Truckin' on down / Piano madness / My girl's a rhythm fan / Heart of gold / Man of my dreams / Way you look tonight, The / Fine romance, A / Boo-hoo / Rita, the rumba queen / Broken-hearted clown / Why can't we make love?.
**Album:** Released Jul '88, on Saville by Conifer Records. Catalogue no: **SVL 191**
**Cass:** Released Jul '88, on Saville by Conifer Records. Catalogue no: **CSVL 191**

## Rudd, Roswell

**INSIDE JOB**
Tracks: / Sacred song / Mysterioso / Inside job.
**Album:** Released Mar '79, on Freedom Catalogue no: **FLP 41029**

**REGENERATION (Russ, Rosswell /Steve Lacy)**
Note: With Misha Mengelberg, Kent Carter, Han Bennink
**CD:** Released '86, on Soul Note Catalogue no: **SNCD 1054**

## Rugolo, Pete

**INTRODUCING PETE RUGOLO**
**Album:** Released Feb '88, on Fresh Sounds (Spain) by Fresh Sounds Records (Spain). Catalogue no: **FS 165**

**RUGOLOMANIA**
**Album:** Released Feb '88, on Fresh Sounds (Spain) by Fresh Sounds Records (Spain). Catalogue no: **FS 166**

## Ruiz, Hilton

**Biographical details:** Hilton Ruiz was born in 1952 in New York. He is a pianist, comoser and bandleader, increasingly successful in post-bop and Latin-jazz circles. He studied classical piano and played a solo recital at Carnegie Hall at the age of 8; he later played and recorded with Charles Mingus, Roland Kirk and others; his trio LPs appeared on Steeplechase while *Crosscurrents* in 1984 on Stash and had some quintet tracks; A gig at the Village Gate in 1987 with Papa Lucca, Eddie Palmieri celebrated his first LP on a major label, the octet set *Something Grand* on RCA Novus, with Sam Rivers. (Donald Clarke 4.2.88)..

**CROSS CURRENTS**
**Album:** Released Nov '87, on Stash (USA) Catalogue no: **ST 248**

**EL CAMINO (THE ROAD)**
Tracks: / West side blues / Come dance with me / Sometimes I / El camino (the road) / Message from the chief / Eastern vibrations.
**Album:** Released Dec '88, on Novus by BMG Records (UK). Catalogue no: **PL 83024**
**CD:** Released Dec '88, on Novus by BMG Records (UK). Catalogue no: **PD 83024**

**FANTASIA**
**Album:** Released Mar '82, on Denon Deleted '88. Catalogue no: **YX 7548**

**SOMETHING GRAND (Ruiz, Hilton Ensemble)**
Tracks: / Home cookin' / Puerto Rican children / Four west / Something grand / Sunrise over Madarao / One step ahead.
**CD:** Released Nov '87, on RCA by BMG Records (UK). Catalogue no: **PD 83011**
**Cass:** Released Nov '87, on RCA by BMG Records (UK). Deleted Nov '88. Catalogue no: **PK 83011**
**Album:** Released Nov '87, on RCA by BMG Records (UK). Catalogue no: **PL 83011**

**STRUT**
Tracks: / Sidewinder, The / Goin' back to New Orleans / Bluz / Aged in soul / All my love is yours / Soca serenade / Why don't you steal my blues / Lush life (Only on CD.).
**Album:** Released May '89, on Novus by BMG Records (UK). Catalogue no: **PL 83053**
**Cass:** Released May '89, on Novus by BMG Records (UK). Catalogue no: **PK 83053**
**CD:** Released May '89, on Novus by BMG Records (UK). Catalogue no: **PD 83053**

## Rummel, Jack

**BACK TO RAGTIME**
**Album:** Released '86, on Stomp Off (USA) Catalogue no: **SOS 1118**

## Rumsey, Howard

**Biographical details:** Howard Rumsey was born in 1917 in California. He began on piano; played drums in an early Stan Kenton band; began jam sessions at the Lighthouse in Hermosa Beach in 1949, became owner of the club: the Lighthouse All Stars and guests were a role call of modern jazz on the West Coast in the 1950's. (Donald Clarke 4.2.88)..

**JAZZ ROLLS ROYCE (Rumsey, Howard Lighthouse All Stars)**
**Album:** Released Feb '88, on Fresh Sounds (Spain) by Fresh Sounds Records (Spain). Catalogue no: **FS 136**

**MUSIC FOR LIGHTHOUSEKEEPING (Rumsey, Howard Lighthouse All Stars)**
**Album:** Released Dec '81, on Contemporary (Import) Catalogue no: **1007 528**

## Runnin' Wild

**RUNNIN' WILD (Original sounds of the jazz age) (Various artists)**
Tracks: / Runnin' wild: *Ellington, Duke* / Loveable and sweet: *Hanshaw, Annette* / There's a rainbow round my shoulder: *Jolson, Al* / My song: *Vallee, Rudy* / Heebie jeebies: *Boswell Sisters* / Loveless love: *Waller, Fats* / Magnolia: *California Ramblers* / Any old time: *Rodgers, Jimmie* / Egyptian Ella: *Lewis, Ted* / How many times?: *Lucas, Nick* / She's got 'It': *Weems, Ted* / Makin' whoopee: *Whiteman, Paul* / California here I come: *Edwards, Cliff* / Mel: *Etting, Ruth* / Four or five times: *McKinney's Cotton Pickers* / Without that gal: *Austin, Gene* / Home again blues: *Original Dixieland Jazz Band* / Lindy: *Original Dixieland Jazz Band* / Oh, you have no idea: *Tucker, Sophie* / You brought a new kind of love to me: *Chevalier, Maurice* / St. James Infirmary: *Bloom, Rube* / Three little words: *Crumit, Frank* / Painting the clouds with sunshine: *Hylton, Jack*.
**Album:** Released 1 Jan '83, on Living Era by Academy Sound & Vision Rec-

ords. Catalogue no: **AJA 5017**
**Cass:** Released Jan '83, on Living Era by Academy Sound & Vision Records. Catalogue no: **ZC AJA 5017**

## Rural Blues

**RURAL BLUES 1949-53 (Roosevelt Sykes etc). (Various artists)**
**Album:** Released Jan '90, on Blues Master Catalogue no: **MB 904**

**SACRED TRADITION, THE**
**Album:** Released Dec '88, on Herwin by Shanachie Records (USA). Catalogue no: **HER 206**

## Rush, Otis

**Biographical details:** Otis Rush was born in 1934 in Mississippi. He began teaching himself guitar at eight, moved to Chicago in 1948 and became one of the greatest of Chicago blues singers, also playing harmonica and drums. Earliest recordings on Cobra from 1956-58 are compiled on Charly; his *Right Place, Wrong Time* from 1971 was one of the most welcome reissues of 1986. (Donald Clarke 27.5.87)..

**CLASSIC RECORDINGS**
Tracks: / All your love / Three times a fool / She's a good 'un / It takes time / Double trouble / My love will never die / My baby is a good 'un / Checking on my baby / Jump sister Bessie / I can't quit you baby / If you were mine / Groaning the blues / Keep on loving me baby / Sit down baby / Love that woman / Violent love.
**Album:** Released Oct '85, on Charly R&B by Charly Records. Catalogue no: **CRB 1107**
**Cass:** Released Jul '86, on Charly R&B by Charly Records. Catalogue no: **TCCRB 1107**

**COBRA RECORDINGS 1956-58**
**CD:** Released '88, on Flyright by Interstate Music. Catalogue no: **FLYCD 01**

**COLD DAY IN HELL**
**Album:** Released Dec '88, on Delmark (USA) by Delmark Records (USA). Catalogue no: **DL 638**

**FINAL TAKES, THE (Rush, Otis & Buddy Guy)**
**Album:** Released Oct '86, on Flyright by Interstate Music. Catalogue no: **FLY 594**

**GROANING THE BLUES**
**Album:** Released '88, on Flyright by Interstate Music. Catalogue no: **FLY 560**

**LIVE AT THE CHICAGO BLUES FESTIVAL (Rush, Otis & Little Walter)**
**Cass:** Released '88, on Masters (Holland) Catalogue no: **CLMC 9291283**
**Album:** Released '88, on Masters (Holland) Catalogue no: **CL 291283**

**OTHER TAKES, THE (1956-58) (Rush, Otis & Magic Sam)**
**Album:** Released Dec '88, on Flyright by Interstate Music. Catalogue no: **FLY 562**

**OTIS RUSH**
Tracks: / Double trouble / Jump sister Bessie / She's a good 'un (take A) / Checking on my baby / Sit down baby / Love that woman / Keep on loving me baby (Take B) / Keep on loving me baby (Take A) / My baby is a good 'un / If you were mine / I can't quit you baby / All your love / Groaning the blues / It takes time / Violent love / Three times a fool / My love will never die / She's a good 'un (take B).
**Album:** Released Jul '86, on Flyright by Interstate Music. Catalogue no: **FLY 650**

**RIGHT PLACE, WRONG TIME**
Tracks: / Tore up / Right place, wrong time / Easy go / Three times a fool / Rainy night in Georgia / Natural ball / I wonder why / Your turn to cry / Lonely man / Take a look behind.
**Album:** Released Apr '79, on Bullfrog Catalogue no: **BULLFROG 301**
**Album:** Released Mar '87, on Edsel by Demon Records. Catalogue no: **ED 220**

**SO MANY ROADS / LIVE IN CONCERT**
**Album:** Released Dec '88, on Delmark (USA) by Delmark Records (USA). Catalogue no: **DL 643**

**TOPS**
Tracks: / Right place, wrong time / Crosscut saw / Tops / Feels so bad / Gambler's blues / Keep on lovin' me baby / I wonder why.
**CD:** Released Jan '90, on Demon by Demon Records. Catalogue no: **FIEND CD 143**
**Album:** Released Jul '89, on Demon by Demon Records. Catalogue no: **FIEND 143**

**TROUBLES TROUBLES**
**Album:** Released Aug '78, on Sonet by Sonet Records. Catalogue no: **SNTF 756**

## Rushing, Jimmy

**Biographical details:** Jimmy Rushing was born in 1902 in Oklahoma City; he died in NYC in 1972. He was a powerful, always musical and always genial blues singer, called 'Mr Five By Five' on account of his generous girth, and most famous for many years with Count Basie from the late 1930s: Basie said it was often Rushing's spirt which kept him going when the road was tough. The classic Basie small-group session of 1936 produced by John Hammond included *Boogie-Woogie* (aka *I May Be Wrong*) and *Evenin'*, Rushing's property forever after; also famous for *Good Morning Blues, Going To Chicago, Sent For You Yesterday And Here You Come Today*. He led his own band briefly, and made many fine freelance recordings in the 50's and '60s. (Donald Clarke 27.5.87)..

**BIG BAND BLUES 1949-52**
Note: Featuring JB Summers, Tiny Tim, Ernie Fields' Orchestra.
**Album:** Released Sep '87, on Krazy Kat by Interstate Music. Catalogue no: **KK 814**

**BLUESWAY SESSIONS / BLUES YEARS**
Tracks: / Baby don't tell on me / Berkely campus blues / Blues in the dark / Everyday I have the blues / Evil blues / Keep the faith baby / Sent for you yesterday / I left my baby / Sonny boy blues / Bad loser / You can't run around / Tell me I'm not too late / Crying blues / Undecided blues / Take me back baby / We remember Pres.
**2 LP Set:** Released Sep '86, on Charly by Charly Records. Catalogue no: **CDX 13**

**ESSENTIAL JIMMY RUSHING, THE**
Tracks: / I may be wrong / See see rider / Sent for you yesterday / How long how long blues / I can't understand / How you want lovin' done? / My friend Mister Blues / Sometimes I think I do / Goin' to Chicago / Everyday / Rock and roll / Good morning blues / Evenin' / Take me back, baby / Take me with you, baby / If this ain't the blues.
**2 LP Set:** Released May '83, on Vogue Jazz (France) by Vogue Records. Catalogue no: **VJD 556**

**GOOD MOURNIN' BLUES (Rushing, Jimmy & The Count Basie Band)**
**Album:** Released Nov '85, on Affinity by Charly Records. Catalogue no: **AFS 1002**

**I-WANT-A-LITTLE-GIRL**
Tracks: / My baby's business / Jimmy's round the clock blues / Thursday blues / Good mornin' blues / I've got to have you, that's all / I-want-a-little-girl / I'm so lonely / Go get some more you fool / Hi-ho Sylvester / Way I feel, The / In the moonlight / She's mine, she's yours / Where were you? / Somebody's spoiling these women / My last affair / Baby, don't tell on me.
**Album:** on Official by Official Records. Catalogue no: **OFF 3020**

**JAZZ ODYSSEY OF JIMMY RUSHING**
**Album:** Released Feb '88, on Fresh Sounds (Spain) by Fresh Sounds Records (Spain). Catalogue no: **FS 270**

**RUSHING LULLABIES**
**Album:** Released Feb '88, on Fresh Sounds (Spain) by Fresh Sounds Records (Spain). Catalogue no: **FS 271**

**SMITH GIRLS, THE**
**Album:** Released Feb '88, on Fresh Sounds (Spain) by Fresh Sounds Records (Spain). Catalogue no: **FS 273**

**YOU AND ME THAT USED TO BE, THE**
Tracks: / You and me that used to be, The / Fine and mellow / When I grow too old to dream / I surrender dear / Linger awhile / Bei mir bist du schon / My last affair / All God's chillun got rhythm / More than you know / Home / Thanks a million.
**Album:** Released Apr '89, on Bluebird (2) by BMG Records (UK). Catalogue no: **NL 86460**
**Cass:** Released Apr '89, on Bluebird (2) by BMG Records (UK). Catalogue no:

**NK 86460**
**CD:** Released Apr '89, on Bluebird (2) by BMG Records (UK). Catalogue no: **ND 86460**

## Russell, George

**Biographical details:** George Russell was born in 1923 in Cincinatti, Ohio; he played drums in a Benny Carter band, but was replaced by Max Roach; he had an offer from Charlie Parker, but fell ill with TB: while in hospital he began work on his textbook on the modal style, inspired by Miles Davies, who said he wanted to be able 'to play all the changes'. His early compositions included *Cubana-Be--Cubana-Bop*, co-written for a Dizzy Gillespie Carnegie Hall Concert in 1947. His book, The Lydian Concept Of Tonal Organisation, was first published in 1953; he made a few albums over the years (sextet briefly included Eric Dolphy in the early 1960s), worked in Scandinavia for a decade and became a faculty member at the New England Conservatory of Music in 1969. He first toured the UK in early 1986 with a sensational international band that included Courtney Pine, Kenny Wheeler, Palle Mikkelborg, two members of Loose Tubes, Keith Copeland on drums; he returned for the Bracknell Festival in 1987. He has been hailed by Ornette Coleman and many others as one of the most widely influential musicians of his generation. (Donald Clarke 27.5.87)..

**AFRICAN GAME, THE**
Tracks: / Event I: Organic life on earth begins / Event II: The Paleolithic game / Event III: Consciousness / Event IV: The survival game / Event V: The human sensing of unity wiht great nature / Event VI: African Empires / Event VII: Cartesian man / Event VIII: The mega-minimalist age / Event IX: The future.
Note: George Russell has been on the leading edge of jazz since the 1940's as a composer and theorist. His compositions have been performed by Dixxie Gillespie's big band, Charlie Parker, John Coltrane, Miles Davis, and others.'The African Game' is a ten movement, rythmically-charged work performed by a twenty-six piece prchestra.
**CD:** Released Jul '87, on Blue Note by EMI Records. Deleted Aug '89. Catalogue no: **BNZ 82**
**CD:** Released Jul '87, on Blue Note by EMI Records. Deleted Aug '89. Catalogue no: **CDP 746 335 2**
**Album:** Released Jul '89, on Blue Note by EMI Records. Catalogue no: **BT 85103**
**Cass:** Released Dec '85, on Blue Note by EMI Records. Deleted '88. Catalogue no: **TCBT 85103**

**ELECTRONIC SONATA FOR SOULS**
**Album:** Released May '85, on Soul Note Catalogue no: **SN 1034**

**JAZZ IN THE SPACE AGE (Russell, George & His Orchestra)**
Tracks: / Chromatic Universe-Part 1 / Dimensions / Chromatic Universe-Part 2 / Lydiot, The / Waltz from outer space / Chromatic Universe-Part 3.
**Album:** Released Jun '86, on Affinity by Charly Records. Deleted '88. Catalogue no: **AFF 152**

**JAZZ WORKSHOP (Russell, George Smalltet)**
Tracks: / Ye hypocrite, ye Beelzebub / Jack's blues / Livingston I pressume / Ezz-thetic / Night sound / Round Johnny rondo / Fellow delegates / Witch hunt / Sad sergeant, The / Knights of the steamtable / Concerto for Billy the Kid / Ballad of Hix Blewitt (alt. take) / Concerto for Billy the Kid (alt. take).
**CD:** Released Jun '88, on Bluebird (2) by BMG Records (UK). Catalogue no: **ND 86289**
**CD:** Released '88, on Bluebird (2) by BMG Records (UK). Catalogue no: **ND 86467**

**LIVE IN AN AMERICAN TIME SPIRAL (Russell, George New York Band)**
**CD:** Released '86, on Soul Note Catalogue no: **SNCD 1049**

**NEW YORK BIG BAND**
**CD:** Released '86, on Soul Note Catalogue no: **SNCD 1039**

**SO WHAT**
Tracks: / So what / Rhymes / War gewessen / Time spiral.
**CD:** Released Jun '87, on Blue Note by EMI Records. Deleted Aug '89. Catalogue no: **BNZ 83**
**CD:** Released Jun '87, on Blue Note by EMI Records. Deleted Aug '89. Catalogue no: **CDP 746 391 2**
**Album:** Released Jul '89, on Blue Note by EMI Records. Catalogue no: **BT 85132**

**STRATUSPHUNK (Russell, George Sextet)**
**Album:** Released Apr '86, on Original Jazz Classics (USA) by Fantasy Inc (USA). Catalogue no: **OJC 232**

**TIME SPACE (Russell, George Big Band)**
**CD:** Released '88, on Polygram by PolyGram UK Ltd. Catalogue no: **SN 1049 CD**

**TRIP TO PRILLARGURI (Russell, George Sextet)**
Tracks: / Theme / Souls / Event III: Consciousness / VIPs / Stratusphink / Esoteric / Circle / Man on the moon.
**Album:** Released Jul '82, on Soul Note Catalogue no: **SN 1029**

## Russell, Hal

**GENERATION (Russell, Hal & NRG Ensemble & Charles Tyler)**
Tracks: / Sinus up / Poodle cut / Sponge / Tatwas / Cascade / Generation.
Note: Hal Russell is Chicago's best-kept secret, playing drums, trumpet, reeds, and much else. He and four young acolytes sound like a whole orchestra, playing precise, biting, witty, jazz-based by unclassifiable music, and making the average pop group sound like posturing children. On their third album (first to be released in Europe) they are joined by guest reedman Tyler, who began recording in the late '60's with Albert Ayler. Russell, born in 1926, once sang novelty vocals with big bands; here he sings on the title track (for first time on record) with the vitality of a teenager. (Chief Records, June 1989)
**CD:** Released Jun '89, on Chief Catalogue no: **CHIEFCD 5**

## Russell, Luis

**Biographical details:** Luis Russel was born 1902 on an island of Panama; he died in NYC in 1963. The pianist, composer and bandleader had one of the best young black bands in the USA when it recorded more than 30 sides for various labels in 1929-34. The band backed Louis Armstrong for two days at the Savoy in 1935; manager Joe Glaser took them over as Luis's permanent backing band and they lost their identity: Russel was music director for Louis until 1943. He later ran a candy shop, worked as a chauffeur etc. but tracks *Call Of The Freaks*, *Saratonga shout*, *Jersey Lightning*, etc. will be classics as long as records are played. (Donald Clarke 27.5.87)..

**1926-30 (Russell, Luis & His Orchestra)**
Tracks: / 29th and dearborn / Sweet Mumtaz / Plantation joys / Please don't turn me down / Dolly mine / Savoy shout / Call of the freaks, The / It's tight like that / New call of the freaks, The / Feelin' the spirit / Jersey lightning / Way he loves is just too bad, The / Jersey lightning / Broadway rhythm / Doctor blues / Saratoga shout / Song of the Swanee / Louisiana swing / Poor li'l me / On revival day.
**Album:** Released Dec '84, on VJM (Vintage Jazz Music) by Vintage Jazz Music Society(VJM). Catalogue no: **VLP 54**

**1929-30**
**CD:** Released Oct '89, on JSP by JSP Records. Catalogue no: **JSPCD 308**

**1930-1934**
Tracks: / Give me your telephone number / Higginbotham blues / Muggin' lightly / Panama / High tension / I got rhythm / Saratoga drag / Ease on down / Honey, that reminds me / You rascal, you / Goin' to town / Say the word / Freakish blues / Darktown strutters' ball / My blue Heaven / Ghost of the freaks / Hokus pokus / Primitive / Ol' man river.
Note: Classic recordings by one of the hottest groups in the history of jazz. Chronological, of course. Featuring: Red Allen, J.C. Higginbotham, Charlie Holmes, Pops Foster, Albert Nicholas, Dickie Wells, Rex Stewart, etc.

**Album:** Released Apr '86, on VJM (Vintage Jazz Music) by Vintage Jazz Music Society(VJM). Catalogue no: **VLP 57**

**LUIS RUSSELL AND ORCHESTRA 1929-30 (Russell, Luis & His Orchestra)**
**Album:** Released Jan '88, on Swaggie (Australia) Catalogue no: **S 828**

**SAVOY SHOUT**
**CD:** Released Aug '89, on JSP by JSP Records. Catalogue no: **JSPCD 308**

## Russell, Pee Wee

**Biographical details:** Pee Wee Russell was born in 1906 in Virginia; he died in 1969. He played reeds, mainly clarinet and was a unique stylist who played progressively even when stuck in a Dixieland contexts. He was an alcoholic. His music was endlessly rewarding and (like his face, which looked like a weather map) unclassifiable. (Donald Clarke 27.5.87)..

**COLLEGE CONCERT, THE (Russell, Pee Wee & Red Allen)**
Tracks: / Blue Monk / I want a little girl / Body and soul / Pee Wee's blues / Two degrees east, three degrees west / Graduation blues.
**Album:** Released Mar '85, on Jasmine by Hasmick Promotions. Deleted Feb '88. Catalogue no: **JAS 78**

**HOT LICOURICE (Russell, Pee Wee & His Rhythm Cats)**
**Album:** Released Oct '79, on Honeydew Catalogue no: **HD 6614**

**INDIVIDUALISM OF..., THE**
Tracks: / Love is just around the corner / Squeeze me / Ballin' the Jack / I'd do most anything for you / California here I come / St. James infirmary / Baby won't you please come home / Lady's in love with you, The / Struttin' with some barbecue / St. Louis blues / Sweet Lorraine / Sentimental journey / If I had you / Coquette / Lady is a tramp, The.
**2 LP Set:** Released Mar '85, on Savoy Jazz (USA) by Malaco Records (USA). Catalogue no: **SJL 2228**

**JAM SESSION IN SWINGVILLE (Russell, Pee Wee & Coleman Hawkins)**
Tracks: / Jammin' in Swingville / Cool sunrise / Spring's swing / Love me or leave me / I want to be happy / Phoenix / So glad / Things ain't what they used to be / I may be wrong / Vic's spot / Years ago.
**2 LP Set:** Released Apr '76, on Prestige Catalogue no: **PR 24051**

**JAZZ REUNION (Russell, Pee Wee & Coleman Hawkins)**
Tracks: / If I could be with you one hour tonight / Tin tin deo / Mariooch / All too soon / 29th and 8th / What am I here for?.
Note: With Jo Jones, Bob Brookmeyer.
**CD:** Released Jul '88, on Candid Catalogue no: **CCD 9020**
**Album:** Released Jul '88, on Candid Catalogue no: **CS 9020**

**OVER THE RAINBOW**
**Album:** Released Jan '83, on Xanadu Catalogue no: **XAN 192**

**PEE WEE RUSSELL AND THE RHYTHM CATS**
**Album:** Released Apr '81, on Shoestring (1) Catalogue no: **SS 109**

**PIED PIPER OF JAZZ THREE DEUCES AND HOT FOUR, THE**
Tracks: / Jig walk / Deuces wild / Last time I saw Chicago / About face / Take me to the land of jazz / Rose of Washington Square / Keepin' out of mischief now / D. A. blues.
**Album:** Released Sep '83, on Teldec (1) by ASV (Academy Sound & Vision). Catalogue no: **6.25490**

**WE'RE IN THE MONEY**
**Album:** Released Jan '89, on Black Lion Catalogue no: **BLP 60909**
**CD:** Released Jan '89, on Black Lion Catalogue no: **760 909**

## Russian...

**AKVARELLI AND TCHARIVINI GITARY (Russian Jazz Groups)**
**Cass:** Released Feb '79, on Melodiya (USSR) Catalogue no: **SM 00386**

**LIGHT JAZZ (Russian Radio Ensemble)**
**Cass:** Released Feb '79, on Melodiya (USSR) Catalogue no: **M 00177**

**WING GROUP-HELMUT ORUSAAR (Russian Jazz Group)**
**Cass:** Released Feb '79, on Melodiya (USSR) Catalogue no: **SM 00393**

## Rutherford, Paul

**ISKRA 1903 (Rutherford, Paul / Derek Bailey / Barry Guy)**
**2 LP Set:** Released Nov '76, on Incus by Incus Records. Catalogue no: **INCUS 3/4**

**LIVE - MOERS (SOLO TROMBONE 1976)**
**Album:** Released Jul '78, on Ring Catalogue no: **RING 01014**

**NEUPH**
Tracks: / Yep / Realign / Three levels / Paunch and Judies / Chefor / Phase 2 / Neuph.
**Album:** Released May '81, on Sweet Folk All by Sweet Folk All Records. Catalogue no: **SFA 092**

## Rypdal, Terje

**AFRIC POPPERBIRD (Rypdal, Terje / Jan Garbarek / Anderson)**
**Album:** Released May '74, on ECM Catalogue no: **ECM 1007**

**AFTER THE RAIN**
**Album:** Released Dec '76, on ECM Catalogue no: **ECM 1083**

**BLUE (Rypdal, Terje / Chasers)**
Tracks: / Curse, The / Kompet Gar / I disremember quite well / Og hva synes vi om det / Last nite / Blue / Tanga / Om bare.
Note: Personnel: Terje Rypdal - electric guitar, keyboards / Bjorn Kjellemyr - electric & acoustic bass / Audun Kleive - drums, percussion.
**CD:** Released Jul '87, on ECM Catalogue no: **831 516 2**
**Album:** Released Jul '87, on ECM Catalogue no: **ECM 1346**

Terje Rypdal

**CHASER**
Tracks: / Ambiguity / Once upon a time / Geysir / Closer look, A / Orion / Chaser / Transition / Imagi (theme).
Note: In collaboration with the two young Norwegan musicians Audun Kleive (drums) and Bjorn Kjellemyr (bass), Rypdal displays all aspects of his guitar virtuosity. One can find rock inspired pieces with expression solos over complex rhythmic patterns next to lyrical ballads with subtle laters of sounds. His composition ideas and improvisational excursions from the centre driving force behind this powerful trio. The trio have just toured the UK and recieved a great response.
**CD:** Released Dec '85, on ECM Catalogue no: **827 256-2**
**Album:** Released Dec '85, on ECM Catalogue no: **ECM 1303**

**DESCENDRE**
Tracks: / Askjed / Circles / Innseiling / Men of mystery / Speil.
Note: Personnel: Terje Rypdal-guitar, keyboard, flute/Pall Mikkelborg-trumpet, flugelhorn, keyboards/Jon Christensen-drums,percussion.
**CD:** Released Jun '86, on ECM Catalogue no: **829 118 2**

**EOS (Rypdal, Terje & David Darling)**
Tracks: / Laster / Eos / Bedtime story / Light years / Melody / Mirage / Adagietto.
**Album:** Released Feb '84, on ECM Catalogue no: **ECM 1263**

**ODYSSEY**
**CD:** Released Sep '88, on ECM Catalogue no: **835 355-2**
**Album:** Released Oct '75, on ECM Catalogue no: **ECM 1067/68**

**TERJE RYPDAL, MIROSLAV VITOUS AND JACK DEJOHNETTE**
Tracks: / Sunrise / Den forste sne / Will / Believer / Flight / Seasons.
Note: Personnel: Terje Rypdal - guitar, synthesizer, organ / Miroslav Vitous-bass, electric piano / Jack Dejonette-drums
**CD:** Released Aug '85, on ECM Catalogue no: **825 470-2**

**SART (Rypdal, Terje/Stenson/Jan Garbarek)**
**Album:** Released May '74, on ECM Catalogue no: **ECM 1015**
**CD:** Released Nov '89, on ECM Catalogue no: **839 305 2**

**SINGLES COLLECTION, THE**
**CD:** Released Apr '89, on ECM Catalogue no: **837 749-2**
**Album:** Released Apr '89, on ECM Catalogue no: **ECM 1383**
**Cass:** Released Apr '89, on ECM Catalogue no: **837 749-4**

**SUNRISE**
**Cass:** Released Jul '85, on ECM Catalogue no: **7104655**

**TERJE RYPDAL (Rypdal, Terje / Fintl / Jan Garbarek)**
**Album:** Released May '74, on ECM Catalogue no: **ECM 1016**

**TO BE CONTINUED**
**Album:** Released Nov '81, on ECM Catalogue no: **ECM 1192**

**UNDISONUS**
**Album:** Released Mar '90, on New Note Catalogue no: **ECM 1389**
**CD:** Released Mar '90, on New Note Catalogue no: **837 755 2**

**WAVES**
Tracks: / Per ulv / Karusell / Stenskoven / Waves / Dain curse, The / Charisma.
Note: Personnel: Terje Rypdal-electric guitar, RMI keyboard computer, ARP synthesizer/Palle Mikkelborg-trumpet, flugelhorn, RMI, tac piano, ring-modulator/Sveinung Hovens jo- 6 & 4 string electric bases/Jo Christensen-drums, percussion.
**Album:** Released Jan '78, on ECM Catalogue no: **ECM 1110**
**CD:** Released Feb '86, on ECM Catalogue no: **827 419-2**

**WHAT COMES AFTER**
**Album:** Released Mar '74, on ECM Catalogue no: **ECM 1031**
**CD:** Released Nov '89, on ECM Catalogue no: **839 306 2**

**WHENEVER I SEEM TO BE AWAY**
**Album:** Released Feb '75, on ECM Catalogue no: **ECM 1045**

**WORKS: TERJE RYPDAL**
Tracks: / Waves / Den forste sne / Hung, The / Better off without you / Innseiling / Rainbow / Topplue, vooter & skjerf / Descendre.
Note: Personnel: Terje Rypdal, Palle Mikkelborg, Jon Christensen, Miroslav Vitous, Jack DeJohnette, Jan Gabarek, Arild Andersen.
**Album:** Released Jun '89, on ECM Catalogue no: **825 428-1**
**CD:** Released Jun '89, on ECM Catalogue no: **825 428-2**

# S

The following information was taken from the Music Master database on 14th April, 1990.

## Sabien, Randy

**IN A FOG (Sabien, Randy Jazz Quintet)**
**Album:** Released Mar '89, on Flying Fish (USA) by Flying Fish Records (USA). Catalogue no: **FF 297**

## Sackville All Stars

**SACKVILLE ALL STARS CHRISTMAS RECORD**
**Album:** Released '89, on Sackville by Spotlite Records. Catalogue no: **SACK 3038**
**Album:** Released Jan '88, on Sackville by Spotlite Records. Catalogue no: **3038**
**CD:** Released Dec '87, on Sackville by Spotlite Records. Catalogue no: **CD 203 038**

**TRIBUTE TO LOUIS ARMSTRONG**
**CD:** Released Feb '89, on Sackville by Spotlite Records. Catalogue no: **SACKCD 3042**
**Cass:** Released Feb '89, on Sackville by Spotlite Records. Catalogue no: **SACKMC 3042**

## Salsaya Big Band

**LIVE IN LUXOR**
**Album:** Released Oct '86, on Timeless by Timeless Records. Catalogue no: **SJP 209**

## Salty Dogs Jazzband

**ACE IN THE HOLE**
**Album:** Released Jun '88, on GHB by Jazzology Records (USA). Catalogue no: **GHB 207**

## Salvador, Sal

**BERNIES TUNES**
**Album:** Released Aug '88, on Stash (USA) Catalogue no: **ST 251**

**BOO BOO BE DOOP**
**Album:** Released Jul '81, on Affinity by Charly Records. Deleted '88. Catalogue no: **AFF 68**

**IN OUR OWN SWEET WAY**
Tracks: / I'm afraid the masquerade is over / Breezeway / Anthropology / Blue monk / Parallelagram / Mr. P.C. / Somewhere over the rainbow / In your own sweet way.
**Album:** Released Apr '83, on Stash (USA) Catalogue no: **ST 224**

**STOP SMOKING OR ELSE BLUES (Salvador, Sal Quartet)**
**Album:** Released Feb '88, on Fresh Sounds (Spain) by Fresh Sounds Records (Spain). Catalogue no: **FS 227**

**TRIBUTE TO THE GREATS**
**Album:** Released Feb '88, on Fresh Sounds (Spain) by Fresh Sounds Records (Spain). Catalogue no: **FS 207**

**WORLD'S GREATEST JAZZ STANDARDS (Salvador, Sal Quartet)**
**Album:** Released Nov '87, on Stash (USA) Catalogue no: **ST 234**

## Sample Of Blue Notes

**SAMPLE OF BLUE NOTES (Various artists)**
Tracks: / Blowin' the blues: *Silver, Horace* / Blue riff: *Turrentine, Stanley* / Sermon: *Smith, Jimmy (USA)* / Minor's holiday: *Jazz Messengers* / I guess I'll hang my tears out to dry: *Gordon, Dexter* / Round midnight: *Various artists* / Calling all cats: *Donaldson, Lou* / Eye of the hurricane: *Various artists* / Love for sale: *Adderley, Cannonball* / Dig dis: *Burrell, Kenny*.
**Album:** Released Sep '87, on Blue Note by EMI Records. Deleted Nov '88. Catalogue no: **BNX 1**
**Cass:** Released Sep '87, on Blue Note by EMI Records. Deleted Nov '88. Catalogue no: **TCBNX 1**
**CD:** Released Sep '87, on Blue Note by EMI Records. Deleted Aug '89. Catalogue no: **CDP 748 337 2**
**CD:** Released Sep '87, on Blue Note by EMI Records. Catalogue no: **CDBNX 1**

## Sampson, Deryck

**BOOGIE EXPRESS**
Tracks: / Boogie in C / Basin street boogie / Steady time special / Kansas City boogie woogie / Homeless on the range / Monday's wash / Blackberry jam / Table top boogie / Boogie serenade / Hen house boogie / Canal street boogie woogie / Boogie express / Flash in de pan / Boogie de concerto.
**Album:** Released Sep '84, on Harlequin by Interstate Music. Catalogue no: **HQ 2006**

## Sampson, Edgar

**Biographical details:** Edgar Samson (1907-73) played violin and saxophones; he also wrote some of the biggest hits of the swing era: he played with Duke Ellington in 1927, Fletcher Henderson 1931-33, Chick Webb 1933-37; he wrote *Stompin' at the Savoy, Don't be that way, Blue Minor, If dreams come true, Blue Lou, Lullaby in rhythm* 1934-38, mostly for Webb, later big hits for Benny Goodman. He led his own band 1949-51, played with Tito Puente and other Latin bands; led his own combos in the 1960's. [Donald Clarke, April 87].

**SWING SOFTLY SWEET SAMPSON**
Tracks: / Lullaby in rhythm / Hoopdee whodee / If dreams come true / Stompin' at the Savoy / I'll be back for more / Happy and satisfied / Cool and groovy / Blue Lou / Blues made me feel this way, The / Light and sweet / Sweetness of you, The / Don't be that way.
**Album:** Released Jun '83, on Jasmine by Hasmick Promotions. Deleted Feb '88. Catalogue no: **JASM 1020**

## Samson, Sam

**SWING IN THE SPRING 1939/42 (Samson, Sam Och Hans Orkester)**
**Album:** Released Jun '86, on Dragon by Dragon Records. Catalogue no: **DRLP 19**

## San Diego Blues

**SAN DIEGO BLUES (Various artists)**
**Album:** Released Apr '79, on Advent by Advent Records. Catalogue no: **ADVENT 2804**

## Sanborn, David

**Biographical details:**
David Sanborn, born in 1945 in Tampa, Florida, plays alto sax and flute, and has been described as the white Junior Walker for his soulful sound. He played with Albert King and Little Milton at 14, with Paul Butterfield Blues Band on and off 1967-72, with Stevie Wonder, Gil Evans, David Bowie and Paul Simon in the early 1970s, began making successful solo albums. (Donald Clarke, 27.3.88)..

**AS WE SPEAK**
**Album:** Released Jul '82, on Warner Bros. by WEA Records. Catalogue no: **BSK 3650**
**CD:** Released Oct '87, on WEA by WEA Records. Catalogue no: **923650 2**
**Album:** Released Jul '83, on WEA (Import) by WEA Records. Catalogue no: **K 56975**

**BACKSTREET**
Tracks: / I told U so / When you smile at me / Believer / Backstreet / Tear for crystal, A / Bums cathedral / Blue beach / Neither one of us.
**CD:** Released Oct '87, on WEA by WEA Records. Catalogue no: **923906 2**
**Cass:** Released Sep '83, on Warner Bros. by WEA Records. Catalogue no: **923906 4**
**Album:** Released Sep '83, on Warner Bros. by WEA Records. Catalogue no: **923906 1**

### CHANGE OF HEART, A
Tracks: / Chicago song / Imogene / High roller / Tin tin / Breaking point / Change of heart, A / Summer / Dream, The.
**Album:** Released Jan '87, on Warner Bros. by WEA Records. Catalogue no: **925479 1**
**CD:** Released Feb '87, on Warner Bros. by WEA Records. Catalogue no: **925479 2**
**Cass:** Released Jan '87, on Warner Bros. by WEA Records. Catalogue no: **925479 4**

### CHICAGO SONG
Tracks: / Chicago song / Imogene.
**12" Single:** Released May '87, on Warner Bros. by WEA Records. Deleted Jul '88. Catalogue no: **W 8392T**
**7" Single:** Released May '87, on Warner Bros. by WEA Records. Deleted Jan '88. Catalogue no: **W 8392**

### CLOSE UP
Tracks: / Slam / J.T. / Leslie Ann / Goodbye / Same girl / Pyramid / Tough / So far away / You are everything.
**Album:** Released Jun '88, on Reprise/Slash (USA) by WEA Records. Catalogue no: **K 925715 1**
**Cass:** Released Jun '88, on Reprise/Slash (USA) by WEA Records. Catalogue no: **K 925715 4**
**CD:** Released Jun '88, on Reprise/Slash (USA) by WEA Records. Catalogue no: **925715 2**

### DREAM, THE (REMIX)
Tracks: / Dream (remix), The / Imogene / Change of heart, A (Extra track on 12" only).
**7" Single:** Released Feb '87, on Warner Bros. by WEA Records. Deleted Jan '88. Catalogue no: **W 8414**
**12" Single:** Released Feb '87, on Warner Bros. by WEA Records. Deleted Jan '88. Catalogue no: **W 8414T**

### HIDEAWAY
Tracks: / Hideaway / Carly's song / Anything you want / Seduction, The / Lisa / If you would be mine / Creeper / Again & again.
**Album:** Released Mar '81, on Warner Bros. by WEA Records. Catalogue no: **BSK 3379**

### LET IT SPEAK
**Album:** Released Mar '84, on Warner Bros. by WEA Records. Catalogue no: **K 56975**

### LET'S JUST SAY GOODBYE
Tracks: / Let's just say goodbye / Seduction, The.
**7" Single:** Released Jul '81, on Warner Bros. by WEA Records. Catalogue no: **LV 46**

### LOVE AND HAPPINESS
Tracks: / Love and happiness / Run for cover / Hideaway (Only on 12" single.).
**7" Single:** Released Nov '84, on Warner Bros. by WEA Records. Deleted '87. Catalogue no: **W 9015**
**12" Single:** Released Nov '84, on Warner Bros. by WEA Records. Deleted '87. Catalogue no: **W 9015 T**

### LOVE AND HAPPINESS (VIDEO)
**VHS:** Released '88, on Kay Jazz (video) by Kay Jazz. Catalogue no: **KJ 077**

### NEITHER ONE OF US
Tracks: / Neither one of us / Let's just say goodbye / Love is not enough.
**12" Single:** Released Jan '84, on Warner Bros. by WEA Records. Catalogue no: **W 9430T**
**7" Single:** Released Jan '84, on Warner Bros. by WEA Records. Catalogue no: **W 9430**

### STRAIGHT TO THE HEART
Tracks: / Hideaway / Straight to the heart / Run for cover / Smile / Lisa / Love and happiness / Lotus blossom / One hundred ways.
**CD:** Released Jan '86, on Warner Bros. by WEA Records. Catalogue no: **9251 50 2**
**Album:** Released Nov '84, on Warner Bros. by WEA Records. Catalogue no: **925150 1**

### TAKIN' OFF
**CD:** Released '89, on WEA by WEA Records. Catalogue no: **927 295 2**

### VOYEUR
Tracks: / Let's just say goodbye / It's you / Wake me when it's over / One in a million / Run for cover / All I need is you / Just for you.
**Cass:** Released May '81, on Warner Bros. by WEA Records. Catalogue no: **D4 56900**
**Album:** Released May '81, on Warner Bros. by WEA Records. Deleted '83. Catalogue no: **K 56900**
**CD:** Released May '81, on Warner Bros. by WEA Records. Catalogue no: **256 900**

## Sanchez, Poncho

### BIEN SABROSO
Tracks: / Ahora / Bien sabroso / Nancy / Keeper of the flame / Brisa / Sin timbal / Una mas / Half and half / I can.
**CD:** Released Jul '88, on Concord Jazz by Concord Jazz Records (USA). Catalogue no: **CCD 4239**
**Album:** Released Jun '84, on Concord Jazz by Concord Jazz Records (USA). Catalogue no: **CJP 239**

### CHILE CON SOUL
Tracks: / Song for Cal / Night in London, A / Mama guela / Soul burst / Will you still be mine / Lover come back to me / Chile con soul / Nueva charanga (CD only.) / Quieto / Commigo (CD only.) / Ti-pon-pa / Cold sweat / Funky broadway.
**CD:** Released Mar '90, on Concord by Concord Jazz Records (USA). Catalogue no: **CCD 4406**
**Cass:** Released Mar '90, on Concord by Concord Jazz Records (USA). Catalogue no: **CJP 406C**

### EL CONGUERO
Tracks: / Siempre me va bien / Mi negra / Shiny stockings / Si no hay amor / Yumbambo / Agua dulce / Night walk / Tin tin deo / Cuidado.
Note: El Conguero (the Conga Player) follows Sanchez's Grammy-nominated album Bien Sabrosol and is his third Concord album as a leader. His years of association with Cal Tjader were an explosive springboard for his own Latin jazz rhythms. Personnel: Poncho Sanchez - congas, bata; Ramon Banda - timbales; Tony Banda - bass; Sal Cracchiolo - trumpet, flugelhorn; Dick Mitchell - tenor & alto sax, flute; David Romero - bongos; Art Velasco - trombone.
**CD:** Released Jul '88, on Concord Jazz by Concord Jazz Records (USA). Catalogue no: **CCD 4286**
**Album:** Released Dec '85, on Concord Jazz by Concord Jazz Records (USA). Catalogue no: **CJP 286**

### FUERTE - STRONG
Tracks: / Fuerte! / Baila mi gente / It could happen to you / Lo llores, mi corazon / Ixtapa / Co co my my / Siempre te amare / Alafia / Daahoud.
Note: Fuerte! is right - Poncho Sanchez's music is strong. He and his band turn in a superlative programme covering more musical territory than any other Latin-jazz aggregation: mambos, cha chas, boleros, bossa novas, guagiras, all expertly performed with precision ensembles and top-notch solos. Poncho Sanchez - congas; Ramon Banda - timbales; Tony Banda - bass; Sal Cracchiolo - trumpet, flugelhorn; Kenny Goldberg - tenor sax, flute; Charlie Otwell - piano; David Romero - bongos; Art Velasco - trombone. (IMS Records, May 1988.)
**CD:** Released May '88, on Concord Jazz by Concord Jazz Records (USA). Catalogue no: **CCD 4340**
**Album:** Released May '88, on Concord Jazz by Concord Jazz Records (USA). Catalogue no: **CJP 340**
**Cass:** Released May '88, on Concord Jazz by Concord Jazz Records (USA). Catalogue no: **CJPC 340**

### GAVIOTA
**CD:** Released Dec '86, on Discovery (USA) by Discovery Records (USA). Catalogue no: **DSCD 930**

### LA FAMILIA
Note: La familia features spicy Latin arrangements of jazz standards, sizzling salsas, and a whole range of Latin rhythms. A highlight of the recording is Poncho's gutsy, soulful vocals on the funky 60's R & B classic, *Let a man be a man.*
Personnel: Poncho Sanchez - congas, perc, lead vocals; Charlie Otwell - piano; Kenny Goldberg - alto & tenor saxophone, flute; Tony Banda - bass, vocals; David Romero - bongos, percussion, vocals, congas; Ramon Banda - timable, bata, drums; Sal Cracchiolo - trombone, flugelhorn; Art Velasco - trombone, vocals. Special guest: Gary Foster - alto sax).
**Cass:** Released Feb '89, on Concord by Concord Jazz Records (USA). Catalogue no: **CJP 369 C**
**CD:** Released Feb '89, on Concord by Concord Jazz Records (USA). Catalogue no: **CCD 4369**
**Album:** Released Feb '89, on Concord by Concord Jazz Records (USA). Catalogue no: **CJP 369**

**PAPA GATO**
Tracks: / Quindembo / Papa Gato / Serenidade / Jumpin' with Symphony Sid / Baila baila / Pan dulce / Tania / Senor blues / Manteca.
Note: Poncho's fourth Concord Picante release is hot, melodic and danceable... rich with solos and ensemble work. Years of performing with vibist Cal Tjader served as a springboard for this giant of Latin jazz.
Personnel: Poncho Sanchez - congas & bata; Justo Almario - alto & tenor saxes, flute; Ramon Banda - timbales; Tony Banda - bass; Sal Cracchiolo - trumpet, flugelhorn; Charlie Otwell - piano; David Romero - bongos; Art Velasco - trombone.
**Album:** Released Mar '87, on Concord Picante by Concord Jazz Records (USA). Catalogue no: **CJP 310**

**PONCHO**
Tracks: / Baila Mi Gente / Morning / Mama Guela / Gaviota.
Note: Poncho Sanchez - congas, vocal chorus; Clare Fischer - keyboards; Johnny Nelson - lead vocals, maracas, guiro; Alex Acuna - timbales, vocal chorus; Victor Pantoja - bongos, vocal chorus; Humberto Cane - bass; Mayo Tiana - trombone; Steve Huffsteter - trumpet, flugelhorn; Gary Foster - alto sax, flute.
**Album:** Released '88, on Discovery (USA) by Discovery Records (USA). Catalogue no: **DS 799**

**SONANDO**
Tracks: / Night in tunisia / Sonando / Summer knows / Con tres tambores bata / Almendra / Sueno / Cals pals / Peruchin / Este san.
Note: This is the recording that established Poncho Sanchez as a premier conga player and percussionist.
Personnel: Poncho Sanchez - congas, percussion; Tony Banda - bass; Gary Foster - saxophone, flute; Steven Huffsteter - trumpet; Dick Mitchell - saxophone, flute; Jose Perico Hernandez - vocal; Ramon Banda - timbales, drums; Luis Conti - bongos, bata, percussion; Mark Levine - trombone; Charlie Otwell - piano.
**Album:** Released Mar '83, on Concord Jazz by Concord Jazz Records (USA). Catalogue no: **CJP 201**
**Cass:** Released Mar '83, on Concord Jazz by Concord Jazz Records (USA). Catalogue no: **CJPC201**
**CD:** Released Nov '89, on Concord Jazz by Concord Jazz Records (USA). Catalogue no: **CCD 4201**

**STRAIGHT AHEAD**
Tracks: / Pensativa / I remember spring / Once again.
Note: Arranged and conducted by Clare Fischer. Personnel: Clare Fischer - piano; Luis Conte - percussion; Oscar Meza - bass; Gary Foster - saxophone, flute; Mayo Tiana - trombone; Poncho Sanchez - conga.
**Album:** Released '88, on Discovery (USA) by Discovery Records (USA). Catalogue no: **DS 813**

## Sanctified Jug Bands

**COMPLETE RECORDINGS IN CHRONOLOGICAL ORDER 1928-30**
Note: Artists: Elder Richard Bryant, Brother Williams, Memphis Sanctified Singers, Holy Ghost Sanctified Singers.
**Album:** Released Sep '87, on Matchbox by Flyright Records. Catalogue no: **MSE 222**

**SANCTIFIED JUG BANDS 1928-30 (Various artists)**
**Album:** Released Sep '87, on Matchbox by Flyright Records. Catalogue no: **MSE 222**

## Sanders, Coon

**NIGHTHAWK BLUES Vol. 1**
**Album:** Released Jan '88, on Broadway (USA) Catalogue no: **BR 144**

## Sanders, Joe

**VICTORY PARADE (Sanders, Joe & His Orchestra/Henry King & His Orch.)**
**Album:** Released Oct '86, on Aircheck (USA) by Kiner Ents.(USA). Deleted '88. Catalogue no: **AIRCHECK 7**

## Sanders, Pharoah

**Biographical details:** Saxophonist Pharoah Sanders' real name is Farrell. He was born in 1940 in Little Rock, Arkansas, played with R&B bands; later with Sun Ra, John Coltrane; began making his own albums in 1964 on ESP, in 1969 on Impulse: the 1969 band pursued Coltrane's spiritual quest with an exotic sound at a gentler level of intensity, with Lonnie Liston Smith and the African-inspired yodel of vocalist Leon Thomas (born in 1937 in East St.Louis, Illinois); both had left by the time *Thembi* was recorded by a sextet, Sanders' fourth Impulse LP and the second to make the pop album chart. *Love will find a way* on Arista in 1977 was the third USA chart entry, with a 23-piece band plus vocalists. (Donald Clarke, April 87).

**AFRICA**
Tracks: / You've got to have freedom / Naima / Origin / Speak low / After the morning / Africa.
**Album:** Released Jan '88, on Timeless by Timeless Records. Catalogue no: **SJP 253**

**BLACK UNITY**
**Album:** Released Oct '85, on Impulse by Impulse Records. Catalogue no: **AS 9026**

**JOURNEY TO THE ONE**
**Album:** Released Sep '88, on Theresa (USA) by Theresa Records (USA). Catalogue no: **TR 108**
**CD:** Released Sep '88, on Theresa (USA) by Theresa Records (USA). Catalogue no: **TRCD 108**

**KARMA**
Tracks: / Creator has a master plan, The / Creater has a master plan, The (part 2) / Colors.
Note: Recorded 1969. Personnel: Pharoah Sanders - tenor sax; Leon Thomas - vocals, percussion; Lonnie Listen Smith - piano; Richard Davis - bass; Reggie Workman - bass; William Hart - drums.
**CD:** Released Jun '89, on MCA (Impulse Jazz) Catalogue no: **MCAD 39122**
**Album:** Released Jun '89, on MCA (Impulse Jazz) Catalogue no: **MCA 39122**

**PHAROAH SANDERS LIVE**
**Album:** Released Sep '88, on Theresa (USA) by Theresa Records (USA). Catalogue no: **TR 116**

**PRAYER BEFORE DAWN, A**
Tracks: / Light at the edge of the world, The / Dedication to James W Clark / Softly for Shyla / After the rain / Greatest love of all, The / Midnight at Yoshi's / Living space / In your own sweet way / Christmas song, The.
Note: Tenor and soprano saxophonist Pharoah Sanders delivers a superb set that features compositions from such diverse talents as John Coltrane, Dave Brubeck, Mel Torme and of course himself. Also featured is the hit song by Whitney Houston *Greatest love of all.* Over 55 minutes of music.
Personnel: Pharoah Sanders - tenor & soprano sax; John Hicks - piano; Alvin Queen - drums.
**Album:** Released Nov '89, on Theresa (USA) by Theresa Records (USA). Catalogue no: **TR 127**
**CD:** Released Nov '89, on Theresa (USA) by Theresa Records (USA). Catalogue no: **TRCD 127**

**REJOICE**
**Album:** Released Sep '88, on Theresa (USA) by Theresa Records (USA). Catalogue no: **TR 112**
**CD:** Released Sep '88, on Theresa (USA) by Theresa Records (USA). Catalogue no: **TRCD 112**

**TAUHID**
**Album:** Released Oct '85, on Impulse by Impulse Records. Catalogue no: **AS 9138**

**THEMBI**
Tracks: / Astral travelling / Red black and green / Thembi / Love / Morning prayer / Bailophone dance.
**Cass:** Released Sep '82, on Jasmine by Hasmick Promotions. Catalogue no: **JAS C53**
**Album:** Released Sep '82, on Jasmine by Hasmick Promotions. Deleted Feb '88. Catalogue no: **JAS 53**

## Sandke, Jordan

**RHYTHM IS OUR BUSINESS (Sandke, Jordan & Jaki Byard & Co.)**
**Album:** Released Mar '87, on Stash (USA) Catalogue no: **ST 259**

## Sandoval, Arturo

**JUST MUSIC**
Tracks: / El misterioso / Sambeando / Georgia on my mind / Libertao carnaval / Saving all my love / Al chicoy / My love.
**Album:** Released Sep '89, on Jazz House Catalogue no: **JHR 008**

**NO PROBLEM**
Tracks: / Nuestro blues / Los elefantes / Donna Lee / Rimsky / Campana / Fiesta mojo.
Note: An exceptional Cuban trumpet player, Arturo Sandoval and his band recorded this album live at Ronnie Scott's Club in August 1986. Sandoval has been a yearly visitor to the Club for the past three years, and his reputation and audience has grown with each visit.
**Album:** Released Nov '88, on Jazz House Catalogue no: **JHR 001**
**Cass:** Released Nov '88, on Jazz House Catalogue no: **JHC 001**

**STRAIGHT AHEAD (Sandoval, Arturo & Chucho Valdes)**
**Album:** Released 12 Apr '89, on Jazz House Catalogue no: **JHR 007**

**TUMBAITO**
**Album:** Released 12 Apr '89, on Messidor (Germany) Catalogue no: **15973**
**CD:** Released 12 Apr '89, on Messidor (Germany) Catalogue no: **15974**

## Sandstrom, Nisse

**YOUNG FOREVER (Sandstrom, Nisse/Horace Parlan/Red Mitchell)**
**Album:** Released Mar '87, on Phontastic (Sweden) Catalogue no: **PHONT 7562**

## Sandvik Big Band

**SANDVIK BIG BAND**
Note: Featuring Ann Kristin/Claes Jansson
**Album:** Released Jun '86, on Dragon by Dragon Records. Catalogue no: **DRLP 26**

## Santa Claus Blues

**SANTA CLAUS BLUES (Various artists)**
Note: Including Louis Prima, Clarence Williams, Louis Armstrong, Johnny Otis, Count Basie.
**CD:** Released Aug '89, on Jass Catalogue no: **JASSCD 3**
**Album:** Released Jun '88, on Jass Catalogue no: **JASS 8**

## Santamaria, Mongo

**HAPPY AS A FAT RAT**
**Album:** Released Mar '89, on Sterns by Sterns African Records Centre. Catalogue no: **VS 61**

**IMAGES: MONGO SANTAMARIA**
**Album:** Released Mar '89, on Sterns by Sterns African Records Centre. Catalogue no: **VS 92**

**MONGO MAGIC**
**Album:** Released Apr '84, on Roulette by Vogue Records. Catalogue no: **520 319**

**MONGO'S GROOVE**
Tracks: / Manteca / Pachanga twist / Dot dot dot / Para ti / Conga pa gozar / Watermelon man / Sweet tater pie / Este mambo / Happy now / Nothing for nothing.
**Album:** Released Oct '87, on BGP by Ace Records. Catalogue no: **BGP 1001**
**Cass:** Released Sep '87, on BGP by Ace Records. Deleted '89. Catalogue no: **BGPC 1001**

**OLE OLA**
Note: Combining the most compatible elements of jazz and pop music with the polyrhythms of Cuba and Africa.
**Cass:** Released Aug '89, on Concord Picante by Concord Jazz Records (USA). Catalogue no: **CJP 387C**
**CD:** Released Aug '89, on Concord Picante by Concord Jazz Records (USA). Catalogue no: **CCD 4387**
**Album:** Released Aug '89, on Concord Picante by Concord Jazz Records (USA). Catalogue no: **CJP 387**

**RED HOT**
Tracks: / Watermelon man / A mi no me enganan / Jai alai / Jamaican sunrise / Afro-Cuban fantasy / Sambita.
**Album:** Released '79, on CBS by CBS Records. Deleted '84. Catalogue no: **CBS 83340**

**SOCA ME NICE**
Tracks: / Con mi ritmo / Cookie / Cu-bop alert / Day tripper / Kathy's waltz / Quiet fire / Soca me nice / Tropical breeze.
Note: Legendary Cuban conga player Mongo Santamaria is hot. *Soca me nice* is full of spicy rhythms, tight ensemble passages and fiery solos.
Personnel: Mongo Santamaria - congas, bongos; Johnny Almendra Andreu - drums, timbales; Humberto Nengue Hernandez - percussion, vocals; Bob Quaranta - piano; Ray Martinez - piano; Ray Vega - trumpet, flugelhorn; Bobby Porcelli - alto & baritone sax, flute; Angelo-Mark Pagan - vocals; Marty Sheller - conductor.
**Cass:** Released Nov '88, on Concord by Concord Jazz Records (USA). Catalogue no: **CJP 362 C**
**CD:** Released Nov '88, on Concord by Concord Jazz Records (USA). Catalogue no: **CCD 4362**
**Album:** Released Nov '88, on Concord by Concord Jazz Records (USA). Catalogue no: **CJP 362**

**SOY YO**
Tracks: / La manzana (the apple) / Sweet love / Soy yo (that's me) / Salazar / Mayeya / Oasis / Smooth operator / Un dia de playa (a day at the beach).
**Cass:** Released Oct '87, on Concord Jazz by Concord Jazz Records (USA). Catalogue no: **CJPC 327**
**CD:** Released Oct '87, on Concord Jazz by Concord Jazz Records (USA). Catalogue no: **CCD 4327**
**Album:** Released Oct '87, on Concord Jazz by Concord Jazz Records (USA). Catalogue no: **CJP 327**

**WATERMELON MAN**
Tracks: / Watermelon man / Funny money / Cut that cane / Get the money / Boogie cha-cha blues / Don't bother me no more / Love oh love / Yeh-yeh / Peanut vendor / Go git it / Bayou roots / Sauvito / El toro / Fat back / Mongo's groove / Creole / Para ti / Jungle bit / My sound / Morning after / Nothing for nothing.
**Album:** Released Apr '81, on Milestone by Ace Records. Deleted Apr '86. Catalogue no: **M 47012**

**YAMBU (Santamaria, Mongo Y Sus Ritmos Afro Cubanos)**
Tracks: / Yeye / Congobel / Macunsere / Timbales & bongo / Yambu / Bricamo / Longoito / Conga pa gozar / Mi guaguanco / Columbia.
**Album:** Released Nov '88, on Globestyle by Ace Records. Catalogue no: **ORB 036**

## Sarafina

**SARAFINA Featuring Hugh Masakela (Various artists)**
**Cass:** Released Aug '88, on Shanachie by Shanachie Records (USA). Catalogue no: **SHANC 43052**
**CD:** Released Aug '88, on Shanachie by Shanachie Records (USA). Catalogue no: **SHANCD 43052**
**Album:** Released Jun '88, on Shanachie by Shanachie Records (USA). Catalogue no: **SHAN 43052**
**CD:** Released Jan '89, on RCA (France) by BMG Records (France). Catalogue no: **BMG 9304.2**
**Cass:** Released Jan '89, on RCA (France) by BMG Records (France). Catalogue no: **BMG 9304.4**
**Cass:** Released Jul '89, on RCA by BMG Records (UK). Catalogue no: **RK 89307**
**CD:** Released Jul '89, on RCA by BMG Records (UK). Catalogue no: **RD 89307**
**Album:** Released Jan '89, on RCA (France) by BMG Records (France). Catalogue no: **BMG 9304.1**

## Sarde, Cliff

**DREAMS OUT LOUD**
**Album:** Released '87, on Passport Jazz (USA) by Jem Records Inc.(USA). Catalogue no: **PJ 88034**
**Cass:** Released '87, on Passport Jazz (USA) by Jem Records Inc.(USA). Catalogue no: **PJC 88034**
**CD:** Released '87, on Passport Jazz (USA) by Jem Records Inc.(USA). Catalogue no: **PJCCD 88034**

## Satchmo Legacy Band

**SALUTE TO POPS VOL.1**
**CD:** Released Sep '89, on Soul Note Catalogue no: **121116-2**
**Album:** Released Sep '89, on Soul Note Catalogue no: **121116-1**

## Sato, Masahiko

**AS IF**
Tracks: / Cajaput trip / Waltz for Debbie / Nardis / Dead end / How my heart sings / As if / My foolish heart / Israel.
Note: Personnel: Masahiko Satoh - piano; Eddie Gomez - bass; Steve Gadd - drums.
**CD:** Released '88, on Denon Catalogue no: **C38-7455**

**TRINITY**
**Album:** Released Jan '82, on Enja (Germany) by Enja Records (West Germany). Catalogue no: **ENJA 2008**

## Sauter, Eddie

**Biographical details:** Eddie Sauter (1914-1981) was one of the great arrangers of the Swing Era, writing for Charlie Barnet, then doing virtually all the writing for Red Norvo and Mildred Bailey in the late 1930's when their popular band was a hit on the radio. Then he worked for Benny Goodman, many others; with Bill Finegan (born 1917), famous for some of Glenn Miller's best arrangements, he formed the Sauter-Finegan band, which had very clever and witty hits in the early 1950's with unusual instrumentation. Finegan revived that band in New York in 1987. (Donald Clarke, April 1987)..

**DIRECTIONS IN MUSIC (Sauter, Eddie/Bill Finegan)**
Tracks: / Doodletown fifers / Azure-te / When hearts are young / April in Paris / Moonlight sleighride / Nina never knew / Love is a simple thing / Foggy day, A / How about choo (how about you?) / Autumn leaves / Two bats in a cave / Over the rainbow / Wild wings in the woods / These foolish things / Horseplay / Dream play / Clarinet a la King / Old folks / Thundisbreak, The (the thunderer).
**CD:** Released Apr '89, on Bluebird (2) by BMG Records (UK). Catalogue no: **ND 86468**
**Cass:** Released Apr '89, on Bluebird (2) by BMG Records (UK). Catalogue no: **NK 86468**
**Album:** Released Apr '89, on Bluebird (2) by BMG Records (UK). Catalogue no: **NL 86468**

**RETURN OF THE DOODLETOWN FIFERS, THE (Sauter, Eddie/Bill Finegan)**
Tracks: / Doodletown fifers / April in Paris / Churchmouse / When hearts are young / One is a lonely number / Doodletown races / Midnight sleighride / Moonlight on the ganges / Foggy day, A / Rain / Thursday's child / Darn that dream.
Note: Eddie Sauter and Bill Finegan and their orchestra were a successful and very adventurous post-war band. This album features tracks from the 50's which were re-recorded in stereo in the early 60's. Includes *Midnight sleighride*, their well-known Christmas track. Original American sleeve. Nothing currently available from Sauter & Finegan. Similar to the sounds of Ray Anthony, Nelson Riddle and Billy May.
**Album:** Released Dec '85, on Capitol by EMI Records. Deleted Nov '88. Catalogue no: **ED 2607691**
**Cass:** Released Dec '85, on Capitol by EMI Records. Deleted Nov '88. Catalogue no: **ED 2607694**

## Savannah Jazzband

**WITH TRADITION (Savannah Jazzband/Mary Asquith)**
**Album:** Released '88, on Tradition Catalogue no: **TSR 029**

## Savitt, Jan

**Biographical details:** Violinist Jan Savitt was born in Russia, probably in 1908; he died in California in 1948. He was a child prodigy who led one of America's most popular dance bands; several hits 1938-42 included the band's theme, *720 in the books*, so-called because that was the number on the arrangement. His popular vocalist Bon-Bon was black, unusual then. (Donald Clarke, April 87).

**FUTURISTIC SHUFFLE 1938-41 (Savitt, Jan & His Orchestra)**
**Album:** Released Jun '88, on Bandstand Catalogue no: **BS 7113**
**Cass:** Released Jun '88, on Bandstand Catalogue no: **BS 7113C**

**IN DISCO ORDER VOL.1**
**Album:** Released Jul '77, on Ajax (USA) Catalogue no: **AJAX 113**

**JAN SAVITT - 1938 VOL.2**
**Album:** Released Apr '79, on Ajax (USA) Catalogue no: **AJAX 152**

**JAN SAVITT - 1938 VOL.3**
**Album:** Released Apr '79, on Ajax (USA) Catalogue no: **AJAX 162**

**JAN SAVITT AND THE TOP HATTERS (Savitt, Jan & The Top Hatters)**
**Album:** Released Aug '89, on Golden Era by Delta Records. Catalogue no: **GELP 15096**

## Savoy Hotel Orpheans

**STOMP OFF, LET'S GO**
Tracks: / Eccentric / Oh Eva / Hard hearted Hannah / Copenhagen / Come on over / Blue evening blues / Oh that sweet in suite 16 / Stomp off, let's go / Dinah / Static strut / Jig walk / Hop skip / I'm telling the birds / Back beats / Little brown baby / Vladivostock / Ain't that too bad? / That's my hap-hap-happiness.
**Cass:** Released 20 Mar '87, on Halcyon (USA) by Submarine Records. Catalogue no: **CHDL 111**
**Album:** Released 20 Mar '87, on Halcyon (USA) by Submarine Records. Catalogue no: **HDL 111**

## Savoy Jazzmen

**JUBILEE**
**Album:** Released May '86, on Burlington Records by Plant Life Records. Catalogue no: **BURL 018**

**LATEST RELEASE**
**Album:** Released May '86, on Burlington Records by Plant Life Records. Catalogue no: **BURL 002**

**ONCE MORE FOR LUCK**
**Album:** Released '88, on Burlington Records by Plant Life Records. Catalogue no: **BURL 024**

**SAVOY RAG**
Tracks: / Button up your overcoat / Savoy rag / Porter's love song to a chambermaid, A / Cakewalking babies from home / Mabel / Chant / Heebie jeebies / Summertime / Buddy's habit / Black and blue / Too busy / Going home.
Note: Recorded live.
**Album:** Released Nov '81, on Burlington Records by Plant Life Records. Catalogue no: **BURL 010**

**YOU'VE GOT THE RIGHT KEY**
Tracks: / 1919 march / Papa dip / Petite Fleur / Shout 'em Aunt Tillie / Jenny's ball / Jeep's blues / Dapper Dan / You've got the right key.
Note: Six-piece outfit from Cambridge recorded at a club session.
**Album:** Released Nov '81, on Burlington Records by Plant Life Records. Catalogue no: **BURL 001**

## Sax Legends

**SAX LEGENDS (Various artists)**
**Album:** Released May '88, on Jazz Life Catalogue no: **2673041**
**CD:** Released May '88, on Jazz Life Catalogue no: **267 304 2**
**Cass:** Released May '88, on Jazz Life Catalogue no: **2673044**

## Saxophone

**SAXOPHONE (Various artists)**
Note: *Saxophone* is a superb collection of performances from some of the all-time great exponents of an instrument which, more than any other, is synonymous with jazz. Featured stars include John Coltrane, Coleman Hawkins, Eric Dolphy, Al Cohn, Cannonball Adderly, Zoot Sims and Nathan Davis.
**CD:** Released May '89, on West Wind Catalogue no: **WWCD 2013**

## Sayama, Masahiro

**PLAY ME A LITTLE MUSIC**
Note: Mainstream jazz from one of Japan's top keyboard players.
**CD:** Released Jul '88, on JVC Catalogue no: **JD 3305**
**Cass:** Released Jul '88, on JVC Catalogue no: **JC 3305**

## Schaefer, Hal

**EXTRAORDINARY JAZZ PIANIST, THE**
Tracks: / You are too beautiful / Yesterdays / You stepped out of a dream / I'll take romance / I can't get started / Tangerine.
Note: Personnel: Hal Schaefer - piano; Fred Atwood - bass; Alvin Stoller - drums.
**Album:** Released '88, on Discovery (USA) by Discovery Records (USA). Catalogue no: **DS 781**

**RCA JAZZ WORKSHOP, THE**
**Album:** Released Feb '88, on Fresh Sounds (Spain) by Fresh Sounds Records (Spain). Catalogue no: **FS 82**

## Schifrin, Lalo

**ANNO DOMINI**
**Album:** Released Mar '86, on BBC by BBC Records & Tapes. Catalogue no: **REB 561**
**Cass:** Released Mar '86, on BBC by BBC Records & Tapes. Catalogue no: **ZCF 561**

**JAWS**
Tracks: / Jaws.
**7" Single:** Released Oct '76, on CTI (1) by Polydor Ltd. Deleted Oct '79. Catalogue no: **CTSP 005**

## Schnitter, David

**GLOWING**
**Album:** Released '88, on Muse by Black & Blue Records. Catalogue no: **MR 5222**

**GOLIATH**
Tracks: / Swing thing / Goliath / My funny valentine / Memories / Night and day.
Note: David Schnitter - tenor sax; Hubert Eaves - keyboards; Cecil McBee - bass; Eddie Moore - drums; Claudio Roditi - trumpet (second and fourth tracks). Recorded: 29 October 1977.
**Album:** Released Apr '81, on Muse by Black & Blue Records. Catalogue no: **MR 5153**

**INVITATION**
Tracks: / Invitation / Blue Monk / Body and soul / Donna Lee / Fat Face Fenner's saloon.
Note: Dave Schnitter - tenor sax; Mickey Tucker - piano; James Leary - bass; Ed Marshall - drums.
**Album:** Released Apr '81, on Muse by Black & Blue Records. Catalogue no: **MR 5108**

**THUNDERING**
Tracks: / Thundering / Stardust / Flying cloud / Caa purange / Herb's blues / There goes the ball game.
**Album:** Released Apr '81, on Muse by Black & Blue Records. Catalogue no: **MR 5197**

## Schoof, Manfred

**DISTANT THUNDER**
**Album:** Released Jan '82, on Enja (Germany) by Enja Records (West Germany). Catalogue no: **ENJA 2066**

## Scobey, Bob

**ALEXANDER'S JAZZ BAND (Scobey, Bob, Alexander's Jazz Band)**
**Album:** Released Dec '86, on Dawn Club by Cadillac Music. Catalogue no: **DC 12004**

**BOB SCOBEY'S FRISCO BAND**
**CD:** Released Apr '87, on London Records by London Records Ltd. Catalogue no: **FCD 60010**

## Scott, Bobby

**COMPOSITIONS OF B. SCOTT, THE**
**Album:** Released Feb '88, on Fresh Sounds (Spain) by Fresh Sounds Records (Spain). Catalogue no: **FS 208**

## Scott, Isaac

**BIG TIME BLUES MAN**
Tracks: / Help / Listen to the blues / Standing on the outside / Seattle blues / Moonbelly / Don't let my baby ride / Let my mind run back / Feast goin' on / On the road again.
**Album:** Released Jul '83, on Red Lightnin' by Red Lightning Records. Deleted Jun '89. Catalogue no: **RL 046**

**ISAAC SCOTT BLUES BAND (Scott, Isaac Blues Band)**
Tracks: / There's gotta be a change / Ice cold / Same old blues / You send me / Rock me / Going back to Oakland / Blues at midnight / Steal away / Honky tonk.
**Album:** Released Sep '82, on Red Lightnin' by Red Lightning Records. Catalogue no: **RL 023**

## Scott, Mabel

**FINE FINE BABY**
Tracks: / Elevator boogie / Give me a man / Don't cry baby / Baseball boogie / Have you ever watched love die / Subway blues / Catch 'em young, treat 'em rough, tell 'em nothin' / Boogie woogie choo choo train / No more cryin' the blues / Disgusted / Somebody goofed / Wailin' daddy / Yes! / Mr. Fine / Mabel blues.
**Album:** Released Aug '87, on Jukebox Lil (Sweden) Catalogue no: **JB 606**

## Scott, Raymond

**Biographical details:** Bandleader Raymond Scott was born in 1909 and was well known for clever novelty arrangements such as *In An Eighteenth Century Drawing Room, Dinner Music For A Pack Of Hungry Cannibals, When Cootie Left The Duke* (which caused a shock in the music business in 1939, when Cootie Williams left Duke Ellington for more money with Benny Goodman.) His intricate arrangements were played by a first rate sextet. Later he led a big band, became music director on radio and TV of *Your Hit Parade* for many years (all the while he was a CBS staff musician) and was married to Dorothy Collins, a regular on the show he'd discovered as a teenager. (Donald Clarke)..

**BUSINESS MAN'S BOUNCE**
**Album:** Released Jul '82, on Golden Era by Delta Records. Catalogue no: **GELP 15029**

**POPULAR MUSIC**
**Album:** Released '84, on Swing House by Submarine Records. Catalogue no: **SWH 31**

**RAYMOND SCOTT AND ORCHESTRA, 1944 (Scott, Raymond & Orchestra)**
**Album:** Released '88, on Hindsight Catalogue no: **HSR 211**

## Scott, Ronnie

**Biographical details:**
Tenor saxophonist and bandleader Ronnie Scott was born in London in 1927. He is best known as co-operator (with Peter King) of one of the most famous jazz clubs in the world for almost 30 years, also for his elderly and terrible jokes, but he is an underrated (even by himself) musician, having studied jazz in New York at the height of the bop era thanks to Geraldo's Navy (bandleader Geraldo hired musicians to work on the Queen Mary, back and forth across the Atlantic). Among his best-known albums include the *Battle Royal,* made in 1951 with two tenors, Victor Feldman on piano; *Serious Gold* was made in 1977 with John Taylor on keyboards (lately of Azimuth), Ron Matthewson on bass and Martin Drew on drums (who still play in the quintet at the club) and Louis Stewart on guitar. (Donald Clarke, April 87)..

**BATTLE ROYAL (Scott, Ronnie & Kenny Graham)**
Tracks: / Not so fast / Battle royal / Fast / Twins' bed / Smoke gets in your eyes / Scott's expedition / Avalon / Love me or leave me / Nemo / Troubled air / Eureka / Seven eleven / All the things you are.
**7" Single:** Released May '81, on Esquire by Titan Int. Prod.. Catalogue no: **ESQ 311**

**GREAT SCOTT VOLUME 1**
**Album:** Released Apr '79, on Esquire by Titan Int. Prod.. Catalogue no: **ESQ 303**

**LIVE AT THE JAZZ CLUB, VOLUME 1 (Scott, Ronnie & His Orchestra)**
Tracks: / Popo / Pantagrulian / Mullenium / Nearness of you, The / Nemo / All the things you are / Champ, The / Daydream / On the alamo / What's new / I may be wrong.
**Album:** Released Jul '87, on Esquire by Titan Int. Prod.. Catalogue no: **ESQ 328**

**MUSIC FROM RONNIE'S**
**Special:** Released Sep '78, on Pye Catalogue no: **11PP 603**

**SERIOUS GOLD**
Tracks: / Invitation / Lazy afternoon / Forty colours / Hey-oke sweet ballad / Send in the clowns / Interfusion.
**Album:** Released Jan '78, on PRT by Castle Communications Records. Catalogue no: **NSPL 18542**
**Cass:** Released Jan '78, on PRT by Castle Communications Records. Catalogue no: **ZCP 18542**

## Scott, Shirley

**BLUE FLAMES (Scott, Shirley/Stanley Turrentine)**
Tracks: / Funky fox, The / Hip knees and legs / Five spot after dark / Grand Street / Flamingo.
**Album:** Released May '88, on Prestige Catalogue no: **PR 7338**
**Cass:** Released May '88, on Prestige Deleted Jan '90. Catalogue no: **PRC 7338**

**SHIRLEY SCOTT**
Tracks: / Blues for members / I've grown accustomed to her face / Marchin' to the riverside / We're goin' home / Lisa and Pam / Toys in the attic / Southern comfort / Blue piano / Freedom dance / Five o'clock whistle / Blues ain't nothin' but some pain, The / I'm getting sentimental over you / Make someone happy / Show in the dark, A / Great Scott / Seventh dawn, The / Hoe down / Shadows of Paris.
**CD:** Released Jan '90, on MCA (Impulse Jazz) Catalogue no: **MCAD 33115**

## Scott, Tony

**Biographical details:** Tony Scott was born in New Jersey in 1921; with Buddy DeFranco he is one of the few musicians to specialise on the clarinet in post-war jazz. He studied ethnic music in the Orient from 1959 to 1965. His verve albums were made in the mid-60's; *52nd Street scene* was made in 1958, with Coleman Hawkins, Jimmy Knepper, Al Cohn, Pee Wee Russell, Oscar Pettifold, Tommy Flanagan and others on various tracks. (Donald Clarke, April 87).

**52ND STREET SCENE**
Tracks: / Blues for the street / Love is just around the corner / Body and soul / Mop mop / Lester leaps in / Lover man (oh where can you be) / Woody 'n' you / Round midnight / Ornithology.
**Album:** Released Feb '83, on Jasmine by Hasmick Promotions. Deleted Feb '88. Catalogue no: **JASM 1011**

**AFRICAN BIRD**
Tracks: / African bird (suite) / Spirits return / Spirits dance / Come back Mother Africa / African bird / Requiem for lost spirits.
Note: Recorded 1981 - 1984. Personnel: Tony Scott, Chris Hunter, Robin Jones, Karl Potter, Duncan Kinnel, Giancarlo Barigozzi, Rex Reason
**Album:** Released May '85, on Soul Note Catalogue no: **SN 1083**

**BOTH SIDES OF TONY SCOTT (Scott, Tony Quartet)**
Tracks: / Cry me a river / My funny Valentine / Star dust / More than you know / Everything happens to me / Counterpoint pleasant / East coast, west side / You and I.
**Album:** Released Jun '88, on Fresh Sounds (Spain) by Fresh Sounds Records (Spain). Catalogue no: **FS 335**

**CHIEF, THE**
**Cass:** Released Feb '90, on Champion by Champion Records. Catalogue no: **CHAMPK 1022**
**Album:** Released Feb '90, on Champion by Champion Records. Catalogue no: **CHAMP 1022**
**Special:** Released Feb '90, on Champion by Champion Records. Catalogue no: **CHAMPCD 1022**

**GET INTO IT**
Tracks: / Get into it / Get into it (version) / That's how I'm living (Available on CD single) / Chief, The (Available on CD single).
**7" Single:** Released Jan '90, on Champion by Champion Records. Catalogue no: **CHAMP 232**
**12" Single:** Released Jan '90, on Champion by Champion Records. Deleted Feb '90. Catalogue no: **CHAMX 12232**
**12" Single:** Released Jan '90, on Champion by Champion Records. Catalogue no: **CHAMP 12232**
**CD Single:** Released Jan '90, on Champion by Champion Records. Catalogue no: **CHAMPCD 232**

**MODERN ART OF JAZZ, THE**
**Album:** Released Feb '88, on Fresh Sounds (Spain) by Fresh Sounds Records (Spain). Catalogue no: **FS 238**

**MUSIC FOR ZEN MEDITATION**
Tracks: / Is not all one? / Murmuring sound of the mountain / Quivering leaf, ask the wind / After the snow the fragrance / To drift like clouds / Za-zan (meditation) / Prajina paramita hridya sutra / Sanzan (moment of truth) / Satori (enlightenment).
**Album:** Released Mar '81, on Verve (Import) Catalogue no: **2304 138**
**CD:** Released Sep '84, on Verve (Germany) Deleted '88. Catalogue no: **817 209 2**

**SUNG HEROES**
Tracks: / Misery (to lady day) / Portrait of Anne Frank / Remembrance of Art Tatum / Requiem for 'Hot Lips' Page / Blues for an African friend / For Stefan Wolpe / Israel / Memory of my father / Lament to manolete.
Note: All compositions by Tony Scott. Featuring: Bill Evans, Scott Lafaro, Paul Motian.
**CD:** Released Sep '86, on Sunnyside Jazz(USA) Catalogue no: **SSC 1015D**
**Album:** Released Sep '86, on Sunnyside Jazz(USA) Catalogue no: **SSC 1015**

**TONY SCOTT PLAYS GYPSY**
**Album:** Released Oct '87, on Fresh Sounds (Spain) by Fresh Sounds Records (Spain). Catalogue no: **FS 248**

## Screaming Saxophones

**SCREAMING SAXOPHONES VOL.1 (Various artists)**
**Album:** Released Jan '86, on Swingtime by Contact Records (Denmark). Deleted Jun '89. Catalogue no: **ST 1002**

## Seals, Son

**Biographical details:** Blues singer and guitarist Son Seals' father owned a club in Osceola, Georgia, where Son was born in 1942; he sat in at the club, toured with Earl Hooker, Albert King, settled in Chicago in 1971. He is part of the marvelous Alligator label family of bluesmen whose records are leased to Sonet in the UK. (Donald Clarke).

**BAD AXE**
Tracks: / Don't pick me for your fool / Going home (where women got meat on their bones) / Just about to lose your clown / Friday again / Cold blood / Out of my way / I think you're fooling me / I can count on my blues / Can't stand to see her cry / Person to person.
**Album:** Released Dec '84, on Sonet by Sonet Records. Catalogue no: **SNTF 927**
**CD:** Released Oct '86, on Sonet by Sonet Records. Catalogue no: **SNTCD 927**

**CHICAGO FIRE**
Tracks: / Buzzard luck / I'm not tired / Leaving home / Landlord at my door / Gentleman from the windy city / Goodbye little girl / Watching every move you make / Crying time again / Nobody wants a loser.
**Album:** Released Sep '80, on Sonet by Sonet Records. Catalogue no: **SNTF 838**

**LIVE 'N' BURNING**
**Album:** Released Jul '88, on Sonet by Sonet Records. Catalogue no: **SNTF 782**

**MIDNIGHT SON**
Tracks: / I believe (you're trying to make a fool out of me) / No, no, baby / Four full seasons of love / Telephone angel / Don't bother me / On my knees / Don't fool with my baby / Strung-out woman / Going back home.
**Album:** Released Jul '77, on Sonet by Sonet Records. Catalogue no: **SNTF 728**

**SON SEALS BLUES BAND (Seals, Son Blues Band)**
Tracks: / Mother-in-law blues / Sitting at my window / Look now, baby / Your love is a cancer / All you love / Cotton pickin' blues / Hot sauce / How could she leave me? / Going home tomorrow / Now that I'm down.
**Album:** Released Jan '75, on Sonet by Sonet Records. Catalogue no: **SNTF 679**

## Seamen, Phil

**PHIL ON DRUMS (Various artists)**
**Album:** Released '88, on Hep Jazz by Hep Records. Catalogue no: **HEP 2037**
**Album:** Released Jul '88, on 77 by 77 Records. Catalogue no: **77 SEU 12/53**

## Sebesky, Don

**FULL CYCLE**
Tracks: / Naima / Django / Intrepid fox / Waltz for Debbie / All blues / Un poco loco.
**Album:** Released '88, on GNP Crescendo (USA) by GNP Crescendo Records (USA). Catalogue no: **GNPS 2164**
**Cass:** Released '88, on GNP Crescendo (USA) by GNP Crescendo Records (USA). Catalogue no: **GNP5 2164**
**Album:** Released Oct '84, on PRT by Castle Communications Records. Catalogue no: **N 6551**

**GIANT BOX**
**CD:** Released '88, on CBS by CBS Records. Deleted 17 Apr '89. Catalogue no: **450564 2**

**MOVING LINES**
**Album:** Released Mar '86, on Doctor Jazz (USA) by CBS Records (USA). Deleted '88. Catalogue no: **ASLP 811**
**Cass:** Released Mar '86, on Doctor Jazz (USA) by CBS Records (USA). Deleted '88. Catalogue no: **ZCAS 811**

## Second Time

**SECOND TIME I MET THE BLUES Best of Chess Blues Vol 2 (Various artists)**
Tracks: / Talk to me baby: *James, Elmore* / Last night: *Little Walter* / Chicago bound: *Rodgers, Jimmie (1)* / Baby please don't go: *Waters, Muddy* / Ten years ago: *Guy, Buddy* / It's my own fault: *Hooker, John Lee* / Help me: *Williamson, Sonny Boy* / You got me: *Brim, John* / I'm a man: *Diddley, Bo* / Evil: *Howlin' Wolf* / Trouble trouble: *Fulson, Lowell* / Time brings about a change: *Witherspoon, Jimmy* / I'm in love with you baby: *Spann, Otis* / Juke: *Little Walter* / Billy's blues (part 2): *Stewart, Billy* /

Diggin' my potatoes: *Washboard Sam* / World's in a tangle, The: *Rodgers, Jimmie (1)* / She's 19 years old: *Waters, Muddy* / Let your conscience be your guide: *Williamson, Sonny Boy* / Leave my wife alone: *Hooker, John Lee* / Before you accuse me: *Diddley, Bo* / I asked for water (and she gave me gasoline): *Howlin' Wolf* / Let me love you baby: *Guy, Buddy* / Thirty days: *Berry, Chuck*.
**CD:** Released Jun '89, on Chess by Vogue Records. Catalogue no: **CDRED 12**

## Sellers, John

**LET PRAISE ARISE**
**Cass:** Released May '85, on Wing by Polydor Ltd. Catalogue no: **TC WING 525**
**Album:** Released May '85, on Wing by Polydor Ltd. Catalogue no: **WING 525**

## Senter, Boyd

**SOLOS AND SENTERPEDES - VOL.1 1927-28**
Tracks: / Down-hearted blues / Boss of the stomps / Grind out, The / I ain't got nobody / T'aint clean / Eniale blues / Just so-so / Prickly heat / Sister Kate / Mobile blues / No more / Original stack o'lee blues / Original Chinese blues / Somebody's wrong.
**Album:** Released Dec '86, on Harlequin by Interstate Music. Catalogue no: **HQ 2044**

## Seventh Ave Stompers

**FIDGETY FEET**
Note: Artists include: Emmett Berry - trumpet; Vic Dickenson - trombone; Buster Bailey - clarinet; Red Richards - piano; Al Lucas - bass; Bobby Donaldson - drums; Joe Wilder - trumpet; Seldon Powell - tenor sax; Ernie Hayes - organ; Bucky Pizzarelli - guitar.
Includes two previously unissued tracks: *Ferry boat romp* and *Blues like they used to be*, as well as cuts like *Basin street blues* and *St Louis blues*.
**Album:** Released Dec '86, on Savoy (France) Deleted May '89. Catalogue no: **WL 70509**

## Seymour, Terry

**TERRY SEYMOUR BIG BAND (Seymour, Terry Big Band)**
**Album:** Released Nov '74, on Wave by Wave Records. Catalogue no: **WAVE LP 14**

## Shafer, Ted

**SAN FRANCISCO JAZZ (Shafer, Ted Jelly Roll Jazz Band)**
**Album:** Released Jun '86, on GHB by Jazzology Records (USA). Catalogue no: **GHB 165**

**SAN FRANCISCO STYLE (Shafer, Ted Jelly Roll Jazz Band)**
**Cass:** Released Mar '90, on Merry Makers Catalogue no: **MC MMRC101**

**TED SHAFERS JELLY ROLL JAZZ BAND VOL.1 (Shafer, Ted Jelly Roll Jazz Band)**
**Album:** Released Jun '88, on Merry Makers Catalogue no: **MMRC 101**

**TED SHAFERS JELLY ROLL JAZZ BAND VOL.2 (Shafer, Ted Jelly Roll Jazz Band)**
**Album:** Released Jun '88, on Merry Makers Catalogue no: **MMRC 102**

**TED SHAFERS JELLY ROLL JAZZ BAND VOL.3 (Shafer, Ted Jelly Roll Jazz Band)**
**Album:** Released Jun '88, on Merry Makers Catalogue no: **MMRC 104**

## Shane, Mark

**BLUEBERRY RHYME With Dave Shapiro**
**Album:** Released Jun '88, on Jazzology (USA) by Jazzology Records (USA). Catalogue no: **JCE 91**

## Shank, Bud

**Biographical details:** Bud Shank was born 27 May, 1926, in Dayton, Ohio. He plays flute and sax and is a composer. He went to California in 1947, played in big bands and studied with trumpeter-bandleader Shorty Rogers, becoming a mainstay on the West Coast jazz scene and a regular at Howard Rumsey's famous Lighthouse Club in Hermosa Beach. He also did a lot of studio work and was heard on film soundtracks. He made nearly 30 albums as a leader on World Pacific/Pacific Jazz '54-70, mostly small-group sets, always with excellent sidesmen, including LPs of pop songs: *Michelle*, with Chet Baker on flugelhorn, was a hit LP in the USA. He also made *Brazil '65* on Capitol with Sergio Mendez and played as a sidesman on LPs by just about everybody. In 1974 he co-formed the L.A. Four with Shelly Manne, Ray Brown and Laurindo Almeida (albums on Concord Jazz) and has made several albums on Concord Jazz since '76 with pianist/composer Bill Mays. (Donald Clarke, April 87).

**BUD SHANK PLAYS CONCERTO FOR ALTO SAX AND ORCHESTRA (Shank, Bud & The Royal Philharmonic Orchestra)**
Tracks: / Here's that rainy day / Body and soul / Concerto for jazz alto saxophone and orchestra.
**Album:** Released Apr '87, on Mole Jazz by Mole Jazz Records. Catalogue no: **MOLE 12**
**CD:** Released Apr '87, on Mole Jazz by Mole Jazz Records. Catalogue no: **MOLECD 12**

**BUD SHANK QUARTET AT JAZZ ALLEY (Shank, Bud Quartet)**
**CD:** Released Jan '89, on JVC/Fantasy Catalogue no: **VDJ 1120**

**LIVE AT THE HAIG**
Tracks: / How about you / Lover man / Ambassador blues / I heard you cried last night / Out of this world / Miles sign off / Set ends.
Note: As a founding member of the LA Four with Shelly Manne, Ray Brown and Laurindo Almeida, Bud Shank is well-known through the groups recordings on Concord. Still an important figure on the West Coast jazz scene, he combines his club and concert work doing freelance movie and TV dates. He has composed countless jingles and TV themes and has performed solo spots in movies such as *The Thomas Crown Affair*, *Assault on*

**Bud Shank - This Bud's for you (Muse)**

a Queen, Sandpiper and Summer '42. These recordings were made in Los Angles, during 1956, at a club called 'The Haig' and have never been issued before. Featuring both Claude Williamson and Miles Davies, this set provides a well balanced programme of West Cost jazz. Personnel: Bud Shank - alto sax & flute/Claude Williamson - piano, has worked with Charlie Barnet, Red Norvo and own groups/Don Prel - bass, worked with Charlie Barnet, Peggy Lee and the Utah Symphony Orchestra/Chuck Flores - drums, worked wtih Maynard Ferguson and Woody Herman.
**Album:** Released Sep '85, on Mole Jazz by Mole Jazz Records. Catalogue no: **VL 02**

**REEDS AND WOODWINDS VOL 1**
**Album:** Released Jul '88, on Ingo Catalogue no: **INGO 17**

**REEDS AND WOODWINDS VOL 2 (Shank, Bud/Bob Cooper)**
**Album:** Released Jul '88, on Ingo Catalogue no: **INGO 18**

**THAT OLD FEELING (Shank, Bud Quartet)**
Tracks: / Whisper not / Dream dancing / Cabin in the sky / El wacko / No Moe / I've told every little star / As time goes by / That old feeling.
**Album:** Released '88, on Boplicity by Ace Records. Catalogue no: **COP 035**

**THIS BUD'S FOR YOU**
Tracks: / I'll be seeing you / Nica's dream / Never never land / Space maker / Visa / Cotton blossom / Bouncing with Bud.
Note: And the Rhythm section of Ron Carter/Kenny Barron/Al Foster. Produced by Bob Golden. Recorded at Classic Sound Studio-NYC on 14.11.84
**Album:** Released May '86, on Muse by Black & Blue Records. Catalogue no: **MR 5309**

## Sharon, Ralph

**MAGIC OF COLE PORTER (Sharon, Ralph Trio)**
Tracks: / You're the top / All thru the night / Easy to love / Get out of town / You'd be so nice to come home to / I concentrate on you / I've got you under my skin / Down in the depths on the 90th floor / So in love / Anything goes / Let's do it / From this moment on / What is this thing called love / Do I love you / Night & day / I love Paris / Love for sale / I love you / It's alright by me / All of you / I get a kick out of you / Why should I / Just one of those things / Long last love / Begin the beguine / Sorta Porter.
**Cass:** Released Feb '90, on Horatio Nelson by Horatio Nelson Records & Tapes Ltd.. Catalogue no: **CSIV 1123**
**CD:** Released Feb '90, on Horatio Nelson by Horatio Nelson Records & Tapes Ltd.. Catalogue no: **CDSIV 1123**

**MAGIC OF GEORGE GERSHWIN, THE (Sharon, Ralph Trio)**
Tracks: / Fascinating rhythm / They all laughed / Somebody loves me / S'wonderful s'marvellous / But not for me / Soon / I loves you Porgy / I got rhythm / They can't take that away from me / Someone to watch over me / Man I love, The / Love is here to stay / There's a boat dat's leavin' soon for New York / Rhapsody in blue / Foggy day, A / Embraceable you / Liza (all the cloud'll roll away) / How long has this been going on / Swanee / Love walked in (Golden Follies) / Oh lady be good.
**CD:** Released Sep '88, on Horatio Nelson by Horatio Nelson Records & Tapes Ltd.. Catalogue no: **CDSIV 1116**
**Cass:** Released Sep '88, on Horatio Nelson by Horatio Nelson Records & Tapes Ltd.. Catalogue no: **CSIV 116**

**MR & MRS JAZZ (Sharon, Ralph & Sue)**
**Album:** Released Feb '88, on Fresh Sounds (Spain) by Fresh Sounds Records (Spain). Catalogue no: **FS 243**

## Sharrock, Sonny

**GUITAR**
**Album:** Released May '86, on Enemy Catalogue no: **ENY 102**

**LIVE IN NEW YORK**
**Album:** Released Feb '90, on Enemy Catalogue no: **ENY 108**
**CD:** Released Feb '90, on Enemy Catalogue no: **ENYCD 108**

**MONKEY POCKIE BOO**
**Album:** Released Sep '79, on Affinity by Charly Records. Deleted '88. Catalogue no: **AFF 35**

**SONNY SHARROCK: LIVE IN NEW YORK**
**CD:** Released Jan '90, on Enemy Catalogue no: **EMY 108 CD**
**Album:** Released Jan '90, on Enemy Catalogue no: **EMY 108**

## Shavers, Charlie

**Biographical details:** Charlie Shavers (1917-71) was one of the most original and popular trumpet players of the Swing Era; he played with the bands of Tiny Bradshaw and Lucky Millinder, then with the John Kirby Sextet from 1937 until 1944 ('the biggest little band in the land'). His best known compositions are *Pastel Blue* (became *Why Begin Again* with words) and *Undecided*, a hit (with words by Sid Robin) for Ella Fitzgerald, the Ames Brothers, etc. He later played with Tommy Dorsey and many others. (Donald Clarke)..

**ART FORD'S JAZZY PARTY July 1958**
Note: With Buck Clayton.
**Album:** Released Oct '87, on Jazz Connoisseur by Spotlite Records. Catalogue no: **AFJP 2**

**CHARLIE SHAVERS**
Tracks: / Deuce-a-rini / Summertime / Echoes of Harlem / Amor / Rose room / She's funny that way / On the spot / Bye bye blackbird / Nature boy / Avalon / St. Louis blues / I want a little girl / I concentrate on you / What is this thing called love? / Pennies from Heaven / I'm forever blowing bubbles / My funny valentine / But beautiful / Bei mir bist du schon.
**Album:** Released Apr '79, on Phoenix (USA) by All Star Talent Inc.(USA). Catalogue no: **LP 21**
**Album:** Released Apr '81, on Hep Jazz by Hep Records. Catalogue no: **HEP 23**

**JAZZ OFF THE AIR Volume 7 (Shavers, Charlie Quartet)**
Tracks: / Undecided / St Louis blues / What is this thing called love / My funny valentine / I'm forever blowing bubbles / Rose room / Pennies from heaven / A tisket a tasket / Over the rainbow / Bernies tune.
**Album:** Released '88, on Spotlite by Spotlite Records. Catalogue no: **SPJ 154**

**LIVE: CHARLIE SHAVERS**
**Album:** Released Jun '84, on Black & Blue (1) by Black & Blue Records. Catalogue no: **33302**

**NOVEMBER 1961 & MARCH 1962 (Shavers, Charlie Quartet)**
Tracks: / Old apple tree / You got nothin' / Snow in Lovers' Lane / My old Kentucky home / Love gave me you / In the good old summertime / Give my regards to Broadway / Ain't gonna get fooled again / Carry me back to old Virginny / She's only a bird in a gilded cage.
**Album:** Released Oct '80, on From The Jazz Vault by Damont Audio Ltd.. Catalogue no: **JV 106**
: by Damont Audio Ltd..

**SWING ALONG**
**Album:** Released Oct '88, on Vogue by Vogue Records. Catalogue no: **500072**

**SWING WITH CHARLIE**
**Album:** Released Oct '88, on Vogue by Vogue Records. Catalogue no: **500084**

**TRUMPET MAN**
Tracks: / Deuce-a-rini / Summertime / Echoes of Harlem / Amor / Rose room / She's funny that way / On the spot / Bye bye blackbird / Nature boy / Avalon.
**Album:** Released Jun '89, on Phoenix (1) by Phoenix Records. Catalogue no: **PHOENIX 21**

## Shaw, Artie

**Biographical details:** Artie Shaw was the other clarinet-playing bandleader of the Swing Era; partisans of Shaw and Benny Goodman sometimes had heated discussions. Shaw was born in 1910 and was among the busiest freelance musicians in New York when he formed his own band; after half a dozen hits he had an international smash with Jerry Gray's arrangement of Cole Porter's *Begin The Beguine* '38 (copied straight by Billy Cotton in this country); his other big hits were *Frenesi* (arranged by the black American composer William Grant Still, with oboe, French horn and strings), *Stardust*, *Dancing In The Dark* and *Summit Ridge Drive*, by the small group the Gramercy Five, with Johnny Guarnieri on harpsichord; all were named among their all time favourite records by disc jockeys in a Billboard poll in 1956. He employed top musicians like Tony Pastor (on tenor sax and novelty vocals), drummer Buddy Rich, trumpeters Billy Butterfield and Roy Eldridge, and at one point Billie Holiday. An intelligent and unpredictable man, he frequently got fed up with the music business, finally quit around 1954, but came back fronting a band in the early 1980's. He married seven times and wrote a novel called *I Love You, I Hate You, Drop Dead!* in 1965. (Donald Clarke)..

**22 ORIGINAL BIG BAND RECORDINGS (Shaw, Artie & his Orchestra)**
**Album:** Released '88, on Hindsight Catalogue no: **HSR 401**

**1938 BAND IN HI-FI, THE**
Tracks: / Sobbin' blues / I can't believe that you're in love with me / It had to be you / My reverie / Sweet Adeline / Who blew out the flame? / Copenhagen / Begin the beguine / You're a sweet little headache / What is this thing called love? / Jungle drums.
Note: With Helen Forrest, Tony Pastor.
**Album:** Released Feb '89, on Jasmine by Hasmick Promotions. Catalogue no: **JASM 2522**
**Cass:** Released Feb '89, on Jasmine by Hasmick Promotions. Catalogue no: **JASMC 2522**
**Album:** Released Apr '79, on Fanfare (USA) Catalogue no: **FANFARE 28 128**

**1949, VOL 1 (Shaw, Artie & his Orchestra)**
Tracks: / Stardust / Tea for two / They can't take that away from me / Things are looking up / Softly as in a morning sunrise / He's funny that way / I only have eyes for you / Let's fall in love / So in love / You do something to me / I get a kick out of you / Begin the beguine / I concentrate on you / 'S wonderful / Orinoco / Carnival / Nightmare.
**Album:** Released Apr '81, on Solid Sender Catalogue no: **SOL 508**

**1949, VOL 2 (Shaw, Artie & his Orchestra)**
Tracks: / Comes love / I cover the waterfront / Krazy kat / Love walked in / Moonglow / So easy / Innuendo / Gue le le / Summit ridge drive / Grabtown grapple, The / Smoke gets in your eyes / Pied piper / Cross your heart / Cool daddy.
**Album:** Released Apr '81, on Solid Sender Catalogue no: **SOL 509**

**1949-1950 VOLUME 3 (Shaw, Artie & his Orchestra)**
Tracks: / Minesota / Smooth and easy / Don't take your love from me / Exactly like you / How deep is the ocean / Together / Too marvellous for words / Very thought of you, The / Love is the sweetest thing / Bedford drive / Love of my life / Fred's delight / Love for sale / Similau / Time on my hands.
Note: Features on all 3 Shaw LP's are Don Fageruist (tp), Zoot Sims, Al Cohn (ts), Dodo Marmarosa (p), Jimmy Raney (d). Arrangements by Johnny Mandel, Tadd Dameron, Gene Roland, John Bartee, Ray Conniff, Roger Segure, Eddie Sauter.
**Album:** Released Apr '81, on Solid Sender Catalogue no: **SOL 510**

**1937-38 VOL. 1 (Shaw, Artie/Rhythm Makers)**
**Album:** Released Mar '90, on Singdom. Catalogue no: **SWDM 7001/2**

**1937-38 VOL. 2 (Shaw, Artie/Rhythm Makers)**
**Album:** Released Nov '86, on Swingdom Catalogue no: **7003/4**
**Cass:** Released Nov '86, on Swingdom Catalogue no: **CAWE 26**

**1937-38 VOL. 3 (Shaw, Artie/Rhythm Makers)**
**Album:** Released Mar '90, on Swingdom. Catalogue no: **SWDM 7005/6**

**ARTIE SHAW**
**Album:** Released Sep '87, on Giants of Jazz by Hasmick Promotions. Catalogue no: **LPJT 6**
**Album:** Released Apr '79, on Bright Orange Catalogue no: **BO 708**

**ARTIE SHAW AND ORCHESTRA VOL. 1 1938 (Shaw, Artie & His Orchestra)**
Tracks: / April in my heart / Night in Shanghai / Small fry / Just a kid named Joe / When I go a-dreamin' / Leapin' at Lincoln / What is this thing called love / Lambeth walk / They say / Shine on harvest moon / Out of nowhere / Simple and sweet / Blue interlude / Apple blossom time / Deep in a dream.
Note: (Broadcasts of 11-2-38, 12-1-38 and 12-2-38). These are the off-the-line high quality broadcasts of the 1938 Shaw band from the Blue Room of the Lincoln Hotel in New York, featuring vocals by Helen Forrest and Tony Pastor occasionally. These are performances and selections that have, to the best of our knowledge, never been released on record to date, legal or otherwise. The liner notes are by Patricia Willard interviewing Artie Shaw himself - what more can we say? Produced by Wally Heider. (Hindsight Catalogue - 1989)
**Album:** Released '88, on Hindsight. Catalogue no: **HSR 139**

**ARTIE SHAW AND ORCHESTRA VOL. 2 1938-9 (Shaw, Artie & His Orchestra)**
Tracks: / Softly as in a morning sunrise / I won't tell a soul / Back bay shuffle / If I had you / Thanks for everything / I used to be colour blind / Together / Stardust / Who blew out the flame / Between a kiss and a sigh / Just you, just me / Let's stop the clock / In the mood / Deep in a dream / Diga diga doo.
Note: Broadcasts of 12-2-38 (second broadcast of the same evening), 12-6-38 and 12-2-38. This is a continuation of HSR 139, Volume 1, both being complete with announcements, audience applause, opening and closing themes - just like you were there. More vocals by Helen Forrest. Liner notes by Patricia Willard talking with Artie about the band during this time and the selections on the record. Produced by Wally Heider. (Hindsight Catalogue - 1989)
**Album:** Released '88, on Hindsight. Catalogue no: **HSR 140**

**ARTIE SHAW AND ORCHESTRA VOL. 3 1939 (Shaw, Artie & His Orchestra)**
**Album:** Released '88, on Hindsight. Catalogue no: **HSR 148**

**ARTIE SHAW AND ORCHESTRA VOL. 4 1939 (Shaw, Artie & His Orchestra)**
**Album:** Released '88, on Hindsight. Catalogue no: **HSR 149**

**ARTIE SHAW COLLECTION (20 golden greats)**
Tracks: / Begin the beguine / Indian love call / Jungle drums / Carioca / Traffic jam / Frenesi / Summit Ridge Drive / Temptation / Stardust / Smoke gets in your eyes / Dancing in the dark / My blue Heaven / It had to be you / Accentuate the positive / 'S wonderful / September song / Summertime / Foggy day, A / These foolish things / They can't take that away from me.
**Cass:** Released Aug '85, on Deja Vu Catalogue no: **DVMC 2013**
**Album:** Released Aug '85, on Deja Vu Catalogue no: **DVLP 2013**

**ARTIE SHAW & HIS MUSICIANS, 1949**
Tracks: / Minesota / Smooth and easy / Don't take your love from me.
**Album:** Released Jul '77, on First Heard by Submarine Records. Catalogue no: **FH 6**

**ARTIE SHAW & HIS ORCHESTRA (Shaw, Artie & his Orchestra)**
Tracks: / 'S wonderful / Man and his dreams, A / April in Paris / Summertime / I cover the waterfront / Blues (end s1) / I could write a book / Don't take your love from me / Beyond the blue horizon / Maid with the flaccid air, The / Time on my hands / Deep purple / Prelude in C major.
**Cass:** Released May '85, on Premier by Premier Records. Catalogue no: **KCBR 1013**
**Album:** Released May '85, on Premier by Premier Records. Catalogue no: **CBR 1013**

**ARTIE SHAW & HIS ORCHESTRA, VOL 1 (Shaw, Artie & his Orchestra)**
Tracks: / Deep in a dream / Nightmare / Softly as in a morning sunrise / I won't tell a soul / If I had you / Thanks for everything / I used to be colour blind / Together / Stardust / Who blew out the flame / Between a kiss and a sigh / Just you, just me / Let's stop the clock / In the mood / Diga diga doo.
**Album:** Released Apr '80, on London Records by London Records Ltd. Catalogue no: **HMA 5065**

**ARTIE SHAW & HIS ORCHESTRA VOL. 2 (Shaw, Artie & His Orchestra)**
Tracks: / Deep in a dream / Nightmare / Softly as in a morning sunrise / I won't tell a soul / If I had you / Thanks for everything / I used to be colour blind / Together / Stardust / Who blew out the flame / Between a kiss and a sigh / Just you, just me / Let's stop the clock / In the

mood / Diga diga doo.
**Album:** Released Apr '80, on London Records by London Records Ltd. Catalogue no: **HMA 5066**

**ARTIE SHAW & HIS ORCHESTRA & STRINGS VOL.1 (Shaw, Artie & His Orchestra)**
**CD:** Released Oct '87, on Musicraft (USA) by Discovery Records (USA). Catalogue no: **MVSCD 50**

**ARTIE SHAW & HIS ORCHESTRA & STRINGS VOL.2 (Shaw, Artie & His Orchestra)**
**CD:** Released Jul '88, on Musicraft (USA) by Discovery Records (USA). Catalogue no: **MVSCD 51**

**ARTIE SHAW ON THE AIR**
Tracks: / Shoot the likker to me John boy / One night stand / I ain't comin' / Chant, The / Serenade to a savage / Carioca / I'm comin', Virginia / Man from Mars / Donkey serenade, The / Lamp is low, The / Octoroon / Them there eyes / Along the Santa Fe trail / Looking for yesterday / Everything's jumpin'.
**Album:** Released Aug '79, on Sandy Hook (USA) Catalogue no: **SH 2016**
**Album:** Released Apr '79, on Aircheck (USA) by Kiner Ents.(USA). Catalogue no: **AIRCHECK 11**

**BEGIN THE BEGUINE**
Tracks: / Nightmare / Indian love call / Back bay shuffle / Any old time / Traffic jam / Comes love / What is this thing called love? / Begin the beguine / Lady be good / Frenesi / Serenade to a savage / Deep purple / Special delivery stomp / Summit Ridge Drive / Temptation / Stardust / Blues (parts 1 & 2) / Moonglow / Moon ray / Carioca.
**CD:** Released Apr '88, on Bluebird (2) by BMG Records (UK). Catalogue no: **ND 86274**
**CD:** Released Oct '87, on Dance Band Days by Prism Leisure. Catalogue no: **DBCD 07**
**Cass:** Released Oct '87, on Dance Band Days by Prism Leisure. Catalogue no: **DBDC 07**
**Album:** Released Oct '87, on Dance Band Days by Prism Leisure. Catalogue no: **DBD 07**

**BEGIN THE BEGUINE, VOL.1 (Shaw, Artie & His Orchestra)**
Tracks: / Love of my life / Ghost of a chance / How deep is the ocean? / I got the sun in the morning / You do something to me / In the still of the night / My heart belongs to Daddy / Night and day.
Note: Classics from the mid 40's with Dodo Marmorosa, Herbie Stewart, Barney Kessel, Ray Linn, Johnny Guarneri and Nick Fatool. The first recording by Mel Torme and his Mel-Tones, Kitty Kallen, Teddy Walters and Hal Stevens.
**Album:** Released '88, on Musicraft (USA) by Discovery Records (USA). Catalogue no: **MVS 503**

**BEGINNING, THE (Shaw, Artie & His Orchestra)**
**Album:** Released '88, on Hep Jazz by Hep Records. Catalogue no: **HEP 1024**

**BEST OF ARTIE SHAW**
Tracks: / Nightmare / Black bay shuffle / Any old time / Stardust / Blues in the night / Carioca / Concerto for clarinet / Begin the beguine / Traffic jam / Frenesi.
**Cass:** Released '84, on RCA by BMG Records (UK). Catalogue no: **NK 89104**
**Album:** Released '84, on RCA by BMG Records (UK). Deleted Jul '89. Catalogue no: **NL 89104**

**BEST OF ARTIE SHAW & HIS ORCHESTRA (Shaw, Artie & His Orchestra)**
Tracks: / Nightmare / Back Bay shuffle / Any old time / Stardust / Blues in the night / Carioca / Concerto for clarinet / Deep purple / Begin the beguine / Traffic jam / Frenesi.
**Album:** Released Aug '80, on RCA by BMG Records (UK). Deleted '85. Catalogue no: **INTS 5022**

**BEST OF ARTIE SHAW (STARCALL) (Shaw, Artie & His Orchestra)**
Tracks: / Frenesi / Stardust / Moonglow / Oh lady be good / All the things you are / Temptation / Begin the beguine / Serenade to a savage / Indian love call / Traffic jam / Nightmare / Dancing in the dark.
**Album:** Released Feb '77, on Star Call by BMG Records (UK). Deleted '80. Catalogue no: **NL 11089**

**BLUE INTERLUDE**
Tracks: / Shine on harvest moon / Blue interlude / April in my heart.
**Cass:** Released Dec '84, on Pathe Marconi (France) Catalogue no: **2M 256 64855**
**Album:** Released Dec '84, on Pathe Marconi (France) Catalogue no: **2M 056 64855**

**BORN TO SWING (Shaw, Artie & His Orchestra)**
Tracks: / Milenburg joys / Stealin' apples / Born to swing / Call of the freaks, The / Posin' / Hold your hat / Someday, sweetheart / Lost in the shuffle / Wake up and live / Azure / I'd rather be right / I'll never let you cry / Meade Lux special / There'll be some changes made.
Note: Recorded: April, July, October, December 1937; February 1938; 1941.
**Album:** Released Apr '81, on Jazz Live (Italy) Catalogue no: **BLJ 8020**

**COMPLETE GRAMERCY FIVE SESSIONS, THE**
Tracks: / Special delivery stomp / Summit ridge drive / Keepin' myself for you / Cross your heart / Dr. Livingstone, I presume / When the quail come back to San Quentin / My blue Heaven / Smoke gets in your eyes / Grabtown grapple, The / Sad sack, The / Scuttlebutt / Gentle grifter, The / Mysterioso (take 1) / Mysterioso (take 2) / Hop, skip and jump.
**CD:** Released Jul '89, on Bluebird (2) by BMG Records (UK). Catalogue no: **ND 87637**
**Album:** Released Jul '89, on Bluebird (2) by BMG Records (UK). Catalogue no: **NL 87637**
**Cass:** Released Jul '89, on Bluebird (2) by BMG Records (UK). Catalogue no: **NK 87637**

**CONCERTO FOR CLARINET (Shaw, Artie & His Orchestra)**
Tracks: / Nightmare / Back bay shuffle / Any old time / Yesterdays / Copenhagen / My heart stood still / Deep purple / Begin the beguine / One night stand / I'm comin' / Virginia / Pastel blue / Carioca / One foot in the groove / I surrender, dear / Oh, lady be good / Traffic jam / Frenesi / Adios mariquita linda / Chantez les bas / April in Paris / Stardust / I'm confessin' (that I love you) / Blues (parts 1 and 2) / Concerto for clarinet / Blues in the night / Solid Sam / Deuces wild / Sometimes I feel like a mother-less child / Bedford drive / Little jazz.
**2 LP Set:** Released '79, on RCA by BMG Records (UK). Deleted '84. Catalogue no: **DPM 2028**

**DEUX GRANDES ANNEES (1938-39)**
Tracks: / Begin the beguine / Indian love call / Comin' on / Back bay shuffle / Any old time / I can't believe that you're in love with me / Non-stop flight / What is this thing called love? / Copenhagen / Softly as in a morning sunrise / It had to be you / My heart stood still / Rosalie / Rose room / This is it / Deep purple / Prosschai / I'm coming, Virginia / Snug as a bug in a rug / One foot in the groove / Out of nowhere / I can't afford to dream / Serenade to a savage / You're a lucky guy / Nightmare / Sobbin' blues / Together / Carioca on you / Sweet Sue / St. Louis blues.
**2 LP Set:** Released '83, on RCA (France) by BMG Records (France). Catalogue no: **PM 43175**

**DIAMOND SERIES: ARTIE SHAW**
Tracks: / Special delivery stomp / Keepin' myself for you / Summit Ridge Drive / Cross your heart / Doctor Livingstone, I presume / When the quail comes back to San Quentin / Smoke gets in your eyes / My blue Heaven / Grabtown grapple, The / Sad sack, The / Scuttlebutt / Gentle drifter, The / Mysterioso / Hop, skip and jump / Confessin' / Beyond the blue horizon.
**CD:** Released Apr '88, on Diamond Series by RCA Records. Catalogue no: **CD 90128**

**HOLLYWOOD PALLADIUM**
Tracks: / Whispers in the night / Canto carbli / There I go / Prelude in C major / Doctor Livingstone, I presume / Nobody knows the trouble I've seen / There'll be some changes made / Time was / Do you know why? / Frenesi / Looking for yesterday / Along the Santa Fe trail / Everything's jumpin'.
**Album:** Released Apr '81, on Hep Jazz by Hep Records. Catalogue no: **HEP 19**

**I CAN'T GET STARTED (Shaw, Artie & His Gramercy Five)**
**Album:** Released Sep '81, on Verve (USA) by Polydor Ltd. Catalogue no: **2304 208**

**INDISPENSABLE ARTIE SHAW (1938-1939) (Shaw, Artie & His Orchestra)**
Tracks: / Begin the beguine / Indian love call / Comin' on / Back bay shuffle / Any old time / I can't believe that you're in love with me / Non-stop flight / What is

this thing called love / Copenhagen / Softly as in a morning sunrise / It had to be you / My heart stood still / Rosalie / Rose room / This is it / Deep purple / Prosschai / I'm coming, Virginia / Snug as a bug in a rug / One foot in the groove / Out of nowhere / I can't afford to dream / Serenade to a savage / You're the lucky guy / Nightmare / Sobbin' blues / Together / Carioca / At sundown / I've got my eyes on you / Sweet Sue / St. Louis blues.
Note: Monophonic recording.
**Cass set:** Released Sep '86, on RCA by BMG Records (UK). Deleted May '89. Catalogue no: **NK 89820**
**2 LP Set:** Released Sep '86, on RCA by BMG Records (UK). Deleted Jul '89. Catalogue no: **NL 89820**

**INDISPENSABLE ARTIE SHAW VOLS. 3/4 (1940-1942) (Shaw, Artie & his Orchestra)**
Tracks: / Frenesi / King for a day / Special delivery stomp / Summit Ridge Drive / Chantez les bas / Stardust / Blues (parts 1 & 2) / What is there to say? / Who's excited? / Prelude in C major / When the quail comes back to San Quentin / Concerto for a clarinet (parts 1 & 2) / Moonglow / Confessin' / Love me a little / Beyond the blue horizon / Blues in the night / Rockin' chair / Take your shoes off, baby / Solid Sam / Just kiddin' around / St. James Infirmary / Deuces wild / Someone's rocking my dreamboat / Carnival / Needlenose / Two in one blues / Sometimes I feel like a motherless child.
**Cass:** Released '86, on RCA by BMG Records (UK). Deleted Oct '88. Catalogue no: **NK 89874**
**2 LP Set:** Released '86, on RCA by BMG Records (UK). Deleted Jul '89. Catalogue no: **NL 89874**

**INDISPENSABLE ARTIE SHAW VOLS. 5/6 1944-45 (Shaw, Artie & His Orchestra)**
Tracks: / Lady day / Jumpin' on the merry-go-round / I'll never be the same / 'S wonderful / Bedford drive / Grabtown grapple, The / Sad sack, The / Little jazz / Tea for two / Summertime / Time on my hands / Foggy day, A / Man I love, The / I could write a book / Thrill of a lifetime / Lucky number / Love walked on / Soon / Natch / They can't take that away from me / Things are looking up / Maid with the flaccid hair, The / No one but you / Dancing on the ceiling / I can't get started with you / Just floatin' along / I can't escape from you / Scuttlebutt / Gentle drifter, The / Mysterioso / Hop, skip and jump.
**2 LP Set:** Released Jan '87, on RCA by BMG Records (UK). Deleted Jul '89. Catalogue no: **NL 89914**
**Cass:** Released Jan '87, on RCA by BMG Records (UK). Deleted Oct '88. Catalogue no: **NK 89914**

**KING OF JAZZ STORY Volume 1**
**Cass:** Released '88, on Joker (USA) by Lifetime Records (USA). Catalogue no: **MC 3620**
**Album:** Released '88, on Joker (USA) by Lifetime Records (USA). Catalogue no: **SM 3620**

**MELODY & MADNESS, VOL 1 (Shaw, Artie & his Orchestra)**
Tracks: / Yam, The / Non-stop flight / Who blew out the flame? / Shoot the rhythm to me, John boy / Back bay shuffle / Yesterdays / What is this thing called love? / Copenhagen / It had to be you / Simple and sweet / Rockin' the state / You got me / In the mood / Shine on harvest moon.
**Album:** Released '82, on Nostalgia by Mainline Records. Catalogue no: **NOST 7609**

**MELODY & MADNESS, VOL 2 (Shaw, Artie & his Orchestra)**
Tracks: / Hold your hat / Jeepers creepers / Saving myself for you / Indian love call / Time out / Serenade to a savage / Softly as in a morning sunrise / Diga diga doo / Begin the beguine / My heart belongs to daddy / Prosschai / Rose room / My own / At sundown.
**Cass:** Released '82, on Nostalgia by Mainline Records. Catalogue no: **NOST 8613**
**Album:** Released '82, on Nostalgia by Mainline Records. Catalogue no: **NOST 7613**

**MELODY & MADNESS, VOL 3 (Shaw, Artie & his Orchestra)**
Tracks: / Zigeuner / I have eyes / Carioca / My heart stood still / I'm comin', Virginia / Deep purple / Diga diga doo / Shoot the rhythm to me, John boy / Together / I cried for you / Back bay shuffle / I want my share of love / Jungle drums / Rosalie.
**Cass:** Released '82, on Nostalgia by Mainline Records. Catalogue no: **NOST 8627**
**Album:** Released '82, on Nostalgia by Mainline Records. Catalogue no: **NOST 7627**

**MELODY & MADNESS, VOL 4 (Shaw, Artie & his Orchestra)**
Tracks: / Non-stop flight / My heart belongs to daddy / Chant, The / Double mellow / Better than average girl / Gang busters / Pastel blue / It's all yours / Prosschai / Nightmare / I'm coming, Virginia / I'm in love with the Honourable Mr. So and So / One foot in the groove.
**Album:** Released '82, on Nostalgia by Mainline Records. Catalogue no: **NOST 7628**

**MELODY & MADNESS, VOL 5 (Shaw, Artie & his Orchestra)**
Tracks: / Serenade to a savage / Rosalie / You're so indiff'rent / Copenhagen / At sundown / Supper time / Snug as a bug in a rug / Diga diga doo / Begin the beguine / Shoot the rhythm to me, John boy / Carioca / It had to be you / Traffic jam.
**Album:** Released '82, on Nostalgia by Mainline Records. Catalogue no: **NOST 7637**

**ORIGINAL SOUNDS OF THE SWING ERA VOL. 7**
**Album:** Released '83, on RCA (Germany) Catalogue no: **CL 05517**

**PIED PIPER, THE (Shaw, Artie & his Orchestra)**
**Album:** Released Jun '81, on First Heard by Submarine Records. Catalogue no: **FH 1005**

**SWINGING BIG BANDS, 1938-45, VOL. 1**
Tracks: / Yesterdays / Rosalie / Love come back to me / Diga diga doo / Stardust / Serenade to a savage / Moonglow / Grabtown grapple, The / Summertime / Temptation / Frenesi / Zigeuner.
**Album:** Released Apr '81, on Joker (USA) by Lifetime Records (USA). Catalogue no: **SM 3620**

**SWINGING BIG BANDS, 1938-40, VOL. 2**
Tracks: / Begin the beguine / Indian love call / Nightmare / Jungle drums / Carioca / Man I love, The / Donkey serenade, The / Lady be good / I surrender, dear / All the things you are / I didn't know what time it was / Summit Ridge Drive.
**Album:** Released Apr '81, on Joker (USA) by Lifetime Records (USA). Catalogue no: **SM 3621**

**SWING GOES ON VOL. 3**
Tracks: / Traffic jam / Begin the beguine / Lover come back to me / Zigeuner / What is this thing called love? / It had to be you / Softly as in a morning sunrise / Octoroon / Nightmare / Back bay shuffle / Jungle drums / Copenhagen.
**Album:** Released '83, on EMI (Germany) by EMI Records. Catalogue no: **IC 054 52712**

**THIS IS ARTIE SHAW**
Tracks: / Begin the beguine / Indian love call / Any old time / Back bay shuffle / Deep in a dream / It had to be you / Jungle drums / Donkey serenade, The / Deep purple / All the things you are / Frenesi / Cross your heart / Summit ridge drive / Temptation / Star dust / My blue Heaven / Smoke gets in your eyes / Moonglow / Dancing in the dark.
**Album:** Released Jul '86, on RCA by BMG Records (UK). Deleted Nov '88. Catalogue no: **NL 89411**
**Album:** Released '83, on RCA (Germany) Catalogue no: **26 28034**
**Cass:** Released Jul '86, on RCA by BMG Records (UK). Deleted Nov '88. Catalogue no: **NK 89411**

**THOU SWELL (Shaw, Artie & his Orchestra)**
Tracks: / Shoot the likker to me John boy / All alone / I'll be with you in apple blossom time / Blue skies / Sweet Lorraine / Same old line, The / Blues, The / It's a long way to Tipperary / Because I love you / Chant, The / My blue Heaven / Streamline / Sugar foot stomp / Thou swell / Pretty girl is like a melody, A / Japanese sandman, The.
Note: Recordings made in 1936 & 1937.
**CD:** Released 1 Oct '88, on Living Era by Academy Sound & Vision Records. Catalogue no: **CD AJA 5056**

**Album:** Released Oct '88, on Living Era by Academy Sound & Vision Records. Catalogue no: **AJA 5056**
**Cass:** Released Oct '88, on Living Era by Academy Sound & Vision Records. Catalogue no: **ZC AJA 5056**

**TRAFFIC JAM**
Tracks: / Man I love, The / Muchodenada / Love is the sweetest thing / Love walked in / You're mine / Oh you crazy moon / Serenade to a savage / Sweet little headache / What is this thing called love? / Thanks for everything / Mood in question / Orinoco / Traffic jam / I'm comin', Virginia / Last two weeks in July / Lilacs in the rain.
**Album:** Released Mar '85, on Big Band Era Catalogue no: **20135**
**Cass:** Released May '88, on Big Band Era Catalogue no: **40135**

**UNCOLLECTED, THE (Shaw, Artie & His Orchestra)**
Note: Previously unreleased material, recorded live, featuring vocalists Helen Forrest and Tony Pastor.
**Album:** Released Apr '85, on Hindsight Catalogue no: **HUK 176**

**WITH STRINGS VOL.2 (Shaw, Artie & His Orchestra)**
Tracks: / What is this thing called love / I believe / Love for sale / I've got you under my skin / Get out of town / Anniversary song.
Note: featuring Mel Torme and his Mel-Tones.
**Album:** Released '88, on Musicraft (USA) by Discovery Records (USA). Catalogue no: **MVS 507**

## Shaw, Charles "Bobo"

**BUGLE BOY BOP (Shaw, Charles "Bobo" & Lester Bowie)**
**Album:** Released '88, on Muse by Black & Blue Records. Catalogue no: **MR 5268**

**CHARLES 'BOBO' SHAW**
Note: Tracks include: Steam away kook 500 / Jackibeetee / Concerentasiah / Be bo bo be.
Artists include Joseph Bowie, The Human Arts Ensemble, Jullius Hemphill, Francois Myomo Mantuila, Alex Blake, Adbul Wadud. Recorded in New York City.
**Album:** Released '81, on Muse by Black & Blue Records. Catalogue no: **MR 5232**

## Shaw, Gene

**DEBUT IN BLUES (Shaw, Gene Sextet)**
Tracks: / Debut in blues / Karachi / Gentle Princess, The / When sunny gets blue / Thieves carnival / Not too cool / Who knows? / Travelog.
**Album:** Released '88, on Arco by Charly Records. Catalogue no: **ARC 501**

## Shaw, Robert

**TEXAS BARRELHOUSE PIANO**
**Album:** Released May '81, on Arhoolie (USA) by Arhoolie Records (USA). Catalogue no: **ARHOOLIE 1010**

## Shaw, Woody

**Biographical details:** American jazz man Woody Shaw was born in 1944 in North Carolina. He played trumpet and flugelhorn and has become a highly regarded composer. He gigged with Chick Corea, Eric Dolphy, Art Blakey and many others. He had become highly regarded composer and bandleader since finding his own voice in the 1970's.
He died in 1989. (Donald Clarke).

**CONCERT ENSEMBLE**
Tracks: / Hello to the wind / Obsequious / Jean Marie / In the land of the blacks.
Note: Personnel: Woody Shaw - trumpet; Rene McLean - alto sax, flute; Frank Foster - tenor & soprano sax; Slide Hampton - trombone; Ronnie Matthews - piano; Stafford James - bass; Louis Hayes - drums. Recorded live at the Berlin Jazz Festival, 6 November 1976.
**Album:** Released May '81, on Muse by Black & Blue Records. Catalogue no: **MR 5139**

**ICHI-BAN (Shaw, Woody/Jun. Cook/R. Matthews/S. James/Guilherme)**
Tracks: / Ichi-ban / Pannonica / Brothers & sisters / Moontrane / Book's bossa.
Note: Recorded in New York, 5 May 1976.
**Album:** Released May '81, on Timeless (Import) by Timeless Records. Catalogue no: **SJP 102**

**IN MY OWN WAY**
**CD:** Released 12 Apr '89, on In & Out by New Note. Catalogue no: **70032**
**Album:** Released 12 Apr '89, on In & Out by New Note. Catalogue no: **70031**

**IRON MEN, THE**
Tracks: / Iron man / Jitterbug waltz / Symmetry / Diversion one / Song of songs / Diversion two.
Note: Musicians include Anthony Braxton, Muhal Richard Abrams, Cecil McBee, Victor Lewis, Arthur Blythe. Recorded: 6, 13 April 1977.
**Album:** Released '81, on Muse by Black & Blue Records. Catalogue no: **MR 5160**

**LITTLE RED'S FANTASY**
Tracks: / Jean Marie / Sashianova / In case you haven't heard / Little Red's fantasy / Tomorrow's destiny.
Note: Personnel: Woody Shaw - trumpet; Frank Strozier - alto sax; Ronnie Matthews - piano; Stafford James - bass; Eddie Moore - drums. Recorded 29 June 1976.
**Album:** Released May '81, on Muse by Black & Blue Records. Catalogue no: **MR 5103**

**LONELY SCHOOL**
Tracks: / Lonely school / Heads up.
**12" Single:** Released Jan '85, on A&M by A&M Records. Deleted '88. Catalogue no: **AMY 231**
**7" Single:** Released Jan '85, on A&M by A&M Records. Deleted '88. Catalogue no: **AM 231**

**LOTUS FLOWER**
**Album:** Released Jul '88, on Enja (Germany) by Enja Records (West Germany). Catalogue no: **ENJA 4018**

**LOVE DANCE**
Tracks: / Love dance / Obsequious / Sunbath / Soulfully I love you / Zoltan.
Note: Personnel: Woody Shaw - trumpet; Steve Turre - trombone, bass trombone; Rene McLean - alto & soprano sax; Billy Harper - tenor sax; Joe Bonner - piano; Cecil McBee - bass; Victor Lewis - drums; Guilherme - percussion; Tony Waters - congas. Recorded November 1975.
**Album:** Released May '81, on Muse by Black & Blue Records. Catalogue no: **MR 5074**

**MOONTRANE, THE**
Tracks: / Moontrane / Are they only dreams? / Tapscott's blues / Sanyas / Katrina ballerina.
Note: Personnel: Woody Shaw - trumpet; Steve Turre - trombone; Azar Lawrence - tenor & soprano sax; Onaje Allen Gumbs - piano, electric piano; Buster Williams or Cecil McBee - bass; Victor Lewis - drums; Guilherme - percussion. Recorded 11, 18 December 1974.
**Album:** Released Apr '81, on Muse by Black & Blue Records. Catalogue no: **MR 5058**

**NIGHT MUSIC**
Tracks: / Orange cresent / To kill a brick / All the things you are / Apex.
**Album:** Released '84, on WEA by WEA Records. Deleted '89. Catalogue no: **K960299-1**

**SETTING STANDARDS**
Tracks: / There is no greater love / All the way / Spiderman blues / Touch of your lips, The / What's new / When lore is new.
Note: Personnel: Woody Shaw - flugelhorn; Cedar Walton - piano; Buster Williams - bass; Victor Jones - drums.
**Album:** Released Jan '86, on Muse by Black & Blue Records. Catalogue no: **MR 5318**

## Shearing, George

**Biographical details:** Pianist George Shearing was born blind in London in 1919. He was already a highly regarded jazz musician when he went to the USA in 1947, sponsored by British-born critic/composer/producer Leonard Feather; in 1949 he invented a much imitated style with his quintet of piano, guitar, vibes, bass and drums, playing in the bop-flavoured 'locked hands' chordal style. He has been one of the most popular jazz musicians in the world ever since. (Donald Clarke)..

**500 MILES HIGH**
**Album:** Released Apr '81, on MPS Jazz Catalogue no: **MPS 68 219**

**ALONE TOGETHER (Shearing, George & Marian McPartland)**
**Album:** Released Dec '81, on Concord Jazz by Concord Jazz Records (USA). Catalogue no: **CJ 171**

**AN ELEGANT EVENING (Shearing, George & Mel Torme)**
Tracks: / I'll be seeing you / Love and the moon / Oh, you crazy moon / No moon at all / After the waltz is over / This

time the dream's on me / Last night, when we were young / You changed my life / I had the craziest dream / Darn that dream / Brigg fair / My foolish heart / You're driving me crazy.
Note: Recorded March 1985 Personnel: George Shearing - piano / Mel Torme - vocals. Recorded in March 1985.
**Cass:** Released Feb '86, on Concord Jazz by Concord Jazz Records (USA). Catalogue no: **CJC 294**
**Album:** Released Feb '86, on Concord Jazz by Concord Jazz Records (USA). Catalogue no: **CJ 294**
**CD:** Released Jul '87, on Concord Jazz by Concord Jazz Records (USA). Catalogue no: **CCD 4294**

**AN EVENING AT CHARLIE'S (Shearing, George & Mel Torme)**
Tracks: / Just one of those things / On Green Dolphin Street / Dream dancing / I'm hip / Then I'll be tired of you / Caught in the middle of my years / Welcome to the club / Nica's dream / Chase me Charlie / Love is just around the corner.
Note: Don Thompson: bass. Donny Osborne: drums. Recorded live at 'Charlie's Georgetown'.
**Album:** Released Sep '84, on Concord Jazz by Concord Jazz Records (USA). Catalogue no: **CJ 248**
**CD:** Released Sep '84, on Concord Jazz by Concord Jazz Records (USA). Catalogue no: **CCD 4248**
**Cass:** Released Sep '84, on Concord Jazz by Concord Jazz Records (USA). Catalogue no: **CJC 248**

**ARTISTRY OF GEORGE SHEARING**
**VHS:** Released '88, on Kay Jazz (video) by Kay Jazz. Catalogue no: **KJ 064**

**BAUBLES,BANGLES & BEADS**
Tracks: / Baubles, bangles and beads.
**7" Single:** Released Oct '62, on Capitol by EMI Records. Deleted Oct '65. Catalogue no: **CL 15269**

**BEST OF GEORGE SHEARING**
Tracks: / Roses of Picardy / Early autumn / East of the sun / Honeysuckle rose / Lullaby of Birdland / September in the rain / Little white lies / You don't know what love is / You stepped out of a dream / September song / Jumpin' with symphony Syd.
**Album:** Released Jun '83, on MFP by EMI Records. Deleted Jun '88. Catalogue no: **MFP 5608**

**BLUES ALLEY JAZZ**
Tracks: / One for the woofer / Autumn in New York / Masquerade is over, The / Soon it's gonna rain / High and inside / For every man there's a woman / This couldn't be the real thing / Up a lazy river.
Note: This was the first of many critically acclaimed recordings by Shearing on the Concord Jazz label. Sophisticated piano sounds in an intimate duo setting. George Shearing (piano) and Brian Torff (bass).
**CD:** Released Nov '89, on Concord Jazz by Concord Jazz Records (USA). Catalogue no: **CCD 4110**

**BREAKIN' OUT (Shearing, George Trio)**
**CD:** Released Dec '87, on Concord Jazz by Concord Jazz Records (USA). Catalogue no: **CCD 4335**

**CHAMPAGNE EVENING (Shearing, George & Mel Torme)**
Tracks: / All God's children / Born to be blue / Simple life / Good morning heartache / Manhattan hoedown / Love / You'd be so nice to come home to / It might as well be Spring / Nightingale sang in Berkeley Square, A / Lullaby of Birdland.
Note: The first-ever recording of Shearing and Torme together.
**Cass:** Released Aug '82, on Concord Jazz by Concord Jazz Records (USA). Catalogue no: **CJC 190**
**Album:** Released Aug '82, on Concord Jazz by Concord Jazz Records (USA). Catalogue no: **CJ 190**

**DEXTERITY**
Tracks: / Dexterity / You must believe in spring / Sakura sakura / Long ago and far away / Can't we be friends / As long as I live / Please send me someone to love / Duke Ellington medley.
Note: With bassist Neil Swainson and a guest appearance from singer Ernestine Anderson on two numbers. Recorded at the Concord Jazz Festival in Japan, 1987. Sleeve notes by Leonard Feather. CD version has three extra tracks.
**CD:** Released Jul '88, on Concord Jazz by Concord Jazz Records (USA). Catalogue no: **CCD 4346**
**Cass:** Released Jul '88, on Concord Jazz by Concord Jazz Records (USA). Catalogue no: **CJ 346 C**
**Album:** Released Jul '88, on Concord Jazz by Concord Jazz Records (USA). Catalogue no: **CJ 346**

**EVENING WITH... (Shearing, George & Mel Torme)**
Tracks: / All God's chillun got rhythm / Born to be blue / Give me the simple life / Good morning heartache / Manhattan hoedown / You'd be so nice to come home to / Nightingale sang in Berkeley Square, A / Love / It might as well be spring / Lullaby of Birdland.
Note: Personnel: George Shearing (piano), Mel Torme (vocals), Brian Torf (bass).
**CD:** Released Mar '87, on Concord Jazz by Concord Jazz Records (USA). Catalogue no: **CCD 4190**

**FIRST EDITION (Shearing, George & Jim Hall)**
Tracks: / Street of dreams / To Antonio Carlos Jobim / Careful / I see nothing to laugh about / Without words / I hear a rhapsody / To Tommy Flanagan / Emily.
Note: George Shearing (piano) and Jim Hall (guitar).
**Cass:** Released Apr '82, on Concord Jazz by Concord Jazz Records (USA). Catalogue no: **CJC 177**
**Album:** Released Apr '82, on Concord Jazz by Concord Jazz Records (USA). Catalogue no: **CJ 177**

**GEORGE SHEARING (Compact/Walkman jazz)**
Tracks: / Lullaby of Birdland / Time after time / How deep is the ocean? / G & G after you've gone / Con alma / Yesterdays / This can't be love / Too close for comfort / Entertainer, The / Love walked in / When I fall in love / Cheryl / It don't mean athing if it ain't....
**CD:** Released Mar '88, on MPS Jazz Catalogue no: **833 284-2**
**Cass:** Released 27 Feb '88, on MPS Jazz Catalogue no: **833 284-4**

**GEORGE SHEARING IN DIXIELAND (Shearing, George/Dixie Six)**
Tracks: / Clap your hands / Truckin' / New Orleans / Take five / Blue Monk / Alice in Dixieland / Mighty like the blues / Destination Moon / Soon / Lullaby of Birdland / Desafinado.
Note: Cassette: One bonus track. CD: Three bonus tracks.
**CD:** Released Sep '89, on Concord Jazz by Concord Jazz Records (USA). Catalogue no: **CCD 4388**
**Album:** Released Sep '89, on Concord Jazz by Concord Jazz Records (USA). Catalogue no: **CJ 388**
**Cass:** Released Sep '89, on Concord Jazz by Concord Jazz Records (USA). Catalogue no: **CJ 388C**

**GETTING IN THE SWING OF THINGS (Shearing, George Trio)**
**Album:** Released May '81, on MPS Jazz Catalogue no: **MPS 68 253**

**GRAND PIANO**
Tracks: / When a woman loves a man / It never entered my mind / Mack the knife / Nobody else but me / Imitations / Taking a chance on love / If I had you / How insensitive / Easy to love / While we're young.
**Album:** Released Nov '85, on Concord Jazz by Concord Jazz Records (USA). Catalogue no: **CJ 281**
**Cass:** Released Nov '85, on Concord Jazz by Concord Jazz Records (USA). Catalogue no: **CJC 281**
**CD:** Released Sep '86, on Concord Jazz by Concord Jazz Records (USA). Catalogue no: **CCD 4281**

**IN CONCERT AT THE PAVILION (Shearing, George & Brian Torff)**
**Album:** Released Nov '80, on Concord Jazz by Concord Jazz Records (USA). Catalogue no: **CJ 132**

**IT'S EASY TO REMEMBER**
Tracks: / It's easy to remember / Nearness of you, The / Wednesday night hop / Poinciana / Consternation / Fourth deuce / Blue moon / Missouri scrambler / Man from Minton's, The / Overnight hop

/ Someone to watch over me / To be or not to bop.
**Album:** Released Feb '83, on Jasmine by Hasmick Promotions. Deleted Jun '87. Catalogue no: **JASM 2009**

**JAZZ CONCERT**
Tracks: / Walkin' / Love is just around the corner / I cover the waterfront / Love walked in / There with you / Bel Aire.
**Cass:** Released Jul '86, on Capitol by EMI Records. Deleted Oct '89. Catalogue no: **TCEMS 1157**
**Album:** Released Jul '86, on Capitol by EMI Records. Deleted Oct '89. Catalogue no: **EMS 1157**

**LIGHT, AIRY AND SWINGING**
**Album:** Released May '81, on MPS Jazz Catalogue no: **MPS 68 094**

**LIVE AT THE CAFE CARLYLE (Shearing, George & Don Thompson)**
Tracks: / Pent-up house / Shadow of your smile / Teach me tonight / Cheryl / Blues for breakfast / P.S. I love you / I cover the waterfront / Tell me a bedtime story / Stratford stomp / Inside.
Note: George Shearing (piano), Don Thompson (bass).
**Cass:** Released Sep '84, on Concord Jazz by Concord Jazz Records (USA). Catalogue no: **CJC 246**
**Album:** Released Sep '84, on Concord Jazz by Concord Jazz Records (USA). Catalogue no: **CJ 246**
**CD:** Released '88, on Concord Jazz by Concord Jazz Records (USA). Catalogue no: **CCD 4246**

**MANY FACETS OF GEORGE SHEARING,**
**Album:** Released May '81, on MPS Jazz Catalogue no: **MPS 68 177**

**MORE GRAND PIANO (solo piano)**
Tracks: / My silent love / Change partners / My favourite things / You don't know what love is / Ramona / People / East of the sun / I can't get started / Dream / Wind in the willows.
**Album:** Released Jul '87, on Concord Jazz by Concord Jazz Records (USA). Catalogue no: **CJ 318**
**Cass:** Released Jul '87, on Concord Jazz by Concord Jazz Records (USA). Catalogue no: **CJC 318**
**CD:** Released Jul '87, on Concord Jazz by Concord Jazz Records (USA). Catalogue no: **CCD 4318**

**MUSIC OF COLE PORTER, THE (Shearing, George / Barry Tuckwell)**
Tracks: / I concentrate on you / Everything I love / I've got you under my skin / Easy to love / In the still of the night / Every time we say goodbye / But in the morning, no / So in love / After you / All through the night / Do I love you?.
Note: George Shearing - piano and arrangements. Barry Tuckwell - french horn. Mike Renzi, Harry Lookofsky, John Clayton, Don Thompson, Grady Tate.
**Cass:** Released Oct '86, on Concord Jazz by Concord Jazz Records (USA). Catalogue no: **CCMC 2010**
**Album:** Released Oct '86, on Concord Jazz by Concord Jazz Records (USA). Catalogue no: **CC 2010**
**CD:** Released Oct '86, on Concord Jazz by Concord Jazz Records (USA). Catalogue no: **CCD 42010**

**MY SHIP**
**Album:** Released May '81, on MPS Jazz Catalogue no: **MPS 68 096**

**ON TARGET (Shearing, George Trio)**
Tracks: / Fjaerlins vingot / Last night when we were young / Amaryllis / Strange enchantment / Look at that face / Songbird / This is all I ask / Portrait of Jennie / Nightingale sang in Berkeley Square.
**Album:** Released Dec '82, on MPS Jazz Deleted Dec '87. Catalogue no: **15551**
**Cass:** Released Nov '89, on Memoir by Memoir Records. Catalogue no: **CMOIR 133**

**PERFECT MATCH, A (Shearing, George/Ernestine Anderson)**
Note: By popular demand this dynamic duo has joined forces to create an entire album together. They are joined by Neil Swainson(bass) and Jeff Hamilton(drums).
**CD:** Released Oct '88, on Concord Jazz by Concord Jazz Records (USA). Catalogue no: **CCD 4357**
**Cass:** Released Oct '88, on Concord Jazz by Concord Jazz Records (USA). Catalogue no: **CJ 357 C**
**Album:** Released Oct '88, on Concord Jazz by Concord Jazz Records (USA). Catalogue no: **CJ 357**

**PIANO**
Tracks: / It had to be you / Daisy / Thinking of you / Sweet and lovely / It's you or no one / Wendy / Am I blue? (CD only.) / Miss Invisible (CD only.) / You're my everything / John O'Groats / Waltz for Claudia / For you / Children's waltz / Happiness is a thing called Joe.
**Album:** Released Jan '90, on Concord by Concord Jazz Records (USA). Catalogue no: **CJ 400**
**CD:** Released Jan '90, on Concord by Concord Jazz Records (USA). Catalogue no: **CCD 4400**
**Cass:** Released Jan '90, on Concord by Concord Jazz Records (USA). Catalogue no: **CJ 400C**

**SHEARING ON STAGE**
Tracks: / September in the rain / On the street where you live / Roses of Picardy / Little Niles / Caravan / I'll remember April / Little white lies / East of the sun / Nothing be de best / Love is just around the corner / Walkin' / I cover the waterfront / Love walked in / Bel-Air.
Note: George Shearing was born in London on 13th August 1919. Blind from birth, he began playing piano at the age of three. After winning a number of Melody Maker polls as top British pianist, he decided to emigrate to the USA in 1947. Settling in New York, he was strongly influenced by the bop style of Bud Powell. The memorable 'Shearing sound' originated around 1949, in some recordings he made with a quintet of piano, vibes, guitar, bass and drums. This sound, bought Shearing enormous commercial success, which was at its peak when these recordings were tapedin the early '60s. They contain some of the swingiest, joyous and most humourous music George ever committed to tape. As this album is released, George is celebrating his seventieth birthday. We thank him for the hours of pleasure he has given us and which he continues to give us. We wish him well. (Renaissance, 1989)
**CD:** Released '89, on Renaissance Catalogue no: **CDREN 004**

**SOLO PIANO-MY SHIP**
Tracks: / My ship / Happy days are here again / When I fall in love / Londonderry air / April in Paris / Entertainer, The / Tenderly / How deep is the ocean / Autumn in New York / Greensleeves / Send in the clowns.
Note: A solo performance by the great George Shearing.A programme of popular standards that will appear to all good music lovers. Surprise track 'Send in the Clowns' features Shearing playing and singing.
**CD:** Released May '87, on MPS Jazz (Germany) Catalogue no: **821 664-2**

**TOP DRAWER (Shearing, George & Mel Torme)**
Tracks: / Smoke gets in your eyes / Hi-fly / Shine on your shoes / Stardust / Away in a manger / Here's to my lady / What's this? / Oleo / How do you say auf wiedersehen?.
**Album:** Released Jul '83, on Concord Jazz by Concord Jazz Records (USA). Catalogue no: **CJ 219**
**Cass:** Released Jul '83, on Concord Jazz by Concord Jazz Records (USA). Catalogue no: **CJC 219**

**TWO FOR THE ROAD (Shearing, George & Carmen McRae)**
**CD:** Released '89, on Concord Jazz by Concord Jazz Records (USA). Catalogue no: **CCD 4128**

**WINDOW**
**Album:** Released May '81, on MPS Jazz Catalogue no: **MPS 68 200**

**YOUNG GEORGE SHEARING, THE 1939 - 1944**
Tracks: / Pretty girl is like a melody, A / Guilty / Can't we be friends? / Rosetta / I don't stand a ghost of a chance / How come you do me like you do? / Coquette / Sweet Lorraine / Stomp in F / More than you know / Time on my hands / Afraid of you.
**Album:** Released Feb '83, on Jasmine by Hasmick Promotions. Deleted Jun '87. Catalogue no: **JASM 2008**

## Sheldon, Jack

**BLUES IN THE NIGHT (Sheldon, Jack & The Swedish All Stars)**
**Album:** Released May '86, on Phontastic (Sweden) Catalogue no: **PHONT 7569**

**HOLLYWOOD HEROES (Sheldon, Jack Quintet)**
Tracks: / Joint is jumpin', The / Pardon my southern accent / Poor butterfly / Lover / Rosetta / I thought about you / I want to be happy.
Note: "On this album Jack and his hand-picked band of 'heroes' demonstrate that having fun and making great music go hand in hand. The tunes have been well chosen: a mixture of strongly melodic standards that have the taste of old wine from a new bottle.... Jack Sheldon's Hollywood Heroes explore new ground and strikingly familiar territory with this lively jazz set. Jack Sheldon, trumpet and vocals; Gene Estes, drums; Doug MacDonald, guitar; Ray Sherman, piano; Dave Stone, bass." (IMS Records, May 1988.)
**Cass:** Released May '88, on Concord Jazz by Concord Jazz Records (USA). Catalogue no: **CJC 339**
**CD:** Released May '88, on Concord Jazz by Concord Jazz Records (USA). Catalogue no: **CCD 4339**
**Album:** Released May '88, on Concord Jazz by Concord Jazz Records (USA). Catalogue no: **CJ 339**

**JACK SHELDON & HIS EXCITING BIG BAND**
**Album:** Released '88, on GNP Crescendo (USA) by GNP Crescendo Records (USA). Catalogue no: **GNPS 9036**

**JACK SHELDON QUARTET, THE**
Tracks: / I love you / Daydream / Cherry / Don't get around much anymore / Bye bye Blackbird / I'm getting sentimental over you / Shadow of your smile / Get out of town / Ours / Poor butterfly / Very thought of you, The.
**Album:** Released Nov '83, on Concord Jazz by Concord Jazz Records (USA). Catalogue no: **CJ 228**

## Shelton, Anne

**Biographical details:** Singer Ann Shelton was born in Dulwich in 1927, and performed on the BBC at age 12. She went to work for bandleader Ambrose rather than be evacuated from WWII London. She was under contract to Ambrose for years, but also worked with Glen Miller and Bing Crosby during the war at their request. She had many hit records before UK charts began (she was the first to sing *Lili Marlene* in English) and continued into the 1950's. With Vera Lynn one of the country's best loved artists from that era, she was also succesful in the USA. She sang *You'll never Know* for the Queen Mother on her 80th birthday, and sang on UK TV with a Glen Miller ghost band in 1984 during celebrations for the 40th anniversary of D-Day. (Donald Clarke)..

**ANNE SHELTON SINGS WITH AMBROSE & HIS ORCHESTRA**
Tracks: / Lady who didn't believe in love, The / Taking a chance on love / Rhyme with everything that's beautiful / Dance with a dolly / It can't be wrong / Daddy / I never mention your name / I'll walk alone / My Yiddishe momma / I know why (and so do you) / So long, Sarah Jane / Where's my love? / Journey's end / All or nothing at all / If you please / Robin Hood / Anywhere / Wedding waltz.
**Album:** Released Apr '84, on Recollections (Decca) by Decca Records. Deleted '86. Catalogue no: **RFL 41**
**Cass:** Released Apr '84, on Recollections (Decca) by Decca Records. Catalogue no: **KRFLC 41**

**ANNE SHELTON'S SENTIMENTAL JOURNEY**
Tracks: / Sentimental journey / Tangerine / Nightingale sang in Berkeley Square, A / Don't fence me in / I'll walk alone / Run rabbit run / When the lights go on again / White cliffs of Dover, The / You'll never know / After all / Don't sit under the apple tree / I left my heart at the stage door canteen / Roll out the barrel / I'll get by / Boogie woogie bugle boy / I'll be seeing you / Chattanooga choo choo / Lili Marlene / Just look around.
**Album:** Released Oct '82, on President by President Records. Catalogue no: **PRX 21**

**ARRIVEDERCI DARLING**
Tracks: / Arrivederci darling.
**7" Single:** Released Dec '55, on H.M.V. by EMI Records. Deleted Dec '58. Catalogue no: **POP 146**

**COLLECTION: ANNE SHELTON**
Tracks: / Cross over the bridge / Song of the trees / Answer me / If I give my heart to you / I remember mama / Crystal ball / If you've never been in love / Song of the barefoot Contessa / If we all said a prayer / Arrivederci, darling / Bridge of sighs / Why does it have to be me / For you, for me / Goodnight, well it's time to go / Tobermory Bay / Book / What have they told you / Teach me tonight / Oh baby mine, I get so lonely / Don't say goodbye.
**Album:** Released '79, on Encore by EMI Records. Deleted '84. Catalogue no: **ONCM 521**

**CRAZY**
Tracks: / Crazy.
**7" Single:** Released Sep '82, on President by President Records. Catalogue no: **PT 510**

**I'LL BE SEEING YOU**
Tracks: / I'll be seeing you / I'll be with you in apple blossom time / Nightingale sang in Berkeley Square, A / Pair of silver wings / At last / Last time I saw Paris, The / I'll never smile again / Fools rush in / Kiss the boys goodbye / Amapola / Blues in the night / Where or when / You'd be so nice to come home to / I never mention your name / How deep is the ocean? / Anniversary song.
**Album:** Released Jul '77, on Decca by Decca International. Deleted '88. Catalogue no: **DVL 2**
**Cass:** Released Jul '77, on Decca by Decca International. Deleted '88. Catalogue no: **KDVC 2**

**LAY DOWN YOUR ARMS**
Tracks: / Lay down your arms.
**7" Single:** Released Aug '56, on Philips by Phonogram Ltd. Deleted Aug '59. Catalogue no: **PB 616**

**MAGIC OF ANNE SHELTON, THE**
Tracks: / Arrivederci darling / Cross over the bridge / Song of the trees / Answer me / Crystal ball / We all said a prayer / Kissing tree, The / If I give my heart to you / I remember mama / If you've never been in love / Song of the barefoot contessa / Jukebox rag / Ay ay ay baio / Bridge of sighs / Why does it have to be me? / For you, for me / Goodnight, well it's time to go / Tobermory Bay / Don't leave me now / Book, The / What have they told you? / Teach me tonight / Oh baby mine, I get so lonely / Don't say goodbye / Love him so much I could scream.
**Cass set:** Released Jun '84, on MFP by EMI Records. Deleted '89. Catalogue no: **41 1048 9**
**2 LP Set:** Released Jun '84, on MFP by EMI Records. Deleted '89. Catalogue no: **41 1048 3**

**SAILOR**
Tracks: / Sailor.
**7" Single:** Released Jan '61, on Philips by Phonogram Ltd. Deleted Jan '64. Catalogue no: **PB 1096**

**SEVEN DAYS**
Tracks: / Seven days.
**7" Single:** Released Apr '56, on Philips by Phonogram Ltd. Deleted Apr '59. Catalogue no: **PB 567**

**SING IT AGAIN, ANNE**
Tracks: / Tangerine / Smoke gets in your eyes / Taking a chance on love / I remember you / How green was my valley / I'll never smile again / How did he look? / Village of St. Bernadette / My Yiddishe momma / Lay down your arms / I got it bad and that ain't good / Perfidia / Happiness is just a thing called Joe / There's a lull in my life / Let there be love / Souvenir d'Italie / Let's face the music and dance / Man that got away, The.
**Album:** Released Dec '83, on President by President Records. Catalogue no: **PLE 510**
**Cass:** Released Jan '84, on President by President Records. Catalogue no: **TC-PLE 510**

**VILLAGE OF ST. BERNADETTE**
Tracks: / Village of St. Bernadette.
**7" Single:** Released Nov '59, on Philips by Phonogram Ltd. Deleted Nov '62. Catalogue no: **PB 969**

## Shepp, Archie

**Biographical details:** Saxophonist, composer and bandleader Archie Shepp was born 24 May 1937 in Florida. He is also a poet, a playwright and a teacher. He worked in R&B bands, then with avant-gardists Cecil Taylor, Bill Dixon, Jihn Tchicai, Don Cherry, John Coltrane. He has toured the world with his own groups. His electric music tries to include everything and sometimes fails, but his body of work is passionately honest. [Donald Clarke, April 87].

**Archie Shepp**

**ARCHIE SHEPP/THE NEW YORK CONTEMPORARY FIVE (Shepp, Archie & New York Contemporary Five)**
Note: MONO production.
**Album:** Released May '86, on Storyville by Storyville Records AB. Catalogue no: **SLP 1009**

**BALLADS FOR TRANE (Shepp, Archie Quartet)**
Tracks: / Soul eyes / You don't know what love is / Wise one / Where are you? / Darn that dream / Theme for Ernie.
Note: Personnel: Archie Shepp (Tenor sax), Al Dailey (Piano), Reggie Workman (Bass), Charlie Persip (Drums).
**CD:** Released '88, on Denon Catalogue no: **C38-7264**

**BIRD FIRE**
**CD:** Released Jul '88, on West Wind Catalogue no: **WWCD 006**
**Album:** Released Jul '88, on West Wind Catalogue no: **WW 006**

**BLASE**
Tracks: / My angel / There is a balm in Gilead / Sophisticated lady / Touareg / Blase.
Note: The LP from which this CD was taken from was recorded in Paris, late in 1969, during a flurry of activity created by the simultaneous presence in that city of a good proportion of America's finest young improvisers. Under the aegis of the BYG organisation they found their way into the recording studio in a variety of combinations; not the least impressive result was a series of three BYG albums by the much recorded Archie Shepp, of which *Blase* is one.
By the time of this date, Shepp was one of the better-known standard-bearers of the avant-garde. He had been a member of the short-lived but influential New York Contemporary Five (with Don Cherry, John Tchicai and Sunny Murray), he had published several antiestablishment broadsides in the widely-read American Jazz magazine *Downbeat* (one, in which he compared the function of his saxophone to that of the machine guns of the Viet Cong, brought down the wrath of half the publication's subscribers), and he had enjoyed the patronage of the great John Coltrane, who had not only made Shepp a part of his important 'Ascension' recording, but had secured the tenorist a recording contract with his own label, leading to brilliant LPs like *Four for Trane, On this night* and *Fire music.*
It didn't take long for commentators to agree that, of all the young hellions, Shepp seemed to possess the most obvious sense of tradition; he showed, for example, a lasting fondness for the ballads of Duke Ellington, which he delivered in a relaxed style reminiscent of Ellington's former sideman, Ben Webster. Futhermore, his style appeared to be surrused with a blues feeling which even those inimical to the avant-garde could understand, and early compositions such as *Hambone* displayed a liking for procedures which would not have been alien to the jazz-for-dancing bands of the South West in the '30s. Against this, his detractors could point to the rambling but extraordinarily intense 'free' performances of his working groups, such as that recorded at the Donaueschingen Festival in 1968, when Shepp and his two trombonists, Roswell Rudd and Grachan Moncur, worked virtually without structures.
Shepp turned up in Paris in 1969 apparently in transit back to America, having visited and played in Morocco. (Hence, perhaps, the inclusion of a piece entitled *Touareg* on this CD, and the original cover photograph, which showed him in North African robes against a Morrocan sky). Lacking the members of his regular group, the BYG producers placed him in a variety of contexts, mostly including members of the Art Ensemble of Chicago, then visiting Paris and various other Americans, both emigres and transients.
*Blase* finds him with a typically mixed selection of comrades, perhaps the most unusual of whom appear on the first two selections. Chicago Beau (Beauchamp) and Julio Finn were Chicago's bluesmen of the younger generation: they were not heard from publically before these sessions, and have been silent since. Their prescence on *My angel* and on the title-track is provocative, in that it leads Shepp to create two pieces rooted strongly in simple blues practices, although there are uncomfortable moments - such as that after the harmonica introduction to *My angel* when the piano enters, making the listener immediately aware of differences in tuning between the instruments. However, once past the initial shock, they appear to reach some accommodation of pitching, and the discrepancy happily fades.
*There is a balm in Gilead*, Shepp's recasting and setting of Isaiah Viii:22, is surely one of the loveliest, most delicate pieces he has ever created. The simple theme is shared between Jeanne Lee's beautiful voice, Shepp at his genlest, and the muted trumpet and the flugelhorn of Lester Bowie, that brilliant member of the Art Ensemble. With discreet support from Dave Burrell's piano and the bowed bass of Malachi Favors (another Art Ensemble stalwart), they indulge in a minimum of decoration, sticking closely to the tune, and it is perhaps not too much to suggest that within' the words and the music each musician discovered some shared experience, stretching back into childhood and the church.
Shared history of another kind, is in Ellington's *Sophisticated lady*, a fine addition to the series of Ducal ballads which Shepp inaugurated with his recording of *Prelude to a kiss* in 1965 and which continues to this day (in 1976, for instance, *Solitude* was a staple of his repertoire). This 'Lady' is possibly not the most poised member of that community, but Lee's vocal and Shepp's smoky obligato intertwine beautifully.
Lastly, a meeting of giants: *Touareg* is a free improvisation for tenor, bass and

drums, featuring two wonderful musicians; Favors, a young giant whose facility and imagination match the best of the post-LaFaro bassists (and whose membership of the Art Ensemble has perhaps prevented him from earning the praise that he would surely have found in a freelance context), and the marvellous Philly Joe Jones, sparkplug of his unforgettable Miles Davis Quintet of the mid '50s. Jones, then resident in Europe (prior to this date he had spent some time in England, teaching young local drummers), had little experience of the kind of improvisation which was by then second nature to Shepp and Favors, but his finely detailed cymbal line dovetails impressively with the bass. Shepp's career does not lack documentation; indeed, he has recorded so prolifically since 1963 that some of his finest achievements are in danger of being overlooked. Blase sees him looking outwards, experimenting with a variety of partners and idioms, and in this respect alone it is a valuable component of his oeuvre. (Richard Williams)
**Album:** Released Feb '78, on Charly by Charly Records. Catalogue no: **AFF 7**
**CD:** Released Mar '87, on Affinity by Charly Records. Catalogue no: **CDCHARLY 77**

**DAY DREAM**
Tracks: / Don't you know I care / Caravan / Day dream / Satin doll / I got it bad and that ain't good / Prelude to a kiss.
**CD:** Released Jun '89, on Denon Catalogue no: **DC 8547**

**DOWN HOME NEW YORK**
Tracks: / Down home New York / Round midnight / May 16th / Fourth world / Straight Street.
Note: Archie Shepp - tenor, soprano saxes, vocals. Charles E McGhee - trumpet, vocals. Ken Werner - piano, vocals. Saheb Sarbib - bass, electric bass, vocals. Marvin Smith - drums, vocals. Bazzi Bartholemew Gray- vocals. Recorded 5, 6, 7, 8 February 1984, Classic Sound studio, New York.
**CD:** Released '86, on Soul Note Catalogue no: **SNCD 1102**
**Album:** Released May '85, on Soul Note Catalogue no: **SN 1102**

**DUET (Shepp, Archie & Dollar Brand)**
Tracks: / Fortunato / Barefoot boy form Queens Town / Left alone / Proof of the man / Ubu suku / Moniebah.
**Album:** Released Mar '82, on Denon Deleted '88. Catalogue no: **YX 7532**
**CD:** Released '88, on Denon Deleted '88. Catalogue no: **C38-7008**

**FIFTH OF MAY (Shepp, Archie & Jasper Van't Hof)**
Note: Tenor saxist Shepp is joined by Dutchman Van't Hof on acoustic piano and electric keyboards.
**CD:** Released Jul '88, on L&R Catalogue no: **CDLR 45.004**
**Album:** Released Jul '88, on L&R Catalogue no: **LR 45.004**

**FIRE MUSIC**
Tracks: / Hambone / Malcolm, Malcolm Semper Malcolm / Los Olvidados.
**Cass:** Released Oct '85, on Impulse by Impulse Records. Deleted Dec '89. Catalogue no: **ASC 86**
**Album:** Released Jun '89, on MCA (Impulse Jazz) Catalogue no: **MCA 39121**
**CD:** Released Jun '89, on MCA (Impulse Jazz) Catalogue no: **MCAD 39121**
**Album:** Released Oct '85, on Impulse by Impulse Records. Catalogue no: **AS 86**

**FORCE (Shepp, Archie & Max Roach)**
Tracks: / Sweet Mao / Suid Afrika, 76.
**2 LP Set:** Released Apr '81, on UNI by MCA Records. Catalogue no: **UNI 28976**

**FOUR FOR TRANE**
Tracks: / Syeeda's song flute / Mr. Syms / Cousin Mary / Niema / Rufus.
**Cass:** Released Aug '82, on Jasmine by Hasmick Promotions. Catalogue no: **JAS C31**
**Album:** Released Aug '82, on Jasmine by Hasmick Promotions. Catalogue no: **JAS 31**

**GOIN' HOME**
**CD:** Released Jul '88, on Steeplechase (USA) Catalogue no: **SCCD 31079**
**Album:** Released Jul '88, on Steeplechase (USA) Catalogue no: **SCS 1079**

**GOOD LIFE, THE**
**Cass:** Released '88, on Varrick (USA) by Rounder Records (USA). Catalogue no: **VR 005C**
**Album:** Released '88, on Varrick (USA) by Rounder Records (USA). Catalogue no: **VR 005**

**HOUSE I LIVE IN, THE (Shepp, Archie Quintet)**
**Album:** Released May '81, on Steeplechase (USA) Catalogue no: **SCC 6013**

**IN MEMORY OF ... (Shepp, Archie & Chet Baker)**
Note: Following closely on Baker's death comes the issue of this session from March 1988. Recorded live in Frankfurt and Paris, Shepp (tenor sax) and Baker (trumpet) play standards with Horace Parlan (piano), Herman Wright (bass) amd Clifford Jarvis (drums). CD version has three extra tracks, cassette two extra tracks.
**CD:** Released Jul '88, on L&R Catalogue no: **CDLR 45.006**
**Album:** Released Jul '88, on L&R Catalogue no: **LR 45.006**
**Cass:** Released Jul '88, on L&R Catalogue no: **LR 65.006**

**INDOMITABLE**
Tracks: / One for the trane (part 1) / One for the trane (part 2).
**Album:** Released '79, on MPS Jazz Deleted '84. Catalogue no: **5C 064 61177**

**LADYBIRD**
Tracks: / Donna Lee / Relaxin' at Camarillo / Now's the time / Ladybird / Flamingo.
**CD:** Released Jun '89, on Denon Catalogue no: **DC 8546**
**Album:** Released Mar '82, on Denon Deleted '88. Catalogue no: **YX 7543**

**LIVE AT THE PAN AFRICAN FESTIVAL**
**Album:** Released Oct '79, on Affinity by Charly Records. Catalogue no: **AFF 41**

**LIVE IN SAN FRANCISCO**
Tracks: / Keep your heart right / Lady sings the blues / In a sentimental mood / Sylvia / Wedding / Wherever June bugs go.
**Album:** Released Feb '84, on Jasmine by Hasmick Promotions. Deleted Feb '88. Catalogue no: **JAS 75**

**LIVE IN TOKYO (Shepp, Archie Quartet)**
Tracks: / Caravan / In a sentimental mood / Steam / Straight Street.
**Album:** Released Mar '82, on Denon Deleted '88. Catalogue no: **YX 7538**

**LOOKING AT BIRD**
**Album:** Released Sep '81, on Steeplechase (USA) Catalogue no: **SCS 1149**

**LOVER MAN**
**CD:** Released Jun '89, on New Note Catalogue no: **CDSJP 287**
**Album:** Released Jun '89, on New Note Catalogue no: **SJP 287**

**MAMA ROSE**
**Album:** Released Jul '88, on Steeplechase (USA) Catalogue no: **SCS 1169**
**CD:** Released Jul '88, on Steeplechase (USA) Catalogue no: **SCCD 31169**

**MAMA TOO TIGHT**
Tracks: / Portait of Robert Thompson, A / Prelude to a kiss / Break strain, The / Dem basses / Mama too tight / Theme for Ernie / Basher.
**Album:** Released Jun '82, on Jasmine by Hasmick Promotions. Deleted Feb '88. Catalogue no: **JAS 18**
**Cass:** Released Jun '82, on Jasmine by Hasmick Promotions. Catalogue no: **JAS C18**

**MONTREUX 1**
Tracks: / Lush life / U-jamaa / Crucificado / Miss Toni.
**Album:** Released '83, on Freedom Catalogue no: **FLP 41027**
**CD:** Released 16 Sep '88, on Freedom Catalogue no: **FCD 741027**

**MONTREUX 2**
Tracks: / Steam / Along came Betty / Blues for Donald Duck.
**Album:** Released Jan '79, on Freedom Import Catalogue no: **FLP 41034**

**ON GREEN DOLPHIN STREET**
Tracks: / On Green Dolphin Street / Enough / Scene is clean, The / In a mellow blues / I thought about you.
Note: Personnel: Archie Shepp (tenor & Soprano saxes), Walter Bishop Jnr. (Piano), Sam Jones (Bass), Joe Chambers (Drums). Recorded at Sound Ideas Studios, New York City, November 28th 1977.

**Album:** Released Mar '82, on Denon Deleted '88. Catalogue no: **YX 7524**
**CD:** Released '88, on Denon Deleted '88. Catalogue no: **C38-7262**

**ON THIS NIGHT**
Tracks: / Mac man / In a sentimental mood / Gingerbread boy / On this night / Original Mr. Sonny Boy Williamson / Pickaninny.
**Album:** Released Aug '82, on Jasmine by Hasmick Promotions. Catalogue no: **JAS 46**
**Cass:** Released Aug '82, on Jasmine by Hasmick Promotions. Catalogue no: **JAS C46**

**PARLAN DUO REUNION (Shepp, Archie & Horace Parlan)**
**CD:** Released Oct '88, on L&R Catalogue no: **CDLR 45.003**
**Album:** Released Oct '88, on L&R Catalogue no: **LR 45.003**

**PASSPORT TO PARADISE Archie Shepp plays Sydney Bechet**
**CD:** Released Jul '88, on West Wind Catalogue no: **WWCD 002**
**Album:** Released Jul '88, on West Wind Catalogue no: **WW 002**

**POEM FOR MALCOLM**
Tracks: / Mamarose / Poem for Malcolm / Rain forest / Oleo.
**Album:** Released Mar '83, on Affinity by Charly Records. Catalogue no: **AFF 78**

**SEA OF FACES, A**
**Album:** Released Jul '78, on Black Saint (Italy) Catalogue no: **BSR 002**

**SOUL SONG**
**Album:** Released Jul '88, on Enja (Germany) by Enja Records (West Germany). Catalogue no: **ENJA 4050**

**SPLASHES (Shepp, Archie Quartet)**
Tracks: / Arrival / Reflexions / Groovin high / Steam / Manhattan.
Note: Archie Shepp, tenor sax; Horace Parlan, piano; Harry Emmery, bass; Clifford Jarvis, drums. Tunes include Groovin' High, Relaxing At Camarillo and Manhattan.
**Album:** Released Jul '88, on L&R Catalogue no: **LR 45.005**
**CD:** Released Jul '88, on L&R Catalogue no: **CDLR 45.005**

**STEAM**
**Album:** Released Jan '82, on Enja (Germany) by Enja Records (West Germany). Catalogue no: **ENJA 2076**

**THERE'S A TRUMPET IN MY SOUL**
Tracks: / Suite: There's a trumpet in my soul, Part 1 / Samba da rua / Zaid, Part 1 / Down in Brazil / Suite: There's a trumpet in my soul, Part 2 / Zaid, Part 2 / It is the year of the rabbit / Zaid, Part 3.
**CD:** Released Dec '87, on Freedom Catalogue no: **FCD 41016**
**Album:** Released Apr '79, on Freedom Import Catalogue no: **FLP 41016**

**THREE FOR A QUARTER ONE FOR A DIME**
**Album:** Released Mar '83, on Jasmine by Hasmick Promotions. Deleted Feb '88. Catalogue no: **JAS 68**

**TRAY OF SILVER**
Tracks: / No smokin / If you could see me now / Nica's dream / Cookin at the continental.
**CD:** Released Jun '89, on Denon Catalogue no: **DC 8548**
**Album:** Released Mar '82, on Denon Deleted '88. Catalogue no: **YX 7806**

**TROUBLE IN MIND (Shepp, Archie & Horace Parlan)**
**CD:** on Steeplechase (USA) Catalogue no: **SCCD 31139**
**Album:** Released Sep '81, on Steeplechase (USA) Catalogue no: **SCS 1139**

**YASMINIA - BLACK WOMAN**
**Album:** Released May '79, on Affinity by Charly Records. Deleted '88. Catalogue no: **AFF 21**

## Sheppard, Andy

**ANDY SHEPPARD**
Tracks: / Java jive / Esme / Twee / Sol / Coming second / Want a toffee? / Liquid.
**Album:** Released Oct '87, on Antilles/New Directions by Island Records. Catalogue no: **AN 8720**
**CD:** Released Feb '89, on Antilles/New Directions by Island Records. Catalogue no: **ANCD 8720**
**Cass:** Released 13 Nov '87, on Freedom Catalogue no: **ANC 8720**

**HERE COMES THE FAMILY (Sheppard, Andy & Family Of Percussion)**
**CD:** Released '88, on Import (label unknown) Catalogue no: **CDMIX 1021**

**INTRODUCTIONS IN THE DARK**
Tracks: / Romantic / Rebecca's / Optics / Conversations / Forbidden fruit.
**Album:** Released Feb '89, on Antilles/New Directions by Island Records. Catalogue no: **ANLP 8742**
**CD:** Released Feb '89, on Antilles/New Directions by Island Records. Catalogue no: **ANCD 8742**
**Cass:** Released Feb '89, on Antilles/New Directions by Island Records. Catalogue no: **ANC 8742**

**JAVA JIVE**
Tracks: / Java jive / Sol.
Note: Saxophonist, composer and bandleader. He also won the Newcomer of the year in the 1988 Jazz awards.
**7" Single:** Released Jun '88, on Antilles/New Directions by Island Records. Catalogue no: **ANN 5**

**SOFT ON THE INSIDE**
**Cass:** Released Apr '90, on Antilles/New Directions by Island Records. Catalogue no: **ANC 8751**
**CD:** Released Apr '90, on Antilles/New Directions by Island Records. Catalogue no: **ANCD 8751**
**Album:** Released Apr '90, on Antilles/New Directions by Island Records. Catalogue no: **AN 8751**

## Sherwood, Bobby

**1944: BOBBY SHERWOOD (Sherwood, Bobby & His Orchestra)**
**Album:** Released Aug '88, on Circle (USA) by Jazzology Records (USA). Catalogue no: **CLP 28**

**ONE NIGHT STAND - 1946**
**Album:** Released Jul '82, on Joyce Catalogue no: **JLP 1028**

**POLITELY**
**Album:** Released Jul '82, on Golden Era by Delta Records. Catalogue no: **GELP 15018**

**SHERWOOD SWINGS**
**Album:** Released '84, on Swing House by Submarine Records. Catalogue no: **SWH 35**

**VICTORY PARADE OF SPOTLIGHT (Sherwood, Bobby & His Orchestra)**
Tracks: / Girlfriend / Floating / New world jumps, The / I don't want to love you / Swingin' at the semloh / Elk's parade, The / Lover, come back to me / Song of the wanderer / Don't you know I care / I dream of you / Accentuate the positive.
**Album:** Released Apr '79, on Aircheck (USA) by Kiner Ents.(USA). Catalogue no: **AIRCHECK 3**

## Sherwood, Bobby & His

**1944-46**
**Album:** Released Mar '90, on Circle (USA) Catalogue no: **CLP 115**

## Shines, Johnny

**Biographical details:** Johnny Shines was born in Tennessee in 1915, worked with the legendary **Robert Johnson** in the 1930's, settled in Chicago in 1941 and became one of the best loved Chicago blues singers/guitarists without giving up his country roots (and for the most part without being able to make a living at it: he worked as a builder). His fine bottleneck guitar and his clear, ringing voice are unforgettable; he has written many fine songs, as well as updating some of Johnsons. (Donald Clarke)..

**1951-55 (Shines, Johnny/Robert Lockwood)**
**CD:** Released 10 Jul '89, on Flyright by Interstate Music. Catalogue no: **FLYCD 10**

**COUNTRY BLUES (Shines, Johnny & Blind Will Dukes)**
Tracks: / Rambling blues / Maggie Lee blues / You're the one that I love / Sweet home Chicago / Shake 'em on down / Moanin' and groanin' the blues / Terraplane blues / Dead shrimp blues / Steady rollin man / Me andthe devil / Mean hearted woman / Ramblin' blues / Hobo blues / Milk cow blues / Mistreated so long / Sail on little woman / Hoodoo man.
**Album:** Released Dec '84, on JSP by JSP Records. Catalogue no: **JSP 1079**

**DUST MY BROOM Job series vol1 (Shines, Johnny/Robert Lockwood)**

**Album:** Released '88, on Flyright by Interstate Music. Catalogue no: **FLY 563**

**HEY BA-BA-RE-BOP**
**Cass:** Released Aug '88, on Rounder (USA) by Rounder Records (USA). Catalogue no: **ROUNDER 2020C**
**Album:** Released May '79, on Rounder (USA) by Rounder Records (USA). Catalogue no: **ROUNDER 2020**

**JOHNNY SHINES' BAND WITH BIG WALTER HORTON (Shines, Johnny Band & Walter Horton)**
**Album:** Released May '86, on Testament Catalogue no: **T 2217**

**JOHNNY SHINES & COMPANY**
Tracks: / Little wolf / Mr. Cover / Shaker / Shotgun whupin' / Lost love letter blues / Stand by me / Blood ran like wind / Chief Tiscaloosa / I'm getting old / Mother's place / Jim string.
**Album:** Released Jun '88, on Blue Moon (1) by Magnum Music Group. Catalogue no: **BMLP 1065**

**LIVE IN ST LOUIS, 1974**
**Album:** Released Jul '88, on Wolf Catalogue no: **120 914**

## Shoemake, Charlie

**AWAY FROM THE CROWD (Shoemake, Charlie Sextet)**
Tracks: / Dandi's smile / He needs me / Away from the crowd / Evening run / Small talk / Gentle man / Sometime yesterday / Young and foolish.
Note: Charlie Shoemake - vibes, Hank Jones - piano, Tom Harrell - trumpet & flugelhorn, Ted Nash - sax, Ed Schuller - bass, Paul Mtian - drums, Sandi Shoemake - vocals.
**Album:** Released Jun '83, on Discovery (USA) by Discovery Records (USA). Catalogue no: **DS 856**

**BLUE SHOE**
Tracks: / Blue shoe / Dream, The / Rainbows / Cure for the common chord / Why, someone tell me, why?.
Note: Charlie Shoemake / vibraphone; Pete Christlieb / tenor sax; Kenny Barron / piano; Mark Helias / bass; Ben Riley / drums. Recorded: 21 July 1979.
**Album:** Released Apr '81, on Muse by Black & Blue Records. Catalogue no: **MR 5221**

**CROSS ROADS (Shoemake, Charlie Sextet)**
Tracks: / Say it isn't so / Child in me / Fleeting resemblance / Cross roads / Recondite / Dunbar's pace / Christmas bells.
**Album:** Released Aug '83, on Discovery (USA) by Discovery Records (USA). Catalogue no: **DS 878**

**I THINK WE'RE ALMOST THERE**
**CD:** Released Dec '86, on Discovery (USA) by Discovery Records (USA). Catalogue no: **DSCD 924**

**INCANDESCENT (Shoemake, Charlie Sextet)**
Note: Featuring Phil Woods, Tom Harrell, Terry Trotter, Ray Drummond, Billy Hart, and Sandi Shoemake.
**Album:** Released '88, on Discovery (USA) by Discovery Records (USA). Catalogue no: **DS 904**

**PLAYS THE MUSIC OF DAVID RAKSIN (Shoemake, Charlie Sextet)**
Tracks: / Too late blues / Mirror, mirror, mirror / Bad and the beautiful, The / Striver, The.
**Album:** Released Apr '84, on Discovery (USA) by Discovery Records (USA). Catalogue no: **DS 894**

**SUNSTROKE**
Tracks: / This happy madness / That's Earl's brother / Sunstroke / You'll love New York / 42nd Street / We'll be together again.
Note: Charlie Shoemake/vibraphone; Dave Schnitter/tenor sax; Kenny Barron/piano; Cecil McBee/bass; Al Foster/drums.
**Album:** Released Apr '81, on Muse by Black & Blue Records. Catalogue no: **MR 5193**

## Shoemake, Sandi

**SLOWLY**
Tracks: / Yardbird suite / You're blase / Flamingo / I wish I knew.
**Album:** Released '88, in Discovery (USA) by Discovery Records. Catalogue no: **DS 889**

## Shore, Dinah

**Biographical details:** Dinah Shore's real name is Frances Rose Shore; she was born in 1917 in Tennessee, began on Nashville radio and adopted *Dinah* (a song from 1925) as her theme and her name. She had hits with Xavier Cugat but was never a regular with a big-name band. She became one of the first pop singers to make it on her own, becoming one of America's most popular on radio and records in the 1940s. She later became a TV star. Unlike some other singers of the era, her warm-voiced, warm-hearted style has never dated. (Donald Clarke).

**BEST OF DINAH SHORE**
Tracks: / Sentimental journey / Chantez-chantez / Hi-lili hi-lo / Blue canary / Sweet violets / What can I say after I say I'm sorry / Blues in the night / Memphis blues / Come rain or come shine / I got it bad / Deep purple / I concentrate on you.
**Album:** Released '81, on RCA by BMG Records (UK). Deleted '86. Catalogue no: **INTS 5062**

**CAPITOL YEARS, THE: DINAH SHORE (Best of)**
Tracks: / I'm old fashioned / I only have eyes for you / Mississippi mud / It's so nice to have a man around the house / Our love is here to stay / Way down yonder in New Orleans / I hadn't anyone till you / Where or when / Easy to love / They can't take that away from me / It's easy to remember / South / Gipsy, The / Somebody loves me / I'm coming Virginia / Laughing on the outside (crying on the inside) / Buttons & bows / Sentimental journey.
**Cass:** Released Sep '89, on Capitol by EMI Records. Catalogue no: **TCEMS 1342**
**CD:** Released Sep '89, on Capitol by EMI Records. Catalogue no: **CDEMS 1342**
**Album:** Released Sep '89, on Capitol by EMI Records. Catalogue no: **792 895 1**
**Album:** Released Sep '89, on Capitol by EMI Records. Catalogue no: **EMS 1342**
**Cass:** Released Sep '89, on Capitol by EMI Records. Catalogue no: **792 895 4**
**CD:** Released Sep '89, on Capitol by EMI Records. Catalogue no: **CDP 792 895 2**
**CD:** Released Sep '89, on Capitol by EMI Records. Catalogue no: **CZ 222**

**'DEED I DO 1942-52**
Tracks: / Deed I do / On the sunny side of the street / Tess's torch song / Time on my hands / How high the moon / Sugar blues / At last / Until the real thing comes along / Night and day / I'm gonna love that guy / I've got the world on a string / Someone like you / It isn't fair / I feel a song coming on / Way you look tonight / Put 'em in a box, tie 'em with ribbon / You do something to me / Beat me daddy-o, eight to the bar / This can't be love / My guy's come back.
**Album:** Released '88, on Hep Jazz by Hep Records. Catalogue no: **HEP 30**

**DINAH SHORES GREATEST HITS**
Tracks: / I'll walk alone / Buttons and bows / Gypsy, The / Blues in the night / Laughing on the outside (crying on the inside) / Jim / Dear hearts and gentle people / It's so nice to have a man around the house / Chantez, chantez.
**Cass:** Released Dec '88, on Capitol (Specials) Catalogue no: **4XL 9447**

**DINAH SINGS, PREVIN PLAYS (Shore, Dinah & Andre Previn)**
Tracks: / Man I love, The / April in Paris / That old feeling / I've got you under my skin / Then I'll be tired of you / Sleepy time gal / My melancholy baby / My funny valentine / It had to be you / I'll be seeing you / If I had you.
**Cass:** Released Apr '84, on Capitol by EMI Records. Deleted Jan '88. Catalogue no: **TC CAPS 2600084**
**Album:** Released Apr '84, on Capitol by EMI Records. Deleted Aug '89. Catalogue no: **CAPS 2600081**

**DINAH SINGS SOME BLUES WITH RED (Shore, Dinah & The Red Norvo Quintet)**
Tracks: / Bye bye blues / I can't face the music / Someday, sweetheart / It's funny to everyone but me / Who / I can't believe that you're in love with me / I ain't got nothin' but the blues / Lucky in love / Do nothing till you hear from me / It's all right with me / Skylark / Lover, come back to me.
Note: This original album features Red Norvo, the esteemed 'vibes' player of the 50's with his Quintet accompanying the

ever popular Dinah Shore. For some time, this album has only been available as an expensive Japanese import.
**Album:** Released Jul '85, on Capitol by EMI Records. Deleted Jan '88. Catalogue no: **EG 2606091**
**Cass:** Released Jul '85, on Capitol by EMI Records. Deleted Jan '88. Catalogue no: **EG 2606094**

**DINAH, YES INDEED!**
Tracks: / It all depends on you / Falling in love with love / Where or when / Easy to love / Get out of town / They can't take that away from me / Sentimental journey / One I love belongs to somebody else, The / I'm old fashioned / Love is here to stay / Taking a chance on love / Yes indeed.
**Cass:** Released Apr '83, on MFP by EMI Records. Deleted '87. Catalogue no: **TCMFP 5606**
**Album:** Released Apr '83, on MFP by EMI Records. Deleted '87. Catalogue no: **MFP 5606**
**Album:** Released '87, on Conifer Catalogue no: **2C 068 85290**

**HOLDING HANDS AT MIDNIGHT**
Tracks: / Nice work if you can get it / Easy to love / Come rain or come shine / Once in a while / It had to be you / You're driving me crazy / That great come and get it day / Moanin' in the mornin' / Under a blanket of blue / Taking a chance on love / I concentrate on you / Yesterdays.
**Cass:** Released Oct '84, on RCA by BMG Records (UK). Deleted '87. Catalogue no: **NK 89467**
**Album:** Released Oct '84, on RCA by BMG Records (UK). Deleted '87. Catalogue no: **NL 89467**

**LAVENDER BLUE**
Tracks: / They didn't believe me / They can't take that away from me / I may be wrong (but I think you're wonderful) / Gypsy, The / Anniversary song / It's easy to remember / Come rain or come shine / It all depends on you / Little white lies / Golden earrings / I'll be seeing you / Lavender blue / Laughing on the outside (crying on the inside) / I get along without you very well.
**Cass:** Released Jun '86, on Memoir by Memoir Records. Catalogue no: **CMOIR 122**
**Album:** Released Jan '87, on Memoir by Memoir Records. Catalogue no: **MOIR 122**

**MOMENTS LIKE THESE**
Tracks: / Deep purple / When the world was young / Moments like this / I'll remember April / These foolish things / I fall in love too easily / What's new? / I can dream, can't I / Now I know / How long as this been going on? / Something wonderful.
**Album:** Released Jun '87, on RCA by BMG Records (UK). Deleted Jul '89. Catalogue no: **NL 90042**
**Cass:** Released Jun '87, on RCA by BMG Records (UK). Deleted Jul '89. Catalogue no: **NK 90042**

## Short, J.D.

**EARLY RECORDINGS 1930-33**
**Album:** Released Aug '85, on Wolf Catalogue no: **WSE 118**

**LEGACY OF THE BLUES-8**
Tracks: / Starry crown blues / My rare dog / By the spoonful / You're tempting me / Slidin' delta / I'm just wastin' my time / Red river run, The / Help me some / East St. Louis / Make me down a pallet.
**CD:** Released '73, on Sonet by Sonet Records. Catalogue no: **SNTCD 648**
**Album:** Released '73, on Sonet by Sonet Records. Catalogue no: **SNTF 648**
**Album:** Released May '89, on GNP Crescendo (USA) by GNP Crescendo Records (USA). Catalogue no: **GNPS 10018**

## Shorter, Wayne

**Biographical details:** Wayne Shorter is one of the biggest stars in jazz today, playing saxaphone, composing and now leading his own group. He was born in 1933 in Newark, New Jersey, played in Art Blakey's Jazz Messengers 1959-93, one of Miles Davies's greatest quintets '64-70, and formed Weather Report with Joe Zawinul in 1970: the popular Weather report stayed togeter until 1985, perhaps too long; Shorter himself is extremely popular, but now he has to invent a style of his own to overcome the electronic hangover, described recently by a London critic as 'mewling synthesisers'. (Donald Clarke 27.5.87).

**ADAM'S APPLE**
Tracks: / Adam's apple / 502 blues (drinkin' and drivin') / El gaucho / Footprints / Teru / Chief Crazy Horse / Collector, The.
**CD:** Released Jun '87, on EMI by EMI Records. Catalogue no: **CDP 746 403 2**
**CD:** Released Jun '87, on EMI by EMI Records. Catalogue no: **BNZ 84**
**Cass:** Released Sep '87, on Blue Note by EMI Records. Deleted Aug '89. Catalogue no: **4BN 84232**
**Album:** Released Jul '89, on Blue Note by EMI Records. Catalogue no: **BST 84232**

**ATLANTIS**
Tracks: / Endangered species / Three Marias, The / Last silk hat, The / When you dream / Who goes there? / Atlantis / Shere Khan / Criancas.
**Cass:** Released Oct '85, on CBS by CBS Records. Catalogue no: **40 26669**
**Album:** Released Oct '85, on CBS by CBS Records. Deleted Jan '89. Catalogue no: **CBS 26669**

**BEST OF WAYNE SHORTER (Blue Note years)**
Tracks: / Speak no evil / Infant eyes / Tom Thumb / Lost / Adam's apple / Footprints / Virgo / Ju ju / Water babies
**CD:** Released Dec '88, on Blue Note by EMI Records. Catalogue no: **BNZ 145**
**CD:** Released Dec '88, on Blue Note by EMI Records. Catalogue no: **CDP 791 141 2**
**Album:** Released Dec '88, on Blue Note by EMI Records. Catalogue no: **B1 91141**

**BLUES A LA CARTE**
Tracks: / Blues a la carte / Harry's last stand / Down in the depths / Pug nose / Black diamond / Mack the knife.
**Album:** Released Nov '85, on Affinity by Charly Records. Catalogue no: **AFF 144**

**ETCETERA**
Tracks: / Etcetera / Penelope / Toy tune / Barracudas / Indian song.
**Album:** Released Feb '81, on Liberty by EMI Records. Deleted '86. Catalogue no: **LBR 1037**

**JOY RYDER**
Tracks: / Someplace called 'where' / Joy ryder / Cathay / Over Shadow Hill way / Anthem / Causeways / Daredevil.
**CD:** Released Mar '88, on CBS by CBS Records. Deleted Jan '90. Catalogue no: **460678 2**
**Cass:** Released Mar '88, on CBS by CBS Records. Deleted Jan '90. Catalogue no: **460678 4**
**Album:** Released Mar '88, on CBS by CBS Records. Deleted Jan '90. Catalogue no: **460678 1**

**JU JU**
Tracks: / Ju ju / Deluge / House of jade / Mahjong / Yes & no / Twelve more bars to go.
**Cass:** Released Sep '87, on Blue Note by EMI Records. Catalogue no: **4BN 84182**
**CD:** Released Apr '87, on Blue Note by EMI Records. Deleted Aug '89. Catalogue no: **BNZ 85**
**CD:** Released Apr '87, on Blue Note by EMI Records. Deleted Aug '89. Catalogue no: **CDP 746 514 2**
**Album:** Released Apr '85, on Blue Note by EMI Records. Catalogue no: **BST 84182**

**NIGHT DREAMER**
Tracks: / Night dreamer / Oriental folk song / Virgo / Virgo (alternate take) / Black Nile / Charcoal blues / Armageddon.
**CD:** Released Apr '88, on Blue Note by EMI Records. Catalogue no: **CDP 784 173 2**
**CD:** Released Apr '88, on Blue Note by EMI Records. Catalogue no: **BNZ 87**

**ODYSSEY OF ISKA**
Tracks: / Wind / Storm / De pois do amor / O vazio (After love emptiness) / Joy.
**CD:** Released Aug '89, on Blue Note by EMI Records. Catalogue no: **CDP 784 363 2**
**CD:** Released Aug '89, on Blue Note by EMI Records. Catalogue no: **BNZ 190**

**PHANTOM NAVIGATOR**
Tracks: / Condition red / Mahogany bird / Remote control / Ya manja / Forbidden, plan-it! / Flagships.
**Album:** Released Mar '87, on CBS by CBS Records. Catalogue no: **450365 1**
**CD:** Released Apr '87, on CBS by CBS Records. Deleted Jan '89. Catalogue no: **450 365 2**
**Cass:** Released Mar '87, on CBS by

**Wayne Shorter - The Vee Jay Years (Affinity)**

CBS Records. Catalogue no: **450365 4**

**SECOND GENESIS**
Tracks: / Ruby and the pearl / Pay as you go / Second Genesis / Mister chairman / Tenderfoot / Albatross / Getting to know you / I didn't know what time it was.
Note: With Cedar Walton, Bob Cranshaw, Art Blakey.
**Album:** Released Mar '84, on Affinity by Charly Records. Catalogue no: **AFF 114**

**SOOTHSAYER, THE**
**Album:** Released Jun '80, on Liberty by EMI Records. Catalogue no: **LBR 1021**
**Album:** Released Sep '84, on Affinity by Charly Records. Catalogue no: **AFF 126**

**SPEAK NO EVIL**
Tracks: / Fee fi fo fum / Dance candaverous / Speak no evil / Infant eyes / Wild flower / Out to lunch / Straight up and down / Witch hunt.
Note: P 1987 Manhattan records,a division of Capitol records Inc.
**CD:** Released Mar '88, on Blue Note by EMI Records. Catalogue no: **CDP 746 509 2**
**CD:** Released Mar '88, on Blue Note by EMI Records. Catalogue no: **BNZ 86**
**Album:** Released Aug '87, on Blue Note by EMI Records. Catalogue no: **BST 84194**

**SUPER NOVA**
Tracks: / Super nova / Swee-pee / Dindi (pronounced "Jin-jee") / Water babies / Capricorn / More than human.
**CD:** Released Nov '88, on Blue Note by EMI Records. Catalogue no: **CDP 784 332 2**
**CD:** Released Nov '88, on Blue Note by EMI Records. Catalogue no: **BNZ 117**
**Album:** Released Jul '89, on Blue Note by EMI Records. Catalogue no: **B1 84332**

**VEE JAY YEARS**
Tracks: / Blues a la carte / Harry's last stand / Down in the depths / Pug nose / Black diamond / Mack the knife / Ruby and the pearl / Pay as you go / Second Genesis / Mister chairman / Tenderfoot / Albatross / Getting to know you.
Note: The Veejay Years helps in charting his progress along the way to fame, (if not exactly a fortune), from the period when Wayne Shorter had yet to become a figure-head in the area of music to which he has contributed so meaningfully. As such, this splendid CD is a must, both for the Shorter aficionado, as well as for those who have begun to respond to his talents in more recent times.
Stan Britt (Music Week). April 1988.
Wayne Shorter's elevation to the present-day hierarchy of jazz hasn't been the result of instant success. True, right from his earliest days in the big-time jazz arena he seems to have created a favourable impression among his fellow musicians - even those of the long-established, hard-to-please variety.
In fact, Shorter's handsome reputation has been achieved by degrees: one important step in the right direction being well and truly consolidated before the next move towards yet another conquest, whether making a significant impact as a saxophone soloist, composer, a valued sideman to some pretty heavy front-men, and more recently, as a respected leader of his own jazz combos.
Perhaps Shorter's first involvement with a jazz figure of some real significance came about during the mid-1950s. When he deputised with Horace Silver's band in Philadelphia. Just a three-gig association, during the 24-year-old native of Newark's near-three years as a US serviceman. It was while touring with an all-Army band that Wayne Shorter first heard the Miles Davis Quintet, with Coltrane, in live performance. Shortly after demobilisation, he actually got the chance to meet Trane - and indeed to participate with the innovative saxman at a jam session. The two became firm friends. A meeting of comparable importance occurred in '59. Shorter was introduced to Josef Zawinul, an immensely promising pianist, freshly asrrived from his native Austria. Zawinul, at that time, was working with Maynard Ferguson's wildly exciting big band. A Zawinul recommendation to the extrovert trumpeter resulted in a three month spell for Shorter with the Ferguson outfit. Following which came a dream job, with Art Blakey's enduring Jazz Messengers. That gig lasted from 1959-1964, during which time Wayne firmly established himself as both a saxophonist of the front rank, as well as a writer of great individual style and real distinction. After which came the plum gig: membership of what was to become known as one of the two most important groups (among so many) fronted by Miles Davis.
For Wayne Shorter, this was graduation...and, it should never be forgotten, graduation with honours. Then, it was out on his own, a fully-fledged instrumentalist-composer in his own right. Weather Report - and a long time reunion with Joe Zawinul - and the kind of world-wide acceptance than both could scarcely have dreamed about, was awaitin', just around the corner.
With Blakey, though, Wayne Shorter really started to come of age. Not yet had he added the soprano-sax to complement his already satisfying contributions to the tenor. And his composing-arranging talents - within the framework of the Messengers and elsewhere - he did absolutely nothing to diminish his fast-growing reputation. Which is where the contents of this Vee-Jay originated Compact Disc comes into the picture.
The Vee-Jay years comprise the results of two Wayne Shorter cecording dates under his own name - in fact, his very first as a session leader. The initial Shorter led date took place in New York in November, '59. Wayne's associates represented an absolutely first rate pick up band in every way; fine individual musicians; musically as well as socially compatible; kindred spirits. Drummer Jimmy Cobb - at thirty-coming-up-thirty-one - was the eldest of the Shorter Quintet. Like bassist Paul Chambers (24), he was attracting wide attention for his crisp, unobtrusive playing with the superb Miles Davis Quintet, which included also John Coltrane, and Wynton Kelly (27), Shorter's choice as pianist for

his debut LP. Youngest member of this impressive studio line-up: Lee Morgan (21), Shorter's front-line colleague in the then current Jazz Messengers line up. Less than one week after the Vee-Jay date, both the latter were appearing in Paris with Art Blakey's explosive combo. The opening *Blues a la carte*, an attractive twelve-bar Shorter original, finds all the soloists on their toes. Shorter, still heavily under the Coltrane influence, eases through his solo in a manner that suggests nevertheless his own quest for individualism isn't that far away. Morgan is as perky and buoyant as it is technically subtle. Chambers adds a typical two-chorus statement, and Cobb's own solo is intellegent, positive and to the point. The slightly convoluted *Harry's last stand* has even more memorablesolos, with Shorter's the more authoritative and hard-driving, complemented by one of Morgan's intense muted offerings, a much too short appearance from Kelly, a nicely articulated solo from Chambers, and Cobb's immaculate brushwork in ample evidence throughout. Both *Down in the depths* and *Black diamond* are cast in a 64-bar-chorus mould. *Depths* contain a succession of superior solos - Kelly's taking honours, but Morgan at his most laid-back. Overall, though, it's the sheer relaxation which pervades the entire performance. Certainly, Trane seems very much on Shorter's mind during his powerful, surging tenor work on *Diamond*. Morgan, in typically brash and super-confident mood, is more than a match for his partner, while Kelly sails sublimely through his own solo. Chambers, once again uses his bow to good effect. And Cobb's outburst is controlled, logical and as economic in duration as before.

The quietly compelling *Pug nose* exudes the same kind of relaxation-in-performance as the afore-mentioned *Down in the depths*. Even the extrovert Morgan contains much of his natural, outgoing instincts, concentrating on the lyrical side of his playing; not surprisingly, his debt to the immortal Fats Navarro asserts itself most appealingly. Finally, *Mack the knife*, the best-known number from Kurt Weill's The Threepenny Opera. Not such a strange choice, as the one non-Shorter item on the programme, as some might think; after all, Louis Armstrong, no less, had had a hit record with Mack three years before, and *Mack the knife* had become even more widely known at the time of the Shorter/Vee-Jay date, thanks to Bobby Darin's Chart-topping revival. It was to be almost exactly eleven months after Shorter's first studio date under his own name that an opportunity to undertake a similar task occurred. (Incidentally, Shorter and Morgan didn't see much of November 10, '59, except for studio walls: apart from the Vee-Jay date, they also visited Rudy Van gelder's Englewood Cliffs, NJ, studios on the same day to help complete the Messengers' latest Blue Note project, later titled Africaine). During the intervening period, Shorter had been consolidating his position as a stalwart Blakey sideman, in his dual role as saxophonist and writer. Since November '59, he'd made half a dozen Messengers LP dates for Blue Note, including the live, two-part Meet You At The Jazz Corner Of The World sessions, taped at Birdland. Both on record as well as for club and concert appearances (including the trip to France), Shorter's contributions to the band's ever-growing book continued to increase at an encouraging rate; and at this time it is more than probable that his progress as a composer of real distinction and originality was more readily apparent than as an instrumentalist still seeking a totally individual voice of his own. Shorter's graduation in both areas was to emerge during the mid-Sixties, when he completed his five-year tenure with Blakey to join Miles. With Davis, Shorter's developing twin talents found full blossom: a superbly gifted musician, just over thirty years old, entered the ranks of the true Giants of Jazz.

But back in 1960, Wayne Shorter remained a hard-working sideman with Art Blakey, and further enhancing his reputation by participating in record dates of others. And just under one year after the initial Vee-Jay session under his own name, the same label recorded Wayne, in Chicago this time, fronting a quartet instead of the previous five-man combo. The line-up, Shorter apart, was completely different - and even without the fiery Morgan, or indeed any other frontline partner. Shorter sounds suitably inspired by the presence of his three eminent colleagues. Bassist Bob Cranshaw, from Evanston, Illinois, had been a respected part of the local (Chicago) jazz scene since the early-Fifties. At the time of the second Shorter session. Cranshaw was currently co-leading, with drummer Walter Perkins, the Modern Jazz Two plus Three. In a matter of a couple of months Cranshaw had moved permanently to New York City. His great tone, superb technique and impeccable time has through the succeeding years made the kind of bass player who has been in constant demand.

Pianist Cedar Walton, from Dallas, Texas, had already moved to the Big Apple, although only a year or so before. The immensely talented Walton had joined the Art Farmer-Benny Golson Jazztet during July 1960 and had quickly become highly-valued member of that popular unit.

Shorter could Scarcely have hoped for a finer replacement of Jimmy Cobb as drummer than Art Blakey; his boss of justover a year and whose band Walton would become a full-time member for almost four years in 1961 (and later, in '73, for a much shorter period). Pittsburgh-born Blakey - celebrating his 40th birthday by providing such a powerful rhythmic uplift to Wayne Shorter's Chicago record date - had long since become elevated to the pantheon of jazz drumming, having established his first most significant reputation as a vital ingredient of the legendary Billy Eckstine Orchestra. Originally a co-operative, the Jazz Messengers has had Art Blakey as its leader since 1956. The Chicago session was different from that in New York the previous year also insofar as the repertoire chosen was not almost exclusively the work of the leader. True, once more Shorter was responsible for five originals, but this time there were three pieces from the standard pop world for the Quartet to improvise on.

That Shorter was continuing to progress as a jazz composer of immense promise can be gauged from even casual listening to any one of the five titles bearing his name, each of which was to recieve its first recording. For instance, the easy flowing, engagingly melodic *Pay as you go* sounds as interesting today as it must have been for Shorter and his colleagues to play in Chicago, over 27 years ago. Shorter himself flows into his own solo in almost Getzian fashion, making effective use of a two-note phrase. Walton's contribution is nicely assertive and never less than wholly creative throughout. *Second genesis* is another Shorter tune with great melodic strength. Once again it's his tenor which takes full advantage of its attractive contours, sailing through his choruses with admirable logic and poise.

Walton complements the tenor statement to perfection. The Cranshaw-Blakey team offers non pareil support at all times. The accent is firmly on rhythm during *Mister chairman* - Wayne's personal dedication to his then boss, maybe? - As all four musicians together reconjugate the verb to swing - and with real emphasis. Here, in particular. Shorter demonstrates just how much he was growing in stature as a premier league tenorman. His improvisations are interesting at all times, his tonal quality is fine - and already he's beginning to move away from the awesome Coltrane influence. His short, four-bar dialogue with Blakey makes for a nice final touch. The ballad side of Wayne Shorter is represented superbly with the out-of-the-ordinary *The albatross*. Shorter injects a lovely yearning quality into his contribution that is entirely apposite; and although he plays with admirable restraint he never eschews real feeling. He also uses the upper register of his instrument to telling effect. A word of praise here forCranshaw whose pivotal bass is amply present.

It doesn't seem fair somehow to single out just one track which perhaps more than the rest demonstrates Blakey's unique percussion qualities. But for a particularly wonderous example of Abdullah Ibn Buhainia in *Ne plus ultra* form, then operate the Time Mode button of your CD player to play at Track II. It's all there - the power, the dynamics, the rhythmic-polyrhythmic qualities that are his alone. The kind of surging drive that seems to lift the soloists aloft, willing them to surpass their best. Shorter, especially, is inspired to play one of his finest recorded solos of this period on *Tenderfoot*. And the exchanges between the pair show just how truly exciting this basic device can be. The non-Shorter pieces recorded in October '60 aren't quite on the same overall standard of excellence as the other items - although in no way does their inclusion inhibit the Quartet. Shorter's smoky tone rivals his fecundity of ideas during the kind of first-class treatment the dreary principal theme from an equally forgettsble 1952 movie (*Ruby and the pearl*) scarcely deserves. Blakey's use of mallets is adroit. Strange, though, that there is no Walton solo on this almost six minute long track. *Getting to know you* from Rogers-Hammerstein's The King and I, likewise hardly seems to be the most promising piece of material for an out-and-out jazz date. But the sprightly tempo with which Shorter kicks off proceedings helps no little. And his and Walton's solos don't lack in any way that essential jazz bite and commitment. (Sadly, lack of space, CD-wise, prevents the inclusion here of the remaining standard, a Rodger's and Hart opus of infinitely superior quality. But Shorter fans need look no further than Charly Records' enticing The Horn - The Tenor Saxophone In Jazz (CD CHARLY 114), wherein the Wayne Shorter Quartets fine version of *I didn't know what time it was* nestles comfortably, rubbing shoulders with a gang of other top-class tracks, featuring other giants of the instrument such as Ben Webster,Zoot Sims, Dexter Gordon, John Coltrane, and Coleman Hawkins).

Developmentally, the advent of the 1960s proved to be an important period in Wayne Shorter's carreer. The juxtaposition of the contents of his two first record dates as leader (or almost all the contents) helps to document, in part at least, that development. In more recent times, Shorter has become almost a cult figure, both as a saxophonist and writer. A youthful veteran who, in turn, has influenced at least one other generation of aspiring jazz musicians. During the past quarter-century he has accomplished much, and rightly earned the respect of his musical peers and the international acclaim of critics and punters alike.

**CD:** Released Jun '88, on Charly by Charly Records. Catalogue no: **CDCHARLY 121**

**WAYNE SHORTER**

**2 LP Set:** Released '88, on GNP Crescendo (USA) by GNP Crescendo Records (USA). Catalogue no: **GNPS 2.2075**

**WAYNING MOMENTS**

Tracks: / Black orpheus (Composer Louis Bonfa.) / Devils' Island (Composer Wayne Shorter.) / Moon of Manakoora (Composer Alfred Newman.) / Dead end (Composer Wayne Shorter.) / Wayning moments (Composer: Eddie Higgins.) / Powder keg (Composer: Wayne Shorter.) / All or nothing at all (Composers: J Lawrence/A Altman.) / Callaway went that-a-way (Composer Wayne Shorter.). Note: A Vee Jay Recording. Licensed from Charly Records International APS.

**CD:** Released Nov '86, on Charly by Charly Records. Catalogue no: **CDCHARLY 32**

**Album:** Released '86, on Affinity by Charly Records. Catalogue no: **AFF 126**

## Shouters

**SHOUTERS (Various artists)**

**Album:** Released Mar '85, on Savoy Jazz (USA) by Malaco Records (USA). Catalogue no: **SJL 2244**

## Sidran, Ben

**Biographical details:** Ben Sidran is a pianist/vocalist, born in Chicago in 1943; he met Steve Miller and Boz Scaggs at the University of Wisconsin and was a member of an early Miller band, but switched to mainstream jazz. He studied at the U. of Sussex and turned his PhD thesis into a book, Black Talk, in 1971; he is now a jazz critic on National Public Radio in the USA. He's made twelve albums on five labels, the latest on Magenta, the jazz subsiduary of Windham Hill. (Donald Clarke 27.5.87)..

**OLD SONGS FOR THE NEW DEPRESSION**

Tracks: / Easy Street / Piano players.

**Album:** Released '82, on Antilles/New Directions by Island Records. Catalogue no: **AN 1004**

**ON THE LIVE SIDE**

Tracks: / Doctor's blues, The / Piano players / Good travel agent, A / Mitsubishi boy / On the cool side / Space cowboy / Last dance.

**CD:** Released '87, on Windham Hill by Windham Hill Records (USA). Deleted '88. Catalogue no: **370 206-2**

**Cass:** Released '87, on Windham Hill by Windham Hill Records (USA). Deleted '88. Catalogue no: **370206-4**

**Album:** Released '87, on Windham Hill by Windham Hill Records (USA). Catalogue no: **370206-1**

**TOO HOT TO TOUCH**

Tracks: / Shine a light on me / Enivre d'amour / Everything happens to me / Freedom jazz dance / On the sunny side / Critics / Too hot to touch / I wanna be a / Pepper / Longing for Bahia.

**Album:** Released Jul '88, on Windham Hill by Windham Hill Records (USA). Catalogue no: **370108-1**

**Cass:** Released Jul '88, on Windham Hill by Windham Hill Records (USA). Catalogue no: **370108-4**

**CD:** Released Jul '88, on Windham Hill by Windham Hill Records (USA). Catalogue no: **370 108-2**

## Silver, Horace

**Biographical details:** Horace Silver is a pianist, composer, bandleader, born in Norwalk, Connecticit on 2 September 1928. His father was Portuguese, from the Cape Verde Islands. He was an early member of Art Blakey's Jazz Messengers; in fact, the earliest recordings of that group were as 'Horace Silver and the Jazz Messengers'. He went on to contribute significantly through the 1950-60s to the sound of the Blue Note and to the beginnings of what is now called funk, with soulful compositions such as *Doodlin'*, *The Preacher*, and *Senor Blues*. There were about 20 Blue Note albums (later owned by Liberty, now by EMI), all with all-star sidemen. In the mid-1960s albums such as *Song For My Father* crossed over to the pop album chart in the USA. He formed his own Silveto label in the early 1980s. (Donald Clarke 27.5.87)..

**BEST OF HORACE SILVER (Blue Note years)**

Tracks: / Opus de funk / Doodlin' / Room 608 (CD only.) / Preacher, The / Senor Blues / Cool eyes (CD only.) / Home cookin' / Soulville (CD only.) / Cookin' at the continental / Peace / Sister Sadie / Blowin' the blues away (CD only.).

**Album:** Released Dec '88, on Blue Note by EMI Records. Catalogue no: **B1 91143**

**CD:** Released Dec '88, on Blue Note by EMI Records. Catalogue no: **CDP 791 143 2**

**CD:** Released Dec '88, on Blue Note by EMI Records. Catalogue no: **BNZ 146**

**BEST OF HORACE SILVER - VOL. 2**

Tracks: / Song for my father / Que pasa / Pretty eyes / Cape Verdean blues, The / Nutville (CD only.) / Mexican hip dance (CD only.) / Gregory is hedre / Jody grind, The / Serenade to a soul sister.

**CD:** Released Feb '90, on Blue Note by EMI Records. Catalogue no: **CDP 793 206 2**

**Album:** Released Feb '90, on Blue Note by EMI Records. Catalogue no: **793 206 1**

**CD:** Released Feb '90, on Blue Note by EMI Records. Catalogue no: **BNZ 233**

**Album:** Released Feb '90, on Blue Note by EMI Records. Catalogue no: **B1 93206**

**BLOWIN' THE BLUES AWAY**

Tracks: / Blowin' the blues away / St. Vitus dance, The / Break city / Peace / Sister Sadie / Baghdad, The / Melancholy mood / How did it happen?.

**CD:** Released Sep '87, on Blue Note by EMI Records. Catalogue no: **BNZ 89**

**Album:** Released Nov '85, on Blue Note by EMI Records. Catalogue no: **BST 84017**

**CD:** Released Sep '87, on Blue Note by EMI Records. Catalogue no: **CDP 746 526 2**

**Cass:** Released Nov '85, on Blue Note by EMI Records. Deleted Jun '88. Catalogue no: **4BN 84017**

**CAPE VERDEAN BLUES, THE (Silver, Horace Quintet)**

Tracks: / Cape Verdean blues, The / African queen, The / Pretty eyes / Nut-

ville / Bonita / Mo' Joe.
**CD:** Released Aug '89, on Blue Note by EMI Records. Catalogue no: **BNZ 229**
**CD:** Released Aug '89, on Blue Note by EMI Records. Catalogue no: **CDP 784 220 2**

**DOIN' THE THING (AT THE VILLAGE VANGUARD)**
Tracks: / Filthy McNasty / Doin' the thing / Cool eyes (alt. take) / It ain't s'posed to be like that / Kiss me right / Gringo.
**CD:** Released Apr '89, on Blue Note by EMI Records. Catalogue no: **CDP 784 076 2**
**CD:** Released Apr '89, on Blue Note by EMI Records. Catalogue no: **BNZ 161**
**Album:** Released Apr '89, on Blue Note by EMI Records. Catalogue no: **B1 84076**

**FINGER POPPIN' WITH THE HORACE SILVER QUINTET (Silver, Horace Quintet)**
Tracks: / Finger poppin' / Juicy Lucy / Swingin' the samba / Sweet stuff / Cookin' at the Continental / Come on home / You happened my way / Mellow D.
Note: This was the first of many Blue Note albums by Horace Silver's finest and longest-lasting band with trumpeter Blue Mitchell and tenor saxophonist Junior Cook. Like all of Silver's efforts, it is meticuously planned and performed as well as being drenched in earthy, soulful, lyrical feeling. Several Silver classics came out of this album, including 'Juicy Lucy', 'Cookin' at the Continental', 'Come on home' and the title tune.
**Album:** Released May '86, on Blue Note by EMI Records. Catalogue no: **BST 84008**
**CD:** Released May '89, on Blue Note by EMI Records. Catalogue no: **BNZ 176**
**CD:** Released May '89, on Blue Note by EMI Records. Catalogue no: **CDP 784 008 2**

**HORACE SILVER & THE JAZZ MESSENGERS (Silver, Horace & The Jazz Messengers)**
Tracks: / Room 608 / Creepin' in / Stop time / To whom it may concern / Hippy / Preachers, The / Hankerin' / Doodlin'.
Note: Featuring three great institutions: the Horace Silver Quintet, Art Blakey & The Jazz Messengers and the definitive Blue Note sound - a classic.
**Cass:** Released Aug '85, on Blue Note by EMI Records. Deleted Nov '88. Catalogue no: **4BN 81518**
**CD:** Released Sep '87, on Blue Note by EMI Records. Catalogue no: **BNZ 88**
**Album:** Released Jul '89, on Blue Note by EMI Records. Catalogue no: **781 518 1**
**CD:** Released Sep '87, on Blue Note by EMI Records. Catalogue no: **CDP 746 140 2**
**Album:** Released Aug '82, on Blue Note by EMI Records. Deleted Jan '88. Catalogue no: **BLP 1518**
**Album:** Released Jul '89, on Blue Note by EMI Records. Catalogue no: **BST 81518**

**HORACE SILVER TRIO**
Tracks: / Safari / Ecaroh / Prelude to a kiss / Message from Kenya / Horoscope / Yeah / How about you / I remember you / Opus de funk / Nothing but the soul / Silverware / Day in, day out / Thou swell (CD only.) / Quicksilver (CD only.) / Knowledge box (CD only.) / Buhaina (CD only.).
**Album:** Released Jul '89, on Blue Note by EMI Records. Catalogue no: **B1 81520**
**CD:** Released Jul '89, on Blue Note by EMI Records. Catalogue no: **CDP 781 520 2**
**Album:** Released Dec '84, on Blue Note by EMI Records. Catalogue no: **VLP 1520**
**CD:** Released Jul '89, on Blue Note by EMI Records. Catalogue no: **BNZ 150**

**SERENADE TO A SOUL SISTER**
Tracks: / Psychedelic Sally / Serenade to a soul sister / Rain dance / Jungle juice / Kindred spirits / Next time I fall in love.
**Album:** Released Nov '86, on Blue Note by EMI Records. Deleted Nov '88. Catalogue no: **BST 84277**

**SIX PIECES OF SILVER**
Tracks: / Cool eyes / Shirl / Camouflage / Enchantment / Senor blues / Senor blues (45 version) / Virgo / For heaven's sake / Tippin' / Senor blues (vocal version).
**CD:** Released Jun '89, on Blue Note by EMI Records. Catalogue no: **CDP 781 539 2**
**CD:** Released Jun '89, on Blue Note by EMI Records. Catalogue no: **BNZ 175**
**Album:** Released Jul '89, on Blue Note by EMI Records. Catalogue no: **B1 81539**
**Album:** Released Sep '84, on Blue Note by EMI Records. Catalogue no: **BLP 1539**

**SONG FOR MY FATHER (Silver, Horace Quintet)**
Tracks: / Song for my father / Natives are restless tonight, The / Calcutta cutie / Que pasa / Kicker, The / Lonely woman / Sanctimonious Sam (CD only.) / Sighin' and cryin' (CD only.) / Silver threads among the soul (CD only.).
**CD:** Released Jun '89, on Blue Note by EMI Records. Catalogue no: **BNZ 200**
**Album:** Released Jul '82, on Blue Note by EMI Records. Catalogue no: **BST 84185**
**CD:** Released Jun '89, on Blue Note by EMI Records. Catalogue no: **CDP 784 185 2**
**Cass:** Released Mar '86, on Blue Note by EMI Records. Catalogue no: **TCBST 84185**

## Simmons, Norman

**I'M THE BLUES (Simmons, Norman Quintet)**
Tracks: / I'm the blues, part 1 / I'm the blues, part 2 / Juicy Lucy / I ain't got nothin' but the blues / Good humour / Los milagros pequenos / Why try to change me now?.
Note: With Jimmy Owens, Clifford Jones, Lisle Atkinson, Vernal Fournier.
**Album:** Released Nov '86, on Milljack (USA) Catalogue no: **MJP 1002**

**MIDNIGHT CREEPER**
Tracks: / Some day my prince will come / Midnight creeper / Confirmation / Blackout / Send in the clowns / Emily.
Note: With Lisle Atkinson, Al Harewood.
**Album:** Released Nov '86, on Milljack (USA) Catalogue no: **MJP 1001**

**RAMIRA THE DANCER (Simmons, Norman Quartet)**
Tracks: / Ramira / Oleo / Stairway to the stars / Blue juice / My shining hour / Where is my lady? / How insensitive / Four.
**Album:** Released Jan '83, on Spotlite by Spotlite Records. Catalogue no: **SPJ LP13**

## Simone, Nina

**Biographical details:** Nina Simone was born Eunice Waymon on 21 Feb 1933 in North Carolina. As pianist, singer and songwriter, she is one of the all-time great cabaret artists, though unpredictable: sometimes she doesn't show up. Her first album, on Bethlehem in the USA in 1959, included top 20 singles *I Loves You Porgy*; the album is now called *My Baby Just Cares For Me* on Charly in the UK. (Donald Clarke 27.5.87).

**60'S VOL 1, THE**
**CD:** Released Jan '90, on Polydor by Polydor Ltd. Catalogue no: **8385432**

**60'S VOL 2, THE**
**CD:** Released Jan '90, on Polydor by Polydor Ltd. Catalogue no: **8385442**

**60'S VOL 3, THE**
**CD:** Released Jan '90, on Polydor by Polydor Ltd. Catalogue no: **8385452**

**AIN'T GOT NO....I GOT LIFE**
Tracks: / Ain't got no....I got life / To love somebody.
**7" Single:** Released Oct '86, on Old Gold by Old Gold Records. Catalogue no: **OG 9609**

**AIN'T GOT NO....I GOT LIFE**
Tracks: / Ain't got no....I got life / Do what you gotta do.
**7" Single:** Released Oct '68, on RCA by BMG Records (UK). Deleted Oct '71. Catalogue no: **RCA 1743**

**AMAZING NINA SIMONE, THE**
Tracks: / Blue prelude / Children go where I send you / Tomorrow / Stompin' at the Savoy / It might as well be spring / You've been gone too long / That's him over there / Chilly winds don't blow / Theme from 'middle of the night' / Can't get out of this mood / Willow weep for me.
**CD:** Released '88, on Official by Official Records. Catalogue no: **OFF 86002**
**Album:** Released '88, on Official by Official Records. Catalogue no: **OFF 6002**
**Cass:** Released '88, on Official by Official Records. Catalogue no: **OFF 46002**

**ARTISTRY OF NINA SIMONE, THE**
Tracks: / Mr. Bojangles / I shall be released / Do what you gotta do / Since I fell for you / I want a little sugar in my bowl / I can't see nobody / Ain't got no....I got life / To love somebody / Turn me on / Seems I'm never tired lovin' you / Romance in the dark / My man's gone now / How long must I wander? / Blues for mama.
**Cass:** Released '84, on RCA International by BMG Records (UK). Catalogue no: **NK 89018**
**Album:** Released '84, on RCA International by BMG Records (UK). Catalogue no: **NL 89018**
**Album:** Released Jul '82, on RCA by BMG Records (UK). Deleted Jul '87. Catalogue no: **INTS 5193**

**AT RONNIE SCOTT'S**
Note: Running time: 57 mins.
**VHS:** Released '88, on Channel 5 by Channel 5 Video. Catalogue no: **CFV 06342**
**VHS:** Released '88, on Hendring Video Catalogue no: **HEN 2 017**

**BACKLASH**
**Cass:** Released Apr '86, on Star Jazz (USA) by Charly Records. Catalogue no: **SJAZZC 6**
**Album:** Released Apr '86, on Star Jazz (USA) by Charly Records. Catalogue no: **SJAZZ 6**

**BALTIMORE**
Tracks: / Baltimore / Everything must change / Family, The / My father / Music for lovers / Rich girl / That's all I want from you / Forget / Balm in gilead / If you pray right.
Note: Recorded: January 1978.
**Album:** Released Feb '84, on CTI (1) by Polydor Ltd. Catalogue no: **CTI 9010**

**BALTIMORE (RE-ISSUE)**
Note: Tracks as original album.
**Album:** Released Mar '88, on CBS by CBS Records. Catalogue no: **460730 1**
**Cass:** Released Mar '88, on CBS by CBS Records. Catalogue no: **460730 4**

**BEST OF NINA SIMONE**
Tracks: / In the morning / I shall be released / Day and night / It be's that way sometime / I want a little sugar in my bowl / My man's gone now / Why? (the king of love is dead) / Compensation / I wish I knew how it would feel to be free / Go to hell / Do what you gotta do / Suzanne.
**Album:** Released Sep '89, on RCA by BMG Records (UK). Catalogue no: **NL 90376**
**Cass:** Released Sep '84, on Philips (Timeless) by PolyGram UK Ltd. Catalogue no: **TIMC 10**
**CD:** Released Sep '89, on RCA by BMG Records (UK). Catalogue no: **ND 90376**
**Album:** Released Sep '84, on Philips (Timeless) by PolyGram UK Ltd. Catalogue no: **TIME 10**
**Cass:** Released Sep '89, on RCA by BMG Records (UK). Catalogue no: **NK 90376**
**CD:** Released Mar '86, on Philips by Phonogram Ltd. Catalogue no: **822 846 2**

**BLACK SOUL**
Tracks: / Here comes the sun / Mr. Bojangles / I think it's going to rain today.
**Cass:** Released Jul '83, on RCA (Germany) Catalogue no: **CK 42220**
**Album:** Released Jul '83, on RCA (Germany) Catalogue no: **CL 42220**

**COLLECTION: NINA SIMONE**
**Cass:** Released '88, on Masters (Holland) Catalogue no: **MAMC 916185**
**Album:** Released '88, on Masters (Holland) Catalogue no: **MA 16185**

**CRY BEFORE I GO**
Tracks: / Trouble in mind / After you've gone / Nobody / Hard walkin' Hanna / Cry before I go / Can't stand to leave / Big legged woman / Funky funky soul.
**Album:** Released Nov '80, on Manhattan Records by President Records. Catalogue no: **MAN 5039**

**DIAMOND SERIES: NINA SIMONE**
Tracks: / Ain't got no....I got life / I loves you, Porgy / Take my hand, precious Lord / To love somebody / I shall be released / Just like Tom Thumb's blues / Times they are a-changin' / Here comes the sun / Just like a woman / Mr. Bojangles / Angel of the morning / Backlash blues / House of the Rising Sun / Blues for mama / Look of love, The / Go to hell.
**CD:** Released Apr '88, on Diamond Series by RCA Records. Catalogue no: **CD 90113**

**DON'T LET ME BE MISUNDERSTOOD**
Tracks: / Don't let me be misunderstood / Last rose of summer / Ne me quitte pas / Work song / Little girl blue / Trouble in mind / Strange fruit / Love me or leave me / Come ye / I put a spell on you / Don't explain / Wild is the wind / What more can I say / Nobody knows you (when you're down and out) / I loves you, Porgy (live) / Mississippi goddam (live).
**Cass:** Released Mar '88, on Mercury (Holland) Catalogue no: **834084**
**Album:** Released Mar '88, on Mercury (Holland) Catalogue no: **834081**
**CD:** Released Mar '88, on Mercury (Holland) Catalogue no: **834 082**

**FINE AND MELLOW**
Tracks: / Fine and mellow / Rags and old iron / Satin doll / Memphis in June / Twelfth of never / I got it bad and that ain't good / Return home, The / Sayonara / It don't mean a thing / Just say I love him / I'll look around / Do nothing till you hear from me / I love to love / Will I find my love? / Black swan.
**Album:** Released Oct '75, on Golden Hour Catalogue no: **GH 607**

**FODDER ON MY WINGS**
Tracks: / I sing just to know that I'm alive / Fodder in her wings / Vous etes seuls, mais je desire etre / Avec vous / Il y a un baume a gilhead / Heaven belongs to you / Liberian calypso / Thandewye / I was just a stupid dog to them / Colour is a beautiful thing / There is no returning.
Note: Recorded in Paris, 1982.
**Album:** Released Mar '84, on IMS by Polydor Ltd. Catalogue no: **1067 885**

**GIN HOUSE BLUES**
Tracks: / Ain't no use / I want a little sugar in my bowl / Gin House blues / Backlash blues / Assignment song / Young gifted and black.
**Album:** Released Jun '80, on Manhattan Records by President Records. Deleted '85. Catalogue no: **MAN 5031**

**HERE COMES THE SUN**
Tracks: / Here comes the sun / Just like a woman / Oh child / Mr. Bojangles / New world coming / Angel of the morning / How long must I wander? / My way.
**Album:** Released Jul '80, on RCA International by BMG Records (UK). Catalogue no: **INTS 5025**
**Cass:** Released Jul '80, on RCA International by BMG Records (UK). Catalogue no: **INTK 5025**
**Album:** Released Oct '85, on RCA (France) by BMG Records (France). Catalogue no: **NL 89421**

**I PUT A SPELL ON YOU**
**Album:** Released Jul '65, on Philips by Phonogram Ltd. Deleted Jul '70. Catalogue no: **BL 7671**

**I PUT A SPELL ON YOU (SINGLE)**
Tracks: / I put a spell on you.
**7" Single:** Released Aug '65, on Philips by Phonogram Ltd. Deleted Aug '68. Catalogue no: **BF 1415**

**I WANT A LITTLE SUGAR IN MY BOWL**
Tracks: / Ain't no use / I want a little sugar in my bowl / Gin house blues / Ain't got no - I got life / Four women / No opportunity necessary.
**Album:** Released Apr '80, on Manhattan Records by President Records. Deleted '85. Catalogue no: **MAN 5007**

**IT'S COLD OUT HERE**
Tracks: / It's cold out here / I sing just to know that I'm alive / Mississippi Goddamn (live) / My baby.
**12" Single:** Released 22 May '89, on Jungle by Jungle Records. Catalogue no: **JUNG 051 T**
**Cassingle:** Released Jun '89, on Jungle by Jungle Records. Catalogue no: **JUNG 051 C**
**7" Single:** Released 22 May '89, on Jungle by Jungle Records. Catalogue no: **JUNG 051**
**CD Single:** Released 22 May '89, on Jungle by Jungle Records. Catalogue no: **JUNG 051 CD**

**LADY MIDNIGHT**
Tracks: / I put a spell on you / Nobody knows you (when you're down and out) / Trouble in mind / Mood indigo / Feeling good / For roar of the grease / Pirate Jenny(live) / I loves you porgy / Wild is the wind / For myself / Beautiful land / This years kisses / Plain gold ring / Don't let me be misunderstood / One September day / Little girl blue / Keep on breaking my heart / Love me or leave me / Ballad of Hollis Brown, The / Strange fruit / Something wonderful (from The

King And I) / Don't explain / Last rose of summer / What more can I say? / Mississippi goddam.
**2 LP Set:** Released 8 Nov '87, on Connoisseur Collection by Connoisseur Collection Ltd.. Catalogue no: **VSOPLP 106**
**Cass:** Released 7 Nov '87, on Connoisseur Collection by Connoisseur Collection Ltd.. Catalogue no: **VSOPMC 106**

**LITTLE GIRL BLUE**
Tracks: / Little girl blue / I loves you, Porgy / For all we know (12" only).
**7" Single:** Released Dec '87, on Charly by Charly Records. Catalogue no: **CYZ 7 123**
**12" Single:** Released Dec '87, on Charly by Charly Records. Catalogue no: **CYZ 123**

**LIVE AND KICKIN'**
**Cass:** Released Nov '89, on Jungle by Jungle Records. Catalogue no: **FREUDC 32**
**CD:** Released Nov '89, on Jungle by Jungle Records. Catalogue no: **FREUDCD 32**
**Album:** Released Nov '89, on Jungle by Jungle Records. Catalogue no: **FREUD 32**

**LIVE AT RONNIE SCOTT'S**
Tracks: / God,God,God / If you knew / Mr. Smith / Fodder in her wings / Be my husband / I loves you Porgy / Other woman, The / Mississippi goddam / Moon over Alabama / For a while / See live woman / I sing just to know that I'm alive / My baby just cares for me.
**CD:** Released 20 Feb '88, on Hendring Catalogue no: **HEN 6017 Y**
**CD:** Released Feb '38, on Windham Hill by Windham Hill Records (USA). Catalogue no: **WHCD 006**

**LIVE AT RONNIE SCOTT'S (2)**
Tracks: / God, God, God / If you knew / Mr.Smith / Fodder on her wings / Be my husband / I loves you, Porgy / Other woman,The / Mississippi goddam / For a while / See live woman / I sing just to know I'm alive / My baby just cares for me.
**Cass:** Released Feb '90, on Essential by Castle Communications Records. Catalogue no: **ESMMC 013**
**CD:** Released Feb '90, on Essential by Castle Communications Records. Catalogue no: **ESMCD 013**

**LIVE AT VINE STREET**
**Album:** Released May '87, on Verve (USA) by Polydor Ltd. Catalogue no: **831 437-1**
**Cass:** Released May '87, on Verve (USA) by Polydor Ltd. Catalogue no: **831 437-4**
**CD:** Released May '87, on Verve (USA) by Polydor Ltd. Catalogue no: **831 437-2**

**LIVE & KICKIN'**
**Album:** Released Feb '90, on Jungle by Jungle Records. Catalogue no: **FREUD 32**

**MAGIC MOMENTS**
**Cass:** Released May '86, on RCA by BMG Records (UK). Catalogue no: **NK 89896**

**MAGIC OF NINA SIMONE, THE**
Tracks: / Work song / You can have him / Little Liza Jane / Fine and mellow / Porgy / Angel of the morning / Lovin' woman / My way / Nina's blues / Here comes the sun.
**Cass:** Released Feb '89, on Venus Catalogue no: **VENUMC 2**

**MISTER BOJANGLES**
Tracks: / Mister bojangles / Turn me on / Ain't got no....I got life (Extra track on 12") / Ozy Mandras (Extra track on Cassingle and C.D.single.).
**12" Single:** Released Feb '88, on Enterprizes Deleted May '89. Catalogue no: **PT 41776**
**7" Single:** Released Feb '88, on Enterprizes Deleted May '89. Catalogue no: **PB 41775**

**MUSIC FOR THE MILLIONS**
Tracks: / I put a spell on you / Mississippi / Goddam / Don't let me be misunderstood / Trouble in mind / Laziest girl in town / I loves you, Porgy / Ne me quitte pas / Gimme some / Nobody knows you (when you're down and out) / Strange fruit / Take care of business / Don't take all night.
**Cass:** Released Dec '83, on Philips (Import) by PolyGram UK Ltd. Catalogue no: **8123 784**
**Album:** Released Dec '83, on Philips (Import) by PolyGram UK Ltd. Catalogue no: **8123 781**

**MY BABY JUST CARES FOR ME**
Tracks: / My baby just cares for me / Little girl blue / I loves you Porgy (Only on 10" single.) / Love me or leave me (Only on 10" single.).
**10" Single:** Released May '82, on Charly by Charly Records. Deleted '85. Catalogue no: **10 CYX 201**
**Cass:** Released '85, on Charly by Charly Records. Catalogue no: **TCCR 30217**
**7" Single:** Released May '82, on Charly by Charly Records. Deleted '85. Catalogue no: **7 CYX 201**
**Album:** Released '85, on Charly by Charly Records. Catalogue no: **CR 30217**
**CD:** Released Mar '86, on Charly by Charly Records. Catalogue no: **CDCHARLY 6**

**MY BABY JUST CARES FOR ME**
Tracks: / My baby just cares for me / Love me or leave me / Little girl blue (Extra track on 12" only).
**12" Single:** Released Oct '87, on Charly by Charly Records. Catalogue no: **CYZ 112**
**7" Single:** Released Apr '85, on Charly by Charly Records. Deleted '87. Catalogue no: **CYZ 7 112**
**CD Single:** Released Nov '87, on Charly by Charly Records. Catalogue no: **CDS 1**

**NE ME QUITTE PAS**
**2 LP Set:** Released Oct '88, on Vogue by Vogue Records. Catalogue no: **406502**
**CD:** Released Oct '88, on Vogue by Vogue Records. Catalogue no: **VGCD 670 030**

**NINA AT TOWN HALL**
Tracks: / Black is the color of my true love's hair / Exactly like you / Other woman, The / Under the lowest / You can have him / Summertime / Cotton eyed Joe / Return home / Wild is the wind / Fine and mellow.
**Album:** Released May '88, on Official by Official Records. Catalogue no: **OFF 6012**
**Cass:** Released May '88, on Official by Official Records. Catalogue no: **OFF 46012**

**NINA SIMONE**
**CD:** Released Feb '90, on Mercury by Phonogram Ltd. Catalogue no: **838 007-4**
**Cass:** Released Feb '90, on Mercury by Phonogram Ltd. Catalogue no: **838 007-2**

**NINA SIMONE**
Tracks: / House of the rising sun / Gin house blues / Ne me quitte pas / When I was a young girl / Devil's workshop / Just in time / Don't let me be misunderstood / Backlash blues / To love somebody / Ain't got no...I got life / Sealine woman / Please read me.
**Album:** Released Oct '82, on Dakota (Countdown). Deleted '84. Catalogue no: **COUNT 9**
**Cass:** Released Oct '82, on Dakota (Countdown). Deleted '84. Catalogue no: **ZC CNT 9**

**NINA SIMONE AT NEWPORT**
Tracks: / Trouble in mind / Porgy / Little Liza Jane / You'd be so nice to come home to / Flo me la / Nina's blues / In the evening by the moonlight.
**CD:** Released Dec '88, on Official by Official Records. Catalogue no: **OFF 86014**
**Cass:** Released Dec '88, on Official by Official Records. Catalogue no: **OFF 46014**
**Album:** Released '88, on Official by Official Records. Catalogue no: **OFF 6014**

**NINA SIMONE COLLECTION (Her golden greats)**
Tracks: / House of the Rising Sun / Gin House blues / Don't let me be misunderstood / He was too good to me / When I was a young girl / Brown baby / Just in time / Zungo / Way I love you, The / Backlash blues / Please read me / Seeline woman / If he changed my name.
**Cass:** Released Dec '87, on Deja Vu Catalogue no: **DVMC 2104**
**Album:** Released Dec '87, on Deja Vu Catalogue no: **DVLP 2104**
**CD:** Released Jun '88, on Deja Vu Catalogue no: **DVCD 2104**

**NINA SIMONE SINGS THE BLUES**
Tracks: / Do I move you? / Day and night / In the dark / Real real / My man's gone now / Backlash blues / I want a little

Zoot Sims

sugar in my bowl / Buck / Since I fell for you / House of the Rising Sun / Blues for mama.
**Album:** Released Aug '85, on RCA by BMG Records (UK). Catalogue no: **NL 89265**
**Album:** Released '83, on RCA (Germany) Catalogue no: **26 21230**
**Cass:** Released Aug '85, on RCA by BMG Records (UK). Catalogue no: **NK 89265**

**NINA SIMONE STORY, THE**
Tracks: / When I was a young girl / Just in time / He was too good to me / House of the rising sun / Life / To love somebody / Don't let me be misunderstood / Devil's workshop / Seeline woman / Gin house blues / Brown baby / I'm gonna say / Promises / Children go where I send you / Zungo / If he changed my name / Backlash blues.
**Cass:** Released Apr '89, on Deja Vu Catalogue no: **DVRE MC 15**
**CD:** Released Apr '89, on Deja Vu Catalogue no: **DVRE CD 15**

**NINA'S BACK**
**CD:** Released Jul '89, on Jungle by Jungle Records. Catalogue no: **FREUDCD 28**
**Album:** Released Feb '86, on VPI Catalogue no: **VPI 1007**
**Cass:** Released Jul '89, on Jungle by Jungle Records. Catalogue no: **FREUDC 28**
**Cass:** Released Feb '86, on VPI Catalogue no: **VPIC 1007**
**Album:** Released Jul '89, on Jungle by Jungle Records. Catalogue no: **FREUD 28**

**'NUFF SAID**
**Album:** Released Feb '69, on RCA Victor by BMG Records (UK). Deleted Feb '74. Catalogue no: **SF 7979**

**OUR LOVE**
Tracks: / Don't let me be misunderstood / How can I make him love me? / I am blessed / Our love / Laziest girl in town / Nobody / Night song.
**Album:** Released May '83, on Barclay (France) by Decca Records. Catalogue no: **B 90118**
**Cass:** Released May '83, on Barclay (France) by Decca Records. Catalogue no: **MB 990118**

**PORTRAIT OF A SONG STYLIST**
**Cass:** Released Oct '89, on Masterpiece by Castle Communications Records. Catalogue no: **HARMC 112**
**CD:** Released Oct '89, on Masterpiece by Castle Communications Records. Catalogue no: **HARCD 112**

**PORTRAIT OF NINA SIMONE**
Tracks: / Four women / Nobody wants you / Assignment song / No opportunity necessary / I love my baby / Strange fruit / I love to love / Ding song / Sinner man / I want a little sugar in my bowl.
**2 LP Set:** Released Aug '83, on Musidisc by Musidisc Records (France). Catalogue no: **ALB 189**

**REPLAY ON NINA SIMONE**
**Cass:** Released Aug '85, on Sierra by Sierra Records. Catalogue no: **CFEDB 5021**
**Album:** Released Aug '85, on Sierra by Sierra Records. Catalogue no: **FEDB 5021**

**RIGHT ON**
**Album:** Released Oct '88, on Vogue (France) by Vogue Records. Catalogue no: **509108**

**TO LOVE SOMEBODY**
Tracks: / To love somebody.
**7" Single:** Released Jan '69, on RCA by BMG Records (UK). Deleted Jan '72. Catalogue no: **RCA 1779**

**VERY RARE EVENING WITH NINA**
**Album:** Released Jan '80, on PM Catalogue no: **PM 018**

## Sims, Zoot

**Biographical details:** Zoot Sims was born John Haley Sims on 29 October 1925 in Inglewood, California; he died on 22 March 1985. He first came to fame as one of the famous Four Brothers reed section in Woody Herman's legendary band of 1947-49, and continued with his warm, personal style as one of the best loved tenor sax players of his generation. He later also played some soprano sax; his albums with trombomist Bobby Brookmeyer and saxist Al Cohn are especiallly well regarded. (Donald Clarke 27.5.87)..

**AFRICAN CHALLENGE**
Tracks: / African challenge.
**12" Single:** Released Sep '84, on Studio One Catalogue no: **Unknown**

**BEST OF ZOOT SIMS**
Tracks: / Willow weep for me / Blues for Louise / Someday, sweetheart / Wrap up / Girl from Ipanema / More than you know / Main stem / I got it bad and that ain't good.
**Cass:** Released '82, on Pablo Jazz (USA) by Pablo Records (USA). Catalogue no: **K10 850**
**Album:** Released '82, on Pablo Jazz (USA) by Pablo Records (USA). Catalogue no: **23 10 850**

**BIG STAMPEDE, THE**
Tracks: / You're my girl / Purple cow, The / Ill wind / Big stampede, The / Too close for comfort / Jerry's jaunt / How now blues / Bye ya.
**CD:** Released Aug '89, on Meteor by Magnum Music Group. Catalogue no: **CDMT 017**
**Album:** Released Aug '89, on Meteor by Magnum Music Group. Catalogue no: **MTLP 017**

**BLUES FOR TWO (Sims, Zoot & Joe Pass)**
Tracks: / Blues for two / Dindi / Remember / Poor butterfly / Black and blue / Pennies from Heaven / I hadn't anyone till you / Take off.
**Album:** Released Mar '83, on Pablo Jazz (USA) by Pablo Records (USA). Catalogue no: **D 2310 879**
**Cass:** Released Mar '83, on Pablo Jazz (USA) by Pablo Records (USA). Catalogue no: **D 10 879**

**BROTHER IN SWING**
**Album:** Released '88, on Vogue by Vogue Records. Catalogue no: **VG 500077**

**DOWN HOME (Sims, Zoot Quartet)**
Tracks: / Jive at five / Doggin' around / Ascap / Avalon / I cried for you / Bill Bailey won't you please come home / Goodnight sweetheart / There'll be some changes made / I've heard that blues before.
**Album:** Released May '82, on Affinity by Charly Records. Catalogue no: **AFF 87**
**CD:** Released Jan '87, on Charly by Charly Records. Catalogue no: **CDCHARLY 59**

**HAPPY OVER HOAGY (Sims, Zoot & Al Cohn Septet)**
**Album:** Released '88, on Jass Catalogue no: **JASS 12**
**CD:** Released '88, on Jass Catalogue no: **JASSCD 5**

**HAWTHORNE NIGHTS**
Tracks: / Hawthorne nights / Main stem / More than you know / Only a rose / Girl from Ipanema / I got it bad / Fillings / Dark clouds.
**Cass:** Released '82, on Pablo Jazz (USA) by Pablo Records (USA). Catalogue no: **K10 783**
**Album:** Released '82, on Pablo Jazz (USA) by Pablo Records (USA). Catalogue no: **2310 783**

**I WISH I WERE TWINS**
Tracks: / I wish I were twins / Georgia / Changes / Touch of your lips, The / Fish horn, The / Come closer to me / You go your way.
**Cass:** Released '82, on Pablo Jazz (USA, by Pablo Records (USA). Catalogue no: **K10 868**
**Album:** Released '82, on Pablo Jazz (USA) by Pablo Records (USA). Catalogue no: **2310 868**

**IF I'M LUCKY (Sims, Zoot & Jimmy Rowles)**
Tracks: / Where our love has gone / Legs / If I'm lucky / Shadow waltz / You're my everything / It's all right with me / Gypsy sweetheart / I hear a rhapsody.
**Album:** Released '82, on Pablo Jazz (USA) by Pablo Records (USA). Catalogue no: **231 0803**
**Cass:** Released '82, on Pablo Jazz (USA) by Pablo Records (USA). Catalogue no: **K10 803**

**IN A SENTIMENTAL MOOD**
**Album:** Released Jun '85, on Sonet by Sonet Records. Catalogue no: **SNTF 932**

**IN PARIS - 1956**
**Album:** Released May '87, on Swing Disque Catalogue no: **SW 8417**

**INNOCENT YEARS, THE (Sims, Zoot Four)**
Tracks: / Pomme au four / I hear a rhapsody / Over the rainbow / Very thought of you, The / If you were mine / Indian summer.
**Cass:** Released Sep '82, on Pablo Jazz (USA) by Pablo Records (USA). Catalogue no: **K10 872**
**Album:** Released Sep '82, on Pablo Jazz (USA) by Pablo Records (USA). Catalogue no: **2310 872**

**JOE & ZOOT (Sims, Zoot & Joe Venuti)**
**2 LP Set:** Released Sep '76, on Vanguard by Start Records Ltd.. Catalogue no: **VJD 523**

**JUST FRIENDS (Sims, John Haley/Harry Sweets Edison)**
Tracks: / Nature boy / How deep is the ocean / My heart belongs to daddy / I understand / Just friends / Blue skies / Until tonight / Little tutu, A.
**Cass:** Released '82, on Pablo Jazz (USA) by Pablo Records (USA). Catalogue no: **K10 841**
**Album:** Released '82, on Pablo Jazz (USA) by Pablo Records (USA). Catalogue no: **231 0841**

**MOTORING ALONG (see Cohn,Al & Zoot Sims)**
**CD:** Released Jun '88, on Sonet by Sonet Records. Catalogue no: **SNTCD 684**

**NASHVILLE (Sims, Zoot & Dick Nash)**
Tracks: / Way you look tonight / Nashville / You don't know what love is / Compatability.
Note: With Hal Daniels (trumpet), Bob Gordon (baritone sax), Paul Atkerson (piano), Rolly Bundock (bass), Jack Sperling (drums).
**Album:** Released Apr '81, on Zim (USA) Catalogue no: **ZMS 2004**

**ONE TO BLOW ON**
Tracks: / September in the rain / Down at the loft / Ghost of a chance / Not so deep / Them there eyes / Our pad / Dark clouds / One to blow on.
Note: Original biograph album as the first release in the Lazer jazz series. An interesting and highly collectable album. (Magnum Music Group, January 1988).
**Album:** Released Dec '87, on Meteor by Magnum Music Group. Catalogue no: **MTLP 012**

**PASSION FLOWER**
Tracks: / It don't mean a thing / In a mellow tone / I got it bad and that ain't good / I let a song go out of my heart / Black butterfly / Do nothing till you hear from me / Your love has faded / Bojangles / Passion flower.
**Album:** Released '82, on Pablo Jazz (USA) by Pablo Records (USA). Catalogue no: **2312 120**
**Cass:** Released '82, on Pablo Jazz (USA) by Pablo Records (USA). Catalogue no: **K 12 120**

**QUIETLY THERE - ZOOT SIMS PLAYS JOHNNY MANDEL**
Tracks: / Rissy / Time for love / Cinnamon and cloves / Low life / Zoot / Emily / Quitly there.
**Album:** Released Sep '84, on Pablo Jazz (USA) by Pablo Records (USA). Catalogue no: **2310 903**
**Cass:** Released Sep '84, on Pablo Jazz (USA) by Pablo Records (USA). Catalogue no: **K10 903**

**SOMEBODY LOVES ME**
Tracks: / Summerset / Honeysuckle rose / Summer thing, A / Somebody loves me / Gee baby / Ain't I good to you / Nirvana / Indiana / Memories of you / Come rain or come shine / Up a lazy river / Send in the clowns / Air mail special / Ham hock blues / Ring dem bells.
Note: Personnel: Zoot Sims (Tenor / Soprano saxes), Bucky Pizzarelli (Guitar), Buddy Rich (Drums), Milton Hinton (Bass).
**CD:** Released '88, on Denon Catalogue no: **DC-8514**
**Cass:** Released '88, on Denon Catalogue no: **MC 8514**

**SOPRANO SAX**
**CD:** Released Jan '89, on JVC/Fantasy Catalogue no: **VDJ 28012**
**CD:** Released May '86, on Pablo Jazz (USA) by Pablo Records (USA). Catalogue no: **CD 20037**

**STRETCHING OUT (Sims, Zoot & Bob Brookmeyer)**
Tracks: / Stretching out / Now will you be good / Pennies from Heaven / King Porter / Ain't misbehavin' / Bee Kay.
**Album:** Released Sep '89, on Fresh Sounds (Spain) by Fresh Sounds Records (Spain). Catalogue no: **FS 44**

**SWINGER, THE**
Tracks: / Moon is low, The / Now I lay me down to dream of you / On the Alamo / Danielle / Mr. J.R. blues / Jeep is jumpin' / She's funny that way / Dream of you.
**Cass:** Released '82, on Pablo Jazz (USA) by Pablo Records (USA). Catalogue no: **K10 861**
**Album:** Released '82, on Pablo Jazz (USA) by Pablo Records (USA). Catalogue no: **23210 861**

**TENOR CONTRASTS VOLUME 2 (Sims, Zoot/Al Cohn/James Moody)**
**Album:** Released Nov '86, on Esquire by Titan Int. Prod.. Catalogue no: **ESQ 320**

**TONITE'S MUSIC TODAY (Sims, Zoot & Bob Brookmeyer)**
**CD:** Released Jun '88, on Black Lion Catalogue no: **BLCD 760907**
**Album:** Released Jun '88, on Black Lion Catalogue no: **BLP 60907**

**WAITING GAME**
Tracks: / Old folks / I wish I knew / Once we loved / It's a blue world / September song / Over the rainbow / Stella by starlight / One I could have loved / You go to my head / Does the sun really shine on the moon?.
**Album:** Released Mar '83, on Jasmine by Hasmick Promotions. Deleted Feb '88. Catalogue no: **JAS 62**

**WARM TENOR (Sims, Zoot & Jimmy Rowles)**
Tracks: / Dream dancing / Old devil moon / Blues for Louise / Jitterbug waltz / You go to my head / Blue prelude / Comes love / You're my thrill.
**Cass:** Released '82, on Pablo Jazz (USA) by Pablo Records (USA). Catalogue no: **K10 831**
**Album:** Released '82, on Pablo Jazz

(USA) by Pablo Records (USA). Catalogue no: **231 0831**

### ZOOT! (Sims, Zoot Quartet)
**Album:** Released Apr '86, on Original Jazz Classics (USA) by Fantasy Inc (USA). Catalogue no: **OJC 228**

### ZOOT AT EASE
**CD:** on Mobile Fidelity Sound Lab(USA) by Mobile Fidelity Records (USA). Catalogue no: **MFCD 842**

### ZOOT PLAYS SOPRANO
Tracks: / Someday, sweetheart / Moonlight in Vermont / Wrap your troubles in dreams / Blues for Louise / Willow weep for me / Wrap up / Ghost of a chance / Baubles, bangles and beads.
**Cass:** Released '82, on Pablo Jazz (USA) by Pablo Records (USA). Catalogue no: **K10 770**
**Album:** Released '82, on Pablo Jazz (USA) by Pablo Records (USA). Catalogue no: **2310 770**

### ZOOT SIMS
**Album:** Released Jul '82, on Jazz Reactivation Catalogue no: **JR 156**
**Album:** Released Jan '87, on Original Jazz Classics (USA) by Fantasy Inc (USA). Catalogue no: **OJC 242**

### ZOOT SIMS & BOB BROOKMEYER (Sims, Zoot & Bob Brookmeyer)
**Album:** Released '88, on Black Lion Catalogue no: **BLP 60914**
**CD:** Released '88, on Black Lion Catalogue no: **BLCD7 60914**

### ZOOT SIMS IN PARIS
**CD:** Released Jan '89, on DRG (USA) by DRG Records (USA). Catalogue no: **CDSW 8417**

### ZOOT SIMS & THE GERSHWIN BROTHERS
Tracks: / Man I love, The / How long has this been going on? / Lady be good / I've got a crush on you / I got rhythm / Embraceable you / 'S wonderful / Someone to watch over me / Isn't it a pity? / Summertime.
**Album:** Released '82, on Pablo Jazz (USA) by Pablo Records (USA). Catalogue no: **2310 744**
**Cass:** Released '82, on Pablo Jazz (USA) by Pablo Records (USA). Catalogue no: **K10 744**

### ZOOT SIMS WITH THE BOB-BROOKMEYER QUINTET (Sims, Zoot & The Bob Brookmeyer Quintet)
**Album:** Released Nov '79, on Pumpkin Catalogue no: **PUMPKIN 108**

### ZOOT SIMS/DICK NASH (Sims, Zoot & Dick Nash)
Tracks: / Way you look tonight / Nashville / You don't know what love is / Compatability.
**Album:** Released Apr '79, on Zim (USA) Catalogue no: **ZM 1008**

### ZOOT SIMS/FRANK ROSOLINO (Sims, Zoot/Frank Rosolino)
**CD:** Released Dec '86, on Vogue by Vogue Records. Catalogue no: **VGCD 600117**

### ZOOTCASE
Tracks: / My silent love / Jane O / Dancing in the dark / Memories of you / Trotting / I wonder who / It had to be / Zoot sings the blues / Zoot sings the blues (take 2) / East of the sun (and west of the moon) / Morning fun / Tangerine / Zootcase / Red door, The / Howdy podner / (An American idyll) Indian summer / Toot number two / What's new?.
**2 LP Set:** Released '79, on Prestige Deleted '84. Catalogue no: **PR 24061**

## Sinatra, Frank

**Biographical details:** Francis Albert Sinatra was born on 12 December 1915 in Hoboken, New Jersey, the son of Italian immigrants. His father, Anthony Sinatra, of Sicilian origin, was an ex-professional boxer who tried various jobs before joining the fire brigade and making the grade as captain. His mother, Natalia Gavaranti, known as Dolly, was from Genoa. She was an energetic woman who became politically active in the local Democratic Party. Sinatra, a slight, only child, had to learn to defend himself in the rough neighbourhood where he grew up. At home his family was, by tradition, musically minded. At 18, against his family's wishes, Sinatra decided to make music his career. Dolly, resigned to this, helped him to start out. He formed a vocal quartet, the Hoboken Four, touring the roadhouses, but it soon broke up as Sinatra gained attention as a solo singer. In February 1939 he married Nancy. He continued to work in the New York area and while at the Rustic Cabin Roadhouse met Harry James (former trumpet player with Benny Goodman), whose band he joined as a vocalist. In 1939, Sinatra began touring with the Tommy Dorsey band and made his first recording, The Sky Fell Down. Up to 1942 he and Dorsey recorded 80 songs together. Sinatra rapidly gained stardom and became known as "The Voice". He topped the hit parades and was the first singer to evoke hysteria among his audience, capturing the hearts of millions of women. In 1944, he was called up by the army but was exonerated. Nonetheless he contributed to the war effort with the special broadcasts and concerts which he gave for the American forces in Europe and North Africa. This enabled him to aquire fame outside the United States. Alongside his singing career Sinatra was also becoming well known as an actor, making many excellent films. Meanwhile he also had a reputation as a womanizer: having a succession of love affairs which, however, did not affect the stability of his marriage with Nancy until he fell passionately in love with Ava Gardner. This completely disrupted his public image. He divorced Nancy to marry Ava and rapidly lost popularity as a singer while his acting career came to a standstill. The Frank-Ava relationship was passionate and stormy and eventually ended in divorce in 1957. Sinatra, who had recorded in the 'forties with RCA and then Columbia -- which refused to renew his contract in 1952 -- signed with Capitol in 1953, when he asked for the star role in the film From Here To Eternity. This film earned him an Academy Award and marked a turning point. He developed a more mature, sophisticated style as a singer while exploiting his business capacities in other fields. In 1961, he founded his own record company Reprise. He was briefly married to actress Mia Farrow, and is now married to Barbara, former wife of Zeppo, one of the famous Marx Brothers. In the early 'seventies, Sinatra announced his retirement but has continued to record and to make personal appearances. (Bob McDonald)
Frank Sinatra is one of the all-time biggest stars in popular music. He was born Francis Albert Sinatra, 12 December 1915 in Hoboken, New Jersey. After his idol Bing Crosby, he became the most innovative and influential of all male singers, perhaps the best interpreter of the finest American songs; though not regarded as a jazz singer, the combination of his attractive baritone and his phrasing gave the impression that he was singing directly to each listener, and appealed accross the board to critics, listeners and fans in both jazz and pop categories. He began in Hoboken clubs, singing for anyone who would have him, often for free; bandleader Harry James hired him in 1939 to sing with his new band, and later the same year he moved to Tommy Dorsey's band, singing solo and with the Pied Pipers, who also included Jo Stafford; he went solo in 1942 (taking arranger Axel Stordahl with him from Dorsey) and had about 90 hit records in ten years (not counting those with Dorsey). He caused the first pop hysteria and was called 'The Sultan Of Swoon' and 'The Voice'. His films in the 1940s included three classics with Gene Kelly: **Anchors Aweigh** in 1945, **Take Me Out To The Ball Game** and **On The Town** in 1949; he recieved a special Oscar in 1946 for the short film **The House I Live In**, a plea for racial and religious tolerance. He had married his sweetheart Nancy; then married actress Ava Gardener in 1950; the relationship was stormy and he co-wrote and recorded *I'm A Fool To Want You* at the time. An outspoken man who had been at the top for a long time, his passionate private life was public gossip and Columbia USA (CBS) shoved songs at him that were not suitable: the press turned against him and his career seemed a shambles. Then he played Maggio in **From Here To Etenity** (won an Oscar in 1954) and switched to Capitol Records, where his series of classic albums, mostly with arranger-conductor Nelson Riddle, put him back at the top where he has stayed ever since. He formed his own Reprise label in 1961, merged it with Warner Bros. in 1963 in a deal that made him very rich. He had more than 60 hit albums, made with Duke Ellington, Count Basie, Gordon Jenkins and many others

as well as Riddle; he also had more than 30 hit singles and nearly 40 hit albums in the UK. He made over 40 more films, not all masterpieces; among the best were musicals **Guys And Dolls** (songs by Frank Losser), **High Society** (Cole Porter), and **Pal Joey** (Rodgers and Hart), all in the mid-1950s. Hit songs written for Sinatra films by ace songwriters Sammy Cahn and Jimmy Van Heusen incl. *The Tender Trap, Love And Marriage, High Hopes* and *Come Blow Your Horn.* It is unfortunate that he is best known among young people today for *Strangers In The Night*, a song not up to his old standard; in 1980 thousands of his fans voted Porter's *I've Got You Under My Skin* as their all time favorite Sinatra record (from *Songs For Swingin' Lovers*, 1956); *In the Wee Small Hours* (1955) is often called the first concept album. All of the Capitol albums were recently digitally remastered and reissued by EMI. He was once engaged to dancer Juliet Prowse; then married to actress Mia Farrow, now to Barbara Marx, widow of Zeppo, one of the original Marx Brothers. His son Frank Sinatra Jr. (born 10 Jan 1944) and daughter Nancy (born 7 June 1940) both had successful careers as vocalists, Nancy helped by producer Lee Hazlewood. (Donald Clarke 27.5.87)..

## 20 CLASSIC TRACKS: FRANK SINATRA

Tracks: / Come fly with me / Around the world / French Foreign Legion / Moonlight in Vermont / Autumn in New York / Let's get away from it all / April in Paris / London by night / It's nice to go travellin' / Come dance with me / Something's gotta give / Just in time / Dancing in the dark / Too close for comfort / I could have danced all night / Saturday night is the loneliest night of the week / Cheek to cheek / Baubles, bangles and beads / Day in, day out.
**Album:** Released Nov '81, on MFP by EMI Records. Catalogue no: **MFP 50530**
**Cass:** Released Nov '81, on MFP by EMI Records. Catalogue no: **TCMFP 50530**

## 20 GOLDEN CLASSICS, VOL 1

**Album:** Released Nov '84, on Astan (USA) Catalogue no: **20035**

## 20 GOLDEN GREATS: FRANK SINATRA

Tracks: / That old black magic / Love and marriage / Fools rush in / Lady is a tramp, The / Swingin' down the lane / All the way / Witchcraft / It happened in Monterey / You make me feel so young / Nice 'n' easy / Come fly with me / High hopes / I've got you under my skin / Chicago / Three coins in the fountain / It's nice to go travellin' / Young at heart / In the wee small hours of the morning / Tender trap, The / Let's do it.
**Cass:** Released Apr '78, on Capitol by EMI Records. Catalogue no: **TCEMTV 10**
**Album:** Released Apr '78, on Capitol by EMI Records. Deleted Aug '89. Catalogue no: **EMTV 10**

## 20 GOLDEN PIECES: FRANK SINATRA

Tracks: / Now is the hour / Don't forget tonight tomorrow / Haunted heart / My shining hour / Hair of gold, eyes of blue / Lady from 29 palms / Little white lies / Suddenly it's spring / It only happens when I dance with you / Very thought of you, The / One hundred years from today / Golden earrings / I'm in the mood for love / You're the top / Right kind of love, The / Let me love you tonight / My happiness / I'll get by / Tenderly / Speak low.
**Cass:** Released Sep '85, on Bulldog Records by President Records. Catalogue no: **BDC 2046**
**Album:** Released Sep '85, on Bulldog Records by President Records. Catalogue no: **BDL 2046**

## ADVENTURES OF THE HEART

Tracks: / I guess I'll have to dream the rest / If only she looked my way / Love me / Nevertheless / We kiss in a shadow / I am loved / Take my love / I could write a book / Mad about you / Sorry / Stromboll / It's only a paper moon.
**Album:** Released Aug '83, on CBS Cameo by CBS Records. Deleted Aug '88. Catalogue no: **32319**

## ALL THE WAY

Tracks: / All the way / Chicago.
**7" Single:** Released Nov '57, on Capitol by EMI Records. Deleted Nov '60. Catalogue no: **CL 14800**
**Album:** Released Sep '84, on Capitol by EMI Records. Catalogue no: **ED 2601791**
**CD:** Released Apr '89, on Capitol by EMI Records. Catalogue no: **CDP 791 150 2**
**CD:** Released Apr '89, on Capitol by EMI Records. Catalogue no: **CZ 195**
**Cass:** Released Sep '84, on Capitol by EMI Records. Catalogue no: **ED 2601794**

## BANG BANG

Tracks: / Bang bang / It was a very good year.
**7" Single:** Released Dec '81, on Reprise (USA) Catalogue no: **K 14515**

## BEST OF FRANK SINATRA

Tracks: / Chicago / Witchcraft / Lady is a tramp / Nice and easy.
**Album:** Released '83, on EMI (Holland) by EMI Records. Catalogue no: **1A 022 58137**
**Album:** Released Dec '68, on Capitol by EMI Records. Deleted Dec '73. Catalogue no: **ST 21140**
**Cass:** Released '88, on EMI (Holland) by EMI Records. Catalogue no: **1A 222 58137**

## BEST OF FRANK SINATRA & TOMMY DORSEY (Sinatra, Frank & Tommy Dorsey)

Tracks: / Stardust / I think of you / There are such things / How about you / I'll never smile again / I'll be seeing you / Without a song / Street of dreams / Poor you / April played the fiddle / This love of mine / One I love, The / I guess I'll have to dream the rest / We three.
**Cass:** Released Jan '84, on RCA (Brazil) Catalogue no: **770 4063**
**Album:** Released Jan '84, on RCA (Brazil) Catalogue no: **107 4063**

## BEST OF OL' BLUE EYES

Tracks: / I've got you under my skin / I have dreamed / Witchcraft / In the wee small hours of the morning / Girl from Ipanema / Last night when we were young / Let me try again / Fly me to the moon / Come rain or come shine / How insensitive / All or nothing at all / Something.
**Album:** Released May '75, on Reprise (USA) Deleted Jan '90. Catalogue no: **K 54042**
**Cass:** Released May '75, on Reprise (USA) Catalogue no: **K4 54042**

## BROADWAY KICK/ADVENTURES OF THE HEART

Tracks: / There's no business like show business / They say it's wonderful / Some enchanted evening / You're my girl / Lost in the stars / Why can't you behave? / I whistle a happy tune / Girl that I marry, The / Can't you just see yourself? / There but for you go I / Bali ha'i / Where is my Bess? / I guess I'll have to dream the rest / If only she'd looked my way / Love me / Nevertheless (I'm in love with you) / We kiss in a shadow / I am loved / Take my love / I could write a book / Mad about you / Sorry / On the island of Stromboli / It's only a paper moon.
**Cass:** Released Jun '85, on CBS (Blue Diamond) by CBS Records. Deleted Aug '87. Catalogue no: **40 22182**
**Album:** Released Jun '85, on CBS (Blue Diamond) by CBS Records. Deleted Aug '87. Catalogue no: **CBS 22182**

## CAPITOL COLLECTORS SERIES, THE

Tracks: / I'm walking behind you / I've got the world on a string / From here to eternity / South of the border / Young at heart / Don't worry 'bout me / Three coins in the fountain / Melody of love / Learnin' the blues / Same old Saturday night / Love and marriage / Love is the tender trap / How little it matters how little we know / Hey jealous lover / Can I steal a little love / All the way / Chicago / Witchcraft / High hopes / Nice 'n' easy.
**CD:** Released Sep '89, on Capitol by EMI Records. Catalogue no: **CDP 792 160 2**
**CD:** Released Sep '89, on Capitol by EMI Records. Catalogue no: **CZ 228**

## CAPITOL YEARS, THE: FRANK SINATRA

Note: A 20 cassette box set of the classic albums from Frank Sinatra's Capitol career. All cassettes are on high quality XDR tape and show the original sleeve designs with notes by Alan Dell. Features his best loved songs with orchestrations by Billy May, the late Nelson Riddle, Gordan Jenkins and many more. This deluxe box set comes complete with a full colour booklet, exclusive to the set, tracing Sinatra's "Capitol years" with

colour photographs and story by Alan Del. This album was bought out in the year of Frank Sinatra's 70th birthday. The twenty albums in the boxed set are: Where are you?/A swingin' affair/Songs for young lovers/Come dance with me/Close to you/Only the lonely/Look to your heart/No one cares/Nice 'n' easy/Point of no return/Sings of love and things.../All the way/Come swing with me/Swingin' session/Songs for swingin' lovers/Wee small hours/This is Sinatra/This is Sinatra - Volume 2./Swing easy/Come fly with me.
**LP Set:** Released Oct '85, on Capitol by EMI Records. Catalogue no: **SINATRA 20**
**Cass set:** Released Nov '86, on Capitol by EMI Records. Deleted Oct '89. Catalogue no: **TCSINATRA 20**

**CHICAGO**
Tracks: / Chicago.
**7" Single:** Released Nov '57, on Capitol by EMI Records. Deleted Nov '60. Catalogue no: **CL 14800**

**CLOSE TO YOU**
Tracks: / Close to you / P.S. I love you / Love locked out / Everything happens to me / It's easy to remember / Don't like goodbyes / With every breath I take / Blame it on my youth / It could happen to you / I've had my moments / I couldn't sleep a wink last night / End of a love affair, The / If it's the last thing I do / There's a flaw in my flute / Wait till you see her.
**Album:** Released Jul '84, on Capitol by EMI Records. Catalogue no: **ED 2601381**
**Album:** Released Apr '84, on Capitol by EMI Records. Catalogue no: **2C 068 54579**
**CD:** Released Mar '88, on Capitol by EMI Records. Catalogue no: **CDP 746 572 2**
**CD:** Released Mar '88, on Capitol by EMI Records. Catalogue no: **BU 19**
**Cass:** Released Jul '84, on Capitol by EMI Records. Catalogue no: **ED 2601384**

**COFFEE SONG, THE**
Tracks: / Coffee song, The.
**7" Single:** Released Nov '61, on Reprise by WEA Records. Deleted Nov '64. Catalogue no: **R 20035**

**COLLECTION: FRANK SINATRA**
**2 LP Set:** Released Apr '86, on Castle Collector Series by Castle Communications Records. Catalogue no: **CCSLP 122**
**Cass:** Released Apr '86, on Castle Collector Series by Castle Communications Records. Catalogue no: **CCSMC 122**

**COLLECTION:FRANK SINATRA (The love songs)**
Tracks: / Tell her you love her / You go to my head / One for my baby / Don't worry 'bout me / Wrap your troubles in dreams / I'll string along with you / Half as lovely / If I had you / Violets for your furs / It all depends on you / Someone to watch over me / When I stop loving you / Out of nowhere / Like someone in love / One I love, The / You are too beautiful / Our love is here to stay / Taking a chance on love / It worries me / It only happens when I dance with you.
**Album:** Released Dec '87, on Deja Vu Catalogue no: **DVLP 2101**
**Cass:** Released Sep '87, on Deja Vu Catalogue no: **DVMC 2015**
**Cass:** Released Dec '87, on Deja Vu Catalogue no: **DVMC 2101**
**CD:** Released Sep '87, on Deja Vu Catalogue no: **DVCD 2015**
**Album:** Released Sep '87, on Deja Vu Catalogue no: **DVLP 2015**

**COME BACK TO SORRENTO**
**Album:** Released Jun '60, on Fontana by Phonogram Ltd. Deleted Jun '65. Catalogue no: **TFL 5082**

**COME DANCE WITH ME**
Tracks: / Come dance with me / Something's gotta give / Just in time / Dancing in the dark / Too close for comfort / I could have danced all night / Saturday night is the loneliest night of the week / Day in, day out / Cheek to cheek / Baubles, bangles and beads / Song is you, The / Last dance.
**Album:** Released May '59, on Capitol by EMI Records. Deleted May '64. Catalogue no: **LCT 6179**
**Album:** Released Jun '84, on Capitol by EMI Records. Catalogue no: **ED 2600801**
**Cass:** Released Jun '84, on Capitol by EMI Records. Catalogue no: **ED 2600804**
**CD:** Released Feb '88, on Capitol by EMI Records. Catalogue no: **ED 2600802**
**CD:** Released Feb '88, on Capitol by EMI Records. Catalogue no: **CDP 748 468 2**

**COME FLY WITH ME**
Tracks: / Come fly with me / Around the world / Isle of Capri / Moonlight in Vermont / Autumn in New York / On the road to Mandalay / Let's get away from it all / April in Paris / London by night / Brazil / Blue Hawaii / It's nice to go travellin'.
**CD:** Released Feb '88, on Capitol by EMI Records. Catalogue no: **CDP 748 469 2**
**Album:** Released Nov '58, on Capitol by EMI Records. Deleted Nov '63. Catalogue no: **LCT 6154**
**Cass:** Released Dec '88, on Capitol (Specials) Catalogue no: **4XL 9190**
**Album:** Released Jun '84, on Capitol by EMI Records. Catalogue no: **ED 2600951**
**Cass:** Released Jun '84, on Capitol by EMI Records. Catalogue no: **ED 2600954**

**COME FLY WITH ME (SINGLE)**
Tracks: / It happened in Monterey / Blue Hawaii / Brazil.
**7" EP:** Released '59, on Capitol by EMI Records. Catalogue no: **EAP 4920**

**COME SWING WITH ME**
Tracks: / Day by day / Sentimental journey / Almost like being in love / Five minutes more / American beauty / Yes indeed / On the sunny side of the street / Don't take your love from me / That old black magic / Lover / Paper doll / I've heard that song before.
**Cass:** Released Sep '84, on Capitol by EMI Records. Catalogue no: **ED 2601804**
**Album:** Released Feb '64, on Capitol by EMI Records. Deleted Feb '69. Catalogue no: **W 1594**
**Album:** Released Sep '84, on Capitol by EMI Records. Catalogue no: **ED 2601801**

**CONCERT SINATRA**
**CD:** Released Oct '86, on Reprise by WEA Records. Catalogue no: **901009 2**
**Album:** Released Jul '63, on Reprise by WEA Records. Deleted Jul '68. Catalogue no: **R 1009**

**CYCLES**
Tracks: / Rain in my heart / Both sides now / Little green apples / Pretty colours / Cycles / Wandering / By the time I get to Phoenix / Moody river / My way of life / Gentle on my mind.
**Album:** on Reprise by WEA Records. Catalogue no: **K 44013**

**DAYS OF WINE AND ROSES**
Tracks: / Days of wine and roses / Moon river / Way you look tonight / Three coins in the fountain / In the cool cool cool of the evening / Secret love / Swinging on a star / It might as well be Spring / Continental, The / Love is a many splendoured thing / All the way.
**Album:** on Reprise by WEA Records. Catalogue no: **K 44003**

**DOOBE DOOBE DOO STRANGERS IN THE NIGHT**
Tracks: / Strangers in the night / In the wee small hours of the morning / Last night when we were young (Track on 12" version only.).
**12" Single:** Released Apr '86, on Reprise (USA) Catalogue no: **W 8699T**
**7" Single:** Released Apr '86, on Reprise (USA) Deleted Jun '87. Catalogue no: **W 8699**

**DUETS**
Note: Featuring Tony Bennett, Doris Day, Jimmy Durante, Judy Garland, Eydie Gorme, Lena Horne, Dean Martin, Natalie Wood, Robert Mitchum etc.
**Album:** Released Jan '89, on Silva Screen by Silva Screen Records. Catalogue no: **PJ 001**

**EARLY YEARS, THE**
Tracks: / Night and day / Blue skies / Stardust / Night we called it a day, The.
Note: Recorded with the Tommy Dorsey and Axel Stordahl big bands.
**Album:** Released May '83, on RCA (Germany) Catalogue no: **26 21726**

**EVERYBODY'S TWISTING**
Tracks: / Everybody's twisting.
**7" Single:** Released Apr '62, on Reprise by WEA Records. Deleted Apr '65. Catalogue no: **R 20063**

**FABULOUS FORTIES, THE**
**Cass:** Released '88, on Joker (USA) by Lifetime Records (USA). Catalogue no: **MC 4194**
**Album:** Released '88, on Joker (USA) by Lifetime Records (USA). Catalogue no: **SM 4194**

**FRANCIS ALBERT SINATRA**
Tracks: / Girl from Ipanema / Dindi / Change partners / Quiet night of quiet stars / Meditation / If you never come to me / How insensitive / Concentrate on you / Baubles, bangles and beads / Once I loved.
**Album:** on Reprise by WEA Records. Catalogue no: **K 44008**

**FRANK**
Tracks: / I hadn't anyone till you / Night and day / Misty / Stardust / Come rain or come shine / It might as well be Spring / Prisoner of love / That's all or nothing at all / Yesterday / I'm getting sentimental over you / Imagination / There are such things / East of the sun (and west of the moon) / Daybreak / Without a song / I'll be seeing you / Take me / It's almost you / Polka dots and moonbeams / It started all over again / One I love belongs to somebody else, The / I'm getting sentimental over you (reprise).
**Album:** on Reprise by WEA Records. Catalogue no: **K 64016**

**FRANK SINATRA (WEA)**
Tracks: / World we knew (over and over), The / Something stupid / This is my love / Born free / Don't sleep in the subway / This town / This is my song, you are there / Drinking again / Some enchanted evening.
**Album:** on Reprise by WEA Records. Catalogue no: **K 44009**
**Album:** Released Oct '67, on Reprise by WEA Records. Deleted Oct '72. Catalogue no: **RSLP 1022**

**FRANK SINATRA**
**Cass set:** Released Dec '81, on World Records by EMI Records. Catalogue no: **CASSETTE 47**
**LP Set:** Released Dec '81, on World Records by EMI Records. Catalogue no: **ALBUM 47**
**Album:** Released Sep '87, on Entertainers Catalogue no: **ENT LP 13001**
**Cass:** Released '88, on Entertainers Catalogue no: **ENT MC 13001**

**FRANK SINATRA AND BING CROSBY (Sinatra, Frank & Bing Crosby)**
Tracks: / Granada / Someone lovelier than you / Imagination / Wanted / Take a change / Young at heart / 'Til we meet again / Among my souvenirs / September song / As time goes by / Meet me tonight in dreamland / It's a long, long trail.
**Cass:** Released '88, on Joker (USA) by Lifetime Records (USA). Catalogue no: **MC 3612**
**Album:** Released Apr '81, on Joker (USA) by Lifetime Records (USA). Catalogue no: **SM 3612**

**FRANK SINATRA CHRISTMAS (Frank's Christmas greats)**
Tracks: / Christmas song, The / White Christmas / O little town of Bethlehem / Adeste fideles / It came upon a midnight clear / Santa Claus is coming to town / Jingle bells / Silent night / Christmas dreaming / Have yourself a merry little Christmas / Hark the herald angels sing.
**Album:** Released Aug '86, on Deja Vu Catalogue no: **DVLP 2079**
**Cass:** Released Aug '86, on Deja Vu Catalogue no: **DVMC 2079**

**FRANK SINATRA COLLECTION, THE**
Tracks: / Nice 'n' easy / Cheek to cheek / I'm gonna sit right down and write myself a letter / As time goes by / Witchcraft / I've got you under my skin / You make me feel so young / I can't get started / I get a kick out of you / Chicago / Come fly with me / Lady is a tramp, The / Tender trap, The / My funny valentine / Night and day / You'd be so nice to come home to / Dancing in the dark / Let's get away from it all / Nice work if you can get it / One for my baby.
Note: Original Capitol recordings digitally remastered
**CD:** Released Dec '87, on EMI by EMI Records. Catalogue no: **CDEMTV 41**
**CD:** Released Dec '87, on EMI by EMI Records. Catalogue no: **CDP 748 616 2**
**Album:** Released Sep '86, on EMI by EMI Records. Catalogue no: **EMTV 41**
**Cass:** Released Sep '86, on EMI by EMI Records. Catalogue no: **TCEMTV 41**

**FRANK SINATRA IN CONCERT**
Tracks: / Come fly with me / I've got a crush on you / I've got you under my skin / Shadow of your smile / Street of dreams / One for my baby / Fly me to the moon / One o'clock jump / You make me feel so young / All of me / September of my years / Get me to the church on time / It was a very good year / Don't worry 'bout me / Makin' whoopee / Where or when / Angel eyes / My kind of town.
**2 LP Set:** Released '74, on Reprise (USA) Catalogue no: **K 64002**

**FRANK SINATRA IN ITALIA**
**Cass:** Released '88, on WEA by WEA Records. Catalogue no: **24-1072-1**

**FRANK SINATRA AND LENA HORNE (Sinatra, Frank & Lena Horne)**
**Cass:** Released Nov '84, on Astan (USA) Catalogue no: **40037**
**Album:** Released Nov '84, on Astan (USA) Catalogue no: **20037**

**FRANK SINATRA - ORIGINAL**
Note: 4 CD pack.
**CD Set:** Released Dec '87, on The Collection by Object Enterprises. Catalogue no: **OX 0001**

**FRANK SINATRA STORY**
**Album:** Released Nov '58, on Fontana by Phonogram Ltd. Deleted Nov '63. Catalogue no: **TFL 5030**

**FRANK SINATRA, VOL. 2**
**Album:** Released '88, on Joker (USA) by Lifetime Records (USA). Catalogue no: **SM 3631**

**FRANK SINATRA, VOL. 3**
**Album:** Released '88, on Joker (USA) by Lifetime Records (USA). Catalogue no: **SM 3632**

**FRANK SINATRA, VOL. 4**
**Album:** Released '88, on Joker (USA) by Lifetime Records (USA). Catalogue no: **SM 3633**

**FRANK SINATRA, VOL. 5**
**Album:** Released '88, on Joker (USA) by Lifetime Records (USA). Catalogue no: **SM 3634**

**FRENCH FOREIGN LEGION**
Tracks: / French foreign legion.
**7" Single:** Released Apr '59, on Capitol by EMI Records. Deleted Apr '62. Catalogue no: **CL 14997**

**GOT THE WORLD ON A STRING**
Tracks: / I've got the world on a string / Them there eyes / If I could be with you / Under a blanket of blue / Just you, just me / Let's fall in love / Hands across the table / You must have been a beautiful baby / Someone to watch over me / I'll string along with you / Thou swell / You took advantage of me / Where or when / This can't be love / Try a little tenderness / Platinum blues / I'm confessin' / Sometimes I'm happy / My funny valentine / That old black magic.
**Cass:** Released Jun '87, on Starburst by Magnum Music Group. Catalogue no: **SMTC 007**
**CD:** Released Jun '88, on Meteor by Magnum Music Group. Catalogue no: **CDSM 007**
**Album:** Released Jun '87, on Starburst by Magnum Music Group. Catalogue no: **SMT 007**

**GRANADA**
Tracks: / Granada.
**7" Single:** Released Sep '61, on Reprise by WEA Records. Deleted Sep '64. Catalogue no: **R 20010**

**GREAT FILMS AND SHOWS**
Tracks: / Night and day / I wish I were in love again / I got plenty o' nuttin' / I guess I'll have to change my plan / Nice work if you can get it / I won't dance / You'd be so nice to come home to / I got it bad and that ain't good (CD only.) / From this moment on / Blue moon / September in the rain / It's only a paper moon / You do something to me / Taking a chance on love / Get happy / Just one of those things / I love Paris / Chicago / High hopes / I believe / Lady is a tramp, The / Let's do it / C'est magnifique / Tender trap, The / Three coins in the fountain / Young at heart / Girl next door, The / They can't take that away from me / Someone to watch over me / Little girl blue / Like someone in love / Foggy day, A / I get a kick out of you / My funny valentine / Embraceable you / That old feeling / I've got a crush on you / Dream / September song / I'll see you again / As time goes by / There will never be another you / I'll remember April / Stormy weather / I can't get started / Around the world / Something's gotta give / Just in time / Dancing in the dark / Too close for comfort / I could have danced all night / Cheek to cheek / Song is you, The / Baubles,

bangles and beads / Almost like being in love / Lover / On the sunny side of the street / That old black magic / I've heard that song before / You make me feel so young / Too marvellous for words / It happened in Monterey / I've got you under my skin / How about you / Pennies from Heaven / You're getting to be a habit with me / You brought a new kind of love to me / Love is here to stay / Old devil moon / Makin' whoopee / Anything goes / What is this thing called love / Glad to be unhappy / I get along without you very well / Dancing on the ceiling / Can't we be friends / All the way / To love and be loved / All my tomorrows / I couldn't sleep a wink last night / Spring is here / One for my baby / Time after time / It's all right with me / It's the same old dream / Johnny Concho theme (wait for me) / Wait till you see her / Where are you / Lonely town / Where or when / I concentrate on you / Love and marriage.
**LP Set:** Released Apr '89, on Capitol by EMI Records. Catalogue no: **FS 1**
**CD Set:** Released Apr '89, on Capitol by EMI Records. Catalogue no: **CDS 792 224 2**
**CD Set:** Released Apr '89, on Capitol by EMI Records. Catalogue no: **CDFS 1**

**GREAT SONGS FROM GREAT BRITAIN**
**Album:** Released Oct '62, on Reprise by WEA Records. Deleted Oct '67. Catalogue no: **R 1006**

**GREATEST HITS: FRANK SINATRA (The early years)**
**Cass:** Released Jun '78, on Embassy by CBS Records. Catalogue no: **40 31677**
**Album:** Released Jun '78, on Embassy by CBS Records. Catalogue no: **CBS 31677**
**CD:** Released Jul '89, on Pickwick by Pickwick Records. Catalogue no: **902 128-2**
**Album:** Released Oct '68, on Reprise by WEA Records. Deleted Oct '73. Catalogue no: **RSLP 1025**
**Cass set:** Released Nov '83, on Reprise (USA) Catalogue no: **923954 4**
**2 LP Set:** Released '83, on Capitol (import) Catalogue no: **5C 180 82263/4**

**GREATEST HITS: FRANK SINATRA, VOL. 1**
Tracks: / Strangers in the night / Summer wind / It was a very good year / Somewhere in your heart / Forget Domani / Something stupid / That's life / Tell her / World we knew, The / When somebody loves you / This town / Softly as I leave you.
**CD:** Released '86, on Reprise by WEA Records. Catalogue no: **K 244011**
**Album:** Released '74, on Reprise (USA) Catalogue no: **K 44011**
**Cass:** Released '74, on Reprise (USA) Catalogue no: **K4 44011**

**GREATEST HITS: FRANK SINATRA, VOL. 2**
Tracks: / Shadow of your smile / Yesterday / Blue lace / For once in my life / Born free / My way / Little green apples / Both sides now / Mrs. Robinson / Call me irresponsible / Gentle on my mind / Love's been good to me.
**Album:** Released Dec '70, on Reprise by WEA Records. Deleted Dec '75. Catalogue no: **RSLP 1032**
**Cass:** Released '74, on Reprise (USA) Catalogue no: **K4 44018**
**Album:** Released '74, on Reprise (USA) Catalogue no: **K 44018**

**HAVE YOURSELF A MERRY LITTLE CHRISTMAS**
Tracks: / White Christmas / Jingle bells / O little town of Bethlehem / Have yourself a merry little Christmas / Christmas dreaming / Silent night, holy night / It came upon a midnight clear / Adeste fideles / Santa Claus is coming to town.
**Album:** Released Nov '89, on CBS by CBS Records. Catalogue no: **460464 1**
**Cass:** Released Nov '89, on CBS by CBS Records. Catalogue no: **460464 4**
**CD:** Released Nov '89, on CBS by CBS Records. Catalogue no: **463105 2**

**HELLO DOLLY (Sinatra, Frank / Count Basie)**
Tracks: / Hello Dolly.
**7" Single:** Released Sep '64, on Reprise by WEA Records. Deleted Sep '67. Catalogue no: **R 20351**

**HIGH HOPES**
Tracks: / High hopes.
**7" Single:** Released Aug '59, on Capitol by EMI Records. Deleted Aug '62. Catalogue no: **CL 15052**

**I BELIEVE I'M GONNA LOVE YOU**
Tracks: / I believe I'm gonna love you.
**7" Single:** Released Dec '75, on Reprise (USA) Deleted Dec '78. Catalogue no: **K 14400**

**I REMEMBER TOMMY**
**Album:** Released Apr '62, on Reprise by WEA Records. Deleted Apr '67. Catalogue no: **R 1003**

**I WILL DRINK THE WINE**
Tracks: / I will drink the wine.
**7" Single:** Released Mar '71, on Reprise (USA) Deleted Mar '74. Catalogue no: **RS 23487**

**IN THE BEGINNING**
Tracks: / I've got a crush on you / If you are but a dream / Nancy / Girl that I marry, The / House that I live in, The / Mean to me / I have but one heart / Moon was yellow, The / Full moon and empty arms / Put your dreams away / Day by day / I couldn't sleep a wink last night / Ol' man river / Time after time / I'm a fool to want you / Saturday night is the loneliest night of the week / Five minutes more / Sunday, Monday or always / Coffee song, The / Dream.
**2 LP Set:** Released Sep '80, on CBS by CBS Records. Catalogue no: **CBS 22108**
**Cass:** Released Sep '80, on CBS by CBS Records. Catalogue no: **40 22108**

**IN THE WEE SMALL HOURS**
Tracks: / In the wee small hours of the morning / Glad to be unhappy / I get along without you very well / Deep in a dream / I see your face before me / Can't we be friends / When your lover has gone / What is this thing called love / I'll be around / Ill wind / It never entered my mind / I'll never be the same / This love of mine / Last night when we were young / Dancing on the ceiling.
**Album:** Released Oct '77, on Capitol by EMI Records. Catalogue no: **CAPS 1008**
**CD:** Released Mar '87, on EMI by EMI Records. Catalogue no: **BU 18**
**Cass:** Released Sep '82, on Capitol by EMI Records. Catalogue no: **TCCAPS 1008**
**CD:** Released Mar '87, on EMI by EMI Records. Catalogue no: **CDP 746 571 2**

**IT MIGHT AS WELL BE SWING (Sinatra, Frank/Count Basie)**
Tracks: / In other words / I wish you love / I believe in you / More / I can't stop loving you / Hello Dolly / I wanna be around / Best is yet to come, The / Good life / Wives and lovers.
**Album:** on Reprise by WEA Records. Catalogue no: **K 44004**
**CD:** Released Oct '86, on Reprise by WEA Records. Catalogue no: **901012 2**
**Album:** Released Sep '64, on Reprise by WEA Records. Deleted Sep '69. Catalogue no: **R 1012**
**Album:** Released '88, on CBS by CBS Records. Catalogue no: **CBS 44004**

**IT'S NICE TO GO TRAVELIN'**
Tracks: / It's nice to go travellin'.
**7" Single:** Released Apr '60, on Capitol by EMI Records. Deleted Apr '63. Catalogue no: **CL 15116**

**I'VE GOT YOU UNDER MY SKIN**
**CD:** Released '88, on Entertainers Catalogue no: **ENT CD 229**
**Album:** Released Nov '87, on Entertainers Catalogue no: **ENT LP 13035**
**Cass:** Released '88, on Entertainers Catalogue no: **ENT MC 13035**

**KISSES AND TEARS**
Tracks: / So they tell me / Help yourself to my heart / If you please / You'll know when it happens / All through the day / There's something missing / Kisses and tears / Meet me at the Copa / My love for you.
**Album:** Released Apr '87, on Meteor by Magnum Music Group. Catalogue no: **MTM 023**

**L.A. IS MY LADY**
Tracks: / L.A. is my lady / Best of everything, The / How do you keep the music playing? / Teach me tonight / It's all right / Mack the knife / Until the real thing comes along / Stormy weather / If I should lose you / Hundred years from today / After you've gone.
**CD:** Released Mar '87, on Qwest (USA) by Qwest Records (USA). Catalogue no: **925145 2**
**Cass:** Released Aug '84, on Qwest (USA) by Qwest Records (USA). Catalogue no: **925145 4**
**Album:** Released Aug '84, on Qwest (USA) by Qwest Records (USA). Catalogue no: **925145 1**

**L.A. IS MY LADY (SINGLE)**
Tracks: / L.A. is my lady / Until the real thing comes along.
**7" Single:** Released Oct '84, on Warner Bros. by WEA Records. Deleted Oct '87. Catalogue no: **W 9223**

**LEARNIN' THE BLUES**
Tracks: / Learnin' the blues.
**7" Single:** Released Aug '55, on Capitol by EMI Records. Deleted Aug '58. Catalogue no: **CL 14296**

**LEGENDARY CONCERTS VOL. 1**
**Cass:** Released May '88, on Commander Catalogue no: **69014**
**Album:** Released May '88, on Commander Catalogue no: **39014**
**CD:** Released May '88, on Commander Catalogue no: **99014**

**LEGENDARY CONCERTS VOL. 2**
**CD:** Released May '88, on Commander Catalogue no: **99015**
**Album:** Released May '88, on Commander Catalogue no: **39015**
**Cass:** Released May '88, on Commander Catalogue no: **69015**

**LEGENDARY CONCERTS VOL 3**
**Album:** Released May '88, on Commander Catalogue no: **39016**
**Cass:** Released May '88, on Commander Catalogue no: **69016**

**LEGENDARY, THE**
**Cass:** Released Mar '90, on Silva Screen by Silva Screen Records. Catalogue no: **MRT 40040**

**LIVE AT MONTECARLO SPORTING CLUB (June 14, 1958)**
**Album:** Released Sep '87, on Lotus Catalogue no: **LOP 14 019**

**LONG AGO AND FAR AWAY**
Tracks: / Little white lies / Suddenly / It's spring / This can't be love / Long ago and far away / One hundred years from today / I'm in the mood for love / Tenderly / Speak low / My happiness / I'll get by / Now is the hour / I found a new baby / You can't be true dear.
**Album:** Released '86, on Topline by Charly Records. Catalogue no: **TOP 121**
**Cass:** Released '86, on Topline by Charly Records. Catalogue no: **KTOP 121**

**LOOK TO YOUR HEART**
Tracks: / Look to your heart / Any time, anywhere / Not as a stranger / Our town / You, my love / Same old Saturday night / Fairytale / Impatient years, The / I could have told you / When I stop loving you / If I had three wishes / I'm gonna live 'til I die.
**Album:** Released Aug '59, on Capitol by EMI Records. Deleted Aug '64. Catalogue no: **LCT 6181**
**Cass:** Released Jul '84, on Capitol by EMI Records. Catalogue no: **ED 2601404**
**Album:** Released Jul '84, on Capitol by EMI Records. Catalogue no: **ED 2601401**

**LOVE AND MARRIAGE**
Tracks: / Love and marriage.
**7" Single:** Released Jan '56, on Capitol by EMI Records. Deleted Jan '59. Catalogue no: **CL 14503**

**LOVE IS A KICK**
Tracks: / You do something to me / Bim bam baby / My blue Heaven / When you're smiling / Saturday night is the loneliest night of the week / Bye bye baby / Continental (you kiss while you're dancing),The / Deep night / Should I / American beauty rose / Five minutes more / Farewell farewell to love.
**Cass:** Released Mar '86, on CBS Cameo by CBS Records. Deleted Aug '87. Catalogue no: **40 32736**
**Album:** Released Mar '86, on CBS Cameo by CBS Records. Deleted Aug '87. Catalogue no: **CBS 32736**

**LOVE AND MARRIAGE**
Tracks: / Love & marriage / Love & marriage.
**7" Single:** Released Mar '84, on EMI Golden 45's by EMI Records. Catalogue no: **G45 9**

**LOVE'S BEEN GOOD TO ME**
Tracks: / Love's been good to me.
**7" Single:** Released Oct '69, on Reprise (USA) Deleted Oct '72. Catalogue no: **RS 20852**

**MAIN EVENT, THE**
Tracks: / Overture / It was a very good year / All the way / My kind of town / Lady is a tramp, The / I get a kick out of you / Let me try again / Autumn in New York / I've got you under my skin / Bad bad Leroy Brown / Angel eyes / You are the sunshine of my life / House I live in, The / My kind of town / My way.
**Album:** Released Feb '75, on Reprise by WEA Records. Deleted Feb '80. Catalogue no: **K 54031**

**MAN ALONE, A**
Tracks: / Man alone, A / Night / I've been to town / From promise to promise / Single man, The / Beautiful strangers / Lonesome cities / Love's been good to me / Empty is / Out beyond the window / Some travelling music.
**Album:** Released Oct '69, on Reprise by WEA Records. Deleted Oct '74. Catalogue no: **RSLP 1030**
**Album:** on Reprise by WEA Records. Catalogue no: **K 44016**

**MAN AND HIS MUSIC, A**
**Album:** Released Jan '66, on Reprise by WEA Records. Deleted Jan '71. Catalogue no: **R 1016**
**CD Set:** Released Jul '87, on Reprise (USA) Catalogue no: **901016 2**

**ME AND MY SHADOW (Sinatra, Frank & Sammy Davis Jr.)**
Tracks: / Me and my shadow.
**7" Single:** Released Dec '62, on Reprise (USA) Deleted Dec '66. Catalogue no: **R 20128**

**MOONLIGHT SINATRA**
**Album:** Released May '66, on Reprise by WEA Records. Deleted May '71. Catalogue no: **R 1018**

**MOST BEAUTIFUL SONGS, THE**
Tracks: / Strangers in the night / Cycles / Swinging on a star / Summer wind / Fine romance, A / Baubles, bangles and beads / My way / Goody goody / Moonlight serenade / It was a very good year / Days of wine and roses / Ring a ding ding / Moon river / Call me irresponsible / Somethin' stupid / Shadow of your smile, The / September song / That's life / Girl from Ipanema / More / Ol' man river / Stardust / Come fly with me / What now my love.
**Album:** on Reprise by WEA Records. Catalogue no: **K 64011**

**MR SUCCESS**
Tracks: / Mr. Success.
**7" Single:** Released Nov '58, on Capitol by EMI Records. Deleted Nov '62. Catalogue no: **CL 14956**

**MUSICAL MONTAGE, A**
**Album:** Released Sep '86, on Artistry Catalogue no: **AR 105**

**MY BEST YEARS, VOL 1**
Tracks: / Pistol packin' mama / I found a new baby / You can't be true, dear / I'm in the mood for love / Love is blue / I'll dance at your wedding / Long ago and far away / My shining hour.
**Album:** Released Oct '82, on IMS by Polydor Ltd. Catalogue no: **DO 90063**

**MY BEST YEARS, VOL 2**
Tracks: / This can't be love / My happiness / I'll get by / Lili Bolero / Hair of gold, eyes of blue / I wonder who's kissing her now / Long ago and far away / Tenderly / Little white lies / Haunted house / I'll string along with you / How soon?.
**Album:** Released Oct '82, on IMS by Polydor Ltd. Catalogue no: **DO 90064**

**MY BLUE HEAVEN**
Tracks: / My blue Heaven.
**7" Single:** Released Apr '61, on Capitol by EMI Records. Deleted Apr '64. Catalogue no: **CL 15193**

**MY KIND OF GIRL (Sinatra, Frank/Count Basie)**
Tracks: / My kind of girl.
**7" Single:** Released Mar '63, on Reprise by WEA Records. Deleted Mar '66. Catalogue no: **R 20148**

**MY WAY**
Tracks: / Watch what happens / Hallelujah, I love her so / Yesterday all my tomorrows / My Way / For once in my life / If you go away / Mrs. Robinson / Didn't we? / Day in the life of a fool, A.
**Album:** Released '74, on Reprise (USA) Catalogue no: **K 44015**
**CD:** Released Nov '86, on Reprise by WEA Records. Catalogue no: **901029 2**
**Cass:** Released '74, on Reprise (USA) Catalogue no: **K4 44015**
**Album:** Released Jun '69, on Reprise by WEA Records. Deleted Jun '74. Catalogue no: **RSLP 1029**

**MY WAY (SINGLE)**
Tracks: / My way.
**7" Single:** Released '77, on Reprise by WEA Records. Deleted '80. Catalogue no: **K 14474**
**7" Single:** Released Jul '81, on Reprise

(USA) Deleted Jun '87. Catalogue no: **K 14008**
**7" Single:** Released Apr '69, on Reprise (USA) Deleted Jan '75. Catalogue no: **RS 20817**

### NEW YORK, NEW YORK (His greatest hits)
Tracks: / I get a kick out of you / Something stupid / Moon river / What now my love / Summer wind / Mrs. Robinson / My way / Strangers in the night / For once in my life / Yesterday / That's life / Girl from Ipanema / Lady is a tramp, The / Bad, bad Leroy Brown / Ol' man river.
**Cass:** Released Mar '86, on Warner Bros. by WEA Records. Catalogue no: **WX 32 C**
**Album:** Released Mar '86, on Warner Bros. by WEA Records. Catalogue no: **WX 32**
**CD:** Released '87, on Warner Bros. by WEA Records. Catalogue no: **923927 2**

### NEW YORK, NEW YORK (SINGLE)
**7" Single:** Released Feb '86, on Warner Bros. by WEA Records. Catalogue no: **K 14502**
**12" Single:** Released Feb '86, on Warner Bros. by WEA Records. Deleted Jan '88. Catalogue no: **K 14502T**

### NICE AND EASY
**Cass:** Released Jul '84, on Capitol by EMI Records. Catalogue no: **ED 2601424**
**Album:** Released Jan '61, on Capitol by EMI Records. Deleted Jan '66. Catalogue no: **W 1417**
**CD:** Released Apr '89, on Capitol by EMI Records. Catalogue no: **CZ 194**
**CD:** Released Apr '89, on Capitol by EMI Records. Catalogue no: **CDP 791 149 2**
**Album:** Released Jul '84, on Capitol by EMI Records. Catalogue no: **ED 2601421**

### NICE AND EASY (SINGLE)
Tracks: / Nice and easy / Come fly with me / One for my baby (Extra track included on 12" version).
**12" Single:** Released Sep '86, on Capitol by EMI Records. Deleted '88. Catalogue no: **12CL 426**
**7" Single:** Released Sep '86, on Capitol by EMI Records. Deleted Oct '87. Catalogue no: **CL 426**
**7" Single:** Released Sep '60, on Capitol by EMI Records. Deleted Sep '63. Catalogue no: **CL 15150**

### NO ONE CARES
Tracks: / When no one cares / Cottage for sale / Stormy weather / Where do you go? / I don't stand a ghost of a chance / Here's that rainy day / I can't get started / Why try to change me now? / Just friends / One I love belongs to somebody else, The.
**Album:** Released Jul '84, on Capitol by EMI Records. Catalogue no: **ED 2601411**
**Cass:** Released Jul '84, on Capitol by EMI Records. Catalogue no: **ED 2601414**

### NOT AS A STRANGER
Tracks: / Not as a stranger.
**7" Single:** Released Sep '55, on Capitol by EMI Records. Deleted Sep '58. Catalogue no: **CL 14326**

### NOW IS THE HOUR
Tracks: / I wonder who's kissing her now / I wish I didn't love you so / How soon / Lady from 29 Palms / You do / Serenade of the bells / Golden earrings / Dance ballerina dance / I'll dance at your wedding / Lili Bolero / Little white lies / Tree in the meadow, A / My happiness / You call everybody darling / Now is the hour.
**Album:** Released Apr '86, on Castle Showcase by Castle Communications Records. Catalogue no: **SHLP 106**
**Cass:** Released Apr '86, on Castle Showcase by Castle Communications Records. Catalogue no: **SHTC 106**

### NOW IS THE HOUR (ASTAN)
**Cass:** Released Nov '84, on Astan (USA) Catalogue no: **40034**
**Album:** Released Nov '84, on Astan (USA) Catalogue no: **20034**

### NOW IS THE HOUR (METEOR)
Tracks: / Now is the hour / Don't forget tonight tomorrow / Haunted heart / My shining hour / Hair of gold / Lady form twenty nine palms / Little white lies / Suddenly it's spring / It only happens when I dance with you / Very thought of you, The.
**Album:** Released Sep '84, on Meteor by Magnum Music Group. Catalogue no: **MTM 003**

### OFF THE RECORD WITH...
Tracks: / I wonder who's kissing her now / Let me love you tonight / I'll get by / This can't be love / I heard you cried last night / Long ago and far away / My happiness / I wish I didn't love you so / Some other time / I'm in the mood for love / Pistol packin' mama / Golden earrings / Serenade of the bells / Lady from 29 palms / After I say I'm sorry / Lover is blue, A / Hair of gold, eyes of blue / Little white lies / Wing and a prayer / Little Bolero / Don't forget tonight tomorrow / I found a new baby / One hundred years from today.
**Cass:** Released Aug '87, on Sierra by Sierra Records. Catalogue no: **CFEDD 1011**
**Album:** Released Aug '87, on Sierra by Sierra Records. Catalogue no: **FEDD 1011**

### OL' BLUE EYES
Tracks: / Witchcraft / Come fly with me / Young at heart / Tender trap, The / All the way.
**LP Pic:** Released 7 Nov '87, on Exclusive Picture Discs Catalogue no: **AR 30080**
**CD:** Released Apr '87, on Card/Grand Prix Catalogue no: **CD 180007**

### OL' BLUE EYES IS BACK
Tracks: / You will be my music / Winners theme (From Maurice.) / Nobody wins / Send in the clowns / Dream away / Let me try again / There used to be a ball park / Noah / You're so right (for what's wrong in my life).
**Album:** Released '73, on Reprise (USA) Catalogue no: **K 44249**
**CD:** Released Nov '86, on Reprise by WEA Records. Catalogue no: **901 155 2**

### OL' MACDONALD
Tracks: / Ol' MacDonald.
**7" Single:** Released Nov '60, on Capitol by EMI Records. Deleted Nov '63. Catalogue no: **CL 15168**

### OLD BLUE EYES (VIDEO)
**VHS:** Released '88, on World Of Video Catalogue no: **SP 2**

### ONE NIGHT STAND WITH FRANK
**Album:** Released May '84, on Joyce (USA) Catalogue no: **JOYCE 1121**

### ORIGINAL RECORDINGS 1939-42
Tracks: / All or nothing at all / Too romantic / Hear my song, Violetta / Yours is my heart alone / I'll never smile again / Whispering / Oh, look at me now / Blue skies / Sinner kissed an angel, A / Somewhere a voice is calling / There are such things / I'll take Tallulah.
**Album:** Released Apr '81, on Joker (USA) by Lifetime Records (USA). Catalogue no: **SM 3055**
**Cass:** Released Apr '81, on Joker (USA) by Lifetime Records (USA). Catalogue no: **MC 3055**

### ORIGINAL SESSIONS, VOL 1
Tracks: / Night and day / Somebody loves me / You make me feel so young / Just one of those things / Nevertheless / On the sunny side of the street / Love me or leave me / You are love / They didn't believe me / Out of nowhere / I've got my love to keep me warm / For you.
**Album:** Released Nov '84, on Meteor by Magnum Music Group. Catalogue no: **MTM 007**

### ORIGINAL SESSIONS, VOL 2
Tracks: / Blue skies / They say it's wonderful / 'S wonderful / Begin the beguine / Ol' man river / Don't blame me / Laura / It all depends on you / I fall in love with you every day / Music stopped, The / I don't stand a ghost of a chance / You do something to me.
**Album:** Released Nov '84, on Meteor by Magnum Music Group. Catalogue no: **MTM 004**

### POINT OF NO RETURN
Tracks: / When the world was young /

I'll remember April / September song / Million dreams ago, A / I'll see you again / There will never be another you / Somewhere along the way / It's a blue world / These foolish things / As time goes by / I'll be seeing you / Memories of you.
**CD:** Released Feb '88, on Capitol by EMI Records. Catalogue no: **ED 2601772**
**Cass:** Released Sep '84, on Capitol by EMI Records. Catalogue no: **ED 2601774**
**CD:** Released Feb '88, on Capitol by EMI Records. Catalogue no: **CDP 748 334 2**
**Album:** Released Sep '84, on Capitol by EMI Records. Catalogue no: **ED 2601771**

## PORTRAIT OF AN ALBUM
Tracks: / Best of everything, The / Until the real thing comes along / It's all right with me / How do you keep the music playing / Hundred years from today, A / After you've gone / Teach me tonight / If I should lose you / Stormy weather / Mack the knife / L.A. is my lady.
Note: You're invited to witness first hand the historic musical collaboration of Frank Sinatra and Quincy Jones in Portrait of an album, the behind the scenes documentary of the making of the album 'L.A. is my lady'. It is definitely an occasion for superlatives. As a member of the invited audience, you sense the energy and the excitement present in the studio. The electricity crackles in the air; indeed you are witnessing musical history in the making. Sinatra and the band are recording live, together in the same room. The way it used to be done. This video affords the insider a unique view of the consummate art of recording. It offers a rarely seen perspective of Sinatra in session, the musician with the impeccable sense of phrasing, the musician's musician. The dress is informal, no black tie for this occasion; the goal is great sound - and you'll see how it's accomplished. Mr. Sinatra is doing what he does best: making music that makes magic. Running time: 65 mins. (MGM/UA Home Video)
**VHS:** Released Feb '85, on MGM by Polydor Ltd. Catalogue no: **SMV 10648**

## PORTRAIT OF SINATRA
Tracks: / Let's face the music and dance / Nancy (with the laughing face) / I've got you under my skin / Let me try again / Fly me to the moon / All or nothing at all / For once in my life / Bonita / My kind of town / Call me irresponsible / All the way / Strangers in the night / Didn't we? / Come fly with me / Second time around / In the wee small hours of the morning / Bad, bad Leroy Brown / Softly as I leave you / Cycles / Send in the clowns / That's life / Little green apples / Song of the Sabia / Goody goody / Empty tables / I believe I'm gonna love you / Stargazer / I sing the songs / I write the songs / You are the sunshine of my life / It was a very good year / Something stupid / Young at heart / You make me feel so young / Yesterday / Pennies from Heaven / Something / If / Star / Love's been good to me / My way.
**Cass set:** Released Mar '77, on Reprise (USA) Catalogue no: **K4 64039**
**2 LP Set:** Released Mar '77, on Reprise (USA) Catalogue no: **K 64039**

## PORTRAITS FROM THE PAST
**CD:** Released Jul '88, on Bravura Catalogue no: **BCD 101**

## RADIO DAYS
**Cass set:** Released '89, on Ditto by Pickwick Records. Catalogue no: **DTO 10304**
**CD:** Released Dec '87, on Pickwick by Pickwick Records. Catalogue no: **PWK 046**

## RADIO YEARS 1939-55, THE
Tracks: / All or nothing / After all / I've got my eyes on you / Polka dots and moonbeams / Deep night / Whispering / Sky fell down, The / On the Isle of May / It's a blue world / Fable of the rose / Marie / I'll get by / Lover is blue, A.
**CD Set:** Released Mar '89, on Meteor by Magnum Music Group. Catalogue no: **CDMTBS 001**

## RADIO YEARS, THE
**CD:** Released '89, on K-Tel by K-Tel Records. Catalogue no: **NCD 5152**
**CD:** Released Dec '87, on Tamy Deleted Jan '89. Catalogue no: **20107**

## RARE RECORDINGS 1935 - 1970
**Cass:** Released Jan '89, on Silva Screen by Silva Screen Records. Catalogue no: **CSH 2040**
**Album:** Released Jan '89, on Silva Screen by Silva Screen Records. Catalogue no: **SH 2040**

## RARE SINATRA, THE
Tracks: / Don't make a beggar of me / Ya better stop / Day in, day out / Memories of you / If it's the last thing I do / I couldn't care less / Take a chance / There's a flaw in my flute / Song is you, The / Where or when / It all depends on you / One I love belongs to somebody else, The.
**Cass:** Released '78, on Capitol by EMI Records. Catalogue no: **TCATAK 66**
**Cass:** Released Sep '88, on Capitol by EMI Records. Deleted Aug '89. Catalogue no: **TCESTK 24311**
**Album:** Released '78, on Capitol by EMI Records. Catalogue no: **ATAK 66**
**Cass:** Released Dec '78, on Capitol by EMI Records. Deleted Nov '88. Catalogue no: **TCEST 24311**
**Cass:** Released Mar '89, on MFP by EMI Records. Catalogue no: **TCMFP 5856**
**Album:** Released Dec '78, on Capitol by EMI Records. Deleted Nov '88. Catalogue no: **EST 24311**
**Album:** Released Mar '89, on MFP by EMI Records. Catalogue no: **MFP 5856**

## RARITIES
Tracks: / Why shouldn't I? / Two hearts are better than one / Girl that I marry, The / Could 'ja? / Things we did last summer, The / Stella by starlight / So far / It only happens when I dance with you / When is sometime? / Where is the one / Nature boy / Bop! goes my heart / It happens every Spring / Accidents will happen / London by night / Bim bam baby.
**CD:** Released 15 May '89, on CBS by CBS Records. Catalogue no: **465165 2**
**Album:** Released 15 May '89, on CBS by CBS Records. Catalogue no: **465165 1**
**Cass:** Released 15 May '89, on CBS by CBS Records. Catalogue no: **465165 4**

## REPLAY ON FRANK SINATRA VOL.1
**Album:** Released Feb '85, on Sierra by Sierra Records. Catalogue no: **FEDB 5001**
**Cass:** Released Feb '85, on Sierra by Sierra Records. Catalogue no: **CFEDB 5001**

## REPLAY ON FRANK SINATRA VOL.2
**Cass:** Released May '86, on Sierra by Sierra Records. Catalogue no: **CFEDB 5029**
**Album:** Released May '86, on Sierra by Sierra Records. Catalogue no: **FEDB 5029**

## REPRISE YEARS, THE
Tracks: / In the still of the night / Granada / I'm getting sentimental over you / Without a song / I get a kick out of you / Night and day / Come rain or come shine / All or nothing at all / Nightingale sang in Berkeley Square / All alone / I won't dance / Ol' man river / I've got you under my skin / In the wee small hours of the morning / Nancy / Way you look tonight / Fly me to the moon / All the way / Luck be a lady / I only miss her when I think of her / September of my years / This is all I ask / It was a very good year / Strangers in the night / Call me irresponsible / Moon love / Don't worry / One for my baby / My kind of town / Poor butterfly / How insensitive / Dindi / By the time I get to Phoenix / Cycles / Didn't we / Something stupid / Love's been good to me / Man alone, A / Goin' out of my head / Something / Train / Lady day / Drinking angels / Send in the clowns / Let me try again / What are you doing the rest of your life / If / Put your dreams my way.
**LP Set:** Released Dec '86, on Reprise (USA) Catalogue no: **K 94003**

## RING-A-DING-DING
**Album:** Released Dec '61, on Reprise by WEA Records. Deleted Dec '66. Catalogue no: **R 1001**

## RIVER STAY 'WAY FROM MY DOOR
Tracks: / River stay 'way from my door.
**7" Single:** Released Jun '60, on Capitol by EMI Records. Deleted Jun '63. Catalogue no: **CL 15135**

## SALOON SONGS
Tracks: / One for my baby / I should care / These foolish things / I guess I'll have to dream the rest / It never entered my mind / When your lover has gone / Body and soul / That old feeling / Ghost of a chance / There's no you / Guess I'll hang my tears out to dry / Why try to change me now.
**Cass:** Released Jul '87, on CBS by

CBS Records. Catalogue no: **460018 4**
**Album:** Released Jul '87, on CBS by CBS Records. Catalogue no: **460018 1**

## SAY HELLO
Tracks: / Say hello / Good thing going.
**7" Single:** Released Nov '81, on Reprise (USA) Catalogue no: **K 14513**

## SCREEN SINATRA
Tracks: / From here to eternity / Three coins in the fountain / Young at heart / Just one of those things / Someone to watch over me / Not as a stranger / Tender trap, The / Wait for me (Johnny Concho theme) / All the way / Chicago / Monique-Song from Kings Go Forth / They came to Cordura / To love and be loved / High hopes / All my tomorrows / It's alright with me / C'est magnifique / Dream.
**Cass:** Released Sep '80, on Capitol by EMI Records. Deleted Jul '88. Catalogue no: **TCCAPS 1038**
**Album:** Released Sep '80, on Capitol by EMI Records. Deleted '88. Catalogue no: **CAPS 1038**
**CD:** Released Mar '89, on MFP by EMI Records. Catalogue no: **CDMFP 6052**
**CD:** Released Mar '89, on MFP by EMI Records. Catalogue no: **CDB 791 875 2**
**Cass:** Released Sep '88, on MFP by EMI Records. Catalogue no: **TCMFP 5835**
**Album:** Released Sep '88, on MFP by EMI Records. Catalogue no: **MFP 5835**

## SEPTEMBER OF MY YEARS
Tracks: / September of my years / How old am I / Don't wait too long / It gets lonely early / This is all I ask / Last night when we were young / Man in the looking glass, The / It was a very good year / When the wind was green / Hello young lovers / I see it now / Once upon a time / September song.
**Album:** on Reprise by WEA Records. Catalogue no: **K 44005**
**CD:** Released Oct '86, on Reprise by WEA Records. Catalogue no: **901014 2**

## SEXY, SWINGING SINATRA
Tracks: / Blue moon / These foolish things / Autumn leaves.
**LP Set:** Released Jan '85, on Pathe Marconi (France) Catalogue no: **PM 155 177 3**

## SHE SHOT ME DOWN
Tracks: / Good thing going / Hey look, no crying / Thanks for the memory / Long night / Bang bang / Monday morning quarterback / South to a warmer place / I loved her / Gal that got away / It never entered my mind.
**Album:** Released Jan '82, on Reprise by WEA Records. Deleted Jan '87. Catalogue no: **L 54117**

## SINATRA
**2 LP Set:** Released '79, on Joker (USA) by Lifetime Records (USA). Catalogue no: **SM 3762/2**
**Cass:** Released Dec '88, on Capitol (Specials) Catalogue no: **4XL 8345**

## SINATRA: A MAN AND HIS MUSIC
**CD:** Released Oct '86, on Reprise by WEA Records. Catalogue no: **901016 2**

## SINATRA AND COMPANY
**Album:** Released Jun '71, on Reprise by WEA Records. Deleted Jun '76. Catalogue no: **RSLP 1033**

## SINATRA AND STRINGS
**Album:** Released Jun '62, on Reprise by WEA Records. Deleted Jun '67. Catalogue no: **R 1004**

## SINATRA AT THE SANDS (Sinatra, Frank/Count Basie)
**Cass:** Released '88, on BBC by BBC Records & Tapes. Catalogue no: **REP 64002**
**CD:** Released Nov '86, on Reprise by WEA Records. Catalogue no: **901019 2**
**Album:** Released Oct '66, on Reprise by WEA Records. Deleted Oct '71. Catalogue no: **RLP 1019**

## SINATRA CHRISTMAS ALBUM, THE
Tracks: / Jingle bells / Christmas song, The / Mistletoe and holly / I'll be home for Christmas / Have yourself a merry little Christmas / Christmas waltz / First Noel, The / Hark the herald angels sing / O little town of Bethlehem / Adeste fideles / It came upon a midnight clear / Silent night / White Christmas (CD only) / Christmas waltz (alternate).
Note: On side 1, Frank Sinatra sings Yuletide favourites of recent years and side 2 is a collectiion of more traditional Christmas fare. A Christmas present for every Christmas. The Orchestra is conducted by Gordon Jenkins.
**Album:** Released Sep '87, on MFP by EMI Records. Deleted '89. Catalogue no: **MFP 5797**
**Cass:** Released Sep '87, on MFP by EMI Records. Deleted '89. Catalogue no: **TCMFP 5797**
**Cass:** Released Nov '83, on Capitol by EMI Records. Deleted Jul '87. Catalogue no: **TC CAPS 1809874**
**Album:** Released Nov '83, on Capitol by EMI Records. Deleted Jul '87. Catalogue no: **CAPS 1809871**
**CD:** Released Nov '87, on Capitol by EMI Records. Catalogue no: **CDP 748 329 2**

## SINATRA FOR THE SINATRA-PHILE
**Album:** Released Nov '88, on Apex Catalogue no: **AX 6**

## SINATRA LOVE SONGS
Tracks: / Nearness of you / If I had you / Nevertheless / You go to my head / My melancholy baby / How deep is the ocean / Embraceable you / She's funny that way / For every man there's a woman / I don't know why (I just do) / Someone to watch over me / Love me.
**Cass:** Released Jul '87, on CBS by CBS Records. Catalogue no: **460016 4**
**Album:** Released Jul '87, on CBS by CBS Records. Catalogue no: **460016 1**

## SINATRA PLUS
**Album:** Released Nov '61, on Fontana by Phonogram Ltd. Deleted Nov '66. Catalogue no: **SET 303**

## SINATRA SCREEN
Tracks: / Continental, The / It's the same old dream / Laura / Stormy weather / I've got a crush on you / House I live in, The / All through the day / I couldn't sleep a wink last night / Time after time / But beautiful / I fall in love too easily / Brooklyn bridge.
**Cass:** Released Jul '87, on CBS by CBS Records. Catalogue no: **460015 4**
**Album:** Released Jul '87, on CBS by CBS Records. Catalogue no: **460015 1**

## SINATRA SINGS RODGERS & HART
**Album:** Released Nov '71, on Starline (EMI) by EMI Records. Deleted Nov '76. Catalogue no: **SRS 5083**

## SINATRA SINGS SONGS FOR PLEASURE
**Album:** Released Dec '66, on MFP by EMI Records. Deleted Dec '71. Catalogue no: **MFP 1120**

## SINATRA SINGS...OF LOVE AND
Tracks: / Nearness of you, The / Hidden persuasion / Moon was yellow, The / I love Paris / Monique / Chicago / Love looks so well on you / Sentimental baby / Mr. Success / They came to Cordura / I gotta right to sing the blues / Something wonderful happens in summer.
**Album:** Released Sep '84, on Capitol by EMI Records. Catalogue no: **ED 2601781**
**Cass:** Released Sep '84, on Capitol by EMI Records. Catalogue no: **ED 2601784**

## SINATRA SOUVENIR
**Album:** Released Jul '61, on Fontana by Phonogram Ltd. Deleted Jul '66. Catalogue no: **TFL 5138**

## SINATRA STAGE
Tracks: / There's no business like show business / Song is you, The / September song / Oh what a beautiful morning / They say it's wonderful / Bess, oh where's my Bess? / Where or when / I could write a book / Why was I born / Lost in the stars / All the things you are / Ol' man river.
**Cass:** Released Jul '87, on CBS by CBS Records. Catalogue no: **460014 4**
**Album:** Released Jul '87, on CBS by CBS Records. Catalogue no: **460014 1**

## SINATRA STANDARDS
Tracks: / Saturday night is the loneliest night in the week / Poinciana / Try a little tenderness / Autumn in New York / April in Paris / Dream / Nancy (with the laughing face) / Put your dreams away / I'm glad there is you / Day by day / Close to you / I'm a fool to want you.
**Cass:** Released Jul '87, on CBS by CBS Records. Catalogue no: **460017 4**
**Album:** Released Jul '87, on CBS by CBS Records. Catalogue no: **460017 1**

## SINATRA SWINGS
Tracks: / Should I / Birth of the blues / Mean to me / It all depends on you / Deep night / Sweet Lorraine / Castle rock / Why can't you behave / My blue Heaven / S'posin' / You can take my word for it

baby / Blue skies.
**Album:** Released Oct '61, on Reprise by WEA Records. Deleted Oct '66. Catalogue no: **R 1002**
**Cass:** Released Jul '87, on CBS by CBS Records. Catalogue no: **460013 4**
**Album:** Released Jul '87, on CBS by CBS Records. Catalogue no: **460013 1**

**SINATRA: THE CONCERTS (20 live greats)**
Tracks: / At long last love / I could have danced all night / Imagination / Moon was yellow, The / Embraceable you / Dancing in the dark / Road to Mandalay, The / Just one of those things / Willow weep for me / Angel eyes / My funny valentine / My blue Heaven / Come fly with me / I get a kick out of you / I've got you under my skin / April in Paris / All the way / Bewitched / Lady is a tramp, The / Night and day.
**Album:** Released Jul '86, on Deja Vu Catalogue no: **DVLP 2061**
**Cass:** Released Jul '86, on Deja Vu Catalogue no: **DVMC 2061**
**CD:** Released Sep '87, on Deja Vu Catalogue no: **DVCD 2061**

**SINATRA: THE DUETS**
Tracks: / Little learning is a dangerous business / Kisses and tears / Love means love / Mama will bark / Good man is hard to find, A / Love me tender / Tea for two / Exactly like you / Camptown races / When you're smiling / Me and my shadow / Take me out to the ball game / Gotta be this or that / How about you / Birth of the blues / Down by the old mill stream / Yes sir / Some enchanted evening / Them there eyes / Beautiful dreamer / Witchcraft / Come fly with me / I begged her / Downtown / These boots are made for walking.
Note: Other artists include Pearl Bailey, Jane Russell, Rosemary Clooney, Elvis Presley,/Dinah Shore, Judy Garland.
**Album:** Released May '86, on Deja Vu Catalogue no: **DVLP 2051**
**CD:** Released Jul '87, on Deja Vu Catalogue no: **DVCD 2051**
**Cass:** Released May '86, on Deja Vu Catalogue no: **DVMC 2051**

**SINATRA: THE RADIO YEARS 1939-55**
Tracks: / All or nothing at all / After all / I've got my eyes on you / Polka dots and moonbeams / Deep night / Whispering / Sky fell down, The / On the isle of may / It's a blue world / Fable of the rose / Marie / A lover is blue / Careless / I'll never smile again / Our love affair / East of the sun / One I love, The / Shadows on the sand / That's how it goes / I get a kick out of you / Let's get lost / Embraceable you / Night and day / Close to you / I couldn't sleep a wink last night / Falling in love with you / Music stopped, The / My ideal / Speak low / People will say we're in love / Long ago and far away / I'll get by / Sweet Lorraine / Swinging on a star / These foolish things / Very thought of you, The / All the things you are / My melancholy baby / Homesick that's all / Till the end of time / What makes the sunset? / I fall in love too easily / I begged her / Don't forget tonight tomorrow / That's for me / I found a new baby / I'm always chasing rainbows / Aren't you glad you're you? / It might as well be spring / Lilly belle / If I loved you / Slowly / Great day / I only have eyes for you / Oh,what it seemed to be / Full moon and empty arms / Exactly like you / I fall in love with you every day / It's a good day / My sugar is so refined / Ole buttermilk sky / Lullaby of broadway / I won't dance / Touch of your hand, The / Why was I born? / All through the day / Make believe / Song is you, The / All the things you are / You can't see the sun when you're crying / Anniversary song, The / You do / Let it snow, let it snow, let it snow / I wish I didn't love you so / Wrap your troubles in dreams / Nature boy / My haunted heart / Little white lies / A tree in the meadow / It only happens when I dance with you / My happiness / O sole mio / I found a new baby / It isn't fair / Body and soul / When you're smiling / I've got a crush on you / My foolish heart / Best things in life are free, The / I love you / Why remind me? / Just you, just me / Somebody loves me / Polka dots and moonbeams / Sorry / Young at heart / Among my souvenirs / September song / As time goes by / Take a chance / Till we meet again / Meet me in dreamland / There's a long long trail / Don't blame me / 'S wonderful / It all depends on you / Night and day / Somebody loves you / Nevertheless / On the sunny side of the street / Love me or leave me / Try a little tenderness / Out of nowhere / I've got my love to keep me warm / What can I say? / Between the devil and the deep blue sea / One hundred years from today / I'm in the mood for love / Tenderly / Hello young lovers / She's funny that way / I don't know why / Come rain or shine.
Note: Includes a medley of Summertime/It ain't necessarily so/Bess, Oh where's my Bess.
**LP Set:** Released Oct '87, on Meteor by Magnum Music Group. Catalogue no: **MTBS 001**

**SINATRA: THE RADIO YEARS (IMPORT)**
Tracks: / Night and day / Laura / Somebody loves me / Tenderly / You make me feel so young / Nevertheless / On the sunny side of the street / Love me or leave me / You are love / They didn't believe me / Out of nowhere / I've got my love to keep me warm / For you / Ol' man river / Music stopped, The / I don't stand a ghost of a chance / You do something to me / Begin the beguine.
**CD:** Released '89, on Tamy Catalogue no: **TAMY 20.107**

**SINATRA: THE UNOBTAINABLE (20 rare greats)**
Tracks: / Old school teacher / If you please / You'll know when it happens / So they tell me / It's all up to you / My love for you / All through the day / Life is so peculiar / There's something missing / Meet me at the Copa / Home on the range / Lilly Belle / Help yourself to my heart / Bop goes my heart / My cousin Louella / Cantana / Chattanooga shoeshine boy / Old master painter, The / Fella with an umbrella / Shine.
**Cass:** Released Aug '86, on Deja Vu Catalogue no: **DVMC 2071**
**Album:** Released Aug '86, on Deja Vu Catalogue no: **DVLP 2071**
**CD:** Released Oct '87, on Deja Vu Catalogue no: **DVCD 2071**

**SINATRA WITH SWINGING BRASS**
**Album:** Released Dec '62, on Reprise by WEA Records. Deleted Dec '67. Catalogue no: **R 1005**

**SINATRA - BASIE (Sinatra, Frank / Count Basie)**
**Album:** Released Feb '63, on Reprise by WEA Records. Deleted Feb '68. Catalogue no: **R 1008**

**SINATRA'S GOLD**
Tracks: / Lady is a tramp, The / Young at heart / My funny valentine / 3 coins in the fountain.
**Cass:** Released Dec '88, on Capitol (Specials) Catalogue no: **4XL 8346**

**SINATRA'S SINATRA**
Tracks: / I've got you under my skin / In the wee small hours of the morning / Second time around / Nancy / Witchcraft / Young at heart / All the way / How little we know / Pocketful of miracles / Oh what it seemed to be / Call me irresponsible / Put your dreams away.
**Album:** Released Oct '63, on Reprise by WEA Records. Deleted Oct '68. Catalogue no: **R 1010**
**Album:** on Reprise by WEA Records. Catalogue no: **K 44002**

**SINATRA'S SWINGIN' SESSION**
Tracks: / When you're smiling / Blue moon / S'posin' / It all depends on you / It's only a paper moon / My blue Heaven / Should I / September in the rain / Always / I can't believe you're in love with me / I concentrate on you / You do something to me / Sentimental baby / Ol' MacDonald / Hidden persuasion.
**Album:** Released Sep '61, on Capitol by EMI Records. Deleted Sep '66. Catalogue no: **W 1491**
**Album:** Released Sep '84, on Capitol by EMI Records. Catalogue no: **ED 2602461**
**Cass:** Released Sep '84, on Capitol by EMI Records. Catalogue no: **ED 2602464**
**CD:** Released Mar '88, on Capitol by EMI Records. Catalogue no: **BU 20**
**CD:** Released Mar '88, on Capitol by EMI Records. Catalogue no: **CDP 746 573 2**

**...SINGS FOR ONLY THE LONELY**
**Album:** Released Dec '58, on Capitol by EMI Records. Deleted Dec '63. Catalogue no: **LCT 6168**
**Album:** Released Jul '84, on Capitol by EMI Records. Catalogue no: **ED 2601391**
**Cass:** Released Jul '84, on Capitol by EMI Records. Catalogue no: **ED 2601394**
**CD:** Released Feb '88, on Capitol by

EMI Records. Catalogue no: **CDP 748 471 2**
**CD:** Released Feb '88, on Capitol by EMI Records. Catalogue no: **ED 2601392**

**SOFTLY AS I LEAVE YOU**
**Album:** Released Mar '65, on Reprise by WEA Records. Deleted Mar '70. Catalogue no: **R 1013**

**SOME NICE THINGS I'VE MISSED**
Tracks: / You turned my world around / Sweet Caroline / Summer knows, The / Tie a yellow ribbon / Satisfy me one more time / If / You are the sunshine of my life / What are you doing the rest of your life? / Bad bad Leroy Brown.
**Album:** Released Aug '74, on Reprise by WEA Records. Catalogue no: **K 54020**

**SONGS BY SINATRA**
Note: Complete radio performances, featuring Jimmy Durante
**Album:** Released Jan '89, on Silva Screen by Silva Screen Records. Catalogue no: **PJ 003**
**Album:** Released Nov '88, on Apex Catalogue no: **AX 7**

**SONGS FOR SWINGIN' LOVERS**
Tracks: / Too marvellous for words / Old devil moon / Pennies from Heaven / Love is here to stay / I've got you under my skin / I thought about you / We'll be together again / Makin'whoopee / Swingin' down the lane / Anything goes / How about you / You make me feel so young / It happened in Monterey / You're getting to be a habit with me / You brought a new kind of love to me.
**CD:** Released Mar '88, on Capitol by EMI Records. Catalogue no: **CDP 746 570 2**
**Cass:** Released Jul '71, on Capitol by EMI Records. Catalogue no: **TCSLCT 6106**
**CD:** Released Mar '88, on Capitol by EMI Records. Catalogue no: **BU 17**
**Album:** Released Jul '71, on Capitol by EMI Records. Catalogue no: **SLCT 6106**
**Album:** Released Nov '58, on Capitol by EMI Records. Deleted Nov '63. Catalogue no: **LCT 6106**

**SONGS FOR YOUNG LOVERS**
Tracks: / Girl next door, The / They can't take that away from me / Violets for your furs / Someone to watch over me / My one and only / Little girl blue / Like someone in love / Foggy day, A / It worries me / I can read between the lines / I get a kick out of you / My funny valentine.
**CD:** Released Feb '88, on Capitol by EMI Records. Catalogue no: **CDP 748 470 2**
**Cass:** Released Jun '84, on Capitol by EMI Records. Catalogue no: **ED 2600744**
**Album:** Released Jun '84, on Capitol by EMI Records. Catalogue no: **ED 2600741**
**CD:** Released Feb '88, on Capitol by EMI Records. Deleted '89. Catalogue no: **ED 2600742**

**STORY IN MUSIC**
**CD:** Released Mar '90, on Silva Screen by Silva Screen Records. Catalogue no: **A220709**

**STRANGERS IN THE NIGHT**
Tracks: / Strangers in the night / Summer wind / All or nothing at all / Call me / You're driving me crazy / On a clear day / My baby just cares for me / Downtown / Yes sir, that's my baby / Most beautiful girl in the world, The.
**Album:** on Reprise by WEA Records. Catalogue no: **K 44006**
**Album:** Released Jul '66, on Reprise by WEA Records. Deleted Jul '71. Catalogue no: **R 1017**
**CD:** Released Nov '86, on Reprise by WEA Records. Catalogue no: **901017 2**

**STRANGERS IN THE NIGHT (SINGLE)**
Tracks: / Strangers in the night / My kind of town.
**7" Single:** Released '79, on Elektra by Elektra Records (UK). Deleted '82. Catalogue no: **K 14043**
**7" Single:** Released May '66, on Reprise (USA) Deleted May '69. Catalogue no: **R 23052**

**STRING ALONG**
Tracks: / I'll string along with you / How soon? / Mimi / After I say I'm sorry / A lover is blue / Speak low / Dance ballerina dance / Serenade of the bells / Devil and the deep blue sea / My heart tells me / I wonder who's kissing her now? / Long ago and far away.
**Album:** Released Oct '85, on Meteor by Magnum Music Group. Catalogue no: **MTM 014**

**SUDDENLY IT'S SPRING**
Tracks: / I wish I didn't love you so / Lili Bolero / Suddenly it's spring / You're the top / Lilly belle / Wing and a prayer / It's all up to you / Some other time / You've got a hold on me / Right kind of love, The.
**Album:** Released Jun '86, on Meteor by Magnum Music Group. Catalogue no: **MTM 018**

**SUMMER WIND**
Tracks: / Summer wind.
**7" Single:** Released Sep '66, on Reprise by WEA Records. Deleted Sep '69. Catalogue no: **RS 20509**

**SUNNY SIDE OF THE STREET**
**Cass:** Released Dec '88, on Magnum Music (Import) by Magnum Music Group. Catalogue no: **510423.8**

**SUPERGOLD**
**2 LP Set:** Released '83, on EMI (Germany) by EMI Records. Catalogue no: **IC 134 81333/4**

**SWING EASY**
Tracks: / Jeepers creepers / Taking a chance on love / Wrap your troubles in dreams / Lean baby / I love you / I'm gonna sit right down and write myself a letter / Get happy / All of me / How could you do a thing like that to me / Why should I cry over you / Sunday / Just one of those things.
**Cass:** Released Jun '84, on Capitol by EMI Records. Catalogue no: **ED 2600814**
**Album:** Released Oct '60, on Capitol by EMI Records. Deleted Oct '65. Catalogue no: **W 587**
**Album:** Released Jun '84, on Capitol by EMI Records. Catalogue no: **ED 2600811**
**CD:** Released Feb '88, on Capitol by EMI Records. Deleted '89. Catalogue no: **ED 2600812**

**SWINGIN' AFFAIR, A**
Tracks: / Night and day / I wish I were in love again / I got plenty o' nuttin' / I guess I'll have to change my plan / Nice work if you can get it / Stars fell on Alabama / No one ever tells you / I won't dance / Lonesome road / At long last love / You'd be so nice to come home to / I got it bad and that ain't good / From this moment on / If I had you / Oh, look at me now.
Note: Orchestra conducted by Nelson Riddle.
**Album:** Released Mar '84, on Capitol by EMI Records. Catalogue no: **CAPS 2600171**
**Cass:** Released Mar '84, on Capitol by EMI Records. Catalogue no: **TCCAPS 2600174**

**SWINGING, SEXY SINATRA**
Tracks: / Autumn leaves / April in Paris / Blues in the night / Ebb tide / One for my baby / Gone with the wind / Stormy weather / That old feeling / How deep is the ocean? / Fools rush in / Try a little tenderness / Embraceable you / September song / I'll see you again / These foolish things / As time goes by / I'll be seeing you / My funny valentine / Come fly with me / Come dance with me / Just in time / I could have danced all night / Baubles, bangles and beads / Dancing in the dark / Cheek to cheek / Something's gotta give / When you're smiling / It's only a paper moon / September in the rain / My blue Heaven / Always / You do something to me / Blue moon / That old black magic / Jeepers creepers / All of me.
**2 LP Set:** Released '83, on EMI (France) by EMI Records. Catalogue no: **2C 152 81700/2**

**TENDER TRAP, THE**
Tracks: / Tender trap, The.
**7" Single:** Released Jan '56, on Capitol by EMI Records. Deleted Jan '59. Catalogue no: **CL 14511**

**TENDERLY**
Tracks: / One hundred years from today / Golden earrings / I'm in the mood for love / You're the top / Right kind of love / Let me love you tonight / My happiness / I'll get by / Tenderly / Speak low.
Note: Ol' blue eyes from his late '40'S radio broadcasts. A collectors' item and a must for all MOR fans. Mono recording.
**Album:** Released Apr '84, on Meteor by Magnum Music Group. Catalogue no: **MTM 001**

**THAT'S LIFE**
Tracks: / That's life.
**7" Single:** Released Dec '66, on Reprise (USA) Deleted Dec '69. Catalogue

no: **RS 20531**
**Album:** Released Feb '67, on Reprise by WEA Records. Deleted Feb '72. Catalogue no: **RSLP 1020**
**CD:** Released Oct '86, on Reprise by WEA Records. Catalogue no: **901020 2**

## THIS IS SINATRA VOL.1
Tracks: / I've got the world on a string / Three coins in the fountain / Love and marriage / From here to eternity / South of the border / Rain (falling from the skies) / Gal that got away / Young at heart / Learnin' the blues / My one and only love / Tender trap, The / Don't worry 'bout me.
Note: (P)1956 Original Sound Recordings made by Capitol Records Inc.
**Cass:** Released Mar '87, on Capitol by EMI Records. Catalogue no: **TCEMS 1237**
**Album:** Released Mar '87, on Capitol by EMI Records. Catalogue no: **ED 2606981**
**Cass:** Released Mar '87, on Capitol by EMI Records. Catalogue no: **ED 2606984**
**Album:** Released Mar '87, on Capitol by EMI Records. Catalogue no: **EMS 1237**

## THIS IS SINATRA VOL.2
Tracks: / Hey jealous lover / Everybody loves somebody / Something wonderful happens in summer / Half as lovely / You're cheatin' yourself (if you're cheatin' on me) / You'll always be the one I love / You forgot all the words / How little we know (how little it matters) / Time after time / Crazy love / Johnny Concho theme (wait for me) / If you are but a dream / So long, my love / It's the same old dream / I believe / Put all your dreams away (for another day).
Note: Orchestra conducted by Nelson Riddle
**Album:** Released Mar '87, on Capitol by EMI Records. Catalogue no: **EMS 1238**
**Cass:** Released Mar '87, on Capitol by EMI Records. Catalogue no: **TCEMS 1238**
**Cass:** Released Mar '87, on Capitol by EMI Records. Catalogue no: **ED 2606994**
**Album:** Released Mar '87, on Capitol by EMI Records. Catalogue no: **ED 2606991**

## THIS LOVE OF MINE
**Cass:** Released Dec '88, on Capitol (Specials) Catalogue no: **4XL 9052**

## THREE COINS IN THE FOUNTAIN
Tracks: / Three coins in the fountain.
**7" Single:** Released Jul '54, on Capitol by EMI Records. Deleted Jul '57. Catalogue no: **CL 14120**

## TO LOVE A CHILD
Tracks: / To love a child / That's what god looks like to me.
**7" Single:** Released Dec '82, on Reprise (USA) Catalogue no: **W 9903**

## TRILOGY
Tracks: / Song is you, The / But not for me / I had the craziest dream / It had to be you / Let's face the music and dance / Street of dreams / My shining hour / All of you / More than you know / They all laughed / You and me (we wanted it all) / Just the way you are / Something / MacArthur Park / New York, New York / Summer me, winter me / Song sung blue / For the good times / Love me tender / That's what God looks like / What time does the next miracle leave? / World war none / Future, The / I've been there / Song without words / Before the music ends (finale).
**LP Set:** Released Apr '80, on Reprise (USA) Deleted Aug '87. Catalogue no: **K 64042**

## ULTIMATE EVENT, THE (VIDEO) (Sinatra, Frank / Liza Minelli / Sammy Davis Jr)
Note: Running time: 103 mins.
**VHS:** Released Aug '89, on Video Collection by Video Collection. Catalogue no: **VC 4077**

## V-DISC RECORDINGS, VOL 1
**Album:** Released Aug '81, on Apex Catalogue no: **AX 1**

## VERY BEST: FRANK SINATRA
**CD:** Released 7 Aug '89, on Arcade Catalogue no: **357 061**

## VOICE 1942-1952, THE (Columbia years, The)
Tracks: / One for my baby / I should care / These foolish things / I guess I'll have to dream the rest / It never entered my mind / When your lover has gone / Body and soul / That old feeling / Ghost of a chance / There's no you / Guess I'll hang my tears out to dry / Why try to change me now / Nearness of you, The / If I had you / Never the less / You go to my head / My melancholy baby / How deep is the ocean / Embraceable you / She's funny that way / For every man there's a woman / I don't know why (I just do) / Someone to watch over me / Love me / Saturday night is the loneliest night in the week / Poinciana / Try a little tenderness / Autumn in New York / April in Paris / Dream / Nancy (with the laughing face) / Put your dreams away / I'm glad there is you / Day by day / Close to you / I'm a fool to want you / Should I / Birth of the blues / Mean to me / It all depends on you / Deep night / Sweet Lorraine / Castle rock / Why can't you behave / My blue Heaven / S'posin / You can take my word for it baby / Blue skies / Continental, The / It's the same old dream / Laura / Stormy weather / I've got a crush on you / House I live in, The / All through the day / I couldn't sleep a wink last night / Time after time / But beautiful / I fall in love too easily / Brooklyn bridge / There's no business like show business / Song is you, The / September song / Oh what a beautiful morning / They say it's wonderful / Bess, oh where's my Bess? / Where or when / I could write a book / Why was I born / Lost in the stars / All the things you are / Ol' man river.
**CD:** Released Jun '87, on CBS by CBS Records. Deleted Jan '89. Catalogue no: **450 222 2**
**2 LP Set:** Released Nov '86, on CBS by CBS Records. Catalogue no: **450 222 1**

## VOICE, THE
Tracks: / I don't know why / Try a little tenderness / Ghost of a chance / Paradise / These foolish things / Laura / She's funny that way / Fools rush in / Over the rainbow / That old black magic / Spring is here / Lover.
**Cass:** Released Oct '84, on CBS Cameo by CBS Records. Deleted Aug '87. Catalogue no: **40 32520**
**CD:** Released Oct '86, on Solid Gold (1) by Creole Records. Deleted '86. Catalogue no: **CD 8601**
**Album:** Released Oct '84, on CBS Cameo by CBS Records. Deleted Aug '87. Catalogue no: **CBS 32520**

## WATERTOWN
**Album:** Released May '70, on Reprise by WEA Records. Deleted May '75. Catalogue no: **RSLP 1031**

## WHEN YOUR LOVER HAS GONE
**Album:** Released Aug '61, on Encore by EMI Records. Deleted Aug '66. Catalogue no: **ENC 101**

## WHERE ARE YOU?
Tracks: / Where are you? / Night we called it a day, The / I cover the waterfront / Maybe you'll be there / Laura / Lonely town / Autumn leaves / I'm a fool to want you / I think of you / Where is the one / There's no you / Baby, won't you please come home.
Note: A classic Sinatra issue, reproduced in superb Digital sound. From the sleeve note by Alan Dell: "Remastering of an album outstanding for the beauty of its sound dimension".
**Album:** Released Mar '84, on Capitol by EMI Records. Catalogue no: **CAPS 2600181**
**Cass:** Released Mar '84, on Capitol by EMI Records. Catalogue no: **TCCAPS 2600184**

## WITCHCRAFT
Tracks: / Witchcraft.
**7" Single:** Released Feb '58, on Capitol by EMI Records. Deleted Feb '61. Catalogue no: **CL 14819**

## WORLD WE KNEW, THE
Tracks: / World we knew, The.
**7" Single:** Released Aug '67, on Reprise (USA) Deleted Aug '70. Catalogue no: **RS 20610**

## YOU MAKE ME FEEL SO YOUNG
Tracks: / Night and day / Laura / Somebody loves me / Little white lies / This can't be love / You make me feel so young / Speak low / You do something to me / Begin the beguine / Tenderly / On the sunny side of the street / Love me or leave me / They didn't believe me / Out of nowhere / I've got my love to keep me warm / For you.
**CD:** Released '87, on Topline by Charly Records. Catalogue no: **TOP CD 522**
**CD:** Released '88, on Entertainers Catalogue no: **ENT CD 213**
**Album:** Released Sep '87, on Entertainers Catalogue no: **ENT LP 13024**
**Cass:** Released '88, on Entertainers Catalogue no: **ENT MC 13024**

Alan Skidmore

**YOU MY LOVE**
Tracks: / You my love.
**7" Single:** Released Jun '55, on Capitol by EMI Records. Deleted Jun '58. Catalogue no: **CL 14240**

**YOUNG AT HEART**
Tracks: / Young at heart.
**7" Single:** Released Jul '54, on Capitol by EMI Records. Deleted Jul '57. Catalogue no: **CL 14064**

**YOUNG, THE 1940-42**
**Album:** Released '88, on Joker (USA) by Lifetime Records (USA). Catalogue no: **SM 4012**

## Singer, Hal

**SWING ON IT**
**Album:** Released Aug '81, on JSP by JSP Records. Catalogue no: **JSP 1028**

## Singers Unlimited

**Biographical details:** The Singers Unlimited took the art of vocalizing / harmonizing to the pinnacle of perfection. Using just four voices and sophisticated recording techniques, the effects achieved border on the impossible..

**ACAPELLA I**
Tracks: / Both sides now / London by night / Here, there and everywhere / Lullaby / Michell / Fool on the hill / Emily / Since you asked / More I cannot wish you / Try to remember.
**Album:** Released Sep '84, on MPS Jazz (Germany) Catalogue no: **815 671-1**
**CD:** Released Aug '84, on Verve Deleted Aug '87. Catalogue no: **815671-2**
**Cass:** Released Sep '84, on MPS Jazz (Germany) Catalogue no: **815 671-4**

**ACAPELLA II**
Tracks: / Clair / Killin' me softly with his song / Yesterday / My romance / Lost in the stars / April in Paris / Girl talk / Nature boy / I don't know where I stand / Autumn in New York / Like someone in love / Indian summer.
**Album:** Released Apr '85, on MPS Jazz (Germany) Catalogue no: **821 860-1**

**ACAPELLA III**
Tracks: / Anything goes / Way we were, The / One more time, Chick Corea / Sweet Lorraine / Jeanie with the light brown hair / Someone to light up my life / Love is here to stay / Entertainer, The / All the things you are / Sometimes I feel like a motherless child / I wish you love.
**Album:** Released Aug '85, on MPS Jazz (Germany) Catalogue no: **821 882-1**

**CHRISTMAS (SINGERS UNLIMITED)**
Tracks: / Dec the halls / Ah bleak and chill the wintry wind / Bright, bright the hollly berries / Nigh Bethlehem / While by my sheep / It came upon a midnight clear / Silent night / Joy to the world / Wassailing song carol of the Russian children / Good King Wenceslas / O come all ye faithful / Coventry carol / Have yourself a merry little Christmas.
**CD:** Released Nov '84, on MPS Jazz (Germany) Deleted Aug '87. Catalogue no: **821 859-2**
**Album:** Released Jan '81, on MPS Jazz Catalogue no: **MPS 68 105**

**COMPACT JAZZ: SINGERS UNLIMITED**
**CD:** Released Jul '87, on MPS Jazz (Germany) Deleted Jan '89. Catalogue no: **831 373-2**

**EVENTIDE**
Tracks: / Deep purple / Air (From the suite D) / Put your dreams away / I loved you / In the still of the night / Mona Lisa / Feelings / Gymnopedie / Yours truly Rosa / Marlies / How beautiful is night / Eventide.
**Album:** Released Aug '85, on MPS Jazz (Germany) Catalogue no: **821 872-1**

**FEELING FREE**
Tracks: / You are the sunshine of my life / Time for love, A / Green Dolphin Street / So many stars / Feeling free with Patrick B / Ja da / Skylark / On a clear day / I'm shadowing you / Where is the love.
Note: The group are accompanied by the orchestras of Robert Farnon and Pat Williams.
**CD:** Released Aug '85, on MPS Jazz (Germany) Deleted Aug '87. Catalogue no: **821 858-2**
**Album:** Released Aug '85, on MPS Jazz (Germany) Catalogue no: **821 858-1**

**FOUR OF US**
**Album:** Released May '81, on MPS Jazz Catalogue no: **MPS 68 106**

**FRIENDS**
**Album:** Released May '81, on MPS Jazz Catalogue no: **MPS 68 150**

**IN TUNE**
**Album:** on MPS Jazz Catalogue no: **MPS 68 085**

**INVITATION**
**Album:** Released Jan '81, on MPS Jazz Catalogue no: **MPS 68 107**

**JUST IN TIME**
**Album:** Released May '81, on MPS Jazz Catalogue no: **MPS 68 179**

**SENTIMENTAL JOURNEY**
Tracks: / More I see you, The / Sleepy time gal / I get along without you very well / Angel eyes / As time goes by / I'll remember April / If I didn't care / Sentimental journey.
Note: With the Robert Farnon Orchestra.
**Album:** Released Apr '85, on MPS Jazz (Germany) Catalogue no: **821 857-1**

**SINGERS UNLIMITED (Compact / Walkman jazz)**
**Cass:** Released Jun '87, on MPS Jazz Catalogue no: **831 373-4**
**CD:** on Polydor by Polydor Ltd. Deleted Aug '87. Catalogue no: **817 486-2**
**CD:** Released Jun '87, on MPS Jazz Catalogue no: **831 373-2**

**SPECIAL BLEND, A**
**Album:** Released May '81, on MPS Jazz Catalogue no: **MPS 68 101**

**WITH ROB MCCONNELL AND THE BOSS**
Tracks: / Tangerine / Laura / Lullaby of the leaves / You are my sunshine / Sophisticated lady / Beautiful friendship, A / It might as well be spring / Chelsea morning / Dindi / Pieces of dreams.

**Album:** Released Apr '85, on MPS Jazz (Germany) Catalogue no: **817 486-1**

## Sissle, Noble

**SISSIE AND HIS SIZZLING SYNCOPATORS (With Tommy Ladnier & Sydney Bechet) (Sissle, Noble / Tommy Ladnier / Sidney Bechet)**
**Album:** Released Dec '86, on Classic Jazz Masters Catalogue no: **CJM 22**

## Sissy Man Blues

**SISSY MAN BLUES (Straight And Gay Blues And Jazz Vocals) (Various artists)**
**CD:** Released Jul '89, on Jass Catalogue no: **CD 504**
**CD:** Released '88, on Jass Catalogue no: **JASSCD 13**

## Sjosten, Lars

**BELLS, BLUES AND BROTHERHOOD (Sjosten, Lars Trio)**
Tracks: / 24th of April / May it do some good / One certain lady / Monologue and dialogue about the blues / Triad / It's from Lester actually / I thought the roof was falling down / Inner voice, The / Bells, blues and brotherhood.
Note: Recorded December 27th, 1981.
**Album:** Released Jul '83, on Dragon by Dragon Records. Catalogue no: **DRLP 46**

**ROOTS AND RELATIONS (Sjosten, Lars Quartet)**
**Album:** Released Apr '89, on Dragon by Dragon Records. Catalogue no: **DRLP 164**

## Skidmore, Alan

**EUROPEAN JAZZ QUINTET**
**Album:** Released Oct'79, on Ego. Catalogue no: **EGO 4012**

**S.O.H.**
**Album:** Released Oct'79, on Ego. Catalogue no: **EGO 4011**

**S.O.S.**
**Album:** Released Jan '77, on Ogun. Catalogue no: **OG 400**

**TRIBUTE TO 'TRANE**
Tracks: / Resolution / Lonnie's lament / Bessie's blues / Crescent / Dear Lord / Naima / Mr. P. C.
**Album:** Released Sep '88, onMiles Music. Catalogue no: **MM 075**

## Skjelbred, Ray

**RAY SKJELBRED & HAL SMITH (Skjelbred, Ray & Hal Smith)**
**Album:** Released Jun '86, on Stomp Off (USA) Catalogue no: **SOS 1097**

**SOLO JAZZ PIANO 1973/1974**
**Album:** on Berkeley Rhythm Deleted '88. Catalogue no: **BR 2**

## Skymasters

**BIG BAND FAVOURITES**
Tracks: / Skyliner / Begin the beguine / Trumpet blues and cantabile / I'm getting sentimental over you / Pink panther (theme from) / One o'clock jump / Opus one / Moonlight serenade / Take the 'A' train / Love / Lean Baby / Sing, sing, sing.
Note: The Skymasters are one of Holland's most popular radio and concert Big Bands. This superb digital recording features the very best in Big Band repetoire including "Take The A Train" (Billy Strayhorn), "Moonlight Serenade" (Glenn Miller), and "One O'Clock Jump" (Count Basie).
**CD:** Released Apr '87, on Philips (Holland) by PolyGram UK Ltd. Catalogue no: **830 301 2**
**Album:** Released Apr '87, on Philips (Holland) by PolyGram UK Ltd. Catalogue no: **830 301 1**
**Cass:** Released Apr '87, on Philips (Holland) by. PolyGram UK Ltd. Catalogue no: **830 301 4**

## Slack, Freddie

**BOOGIE WOOGIE**
**Album:** Released May '85, on Oldie Blues Catalogue no: **OL 2829**

**BOOGIE WOOGIE ON THE 88**
Tracks: / Rockin' the boogie / Cow cow boogie / Humoresquire / Down the road a piece / After sours / Between 18th and 19th on Chestnut Street / Rhum boogie / Bolero / Pig foot Pete / Rain drops / Beat me daddy eight to the bar / Beating with chopsticks.
**Album:** Released '88, on Official by Official Records. Catalogue no: **OFF 12000**

## Slim, Bumble Bee

**BUMBLE BEE SLIM 1931-37**
Note: With: Big Bill Broonzy, Washboard Sam etc.
**Album:** Released Jul '87, on Document Catalogue no: **DLP 506**

**BUMBLE BEE SLIM 1934-37**
**Album:** Released Dec '88, on Best Of Blues (USA) by Blue Island Records (USA). Catalogue no: **BOB 9**

**EVERYBODY'S FISHING**
**Album:** Released Jan '77, on Magpie by Interstate Music. Deleted '88. Catalogue no: **PY 1808**

## Slim, Lightning

**BEST OF LP'S**
**CD:** Released 10 Jul '89, on Flyright by Interstate Music. Catalogue no: **FLYCD 08**

**FEATURE SIDES, THE 1954**
Note: Mono recording.
**Album:** Released Oct '86, on Flyright by Interstate Music. Catalogue no: **FLY 583**

## Slim, Magic

**CHICAGO BLUES SESSIONS 10 (Slim, Magic/Nick Holt)**
**Album:** Released '89, on Wolf Catalogue no: **WOLF 120 856**

## Slim, Memphis

**20 GREATEST HITS: MEMPHIS SLIM**
**Album:** Released '88, on Masters (Holland) Catalogue no: **CL 23983**

**ALL KINDS OF BLUES**
Tracks: / Blues is trouble / Grinder man blues / Three in one boogie / Letter home / Churnin' man blues / Two of a kind / Blacks, The / If you see Kay / Frankie and Johnny Boogie / Mother earth.
**CD:** Released Apr '87, on Carrere (France) Catalogue no: **98415**
**Album:** Released May '84, on Original Blues Classics (USA) by Fantasy Inc (USA). Catalogue no: **OBC 507**

**AMBASSADOR OF THE BLUES, THE**
Tracks: / Lonesome / Cold blooded woman / One man's mad / Let the good times roll Creole / Where is the mare rack / Pigalle love / Four walls / It's been so long / Big Bertha / I'm lost without you / I'll just keep on singin' the blues / True love.
**Album:** Released '88, on Blue Moon (1) by Magnum Music Group. Catalogue no: **BMLP 1061**
**Album:** Released '88, on Official by Official Records. Catalogue no: **OFF 6016**

**AT RONNIE SCOTT'S**
Note: Running time: 85 mins.
**CD:** Released Dec '87, on Hendring Catalogue no: **HEN 6039 Y**

**BLUES EVERY WHICH WAY, THE (Slim, Memphis & Willie Dixon)**
**Album:** Released Jun '81, on Verve (USA) by Polydor Ltd. Catalogue no: **2304 505**

**BLUES IS EVERYWHERE**
**Album:** Released Oct '88, on Vogue (France) by Vogue Records. Catalogue no: **512601**
**CD:** Released May '87, on Vogue by Vogue Records. Catalogue no: **VGCD 600109**
**Album:** Released May '89, on GNP Crescendo (USA) by GNP Crescendo Records (USA). Catalogue no: **GNPS 10002**

**BLUES... MY OWN WAY**
Tracks: / No mail blues / Gonna need my baby some day / Question, The / Never let me love / Train time / Blue evening / Treat me like I treat you / My country girl / Four years of torment / Back alley / Living the life I love / Come back, The / Five o'clock blues / Call before you go home / This is my lucky day / I love my baby.
**Album:** Released May '88, on Official by Official Records. Catalogue no: **OFF 6006**

**BOOGIE WOOGIE PIANO**
Tracks: / Panic street / Hustler / Carried away / Bluesnick / Back home / Olympia boogie / Sonophone boogie / Blue Slim / Musing / West Side trot / Hotfan's delight.
**Album:** Released Feb '84, on CBS by CBS Records. Deleted '87. Catalogue no: **CBS 21106**
**Cass:** Released Feb '84, on CBS by CBS Records. Deleted Nov '87. Catalogue no: **40 21106**

**CHICAGO BOOGIE**
Note: With Alexis Korner. Stan Grieg. Recorded 1960. Tracks include: Chicago boogie/Sad and lonesome/Memphis woman/Bertha Mae/'Frisco bay blues/Misery etc.
**Album:** Released Sep '87, on Black Lion Catalogue no: **BLP 30196**

**COLLECTION: MEMPHIS SLIM (20 Blues Greats)**
Tracks: / Baby please come home / Sassy Mae / Rock me, baby / Caldonia / Strollin' thru the park / Ballin' the jack / Forty years or more / Pigalle love / Ramble this highway / Gone again / Piney Brown blues / Only fools have fun / Little lonely girl / Long time baby / Careless love / Freedom / All by myself / Everyday I have the blues / I am the blues / This little woman.
**Album:** Released Aug '86, on Deja Vu Catalogue no: **DVLP 2075**
**Cass:** Released Aug '86, on Deja Vu Catalogue no: **DVMC 2075**

**DIALOGUE IN BOOGIE**
**Album:** Released '88, on Zeta Catalogue no: **ZET 711**
**Cass:** Released Jul '83, on Happy Bird (Germany) Catalogue no: **MB 990120**
**Album:** Released Jul '83, on Happy Bird (Germany) Catalogue no: **B 90120**

**GREATEST HITS: MEMPHIS SLIM**
**Album:** Released '88, on Masters (Holland) Catalogue no: **MA 23983**

**I'LL JUST KEEP ON SINGIN' THE BLUES**
Tracks: / Lonesome / Cold blooded woman / One man's man / Let the good times roll creole / What is the mare rack / Pigalle love / Four walls / It's been too long / Big Bertha / I'm lost without you / I'll just keep on singin' the blues / True love.
**Album:** Released '81, on Muse by Black & Blue Records. Catalogue no: **MR 5219**

**LEGACY OF THE BLUES-7**
Tracks: / Everyday I have the blues / I am the blues / Long time gone / I feel like ballin' the Jack / Let's get with it / Broadway boogie / Gambler's blues / Freedom / Sassy Mae.
**Album:** Released May '89, on GNP Crescendo (USA) by GNP Crescendo Records (USA). Catalogue no: **GNPS 10017**
**Album:** Released '73, on Sonet by Sonet Records. Catalogue no: **SNTF 647**
**CD:** Released '73, on Sonet by Sonet Records. Catalogue no: **SNTCD 647**

**LIVE AT RONNIE SCOTT'S**
**CD:** Released Dec '86, on Hendring Video Catalogue no: **WHCD 002**

**LIVE: FROM THEATRE MUNICIPAL, BAYONNE, FRANCE**
**Album:** Released Sep '86, on Storyville by Storyville Records AB. Catalogue no: **SLP 4058**

**MEMPHIS SLIM**
Tracks: / I guess I'm a fool / Rock in the pad / Havin' fun / Marack / Mother earth / Really got the blues / Tia Juana / I'm crying / Reverend bounce / Slim blues / Blues for my baby.
**Cass:** Released Apr '87, on Chess by Vogue Records. Catalogue no: **GCHK 78024**
**Album:** Released Apr '87, on Chess by Vogue Records. Catalogue no: **GCH 8024**

**MEMPHIS SLIM & PAUL JONES AT RONNIE SCOTTS**
**VHS:** Released '88, on Castle Hendring Video by Castle Communications Records. Catalogue no: **HEN 2 039 G**

**MEMPHIS SLIM STORY, THE**
Tracks: / All by myself / Sassy Mae / Baby please come home (1st version) / Gone again / Rock my baby / Careless love / Gambler's blues / Broadway boogie / Ballin' the Jack / Pigalle love / Ramble this highway / Baby please come home (2nd version) / Little lonely girl / Caldonia / This little woman / Strollin' thru' the park / I am the blues / Long time baby / Freedom / Only fools have fun / Let's get with it / Forty years or more.
**Cass:** Released Apr '89, on Deja Vu Catalogue no: **DVRE MC 18**
**CD:** Released Apr '89, on Deja Vu Catalogue no: **DVRE CD 18**

**MEMPHIS SLIM USA**
Tracks: / Born with the blues / Just let it be me / Red haired boogie / Blue and disgusted / New key to the highway / I'd take her to Chicago / Harlem bound / El capitan / I just landed in your own / John Henry / I believe I'll settle down / Bad luck and troubles / Late afternoon blues / Memphis Slim U.S.A.
**CD:** Released Apr '87, on Candid Catalogue no: **CCD 9024**
**Album:** Released Apr '87, on Candid Catalogue no: **CS 9024**

**MESSIN' AROUND WITH THE BLUES**
**Album:** Released Jul '88, on Bellaphon Catalogue no: **BID 8018**
**Cass set:** Released Mar '88, on Gusto (USA) by Gusto Records (USA). Catalogue no: **GD 5038**

**PARISIAN BLUES**
Note: Two classic blues sessions on one CD containing over 70 minutes of music. The first session features Memphis Slim with fellow pianist and singer Roosevelt Sykes and the vocal performances are shared by both musicians. The second session features Memphis Slim with a group that includes guitarist Buddy Guy and harmonica player Junior Wells. The recording was made during September 1970 while the group were on tour with the Rolling Stones.
**CD:** Released Feb '89, on Polygram (France) by PolyGram UK Ltd. Catalogue no: **834658 2**

**REAL FOLK BLUES**
**Album:** Released Oct '88, on Vogue (France) by Vogue Records. Catalogue no: **515024**

**ROCK ME, BABY (Slim, Memphis & Alexis Korner)**
Tracks: / Pinetop's blues / Blue this evening / Caught the old coon at last / We're just two of the same old kind / Don't think you're smart / I'm going to Kansas City / Got a little old mama / Rock me, baby / In the evening.
**Album:** Released Sep '85, on Black Lion Catalogue no: **BLP 30122**

**ROCKIN' THE BLUES**
Tracks: / Gotta find my baby / Comeback, The / Messin' around / Sassy Mae / Lend me your love / Guitar cha cha / Stroll on little girl / Rockin' the house / Wish me well / Blue and lonesome / My gal keeps me crying / Slim's blues / Steppin' out / Mother Earth / What's the matter / This time I'm through.
**Album:** Released Nov '81, on Charly R&B by Charly Records. Catalogue no: **CRB 1030**
**CD:** Released 23 Feb '90, on Charly R&B by Charly Records. Catalogue no: **CDCHARLY 210**

**STEADY ROLLIN' BLUES**
**Album:** Released Jan '88, on OBC Catalogue no: **OBC 523**

**STEPPIN' OUT (Live at Ronnie Scott's)**
Tracks: / Health shaking / Mother earth / Rock this house tonight / If you see Kay / Feel so good / Tribute to Gaillard / Four hundred years / Steppin' out / Baby please come home / Where do I go from here / Didn't we / Christina / Animal / Beer drinking woman / What is this world coming to / Bye bye blues.
**Cass:** Released Feb '90, on Essential by Castle Communications Records. Catalogue no: **ESMMC 016**
**CD:** Released Feb '90, on Essential by Castle Communications Records. Catalogue no: **ESMCD 016**

**TOGETHER AGAIN ONE MORE TIME (Slim, Memphis & Matt Murphy)**
**Album:** Released Dec '88, on Antones Catalogue no: **AN 003**

**TRAVELLING WITH THE BLUES**
**Album:** Released '88, on Storyville by Storyville Records AB. Catalogue no: **SLP 118**
**Album:** Released Sep '86, on Storyville by Storyville Records AB. Catalogue no: **SLP 4033**

**TRIBUTE**
**CD:** Released Jun '88, on Candid Catalogue no: **CCD 9023**
**Album:** Released Jun '86, on Candid Catalogue no: **CS 9023**

**UNISSUED 1963 BLUES FESTIVAL, THE (Slim, Memphis / Sonny Boy Williamson / etc)**
**Album:** Released Jan '87, on Red Lightnin' by Red Lightning Records. Catalogue no: **RL 060**

**USA**
**Album:** Released Dec '88, on Pearl (USA) by Delmark Records (USA).

**Bessie Smith - The Bessie Smith Story (Deja Vu)**

Catalogue no: **PL 10**

**WILLIE'S BLUES (Slim, Memphis & Willie Dixon)**
**Album:** Released May '84, on Original Blues Classics (USA) by Fantasy Inc (USA). Catalogue no: **OBC 501**

**WORRIED LIFE**
**CD:** Released Mar '90, on Roots Catalogue no: **RTS 33013**

## Slinger, Cees

**CEES SLINGER / PHILLY JOE / CLIFFORD JORDAN AND ISLA ECKINGER**
**Album:** Released Oct '86, on Timeless by Timeless Records. Catalogue no: **SJP 225**

## Slipstream

**SLIPSTREAM - THE BEST OF BRITISH JAZZ FUNK (Various artists)**
Tracks: / London Town: *Light Of The World* / Girl: *Various artists* / Feels like the right time: *Shakatak* / Southern Freeez: *Freeez* / Turn it on: *Level 42* / Locomoto: *Inversions* / You know you can do it: *Central Line* / Slipstream: *Morrissey Mullen* / Shaping up: *Hipnosis* / W.T.L.D.L.T.W.: *Multivision* / Roberto Who: *Cayenne* / Incognito: *Incognito.*
**Album:** Released Nov '81, on Beggars Banquet by Beggars Banquet Records. Deleted Aug '87. Catalogue no: **BEGA 31**
**Cass:** Released Nov '81, on Beggars Banquet by Beggars Banquet Records. Deleted Aug '87. Catalogue no: **BEGC 31**

## Small Labels

**SMALL LABEL GEMS OF THE FORTIES VOL. 1 (Vakeros, The)**
**Album:** Released Apr '81, on Solid Sender Catalogue no: **SOL 512**

**SMALL LABEL GEMS OF THE FORTIES VOL. 2 (Vakeros, The)**
**Album:** Released Apr '81, on Solid Sender Catalogue no: **SOL 513**

**SMALL LABEL GEMS OF THE FORTIES VOL. 3 (Vakeros, The)**
**Album:** Released Apr '81, on Solid Sender Catalogue no: **SOL 514**

**SMALL LABELS 1927-1935, THE (Various artists)**
Note: Artists include: Chicago redheads/Chick Bullock etc.
**Album:** Released Jul '86, on Collectors Items Catalogue no: **CI 010**

## Smith, Bessie

**Biographical details:** The greatest female blues singer of all --*The Empress of the Blues*-- was born in Tennessee in 1894 and died from injuries received in a car crash in Mississippi in 1937. She was orphaned at the age of seven and sang in the streets for pennies, eventually becoming a headliner in black vaudeville and the toast of New York's smart set (for whom her respect was not total: a hard-drinking woman, she took no nonsense from anyone). Her big, powerful voice, packing a huge emotional wallop, led to records for American Columbia from 1923-31; John Hammond brought her back into the studio for one last date in 1933 when she was no longer a commercial proposition. (As one era ended another began: a month later Hammond produced the great Billie Holiday's first records.) One-hundred-and-sixty of Bessie Smith's recordings survive, all now on CBS in five two-disc sets, with accompaniment by musicians such as Louis Armstrong and members of Fletcher Henderson's band of the period. In 1929 she made a short film, *St Louis Blues*, with a choir and band led by James P. Johnson. (Donald Clarke, March 1987.).

**ANY WOMAN'S BLUES**
Tracks: / Jailhouse blues / St. Louis gal / Sam Jones blues / Cemetery blues / Far away blues / I'm going back to my used to be / Whoa, Tillie / Take your time / My sweetie went away / Any woman's blues / Chicago bound blues / Mistreating Daddy / Frosty morning blues / Haunted house blues / Eavesdropper's blues / Easy come, easy go / Graveyard dream blues / I'm wild about that thing / You've got to give me some / Kitchen man / I've got what it takes / Nobody knows you (when you're down and out) / Take it right back / He's got me goin' / It makes my love come down / Wasted life blues / Dirty nogooder's blues / Blue spirit blues / Worn out papa blues / You don't understand / Don't cry baby / Keep it to yourself / New Orleans hop slop blues.
**Album:** Released '74, on CBS by CBS Records. Catalogue no: **CBS 66262**

**BESSIE SMITH 1925-33**
Tracks: / Careless love blues / Money blues / Good man is hard to find, A / I'm wild about that thing / Nobody knows you (when you're down and out).
**CD:** Released '89, on Hermes by Nimbus Records. Catalogue no: **HRM 6003**

**BESSIE SMITH COLLECTION (20 golden greats)**
Tracks: / Alexander's ragtime band / Gin House blues / Careless love blues / Nobody's blues but mine / What's the matter now? / Baby doll / Hard time blues / After you've gone / At the Christmas ball / Young woman's blues / Florida bound blues / I've been mistreated and I don't like it / Jazzbo Brown from Memphis Town / My man blues / I want ev'ry bit of it / New Gulf Coast blues / Squeeze me / Hard-driving papa / Lonesome desert blues / St. Louis blues.
**Cass:** Released Aug '85, on Deja Vu Catalogue no: **DVMC 2008**
**CD:** Released Dec '87, on Deja Vu Catalogue no: **DVCD 2008**
**Album:** Released Aug '85, on Deja Vu Catalogue no: **DVLP 2008**

**BESSIE SMITH STORY, THE (See panel above)**
Tracks: / Careless love blues / J.C. Holmes blues / He's gone blues / Nobody's blues but mine / I ain't got nobody / My man blues / New Gulf Coast blues / I've been mistreated and I don't like it / Lonesome desert blues / Squeeze me / What's the matter now? / I want every bit of it / Jazzbo Brown from Memphis Town / Gin house blues / Money blues / Baby

doll / Hard driving papa / Lost your head blues / Hard time blues / One and two blues / Young woman's blues / Preachin' the blues / Backwater blues / After you've gone / Alexander's ragtime band.
**Cass:** Released Apr '89, on Deja Vu Catalogue no: **DVRE MC 11**
**CD:** Released Apr '89, on Deja Vu Catalogue no: **DVRE CD 11**

**CLASSICS - VOL.3 - 1928/31**
**Cass:** Released Aug '81, on Neovox by Neovox Records. Catalogue no: **NEO 751**

**COLLECTION: BESSIE SMITH**
**CD:** Released May '89, on CBS (import) by CBS Records. Catalogue no: **463 339 2**
**Cass:** Released May '89, on CBS (import) by CBS Records. Catalogue no: **463 339 4**
**Album:** Released May '89, on CBS (import) by CBS Records. Catalogue no: **463 339 1**

**EMPRESS, THE (Including C.Hawkins,F.Henderson,L.Armstrong)**
Tracks: / Sing Sing Prison blues / Follow the deal on down / Sinful blues / Woman trouble blues / Love me daddy blues / Dying gambler's blues / St. Louis blues / Reckless blues / Sobbin' hearted blues / Cold in hand blues / You've been a good ole wagon / Cake walking babies from home / Yellow dog blues / Soft pedal blues / Dixie flyers blues / Nashville woman's blues / Muddy water / There'll be a hot time in the old town tonight / Trombone cholly / Send me to the 'lectric chair / Them's graveyard words / Hot springs blues / Lock and key / Mean old bedbug blues / Good man is hard to find, A / Homeless blues / Looking for my man blues / Dyin' by the hour / Foolish man blues / Thinking blues / Pickpocket blues.
**2 LP Set:** Released Sep '86, on Avan-Guard Catalogue no: **B2VL 082**

**EMPRESS OF THE BLUES**
Note: Featuring Fletcher Henderson, Louis Armstrong, Coleman Hawkins etc.
**Album:** Released Sep '87, on Giants of Jazz by Hasmick Promotions. Catalogue no: **LPJT 36**

**JAZZ CLASSICS IN DIGITAL STEREO**
Tracks: / Empty bed blues / Alexander's Ragtime Band / Preachin' the blues / Keep it to yourself / Trombone Cholly / At the Christmas Ball / Kitchen man / You've got to give me some / He's got me goin' / Devil's gonna git you / Send me to the 'lectric chair / Baby doll / Take me for a buggy ride / Young woman's blues.
Note: Features Bessie with such jazz giants as Coleman Hawkins,James P. Johnson, Charlie Green, Joe Smith, Fletcher Henderson Ahd Jack Teagarden
**Album:** Released Sep '86, on BBC by BBC Records & Tapes. Catalogue no: **REB 602**
**CD:** Released Sep '86, on BBC by BBC Records & Tapes. Catalogue no: **BBC CD 602**

**MOTHER OF THE BLUES**
**CD:** Released Mar '90, on Roots Catalogue no: **RTS 33**

**NOBODY'S BLUES BUT MINE**
Tracks: / Careless love blues / J.C. Holmes blues / I ain't goin' to play no second fiddle / He's gone blues / Nobody's blues but mine / I ain't got nobody / My man blues / New Gulf Coast blues / Florida bound blues / At the Christmas ball / I've been mistreated and I don't like it / Red mountain blues / Golden rule blues / Lonesome desert blues / Them has been blues / Squeeze me / What's the matter now? / I want ev'ry bit of it / Jazzbo Brown from Memphis town / Gin house blues / Money blues / Baby doll / Hard-driving papa / Lost your head blues / Hard time blues / Honey man blues / One and two blues / Young woman's blues / Preachin' the blues / Backwater blues / After you've gone / Alexander's ragtime band.
**LP Set:** Released '79, on CBS by CBS Records. Catalogue no: **CBS 67232**

**ST. LOUIS BLUES (Smith, Bessie & Various artists)**
Tracks: / I cover the waterfront / Somebody loves me / Do that thing / I don't know, I don't care blues / Freight train blues / Sorrowful blues / Don't shake it no more / Praying blues.
**Album:** Released Apr '81, on Jazz Live (Italy) Catalogue no: **BLJ 8001**

**WHOLE ST. LOUIS BLUES SOUNDTRACK**
**Album:** Released Apr '81, on Jazz Live (Italy) Catalogue no: **BLJ 8025**

**WORLDS GREATEST BLUES SINGER**
Tracks: / Down hearted blues / Gulf coast blues / Aggravatin' papa / Beale Street mama / Baby won't you please come home? / Oh daddy (you won't have no mama at all) / T'aint nobody's business if I do / Keeps on a rainin' (Papa, he can't make no time) / Mama's got the blues / Outside of that / Bleeding hearted blues / Yodelling blues / If you don't know who will / Nobody in town can bake a sweet jelly roll like mine / See if I care / Baby have pity on me / On revival day / Moan, you moaners / Hustlin' Dan / Black mountain blues / In the house blues / Long old road / Blue blue / Shipwreck blues / Need a little sugar in my bowl / Safety mama / Do your duty / Gimme a pigfoot and a bottle of beer / Take me for a buggy ride / Down in the dumps.
**2 LP Set:** Released 15 Aug '87, on CBS by CBS Records. Catalogue no: **CBS 66258**

## Smith, Charlie

**JAZZVILLE VOL.3 (Smith, Charlie Trio/Aaron Sachs Sextet)**
**Album:** Released Feb '88, on Fresh Sounds (Spain) by Fresh Sounds Records (Spain). Catalogue no: **FS 244**

**TESTIFYIN' (Smith,Charles/Chuck Armstrong/Ted Ford)**
Tracks: / My great loss (ashes to ashes) / Glad to be home / I'm useless / Why can't I cry / Only time you say you love me, The / Stand up and take it like a man / Pull me out of the water / Two pillows / Why does it hurt so bad / How sweet it is to be loved by you / I'm gonna forget about you / Keep your mind on me / She's gonna come back / Pretty girls everywhere / Please give me another chance / You're gonna need me.
Note: Original sound recordings made by Sound Stage 7/77 Records.
**Album:** Released Mar '87, on Charly R&B by Charly Records. Catalogue no: **CRB 1153**

## Smith, Clara

**Biographical details:** One of four famous women blues singers -- all Smiths and none related -- Clara Smith was born in Spartanburg, Carolina in 1894 and died in Detroit, Michegan in 1935. The greatest of the four was Bessie and the others were Mamie and Trixie. Clara's voice was higher and lighter than Bessie's but she was an all-rounder, singing pop and vaudeville songs as well as the blues, and was very popular in her day. Like Bessie, she recorded for Columbia: they recorded two duets in 1923. (Donald Clarke, March 1987.).

**CLARA SMITH VOL.1 (1923)**
**Album:** Released '74, on VJM (Vintage Jazz Music) by Vintage Jazz Music Society(VJM). Catalogue no: **VLP 15**
**Album:** Released '89, on Document Catalogue no: **DLP 566**

**CLARA SMITH VOL.2 (1923-24)**
**Album:** Released '74, on VJM (Vintage Jazz Music) by Vintage Jazz Music Society(VJM). Catalogue no: **VLP 16**
**Album:** Released '89, on Document Catalogue no: **DLP 567**

**CLARA SMITH VOL.3 (1924)**
**Album:** Released '89, on Document Catalogue no: **DLP 568**
**Album:** Released '74, on VJM (Vintage Jazz Music) by Vintage Jazz Music Society(VJM). Catalogue no: **VLP 17**

**CLARA SMITH VOL.4 (1925-26)**
**Album:** Released '89, on Document Catalogue no: **DLP 569**

**CLARA SMITH VOL.5 (1926-28)**
**Album:** Released '89, on Document Catalogue no: **DLP 570**

Jimmy Smith - Go For Watcha Know (Blue Note)

**CLARA SMITH VOL.6 (1928-30)**
**Album:** Released '89, on Document Catalogue no: **DLP 571**

**CLARA SMITH VOL.7 (1930-32)**
**Album:** Released '89, on Document Catalogue no: **DLP 572**

## Smith, Clarence

**COMPILATION 1928-29-30 (Smith, Clarence 'Pinetop' & Romeo Nelson)**
**Album:** Released Apr '86, on Oldie Blues Catalogue no: **OL 2330**

**COMPILATION (1929-30) (Smith, Clarence 'Pinetop' & Romeo Nelson)**
**Album:** Released '88, on Oldie Blues Catalogue no: **OL 2831**

## Smith, Derek

**DARK EYES (Smith, Derek Trio)**
**Album:** Released Apr '85, on East Wind Catalogue no: **EWIND 711**

**DEREK SMITH PLAYS THE MUSIC OF JEROME KERN**
Tracks: / Ol' man river / Fine romance, A / Folks who live on the hill, The / I'm old fashioned / Long ago and far away / Way you look tonight / I won't dance.
**Album:** Released '81, on Progressive (USA) by Jazzology Records (USA). Catalogue no: **PRO 7055**

**LOVE FOR SALE (Smith, Derek Trio)**
Tracks: / Love for sale / Summertime / Tristesse / Too close for comfort / One to warm up on / Autumn leaves / Sweet Lorraine / Day in the life of a fool, A.
Note: Derek Smith -- piano, George Duvivier -- bass, Bobby Rosengarden -- drums.
**Album:** Released Apr '81, on Progressive (USA) by Jazzology Records (USA). Catalogue no: **PRO 7002**

**MAN I LOVE, THE (Smith, Derek Quartet)**
Tracks: / Man I love, The / Yesterdays / Topsy / There's a small hotel / These foolish things / Between the Devil and the deep blue sea / I'm in the mood for love.
Note: Derek Smith -- piano, Scott Hamilton -- tenor sax, George Mraz -- bass, Billy Hart -- drums.
**Album:** Released Apr '81, on Progressive (USA) by Jazzology Records (USA). Catalogue no: **PRO 7035**

## Smith, Funny Papa

**ORIGINAL HOWLING WOLF, THE**
**Album:** Released Dec '88, on Yazoo (USA) by Shanachie Records (USA). Catalogue no: **L 1031**

## Smith, Hal

**HAL SMITH TRIO (Smith, Hal Trio)**
**Album:** Released Apr '89, on Jazzology (USA) by Jazzology Records (USA). Catalogue no: **J 156**

**HAL SMITH'S CREOLE SUNSHINE ORCHESTRA (Smith's Hal Creole Sunshine Orchestra)**
**Album:** Released Jun '86, on Stomp Off (USA) Catalogue no: **SOS 1077**

**HAL SMITH'S RHYTHMAKERS (Smith, Hal/ Butch Thompson)**
**Album:** Released '88, on Jazzology (USA) by Jazzology Records (USA). Catalogue no: **J 136**

## Smith, Jabbo

**SWEET 'N' LOW DOWN (Smith, Jabbo & His Rhythm Aces)**
Tracks: / Black and tan fantasy / Take me to the river / What more can a poor fellow do? / Sweet and low down / Sleepytime blues / Jazz battle / Little willie blues / Take your time / Sau sha stomp / Let's get together / Michigander blues / Decatur street tutti / Till times get better / Ace of rhythm.
**Cass:** Released Jul '86, on Affinity by Charly Records. Catalogue no: **TCAFS 1029**
**Album:** Released Jul '86, on Affinity by Charly Records. Catalogue no: **AFS 1029**

## Smith, Jimmy (USA)

**Biographical details:** Jimmy Smith, born in Norristown, Pennsylvania in 1925, became the most popular and influential jazz organist of all, his trio format widely imitated. About 20 albums for Blue Note, 1956-63, were issued, followed by Verve singles and albums, 1962-70, which crossed over to the American pop chart. (Donald Clarke, 1987.).

**BACK AT THE CHICKEN SHACK**
Tracks: / Back at the Chicken Shack (Track 1) / When I grow too old to dream (Track 2) / Minor chant (Track 3) / Messy Bessie (Track 4) / On the sunny side of the street (Track 5).
Note: This was the first and most celebrated meeting of pioneer organist Jimmy Smith
**CD:** Released Jun '87, on Blue Note by EMI Records. Catalogue no: **BNZ 90**
**CD:** Released Jun '87, on Blue Note by EMI Records. Catalogue no: **CDP 746 402 2**
**Album:** Released Nov '85, on Blue Note by EMI Records. Deleted Nov '88. Catalogue no: **BST 84117**
**Cass:** Released Sep '87, on Blue Note by EMI Records. Deleted Nov '88. Catalogue no: **4BN 84117**

**BASHIN (Unpredictable Jimmy Smith, The) (Smith, Jimmy & Big Big Band)**
Tracks: / Walk on the wild side / Ol' man river / In a mellow tone / Step right up / Beggar for the blues / Bashin' / I'm an old cowhand.
**CD:** Released May '82, on Verve (USA) by Polydor Ltd. Deleted Aug '87. Catalogue no: **823 308-2**
**Album:** Released Jun '81, on Verve Deleted '86. Catalogue no: **230 448 1**
**Album:** Released May '82, on Verve (USA) by Polydor Ltd. Deleted Mar '88. Catalogue no: **823 308-1**
**Cass:** Released May '82, on Verve (USA) by Polydor Ltd. Deleted Mar '88. Catalogue no: **823 308-4**

**BEST OF JIMMY SMITH (Blue Note years)**
Tracks: / Sermon / Fungii mama (CD

only.) / When Johnny comes marching home / Jumpin' the blues / Back at the chicken shack / Champ, The (CD only.) / All day long (CD only.).
**CD:** Released Dec '88, on Blue Note by EMI Records. Catalogue no: **BNZ 147**
**CD:** Released Dec '88, on Blue Note by EMI Records. Catalogue no: **CDP 791 140 2**
**Album:** Released Dec '88, on Blue Note by EMI Records. Catalogue no: **B1-91140**

**CAT STRIKES AGAIN, THE (Smith, Jimmy & Lalo Schifrin)**
**CD:** Released Feb '86, on Delta (1) by Delta Records. Deleted '88. Catalogue no: **DELTA 11025**

**CAT, THE**
Tracks: / Joy house theme / Basin Street blues / Cat, The / Carpetbagger's theme / St. Louis blues / Chicago serenade / Delon's blues / Blues in the night / Love cage (theme from).
**Album:** Released May '82, on Verve (USA) by Polydor Ltd. Deleted '88. Catalogue no: **2304 153**
**CD:** Released '83, on Verve Deleted Mar '88. Catalogue no: **810 046-2**
**Cass:** Released Apr '89, on Polydor by Polydor Ltd. Catalogue no: **810 046 4**
**Cass:** Released Jun '84, on Verve (USA) by Polydor Ltd. Catalogue no: **1912 205**
**Album:** Released Apr '89, on Polydor by Polydor Ltd. Catalogue no: **810 046 1**

**CHAMP, THE**
**Album:** Released Sep '84, on Blue Note by EMI Records. Catalogue no: **BLP 1514**

**CRAZY BABY**
Tracks: / When Johnny comes marching home / Makin' whoopee / Night in Tunisia / Sonnymoon for two / Mack the knife / What's new / Alfredo.
Note: Produced by Alfred Lion.
**Album:** Released Nov '86, on Blue Note by EMI Records. Catalogue no: **BST 84030**

**GO FOR WHATCHA KNOW (See panel on previous page)**
Tracks: / Fungii mama / Go for whatcha know / Bass face / She's out of my life / We can make it work / No substitute.
Note: Jimmy Smith (organ); Kenny Burrell (guitar); Stanley Turrentine (tenor saxophone); Monty Alexander (piano on *She's out of my life* and *We can make it work*); Grady Tate (drums/vocal on *She's out of my life*); Kenny Washington (drums on *She's out of my life*); Buster Williams (bass on *Bass face, She's out of my life* and *We can make it work* and Errol 'Crusher' Bennett (percussion on *Fungii mama* and *We can make it work.* Recorded in Englewood Cliffs, New Jersey, on January 2nd/3rd, 1986.
**Album:** Released Jul '89, on Blue Note by EMI Records. Catalogue no: **BT 85125**
**CD:** Released Sep '86, on Blue Note by EMI Records. Catalogue no: **CDP 746 297 2**
**CD:** Released Sep '86, on Blue Note by EMI Records. Catalogue no: **BNZ 93**

**GOT MY MOJO WORKING**
Tracks: / High heel sneekers / Satisfaction / One two three / Mustard greens / Got my mojo working / Johnny come lately / C jam blues / Hobson's hop.
**Album:** Released Mar '83, on Verve Catalogue no: **2304 191**
**Album:** Released Jun '66, on Verve Deleted Jun '71. Catalogue no: **VLP 912**

**GOT MY MOJO WORKING (SINGLE)**
Tracks: / Got my mojo working.
**7" Single:** Released Apr '66, on Verve Deleted May '69. Catalogue no: **VS 536**

**HOME COOKIN'**
**Album:** Released Sep '84, on Blue Note by EMI Records. Deleted '87. Catalogue no: **BST 84050**

**HOUSE PARTY**
Tracks: / J.O.S. / What is this thing called love / Just friends / Cherokee / Blues after all / Au privave / Lover man.
Note: This is the companion album to The Sermon, with two all-star groups including Lou Donaldson, Lee Morgan, Curtis Fuller, Kenny Burrell and Art Blakey.
**Cass:** Released Aug '85, on Blue Note by EMI Records. Deleted Nov '88. Catalogue no: **4BN 84002**
**CD:** Released May '87, on Blue Note by EMI Records. Catalogue no: **CDP 746 546 2**
**CD:** Released May '87, on Blue Note by EMI Records. Catalogue no: **BNZ 91**
**Album:** Released Jul '89, on Blue Note by EMI Records. Catalogue no: **BST 84002**

**JIMMY SMITH (Compact/Walkman jazz)**
**Cass:** Released Jun '87, on Verve Catalogue no: **831 374-4**
**CD:** Released Jun '87, on Verve Catalogue no: **831 374-2**

**JIMMY SMITH AT THE ORGAN**
Tracks: / Stranger In Paradise / It's A Sin To Tell A Lie / Night Winds / You Go To My Head / Sleepwalk 9 / Lost in lonliness / Dancing On The Ceiling / Blue Mist / Jungle bunny / Mr. Jim.
**Cass:** Released Mar '88, on Exel Catalogue no: **XELMC 102**
**CD:** Released Mar '88, on Exel Catalogue no: **XELCD 102**
**Album:** Released Mar '88, on Exel Catalogue no: **XELLP 102**

**JIMMY SMITH PLAYS THE BLUES (Compact/Walkman jazz)**
**CD:** Released 14 Aug '88, on Verve Deleted May '90. Catalogue no: **829 537-2**
**Cass:** Released 14 Aug '88, on Verve Catalogue no: **829 537-4**

**KEEP ON COMIN'**
Tracks: / Keep on comin' / Be yourself / No problem / Summertime / Yesterdays / Callitwhachawanna / Piano medley.
**Album:** Released '84, on WEA by WEA Records. Deleted '89. Catalogue no: **K960301-1**

**MIDNIGHT SPECIAL**
**Cass:** Released Sep '84, on Blue Note by EMI Records. Catalogue no: **BSC 84978**
**Album:** Released Apr '83, on Blue Note by EMI Records. Deleted Jan '88. Catalogue no: **BST 84078**
**Album:** Released Sep '84, on Blue Note by EMI Records. Deleted '87. Catalogue no: **BST 84978**

**MR.JIM**
Tracks: / Stranger in paradise / It's a sin to tell a lie / Night winds / You go to my head / Tenderly / Caravan / Bongo rock / Cherokee.
**Album:** Released Feb '81, on Manhattan Records by President Records. Deleted '85. Catalogue no: **MAN 5038**

**OFF THE TOP**
**CD:** Released Apr '84, on Elektra (Musician) by Elektra Records (USA). Catalogue no: **960 175-2**
**Album:** Released Oct '82, on Elektra (Musician) by Elektra Records (USA). Deleted Oct '87. Catalogue no: **K 52418**
**CD:** Released Apr '84, on Elektra by Elektra Records (UK). Catalogue no: **960 175-2**

**ORGAN GRINDER SWING**
**CD:** Released Jan '86, on Verve Deleted Mar '88. Catalogue no: **825 675-2**

**PRAYER MEETING**
Tracks: / Prayer meeting / I almost lost my mind / Stone cold dead / In the market / When the saints go marching in / Red top / Picnicking.
**CD:** Released Nov '88, on Blue Note by EMI Records. Deleted Aug '89. Catalogue no: **CZ 95**
**Cass:** Released Nov '84, on Blue Note by EMI Records. Deleted Nov '88. Catalogue no: **TC-BST 84164**
**CD:** Released Nov '88, on Blue Note by EMI Records. Catalogue no: **CDP 784 164 2**
**Album:** Released Mar '86, on Blue Note by EMI Records. Deleted '87. Catalogue no: **BST 84164**
**CD:** Released Nov '88, on Blue Note by EMI Records. Catalogue no: **BNZ 121**

**SERMON, THE**
Tracks: / Sermon / You came a long way from St. Louis / Ape woman / Georgia on my mind / G'won train / Any number can win / What'd I say / Ruby / Tubs / Blues for C.A..
**CD:** Released May '87, on Blue Note by EMI Records. Catalogue no: **BNZ 92**
**Album:** Released Apr '85, on Blue Note by EMI Records. Catalogue no: **BST 84011**
**CD:** Released May '87, on Blue Note by EMI Records. Catalogue no: **CDP 746 097 2**
**Album:** Released '79, on Blue Note by EMI Records. Deleted '84. Catalogue no: **2332085**
**Cass:** Released Apr '85, on Blue Note by EMI Records. Deleted Jun '88. Catalogue no: **4BN 84011**

**WHO'S AFRAID OF VIRGINIA WOOLF**
Tracks: / Slaughter on Tenth Avenue / Who's afraid of Virginia Woolfe / John Brown's body / Wives and lovers / Women of the world / Bluesette.
**CD:** Released Feb '85, on Polydor by Polydor Ltd. Deleted Mar '88. Catalogue no: **823 309-2**

## Smith, Johnny

**Biographical details:** Guitarist Johnny Smith's 1952 record of *Moonlight in Vermont* - with Stan Guest - was a jukebox hit. Born in Birmingham, Alabama, in 1922, Smith recorded for Roost from 1952 to 1963. (Donald Clarke, March 1987).

**FOURSOME VOL.2**
**Album:** Released Feb '88, on Fresh Sounds (Spain) by Fresh Sounds Records (Spain). Catalogue no: **FS 126**

**MOONLIGHT IN VERMONT (Smith, Johnny Quintet)**
**Album:** Released Feb '88, on Fresh Sounds (Spain) by Fresh Sounds Records (Spain). Catalogue no: **FS 92**
**2 LP Set:** Released Jan '78, on Vogue by Vogue Records. Catalogue no: **VJD 539**

**NEW QUARTET, THE**
**Album:** Released Feb '88, on Fresh Sounds (Spain) by Fresh Sounds Records (Spain). Catalogue no: **FS 127**

## Smith, Keith

**BALL OF FIRE (Smith, Keith & Vic Dickenson)**
Tracks: / Medi two / You're a lucky guy / I've got a feeling / After you've gone / Cherry Red rides again / Gee baby / Ball of fire / This one's for you, Lennie.
**Album:** Released Sep '79, on Hefty Jazz Catalogue no: **HJ 103**

**KEITH SMITH & ALTON PURNELL LIVE (Smith, Keith Band & Alton Purnell)**
**Album:** Released '74, on 77 by 77 Records. Catalogue no: **77 LEU 12/13**

**KEITH SMITH'S AMERICAN ALL-STARS IN EUROPE 1966 (Smith, Keith & His American All-Stars)**
Tracks: / Struttin' with some barbecue / Beale Street blues / Bugle boy / Melancholy blues / Panama rag / Royal Garden blues / See you kidder / Hindustan / Preaching / Shake it don't break it.
**Album:** Released Sep '79, on Hefty Jazz Catalogue no: **HJ 102**

**KEITH SMITH'S HEFTY JAZZ**
**Album:** Released Jun '88, on Jazzology (USA) by Jazzology Records (USA). Catalogue no: **J 145**

**TORONTO 66 (Smith, Keith with The American All Stars)**
**Album:** Released '74, on 77 by 77 Records. Catalogue no: **77LEU 12/13**

**UP JUMPED THE BLUES (Smith, Keith, Chosen Five & Benny Waters)**
**Album:** Released Sep '79, on Hefty Jazz Catalogue no: **HJ 105**

**WAY DOWN YONDER IN NEW ORLEANS (Smith, Keith & Sammy Rimmington)**
Tracks: / Down in the jungle town / Put a shine on your shoes / Black and blue / Way down yonder in New Orleans / Snag it / Ting a ling / Someday you'll be sorry / Memphis blues / Hymn for George / Struttin' with some barbecue.
**Album:** Released Sep '79, on Hefty Jazz Catalogue no: **HJ 101**

## Smith, Leo

**Biographical details:** Trumpeter and composer Smith, born in Mississippi in 1941, was a member of the AACM in Chicago in the 60's, along with the members of the Art Ensemble. *The burning of the stones* on his album *Spirit catcher* is scored for three harps whose parts are notated, while Smith improvises with a mute: a beautiful piece beautifully recorded. Most of his LPs are on his own Kabell label in America. (Donald Clarke, March 1987).

**DIVINE LOVE**
**Album:** Released May '79, on ECM Catalogue no: **ECM 1143**

**HUMAN RIGHTS**
**Album:** on Gramm Catalogue no: **GRAMM 24**

**PROCESSION OF THE GREAT ANCESTRY**
Tracks: / Blues: Jah jah is the greatest love / Procession of the great ancestry / Flower that seeds the earth, The / Third world, grainery of pure earth, The / Who killed David Walker? / Celestial sparks in the sanctuary / Nuru light: The prince of peace.
Note: An AACM alumni, trumpeter Smith is described by Anthony Braxton as a genius (it takes one to know one). On this 1983 set he is joined by Bobby Naughton on vibes, Joe Fonda on bass, Kahil El Zabar on percussion, and guests on various tracks. (Chief Records, June 1989)
**CD:** Released Jun '89, on Chief Catalogue no: **CHIEFCD 6**

**SPIRIT CATCHER**
**Album:** Released Sep '79, on Nessa Catalogue no: **N 19**

## Smith, Lonnie Liston

**Biographical details:** Keyboardist, composer and bandleader Smith, who was born in Richmond, Virginia, in 1940, has had most of his albums produced by Bob Theile, producer of John Coltrane's LPs on Impulse, since Smith recorded for Impulse with Pharoah Sanders. Smith, who also plays trumpet and tuba, wrote the Sanders album *Jewel of thought* and in 1973-74 he played with Miles Davis, at whose suggestion three CBS albums were made. (Donald Clarke, March 1987.).

**BEST OF LONNIE LISTON SMITH**
Tracks: / Quiet moments / Space princess / In the park / Give peace a chance / Fruit music / Gift of love / Journey into love.
**Cass:** Released Jan '81, on CBS by CBS Records. Catalogue no: **40 84348**
**Album:** Released Jan '81, on CBS by CBS Records. Catalogue no: **CBS 84348**

**BEST OF LONNIE LISTON SMITH, THE**
Tracks: / Expansions / Love beams / Song of love / Meditations / Voodoo woman / Space lady / Starlight and you starbeams.
**Album:** Released Apr '80, on RCA by BMG Records (UK). Deleted '85. Catalogue no: **PL 12897**

**DREAMS OF TOMORROW**
Tracks: / Lonely way to be / Mystic woman / Love I see in your eyes, The / Dreams of tomorrow / Never too late / Rainbows of love / Divine light / Garden of peace.
**Album:** Released Jul '83, on Doctor Jazz (USA) by CBS Records (USA). Catalogue no: **ASLP 1000**
**Cass:** Released Jul '83, on Doctor Jazz (USA) by CBS Records (USA). Catalogue no: **ZCAS 1000**

**EXPANSIONS**
Tracks: / Expansions / Voodoo woman.
**12" Single:** Released Nov '83, on Bluebird (2) by BMG Records (UK). Catalogue no: **BRT 4**

**GIVE PEACE A CHANCE**
Tracks: / Give peace a chance / Sunburst.
**12" Single:** Released Jun '80, on CBS by CBS Records. Deleted '83. Catalogue no: **13 8660**

**GOLDEN DREAMS**
Tracks: / Get down everybody (it's time for world peace) / Quiet dawn / Sunbeams / Meditations / Peace and love / Goddess of love / Inner beauty / Golden dreams / Journey into space / Astral travelling / Let us go into the house of the Lord / I mani / In search of truth.
**CD:** Released Nov '88, on Bluebird (2) by BMG Records (UK). Catalogue no: **ND 86886**

**GOTCHA**
Tracks: / Sweet honey wine / I need your love / What's done is done / Do it / Journey to within / My Latin sky.
**Album:** Released Apr '79, on TK Deleted '84. Catalogue no: **TKR 83356**

**IF YOU TAKE CARE OF ME**
Tracks: / If you take care of me / Just us two.
**7" Single:** Released Feb '85, on Doctor Jazz (USA) by CBS Records (USA). Catalogue no: **7AS 3500**

**LOVE GODDESS**
Tracks: / Love goddess / Obsession / Heaven / Monk's mood / Star flower / Giving you the best that I've got / Don't write cheques that your body can't cash / Dance floor / I'm your melody (Only on cassette and CD.) / Blue in green (Only on cassette and CD.) / Blue Bossa (Only on cassette and CD.) / Child is born, A (Only on cassette and CD.).
**Cass:** Released Mar '90, on Star Track

Catalogue no: **STAMC 4021**
**Album:** Released Mar '90, on Star Track Catalogue no: **STA 4021**
**CD:** Released Mar '90, on Star Track Catalogue no: **STACD 4021**

**LOVE IS THE ANSWER**
Tracks: / In the park / Love is the answer / Speak about it / Bridge through time / On the real side / Enchantress / Give peace a chance / Free and easy.
**Album:** Released Jul '80, on CBS by CBS Records. Deleted Jul '85. Catalogue no: **CBS 84365**

**LOVELAND**
Tracks: / Sunburst / Journey into love / Floating through space / Bright moments / We can dream / Springtime magic / Loveland / Explorations.
**Album:** Released '74, on CBS by CBS Records. Catalogue no: **82837**

**NEVER TOO LATE**
Tracks: / Never too late / Divine light.
**12" Single:** Released Jul '83, on Doctor Jazz (USA) by CBS Records (USA). Deleted Jul '86. Catalogue no: **ASL 100**
**7" Single:** Released Jul '83, on Doctor Jazz (USA) by CBS Records (USA). Deleted Jul '86. Catalogue no: **7 AS 100**

**REJUVENATION**
**Album:** Released Mar '86, on Doctor Jazz (USA) by CBS Records (USA). Deleted '88. Catalogue no: **ASLP 810**
**Cass:** Released Mar '86, on Doctor Jazz (USA) by CBS Records (USA). Deleted '88. Catalogue no: **ZCAS 810**

**RENAISSANCE**
Tracks: / Space lady / Mardi gras / Starlight and you / Mongotee / Song of love / Between here and there / Renaissance.
**Album:** Released Jan '77, on RCA by BMG Records (UK). Deleted '80. Catalogue no: **PL 11822**

**SILHOUETTES**
Tracks: / Warm / If you take care of me I'll take care of you / Silhouettes / Summer afternoon / Enlightenment / City of lights / Once again love / Just us two.
Note: Produced by Bob Thiele Jnr.
**Cass:** Released Nov '84, on Doctor Jazz (USA) by CBS Records (USA). Catalogue no: **ZCAS 805**
**Album:** Released Nov '84, on Doctor Jazz (USA) by CBS Records (USA). Catalogue no: **ASLP 805**

**SONG FOR THE CHILDREN**
Tracks: / Song for the children / Lover's dream / Aquarian cycle / Street festival / Midsummer magic / Nightlife / Gift of love / Fruit music.
**Album:** Released Feb '80, on CBS by CBS Records. Deleted '85. Catalogue no: **83809**

**THINK**
Tracks: / Son of Ice Bag / Call of the wild / Think / Three blind mice / Slouchin'.
Note: Produced by Francis Wolff.
**Album:** Released Jul '89, on Blue Note by EMI Records. Catalogue no: **BST 84290**
**CD:** Released Mar '89, on Blue Note by EMI Records. Catalogue no: **BNZ 136**
**Album:** Released Jul '89, on Blue Note by EMI Records. Catalogue no: **784 290 1**
**CD:** Released Mar '89, on Blue Note by EMI Records. Catalogue no: **CDP 784 290 2**

## Smith, Louis

**LOUIS SMITH QUINTET (Smith, Louis Quintet)**
**Album:** Released '78, on Steeplechase (USA) Catalogue no: **SCS 1096**

**PRANCIN'**
**Album:** Released Sep '79, on Steeplechase (USA) Catalogue no: **SCS 1121**

## Smith, Mamie

**CRAZY BLUES**
Tracks: / That thing called love / You can't keep a good man down / Crazy blues / It's right here for you / Fare thee honey blues / Road is rocky, The / Mem'ries of you mammy / If you don't want me blues / Don't care blues / Lovin' Sam from Alabam / Jazzbo Ball / What have I done / Frankie blues / "U" need some loving blues / Dangerous blues / Daddy, your mama is lonesome for you.
**Album:** on Official by Official Records. Catalogue no: **OFF 6037**

**GOIN' CRAZY WITH THE BLUES**
**Album:** Released May '89, on Document Catalogue no: **DLP 555**

**MAMIE SMITH VOL.1 (Crazy blues)**
**Album:** Released May '89, on Document Catalogue no: **DLP 551**

**MAMIE SMITH VOL.2 (Get hot)**
**Album:** Released May '89, on Document Catalogue no: **DLP 552**

**MAMIE SMITH VOL.3 (Mamie Smith blues 1922)**
**Album:** Released May '89, on Document Catalogue no: **DLP 553**

**MAMIE SMITH VOL.4 (First lady of the blues)**
**Album:** Released May '89, on Document Catalogue no: **DLP 554**

## Smith, Marvin

**KEEPER OF THE DRUMS**
Tracks: / Just have fun / Miss Ann / Love will find a way / Song of joy / Creeper, The / Now I know / Thinking of you / Simple samba song, A.
**Cass:** Released Sep '87, on Concord Jazz by Concord Jazz Records (USA). Catalogue no: **CJC 325**
**Album:** Released Sep '87, on Concord Jazz by Concord Jazz Records (USA). Catalogue no: **CJ 325**
**CD:** Released Oct '87, on Concord Jazz by Concord Jazz Records (USA). Catalogue no: **CCD 4325**

**ROAD LESS TRAVELLED, THE (Smith, Marvin 'Smitty')**
Tracks: / Neighbourhood, The / Wish you were here with me part 1 / Gothic 17 / Road less travelled, The / I'll love you always / Salsa blue / Concerto in B.G. / Wish you were here with me part 2.
**CD:** Released Jul '89, on Concord by Concord Jazz Records (USA). Catalogue no: **CCD 4379**
**Cass:** Released Jul '89, on Concord by Concord Jazz Records (USA). Catalogue no: **CJ 379C**
**Album:** Released Jul '89, on Concord by Concord Jazz Records (USA). Catalogue no: **CJ 379**

## Smith St Society

**TAKE ME TO THE LAND OF JAZZ**
**Album:** Released Jun '88, on GHB by Jazzology Records (USA). Catalogue no: **GHB 208**

## Smith, Stuff

**Biographical details:** The most influential of jazz violinists, Smith was born Hezekiah Leroy Gordon Smith in 1909 in Portsmouth, Ohio, and died in Munich in 1967. He played an amplified instrument and led swinging groups on 52nd Street which were not recorded often enough. He recorded on Vocalion and American Decca in 1936 and 1937, later on Varsity (1939-40) and Verve in the 50's. (Donald Clarke, March 1987.).

**DESERT SANDS**
Tracks: / Desert sands / Soft winds / Things ain't what they used to be / It don't mean a thing / Time and again / I know that you know.
Note: Stuff Smith -- violin, Oscar Peterson -- piano, Barney Kessel -- guitar, Ray Brown -- bass. Recorded in 1957.
**Album:** Released May '82, on Verve Catalogue no: **2304 536**

**LIVE AT MONTMATRE**
**Album:** Released Feb '90, on Storyville by Storyville Records AB. Catalogue no: **SLP 4142**
**CD:** Released Feb '90, on Storyville by Storyville Records AB. Catalogue no: **STCD 4142**

**LIVE IN PARIS 1965**
**Album:** Released Oct '88, on France's Concert Catalogue no: **FC 120**
**CD:** Released Oct '88, on France's Concert Catalogue no: **FCD 120**

**STUFF SMITH AND ONYX CLUB (Smith, Stuff & His Onyx Club Orchestra)**
**Album:** Released '88, on Collector's Classics Catalogue no: **12-12**

**STUFF SMITH TRIO 1943 (Smith, Stuff Trio)**
**Album:** Released Apr '89, on Circle Catalogue no: **CLP 132**

**SWINGIN' STUFF (Smith, Stuff Quartet)**
Tracks: / Bugle blues / Only time will tell / C jam blues / One o'clock jump / My blue Heaven / Blues for Timmy.
**Album:** Released '86, on Storyville by Storyville Records AB. Catalogue no: **SLP 4087**

**VARSITY SESSION THE VOL. 2 (Smith, Stuff & His Orchestra)**
**Album:** Released Jul '81, on Storyville by Storyville Records AB. Catalogue no: **SLP 703**

## Smith, Tab

### I DON'T WANT TO PLAY IN YOUR KITCHEN
**Album:** Released Aug '87, on Saxophonograph (Sweden) Catalogue no: **BP 503**

### JOY AT THE SAVOY
**Album:** Released Aug '87, on Saxophonograph (Sweden) Catalogue no: **BP 509**

### WORLD'S GREATEST ALTOIST - THESE FOOLISH THINGS
Tracks: / I can't believe that you're in love with me / It's no sin / Spider rock / My baby / Cherry / Slow and easy / Seven up / Moondream / These foolish things / T.G. blues / Love is a wonderful thing / Can't we take a chance / You belong to me / Ace high / Cottage for sale / All my life.
**Album:** Released Aug '89, on Saxophonograph (Sweden) Catalogue no: **BP 511**

## Smith, Tommy

### ALLY THE WALLYGATOR (Promo only)
Tracks: / Ally the wallygator / Pillow talk / Ever never land.
Note: Both tracks taken from album Step By Step.
**12" Single:** on Blue Note Int. by EMI Records. Catalogue no: **12BLTP 1**

### GIANT STRIDES
**Album:** Released Feb '87, on GFM Catalogue no: **GFM LP8001**

### PEEPING TOM
Tracks: / New road, The / Follow your heart / Merry go round / Slip of the tongue / Interval time (CD only.) / Simple pleasures (CD only.) / Peeping Tom / Quiet picnic (CD only.) / Affairs, please / Harlequin / Boats and boxes (CD only.) / Biting at the apple / Baked air (CD only.).
**CD:** Released May '90, on Blue Note Int. by EMI Records. Catalogue no: **CDP 794 335 2**
**CD:** Released May '90, on Blue Note Int. by EMI Records. Catalogue no: **CDBLT 1002**
**Cass:** Released May '90, on Blue Note Int. by EMI Records. Catalogue no: **TCBLT 1002**
**Cass:** Released May '90, on Blue Note Int. by EMI Records. Catalogue no: **794 335 4**
**Album:** Released May '90, on Blue Note Int. by EMI Records. Catalogue no: **BLT 1002**
**Album:** Released May '90, on Blue Note Int. by EMI Records. Catalogue no: **794 335 1**

### STEP BY STEP
Tracks: / Ally the wallygator / Step by step / Ghosts / Pillowtalk / Time piece / Springtim / Freetime (CD only.) / Ever never land (CD only.).
Note: Produced by Gary Burton. Arranged by Tommy Smith.,
**Cass:** Released Mar '89, on Blue Note Int. by EMI Records. Catalogue no: **TCBLT 1001**
**CD:** Released Mar '89, on Blue Note Int. by EMI Records. Catalogue no: **CDBLT 1001**
**Album:** Released Mar '89, on Blue Note Int. by EMI Records. Catalogue no: **BLT 1001**
**CD:** Released Mar '89, on Blue Note Int. by EMI Records. Catalogue no: **CDP 791 930 2**

## Smith, Willie

**Biographical details:** One of the great all-round entertainers of the swing era, Willie Smith was born in Charleston, South Carolina, in 1910 and died in Los Angeles in 1967. He played alto sax, wrote arrangements and sang in the vocal trio with the popular band of Jimmy Lunceford from 1929 to 1942, then played for nearly 20 years with Harry James except for short periods with Duke Ellington and Billy May in '51 and '53. He also toured with Jazz at the Philharmonic and recorded with Nat King Cole. (Donald Clarke, March 1987.).

### TEA FOR TWO
Tracks: / Morning after / I had a premonition / My heart is a heartless ring / I'm a heck of a guy / Flight of the jitterbug / St. Louis blues / I've got it bad / Blue skies / How high the moon / Tea for two / Moon child.
**Album:** Released Apr '81, on Jazz Live (Italy) Catalogue no: **BLJ 8040**

## Smith, Willie 'Lion'

### GRAND PIANO (DUETS) (Smith, Willie The Lion & Don Ewell)
Tracks: / I've found a new baby / Porter's love song, A / I would do anything for you / Some of these days / Just you, just me / Everybody loves my baby / Can't we be friends / You took advantage of me / Keepin' out of mischief now / Sweet Georgia Brown.
**Album:** Released Jan '83, on Swaggie (Australia) Catalogue no: **S 1228**
**Album:** Released Apr '81, on Sackville by Spotlite Records. Catalogue no: **2004**

### HARLEM PIANO (Smith, Willie The Lion & Luckey Roberts)
**Album:** Released Jul '81, on Good Time Jazz(USA) by Fantasy Inc (USA). Catalogue no: **1010 035**

### MEMOIRS OF WILLIE 'THE LION'
Tracks: / Relaxin' / Sand dune / Alexander's ragtime band / Shine / That barbershop chord / Redhead / Where's my red red rose? / Blue skies / Nagasaki / Running wild / Diga diga doo / Got everything but you / Doin' the new low down / Love will find a way / I'm just wild about Harry / Memories of you / Porter's love song to a chambermaid, A / Old-fashioned love / Carolina shout / Ain't misbehavin' / Keepin' out of mischief now / Sophisticated lady / Solitude / Portrait of the Duke / Satin doll / When it's sleepy time down South / Sheik of Araby, The / Keep your temper / Bring on the band / Old stamping ground / Harlem joys / Love remembers / I'm all out of breath / Tango a la Caprice / Sneakaway.
**Album:** Released Jan '83, on RCA (France) by BMG Records (France). Catalogue no: **PL 43171**

### MEMORIAL
**2 LP Set:** Released Oct '88, on Vogue by Vogue Records. Catalogue no: **400021**

### ORIGINAL 14 PLUS TWO
Tracks: / Morning air / Echoes of spring / Concentrating / Fading star / Passionette / Rippling waters / Sneakaway / Finger buster / What is there to say? / Between the Devil and the deep blue sea / Boy in the boat, The / Tea for two / I'll follow you / Stormy weather / Three keyboards / Lion and the lamb.
**Album:** Released Sep '83, on Teldec (1) by ASV (Academy Sound & Vision). Catalogue no: **6.25491**
**Album:** Released May '87, on Commodore Class Catalogue no: **6 24591**

### PORK AND BEANS
Tracks: / Pork and beans / Moonlight cocktail / Spanish Venus / Junk man rag / Squeeze me / Love will find a way / I'm just wild about Harry / Memories of you / Alexander's ragtime band / All of me / Ain't misbehavin' / Man I love, The / Summertime / Ain't she sweet.
**Album:** Released Jan '85, on Black Lion Catalogue no: **BLP 30123**

### WILLIE 'THE LION' SMITH
**Album:** Released '88, on GNP Crescendo (USA) by GNP Crescendo Records (USA). Catalogue no: **GNPS 9011**

### WILLIE 'THE LION' SMITH VOL 1
Tracks: / Echo of spring / Here comes the band / Relaxin' / Contrary motions / Zig zag / Twelfth Street rag / Late hours / Portrait of the Duke / Dardanella / Quand Madelon / Cuttin' out / Charleston / Carolina shout / I'm gonna ride the rest of the way.
**Album:** Released Jan '82, on Jazz Reactivation Catalogue no: **JR 113**

### WILLIE 'THE LION' SMITH VOL 2
Tracks: / Darktown strutters' ball / Ain't misbehavin' / Stormy weather / Get together blues / Nagasaki / Can you hear me? / Trains and planes / Pretty baby / Conversation on Park Avenue / Sweet Sue.
**Album:** Released May '83, on Jazz Reactivation Catalogue no: **JR 132**

## Snidero, Jim

### MIXED BAG (Snidero, Jim Quintet)
**Album:** Released Apr '89, on Criss Cross Catalogue no: **CRISS 1032**

## Snow, Phoebe

**Biographical details:** Born in 1952 in Teaneck, New Jersey, Snow is a jazz-influenced singer, guitarist and songwriter. She began writing poems and setting them to music. Her first album was on Leon Russell's Shelter label: *Phoebe Snow* (1974) included *Poetry Man*, a Top Five hit in America. Backing on various tracks has included musicians of the calibre of Stan Getz, Teddy Wilson and Ron Carter. All Snow's albums have charted in the US and are still available there. (Donald Clarke, March

1987.).

**AGAINST THE GRAIN**
Tracks: / Every night / Do right woman, dor right man / He's not just another man / Random time / In my life / You have not won / Mama don't break down / Oh L.A. / Married men / Keep a watch on the shoreline.
**Album:** Released Feb '79, on CBS by CBS Records. Deleted Feb '84. Catalogue no: **CBS 82915**

**BEST OF PHOEBE SNOW**
Tracks: / Two fisted love / All over / Poetry man / Teach me tonight / Don't let me down / Shaky ground / Love makes a woman / Never letting go / Every night / Harpo's blues.
**Album:** Released Jun '81, on CBS by CBS Records. Deleted '86. Catalogue no: **CBS 84909**
**Album:** Released Apr '85, on CBS by CBS Records. Catalogue no: **CBS 32643**
**Cass:** Released Apr '85, on CBS by CBS Records. Catalogue no: **40 32643**

**EVERY NIGHT**
Tracks: / Every night.
**7" Single:** Released Jan '79, on CBS by CBS Records. Deleted Jan '82. Catalogue no: **CBS 6842**

**GAMES**
Tracks: / Games / Down in the basement.
**7" Single:** Released Apr '81, on Atlantic by WEA Records. Catalogue no: **K 11566**

**GASOLINE ALLEY**
Tracks: / Gasoline Alley / I believe in you.
**7" Single:** Released Jun '81, on Mirage (USA) Catalogue no: **K 11663**

**IF I CAN JUST GET THROUGH THE NIGHT**
Tracks: / If I can just get through the night / Soothin' / Our love is insane.
**7" Single:** Released Apr '89, on Elektra by Elektra Records (UK). Catalogue no: **EKR 91**
**12" Single:** Released Apr '89, on Elektra by Elektra Records (UK). Catalogue no: **EKR 91T**
**CD Single:** Released Apr '89, on Elektra by Elektra Records (UK). Deleted Jan '90. Catalogue no: **EKR 91CD**

**IT LOOKS LIKE SNOW**
Tracks: / Autobiography / Teach me tonight / Stand up on the rock / In my girlish days / Mercy on those / Don't let me down / Drink up the melody / Fat chance / My faith is blind / Shakey ground.
**Album:** Released Feb '77, on CBS by CBS Records. Deleted '81. Catalogue no: **CBS 81714**

**ROCK AWAY**
Tracks: / Cheap thrills / Baby please / Gasoline Alley / Rock away / Mercy, mercy, mercy / Games / Down in the basement / Shoo-rah-shoo-rah / Something good / I believe in you / Two fisted love / All over / Poetry man / Teach me tonight / Don't let me down / Shakey ground / Love makes a woman / Never letting go / Every night / Harpo's blues.
**Album:** Released Apr '81, on Mirage (USA) Catalogue no: **K 50780**
**Cass:** Released Apr '81, on Mirage (USA) Catalogue no: **K4 50780**

**SOMETHING REAL**
Tracks: / Mr. Wondering / Touch your soul / I'm your girl / Soothin' / Cardiac arrest / Something real / We might never feel this way / If I can just get through the night / Best of my love.
**Cass:** Released Apr '89, on Elektra by Elektra Records (UK). Catalogue no: **EKT 56 C**
**CD:** Released Apr '89, on Elektra by Elektra Records (UK). Catalogue no: **960 852 2**
**Album:** Released Apr '89, on Elektra by Elektra Records (UK). Catalogue no: **EKT 56**

## Solal, Martial

**Biographical details:** French jazz pianist and composer Solal was born in Algiers in 1927. He replaced the great Bud Powell in the famous Paris-based rhythm section with Kenny Clarke on drums and bassist Pierre Michelot to play on many fine albums in the 1950's and 60's. He has also led his own groups, played solo concerts, done film work and been a teacher. He is very highly regarded by critics and jazz fans and would probably have become more famous sooner if he had been an American. (Donald Clarke, March 1987.).

**BIG A BAND**
**Album:** Released '85, on CY (France) Catalogue no: **733617**

**LIVE 1959/85**
**CD:** Released '86, on Accord (France) by Musidisc Records (France). Catalogue no: **239 963**

**SOLAL '56**
**Album:** Released Nov '88, on Vogue by Vogue Records. Catalogue no: **500110**

**SOLO SOLAL**
**Album:** Released May '81, on MPS Jazz Catalogue no: **MPS 68 221**

**SUITE FOR TRIO**
**Album:** Released May '81, on MPS Jazz Catalogue no: **MPS 68 002**

## Soloff, Lew

**BUT BEAUTIFUL**
**CD:** Released Sep '88, on Electric Bird Catalogue no: **K32Y 6209**
**Album:** Released Sep '88, on Electric Bird Catalogue no: **K 28P 6468**

**HANALEI BAY**
Tracks: / Salazar / My buddy / Hanalei bay / Feliciade, A / La toalla / Emily / Well you needn't.
Note: Ex-member of Blood,Sweat & Tears trumpeter Lew Soloff presents an album of fusion jazz using both acoustic and electric instruments. The material ranges from the beautiful ballads *My buddy* and *A felicidade* to the latin percussive *Handel Bay*. Gil Evans is featured on electric piano.
Personnel: Lew Soloff - trumpet, flugehorn; Gil Evans - electric piano; Pete Levin - synthsizer; Hiram Bullock - guitars; Mark Egon - bass; Adam Nussbaum-drums; Kenwood Dennard - drums; Manolo Badrena - percussion.
**Album:** Released '86, on King Catalogue no: **K28P 6365**

**YESTERDAYS**
**CD:** Released Oct '87, on King (Japan) Catalogue no: **K32Y 6120**
**Album:** Released Apr '87, on King (Japan) Catalogue no: **K 28P 6448**

## Some People

**BLUE HEAVEN**
Tracks: / Blue heaven / Like the stranger.
**7" Single:** Released Nov '88, on Breakin' by Breakin' Records. Catalogue no: **7 BRK 6**

## Some People Play

**SOME PEOPLE PLAY GUITAR LIKE A LOTTA PEOPLE DON'T (Various artists)**
Tracks: / Tell me, baby: *Grossman, Stefan* / Good gal: *Mann, Woody* / Old devil: *Mann, Woody* / Crosstown blues: *Mann, Woody* / Bad luck blues: *Bookbinder, Roy* / Delta swing: *Sandberg, Larry* / I got mine: *Bookbinder, Roy* / Bye bye baby blues: *Bookbinder, Roy* / Swingin' blues: *Davis, Rev. Gary* / Darktown strutters' ball: *Davis, Rev. Gary* / Who's been here?: *Mann, Woody* / Good morning little schoolgirl: *Grossman, Stefan.*
**Album:** Released '74, on Kicking Mule by Sonet Records. Catalogue no: **SNKF 102**

## Somers, Debroy

**DEBROY SOMERS & HIS BAND 1927-32 (Somers, Debroy & His Band)**
Tracks: / Savoy sea songs medley / Masquerade / Red roofed chalet, A / Laughing Marionette / Roses for remembrance / In a little Spanish town / Slipping round the corner / Going home / Night time brings dreams of you / So blue / Night when love was born, The / You're just the one girl for me / Rag doll / Sunset down in Somerset / Good news selection / Just imagine / Best things in life are free, The / Lucky in love / Varsity drag.
**Album:** Released Jul '84, on Joy by President Records. Catalogue no: **JOYD 282**

## Son Of Jazz

**SON OF JAZZ FOR ABSOLUTE BEGINNERS/ (Various artists)**
Tracks: / Doctor Jazz: *Morton, Jelly Roll* / St. Louis shuffle: *Henderson, Fletcher & His Orchestra* / Ain't misbehavin': *Bechet, Sidney* / Handful of keys: *Waller, Fats* / Flaming youth: *Ellington, Duke* / Blue washboard stomp: *Dodds, Johnny Washboard Band* / I got a right to sing the blues: *Armstrong, Louis/his orchestra* / Maple leaf rag: *New Orleans Feetwarmers* / Hyena stomp: *Morton, Jelly Roll* / Texas stomp: *Big Maceo* / I'm

gonna stomp: *Eddie's Hot Shots* / It should be you: *Allen, Henry 'Red' & his Orchestra* / Oh didn't he ramble?: *Morton, Jelly Roll* / Mr. Henry Lee: *Eddie's Hot Shots* / Edna: *King Oliver & Orchestra.*
**Album:** Released Jan '87, on RCA by BMG Records (UK). Deleted Jul '89. Catalogue no: **NL 89963**
**Cass:** Released Jan '87, on RCA by BMG Records (UK). Deleted Jul '89. Catalogue no: **NK 89963**

## Sondergaard, Jens

**NO COAST**
**Album:** Released Jun '88, on Storyville by Storyville Records AB. Catalogue no: **SLP 4126**

## Songsters & Saints

**SONGSTERS & SAINTS VOL.1 Various blues & gospel artists (Various artists)**
Note: Mono. 2 LP set. Artists include: Peg Leg Howell, Memphis jug band, Julius Daniels, George Owens/Will Bennett/Hezekiah Jenkins/Rev. Jim Beal/Rev. A.W. Nix/Rev. J.E.Burch/Rev. Leora Ross.
**2 LP Set:** Released Dec '88, on Matchbox by Flyright Records. Catalogue no: **MSE 2001/2**
**2 LP Set:** Released Nov '84, on Matchbox by Flyright Records. Catalogue no: **MSEX 2001/2**

**SONGSTERS & SAINTS VOL.2 Various blues & gospel artists (Various artists)**
**2 LP Set:** Released Dec '88, on Matchbox by Flyright Records. Catalogue no: **MSE 2003/4**
**2 LP Set:** Released May '85, on Matchbox by Flyright Records. Catalogue no: **MSEX 2003/4**

## Sons Of Bix

**OSTRICH WALK**
**Album:** Released Jun '86, on Jazzology (USA) by Jazzology Records (USA). Catalogue no: **J 59**

## Sophisticated...

**SOPHISTICATED GENTLEMEN (Various artists)**
Tracks: / Where do I begin...: *Various artists* / As time goes by: *Damone, Vic* / I left my heart: *Bennett, Tony* / Softly as I leave you: *Monro, Matt* / Dream a little dream of me: *Various artists* / It's impossible: *Martino, Al* / Night and day: *Mathis, Johnny* / More: *Cole, Nat "King"* / Just walking in the rain: *Ray, Johnnie* / Take me to your heart: *Hill, Vince* / Lazy river: *Carmichael, Hoagy* / What kind of fool am I: *Goulet, Robert* / Edelweiss: *Hill, Vince* / On a clear day: *Mathis, Johnny* / All I do is dream of you: *Martin, Dean* / My foolish heart: *Martino, Al* / Unforgettable: *Cole, Nat "King"* / Love for sale: *Bennett, Tony* / I can't stop loving you: *Monro, Matt* / On the street where you live: *Damone, Vic* / Hey there: *Ray, Johnnie* / Something stupid: *Williams, Andy.*
**2 LP Set:** Released 7 Nov '87, on Connoisseur Collection by Connoisseur Collection Ltd.. Catalogue no: **VSOPLP 103**
**Cass:** Released 7 Nov '87, on Connoisseur Collection by Connoisseur Collection Ltd.. Catalogue no: **VSOPMC 103**

**SOPHISTICATED GENTLEMEN VOL.2 (Various artists)**
Tracks: / Shadow of your smile: *Como, Perry* / On the street where you live: *Whitfield, David* / Best things in life are free, The: *Lanza, Mario* / Moon river: *Williams, Danny* / Ain't misbehavin': *Armstrong, Louis* / All by myself: *Darin, Bobby* / Rainy night in Georgia: *Benton, Brook* / Mack the knife: *Darin, Bobby* / Love is a many splendoured thing: *Williams, Danny* / Answer me: *Whitfield, David* / My melancholy baby: *Bowly, Al* / Take me: *Rushing,Jimmy / Count Basie & his Orchestra* / Jealousy: *Various artists* / Fools rush in: *Benton, Brook* / King Joe: *Robeson, Paul* / Love is the sweetest thing: *Bowly, Al* / How long: *Rushing,Jimmy / Count Basie & his Orchestra* / Honeysuckle rose: *Murphy, Mark* / Moonglow: *Como, Perry* / Blue skies: *Darin, Bobby* / High noon: *Laine, Frankie* / Memories: *Lanza, Mario* / Nobody knows the trouble I've seen: *Robeson, Paul* / I only have eyes for you: *Murphy, Mark.*
**Cass:** Released Nov '88, on Connoisseur Collection by Connoisseur Collection Ltd.. Catalogue no: **VSOPMC 127**
**2 LP Set:** Released Nov '88, on Connoisseur Collection by Connoisseur Collection Ltd.. Catalogue no: **VSOPLP 127**
**CD:** Released Nov '88, on Connoisseur Collection by Connoisseur Collection Ltd.. Catalogue no: **VSOPCD 127**

**SOPHISTICATED GENTLEMEN VOL.3 (Various artists)**
Tracks: / Lady is a tramp: *Greco, Buddy* / Oh look at me now: *Darin, Bobby* / What kind of fool am I?: *Vale, Jerry* / Stranger in paradise: *Bennett, Tony* / Shadow of your smile: *Monro, Matt* / I'll buy you a star: *Mathis, Johnny* / At long last love: *Greco, Buddy* / Sunday in New York: *Darin, Bobby* / Sunrise sunset: *Vale, Jerry* / For once in my life: *Bennett, Tony* / Walking happy: *Monro, Matt* / Stairway to the stars: *Mathis, Johnny* / In the still of the night: *Damone, Vic* / Street of dreams: *Rawls, Lou* / Day in day out: *Cole, Nat "King"* / I don't know enough: *Jones, Jack* / Canadian sunset: *Williams, Andy* / Spanish eyes: *Martino, Al* / Change partners: *Damone, Vic* / Beautiful friendship: *Rawls, Lou* / To the ends of the earth: *Cole, Nat "King"* / This love of mine: *Jones, Jack* / Man and a woman, A: *Williams, Andy* / Three coins in the fountain: *Martino, Al.*
**Cass:** Released Nov '89, on Connoisseur Collection by Connoisseur Collection Ltd.. Catalogue no: **VSOPMC 146**
**2 LP Set:** Released Nov '89, on Connoisseur Collection by Connoisseur Collection Ltd.. Catalogue no: **VSOPLP 146**
**CD:** Released Nov '89, on Connoisseur Collection by Connoisseur Collection Ltd.. Catalogue no: **VSOPCD 146**

**SOPHISTICATED LADIES (Various artists)**
Tracks: / When I fall in love: *Day, Doris* / I've got you: *Shore, Dinah & Andre Previn* / Summertime: *Holiday, Billie* / Younger than...: *Whiting, Margaret* / As time goes by: *Lee, Peggy* / Over the rainbow: *Garland, Judy* / Fever: *Lee, Peggy* / What is this thing: *Smith, Keely* / Come rain or come shine: *Garland, Judy* / Too old to cut the mustard: *Clooney, Rosemary* / Blowin' in the wind: *Dietrich, Marlene* / It ain't necessarily so: *Franklin, Aretha* / I'll never stop loving you: *Day, Doris* / Moonlight in Vermont: *Whiting, Margaret* / It might as well be...: *Vaughan, Sarah* / Keep on a-rainin': *Smith, Bessie.*
**2 LP Set:** Released 7 Nov '87, on Connoisseur Collection by Connoisseur Collection Ltd.. Catalogue no: **VSOPLP 102**
**Cass:** Released 7 Nov '87, on Connoisseur Collection by Connoisseur Collection Ltd.. Catalogue no: **VSOPMC 102**

**SOPHISTICATED LADIES VOL.2 (Various artists)**
Tracks: / Every time we say goodbye: *Fitzgerald, Ella* / Girl from Ipanema: *Gilberto, Astrud* / Killing me softly with his song: *Laine, Cleo* / Sweet Georgia Brown: *Vaughan, Sarah* / Careless love: *Washington, Dinah* / La vie en rose: *Piaf, Edith* / Cry me a river: *Washington, Dinah* / I can dream, can't I: *Shore, Dinah* / Summertime: *Staton, Dakota* / Non, je ne regrette rien: *Piaf, Edith* / September song: *Lenya, Lotte* / Eleanor Rigby: *Laine, Cleo* / I'm beginning to see the light: *Reese, Della* / I'd love you to want me: *Minnelli, Liza* / Walk over God's heaven: *Jackson, Mahalia* / Late late show, The: *Staton, Dakota* / Let's do it: *Kitt, Eartha* / Saga of Jenny: *Lenya, Lotte* / Didn't it rain: *Jackson, Mahalia* / Manhattan: *Fitzgerald, Ella* / Take the 'A' train: *Vaughan, Sarah* / Old fashioned girl: *Kitt, Eartha* / Certain smile, A: *Gilberto, Astrud* / You are the sunshine of my life: *Minnelli, Liza.*
**2 LP Set:** Released Nov '88, on Connoisseur Collection by Connoisseur Collection Ltd.. Catalogue no: **VSOPLP 126**
**Cass:** Released Nov '88, on Connoisseur Collection by Connoisseur Collection Ltd.. Catalogue no: **VSOPMC 126**
**CD:** Released Nov '88, on Connoisseur Collection by Connoisseur Collection Ltd.. Catalogue no: **VSOPCD 126**

**SOPHISTICATED LADIES VOL.3 (Various artists)**
Tracks: If I were a bell: *Bassey, Shirley* / So tired: *Starr, Kay* / This girl's in love with you: *Warwick, Dionne* / Fascinating rhythm: *Clark, Petula* / I wish you love: *Smith, Keely* / You must have been a beautiful baby: *Lee, Peggy* / I thought about you: *Zadora, Pia* / Caravan song: *Dickson, Barbara* / No moon at all: *Staton, Dakota* / Talking in your sleep:

*Gayle, Crystal* / Something wonderful: *Whiting, Margaret* / When will I see you again: *Three Degrees* / Can't help lovin' dat man: *Bassey, Shirley* / Wheel of fortune, The: *Starr, Kay* / Close to you: *Warwick, Dionne* / Darn that dream: *Clark, Petula* / It's been a long, long time: *Smith, Keely* / Man I love, The: *Lee, Peggy* / I had the craziest dream: *Zadora, Pia* / As time goes by: *Dickson, Barbara* / Someone to watch over me: *Staton, Dakota* / Don't it make your brown eyes blue: *Gayle, Crystal* / Tree in the meadow, A: *Whiting, Margaret* / Take good care of yourself: *Three Degrees.*
**2 LP Set**: Released Dec '89, on Connoisseur Collection by Connoisseur Collection Ltd.. Catalogue no: **VSOPLP 145**
**Cass**: Released Dec '89, on Connoisseur Collection by Connoisseur Collection Ltd.. Catalogue no: **VSOPLMC145**
**CD**: Released Dec '89, on Connoisseur Collection by Connoisseur Collection Ltd.. Catalogue no: **VSOPCD 145**

**SOPHISTICATED SOUNDS (Soul For The Connoisseur) (Various artists)**
Tracks: / Since I found love: *Hadley, Sandy* / You could be my remedy: *Various artists* / Call on Billy: *Soul, Billy T.* / I'm a lover: *Carter, Chuck* / Hurt, The: *North, Freddie* / I wouldn't change a thing about you: *Wyatt, Johnny* / You say: *Esquires* / You must be losing: *Raye, Jimmy* / Love is a good foundation: *Uggams, Leslie* / I don't want to lose you: *Wynn, Mel* / Change, The: *Eady, Ernestine* / Yesterday's kisses: *Big Maybelle* / You got my love: *Wells, Donnie* / I gonna have a party: *Bruce, Ed* / Lover: *Hunt, Tommy.*
**Album:** Released Jun '88, on Kent by Ace Records. Catalogue no: **KENT 079**

## Soprano Summit

**LIVE AT BIGHORN JAZZ FESTIVAL**
**Album:** Released Jun '88, on Jazzology (USA) by Jazzology Records (USA). Catalogue no: **J 56**

## Soul Jazz...

**SOUL JAZZ VOL.1 (Various artists)**
Tracks: / Honky tonk: *Butler, Billy* / Return of the prodigal son: *Green, Byrdie* / I've got the blues: *Moody, James* / Mom and dad: *Earland, Charles* / 322 wow: *Lytle, Johnny* / Up to date: *Smith, Johnny "Hammond"* / Dat dere: *Cannonball Adderley Quartet* / Light, The: *Ammons, Gene.*
**Album:** Released 5 Jun '89, on BGP by Ace Records. Catalogue no: **BGP 1028**

## Soul Of Black Music

**SOUL OF BLACK MUSIC - GOSPEL (Various artists)**
**2 LP Set:** Released Jun '84, on Vogue by Vogue Records. Catalogue no: **426001**

**SOUL OF BLACK MUSIC VOL 1 (Various artists)**
Tracks: / Borrowed time: *Various artists* / Gamblin' man: *Various artists* / Jesus you've been good: *Various artists* / Going home to get my crown: *Various artists* / I'm going to serve Jesus: *Various artists* / Grandma's hands: *Various artists* / I'll be satisfied: *Various artists* / Lord I've done what you told me to do: *Various artists* / I'm holding on: *Various artists* / What am I going to do: *Various artists* / Won't it be grand: *Various artists* / My soul: *Various artists* / I've already been to the water: *Various artists* / Sleep on mother: *Various artists.*
**Album:** Released Sep '79, on Sonet by Sonet Records. Catalogue no: **SNTF 795**

**SOUL OF BLACK MUSIC VOL 2 (Various artists)**
Tracks: / Ezekiel: *Various artists* / Nobody's fault but mine: *Various artists* / Stop by: *Various artists* / He's working it out: *Various artists* / May the work I've done speak for me: *Various artists* / What about me: *Various artists* / New walk: *Various artists* / When we got to heaven: *Various artists* / I love to praise Him: *Various artists* / Stand by me: *Various artists* / Everyday will be Sunday: *Various artists* / Through it all: *Various artists* / How much do I owe: *Various artists* / Walk through the valley: *Various artists.*
**Album:** Released Sep '79, on Sonet by Sonet Records. Catalogue no: **SNTF 796**

## Soul Stirrers

**SOUL STIRRERS**
**Cass:** Released Jul '89, on Miracle by Gull Records. Catalogue no: **ZCMIR 5013**
**Album:** Released Jul '89, on Miracle by Gull Records. Catalogue no: **MIR 5013**

**SOUL STIRRERS: A TRIBUTE TO SAM COOKE (Various artists)**
Tracks: / My loved ones: *Various artists* / Striving: *Various artists* / Hello sunshine: *Various artists* / That's heaven to me: *Various artists* / Farther along: *Various artists* / Slow train: *Various artists* / Don't move that mountain: *Various artists* / God is standing by: *Various artists* / Peace in the valley: *Various artists* / Son,The: *Various artists* / Heaven is my home: *Various artists.*
**Album:** Released Jul '88, on Chess by Vogue Records. Catalogue no: **GCH 8086**
**Cass:** Released '89, on Chess by Vogue Records. Catalogue no: **GCHK 78086**

**STAND BY ME FATHER**
Tracks: / Put a little love in your heart / Stand by me Father / He's my guide / Without God in my life / Set me free / In Heaven with him / Glory bound train / Amazing Grace.
**Cass:** Released 12 Jul '89, on Miracle Records Catalogue no: **ZCMIR 5013**
**Album:** Released 12 Jul '89, on Miracle Records Catalogue no: **MIR 5013**

**WILL THE REAL SOUL STIRRERS PLEASE STAND UP**
Tracks: / If you love Jesus raise your hand / Nobody's child / Hey brother / Are you holding on / Until then / Touch the hem of His garment / He'll welcome us / They crucified Him / Walk along with me / Stop on board and follow me.
**Album:** Released Jul '88, on Miracle Records Catalogue no: **MIR 5006**
**Cass:** Released Aug '88, on Miracle Records Catalogue no: **ZCMIR 5006**

## Sound Of Harlem

**SOUND OF HARLEM (Various artists)**
**Album:** Released Jul '82, on Jazz Document Catalogue no: **VA 7999**

## Sound Of Picante

**SOUND OF PICANTE (Various artists)**
Tracks: / Bye bye blues: *Various artists* / Summer knows, The: *Various artists* / Fiz a cama na varanda: *Various artists* / Rainfall: *Various artists* / Tango allegra: *Various artists* / Don't cry for me Argentina: *Various artists* / Maria Cervantes: *Various artists* / Happy lypso: *Various artists* / Sin Timbal: *Various artists.*
Note: A collection of classic performances recorded for the Concorde Picante label. Personnel: Monty Alexander-piano / Laurinder Almeida - guitar / Charlie Byre - guitar / Tania Maria-piano, vocal / Tito Puente - vibes & percussion / Poncho Sanchez - congas & percussion / Cal Tjader-vibes.
**Cass:** Released Apr '86, on Concord Picante by Concord Jazz Records (USA). Catalogue no: **CJPC 295**
**Album:** Released Apr '86, on Concord Picante by Concord Jazz Records (USA). Catalogue no: **CJP 295**

## Sounds Of Memphis

**SOUNDS OF MEMPHIS 1933-39 (Various artists)**
**Album:** Released Sep '87, on Earl Archives Catalogue no: **BD 2006**

## Sounds Of The Swing

**MORE SOUNDS OF THE SWING YEARS (Various artists)**
Note: Telecast, 8 March 1960. A successful swing sequel to SG 8001, which was also hosted by Ronald Reagan, this second discomentary presents Woody Herman, Freddy Slack, Charlie Barnet and Stan Kenton, plus the vocals of Ella Mae Morse, Eddy Howard, Jo Stafford, Dinah Washington and Vaughn Monroe. Songs include Cow Cow Boogie, Temptation, To Each His Own, What A Difference A Day Makes and seven more.
**Album:** Released Apr '88, on Sounds Great Catalogue no: **SG 8003**

**SOUNDS OF THE SWING YEARS (Various artists)**
Note: Telecast, 9 February 1960. A look at one of the most memorable periods of American popular music. Hosted by Ro-

nald Reagan, this discomentary brings together many of the stars of the era, including Count Basie, Gene Krupa, Bob Crosby, Glen Gray and Woody Herman playing such swing classics as One O'Clock Jump, Drum Boogie, South Rampart Street Parade, No Name Jive and many more.
**Album:** Released Apr '88, on Sounds Great Catalogue no: **SG 8001**

## South, Eddie

**EDDIE SOUTH (South, Eddie & others)**
**Album:** Released '88, on DRG (USA) by DRG Records (USA). Catalogue no: **SW 8405**
**Cass:** Released '88, on DRG (USA) by DRG Records (USA). Catalogue no: **SWC 8405**

## South Frisco Jazz Band

**BROKEN PROMISES**
**Album:** Released '89, on Stomp Off (USA) Catalogue no: **SOS 1180**

**IN SEARCH OF THE FAMOUS GROUSE**
**Album:** Released Jan '88, on Stomp Off (USA) Catalogue no: **SOS 1143**

**SAN FRANCISCO JAZZ**
**Album:** Released Jun '88, on Merry Makers Catalogue no: **MMRC 113**

**SOUTH FISCO JAZZ BAND VOL. 3**
**Album:** Released Jun '86, on Stomp Off (USA) Catalogue no: **SOS 1103**

## South Side Blues

**SOUTH SIDE BLUES - CHICAGO: LIVING LEGENDS (Various artists)**
Tracks: / Mississippi sheiks: *Various artists* / Mama Yancey, Little brother Montgomery: *Various artists* / Henry Benson: *Various artists*.
**Album:** Released Jan '85, on Riverside (1) Catalogue no: **OBC 508**

## Southampton All Stars

**TRIBUTE TO GLENN MILLER (Southampton All Stars Orchestra)**
**Cass:** Released Jun '86, on All That's Jazz Catalogue no: **VOL 2**

## Southern...

**SOUTHERN SANCTIFIED SINGERS (Various artists)**
**Album:** Released Oct '88, on Roots (Germany) Catalogue no: **RL 328**

## Southern Blues

**SOUTHERN BLUES (Various artists)**
**2 LP Set:** Released Mar '85, on Savoy Jazz (USA) by Malaco Records (USA). Catalogue no: **SJL 2255**

## Southern Jazz Group

**SOUTHERN JAZZ GROUP, 1950**
**Album:** Released Oct '89, on Swaggie (Australia) Catalogue no: **S 1415**

**SOUTHERN JAZZ GROUP VOL. 1 1946-1950**
**Album:** Released Dec '86, on Dawn Club by Cadillac Music. Catalogue no: **DC 12021**

**SOUTHERN JAZZ GROUP VOL. 2 1946-1950**
**Album:** Released Dec '86, on Dawn Club by Cadillac Music. Catalogue no: **DC 12022**

**SOUTHERN JAZZ GROUP VOL. 3 1946-1950**
**Album:** Released Dec '86, on Dawn Club by Cadillac Music. Catalogue no: **DC 12023**

**SOUTHERN JAZZ GROUP VOL. 4 1946-1950**
**Album:** Released Dec '86, on Dawn Club by Cadillac Music. Catalogue no: **DC 12024**

## Southern, Jeri

**Biographical details:** Born Genevieve Hering in Nebraska in 1926, Southern was an exceptionally fine cabaret singer even more popular in Britain than America: her 1952 version of *When I Fall In Love* sold better here than the huge US Doris Day hit. Southern quit in the early 60's to teach singing. (Donald Clarke, March 1987.).

**COFFEE, CIGARETTES & MEMORIES**
**Album:** Released Feb '88, on Fresh Sounds (Spain) by Fresh Sounds Records (Spain). Catalogue no: **FS 255**

**FIRE DOWN BELOW**
Tracks: / Fire down below.
**7" Single:** Released Jun '57, on Brunswick by Decca Records. Deleted Jun '60. Catalogue no: **05665**

**JERI SOUTHERN MEETS COLE PORTER**
Tracks: / I concentrate on you / Don't look at me that way / Get out of town / It's alright with me / Let's fly away / Why shouldn't i / It's bad for me / You're the top.
**Cass:** Released Oct '84, on Pathe Marconi (France) Catalogue no: **PM 1553014**
**Album:** Released Oct '84, on Pathe Marconi (France) Catalogue no: **PM 1553011**

**JERI SOUTHERN MEETS JOHNNY SMITH**
**Album:** Released Feb '88, on Fresh Sounds (Spain) by Fresh Sounds Records (Spain). Catalogue no: **FS 156**

**LIVE AT THE CRESCENDO**
Tracks: / I thought of you last night / I get a kick out of you / Dancing on the ceiling / Blame it on my mouth / Remind me / You better go now / I'm just a woman / Something I dreamed last night / Nice work if you can get it / When I fall in love.
**Album:** Released Nov '85, on Capitol T (USA) Catalogue no: **T 1278**

**SOUTHERN BREEZE**
**Album:** Released Feb '88, on Fresh Sounds (Spain) by Fresh Sounds Records (Spain). Catalogue no: **FS 123**

**WHEN I FALL IN LOVE**
Tracks: / When I fall in love / Fire down below / You better go now / I thought of you last night / Occasional man, An / Where walks my true love / Candlelight conversation / Just in time / I'm in love with the honourable Mr. So and So / Autumn in New York / You make me feel so young / All in fun / Little girl blue / Someone to watch over me / Cabin / Every time we say goodbye.
**Album:** Released Apr '84, on MCA by MCA Records. Deleted Jan '88. Catalogue no: **MCL 1791**
**Cass:** Released Apr '84, on MCA by MCA Records. Deleted Jan '88. Catalogue no: **MCLC 1791**

**YOU BETTER GO NOW**
Tracks: / You better go now / Give me time / Something I dreamed last night / Man that got away, The / When I fall in love / Just got to have him around / Dancing on the ceiling / Speak softly to me / What good am I without you / I though of you last night / That ole devil called love / Remind me.
**Album:** Released '89, on Official by Official Records. Catalogue no: **OFF 12007**

## Southern Stompers

**FASCINATING RHYTHM (Southern Stompers 1974)**
**Album:** Released Apr '79, on VJM (Vintage Jazz Music) by Vintage Jazz Music Society(VJM). Catalogue no: **LC 22S**

**STEVE LANE'S JUBILEE RECORD (Southern Stompers 1950-75)**
**Album:** Released Apr '79, on VJM (Vintage Jazz Music) by Vintage Jazz Music Society(VJM). Catalogue no: **SLC 26**

## Southern Swing

**SOUTHERN SWING**
Note: With C.Walker/G.Brown/J.Haworth/A.Andrews/C.Hillary.
**Cass:** Released Jun '86, on All That's Jazz Catalogue no: **VOL 3**

## Southside Screamers

**SOUTHSIDE SCREAMERS (Chicago blues 1948-58) (Various artists)**
**Album:** Released Feb '85, on St.George (USA) Catalogue no: **STG 1003**

## Spand, Charlie

**CHARLIE SPAND 1929-40**
**Album:** Released Apr '89, on Blues Document Catalogue no: **BD 2035**

## Spanier, Muggsy

**Biographical details:** A trumpet player in the Chicago style of white small-group jazz, Muggsy Spanier (1906-67) was born Francis Joseph Spanier in Chicago. Benny Goodman and others in the genre went on to play the big band swing style but Spanier stuck to what came to be called Dixieland. His New Orleans Ragtime Band lasted only a year but had a legendary residency at Nick's in New

York in 1939 and recorded 16 sides that still have much charm. His associates on earlier records included Frank Teschemacher (1906-32), the much-loved redman who died in a car crash, and pianist Frank Melrose (1907-41), who was the victim of a mysterious murder. (Donald Clarke, March 1987.).

**AT CLUB HANGOVER**
**Album:** Released Jan '88, on Storyville by Storyville Records AB. Catalogue no: **SLP 249**

**CLASSIC SMALL GROUPS Vol. 2 (Various artists)**
**Album:** Released '88, on Meritt (USA) Catalogue no: **MERITT 7**

**COLUMBIA - GEM OF THE OCEAN (Spanier, Muggsy & His Huge Dixieland Band)**
**CD:** Released '88, on Mobile Fidelity Sound Lab(USA) by Mobile Fidelity Records (USA). Catalogue no: **MFCD 857**

**FRANCIS JOSEPH MUGGY SPANIER 1926-9**
**Album:** Released Jan '88, on Gaps Catalogue no: **GAPS 150**

**HESITATIN BLUES**
Tracks: / Hesitatin blues / Little David play your harp / Judy / American patrol / Chicago / Baby brown / When my dreamboat comes home / Wreck of the old '97 / No lovers allowed / Careless love / More than you know / Can't we be friends / My wild Irish rose / Oh Dr Ochsner / Since we fell out of love / Washington and Lee swing / Two o'clock jump.
Note: Mono
**Album:** Released Oct '86, on Affinity by Charly Records. Catalogue no: **AFS 1030**
**Cass:** Released Sep '86, on Affinity by Charly Records. Catalogue no: **TCAFS 1030**

**HOT HORN**
**Album:** Released Jun '86, on Storyville by Storyville Records AB. Catalogue no: **SLP 4053**

**HOT HORN 1944 (Spanier, Muggsy & His Ragtimers)**
**Album:** Released '87, on Commodore Class Catalogue no: **6.26167**

**MUGGSY SPANIER AND PEE WEE (Spanier, Muggsy & Pee Wee Russell)**
Note: With Bob Haggart/G Wettling etc.
**Cass:** Released Jun '86, on Holmia Cassettes Catalogue no: **HM 06**

**MUGGSY SPANIER COLLECTION 20 golden greats**
Tracks: / I can't give you anything but love / Sugar / Tin roof blues / Indiana / Sweet Lorraine / Three little words / Dixieland one-step / I ain't gonna give nobody none of my jelly roll / Fidgety feet / Alice blue gown / St. Louis blues / Angry / Lucky to me / Livery stable blues / Relaxing at the Touro / I'm sorry I made you cry / Bugle call rag / Dippermouth blues / Muskrat ramble / Lady be good.
Note: Mono production. Featuring Miff Mole, Lou McGairty, Pee Wee Russell.
**Album:** Released Jan '87, on Deja Vu Catalogue no: **DVLP 2090**
**Cass:** Released Jan '87, on Deja Vu Catalogue no: **DVMC 2090**

**MUGGSY SPANIER & FRANK (Spanier, Muggsy & Frank Teschemaker)**
Tracks: / Buddy's habits / Chicago blues / Mobile blues / Really a pain / Hot mittens / Everybody loves my baby / Why couldn't it be me / Why couldn't it be poor little me / China boy / Bull frog blues / Nobody's sweetheart / Sister Kate / Jazz me blues / Darktown strutters' ball / Whoopee stomp.
**Album:** Released Apr '81, on Joker (USA) by Lifetime Records (USA). Catalogue no: **SM 3088**

**MUGGSY SPANIER & HIS ALL STARS**
Tracks: / Jazz me blues / Pat's blues / Squeeze me / Pee Wee speaks / At the jazz band ball / Relaxin' at the Touro / You are lucky to me / Tin roof blues / Cherry / That's a plenty.
**Album:** Released Apr '81, on Joker (USA) by Lifetime Records (USA). Catalogue no: **SM 3575**

**MUGGSY SPANIER & HIS RAGTIME BAND VOL.1**
Tracks: / Big butter & egg man / Someday, sweetheart / Eccentric / That da da strain / At the Jazz Band Ball / Sister Kate / Dippermouth blues / Livery stable blues / Riverboat shuffle / Relaxin' at the Touro / At sundown / Bluin' the blues / Lonesome road / Dinah / Black and blue / Mandy make up your mind.
**Album:** Released Apr '81, on Joker (USA) by Lifetime Records (USA). Catalogue no: **SM 3574**
**Cass:** Released '88, on Joker (USA) by Lifetime Records (USA). Catalogue no: **MC 3574**

**MUGGSY SPANIER, MIFF MOLE & LOU MCGARITY (Spanier, Muggsy, Miff Mole & Lou McGarity)**
**Album:** Released '88, on Storyville by Storyville Records AB. Catalogue no: **SLP 4020**

**MUGGSY SPANIER (WITH EDDIE CONDON ETC)**
Note: Featuring Sidney Bechet, Eddie Condon, Pee Wee Russell, Bob Haggart etc.
**Album:** Released Sep '87, on Giants of Jazz by Hasmick Promotions. Catalogue no: **LPJT 16**

**MUGGSY SPANIER WITH G BRUNIES AND A NICHOLAS (Spanier, Muggsy, G Brunies & A Nicholas)**
**Album:** Released Jun '88, on Jazzology (USA) by Jazzology Records (USA). Catalogue no: **J 33**

**MUGGSY SPANIER VOL.2 (Spanier, Muggsy & His Dixieland All Stars)**
**Album:** Released Nov '86, on Storyville by Storyville Records AB. Catalogue no: **SLP 4056**

**NICK'S - NEW YORK**
Tracks: / Angry / Weary blues / Snag it / Alice blue gown / Sweet Lorraine / Oh, lady be good / Sugar / September rain.
**Album:** Released May '87, on Commodore Class Catalogue no: **6.25494**

**ON V-DISC 1944-45**
**Album:** Released Jul '87, on Everybody's (Sweden) Catalogue no: **E-1020**

**ONE OF A KIND**
**Album:** Released Dec '87, on Glendale (USA) by Glendale Records (USA). Catalogue no: **GL 6024**

**RARE CUSTOM 45'S**
Note: Includes George Brunis, Peanuts Hucko, Floyd Bean, Doc Cenardo.
**Album:** Released May '88, on I.A.J.R.C (USA) by Vintage Jazz Music Society(VJM). Catalogue no: **IAJRC 42**

**RICHMOND AND CHICAGO DAYS, 1924-28**
Tracks: / Steady roll blues / Mobile blues / Really a pain / Chicago blues / Hot mittens / Buddy's habits / Someday, sweetheart / Why can't it be poor little me? / Everybody loves my baby / Bullfrog blues / China boy / Jazz me blues / Sister Kate / Nobody's sweetheart / Friars Point shuffle / Darktown strutters' ball.
Note: With the Stomp Six, Charles Pierce & His Orchestra, the Jungle Kings, the Bucktown Five.
**Album:** Released Dec '88, on Swaggie (Australia) Catalogue no: **S 806**
**Cass:** Released Sep '87, on Fountain by Retrieval Records. Catalogue no: **CFJ 108**

**SPANIER IN CHICAGO, 1954**
**Album:** Released Apr '79, on VJM (Vintage Jazz Music) by Vintage Jazz Music Society(VJM). Catalogue no: **LC 2**

**TIN ROOF BLUES (Spanier, Muggsy & Earl Hines)**
Tracks: / Deep forest / Tiger rag / Tin roof blues / Limehouse blues / Memphis blues / High society / Boogie woogie on St. Louis blues / Struttin' with some barbecue / Ugly chile / Bugle call rag / Wang wang blues / Rosetta / Billy Bailey / St. James' infirmary / Wolverine blues / Lazy river / That's a plenty / If I could be with you one hour tonight / Royal Garden blues.
**2 LP Set:** Released May '83, on Vogue Jazz (France) by Vogue Records. Catalogue no: **VJD 549**

## Spann, Otis

**Biographical details:** Born in Jackson, Mississippi, in 1930, Spann was a legend in his own lifetime when he died of cancer in 1970 in Chicago. With Muddy Waters and Little Walter he was one of the greatest of the originators of postwar Chicago blues. He came to Chicago in the early 1950's and played almost continuously in Waters' band from 1953, also recording with Howlin' Wolf and Bo Diddley, as house pianist at Chess and as a solo artist for Chess and Checker.

(Donald Clarke, March 1987.).

**BLUES IS WHERE IT'S AT, THE**
**Album:** Released Sep '87, on Crosscut by Topic Records. Catalogue no: **CCR 1016**

**BLUES NEVER DIE**
Tracks: / Blues never die / I got a feeling / One more mile to go / Feelin' Good / After while / Dust my broom / Straighten up baby / Come on / Must have been the Devil / Lightning / I'm ready.
**Album:** Released Feb '88, on Ace by Ace Records. Catalogue no: **CH 231**

**BLUES OF OTIS SPANN**
Tracks: / Rock me, mama / I came from Clarksdale / Keep your hands out of my pocket / Spann's boogie / Sarah Street / Blues don't like nobody / Country boy / Pretty girls everywhere / Meet me in the bottom / Lost sheep in the fold / I got a feeling / Jangle boogie / Natural days / You're gonna need my help / Stirs me up.
Note: This 1964 album features guest musicians Eric Clapton, Jimmy Page, Muddy Waters.
**Album:** Released Aug '85, on See For Miles by See For Miles Records. Catalogue no: **SEE 54**

**CANDID SPANN, VOL 1**
Tracks: / Hard way, The / Take a little walk with me / Otis in the dark / Baby child / Little boy blue / Country boy / Beat up team / My daily wish / Great northern stomp / I got rambling on my mind / No. 2 / Worried life blues / Instrumental boogie / Captain's apprentice, The / Knocker upper man / Fine time / Joe Hill / Cape May / Fine time Lucille / Harvest has been taken in, The / Tottie poem / We got married on Sunday / Greenland whale fisheries / Harry Eddom / Moon was a warning, The.
**Album:** Released Jan '83, on Crosscut by Topic Records. Catalogue no: **CCR 1003**

**CANDID SPANN, VOL 2**
Tracks: / It must have been the devil / Otis' blues / Going down slow / Half ain't been told / Monkey face women / This is the blues / Strange woman / Evil ways / Come day go day / Walking the blues / When things go wrong / Bad condition / My home in the delta.
**Album:** Released Jan '83, on Crosscut by Topic Records. Catalogue no: **CCR 1004**

**CRACKED SPANNER HEAD**
Tracks: / Crack your head / Iced Nehi / Wagon wheel / No sense in worrying / Dollar twenty-five / Everything's gonna be alright / Lucky so and so / Sometimes I wonder / Mr. Highwayman / What will become of me / Country boy / My home in the desert / Pretty girls everywhere / You gonna need my help.
**CD:** Released Oct '88, on Deram by Decca International. Catalogue no: **820 177 2**

**CRYIN' TIME**
Tracks: / Home to Mississippi / Blues is a botheration / You said you'd be on time / Crying time / Blind man / Someday / Twisted snake / Green flowers / New boogaloo, The / Mule kicking in my stall.
**Album:** Released Apr '78, on Vanguard by Start Records Ltd.. Catalogue no: **VSD 6514**

**HALF AIN'T BEEN TOLD**
**Album:** Released '88, on Black Cat by Black Cat Records. Catalogue no: **BC 001**

**NOBODY KNOWS CHICAGO LIKE I DO**
Tracks: / Popcorn man / Brand new house / Nobody knows Chicago like I do / Steel mill blues / Down on Sarah street / T'aint nobody's bizness if I do / Chicago blues / My home is on the delta / Spann blues.
**Album:** Released Nov '83, on Charly R&B by Charly Records. Catalogue no: **CRB 1062**

**OTIS SPANN IS THE BLUES**
Tracks: / Hard way, The / Take a little walk with me / Otis in the dark / Little boy blue / Country boy / Beat-up team / My daily wish / Great northern stomp / I got rambling on my mind / Worried life blues.
Note: Recorded 1960.
**Album:** Released Dec '85, on Candid Catalogue no: **CS 9001**
**CD:** Released Sep '87, on Candid Catalogue no: **CCD 9001**
**Album:** Released Mar '83, on Crosscut by Topic Records. Deleted Mar '88. Catalogue no: **CCR 1003**

**RAREST**
**Album:** Released Apr '84, on JSP by JSP Records. Catalogue no: **JSP 1070**

**TAKE ME BACK HOME**
**Album:** Released Aug '84, on Black Magic by Topic Records. Catalogue no: **BM 9004**

**THIS IS THE BLUES**
**CD:** Released Mar '90, on Roots Catalogue no: **RTS 33014**

**WALKING THE BLUES**
Note: With Robert Lockwood/St Louis Jimmy. Tracks include: It must have been the devil / Otis blues / Going down slow / Half ain't been told / Monkey face woman / This is the blues / Evil ways / Come day go day / Walkin the blues etc.
**CD:** Released Jul '87, on Candid Catalogue no: **CCD 9025**
**Album:** Released Jul '87, on Candid Catalogue no: **CS 9025**

## Spaulding, James

**PLAYS THE LEGACY OF DUKE**
**Album:** Released Feb '90, on Storyville by Storyville Records AB. Catalogue no: **SLP 4034**
**Album:** Released Jan '88, on Storyville by Storyville Records AB. Catalogue no: **SLP 1019**

## Speckled Red

**Biographical details:** Speckled Red was Rufus G. Perryman (born 23rd October 1892 in Monroe, Louisina; died 2nd January 1973 in St. Louis, Missouri),

Sphere

blues singer and powerful pianist in the barrelhouse style. He was one of 16 children; his more famous brother William was Piano Red and and they both got their nicknames because of their mottled complexions: they were albinos. Speckled Red was famous for *The Dirty Dozens*, first recorded in 1929; it was a rhyming song for teaching bible stories to children, turned into a lesson in the twelve levels of invective; the twelfth level of insult accused the insultee of being intimate with his mother. (Donald Clarke)..

**1929-38**
**Album:** Released Apr '84, on Wolf Catalogue no: **WSE 113**

**SPECKLED RED IN LONDON, 1960**
Tracks: / Woke up this morning / Dirty mistreater / I've had my fun / Caledonia / It feels so good / Oh red / Milk cow blues / Bugle call stomp / Early in the morning / Blu-Della boogie / Dad's piece / Tain't nobody's bizness if I do.
**Album:** Released Apr '79, on VJM (Vintage Jazz Music) by Vintage Jazz Music Society(VJM). Catalogue no: **LC 11**

## Spencer, Earle

**BIG BAND PIONEER**
**Album:** Released '89, on I.A.J.R.C (USA) by Vintage Jazz Music Society(VJM). Catalogue no: **IAJRC 41**

**EARLE SPENCER & HIS NEW BAND**
**Album:** Released Jul '77, on First Heard by Submarine Records. Catalogue no: **FH 16**

## Sphere

**FLIGHT PATH**
Tracks: / If I should lose you / Pumpkin's delight / Played twice / El Sueno / Christina / Flight path.
**Album:** Released Apr '84, on Elektra (Musician) by Elektra Records (USA). Deleted Apr '89. Catalogue no: **960 313 1**

**FOUR FOR ALL**
**Cass:** Released Aug '87, on Verve (Germany) Catalogue no: **831674-4**
**Album:** Released Aug '87, on Verve (Germany) Catalogue no: **831674-1**
**CD:** Released Aug '87, on Verve (Germany) Catalogue no: **831 674 2**

**FOUR IN ONE**
Tracks: / Four in one / Light blue / Monk's dream / Evidence / Reflections / Eronel.
**Album:** Released Oct '82, on Elektra (Musician) by Elektra Records (USA). Deleted Oct '87. Catalogue no: **K 52415**

**PRESENT TENSE**
**Album:** Released '88, on Cadillac by Cadillac Music. Catalogue no: **SGC 1012**

**SPHERE**
Note: Featuring: Andy Sheppard, Geoff Williams, Peter Maxfield, Alan Edwards.
**Album:** Released Feb '88, on Cadillac by Cadillac Music. Catalogue no: **SGC 1010**

## Spirits Of Rhythm

**RHYTHM PERSONIFIED (1933/4)**
**Album:** Released Feb '85, on JSP by JSP Records. Catalogue no: **JSP 1088**

## Spivak, Charlie

**Biographical details:** Charlie Spivak was born 17 Febuary 1906 in New Haven, Conneticut. He was an excellent sideman and lead trumpet with the Ben Pollack, Ray Noble, Bob Crosby, Tommy Dorsey and Jack Teagarden bands, formed his own band in 1940 with backing from Glenn Miller and had hits through that decade with arrangements by Sonny Burke, Jimmy Mundy and Nelson Riddle. (Donald Clarke 27.5.87)..

**1942: CHARLIE SPIVAK (Spivak, Charlie & His Orchestra)**
**Album:** Released Aug '88, on Jazzology (USA) by Jazzology Records (USA). Catalogue no: **SLP 16**

**1946 (Spivak, Charlie And His Orchestra)**
**Album:** Released Oct '86, on Circle (USA) by Jazzology Records (USA). Catalogue no: **CLP 80**

**CHARLIE SPIVAK, 1943-46**
Tracks: / Stardreams / Mean to me / Serenade in blue / I used to love you / Cuddle up a little closer / Blue Lou / Laura / More than you know / Stardust / Accentuate the positive / Solitude / Travlin' light / Blue champagne / Let's go home / It's the same old dream / Saturday night.
Note: Spivak's "Sweetest trumpet in the world" beautifully demonstrates its billing, soloing on his theme "Stardreams", "Mean to me", Serenade in blue", "Laura", a classic full five minute "Stardust", "Travellin' light", "Blue champagne" and "It's the same old dream". The superb band, which began as Glenn Millers collective protege, pays affectionate tribute to its mentor in several selections, i.e. the Miller-style trombone section is prominent on Jimmy Mundy's arrangement of "Travelin'...". Outstanding charts are by Sonny Burke, Nelson Riddle, Neal Hefti, Fred Norman and Mundy.
**Album:** Released '88, on Hindsight Catalogue no: **HSR 105**
**Album:** Released Feb '79, on London Records by London Records Ltd. Deleted Feb '84. Catalogue no: **HMP 5044**

**CHARLIE SPIVAK & JIMMY JOY 1945 (Spivak, Charlie And His Orchestra)**
Tracks: / Star dreams / Into each life some rain must fall / Wonderful winter / Every time we say goodbye / If you were but a dream / Right as rain / Even Steven / Shine on harvest moon / Blue skies / I dream of you / Savoy is jumpin', The / How many hearts have you broken? / Green eyes / Don't ever change / Dark eyes.
**Album:** Released Apr '79, on Aircheck (USA) by Kiner Ents.(USA). Catalogue no: **AIRCHECK 6**

**HOP SKIP AND JUMP**
Tracks: / Slow and easy / This love of mine / Mean to me / Stardust / Blue champagne / Comin' through the Rye / Let's go home / Charley horse / Everything happens to me / I understand / Cuddle up / Travelin' light / Got the moon in my pocket / Combination solid / Hop skip and jump / Serenade in blue.
**Cass:** on Astan (USA) Catalogue no: **40181**
**Album:** Released Sep '89, on Big Band Era Catalogue no: **20181**

**NOW 1981 (Spivak, Charlie & His Orchestra)**
**Album:** Released Aug '88, on Jazzology (USA) by Jazzology Records (USA). Catalogue no: **SLP 17**

**ONE WAY PASSAGE**
**Album:** Released Jun '79, on First Heard by Submarine Records. Catalogue no: **FH 28**

**STAR DREAMS (Spivak, Charlie Orchestra & Dubby Spivak)**
**Album:** Released Dec '88, on Circle (USA) by Jazzology Records (USA). Catalogue no: **CLP 100**

## Spivey, Victoria

**EASY RIDERS JAZZ BAND, THE**
**Album:** Released Jun '88, on GHB by Jazzology Records (USA). Catalogue no: **GHB 17**

## Spontaneous Music ...

**BIOSYSTEM (Spontaneous Music Ensemble)**
**Album:** Released May '78, on Incus by Incus Records. Catalogue no: **INCUS 24**

**LIVE AT NOTRE DAME HALL (Spontaneous Music Ensemble)**
Note: Featuring Lol Coxhill
**Album:** Released Mar '87, on Sweet Folk All by Sweet Folk All Records. Catalogue no: **SFA 112**

**SO WHAT DO YOU THINK (Spontaneous Music Ensemble)**
**Album:** Released Apr '81, on Tangent (1) by Tangent Records. Catalogue no: **TGS 118**

**SOURCE, THE (Spontaneous Music Ensemble)**
**Album:** Released Apr '81, on Tangent (1) by Tangent Records. Catalogue no: **TNGS 107**

**SPONTANEOUS MUSIC ENSEMBLE (Spontaneous Music Ensemble)**
**Album:** Released Mar '83, on Affinity by Charly Records. Deleted '88. Catalogue no: **AFF 81**

## Spotts, Roger Hamilton

**ROGER HAMILTON SPOTTS' BIG BAND**
**Album:** Released Nov '88, on Sea Breeze Catalogue no: **SBSEAPEA 5004**

## Sprague, Peter

### BRID RAGA (Peter Sprague, Bill Mays, Sam Most)
**Album:** Released '88, on Xanadu Catalogue no: **XAN 184**

### MESSAGE SENT ON THE WIND, THE
**Album:** Released '88, on Xanadu Catalogue no: **XAN 193**

### MUSICA DEL MAR
Tracks: / I hear a rhapsody / My folk's song / Just one of those things / You stepped out of a dream / Chick's tune / Musica del mar / I thought about you / Invention in D / Chanting with Charles.
Note: Peter Sprague, acoustic and electric guitars; George Cables, piano; Bob Magnusson, bass; Eddie Moore, drums.
**Album:** Released Apr '84, on Concord Jazz by Concord Jazz Records (USA). Catalogue no: **CJ 237**

### NA PALI COAST
Tracks: / Japanese waltz / Magic Mizz Melissa / Children's song No 6 / Na pali coast / I could write a book / If I should lose you / I didn't know about you / Coltrane.
Note: Peter Sprague, acoustic and electric guitars; Steve Kujala, flute; Tipp Sprague, tenor sax; Bob Magnusson, bass; Peter Erskine, drums.
**Album:** Released May '84, on Springtime by Springtime Records. Catalogue no: **SPR 1013**
**Album:** Released Sep '85, on Concord Jazz by Concord Jazz Records (USA). Catalogue no: **CJ 277**

## Spyro Gyra

### ACCESS ALL AREAS
**2 LP Set:** Released Aug '84, on MCA by MCA Records. Catalogue no: **MCSP 310**

### ALTERNATIVE CURRENT
Tracks: / Shakedown / Taking the plunge / PG / I believe in you / Binky's dream no. 6 / Sunflurry / Heartbeat / Mardi Gras / Alternating currents.
**Album:** Released Oct '85, on MCA by MCA Records. Catalogue no: **MCF 3289**

### BREAKOUT
Tracks: / Bob goes to the store / Freefall / Doubletake / Breakout / Body wave / Whirlwind / Swept away / Guiltless.
**Album:** Released Aug '86, on MCA by MCA Records. Deleted Apr '88. Catalogue no: **MCF 3334**
**CD:** Released '87, on MCA by MCA Records. Deleted Apr '88. Catalogue no: **MCAD 5753**
**Cass:** Released Aug '86, on MCA by MCA Records. Deleted Apr '88. Catalogue no: **MCFC 3334**

### CARNIVAL
Tracks: / Cafe amore / Dizzy / Awakening / Cashaca / Foxtrot / Sweet 'n' savvy / Bittersweet / Carnival.
**Album:** Released Dec '80, on MCA by MCA Records. Deleted Dec '85. Catalogue no: **MCF 3087**
**Album:** Released Sep '82, on MCA by MCA Records. Deleted Jan '88. Catalogue no: **MCL 1711**
**CD:** Released '87, on MCA by MCA Records. Catalogue no: **MCAD 1663**
**Cass:** Released Sep '82, on MCA by MCA Records. Deleted Jan '88. Catalogue no: **MCLC 1711**

### CATCHING THE SUN
Tracks: / Catching the sun / Cockatoo / Autumn of our love / Laser material / Percolator / Philly / Lovin' you (interlude) lovin' you / Here again / Safari.
**Cass:** Released '83, on MCA by MCA Records. Deleted Apr '88. Catalogue no: **MCLC 1763**
**Album:** Released Feb '80, on MCA by MCA Records. Deleted Feb '85. Catalogue no: **MCG 4009**
**Album:** Released '83, on MCA by MCA Records. Deleted Apr '88. Catalogue no: **MCL 1763**
**CD:** Released Apr '87, on MCA by MCA Records. Deleted Apr '88. Catalogue no: **MCAD 1487**

### CATCHING THE SUN (SINGLE)
Tracks: / Catching the sun / Percoloator / Cockatoo.
**7" Single:** Released Feb '80, on MCA by MCA Records. Deleted Feb '83. Catalogue no: **MCA 568**

### CITY KIDS
Tracks: / City kids / Serpent in Paradise / Ballad, A / Nightlife / Islands in the sky / Conversations / Silver lining / Haverstraw road.
**Cass:** Released Aug '83, on MCA by MCA Records. Deleted Jan '88. Catalogue no: **MCFC 3178**
**Album:** Released Aug '83, on MCA by MCA Records. Deleted Jan '88. Catalogue no: **MCF 3178**

### FREETIME
Tracks: / Freetime / Telluride / Summer strut / Elegy for Trane / Pacific sunrise / Amber dream / String soup.
**CD:** Released '87, on MCA by MCA Records. Deleted Dec '89. Catalogue no: **MCAD 1468**
**Album:** Released Oct '81, on MCA by MCA Records. Catalogue no: **MCF 3119**

### FREETIME (SINGLE)
Tracks: / Freetime / String soup.
**12" Single:** Released Nov '81, on MCA by MCA Records. Deleted Nov '84. Catalogue no: **MCAT 746**
**7" Single:** Released Nov '81, on MCA by MCA Records. Deleted Nov '84. Catalogue no: **MCA 746**

### INCOGNITO
**CD:** Released Feb '87, on MCA by MCA Records. Catalogue no: **MCAD 5368**
**Album:** Released Dec '82, on MCA by MCA Records. Deleted Dec '87. Catalogue no: **MCF 3151**

### MORNING DANCE
Tracks: / Morning dance / Jubilee / Rasul / Song for Lorraine / Starburst / It does'nt matter / Little Linda / End of Romanticism / Heliopolis.
**Cass:** Released Feb '84, on MCA by MCA Records. Catalogue no: **MCLC 1788**
**Album:** Released Jul '79, on Infinity by MCA Records (USA). Deleted Jul '84. Catalogue no: **INS 2003**
**Album:** Released Feb '84, on MCA by MCA Records. Catalogue no: **MCL 1788**
**CD:** Released Apr '89, on MCA by MCA Records. Catalogue no: **DMCL 1788**
**CD:** Released Feb '84, on MCA by MCA Records. Deleted '88. Catalogue no: **DIDX 201**

### MORNING DANCE (SINGLE)
Tracks: / Morning dance.
**7" Single:** Released Jul '79, on Infinity by MCA Records (USA). Deleted Jul '82. Catalogue no: **INF 111**

### MORNING DANCE / CATCHING THE SUN
Tracks: / Catching the sun / Cockatoo / Autumn of our love / Laser material / Percolator / Philly / Loving you / Here again / Safari / Morning dance / Jubilee / Rasul / Song for Lorraine / Starburst / Heliopolis / It doesn't matter / Little Linda / End of romanticism.
**Cass set:** Released Apr '82, on MCA (Twinpax Cassettes) by MCA Records. Deleted Jan '88. Catalogue no: **MCA 2 100**

### POINT OF VIEW
Note: Personnel - Spyro Gyra: Jay Beckenstein (sax), Richie Morales (drums), Dave Samuels (marimba/vibes), Tom Schuman (kbds), Oscar Cartaya (bass), Jay Azzolina (gtr). Additional: Julio Fernandez (gtr), Roger Squitero (perc).
**CD:** Released Jun '89, on MCA (Jazz Today) Catalogue no: **MCAD 6309**
**Cass:** Released Jun '89, on MCA (Jazz Today) Catalogue no: **MCAC 6309**
**Album:** Released Jun '89, on MCA (Jazz Today) Catalogue no: **MCA 6309**

### SPYRO GYRA
Tracks: / Shaker song / Opus O'opus / Mallet ballet / Pygmy funk / Cascade / Leticia / Mead / Paula / Paw prints / Galadriel.
**Cass:** Released Aug '81, on Infinity by MCA Records (USA). Deleted Jan '88. Catalogue no: **MCLC 1626**
**Album:** Released Nov '82, on Fame by EMI Records. Catalogue no: **FA 3047**
**Album:** Released Nov '79, on Infinity by MCA Records (USA). Deleted '84. Catalogue no: **INS 2008**
**Album:** Released Aug '81, on Infinity by MCA Records (USA). Deleted Jan '88. Catalogue no: **MCL 1626**

### SPYRO GYRA/ CARNIVAL
Tracks: / Shaker song / Opus d'opus / Mallet ballet / Pygmy funk / Cascade / Leticia / Mead / Paula/paw prints / Galadriel / Cafe amore / Dizzy / Awakening / Cashaca / Foxtrot / Sweet and savvy / Bitter sweet / Carnival.
**Cass set:** Released Oct '83, on MCA (Twinpax Cassettes) by MCA Records. Deleted Jan '88. Catalogue no: **MCA 2 110**

**STORIES WITHOUT WORDS**
Tracks: / Cayo Hueso / Serpentine shelly / Del corazon / Early light / Nu sungo / Chrysalis / Joy ride / Pyramid.
**Album:** Released Jul '87, on MCA by MCA Records. Deleted Apr '88. Catalogue no: **MCF 3390**
**CD:** Released Jul '87, on MCA by MCA Records. Catalogue no: **DMCF 3390**
**Cass:** Released Jul '87, on MCA by MCA Records. Deleted Apr '88. Catalogue no: **MCFC 3390**

## St Claire, Bette

**AT BASIN STREET EAST**
**Album:** Released Feb '88, on Fresh Sounds (Spain) by Fresh Sounds Records (Spain). Catalogue no: **FS 222**

## St. Louis...

**BLUES FROM ST. LOUIS 1929-30 (Various artists)**
Note: Tracks by: Blind Terry Darby, James 'Stump' Johnson, Leroy Henderson, Clifford Gibson.
**Album:** Released '88, on Earl Archives Catalogue no: **BD 2017**

**ST LOUIS BLUES 1929-35 (Various artists)**
**Album:** Released Dec '88, on Yazoo (USA) by Shanachie Records (USA). Catalogue no: **L 1030**

**ST. LOUIS BLUES MARCH (Various artists)**
**CD:** on Polygram by PolyGram UK Ltd. Catalogue no: **810 023-2**

**ST LOUIS JIMMY ODEN (Various artists)**
**Album:** Released '89, on Blues Document Catalogue no: **BD 2068**

**ST LOUIS TOWN 1929-33**
**Album:** Released Dec '88, on Yazoo (USA) by Shanachie Records (USA). Catalogue no: **L 1003**

**ST.LOUIS PIANO BLUES 1929-54 (Various artists)**
Note: Includes: Wesley Wallace, Robert Peeples, Sylvester Palmer, Jesse Johnson, Henry Brown.
**Album:** Released '88, on Document Catalogue no: **DLP 529**

## St Louis King Of Rhythm

**RHYTHM & BLUES SHOWTIME WITH...**
**2 LP Set:** Released Dec '88, on Timeless by Timeless Records. Catalogue no: **SJP 231/232**

## St. Louis Ragtimers

**SHOWBOAT ERA**
**Album:** Released Aug '88, on Audiophile (USA) by Jazzology Records (USA). Catalogue no: **AP 122**

**ST. LOUIS RAGTIMERS, VOL. 1, THE**
**Album:** Released Aug '88, on Audiophile (USA) by Jazzology Records (USA). Catalogue no: **AP 75**

**ST. LOUIS RAGTIMERS, VOL. 2, THE**
**Album:** Released Aug '88, on Audiophile (USA) by Jazzology Records (USA). Catalogue no: **AP 81**

**ST. LOUIS RAGTIMERS, VOL. 4, THE**
**Album:** Released Aug '88, on Audiophile (USA) by Jazzology Records (USA). Catalogue no: **AP 116**

## St. Louis Symphony Orch.

**GERSHWIN IN THE MOVIES 1/2 (St. Louis Symphony Orchestra)**
Note: With Wilhelmina Fernandez . Orchestra led by Leonard Slatkin.
**2 LP Set:** Released May '87, on SPI Milan (France) Catalogue no: **A 249/250**
**CD Set:** Released May '87, on SPI Milan (France) Catalogue no: **CDCH 249/250**
**Cass set:** Released May '87, on SPI Milan (France) Catalogue no: **C 249/250**

**GERSHWIN IN THE MOVIES VOL.1 1931-1945 (St. Louis Symphony Orchestra)**
Tracks: / Embraceable you / They all laughed / Love is here to stay / Strike up the band / Fascinating rhythm / But not for me / Rhapsody in blue / Man I love, The / Seconde rhapsodie.
Note: With Wilhelmina Fernandez. Orchestra led by Leonard Slatkin.
**CD:** Released Jan '89, on SPI Milan (France) Deleted Jan '89. Catalogue no: **CD 249**
**Album:** Released Mar '87, on SPI Milan (France) Catalogue no: **A 249**
**Cass:** Released Mar '87, on SPI Milan (France) Catalogue no: **C 249**

**GERSHWIN IN THE MOVIES VOL.2 1951-1959 (St. Louis Symphony Orchestra)**
Tracks: / I'll build a stairway to paradise / Somebody loves me / American in Paris, An / Someone to watch over me / 'S wonderful / Introduction / Porgy sings / Fugue / Ouragan / Bonjour free.
Note: With Wilhelmina Fernandez. Orchestra directed by Leonard Slatkin.
**Cass:** Released Mar '87, on SPI Milan (France) Catalogue no: **C 250**
**Album:** Released Mar '87, on SPI Milan (France) Catalogue no: **A 250**

## Stacy, Jess

**Biographical details:** Jess Stacy was born on 11th August 1904 in Missouri. he was best known as a Pianist with Benny Goodman 1935-39 and later at intervals; he was married to vocalist Lee Wiley. At Goodman's famous Carnegie Hall concert in January 1938 he played an unexpected solo on *Sing Sing Sing* which has gone down in history as one of the most beautiful moments in Jazz. He also led his own bands at various times, often with Wiley singing. (Donald Clarke 27.3.88).

**BLUE NOTION**
**Album:** Released Jun '88, on Jazzology (USA) by Jazzology Records (USA). Catalogue no: **JCE 90**

**JESS STACY AND FRIENDS**
Note: Solos by Lee Wiley, Specs Powell.
**Album:** Released May '87, on Commodore Class Catalogue no: **6.24298**

**JESS STACY ON THE AIR**
Tracks: / Someone to watch over me / Lady be good / Cherry / Rosetta / Honeysuckle rose / Keepin' out of mischief now / Three little words / Jumpin' with Jess / DA blues / After you've gone / Sweet Lorraine / I wish I could shimmy like my sister Kate / China boy / You're driving me crazy.
**Album:** Released Oct '86, on Aircheck (USA) by Kiner Ents.(USA). Catalogue no: **AIRCHECK 26**

**PIANO SOLOS (1935-56)**
**Album:** Released Jan '83, on Swaggie (Australia) Catalogue no: **S 1248**

**STACY 'N' SUTTON (Stacy, Jess/Ralph Sutton)**
Tracks: / Fascinating rhythm / You took advantage of / Indiana / Oh baby / Stars fell on Alabama / If I could be with you / I want to be happy / I can't get started / Jeepers creepers / I'll dance at your wedding / Fussin' / Eye opener, The / T'aint nobody's business if I do / Sneakaway / I got rhythm.
**Album:** Released Jun '86, on Affinity by Charly Records. Catalogue no: **AFS 1020**

**WITH LEE WILEY, SPECS POWELL AND SOLOS 1938 & 1944**
Tracks: / Ramblin' / Candlelights / Complainin' / Ain't goin' nowhere / She's funny that way / You're driving me crazy / Sell out, The / Ec-stacy / Down to Steamboat Tennessee / Sugar / After you've gone / Blues fives u.a..
**Album:** Released Aug '82, on Commodore Class Catalogue no: **AG6 24298**

## Stafford, Jo

**Biographical details:** Jo Stafford was born on 12th november, 1920 in California; she is one of the most highly regarded of pop singers by public, critics and musicians alike. She joined the vocal group the Pied Pipers; they joined Tommy Dorsey in 1940 (Frank Sinatra was a member for a while), left Dorsey in 1942; she went solo in 1944 with her husband, arranger Paul Weston: she had nearly 50 hits on Capitol 1944-50 and about 30 more on USA Columbia 1950-57. She and Weston (as Jonathan and Darlene Edwards) did a comedy act of slightly wrong notes, hilarious and requiring great skill. Her original hit singles and albums are now available on the California Corinthian label. (Donald Clarke 27.3.88).

**BROADWAY REVISITED (Romantic ballads from the theatre)**
Tracks: / My romance / Something to remember you by / They say it's wonderful / I'm always chasing rainbows / Make the man love me / Dancing in the dark / September song / Spring is here / If I were a bell / Mountain high, valley low / I'm your girl / Night and day.
**Album:** Released Jul '88, on Corinthian (USA) by Corinthian Records (USA). Catalogue no: **COR 118**

**G.I. JO (Jo Stafford Sings Songs Of World War II)**
Tracks: / I'll walk alone / I left my heart at the stage door canteen / No love / Do nothing / We mustn't say goodbye / You'll never know / I'll remember April / It could happen to you / I don't want to walk without you / I fall in love too easily / I'll be seeing you.
**CD:** Released Sep '87, on Corinthian (USA) by Corinthian Records (USA). Catalogue no: **COR 105CD**
**Album:** Released Mar '79, on Corinthian (USA) by Corinthian Records (USA). Catalogue no: **COR 105**

**GREATEST HITS: JO STAFFORD**
**Cass:** Released Dec '88, on Capitol (Specials) Catalogue no: **4XL 9399**

**HITS OF JO STAFFORD, THE**
Tracks: / You belong to me / Shrimp boats / Yesterdays / Make love to me / Georgia on my mind / Jambalaya / Come rain or come shine / No other love / Day by day / Gentleman is a dope, The / I'll be seeing you / Trolley song, The.
Note: 1963 album reproduced in its original sleeve, featuring Joe Stafford with musicians directed by her husband, Paul Weston.
**Album:** Released Jul '84, on MFP by EMI Records. Deleted Jul '87. Catalogue no: **MFP 41 5668-1**
**Cass:** Released Jul '84, on MFP by EMI Records. Deleted Jul '87. Catalogue no: **MFP 41 5668-4**

**INTRODUCING JO STAFFORD**
Tracks: / Begin the beguine / Congratulations / Why can't you behave? / Scarlet ribbons / Too marvellous for words / Over the rainbow / Just reminiscing / Walkin' my baby back home / I remember you / Happy times / Baby, won't you please come home / Smoke dreams / Roses of Picardy / If I ever love again / Sometime / Always true to you in my fashion.
**Cass:** Released Nov '87, on Capitol by EMI Records. Deleted Jan '90. Catalogue no: **TCEMS 1273**
**Album:** Released Nov '87, on Capitol by EMI Records. Catalogue no: **EMS 1273**

**JAMBALAYA**
Tracks: / Jambalaya.
**7" Single:** Released Dec '52, on Columbia by EMI Records. Deleted Dec '55. Catalogue no: **DB 3169**

**JO PLUS BLUES (The Best Of The Blues)**
Tracks: / Blues is an old old story, The / John Henry / Sometimes I feel like a motherless child / Nobody knows the trouble I've seen / Blues is a tale of trouble, The / Kansas City blues / Memphis blues / Blues is a travelling thing, The / He's gone away / Every night when the sun goes in / Seems like when it comes in the morning / Times change / Lover man / Blues in the night.
**Album:** Released Mar '79, on Corinthian (USA) by Corinthian Records (USA). Catalogue no: **COR 114**

**JO PLUS BROADWAY (A Swinging Album Of Broadway Hits)**
Tracks: / Love for sale / Happiness is just a thing called Joe / How high the moon / Speak low / It never entered my mind / Taking a chance on love / Anything goes / Gentleman is a dope, The / I got it bad / Old devil moon / Any place I hang my hat is home / Tomorrow mountain.
**Album:** Released Mar '79, on Corinthian (USA) by Corinthian Records (USA). Catalogue no: **COR 112**

**JO PLUS JAZZ**
Tracks: / Just squeeze me / For you / Midnight sun / You'd be so nice to come home to / Folks who live on the hill, The / I didn't know about you / What can I say, after I say I'm sorry? / Dream of you / Imagination / S'posin' / Daydream / I've got the world on a string.
Note: Musicians include such stars as Ben Webster, Johnny Hodges and Jimmy Rowles.
**Album:** Released Mar '79, on Corinthian (USA) by Corinthian Records (USA). Catalogue no: **COR 108**
**CD:** Released Jul '88, on Corinthian (USA) by Corinthian Records (USA). Catalogue no: **COR 108 CD**

**JO STAFFORD: BY REQUEST (Fan Favourites Through The Years)**
Tracks: / As I love you / Early autumn / September in the rain / I cover the waterfront / Don't worry 'bout me / Blue skies / Young and foolish / Easy come, easy go / Sleepy time down south / Dancing on the ceiling / If / King of Paris, The.
**Album:** Released Jul '88, on Corinthian (USA) by Corinthian Records (USA). Catalogue no: **COR 119**

**JO STAFFORD: INTERNATIONAL HITS (Continental Requests And Us Hits)**
Tracks: / Little man with a candy cigar / Come rain or come shine / Allentown Jail / Long ago and far away / September song / Around the corner / Stardust / Keep it a secret / Symphony / On London Bridge / No other love / Teach me tonight.
**Album:** Released Jul '88, on Corinthian (USA) by Corinthian Records (USA). Catalogue no: **COR 115**

**JO STAFFORD SINGS AMERICAN FOLK (The famous Capitol album)**
Tracks: / Shenandoah / Black is the colour / Old Joe Clark / Poor wayfaring stranger / Barbara Allen / Single girl / Red Rosey Bush / I wonder as I wander / Cripple Creek / Nightingale, The / Johnny has gone for a soldier / Sourwood Mountain.
**Album:** Released Mar '79, on Corinthian (USA) by Corinthian Records (USA). Catalogue no: **COR 110**

**JO STAFFORD'S GREATEST HITS (Stafford's Best On Columbia)**
Tracks: / You belong to me / Yesterdays / Jambalaya / I should care / Gentleman is a dope, The / Make love to me / Embraceable you / Shrimp boats / All the things you are / St. Louis blues.
**Album:** Released Mar '79, on Corinthian (USA) by Corinthian Records (USA). Catalogue no: **COR 106**
**Cass:** Released Mar '79, on Corinthian (USA) by Corinthian Records (USA). Catalogue no: **COR 106C**

**MAKE LOVE TO ME**
Tracks: / Make love to me.
**7" Single:** Released May '54, on Philips by Phonogram Ltd. Deleted May '57. Catalogue no: **PB 233**

**MUSIC OF MY LIFE (America's Most Versatile Singing Star)**
Tracks: / Night we called it a day, The / Georgia on my mind / Day by day / Candy / If it takes me all my life / One I love, The / I'll never smile again / Tennessee waltz / On the Alamo / Sunday kind of love, A / All the things you are / Whatcha know, Joe?.
**Album:** Released Jul '88, on Corinthian (USA) by Corinthian Records (USA). Catalogue no: **COR 123**
**Cass:** Released Jul '88, on Corinthian (USA) by Corinthian Records (USA). Catalogue no: **COR 123C**

**OLD RUGGED CROSS (Stafford, Jo/Gordon MacRae)**
Tracks: / Whispering hope / Abide with me / In the garden / Beyond the sunset / Beautiful Isle of somewhere / It is no secret / I found a friend / Old rugged cross, The / Rock of ages / Star of hope / Now the day is over / Perfect day.
**Cass:** Released Jun '87, on MFP by EMI Records. Catalogue no: **TCMFP 5798**
**Album:** Released Jun '87, on MFP by EMI Records. Catalogue no: **MFP 5798**

**SKI TRAILS (Winter Favourites For The Fireside)**
Tracks: / Baby, it's cold outside / Moonlight in Vermont / Let it snow, let it snow, let it snow / By the fireside / Winter weather / It happened in Sun Valley / I've got my love to keep me warm / Nearness of you, The / Winter wonderland / June in January / Whiffenpoof song, The / Sleigh ride.
**Album:** Released Mar '79, on Corinthian (USA) by Corinthian Records (USA). Catalogue no: **COR 113**

**SONGS OF FAITH, HOPE AND LOVE (Whispering Hope And The Best Of Religious Songs)**
Tracks: / Whispering hope / It is no secret / Beautiful Isle of somewhere / I found a friend / Suddenly there's a valley / Lord's my shepherd, The / Beautiful garden of prayer, The / He bought my soul at Calvary / Each step of the way / Star of hope / Lord, keep Your hand on me / Peace in the valley.
**Album:** Released Mar '83, on Corinthian (USA) by Corinthian Records (USA). Catalogue no: **COR 111**

**STARRING JO STAFFORD**
Tracks: / Serenade of the bells / On the Alamo / No other love / Red river valley / Ivy / Fools rush in / Sunday kind of love,

A / Gentleman is a dope, The / Symphony / Tumbling tumbleweeds / You keep coming back like a song / Day by day.
**Cass:** Released Jun '85, on Capitol by EMI Records. Deleted Jan '90. Catalogue no: **ED 2604294**
**Album:** Released Jun '85, on Capitol by EMI Records. Catalogue no: **ED 2604291**

**STARS OF THE 50'S**
**Album:** Released Aug '84, on EMI (Holland) by EMI Records. Catalogue no: **5C 050 81048**

**SUDDENLY THERE'S A VALLEY**
Tracks: / Suddenly there's a valley.
**7" Single:** Released Dec '55, on Philips by Phonogram Ltd. Deleted Dec '59. Catalogue no: **PB 509**

**YOU BELONG TO ME**
Tracks: / You belong to me.
**7" Single:** Released Nov '52, on Columbia by EMI Records. Deleted Nov '55. Catalogue no: **DB 3152**

**YOU'LL NEVER WALK ALONE (Stafford, Jo/Gordon MacRae)**
**Cass:** Released Dec '88, on Capitol (Specials) Catalogue no: **4XL 9536**
**Album:** Released '81, on Word (UK) by Word Records (UK). Deleted '88. Catalogue no: **WRD R 3024**

## Staple Singers

**ARE YOU READY**
Tracks: / Are you ready / Love works in strange ways.
**12" Single:** Released Oct '85, on Epic by CBS Records. Deleted Oct '88. Catalogue no: **TA 6580**
**7" Single:** Released Oct '85, on Epic by CBS Records. Deleted Oct '88. Catalogue no: **A 6580**

**AT THEIR BEST**
**Cass:** Released May '88, on Supreme by Supreme Records. Catalogue no: **2651214**

**BEALTITUDE: RESPECT YOURSELF**
Tracks: / This world / Respect yourself / Name the missing word / I'll take you there / This old town / We the people / Are you sure / Who do you think you are / I'm just another soldier / Who.
**Album:** Released Aug '87, on Stax by Fantasy Inc (USA). Catalogue no: **SXE 001**

**BEST OF THE STAPLES**
**Album:** Released Dec '88, on Stax by Fantasy Inc (USA). Catalogue no: **SX 006**

**BRAND NEW DAY**
Tracks: / Brand new day / Childs life / Come out of your shell / If it wasn't for a woman / He / Garden party / I believe in music / Which way did it go / This time around / You've got to make an effort / Unity.
**Album:** Released Apr '80, on Stax by Fantasy Inc (USA). Deleted '85. Catalogue no: **STM 7009**

**HOLD ON TO YOUR DREAM**
Tracks: / Ride it on out / There's got to be rain in your life / Message in our music / Cold and windy nights / Stupid Louie / Hold on to your dream / Show off the real you / Old flames / Love came knocking.
**Cass:** Released Oct '81, on 20th Century by 20th Century Records. Catalogue no: **C 636**
**Album:** Released Oct '81, on 20th Century by 20th Century Records. Catalogue no: **T 636**

**IF YOU'RE READY (COME GO WITH**
Tracks: / If you're ready (come go with me).
**7" Single:** Released Jun '74, on Stax by Fantasy Inc (USA). Deleted Jun '77. Catalogue no: **2025 224**

**I'LL TAKE YOU THERE**
Tracks: / I'll take you there / I'm just another soldier.
**7" Single:** Released Sep '87, on Stax by Fantasy Inc (USA). Catalogue no: **STAX 815**
**7" Single:** Released Jun '72, on Stax by Fantasy Inc (USA). Deleted Jun '75. Catalogue no: **2025 110**
**7" Single:** Released Mar '82, on Stax by Fantasy Inc (USA). Catalogue no: **STAX 1002**

**LONG WALK TO DC**
Tracks: / Long walk to D.C..
**7" Single:** Released Oct '87, on Stax by Fantasy Inc (USA). Catalogue no: **STAX 817**

**PRAY ON**
Tracks: / Pray on / Don't drive me away / Downward road / Will the circle be unbroken / Stand by me / Ain't that good news / If I could hear my mother / Going away / Don't knock / Uncloudy day / I know I got religion / Somebody save me / Let's go home / This may be the last time / I had a dream / Calling me.
**Album:** Released Apr '86, on New Cross by Charly Records. Catalogue no: **GNC 1002**

**RESPECT YOURSELF (SINGLE)**
Tracks: / Respect yourself / This world / Heavy makes you happy / Long walk to DC.
**7" Single:** Released 13 Jun '87, on Stax by Fantasy Inc (USA). Catalogue no: **STAX 805**
**12" Single:** Released Nov '87, on Stax by Fantasy Inc (USA). Deleted Jan '90. Catalogue no: **STAT 805**

**RESPECT YOURSELF - THE BEST OF THE STAPLE SINGERS**
Tracks: / Heavy makes you happy / Long walk to DC / This world / Respect yourself / I see it / We'll get over / Take you there / Oh la de da / Are you sure / If you're ready (come go with me) / Touch a hand, make a friend / City in the sky / People come out of your shell / You've got to earn it (Available on CD only) / Love is plentiful (Available on CD only) / Got to be some changes (Available on CD only) / Be what you are (Available on CD only) / This old town (Available on CD only) / Slow train (Available on CD only) / My main man (Available on CD only).
**Cass:** Released Mar '88, on Stax by Fantasy Inc (USA). Catalogue no: **SXC 006**
**CD:** Released Oct '87, on Stax by Fantasy Inc (USA). Catalogue no: **CDSX 006**
**CD:** Released '88, on Mobile Fidelity Sound Lab(USA) by Mobile Fidelity Records (USA). Catalogue no: **MFCD 832**
**Album:** Released Mar '88, on Stax by Fantasy Inc (USA). Catalogue no: **SX 006**

**SLIPPERY PEOPLE**
Tracks: / Slippery people.
**7" Single:** Released Sep '84, on Epic by CBS Records. Catalogue no: **A 4784**
**12" Single:** Released Sep '84, on Epic by CBS Records. Catalogue no: **TA 4784**

**STAND BY ME**
Tracks: / Stand by me / If I could hear my mother pray / God's wonderful love / Calling me / Uncloudy day / I know I've got religion / Swing low sweet chariot / On my way to heaven / I'm coming home / I had a dream / Help me Jesus / Love is the way / Let's go home / This may be the last time / I'm leaning / Going away / Downward road / Pray on / Good news / Day is passed and gone / Don't knock / Will the circle be unbroken / Born in Bethlehem / I've been scorned / Sit down servant / Two wings.
**2 LP Set:** Released Jan '77, on DJM Deleted '80. Catalogue no: **DJD 28028**

**STAPLE SINGERS**
Tracks: / Are you ready? / Life during wartime / Nobody can make it on there own / Back to the war / Reason to love / We stand (together, forever) / Start walking / Love works in strange ways.
**Cass:** Released Nov '85, on Epic by CBS Records. Catalogue no: **40 26537**
**Album:** Released Nov '85, on Epic by CBS Records. Catalogue no: **EPC 26537**

**STAPLE SINGERS AT THEIR BEST**
Tracks: / If you're ready (come go with me) / Respect yourself / This world / You're gonna make me cry / Touch a hand, make a friend / City in the sky / I'll take you there / You've got to earn it / Oh la de da / Heavy makes you happy / Be what you are / My main man / Long walk to DC.
**Cass:** Released Mar '82, on Stax by Fantasy Inc (USA). Catalogue no: **STAXK 5004**
**Album:** Released Mar '82, on Stax by Fantasy Inc (USA). Catalogue no: **STAXL 5004**

**STAPLE SINGERS, THE**
**Cass:** Released Oct '84, on Audio Fidelity(USA) by Audio Fidelity (USA). Catalogue no: **ZCGAS 745**

**STAPLE SINGERS, THE (STAX)**
**Album:** Released Dec '88, on Stax by Fantasy Inc (USA). Catalogue no: **SX**

001

**THIS IS OUR NIGHT**
Tracks: / This is our night / Turning point.
**12" Single:** Released Jan '85, on Epic by CBS Records. Catalogue no: **TA 5008**
**7" Single:** Released Jan '85, on Epic by CBS Records. Catalogue no: **A 5008**

**TURNING POINT**
Tracks: / This is our night / Slippery people / Bridges instead of walls / Turning point / Right decision / H-a-t-e / On my own again / That's what friends are for.
**Album:** Released Dec '84, on Epic by CBS Records. Catalogue no: **EPC 26212**

**WE'LL GET OVER**
Tracks: / Give a damn / Everyday people / End of the road / Tend to your own business / Solon Bushi (Japanese folk song) / Challenge, The / God bless the children / Games people play / Wednesday in your garden, A / Gardener, The / When do I get paid.
Note: Produced by legendary guitarist, producer and arranger Steve Cropper. Re-issue.
**Album:** Released Jan '87, on Stax by Fantasy Inc (USA). Catalogue no: **MPS 8532**
**Cass:** Released Jan '87, on Stax by Fantasy Inc (USA). Catalogue no: **MPS 585532**

## Starita, Ray

**RHAPSODY IN RHYTHM (Starita, Ray & His Ambassadors)**
Tracks: / Rhapsody in rhythm / Crazy rhythm / Love lies / Every little moment / Spread a little happiness / That's what I call keen / Through / Blues hills of Pasedena / Un-tcha-am-tcha-da-da-da / There's somebody new / Blue days are over / Come on baby / Blue river / My dream memory / Gee it must be love / Dancing in your sleep / Sunshine of Marseilles / If I had three wishes / It's not you / There's always tomorrow.
**Album:** Released Apr '83, on Saville by Conifer Records. Catalogue no: **SVL 155**

## Starr, Kay

**Biographical details:** Kay Starr was born in 1922 in Oklahoma; she sang with the bands of Bob Crosby and Charlie Barnet, then was one of the biggest USA pop stars from 1948 on Capitol with her big voice, distinctive vocal colour; *Wheel of fortune* was No. 1 for ten weeks in 1952; she was double-tracked for duets with herself, unusual then and particularly effective on *Side by side*. She switched to RCA and *Rock 'n' roll waltz* was No. 1 for six weeks in 1955; then she went back to Capitol. (Donald Clarke 27.3.87).

**1947: KAY STARR**
**Album:** Released Jun '86, on Hindsight (UK) by Michele International Records. Catalogue no: **HUK 214**

**AM I A TOY OR A TREASURE**
Tracks: / Am I a toy or a treasure.
**7" Single:** Released Oct '54, on Capitol by EMI Records. Deleted Oct '57. Catalogue no: **CL 14151**

**BACK TO THE ROOTS**
**Album:** Released '88, on GNP Crescendo (USA) by GNP Crescendo Records (USA). Catalogue no: **GNPS 2090**
**Cass:** Released '88, on GNP Crescendo (USA) by GNP Crescendo Records (USA). Catalogue no: **GNP5 2090**

**BLUE STARR**
Tracks: / It's a lonesome old town / You're driving me crazy / House is haunted, The / We three / I really don't want to know / Blue Starr / Wedding bells / It's funny to everyone but me / Little white lies / Just like a butterfly (that's caught in the rain) / Blue & sentimental.
**Album:** Released Jun '87, on RCA by BMG Records (UK). Deleted Jul '89. Catalogue no: **NL 90045**
**Cass:** Released Jun '87, on RCA by BMG Records (UK). Deleted Jul '89. Catalogue no: **NK 90045**

**CHANGING PARTNERS**
Tracks: / Changing partners.
**7" Single:** Released Mar '54, on Capitol by EMI Records. Deleted Mar '57. Catalogue no: **CL 14050**

**COMES A-LONG A-LOVE**
Tracks: / Comes a-long a-love.
**7" Single:** Released Dec '52, on Capitol by EMI Records. Deleted Dec '55. Catalogue no: **CL 13808**

**FABULOUS FAVOURITES**
Tracks: / Wheel of fortune / Rock and roll waltz / Side by side / Comes along a love / Bonapartes retreat / Half a photograph / Mississippi / So tired / I'm the lonesomest gal in town / Hoop dee doo / Allez vous en go away / Foolin' around.
**Album:** Released Jun '83, on MFP by EMI Records. Deleted Jun '88. Catalogue no: **MFP 5603**

**IN A BLUE MOOD**
Tracks: / After you've gone / Woman likes to be told, A / Maybe you'll be there / I'm waiting for ships that never come in / What will I tell my heart? / Evenin' / He's funny that way / I got the spring fever blues / Don't tell him what happened to me / I got it bad and that ain't good / Everybody's somebody's fool / Until the real thing comes along.
**Album:** Released Jul '85, on Capitol by EMI Records. Deleted Nov '88. Catalogue no: **EG 2606101**
**Cass:** Released Jul '85, on Capitol by EMI Records. Deleted Jul '87. Catalogue no: **EG 2606104**

**IN THE 40'S**
**Album:** Released '88, on Hindsight Catalogue no: **HSR 214**

**JAZZ SINGER**
Tracks: / I never knew / My man / Breezin' along eith the wind / All by myself / Hard hearted Anna / Me too / Happy days & lonely nights / I only want a buddy, not a sweetheart / Hummin' to myself / My honey's arms / Sunday / Anything for you.
**Album:** Released Sep '83, on Capitol by EMI Records. Deleted Jun '88. Catalogue no: **CAPS 1867481**
**Cass:** Released Sep '83, on Capitol by EMI Records. Deleted '87. Catalogue no: **TC CAPS 1867484**

**JUST PLAIN COUNTRY**
Tracks: / Pins and needles in my heart / Crazy / Four walls / My last date (with you) / Blues stay away from me / Walk on by / Oh, lonesome me / I can't help it (if I'm still in love with you) / I really don't want to know / Singing the blues / Don't worry.
**Cass:** Released Sep '87, on Stetson by Hasmick Promotions. Catalogue no: **HATC 3049**
**Album:** Released Sep '87, on Stetson by Hasmick Promotions. Catalogue no: **HAT 3049**

**KAY STARR COUNTRY**
**Album:** Released '88, on GNP Crescendo (USA) by GNP Crescendo Records (USA). Catalogue no: **GNPS 2083**
**Cass:** Released '88, on GNP Crescendo (USA) by GNP Crescendo Records (USA). Catalogue no: **GNP5 2083**

**KAY STARR STYLE, THE**
Tracks: / Side by side / Someday sweetheart / What can I say after I say I'm sorry.
**Cass:** Released Oct '84, on Pathe Marconi (France) Catalogue no: **PM 1552964**
**Album:** Released Oct '84, on Pathe Marconi (France) Catalogue no: **PM 1552961**

**MOVIN'**
**Album:** Released Mar '60, on Capitol by EMI Records. Deleted Mar '65. Catalogue no: **T 1254**

**PURE GOLD: KAY STARR**
Tracks: / Rock and roll waltz / Rockin' chair / Georgia on my mind / My heart reminds me / Oh, how I miss you tonight / It's a lonesome old town / Dry bones / Fit as a fiddle / You're driving me crazy / Wrap your troubles in dreams / I'll never say "never again" again / Only love me.
**Album:** Released Jun '81, on RCA International by BMG Records (UK). Catalogue no: **INTS 5090**
**Cass:** Released Jun '81, on RCA International by BMG Records (UK). Catalogue no: **INTK 5090**

**ROCK AND ROLL WALTZ**
Tracks: / Rock and roll waltz.
**7" Single:** Released Feb '56, on H.M.V. by EMI Records. Deleted Feb '59. Catalogue no: **POP 168**

**ROCK AND ROLL WALTZ (OLD GOLD)**
Tracks: / Rock and roll waltz / Wheel of fortune.
**7" Single:** Released Apr '87, on Old Gold by Old Gold Records. Deleted Sep '89. Catalogue no: **OG 9724**

**SIDE BY SIDE**
Tracks: / Side by side.

**7" Single:** Released Apr '53, on Capitol by EMI Records. Deleted Apr '56. Catalogue no: **CL 13871**

**WHEEL OF FORTUNE AND OTHER HITS**
**Cass:** Released '89, on Capitol (Specials) Catalogue no: **4XL-9286**

**WHEEL OF FORTUNE (SINGLE)**
Tracks: / Wheel of fortune.
**7" Single:** Released '80, on Capitol by EMI Records. Catalogue no: **LR 1870**

## Stars Of Faith

**OF BLACK NATIVITY**
Tracks: / My sweet Lord / I'm glad about it / This joy / Hard way, The / I'm a soldier / My hope is built / We shall be changed / Come over here / Get away Jordan / Too late.
**2 LP Set:** Released Sep '83, on Musidisc by Musidisc Records (France). Catalogue no: **ALB 161**

## Stash Christmas Album

**STASH CHRISTMAS ALBUM (16 Blues & Jazz Classics) (Various artists)**
**Album:** Released Mar '87, on Stash (USA) Catalogue no: **ST 125**

## State Street Ramblers

**Biographical details:** see under - Dixie Four..

**STATE STREET RAMBLERS 1931 VOL. 2**
**Album:** Released '88, on Herwin by Shanachie Records (USA). Catalogue no: **HERWIN 105**

## State Street

**STATE STREET SWINGERS AND CHICAGO BLACK SWANS**
**Album:** Released Aug '89, on Blues Document Catalogue no: **BD 2047**

## Station Hall Jazz Band

**NEW ORLEANS DIXIE**
Note: 18 popular jazz standards played by the Staion Hall Jazz Band
**CD:** Released May '87, on Delta (1) by Delta Records. Deleted '88. Catalogue no: **19 406**

## Staton, Dakota

**Biographical details:** Jazz-oriented singer Dakota Staton was born in 1932. Her Top Five album, *The Late Late Show*, in 1958, included one of the earliest recordings of Erroll Garner's *Misty*. She also recorded with George Shearing. (Donald Clarke, March 1987.).

**CRAZY HE CALLS ME**
Tracks: / Crazy he calls me / Idaho / Invitation / Can't live without him anymore / I never dreamt / Party's over, The / Angel eyes / No moon at all / What do you know about love / Morning, noon or night / How does it feel? / How high the moon.
**Album:** Released Oct '87, on Jasmine by Hasmick Promotions. Catalogue no: **JAS 303**
**Cass:** Released Oct '87, on Jasmine by Hasmick Promotions. Catalogue no: **JAS C303**

**LATE LATE SHOW**
Tracks: / Broadway / Trust in me / Summertime / Misty / Foggy day, A / What do you see in her? / Late late show, The / My funny valentine / Give me the simple life / You showed me the way / Moonray / Ain't no use.
Note: Orchestra conducted by Van Alexander.
**Album:** Released Apr '84, on Capitol by EMI Records. Deleted Feb '90. Catalogue no: **CAPS 2600101**
**Cass:** Released Apr '84, on Capitol by EMI Records. Deleted Jul '87. Catalogue no: **TC CAPS 260 010-4**

**LET ME OFF UPTOWN**
Tracks: / When lights are low / Willow weep for me / But not for me / You don't know what love is / Best thing for you, The / Song is you, The / Avalon / Until the real things come along / If I should lose you / Gone with the wind / Let me off uptown / Anything goes / When sunny gets blue / They all laughed / Too close for comfort / Cherokee / September in the rain / East of the sun / It's you or no one / Song is ended, The / Goodbye / Love walked in.
Note: Dakota Staton swingin' 22 great standards as only she can. Backed by fabulous big band arrangements and featuring solos by amongst others, Taft Jordan, Joe Wilder, Jerome Richardson, Hank Jones, Jonah Jones and Harry Edison.
**CD:** Released '89, on Renaissance Catalogue no: **CDREN 005**

## Stax Blues Masters

**STAX BLUES MASTERS, VOL 1: BLUE MONDAY (Various artists)**
Tracks: / They want money: *Little Sonny* / Driving wheel: *King, Albert* / Creeper, The: *Robinson, Freddie* / Eight men, four women: *Little Milton* / Things that I used to do: *Little Sonny* / Bad luck: *King, Albert* / More bad luck: *King, Albert* / Born under a bad sign: *King, Albert* / Blues with a feeling: *Little Sonny* / Married woman: *Little Milton* / I wonder: *Robinson, Freddie* / Blue Monday: *Little Milton* / After hours: *Robinson, Freddie*.
Note: Tracks include those listed above.
**Album:** Released Mar '82, on Stax by Fantasy Inc (USA). Catalogue no: **STAXL 5005**

## Steig, Jeremy

**OUTLAWS**
**Album:** Released Jan '82, on Enja (Germany) by Enja Records (West Germany). Catalogue no: **ENJA 2098**

**SOMETHING ELSE (Steig, Jeremy / Jan Hammer)**
Tracks: / Home / Cakes / Swamp carol / Down stretch / Give me some / Come with me / Dance of the mind / Up tempo thing / Elephant hump / Rock No.6 / Slow blues in G / Rock No.9 / Something else.
Note: Personnel: Jeremy Steig (Flutes), Jan Hammer (Electric Piano / Chinese gong), Gene Perla, (Electric & upright bass), Eddie Gomez (Upright bass on "Down stretch" and "Come with me"), Don Alias (Drums / percussion).
**CD:** Released '88, on Denon Catalogue no: **DC-8512**
**Cass:** Released '88, on Denon Catalogue no: **MC 8512**

## Stein, Andy

**GOIN' PLACES (Stein, Andy & Friends)**
**Album:** Released Jan '88, on Stomp Off (USA) Catalogue no: **SOS 1146**

## Stein, Lou

**LOU STEIN AND FRIENDS (Stein, Lou & Friends)**
Tracks: / Honeysuckle rose / I'll be seeing you / Sweetest sounds, The / Dancing in the dark / Fine romance, A / Foggy day, A / All the things you are / What is this thing called love / Georgia / I'll remember April / Younger than Spring time / Let's face the music and dance.
**Album:** Released May '81, on World Jazz Deleted '86. Catalogue no: **WJLPS 17**

**LOU STEIN TRIO (Stein, Lou Trio)**
Tracks: / Take the 'A' train / No man alone / Li'l darlin' / My funny valentine / Shadow of your smile / Glad / Jumpin' at the keyboard / Hello little friend / Ballade, The / Something / Yesterday.
**Album:** Released '82, on Jump (Import) Catalogue no: **J 0128**

**PIANO SOLO**
**Album:** Released Jul '87, on Audiophile (USA) by Jazzology Records (USA). Catalogue no: **AP 198**

## Stenson, Bobo

**VERY EARLY (Stenson,Bobo Trio)**
**Album:** Released Apr '89, on Dragon by Dragon Records. Catalogue no: **DRLP 148**

## Stevens, John

**APPLICATION, INTERACTION AND... (Stevens, John/Trevor Watts / Barry Guy)**
**Album:** Released '83, on Spotlite by Spotlite Records. Catalogue no: **SPJ 513**

**FREEBOP**
Tracks: / Blue line / Rhythm is / Take care / Okko / Kook.
**Album:** Released '83, on Affinity by Charly Records. Catalogue no: **AFF 101**

**LIFE OF RILEY, THE**
**Album:** Released Dec '88, on Affinity by Charly Records. Catalogue no: **AFF 130**

**LONGEST NIGHT, VOL 1 (Stevens, John & Evan Parker)**
**Album:** Released Feb '78, on Ogun by Cadillac Music. Catalogue no: **OG 120**

**LONGEST NIGHT, VOL 2 (Stevens, John & Evan Parker)**
**Album:** Released Jun '78, on Ogun by Cadillac Music. Catalogue no: **OG 420**

**NO FEAR (Stevens, John / Trevor Watts / Barry Guy)**
**Album:** Released '83, on Spotlite by

Spotlite Records. Catalogue no: **SPJ 508**

## Stewart, Jimmy

**TOUCH, THE**
Tracks: / Gipsy 86 / Dreams / Jim's tune / Touch, The / Rainbow / Tune for Bill and Jim, A / Wes / Personal touch.
Note: American guitarist Jimmy Stewart With a programme of his own compositions. Each piece is dedicated to the foremost jazz guitarists,simulating the styles and sounds of their respective eras. As well as his collaboration with one of the most important guitarists of the 60's and 70's Gabor Szabo, Stewart has performed with countless other stars, including Ray Charles, Quincy Jones, Andy Williams and Michael Jackson
Personnel: Ryo Okomoto-synthesiser
**Album:** Released Jan '87, on Black Hawk (USA) by Blackhawk Records (USA). Catalogue no: **BKH 50301**

## Stewart, Louis

**ACOUSTIC GUITAR DUETS (Stewart, Louis & Martin Taylor) (See panel below)**
Tracks: / Pick yourself up / Morning of the carnival / Jive at five / Coming through the rye / Cherokee / Stompin' at the Savoy / Darn that dream / Farewell to Erin.
Note: Recorded at Trend Studios, Dublin, Wednesday 3rd July and Monday 8th July 1985.
**Album:** Released Jun '88, on Livia Catalogue no: **LRLP 7**

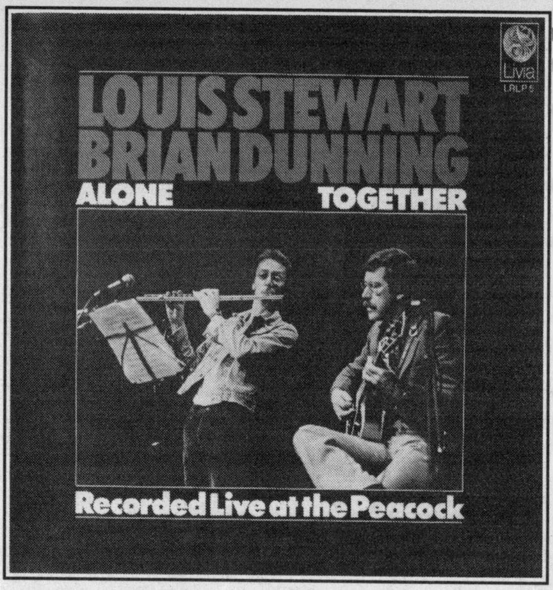


**Louis Stewart - Alone Together (Livia)**

**Cass:** Released Jun '88, on Livia Catalogue no: **LRCS 7**

**ALONE TOGETHER (Live at The Peacock) (Stewart, Louis & Brian Dunning) (See panel above)**
Tracks: / There will never be another you / Windows / Definitely doctored / Inner urge / Israel / Alone together / Triste / Donna Lee.
Note: Recorded by Gerald Davis at the Peacock Theatre, Dublin, August 15th/ 16th/ 17th 1979 and remastered under the supervision of Louis Stewart at Pat Hayes Sound Studios, Bray 27th August 1979. Produced by Gerald Davis. This album is not the result of a happy accident. It is one that has been eagerly anticipated for some time and it finally became possible when Louis Stewart and Brian Dunning played three lunchtime concerts at the Peacock Theatre to packed and appreciative houses. The programmes varied slightly from day to day and the choice for the album was agreed by Brian and Louis. *Definitely doctored* is Brian's title for the free piece played on the last day and refers to the fact that part of the intro has been cut. This is virually the only editing on the album and the music you hear is exactly as taped live. it represents Louis Stewart and Brian Dunning on top form and it is a tribute to the quality of the performances that both musicians, perfectionists as they are, feel that it represents them at their best. (Livia Records, 1979)
**Album:** Released Jun '88, on Livia Catalogue no: **LRLP 5**

**BAUBLES,BANGLES AND BEADS (Stewart Louis & Peter Ind)**
**Album:** Released Apr '79, on Wave by Wave Records. Catalogue no: **WAVE**

**Louis Stewart - Acoustic Guitar Duets (Livia)**

**Louis Stewart - Out on his own (Livia)**

**LP 12**

**GOOD NEWS**
**Album:** Released '88, on Villa Catalogue no: **VILLA 001**

**I THOUGHT ABOUT YOU**
Tracks: / I thought about you / Litha / Smiling Billy / Unit 7 / November girl / Straight no chaser.
**Album:** Released Nov '80, on Lee Lambert by Lee Lambert Records. Deleted Nov '85. Catalogue no: **LAM 103**

**OUT ON HIS OWN (See panel above)**
Tracks: / Blue bossa / Windows / Darn that dream / Wave / She moved through the fair / Make someone happy / I'm all smiles / Stella by starlight / Lazy afternoon / Invitation / I'm old fashioned / General Mojo's well laid plan / What's new ?.
Note: Recorded November 1976/ January 1977 at Pat Hayes Sound Stories. In Ireland, for some years now, Louis Stewart had earned the ungrudging admiration of those lucky enough to hear him; to many he is in a category beyond praise and few will dispute that he merits the ulitmate accolade, *Out on his own*. Since his move to London and exposure to an international audience this opinion has come to be shared abroad particularly by musicians and critics. Derek Jewell, the knowledgable and influential Sunday Times critic has this to say: 'I have been listening to Louis Stewart for some years now, and particularly his work with the quartet and quintet in which he shares front line duties with the British tenor saxist Ronnie Scott. As a member of that band, he has always seemed to me a completely outstanding musician. Indeed, there can be few bands in the world with so distinctive a sound as that current Scott group. Louis has an uncanny sense of the particular contrasts, dynamics and surprises needed to make the band work. Yet even the experience of hearing him with other musicians did not totally prepare me for the brilliance of this solo album. Stewart is revealed here as a guitar vituoso already of considerable maturity - a virtuoso in anyone's language, and in the jazz field (if we must use categories) a musician to be spoken of in the same league as Django Reinhardt, Wes Montgomery, or, among contemporary virtuosos, Joe Pass. The sheer technical mastery of his instrument is staggering; how many fingers has this man got? There are endless themes, variations, counter themes, rythms runs all played with such ease that most other guitarists sound thick fingered.
Stewart's approach, like that of Joe Pass, is orchestral. He puts so much into whatever he plays, and so often on this collection of tunes he passes one particular acid test superbly: he makes very familiar compositions sound as if they had been minted yesterday. In a sense, his style is a history of jazz guitar. To give two examples only: he's as flamboyant as Django at times, and at others his octave-playing is out of Wes Montgomery's file. In his particular blend of history, however, lies his true individuality. Louis Stewart is a master. This album will come, I believe, to be accepted as one of his masterworks. '...high praise indeed. But perhaps we should leave the last word to Louis' colleague, Ronnie Scott, himself one of the finest and most discriminating of jazzmen. 'Louis is a superbly talented natural musician. In my book he's one of the world's great jazz guitarists'. (Livia Records)
**Cass:** Released Jun '88, on Livia Catalogue no: **LRCS 1**
**Album:** Released Jun '88, on Livia Catalogue no: **LRLP 1**

## Stewart, Rex

**ART FORD'S JAZZ PARTY (September 1958)**
Note: With Charlie Shavers / Marty Napoleon / King Curtis / J.C. Higginton / Jimmy Rushing / Red Allen / Lester Young / Vinnie Burle / Osie Johnson, etc.
Tracks include: Bugle call rag / Boy meets horn / The best things in life / Goin' to Chicago / Indian Summer / Mean to me / Avalon, etc..
**Album:** Released Oct '87, on Jazz Connoisseur by Spotlite Records. Catalogue no: **AFJP 6**

**BIG JAZZ 1940 (Stewart, Rex & Jack Teagarden)**
**Album:** Released Jul '87, on Everybody's (Sweden) Catalogue no: **E-1010**

**HOLLYWOOD JAM (Stewart, Rex All Stars Band)**
Tracks: / Blues jam / Someday, sweeheart / Muskrat ramble / Mood indigo / Sheik of Araby, The.
Note: Lamplighters Show broadcast - 19 March 1945 - featuring Duke Ellington, Barney Bigard and other top stars.
**Album:** Released Oct '82, on Duke by Melodisc Records. Catalogue no: **D 1017**

**RENDEZVOUS WITH REX**
Tracks: / Tillie's twist / Pretty ditty / Tell me more / Trade winds / My kind of gal / Blue echo.
Note: Licensed from Decca Records Ltd. Copyright Control
**Album:** Released Dec '86, on Affinity by Charly Records. Catalogue no: **AFF 165**

## Stewart, Slam

**Biographical details:** Stewart, Slam is a bassist and vocalist, born Leroy Stewart on 21 September 1914in Englewood, New Jersey. He teamed with Slim Galliard in 1937 as Slim & Slam; their hits included *Flat Foot Floogie*. He practices one of the most distinctive and delightful gimmicks in jazz, bowing a bass solo and humming in unison and octave above. One of his best know recording sessions was late '43 with the Lester Young Quartet. He appeared in the early 1980's with Illinois Jacquet at the late lamented Canteen. Guitarist Bucky Pizzarelli was born in 1926, also in New Jersey, which also gave us Count Basie, Frank Sinatra, Bruce Springsteen... (Donald Clarke)..

**DIALOGUE (Stewart, Slam & Bucky Pizzarelli)**
Tracks: / Slam blow / It's only a paper moon / That's my kick / Very thought of you, The / Jersey bounce / Night wind / Masquerade / B & S blues / I got rhythm.
**Album:** Released Jan '80, on Sonet by Sonet Records. Catalogue no: **SNTF 811**
**Album:** Released Apr '81, on Stash (USA) Catalogue no: **ST 201**

**NEW YORK, NEW YORK**
**Album:** Released Apr '81, on Stash (USA) Catalogue no: **ST 204**

## Stitt, Sonny

**AT THE D.J. LOUNGE**
Tracks: / McKie's / It all depends on you / Blue moon / I'm in the mood for love / Free love.
**Album:** Released '88, on Chess by Vogue Records. Catalogue no: **GCH 8085**
**Cass:** Released '89, on Chess by Vogue Records. Catalogue no: **GCHK 78085**

**CHAMP, THE**
Tracks: / Champ, The / Sweet and lovely / Midgets, The / Eternal triangle, The / All the things you are / Walkin'.
Note: With Joe Newman, Duke Jordan, Sam Jones, Roy Brooks. Recorded 18 April 1973.
**Album:** Released Apr '81, on Muse by Black & Blue Records. Catalogue no: **MR 5023**

**CONSTELLATION (See panel below)**
Tracks: / Constellation / (I don't stand a) ghost of a chance / Webb city / By accident / Ray's idea / Casbah / It's magic / Topsy.
Note: Personnel: Sonny Stitt - alto & tenor saxophones / Barry Harris - piano / Sam Jones - bass / Roy Brooks - drums. Produced by Don Schlitten. A&R co-ordinator: Joe Fields.
Recorded at RCA studio, NYC June 27 1972. Engineer: Paul Goodman. Mastering engineer: Joe Brescio, the cutting room NYC.
**Album:** Released May '86, on Muse by Black & Blue Records. Catalogue no: **MR 5323**

**FEATURING HOWARD MCGHEE**
**CD:** Released May '88, on Jazz Life Catalogue no: **247 324 2**
**Album:** Released May '88, on Jazz Life Catalogue no: **2273242**
**Cass:** Released May '88, on Jazz Life Catalogue no: **2173242**

**GOOD LIFE (Stitt, Sonny & Hank Jones)**
**CD:** Released Oct '87, on Black Hawk (USA) by Blackhawk Records (USA). Catalogue no: **CDBKH 528**
**Album:** Released Oct '87, on Black Hawk (USA) by Blackhawk Records (USA). Catalogue no: **BKH 528**

**IN WALKED SONNY (Stitt, Sonny / Art Blakey & The Jazz Messengers)**
Tracks: / Blues march / It might as well be spring / Birdlike / I can't get started / Ronnie's a dynamite lady / In walked Sonny.

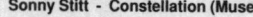

**Sonny Stitt - Constellation (Muse)**

**CD:** Released Jun '88, on Sonet by Sonet Records. Catalogue no: **SNTCD 691**
**Album:** Released '76, on Sonet by Sonet Records. Catalogue no: **SNTF 691**

**JUST FRIENDS (Stitt, Sonny & Red Holloway)**
Tracks: / Way you look tonight / Forecast / You don't know what love is / Getting sentimental over you / Lester leaps in / Just friends / All God's chillun got rhythm.
**Album:** Released Dec '87, on Affinity by Charly Records. Catalogue no: **AFF 181**

**LAST STITT SESSION, THE**
Tracks: / Steamroller / I'll be seeing you / Out of nowhere / Sweet Georgia Brown / Keepin' it / This is always / Makin' it / Angel eyes.
**Album:** Released May '83, on Muse by Black & Blue Records. Catalogue no: **MR 5269**

**LAST STITT SESSIONS VOL. 2**
**Album:** Released '88, on Muse by Black & Blue Records. Catalogue no: **MR 5280**

**LOVERMAN (Stitt, Sonny & The Giants)**
Tracks: / Night work / Matter horns / Loverman / Satin doll / Don't blame me / Hello.
Note: Sonny Stitt, Howard McGhee, Walter Bishop, Tommy Potter, Kenny Clarke.
**Album:** Released Jul '88, on Black Lion Catalogue no: **BLM 52009**

**MADE FOR EACH OTHER**
**Album:** Released '74, on Delmark (USA) by Delmark Records (USA). Catalogue no: **DS 426**

**MOONLIGHT IN VERMONT**
Tracks: / West 46th street / Who can I turn to? / Moonlight in Vermont / Flight cap blues / It might as well be spring / Constellation / Blues for PCM.
Note: Personnel: Sonny Stitt (Alto/Tenor saxes), Barry Harris (Piano), Reggie Workman (Bass), Tony Williams (Drums).
**CD:** Released '88, on Denon Catalogue no: **C38-7046**
**Album:** Released Mar '82, on Denon Deleted '88. Catalogue no: **YX 7530**

**MY BUDDY (Sonny Stitt plays G.Ammons)**
**Album:** Released Jun '77, on Muse by Black & Blue Records. Catalogue no: **MR 5091**

**NIGHT WORK (Stitt, Sonny & The Giants)**
Tracks: / Night work / Matter horns / Lover man / Satin doll / Don't blame me / Hello.
Note: With Howard McGhee, Walter Bishop Jr, Tommy Potter, Kenny Clarke.
**Album:** Released Sep '85, on Black Lion Catalogue no: **BLP 30154**

**NOW**
Tracks: / Surfin' / Lester leaps in / Es-

trellita / Please don't talk about me when I'm gone / Touchy / Never / Sh / My mother's eyes / Getting sentimental over you.
**Cass:** Released Jun '82, on Jasmine by Hasmick Promotions. Catalogue no: **JAS C25**
**Album:** Released Jun '82, on Jasmine by Hasmick Promotions. Deleted Feb '88. Catalogue no: **JAS 25**

**SALT AND PEPPER (Stitt, Sonny & Paul Gonsalves)**
Tracks: / Salt and pepper / S'posin (I should fall in love with you) / Lord of the flies (theme from) / Perdido / Stardust.
**Album:** Released Jun '82, on Jasmine by Hasmick Promotions. Deleted Feb '88. Catalogue no: **JAS 26**
**Cass:** Released Jun '82, on Jasmine by Hasmick Promotions. Catalogue no: **JAS C26**

**SAXOPHONE SYNDICATE**
Tracks: / Chase is on, The / When the blues come on / This can't be love / Last time for love / You're cheating yourself / Knittin' / Tender trap, The / Things I love, The / Way you look tonight, The / Forecast / You don't know what love is / I'm getting sentimental over you / Lester leaps in / Just friends / All God's children got rhythm.
**CD:** Released Sep '89, on Affinity by Charly Records. Catalogue no: **CDAFF 754**

**SONNY**
**Album:** Released Oct '88, on Vogue by Vogue Records. Catalogue no: **500074**

**SONNY STITT**
**CD:** Released Jul '89, on Cleo Catalogue no: **CLCD 5026**
**Album:** Released 10 Jul '89, on Black Lion Catalogue no: **BLP 60130**

**SONNY STITT MEETS SADIK HAKIM (Stitt, Sonny & Sadik Hakim)**
Tracks: / Christopher Street jump / Little girl blue / Easy to love / You are the sunshine of my life / South Georgia blues / All God's chillun got rhythm / Round midnight / Fine and dandy.
Note: With Buster Williams, J.R. Mitchell. Recorded 15 April 1978.
**Album:** Released '81, on Progressive (USA) by Jazzology Records (USA). Catalogue no: **PRO 7034**

**SONNY STITT WITH THE NEW YORKERS (Stitt, Sonny/The New Yorkers)**
**Album:** Released 7 Nov '87, on Fresh Sounds (Spain) by Fresh Sounds Records (Spain). Catalogue no: **FS 274**

**SONNY, SWEETS & JAWS (Stitt, Sonny/Sweets Edison/Eddie Lockjaw Davis)**
Tracks: / Lady be good / What's new? / There is no greater love / Chef, The / I can't get started / Lester leaps in.
**Cass:** Released '89, on Kingdom Jazz by Kingdom Records. Catalogue no: **CGATE 7007**
**Album:** Released '84, on Kingdom Jazz by Kingdom Records. Catalogue no: **GATE 7007**

**SONNY'S BACK**
Tracks: / Canadian sunset / Sonny's bounce / Soon / Dodge City / It might as well be spring / Constellation / Street of dreams.
Note: With Ricky Ford, Barry Harris, George Duvivier, Leroy Williams. Recorded 7 April, 14 July 1980.
**Album:** Released '81, on Muse by Black & Blue Records. Catalogue no: **MR 5204**

**SONNY'S BUBBA'S SESSIONS**
Tracks: / Sonny's blues / Old folks / Lax / Yesterdays / What's new? / Four.
**Cass:** Released '89, on Kingdom Jazz by Kingdom Records. Catalogue no: **CGATE 7012**
**Album:** Released Nov '83, on Kingdom Jazz by Kingdom Records. Catalogue no: **GATE 7012**

**SUPER STITT**
Tracks: / How high the moon / Body and soul / Pennies from Heaven / Every tub / Thou swell / Baritone blues / Blue and sentimental.
Note: Personnel: Sonny Stitt - alto, tenor & baritone sax; Dean Earl - piano; Bernie Griggs - bass; Marquis Foster - drums.
**Album:** Released Apr '81, on Phoenix (USA) by All Star Talent Inc.(USA). Catalogue no: **LP 15**

**SUPER STITT VOL.2**
Tracks: / Sweet Georgia Brown / I'm in the mood for love / Tri-horn blues / If I should lose you / Indiana / Wigmen / Melancholy baby / Flyin' home.
Note: Personnel: Sonny Stitt - alto, tenor & baritone sax; Dean Earl - piano; Bernie Griggs - bass; Marquis Foster - drums.
**Album:** Released Apr '81, on Phoenix (USA) by All Star Talent Inc.(USA). Catalogue no: **LP 23**

**TENOR BATTLES (Stitt, Sonny & Eddie Lockjaw Davis)**
Tracks: / Rollercoaster / Don't blame me / Whoops / All the things you are.
Note: With Doc Bagby and Charlie Rice. Recorded New York, spring 1954.
**Album:** Released Apr '81, on Phoenix (USA) by All Star Talent Inc.(USA). Catalogue no: **LP 19**

## Stobart, Kathy

**ARDERIA (Featuring Marion Williams Vocal)**
Tracks: / Arbeia / Detour ahead / Pieces of dreams / As is / 2HS / If I thought you'd ever change your mind / Enchanted into cry of triumph.
**Album:** Released '83, on Spotlite by Spotlite Records. Catalogue no: **SPJ 509**

**SAXPLOITATION (Stobart, Kathy/Joe Temperley 5)**
Tracks: / Softly as in a morning sunrise / My funny valentine / Tickle toe / Drop me off in Harlem / In a sentimental mood / Blues in the closet / Crazy he calls me / Cottontail.
**Album:** Released '83, on Spotlite by Spotlite Records. Catalogue no: **SPJ 503**

## Stockhausen, Markus

**COSI LONTANO...QUASI DENTRO So far almost inside**
Note: Assembled around bassist, Gary Peacock and trumpeter, Markus Stockhausen, this quartet draws as much on jazz as on New Music for their inspiration. This music was improvised on the spot and displays a rare intensity, freedom and alertness of spontaneous interaction. An enthusiastic review between serious contemporary and improvised music.
Personnel: Markus Stockhausen - trumpet, flugelhorn, synthesiser; Gary Peacock - bass; Fabrizio Ottaviucci - piano; Zoro Babel - drums.
**CD:** Released Feb '89, on ECM Catalogue no: **837 111-2**
**Album:** Released Feb '89, on ECM Catalogue no: **ECM 1371**

## Stockholm 1961

**STOCKHOLM 1961 (Various artists)**
Tracks: / Jackie-ing: *Various artists* / I'm getting sentimental over you: *Various artists* / Crepuscle with Nellie: *Various artists* / Ba-lu Bolivar ba-lues-are: *Various artists* / Rhythm a ning: *Various artists* / Epistrophy: *Various artists* / Just a gigolo: *Various artists* / Well, you needn't: *Various artists* / 'Round midnight: *Various artists* / Bemsha swing: *Various artists* / Blue Monk: *Various artists* / Epistrophy: *Various artists* / Body and soul: *Various artists*.
Note: Featuring: Thelonious Monk, Charlie Rouse, John Ore, Frankie Dunlop. Recorded at the Concert House, Stockholm, Sweden, May 16, 1961, by the Swedish radio.
A lesson in jazz wrote the Swedish jazz magazine Orkester Jounalen after Thelonious Monk's two concerts in Stockholm on May 16, 1961. 'Everything was so consistent and uniform, yet so varied' stated Bertil Sundin, and his co-critic Lars Werner, himself a jazz pianist with be-bop roots, was equally enthusiastic: 'He has complete control of his instrument which enables him to achieve his goals'. Carl Erik Lindgren reviewed the concerts in the Swedish jazz magazine Estrad: Monk manages to make every experienced listener of modern jazz un-easy by, without the slightest effort, avoiding commonplace phrasing. He also troubles you by playing so basically simple and obviously. He further disturbs you with his majestic dominance on stage, and one is entirely agitated when one hears the swing he projects his ideas with. This humble critic is also almost forgetting to say how beautifully he plays.
Now to the visual impression. Hardly anyone, no matter what he thinks about Monk, can avoid being somewhat shocked at his appearance on stage. He wore a cap during the first concert and a thick ski bonnet during the second. This entrance into the classy Stockholm Con-

cert House - had it been in the Swedish provinces and a Swedish musician - would have caused a big scandal. At the piano - an incomparable fervour, a musician who was enraptured. The sweat ran on his brow under his hats, his body swayed to and fro in cunvulsive jerks, his feet moved about as it they were in a cramp. Yes, Monk has mastered the art of visually captivating the audience. Bertil Sundin again: 'He suddenly comes in on stage with his hat on, doesn't look at the audience, stands in back of the piano so all you see of him is his legs, while the drummer plays an intro, then he sits down at the piano and the music just flows out. His entrance was a shock. The second tune, *I'm getting sentimental over you*, it swung so much that one could hardly sit still.

Lars Werner: 'No it was impossible, but what I thought was so fine in the first tune was ... the theme was always there. When Charlie Rouse played a solo, Monk used the theme as an accompaniment and later when he played solo, he started with the theme and then made variations upon it - it was there all the time ... the rhythmical accents came again and again. Everything that Monk played was meaningful and thematic, never any loose ends. Everyone was not so enthusiastic. Estrad's Lars Resberg chose not to attend the concert because as he wrote, it was about crippled sick, commical jazz. But anyway, he reviewed the second concert that was broadcast on Swedish radio -and- he took the opportunity to put down not only Monk, but other critics who liked him and fans as well: 'Every town and community had its backward child, every village its idiot that the children mock with a fearful joy and make fun of. That was in yesteryear. Today we know better and can take care of our less fortunate friends and have an understanding of their difficult situations. That is to say, everywhere - with the exception of the world of jazz. Here, we still cultivate a kind of degeneration of music, allowing each and all of us to experience and enjoy any kind of musical presentation. Monk's is a typical case - never in my life have I seen such 'visual' reviews of any concert.

Resberg could at least by the side of his radio, enjoy a formidable accompaniment and wonderful tenor by Charlie Rouse. But ... 'What about Monk when one is at a loss for the visual aspect of a hatted bop beserk? - Yes, I recall what Harry Arnold said about Monk's solo recordings. Harry was right: Monk can't play the piano, not as an accompanist nor as a soloist'. Embarrasing effects are more the rule than the exception - chromatic chord changes, whole tone scales, second intervals in absurdity. Thank heavens that there are other ways to enjoy jazz than this.

Thelonious Monk gave two concerts on this night, his first appearance in Sweden. The warm-up band this Tuesday evening was Staggan Abeleen's Quintet, a young Swedish group which played in the Jazz Messenger style. Monk's both performances are here - completely - in the order the tunes were played. 'One of our greatest jazz experiences' said Werner and Sundin. 'I have never seen so many shocked critics and musicians after a concert, and it felt good to know that I was not alone in that respect' wrote Carl Erik Lindgren. (Ake Karlsson)

**2 LP Set:** Released Feb '88, on Dragon by Dragon Records. Catalogue no: **DRLP 151/52**

## Stokes, Frank

**1927-29 THE REMAINING TITLES**

Tracks: / Half cup of tea / Ain't gonna be like I used to be / Hunting blues / Rockin' on the hill / Filling in blues (parts 1 & 2) / South Memphis blues / Bunker Hill blues / Right now blues / Shiney town blues / Downtown blues / Bedtime blues / What's the matter blues / It won't be long now / I got mine / T'aint nobody's business if I do (Parts 1 & 2) / Take me back / How long / Frank Stoke's dream.

**Album:** Released Nov '84, on Matchbox by Flyright Records. Catalogue no: **MSE 1002**

**CREATOR OF THE MEMPHIS BLUES**

**Album:** Released Dec '88, on Yazoo (USA) by Shanachie Records (USA). Catalogue no: **L 1056**

**FRANK STOKES**

**Album:** Released Oct '88, on Roots (Germany) Catalogue no: **RL 308**

**FRANK STOKES DREAM (Memphis Blues Anthology)**

**Album:** Released Dec '88, on Yazoo (USA) by Shanachie Records (USA). Catalogue no: **L 1008**

## Stone, Lew

**10.30 TUESDAY NIGHT (Stone, Lew & His Band)**

**Album:** Released '63, on Ace Of Clubs by Decca Records. Deleted '88. Catalogue no: **ACL 1147**

**COFFEE IN THE MORNING (Stone, Lew & His Band)**

Tracks: / Coffee in the morning / Riptide / Looking for a little bit of blue / Emaline / Because it's love / White jazz / I hate myself / Josephine / Rollin' home / What a little moonlight can do / My song for you / Love in bloom / Freckle face you're wonderful / Wagon wheels / Blue jazz / Out for no good / With my eyes wide open, I'm dreaming / Mauna loa.

**Album:** Released Sep '83, on President by President Records. Catalogue no: **PLE 505**

**Cass:** Released Jan '84, on President by President Records. Catalogue no: **TC-PLE 505**

**ECHO OF A SONG, THE (Stone, Lew & His Band)**

Tracks: / All of me / Save the last dance for me / One more kiss / By the fireside / Was that the human thing to do / Now that you're gone / Goodnight, Vienna / My sweet Virginia / Can't we talk it over / Just humming alone / Auf wiedersehen my dear / Rain on the roof / It ain't no fault of mine / Echo of a song, The.

**Album:** Released Dec '82, on Halcyon (USA) by Submarine Records. Catalogue no: **HAL 12**

**GET HAPPY**

Tracks: / Beale Street blues / Transatlantic lullaby / Farewell blues / In Santa Lucia / Speakeasy / Who'll buy an old gold ring / Nine pins in the sky / P.S. I love you / Let it snow, let it snow, let it snow / Get happy / Weep no more my baby / My wubba dolly / Two cigarettes in the dark / Wednesday night hop / Lonely feet / Papa tree-top tall / At the Jazz Band Ball / Little drummer boy.

**Album:** Released Apr '81, on Decca by Decca International. Deleted Apr '86. Catalogue no: **RFL 7**

**GOLDEN AGE OF LEW STONE (Stone, Lew & His Band)**

**Cass:** Released Jul '85, on Golden Age by EMI Records. Catalogue no: **GX 41 2534 4**

**Album:** Released Jul '85, on Golden Age by EMI Records. Catalogue no: **GX 41 2534 1**

**POP GOES YOUR HEART (Stone, Lew & His Band)**

Tracks: / Long may we love / He didn't even say goodbye / Continental, The / Caranga / June in January / Winter wonderland / I ain't got nobody / Pop goes your heart / Beauty must be loved / Because of once upon a time / Maybe I'm wrong again / I was lucky / Seein' is believin' / Anything goes / I get a kick out of you / Lovely to look at / She's a Latin from Manhattan / East of the sun and west of the moon / Cheek to cheek / Isn't this a lovely day?.

**Cass:** Released '88, on Saville by Conifer Records. Catalogue no: **CSVL 196**

**Album:** Released '88, on Saville by Conifer Records. Catalogue no: **SVL 196**

**PRESENTING LEW STONE 1934-35 (Stone, Lew & His Band)**

**2 LP Set:** Released '73, on Retrospect by EMI Records. Catalogue no: **SH 177/8**

**SING ME A SWING SONG**

Tracks: / Stone favourites - part one / He didn't even say goodbye / My old dog / Wanderer / Tina / Where is the sun / Stars fell on Alabama / So close to the forest / Long may we love / Girl with the dreamy eyes / Sing me a swing song / Two trumpet toot / House hop / You never looked so beautiful / What are we gonna do with baby / Carelessly / Ebony shadows / Stone favourites - part two.

**Cass:** Released Dec '88, on Burlington Records by Plant Life Records. Catalogue no: **4 BUR 014**

**Album:** Released Dec '88, on Burlington Records by Plant Life Records. Catalogue no: **BUR 014**

**WITH AL BOWLLY**

**Cass:** Released Aug '87, on Halcyon

(USA) by Submarine Records. Catalogue no: **CHAL 14**

## Storeyville Jazz Band

**STOREYVILLE JAZZ BAND**
**Album:** Released May '86, on Daylight by Daylight Records. Catalogue no: **LD 5010**

## Storm Is Passing By

**STORM IS PASSING BY (Early post-war gospel) (Various artists)**
**Cass:** Released Aug '89, on Global Village Catalogue no: **GVMMC 203**

## Stormy Weather

**PULSE**
**Album:** Released Apr '88, on Spotlite by Spotlite Records. Catalogue no: **SPJ 535**

**STORMY WEATHER, 1933 (Various artists)**
Note: Including Art Tatum, Earl Hines, Benny Goodman.
**Album:** Released May '88, on Nostalgia by Mainline Records. Catalogue no: **NOST 7647**

## Stormy Weather (film)

**STORMY WEATHER (Film soundtrack) (Various artists)**
Note: Starring Lena Horne and Cab Calloway.
**Album:** Released Jan '89, on Silva Screen by Silva Screen Records. Catalogue no: **SH 2037**
**Cass:** Released Jan '89, on Silva Screen by Silva Screen Records. Catalogue no: **CSH 2037**

## Story Of....

**STORY OF THE BLUES (Various artists)**
**Cass set:** Released May '82, on CBS by CBS Records. Deleted '86. Catalogue no: **40 22135**
**2 LP Set:** Released May '82, on CBS by CBS Records. Deleted Jan '89. Catalogue no: **CBS 22135**

**STORY OF THE BLUES VOL.1 (Various artists)**
**LP Set:** Released Oct '84, on CBS by CBS Records. Catalogue no: **CBS 66426**

**STORY OF THE GIANTS OF JAZZ (Various artists)**
**CD:** Released Oct '88, on Vogue by Vogue Records. Catalogue no: **VGCD 670 201**
**CD:** Released Dec '86, on Vogue by Vogue Records. Catalogue no: **VG 600 086**

## Straighten Up & Fly

**STRAIGHTEN UP AND FLY RIGHT (Various artists)**
Tracks: / Flying home: *Hampton, Lionel & His Orchestra* / Roll 'em Pete: *Turner,Joe/Pete Johnson* / Sun didn't shine,The: *Golden Gate Quartet* / Straighten up and fly right: *Cole, Nat "King"* / I Wonder: *Grant, Cecil* / Choo choo ch' boogie: *Jordan, Louis* / Call it stormy Monday: *Walker, T-Bone* / Good rockin' tonight: *Harris, Wynonie* / Give me a simple prayer: *Ravens* / Well,oh well: *Bradshaw, Tiny & His Orchestra* / Hello central: *Hopkins, Lightnin'* / One Mint Julep: *Clovers* / Hound Dog: *Thornton, Willie Mae 'Big Mama'* / Mama,he treats your daughter mean: *Brown, Ruth* / Crying in the Chapel: *Till, Sonny & The Orioles* / Hoochie Coochie man: *Waters, Muddy.*
Note: Mono recording.Rhythm and Blues from the close of Swing Era to the dawn of Rock 'N' Roll.
**Album:** Released Sep '86, on New World (USA) by New World Records (USA). Catalogue no: **NW 261**

## Strayhorn, Billy

**BILLY STRAYHORN & ELLINGTON ORCHESTRA (Strayhorn, Billy & Ellington Orchestra)**
**Album:** Released Nov '88, on Musica Jazz Catalogue no: **2MJP 1055**

**CUE FOR SAXOPHONE (Strayhorn, Billy Septet)**
Tracks: / Cue's blue now / Gone with the wind / Cherry / Watch your cue / You brought a new kind of love to me / When I dream of you / Rose room.
**Album:** Released Dec '86, on Affinity by Charly Records. Catalogue no: **AFF 166**
**CD:** Released Jun '88, on London Records by London Records Ltd. Catalogue no: **820 604 2**

## Strazzeri, Frank

**KAT DANCIN'**
Tracks: / Speak low / Remember / Trees / Moment to moment / Soultrane.
Note: Frank Strazzeri-piano, John Patitucci-bass, Ralph Penland-drums.
**CD:** Released '88, on Discovery (USA) by Discovery Records (USA). Catalogue no: **DSCD 833**
**Album:** Released '88, on Discovery (USA) by Discovery Records (USA). Catalogue no: **DS 933**

**MAKE ME RAINBOWS**
**Album:** Released Feb '88, on Fresh Sounds (Spain) by Fresh Sounds Records (Spain). Catalogue no: **FS 312**

**RELAXIN'**
**Album:** Released Jul '88, on Sea Breeze Catalogue no: **SB 1007**

## Streetwalking Blues

**STREETWALKING BLUES (Various artists)**
**Album:** Released Apr '81, on Stash (USA) Catalogue no: **ST 117**

## String Trio Of NewYork

**FIRST STRING**
**Album:** Released Sep '79, on Black Saint (Italy) Catalogue no: **BSR 0031**

**STRING TRIO OF NEW YORK AND JAY CLAYTON (String Trio Of New York & Jay Clayton)**
**Album:** Released Jul '88, on West Wind Catalogue no: **WW 008**
**CD:** Released Jul '88, on West Wind Catalogue no: **WWCD 008**

## Strozier, Frank

**REMEMBER ME (Strozier, Frank Sextet)**
**Album:** Released Jul '77, on Steeplechase (USA) Catalogue no: **SCS 1066**

**WALTZ OF THE DEMONS**
Tracks: / W K Blues / Waltz of the demons / Starlings theme / I don't know / Runnin' / Off shore.
**Album:** Released Dec '86, on Atlantis by Charly Records. Deleted May '88. Catalogue no: **ATS 5**
**Cass:** Released Dec '86, on Atlantis by Charly Records. Catalogue no: **KATS 5**
**Album:** Released Jan '81, on Affinity by Charly Records. Deleted '88. Catalogue no: **AFF 49**

**WHAT'S GOING ON ? (Direct Cut album) (Strozier, Frank Quintet)**
**Album:** Released Feb '79, on Steeplechase (USA) Catalogue no: **SDC 17001**

## Strutters, Harry

**BORNEO (Strutters, Harry Hot Rhythm Orchestra)**
Tracks: / Borneo / Black Beauty / Barnacle Bill / Rockin' in rhythm / Doodlin' blue / Wherever there's love / Zonky / Symphonic raps / St. James infirmary blues / Froggie Moore / Nagasaki / East St. Louis toodle-oo / Everybody stomp.
**Album:** Released Jul '87, on Black Lion Catalogue no: **BLM 51108**

**HARRY STRUTTERS' HOT RHYTHM ORCHESTRA (Strutters, Harry Hot Rhythm Orchestra)**
Tracks: / Rhythm king / Charleston / Am I blue / Copenhagen / Take your tomorrows / Ice cream / How could Red Riding Hood? / Sugar foot strut / Jazz me blues / Mooche / Chili bom bom / Candy lips.
**Album:** Released '88, on Black Lion Catalogue no: **BLP 12130**

**TOTUS PORCUS**
**Album:** Released '88, on Black Lion Catalogue no: **BLP 12196**

## Suckin & Blowin

**POST WAR BLUES HARP**
**Album:** Released Dec '88, on Sundown by Magnum Music Group. Catalogue no: **SG 709-03**

## Sudhalter, Dick

**FRIENDS WITH PLEASURE**
**Album:** Released Aug '88, on Audiophile (USA) by Jazzology Records (USA). Catalogue no: **AP 159**

## Sugar Blue

**CROSSROADS**
**Album:** Released Oct '80, on T.O.L Deleted '83. Catalogue no: **TOL 1**

**PONTIAC**
Tracks: / Pontiac.
**7" Single:** Released Oct '80, on Blue Sound Deleted '85. Catalogue no: **BS 3501**

## Sullivan, Ira

**BIRD LIVES (Sullivan, Ira & Chicago Jazz Quintet)**
Tracks: / Klactoveesedstein / In other words / Shaw 'nuff / Perhaps / Love letters / Mohawk.
**Album:** Released Dec '81, on Affinity by Charly Records. Deleted '88. Catalogue no: **AFF 71**

**DOES IT ALL**
**Album:** Released '88, on Muse by Black & Blue Records. Catalogue no: **MR 5242**

**HORIZONS**
Tracks: / E flat tuba G / Norwegian wood / Everything happens to me / Adah / Horizon / Oh gee / Nineveh.
**Album:** Released Sep '83, on Discovery (USA) by Discovery Records (USA). Catalogue no: **DS 873**

**INCREDIBLE IRA SULLIVAN PLAYS**
Tracks: / Lonely moments / Our delight / Bernie's tune / Kim's lament / Can't get out of this mood / On the seventh day / Satin doll.
**Album:** Released Apr '81, on Stash (USA) Catalogue no: **ST 208**

**IRA SULLIVAN**
**Album:** Released May '79, on Flying Fish (USA) by Flying Fish Records (USA). Catalogue no: **FF 075**

**IRA SULLIVAN QUARTET**
**Album:** Released '74, on Delmark (USA) by Delmark Records (USA). Catalogue no: **DL 402**

**NICKY'S TUNE**
**Album:** Released '74, on Delmark (USA) by Delmark Records (USA). Catalogue no: **DS 422**

## Sullivan, Joe

**AND THE ALLSTARS**
Tracks: / Jazz me blues / Save it pretty mama / Memphis blues / Coquette / Basin Street blues / That da da strain.
Note: High medley: On the sunny side of the street/Sweet Lorraine/Honeysuckle Rose/ Sister Kate/Royal Garden blues
**Album:** Released '81, on Shoestring (1) Catalogue no: **SS 114**

**AT THE PIANO**
**Album:** Released Apr '81, on Shoestring (1) Catalogue no: **SS 104**

**GIN MILL**
**Album:** Released '88, on Pumpkin Catalogue no: **PUMPKIN 112**

**PIANO MAN (1935/40)**
**Album:** Released May '88, on Blu-Disc (USA) Catalogue no: **T 1005**

## Sullivan, Maxine

**CLOSE AS PAGES IN A BOOK (Sullivan, Maxine & Bob Wilber)**
Tracks: / As long as I live / Gone with the wind / Rockin' rhythm / Darn that dream / Every time / Harlem butterfly / Loch Lomond / Too many tears / Jeepers creepers / Restless / You're driving me crazy / Close as pages in a book.
**Album:** Released May '88, on Audiophile (USA) by Jazzology Records (USA). Catalogue no: **AP 203**
**Album:** Released Mar '79, on Monmouth Evergreen Catalogue no: **MES 6919**

**GOOD MORNING LIFE**
**Album:** Released Jun '86, on Audiophile (USA) by Jazzology Records (USA). Catalogue no: **AP 193**

**GREAT SONGS OF THE COTTON CLUB, THE**
Tracks: / Happy as the day is long / You gave me ev'rything but love / As long as I live / Raisin' the rent / 'Neath the pale Cuban moon / Ill wind / Between the devil and the deep blue sea / I love a parade / Harlem holiday / Get yourself a new broom / Stormy weather / In the silence of the night / That's what I hate about love / Primitive prima donna / I've got the world on a string.
Note: Maxine Sullivan was one of the original Cotton Club stars. On this new recording she sings the songs of Harold Arlen and Ted Koehler, house writers for the Cotton Club between 1930 and 1934. This album features three songs previously not recorded and three others which have never appeared on LP.
**Album:** Released Jul '85, on SPI Milan (France) Catalogue no: **A 270**
**Cass:** Released Jul '85, on SPI Milan (France) Catalogue no: **C 270**
**CD:** Released Jul '87, on SPI Milan (France). Catalogue no: **CD 270**
**CD:** Released '88, on Mobile Fidelity Sound Lab(USA) by Mobile Fidelity Records (USA). Catalogue no: **MFCD 836**

**I LOVE TO BE IN LOVE (See also under Hyman, Dick) (Sullivan, Maxine / Dick Hyman)**
**Album:** Released Mar '90, on Tono Catalogue no: **TDJ101**

**IT WAS GREAT FUN**
**Album:** Released Jun '88, on Audiophile (USA) by Jazzology Records (USA). Catalogue no: **AP 185**

**MAXINE (Sullivan, Maxine & Ted Easton's Jazzband)**
**Album:** Released Aug '88, on Audiophile (USA) by Jazzology Records (USA). Catalogue no: **AP 167**

**MAXINE SULLIVAN AND IKE ISAACS (Sullivan, Maxine & Ike Isaacs Quartet)**
**Album:** Released Jun '88, on Audiophile (USA) by Jazzology Records (USA). Catalogue no: **AP 154**

**MAXINE SULLIVAN AND SCOTT HAMILTON (Sullivan, Maxine & Scott Hamilton)**
Note: Singer Sullivan's last concert appearance -- 1986 -- with Hamilton on tenor, John Bunch on piano and supporting musicians.
**CD:** Released Jul '88, on Concord Jazz by Concord Jazz Records (USA). Catalogue no: **CCD 4351**

**MAXINE SULLIVAN WITH ELLIS (See also under Larkins, Ellis) (Sullivan, Maxine & Ellis Larkins)**
**Album:** Released Mar '90, on Tono Catalogue no: **TJ6001**

**MAXINE SULLIVAN WITH THE BOB HAGGART QUINTET (Sullivan, Maxine with The Bob Haggart Quintet)**
**Album:** Released Jul '87, on Audiophile (USA) by Jazzology Records (USA). Catalogue no: **AP 210**

**QUEEN, THE (VOL.1)**
**Album:** Released Jul '82, on Kenneth Catalogue no: **KS 2052**

**QUEEN, THE (VOL.2)**
**Album:** Released '88, on Kenneth Catalogue no: **KS 2053**

**QUEEN, THE (VOL.3)**
**Album:** Released '88, on Kenneth Catalogue no: **KS 2054**

**SINGS THE MUSIC OF BURTON LANE**
**Album:** Released Sep '86, on Stash (USA) Catalogue no: **ST 257**

**SINGS THE MUSIC OF JULES STYNE (Sullivan, Maxine/Keith Ingram Sextet)**
**Cass:** Released '88, on Atlantic by WEA Records. Catalogue no: **817 834**
**Album:** Released '88, on Atlantic by WEA Records. Catalogue no: **817 831**

**SPRING IS NOT EVERYTHING**
**CD:** Released '89, on Audiophile (USA) by Jazzology Records (USA). Catalogue no: **APCD 229**

**SULLIVAN - SHAKESPEARE - HYMAN**
Tracks: / When I was as a tiny little boy / O mistress mine / Winter and spring / It was a lover and his lass / Take, oh, those lips away / Blow, blow, thou winter wind / Under the greenwood tree / Sigh no more, ladies / Come away, come away / Death / When daffodils begin to peer / Lawn as white as driven snow / Take, oh, take / There's never been a time / Where do I go from here? / Storybook children / Take my hand for a while.
Note: Setting of Shakespeare by Dick Hyman.
**Album:** Released Mar '79, on Monmouth Evergreen Catalogue no: **MES 7038**

**UPTOWN (Sullivan, Maxine with the Scott Hamilton Quintet)**
Tracks: / You were meant for me / I thought about you / Goody goody / Something to remember you by / Wrap your troubles in dreams / You're a lucky guy / Georgia on my mind / By myself / I got the right to sing the blues / Just one of those things.
Note: And yet another legend comes to Concord Records. Cotton Club veteran Maxine Sullivan will take you uptown for a great set of swingin standards backed by the impeccable Scott Hamilton and his band. Maxine is a classic with new release her great delivery and rhythmic control confirm her structure as a seasoned pro.
**Cass:** Released Dec '85, on Concord

Jazz by Concord Jazz Records (USA). Catalogue no: **CJC 288**
**Album:** Released Dec '85, on Concord Jazz by Concord Jazz Records (USA). Catalogue no: **CJ 288**

**WE JUST COULDN'T SAY GOODBYE (Sullivan, Maxine & Art Hodes' Band)**
**Album:** Released Aug '88, on Audiophile (USA) by Jazzology Records (USA). Catalogue no: **AP 128**

## Sulzmann, Stan

**EVERYBODY'S SONG BUT MY OWN (Sulzmann, Stan & John Taylor)**
Tracks: / Introduction to no particular song / Little fella, The / Old ballad / My old man / Everybody's song but my own? / Gigolo / Sea lady / Gnu suite (part 1) / Sweet Yakity Waltz / In the mood.
**Cass:** Released Sep '88, on Loose Tubes by Loose Tubes Records. Catalogue no: **LTMC 004**
**Album:** Released Jul '87, on Loose Tubes by Loose Tubes Records. Catalogue no: **LTLP 004**

**KRARK (With Tony Hymas)**
**Album:** Released Apr '88, on Mosaic by Mosaic Records (UK). Catalogue no: **GCM 792**

**ON LOAN WITH GRATITUDE**
**Album:** Released Aug '77, on Mosaic by Mosaic Records (UK). Catalogue no: **GCM 772**

## Sumlin, Hubert

**BLUES ANYTIME**
**Album:** Released '88, on L&R Catalogue no: **LR 42 004**

**FUNKY ROOTS**
**Album:** Released Oct '88, on Vogue (France) by Vogue Records. Catalogue no: **512503**

**GAMBLIN' WOMEN (Sumlin, Hubert & Carey Bell)**
**Album:** Released '88, on L&R Catalogue no: **LR 42.008**

**HUBERT SUMLIN'S BLUES PARTY**
Tracks: / Hidden charms / West side soul / Soul that's been abused, The / Letter to my girlfriend / How can you leave me, little girl / Blue guitar / Down in the bottom / Poor me, pour me another drink / Living the blues.
**Album:** Released Jun '87, on Demon by Demon Records. Catalogue no: **FIEND 94**
**Album:** Released '88, on Black Top (USA) by Rounder Records (USA). Catalogue no: **BT 1036**
**CD:** Released '88, on Black Top (USA) by Rounder Records (USA). Catalogue no: **BT 1036CD**
**Cass:** Released '88, on Black Top (USA) by Rounder Records (USA). Catalogue no: **BT 1036C**

## Summers, Bob

**INSIDE OUT (Summers, Bob Quintet)**
Tracks: / Autumn leaves / There will never be another you / For Heaven's sake.
Note: Bob Summers-trumpet & flugelhorn, Lanny Morgan-alto sax, Frank Strazzeri-piano, John Heard-bass, Chuck Flores-drums.
**Album:** Released Jun '84, on Discovery (USA) by Discovery Records (USA). Catalogue no: **DS 897**

**JOY SPRING (Summers, Bob Quintet)**
**CD:** Released Jul '88, on Discovery (1) by Oryx Records. Catalogue no: **DSCD 946**

## Sun Ra

**BLUE DELIGHT**
**Album:** Released Sep '89, on A&M by A&M Records. Catalogue no: **AMA 5260**
**CD:** Released Sep '89, on A&M by A&M Records. Catalogue no: **CDA 5260**
**Cass:** Released Sep '89, on A&M by A&M Records. Catalogue no: **AMC 5260**

**COSMOS**
**Album:** Released May '79, on Cobra (France) by Cobra Records (France). Catalogue no: **COB 37001**

**COSMOS SUN CONNECTION**
**Album:** Released Feb '86, on Saturn Catalogue no: **SRRRD 1**

**DANCING SHADOWS**
Tracks: / Dancing shadows / Imagination / Exotic forest / Sun Ra and his band from outer space / Shadow world / Theme of the stargazers / Outer spaceways incorporated / Next stop Mars.
**Album:** Released Sep '84, on Happy Bird (Germany) Catalogue no: **B 90130**

**HELIOCENTRIC WORLDS OF SUN RA VOL. 1**
**Album:** Released '88, on ESP Base Catalogue no: **ESP 1014**
**Album:** Released Apr '81, on ESP by ESP Records. Catalogue no: **ESP 1017**

**LOVE IN OUTER SPACE (Sun Ra & His Arkestra)**
Note: *Love In Outer Space* is the second Sun Ra's album on Leo Records. This time it is a alive performance in Utrecht in 1983, which is more mainstream that the previous release *A Night In East Berlin*. The new release is abundant with stunning solos by John Gilmore, tremendous drumming interludes by the whole Arkestra, and bluesy piano outings by the leader." (Leo Records, March 1988).
**Album:** Released 1 Mar '88, on Leo by Leo Records. Catalogue no: **LR 154**
**CD:** Released Sep '88, on Leo by Leo Records. Catalogue no: **CDLR 154**

**NIGHT IN EAST BERLIN, A (Sun Ra & His Cosmo Discipline Arkestra)**
**Album:** Released Sep '87, on Leo by Leo Records. Catalogue no: **LR 149**

**NOTHING IS...**
**Album:** Released '88, on ESP Base Catalogue no: **ESP 1045**

**NUCLEAR WAR**
**Album:** on UNKNOWN Catalogue no: **Unknown**

**NUCLEAR WAR (SINGLE)**
Tracks: / Nuclear war.
**7" Single:** Released Nov '83, on Y Deleted '86. Catalogue no: **RA 1**

**OTHER WORLDS**
Tracks: / Heliocentric / Outer nothingness / Other worlds / Cosmos, The / Of heavenly things / Nebulae dancing in the sun.
**Album:** Released Sep '84, on Happy Bird (Germany) Catalogue no: **B 90131**

**OUT THERE A MINUTE**
**Album:** Released Mar '89, on Blast First by Blast First Records. Catalogue no: **BFFP 42**
**Cass:** Released Mar '89, on Blast First by Blast First Records. Catalogue no: **BFFP 42C**
**CD:** Released Mar '89, on Blast First by Blast First Records. Catalogue no: **BFFP 42CD**

**PICTURES OF INFINITY (Sun Ra & His Arkestra)**
Tracks: / Saturn / Song of the sparer / Spontaneous simplicity / Somewhere there / Outer spaceways incorporated.
**Album:** Released Jan '85, on Black Lion Catalogue no: **BLP 30103**

**SOLAR-MYTH APPROACH, THE (CD) (Sun Ra & His Solar Myth Orchestra)**
Tracks: / Spectrum / Realm of lightning / Satellites are spinning / Legend / Seen III, took 4 / They'll come back / Adventures of Bugs Hunter / Utter nots, The / outer spaceways / Scene I, take 1 / Pyramids / Ancient Ethiopa.
**CD:** Released Jan '90, on Affinity by Charly Records. Catalogue no: **CDAFF 760**

**SOLAR-MYTH APPROACH, VOL 1**
Tracks: / Spectrum / Realm of lightning / Satellites are spinning, The / Legend / Seen III, took 4 / They'll come back / Adventure of Bugs Hunter.
**Album:** Released Feb '78, on Affinity by Charly Records. Catalogue no: **AFF 10**

**SOLAR-MYTH APPROACH, VOL 2**
Tracks: / Utter nots, The / Outer spaceways (inc. scene 1 take 1) / Pyramids / Interpretation / Ancient Ethiopia / Strange worlds.
**Album:** Released '83, on Affinity by Charly Records. Catalogue no: **AFF 76**

**SOLO PIANO, VOL 1**
**Album:** Released Jul '78, on Improvising Artists Catalogue no: **IAI 3738 50**

**SOLO PIANO, VOL 2**
**Album:** Released '78, on Improvising Artists Catalogue no: **IAI 3738 58**

**SOUND OF JOY**
**Album:** Released '74, on Delmark (USA) by Delmark Records (USA). Catalogue no: **DS 414**

**STRANGE CELESTIAL ROAD**
**Cass:** Released '88, on Rounder (USA) by Rounder Records (USA). Catalogue no: **ROUNDER 3035C**
**Album:** Released Sep '82, on Y Cata-

logue no: **Y19 LP**
**Album:** Released '88, on Rounder (USA) by Rounder Records (USA). Catalogue no: **ROUNDER 3035**

**SUN MYTH, THE**
Tracks: / Sun myth / House of beauty / Cosmic choas.
**Album:** Released Sep '84, on Happy Bird (Germany) Catalogue no: **B 90132**

**SUN RA**
Tracks: / For the sunrise / Of the other tomorrow / From out where others dwell / On sound infinity spheres / House of eternal being, The / Gods of the thunder rain / Lights on a satellite / Take the 'A' train / Prelude / El is the sound of joy / Encore 1 / Encore 2 / We travel the spaceways.
**Album:** Released Apr '79, on Inner City Catalogue no: **IC 1039**

**SUN RA - A JOYFUL NOISE (VIDEO)**
**VHS:** Released '88, on Kay Jazz (video) by Kay Jazz. Catalogue no: **KJ 003**

**SUN RA ARKESTRA NEETS SALAH RAGAB IN EGYPT**
**Album:** Released May '84, on Praxis (Greece) Catalogue no: **CM 106**

**SUN SONG**
**Album:** Released '74, on Delmark (USA) by Delmark Records (USA). Catalogue no: **DL 411**

## Sunnyland Slim

**DECORATION BLUES (Sunnyland Slim Blues Band)**
**Album:** Released '88, on L&R Catalogue no: **LR 42.015**

**DEVIL IS A BUSY MAN**
Tracks: / Ain't nothin' but a child / Brown skinned woman / Hit the road again / Gin drinkin' baby / Going back to Memphis / Devil is a busy man / Shake it baby / Bassology / I want my baby / Blue baby / Jivin' boogie / My heavy load / Keep your hands out of my money / Mud kickin' woman / Every time I get to drinkin'.
**Album:** on Official by Official Records. Catalogue no: **OFF 6043**

**LEGACY OF THE BLUES-11**
Tracks: / Couldn't find a mule / Gonna be my baby / Woman I ain't gonna drink no more whisky / Days of old / She got a thing goin' on / She's so mellow / Get hip to yourself / Bessie Mae / I had it so hard / She used to love me.
**Album:** Released '75, on Sonet by Sonet Records. Catalogue no: **SNTF 671**
**CD:** Released '75, on Sonet by Sonet Records. Catalogue no: **SNTCD 671**
**Album:** Released May '89, on GNP Crescendo (USA) by GNP Crescendo Records (USA). Catalogue no: **GNPS 10021**

**SUNNYLAND SPECIAL (Job Series Vol. 4)**
**Album:** Released '88, on Flyright by Interstate Music. Catalogue no: **FLY 566**

## Sunset All Stars

**JAMMIN' AT SUNSET, VOL 1**
Tracks: / I found a new baby / I surrender, dear / Tea for two / Skylark / California clipper / Ventura jump / Windjammer / I don't stand a ghost of a chance with you / All the things you are / Experiment perilous.
Note: Buddy Childers, Howard McGhee, Vido Musso, Andre Previn, Arnold Ross, Willie Smith, Lucky Thompson, Charlie Ventura.
**Album:** Released Jan '85, on Black Lion Catalogue no: **BLP 30112**

**JAMMIN' AT SUNSET, VOL 2**
Tracks: / Get happy / Blues in my heart / Sweets / It was meant to be / Jefferson jump / Nothin' from nothin' / I found a new baby / I never knew / These foolish things / My blue Heaven / I cover the waterfront / Messin' on Melrose.
Note: Emmett Berry, Lem Davis, Vic Dickenson, Harry Edison, Dodo Marmarosa, Vido Musso, Arnold Ross, Willie Smith.
**Album:** Released Jan '85, on Black Lion Catalogue no: **BLP 30113**

## Sunshine, Monty

**MONTY SUNSHINE'S JAZZ BAND (Sunshine's, Monty Jazz Band)**
**Album:** Released Jun '86, on Stomp Off (USA) Catalogue no: **SOS 1110**

**ON SUNDAY**
**Album:** Released May '87, on Wam Catalogue no: **WAM/O No.10**

**PORTRAIT VOL 2**
**Album:** Released May '87, on Wam Catalogue no: **WAM/O No.12**

**SUNSHINE IN LONDON**
Tracks: / St. Phillip Street breakdown / Dusty road / Just a closer walk with thee / Careless love / C jam blues / You rascal you / Burgundy Street blues / East coast trot / When you and I were young, Maggie / High society.
**Album:** Released Dec '79, on Black Lion Catalogue no: **BLP 12135**

## Suonsaari, Klaus

**REFLECTING TIMES (Suonsaari, Klaus Quintet)**
Note: Bob Berg, Tom Harrell, Niels Lan Doky, Ray Drummond.
**Album:** Released Jun '88, on Storyville by Storyville Records AB. Catalogue no: **SLP 4125**
**CD:** Released Feb '89, on Storyville by Storyville Records AB. Catalogue no: **STCD 4125**

## Super Blues

**SUPER BLUES (Various artists)**
**Album:** Released Oct '86, on Chess (PRT) Deleted '88. Catalogue no: **BRP 2012**

## Super Rhythm 'N' Blues

**SUPER RHYTHM 'N' BLUES (Various artists)**
Tracks: / Keep on knowin': *Various artists* / I found my baby there: *Charles, Ray* / Letter, The: *King, B.B.* / Could this be love: *Tex, Joe* / I thank God: *Cooke, Sam* / Big fine woman: *Hooker, John Lee* / Lovin' woman: *Simone, Nina* / Blues are bluer: *Holiday, Billie* / Cry baby cry: *Angels* / Need him: *Various artists* / Wild child: *Phillips, Esther* / Walkin' and talkin': *Charles, Ray* / Please love me: *King, B.B.* / I'm tramping: *Various artists* / Porgy: *Simone, Nina* / Deep river: *Cooke, Sam* / My man: *Holiday, Billie* / See what you have done: *Charles, Ray* / Blues for Christmas: *Hooker, John Lee* / That's heaven to me: *Cooke, Sam* / Feel like I wanna cry: *Phillips, Esther* / I just can't take it: *Tex, Joe* / I'm wondering: *Charles, Ray* / Milky white way: *Various artists* / Maybellene: *Berry, Chuck* / Memphis: *Berry, Chuck* / Lover come back to me: *Holiday, Billie* / Did you cry the blues: *Charles, Ray* / Peace breaker: *Pickett, Wilson* / Why don't you love me: *Hendrix, Jimi & Little Richard* / Long tall Sally: *Various artists* / Baby call on me: *Pickett, Wilson* / Let the good times roll: *Shirley & Lee* / My prayer: *Platters* / Goodnight Irene: *Hendrix, Jimi & Little Richard* / Sweet little sixteen: *Berry, Chuck*.
Note: Artists Include: Sam Cooke/Little Richard/Wilson Pickett: And more star names, as well as classic cuts from Billie Holiday and Ray Charles.
**Album:** Released Dec '85, on Pathe Marconi (France) Catalogue no: **2M 126 54315/16/17**

## Super Sax

**SUPER SAX (Various artists)**
Tracks: / Flutie: *Lateef, Yusef* / Big foot: *Lateef, Yusef* / Lester leaps in: *Young, Lester* / D B blues: *Young, Lester* / Happy bird blues: *Parker, Charlie All Stars* / Cool blues: *Parker, Charlie* / Breeze and I, The: *Pepper, Art* / Long ago & far away: *Pepper, Art* / Love for sale: *Sims, John Haley 'Zoot'* / Strike up the band: *Sims, John Haley 'Zoot'*.
Note: Charlie Parker, Art Pepper.
**Album:** Released Mar '88, on Exel Catalogue no: **XELLP 101**
**Cass:** Released Mar '88, on Exel Catalogue no: **XELMC 101**
**CD:** Released Mar '88, on Exel Catalogue no: **XELCD 101**

## Supersax

**CHASIN' THE BIRD**
Tracks: / Shaw 'nuff / Night in Tunisia / Drifting on a reed / Song is you, The / Oop bop sh'bam / Round midnight / Now's the time / Dizzy atmosphere / Chasin' the bird / Parker's mood.
**CD:** Released Nov '84, on Polydor by Polydor Ltd. Deleted Aug '87. Catalogue no: **821 867-2**

**EMBRACEABLE YOU**
**Album:** Released Aug '84, on CBS (import) by CBS Records. Catalogue no: **25604**
**Cass:** Released Aug '84, on CBS (import) by CBS Records. Catalogue no: **40 25604**

**STRAIGHTEN UP & FLY RIGHT**
Tracks: / Koko / Super sax / Bamboo /

Chi chi / Country / Straighten up and fly right / April in Paris / Some day my prince will come / Laura.
**Album:** Released Feb '88, on CBS by CBS Records. Catalogue no: **450384 1**
**Cass:** Released Feb '88, on CBS by CBS Records. Catalogue no: **450384 4**

### SUPERSAX & L.A. VOICES VOL.2
**Cass:** Released May '85, on CBS (import) by CBS Records. Catalogue no: **40 26324**
**Album:** Released May '85, on CBS (import) by CBS Records. Catalogue no: **26324**

## Surman, John

### AMAZING ADVENTURES OF SIMON SIMON
Tracks: / Nestor's saga (the tale of the ancient) / Buccaneers / Kentish hunting (Lady Margaret's air) / Pilgrim's way (to the seventeenth walls) / Within the halls of Neptune / Phoenix and the fire / Fide et amore (by faith and love) / Merry pranks (the jester's song) / Fitting epitaph, A.
Note: Personnel: John Surman - soprano & baritone sax, bass clarinet, synthesizer; Jack DeJohnette - drums, congas, electric piano.
**CD:** Released Aug '86, on ECM Catalogue no: **829 160 2**
**Album:** Released Dec '81, on ECM Catalogue no: **ECM 1193**

### PRIVATE CITY
Note: Fourth solo album from John features original composition pieces written for Private City, a ballet premiered at Sadler's Wells Royal Ballet last year. The album draws inspiration from many sources including Surman's own jazz background to the celtic tradtition. (New Note, August 1988)
**Album:** Released Sep '88, on ECM Catalogue no: **ECM 1366**
**CD:** Released Sep '88, on ECM Catalogue no: **835 780-2**

### SONATINAS
**Album:** Released Apr '81, on Steam Catalogue no: **SJ 106**

### S.O.S
**Album:** Released Jan '77, on Ogun by Cadillac Music. Catalogue no: **OG 400**

### SURMAN FOR ALL SAINTS
Tracks: / Round the round / Twelve alone / Electric plunger / Cascadence / Walls / Satisfied air / Matador / Saints alive / Bari-carolle.
**CD:** Released Jan '89, on ECM Catalogue no: **825 407-2**
**Album:** Released May '85, on ECM Catalogue no: **ECM 1295**
**Album:** Released Jun '79, on Ogun by Cadillac Music. Catalogue no: **OG 529**

### UPON REFLECTION
Tracks: / Edges of illusion / Filigree / Caithness to Kerry / Beyond a shadow / Prelude and rustic dance / Lampfighter / Following behind / Constellation.
Note: Personnel: John Surman - soprano & baritone sax, bass clarinet, synthesizers.
**CD:** Released '82, on ECM Catalogue no: **825 472-2**
**Album:** Released '82, on ECM Catalogue no: **ECM 1148**

### WITHHOLDING PATTERN
Tracks: / Doxology / Changes of season / All cat's whiskers and bees' knees / Holding pattern 1 / Skating on thin ice / Snooper, The / Wildcat blues / Holding pattern 2.
Note: Another long-awaited solo album from John Surman - who has just finished a very successful Jazz Services tour in the UK. Surman has built up a strong following in the UK over the years and plays here as often as he can.
**CD:** Released May '86, on ECM Catalogue no: **8254072**

## Sutton, Ralph

### ALLIGATOR CRAWL
**Album:** Released '89, on Jazzology (USA) by Jazzology Records (USA). Catalogue no: **JCE 92**

### BIX BEIDERBECKE SUITE
Tracks: / In the dark / Flashes / Candlelights / In a mist.
**Album:** Released May '87, on Commodore Class Catalogue no: **AG6.25525**

### FEB 7, 8 1982 Great piano solos (Sutton, Ralph & Cosenza Jazz Workshop)
**Album:** Released May '88, on FDC Catalogue no: **FDC 3003**

### LIVE: RALPH SUTTON
**Album:** Released Aug '79, on Flyright by Interstate Music. Catalogue no: **FLY 204**

### OFF THE CUFF Live
**Album:** Released Jul '87, on Audiophile (USA) by Jazzology Records (USA). Catalogue no: **AP 163**

### PARTNERS IN CRIME (Sutton, Ralph & Bob & Len Barnard)
Tracks: / Swing that music / One morning in May / Old folks / Rain / I never knew / Slow boat to China / It's wonderful / How can you face me? / West End avenue blues / Diga diga doo.
**Album:** Released Aug '86, on Vanguard by Start Records Ltd.. Catalogue no: **SVL 505**
**Cass:** Released Aug '86, on Vanguard by Start Records Ltd.. Catalogue no: **SVC 505**

### PIANO SOLOS
**Album:** Released '88, on Eighty-Eight Upright Catalogue no: **88 UR 004**
**Album:** Released '88, on Sackville by Spotlite Records. Catalogue no: **SACK 2012**

### RAGTIME PIANO
**Album:** Released '88, on Vogue by Vogue Records. Catalogue no: **VG 500871**

### RALPH SUTTON QUARTET
**Album:** Released Jan '88, on Storyville by Storyville Records AB. Catalogue no: **SLP 4013**
**Album:** Released Nov '86, on Storyville by Storyville Records AB. Catalogue no: **SLP 275**

### SUTTON, RALPH & THE ALL STARS (Sutton, Ralph & The All Stars)
Note: Mono.
**Album:** Released Jul '86, on Jazz Archives (USA) by Jazz Archives Inc.(USA). Catalogue no: **JA 45**

## Suzuki, Yoshio Chin

### MORNING PICTURE
Note: Virtuoso Japanese bass player Suzuki has become an integral part of the American jazz scene. He played with Stan Getz and was with Art Blakey's Jazz Messengers for several years.
**CD:** Released Jul '88, on JVC Catalogue no: **JD 3306**
**Album:** Released Jul '86, on Pan East Catalogue no: **NEWLP 103**
**Cass:** Released Jul '88, on JVC Catalogue no: **JC 3306**
**CD:** Released '88, on Pan East Catalogue no: **NEWCD 103**
**Cass:** Released Jul '86, on Pan East Catalogue no: **NEWMC 103**

## Swallow, Steve

### CARLA (Swallow, Steve Sextet)
Tracks: / Deep trouble / Crab alley / Fred and Ethel / Read my lips / Afterglow / Hold it against me / Count the ways / Last night.
**CD:** Released Oct '87, on Watt (ECM) Catalogue no: **833 492 2**
**Album:** Released Oct '87, on Watt (ECM) Catalogue no: **XW 2**

## Swamp Blues

### SWAMP BLUES VOL.2
Tracks: / Coolin' aboard / Storm in Texas / Gray's bounce / Hoo doo blues / Worries life blues / I want some body / I don't know why / Honey bee blues / Baton rouge breakdown / Showers of rain / Number ten at the station and number twelve is on the road / Baby please don't go.
**Album:** Released Sep '78, on Sonet by Sonet Records. Catalogue no: **SNTF 774**

## Swan Silvertones

### GET IT RIGHT WITH THE SWAN SILVERTONES
**Album:** Released Jun '88, on Rhino (USA) by Rhino Records (USA). Catalogue no: **RNLP 70081**

### GET YOUR SOUL RIGHT
Tracks: / Is God satisfied with me / At the cross / I'll search heaven / What about you? / Great day in September / Seek, seek / Singin' in my soul / Sinner man / Sign of the judgement / Oh Mary don't you weep / Lady called mother, A / Get your soul right / Move somewhere / Stand up and testify / He saved my soul / Brighter day ahead.
**Album:** Released Apr '86, on New Cross by Charly Records. Catalogue no: **GNC 1003**

## Swartz, Harvey

### IT'S ABOUT TIME (Swartz, Harvey & Urban Earth)
Note: Bassist Harvie Swartz presents his fourth album as leader. This album features *Urban Earth*, the same band that made Harvie's last offering *Smart moves* a contempory jazz success. Billy Drewes (saxophone), Jay Azzolina (guitar), Harris Simon (keyboards) and Yves Gerard (drums)
**Cass:** Released Feb '89, on Gaia (USA) by Gaia Records (USA). Catalogue no: **139011 4**
**Album:** Released Feb '89, on Gaia (USA) by Gaia Records (USA). Catalogue no: **139011 1**
**CD:** Released Feb '89, on Gaia (USA) by Gaia Records (USA). Catalogue no: **139011 2**

### UNDERNEATH IT ALL
Tracks: / Rainbow / Beauty within the beat / Firewalk / Underneath it all / Leaving.
**Album:** Released Jul '83, on Gramavision Catalogue no: **GR 8202**

### URBAN EARTH
**Album:** Released Dec '85, on Gramavision Catalogue no: **GR 8503**

## Swedish Jazz Kings

### AFTER TONIGHT, VOL. 2
**Album:** Released May '89, on Stomp Off (USA) Catalogue no: **SOS 1188**

### TRIBUTE TO CLARENCE WILLIAMS, A
**Album:** Released Oct '86, on Stomp Off (USA) Catalogue no: **SOS 1122**

## Swedish Radio Jazz

### RAINBOW SKETCHES
**Album:** Released '78, on Four Leaf Clover Catalogue no: **CAM CMLP 5906**

## Sweet Home Chicago

### SWEET HOME CHICAGO (Various artists)
**Album:** Released '82, on Delmark (USA) by Delmark Records (USA). Catalogue no: **DS 618**

## Sweet Honey In The Rock

### BREATHS (Best of Sweet Honey In The Rock)
Tracks: / Breaths / Stranger blues / Joanne little / Ella's song / More than a paycheck / Mandiacapella / Study war no more / Waters of Babylon (Rivers of Babylon) / Oughta be a woman / On children / Chile your waters run red through Soweto / Azanian freedom song.
**Cass:** Released Oct '87, on Cooking Vinyl by Cooking Vinyl Records. Catalogue no: **COOKC 008**
**CD:** Released Apr '88, on Cooking Vinyl by Cooking Vinyl Records. Catalogue no: **COOKCD 008**
**Album:** Released Sep '87, on Cooking Vinyl by Cooking Vinyl Records. Catalogue no: **COOK 008**

### FEEL SOMETHING DRAWING ME ON
**Album:** Released Mar '89, on Flying Fish (USA) by Flying Fish Records (USA). Catalogue no: **FF 375**
**Album:** Released Mar '86, on Spindrift by Celtic Music. Catalogue no: **SPIN 124**

### GOOD NEWS
Tracks: / Breaths / Chile your waters run red through Soweto / Good news / If you had lived / On children / Alla that's all right, but / Echo / Oh death / Biko / Oughta be a woman / Time on my hands / Sometime.
**Album:** Released Aug '89, on Cooking Vinyl by Cooking Vinyl Records. Catalogue no: **COOK 027**
**CD:** Released Aug '89, on Cooking Vinyl by Cooking Vinyl Records. Catalogue no: **COOKCD 027**
**Cass:** Released Aug '89, on Cooking Vinyl by Cooking Vinyl Records. Catalogue no: **COOKC 027**
**Album:** Released Mar '89, on Flying Fish (USA) by Flying Fish Records (USA). Catalogue no: **FF 245**

### LIVE AT CARNEGIE HALL
Tracks: / Beautitudes / Where are the keys to the kingdom / Emergency / Are my hands clean / Peace / My lament / Run run mourner run / Letter to Dr. Martin Luther King / Ode to the international debt / Your worries ain' like mine / Song of the exile / Denko / Drinking of the wine / Wade in the water (CD only.) / Our side won (CD only.).
**Cass:** Released May '88, on Cooking Vinyl by Cooking Vinyl Records. Catalogue no: **COOKC 012**
**CD:** Released May '88, on Cooking Vinyl by Cooking Vinyl Records. Catalogue no: **COOKCD 012**
**Album:** Released Feb '89, on Flying Fish (USA) by Flying Fish Records (USA). Catalogue no: **FF 106**
**Album:** Released May '88, on Cooking Vinyl by Cooking Vinyl Records. Catalogue no: **COOK 012**

### OTHER SIDE, THE
**Album:** Released Mar '89, on Flying Fish (USA) by Flying Fish Records (USA). Catalogue no: **FF 366**
**Album:** Released Mar '86, on Spindrift by Celtic Music. Catalogue no: **SPIN 123**

## Sweet Substitute

### BACK IN THE WORLD AGAIN
Tracks: / Back in the world again / We just couldn't say goodbye.
**7" Single:** Released Apr '79, on Decca by Decca International. Deleted '82. Catalogue no: **F 13833**

### I GIVE IN
Tracks: / I give in.
**7" Single:** Released '78, on Decca by Decca International. Deleted '88. Catalogue no: **F 13820**

### LULLABY OF BROADWAY
Tracks: / Lullaby of Broadway / Sleepy Susie.
**7" Single:** Released Nov '82, on Black Lion Catalogue no: **BS 7100**

### MUSICAL CHRISTMAS CARD
Tracks: / Musical Christmas card / I give in.
**7" Single:** Released Nov '79, on Decca by Decca International. Deleted '82. Catalogue no: **F 13826**

### SOPHISTICATED LADIES
Tracks: / Lullaby of Broadway / Sophisticated lady / Tiger blues / Sleepy Suzie / Take me to the Mardi Gras / I got an uncle in Harlem / Good morning heartache / Dear Mr.Berkeley / Sweet misery / Do you know what it means to miss New Orleans? / Satin doll.
Note: With Kenny Baker, Digby Fairweather, Pat Halcox, Chris Barber, Johnny McCallum, Bert Ezzard, Eddie Blair, Pete Strange, Billy Lamb, Jack Thirwell, Randy Colville, Bill Skeat, Danny Moss, Henry Mackenzie, Bernie George, Denny Wright, Barney Bates, Len Skeat, Stan Bourke, Alyn Ainsworth, Harvey Weston, Andy Leggett, John Crocker, Peter Wingfield, Vic Pitt, Norman Emberson, Roger Hill.
**Album:** Released Oct '82, on Black Lion Catalogue no: **BLM 51010**

### TAKE ME TO THE MARDI GRAS
Tracks: / Take me to the mardi gras / Do you know what it means to miss New Orleans.
**7" Single:** Released Oct '80, on Logo by Logo Records. Deleted Oct '83. Catalogue no: **GO 393**

### TEN CENTS A DANCE
**Cass:** Released Aug '77, on Decca by Decca International. Deleted '81. Catalogue no: **KSKC 5276 81**
**Album:** Released Aug '77, on Decca by Decca International. Deleted '88. Catalogue no: **SKL 5276**

## Swing

### STARS OF SWING 1935-37 (Various artists)
Tracks: / China boy: *Gardner, Freddy* / Swing me sweetly: *Davis, Lew* / When you're smiling: *Gonella, Nat* / Japanese sandman: *Gardner, Freddy* / Hummin' to myself: *Whyte, Duncan* / Keep goin': *Firman, Bert* / Ain't misbehavin': *Young, Arthur* / Swing as it comes: *Firman, Bert* / Baby won't you please come home: *Gardner, Freddy* / Tiger rag: *Gonella, Nat* / Ida, sweet as apple cider: *Miranda, Jack* / Blue strings: *Firman, Bert* / I never knew: *Davis, Lew* / Entr'acte: *Black hand gang* / Bread and jam: *Miranda, Jack* / Blind man's buff: *Young, Arthur.*
**Album:** Released Jan '88, on Harlequin by Interstate Music. Catalogue no: **HQ 3015**

### SWING
Tracks: / Big bucks / Right idea, The / Serenade in blue / Tweedlee dee / Caravan / Mirage / Let the good times roll / Dancing in the dark / Closer I get to you, The / Tocadero ballroom / Crazy he calls me / Make love to me baby.
**Album:** Released Nov '81, on Planet Catalogue no: **K 52329**
**Cass:** Released Nov '81, on Planet Catalogue no: **K4 52329**

**SWING - BIG BANDS (Classic years vol. 8) (Various artists)**
Tracks: / King Porter stomp: *Various artists* / Blazin': *Various artists* / Hot and anxious: *Various artists* / Old man Harlem: *Various artists* / Copenhagen: *Various artists* / Don't be that way: *Various artists* / Congo caravan: *Various artists* / Farewell blues: *Various artists* / Corky jada: *Various artists* / Royal Garden blues: *Various artists* / Exposition swing: *Various artists* / Dippermouth blues: *Various artists* / Woman on my weary mind: *Various artists* / Skeleton in the closet, The: *Various artists* / Harlem shout: *Various artists.*
Note: Includes Fletcher Henderson, Dorsey Brothers, Duke Ellington, Artie Shaw & Jimmy Lunceford.
**Cass:** Released Feb '88, on BBC by BBC Records & Tapes. Catalogue no: **ZCF 655**
**CD:** Released Feb '88, on BBC by BBC Records & Tapes. Catalogue no: **BBC CD 655**
**Album:** Released Feb '88, on BBC by BBC Records & Tapes. Catalogue no: **REB 655**

**SWING - SMALL GROUPS 1931-1936 (Classic years vol. 10) (Various artists)**
Tracks: / My melancholy baby: *Various artists* / Beale street blues: *Various artists* / Fan it: *Various artists* / Never had no livin': *Various artists* / Tomboy: *Various artists* / Toledo shuffle: *Various artists* / Buzzard, The: *Various artists* / Muskrat ramble: *Various artists* / Swing is here: *Various artists* / Blues jumped a rabbit, The: *Various artists* / Mutiny in the parlour: *Various artists* / Frolic Sam: *Various artists* / Warmin' up: *Various artists* / Rhythm saved the world: *Various artists* / Paswonky: *Various artists* / Shoe shine boy: *Various artists.*
Note: Includes Benny Goodman, Red Nichols, Red Norvo, Gene Krupa, Teddy Wilson & Bunny Berigan.
**CD:** Released Feb '88, on BBC by BBC Records & Tapes. Catalogue no: **BBC CD 666**
**Cass:** Released Feb '88, on BBC by BBC Records & Tapes. Catalogue no: **ZCF 666**
**Album:** Released Feb '88, on BBC by BBC Records & Tapes. Catalogue no: **REB 666**

## Swing Classics

**SWING CLASSICS VOL. 1 1944-1945**
Note: Mono production: With Hot Lips Page/Shavers etc.
**Album:** Released Jun '86, on Storyville by Storyville Records AB. Catalogue no: **SLP 818**

## Swing Collection

**SWING COLLECTION (Various artists)**
**Album:** Released Mar '90, on Deja Vu Catalogue no: **DVLP 7029**
**CD:** Released Jul '88, on Deja Vu Catalogue no: **DVCD 2029**
**Album:** Released Nov '85, on Deja Vu Catalogue no: **DVLP 2029**
**Cass:** Released Nov '85, on Deja Vu Catalogue no: **DVMC 2029**

## Swing Era

**SWING ERA (Various artists)**
Tracks: / Jumpin' at The Woodside: *Basie, Count* / Lady be good: *Basie, Count* / My daddy rocks me: *Mezzrow, Mezz* / Tempo and swing: *Hampton, Lionel* / How high the moon: *Ellington, Duke* / Cottontail: *Ellington, Duke* / That's a plenty: *Webb, Chick* / Yesterdays: *Hawkins, Coleman* / St. Louis blues: *Bechet, Sidney* / Flying home: *Hampton, Lionel* / Exactly like you: *Hines, Earl* / Lazy river: *Various artists.*
**Album:** Released Apr '81, on Joker (USA) by Lifetime Records (USA). Catalogue no: **SM 3113**

## Swing Jackpot

**SWING JACKPOT (Various artists)**
**Album:** Released Jul '87, on Jazz Archives (USA) by Jazz Archives Inc.(USA). Catalogue no: **JA 50**

## Swing Party

**SWING PARTY (Various artists)**
Note: Featurin, Miller, Shaw, Dorsey, Goodman, James, Herman, Lunceford, Brown.
**Album:** Released Sep '87, on Lotus Catalogue no: **LOP 14 102**

## Swing Piano

**SWING PIANO (Various artists)**
Note: Mono production. Featuring Earl Hines; Art Tatum; Teddy Wilson.
**Album:** Released May '86, on Storyville by Storyville Records AB. Catalogue no: **SLP 829**

## Swing Sounds

**SWING SOUNDS (Various artists)**
**Album:** Released Apr '81, on Jazz Live (Italy) Catalogue no: **BLJ 8016**

## Swing Street

**SWING STREET VOL. 1 (Various artists)**
**Album:** Released '88, on Tax Catalogue no: **TAX 8026**
**Album:** Released '88, on Timeless by Timeless Records. Catalogue no: **TAX 8028**

**SWING STREET VOL. 2 1931-41 (Various artists)**
Note: Fats Waller/5 Spirits Of Rhythm etc.
**Album:** Released Aug '87, on Tax Catalogue no: **M 8030**

**SWING STREET VOL 3 (Various artists)**
**Album:** Released '88, on Tax Catalogue no: **TAX 8034**

## Swing Under The Nazis

**CLANDESTINE RECORDINGS OF THE FRANKFURT HOT CLUB 1941-1944 (Various artists)**
Tracks: / Bugle call rag: *Various artists* / Stomp: *Various artists* / Blues: *Various artists* / Margie: *Various artists* / Sheik of Araby, The: *Various artists* / Honeysuckle rose: *Various artists* / I can't give you...: *Various artists* / Undecided: *Various artists* / I've found a new baby: *Various artists* / On the sunny side of the street: *Various artists* / My blue Heaven: *Various artists* / Sweet Sue: *Various artists* / Lady be good: *Various artists.*
Note: Artists include: Hans Otto Jung / Karlo Bohlander / Rudi Thomsen / Mark Bunner / Karl Petry / Hans Berry / Freddy De Bondt / Robert Pauwels / Tinus Bruyn / Andre Smit / Horst Lippman. Mono recording.
**Album:** Released Nov '86, on Harlequin by Interstate Music. Catalogue no: **HQ 2051**

## Swinging Dixieland

**SWINGING DIXIELAND (Various artists)**
**Album:** Released '88, on Phontastic (Sweden) Catalogue no: **PHON 9**

## Swinging Flicks

**SWINGING FLICKS, VOL 1 (1936-52) (Various artists)**
Tracks: / Let me off uptown: *Various artists* / Semper fidelis: *Various artists* / When the saints go marching in: *Various artists* / Mood indigo: *Various artists* / Boardwalk boogie: *Various artists* / Until today: *Various artists* / Jazznocracy: *Various artists* / You: *Various artists* / Wait till the sun shines Nellie: *Various artists* / Four or five times: *Various artists* / Mooche, The: *Various artists* / Feed the kitty: *Various artists* / Mr. X blues: *Various artists* / Take everything: *Various artists* / Hot chocolate: *Various artists.*
Note: With Ray Hutton, Rita Rio, Wingy Manone, Duke Ellington, Gene Krupa, Bunny Berigan, Dean Hudson, Lucky Millinder, Bob Chester, Cecil Scott.
**Album:** Released Jun '88, on Bandstand Catalogue no: **BS 7129**

**SWINGING FLICKS, VOL 2 (1939-51) (Various artists)**
Tracks: / Dipsy doodle: *Various artists* / Lonesome road: *Various artists* / Basin Street boogie: *Various artists* / Reed rapture: *Various artists* / Time takes care of everything: *Various artists* / Ride, ride, ride: *Various artists* / Calloway boogie: *Various artists* / Anvil chorus: *Various*

*artists* / Whatcha know, Joe?: *Various artists*/ Margie: *Various artists*/ Take the 'A' train: *Various artists* / Barnyard bounce: *Various artists* / La Rosita: *Various artists* / Solid jive: *Various artists*.
Note: With Lucky Millinder, Cab Calloway, Les Brown, Stan Kenton, Tony Pastor, Larry Clinton, Al Donahue, Jimmy Dorsey, Ray Bauduc, Bradley/ McKinley, Duke Ellington.
**Album:** Released Jun '88, on Bandstand Catalogue no: **BS 7130**

## Swingle Singers

**ANYONE FOR MOZART, BACH, HANDEL,**
**CD:** Released Nov '86, on Philips (Germany) by PolyGram UK Ltd. Catalogue no: **826 948-2**

**BEST OF THE SWINGLE SINGERS Compact/Walkman jazz**
Tracks: / Le marche de limoges / Little David's fugue / Andante / Ricercare A6 / Romance Espagnole / Alexander's fugue / Little prelude and fugue.
**Cass:** Released May '87, on Mercury by Phonogram Ltd. Catalogue no: **830701-4**
**CD:** Released May '87, on Mercury by Phonogram Ltd. Catalogue no: **830701-2**

**COMPACT JAZZ: SWINGLE SINGERS**
Tracks: / Air for G String / Etude Op.25 no.2 / Aranjuez mon amour.
**CD:** on Phonogram by Phonogram Ltd. Catalogue no: **831 701-2**
**Cass:** Released Jul '87, on Phonogram by Phonogram Ltd. Catalogue no: **831 701-4**

**FOLIO**
Tracks: / Flight of the bumble bee / Reverie / Sonata / Clair de lune / Prelude / Minuet / Intermezzo / Pavanne / Rondo / La fille aux cheveux de lin / Fur elise / Swan.
**Album:** Released Jun '80, on Columbia by EMI Records. Deleted '85. Catalogue no: **SCX 6631**

**JAZZ SEBASTIAN BACH**
Tracks: / Choral prelude no. 1 / Aria / Prelude in F / Bourre / Sinfonia / Canon / Invention in C / Fuges in D & D minor.
**Album:** Released Feb '64, on Philips by Phonogram Ltd. Deleted Feb '69. Catalogue no: **BL 7572**
**CD:** Released '88, on Polydor by Polydor Ltd. Catalogue no: **824 703 2**
**Album:** Released Sep '85, on Philips (Europe) by PolyGram UK Ltd. Catalogue no: **824 544 1**
**Cass:** Released Sep '85, on Philips (Europe) by PolyGram UK Ltd. Catalogue no: **824 544 4**

**NOTHING BUT BLUE SKIES**
**Cass:** Released May '88, on Trax by Filmtrax Records. Deleted Jan '90. Catalogue no: **MODEMC 1009**
**Album:** Released May '88, on Trax by Filmtrax Records. Deleted Jan '90. Catalogue no: **MODEM 1009**
**CD:** Released May '88, on Trax by Filmtrax Records. Deleted Jan '90. Catalogue no: **MODCD 1009**

**PLACE VENDOME (Swingle Singers & MJQ)**
Tracks: / Little David's fugue / When I am laid in earth / Vendome / Ricercare A6 / Air for G String / Alexander's fugue / Three windows.
**Cass:** Released Sep '85, on Philips (Europe) by PolyGram UK Ltd. Catalogue no: **824 545 4**
**Album:** Released Sep '85, on Philips (Europe) by PolyGram UK Ltd. Catalogue no: **824 545 1**

**SWINGLE SINGERS CHRISTMAS ALBUM**
Tracks: / Jingle bells / God rest ye merry gentlemen / White christmas / O Tannenbaum / We three kings.
**Album:** Released Dec '80, on Festivo (Holland) Deleted '85. Catalogue no: **6570 220**

## Swingtime

**SWING TIME (VIDEO) (Various artists)**
**VHS:** Released '88, on Channel 5 by Channel 5 Video. Catalogue no: **CFV 01082**

**SWINGTIME**
**CD:** Released Feb '88, on London Records by London Records Ltd. Catalogue no: **820 044-2**

**SWINGTIME VIDEO SAMPLER, THE (Various artists)**
Tracks: / Don't be that way: *James, Harry* / Sophisticated lady: *Ellington, Duke* / Chattanooga choo choo: *Beneke, Tex* / Cherokee: *Barnet, Charlie* / I've got the world on a string: *Brown, Les* / April in Paris: *Basie, Count* / Hamp's boogie woogie: *Hampton, Lionel* / Concerto to end all concertos: *Kenton, Stan* / Table d'hote: *Shaw, Artie* / John silver: *Dorsey, Jimmy* / Organ grinders swing & stardust: *Hutton, Ina Ray* / Who's sorry now: *Bobcats* / Basin street blues: *Teagarden, Jack* / Route 66: *Cole, Nat King Trio* / Boo hoo: *Lombardo, Guy* / I'm looking for four leaf clover: *Mooney, Art* / Ain't she sweet: *Welk, Lawrence* / Shanty in old shanty town: *Long, Johnny* / Why don't you do right: *Lee, Peggy* / Brass bell,The: *Firehouse Five Plus Two.*
Note: 20 complete performances. Featuring Harry James, Duke Ellington, Tex Beneke, Charlie Barnet, Les Brown, Count Basie, Lionel Hampton, Stan Kenton, Artie Shaw, Jimmy Dorsey, Ina Ray Hutton, Bobcats (of Crosby fame), Jack Teagarden, Nat King Cole & His Trio, Guy Lombardo, Art Mooney, Lawrence Welk, Johnny Long, Peggy Lee and Firehouse Five & Two.
**VHS:** Released May '89, on Charly Video Catalogue no: **VIDSAM 100**

## Swope, Earl

**LOST SESSION, THE (Swope, Earl Sextet & Lennie Tristano)**
Tracks: / Tea for two / Tea for two (version 2) / Blue Lou / These foolish things / These foolish things (version 2) / Talk of the town / Talk of the town (version 2) / Yesterdays / What is this thing called love / Don't blame me / I found a new baby / I can't get started / Night in Tunisia.
**Album:** Released Nov '82, on Nostalgia by Mainline Records. Catalogue no: **NOST 7635**

## Sykes, Roosevelt

**BLUES FROM BOTTOMS**
**Album:** Released '73, on 77 by 77 Records. Catalogue no: **77LEU 12/50**

**BOOGIE HONKEY (Sykes, Roosevelt & The Original Honeydrippers)**
**Album:** Released '88, on Oldie Blues Catalogue no: **OL 2818**

**COUNTRY BLUES PIANO ACE**
**Album:** Released Dec '88, on Yazoo (USA) by Shanachie Records (USA). Catalogue no: **L 1033**

**DIRTY MOTHER FOR YOU**
**Album:** Released Feb '89, on Bluetime (Denmark) by Contact Records (Denmark). Catalogue no: **BT 2008**

**FEEL LIKE BLOWING MY HORN**
**Album:** Released '74, on Delmark (USA) by Delmark Records (USA). Catalogue no: **DS 632**
**Album:** Released Dec '88, on Delmark (USA) by Delmark Records (USA). Catalogue no: **DL 632**

**HONEYDRIPPER'S DUKE'S MIXTURE VOL.4, THE**
Tracks: / Rock me / Going down slow / Ice cream freezer / Lost my boogie / Sweet Georgia Brown / St. James infirmary / Honeysuckle rose / Basin Street blues / Woman is in demand, A / Dirty mother for you.
**Album:** Released Nov '79, on Barclay (France) by Decca Records. Catalogue no: **80604**

**ORIGINAL HONEYDRIPPER, THE**
Tracks: / Cow cow blues / Drivin' wheel / What'd I say / Viper song / Early morning blues / Dirty mother for you / I'm a nut / Running the boogie / Honeysuckle rose / Too smart too soon / Sweet home Chicago / I like what you did / Please don't talk about me when I'm gone.
**Album:** Released '88, on Blind Pig (USA) by Blind Pig Records (USA). Catalogue no: **BP-005**
**Album:** Released Mar '89, on Blue Moon (1) by Magnum Music Group. Catalogue no: **BMLP 068**

**RAINING IN MY HEART (Uniteds)**
**Album:** Released Dec '88, on Delmark (USA) by Delmark Records (USA). Catalogue no: **DL 642**

**ROCK IT 1946-54**
**Album:** Released '89, on Wolf Catalogue no: **WBJ 004**

**ROOSEVELT SYKES (Live at Webster College, St. Louis, Feb. 1974)**
Note: Recorded live at Webster College, St Louis, February 1974.
**Album:** Released Jul '88, on Document Catalogue no: **DLP 526**

**Album:** Released Feb '88, on Matchbox by Flyright Records. Catalogue no: **MSE 1011**

**ROOSEVELT SYKES 1929-41**
**Album:** Released '88, on Earl Archives Catalogue no: **BD 2013**

**ROOSEVELT SYKES 1929-1942**
Note: Mono.
**Album:** Released Oct '86, on Best Of Blues (USA) by Blue Island Records (USA). Catalogue no: **BOB 3**

## Synger, Liller

**BUCKET SUCCESSOR**
**Album:** Released '88, on Storyville by Storyville Records AB. Catalogue no: **SLP 431**

**LILLER SYNGER**
**Album:** Released '88, on Storyville by Storyville Records AB. Catalogue no: **SLP 606**

## Szabo, Gabor

**BELSTA RIVER**
**Album:** Released '88, on Four Leaf Clover Catalogue no: **FLC 5030**

**HIGH CONTRAST (Szabo, Gabor & Bobby Womack)**
Tracks: / Breezin' / Amazon / Fingers / Azure blue / Just a little communication / If you don't want my love, give it back / I remember when.
**Cass:** Released '88, on Affinity by Charly Records. Catalogue no: **TCAFF 193**
**Album:** Released Sep '88, on Affinity by Charly Records. Catalogue no: **AFF 193**

**SMALL WORLD**
**Album:** Released '88, on Four Leaf Clover Catalogue no: **FLC 6001**

# T

The following information was taken from the Music Master database on April 14th, 1990.

## Taj Mahal

### AT RONNIE SCOTT'S 1988 (VIDEO)
**VHS:** Released Sep '89, on Hendring Video Catalogue no: **HEN 2 161 G**

### BIG BLUES (Live at Ronnie Scott's)
Tracks: / Big Blues / Mail box blues / Staggerlee / Come on in my kitchen / Local local girl / Soothin' / Fishin' blues / Statesboro' blues / Everybody is somebody.
**CD:** Released Feb '90, on Essential by Castle Communications Records. Catalogue no: **ESMCD 002**
**Cass:** Released Feb '90, on Essential by Castle Communications Records. Catalogue no: **ESMMC 002**

### COLLECTION: TAJ MAHAL
Tracks: / Fishin' blues / Leaving trunk / Six days on the road / Dust my broom / Going up the country / Candy man / Staggerlee / Diving duck blues / Clara (St. Kitts woman) / Statesboro blues / Lot of love, A / Take a giant step / Further down the road / Little red hen / E-Z rider / Texas woman blues / Free song, A / Oh mama, don't you know / Railroad bill / Everybody's got to change sometime.

**Cass:** Released '87, on Castle Collector Series by Castle Communications Records. Catalogue no: **CCSMC 180**
**CD:** Released '87, on Castle Collector Series by Castle Communications Records. Catalogue no: **CCSCD 180**
**2 LP Set:** Released '87, on Castle Collector Series by Castle Communications Records. Catalogue no: **CCSLP 180**

### EVERYBODY IS SOMEBODY
Tracks: / French letter / Deed I do* / Every body is somebody.
**12" Single:** Released Mar '87, on Sonet by Sonet Records. Catalogue no: **SONL 2318**
**7" Single:** Released Mar '87, on Sonet by Sonet Records. Catalogue no: **SON 2318**

### FIRST LP
**Cass:** Released Nov '85, on Demon by Demon Records. Catalogue no: **CED 166**

### GIANT STEP
Tracks: / Linin' Track / Country blues no. 1 / Wild ox man / Little Rain Blues / Little soulful tune, A / Candy Man / Cluck Old Hen / Colored Aristocracy / Blind boy rag / Stagger Lee / Cajun tune / Fishin' Blues / Annie's lover.
**CD:** Released Apr '88, on Edsel by Demon Records. Catalogue no: **EDCD 264**
**2 LP Set:** Released Dec '88, on Edsel by Demon Records. Catalogue no: **DED 264**

### GOING HOME
Tracks: / Stateboro blues / Dust my broom / You don't miss your water / Good morning Miss Brown / Six days on the road / Sweet home Chicago / Little red hen / Frankie and Albert / Johnny too bad / New E-Z rider blues / Backjack Davey / Blackjack Davey / Satisfied and tickled too / Brown eyed handsome man / Clara (St Kitts woman).
**Cass:** Released Jul '80, on CBS by CBS Records. Catalogue no: **40 31844**
**Album:** Released Jul '80, on CBS by CBS Records. Deleted Jan '89. Catalogue no: **CBS 31844**

### LIVE AND DIRECT
Tracks: / Jorge Ben / Reggae no. 1 / You're gonna need somebody / Little brown dog / Take a giant step / L-O-V-E love / And who / Suva serenade / Airplay.
**CD:** Released Nov '87, on Teldec (Germany) by ASV (Academy Sound & Vision). Catalogue no: **8.26519**

### NATCH'L BLUES, THE
Tracks: / Good morning Miss Brown / Corinna / I ain't gonna let nobody steal my mail,.. / Done changed my way of living / She caught the Katy / Cuckoo, The / You don't miss your water / Lot of love, A.
**Album:** Released May '87, on Edsel by Demon Records. Catalogue no: **ED 231**

### SOOTHIN'
Tracks: / Soothin' / Kauai Kalypso / Local Local girl.
**7" Single:** Released Aug '87, on Sonet by Sonet Records. Catalogue no: **SON 2325**
**12" Single:** Released Aug '87, on Sonet by Sonet Records. Catalogue no: **SONL 2325**

### TAJ (see panel on next page)
Tracks: / Everybody is somebody / Paradise / Do I love her / Light of the Pacific / Deed I do / Soothin' / Pillow talk / Local local girl / Kauai calypso / French letter.
Note: Produced by Taj Mahal. Executive producer Jonathan F.P. Rose.
**CD:** Released '88, on Sonet by Sonet Records. Catalogue no: **SNTCD 975**
**Album:** Released Jan '87, on Sonet by Sonet Records. Catalogue no: **SNTF 975**

### TAJ MAHAL
Tracks: / Leaving trunk / Statesboro blues / Checkin' up on my baby / Everybody's got to change sometime / EZ rider / Dust my broom / Diving duck blues / Celebrated walkin' blues.
**Album:** Released Dec '85, on Edsel by Demon Records. Catalogue no: **ED 166**
**Cass:** Released Dec '85, on Edsel by Demon Records. Catalogue no: **CED 166**

### TAKE A GIANT STEP
Tracks: / Jorge Ben / Reggae number one / You're gonna need somebody on your bond / Little brown dog / Take a giant step / Airplay / L-O-V-E love / And who / Suya serenade.
**Cass:** Released '83, on Magnet by WEA Records. Deleted Jun '88. Catalogue no: **ZCMAG 5035**
**Album:** Released '83, on Magnet by WEA Records. Deleted '87. Catalogue no: **MAGL 5035**

### TAKE A GIANT STEP (SINGLE)
Tracks: / Take a giant step / Jorge Ben.
**7" Single:** Released Aug '80, on Magnet by WEA Records. Deleted '83. Catalogue no: **MAG 172**

## Tate, Buddy

**Biographical details:** Tate is one of a long line of great tenor saxophonists born in Texas (in 1913).
He played with Count Basie, Lucky Millinder, Jimmy Rushing, Hot Lips Page and was then resident at the Celebrity Club in Harlem for 21 years until pushed out by rock music.
He has recorded regularly all that time, with Buck Clayton, Rushing and many others as a sideman, and his still at it, most recently on Concord Jazz. (See also Scott Hamilton.)
(Donald Clarke 13.1.88).

### BALLAD ARTISTRY OF BUDDY TATE,
Note: Featuring the Ed Bickert Trio.
**Album:** Released Sep '87, on Sackville by Spotlite Records. Catalogue no: **3034**

### BUDDY TATE AND THE MUSE ALL STARS
Tracks: / Jumpin' at the Woodside / Blue creek / Candy / Tangerine / She's got it.
**Album:** Released Apr '81, on Muse by Black & Blue Records. Catalogue no: **MR 5198**

### GREAT BUDDY TATE, THE
**Album:** Released Nov '81, on Concord Jazz by Concord Jazz Records (USA). Catalogue no: **CJ 163**

### INSTRUMENTAL FOR DANCING (Tate, Buddy & Frank Culley)
**Album:** Released Dec '84, on Krazy Kat by Interstate Music. Catalogue no: **KK 784**

### JUMPIN' ON THE WEST COAST
Tracks: / Tate's a jumpin' / Blue and sentimental / Vine Street breakdown /

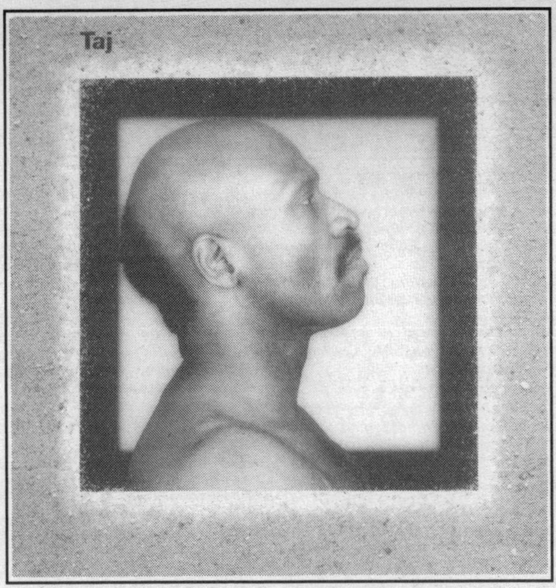


Taj Mahal - Taj (Sonet)

Ballin' from day to day / Six foor two blues / Kansas City local / Things you done for me, baby, The / Early morning blues / Good morning judge.
**Album:** Released Jul '88, on Black Lion Catalogue no: **BLP 30128**

**JUST JAZZ (Tate, Buddy & Al Grey)**
**Album:** Released Nov '86, on Uptown (USA) Catalogue no: **UP 27 21**

**KANSAS CITY JOYS**
Note: Features Paul Quinichette and Jay McShann.
**Album:** Released May '77, on Sonet by Sonet Records. Catalogue no: **SNTF 716**

**KANSAS CITY WOMAN**
Note: Compositions and arrangements by Buck Clayton. (With Bruce Turner/Kathleen Stobart/Mick Pyne/Dave Green/Tony Mann.
Tracks: / Kansas City woman / The one for me / Pamela / Candyville / Outswinger / Steevos / Clarinet Lemonade / Swinging Scorpio.
**Album:** Released May '79, on Black Lion Catalogue no: **BLP 30163**

**LONG TALL TENOR (Tate, Buddy & Humphrey Lyttelton)**
Tracks: / I cover the waterfront / Sweetie / Rompin' with Buck / Buddy Tate from Texas State / Rock a bye Basie / Buddy's bit / I cried for you.
**Album:** Released Sep '86, on Calligraph Catalogue no: **CLGLP 008**

**QUARTET**
Tracks: / June night / If you could see me now / Alone together / Bye bye blackbird / Georgia on my mind / Someday, sweetheart / I remember April.
**Album:** Released Apr '83, on Sackville by Spotlite Records. Catalogue no: **3027**

**SHERMAN SHUFFLE**
Tracks: / Curtains of the night / Back in your own back yard / Have you met Miss Jones / Sherman shuffle / Best things in life are free, The / Lover man / Body and soul / Warm valley / Potentate.
**Album:** Released Apr '81, on Sackville by Spotlite Records. Catalogue no: **3017**

**SWINGING LIKE....TATE (Tate, Buddy & His Orchestra)**
Tracks: / Bottle it / Walk that walk / Miss Sadie Brown / Moon eyes / Rockin' Steve / Rompin' with Buck.
Note: Licensed from Decca Records Ltd. A Felsted recording
**Album:** Released Nov '86, on Affinity by Charly Records. Catalogue no: **AFF 171**
**CD:** Released Jun '88, on London Records by London Records Ltd. Catalogue no: **820 599 2**

**TATE A TETE AT LA FONTAIN (Tate. Buddy & Tete Montoliu)**
**Album:** Released Jan '88, on Storyville by Storyville Records AB. Catalogue no: **SLP 4030**

**TEXAS TWISTER, THE**
**Album:** Released '88, on New World (USA) by New World Records (USA). Catalogue no: **NW 352**
**CD:** Released '88, on New World (USA) by New World Records (USA). Catalogue no: **NWCD 352/2**

## Tatum, Art

**Biographical details:** Tatum was born in 1910 in Ohio and died in 1956 in Los Angeles. As one of the greatest pianists in the history of jazz, his astonishing technique was admired by everyone else including other pianists such as

Buddy Tate

Vladimir Horowitz. He was virtually blind from birth, began gigging as a teenager and made his first solo record in 1933; he recorded exclusively for American Decca (now MCA) well into the 1940s including solo and with a small combo, but mostly as a trio with bass and guitar. Unbelievably, he was neglected in the late 1940s, but recorded with a trio on Dial and Capitol, then extensively for Norman Granz (now on Pablo) until he died of Uremia. He was probably influenced by the harmonic richness of the music of Duke Ellington and admitted the influence of Fats Waller, who once referred to him as God. He was not a composer, but embroidered standards; his quartet album with Ben Webster from 1955 in the *Pablo Group Masterpieces Series* is one of the most beautiful jazz records ever made. (Donald Clarke 13.1.88).

**20TH CENTURY PIANO GENIUS**
**2 LP Set:** Released Aug '87, on Emarcy Catalogue no: **826 129**

**1945: ART TATUM**
Tracks: / Body and soul / I guess I'll have to change my plan / What is this thing called love? / Crazy rhythm / Sweet Georgia Brown / Can't we be friends? / Limehouse blues / Among my souvenirs / I'm gonna sit right down and write myself a letter / Stay as sweet as you are / Sugar foot stomp / You took advantage of me.
**Album:** Released Apr '81, on Joker (USA) by Lifetime Records (USA). Catalogue no: **SM 3117**

**ART OF TATUM, THE**
**Album:** Released May '88, on Jazz Life Catalogue no: **2673751**
**CD:** Released May '88, on Jazz Life Catalogue no: **267 375 2**
**Cass:** Released May '88, on Jazz Life Catalogue no: **2673754**

**ART TATUM**
Note: Featuring Lionel Hampton, Barney Kessell, Buddy Rich, Benny Carter & Ben Webster
**Album:** Released Sep '87, on Giants of Jazz by Hasmick Promotions. Catalogue no: **LPJT 63**

**ART TATUM 1940-44**
**Album:** Released Sep '87, on Giants of Jazz by Hasmick Promotions. Catalogue no: **LPJT 1**

**ART TATUM AT THE CRESCENDO-VOL.1**
**Album:** Released '88, on GNP Crescendo (USA) by GNP Crescendo Records (USA). Catalogue no: **GNPS 9026**
**Album:** Released '88, on GNP Crescendo (USA) by GNP Crescendo Records (USA). Catalogue no: **GNPS 9025**

**ART TATUM COLLECTION (20 golden greats)**
Tracks: / Smoke gets in your eyes / Willow weep for me / Somebody loves me / Blue skies / Sweet Lorraine / Someone to watch over me / I cover the waterfront / I won't dance / On the sunny side of the street / My heart stood still / Japanese sandman / What does it take (to win your love) / Nice work if you can get it / She's funny that way / Don't blame me / Taboo / Dardanella / It's the talk of the town / Dancing in the dark / I gotta right to sing the blues.
**Album:** Released Jul '86, on Deja Vu Catalogue no: **DVLP 2064**
**Cass:** Released Jul '86, on Deja Vu Catalogue no: **DVMC 2064**

**ART TATUM ON THE AIR**
Tracks: / Tiger rag / Young and healthy / Morning, noon and night / When day is done / Stardust / Chinatown, my Chinatown / Lulu's back in town / Humoresque / I know that you know / Sweet Lorraine / How high the moon / Ain't misbehavin' / Song of the vagabonds / Smoke gets in your eyes.
**Album:** Released Feb '78, on Aircheck (USA) by Kiner Ents.(USA). Catalogue no: **AIRCHECK 21**

**ART TATUM, VOLS 1 & 2**
Tracks: / It's only a paper moon / Just a gigolo / Three little words / I gotta right to sing the blues / On the sunny side of the street / Somebody loves me / Why was I born? / If I could be with you one hour tonight / Mean to me / You took advantage of me / Body and soul / I guess I'll have to change my plan / Can't we be friends? / Among my souvenirs / I'm gonna sit right down and write myself a letter / Stay as sweet as you are / Fine and dandy / I've got the world on a string / What is this thing called love? / Crazy rhythm / Limehouse blues / All God's chillun got rhythm / I gotta right to sing the blues / I'm coming, Virginia.
**2 LP Set:** Released Jun '75, on Vogue by Vogue Records. Catalogue no: **VJD 511**

**ART TATUM AND ERROLL GARNER (Tatum, Art & Erroll Garner)**
**Album:** Released 12 Feb '88, on Fresh Sounds (Spain) by Fresh Sounds Records (Spain). Catalogue no: **FS 306**

**ARTISTRY OF TATUM, THE**
**2 LP Set:** Released Oct '88, on Vogue by Vogue Records. Catalogue no: **400031**

**BEST OF ART TATUM**
Tracks: / Night and day / Willow weep for me / Blues in my heart / Caravan / Foggy day, A / Hallelujah / Can't we be friends? / Have you met Miss Jones? / Elegy / Love for sale.
Note: A brilliant pianist with a fantastic line-up: Roy Eldridge, John Simmons, Alvin Stoller, Benny Carter, Louis Bellson, Buddy de Franco, Red Callender, Bill Douglass, Lionel Hampton, Buddy Rich, Ben Webster, Jo Jones. (Recorded in 1983.)
**Album:** Released Oct '84, on Pablo Jazz (USA) by Pablo Records (USA). Catalogue no: **2310 887**

**COMPLETE ART TATUM 1, THE**
**CD:** Released Feb '90, on Capitol by EMI Records. Catalogue no: **CDP 7928662**

**COMPLETE ART TATUM 2, THE**
**CD:** Released Feb '90, on Capitol by EMI Records. Catalogue no: **CDP 7928672**

**COMPLETE CAPITOL RECORDINGS, THE**
Tracks: / Willow weep for me / I cover the waterfront / Aunt Hagar's blues / Nice work if you can get it / Someone to watch over me / Dardanella / Time on my hands / Sweet Lorraine / Somebody loves me / Don't blame me / My heart stood still / You took advantage of me / I gotta right to sing the blues / How high the moon / Makin' whoopee / Going home / Blue skies / It's the talk of the town / Dancing in the dark / Tenderly / Melody in F / September song / Would you like to take a walk / Tea for two / Out of nowhere / Lover / Just one of those things / Indiana.
**Cass:** Released Jun '88, on Affinity by Charly Records. Catalogue no: **TCAFFD 191**
**2 LP Set:** Released Jun '88, on Affinity by Charly Records. Catalogue no: **AFFD 191**

**COMPLETE CAPITOL RECORDINGS VOL.1**
Tracks: / My heart stood still / You took advantage of me / I gotta right to sing the blues / How high the moon / Makin' whoopee / Goin' home / Blue skies / It's the talk of the town / Dancing in the dark / Tenderly / Just one of those things / Indiana (back home again in Indiana) / Love / Would you like to take a walk?.
**CD:** Released Feb '90, on Capitol by EMI Records. Catalogue no: **CZ 278**

**COMPLETE CAPITOL RECORDINGS VOL. 2**
Tracks: / My heart stood still / You took advantage of me / I gotta right to sing the blues / How high the moon / Makin' whoopee / Goin' home / Blue skies / It's the talk of the town / Dancing in the dark / Tenderly / Just one of those things / Indiana (back home again in Indiana) / Love / Would you like to take a walk?.
**CD:** Released Feb '90, on Capitol by EMI Records. Catalogue no: **CZ 269**
**CD:** Released Feb '90, on Capitol by EMI Records. Catalogue no: **CDP 792 867 2**

**COMPLETE TRIO SESSIONS VOL 1 (Featuring Tiny Grimes & Slam Stewart)**
Tracks: / I got rhythm / Cocktails for two / I ain't got nobody / After you've gone / Moonglow / Deep purple / I would do anything for you / Liza / Tea for two / Honeysuckle Rose / Man I love, The / Dark eyes / Body and soul / I know that you know.
**Album:** Released '88, on Official by Official Records. Catalogue no: **OFF 3001**
**CD:** Released Dec '88, on Official by Official Records. Catalogue no: **OFF 83001**

**COMPLETE TRIO SESSIONS VOL 2 (Featuring Tiny Grimes & Slam Stewart)**
Tracks: / On the sunny side of the street / Flying home / Boogie / Topsy / If I had you / Soft winds / Long, long ago / Vari-

ations on a theme by Flotow / If I had you / Warm up with sandman / Thou swell 1 / Thou swell 2 / Thou swell 3.
**CD:** Released Dec '88, on Official by Official Records. Catalogue no: **OFF 83002**
**Album:** Released '88, on Official by Official Records. Catalogue no: **OFF 3002**

**FIRST RECORDINGS (In Concert)**
Tracks: / Tiger Rag / Tea for two / St. Louis blues / Tiger rag / Sophisticated lady / How High the moon / Humouresque / Tatum-pole boogie / Someone to watch over me / Yesterdays / I know that you Know / Willow weep for me / Man I love, The / Kerry dance, the.
**Cass:** Released Jul '86, on CBS by CBS Records. Deleted Aug '87. Catalogue no: **40 26550**
**Album:** Released Jul '86, on CBS by CBS Records. Deleted Aug '87. Catalogue no: **CBS 26550**

**GENIUS OF KEYBOARD, THE**
Tracks: / Blue Lou / Gone with the wind / Foggy day, A / September song / Love for sale / You took advantage of me / Makin' whoopee / Willow weep for me / Hallelujah / Once in a while / This can't be love / All the things you are / My blue Heaven / I cover the waterfront / Somebody loves me.
**CD:** Released Jun '88, on Giants of Jazz by Hasmick Promotions. Catalogue no: **GOJCD 53019**

**GENIUS, THE**
Tracks: / Fifty second street blues / Midnight melody / Gang o'notes / Just before dawn / Between midnight and dawn / Apollo boogie / Hallelujah / Song of the vagabonds / Runnin' wild / Memories of you / Poor butterfly / Kerry dance, The.
**Album:** Released Jan '85, on Black Lion Catalogue no: **BLP 30124**

**GET HAPPY**
Tracks: / Happy feet / Royal Garden blues / Ain't misbehavin' / Stardust / In a sentimental mood / Man I love, The / Running wild / I can't get started / Get happy / Begin the beguine / It had to be you / Humoresque / Hallelujah / Lullaby in rhythm / Oh, you crazy moon / Over the rainbow.
**Album:** Released Jul '77, on Black Lion Catalogue no: **BLP 30194**

**GROUP MASTERPIECES (Tatum, Art Trio)**
Tracks: / Just one of those things / More than you know / Some other Spring / Blue Lou / Love for sale / Is'nt it romantic / I,ll never be the same / I'll guess I'll have to change my plans / Trio Blues.
Note: Personnel: Art Tatum, Red Callender, Jo Jones.
**CD:** Released Jul '86, on Pablo Jazz (USA) by Pablo Records (USA). Catalogue no: **J33J 20035**

**KEYSTONE SESSIONS**
**Album:** Released Mar '79, on Varese International Catalogue no: **VS 81021**

**LIVE AT THE CRESCENDO**
**CD:** Released Dec '86, on Vogue by Vogue Records. Catalogue no: **VGCD 600116**

**MASTERS OF JAZZ VOL.8**
**Album:** Released May '86, on Storyville by Storyville Records AB. Catalogue no: **SLP 4108**

**MOODS**
Tracks: / It had to be you / Oh, you crazy moon / Over the rainbow / Day in, day out / Exactly like you / Hallelujah, Hallelujah / Memories of you / Yesterdays / Jitterbug waltz / I cover the waterfront / Love for sale / Just like a butterfly / Sweet Lorraine.
**Album:** on Official by Official Records. Catalogue no: **OFF 3042**
**CD:** on Official by Official Records. Catalogue no: **OFF 83042**

**PIANO MASTERY**
Tracks: / Humoresque / It had to be you / Begin the beguine / Where or when / Night and day / Poor butterfly / Don't blame me / Man I love, The / Ja da / I found a new baby / Somebody loves me / Exactly like you.
**Album:** Released Apr '81, on Shoestring (1) Catalogue no: **SS 105**

**PIANO SOLO**
**Album:** Released '88, on Zeta Catalogue no: **ZET 708**
**Album:** Released Mar '84, on EMI (France) by EMI Records. Catalogue no: **2M 056 80800**
**Cass:** Released Mar '84, on EMI (France) by EMI Records. Catalogue no: **2M 256 80800**

**PIANO SOLO INEDITS 1940/41**
**CD:** Released Oct '89, on Jazz Anthology by Musidisc Records (France). Catalogue no: **550052**

**PIANO SOLOS**
**Album:** Released '88, on Jazz Piano Catalogue no: **JP 5005**

**PURE GENIUS (DOUBLE ALBUM)**
Note: This double album covers Tatum's early years, from the age of 21.
**2 LP Set:** Released May '84, on Affinity by Charly Records. Catalogue no: **AFFD 118**

**PURE GENIUS (Cleveland Ohio Broadcast 1934, LA 1945 NYC 1945)**
Tracks: / Young and Healthy / Morning noon and night / When day is done / Stardust / Chinatown my Chinatown / Man I love, The / Taboo / Somebody loves Me / Why was I born / If I could be with you one hour tonight / Tea for two / Mean to me / It's only a paper Moon / Just a gigolo / Three little Words / I Gotta right to sing the blues.
**Cass:** Released Sep '86, on Atlantis by Charly Records. Catalogue no: **TCATS 3**
**Album:** Released Sep '86, on Atlantis by Charly Records. Catalogue no: **ATS 3**

**REMARKABLE ART OF TATUM, THE (Tatum, Art Trio)**
Note: Featuring Tiny Grimes, Slam Stuart.
**Album:** Released Aug '88, on Audiophile (USA) by Jazzology Records (USA). Catalogue no: **AP 88**

**SONG OF THE VAGABONDS**
Tracks: / Tea for two / Poor butterfly / I've got a right to sing the blues / Taboo / Ain't misbehavin' / Royal Garden blues / I got rhythm / Hallelujah / Song of the vagabonds / Lover / Memories of you / Running wild / Yesterdays / Kerry dance.
Note: With Tiny Grimes, Slam Stewart, Roy Eldridge, Charlie Shavers, Vic Dickenson, Benny Morton, Ben Webster, Edmund Hall, Sid Catlett. Recorded 1944-45.
**Album:** Released Jul '87, on Black Lion Catalogue no: **BLP 30166**

**STRANGE AS IT SEEMS**
**Album:** Released Jul '86, on Collectors Items Catalogue no: **CI 011**

**TATUM GROUP MASTERPIECES, THE (Sept. 1956) (Tatum, Art & Ben Webster)**
**CD:** Released Jan '89, on JVC/Fantasy Catalogue no: **VDJ 28009**
**CD:** Released May '86, on Pablo Jazz (USA) by Pablo Records (USA). Catalogue no: **CD 20034**

**TATUM GROUP MASTERPIECES, VOL 1**
Tracks: / What is this thing called love? / I'll never be the same / Makin' whoopee / Hallelujah / Perdido / More than you know / How high the moon.
Note: With Lionel Hampton - vibes; Buddy Rich - Drums.
**Album:** Released Jul '85, on Pablo Jazz (USA) by Pablo Records (USA). Catalogue no: **2310 720**
**Cass:** Released Jul '85, on Pablo Jazz (USA) by Pablo Records (USA). Catalogue no: **K10 720**

**TATUM GROUP MASTERPIECES VOL. 2**
Tracks: / Verve blues / Plaid / Somebody loves me / September song / Deep purple.
Note: With Lionel Hampton, Harry Edison, Red Callender, Barney Kessel, Buddy Rich.
**Album:** Released Aug '77 on Pablo Jazz (USA) by Pablo Records (USA). Deleted '83. Catalogue no: **2310 731**
**Cass:** Released Aug '77 on Pablo Jazz (USA) by Pablo Records (USA). Deleted '83. Catalogue no: **K10 731**

**TATUM GROUP MASTERPIECES VOL. 3**
Tracks: / Blues in C / Undecided / Under a blanket of blue / Blues in B flat / Foggy day, A / Street of dreams / 'S wonderdul.
Note: With Benny Carter and Louis Bellson.
**Album:** Released Mar '78, on Pablo Jazz (USA) by Pablo Records (USA). Catalogue no: **2310 732**
**Cass:** Released Mar '78, on Pablo Jazz (USA) by Pablo Records (USA). Catalogue no: **K10 732**

**TATUM GROUP MASTERPIECES VOL. 4**
Tracks: / Old-fashioned love / Blues in my heart / My blue heaven / Hands accross the table / You're mine / You /

Idaho.
Note: With Benny Carter and Louis Bellson.
**Album:** Released Mar '78, on Pablo Jaz (USA) by Pablo Records (USA). Catalogue no: **2310 733**

## TATUM GROUP MASTERPIECES VOL.5
Tracks: / Night and day / I won't dance / In a sentimental mood / Moon is low, The / Moon song / You took advantage of me / This can't be love / I surrender, dear.
Note: With Roy Eldridge, John Simmons, Alvin Stollerwith.
**Cass:** Released Aug '77, on Pablo Jazz (USA) by Pablo Records (USA). Catalogue no: **K10 734**

## TATUM GROUP MASTERPIECES VOL.6
Tracks: / Just one of those things / More than you know / Some other spring / If / Blue Lou / Love for sale / Isn't it romantic? / I'll never be the same / I guess I'll have to change my plan / Trio blues.
Note: With Red Callender and Jo Jones.
**Album:** Released Aug '77, on Pablo Jazz (USA) by Pablo Records (USA). Catalogue no: **2310 735**
**Cass:** Released Aug '77, on Pablo Jazz (USA) by Pablo Records (USA). Catalogue no: **K10 735**

## TATUM GROUP MASTERPIECES VOL.7
Tracks: / Deep night / This can't be love / Memories of you / Once in a while / Foggy day, A / Lover man / You're mine / You / Makin' whoopee.
Note: With Buddy de Franco, Red Callender, Bill Douglass.
**Album:** Released Mar '78, on Pablo Jazz (USA) by Pablo Records (USA). Catalogue no: **2310 736**
**Cass:** Released Mar '78, on Pablo Jazz (USA) by Pablo Records (USA). Catalogue no: **K10 736**

## TATUM GROUP MASTERPIECES VOL.8
Tracks: / Gone with the wind / All the things you are / Have you met Miss Jones? / My one and only love / Night and day / My ideal / Where or when.
Note: With Ben Webster, Red Callender, Bill Douglass.
**Album:** Released Aug '77, on Pablo Jazz (USA) by Pablo Records (USA). Catalogue no: **2310 737**
**Cass:** Released Aug '77, on Pablo Jazz (USA) by Pablo Records (USA). Catalogue no: **K10 737**

## TATUM GROUP MASTERPIECES VOL.9
Tracks: / This can't be love / Stars fell on Alabama / Lover man / Prisoner of love / Love for sale / Body and soul / Please be kind.
Note: With Lionel Hampton - vibes; Buddy Rich - drums.
**Album:** Released Mar '79, on Pablo Jazz (USA) by Pablo Records (USA). Catalogue no: **2310 775**
**Cass:** Released Mar '79, on Pablo Jazz (USA) by Pablo Records (USA). Catalogue no: **K10 775**

## TATUM SOLO MASTERPIECES VOL.1
Tracks: / Moonglow / Love for sale / Body and soul / Just a sittin and a rockin / Paper moon / Have you met Miss Jones? / Stay as sweet as you are / My last affair / Willow weep for me.
**Album:** Released Apr '78, on Pablo Jazz (USA) by Pablo Records (USA). Catalogue no: **2310 723**
**Cass:** Released Apr '78, on Pablo Jazz (USA) by Pablo Records (USA). Catalogue no: **K10 723**

## TATUM SOLO MASTERPIECES VOL.2
Tracks: / Elegy / This can't be love / There will never be another you / Gone with the wind / Ghost of a chance / Lover come back to me / I'll see you in my dreams / Heatwave / September song.
**Cass:** Released Apr '78, on Pablo Jazz (USA) by Pablo Records (USA). Catalogue no: **K10 729**
**Album:** Released Apr '78, on Pablo Jazz (USA) by Pablo Records (USA). Catalogue no: **2310 729**

## TATUM SOLO MASTERPIECES VOL.3
Tracks: / Yesterdays / Tenderly / Jitterbug waltz / Love me or leave me / Deep purple / Begin the beguine / Dixieland band / All the things you are / Crazy rhythm / Prisoner of love.
**Cass:** Released May '78, on Pablo Jazz (USA) by Pablo Records (USA). Catalogue no: **K10 730**
**Album:** Released May '78, on Pablo Jazz (USA) by Pablo Records (USA). Catalogue no: **2310 730**

## TATUM SOLO MASTERPIECES VOL.4
Tracks: / Aunt Hagar's blues / Isn't this a lovely day / Ill wind / I've got the world on a string / Stardust / Man I love, The / What's new? / They can't take that away from me.
**Album:** Released May '78, on Pablo Jazz (USA) by Pablo Records (USA). Catalogue no: **2310 789**
**Cass:** Released May '78, on Pablo Jazz (USA) by Pablo Records (USA). Catalogue no: **K10 789**

## TATUM SOLO MASTERPIECES VOL.5
Tracks: / Makin' whoopee / Don't worry 'bout me / That old feeling / Louise / Fine and dandy / Stompin' at The Savoy / Blue moon / I cover the waterfront / Stars fell on Alabama / You're driving me crazy.
**Album:** Released May '78, on Pablo Jazz (USA) by Pablo Records (USA). Catalogue no: **2310 790**
**Cass:** Released May '78, on Pablo Jazz (USA) by Pablo Records (USA). Catalogue no: **K10 790**

## TATUM SOLO MASTERPIECES VOL.6
Tracks: / I've got a crush on you / There's a small hotel / Night and day / Way you look tonight / Cherokee / I'm coming, Virginia / Do nothing till you hear from me / You're blase / Ain't misbehavin'.
**Cass:** Released Aug '78, on Pablo Jazz (USA) by Pablo Records (USA). Catalogue no: **K10 791**
**Album:** Released Aug '78, on Pablo Jazz (USA) by Pablo Records (USA). Catalogue no: **2310 791**

## TATUM SOLO MASTERPIECES VOL.7
Tracks: / Mighty like a rose / What does it take (to win your love) / Taboo / Humoresque / Smoke gets in your eyes / Moon song / Dancing in the dark / Japanese sandman / So beats my heart for you.
**Cass:** Released Aug '78, on Pablo Jazz (USA) by Pablo Records (USA). Catalogue no: **K10 792**
**Album:** Released Aug '78, on Pablo Jazz (USA) by Pablo Records (USA). Catalogue no: **2310 792**

## TATUM SOLO MASTERPIECES VOL.8
Tracks: / In a sentimental mood / Blue skies / These foolish things / She's funny that way / Sweet Lorraine / Sunny side of the street / I won't dance / You go to my head / Talk of the town.
**Cass:** Released '78, on Pablo Jazz (USA) by Pablo Records (USA). Catalogue no: **K10 793**
**Album:** Released '78, on Pablo Jazz (USA) by Pablo Records (USA). Catalogue no: **2310 793**

## TATUM SOLO MASTERPIECES VOL.9
Tracks: / Too marvellous for words / You took advantage of me / Sophisticated lady / I'm in the mood for love / Everything I have is yours / Blue Lou / Embraceable you / I didn't know what time it was / Tea for two / Come rain or come shine.
**Cass:** Released '78, on Pablo Jazz (USA) by Pablo Records (USA). Catalogue no: **K10 835**
**Album:** Released '78, on Pablo Jazz (USA) by Pablo Records (USA). Catalogue no: **2310 835**

## TATUM SOLO MASTERPIECES VOL.10
Tracks: / After you've gone / When your lover has gone / Very thought of you, The / Please be kind / Indiana / I surrender, dear / Blues in my heart / Would you like to take a walk? / I can't give you anything but love.
**Album:** Released May '81, on Pablo Jazz (USA) by Pablo Records (USA). Catalogue no: **2310 862**
**Cass:** Released May '81, on Pablo Jazz (USA) by Pablo Records (USA). Catalogue no: **K10 862**

## TATUM SOLO MASTERPIECES VOL.11
Tracks: / I only have eyes for you / If you hadn't gone away / Without a song / I gotta right to sing the blues / I hadn't anyone till you / S'posin' / Mean to me / You're mine, you / I'll see you again / Moon is low, The.
**Album:** Released Sep '81, on Pablo Jazz (USA) by Pablo Records (USA). Catalogue no: **2310 864**
**Cass:** Released Sep '81, on Pablo Jazz

(USA) by Pablo Records (USA). Catalogue no: **K10 864**

**TATUM SOLO MASTERPIECES, VOL 12**
Tracks: / Lullaby in rhythm / Boulevard of broken dreams / Judy / Someone to watch over me / Danny boy / Happy feet / Out of nowhere / Over the rainbow / Just like a butterfly (that's caught in the rain) / Memories of you.
**Cass:** Released '82, on Pablo Jazz (USA) by Pablo Records (USA). Catalogue no: **K10 870**

**V-DISCS, THE**
**CD:** Released Aug '89, on Black Lion Catalogue no: **BLCD7 60114**
**Album:** Released '79, on Black Lion Catalogue no: **BLP 60114**

## Taylor, Art

**A.T'S DELIGHT**
Tracks: / Syeeda's song flute / Epistrophy / Move / High seas / Kookoo & fungi / Blue interlude.
**Album:** Released Jul '89, on Blue Note by EMI Records. Catalogue no: **BST 84047**
**CD:** Released May '89, on Blue Note by EMI Records. Catalogue no: **BNZ 177**
**CD:** Released May '89, on Blue Note by EMI Records. Catalogue no: **CDP 784 047 2**

**TAYLORS WAILERS**
**Album:** Released Jun '86, on Original Jazz Classics (USA) by Fantasy Inc (USA). Catalogue no: **OJC 094**

## Taylor, Billy

**Biographical details:** Taylor was born in 1921 in North Carolina; he is a fine jazz pianist who has become better known as a writer, broadcaster and teacher. *Where've You Been* features Keith Copeland on drums, Victor Gaskin on bass, Joe Kennedy on violin. Taylor was co-founder of the Jazzmobile in 1965, which gives free concerts in the streets for children; was musical director of the David Frost TV talk show, the first black to hold such a position (many years later he is still the only one). He published Jazz Piano in 1982, based on his radio series; he does a jazz interview segment once a month or so on a Sunday Morning TV show on CBS in the USA. (Donald Clarke 13.1.88).

**CROSS SECTION**
Tracks: / Eddie's theme / Lullaby of Birdland / Tune for Tex / Billy's beat / I love to mambo / Early morning mambo / Mood for Mendes / Goodbye / Moonlight in Vermont / I'll be around / Candido / Mambo azul.
**Album:** Released Jan '89, on Prestige Catalogue no: **PR 7071**

**I WISH I KNEW (HOW IT WOULD FEEL)**
Tracks: / I wish I knew(how it would feel to be free)(themefromfilm86) / Right here, right now / Freedom* (* Track on 12" version only.).
Note: The Billy Taylor Trio with orchestra conducted by Oliver Nelson.
**7" Single:** Released Sep '86, on Capitol by EMI Records. Deleted Oct '87. Catalogue no: **CL 369**
**12" Single:** Released Sep '86, on Capitol by EMI Records. Deleted Oct '87. Catalogue no: **12CL 369**

**WHERE'VE YOU BEEN (Taylor, Billy Quartet)**
**Album:** Released Aug '81, on Concord Jazz by Concord Jazz Records (USA). Catalogue no: **CJ 145**

**WHITE NIGHTS AND JAZZ IN LENINGRAD (Taylor, Billy Trio)**
Tracks: / Secret love / Pensativa / Child is born, A / C-A-G / I remember you / Your smile / My romance / Jingles / Morning.
**CD:** Released '88, on Taylors by H.R. Taylor Records. Catalogue no: **T 1001 CD**

## Taylor, Cecil

**Biographical details:** Cecil Taylor was born in 1933 in New York City. As a pianist, composer and leader of various groups he is one of the most important musicians to emerge from jazz roots since World War 2, described as a 'Bartok in reverse', taking what he wants from European music without compromising his blues roots. He treats the piano as the percussion instrument it is: 88 tuned drums. He was initially influenced by Fats Waller (the depth of his individual notes) and by Dave Brubeck (his thick chordal clusters); in terms of complete technical mastery of the instrument he is the successor to Art Tatum. He was one of the subjects of A.B. Spellman's classic book Black Music:Four Lives in 1968. His collaborations with bassist Buell Neidlinger from around 1960 are on Candid; his Blue Note albums *Conquistador!* and *Unit Structures* were among the most beautiful and influential small-group albums of that era's avant-garde. He has never stopped innovating, but does not regard his own music as difficult; he loves to play for anyone who will listen, and lots of people are listening: after many years of relative neglect he has become a concert artist in demand all over the world. (Donald Clarke 13.1.88).

**3 PHASIS**
**Album:** Released Sep '86, on New World (USA) by New World Records (USA). Catalogue no: **NW 303**

**AIR ABOVE MOUNTAINS**
**Album:** Released Jan '82, on Enja (Germany) by Enja Records (West Germany). Catalogue no: **ENJA 3005**

**CECIL TAYLOR QUARTET IN EUROPE (Taylor, Cecil Quartet)**
**Album:** Released Apr '79, on Jazz Connoisseur by Spotlite Records. Catalogue no: **JC 111**

**CECIL TAYLOR UNIT**
Tracks: / Idut / Serdab / Holiday en masque.
**Album:** Released Jul '86, on New World (USA) by New World Records (USA). Catalogue no: **NW 201**
**CD:** Released '88, on New World (USA) by New World Records (USA). Catalogue no: **NWCD 201**

**CELL WALK FOR CELESTE**
**CD:** Released May '89, on Candid Catalogue no: **CCD 9034**
**Album:** Released May '89, on Candid Catalogue no: **CS 9034**

**CHINAMPAS**
Note: "Chinampa is an Aztec word meaning 'floating gardens'. It's been a life-long ambition for Cecil Taylor to record an album of his poetry. Make no mistake - he does not play the piano. He accompanies himself on timpani, bells and other small instruments. On some poems the voice is overdubbed. The album is released as a collector's item. Special limited edition of 500 copies never to be pressed again."(Leo Records, March 1988).
**Album:** Released 1 Mar '88, on Leo by Leo Records. Catalogue no: **LR 153**

**CONQUISTADOR**
Tracks: / Conquistador (17.51) / With (exit) (19.17).
**Album:** Released Aug '89, on Blue Note by EMI Records. Catalogue no: **B1 84260**
**CD:** Released May '87, on Blue Note by EMI Records. Deleted '89. Catalogue no: **BNZ 94**
**Album:** Released Jul '82, on Blue Note by EMI Records. Deleted '88. Catalogue no: **BST 84260**
**CD:** Released May '87, on Blue Note by EMI Records. Catalogue no: **CDP 746 535 2**

**DARK TO THEMSELVES (Taylor, Cecil Unit)**
**Album:** Released Jan '82, on Enja (Germany) by Enja Records (West Germany). Catalogue no: **ENJA 2084**

**EMBRACED**
**Cass:** Released May '78, on Pablo Jazz (USA) by Pablo Records (USA). Catalogue no: **K20 108**
**2 LP Set:** Released May '78, on Pablo Jazz (USA) by Pablo Records (USA). Catalogue no: **2620 108**

**INDENT**
Tracks: / Indent: first layer / Indent: second layer (part 1) / Indent: second layer (part 2) / Indent: third layer.
**Album:** Released 7 Nov '87, on Freedom Catalogue no: **FLP 41038**
**CD:** Released Dec '87, on Freedom Catalogue no: **FCD 41038**

**INNOVATIONS**
**Album:** Released Jul '74, on Freedom Catalogue no: **28 422**

**JUMPIN' PUMPKINS**
Note: With Clark Terry/Roswell Rudd/Steve Lacey/Archie Shepp/Charles Shepp/Charles Davis/Buell Neidinger/Billy Higgins/Dennis Charles. (Tracks include: Jumpin' punkins/O.P. I forgot/Things ain't what they used to be. Recorded 1961.)
**Album:** Released Jul '87, on Candid Catalogue no: **CS 9013**
**CD:** Released Nov '87, on Candid Catalogue no: **CCD 9013**

**LIVE IN BOLOGNA (Taylor, Cecil Unit)**
Note: In October-November 1987 Cecil Taylor out together his new unit and toured California and Europe. The unit consisted of Leroy Jenkins, Carlos Ward, William Parker and Thurman Barker. Live recordings of the tour testify that the maestro is back in great shape. (Leo Records March 1988).
**2 LP Set:** Released 1 Mar '88, on Leo by Leo Records. Catalogue no: **LR 404/405**

**LIVE IN THE BLACK FOREST**
**Album:** Released Jun '81, on MPS Jazz Catalogue no: **MPS 68 220**

**LIVE IN VIENNA (Taylor, Cecil Unit)**
**2 LP Set:** Released Oct '88, on Leo by Leo Records. Catalogue no: **LR 408/9**

**LOOKING AHEAD**
Tracks: / Luyah, the glorious step / African violets / Of what / Wallering / Toll / Excursion on a wobbly rail.
**CD:** Released Jan '89, on JVC/Fantasy Catalogue no: **VDJ 1633**
**Album:** Released Sep '86, on Boplicity by Ace Records. Deleted '88. Catalogue no: **COP 030**

**NEFERTITI-BEAUTIFUL ONE**
**2 LP Set:** Released Oct '76, on Freedom Catalogue no: **FLP 41095/2**

**NEW YORK CITY RHYTHM AND BLUES (Taylor, Cecil & Buell Neidlinger)**
Tracks: / OP / Cell walk for Celeste / Cindy's main mood / Things ain't what they used to be.
**CD:** Released May '89, on Candid Catalogue no: **CCD 9017**
**Album:** Released Jun '86, on Candid Catalogue no: **CS 9017**

**PRAXIS**
**2 LP Set:** Released May '84, on Praxis (Greece) Catalogue no: **CM 104/105**

**SILENT TONGUES**
Tracks: / Abyss / Petals & filaments / Jitney / Taylor crossing part one / Crossing part two / After all / Jitney No. 2 / After all No. 2.
**Album:** Released Jun '79, on Freedom Catalogue no: **FLP 41005**
**CD:** Released Sep '87, on Freedom Catalogue no: **FCD 41005**

**STUDENT STUDIES**
Tracks: / Amplitude / Niggle fenigle / Student studies part 1 / Student studies part 2.
**2 LP Set:** Released Mar '83, on Affinity by Charly Records. Deleted May '88. Catalogue no: **AFFD 74**

**TZOTZIL MUMMERS TZOTZIL**
**Album:** Released Feb '89, on Leo by Leo Records. Catalogue no: **LR 162**

**UNIT STRUCTURES**
Tracks: / Steps / Enter, evening (soft line structure) / Enter, evening (alt. take) / Unit structure / As of now / Section / Tales (8 whisps).
**CD:** Released Jul '89, on Blue Note by EMI Records. Catalogue no: **CDP 784 237 2**
**Album:** Released Dec '84, on Blue Note by EMI Records. Catalogue no: **BST 84237**
**Album:** Released '79, on Blue Note by EMI Records. Deleted '84. Catalogue no: **BNS 40023**
**CD:** Released Jul '89, on Blue Note by EMI Records. Catalogue no: **BNZ 218**

**WHAT'S NEW?**
Tracks: / What's new? / Nefertiti, the beautiful one, has come (first variation) / Lena (second variation) / Nefertiti, the beautiful one, has come (second variation).
**Album:** Released Sep '85, on Freedom Catalogue no: **FLP 40124**

**WINGED SERPENT (Taylor,Cecil Segments 11)**
**CD:** Released '86, on Soul Note Catalogue no: **SN 1089**

**WORLD OF CECIL TAYLOR, THE**
Note: Tracks include: Air/This nearly was mine/Port of call/E.B./Lazy afternoon. Recorded 1960.
**CD:** Released Nov '87, on Candid Catalogue no: **CCD 9006**
**Album:** Released Dec '85, on Candid Catalogue no: **CS 9006**

**Cecil Taylor - Tzotzil Mummers Tzotzil (Leo)**

## Taylor, Eddie

**BIG TOWN PLAYBOY**
Tracks: / Bad boy / E.T. blues / Ride em on down / Big town playboy / You'll always have a home / Don't knock at my door / Bongo beat / I'm gonna love you / Lookin' for trouble / Find my baby / Stroll out west / Trainfare / Leave this neighbourhood / I'm sittin' here / Do you want me to cry.
**Album:** Released Mar '81, on Charly R&B by Charly Records. Catalogue no: **CRB 1015**

**I FEEL SO BAD**
**Album:** Released Apr '79, on Advent by Advent Records. Deleted '88. Catalogue no: **ADVENT 2802**

**MY HEART IS BLEEDING (Taylor, Eddie Blues Band)**
**Album:** Released '88, on L&R Catalogue no: **LR 42.009**

**READY FOR EDDIE (Taylor, Eddie Playboy)**
Tracks: / I'm a country boy / Seems like a million years / Gamblin' man / After hours / Sloppy drunk / Ready for Eddie / You don't love me / Too late to cry / You'll always have a home / Playboy boogie / My little machine / Cross-cut saw.
**Album:** Released Oct '86, on Big Bear by Big Bear Records. Deleted '88. Catalogue no: **BRP 2032**
**Album:** Released May '82, on Big Bear by Big Bear Records. Deleted '88. Catalogue no: **BEAR 6**

**STILL NOT READY FOR EDDIE**
**Album:** Released Dec '88, on Antones Catalogue no: **AN 005**

## Taylor, Eva

**EVA TAYLOR 1925-26 (Taylor, Eva & Clarence Williams)**
**Album:** Released '88, on Fountain by Retrieval Records. Catalogue no: **FJ 121**

**LEGENDARY EVA TAYLOR & MAGGIES BLUE 5, THE**
**Album:** Released '88, on Kenneth Catalogue no: **KS 2042**

## Taylor, Hound Dog

**Biographical details:** Was born Theodore Roosevelt Taylor in 1917 in Natchez, Mississippi; he died in Chicago in 1975. As a blues singer, guitarist and pianist, he said of himself, 'When I die, they'll say, "he couldn't play shit, but he sure made it sound good!"' He formed his House Rockers trio with Brewer Phillips' rhythm guitar serving as a bass line and Ted Harvey on drums; Bruce Iglauer managed them and formed his successful Alligator label in Chicago to record them (on Sonet in other countries). Playing slide on a cheap Japanese guitar, using a brass-lined piece of steel chair leg, Hound Dog created some of the most irresistible music of its kind; structurally it is blues, but he called it rock 'n' roll, and who are we to argue? (Donald Clarke 13.1.88).

**BEWARE OF THE DOG (Taylor, Hound Dog And The House Rockers)**
Tracks: / Give me back my wig / Sun is shining, The / Kitchen sink boogie / Dust my broom / Comin' around the mountain / Let's get funky / Rock me / It's alright / Freddie's blues.
Note: Sadly, Hound Dog Taylor never saw the release of this, his first 'live' album. He died in Chicago in December 1975. But this isn't a sombre 'memorial' LP - Hound Dog wouldn't have wanted that. He wanted to be remembered with the same kind of irreverance that he put into his music and his life. As he used to say, 'When I die, don't have a funeral - have a party!' 'Beware of The Dog' successfully captures the inimitable personality of Hound Dog Taylor for posterity. (Alligator catalogue 7/88)
**Album:** Released May '76, on Sonet by Sonet Records. Catalogue no: **SNTF 701**

**GENUINE HOUSEROCKING MUSIC**
Tracks: / Ain't got nobody / Gonna send you back to Georgia / Fender bender / My baby's coming home / Blue guitar / Sun is shining / Phillips goes bananas / What'd I say / Kansas City / Crossroads.
Note: Previously unreleased recordings from Hound Dog Taylor and the House Rockers. 'They made a lot of noise for three men with two guitars and a drum set. Between the incredible distortion from Hound Dog's supercheap Japanese guitar, the sustain from his brass-lined steel slide (made from the leg of a kitchen chair), the sheet metal tone of Brewer Phillips' ancient Fender, their cracked-speaker Sears Silverton amplifiers, and Ted Harvey's simple, kickass drumming, they could indeed rock the house. (Alligator catalogue 7/88)
**Album:** Released Jul '88, on Alligator (Sonet) by Alligator Records (USA). Catalogue no: **SNTF 879**

**HOUND DOG TAYLOR AND THE HOUSE ROCKERS (Taylor, Hound Dog & The House Rockers)**
Note: When Bruce Iglauer launched his Alligator label in 1971, driving across the USA visiting radio stations and store with a car full of Hound Dog Taylor albums, he couldn't have imagined that the label would become America's leading blues record company, featuring the best contemporary artists. But he set a high standard with the first release - featuring the great Chicago bluesman Hound Dog Taylor and Band - and has maintained it ever since. (Alligator catalogue 7/88)
**Album:** Released May '75, on Sonet by Sonet Records. Catalogue no: **SNTF 676**

**HOUSE ROCKIN' BOOGIE**
Tracks: / Ships on the ocean / Rockin' with the dog / Everyday I have the blues / No hair / Walking the ceiling / Mother in law blues / Stinging the blues / Rockin' boogie.
**Album:** Released Dec '82, on JSP by JSP Records. Catalogue no: **JSP 1049**

**KINGS OF THE SLIDE GUITAR (Taylor, Hound Dog/Johnny Littlejohn)**
Tracks: / Watch out, hound dog / Scrappin' / Sittin' here alone / Downhome special / What in the world / Can't be still / Bloody tears / I had a dream / When I think about my baby / Keep on running / She's too much.
**Album:** Released Jun '84, on JSP by JSP Records. Catalogue no: **JSP 1074**

**NATURAL BOOGIE (Taylor, Hound Dog And The House Rockers)**
Note: Hound Dog Taylor and the House Rockers' incredibly raw, no-holds-barred slide guitar boogie made them one of Chicago's most popular bands. Before Hound Dog's death, they toured the world over, inciting crowds everywhere to fits of spontaneous dancing and rampant craziness. 'Natural Boogie', the second studio album by Hound Dog Taylor and the House Rockers, includes Taylor's classic 'Take Five'. (Alligator catalogue 7/88)
**Album:** Released Jul '88, on Alligator (Sonet) by Alligator Records (USA). Catalogue no: **SNTF 678**

## Taylor, Koko

**Biographical details:** Koko was born in Memphis, Tennesee in 1935; she is a blues singer in the great female line of Bessie Smith and Victoria Spivey, but also very much Chicago style, with more than a dash of Muddy Waters. She had a big R&B hit with Willie Dixon's *Wang Dang Doodle* in 1966 and now records for Alligator/Sonet. In 1987 her excellent band the Blues Machine including Michael 'Mr Dynamite' Robinson and Eddie King, guitars; Jerry Murphey, bass; Clyde 'Youngblood' Tyler, drums. (Donald Clarke 13.1.88).

**AUDIENCE WITH THE QUEEN, AN (Live from Chicago)(See panel below)**
Tracks: / Let the good times roll / I'm a woman / Going back to IUKA / Devil's gonna have a field day, The / Come to Mama / I'd rather go blind / Let me love you / Wang dang doodle.
**Album:** Released May '87, on Alligator (Sonet) by Alligator Records (USA). Catalogue no: **SNTF 988**

Koko Taylor - An Audience With The Queen (Sonet)

**BLUES IN HEAVEN**
Tracks: / I got what it takes / What kind of man is this / Wang dang doodle / Separate or integrate / Good advice / Egg or the hen / Just love me / Insane asylum / Tell me the truth / Nitty gritty / Blues heaven / I got all you need.
**Album:** Released 26 Aug '88, on Vogue (France) by Vogue Records. Catalogue no: **515042**
**Cass:** Released 26 Aug '88, on Vogue (France) by Vogue Records. Catalogue no: **715042**

**EARTH SHAKER**
Note: Strong studio set from Chicago's premier blues lady, backed by her impeccably tight and commanding band, featuring a new version of her hit 'Wang Dang Doodle', plus 'Hey Bartender', 'Spoonful' and 'Let The Goodtimes Roll'. The hardest working woman in show business today. (Alligator catalogue 7/88)
**Album:** Released Aug '78, on Sonet by Sonet Records. Catalogue no: **SNTF 775**

**FROM THE HEART OF A WOMAN**
Tracks: / Something strange is going on / I'd rather go blind / Keep your hands off him / Thanks but no thanks / If you got a heartache / Never trust a man / Sure had a wonderful time last night / Blow top blues / If walls could talk / It took a long time.
Note: Strong studio album featuring Koko Taylor and her regular four-piece band with special guests Billy Branch on harmonica and A.C Reed on tenor sax. 'Koko Taylor is simply the premier lady of Chicago blues, with an impeccably tight, commanding band. - Performance Magazine. 'The most impassioned and exciting of women blues singers.' - New York Times. (Alligator catalogue 7/88)
**Album:** Released Sep '81, on Alligator (Sonet) by Alligator Records (USA). Catalogue no: **SNTF 868**

**I GOT WHAT IT TAKES**
Tracks: / Trying to make a living / I got what it takes / Mama / Voodoo woman / Be what you want to be / Honky tonky / Big boss man / Blues never die / Find a fool / Happy home / What's what I'm crying.
**CD:** Released Jun '88, on Vogue by Vogue Records. Catalogue no: **VG 600 179**
**Album:** Released Aug '76, on Sonet by Sonet Records. Catalogue no: **SNTF 687**

**KOKO TAYLOR**
Tracks: / I love you like a woman / i love a lover like you / Don't mess with the messer / I don't care who knows / Wang dang doodle / I'm a little mixed up / Nitty gritty / Fire / Whatever I am,you made me / Twenty-nine ways / Insane asylum / Yes / It's good for you.
**Album:** Released Oct '87, on Chess by Vogue Records. Catalogue no: **GCH 8039**
**CD:** Released Jun '88, on MCA (USA) by MCA Records (USA). Catalogue no: **CHD 31271**
**Cass:** Released Oct '87, on Chess by Vogue Records. Catalogue no: **GCHK 78039**

**LOVE YOU LIKE A WOMAN**
Tracks: / I got what it takes / What kind of man is this / Don't mess with the messer / Whatever I am,you made me / I'm a little mixed up / Wang dang doodle / Blues heaven / All you need (I got) / Tell me the truth / Good advice / Egg or the hen / Just love me / Fire / Insane asylum / Seperate or integrate / I don't care who knows / Love you like a woman / Yes,it's good for you / Twenty nine ways / Nitty gritty / I love a lover like vou.
**CD:** Released '89, on Cness by Vogue Records. Catalogue no: **CD CHESS 1007**

**QUEEN OF THE BLUES**
Note: "Koko Taylor tears through ten killer songs, with a little help from her top-notch band and guests Son Seals, Albert Collins, Lonnie Brooks and James Cotton. Proof beyond doubt that Koko is still the Queen of the Blues can be found on tracks like 'Beer Bottle Boogie', 'Evil', 'Something Inside Me' and 'I cried Like A Baby'". (Alligator catalogue 7/88)
**Album:** Released Aug '85, on Alligator (Sonet) by Alligator Records (USA). Catalogue no: **SNTF 941**

## Taylor, Little Johnny

**AS LONG AS I DON'T SEE YOU**
Tracks: / As long as I don't see you.
**7" Single:** Released Jul '80, on Charly by Charly Records. Deleted '87. Catalogue no: **CTD 118**

**I SHOULDA BEEN A PREACHER**
Tracks: / Somebody's got to pay / Help yourself / Things I used to do, The / Driving wheel / True love / I smell trouble / Double or nothing / Sometimey woman / All I want is you / You'll need another favour / First class love / If you love me / My heart is filled with pain / Since I found a new love / Please come home for Christmas.
**Album:** Released Sep '82, on Red Lightnin' by Red Lightning Records. Catalogue no: **RL 030**

**PART-TIME LOVE**
Tracks: / You're the one / As quick as I can / What you need is a ball / You gotta go on / She tried to understand / Since I found a new love / Darling, believe me / She's yours, she's... / Stay sweet / Somewhere down the line / Part time love.
**Album:** Released Nov '87, on Ace by Ace Records. Catalogue no: **CH 229**
**CD:** Released Dec '87, on Chris Wellard by Chris Wellard Distribution. Catalogue no: **CD 229**
**Album:** Released Mar '81, on Charly R&B by Charly Records. Catalogue no: **CRB 1012**

**STUCK IN THE MUD**
Tracks: / Stuck in the mud / Full Time Love / I will give it all / Back To You / First Class Love / There Is Something On Your Mind / Everybody Knows About My Good Thing / You can help yourself / Your fade is further on down the road.
**Cass:** Released Apr '88, on Ichiban by Ichiban Records (UK). Catalogue no: **ZCICH 1022**
**Album:** Released Apr '88, on Ichiban by Ichiban Records (UK). Catalogue no: **ICH 1022**

**UGLY MAN**
Tracks: / Have you ever been to Kansas City / Never be lonely and blue / LJT / Ugly man / It's my fault, darlin' / I enjoy you / How can a broke man survive / King-size souvenir / Have you ever been to Kansas City (Reprise).
**Album:** Released Sep '89, on Ichiban by Ichiban Records (UK). Catalogue no: **ICH 1042**
**Cass:** Released Sep '89, on Ichiban by Ichiban Records (UK). Catalogue no: **ZCICH 1042**
**CD:** Released Sep '89, on Ichiban by Ichiban Records (UK). Catalogue no: **CDICH 1042**

## Taylor, Martin

**SARABANDA**
Note: Martin Taylor has garnered numerous honours, including the Down Beat critic's jazz poll 'Artist Deserving Wider Recognition' and 'Jazz Guitarist of the Year' for both 1987 and 1988 in the British Jazz Awards. Sarabanda is Martin's debut album for Gaia and is currently on the of the biggest selling jazz albums in the US. The featured personnel includes such stars as John Patitucci on bass, Paulinho da Costa on percussion and special guest Stephane Grappelli performing on one track.
**Album:** Released Feb '89, on Gaia (USA) by Gaia Records (USA). Catalogue no: **139018 1**
**CD:** Released Feb '89, on Gaia (USA) by Gaia Records (USA). Catalogue no: **139018 2**
**Cass:** Released Feb '89, on Gaia (USA) by Gaia Records (USA). Catalogue no: **139018 4**

**SKYE BOAT**
Tracks: / Mouse's spinney / Check it out / St. Thomas / Falling in love with love / Body and soul / Billie's bounce / Stompin' at the Savoy.
Note: Guitarist Taylor, who has toured extensively with Stephane Grappelli, is joined here by Peter Ind and Jimmy Smith.
**Album:** Released Jun '82, on Concord by Concord Jazz Records (USA). Catalogue no: **CJ 184**

**TAYLOR MADE (Martin Taylor, John Richardson, Peter Ind)**
**Album:** Released '88, on Wave by Wave Records. Catalogue no: **WAVE 17**

**TRIBUTE TO ART TATUM**
**Album:** Released Nov '86, on Hep Jazz by Hep Records. Catalogue no: **HEP 2032**

**TRIPLE LIBRA (Taylor, Martin & Peter Ind)**
**Album:** Released '88, on Wave by Wave Records. Catalogue no: **WAVE 24**

## Taylor, Montana

**MONTANA'S BLUES**
**Album:** Released '88, on Oldie Blues Catalogue no: **OL 2815**

**Taylor, RustyGIVE ME A CALL (Taylor, Rusty & Jazz Makers)**
**Album:** Released '88, on Stomp Off (USA) Catalogue no: **SOS 1082**

**GOOD OLD BAD OLD DAYS**
**Album:** Released Dec '82, on Stomp Off (USA) Catalogue no: **SOS 1028**

**RUSTY TAYLOR'S JAZZ REVIEW**
**Album:** Released '89, on Stomp Off (USA) Catalogue no: **SOS 1186**

## Teagarden, Jack

**Biographical details:** Teagarden was born in Vernon, Texas in 1905; he died in New Orleans in 1964. His sister Norma played piano; brother Charlie was a well-known trumpet player. Jack was one of the greatest and best-loved trombone players and vocalists in the history of jazz; he invented jazz trombone playing in the Southwest while Jimmy Harrison and Miff Mole were doing it in the North, and caused a sensation when he reached New York, his style described as doing it the hard way and making it sound easy: both his playing and blues and ballad singing had a laid-back Southern quality. He played with Paul Whiteman for many years, also recording with Benny Goodman and Fats Waller in the early 1930s; he was persuaded to form a big band around 1940: it was not a big commercial success but made fine music, Kitty Kallen and the teenage jazz singer David Allyn among the bands singers (The Varsity Sides). He was honoured guest at Louis Armstrong's legendary Town Hall concert of 1947 (they sang a classic duet on *Old Rockin' Chair's Got Me*) and toured with Armstrong's combo; he recorded on Capitol in the 1950s including albums with Bobby Hackett. Songs associated with Teagarden include *I Ain't Lazy, I'm Just Dreaming, I Gotta Right To Sing The Blues, Meet Me Where They Play The Blues, A Hundred Years From Today, Basin Street Blues*, and many others. (Donald Clarke 13.1.88).

**1939: JACK TEAGARDEN (Teagarden, Jack & His Orchestra)**
**Album:** Released Aug '87, on Tax Catalogue no: **M 8024**

**1943**
Tracks: / Wolverine blues / Clarinet marmalade / All or nothing at all / Chinatown, my Chinatown / Somewhere a voice is calling / Night and day / Aunt Hagar's blues / Dark eyes / Octoroon / Swinging on a garden gate / Nobody knows the trouble I've seen / Rhythm hymn / Baby won't you please come home / Fort Knox jump / Ah sweet mystery of life.
**Album:** Released Apr '81, on Queendisc (Italy) Catalogue no: **QU 040**

**BIG BAND GEMS**
**Album:** Released '88, on Blu-Disc (USA) Catalogue no: **T 5003**

**BIG T AND MIGHTY MAX (Teagarden, Jack & Max Kaminsky)**
**Album:** Released May '87, on Commodore Class Catalogue no: **6.24060**

**BIRTH OF A BAND**
**Cass:** Released May '86, on Giants of Jazz by Hasmick Promotions. Catalogue no: **GOJC 1038**
**Album:** Released May '86, on Giants of Jazz by Hasmick Promotions. Catalogue no: **GOJ 1038**

**BIG T & THE CONDON GANG**
**Album:** Released '88, on Pumpkin Catalogue no: **PUMPKIN 106**

**CLASSIC SMALL GROUPS Vol. 1 (Various artists)**
**Album:** Released '88, on Meritt (USA) Catalogue no: **MERITT 6**

**DIXIELAND BIG BAND ALL STARS**
Tracks: / Introduction / South Rampart Street parade / My inspiration / Basin street blues / That naughty waltz / Milenberg Joys / Barcarolle / High society / Pagan love song / Paducah parade / South Rampart Street parade No 2 / Dixieland, The / Riverboat shuffle / Honeysuckle rose.
**Album:** Released Jan '88, on Jasmine by Hasmick Promotions. Catalogue no: **JASM 2510**
**Cass:** Released 12 Feb '88, on Jasmine by Hasmick Promotions. Catalogue no: **JASMC 2510**

**HOLLYWOOD BOWL CONCERT, 1963 (Teagarden, Jack & Bobby Hackett)**
Tracks: / Sweet Georgia Brown / St. James' Infirmary / Fidgety feet / My funny valentine / Struttin' with some barbecue / When it's sleepy time down South / Muskrat ramble.
**Album:** Released Apr '81, on Shoestring (1) Catalogue no: **SS 102**

**HUNDRED YEARS FROM TODAY, A**
Tracks: / You rascal you / That's what I like about you / Chances are / I got the ritz from the one I love / I've got it / Plantation moods / Shake your hips / Somebody stole Gabriel's horn / Love me / Blue river / Hundred years from today, A / I just couldn't take it baby / Fare-thee-well / Ol pappy / Junk man / Stars fell on Alabama / Your guess is just as good as mine.
**Album:** Released Oct '89, on Conifer Happy Days by Conifer Records. Catalogue no: **CHD 153**
**Cass:** Released Oct '89, on Conifer Happy Days by Conifer Records. Catalogue no: **MCHD 153**

**I GOTTA RIGHT TO SING THE BLUES**
Tracks: / That's a serious thing / I'm gonna stomp Mr. Henry Lee / Dinah / Never had a reason to believe in you / Tailspin blues / Dancing with tears in my eyes / Sheik of Araby, The / Basin Street blues / You rascal you / Two tickets to Georgia / I gotta right to sing the blues / Ain't cha glad? / Texas tea party / Hundred years from today / Fare thee well to Harlem / Christmas night in Harlem / Davenport blues.
Note: 'Mr. T' plays and sings with Benny Goodman, Red Nichols, Glenn Miller, Paul Whiteman, Eddie Condon, Mezz

**Jack Teagarden - I Gotta Right To Sing The Blues (ASV)**

Mezzrow - Joe Sullivan - Gene Krupa - Jimmy Dorsey - Pee Wee Russell - Adrian Rollini - Johnny Mercer - Joe Venuti - Fats Waller.
**Cass:** Released 1 Feb '89, on Living Era by Academy Sound & Vision Records. Catalogue no: **ZC AJA 5059**
**Album:** Released 1 Feb '89, on Living Era by Academy Sound & Vision Records. Catalogue no: **AJA 5059**
**CD:** Released 1 Feb '89, on Living Era by Academy Sound & Vision Records. Catalogue no: **CD AJA 5059**

**JACK TEAGARDEN 1943**
**Album:** Released '88, on Queen Catalogue no: **QUEEN 040**
**Album:** Released Apr '81, on Queendisc (Italy) Catalogue no: **QU 012**
**Album:** Released Jul '82, on Commodore Class Catalogue no: **AG6 24060**
**Album:** Released Apr '81, on Queendisc (Italy) Catalogue no: **QU 027**
**Album:** Released Apr '81, on Rarities Catalogue no: **RARITIES 39**

**JACK TEAGARDEN ALLSTARS (Hangover Club, San Francisco, 1954) (Teagarden, Jack Allstars)**
**Album:** Released Jul '88, on FDC Catalogue no: **FDC 1026**

**JACK TEAGARDEN AND EARL HINES (Teagarden, Jack & Earl Hines)**
**Album:** Released Jun '86, on Magic (1) by Submarine Records. Catalogue no: **AWE 20**

**JACK TEAGARDEN, EDDI CONDON ALL STARS (Various artists)**
**Album:** Released '88, on Pumpkin Catalogue no: **PUMPKIN 115**

**JACK TEAGARDEN IN CONCERT**
**Album:** Released Jul '88, on Sounds Catalogue no: **SOUNDS 1203**

**JACK TEAGARDEN AND RED NICHOLS 1929-31 (Teagarden, Jack & Red Nichols)**
**Album:** Released Jan '88, on Gaps Catalogue no: **GAPS 180**

**JACK TEAGARDEN AND THE CONDON GANG (Teagarden, Jack & Condon Gang)**
**Album:** Released '79, on Pumpkin Catalogue no: **PUMPKIN 104**

**JAZZ ORIGINAL**
Tracks: / King Porter stomp / Eccentric / Davenport blues / Original dixieland one-step / Bad actin' woman / Mis'ry and the blues / High society / Music to love by / Meet me where they play the blues / Riverboat shuffle / Milenberg joys / Blue funk.
Note: An original Bethlehem recording.
**CD:** Released '87, on Charly by Charly Records. Catalogue no: **CDCHARLY 80**
**Album:** Released Jun '85, on Affinity by Charly Records. Catalogue no: **AFF 141**

**LIVE: MODERN JAZZ ROOM, OHIO 1958 (Teagarden, Jack Sextet & Don Ewell)**
**Album:** Released Nov '88, on Pumpkin Catalogue no: **P 121**

**MASTERS OF JAZZ VOL.10**
**CD:** Released Feb '89, on Storyville by Storyville Records AB. Catalogue no: **STCD 4110**
**Album:** Released May '86, on Storyville by Storyville Records AB. Catalogue no: **SLP 4110**

**MEMORIAL**
**Album:** Released '74, on Musidisc by Musidisc Records (France). Catalogue no: **CV 1073**

**ON OKINAWA (Teagarden, Jack Allstars)**
**Album:** Released May '88, on I.A.J.R.C (USA) by Vintage Jazz Music Society(VJM). Catalogue no: **IAJRC 33**

**ON THE AIR 1936-1938**
Tracks: / Music goes round and around, The / Announcer's blues / Got a 'bran new suit / St Louis blues / I hope Gabriel likes my music / Alexander's ragtime band / I'm comin', Virginia / Flat foot floogie / Small fry / Aunt Hagar's blues / FDR Jones / Mutiny in the nursery / Jeepers creepers / Christmas night in Harlem / John Peel.
**Album:** Released May '79, on Aircheck (USA) by Kiner Ents.(USA). Catalogue no: **AIRCHECK 24**

**SHINE (Teagarden, Jack & Pee Wee Russell)**
Tracks: / Shine / St. James' Infirmary / World is waiting for the sunrise, The / Big eight blues / Baby won't you please come home? / Dinah / Zutty's hootie blues / There'll be some changes made / I've found a new baby / Everybody loves my baby.
**Album:** Released Apr '81, on Joker (USA) by Lifetime Records (USA). Catalogue no: **SM 3096**

**STANDARD LIBRARY OF JAZZ VOL 2**
**Album:** Released Jul '81, on Storyville by Storyville Records AB. Catalogue no: **SLP 704**

**STARS FELL ON ALABAMA**
**Album:** Released Feb '89, on Giants of Jazz by Hasmick Promotions. Catalogue no: **LPJT 77**
**Cass:** Released Feb '89, on Giants of Jazz by Hasmick Promotions. Catalogue no: **MCJT 77**

**SWINGING GATE,THE**
**Album:** Released Oct '84, on Giants of Jazz by Hasmick Promotions. Catalogue no: **GOJ 1026**

**TEXAS TROMBONE LIVE**
**CD:** Released Aug '89, on Starline (Jazz) Catalogue no: **CDSG 403**

**THAT'S A SERIOUS THING**
Tracks: / I'm gonna stomp Mr. Henry Lee / That's a serious thing / She's a great great girl / My kinda love / Tailspin blues / Never had a reason to believe in you / Ridin' but walkin' / Fare theee well to Harlem / Nobody's sweetheart / Blue Lou / Blues, The (take 1) / St. Louis blues / St. James infirmary / Jack Armstrong blues / I cover the waterfront / There'll be some changes made.
**CD:** Released Apr '90, on RCA by BMG Records (UK). Catalogue no: **ND 90440**
**Album:** Released Apr '90, on RCA by BMG Records (UK). Catalogue no: **NL 90440**
**Cass:** Released Apr '90, on RCA by BMG Records (UK). Catalogue no: **NK 90440**

**TROMBONE T FROM TEXAS**
Tracks: / I gotta right to sing the blues / Love me or leave me / Jeepers creepers / Basin street blues / Blues to the lonely / Beale street blues / Someday, sweetheart / After you've gone / Nobody knows the trouble I've seen / Body and soul / Riverboat shuffle / Love me / Prelude to the blues / Farewell blues / Aunt Hagar's blues / Somebody loves me.
**Cass:** Released Jan '86, on Affinity by Charly Records. Catalogue no: **TCAFS 1015**
**Album:** Released Jan '86, on Affinity by Charly Records. Catalogue no: **AFS 1015**

**UNFORGETTABLE JACK TEAGARDEN,**
**Album:** Released Jul '86, on Halcyon (USA) by Submarine Records. Catalogue no: **HDL 104**

**VARSITY SIDES**
Tracks: / If I could be with you one hour tonight / My melancholy baby / Can't we talk it over / Blues, The / Love for sale / Moon and the willow tree, The / Wham / Devil may care / Night on the Shalimar / I hear bluebirds / Fatima's drummer boy / Now I lay me down(to dream of you) / Wait till I catch you in my dreams / And so do I / River home.
**Cass:** Released Jan '87, on RCA by BMG Records (UK). Deleted May '89. Catalogue no: **WK 70827**
**Album:** Released Jan '87, on RCA by BMG Records (UK). Deleted Nov '89. Catalogue no: **WL 70827**

## Temperance Seven

**Biographical details:** The 'Seven' were formed at the Royal College of Art in the mid-'50s, playing semi-hot dance music in late-'20s style, members (usually nine) dressed accordingly. Among the original members was jazz buff/recording engineer (now famous for high-quality transfers of old 78s) John R.T. Davies on trombone, using pseudonym Sheik Wadi El Yadounir and wearing a fez. They kept going well into the '60s; there were subsequent editions of the group and they still gig occasionally, original members sometimes sitting in. (Donald Clarke 13.1.88).

**CHARLESTON**
Tracks: / Charleston.
**7" Single:** Released Dec '61, on Parlophone by EMI Records. Deleted '64. Catalogue no: **R 4851**

**HARD HEARTED HANNAH**
Tracks: / Hard hearted Hannah / Chili bom bom.
**7" Single:** Released Sep '61, on Parlophone by EMI Records. Deleted '64. Catalogue no: **R 4823**

**HOT TEMPERANCE SEVEN**
**Album:** Released May '87, on Wam Catalogue no: **WAM/O No.5**

**PASADENA**
Tracks: / Pasadena.
**7" Single:** Released Jun '61, on Parlophone by EMI Records. Deleted '64. Catalogue no: **R 4781**

**TEA FOR EIGHT**
**Album:** Released Mar '90, on Upbeat Catalogue no: **URR 101**
**CD:** Released Mar '90, on Upbeat Catalogue no: **URCD 101**

**TEMPERANCE SEVEN 1961**
**Album:** Released Nov '61, on Parlophone by EMI Records. Deleted '64. Catalogue no: **PMC 1152**

**TEMPERANCE SEVEN PLUS ONE**
**Album:** Released May '61, on Argo (USA) by PolyGram Classics (USA). Deleted '64. Catalogue no: **RG 11**

**YOU'RE DRIVING ME CRAZY**
Tracks: / You're driving me crazy / Pasadena.
**7" Single:** Released Jun '80, on H.M.V. by EMI Records. Deleted '83. Catalogue no: **POP 2007**
**7" Single:** Released Mar '61, on Parlophone by EMI Records. Deleted '64. Catalogue no: **R 4757**
**7" Single:** Released Oct '83, on Old Gold by Old Gold Records. Deleted Jul '88. Catalogue no: **OG 9385**

## Tennessee Legends

**TENNESSEE LEGENDS (Various artists)**
Note: Artists include: Sleepy John Estes/Furry Lewis/Gus Cannon etc.
**Album:** Released Jun '86, on Southland by Delta Records. Catalogue no: **SLP 14**

## Tennessee Tooters

**1924-1926 (Tennessee Tooters & The Hottentots)**
**2 LP Set:** Released Dec '82, on Fountain by Retrieval Records. Catalogue no: **DFJ 117**

**TENNESSEE TOOTERS & THE HOTTENTOTS (Tennessee Tooters & The Hottentots)**
**Album:** Released '88, on Fountain by Retrieval Records. Catalogue no: **FJ 117**

## Tenor Sax Album

**TENOR SAX ALBUM (Various artists)**
Tracks: / Girl of my dreams: *Quebec, Ike Quintet* / I.Q. blues: *Quebec, Ike Quintet* / Scuffin': *Quebec, Ike Quintet* / Jim dawg: *Quebec, Ike Quintet* / Honeysuckle rose: *Webster, Ben Quartet* / I surrender, dear: *Webster, Ben Quartet* / Blue skies: *Webster, Ben Quartet* / Kat's fur: *Webster, Ben Quartet* / Body and soul: *Webster, Ben Quartet* / Lunatic: *Hardee, John Quintet* / Can't help lovin' dat man: *Hardee, John Quintet* / Bad man's bounce: *Hardee, John Quintet* / Baby watch that stuff: *Hardee, John Quintet* / Misty morning blues: *Taylor, Billy Quintet* / Take the 'A' train: *Taylor, Billy Quintet* / Don't blame me: *Jacquet, Illinois Sextet* / Savoy blip: *Berry, Emmett Sextet* / Jacquet in the box: *Jacquet, Illinois Sextet* / Doggin' with doggett: *Berry, Emmett Sextet* / Minor romp: *Berry, Emmett Sextet* / Berry's blues: *Berry, Emmett Sextet* / Last stop: *Hawkins, Coleman Combo* / Should I: *Hawkins, Coleman Combo* / Flight eleven: *Hawkins, Coleman Combo* / Modern fantasy: *Hawkins, Coleman Combo* / Confessin': *Hawkins, Coleman Combo* / September song: *Hawkins, Coleman Combo* / They can't take that away from me: *Hawkins, Coleman Combo.*
**Cass:** Released Mar '86, on RCA by BMG Records (UK). Catalogue no: **WK 70812**
**Album:** Released Mar '86, on RCA by BMG Records (UK). Catalogue no: **WL 70812**
**2 LP Set:** Released Mar '85, on Savoy Jazz (USA) by Malaco Records (USA). Catalogue no: **SJL 2220**

## Tenth Anniversary...

**TENTH ANNIVERSARY ANTHOLOGY (Various artists)**
Note: Featuring Otis Rush, Eddie Taylor, Buddie Guy, Sunnyland Slim, Albert Collins, Snooky Prior. (Live)
**Album:** Released Jun '88, on Bedrock by Bedrock Records. Catalogue no: **BEDLP 8**
**Album:** Released Dec '88, on Antones Catalogue no: **AN 004**

## Territory Bands

**TERRITORY BANDS,THE (Various artists)**
Note: Artists include: Don Albert and his Orchestra/Ernie Fields and his Orchestra/Carolina Cotton Pickers Orchestra/Boots and his Buddies.
**Album:** Released Oct '86, on Jazz Information (Sweden) Catalogue no: **CAH 3005**
**Album:** Released Aug '87, on Tax Catalogue no: **M 8009**
**Album:** Released Aug '87, on Classic Jazz Masters Catalogue no: **CJM 10**

## Terry, Clark

**Biographical details:** Was born in 1920 in St Louis. He is a very popular trumpet player, his mainstream style out of Charlie Shavers and Rex Stewart but influenced by boppers. He was one of the first to adopt the mellower flugelhorn as a second instrument and also has an amusing mumbling vocal style. He played with Lionel Hampton, Charlie Barnet, Count Basie after World War 2, then Duke Ellington through the 1950s. He worked with Quincy Jones, then joined the band on Johnny Carson's Tonight show on TV (1960-72) led by Doc Severinson, which brought wider public popularity. (Donald Clarke 13.1.88).

**AIN'T MISBEHAVIN'**
Tracks: / Jitterbug waltz / Your feets too big / Honeysuckle rose / Mean to me / It's a sin to tell a lie / Ain't misbehavin' / Squeeze me / Handful of keys / Black and blue / I can't give you anything but love / Joint is jumpin', The.
**Cass:** Released Sep '79, on Pablo Jazz (USA) by Pablo Records (USA). Catalogue no: **K 12 105**
**Album:** Released Sep '79, on Pablo Jazz (USA) by Pablo Records (USA). Catalogue no: **2312 105**

**Clark, Terry**

**ALTERNATE BLUES**
Tracks: / Alternate one / Alternate two / Alternate three / Alternate four / Wrap your troubles in dreams / Here's that rainy day / Gypsy / If I should lose you.
**Cass:** Released Sep '82, on Pablo Jazz (USA) by Pablo Records (USA). Catalogue no: **K 12 136**
**Album:** Released Sep '82, on Pablo Jazz (USA) by Pablo Records (USA). Catalogue no: **2312 136**

**BIG B-A-D BAND LIVE AT BUDDY'S**
Tracks: / Modus operandi / Come Sunday / Gap sealer / Jeep's blues / Swiss Air / Big bad blues / Sugar cubes.
**Album:** Released Jan '77, on Vanguard by Start Records Ltd.. Catalogue no: **VSD 79373**

**CLARK TERRY AND HIS JOLLY GIANTS (Terry, Clark & His Jolly Giants)**
**Album:** Released Nov '77, on Vanguard by Start Records Ltd.. Catalogue no: **VHD 79365**

**COLOUR CHANGES**
Note: Features Yusef Lateef. Tracks include: Blue Waltz/Brother Terry/Fluttin' and fluglin'/No problem/La rive gauche/Nahstye blues/Chat Qui peche.
**Album:** Released Oct '87, on Candid Catalogue no: **CS 9009**
**CD:** Released Jul '87, on Candid Catalogue no: **CCD 9009**

**DUKE WITH A DIFFERENCE**
**Album:** Released Apr '86, on Original Jazz Classics (USA) by Fantasy Inc (USA). Catalogue no: **OJC 229**

**EFFERVESCENT**
Tracks: / Perdido / On the trail / Jazzhouse blues / In der Heimat gibt's ein Widerseh'n / Straight no chaser / Wham / Take the 'A' train.
**Album:** Released '79, on MPS Jazz Deleted '84. Catalogue no: **5C 064 61175**

**FUNK DUMPLIN'S (Terry, Clark Quintet)**
**Album:** Released Apr '81, on Matrix (Denmark) Catalogue no: **MTX 1002**

**HAPPY HORNS OF CLARK TERRY**
Tracks: / Rockin' in rhythm / In a mist / Return to Swahili / Ellington rides again / Impulsive / Do nothing till you hear from me / Jazz conversations / High towers.
**Cass:** Released Jun '82, on Jasmine by Hasmick Promotions. Catalogue no: **JAS C28**
**Album:** Released Jun '82, on Jasmine by Hasmick Promotions. Deleted Feb '88. Catalogue no: **JAS 28**

**IN PARIS 1960**
**Album:** Released '88, on DRG (USA) by DRG Records (USA). Catalogue no: **SW 8406**

**IT'S WHAT'S HAPPENIN'**
Tracks: / Electric mumbles / Secret love / Take me back to Elkhart / Take the 'A' train / Tee pee time / On the trail.
**Album:** Released Aug '82, on Jasmine by Hasmick Promotions. Deleted Feb '88. Catalogue no: **JAS 43**
**Cass:** Released Aug '82, on Jasmine by Hasmick Promotions. Catalogue no: **JAS C43**

**LIVE ON 57TH STREET (Terry, Clark Big Bad Band)**
Tracks: / Dirty old man / On the trail / Fading fleur / Hymn for Kim / Take the 'A' train / Shell game / Here's that rainy day / Rock skipping at the Blue Note.
**Album:** Released Jul '78, on Big Bear by Big Bear Records. Deleted '88. Catalogue no: **BEAR 13**

**MEMORIES OF DUKE**
Tracks: / Passion flower / Happy-go-lucky local / Echoes of Harlem / Sophisticated lady / Things ain't what they used to be / I let a song go out of my heart / Cottontail / Everything but you / Come Sunday.
**Album:** Released '78, on Pablo Jazz (USA) by Pablo Records (USA). Catalogue no: **2312 118**
**Cass:** Released '78, on Pablo Jazz (USA) by Pablo Records (USA). Catalogue no: **K 12 118**

**MOTHER - MOTHER (Terry, Clark & Zoot Sims)**
Tracks: / First movement / Jubilation (second movement) / Exultation (third movement) / Revelation (fourth movement).
**Album:** Released Aug '80, on Pablo Jazz (USA) by Pablo Records (USA). Catalogue no: **2312 115**
**Cass:** Released Aug '80, on Pablo Jazz (USA) by Pablo Records (USA). Catalogue no: **K 12 115**

**SERENADE TO A BUS SEAT (Terry, Clark Quintet)**
**Album:** Released Jun '86, on Original Jazz Classics (USA) by Fantasy Inc (USA). Catalogue no: **OJC 066**

**TAKE DOUBLE (Terry, Clark & Jon Faddis)**
Tracks: / Straight up / Take double / Traffic jam / Blues for K.K. / Miami stretch / It don't mean a thing / Climbing old Fuji.
**CD:** Released Mar '88, on ECM Catalogue no: **830 242 2**

**TOP AND BOTTOM BRASS**
**Album:** Released Sep '88, on Riverside (USA) by Fantasy Inc (USA). Catalogue no: **RSLP 295**

**YES, THE BLUES**
Tracks: / Diddlin' / Railroad porter blues / Swingin' the blues / Marina Bay rednecks / Quicksand / Snapper / Kidney stew.
**CD:** Released '88, on Pablo Jazz (USA) by Pablo Records (USA). Catalogue no: **103 112 2**
**Album:** Released Jul '81, on Pablo Jazz (USA) by Pablo Records (USA). Catalogue no: **D 2312 127**
**Cass:** Released Jul '81, on Pablo Jazz (USA) by Pablo Records (USA). Catalogue no: **K 12 127**

## Terry, Pat

**ALL JAZZED UP**
**Album:** Released Aug '88, on Circle (USA) by Jazzology Records (USA). Catalogue no: **CLP 54**

## Terry, Sonny

**BROWNIE & SONNY'S BLUES (Terry, Sonny & Brownie McGee with Earl Hooker)**
**Album:** Released Oct '88, on Vogue (France) by Vogue Records. Catalogue no: **512505**

**HARMONICA BLUES**
**Album:** Released Sep '86, on Storyville by Storyville Records AB. Catalogue no: **SLP 4008**

**SONNY AND BROWNIE (Terry, Sonny & Brownie McGhee)**
**CD:** Released Jun '89, on A&M by A&M Records. Catalogue no: **CDA 0829**

**SONNY IS KING**
**Album:** Released Jan '88, on OBC Catalogue no: **OBC 521**

**SONNY TERRY 1938-55 (Terry, Sonny & Brownie McGhee)**
**Album:** Released Dec '88, on Document Catalogue no: **DLP 536**

**SONNY TERRY 1952**
Tracks: / Wine head woman / Four o'clock blues / Baby let's have some fun / Bad luck blues / Lonesome room / News for you baby / No love blues.
**Album:** Released Jan '87, on Krazy Kat by Interstate Music. Catalogue no: **KK 807**

**SONNY TERRY AND BROWNIE MCGHEE (Terry, Sonny & Brownie McGhee)**
**Album:** Released '89, on Beat Goes On by Andy's Records. Catalogue no: **BGOLP 75**
**CD:** Released '89, on Beat Goes On by Andy's Records. Catalogue no: **BGOCD 75**

**SONNY'S STORY**
Tracks: / I ain't gonna be your dog no more / My baby done gone / Worried blues / High powered woman / Pepper-headed woman / Sonny's story / I'm gonna get on my feet after a while / Four o'clock blues / Telephone blues / Great tall engine.
**Album:** Released Jun '84, on Prestige Catalogue no: **OBC 503**

**SPORTING LIFE BLUES (Terry, Sonny & Brownie McGhee)**
Note: Previously unissued 50's recordings.
**Cass:** Released Apr '88, on JSP by JSP Records. Catalogue no: **JSP CC 1110**
**Album:** Released Sep '87, on JSP by JSP Records. Catalogue no: **JSP 1110**

**TOUGHEST TERRY & BADDEST BROWN (Terry, Sonny & Buster Brown)**
**Album:** Released Nov '87, on Sundown by Magnum Music Group. Catalogue no: **CG 709-11**

**WALK ON (Terry, Sonny & Brownie McGhee)**
Tracks: / Gonna lay my body down / Drinking in the blues / Po' boy / Just rode in your town / Sun's gonna shine / Everybody's blues / Trouble in mind / I'm a stranger here myself / Down by the riverside / Walk on / Blues for the lowlands / Right on that shore / Blowin' the fuses.
**Album:** Released '86, on Bulldog Records by President Records. Catalogue no: **BDL 1018**
**Cass:** Released Nov '84, on Astan (USA) Catalogue no: **40051**
**Album:** Released Nov '84, on Astan (USA) Catalogue no: **20051**
**Cass:** Released '86, on Bulldog Records by President Records. Catalogue no: **BDC 1018**

**WHOOPIN'**
Note: "The master of country blues harmonica meets the super-hot guitarist and the great blues bassist in a terrific supersession. 'Could be the single most interesting thing Sonny has done for years 'Blues & Rhythm. 'With this extraordinary sethe jumps back to his place of honour in the annals of the blues' Jazz Express 'Sonny Terry blows a mean harp'Kerrang!" (Alligator catalogue 7/88) Personnel: Sonny Terry, Johnny Winter and Willie Dixon.
**Album:** Released Mar '87, on Alligator (Sonet) by Alligator Records (USA). Catalogue no: **SNTF 915**

**WHOOPIN' THE BLUES**
Tracks: / Whoopin' the blues / All alone blues / Worried man blues / Leaving' blues / Scream' and cryin' blues / Riff and harmonica jump / Crow Jane blues / Beer garden blues / Hot headed woman / Custard pie blues / Early morning blues / Harmonica rag / Dirty mistreater don't you know / Telephone blues.
**Album:** Released May '86, on Charly R&B by Charly Records. Catalogue no: **CRB 1120**

**WIZARD OF THE HARMONICA**
**Album:** Released Jul '81, on Storyville by Storyville Records AB. Catalogue no: **SLP 218**

**YOU HEAR ME TALKIN' (Terry, Sonny & Brownie McGhee)**
Tracks: / You hear me talkin' / Going down slow / Raise a ruckus tonight / C.C. rider / Cindy Cindy / Right now / Worried life blues / John Henry / Crawdad hole / Ain't gonna study war no more / Take this hammer / That good old jelly roll.
Note: Recorded between 1959 and 1961.
**Album:** Released Aug '83, on Happy Bird (Germany) Catalogue no: **B 90081**

## Texas...

**TEXAS COUNTRY BLUES 1948-1952 (Various artists)**
**Album:** Released Dec '86, on Krazy Kat by Interstate Music. Catalogue no: **KK 7434**

**TEXAS RHYTHM AND BLUES (Various artists)**
Tracks: / Love me, pretty baby: *Booker, Connie Mack* / All alone: *Booker, Connie Mack* / Whoopin' and hollerin': *Stevens, Preacher* / Blue memories: *Kimble, Quinn* / Feel my broom: *Kimble, Quinn* / I'll be there: *Daniels, Melvin & The King Curtis Orchestra* / If you don't want my lovin': *Daniels, Melvin & The King Curtis Orchestra* / Boogie in the moonlight: *Daniels, Melvin & The King Curtis Orchestra* / Hey hey little girl: *Daniels, Melvin & The King Curtis Orchestra* / Craw fishin': *Garlow, Clarence Bonton* / Route 90: *Garlow, Clarence Bonton.*
**Album:** Released Dec '88, on Ace by Ace Records. Catalogue no: **CH 29**

## Texas Blues

**TEXAS BLUES (Various artists)**
**Album:** Released May '81, on Arhoolie (USA) by Arhoolie Records (USA). Catalogue no: **ARHOOLIE 2006**
**Album:** Released Jul '87, on Fountain by Retrieval Records. Catalogue no: **FB 305**

**TEXAS BLUES, (1950S)**
**Album:** Released '88, on Blues Classics(USA) by Arhoolie Records (USA). Catalogue no: **BC 16**

**TEXAS BLUES, (1927-35) (Various artists)**
**Album:** Released '89, on Document Catalogue no: **DLP 558**

**TEXAS BLUES (1927-52) (Various artists)**
**Album:** Released '88, on Paltram Catalogue no: **PL 102**

**TEXAS BLUES (1928-29) (Various artists)**
**Album:** Released Sep '87, on HK Catalogue no: **HK 4003**

**TEXAS BLUES VOL.2 (Various artists)**
**Album:** Released '88, on Arhoolie (USA) by Arhoolie Records (USA). Catalogue no: **ARHOOLIE 1017**

## Texas Guitar Greats

**TEXAS GUITAR GREATS (Various artists)**
**Album:** Released '88, on Home Cooking (USA) by Flat Town Music Co.(USA). Catalogue no: **HCS 109**
**Cass:** Released '88, on Home Cooking (USA) by Flat Town Music Co.(USA). Catalogue no: **HCS 109 TC**

## Texas In The Thirties

**TEXAS IN THE THIRTIES (1935-38) (Various artists)**
**Album:** Released Dec '88, on Document Catalogue no: **DLP 540**

## Texas Piano Styles

**TEXAS PIANO STYLES (1929-37) (Various artists)**
Note: Featuring Whistlin' Jack Moore
**Album:** Released '88, on Wolf Catalogue no: **WSE 132**

## Texas Tenors

**TEXAS TENORS (Guerrero, Paul)**
**Album:** Released Feb '89, on Jazz Mark Catalogue no: **JAZZ MARK 104**

## That Newport Jazz

**THAT NEWPORT JAZZ (All star performances recorded live at Newport Jazz Festival) (Various artists)**
Tracks: / Undecided: *Various artists* / These foolish things: *Various artists* / Sweet Georgia Brown: *Various artists* / Stardust: *Various artists* / Chasin' at Newport: *Various artists* / Rosetta: *Various artists* / Just you, just me: *Various artists* / When your lover has gone: *Various artists* / Lester leaps in: *Various artists.*
**Cass:** Released Jul '87, on CBS by CBS Records. Catalogue no: **40 21139**
**Album:** Released Jul '87, on CBS by CBS Records. Deleted Aug '88. Catalogue no: **CBS 21139**

## That Toddlin' Town...

**THAT TODDLIN' TOWN - CHICAGO (Various artists)**
**Album:** Released Jan '83, on Swaggie (Australia) Catalogue no: **S 1256**

## That's The Way I Feel Now

**THAT'S THE WAY I FEEL NOW (A tribute to Thelonious Monk) (Various artists)**
Tracks: / Thelonious: *Various artists* / Little rootie tootie: *Various artists* / Reflections: *Various artists* / Blue Monk: *Various artists* / Misterioso: *Various artists* / Pannonica: *Various artists* / Ba-lue bolivar ba-lues are: *Various artists* / Brilliant corners: *Various artists* / Ask me now: *Various artists* / Monk's mood: *Various artists* / Four in one: *Various artists* / Functional: *Various artists* / Evidence: *Various artists* / Shuffle boil: *Various artists* / In walked Bud: *Various artists* / Criss cross: *Various artists* / Jackie-ing: *Various artists* / Round midnight: *Various artists* / Friday the 13th: *Various artists* / Work: *Various artists* / Gallop's gallop: *Various artists.*
**CD:** Released '88, on A&M by A&M Records. Catalogue no: **396 600-2**
**Cass:** Released Aug '84, on A&M by A&M Records. Deleted '88. Catalogue no: **CLM 66600**
**CD:** Released '88, on A&M by A&M Records. Catalogue no: **32XB 29**
**Album:** Released Aug '84, on A&M by A&M Records. Deleted '88. Catalogue no: **AMLM 66600**

## Theard, Sam

**LOVIN' SAM FROM DOWN IN 'BAM**
**Album:** Released Aug '89, on Blues Document Catalogue no: **BD 2044**

## Them Dirty Blues

**THEM DIRTY BLUES (Various artists)**
**CD:** Released Jul '89, on Jass Catalogue no: **CD 511/2**

## These Foolish Things

**THESE FOOLISH THINGS, 1936 (Various artists)**
Note: With Jimmie Lunceford, Buddy Berigan, Harry James.
**Album:** Released Mar '87, on Nostalgia by Mainline Records. Catalogue no: **NOST 7658**

## They All Played..

**THEY ALL PLAYED BANJO**
**Album:** Released '88, on Fountain by Retrieval Records. Catalogue no: **FG 403**

**THEY ALL PLAYED MAPLE LEAF RAG (Various artists)**
**Album:** Released '74, on Herwin by Shanachie Records (USA). Catalogue no: **HERWIN 401**

## They Called It Crooning

**THEY CALLED IT CROONING (Various artists)**
Tracks: / Where the blue of the night: *Crosby, Bing* / Cheerful little earful: *Ellis, Segar* / My song: *Bullock, Chick* / She's a new kind of old-fashioned girl: *Smith, Jack* / Got a date with an angel: *O'Malley, Pat* / Living in dreams: *Columbo, Russ* / Orange blossom time: *Edwards, Cliff* / She's wonderful: *Shalson, Harry* / Am I blue?: *Bellew, Smith* / Here lies love: *Browne, Sam* / Thrill is gone, The: *Vallee, Rudy* / Ain't misbehavin': *Austin, Gene* / My sweet Virginia: *Bowlly, Al* / Please: *Rosing, Val* / Little by little: *Marvin, Johnny* / You're a real sweetheart: *Coslow, Sam* / Sweet Sue: *Metaxa, George* / Tell your father: *Richman, Harry.*
**Cass:** Released 1 Feb '84, on Living Era by Academy Sound & Vision Records. Catalogue no: **ZC AJA 5026**
**Album:** Released 1 Feb '84, on Living Era by Academy Sound & Vision Records. Catalogue no: **AJA 5026**

## Thielemans, Toots

**Biographical details:** Was born Jean Baptiste Thielemans in 1922 in Brussels; he plays jazz harmonica and guitar, also composes and whistles. He toured Europe with Benny Goodman in 1950, has lived in the USA since 1951, worked with George Shearing through the '50s. He has led his own groups, visited Europe many times; his enormous amount of studio work includes Quincy Jones' hit LPs 1969-71, film soundtrack work including Midnight Cowboy in 1969; his best-known tune *Bluesette* has at least 100 recordings. (Donald Clarke 13.1.88).

**APPLE DIMPLE**
Tracks: / Take the 'A' train / Sunday in New York / Looking for Mr. Goodbar / Honesty / Midnight cowboy / Harlem nocturne / Still crazy after all these years.
Note: Personnel: Toots Thielemans (Harmonica / Guitar), Masahiko Matsuki (Guitar), Akira Okazawa (Bass), Yuichi Togashiki (Drums), Tadaomi Anai (Percussion). There is also a horn and string section.
**CD:** Released '88, on Denon Catalogue no: **C38-7578**

**AUTUMN LEAVES**
Tracks: / I do it for you, love / Dat mistige rooie beest / Lady be good / Old friends / Bye bye blackbird / Dirty old man / Tenor madness / Strange boogie man / Autumn leaves.
**Cass:** Released May '85, on Soul Note Catalogue no: **823 442-4**
**Album:** Released May '85, on Soul Note Catalogue no: **823 442-1**

**COLLAGE COLLECTION (Thielemans, Toots & Jan Akkerman)**
**Album:** Released '88, on CBS by CBS Records. Catalogue no: **CBS 88557**

**DO NOT LEAVE ME (Thielemans, Toots & His American Band)**
**CD:** Released Aug '89, on Stash (USA) Catalogue no: **STCD 12**

**HARMONICA JAZZ**
Tracks: / Scotch on the rocks / Sophisticated lady / Cocktails for two / Don't be that way / Stars fell on Alabama / I let a song go out of my heart / I'm putting all my eggs in one basket / Skylark / Diga diga doo / So rare / On the Alamo / Sonny boy.
**Album:** Released Feb '84, on CBS by CBS Records. Catalogue no: **CBS 21108**
**Cass:** Released Feb '84, on CBS by CBS Records. Catalogue no: **40 21108**

**JUST FRIENDS**
Note: Personnel: Toots Thielemans, Johnny Teupen and Paul Kuhn.
**CD:** Released '86, on Delta (1) by Delta Records. Deleted '88. Catalogue no: **11 059**

**LIVE IN THE NETHERLANDS**
Note: Personnel: Toots Thielemans, Joe Pass, Niels Henning and Orsted Pederson
Tracks: / Blues in the closet / Mooche / Thriving from a riff / Autumn leaves / Someday my prince will come.
**Cass:** Released Sep '82, on Pablo Jazz (USA) by Pablo Records (USA). Catalogue no: **K08 233**
**Album:** Released Sep '82, on Pablo Jazz (USA) by Pablo Records (USA). Catalogue no: **230 8233**

**LIVE IN THE NETHERLANDS (80) (Thielemans, Toots/Joe Pass)**
**CD:** Released May '86, on Pablo Jazz (USA) by Pablo Records (USA). Catalogue no: **CD 20040**

**LIVE: TOOTS THEILEMANS**
**Album:** Released Aug '81, on Polydor by Polydor Ltd. Catalogue no: **2489 175**

**MUSIC FOR THE MILLIONS**
Tracks: / What are you doing the rest of your life / First time I ever saw your face / Open your window / Friendly persuasion / Glimmies theme / Big bossa / Love remembered / You've got it bad girl.
**Album:** Released Aug '83, on Kingdom by Kingdom Records. Deleted '88. Catalogue no: **GATE 7012**
**Cass:** Released Jun '83, on Polydor (Germany) by Polydor Ltd. Catalogue no: **3212 033**
**Album:** Released Jun '83, on Polydor (Germany) by Polydor Ltd. Catalogue no: **2426 039**

**ONLY TRUST YOUR HEART**
Note: Recognised world-wide as the ultimate jazz harmonica player, Toots Thilemans lives up to his reputation with this superb album on Concord - his first for the label. All-star support is provided by Fred Hersch on piano, Marc Johnson and Harvie Swartz on bass and Joey Baron on drums. (New Note, August 1988)
**CD:** Released Sep '88, on Concord by Concord Jazz Records (USA). Catalogue no: **CCD 4355**
**Cass:** Released Sep '88, on Concord by Concord Jazz Records (USA). Catalogue no: **CJ 355 C**
**Album:** Released Sep '88, on Concord by Concord Jazz Records (USA). Catalogue no: **CJ 355**

**SILVER COLLECTION, THE**
Tracks: / Do it for your love / My little suede shoes / You're my blues machine / Dirty old man / Summer of '42 / Bluesette / Muskrat ramble / Mooche, The / What are you doing the rest of your life / Gentle rain, The / First time ever I saw your face, The / Big bossa / Ben / You've got it bad girl / Love remembered / Old friend.
**CD:** Released Jun '85, on Polydor by Polydor Ltd. Deleted Mar '88. Catalogue no: **825 086-2**

**SOUL OF TOOTS THIELEMANS, THE**
**Album:** Released Feb '88, on Fresh Sounds (Spain) by Fresh Sounds Records (Spain). Catalogue no: **FS 184**

**SUN GAMES**
Tracks: / Sun games / Palestina / Nancy's dance / Swimming pool / Broken circles / I love chick / Tarsican / Lush life / Monkey.
**Album:** Released Dec '83, on Timeless by Timeless Records. Catalogue no: **SJP 167**

**TOOTS THIELEMANS IN TOKYO**
Tracks: / What is this thing called love / Night train / Fallin' in love with love / In the wee small hours of the morning / Shade of love / Georgia on my mind.
**CD:** Released Jun '89, on Denon Catalogue no: **DC 8551**

**WORLD HITS PLAYED ON THE MOUTH ORGAN (Thielemans, Toots / Benny clark)**
**CD:** Released Oct '86, on Delta (1) by Delta Records. Deleted '88. Catalogue no: **11053**
**Album:** Released May '86, on Storyville by Storyville Records AB. Catalogue no: **SLP 4073**

**YESTERDAY AND TODAY (Thielemans, Toots / Svend Asmussen)**
Tracks: / Sophisticated lady / Mr. Nashville / Who can sail without the wind / Yesterday and today / Spirit feel / Denise / Blues on blue.
**CD:** Released Jun '88, on Sonet by Sonet Records. Catalogue no: **SNTCD 822**
**Album:** Released '88, on Scratch (Germany) by Gama Records. Catalogue

no: **805528**
**Album:** Released Jul '88, on Sonet by Sonet Records. Catalogue no: **SNTF 822**

**YOUR PRECIOUS LOVE**
**Album:** Released Aug '85, on Sonet by Sonet Records. Catalogue no: **SNTF 939**

## Thigpen, Ed

**ACTION-RE-ACTION**
**Album:** Released '88, on GNP Crescendo (USA) by GNP Crescendo Records (USA). Catalogue no: **GNPS 2098**
**Album:** Released '76, on Sonet by Sonet Records. Catalogue no: **SNTF 689**

## Thilo, Jesper

**FROG (Thilo, Jesper/Terry Clark Quintet)**
**Album:** Released '88, on Storyville by Storyville Records AB. Catalogue no: **SLP 4072**

**JESPER THILO QUARTET & HARRY EDISON (Thilo, Jesper Quartet)**
**Album:** Released '88, on Storyville by Storyville Records AB. Catalogue no: **SLP 4120**
**CD:** Released Feb '89, on Storyville by Storyville Records AB. Catalogue no: **STCD 4120**

**SWINGIN' FRIENDS (Thilo, Jesper Quartet)**
Note: with Kenny Drew, Billy Hart etc.
**Album:** Released Jan '88, on Storyville by Storyville Records AB. Catalogue no: **SLP 4065**

## Thirties Girls On The Air

**THIRTIES GIRLS: ON THE AIR (Various)**
Tracks: / Can't help it / I surrender dear / I've got a cousin in Milwaukee / Sittin' up, waitin' for you / When you love only one / Moanin' low / Body and soul / Lost my man / Pardon my southern accent / Time was / Dream ship / It's love I'm after / For sentimental reasons.
**Album:** Released Feb '88, on Totem Catalogue no: **TOTEM 1026**

## This Is Dixieland

**THIS IS DIXIELAND (Various artists)**
**Album:** Released Dec '83, on Philips (Import) by PolyGram UK Ltd. Catalogue no: **6424 061**

## This Is Jazz

**THIS IS JAZZ (Radio Series Live 1947) (Various artists)**
**Album:** Released Mar '88, on Delta (1) by Delta Records. Catalogue no: **20 800**

**THIS IS JAZZ VOL.1 (Broadcasts) (Various artists)**
**Album:** Released Apr '81, on Rarities Catalogue no: **RARITIES 33**

**THIS IS JAZZ VOL.2 (Various artists)**
**Album:** Released Apr '81, on Rarities Catalogue no: **RARITIES 35**

## This Is Jazz Broadcasts

**THIS IS JAZZ BROADCASTS VOL.1 (Various artists)**
Tracks: / High society: *Various artists* / Tiger rag: *Various artists* / Basin street blues: *Miller, Punch* / Dippermouth blues: *Various artists* / Sister Kate: *Miller, Punch* / Ain't misbehavin': *Various artists* / That's a plenty: *Various artists* / Baby won't you please come home: *Various artists* / I know that you know: *Various artists* / Caprice rag: *Various artists* / Charleston: *Various artists* / Way down yonder in New Orleans: *Various artists* / Blues: *Various artists.*
**Album:** Released May '87, on Rhapsody by President Records. Catalogue no: **RHA 6036**

**THIS IS JAZZ BROADCASTS VOL.2 (Various artists)**
Tracks: / Sensation rag: *Various artists* / You're some pretty doll: *Various artists* / Twelfth St. rag: *Various artists* / Buddy Bolden's blues: *Various artists* / Black and blue: *Various artists* / Summertime: *Various artists* / Farewell blues: *Various artists* / Maple leaf rag: *Various artists* / Basin street blues: *Various artists* / Polka dot stomp: *Various artists* / Kansas City man blues: *Various artists* / Jazz me blues: *Various artists* / Carolina shout: *Various artists* / Panama march (rag): *Various artists* / Way down yonder in New Orleans: *Various artists.*
**Album:** Released May '87, on Rhapsody by President Records. Catalogue no: **RHA 6037**

## This Is The Big Band Era

**THIS IS THE BIG BAND ERA (Various artists)**
Tracks: / South: *Moten, Bennie Kansas City Orchestra* / Song of India: *Dorsey, Tommy & His Orchestra* / Sing, sing, sing: *Goodman, Benny & His Orchestra* / I can't get started: *Berigan, Bunny & His Orchestra* / Don't be that way: *Goodman, Benny & His Orchestra* / Begin the beguine: *Shaw, Artie & his Orchestra* / And the angels sing: *Elman, Ziggy & His Orchestra* / Twelfth Street rag: *Hampton, Lionel & His Orchestra* / Cherokee: *Barnet, Charlie & His Orchestra* / In the mood: *Miller, Glenn & His Orchestra* / Boogie woogie on St. Louis blues: *Hines, Earl 'Fatha' & His Orchestra* / Frenesi: *Shaw, Artie & his Orchestra* / After hours: *Hawkins, Erskine & His Orchestra* / Pompton turnpike: *Barnet, Charlie & His Orchestra* / Take the 'A' train: *Ellington, Duke/His Orchestra* / String of pearls, A: *Miller, Glenn & His Orchestra* / Opus one: *Dorsey, Tommy & His Orchestra* / Tippin' in: *Hawkins, Erskine & His Orchestra* / Mister Roberts' roost: *Basie, Count & His Orchestra* / Study in brown: *Clinton, Larry & His Orchestra.*
**Album:** Released '83, on RCA (Germany) Catalogue no: **26 28037**

## Thomas, Henry

**RAGTIME TEXAS**
**2 LP Set:** Released Sep '75, on Herwin by Shanachie Records (USA). Catalogue no: **HERWIN 409**

## Thomas, Joe

**BLOWNIN' IN FROM K.C.**
**Album:** Released Jul '83, on Uptown (USA) Catalogue no: **UP 27 12**

**JUMPING WITH JOE**
**Album:** Released Sep '87, on Swingtime by Contact Records (Denmark). Catalogue no: **ST 1017**

**MAKE YOUR MOVE**
Tracks: / Make your move / Your love is so good to me / Caught you lying again / Plato's retreat / Let me be the one / Get on back / Sugar shack.
**Album:** Released '79, on TK Deleted '84. Catalogue no: **TKR 83374**

**MAKE YOUR MOVE (SINGLE)**
Tracks: / Make your move / Get on back.
**7" Single:** Released Jun '79, on TK Deleted '82. Catalogue no: **TKR 7544**

**RAW MEAT**
**Album:** Released Feb '83, on Uptown (USA) Catalogue no: **UP 27 01**

## Thomas, Leon

**PIECE OF CAKE, A (Thomas, Leon & Freddy Hubbard)**
**Album:** Released '81, on Palcoscenico (Italy) Catalogue no: **PAL 15006**

## Thomas, Rene

**MEETING MISTER THOMAS (Thomas, Rene Quintet)**
**Album:** Released Feb '88, on Fresh Sounds (Spain) by Fresh Sounds Records (Spain). Catalogue no: **FS 214**

## Thomas, Walter

**HOT JAZZ**
**Album:** Released '88, on Harlequin by Interstate Music. Catalogue no: **HQ 2032**

## Thompson, Barbara

**Biographical details:** Was born in 1944 in Oxford. As a saxophonist, composer and bandleader she is one of the UK's premier fusion artists, with the accent on melody rather than studio gimmicks. She plays alto, tenor and soprano saxes and flutes; also other instruments; she studied at the Royal College of Music; played with Howard Riley Trio, Don Rendell, John Dankworth, Manfred Mann; she and her husband, drummer Jon Hiseman (who played with Graham Bond, Georgie Fame, John Mayall and Colosseum) played in the New Jazz Orchestra; they were founder members of the United Jazz & Rock Ensemble; she formed her fusion combo Paraphernalia in 1975 and Hiseman joined in 1979. They now operate their own studio at home and Hiseman runs their music publishing company. *Hevenly Bodies* is a collection of Thompson compositions, playing eight instruments and sidemen including members of paraphernalia. She and Hiseman made a BBC documentary in 1979 about being busy musicians/parents, recently made an amusing TV advert for a domestic labour-saving devise, leaving Mom and Dad free to jam in the living room. Latest lineup of Paraphernalia includes Dave

Ball on bass (replaced by Phil Mulford on 1987 tour), Peter Lemer on keyboards, Paul Dunne on guitar. (Donald Clarke 13.1.88).

**BARBARA THOMPSON/ ROD ARGENT**
Tracks: / Ghosts / With you / Poltergeist.
**Album:** Released Mar '82, on MCA by MCA Records. Deleted Mar '87. Catalogue no: **MCF 3125**

**BARBARA THOMPSON'S PARAPHERNALIA**
**Album:** Released Jan '80, on MCA by MCA Records. Deleted Jan '85. Catalogue no: **MCF 3047**

**CRY FROM THE HEART, A (Live in London) (Thompson, Barbara Paraphernalia)**
**CD:** Released 3 Oct '88, on TM (Temple Music) by TM Records. Catalogue no: **CDTM 212**
**2 LP Set:** Released 3 Oct '88, on TM (Temple Music) by TM Records. Catalogue no: **ZTM 212**
**Cass:** Released 3 Oct '88, on TM (Temple Music) by TM Records. Catalogue no: **ZCTM 212**

**FANTASY**
**Album:** Released Mar '84, on Original Catalogue no: **TM 5**
**Cass:** Released Mar '84, on Original Catalogue no: **ZCTM 5**

**HEAVENLY BODIES**
**Album:** Released Oct '86, on Miles Music by Miles Music Records. Catalogue no: **TM 10**
**CD:** Released '86, on TM (Temple Music) by TM Records. Catalogue no: **CDTM 10**
**Cass:** Released Oct '86, on Miles Music by Miles Music Records. Catalogue no: **ZCTM 10**

**JUBIABA**
Tracks: / Funky flunky / Seega / Helena / Cuban thing / Black pearl / Touch of blue / Slum goddess.
**Album:** Released Aug '82, on MCA by MCA Records. Deleted Jan '88. Catalogue no: **MCL 1700**

**MOTHER EARTH (Thompson, Barbara Paraphernalia)**
**Cass:** Released Sep '84, on TM (Temple Music) by TM Records. Catalogue no: **ZCTM 1**
**Album:** Released Sep '84, on TM (Temple Music) by TM Records. Catalogue no: **TM 1**

**PARAPHERNALIA 'LIVE'**
**2 LP Set:** Released Oct '81, on MCA by MCA Records. Deleted Oct '86. Catalogue no: **MCL 1605**
**2 LP Set:** Released Nov '80, on MCA by MCA Records. Deleted Nov '85. Catalogue no: **MCSP 309**

**PURE FANTASY (Thompson, Barbara Paraphernalia)**
Tracks: / Pure fantasy / Mother earth suite.
**CD:** Released Sep '86, on TM (Temple Music) by TM Records. Catalogue no: **CDTM 5**
**Album:** Released Sep '86, on TM (Temple Music) by TM Records. Catalogue no: **TM 5**
**Cass:** Released Sep '86, on TM (Temple Music) by TM Records. Catalogue no: **ZCTM 5**

**SPECIAL EDITION**
Tracks: / Country dance / Fear of spiders / City lights / Little Annie ooh (live) / Fields of flowers / Dusk: nightwatch / Listen to the plants / Out to lunch (live) / Sleepwalker / Midday riser / Times past / Voices behind locked doors (live).
**Cass:** Released Jun '87, on Miles Music by Miles Music Records. Catalogue no: **ZCTM 11**
**CD:** Released 3 Jul '89, on Line by Line Records (W.Germany). Catalogue no: **CDTM 11**

**SUNSET**
Tracks: / Sunset / Frankfurt fayre.
**7" Single:** Released Sep '80, on MCA by MCA Records. Deleted Sep '83. Catalogue no: **MCA 621**
**12" Single:** Released Sep '80, on MCA by MCA Records. Deleted Sep '83. Catalogue no: **MCAT 621**

**WILDE TALES**
**Album:** Released Jul '84, on MCA by MCA Records. Deleted Jul '89. Catalogue no: **MCL 1796**

**WITH YOU (Thompson, Barbara & Rod Argent)**
Tracks: / With you / Ghosts / Poltergeist.
**12" Single:** Released Feb '82, on MCA by MCA Records. Catalogue no: **MCAT 761**
**7" Single:** Released Feb '82, on MCA by MCA Records. Catalogue no: **MCA 761**

## Thompson, Butch

**A' SOLAS**
**Album:** Released Jan '84, on Stomp Off (USA) Catalogue no: **SOS 1037**

**BUTCH THOMPSON AND HAL SMITH (Thompson, Butch & Hal Smith)**
**Album:** Released Jun '86, on Stomp Off (USA) Catalogue no: **SOS 1075**

**BUTCH THOMPSON AND HIS BERKELEY GANG (Thompson, Butch & his Berkeley Gang)**
**Album:** Released Mar '87, on Stomp Off (USA) Catalogue no: **SOS 1127**

**IN CHICAGO (Thompson, Butch & His Boys & Frank Chase)**
**Album:** Released Jul '87, on Jazzology (USA) by Jazzology Records (USA). Catalogue no: **J 146**

**MILENBERG JOYS**
Note: Personnel: Butch Thompson, Hal Smith, Charlie Devore.
**Album:** Released Oct '86, on Stomp Off (USA) Catalogue no: **SOS 1116**

**ONE IN A MILLION (Thompson, Butch & Chicago Rhythm)**
**Album:** Released '88, on Stomp Off (USA) Catalogue no: **SOS 1059**

**PLAYS JELLY ROLL MORTON**
**Album:** Released Mar '77, on Center (USA) by Biograph Records (USA). Catalogue no: **CEN 4**

**PLAYS JELLY ROLL MORTON VOL.2**
**Album:** Released Mar '77, on Center (USA) by Biograph Records (USA). Catalogue no: **CEN 9**

## Thompson, Don

**BEAUTIFUL FRIENDSHIP, A (Thompson, Don Quartet)**
Tracks: / Even Steven / My one and only love / Blues for Jim-San / I've never been in love before / Beautiful friendship, A / For Scott La Faro / East it / Dreams.
Note: Don Thompson, piano, bass; John Abercrombie, guitar; Dave Holland, bass; MichaelSmith, drums.
**Album:** Released Jul '84, on Concord Jazz by Concord Jazz Records (USA). Catalogue no: **CJ 243**

**COAST TO COAST**
**Album:** Released '74, on Amberlee by Amberlee Records. Catalogue no: **AML 307**

**COUNTRY PLACE**
**Album:** Released Jan '80, on PM Deleted '80. Catalogue no: **PM 008**

## Thompson, Eddie

**Biographical details:** Eddie Thompson (1926-86) was a much-loved UK jazz pianist who attended the same school for the blind as George Shearing. He was the house pianist at Ronnie Scott's club 1959-60 and lived in the USA from 1962 to 1972. One of his last albums was a duo with trombonist Roy Williams, who was born in 1937 in Bolton, Lancashire. (Donald Clarke 13.1.88).

**AIN'T SHE SWEET (Thompson, Eddie Trio/Spike Robinson)**
**Album:** Released Apr '81, on Hep Jazz by Hep Records. Catalogue no: **HEP 2002**

**AT CHESTERS (Thompson, Eddie Trio/Spike Robinson)**
**Album:** Released Aug '85, on Hep Jazz by Hep Records. Catalogue no: **HEP 2028**

**AT CHESTERS VOL 2 (Thompson, Eddie Trio/Spike Robinson)**
**Album:** Released Jan '87, on Hep Jazz by Hep Records. Catalogue no: **HEP 2031**

**BY MYSELF**
**Album:** Released '74, on 77 by 77 Records. Catalogue no: **77LUE 12 39**

**I HEAR MUSIC**
**Album:** Released Mar '88, on Dormouse Catalogue no: **DM 17**

**MEMORIES OF YOU (Thompson, Eddie Trio/Spike Robinson)**
**Album:** Released Jul '84, on Hep Jazz by Hep Records. Catalogue no: **HEP 2021**

**PUT ON A HAPPY FACE**
Tracks: / Put on a happy face.
**7" Single:** Released Aug '79, on Hobo Deleted '80. Catalogue no: **HOS 007**

**WHEN THE LIGHTS ARE LOW (Thompson, Eddie & Roy Williams)**
**Album:** Released '88, on Hep Jazz by

Hep Records. Catalogue no: **HEP 2007**

## Thompson, Lucky

**Biographical details:** Was born Eli Thompson in 1924 in Detroit. He is a unique tenor saxophonist who also took up soprano in the late '50s. He played with Lionel Hampton and Count Basie in the 1940s, also recorded for Dial on the West Coast in 1946 with Dizzy Gillespie and Charlie Parker; also played with Boyd Raeburn, Miles Davis, Jo Jones, Milt Jackson, many others. He was also a teacher, lived in Europe for long periods, and has been inactive as a recording artist for some years, to the regret of his many fans. (Donald Clarke 13.1.88).

**IN PARIS 1956**
**Album:** Released '88, on DRG (USA) by DRG Records (USA). Catalogue no: **SW 8404**

**LUCKY THOMPSON FEATURING OSCAR PETTIFORD**
Tracks: / Tom-kattin' / Old reliable / Lady's vanity / Translation / Tricrotism / Bo-bi my boy / Body and soul / O.P. meets L.T..
**Album:** Released Mar '84, on Jasmine by Hasmick Promotions. Deleted Feb '88. Catalogue no: **JASM 1037**

**LUCKY THOMPSON WITH GERARD PONCHONET (Thompson, Lucky / Gerard Pochonet Quartet)**
**Album:** Released Feb '88, on Fresh Sounds (Spain) by Fresh Sounds Records (Spain). Catalogue no: **FS 246**

**TEST PILOT**
**Album:** Released Jan '86, on Swingtime by Contact Records (Denmark). Deleted Jun '89. Catalogue no: **ST 1005**

## Thompson, Rev. Johnny

**GLORIOUS FEELING (Thompson, Rev. Johnny & Gospel Singers)**
**Album:** Released Sep '86, on Calligraph Catalogue no: **CLGLP 009**

## Thompson, Sir Charles

**Biographical details:** Was born in 1918 in Springfield, Ohio; he is a pianist, organist, composer and arranger. He played on Buck Clayton's *Jam Session* albums in the 1950s on CBS, later for Vanguard, other labels; his knight's nickname denotes elegant lightness with substance: like Nat Pierce he is capable of sounding remarkably like Count Basie at the keyboard. (Donald Clarke 13.1.88).

**FOR THE EARS**
Note: Personnel: Honda, Corea, Vitous and Haynes.
Tracks: / For the ears / Oh Joe / Memories of you / Bop this / Honeysuckle Rose / Swingtime in the Rockies / These foolish things / Sweet Georgia Brown / It's the talk of the town / Fore / Dynaflow / Under the sweetheart tree / Ready for Freddie / Sonny Howar's blues / Best by test / Hey there / Love for sale / Stompin' at the Savoy / Mister Sandman.
**2 LP Set:** Released May '83, on Vogue Jazz (France) by Vogue Records. Catalogue no: **VJD 559**

**PORTRAIT OF A PIANO**
**Album:** Released Sep '87, on Sackville by Spotlite Records. Catalogue no: **3037**

## Thompson, Sonny

**CAT ON THE KEYS**
**Album:** Released Mar '89, on Swingtime by Contact Records (Denmark). Catalogue no: **ST 1027**

**SWINGS IN PARIS**
**Album:** Released Mar '74, on Black & Blue (1) by Black & Blue Records. Catalogue no: **33 051**

## Thorburn, Billy

**LET'S BREAK THE GOOD NEWS**
Tracks: / Let's break the good news / With the wind and the rain in your hair / Wish me luck as you wave me goodbye / I'd never fall in love again / All over the place / All alone with my shadow / Memory of a rose, The / Love makes the world go round / It's foolish but it's fun / Faithful forever / If I could paint a memory / There'll come another day / I-spy / You're so sweet to remember / Too many irons in the fire / I'm happy for your sake.
Note: A new 16-track compilation from Billy Thorburn's highly successful group The Organ,Dance Band & Me featuring renowned organist Robinson Cleaver who celebrates his 80th birthday in May.Jazz enthusiast,Hugh Palmer provides us with full personnels for each track plus an informative sleeve note tracing the history of Billy Thorburn and his musicians through his varied and successful employment from beginning as a 9 years old choirmaster to the height of his recording career.This album will have 3-fold appeal,satisfying the followers of Billy Thorburn as well as dance band enthusiast and fans of the largely extinct theatre organ.All tracks have been transferred using the direct metal mastering technique for the best sound quality.
**Cass:** Released May '86, on Retrospect by EMI Records. Deleted Jan '88. Catalogue no: **TCSH 504**
**Album:** Released May '86, on Retrospect by EMI Records. Deleted Jun '89. Catalogue no: **SH 504**

**ORGAN, THE DANCE BAND AND ME, THE (Thorburn, Billy & Robinson Cleaver)**
Tracks: / Never took a lesson in my life / You made me care / It costs so little but means so much / I hear bluebirds / Riding on a rainbow / In a little rocky valley / Nearness of you, The / Scatterbrain / Arm in arm / I'll never make the same mistake again / What do you think these ruby lips were made for? / Safe in my heart / Don't ever walk in the shadows / Journey to a star / I'm all alone / There'll come another day / I've seen you before / It's always you.
Note: Vocals by Alan Kane, Terry Devon, Jimmy Messini, Barbara Palmer, Wally Windsor, Helen Clare, Don Adams, Chick Henderson, Pamela Rainer.
**Cass:** Released Aug '84, on President by President Records. Catalogue no: **TC-PLE 514**
**Album:** Released Aug '84, on President by President Records. Catalogue no: **PLE 514**

## Thore Jederby

**MORNING JUMP (Thore Jederby Jazz Groups(1940-1948))**
**Album:** Released Jun '86, on Dragon by Dragon Records. Catalogue no: **DRLP 51**

## Thornhill, Claude

**Biographical details:** Claude Thornhill (1909-65) was a pianist, arranger and bandleader whose elegant records in the 1940s added to the colour available in American popular music: he employed two French horns and hired Gil Evans, later Gerry Mulligan as arrangers; his above-average dance band music was influential, including his famous theme *Snowfall*, a little tone-poem. 2-disc *Tapestries* on Affinity has 32 tracks from his heyday, 17 arranged by Evans. (Donald Clarke 13.1.88).

**1941 AND 1947 (Thornhill, Claude and his Orchestra)**
**Album:** Released Jun '86, on Circle (USA) by Jazzology Records (USA). Catalogue no: **CLP 19**

**CLAUDE THORNHILL AND ORCHESTRA 1947 (Thornhill, Claude and his Orchestra)**
Tracks: / Snowfall / Robbins' nest / Cabin in the sky / Deed I do / Happy stranger / Medley:Jealous/Swinging down the lane/Breezing / Along with the breeze / Just about this time last night / Donna Lee / Poor little rich girl / Polka dots and moonbeams / I may be wrong / Adios / Sometimes I'm happy / Puttin' and takin' / Sunday drivin' / Anthropology.
Note: Exciting versions of the ballads, pop novelties and jazz of the Thornhill Orchestra--different from the Columbia releases--are collected here from a series of '47 transcriptions. This was the musician's favourite band. Arranger credits alone are ear-boggling--Gil Evans, Gerry Mulligan, Bill Borden, Rusty Dedrick, John Hefti (Neal's older brother) and Thornhill. Alto saxophonist Lee Konitz, guitarist Gary Galbraith, clarinetist Danny Polo, tenor saxophonist Mickey Folus and the pianist leader are the inspired instrumental soloists. Fran Warren and Gene Williams are the tastefully distinctive vocalists. (Hindsight Catalogue - 1989)
**Album:** Released '88, on Hindsight Catalogue no: **HSR 108**
**Album:** Released Feb '79, on London Records by London Records Ltd. Deleted Feb '84. Catalogue no: **HMP 5040**

**SNOWFALL (Thornhill, Claude & His Orchestra)**
**Album:** Released Feb '88, on Fresh Sounds (Spain) by Fresh Sounds Rec-

ords (Spain). Catalogue no: **FS 212**

**SONG IS YOU, THE**
Tracks: / Anthropology / Baia / Arab dance / Royal Garden blues / Polka dots and moonbeams / Sometimes I'm happy / September song / Godchild / Robbins' nest / I don't know why / Song is you, The / April in Paris / La paloma / Lover man / Elevation.
**Album:** Released Apr '81, on Hep Jazz by Hep Records. Catalogue no: **HEP 17**

**TAPESTRIES**
Tracks: / Snowfall / Stop, you're breaking my heart / Portrait of a Guinea farm / Autumn nocturne / I'm somebody nobody loves / Smiles / Night and day / Buster's last stand / There's a small hotel / I don't know why (I just do) / Under the willow tree / Arab dance / I get the blues when it rains / Sunday kind of love, A / Early autumn / La paloma (grey dove) - take 1 / La paloma (grey dove) - take 2 / Warsaw concerto / Thrivin' on a riff (take 1) / Thrivin' on a riff (take 2) / Sorta kinda / Robbins' nest / Lover man / Polka dots and moonbeams / Donna Lee / How am I to know? / For Heaven's sake / Whip-poor-will / That old feeling / Coquette / Yardbird suite / Let's call it a day.
**2 LP Set:** Released Sep '87, on Affinity by Charly Records. Catalogue no: **AFSD 1040**
**CD:** Released Oct '87, on Charly by Charly Records. Catalogue no: **CDCHARLY 82**

## Thornton, Big Mama

**BALL AND CHAIN**
Note: Personnel: Willie Mae 'Big Mama' Thornton, Lightning Hopkins and Larry Williams.
**Album:** Released May '81, on Arhoolie (USA) by Arhoolie Records (USA). Catalogue no: **ARHOOLIE 1039**

**BIG MAMA THORNTON**
Note: Doubleplay cassette contains albums: In Europe - 1028; With Muddy Waters Band - 1032.
**Album:** Released '81, on Arhoolie (USA) by Arhoolie Records (USA). Catalogue no: **ARHOOLIE 1032**
**Cass:** Released '88, on Arhoolie (USA) by Arhoolie Records (USA). Catalogue no: **C 204**

**IN EUROPE**
**Album:** Released May '81, on Arhoolie (USA) by Arhoolie Records (USA). Catalogue no: **ARHOOLIE 1028**

**QUIT SNOOPIN' ROUND MY DOOR (Thornton, Willie Mae 'Big Mama')**
Tracks: / Rockabye baby / Hard times / I ain't no fool either / You don't move me no more / No Jody for me / Let your tears fall baby / Every time I think of you / Mischievious boogie / How come / Just like a dog / I've searched the world over / Nightmare / Story of my blues / Stop a-hoppin on me / Laugh laugh laugh / Fish.
**Album:** Released Sep '86, on Ace by Ace Records. Catalogue no: **CH 170**

**STRONGER THAN DIRT / THE WAY IT IS**
Tracks: / Born under a bad sign / Hound dog / Ball & chain / Summertime / Rollin' stone / Lets go get stoned / Funky Broadway / That lucky old sun / Ain't nothin' you can do / I shall be released / Little red rooster / One black rat / Rock me baby / Wade in the water / Sweet little angel / Baby please don't go / Got my mojo working / Watermelon man / Don't need no doctor.
**Cass:** Released May '88, on Charly by Charly Records. Catalogue no: **TCCDX 24**
**2 LP Set:** Released May '88, on Charly by Charly Records. Catalogue no: **CDX 24**

**YOU OLE HOUN' DAWG**
Tracks: / Hound dog / Walking blues / My man called me / Cotton picking blues / Willie Mae's blues / Big change, The / Partnership blues / I'm all fed up / I smell a rat / I just can't help myself / Yes baby / Tarzan and the signified monkey / They call me Big Mama / Before day (Big Mama's blues) / Me and my chauffeur.
**Album:** Released 2 Oct '89, on Ace by Ace Records. Catalogue no: **CHAD 277**

## Those Ragtime Years

**THOSE RAGTIME YEARS 1899-1916 (Various artists)**
Tracks: / Hot foot Sue: *Various artists* / Rice's ragtime opera: *Various artists* / Ragtime skedaddle: *Various artists* / Mississippi river song: *Various artists* / Ain't yer gwine say: *Various artists* / St. Louis rag: *Various artists* / Peaceful Henery: *Various artists* / American rag: *Various artists* / Operatic rag: *Various artists* / St. Louis tickle: *Various artists* / Wild cherries: *Various artists* / Red rose rag: *Various artists* / Tickled to death: *Various artists* / Fiddlesticks rag: *Various artists* / Turkey trot: *Various artists* / Powder rag: *Various artists* / Be my little baby bumble bee: *Various artists* / I'll dance till de sun breaks through: *Various artists* / College rag: *Various artists* / Rum-tum-tiddle: *Various artists* / Red pepper rag: *Various artists* / I want to be in Dixie: *Various artists* / You made me love you: *Various artists* / On San Francisco bay: *Various artists* / Land of cotton: *Various artists* / Hiawatha: *Various artists* / Lumbrin' Luke: *Various artists* / Gaby glide, The: *Various artists* / Wedding glide: *Various artists* / I want a dancing man: *Various artists* / Hors d'ouvres: *Various artists* / You can't get away from it: *Various artists* / Are you from Dixie: *Various artists* / Dear old Shepherds Bush: *Various artists* / Down home rag: *Various artists.*
**2 LP Set:** Released Feb '77, on Retrospect by EMI Records. Catalogue no: **SHB 41**

## Threadgill, Henry

**Biographical details:** Threadgill is a saxophonist, composer and bandleader who was born in Chicago in 1944. He was a founder member of Chicago's AACM music collective and of the trio **Air**; he formed his sextet (six pieces plus Threadgill) and made three LPs on the small American label About Time; *You Know the Number* (1986) is the first on a major label. '87 on new RCA Novus imprint, with Threadgill on alto and tenor saxophones plus bass flute, Deidre Murray on cello, Frank Lacy on trombone, Rasul Sadik on trumpet, Fred Hopkins on bass, Pheeron akLaff, Reggie Nicholson on drums. Hopkins and akLaff also play in New Air; others play in Oliver Lake's combo as well. Threadgill's contemporary music uses classical harmonies and gospel voicing as well as the earliest jazz principle of collective improvisation; his group is tightly drilled yet at ease. (Donald Clarke 13.1.88).

**EASILY SLIP INTO ANOTHER WORLD**
Tracks: / I can't wait till I get home / Black hands bejewelled / Spotted Dick is pudding / Let me look down your throat or say ah / My rock / Hail / Award the squadtett.
**CD:** Released Dec '88, on Novus by BMG Records (UK). Catalogue no: **PD 83025**
**Album:** Released Dec '88, on Novus by BMG Records (UK). Catalogue no: **PL 83025**

**RAG BUSH AND ALL**
Tracks: / Off the rag / Devil is on the loose & dancing with a monkey / Gift / Sweet holy rag.
**Album:** Released May '89, on RCA by BMG Records (UK). Catalogue no: **PL 83052**
**CD:** Released May '89, on RCA by BMG Records (UK). Catalogue no: **PD 83052**
**Cass:** Released May '89, on RCA by BMG Records (UK). Catalogue no: **PK 83052**

**YOU KNOW THE NUMBER (Threadgill, Henry Sextet)**
Tracks: / Bermuda blues / Silver and gold baby / Thomas Cole, Theme from / Good times / To be announced / Those who eat cookies.
**Cass:** Released Nov '87, on RCA by BMG Records (UK). Deleted Nov '88. Catalogue no: **PK 83013**
**CD:** Released Nov '87, on RCA by BMG Records (UK). Catalogue no: **PD 83013**
**Album:** Released Nov '87, on RCA by BMG Records (UK). Catalogue no: **PL 83013**

## Three Sounds

**BABE'S BLUES**
Tracks: / Babe's blues / Wait a minute / Work song / Blue Daniel / Sweet and lovely / Shiny stockings / Walking the floor over you / Between the devil and the deep blue sea / Stairway to the stars / Lazy cat.
Note: Imported by Pathe Marconi copyright paid in France.
**Album:** Released Dec '86, on Blue Note by EMI Records. Deleted Jun '88. Catalogue no: **BST 84434**
**CD:** Released Mar '89, on Blue Note by EMI Records. Deleted Jan '90. Catalogue no: **BNZ 137**
**CD:** Released Mar '89, on Blue Note by

EMI Records. Deleted Jan '90. Catalogue no: **CDP 784 434 2**

**INTRODUCING THE THREE SOUNDS**
Tracks: / Tenderly / Willow weep for me / Both sides / Blue bells / It's nice / Going home / Would'n you / O sole mio / Bobby / Mo-ge / It might as well be spring / Soft touch / Don't get around much anymore / Going home (alternative take).
**CD:** Released May '87, on Blue Note by EMI Records. Deleted Jan '90. Catalogue no: **BNZ 95**
**CD:** Released May '87, on Blue Note by EMI Records. Deleted Jan '90. Catalogue no: **CDP 746 531 2**

## Tiger Rag

**TIGER RAG (Various artists)**
**CD:** Released Jun '88, on Compact Selection Catalogue no: **TQ 152**

**TIGER RAG, 1931 (Various artists)**
Note: Featuring Bing Crosby, Joe Venuti, Eddie Lang, Duke Ellington.
**Album:** Released '82, on Nostalgia by Mainline Records. Catalogue no: **NOST 7619**

## Timeless Compilation

**TIMELESS COMPILATION (Various artists)**
**CD:** Released Oct '89, on Total Catalogue no: **PWMCD 1**
**Cass:** Released Oct '89, on Total Catalogue no: **PWMC 1**
**Album:** Released Oct '89, on Total Catalogue no: **PWM 1**

## Timeless All Stars

**ESSENCE**
**CD:** Released Mar '90, on delos Catalogue no: **JJCD44**
**CD:** Released '88, on Delos (USA) Catalogue no: **DCD 4006**

**IT'S TIMELESS (LIVE AT KEYSTONE KORNER) (Curtis Fuller, Harold Land)**
**Album:** Released Apr '84, on Timeless by Timeless Records. Catalogue no: **SJP 178**

**MESSINA**
Tracks: / Messina / Lupe.
**CD 3":** Released '88, on Delos (USA) Catalogue no: **D/PC 2105**

**TIMELESS HEART**
**Album:** Released '88, on Timeless by Timeless Records. Catalogue no: **SJP 182**

## Timmons, Bobby

**Biographical details:** An influential pianist and composer, born in 1935 in Philadelphia; he died in 1974. His gospel-influenced post-bop jazz was a precursor of funk. He followed **Horace** Silver into Art Blakey's Jazz Messengers in 1958, where he wrote *Moanin'*; he played with Cannonball Adderley 1959-60, where he wrote *Dis Here* and *Dat Dere*. He led his own groups, died of cirrhosis. (Donald Clarke 13.1.88).

**BOBBY TIMMONS IN PERSON**
**Album:** Released Sep '88, on Riverside (1) Catalogue no: **RSLP 391**

**THIS HERE**
**Album:** Released Aug '84, on Riverside (USA) by Fantasy Inc (USA). Catalogue no: **OJC 104**

**THIS HERE IS BOBBY TIMMONS**
**CD:** Released Apr '86, on Vanguard (USA) by CBS Records. Deleted '88. Catalogue no: **VDJ 1529**
**CD:** Released Apr '86, on Carrere (France) Catalogue no: **98953**

## Tippett, Keith

**Biographical details:** Was born in Bristol in 1947. As a leading UK jazz pianist and composer he has led various groups, recorded duo albums with pianists Stan Tracey and Howard Riley. His wife is vocalist/guitarist Julie (nee Driscoll; used to play with Brian Auger) who has also recorded with Bobby Bradford and John Stevens. (Donald Clarke 13.1.88).

**COUPLE IN SPIRIT**
Tracks: / Daybreak / Marching (We shall remember them) / Brimstone spring lullaby / Key at dusk, The / Morning psalm / Evening psalm / Grey mist with yellow waterfall entwines evening turquoise / Choir and the sunset improvisors, The.
**Cass:** Released Sep '88, on Editions EG by E.G. Records. Catalogue no: **EGEDC 52**
**CD:** Released Sep '88, on Editions EG by E.G. Records. Catalogue no: **EEGCD 52**
**Album:** Released Sep '88, on Editions EG by E.G. Records. Catalogue no: **EGED 52**

**FRAMES**
**2 LP Set:** Released Feb '79, on Ogun by Cadillac Music. Deleted Feb '84. Catalogue no: **OGD 003/004**

**LIVE: KEITH TIPPETT (Tippett's, Keith Septet)**
**2 LP Set:** Released Jun '86, on Ogun by Cadillac Music. Catalogue no: **OGD 008/9**

**LOOSE KITE N A GENTLE... (Tippett's, Keith Septet)**
**Album:** Released '88, on Ogun by Cadillac Music. Catalogue no: **OG 007-8**

**MERCY DASH**
Note: Personnel: Keith Tippet, Joe Galivan, Elton Dean and Hugh Hopper.
**Album:** Released Dec '86, on Culture Press by Vista Sounds Records. Deleted '88. Catalogue no: **CP 2001**

**OVARY LODGE**
**Album:** Released Jan '77, on Ogun by Cadillac Music. Catalogue no: **OG 600**

## Tippetts, Julie

**VOICE**
Note: Personnel: Julie Tippetts, M Nichols, P Minton and B Eley.
Album: Released Apr '74, on Ogun by Cadillac Music. Catalogue no: **OG 110**

## Tirabasso, John

**LIVE AT DINO'S (Tirabasso, John Quartet)**
Note: Gary Foster-alto sax, Frank Strazzeri-piano, Putter Smith-bass.
**Album:** Released '88, on Discovery (USA) by Discovery Records (USA). Catalogue no: **DS 884**

**Keith Tippett**

## Tjader, Cal

**Biographical details:** Was born in 1925 in St Louis, Missouri; he died in 1982 in the Philippine Islands; he played vibes, piano and percussion instruments.
He played with Dave Brubeck around 1950 and with George Shearing in the early '50s; his long series of albums of Latin jazz on *Fantasy* were very popular and are already being reissued; he also recorded for *Verve* and most recently for Concord Jazz.
His sidemen were always first-rate, including (on Verve) Lalo Schifrin, Willie Bobo, Donald Byrd, Kenny Burrell; Of the Concord LPs, *The Shining Sea* is straight jazz, with Hank Jones and Scott Hamilton; one of his Latin albums on *Concord* won a Grammy.
(Donald Clarke 13.1.88).

**A FUEGO VIVO**
**CD:** Released Jul '88, on Concord Jazz by Concord Jazz Records (USA). Catalogue no: **CCD 4176**
**Cass:** Released Apr '82, on Concord by Concord Jazz Records (USA). Catalogue no: **CJ 176 C**
**Album:** Released Apr '82, on Concord by Concord Jazz Records (USA). Catalogue no: **CJ 176**

**BREATHE EASY**
**Album:** Released '79, on Galaxy (1) by President Records. Deleted '84. Catalogue no: **GXY 5107**

**CAL'S PALS**
Tracks: / Perdido / Tambu in 7/4 / Ran kan kan / Noa noa / Curtain call / Mambo show / Te cres que / Cubano chant / Ginza samba / Why do you do right (get me some money too!).
**Album:** Released Sep '87, on BGP by Ace Records. Catalogue no: **BGP 1003**
**Cass:** Released Sep '87, on BGP by Ace Records. Deleted '89. Catalogue no: **BGPC 1003**

**GAZAME**
**Album:** Released Nov '80, on Concord Jazz by Concord Jazz Records (USA). Catalogue no: **CJ 133**

**GOOD VIBES**
Tracks: / Guarachi guaro / Doxy / Shoshana / Speak low / Broadway / Cuban fantasy / Good vibes.
**Album:** Released Oct '84, on Concord Jazz by Concord Jazz Records (USA). Catalogue no: **CJP 247**

**HURACAN**
**Album:** Released Jan '81, on Crystal Clear Catalogue no: **CCS 8003**

**LA ONDA VA BIEN**
**CD:** Released '88, on Concord Jazz by Concord Jazz Records (USA). Catalogue no: **CCD 4113**

**SHINING SEA, THE**
**Album:** Released Nov '81, on Concord Jazz by Concord Jazz Records (USA). Catalogue no: **CJ 159**

**SOLAR HEAT**
Tracks: / Ode to Billy Joe / Never my love / Felicidade / Mambo sangria / Here / Fried bananas / Amazon / La Bamba / Eye of the devil / Solar heat.
**Album:** Released Oct '82, on Rhapsody by President Records. Catalogue no: **RHAP 13**

**SONA LIBRE**
Tracks: / Hip walk / Sally's tomato / O barquinho / El muchacho / Insight / My reverie / Morning of the carnival / Azul / Invitation / Alonzo.
Note: Digital stereo recording.
**CD:** Released Apr '84, on Verve Catalogue no: **815 058-2**

## Togashi, Masahiko

**BREATH**
**CD:** Released '88, on Denon Catalogue no: **C38 7281**

**VARIATION (Togashi, Masahiko Quartet)**
**CD:** Released '88, on Denon Catalogue no: **C38 7693**

## Tolliver, Charles

**Biographical details:** Born in 1942 in Florida, trumpeter and composer Tolliver was influenced by Clifford Brown, later Freddie Hubbard. He played on albums by Art Blakey, Jackie McLean and others on Blue Note and was co-founder of the artists' label Strata-East in 1971. His own albums have appeared on several labels. (Donald Clarke 13.1.88).

**CHARLES TOLLIVER AND HIS ALL STARS (Tolliver, Charles & His All Stars)**
Tracks: / Earl's world / Peace with myself / Right now / Household of Saud / Lil's paradise / Paper man.
Note: Charles Tolliver, Herbie Hancock, Gary Bartz, Ron Carter, Joe Chambers.
**Album:** Released Jul '88, on Black Lion Catalogue no: **BLP 30117**

**IMPACT**
**Album:** Released Jan '82, on Enja (Germany) by Enja Records (West Germany). Catalogue no: **ENJA 2016**

## Tolvan Big Band

**MONTREAUX AND MORE**
**Album:** Released Mar '90, Catalogue no: **DRLP61**

**SPLIT VISION**
**Album:** Released Jun '86, on Dragon by Dragon Records. Catalogue no: **DRLP 44**

## Torff, Brian

**MANHATTAN HOE-DOWN**
**Album:** Released Aug '88, on Audiophile (USA) by Jazzology Records (USA). Catalogue no: **AP 182**

## Torme, Mel

**Biographical details:** Was born in Chicago in 1925; he is a songwriter, a writer, an actor and plays piano and drums as well as one of the great jazz-oriented popular singers.
He sang on radio at the age of 4, acted in radio soap operas at 9; formed vocal group the Mel-Tones, recording under that name, and with Artie Shaw in the 1940s.
He began writing hit songs at 15, his best-known song being *The Christmas Song* (*Chestnuts Roasting On An Open Fire*). He went solo and had hits on Capitol 1949-52.
He was known as *The Velvet Fog* during the Mel-Tones period, but his range increased and he became an even better singer in the '50s, recording for *Bethlehem* (now on *Affinity*) and on *Verve*.

He often worked with ace arranger Marty Paich, but later arranged and produced his own albums; his latest are on Concord Jazz. (Donald Clarke 13.1.88).

**BACK IN TOWN (Torme, Mel and the Mel-Tones)**
Tracks: / Makin' whoopee / Baubles, bangles and beads / What is this thing called love? / Truckin' / Bunch of the blues, The / Some like it hot.
**Album:** Released Feb '84, on Verve (France) Catalogue no: **2304 384**

**COMING HOME BABY**
Tracks: / Coming home baby.
**7" Single:** Released Jan '63, on London-American Deleted Jan '66. Catalogue no: **HLK 9643**

**DUKE ELLINGTON AND COUNT BASIE**
Tracks: / I'm gonna go fishin / Don't get around much anymore / I like the sunrise / Take the 'A' train / Reminiscin' in tempo / Outskirts of town, the / Just a sittin' and a rockin' / Down for double / I'm gonna move to the outskirts of town / Blue and sentimental / Oh what a night for love / Sent for you yesterday / In the evening when the sun goes down.
**Cass:** Released Aug '85, on Verve Catalogue no: **VRVC 8**
**Album:** on Verve Deleted Mar '87. Catalogue no: **823 248-1**
**CD:** Released Aug '85, on Verve Deleted Mar '88. Catalogue no: **823 248-2**
**Album:** Released Aug '85, on Verve Catalogue no: **VRV 8**

**FINE AND DANDY**
**CD:** on Musicraft (USA) by Discovery Records (USA). Catalogue no: **MVSCD 60**

**FOGGY DAY, A (Torme, Mel and the Mel-Tones)**
**CD:** on Musicraft (USA) by Discovery Records (USA). Catalogue no: **MVSCD 54**

**GONE WITH THE WIND**
Tracks: / Day you came along, The / Mimi / Magic town / I'll always be in love with you / It's easy to remember / How long has this been going on / Little kiss each morning a little kiss each night, A / When is sometime / Gone with the wind / What are you doing New Year's Eve.
**Album:** Released '88, on Musicraft (USA) by Discovery Records (USA). Catalogue no: **MVS 2005**

**GREAT SINGERS OF THE FIFTIES**
**Album:** Released Jan '79, on Jazz Greats Catalogue no: **GP 705**

**GREAT SONG STYLISTS VOL.2**
Tracks: / Limehouse blues / Nightingale sang in Berkeley Square, A / I've got a lovely bunch of coconuts / These foolish things / Geordie / My one and only Highland fling / White cliffs of Dover, The / Danny boy / Let there be love / Greensleeves / Try a little tenderness / London pride / Time was / You've got me goin' ev'ry which way.
**Album:** Released Jun '83, on Apex Catalogue no: **AX 5**

**I CAN'T GIVE YOU ANYTHING BUT LOVE**
Tracks: / I can't give you anything but love / I'm yours / Little white lies / Love, you funny thing / Cottage for sale / Love is the sweetest thing / You're driving me crazy / Who cares what people say / My baby just cares for me / If I had a girl like you.
**Album:** Released Aug '83, on Musicraft (USA) by Discovery Records (USA). Catalogue no: **MVS 2000**

**I DIG DUKE AND COUNT**
**Album:** Released Dec '79, on Verve (USA) by Polydor Ltd. Catalogue no: **2304 402**

**IN CONCERT - TOKYO (Torme, Mel & Marty Paich Dektette)**
Tracks: / It don't mean a thing / Cotton tail / More than you know / Sweet Georgia Brown / Just in time / When the sun comes out / Carioca, The / Too close for comfort / City, The / Bossa nova pot pourri / On the street where you live.
Note: Personnel: Mel Torme (vocals), Marty Paich (cond/arr/DX7), Dan Barrett (tbn), Chuck Berghofer (bass), Bob Efford (baritone sax), Bob Enevoldsen (valve tbn), Allen Farnham (piano), Gary Foster (alto sax), Warren Luning (tpt), Ken Peplowski (tenor sax), Jim Self (tuba), Jack Sheldon (tpt), John von Ohlen (drums). Recorded in Tokyo, 1988.
**Cass:** Released Jun '89, on Concord Jazz by Concord Jazz Records (USA). Catalogue no: **CJ 382 C**
**Album:** Released Jun '89, on Concord Jazz by Concord Jazz Records (USA). Catalogue no: **CJ 382**
**CD:** Released Jun '89, on Concord Jazz by Concord Jazz Records (USA). Catalogue no: **CCD 4382**

**IT HAPPENED IN MONTEREY (Torme, Mel & Mel-Tones)**
Tracks: / Dream awhile / Try a little tenderness / Born to be blue / There's no business like show business / That's where I came in / Night and day / Fine and dandy / There's no-one but you / It happened in Monterey / Willow Road / South America take it away.
Note: Sonny Burke and his orchestra.
**Album:** Released '88, on Discovery (USA) by Discovery Records (USA). Catalogue no: **MVS 510**

**IT'S A BLUE WORLD**
Tracks: / I got it bad and that ain't good / Till the clouds roll by / Isn't it romantic? / I know why / All this and Heaven too / How long has this been going on? / Polka dots and moonbeams / You leave me breathless / I found a million dollar baby / Wonderful one / It's a blue world / Stay as sweet as you are.
**Album:** Released May '85, on Affinity by Charly Records. Catalogue no: **AFF 138**

**LIVE AT THE CRESCENDO (AFFINITY)**
Tracks: / It's only a paper moon / What is this thing called love / One for my baby / Love is just a bug / Nightingale sang in berkely square / Autumn leaves / Just one of those things / Girl next door / Lover come back to me / Looking at you / Tender trap / I wish i was in love again / It's d'lovely / It's alright with me / Manhattan / Taking a chance on love / Home by the sea / I got plenty of nothing / Nobody's heart.
**2 LP Set:** Released Oct '82, on Affinity by Charly Records. Catalogue no: **AFF 100**

**LIVE AT THE CRESCENDO (CHARLY)**
Tracks: / Love is just a bug / Nobody's heart / It's only a paper moon / What is this thing called love / I got plenty o' nuttin' / Taking a chance / One for my baby / Nightingale sang in Berkeley Square, A / Just one of those things / Autumn leaves / Girl next door / Lover come back to me / I'm beginning to see the light / Looking at you / Tender trap, The / Tenderly / I wish I was in love again / It's de-lovely / It's allright with me / Home by the sea / Manhattan.
**CD:** Released '87, on Charly by Charly Records. Catalogue no: **CDCHARLY 60**

**LIVE AT THE CRESCENDO (MCA)**
**Album:** Released Jul '82, on MCA by MCA Records. Deleted Jul '87. Catalogue no: **MCL 1683**

**LULU'S BACK IN TOWN (See also under Paich, Marty) (Torme, Mel & Marty Paich)**
**CD:** Released Mar '90, on Giants of Jazz by Hasmick Promotions. Catalogue no: **GOJCD53010**
**Album:** Released Jun '85, on Charly by Charly Records. Catalogue no: **AFF 85**
**CD:** Released Mar '86, on Charly by Charly Records. Catalogue no: **CDCHARLY 5**

**LULU'S BACK IN TOWN (CD)**
Tracks: / Lulu's back in town / They can't take that away from me / Nice work if you get it / Way you look tonight / Foggy day, A / Lullaby of Birdland / Lady is a tramp, The / Let's call the whole thing off / When April comes again / Fine romance, A / Cheek to cheek / Let's face the music and dance / Piccolino, The / Blues, The / Top hat, white tie and tails / Something's gotta give / Carioca / Sing for your supper / When the sun comes out / I love to watch the moonlight / I like to recognise the tune / Keeping myself for you / Fascinating rhythm.
**CD:** Released '88, on Giants of Jazz by Hasmick Promotions. Catalogue no: **GOJCD 0230**

**MEL TORME (Compact / Walkman jazz)**
Tracks: / Too close for comfort / Stranger in town, A / Don't get around much anymore / Body and soul / Surrey with the fringe on top / Welcome to the club / Sent for you yesterday / Truckin'.
**Cass:** Released 27 Feb '88, on Verve Catalogue no: **833 282-4**
**Cass:** Released '88, on Entertainers Catalogue no: **ENT MC 13009**
**CD:** Released Mar '88, on Verve Catalogue no: **833 282-2**
**Cass:** Released Oct '84, on Audio Fidelity(USA) by Audio Fidelity (USA). Catalogue no: **ZCGAS 740**
**Album:** Released '88, on Entertainers Catalogue no: **ENT LP 13009**

**MEL TORME (2)**
Tracks: / That old feeling / Blues in the night / 'Round midnight / I don't want to cry anymore.
**Album:** Released Jan '83, on Verve (Import) Deleted Jan '88. Catalogue no: **IMS 2304 500**

**MEL TORME COLLECTION (20 golden greats)**
Tracks: / That old black magic / Blue moon / Get out of town / Jeepers creepers / From this moment on / Our love is here to stay / Mountain greenery / Bernie's tune / Old devil moon / Get happy / Don't you believe it / Along with me / Changing my tune / They can't convince me / Guilty / For you, for me, for evermore / You're driving me crazy / Goody goody / Christmas song, The / I believe.
**Cass:** Released Nov '85, on Deja Vu Catalogue no: **DVMC 2046**
**Album:** Released Nov '85, on Deja Vu Catalogue no: **DVLP 2046**

**MEL TORME AND FRIENDS RECORDED LIVE AT MARTY'S, NEW YORK CITY (Torme, Mel & Friends)**
Tracks: / Let's take a walk around the block / New York state of mind / When the world was young / Pick yourself up / Silly habits / Mountain greenery / Cottage for sale / Take a letter, Miss Jones / Real thing, The / Lines for Lyons / Venus de Milo / Walking shoes / Watch what happens / Fly me to the moon / You and the night and the music / Shakin' the blues away / Isn't it romantic / Summertime / They pass by, singin' / I got plenty o' nuttin / It take a long pull to get there / It ain't necessarily so / Strawberry woman / Oh Bess, oh where's my Bess? / Bess you is my woman / Folks who live on the hill, The / Chase me Charlie / Best is yet to come, The / Isn't it a pity / Wave / I guess I'll have to change my plan / Love for sale.
Note: Friends: Cy Coleman: songwriter, Janis Ian: singer, Gerry Mulligan: saxophone, Jonathan Schwartz: dj/singer. Trio accompaniment: Mike Renzie: piano, Rufus Reid or Jay Lionhart: bass,

Donny Osborne: drums. Duration 80 minutes approx.
**Album:** Released Apr '84, on Finesse Deleted '87. Catalogue no: **FIND 5661**
**Cass:** Released Apr '84, on Finesse Deleted '87. Catalogue no: **ZCFID 5661**

## MEL TORME (GLENDALE)
Tracks: / Easy to remember / My funny valentine / September song / April showers / Blues in the night.
Note: Tracks include those listed above.
**Album:** Released Jul '88, on Glendale (USA) by Glendale Records (USA). Catalogue no: **GL 6018**

## MEL TORME LIVE
Tracks: / You're driving me crazy / You're the top / When the red, red robin comes bob, bob, bobbin' along / Everything happens to me / It's a most unusual day / Pythagoras how you stagger us / French lesson, The / It's dark on observatory hill / I've got the sun in the morning and the moon at night / On a slow boat to China.
**Cass:** Released Sep '89, on Jasmine by Hasmick Promotions. Catalogue no: **JASMC 2529**
**Album:** Released Jan '88, on Sounds Great Catalogue no: **SG 5012**
**Album:** Released Sep '89, on Jasmine by Hasmick Promotions. Catalogue no: **JASM 2529**

## MEL TORME SINGS
Tracks: / I'm getting sentimental over you / I can't believe that you're in love with me / Prelude to a kiss / I've got the world on a string / Devil and the deep blue sea / I surrender dear / I let a song go out of my heart / Don't worry 'bout me / One morning in May / I can't give you anything but love.
**Cass:** Released Nov '84, on Astan (USA) Catalogue no: **40069**
**Album:** Released Nov '84, on Astan (USA) Catalogue no: **20069**
**Album:** Released Jul '82, on Bulldog Records by President Records. Catalogue no: **BDL 1017**

## MEL TORME SINGS ABOUT LOVE
**Album:** Released Aug '88, on Audiophile (USA) by Jazzology Records (USA). Catalogue no: **AP 67**

## MEL TORME, VOL.1
Tracks: / Foggy day, A / I cover the waterfront / But beautiful / Until the real thing comes along / Makin' whoopee / Three little words / It's dream time.
**Album:** Released '88, on Musicraft (USA) by Discovery Records (USA). Catalogue no: **MVS 508**

## MEL TORME WITH THE MEL-TONES - LIVE!
**Album:** Released Feb '89, on Sounds Great Catalogue no: **SG 5006**

## MEL TORME / ROB MCCONNELL AND BOSS BRASS
Tracks: / Just friends / September song / Don'cha go 'way mad / House is not a home, A / Song is you, The / Cow cow boogie / Handful of stars, A / Stars fell on Alabama / It don't mean a thing / Do nothing till you hear from me / Mood indigo / Take the 'A' train / Sophisticated lady / Satin doll.
**Album:** Released Oct '86, on Concord Jazz by Concord Jazz Records (USA). Catalogue no: **CJ 306**
**Cass:** Released Oct '86, on Concord Jazz by Concord Jazz Records (USA). Catalogue no: **CJC 306**
**CD:** Released Jan '87, on Concord Jazz by Concord Jazz Records (USA). Catalogue no: **CCD 4306**

## MOUNTAIN GREENERY
Tracks: / Mountain greenery.
**7" Single:** Released Apr '56, on Vogue by Vogue Records. Deleted Apr '59. Catalogue no: **Q 72150**

## MUSICAL SOUNDS ARE THE BEST SONGS
Tracks: / Flat foot floogie / Hut sut song, The / All of you / Just one more chance / It don't mean a thing / Tutti frutti / Cement mixer / Hold tight / Blue skies / Rose O'Day / Spellbound / I's a muggin'.
**Album:** Released Feb '83, on Jasmine by Hasmick Promotions. Catalogue no: **JASM 1004**

## PRIME TIME
**Album:** Released Jan '79, on Jazz Greats Catalogue no: **GP 701**

## RETROSPECTIVE, A 1956-68
**CD:** Released '88, on Stash (USA) Catalogue no: **STCD 4**

## REUNION (Torme, Mel & Marty Paich Dektette)
Tracks: / Sweet Georgia Brown / I'm wishing / Blues, The / Trolley song, The / More than you know / For whom the bell tolls / When you wish upon a star / Walk between raindrops / Bossa nova potpurri / Get me to the church on time / Goodbye look, The / Spain ( I can recall).
**CD:** Released Dec '88, on Concord Jazz by Concord Jazz Records (USA). Catalogue no: **CCD 4360**
**Album:** Released Dec '88, on Concord Jazz by Concord Jazz Records (USA). Catalogue no: **CJ 360**
**Cass:** Released Dec '88, on Concord Jazz by Concord Jazz Records (USA). Catalogue no: **CJ 360 C**

## ROUND MIDNIGHT
**Album:** Released Jun '86, on Stash (USA) Catalogue no: **ST 252**

## SINGS HIS CALIFORNIA SUITE (Torme, Mel Orchestra)
Tracks: / Mountain desert / We think the west coast is the best coast in the land / Coney Island / Miami waltz, The / They go to San Diego / Sunday night in San Fernando / Got the gate on the Golden Gate / Prelude to poor little extra girl / Poor little extra girl.
**Album:** Released Nov '84, on Discovery (USA) by Discovery Records (USA). Catalogue no: **DS 910**

## SMOOTH ONE, THE
**Cass:** Released Jun '88, on Starline (Jazz) Catalogue no: **SLC 61005**

**Mel Tormé - Swings (Verve)**

**SONGS OF NEW YORK**
**CD:** Released Oct '87, on WEA by WEA Records. Catalogue no: **780 078-2**

**SWINGS (See panel on previous page)**
Tracks: / Too close for comfort / Once in love with Amy / Sleeping Bee, A / On the street where you live / All I need is a girl / Just in time / Hello young lovers / Surrey with the fringe on top / Old devil moon / Whatever Lola wants (Lola gets) / Too darn hot / Lonely town / I'm gonna go fishin' / Don't get around much anymore / I like the sunrise / Take the 'A' train / Reminiscing in tempo / Just a sittin' and a' rockin' / Down for the double / I'm gonna move to the outskirts of town / Blue and sentimental / Oh what a night for love / Sent for you Yesterday / In the evening.
**2 LP Set:** Released , on Verve by Polydor Ltd. Catalogue no: **VSP 17/18**

**SWINGS SCHUBERT ALLEY**
Tracks: / Too close for comfort / Once in love with Amy / Sleeping bee / On the street where you live / Just in time / Whatever Lola wants (Lola gets) / Surrey with the fringe on top / Old devil moon / Too darn hot / Lonely town.
**Album:** Released Sep '81, on Verve (USA) by Polydor Ltd. Catalogue no: **2304 235**
**CD:** Released Oct '84, on Verve Deleted Mar '88. Catalogue no: **821 581-2**

**THAT'S ALL**
Tracks: / I've got you under my skin / That's all / What is there to say / Do I love you / Folks that live on the hill / Isn't it a pity / Ho ba la / PS I love you / Nearness of you / My romance / Second time around / Haven't we met.
**Album:** Released Aug '83, on CBS Cameo by CBS Records. Deleted '88. Catalogue no: **32313**

**THERE'S NO BUSINESS LIKE SHOW BUSINESS (Torme, Mel & Mel-Tones)**
Tracks: / It happened in Monterey / South America / Take it away / There's no one but you / Dream awhile / Try a little tenderness / Fine and dandy.
**Album:** Released Oct '82, on Musicraft (USA) by Discovery Records (USA). Catalogue no: **MVS 510**

**TORME**
Tracks: / All in love is fair / First time ever I saw your face, The / New York state of mind / Stars / Send in the clowns / Ordinary fool / When the world was young / Yesterday when I was young / Bye bye blackbird.
**Album:** Released Oct '84, on Verve (USA) by Polydor Ltd. Catalogue no: **823 010 4**
**CD:** Released Jan '87, on Rhapsody by President Records. Catalogue no: **RHCD 3**
**Album:** Released Aug '80, on Rhapsody by President Records. Catalogue no: **RHAP 3**
**Album:** Released Oct '84, on Verve (USA) by Polydor Ltd. Catalogue no: **2304 500**

**TORME SINGS ASTAIRE (Torme, Mel & Marty Paich Dektette)**
Tracks: / Nice work if you can get it / Something's gotta give / Foggy day, A / Fine romance, A / Let's call the whole thing off / Top hat, white tie and tails / Way you look tonight / Piccolino, The / They can't take that away from me / Cheek to cheek / Let's face the music and dance / They all laughed.
**Album:** Released Nov '83, on Affinity by Charly Records. Catalogue no: **AFF 107**
**CD:** Released Aug '87, on Charly by Charly Records. Catalogue no: **CDCHARLY 96**
**Cass:** Released Nov '83, on Affinity by Charly Records. Catalogue no: **TCAFF 107**

**VINTAGE YEAR (Torme, Mel & George Shearing)**
Tracks: / Whisper not / Love me or leave me / Out of this world / Some day I'll find you / Midnight sun / New York, New York / Since I fell for you / Way you look tonight / Anyone can whistle / Tune for humming, A / When Sunny gets blue / Little man you've had a busy day / Folks who live on the hill, The (Bonus track on CD only.) / Bittersweet (Bonus track on CD only.).
Note: "Recorded live at the fabulous Paul Masson Mountain Winery, Mel Torme and George Shearing are, quite simply, stunning
**Album:** Released May '88, on Concord Jazz by Concord Jazz Records (USA). Catalogue no: **CJ 341**
**Cass:** Released May '88, on Concord Jazz by Concord Jazz Records (USA). Catalogue no: **CJC 341**
**CD:** Released May '88, on Concord Jazz by Concord Jazz Records (USA). Catalogue no: **CCD 4341**

## Toshiko Mariano Quartet

**TOSHIKO MARIANO QUARTET**
**CD:** Released Jun '88, on Candid Catalogue no: **CCD 9012**
**Album:** Released May '86, on Candid Catalogue no: **CS 9012**

## Touff, Cy

**CY TOUFF, HIS OCTET AND QUINTET (Touff, Cy Octet & Quintet)**
**Album:** Released Feb '88, on Fresh Sounds (Spain) by Fresh Sounds Records (Spain). Catalogue no: **FS 51**

**TOUFF ASSIGNMENT**
**Album:** Released Feb '88, on Fresh Sounds (Spain) by Fresh Sounds Records (Spain). Catalogue no: **FS 62**

## Toussaint, Allen

**Biographical details:** Was born in 1938 in New Orleans; as a producer he has been making hits since he was a teenager, working for Dave Bartholomew at Cosimo Matassa's studio on Fats Domino records; he arranged Lee Allen's hit *Walking For Mr Lee* in 1958; his own first LP on RCA included *Java*, a hit for Al Hirt; he later worked for Joe Banashak's Minit label, overseeing huge R&B hits like Ernie K-Doe's *Mother-In-Law*. After military service he formed a partnership with Marshal Sehorn in 1965; they opened their famous Sea Saint studio in 1972. His songs have been widely covered and he has produced dozens of hit LPs, as well as several fine albums of his own. (Donald Clarke 13.1.88).

**FROM A WHISPER TO A SCREAM (Retro 85-88)**
Tracks: / From a whisper to a scream / Chokin' kind / Sweet touch of love / What is success / Working in the coalmine / Everything i do gonna be funky / Either / Louie / Cast your fate to the wind / Number nine / Pickles.
**Album:** Released Mar '85, on Kent by Ace Records. Catalogue no: **KENT 036**

**SOUTHERN NIGHTS**
Tracks: / Last train / Worldwide / Back in baby's arms / Country John / Basic lady / Southern nights / You will not lose / What do you want the girl to do / When the party's over / Cruel way to go down.
**Album:** Released Mar '85, on Edsel by Demon Records. Catalogue no: **ED 155**

**WILD SOUNDS OF NEW ORLEANS**
Tracks: / Up the creek / Tim Tam / Me And You / Bono / Java / Happy Times / Nowhere to go / Nashua / Po' Boy Walk / Pelican parade.
**Album:** Released Apr '88, on Edsel by Demon Records. Catalogue no: **ED 275**

**WITH THE STOKES**
**Album:** Released Jul '84, on Bandy (USA) Deleted '88. Catalogue no: **BANDY 70014**

**WORKING IN THE COALMINE**
Tracks: / Working down the coal mine / Down in the sewer.
**7" Single:** Released Apr '80, on Magnet by WEA Records. Deleted Apr '83. Catalogue no: **MAG 170**

## Town Hall Jazz

**LIVE - ON THE SUNNY SIDE OF THE STREET**
Tracks: / On the sunny side of the street / What's going on? / Mighty fine wine / For Heaven's sake / Cecil the Great / Mulligan stew / Ebb tide.
Note: Interesting line-up includes Joe Newman, Russell Jacquet (trumpets), Illinois Jacquet, James Moody (tenor saxes), Gerry Mulligan, Cecil Payne (baritone saxes), Kenny Drew (piano), Kenny Burrell (guitar), Roy Haynes (drums).
**Album:** Released Apr '81, on Jath Catalogue no: **JATH 11436**

## Towner, Ralph

**BATIK**
**Album:** Released '78, on ECM Catalogue no: **ECM 1121**

**BLUE SUN**
**CD:** Released Oct '86, on ECM Catalogue no: **829 162 2**
**Album:** Released Apr '83, on ECM Catalogue no: **ECM 1250**

**CITY OF EYES**
Note: City of eyes if Ralph Towner's first recording under his own name since the acclaimed 'Blue sun' album of '83. Re-

corded in '86 and '88, all the compositions are by Towner and include four solo guitar pieces. Elsewhere a formidable ensemble is featured: Markus Stockhausen (trumpets), Paul McCandless (oboe & English horn), Gary Peacock (bass) and Jerry Granelli (acoustic & electronic drums). Those familiar with Towner's Solstice recordings will especially welcome this new album.
**Album:** Released May '89, on ECM Catalogue no: **ECM 1388**
**CD:** Released May '89, on ECM Catalogue no: **837 754-2**

**DIARY**
Tracks: / Dark spirit / Entry in a diary / Images unseen / Icarus / Mon enfant / Ogden road / Erg / Silence of a candle, The.
Note: Ralph Towner-12 string and classical guitar, piano, gongs.
**Album:** Released Feb '75, on ECM Catalogue no: **ECM 1032**
**CD:** Released Aug '86, on ECM Catalogue no: **829 157 2**

**FIVE YEARS LATER (Towner, Ralph & John Abercrombie)**
**Album:** Released Mar '82, on ECM Catalogue no: **ECM 1207**

**MATCHBOOK (Towner, Ralph & Gary Burton)**
**CD:** Released Oct '88, on ECM Catalogue no: **835 014-2**
**Album:** Released Jun '75, on ECM Catalogue no: **ECM 1056**

**OLD FRIENDS, NEW FRIENDS**
**CD:** Released Oct '86, on ECM Catalogue no: **829 196 2**

**SARGASSO SEA (Towner, Ralph & John Abercrombie)**
**Album:** Released Oct '76, on ECM Catalogue no: **ECM 1080**
**CD:** Released Sep '88, on ECM Catalogue no: **835 015-2**

**SLIDE SHOW (Towner, Ralph & Gary Burton)**
Tracks: / Maelstrom / Vessel / Around the bend / Blue in green / Beneath an evening sky / Donkey jamboree / Continental breakfast / Charlotte's tangle / Innocenti.
Note: More than 10 years after their duet album "Matchbook", these two musicians got together again to record a fresh and inspired statement of the art of improvisors. "Slide show" presents both new and familiar compositions by Ralph Towner plus a vital version of the Miles Davis/Bill Evans standard "Blue & Green". The tunes range from fine lyrical songs to humorous calypso-like music. The interaction between these two fine musicians is breathtaking. Ralph Towner - classical and 12-string guitars. Gary Burton-vibraphone, marimba.
**Album:** Released Feb '86, on ECM Catalogue no: **ECM 1306**
**CD:** Released Feb '86, on ECM Catalogue no: **827 257-2**

**SOLO CONCERT**
Tracks: / Spirit lake / Ralph's piano waltz / Train of thought / Zoetrope / Nardis / Chelsea courtyard / Timeless.
**CD:** Released Dec '85, on ECM Catalogue no: **827 668-2**

**SOLSTICE**
Tracks: / Oceanus / Visitation / Drifting petals / Numbus / Winter solstice / Piscean dance / Red and black / Sand.
Note: Personnel: Ralph Towner-12 string an classical guitar, piano/Jan Garbarek-tenor and soprano saxophones, flute/Eberhard Weber-bass cello/John Christensen-drums, percussion.
**Album:** Released '82, on ECM Catalogue no: **ECM 1060**
**CD:** Released '82, on ECM Catalogue no: **825 458-2**

**SOUNDS AND SHADOWS (Towner, Ralph 's Solstice)**
**Album:** Released Nov '77, on ECM Catalogue no: **ECM 1095**

**TRIOS**
**Album:** Released '75, on ECM Catalogue no: **ECM 1025**

**TRIOS AND SOLOS (Towner, Ralph & Glen Moore)**
Note: With Paul McCandless and Collin Walcott.
**CD:** Released Jul '88, on ECM Catalogue no: **833 328-2**

**WORKS: RALPH TOWNER**
Tracks: / Oceanus / Blue sun / New moon / Beneath an evening sky / Prince and the sage, The / Nimbus.
Note: Personnel: Ralph Towner, Jan Gabarek, Eberhard Weber, Kenny Wheeler, Eddie Gomez, Jon Christensen.
**CD:** Released Jun '89, on ECM Catalogue no: **823 268-2**
**Album:** Released Jun '89, on ECM Catalogue no: **823 268-1**
**Cass:** Released Nov '83, on ECM Catalogue no: **3100 390**

## Townsend, Henry

**HENRY TOWNSEND AND HENRY SPAULDING 1929-37 (Townsend, Henry & Henry Spaulding)**
Note: Complete recordings in chronological order
**Album:** Released Jan '88, on Wolf Catalogue no: **WSE 117**

**ST. LOUIS BLUES**
**Album:** Released Mar '87, on Wolf Catalogue no: **120.495**

## Tracey, Clark

**Biographical details:** Was born in 1961 in London; he is a drummer, the son of Stan Tracey; he worked with his father and backed many a big visiting American star, and now leads his own highly rated quartet. (Donald Clarke 13.1.88).

**STIPERSTONES (Tracey, Clark Quintet)**
Tracks: / Nipstone rock / Scattered rock / Cranberry rock / Devil's chair / Shepherd's rock / Manstone rock / Nipstone rock (reprise).
**Album:** Released Mar '88, on Steam Catalogue no: **SJ 115**

Stan Tracey

**SUDDENLY LAST TUESDAY (Tracey, Clark Quintet)**
**Album:** Released Jun '86, on Cadillac by Cadillac Music. Catalogue no: **SGC 1013**

## Tracey, Stan

**Biographical details:** Was born in 1926 in London; the pianist and composer has stuck out a long, often thankless career to become one of the most highly rated UK jazzmen. He turned professional at 16, was house pianist at Ronnie Scott's club 1969-70, recording with Zoot Sims, Ben Webster etc; he recorded with Sonny Rollins on his soundtrack for film Alfie in 1966. He has gigged all over Europe with groups up to tentet and larger bands as well as solo. His best-known compositions is *Under Milkwood*, inspired by Dylan Thomas's play, recorded in 1965 by a quartet including Bobby Wellins (born in Glasgow in 1936), and in 1976 at Wigmore Hall, narrated by Donald Houston, with Art Themen on tenor (born in 1939). Other LPs include solo albums, duos with Keith Tippett and John Surman, and various small group sets; his solo Plays *Duke Ellington* is very highly rated. (Donald Clarke 13.1.88).

**ALONE (AT WIGMORE HALL 1974)**
**Album:** Released Jul '78, on Cadillac by Cadillac Music. Catalogue no: **SGC 1003**

**BRACKNELL CONNECTION**
**Album:** Released Apr '81, on Steam Catalogue no: **SJ 103**

**CAPTAIN ADVENTURE**
**Album:** Released Apr '81, on Steam Catalogue no: **SJ 102**

**GENESIS AND MORE... (Tracey, Stan & His Orchestra)**
Tracks: / Beginning, The / Light, The / Firmament, The / Gathering, The / Sun, moon & the stars, The / Feather, fin & limb / Sixth day, The.
Note: A prolific composer,Stan Tracey is probably best known for his interpretation ofDylan Thomas's "Under Milk Wood".His new work "Genesis" based on the creation has already been performed at Ronnie Scott's Club (residency 28th February--7th March).Reviews have been extremely good for both the performance and the album. Over 60 minutes of music.
**Album:** Released Mar '87, on Steam Catalogue no: **SJ 114**
**CD:** Released Nov '89, on Steam Catalogue no: **SJCD 114**
**Cass:** Released Nov '89, on Steam Catalogue no: **SJCAS 114**

**HELLO, OLD ADVERSARY**
**Album:** Released Apr '81, on Steam Catalogue no: **SJ 107**

**LIVE AT RONNIE SCOTT'S (Tracey's, Stan Hexad)**
**Album:** Released Jun '86, on Steam Catalogue no: **SJ 113**

**NOW**
**Album:** Released '88, on Steam Catalogue no: **SJ 110**

**ORIGINAL (Tracey, Stan & Mike Osborne)**
**Album:** Released '74, on Cadillac by Cadillac Music. Catalogue no: **SGC 1002**

**PLAYS DUKE ELLINGTON**
Tracks: / I let a song go out of my heart / Prelude to a kiss / Satin doll / In a mellow tone / Day dream / Great times / Sophisticated lady / Black butterfly / Lotus blossom.
**CD:** Released Jan '90, on Mole Catalogue no: **CDMOLE 10**
**Album:** Released '86, on Mole Catalogue no: **MOLE 10**

**POET'S SUITE, THE (Tracey, Stan Quartet)**
**Album:** Released '88, on Steam Catalogue no: **SJ 111**

**SALISBURY SUITE**
**Album:** Released Apr '81, on Steam Catalogue no: **SJ 105**

**SOUTH EAST ASSIGNMENT (Tracey, Stan Quartet)**
**Album:** Released '88, on Steam Catalogue no: **SJ 108**

**TANDEM (Tracey, Stan & Mike Osborne)**
**Album:** Released Mar '77, on Ogun by Cadillac Music. Catalogue no: **OG 210**

**TNT (Tracey, Stan/Keith Tippett)**
**Album:** Released '79, on Steam Catalogue no: **SJ 104**

**WE STILL LOVE YOU MADLY (tribute to Duke Ellington) (Tracey, Stan & His Orchestra)**
Tracks: / I'm beginning to see the light / Mood indigo / Blue feeling / I let a song go out of my heart / Stomp look and listen / Festival junction / In a sentimental mood / Just squeeze me / Lay by.
**CD:** Released 12 Apr '89, on Mole Jazz by Mole Jazz Records. Catalogue no: **MOLECD 13**
**Album:** Released 12 Apr '89, on Mole Jazz by Mole Jazz Records. Catalogue no: **MOLE 13**
**Cass:** Released 12 Apr '89, on Mole Jazz by Mole Jazz Records. Catalogue no: **MOLEMC 13**

## Trad Jazz

**TRAD JAZZ (Various artists)**
Tracks: / Royal garden blues: *Various artists* / April showers: *Various artists* / Winin' boy blues: *Various artists* / Alexander's ragtime band: *Various artists* / Snag it: *Various artists* / Pananma rag: *Various artists* / Saved by the blues: *Various artists* / Sister Kate: *Various artists* / We shall march through the streets of the city: *Various artists* / Bei mir bist du schen: *Various artists* / Hot time in the old town tonight: *Various artists* / Louisiana: *Various artists* / Gettysburg march: *Various artists* / T'aint no sin: *Various artists* / Go Ghana: *Various artists* / There'll be some changes made: *Various artists* / Ostrich walk: *Various artists* / Beale Street blues: *Various artists* / Stop, look and listen: *Various artists* / When the Saints go marching in: *Various artists.*
**Album:** Released Apr '79, on Pye Deleted Apr '84. Catalogue no: **GH 669**
**Cass:** Released May '89, on PRT by Castle Communications Records. Catalogue no: **C 907**
**CD:** Released May '89, on PRT by Castle Communications Records. Catalogue no: **GHCD 7**

## Trad Jazz Festival

**TRAD JAZZ FESTIVAL (Various artists)**
Tracks: / Marching through Georgia: *Various artists* / American patrol: *Various artists* / Tishomingo blues: *Various artists* / Whistling Rufus: *Various artists* / Sur le pont d'Avignon: *Various artists* / Delia's gone: *Various artists* / One sweet letter from you: *Various artists* / Dinah: *Various artists* / Travelling blues: *Various artists* / Petite Fleur: *Various artists* / Easter parade: *Various artists.*
**Cass:** Released Jul '82, on Ditto by Pickwick Records. Catalogue no: **DTO 10019**

## Traditional Jazz...

**TRADITIONAL JAZZ (Various artists)**
**2 LP Set:** Released Oct '88, on Vogue by Vogue Records. Catalogue no: **416038**

**TRADITIONAL JAZZ IN RURAL (Various artists)**
**Album:** Released '88, on Truth (2) Catalogue no: **TLP 1001**

## Transatlantic Jazz

**FIRST CROSSING**
**Album:** Released Oct '87, on Fresh Sounds (Spain) by Fresh Sounds Records (Spain). Catalogue no: **FS 239**

## Tribute To...

**GLENN MILLER TRIBUTE (Various artists)**
Note: An hour of music and memories -- recorded 5 June, 1945 -- in honour of Miller by some of his closest friends, including Tex Beneke, Gene Krupa, Count Basie, Cab Calloway and Benny Goodman. Songs include Ida, Drum Boogie, B-Flat, Gotta Be This Or That and Robin Hood.
**Album:** Released Apr '88, on Sounds Great Catalogue no: **SG 8009**

**TRIBUTE TO DUKE (Various artists)**
**CD:** Released Jan '90, on GRP by GRP Records (USA). Catalogue no: **CCD 4050**

**TRIBUTE TO MONK AND BIRD, A (Various artists)**
Tracks: / Air conditioning: *Various artists* / Au privave: *Various artists* / Ba-lue bolivar ba-lues are: *Various artists* / Straight no chaser: *Various artists* / Mis-

terioso: *Various artists* / Perhaps: *Various artists*.
**Album:** Released Mar '88, on Affinity by Charly Records. Catalogue no: **AFFD 187**

**TRIBUTE TO PAUL WHITEMAN (Various artists)**
Note: Telecast 24 March, 1960. With Peggy Lee, Jack Teagarden, Bing Crosby and Peter Nero.
**Album:** Released Jan '88, on Sounds Great Catalogue no: **SG 8015**

**TRIBUTE TO TOMMY DORSEY (Various artists)**
Note: Telecast, 1 December, 1956. After Dorsey's death close friend Jackie Gleason gathered together members of Dorsey bands past and present for this one-hour musical special. Tunes include Royal Garden Blues, Daybreak, I'll Never Smile Again and an 11-part medley of Dorsey standards.
**Album:** Released Jan '88, on Sounds Great Catalogue no: **SG 8014**

## Tristano, Lennie

**Biographical details:** Was born in 1919 in Chicago during an epidemic of measles; he went totally blind by the time he was 11 years old. He died in 1978. As a pianist and composer his unique approach to harmony made him a legend and an important teacher, although he rarely played in public and made few records. He also played reeds as a youngster, absorbing everything. His students included Warne Marsh, Lee Konitz and Billy Bauer (guitarist with the Woody Herman band). *The Lost Session* was made with the trombonist Earl Swope in 1945; he went to New York City in 1946 and 19 tracks made for Keynote in the late '40s have just been reissued. At sextet sessions in 1949-50, two tracks were probably the first attempts at 'free jazz' ever made; Capitol was outraged and tried to refuse to pay for the dates. These are now in Affinity's *Crosscurrents* album with tracks on the other side by Tadd Dameron. Tristano was later associated with the British bassist Peter Ind, who now runs the North London jazz club, the Bass Clef. (Donald Clarke 13.1.88).

**BLUES OF A KIND**
**Album:** Released Aug '89, on Braba Catalogue no: **BB 01**

**COOL IN JAM**
**Album:** Released Apr '81, on Jazz Live (Italy) Catalogue no: **BLJ 8033**

**CROSS CURRENTS (Tristano, Lennie & Tadd Dameron)**
Tracks: / Wow / Crosscurrent / Yesterdays / Marionette / Sax of a King / Intuition / Digression / Sid's delight / Casbah / John's delight / What's new / Heaven's doors are open wide / Focus.
**Album:** Released '86, on Affinity by Charly Records. Catalogue no: **AFF 149**

**IN EUROPE (Tristano, Lennie/Lee Konitz)**
**Album:** Released Apr '81, on Unique Jazz by Spotlite Records. Catalogue no: **UJ 21**

**LENNIE TRISTANO**
Tracks: / Line up / Requiem / Turkish mambo / East thiry-second / These foolish things / You go to my head / If I had you / Ghost of a change / All the things you are.
**Album:** Released '77, on Atlantic by WEA Records. Deleted '82. Catalogue no: **K 50245**

**MANHATTAN STUDIO**
**Album:** Released Sep '83, on Elektra by Elektra Records (UK). Deleted Jan '88. Catalogue no: **960 264 1**

**NEW SOUNDS IN THE FORTIES (Tristano, Lennie/Boyd Raeburn)**
**Album:** Released Apr '81, on Jazz Live (Italy) Catalogue no: **BLJ 8007**

## Trombone..

**I MAESTRI DI TROMBONE (Various artists)**
Note: Features Kid Ory, Tommy Dorsey, Trummy Young, Kai Winding, Miff Mole.
**Album:** Released May '88, on Musica Jazz Catalogue no: **2MJP 1054**

**TROMBONE ALBUM, THE (Various artists)**
**2 LP Set:** Released Oct '85, on Savoy (France) Catalogue no: **WL 70523**

## Troup, Bobby

**Biographical details:** Is a songwriter, pianist and vocalist who was born in 1918 in Harrisburg, Pennsylvania. He was a staff songwriter with Tommy Dorsey; wrote, produced and directed service musicals during World War 2; wrote hits *(Get Your Kicks On) Route 66!* and *Baby, Baby All The Time* for Nat Cole Trio in 1946, settled in Hollywood. He was married to Julie London, produced her albums; many film songs included *The Girl Can't Help It*, title song of the delightful rock 'n' roll movie in 1956: he must be the only songwriter who co-wrote with Johnny Mercer (*I'm With You*) and also wrote a hit for Little Richard. (Donald Clarke 13.1.88).

**BOBBY TROUP PLAYS JOHNNY MERCER**
Tracks: / Jamboree ones / Midnight sun / Come rain or come shine / Laura / That old black magic / One for my baby / Cuckoo in the clock / Day in, day out / Jeepers, creepers / Lazy Mood (Love's got me in a) / Skylark / I'm with you.
Note: A Bethleham Recording. This compilation P 1987 Charly Records Ltd. This compilation C 1987 Charly Records Ltd.
**Album:** Released Jun '87, on Affinity by Charly Records. Deleted '88. Catalogue no: **AFF 174**

**DISTINCTIVE STYLE OF BOBBY TROUP, THE**
**Album:** Released Aug '87, on Fresh Sounds (Spain) by Fresh Sounds Records (Spain). Catalogue no: **FS 234**

**IN A CLASS BEYOND COMPARE**
Note: Featuring Al Viola, Bobby Enevoldson.
**Album:** Released Aug '88, on Audiophile (USA) by Jazzology Records (USA). Catalogue no: **AP 98**

## Trumbauer, Frankie

**Biographical details:** Was born in 1901 in Carbondale, Illinois and died in 1956 in Kansas City. He played C-melody sax, also sang and played other instruments; his nickname was 'Tram'. He was the best white saxophonist of the 1920s, a great technician who could play hot and also liked to play pretty; he influenced Lester Young, Benny Carter, Buddy Tate and many others, and was unjustly neglected long before his death. He worked with Bix Beiderbecke in the Jean Goldkette band, where Tram was music director; Bix & Tram's classic small-group sides in 1927 included *Singin' The Blues*, the finest white jazz of the day; they also worked together with Adrian Rollini and Paul Whiteman. Tram co-led the Three Ts in 1936 with brothers Charlie and Jack Teagarden. He later became a pilot, worked in civil aeronautics and played at a Bix tribute in 1952. (Donald Clarke 13.1.88).

**JACK TEAGARDEN & FRANKIE TRUMBAUER (Trumbauer, Frankie / Teagarden, Jack)**
Tracks: / Dixie Lee / Clambake / Fare thee well to Harlem / I'm so in love with you / Basin street blues / Christmas night in Harlem / Beale street blues / Prohibition / Wildcat / Bouncing ball / F blues / Nobody's sweetheart / Wabash blues / Flight of the haybag / Old man of the mountain, The / I'm the mayor of Alabam' / China boy.
**Album:** Released Apr '79, on Aircheck (USA) by Kiner Ents.(USA). Catalogue no: **AIRCHECK 9**

## Trumpet...

**TRUMPET CALLS FOR THE ARMY (Close, A.E.)**
**Cass:** Released Jul '83, on Major Richards Catalogue no: **CDR 44**

**TRUMPET KINGS (Various artists)**
**Album:** Released Oct '75, on Pablo Jazz (USA) by Pablo Records (USA). Catalogue no: **231 0754**
**Cass:** Released Oct '75, on Pablo Jazz (USA) by Pablo Records (USA). Catalogue no: **K10 754**

## Trumpet Album

**TRUMPET ALBUM (Various artists)**
**Album:** Released Mar '85, on Savoy Jazz (USA) by Malaco Records (USA). Catalogue no: **SJL 2237**

## Trumpet Blues

**TRUMPET BLUES 1925/29 (Various artists)**
**Album:** Released '78, on Historical (USA) by Biograph Records (USA). Catalogue no: **HLP 27**

## Trumpet Time

**TRUMPET TIME (Various artists)**
Note: Including Louis Armstrong, Buck Clayton, Eldridge, B. Hackett, Y. Lawson.
**Album:** Released Mar '87, on Jazz Society Catalogue no: **AA 511**

## Tucker, Bessie

**1928 RECORDINGS (also see Ida Mae Mack) (Tucker, Bessie & Ida Mae Mack)**
**Album:** Released Jul '79, on Magpie by Interstate Music. Catalogue no: **PY 1815**

**QUEEN OF TEXAS BLUES (1928-29)**
**Album:** Released Aug '89, on Document Catalogue no: **DLP 556**

**RARE BLUES (1927 - 1935)**
**Album:** Released Jan '74, on Historical (USA) by Biograph Records (USA). Catalogue no: **HLP 4**

## Tucker, Mickey

**Biographical details:** Mickey Tucker was born in Durham, North Carolina in 1941; he is a fine jazz pianist and composer who deserves to be better known. He recorded with Roland Kirk, James Moody, drummer Jake Hanna and many others; his own albums have been highly praised with roots in Fats Waller and Earl Hines and technique to match: his solos are full of pleasant surprises, with often furious energy. He appeared at Ronnie Scott's in 1985 with Benny Golson..

**CRAWL, THE**
**Album:** Released Apr '81, on Muse by Black & Blue Records. Catalogue no: **MR 5223**

**MISTER MYSTERIOUS**
**Album:** Released Apr '81, on Muse by Black & Blue Records. Catalogue no: **MR 5174**

**SWEET LOTUS LIPS**
Tracks: / Gettin' there / Return ticket / All of you / Sweet lotus lips / Portrait of a peaceful scene / There for a woogie boogie / Kap'n'kryptonito / Tribute to Bean, A / Japanese soundscope / Bogue ballad bossa.
**CD:** Released Jun '89, on Denon Catalogue no: **DC 8552**
**Album:** Released Mar '82, on Denon Deleted '88. Catalogue no: **YX 7535**

**BOOGIE WOOGIE, THEME FROM**
**Album:** Released Mar '82, on Denon Deleted '88. Catalogue no: **YX 7804**

## Tucker, Sophie

**Biographical details:** Sophie Tucker was born Sophie Kalish-Abuza in 1884, on the run from Russian pogroms; she died in New York City in 1966. She had 20 big hits between 1910 and 1937 including two recordings of her theme *Some Of These Days*; she recorded with jazzmen like Miff Mole, Jimmy Dorsey, Red Nichols, Eddie Lang. Her material was often extremely blue and could not be broadcast. She made her London debut in 1922 at the Hippodrome in a revue with comic George Robey; the Lord Chamberlain objected to her references to the Prince Of Wales; at her first Royal Command Performance in 1934: she greeted George V with *Hiya, King!*. She made several films, appeared in Cole Porter musical *Leave It To Me*; described as a battleship with a voice like 70 trombones', she handed out advice to ladies in half-sung, half-spoken style; marked later decades with *Life Begins at 40, I'm Having More Fun Now I'm Fifty, I'm Having More Fun Since I'm Sixty, I'm Starting All Over Again.* She last performed in 1963. (Donald Clarke 13.1.88).

**ALL OF ME**
**Album:** Released '88, on Look by Look Records. Catalogue no: **LKLP 6046**

**FOLLOW A STAR**
Tracks: / Follow a star / That's where the south begins / Oh you have no idea / Washing the blues from my soul / Making wickey wackey down in Waikiki / There's something Spanish in my eyes / I'm the last of the red hot mamas / If your kisses can't hold the man you love / 'Cause I fell lowdown / I can never think of the words / That man of my dreams / What good am I without you? / Aren't women wonderful? / Some of these days.
**Album:** Released 1 Mar '87, on Living Era by Academy Sound & Vision Records. Catalogue no: **AJA 5046**
**Cass:** Released 1 Mar '87, on Living Era by Academy Sound & Vision Records. Catalogue no: **ZC AJA 5046**

**GOLDEN AGE OF SOPHIE TUCKER, THE**
**Cass:** Released Jul '85, on Golden Age by EMI Records. Catalogue no: **GX 41 2533 3**
**Album:** Released Jul '85, on Golden Age by EMI Records. Catalogue no: **GX 41 2533 1**

**LAST OF THE RED HOT MAMA'S**
Tracks: / Aggravatin' Papa / Hule Lou / Some of these days / Red hot Mama / You've got to see Mama every night / After you've gone / I ain't nobody / 50,000,000 Frenchmen can't be wrong / My yiddishe momma / What'll you do / One sweet letter from you / There'll be some changes made / I ain't taking orders from no one.
**Album:** Released Aug '83, on CBS Cameo by CBS Records. Deleted '88. Catalogue no: **32318**

**SOME OF THESE DAYS**
**Album:** Released Aug '76, on Retrospect by EMI Records. Catalogue no: **SH 234**
**Cass:** Released Aug '76, on Retrospect by EMI Records. Catalogue no: **TC SH 234**

**SOPHIE TUCKER COLLECTION (20 Golden Greats)**
Tracks: / Red hot mama / My Yiddishe momma / Hula Lou / Stay at home, papa / Man I love, The / Louisville lady / What'll you do? / I've got a cross-eyed papa / When a lady meets a gentleman down South / Oh, you have no idea / Some of these days / No one man is ever going to worry me / Aggravatin' papa / I ain't taking orders from no one / Life begins at forty / He hadn't up 'til yesterday.
**Album:** Released Jan '87, on Deja Vu Catalogue no: **DVLP 2099**
**Cass:** Released Jan '87, on Deja Vu Catalogue no: **DVMC 2099**

## Tucker, Tommy

**1933: TOMMY TUCKER (Tucker, Tommy & His Californians)**
**Album:** Released Aug '88, on Circle (USA) by Jazzology Records (USA). Catalogue no: **CLP 124**

**1942: TOMMY TUCKER (Tucker, Tommy & His Orchestra)**
**Album:** Released Aug '88, on Circle (USA) by Jazzology Records (USA). Catalogue no: **CLP 15**

**HI HEEL SNEAKERS**
Tracks: / High heel sneakers / Is that the way God planned it.
**7" Single:** Released Sep '82, on Red Lightnin' by Red Lightning Records. Deleted Jun '89. Catalogue no: **RL 450031**

**MEMPHIS BADBOY**
Tracks: / Miller's cave / Man in love, The / Lovin' Lil / You learn something now everyday / Ghost of Mary Lou, The / You don't love me / Miller's cave (2) / Will the circle be unbroken / I couldn't believe it was true / Joe Bodine / I ain't had enough / You hitched your wagon to a loser / Bridge of life, The / Glory train / Will the circle be unbroken (part 2).
**Album:** Released Sep '87, on Zu Zazz by Zu Zazz Records. Catalogue no: **Z 2001**

**MOTHER TUCKER**
**Album:** Released Aug '84, on Red Lightnin' by Red Lightning Records. Catalogue no: **RL 022**

**ROCKS IS MY PILLOW, COLD GROUND IS MY BED**
Tracks: / Alimony / Made your move too soon / J.R.'s blues / Isn't she sweet / Five long years / I just want to make love to you / Watch out / You're the one.
**Album:** Released Sep '82, on Red Lightnin' by Red Lightning Records. Catalogue no: **RL 0037**

## Turner, Big Joe

**Biographical details:** Turner, a vocalist and pianist in the East Coast stride style with blues feeling, was born in 1907 in Baltimore. He went to New York City around 1925 and played with Benny Carter, Louis Armstrong and others; he accompanied Adelaide Hall in the 1930's and came to Europe with her; he returned to Europe in 1948 and was based in Paris. He is often confused with blues singer Big Joe Turner; to confuse matters further, they both had recorded for the Continental labels Black and Blue and MPS. (Donald Clarke 13.1.88).

**ANOTHER EPOCH STRIDE PIANO**
**Album:** Released '82, on Pablo Jazz

(USA) by Pablo Records (USA). Catalogue no: **231 0763**
**Cass:** Released '82, on Pablo Jazz (USA) by Pablo Records (USA). Catalogue no: **K10 763**

**BEST OF JOE TURNER**
**Album:** Released '82, on Pablo Jazz (USA) by Pablo Records (USA). Catalogue no: **231 0848**
**Cass:** Released '82, on Pablo Jazz (USA) by Pablo Records (USA). Catalogue no: **K10 848**

**BIG JOE RIDES AGAIN**
**Album:** Released Jun '88, on Atlantic by WEA Records. Catalogue no: **90668**

**BIG JOE TURNER**
Tracks: / Roll em' Pete / Cherry red / Testing the blues / Morning glories / Low down dog / St. Louis blues / You're driving me crazy.
**Album:** Released 10 Jul '89, on KC Catalogue no: **KC 108**
**Album:** Released '88, on Southland by Delta Records. Catalogue no: **SLP 13**

**BIG JOE TURNER MEMORIAL ALBUM**
Tracks: / Miss Bump Suzie / Chill is on, The / I'll never stop loving you / Don't you cry / Poor lover's blues / Still in love / Baby I still want you / T.V. mama / Married woman / You know I love you / Midnight cannonball / In the evening / Morning noon and night / Ti-Ri-Lee / Lipstick, powder and paint / Rock a while / After a while / Trouble in mind / World of trouble / Love rollercoaster / I need a girl / Teenage letter / Wee baby blues / (We're gonna) Jump for joy / Sweet Sue / My reasons for living / Love oh careless love / Got you on my mind / Chains of love / My little honeydripper / Tomorrow night / Honey, hush.
**Cass set:** Released Jun '87, on Atlantic by WEA Records. Catalogue no: **781 663-4**
**2 LP Set:** Released Jun '87, on Atlantic by WEA Records. Catalogue no: **781 663-1**

**BLUES TRAIN (Turner, Big Joe & Roomful of Blues)**
Tracks: / Crawdad hole / Red sails in the sunset / Cocka-doodle-doo / Jumpin' for Joe / I want a little girl / I know you love me / Last night / I love the way (my baby sings the blues) / Blues train.
**Album:** Released Aug '86, on Muse by Black & Blue Records. Catalogue no: **MR 5293**
**CD:** Released Feb '87, on Muse (USA) by Muse Records (USA). Catalogue no: **MCD 5293**
**Cass:** Released Aug '86, on Muse (USA) by Muse Records (USA). Catalogue no: **MRC 5293**

**BOOGIE WOOGIE AND MORE**
Tracks: / Goin' away blues / Roll 'em, Pete / Cherry red / Baby, look at you / Lovin' mama blues / Cafe Society rag / How long, how long blues / Shake it and break it / Low down dirty shame blues / Joe Turner blues / Beale street blues / I got a gal for every day in the week / It's the same old story / Around the clock (part 1) / Around the clock (part 2) / Married woman blues.
**Album:** on Official by Official Records. Catalogue no: **OFF 6028**

**BOSS OF THE BLUES (That's jazz - Vol.14)**
Tracks: / Cherry red / Roll 'em Pete / I want a little girl / Low down dog / Wee baby blues / You're driving me crazy / How long blues / Morning glories / St. Louis blues / Piney Brown blues.
**CD:** Released '88, on Atlantic by WEA Records. Catalogue no: **K 781 459 2**
**Album:** Released Jul '76, on Atlantic by WEA Records. Catalogue no: **K 50244**

**BOSSES OF THE BLUES (Turner, Joe & T Bone Walker)**
Tracks: / Lonesome train / Corinne Corinna / How long, how long blues / Careless love / Two loves have I / Every day I have the blues / Vietnam / Shake it baby / Cold, cold feeling / Sail on.
**CD:** Released Nov '89, on Bluebird (2) by BMG Records (UK). Catalogue no: **ND 88311**
**Album:** Released Nov '89, on Bluebird (2) by BMG Records (UK). Catalogue no: **NL 88311**
**Cass:** Released Nov '89, on Bluebird (2) by BMG Records (UK). Catalogue no: **NK 88311**

**GREAT RHYTHM AND BLUES OLDIES**
**Album:** Released Feb '83, on Carosello Catalogue no: **BRP 2024**

**GREAT RHYTHM AND BLUES - VOL.4**
Tracks: / Honey hush / Chains of love / Roll 'em Pete / Piney Brown blues / Cherry red / Nothin' from nothin' blues / Shake, rattle and roll / Corina Corina / T.V. mama / Wee baby blues / Squeeze me, baby.
**Album:** Released Jul '82, on Bulldog Records by President Records. Catalogue no: **BDL 1003**

**GREATEST HITS: BIG JOE TURNER**
**Album:** Released Jun '88, on Atlantic by WEA Records. Catalogue no: **817521**
**Album:** Released Sep '87, on Atlantic (Import) by WEA Records. Catalogue no: **817521**

**HAVE NO FEAR, BIG JOE IS HERE**
Tracks: / S.K. Blues / Watch that jive / Howling wind / Low down dog / Mad blues / Playboy blues / My gal's a jockey / Sally Zu-Zazz / Oowee baby blues / Lucille Lucille / Careless love / Hollywood bed / Johnson & Turner blues / I got love for sale.
**Cass set:** Released Jul '86, on RCA by BMG Records (UK). Deleted Jun '88. Catalogue no: **WK 70822**
**2 LP Set:** Released Jul '86, on RCA by BMG Records (UK). Catalogue no: **WL 70822**
**2 LP Set:** Released Mar '85, on Savoy Jazz (USA) by Malaco Records (USA). Catalogue no: **SJL 2223**

**HAVE NO FEAR, JOE TURNER IS HERE**
Tracks: / Rocks in my bed / So long / Howlin' wind / Woman you must be crazy / How come my dog don't bark.
**Cass:** Released '82, on Pablo Jazz (USA) by Pablo Records (USA). Catalogue no: **K10 863**
**Album:** Released '82, on Pablo Jazz (USA) by Pablo Records (USA). Catalogue no: **231 0863**

**HONEY HUSH**
Tracks: / Shake, rattle and roll / Chains of love / Roll 'em hawk / Piney Brown blues / Cherry red / Nothin' from nothin' blues / Honey hush / Corina Corina / T.V. mama / Wee baby blues / Squeeze me baby.
**Album:** Released Aug '88, on Magnum Force by Magnum Music Group. Catalogue no: **MFLP 064**

**I DON'T DIG IT**
Tracks: / Goin' to Chicago blues / I can't give you anything but love / Blues in the night / Rocks in my bed / Sun risin' blues / Mardigras boogie / Cry baby blues / Rainy weather blues / I don't dig it / Boogie woogie baby / My heart belongs to you / Born to gamble / I love you, I love you / Oo-ouch-stop / Wish I had a dollar / Fuzzy wuzzy honey.
**Album:** Released May '86, on Jukebox Lil (Sweden) Catalogue no: **JB 618**

**IN THE EVENING**
**Cass:** Released '82, on Pablo Jazz (USA) by Pablo Records (USA). Catalogue no: **K10 776**
**Album:** Released '82, on Pablo Jazz (USA) by Pablo Records (USA). Catalogue no: **231 0776**

**JUMPIN' THE BLUES (Turner, Joe / Pete Johnson)**
**Album:** Released May '81, on Arhoolie (USA) by Arhoolie Records (USA). Catalogue no: **ARHOOLIE 2004**

**JUMPIN' TONIGHT**
**Album:** Released Apr '85, on Pathe Marconi (France) Catalogue no: **PM 1561431**

**JUMPIN' WITH JOE**
Tracks: / Bump Miss Susie / Honey bush / Ti-ri-lee / Oke-she-moke-she-pop / T.V. mama / Shake, rattle and roll / In the evening when the sun goes down / Well all right / Morning, noon and night / Hide and seek / Flip flop and fly / Chicken and the hawk / Boogie woogie country girl / Lipstick, powder and paint / Teenage letter / We're gonna jump for joy.
**Cass:** Released Apr '84, on Charly R&B by Charly Records. Deleted '88. Catalogue no: **TCCRB 1070**
**Album:** Released Apr '84, on Charly R&B by Charly Records. Deleted '88. Catalogue no: **CRB 1070**

**KANSAS CITY, HERE I COME**
Tracks: / Down home blues / Call the plumber / Since I fell for you / Kansas City here I come / Big leg woman / Sweet sixteen / Time after time.
**Album:** Released Sep '84, on Pablo

Jazz (USA) by Pablo Records (USA). Catalogue no: **231 0904**

**KANSAS CITY SHOUT (Turner, Joe, Count Basie & Eddie Vinson)**
**Cass:** Released '82, on Pablo Jazz (USA) by Pablo Records (USA). Catalogue no: **K10 859**
**Album:** Released '82, on Pablo Jazz (USA) by Pablo Records (USA). Catalogue no: **231 0859**

**MIDNIGHT SPECIAL**
Tracks: / I left my heart in San Francisco / I'm gonna sit right down / I can't give you anything but love / You're driving me crazy / So long / After my laughter came the tears / Midnight special / Stoop down baby.
**Album:** Released Sep '80, on Pablo Jazz (USA) by Pablo Records (USA). Deleted Sep '85. Catalogue no: **201 084 4**
**Cass:** Released '82, on Pablo Jazz (USA) by Pablo Records (USA). Catalogue no: **K10 844**
**Album:** Released '82, on Pablo Jazz (USA) by Pablo Records (USA). Catalogue no: **231 0844**

**NOBODY IN MIND (Turner, Joe & Jimmy Witherspoon)**
**Album:** Released '82, on Pablo Jazz (USA) by Pablo Records (USA). Catalogue no: **231 0760**

**PATCHA PATCHA (Turner, Joe & Jimmy Witherspoon)**
Tracks: / Patcha patcha / Blues lament / You got me runnin' / Kansas City on my mind / JT's blues / I want a little girl.
**Album:** Released Sep '86, on Pablo Jazz (USA) by Pablo Records (USA). Catalogue no: **231 0913**
**Cass:** Released Sep '86, on Pablo Jazz (USA) by Pablo Records (USA). Catalogue no: **K10 913**

**ROCK THIS JOINT**
Tracks: / Roll me baby / Low down dog / Stormy Monday blues / Roll 'em Pete / Shake, rattle and roll / When the sun goes down / Morning noon and night / Hide and seek / How long blues.
**Album:** Released '88, on Masters (Holland) Catalogue no: **CL 19983**
**Cass:** Released '88, on Masters (Holland) Catalogue no: **CLMC 919983**
**Album:** Released Dec '84, on Magnum Force by Magnum Music Group. Catalogue no: **MFM 022**

**ROOMFUL OF BLUES**
Tracks: / Crawdad hole / Red sails in the sunset / Cock-a-doodle-doo / Jumpin' for Joe / I want a little girl / Blues train / I know you love me / Last night / I love the way (my baby sings the blues).
**Album:** Released May '83, on Muse by Black & Blue Records. Catalogue no: **MR 5293**

**STEPPIN' OUT**
Tracks: / Adam Bit The apple / Still In The Dark / Just a travellin' man / Life is like a card game / Feeling Happy / After 'While You'll Be Sorry / When the rooster crows / Dawn Is breaking through / Roll 'em Pete / Kansas City Blues / Jockey blues / Playful Baby / Yancey Special / Pete's boogie special / Swanee River boogie.
**Album:** Released Mar '88, on Ace by Ace Records. Catalogue no: **CHD 243**
**Album:** Released May '88, on Ace by Ace Records. Catalogue no: **CH 243**

**STRIDDIN' IN PARIS**
**Album:** Released Nov '88, on Vogue by Vogue Records. Catalogue no: **500101**

**THINGS THAT I USED TO DO**
**Cass:** Released '82, on Pablo Jazz (USA) by Pablo Records (USA). Catalogue no: **K10 800**
**Album:** Released '82, on Pablo Jazz (USA) by Pablo Records (USA). Catalogue no: **231 0800**

**TRUMPET KINGS MEET JOE TURNER, THE**
**Cass:** Released '82, on Pablo Jazz (USA) by Pablo Records (USA). Catalogue no: **K10 717**
**Album:** Released '82, on Pablo Jazz (USA) by Pablo Records (USA). Catalogue no: **231 0717**

## Turner, Bruce

**DIRTY BOPPER, THE (Turner, Bruce Quartet)**
**Album:** Released Sep '85, on Calligraph Catalogue no: **CLGLP 003**

## Turrentine, Stanley

**Biographical details:** Stanley Turrentine is a tenor saxist born in 1934 in Philadelphia. He played with Ray Charles, then Eric Bostic, Max Roach; formed his own group and married organist Shirley Scott, working with her through the 1960s, also making his own LPs on Blue Note, as well as recording with Ike Quebec and others. He split with Scott in 1971; turned to pop/soul vein on CTI, then Fantasy, always with funky, blues-tinged feeling: some of his jazz albums reached the pop 200 LPs in the USA. He was back on Blue Note in 1987 with *Wonderland* (tunes by Stevie Wonder). (Donald Clarke 13.1.88).

**BEST OF STANLEY TURRENTINE**
Tracks: / Little Sheri / Since I fell for you / River's invitation / In memory of (CD only.) / Smile Stacy / God bless the child / Feeling good (CD only. From The Roar Of The Greasepaint, The Smell Of The Crowd.) / Lonesome lover (CD only.) / Plum.
**Album:** Released Feb '90, on Blue Note by EMI Records. Catalogue no: **B1 93201**
**CD:** Released Feb '90, on Blue Note by EMI Records. Catalogue no: **BNZ 231**
**Album:** Released Feb '90, on Blue Note by EMI Records. Catalogue no: **793 201 1**
**CD:** Released Feb '90, on Blue Note by EMI Records. Catalogue no: **CDP 793 201 2**

**BLUE HOUR**
Tracks: / I want a little girl / Gee baby ain't I good to you / Blue riff / Since I fell for you / Willow weep for me.
**Album:** Released Dec '85, on Blue Note by EMI Records. Deleted Nov '88. Catalogue no: **BST 84057**
**CD:** Released Apr '89, on Blue Note by EMI Records. Catalogue no: **CDP 784 057 2**
**CD:** Released Apr '89, on Blue Note by EMI Records. Catalogue no: **BNZ 138**

**COMIN' YOUR WAY**
Tracks: / My girl is just enough woman for me / Then I'll be tired of you / Fine I'il lass / Thomasville / Someone to watch over me / Stolen sweets / Fin I'il lass (alt. take) (CD only.) / Just in time (CD only.).
**CD:** Released Aug '89, on Blue Note by EMI Records. Catalogue no: **BNZ 191**
**Album:** Released Jan '88, on Blue Note by EMI Records. Catalogue no: **BLJ 84065**
**CD:** Released Aug '89, on Blue Note by EMI Records. Catalogue no: **CDP 784 065 2**

**HOME AGAIN**
Tracks: / Paradise / You can't take my love / I'll be there / I knew it couldn't happen / Blow / At the club / Gemini / Holy one.
**Album:** Released Dec '82, on Elektra by Elektra Records (UK). Deleted Dec '87. Catalogue no: **960 201 1**
**Album:** Released Feb '83, on Elektra by Elektra Records (UK). Deleted Feb '88. Catalogue no: **E 0201**

**IN CONCERT VOLS. 1 AND 2**
**CD:** Released Jan '88, on CBS by CBS Records. Deleted 17 Apr '89. Catalogue no: **450561 2**

**JOYRIDE**
Tracks: / River's invitation / I wonder where our love has gone / Little Sheri / Mattie / Bayou / Taste of honey, A.
**Album:** Released Jul '89, on Blue Note by EMI Records. Catalogue no: **BST 84201**
**CD:** Released Apr '87, on Blue Note by EMI Records. Deleted Jan '90. Catalogue no: **BNZ 96**
**CD:** Released Apr '87, on Blue Note by EMI Records. Deleted Jan '90. Catalogue no: **CDP 746 100 2**

**JUBILEE SHOUT**
Tracks: / Jubilee shout / My ship / You said it / Brother Tom / Cotton walk / You better go now.
**CD:** Released Mar '89, on Blue Note by EMI Records. Catalogue no: **BNZ 139**
**Album:** Released Aug '86, on Blue Note by EMI Records. Catalogue no: **BST 84122**
**CD:** Released Mar '89, on Blue Note by EMI Records. Catalogue no: **CDP 784 122 2**

**LA PLACE**
Tracks: / Terrible T / Cruisin' / Night breeze / Take 4 / Touching / La place street / Sparkle.
**Album:** Released Jan '90, on Blue Note by EMI Records. Catalogue no: **790 261 1**

**Album:** Released Jan '90, on Blue Note by EMI Records. Catalogue no: **B1 90261**
**CD:** Released Jan '90, on Blue Note by EMI Records. Catalogue no: **CDP 790 261 2**
**CD:** Released Jan '90, on Blue Note by EMI Records. Catalogue no: **CDB1 90261**

**LOOK OUT**
Tracks: / Look out / Journey into melody / Return engagement / Little Sheri / Tin tin deo / Yesterdays / Tiny capers / Minor chant.
**CD:** Released Jun '87, on Blue Note by EMI Records. Catalogue no: **CDP 746 543 2**
**CD:** Released Jun '87, on Blue Note by EMI Records. Catalogue no: **BNZ 98**

**NEW TIME SHUFFLE**
**Album:** Released Jun '80, on Liberty by EMI Records. Catalogue no: **LBR 1026**

**PAPA T**
Tracks: / Papa T part 1 / Papa T part 2.
**7" Single:** Released Jan '78, on Fantasy by Ace Records. Deleted '81. Catalogue no: **FTC 149**

**PIECES OF A DREAM**
**CD:** Released Nov '86, on Fantasy (import) by Fantasy Inc (USA). Catalogue no: **FCD 6109465**

**STANLEY TURRENTINE**
**2 LP Set:** Released May '79, on Blue Note by EMI Records. Catalogue no: **BND 4006**

**STRAIGHT AHEAD**
Tracks: / Plum / Child is born, A / Other side of time / Straight ahead / Longer you wait, The / Ah Rio.
Note: Another member of the original Blue Note roster, Stanley Turrentine returns to the label to the label to produce an album with enormous appeal within and beyond the mainstream jazz audience. An all star line up for the album features Jimmy Smith, Les McCann, Ron Carter and George Benson.
**CD:** Released Jul '89, on Blue Note by EMI Records. Catalogue no: **CDP 746 110 2**
**CD:** Released Jul '89, on Blue Note by EMI Records. Catalogue no: **BNZ 219**
**Album:** Released Jul '89, on Blue Note by EMI Records. Catalogue no: **BT 85105**

**SUGAR**
**CD:** Released '88, on CBS by CBS Records. Deleted 17 Apr '89. Catalogue no: **450573 2**

**TENDER TOGETHERNESS**
Tracks: / Hermanos / I'll give you my love / Tamarac / After the love is gone / Cherubim / Only you and me / World chimes / Pure love / Havin' fun with Mr. T.
**Album:** Released Nov '81, on Elektra by Elektra Records (UK). Deleted Nov '86. Catalogue no: **K52313**

**THAT'S WHERE IT'S AT**
Tracks: / Smile Stacey / Soft pedal blues / Pia / We'll se yaw'll after while, ya heah / Dorene don't cry / Light blue.
Note: Produced by Alfred Lion.
**CD:** Released Jun '89, on Blue Note by EMI Records. Catalogue no: **BNZ 178**
**Album:** Released Jul '89, on Blue Note by EMI Records. Catalogue no: **BST 84096**
**CD:** Released Jun '89, on Blue Note by EMI Records. Catalogue no: **CDP 784 096 2**

**USE THE STAIRS**
Tracks: / Tomorrow / Sometimes bread / Georgia on my mind / Lamp is low / Till the very end / On a misty night / Jor-du / Pay the price.
**Album:** Released Apr '81, on Fantasy by Ace Records. Catalogue no: **F 9604**

**WHAT ABOUT YOU**
Tracks: / Heritage / Feel the fire / Disco dancing / Manhattan skyline / My wish for you / Wind and sea.
**Album:** Released Feb '79, on Fantasy by Ace Records. Deleted Feb '84. Catalogue no: **FT 551**

**WONDERLAND (The music of Stevie Wonder)**
Tracks: / Bird of beauty / Creepin' / Living for the city / Boogie on reggae women / Rocket love / Don't you worry 'bout a thing / Sir Duke / You and I.
Note: The master of the soulful tenor sax has come up with an extraordinary album in "Wonderland". Conceived as a vehicle to explore the compositions of Stevie Wonder, Turrentine has not selected a stack of singles and done cover versions of them. Here he has selected the producer-pianist Ronnie Foster a wide range of sophisticated (and swinging) Wonder tunes that make sense in the jazz/R & B realm. With apowerhouse rhythym section that bassist Abe Laboriel, drummer Harvey Mason and percussionistPaulinho Da Costa, Turrentine brings new life and flavour to Stevie's music. The ballad "You And I" is among Stanley's most tender and soulful achievments. The cookers like "Boogie On, Reggae Woman", which features a hot harmonica solo by Wonder himself, get plenty of jazz fire from Stanley. And Stevies jazzy pieces like "Sir Duke" and "Living For The City" are given new dimension [EMI release sheet, May 1987]
**CD:** Released Jul '87, on Blue Note by EMI Records. Catalogue no: **CDP 746 762 2**
**Album:** Released Jul '89, on Blue Note by EMI Records. Catalogue no: **BT 85140**
**CD:** Released Jul '87, on Blue Note by EMI Records. Catalogue no: **BNZ 97**

**Z.T.'S BLUES**
Tracks: / Z.T.'s blues / More than you know / Lamp is low, The / Way you look tonight / For heaven's sake / I wish I knew / Be my love.
**Album:** Released Jul '89, on Blue Note by EMI Records. Catalogue no: **BST 84424**
**Cass:** Released Sep '87, on Blue Note by EMI Records. Deleted Jun '88. Catalogue no: **4BN 84424**
**Album:** Released Jul '89, on Blue Note by EMI Records. Catalogue no: **784 424 1**
**CD:** Released Feb '89, on Blue Note by EMI Records. Catalogue no: **BNZ 140**
**CD:** Released Feb '89, on Blue Note by EMI Records. Catalogue no: **CDP 784 424 2**

## Twenty Geants

**20 GEANTS DU PIANO JAZZ (Various artists)**
**CD:** Released Jul '87, on Vogue by Vogue Records. Catalogue no: **VGCD 600 149**

## Twenty Golden Greats...

**20 GOLDEN GREATS FROM THE BIG BAND ERA (Various artists)**
Tracks: / Trumpet blues and cantabile: *Various artists* / One o'clock jump: *Various artists* / Yes indeed: *Various artists* / Intermission riff: *Various artists* / You made me love you: *Various artists* / Four brothers: *Various artists* / Artistry in rhythm: *Various artists* / I've got a gal in Kalamazoo: *Various artists* / I'll never smile again: *Various artists* / Jeeps blues: *Various artists* / Solitude: *Various artists* / Don't be that way: *Various artists* / Midnight sun: *Various artists* / Red bank boogie: *Various artists* / La paloma: *Various artists* / Stardust: *Various artists* / Skyliner: *Various artists* / Goosey gander: *Various artists* / Well, get it: *Various artists*.
Note: Featuring: Ben Webster, Conte Candoli, Juan Tizol, Vido Musso, Nick Fatool, Al Cohn and other members of the original big band.
**CD:** Released Jun '87, on Hermes by Nimbus Records. Catalogue no: **HRM 7005**

## Twenty Golden Memories

**20 GOLDEN MEMORIES (Various artists)**
**Album:** Released '88, on Masters (Holland) Catalogue no: **MA 16287**
**Cass:** Released Dec '88, on Masters (Holland) Catalogue no: **MAMC 916287**

## Twenty Great...

**20 GREAT BIG BAND HITS (Various artists)**
**Cass:** Released Jun '86, on Astan (USA) Catalogue no: **40190**

## Twenty Seven ...

**27 CLASSIC JAZZ MASTERS (Various artists)**
**Album:** Released Jan '90, on CBS (import) by CBS Records. Catalogue no: **465 192 1**
**Cass:** Released Jan '90, on CBS (import) by CBS Records. Catalogue no: **465 192 4**
**CD:** Released Jan '90, on CBS (import) by CBS Records. Catalogue no: **465 192 2**

## Tyler, Alvin 'Red'

**Biographical details:** Alvin 'Red' Tyler was born in New Orleans in 1925; he is the leg'endary tenor saxophonist who joined the Dave Bartholemew band in the late '40s and subsequently played on a great many R&B hits by Fats Domino and many others. *Heritage* is a jazz album, his first proper album as a leader, and should be well worth a listen. (Donald Clarke 13.1.88).

**GRACIOUSLY**
**CD:** Released '88, on Rounder (USA) by Rounder Records (USA). Catalogue no: **CD 2061**
**Album:** Released '88, on Rounder (USA) by Rounder Records (USA). Catalogue no: **ROUNDER 2061**
**Cass:** Released '88, on Rounder (USA) by Rounder Records (USA). Catalogue no: **ROUNDER 2061C**

**HERITAGE**
**Cass:** Released '88, on Rounder (USA) by Rounder Records (USA). Catalogue no: **ROUNDER 2047C**
**Album:** Released '88, on Rounder (USA) by Rounder Records (USA). Catalogue no: **ROUNDER 2047**
**CD:** Released '88, on Rounder (USA) by Rounder Records (USA). Catalogue no: **CD 2047**
**Album:** Released Feb '87, on Rounder Europa (USA) Catalogue no: **REU 1002**

**ROCKIN' AND ROLLIN' (Tyler, Alvin and The Gyros)**
**Album:** Released Dec '88, on Ace by Ace Records. Catalogue no: **CH 182**

## Tyner, McCoy

**Biographical details:** McCoy Tyner was born in 1938 in Philadelphia; he was an important part of the epochal John Coltrane quartet 1960-65 and has become a jazz superstar in his own right. Albums for Impulse are now on Jasmine in the UK; he also recorded for Milestone and Blue Note. He is a master of structure, using it in his improvising like a composer, and of tension and release; he rarely plays 'free' but stretches rhythms and tonalities to their limit with unerring judgement; his sound is bright, exultant, affirmative: life enhancing. As his old Blue Note LPs were being reissued he came back to that label for *Double Trios* in 1987, including standards such as *Lover Man*, played as no one else could play them. (Donald Clarke 13.1.88).

**BON VOYAGE**
Tracks: / Bon voyage / Don't blame me / Summertime / You stepped out of a dream / Jazz walk / How deep is the ocean / Blues for Max.
**Album:** Released 22 Jan '88, on Timeless by Timeless Records. Catalogue no: **SJP 260**

**DIMENSIONS**
Tracks: / One for Dea / Prelude to a kiss / Precious one / Just in time / Understanding / Uncle Bubba.
**Album:** Released Jun '84, on Elektra by Elektra Records (UK). Deleted Jun '89. Catalogue no: **9603501**

**DOUBLE TRIOS**
Tracks: / Latino suite / Lil' darlin' / Dreamer / Satin doll / Down home / Sudan lover / Lover man / Rhythm a ning.
Note: That McCoy Tyner remains one of the pre-eminent jazz keyboard stylists is demonstrated, with utter conviction, by his consistently uplifting playing throughout the contents of this, his debut offering of Denon. An absolutely essential purchase of all Tyner fans. (Denon 10/88). Personnel (On "Latino suite", "Lil' darlin", "Dreamer" and "Satin doll": McCoy Tyner (Piano), Avery Sharpe (Bass), Louis Hayes (Drums), Steve Thornton (Percussion). Personnel on all other tracks: McCoy Tyner (Piano), Marcus Miller (Electric bass), Jeff 'Tain' Waits (Drums), Steve Thornton (Percussion).
**CD:** Released Oct '88, on Denon Catalogue no: **CY 1128**
**Cass:** Released Oct '88, on Denon Catalogue no: **CC 12**

**EXPANSIONS**
Tracks: / Vision / Song of happiness / Smitty's place / Peresina / I thought I'd let you know.
**CD:** Released Mar '89, on Blue Note by EMI Records. Catalogue no: **BNZ 141**
**CD:** Released Mar '89, on Blue Note by EMI Records. Catalogue no: **CDP 784 338 2**
**Album:** Released Jul '89, on Blue Note by EMI Records. Catalogue no: **BST 84338**

**FLY WITH THE WIND**
**CD:** Released Apr '87, on Carrere (France) Catalogue no: **98164**
**CD:** Released Nov '86, on Fantasy (import) by Fantasy Inc (USA). Catalogue no: **FCD 6019067**

**FOCAL POINT**
Tracks: / Mes trois fils / Parody / Indo-serenade / Mode for dulcimer / Departure / Theme from Nana.
**Album:** Released Jan '77, on Milestone by Ace Records. Deleted '81. Catalogue no: **M 9072**

**GREETING**
Tracks: / Hand in hand / Fly with the wind / Pictures / Naima / Greeting.
**Album:** Released '79, on Milestone by Ace Records. Deleted '84. Catalogue no: **M 9085**

**HORIZON**
Tracks: / Horizon / Woman of tomorrow / Motherland / One for honour / Just feelin'.
**Album:** Released Oct '80, on Milestone by Ace Records. Deleted Oct '85. Catalogue no: **M 9094**

**INCEPTION**
Tracks: / Inception / Blues for Gwen / Speak / We'll be together again / For heaven's sake / Blue monk / Days of wine and roses / There is no greater love / Sunset effendi / Satin doll / 'Round midnight / Star eyes / Groove waltz.
Note: Personnel: McCoy Tyner (piano), Art Davis (bass), Elvin Jones (drums).
**CD:** Released Jun '89, on MCA (Impulse Jazz) Catalogue no: **MCAD 42000**

**IT'S ABOUT TIME (Tyner, McCoy & Jackie McLean)**
Tracks: / Spur of the moment / You taught my heart to sing / It's about time / Hip toe / No flowers please / Travellin'.
Note: Featuring Ron Carter on bass, Al Foster on drums and an exceptional trumpeter, Jon Faddis. The music was composed by McCoy Turner with the exception of one title by Carter.
**CD:** Released Jul '87, on Blue Note by EMI Records. Deleted Jan '90. Catalogue no: **BNZ 101**
**Album:** Released Jul '89, on Blue Note by EMI Records. Catalogue no: **BT 85102**
**CD:** Released Jul '87, on Blue Note by EMI Records. Deleted Jan '90. Catalogue no: **CDP 746 291 2**
**Cass:** Released Dec '85, on Blue Note by EMI Records. Deleted Jul '87. Catalogue no: **TCBT 85102**

**LA LEYENDA DE LA HORA**
Tracks: / La vida feliz / Ja'cara / La habana sol / Walk spirit, talk spirit / La busca.
**Album:** Released Nov '81, on CBS by CBS Records. Deleted Nov '86. Catalogue no: **CBS 85143**

**LIVE AT MUSICIANS EXCHANGE**
Tracks: / Senor Carlos / Lover man / You taught my heart to sing / Port au blues / Island birdie / What's new? / Hip toe (CD only.).
**Cass:** Released '89, on Kingdom Jazz by Kingdom Records. Catalogue no: **CGATE**
**CD:** Released Apr '88, on Kingdom Jazz by Kingdom Records. Catalogue no: **CDGATE 7021**
**Album:** Released Apr '88, on Kingdom Jazz by Kingdom Records. Catalogue no: **GATE 7021**

**LIVE AT SWEET BASIL (Tyner, McCoy Trio)**
**CD:** Released '89, on King Catalogue

no: **292 E 6033**

**LOOKING OUT**
Tracks: / Love surrounds us everywhere / Hannibal / I'll be around / Senor Carlos / In search of my heart / Island birdie.
**Album:** Released Sep '82, on CBS by CBS Records. Deleted Jan '88. Catalogue no: **CBS 85895**

**NIGHTS OF BALLADS AND BLUES**
Tracks: / Satin doll / We'll be together again / Round midnight.
Note: Personnel: McCoy Tyner (piano), Steve Davis (bass), Lex Humphries (drums).
**CD:** Released Jun '89, on MCA (Impulse Jazz) Catalogue no: **MCAD 42000**
**Cass:** Released Aug '82, on Jasmine by Hasmick Promotions. Catalogue no: **JAS C35**
**Album:** Released Aug '82, on Jasmine by Hasmick Promotions. Deleted Feb '88. Catalogue no: **JAS 35**

**PASSION DANCE**
Tracks: / Moment's notice / Passion dance / Search for peace / Promise / Song of the New World.
**Album:** Released Apr '80, on Milestone by Ace Records. Deleted '85. Catalogue no: **M 9091**

**PLAYS ELLINGTON**
Tracks: / Dukes place / Caravan / Solitude / Searchin' / Mr. Gentle and Mr. Cool / Satin doll / Gypsy without a song.
**Cass:** Released '82, on Jasmine by Hasmick Promotions. Catalogue no: **JAS C56**
**Album:** Released '82, on Jasmine by Hasmick Promotions. Catalogue no: **JAS 56**

**REAL MCCOY, THE**
Tracks: / Passion dance / Contemplation / Four by five / Search for peace / Blues on the corner.
**Album:** Released Jul '89, on Blue Note by EMI Records. Catalogue no: **BST 84264**
**CD:** Released May '87, on Blue Note by EMI Records. Catalogue no: **BNZ 100**
**CD:** Released May '87, on Blue Note by EMI Records. Catalogue no: **CDP 746 512 2**

**REFLECTIONS**
Tracks: / Ebony queen / Native song / Above the rainbow / Rebirth / Naima / Impressions / Ruby, my dear / Offering / Nebula / My one and only love / Desert cry / Afro blue / Song of the new world.
**2 LP Set:** Released Mar '82, on Milestone by Ace Records. Catalogue no: **M 47062**

**REVELATIONS**
Tracks: / Yesterdays / You taught my heart to sing / In a mellow tone / View from the hill / Lazy bird / Don't blame me / Rio / How deep is the ocean / Someone to watch over me / Contemplation / Autumn leaves (CD only.) / Peresina (CD only.) / When I fall in love (CD only.).
**Album:** Released Jul '89, on Blue Note by EMI Records. Catalogue no: **B1 91651**
**CD:** Released May '89, on Blue Note by EMI Records. Catalogue no: **CDP 791 651 2**
**Album:** Released Jul '89, on Blue Note by EMI Records. Catalogue no: **791 651 1**

**TENDER MOMENTS**
Tracks: / Mode to John / Man from Tanganyika / High priest, The / Utopia / All my yesterdays / Lee plus three.
**Album:** Released Jul '89, on Blue Note by EMI Records. Catalogue no: **BST 84275**
**CD:** Released Apr '88, on Blue Note by EMI Records. Deleted Jan '90. Catalogue no: **BNZ 99**
**CD:** Released Apr '88, on Blue Note by EMI Records. Deleted Jan '90. Catalogue no: **CDP 784 275 2**

**TIME FOR TYNER**
Tracks: / African village / Little Madimba / May street / I didn't know what time it was / Surrey with the fringe on top / I've grown accustomed to your face.
Note: For this 1968 recording Tyner's regular trio was joined by another outstanding Blue Note artist, vibist Bobby Hutcherson.
**Album:** Released Jul '89, on Blue Note by EMI Records. Catalogue no: **BST 84307**
**CD:** Released Jul '89, on Blue Note by EMI Records. Catalogue no: **BNZ 192**
**CD:** Released Jul '89, on Blue Note by EMI Records. Catalogue no: **CDP 784 307 2**

# U

The following information was taken from the Music Master database on 14th, 1990.

## UCS All Stars

### LIVE AT FROGNALL

**Album:** Released '83, on Spotlite by Spotlite Records. Catalogue no: **SPJ LP 23**

## Ulmer, James "Blood"

**Biographical details:** 'Blood' was born in 1942 in South Carolina. The guitarist, vocalist and composer also plays flute; he is an uncategorisable musician, a sort of avant-garde bluesman full of controlled passion. He sang gospel music and learned the guitar as a child; in the 1970s in NYC he worked with Art Blakey, Paul Bley and others; he studied with Ornette Coleman in 1974 and gigged with him. He played on albums by Arthur Blythe in 1979-80 on CBS, made his own LP (with Coleman in the lineup) on Artist's House, then on CBS, Rough Trade and Blue Note. (Donald Clarke 15.5.87).

### AMERICA: DO YOU REMEMBER THE LOVE ?

Tracks: / I belong in the USA / Lady blue / After dark / Show me your love / Black sheep / Wings.

Note: From his sixties roots in R & B bars bands to the first ranks of funk-jazz with organist John Patton (with whom he recorded on Blue Note some 18 years ago) to harmelodic experiments with jazz pioneer Ornette Coleman, guitarist James 'Blood' Ulmer has always been a true American original, absorbing and assimilating all that passes through him. After a self produced album with Ornette and three successful albums on CBS, Ulmer established himself on the international jazz and avant garde scenes as a distinctive and creative voice. for his Blue Note debut, he has surrounded himself with his visionary peers: bassist and producer Bill Laswell and drummer and band leader Ronald Shannon Jackson. On six high individual pieces, two of which include Blood's haunting vocals, Ulmer draws upon American echoes that conjure up every sound from Charlie Christian to Grant Green to Ry Cooder to Duane Eddy. Here is an American original. Someone to deal with ...someone to enjoy: James'Blood'Ulmer.

**Album:** Released Apr '87, on Blue Note by EMI Records. Deleted '89. Catalogue no: **BT 85136**

**CD:** Released Jun '87, on Blue Note by EMI Records. Deleted Jan '90. Catalogue no: **BNZ 102**

**CD:** Released Jun '87, on Blue Note by EMI Records. Deleted Jan '90. Catalogue no: **CDP 746 755 2**

### ARE YOU GLAD TO BE IN AMERICA

**Album:** Released '84, on Rough Trade by Rough Trade Records. Catalogue no: **ROUGH 16**

### BLACK ROCK

Tracks: / Open house / Black rock / Moon beam / Family affair / More blood / Love has two faces / Overnight / Fun house / We bop.

**Album:** Released Dec '82, on CBS by CBS Records. Deleted Dec '87. Catalogue no: **CBS 25064**

### EYE LEVEL

Tracks: / Eye level / Blues.

**12" Single:** Released Aug '84, on Rough Trade by Rough Trade Records. Catalogue no: **RTT 128**

### FREELANCING

Tracks: / Timeless / Pleasure control / Night lover / Where did all the girls come from / High time / Hi Jack / Freelancing / Stand up to yourself / Rush hour / Happy time.

**Album:** Released Dec '81, on CBS by CBS Records. Deleted '86. Catalogue no: **CBS 85224**

### LIVE AT THE CARAVAN

**Album:** Released Apr '87, on Caravan Of Dreams (USA) Catalogue no: **CDP 85004**

### ODYSSEY

Tracks: / Church / Little red house / Love dance / Are you glad to be in America / Election / Odyssey / Please tell her / Swing and things.

**Album:** Released Apr '84, on CBS by CBS Records. Deleted '89. Catalogue no: **CBS 25602**

### PART TIME

**Album:** Released '84, on Rough Trade by Rough Trade Records. Catalogue no: **ROUGH 65**

### REVEALING

Tracks: / Revealing / D.H. / M.O. / Little tree.

**Album:** Released Mar '90, on In & Out by New Note. Catalogue no: **70071**

**CD:** Released Mar '90, on In & Out by New Note. Catalogue no: **70072**

## Unforgettable...

### UNFORGETTABLE PERFORMANCES OF THE WORLD WAR YEARS

**Michal Urbaniak**

**(Various artists)**
Note: Artists include Count Basie, Art Tatum etc.
**Album:** Released Nov '86, on Kaydee Catalogue no: **KAYDEE 2**

## United Jazz & Rock

**LIVE OPUS 6**
**Album:** Released Sep '84, on Original Catalogue no: **TM6 28642**

## Uptown Blues

**UPTOWN BLUES (Various artists)**
**Album:** Released Dec '88, on Yazoo (USA) by Shanachie Records (USA). Catalogue no: **L 1042**

## Uptown Jazzband

**IN COLONIAL YORK PA**
**Album:** Released '88, on Stomp Off (USA) Catalogue no: **SOS 1030**

## Urban Blues

**URBAN BLUES Various original artists 1940's/50's (Various artists)**
Tracks: / Rockin' boogie: *Lutcher, Joe & His Society Cats* / Life is a card game: *Turner, Big* / I can't lose with the stuff I use: *Williams, Lester & His Band* / Bachelor blues, The: *Mayfield, Percy & His Orchestra* / Please Mr. Jailer: *Carr, Wynona & The Bumps Blackwell Band* / When the clock strikes twelve: *Smith, Eddie & His Orchestra* / Please don't go: *Dixon, Floyd* / I need love so bad: *Mayfield, Percy & His Orchestra* / If you knew how much I love you: *Williams, Lester & His Band* / After 'while you'll be sorry: *Turner, Big* / Something's goin' on in my room: *Daddy Cleanhead & The Chuck Higgins Band.*
**Album:** Released Aug '77, on Sonet by Sonet Records. Catalogue no: **SNTF 5023**

## Urban Jazz

**URBAN JAZZ The original illicit grooves (Various artists)**
Tracks: / Soul sauce: *Tjader, Cal* / Cantaloupe woman: *Green, Grant* / Eight counts for Rita: *Smith, Jimmy (USA)* / In the middle: *Brown, James* / You're starting too fast: *Pate, Johnny* / Betty Boop: *Earland, Charles* / Spinning wheel: *New Jersey Kings* / That ain't too cool: *Pate, Johnny.*
**Album:** Released 6 Mar '89, on Urban by Polydor Ltd. Catalogue no: **837 930-1**
**Cass:** Released 6 Mar '89, on Urban by Polydor Ltd. Catalogue no: **837 930-4**
**CD:** Released 6 Mar '89, on Urban by Polydor Ltd. Catalogue no: **837 930-2**

## Urbaniak, Michal

**CINEMODE**
**Album:** Released Mar '89, on Sonet by Sonet Records. Catalogue no: **SNTF 1009**

**RECITAL (Urbaniak, Michel/Vladislav Sendecki)**
**Album:** Released Jul '86, on Four Leaf Clover Catalogue no: **FLC 5073**

**SONGS FOR POLAND**
**Album:** Released '89, on Sonet by Sonet Records. Catalogue no: **SNTF 1025**
**CD:** Released Mar '90, on Sonet by Sonet Records. Catalogue no: **SNTCD 1025**

**TAKE GOOD CARE OF MY HEART**
**Album:** Released Jul '88, on Steeplechase (USA) Catalogue no: **SCS 1195**
**CD:** Released Jul '88, on Steeplechase (USA) Catalogue no: **SCCD 31195**

# V

The following information was taken from the Music Master database on April 14th, 1990.

## Vache, Allan

**HIGH SPEED SWING**
**Album:** Released Jan '87, on Audiophile (USA) by Jazzology Records (USA). Catalogue no: **AP 192**

**JAZZ MOODS**
**Album:** Released Jul '87, on Audiophile (USA) by Jazzology Records (USA). Catalogue no: **AP 176**

## Vache, Warren

**BLUES WALK (Vache, Warren With Scott Hamilton & John Bunch.)**
**Album:** Released Jan '79, on Dreamstreet (USA) by Dreamstreet Records (USA). Catalogue no: **DR 101**

**EASY GOING (Vache, Warren Sextet)**
Tracks: / Little girl / Easy going bounce / Warm valley / You'd be so nice to come home to / Michelle / It's been so long / Was I to blame for falling in love with you? / London by night / Mandy make up your mind / Moon song (That wasn't meant for me).
Note: Personnel: Warren Vache - cornet & flugelhorn / Howard Alden - guitar / Dan Barrett - trombone / John Harkins - piano / Jack Lesberg - bass / Chuck Riggs - drums.
**CD:** Released Jul '87, on Concord Jazz by Concord Jazz Records (USA). Catalogue no: **CCD 4323**
**Album:** Released Jul '87, on Concord Jazz by Concord Jazz Records (USA). Catalogue no: **CJ 323**
**Cass:** Released Jul '87, on Concord Jazz by Concord Jazz Records (USA). Catalogue no: **CJC 323**

**FIRST TIME OUT**
Note: with Bucky Pizarelli/Kenny Davern etc.
**Album:** Released Mar '79, on Monmouth Evergreen Catalogue no: **MES 7081**
**Album:** Released Jan '87, on Audiophile (USA) by Jazzology Records (USA). Catalogue no: **AP 196**

**IRIDESCENCE**
**Album:** Released Aug '81, on Concord by Concord Jazz Records (USA). Catalogue no: **CJ 153**

**MIDTOWN JAZZ**
Tracks: / I'm old fashioned / Rhythm-a-ning / Tempus fugit / Two for the road / We'll be together again / Time for love, A / I let a song go out of my heart / Out of nowhere / Love in the spring / I remember April.
**Album:** Released Mar '83, on Concord Jazz by Concord Jazz Records (USA). Catalogue no: **CJ 203**

**WARREN VACHE & THE BEAUX-ARTS STRING QUARTET (Vache, Warren & The Beaux-Arts String Quartet)**
**CD:** Released '89, on Concord Jazz by Concord Jazz Records (USA). Catalogue no: **CCD 4392**

## Valentine, Kid Thomas

**ALGIERS STOMPERS**
**Album:** Released Jun '88, on GHB by Jazzology Records (USA). Catalogue no: **GHB 80**

**AT MOULIN ROUGE**
**Album:** Released Mar '77, on Center (USA) by Biograph Records (USA). Catalogue no: **CEN 14**

**AT THE OLD GRIST MILL (Valentine, Kid Thomas & His New Orleans Joymakers)**
**Album:** Released Jun '86, on GHB by Jazzology Records (USA). Catalogue no: **GHB 73**

**ECHOES OF NEW ORLEANS VOL.2**
**Album:** Released '78, on Storyville by Storyville Records AB. Catalogue no: **SLP 212**

**HIS NEW ORLEANS JAZZ BAND**
**Album:** Released Jun '75, on Arhoolie (USA) by Arhoolie Records (USA). Catalogue no: **F 1016**

**IN DENMARK VOL.1 (Valentine, Kid Thomas & Louis Nelson)**
**Album:** Released Jun '77, on Storyville by Storyville Records AB. Catalogue no: **SLP 241**

**IN SCANDINAVIA**
**Album:** Released Sep '74, on Rarities Catalogue no: **RARITIES 16**

**JAZZOLOGY POLL WINNERS 1964 (Thomas,Kid/George Lewis / Don Ewell)**
**Album:** Released Sep '86, on GHB by Jazzology Records (USA). Catalogue no: **GHB 200**

**KID THOMAS' DIXIELAND BAND (Recorded New Orleans 1968) (Valentine, Kid Thomas & His Dixieland Band)**
**Album:** Released Apr '79, on Nola Catalogue no: **NOLA LP 14**
**Cass:** Released Apr '79, on Nola Catalogue no: **TC 014**

**KID THOMAS, EMANUEL PAUL & BARRY MARTYN**
**Album:** Released '74, on 77 by 77 Records. Catalogue no: **77LA12/26**

**KID THOMAS' JAZZBAND (Valentine, Kid Thomas Jazz Band)**
**Album:** Released '88, on CSA by CSA Records. Catalogue no: **CLPS**

**KID THOMAS & LOUIS NELSON IN DENMARK 2 (Valentine, Kid Thomas & Louis Nelson)**
**Album:** Released '88, on Storyville by Storyville Records AB. Catalogue no: **SLP 246**

**KID THOMAS & THE NEW BLACK EAGLE JAZZ BAND (Valentine, Kid Thomas & The New Black Eagle Jazz Band)**
**Album:** Released Jun '86, on GHB by Jazzology Records (USA). Catalogue no: **GHB 145**

**KID THOMAS VALENTINE (Valentine, Kid Thomas/Louis Nelson / New Iberia Stompers)**
**Cass:** Released Sep '86, on 504 Catalogue no: **TCS 7**

**KID THOMAS VALENTINE'S CREOLE JAZZ BAND**
**Album:** Released Sep '79, on 77 by 77 Records. Catalogue no: **77LA 12/9**

**KID THOMAS / RAYMOND BURKE & THE ORIGINAL ALGIERS (Valentine, Kid Thomas & Raymond Burke)**
**Album:** Released Feb '87, on Jazzology (USA) by Jazzology Records (USA). Catalogue no: **JCE 30**

**LOVE SONGS OF THE NILE**
**Album:** Released Mar '87, on GHB by Jazzology Records (USA). Catalogue no: **GHB 183**

**NEW ORLEANS JAZZ**
**Album:** Released May '81, on Arhoolie (USA) by Arhoolie Records (USA). Catalogue no: **ARHOOLIE 1016**

**ON STAGE (Valentine, Kid Thomas & The Algiers Stompers)**
**Album:** Released '88, on GHB by Jazzology Records (USA). Catalogue no: **GHB 53**

**PORTRAIT OF KID THOMAS VALENTINE**
**Album:** Released Feb '90, on Storyville by Storyville Records AB. Catalogue no: **SLP233**

**RAGTIME STOMPERS (Valentine, Kid Thomas & George Lewis)**
**Album:** Released Jun '88, on GHB by Jazzology Records (USA). Catalogue no: **GHB 5**

**ROCKIN' THIS JOINT TONIGHT (Kid Thomas)**

Tracks: / Rockin' this joint tonight / Wail baby wail / Lookie there.
**7" Single:** Released May '84, on JSP by JSP Records. Catalogue no: **JSP 4505**

**ROCKIN' THIS JOINT TONITE (Valentine, Kid Thomas, Floyd Dixon & Ace Holder)**
Tracks: / Rockin' this joint tonite / You are an angel / Wail baby wail / Lookie there / Cozy lounge blues / Five long years / Don't leave me baby / Late freight twist / Me quieres / Tell me tell me / Leave me woman alone / Happy anniversary / Wabba Suzy Q.
**Album:** Released Feb '79, on JSP by JSP Records. Catalogue no: **JSP 1002**

**WITH SAMMY RIMINGTON 1981 (Valentine, Kid Thomas & Sammy Rimington)**
**Album:** Released '88, on Black Label (USA) by House Of America Records (USA). Catalogue no: **DTS 033**
**Album:** Released 8 Apr '89, on GHB by Jazzology Records (USA). Catalogue no: **GHB 291**

## Vallee, Rudy

**Biographical details:** Perhaps the first teen idol, singing to swooning girls through a megaphone - he predicted the demise of his own style with the rise of Bing Crosby - Vallee was born in Vermont in 1901 and died in California in 1986. With his famous greeting, "Heigh-ho, everybody", he starred in films and on Broadway and radio. His first film, *The vagabond lover*, in 1929, yielded his theme, the co-written *I'm Just A vagabond lover*. Later he played wealthy, stuffed-shirt types who never got the girl and became a good comic actor. In 1961 he starred as a caricature of the old college type in Frank Loesser's musical *How To Succeed In Business Without Really Trying*, in the film version in '67 and in a San Francisco revival at ther age of 74. Other hits, many co-written, included *Life is just a bowl of cherries*, *Dancing with tears in my eyes*, *The Whiffenpoof song* and *Say it isn't so*. He ran two publishing companies, wrote three autobiographies and had four wives. (Donald Clarke, January 1988.)..

**HEIGH-HO EVERYBODY, THIS IS RUDY VALLEE**
Tracks: / Heigh ho everybody, heigh ho / Betty co-ed / If I had a girl like you / Let's do it / I still remember / Salaaming the rajah / My heart belongs to the girl who belongs to somebody else / One in the world, The / I'll be reminded of you / You'll do it someday, so why not now? / Kitty from Kansas City / That's when I learned to love you / Outside / Dream sweetheart / Love made a gypsy out of me / Perhaps / Little kiss each morning a little kiss each night, A / Verdict is life with you, The / Lover come back to me / Stein song, The.
**Cass:** Released 1 Nov '81, on Living Era by Academy Sound & Vision Records. Catalogue no: **ZC AJA 5009**
**Album:** Released 1 Nov '81, on Living Era by Academy Sound & Vision Records. Catalogue no: **AJA 5009**

**RUDY VALLEE AND HIS CONNECTICUT YANKEES (Vallee, Rudy/his Connecticut Yankees)**
Tracks: / Deep night / Little kiss each morning a little kiss each night, A / I love the moon / M-a-r-y I love you / Stein song, The / St. Louis blues / Kitty from Kansas city / How come you do me like you do / Betsy co-ed / Would you like to take a walk? / Ninety-nine out of a hundred wanna be loved / When Yuba plays the rumba on the tuba / This is the missus / Life is just a bowl of cherries.
Note: Produced by Submarine records.
**Cass:** Released Sep '86, on Halcyon (USA) by Submarine Records. Catalogue no: **CHDL 105**
**Album:** Released Sep '86, on Halcyon (USA) by Submarine Records. Catalogue no: **HDL 105**

**RUDY VALLEE: ON THE AIR**
Tracks: / We did it before and we can do it again / I don't want to walk without you.
**Album:** Released Jan '78, on Totem Catalogue no: **TOTEM 1027**

**SING FOR YOUR SUPPER**
Tracks: / Naturally / Flying down to Rio / Sing for your supper / Stranger in Paree, A / Vieni vieni / Whiffenpoof song, The / Nasty man / You and me that used to be, The / Drunkard song, The (There is a Tavern in the t / I'm just a vagabond lover / Me minus you / Latin Quarter, The / Orchids in the moonlight / Life is a song / This can't be love / Ha-cha-cha / I wanna go back to Bali / Goodnight, my love.
**CD:** Released '89, on Movie Stars by Conifer Records. Catalogue no: **CMSCD 005**
**Album:** Released '89, on Movie Stars by Conifer Records. Catalogue no: **CMS 005**
**Cass:** Released '89, on Movie Stars by Conifer Records. Catalogue no: **CMSC 005**

## Van Damme, Art

**ART VAN DAMME AND FRIENDS (Various artists)**
Tracks: / Let yourself down: *Various artists* / Satin doll: *Various artists* / I didn't know what time it was: *Various artists* / Cheek to cheek: *Various artists* / Rosetta: *Various artists*.
**Album:** Released '84, on Accordion Record Club by Accordion Record Club. Catalogue no: **NLP 107**

## Van't Hof, Jasper

**PILI-PILI**
Tracks: / Pili-pili.
**12" Single:** Released Jan '85, on WEA by WEA Records. Catalogue no: **X 9243**

## Varekamp, Victoria

**HOT DOGS & VICTORIA VAREKAMP (Varekamp, Victoria & the Hot Dogs)**
**Album:** Released '88, on Stomp Off (USA) Catalogue no: **SOS 1033**

## Vaudeville Blues

**VAUDEVILLE BLUES (Various artists)**
**Album:** Released Apr '78, on VJM (Vintage Jazz Music) by Vintage Jazz Music Society(VJM). Catalogue no: **VLP 30**

## Vaughan, Sarah

**Biographical details:** As with Ella Fitzgerald there is argument about whether Vaughan -- also known as Sassy, Sass and The Divine One -- is a jazz singer, and, as with Ella, the argument is academic: with her effortless swing, wide vocal range, rare but accurate scatting, perfect pitch and vocal colour she is one of the century's great singers. She joined the Earl Hines band in 1944 and when Billy Eckstine left to form his own band she was a founder member. She soon went solo, often duetting with Eckstine. Most of her recordings were on Mercury and Verve, now owned by Polydor, and she later recorded for Norman Granz's Pablo label. She often sang with symphony orchestras in the 1980's (*Gershwin Live!* with the Los Angeles Philharmonic, conducted by Michael Tilson Thomas; also sang in London studio recording of *South Pacific* '86 on CBS, with Kiri Te Kanawa, Jose Carreras in leading roles.). One of her most unusual projects was recording songs based on poems by Pope John Paul II at a live concert in Dusseldorf in 1985: *The Planet Is Alive ... Let It Live* had the Pope's poems adapted in English by lyricist Gene Lees to music by Italian composers.Tragically she died on 4/4/90.

**16 ORIGINAL HITS: SARAH VAUGHAN**
**Cass:** Released Sep '87, on Timeless Treasures Catalogue no: **MC 1632**

**AFTER HOURS**
Tracks: / My favourite things (From The Sound of Music.) / Ev'ry time we say goodbye / Wonder why / Easy to love / Sophisticated lady / Great day / Ill wind / If love is good to me / In a sentimental mood / Vanity.
**Album:** Released Oct '89, on Roulette (EMI) by EMI Records. Catalogue no: **ROU 1003**
**CD:** Released Oct '89, on Roulette (EMI) by EMI Records. Catalogue no: **CDP 793 271 2**
**Album:** Released Oct '89, on Roulette (EMI) by EMI Records. Catalogue no: **793 271 1**
**CD:** Released Oct '89, on Roulette (EMI) by EMI Records. Catalogue no: **CZ 235**

**BEST OF SARAH VAUGHAN (Compact / Walkman jazz)**
Tracks: / How high the moon / Misty / Take the 'A' train / Summertime / Sweetest sounds, the / Poor butterfly / Shulie a bop / Embraceable you.
**Cass:** Released May '87, on Mercury by Phonogram Ltd. Catalogue no: **830 699-4**
**CD:** Released May '87, on Mercury by Phonogram Ltd. Catalogue no:**830 699-2**

**BRAZILIAN ROMANCE**
Tracks: / Make this city ours tonight / Romance / Love and passion / So many stars / Photography / Nothing will be as it was / It's simple / Obsession / Wanting more / Your smile.
**Cass:** Released Oct '87, on CBS (Masterworks) by CBS Records. Deleted Jan '90. Catalogue no: **4601564**
**CD:** Released Nov '87, on CBS by CBS Records. Catalogue no: **460 156 2**
**Album:** Released Oct '87, on CBS (Masterworks) by CBS Records. Deleted 10 Jul '89. Catalogue no: **460 156-1**

**BROKEN HEARTED MELODY**
Tracks: / Broken hearted melody.
**7" Single:** Released Sep '59, on Mercury (EMI) Deleted '62. Catalogue no: **AMT 1057**

**BROKEN HEARTED MELODY (OLD GOLD)**
Tracks: / Broken hearted melody / Passing strangers.
**7" Single:** Released Jan '85, on Old Gold by Old Gold Records. Catalogue no: **OG 9476**

**CBS YEARS, THE**
**Cass:** Released Nov '89, on CBS by CBS Records. Catalogue no: **465 597 4**
**CD:** Released Nov '89, on CBS by CBS Records. Catalogue no: **465 597 2**
**Album:** Released Nov '89, on CBS by CBS Records. Catalogue no: **465 597 1**

**COMPACT JAZZ: SARAH VAUGHAN**
Tracks: / Lullaby of Birdland / Summertime / Embraceable you.
**Cass:** Released Jul '87, on Phonogram by Phonogram Ltd. Catalogue no: **831 699-4**
**CD:** Released Jul '87, on Phonogram by Phonogram Ltd. Catalogue no: **831 699-2**

**COPACABANA**
Tracks: / Copacabana / Smiling hour / To say goodbye / Dreamer / Gentle rain, The / Tete / Dindi / Double rainbow / Bonita.
**Album:** Released '82, on Pablo Jazz (USA) by Pablo Records (USA). Catalogue no: **2312 125**
**Cass:** Released '82, on Pablo Jazz (USA) by Pablo Records (USA). Catalogue no: **K 12 125**

**CRAZY AND MIXED UP**
Tracks: / I didn't know what time it was / That's all / Autumn leaves / Love dance / Island, The / In love in vain / Seasons / You are too beautiful.
**CD:** Released Jul '86, on Pablo Jazz (USA) by Pablo Records (USA). Catalogue no: **J33J 20043**

**DIVINE**
**Album:** Released '88, on Entertainers Catalogue no: **ENT LP 13036**
**2 LP Set:** Released Oct '88, on Vogue by Vogue Records. Catalogue no: **400009**
**CD:** Released '88, on Entertainers Catalogue no: **ENT CD 225**
**Cass:** Released '88, on Entertainers Catalogue no: **ENT MC 13036**

**DIVINE ONE, THE**
Tracks: / Have you met Miss Jones? / Ain't no use / Every time I see you / You stepped out of a dream / Gloomy Sunday / What do you see in her / Jump for joy / When your lover has gone / I'm gonna laugh you out of my life / Wrap your troubles in dreams / Somebody else's dream / Trouble is a man.
**CD:** Released Dec '86, on Vogue by Vogue Records. Catalogue no: **VG 600 017**

**DIVINE SARAH, VOL.1, THE**
Tracks: / If you could see me now / My kinda love / I've got a crush on you / I'm through with love / Everything I have is yours / Body and soul / I cover the waterfront / Tenderly / Don't blame me / Motherless child / I don't stand a ghost of a chance with you.
Note: Featuring Bud Powell, Kenny Clarke, Al McKibbon, plus Ted Dale's Orchestra.
**Album:** Released '88, on Musicraft (USA) by Discovery Records (USA). Catalogue no: **MVS 504**

**DUKE ELLINGTON SONG BOOK, VOL. 1**
Tracks: / In a sentimental mood / I'm just a lucky so and so / Solitude / I let a song go out of my heart / I didn't know about you / All too soon / Lush life / In a mellow tone / Sophisticated lady / Daydream.
**Cass:** Released '82, on Pablo Jazz (USA) by Pablo Records (USA). Catalogue no: **K 12 111**
**Album:** Released '82, on Pablo Jazz (USA) by Pablo Records (USA). Catalogue no: **2312 111**

**DUKE ELLINGTON SONG BOOK, VOL. 2**
Tracks: / I ain't got nothin' but the blues / Black butterfly / Chelsea Bridge / What am I here for? / Tonight I shall sleep / Rocks in my bed / I got it bad and that ain't good / Everything but you / Mood indigo / It don't mean a thing / Prelude to a kiss.
**Album:** Released '82, on Pablo Jazz (USA) by Pablo Records (USA). Catalogue no: **2312 116**
**Cass:** Released '82, on Pablo Jazz (USA) by Pablo Records (USA). Catalogue no: **K 12 116**

**FOGGY DAY, A**
**Cass:** Released Nov '84, on Astan (USA) Catalogue no: **40117**
**Album:** Released Nov '84, on Astan (USA) Catalogue no: **20117**

**GERSHWIN LIVE (Vaughan, Sarah / Michael Tilson Thomas)**
Tracks: / Porgy and Bess medley / But not for me / Do it again / Embraceable you / Someone to watch over me / Man I love / Sweet and lowdown / Fascinating rhythm / My man's gone now / Nice work if you can get it / They can't take that away from me / 'S wonderful / Swanee / Strike up the band / Foggy day / I've got a crush on you.
Note: Song include Fascinating rhythm, Do it again.
**Cass:** Released Sep '82, on CBS by CBS Records. Catalogue no: **40 73650**
**CD:** Released Feb '86, on CBS by CBS Records. Catalogue no: **MK 73650**
**Album:** Released Sep '82, on CBS by CBS Records. Catalogue no: **CBS 73650**

**GOLDEN HITS: SARAH VAUGHAN**
Tracks: / Moonlight in Vermont / Poor butterfly / Misty / Broken-hearted melody / Autumn in New York / Smooth operator / Yesterday / Close to you / Eternally / Whatever Lola wants (Lola gets) / Lullaby of Birdland / How important can it be? / Make yourself comfortable / Tea for two.
**Cass:** Released Apr '83, on Mercury (Import) Catalogue no: **7259 149**
**Album:** Released Apr '83, on Mercury (Import) Catalogue no: **9279 149**

**HOW LONG HAS THIS BEEN GOING ON**
Tracks: / I got the world on a string / Midnight sun / How long has this been going on? / You're blase / Easy living / More than you know / My old flame / Teach me tonight / Body and soul / When your lover has gone.
**Album:** Released '82, on Pablo Jazz (USA) by Pablo Records (USA). Catalogue no: **2312 821**
**Cass:** Released '82, on Pablo Jazz (USA) by Pablo Records (USA). Catalogue no: **K 12 821**
**CD:** Released Jul '86, on Pablo Jazz (USA) by Pablo Records (USA). Catalogue no: **J33J 20044**

**IN THE LAND OF HI-FI**
**CD:** Released Jul '87, on Philips by Phonogram Ltd. Deleted Nov '88. Catalogue no: **826 454-2**

**IRVING BERLIN SONGBOOK (Vaughan, Sarah/Billy Eckstein)**
Tracks: / Alexander's ragtime band / Isn't this a lovely day / I've got my love to keep me warm / All of my life / Cheek to cheek / You're just in love / Remember / Always / Easter parade / Girl that I marry, The / Now it can be told / Thanks for the memory / Start believing me now / My funny valentine / Foggy day, A / Send in the clowns / Like someone in love / Detour ahead / Three little words / You may not be an angel / If you could see me now.
**Cass:** Released '86, on Topline by Charly Records. Catalogue no: **KTOP 135**
**Cass:** Released Feb '85, on Emarcy Catalogue no: **825 526-4**
**Album:** Released Feb '85, on Emarcy Catalogue no: **825 526-1**
**Album:** Released '86, on Topline by Charly Records. Catalogue no: **TOP 135**
**CD:** Released Feb '85, on Emarcy Catalogue no: **825 526-2**

**LET'S**
Tracks: / Let's / Serenata.
**7" Single:** Released Dec '60, on Columbia by EMI Records. Deleted '63. Catalogue no: **DB 4542**

**LIKE SOMEONE IN LOVE**
Tracks: / Detour ahead / Three little words / I'll string along with you / If you could see me now / Thanks for the memory / Start believing me now / My funny valentine / Foggy day, A / Send in the clowns / Like someone in love.
**CD:** Released May '87, on Topline by Charly Records. Catalogue no: **TOP CD 519**

**LIVE IN JAPAN**
**CD:** Released '88, on Mobile Fidelity Sound Lab(USA) by Mobile Fidelity Records (USA). Catalogue no: **MFCD 2-844**
**Cass:** Released Dec '89, on Accord (France) by Musidisc Records (France). Catalogue no: **557302**
**CD:** Released Dec '89, on Accord (France) by Musidisc Records (France). Catalogue no: **557304**

**LOVER MAN, VOL.3**
Tracks: / Love me or leave me / Button up your overcoat / I'm through with love / What a difference a day made / Nature boy / It's magic / Ghost of a chance / Lover man /.Gentleman friend / I feel so smoochie.
**Album:** Released '88, on Musicraft (USA) by Discovery Records (USA). Catalogue no: **MVS 2006**

**LULLABY OF BIRDLAND**
**Album:** Released Dec '83, on Mercury (USA) by PolyGram Rec.Inc.(USA). Catalogue no: **6336 709**

**MAGIC OF SARAH VAUGHAN, THE**
Tracks: / That old black magic / Separate ways / Mary Contrary / I've got the world on a string / What's so bad about it / Misty / Careless / Are you certain / Broken hearted melody / Friendly enemies / Sweet affection.
**Cass:** Released Feb '89, on Venus Catalogue no: **VENUMC 1**

**MAN I LOVE, THE**
Tracks: / Trouble is a man / I'm gonna sit right down and write myself a l. / I can't get started / Man i love / One i love / It's you or no-one / Once in a while / I get a kick out of you / I'll wait & pray / I'm glad there is you / Time and again.
**Album:** Released Jan '84, on Musicraft (USA) by Discovery Records (USA). Catalogue no: **MVS 2002**

**MY FIRST 15 SIDES**
Tracks: / I'll wait and pray / Signing off / Interlude / No smokes blues / East of the sun / Lover man oh, where can you be / What more can a woman do? / I'd rather have a memory than a dream / Mean to me / All too soon / I'm scared / You go to my head / I could make you love me / It might as well be spring / We're through.
**Album:** Released May '88, on Official by Official Records. Catalogue no: **OFF 3003**
**Cass:** Released May '88, on Official by Official Records. Catalogue no: **OFF 43003**
**CD:** Released Dec '88, on Official by Official Records. Catalogue no: **OFF 83003**

**NO COUNT SARAH**
Tracks: / Smoke gets in your eyes / Doodlin' / Darn that dream / Just one of those things / Moonlight in Vermont / No 'count blues / Cheek to cheek / Stardust / Missing you.
Note: Personnel: Sarah Vaughan- vocals/Wendell Culley, Thad Jones, Snooky Young, Joe Newman- trumpets/Henry Coker, Al Grey, Benny Powell- trombones/Frank Wess, Frank Foster, Billy Mitchell, Charlie Fowlkes, Marchall Royal- reeds / Freddie Green- guitar / Ronnell Bright- piano / Richard Davis- bass / Sonny Payne- drums. Recorded in New York.
**Album:** Released Mar '60, on Mercury by Phonogram Ltd. Deleted '65. Catalogue no: **MMC 14021**
**CD:** Released May '86, on Emarcy Catalogue no: **824 057 2**

**O, SOME BRASILEIRO DE**
**Album:** Released Jan '84, on RCA (Brazil) Catalogue no: **110 0018**
**Cass:** Released Jan '84, on RCA/Camden by BMG Records (UK). Catalogue no: **710 0315**

**PASSING STRANGERS (Vaughan, Sarah / Billy Eckstein)**
Tracks: / Passing strangers / Alexander's ragtime band / Isn't this a lovely day / I've got my love to keep me warm / All of my life / Cheek to cheek / You're just in love / Remember / Always / Easter parade / Girl that I marry, The / Now it can be told.
**Cass set:** Released '78, on Mercury by Phonogram Ltd. Catalogue no: **7599 366**
**Album:** Released Jul '84, on Philips (Timeless) by PolyGram UK Ltd. Catalogue no: **TIME 02**
**2 LP Set:** Released '78, on Mercury by Phonogram Ltd. Catalogue no: **6641 868**
**Album:** Released Aug '80, on Mercury by Phonogram Ltd. Deleted '85. Catalogue no: **6463 041**
**Cass:** Released Jul '84, on Philips (Timeless) by PolyGram UK Ltd. Catalogue no: **TIMEC 02**

**PASSING STRANGERS (SINGLE)**
Tracks: / Passing Strangers / Wedding.
**7" Single:** Released Oct '80, on Classic Cuts Catalogue no: **CUT 106**

**RODGERS & HART SONGBOOK, THE**
Tracks: / My funny valentine / LIttle girl blue / Tree in the park, A / It's got to be love / Ship without a sail, A / Bewitched / Thou swell / It never entered my mind / It's easy to remember / Why can't I / My romance / My heart stood still.
Note: The programme on this record has been compiled from recordings made between 1954 and 1958 and has never been issued in this format before. These recordings have been digitally remastered.
**CD:** Released Dec '85, on Polydor by Polydor Ltd. Catalogue no: **824 864-2**
**Album:** Released Dec '85, on Pablo Jazz (USA) by Pablo Records (USA). Catalogue no: **824 864-1**
**Cass:** Released Dec '85, on Pablo Jazz (USA) by Pablo Records (USA). Catalogue no: **824 864-4**

**ROUND MIDNIGHT**
**Album:** Released '88, on Zeta Catalogue no: **ZET 701**

**SARAH + 2**
**CD:** Released Oct '88, on Vogue by Vogue Records. Catalogue no: **VGCD 600 182**
**Album:** Released Dec '87, on Fresh Sounds (Spain) by Fresh Sounds Records (Spain). Catalogue no: **FS 298**

**SARAH VAUGHAN**
Tracks: / Lullaby of birdland / April in Paris / He's my guy / Jim / You're not the kind / Embraceable you / I'm glad there is you / September song / It's crazy.
Note: Personnel: Orchestra conducted by Ernie Wilkins/H. Mann- flute/C. Brown- trumpet/P. Quioichette- tener sax/J. Benjamin- bass/J. Jones- piano/R. Haynes- drums. Recorded New York 1954.
**Cass:** Released '88, on Entertainers Catalogue no: **ENT MC 13006**
**Album:** Released Sep '87, on Entertainers Catalogue no: **ENT LP 13006**
**CD:** Released May '85, on Emarcy Catalogue no: **814 641 2**
**Cass:** Released Oct '84, on Audio Fidelity(USA) by Audio Fidelity (USA). Catalogue no: **ZCGAS 728**

**SARAH VAUGHAN COLLECTION (20 golden greats)**
Tracks: / Scat blues / I feel pretty / Won't you come home, Bill Bailey / Polka dots and moonbeams / Embraceable you / What is this thing called love? / East of the sun / Gentleman friend / Motherless child / Signing off / What a difference a day made / Tenderly / Lord's Prayer, The / Time after time / You or no one / September song / One I love belongs to somebody else, The / Hundred years from today / I cried for you / Sometimes I'm happy.
**Album:** Released Nov '85, on Deja Vu Catalogue no: **DVLP 2023**
**Cass:** Released Nov '85, on Deja Vu Catalogue no: **DVMC 2023**

**SARAH VAUGHAN LIVE (Compact / Walkman jazz)**
**CD:** Released '88, on Mercury by Phonogram Ltd. Catalogue no: **832572-2**
**Cass:** Released '88, on Mercury by Phonogram Ltd. Catalogue no: **832572-4**

**SARAH VAUGHAN, VOL 1**
Tracks: / Just in time / When Sunny gets blue / All I do is dream of you / I understand / Goodnight sweetheart / Baby won't you please come home / When lights are low / Key largo / Just squeeze me / All or nothing at all / Very thought of you, The.
**Album:** Released Jan '82, on Jazz Reactivation Catalogue no: **JR 109**

**SARAH VAUGHAN, VOL 2**
Tracks: / I believe in you / Honeysuckle

rose / Moonlight on the Ganges / Lady's in love with you / After you've gone / Garden in the rain / I can't give you anything but love / Trolley song / I'm gonna live till I die / Falling in love with love / Great day / Nobody else but me.
**Album:** Released May '83, on Jazz Reactivation Catalogue no: **JR 128**
**Album:** Released May '79, on Pye Catalogue no: **N 103**
**Cass:** Released May '79, on Pye Catalogue no: **ZCN 103**

**SARAH VAUGHAN (with Count Basie & Benny Carter) (Vaughan, Sarah/Count Basie)**
**CD:** Released Dec '86, on Vogue by Vogue Records. Catalogue no: **VG 600 106**

**SASSY SWINGS AGAIN**
Tracks: / Sweet Georgia Brown / Take the 'A' train / I left my heart in San Francisco / S'posin' / Everyday / I have the blues / I want to be happy / All alone / Sweetest sounds, The / On the other side of the tracks / I had a ball.
**CD:** Released Sep '84, on Verve (USA) by Polydor Ltd. Catalogue no: **814 587 2**

**SEND IN THE CLOWNS (Vaughan, Sarah / Count Basie)**
Tracks: / I gotta right to sing the blues / Just friends / Ill wind / If you could see me now / I hadn't anyone till you / Send in the clowns / All the things you are / Indian summer / When your lover has gone / From this moment on.
**Cass:** Released '82, on Pablo Jazz (USA) by Pablo Records (USA). Catalogue no: **K 12 130**
**Album:** Released '82, on Pablo Jazz (USA) by Pablo Records (USA). Catalogue no: **2312 130**

**SINGS GREAT SONGS FROM HIT SHOWS**
**Album:** Released Jan '88, on Memoir by Memoir Records. Catalogue no: **MOIR 127**
**Cass:** Released Jan '88, on Memoir by Memoir Records. Catalogue no: **MOIRC 127**

**SPOTLIGHT ON SARAH VAUGHAN**
Tracks: / You're mine now / Best is yet to come, The / Witchcraft / So long / Second time around / I could write a book / Marie / Baubles, bangles and beads / Fly me to the moon / Moonglow / Invitation / On Green Dolphin Street / Dreamy / Hands across the table / More I see you, The / I'll be seeing you / Star eyes / You've changed / Trees / Why was I born? / My ideal / Crazy he calls me / Stormy weather / Moon over Miami.
**Cass set:** Released Oct '84, on PRT by Castle Communications Records. Catalogue no: **ZCSPT 6804**
**2 LP Set:** Released Oct '84, on PRT by Castle Communications Records. Catalogue no: **SPOT 6804**

**SUMMERTIME**
**Cass:** Released Aug '84, on CBS (I love Jazz) by CBS Records. Catalogue no: **40 21114**
**Album:** Released Aug '84, on CBS (I love Jazz) by CBS Records. Deleted Aug '88. Catalogue no: **CBS 21114**

**TENDERLY**
Tracks: / It's you or no one / Tenderly / Lord's Prayer, The / What a difference a day made / Gentleman friend / East of the sun / Motherless child / One I love belongs to somebody else, The / September song / Time after time / Hundred years from today / Signing off.
**Album:** Released Jul '82, on Bulldog Records by President Records. Catalogue no: **BDL 1009**
**Album:** Released Nov '84, on Astan (USA) Catalogue no: **20070**
**Cass:** Released Nov '84, on Astan (USA) Catalogue no: **40070**

**TIME AFTER TIME (Vaughan, Sarah / Teddy Wilson)**
Tracks: / September song / Just one of those things / When we're alone / I want to be happy / Moon faced and starry eyed / Sheik of Araby / Whispering / Time after time / Moonlight on the Ganges / Don't worry about me / Chinatown my Chinatown / Bess you is my woman.
**Album:** Released Aug '83, on Musicraft (USA) by Discovery Records (USA). Catalogue no: **MVS 2001**

**TIME IN MY LIFE, A**
**CD:** Released Oct '86, on Mobile Fidelity Sound Lab(USA) by Mobile Fidelity Records (USA). Catalogue no: **MFCD 855**

**TWO SOUNDS OF SARAH VAUGHAN**
Tracks: / I believe in you / Honeysuckle rose / When Sunny gets blue / Just in time / All I do is dream of you / Lady's in love with you, The / Just squeeze me / Very thought of you, The / After you've gone / Key Largo / Garden in the rain / Baby won't you please come home? / When lights are low / I can't give you anything but love / Trolley song, The / All or nothing at all / Moonlight in the Ganges / I'm gonna live 'til I die / Great days / I understand / Falling in love with love / Nobody else but me / Goodnight sweetheart.
**Cass:** Released May '83, on Vogue Jazz (France) by Vogue Records. Catalogue no: **ZCVJD 543**

**VAUGHAN AND VIOLINS**
Tracks: / Gone with the wind / Day by day / Please be kind / Live for love / I'll close my eyes / Misty / Midnight sun will never set, The / That's all / I'm lost / Love me / Thrill is gone, The.
Note: Also featuring Quincy Jones Orchestra.
**Album:** Released Dec '85, on Memoir by Memoir Records. Catalogue no: **MOIR 113**
**Cass:** Released Dec '85, on Memoir by Memoir Records. Catalogue no: **CMOIR 113**

**YOU'RE MINE YOU (with Quincy Jones) (Vaughan, Sarah & Quincy Jones)**
**Album:** Released Jun '88, on Fresh Sounds (Spain) by Fresh Sounds Records (Spain). Catalogue no: **FS 318**

## Ventura, Charlie

**Biographical details:** Born in 1916 in Philadelphia, tenor saxist Charlie Ventura was a showman with a touch of vulgarity who was very popular with several Gene Krupa bands from 1942 as well as leading his own combos, influenced by the jump bands of Louis Jordan and Illinois Jacquet and also by modern jazz. His '51 quartet included drummer Buddy Rich; his late 40's work featured the excellent vocal duo Jackie Cain and Roy Kral. (Donald Clarke, January 1988.).

**BIRDLAND**
**Album:** Released Feb '88, on Fresh Sounds (Spain) by Fresh Sounds Records (Spain). Catalogue no: **FS 177**

**BOP FOR THE PEOPLE (Ventura, Charlie Featuring Jackie Cain / Roy Kral)**
Tracks: / Yesterdays / Peanut vendor / Euphoria / Fine and dandy / East of Suez / Great lie, The / Turnpike / If I had you / I'm forever blowing bubbles / Pennies from Heaven / How high the moon / They can't take that away from me / Honey jump, The.
**Album:** Released '83, on Affinity by Charly Records. Deleted '87. Catalogue no: **AFF 104**

**CHARLIE BOY (1946)**
**Album:** Released Apr '81, on Phoenix (USA) by All Star Talent Inc.(USA). Catalogue no: **LP 6**

**CHARLIE VENTURA & HIS BAND**
Tracks: / Birdland / Flamingo / Body and soul / Lullaby in rhythm / Boptura / Over the rainbow / Dark eyes / High on an open mike.
**Album:** Released Jan '82, on Jazz Reactivation Catalogue no: **JR 103**

**CHARLIE VENTURA IN CONCERT**
**Album:** Released '87, on GNP Crescendo (USA) by GNP Crescendo Records (USA). Catalogue no: **GNPS 1**

**CHARLIE VENTURA QUINTET IN HI-FI (Ventura Quintet,Charlie)**
Tracks: / High on an open mike / Charlies ant / Cry me a river / Love and the weather / Euphoria / Parlay 2 / Jazz roost / Sleep till noon / East of suez / Bernies tune.
**Album:** Released Aug '84, on Harlequin by Interstate Music. Catalogue no: **HQ 2009**

**EUPHORIA**
**Album:** Released Mar '85, on Savoy Jazz (USA) by Malaco Records (USA). Catalogue no: **SJL 2243**

**IN CHICAGO-1947 (Ventura Quintet,Charlie)**
**Album:** Released Apr '81, on Zim (USA) Catalogue no: **ZM 1004**

**TOWN HALL CONCERT VOL.2**
**Album:** Released '74, on London Records by London Records Ltd. Catalogue no: **HMC 5002**

## Venuti, Joe

**Biographical details:** He recorded legendary duets with Eddie Lang in the 1920s, was eclipsed in the 1960s due to alcoholism but came back for a second career, with modern recordings on Sonet, Flying Fish and Concord Jazz. Venuti was a notorious practical joker, pushing a piano out of a hotel room window, pouring jelly into Bix Beiderbecke's bathwater, putting flour in the tub during the filming of Paul Whiteman's King Of Jazz and so on. (Donald Clarke, January 1988).

**BIG BANDS OF JOE VENUTI 1928-30 (Venuti, Joe Big Band)**
Note: Mono.
**Album:** Released Feb '87, on JSP by JSP Records. Catalogue no: **JSP 1111**

**DOIN' THINGS**
Tracks: / Man from the south / Ragging the scale / Sensation / Jig saw puzzle blues / Put & take / To to blues / Wild dog / Runnin' ragged / Doin' things / Beale street blues / After you've gone / Wild cat / Farewell blues / Someday sweetheart / I've found a new baby / I'll never be the same again.
**Album:** Released '84, on Decca by Decca International. Deleted '89. Catalogue no: **RAL 502**

**ELECTRIC JOE**
Note: Previously released on Jump (Import), '81 Dist Jazz Horizons Cat.No.J 0143
**Album:** Released '88, on Jump (Import) Catalogue no: **JUMP 0143**

**INCREDIBLE JOE VENUTI, THE**
**Album:** Released Jul '87, on Audiophile (USA) by Jazzology Records (USA). Catalogue no: **AP 118**

**JANUARY 28TH & 30TH,1957 (Venuti, Joe & His Blue Four)**
Tracks: / Howdown lowdown / Hot 'n' trot / Bohemian bounce / Concerto for new sounds / Blue Five swing / Black rhythm / Nobody loves me / Fickle fiddle / Fleur-de-lis / Gee it's great / Desert flower / Distant lake.
**Album:** Released Oct '80, on From The Jazz Vault by Damont Audio Ltd.. Catalogue no: **JV 109**

**JAZZ ME BLUES**
**Album:** Released Apr '81, on Jump (Import) Catalogue no: **J 0124**

**JOE IN CHICAGO**
**Album:** Released May '79, on Flying Fish (USA) by Flying Fish Records (USA). Catalogue no: **FF 077**

**JOE VENUTI AND EDDIE LANG, VOL.1 (Venuti, Joe & Eddie Lang)**
**CD:** Released Aug '89, on JSP by JSP Records. Catalogue no: **JSPCD 309**

**JOE VENUTI AND EDDIE LANG, VOL.2 (Venuti, Joe & Eddie Lang)**
**CD:** Released Aug '89, on JSP by JSP Records. Catalogue no: **JSPCD 310**
**Album:** Released Jan '83, on Swaggie (Australia) Catalogue no: **S 1266**
**Album:** Released '88, on Swaggie (Australia) Catalogue no: **S 817**

**JOE VENUTI AND HIS BAND-1945 (Venuti, Joe & His Band)**
**Album:** Released Jul '82, on Golden Era by Delta Records. Catalogue no: **GELP 15061**

**JOE VENUTI & HIS ORCHESTRA**
**Album:** Released Mar '76, on London Records by London Records Ltd. Catalogue no: **HMG 5023**

**JOE VENUTI JAZZ GROUP (Venuti, Joe Jazz Group & Gil Cuppini Big Band)**
**Album:** Released '88, on Jump (Import) Catalogue no: **JUMP 0118**

**JOE VENUTI QUARTET (Venuti, Joe Quartet)**
**Album:** Released Apr '81, on Jump (Import) Catalogue no: **J 0110**

**JOE VENUTI VOL. 2**
**Album:** Released May '88, on JSP by JSP Records. Catalogue no: **JSP 1112**

**JOE VENUTI'S JAZZ GROUP**
**Album:** Released Apr '81, on Jump (Import) Catalogue no: **J 0118**

**MAD FIDDLER FROM PHILLY, THE**
**Album:** Released Apr '81, on Shoestring (1) Catalogue no: **SS 111**

**PLAYS GEORGE GERSHWIN & JEROME KERN**
**Album:** Released Apr '81, on Jump (Import) Catalogue no: **J 0121**

**'S WONDERFUL GIANTS OF SWING**
**Album:** Released Feb '79, on Flying Fish (USA) by Flying Fish Records (USA). Catalogue no: **FLY 0006**

**SLIDING BY (Venuti, Joe & Bucky Pizzarelli)**
Tracks: / Sliding by / Red velvet / That's a plenty / But not for me / Clarinet marmalade / Lover / Black satin / Rhapsodic / Sophisticated lady / Sweet Georgia Brown.
**Album:** Released Jan '78, on Sonet by Sonet Records. Catalogue no: **SNTF 734**

**VENUTIANA**
**Album:** Released '88, on Jump (Import) Catalogue no: **JUMP 0132**
**Album:** Released Apr '81, on Jump (Import) Catalogue no: **J 0132**

**VIOLIN JAZZ**
**Album:** Released Jan '79, on Yazoo (USA) by Shanachie Records (USA). Catalogue no: **L 1062**

## VerPlanck, Marlene

**I LIKE TO SING**
**Album:** Released Sep '86, on Audiophile (USA) by Jazzology Records (USA). Catalogue no: **AP 186**

**I THINK OF YOU WITH EVERY**
**Album:** Released Jun '88, on Audiophile (USA) by Jazzology Records (USA). Catalogue no: **AP 62**

**LOVES JOHNNY MERCER**
**CD:** Released Apr '89, on Audiophile (USA) by Jazzology Records (USA). Catalogue no: **APCD 138**
**Album:** Released Jun '88, on Audiophile (USA) by Jazzology Records (USA). Catalogue no: **AP 138**

**NEW YORK SINGER, A**
**Album:** Released Jun '88, on Audiophile (USA) by Jazzology Records (USA). Catalogue no: **AP 160**

**PURE AND NATURAL**
**Album:** Released Aug '88, on Jazzology (USA) by Jazzology Records (USA). Catalogue no: **AP 235**

**SINGS ALEC WILDER**
Note: Mel Lewis - drums. Double album.
**Album:** Released Feb '87, on Audiophile (USA) by Jazzology Records (USA). Catalogue no: **AP 218**

**WARMER PLACE, A**
**Album:** Released '89, on Audiophile (USA) by Jazzology Records (USA). Catalogue no: **AP 169**

**YOU'D BETTER LOVE ME**
**Album:** Released Jun '88, on Audiophile (USA) by Jazzology Records (USA). Catalogue no: **AP 121**

## Verve Jazz Best

**VERVE JAZZ BEST VOL.3 (Various artists)**
Tracks: / Organ grinder's swing: *Smith, Jimmy (USA)* / Cheek to cheek: *Fitzgerald, Ella & Louis Armstrong* / Samba triste: *Getz, Stan & Charlie Byrd* / Aqua de beber: *Gilberto, Astrud* / You'd be so nice to come home to: *Hawkins, Coleman & Ben Webster* / Too close for comfort: *Torme, Mel* / Caravan: *Montgomery, Wes* / I can't give you anything but love: *Fitzgerald, Ella* / Moonglow: *Hampton, Lionel/Teddy Wilson/Gene Krupa* / Just a sittin and a rockin: *Harper, Toni* / East of the sun (and west of the moon): *Various artists* / Moonlight in Vermont: *Holiday, Billie* / You look good to me: *Oscar Peterson Trio.*
**Album:** Released Apr '86, on Verve (USA) by Polydor Ltd. Catalogue no: **827 542-1**
**Cass:** Released Apr '86, on Verve (USA) by Polydor Ltd. Catalogue no: **827 542-4**

## Vesala, Edward

**LUMI**
Tracks: / Wind, The / Frozen melody / Calypso bulbosa / Third moon / Lumi / Camel walk / Fingo / Early messenger / Together.
Note: Personnel: Edward Vesala - drums, percussion / Eskko Heikkinen - trumpet, piccolo trumpet / Penti Lahti - alto & baritone saxophones, flutes / Jorma Tapio -alto saxaphone, clarinet, bass clarinet, flute / Tapani Rinne - tenor & soprano saxophones, clarinet, bass clarinet / Kari Heinila - tenor & soprano saxophones, flute / Tom Bildo - trombone, tuba / Iro Haarla - piano, harp / Raoul Bjorkenheim - guitar /Haka - bass.
**Album:** Released Jul '87, on ECM Catalogue no: **ECM 1339**
**CD:** Released Jul '87, on ECM Catalogue no: **831 517 2**

## Vig, Tommy

**ENCOUNTER WITH TIME (Vig, Tommy & His Orchestra)**
Note: Al Porcino, Buddy Childers, Gus Mancuso, Charlie Loper, Carl Fontana, Frank Rosolino, Ken Shroyer, Charlie McLean, Bill Perkins, Irv Gordon, Don Hannah, Mike Wofford, Victor Feldman, Herb Mickman, Red Mitchell, Shelly Manne, Tommy Vig.
**Album:** Released '88, on Discovery (USA) by Discovery Records (USA). Catalogue no: **DS 780**

**SPACE RACE (Vig, Tommy Orchestra)**
**CD:** Released Dec '86, on Discovery (USA) by Discovery Records (USA). Catalogue no: **DSCD 925**

## Vinson, Eddie

**Biographical details:** Born in 1917 in Houston, Texas, alto saxist, blues singer and bandleader Vinson, whose nickname comes from his bald head, is a rhythm-and-blues stalwart who is also highly regarded in jazz circles. He recorded as a singer with the Cootie Williams Band from 1942 to 1945 (tracks now on Affinity) and was regarded as one of the best big band singers of the decade. He formed his own band and recorded for Mercury and King (1945-52). As well as making many albums as a solo artist he worked with Cannonball Adderley, Arnett Cobb, Jay McShann, Johnny Otis and others. (Donald Clarke, January 1988.).

**BACK IN TOWN (Live at Sandys)**
**Album:** Released '81, on Muse by Black & Blue Records. Catalogue no: **MR 5208**
**CD:** Released Jan '87, on Charly by Charly Records. Catalogue no: **CDCHARLY 50**
**Album:** Released Mar '83, on Charly R&B by Charly Records. Catalogue no: **CRB 1046**

**BATTLE OF THE BLUES VOL. 4 (Vinson, Eddie, Roy Brown & Wynomie Harris)**
Tracks: / Big mouth gal / Bring it back / If you don't think I'm sinking / Trouble at midnight / Peas and rice / Rock Mr. Blues / Lonesome train / Old age boogie / Balt headed blues / Grandma plays the numbers / Good bread alley / Queen of diamonds.
**CD:** Released Mar '90, on King Catalogue no: **KCD 668**
**Album:** Released Dec '87, on Sing Catalogue no: **SING 668**

**CHERRY RED BLUES**
**Album:** Released Jul '88, on Bellaphon Catalogue no: **BID 8023**
**Cass set:** Released Mar '88, on Gusto (USA) by Gusto Records (USA). Catalogue no: **GD 5035**

**CLEAN MACHINE, THE**
**Album:** Released Apr '81, on Muse by Black & Blue Records. Catalogue no: **MR 5116**

**CLEANHEAD & CANNONBALL (Vinson, Eddie & Cannonball Adderley)**
Note: Blues singer & alto player Eddie 'Cleanhead' Vinson recorded in September 1961 with the Cannonball Adderley Quintet and never before released. Personnel: Eddie (vocals & alto sax), Cannonball Adderley (alto sax), Nat Adderley (cornet), Joe Zawinul (piano), Sam Jones (bass), Louis Hayes (drums).
**CD:** Released Oct '88, on Landmark (USA) by Fantasy Inc (USA). Catalogue no: **LCD 13092**
**Album:** Released Oct '88, on Landmark (USA) by Fantasy Inc (USA). Catalogue no: **LLP 1309**

**CLEANHEAD & ROOMFUL OF BLUES**
Tracks: / House of joy / Friend of mine, A / Movin with Lester / No bones / That's the groovy thing / Past sixty blues / Street light / Farmer's daughter blues.
Note: All tunes except 1 and 4 arranged by Roomful of Blues and Eddie 'Cleanhead' Vinson.Personnel: Eddie 'Cleanhead' Vinson-alto saxophone (plus vocals on 2,6,8) Greg Piccolo-tenor saxophone & leader. Rich Ltaille-alto saxophone. Doug James- baritone saxophone. Bob Enos-trumpet. Porky Cohen- trombone. Al Copley- piano. Ronnie Earl Horvath- guitar. Jimmy Wimpfheimer- bass. John Rossi- drums.
**Album:** Released Aug '86, on Muse by Black & Blue Records. Catalogue no: **MR 5282**

**FUN IN LONDON**
**Album:** Released Mar '82, on JSP by JSP Records. Catalogue no: **JSP 1012**
**CD:** Released Nov '87, on JSP by JSP Records. Catalogue no: **JSP CD 204**

**I WANT A LITTLE GIRL**
Tracks: / I want a little girl / Somebody got to go / Blues in the closet / No good for me / Stormy Monday / Straight, no chaser / Worried mind blues.
**Cass:** Released '82, on Pablo Jazz (USA) by Pablo Records (USA). Catalogue no: **K10 866**
**Album:** Released '82, on Pablo Jazz (USA) by Pablo Records (USA). Catalogue no: **231 0866**

**JAMMIN' THE BLUES**
Tracks: / Just a dream / Laura / Person to person / Now's the time / Hold it right there / Home boy / C jam blues.
Note: With Hal Singer, Peter Wingfield, Jerome Rimson, Joe Wright, Peter Van Hook. Recorded 1974.
**Album:** Released Jul '87, on Black Lion Catalogue no: **BLP 30168**

**KANSAS CITY SHOUT (Vinson, Eddie, Count Basie & Joe Turner)**
**Album:** Released '82, on Pablo Jazz (USA) by Pablo Records (USA). Catalogue no: **231 0859**
**Cass:** Released '82, on Pablo Jazz (USA) by Pablo Records (USA). Catalogue no: **K10 859**

**MEAT'S TOO HIGH**
**CD:** Released Feb '89, on JSP by JSP Records. Catalogue no: **JSPCD 223**

**MIDNIGHT CREEPER**
**Album:** Released May '89, on Blue Moon (1) by Magnum Music Group. Catalogue no: **BMLP 1063**

**MR. CLEANHEAD STEPS OUT**
**Album:** Released Aug '85, on Saxophonograph (Sweden) Catalogue no: **BP 507**

**MR. CLEANHEAD'S BACK IN TOWN**
Tracks: / Home boy / Meats too high / Somebody's got to go / Somebody else is taking my place / Investigation blues / If you were my buddy / Old maid boogie / That's all / Travelling.
**Album:** Released Jul '82, on JSP by JSP Records. Catalogue no: **JSP 1046**

**REAL "MR. CLEANHEAD", THE**
Tracks: / Suffer fool / Big chief / Tomorrow may never come / Anxious heart / Old man boogie / You can't have my love no more / Juice head baby / Cherry red blues / Somebody's got to go / Too many women blues / Just a dream / Cleanhead blues / When a woman loves / King for a day blues / Railroad porter's blues.
**Album:** on Official by Official Records. Catalogue no: **OFF 6041**

## Vintage Bands

**VINTAGE BANDS, THE (Various artists)**
Tracks: / Music, Maestro, please: *Hylton, Jack/his orchestra* / Alexander's ragtime band: *Roy, Harry & His Orchestra* / Nagasaki: *Gonella, Nat/his Georgians* / Nobody loves a fairy when she's forty: *Cotton, Billy & His Band* / My brother makes the noises for the talkies: *Payne, Jack & His BBC Dance Orchestra* / Stay as sweet as you are: *Stone, Lew & His Orchestra* / In the mood: *Loss, Joe & His Orchestra* / Let's face the music and dance: *Fox, Roy & His Orchestra* / Nightingale sang in Berkeley Square, A: *Gibbons, Carroll & The Savoy Hotel Orpheans* / Dancing in the dark: *Ambrose* / Here's to the next time: *Hall, Henry & The BBC Dance Orchestra* / Say it with music: *Payne, Jack & His BBC Dance Orchestra* / I'm going to get lit up when the lights go up in London: *Gibbons, Carroll & The Savoy Hotel Orpheans* / Change partners: *Loss, Joe & His Orchestra* / Did you ever see a dream walking?: *Hall, Henry & The BBC Dance Orchestra* / Shine: *Cotton, Billy & His Band* / She had to go and lose it at the Astoria: *Roy, Harry & His Orchestra* / Easy to remember: *Stone, Lew & His Orchestra* / Have you met Miss Jones?: *Hylton, Jack/his orchestra* / I can't dance, I got ants in my pants: *Gonella, Nat/his Georgians* / Night is young and you're so beautiful, The: *Fox, Roy & His Orchestra* / Let's put out the lights: *Ambrose.*
**CD:** Released May '88, on Compacts For Pleasure by Music For Pleasure Records. Catalogue no: **CDB 752 033 2**
**Cass:** Released May '86, on Hour Of Pleasure by EMI Records. Catalogue no: **HR 8114**

**CD:** Released May '88, on Compacts For Pleasure by Music For Pleasure Records. Catalogue no: **CC 206**
**Cass:** Released May '86, on Hour Of Pleasure by EMI Records. Catalogue no: **HR 4181144**

## Vintage Irving Berlin

**VINTAGE IRVING BERLIN (Various artists)**
Tracks: / Oh how I hate to get up in the morning: *Berlin, Irving* / Mandy: *Van & Schenck* / Pretty girl is like a melody ,A: *Steele, John* / Rockabye baby: *Moore, Grace* / Shakin' the blues away: *Etting, Ruth* / It all belongs to me: *Etting, Ruth* / Where is the song of songs for me: *Velez,Lupe* / Let me sing and I'm happy: *Jolson, Al* / Puttin on the ritz: *Richman, Harry* / Not for all the tea in China: *Webb, Clifton* / How's chances: *Webb, Clifton* / Heatwave: *Waters, Ethel* / How deep is the ocean: *Merman, Ethel* / Cheek to cheek: *Rogers, Ginger* / Louisiana purchas: *Bruce, Carol.*
**Album:** Released Sep '86, on New World (USA) by New World Records (USA). Catalogue no: **NW 238**

## Viper Mad Blues

**VIPER MAD BLUES (16 songs of dope) (Various artists)**
Note: 16 songs of dope & depravity. Includes Cab Calloway, Fats Waller and Larry Adler.
**Album:** Released Jun '88, on Jass Catalogue no: **JASS 4**

## Vitous, Miroslav

**EMERGENCE**
Tracks: / Epilogue / Transformation / Atlantis suite: / Atlantis suite-Emergence of the spirit / Atlantis suite-Matter and spirit / Atlantis suite-choice, The / Atlantis suite-Destruction into energy / Wheel of fortune (when the face gets pale) / Regards to Gershwin's honeyman / Alice in Wonderland / Morning lake for ever / Variations on Spanish themes.
**CD:** Released Dec '86, on ECM Catalogue no: **827 855-2**
**Album:** Released Jan '87, on ECM Catalogue no: **EMC 1312**

**GUARDIAN ANGELS**
**CD:** Released Feb '90, on Storyville by Storyville Records AB. Catalogue no: **STCD 4155**

**JOURNEY'S END**
Tracks: / U dunaje u prespurka / Tess / Carry on no. 1 / Paragraph jay / Only one / Windfall.
**Album:** Released Mar '83, on ECM Catalogue no: **ECM 1242**

**MIROSLAV**
**CD:** Released 16 Sep '88, on Freedom Catalogue no: **FCD 741040**

**MIROSLAV VITOUS GROUP (Vitous / Surman / Kirkland / Christensen)**
**Album:** Released Apr '81, on ECM Catalogue no: **ECM 1185**

**MOUNTAIN IN THE CLOUDS (THAT'S JAZZ SERIES)**
Tracks: / Freedom jazz dance / Mountain in the clouds / Epilogue / Cerecka / Indinate search / I will tell him on you / When face gets pale.
**Album:** Released Oct '77, on Atlantic by WEA Records. Catalogue no: **K 50406**

## Vocal Group Album

**VOCAL GROUP ALBUM (Various artists)**
**2 LP Set:** Released Mar '85, on Savoy Jazz (USA) by Malaco Records (USA). Catalogue no: **SJL 2241**

## Voice Of The Blues

**VOICE OF THE BLUES (Bottleneck masterpieces) (Various artists)**
**Album:** Released Dec '88, on Yazoo (USA) by Shanachie Records (USA). Catalogue no: **L 1046**

## Von Freeman

**SERENADE AND BLUES**
Tracks: / Serenade in blue / After dark / Time after time / Von Freeman's blues / I'll close my eyes.
Note: With David Shipp, bass; John Young, piano; Wilbur Campbell, drums. Von Freeman, Chico Freeman's father, is himself a Chicago legend, born in 1922. This is one of two superbly relaxed and witty sets made in 1975. John Young is a highly rated recording artist in his own right, and the jaunty lope of the rhythm section as a whole has to be heard to be believed. 'Just like I'd play at the enterprise lounge' said Von. (Chief Records, June 1989)
**Album:** Released Sep '79, on Nessa Deleted '83. Catalogue no: **N 11**
**CD:** Released Jun '89, on Chief Catalogue no: **CHIEFCD 3**

**YOUNG AND FOOLISH (Von Freeman Quartet)**
Tracks: / I'll close my eyes / Young and foolish / Bye bye blackbird.
**Album:** Released '88, on Affinity by Charly Records. Catalogue no: **AFF 184**

# W

The following information was taken from the Music Master database on 14th April, 1990

## Wadham, John

**DRUMS AND FRIENDS (Wadham, John & Louis Stewart) (see panel below)**
Tracks: / Clarence's place / Floatin' / Winter song / Pompeiian.
**Album:** Released Jun '88, on Livia. Catalogue no: **LRLP 2**

## Waine, Raney

**FOURMOST GUITARS WITH RANEY WAINE**
Tracks: / Two dreams of soma / I'm old fashioned / You stepped out of a dream / Time was / Scholars mate / Easy mate / Easy living / Ain't misbehavin' / Gone with the wind / If I love again / Li'l basses / Yesterdays.
**Album:** Released Jun '84, on Jasmine by Hasmick Promotions. Deleted Feb '88. Catalogue no: **JASM 1041**

## Waldo, Terry

**TERRY WALDO AND THE GOTHAM CITY BAND (Waldo, Terry & The Gotham City Band)**
**Album:** Released Mar '87, on Stomp Off (USA) Catalogue no: **SOS 1120**

## Waldos Gutbucket

**WALDOS GUTBUCKET SYNCOPATORS**
**Album:** Released '88, on Stomp Off (USA) Catalogue no: **SOS 1036**

## Waldo's Ragtime

**WALDO'S RAGTIME ORCHESTRA VOL.2**
**Album:** Released Jun '86, on Stomp Off (USA) Catalogue no: **SOS 1069**

## Waldron, Mal

**Biographical details:** Pianist and composer Mal Waldron, born in New York in 1926, worked with Charles Mingus in the mid-50's, accompanied Billie Holiday in the late 50's then became virtually house pianist on the Prestige label. Among many great LPs, *The Quest* ('61), with Eric Dolphy, Booker Little, Ron Carter and Charlie Persip, includes seven Waldron tunes and remains among the finest examples of what was called at the time "the new music". Dolphy led the outfit in the famous *Live At The Five Spot 1961* sets with Waldron, Little, Richard Davis and Ed Blackwell - they are also compiled as *The Great Concert Of Eric Dolphy*. As well as jazz Mal Waldron wrote music for ballet and films. He went to Europe in the 60's and re-located in Munich, with many visits to Japan. (Donald Clarke, March 1988.).

**BLACK GLORY**
**Album:** Released Jan '82, on Enja (Germany) by Enja Records (West Germany). Catalogue no: **ENJA 2004**

**BLUES FOR LADY DAY (A personal tribute to Billie Holiday)**
Tracks: / Blues for Lady Day / Just friends / Don't blame me / You don't know what love is / Man I love, The / You're my thrill / Strange fruit / Easy living / Mean to me.
**Album:** Released Jul '87, on Black Lion Catalogue no: **BLP 30142**

**CALL, THE**
**Album:** Released '79, on Japo (ECM) Catalogue no: **JAPO 60001**

**ENCOUNTERS (Waldron, Mal/Dave Friesen)**
**Album:** Released '88, on Muse by Black & Blue Records. Catalogue no: **MR 5305**

**FREE AT LAST (Waldron, Mal Trio)**
Tracks: / Rat now / 1-3-234 / Willow weep for me / Balladina / Rock my soul / Boo.
**CD:** Released Aug '89, on ECM Catalogue no: **831 332 2**
**Album:** Released '76, on ECM Catalogue no: **ECM 1001**

**HARD TALK (Waldron, Mal Quintet)**
**Album:** Released Jan '82, on Enja (Germany) by Enja Records (West Germany). Catalogue no: **ENJA 2050**

**LEFT ALONE '86 (Waldron, Mal & Jackie McLean)**
Note: Mal Waldron, for many years pianist to Billie Holiday, joins forces with alto sax player Jackie McLean, friend & contemporary of Charlie Parker & a major influence on a whole generation of altoists. These quartet performances feature 4 well-known standards, associated with Billie Holiday, plus 4 compositions by Mal Waldron.
Mal Waldron - piano; Jackie McLean - alto sax; Herbie Lewis - bass; Eddie Moore - drums. Recorded in September 1986.
**CD:** Released Oct '88, on Paddlewheel/King Catalogue no: **K32Y 6167**
**Album:** Released Oct '88, on Paddlewheel/King Catalogue no: **K 28P 6453**

**John Wadham - Drums and friends (Livia)**

**MAL 1 (Waldron, Mal Quintet)**
**CD:** Released Apr '86, on JVC/Fantasy Catalogue no: **VDJ 1513**
**CD:** Released '88, on Fantasy (import) by Fantasy Inc (USA). Catalogue no: **FCD 6377090**

**MAL 4 (Waldron, Mal Trio)**
**CD:** Released Nov '86, on JVC/Fantasy Catalogue no: **VDJ 1545**

**MINGUS LIVES**
**Album:** Released Jan '82, on Enja (Germany) by Enja Records (West Germany). Catalogue no: **ENJA 3075**

**MOODS**
**Album:** Released Jan '82, on Enja (Germany) by Enja Records (West Germany). Catalogue no: **ENJA 3021**

**ONE ENTRANCE MANY EXITS**
**Album:** Released Jul '86, on Palo Alto Catalogue no: **PA 8014**
**Cass:** Released Jul '86, on Palo Alto Catalogue no: **PAC 8014**

**ONE UPMANSHIP (Waldron, Mal Quintet/Steve Lacy)**
**Album:** Released Jan '82, on Enja (Germany) by Enja Records (West Germany). Catalogue no: **ENJA 2092**

**QUEST, THE (Waldron, Mal/Eric Dolphy)**
Tracks: / Status seeking / Duquility / Thirteen / We did it / Warm canto / Warp and woof / Fire waltz.
**Album:** Released Feb '84, on New Jazz (USA) by Fantasy Inc (USA). Catalogue no: **OJC 082**

**SET ME FREE**
Tracks: / Set me free / You were always there / Yeah / Jamaica libre / Desillusion / Atilla the hun.
**Album:** Released Apr '85, on Affinity by Charly Records. Deleted '88. Catalogue no: **AFF 116**

**SIGNALS**
**Album:** Released Feb '79, on Freedom Catalogue no: **FLP 41042**

**SUPER QUARTET - LIVE AT SWEET BASIL, THE**
Note: Pianist Mal Waldron and his quartet recorded live at New York's Sweet Basil during July 1988. Featuring Steve Lacy on soprano sax, the quartet performs compositions by Mal Waldron and Thelonious Monk.
**CD:** Released Feb '89, on King Catalogue no: **K32Y 6208**
**Album:** Released Feb '89, on King (Japan) Catalogue no: **K 28P 6471**

**TOUCH OF BLUES, A**
**Album:** Released Jan '82, on Enja (Germany) by Enja Records (West Germany). Catalogue no: **ENJA 2062**

**UP POPPED THE DEVIL**
**Album:** Released Jan '82, on Enja (Germany) by Enja Records (West Germany). Catalogue no: **ENJA 2034**

**WHAT IT IS (Waldron, Mal Quartet)**
**Album:** Released Apr '82, on Enja (Germany) by Enja Records (West Germany). Catalogue no: **ENJA 4010**

**YOU AND THE NIGHT AND THE MUSIC**
Tracks: / Way you look tonight / Bag's groove / Round midnight / You and the night and the music / Georgia on my mind / Billie's bounce / Waltz for my mother.
**Album:** Released Jul '86, on King (Japan) Catalogue no: **K 28P 6272**

## Walker Jazz Band

**BIG BAND STORY VOLUME 2**
**CD:** Released Feb '86, on Pierre Verany (France) Catalogue no: **PV 785093**

## Walker, Jimmy

**ORIGINAL SOUTHSIDE BLUES PIANO**
**Album:** Released Jan '88, on Wolf Catalogue no: **120 712**

## Walker, Joe Louis

**ALONE**
Tracks: / Alone / Cold is the night / Shade tree mechanic.
**12" Single:** Released Oct '88, on Ace by Ace Records. Deleted Jan '90. Catalogue no: **NST 125**

**BLUE SOUL**
Tracks: / Prove your love / Ain't nothin' goin' on / T.L.C. / Personal baby / Since you've been gone / Alligator / Dead sea / City of angels / I'll get to Heaven on my own.
**CD:** Released Oct '89, on Demon by Demon Records. Catalogue no: **FIENDCD 159**
**Album:** Released Oct '89, on Demon by Demon Records. Catalogue no: **FIEND 159**

**COLD IS THE NIGHT**
Tracks: / Why do you run / Madness of it all (was once was and still is) (instrumental version) / Cold is the night / Ten more shows to play / Moanin' news / One woman / I need someone / Brother go ahead and take her / Fuss and fight / Gettin' even / Ridin' high / Don't play games.
Note: Debut album from the American blues guitarist/vocalist.
**CD:** Released Jan '89, on Sound by Target Records. Catalogue no: **HCD 8006**
**Album:** Released Apr '87, on Ace by Ace Records. Catalogue no: **CH 208**

**GIFT, THE**
Tracks: / One Time Around / Thin Line / 747 / Gift, The / What About You? / Shade Tree Mechanic / 1/4 To 3 / Mama Didn't Raise No Fool / Everybody's Had The Blues / Main goal.
**CD:** Released Jan '89, on Sound by Target Records. Catalogue no: **HCD 8012**
**Album:** Released Feb '88, on Ace by Ace Records. Catalogue no: **CH 241**
**Cass:** Released Apr '88, on Ace by Ace Records. Deleted Jan '90. Catalogue no: **CHC 241**
**CD:** Released Apr '88, on Ace by Ace Records. Catalogue no: **CDCH 241**

## Walker, Junior

**Biographical details:** The American saxophonist and singer was born in Arkansas as Autry DeWalt Jr and given his stage name by his father. He took up the sax at school and assembled his first band in 1961, shortly after leaving. He signed to Harvey Records, a label owned by Harvey Fuqua, brother-in-law of Motown founder Berry Gordy. By 1965 Harvey Records had been incorporated into the Motown family. In that year Junior Walker stormed into the American charts with his debut smash hit *Shotgun*, a rousing, pounding dance number which reached No 4 on the Billboard Hot Hundred. It set the scene for a succession of raw rhythm and blues hits, mainly instrumental but featuring raucous vocals, which sounded gruffer than those of most of his Motown colleagues. These hits continued into the late 60's, often reaching the US pop Top Forty but not the Top Ten. His first British Top Forty single was 1966's *How sweet it is*, version of the Marvin Gaye hit. The singles were credited to Junior Walker & The All-Stars, his funky backing group. In the late 60's Walker mellowed his sound and progressed to a smoother, more sophisticated style. He was quickly rewarded with the smash, *What does it take (to win your love)?*, a mid-tempo ballad which cruised to UK No 4 in summer '69 and thus tied with *Shotgun* to become his joint biggest American hit. Greater emphasis was now placed on the (far less raucous) vocals, although his sax prowess was still very much in evidence. Early 70's hits included two which reached the UK Top Twenty, the lush but slinky *Walk in the night* and *Take me, girl, i'm ready*, plus a smaller success with string-laden ballad Way Back Home. The roots of Walker's honky style lay in the R & B sounds of the late 40's and early 50's: he had successfully adapted them to the needs of 60's and 70's soul fans. He suffered a commercial nosedive after 1973 and never regained his chart fortunes, despite revival attempts by Motown and his subsequent record company, Warner Bros. However, his virtuosity has remained intact and in 1981 he contributed a classic sax solo on Foreigner's US Top Five single *Urgent*. (Bob MacDonald, April 1985.)
Junior Walker was born in 1942 in Arkansas; the alto saxist formed the All Stars and had 21 Hot 100 hits in the USA charts in 1965-72, many instrumentalists (though Junior also sang). Biggest were the first, *Shotgun* and *What does it take (to win your love)* in 1969, both top 5; the good time music was an echo of the jump-bands of the late 40s, while later hits were often ballads, sometimes with strings. Ten hit LPs in USA incl. *Soul session* '66, entirely instrumental; *Greatest hits* '69 reached top 50. he still toured in the '80s, sometimes with son Autry DeWalt III on drums. (Donald Clarke).

**ANTHOLOGY - JUNIOR WALKER**

**(Walker, Junior & The All Stars)**
Tracks: / Shotgun / Do the boomerang / Shake and fingerpop / Cleo's back / Cleo's mood / I am a roadrunner / How sweet it is to be loved by you / Money (that's what I want) / Pucker up buttercup / Shoot your shot / Come see about me / Hip city (part 1) / Home cookin' / What does it take to win your love / These eyes / I've got to find a way to win Maria back / Gotta hold on to this feeling / Do you see my love (for you growing) / Holy holy / Take me girl I'm ready / Right on brothers and sisters / Don't blame the children / Moody junior / Way back home / Walk in the night.
**2 LP Set:** Released Oct '81, on Motown by BMG Records (UK). Catalogue no: **TMSP 1129**

**BACK STREET BOOGIE**
Tracks: / Back street boogie / Girl I wanna marry you / Wishing on a star / Hole in the wall / Don't let me go astray / Tiger in my tank / Sax attack.
**Album:** Released Feb '80, on Warner Bros. by WEA Records. Deleted '85. Catalogue no: **K 56668**

**BLOW THE HOUSE DOWN**
Tracks: / Sex pot / Rise and shine / Closer than close / Ball baby / T-oo (t double oo) / Urgent / In and out / Blow the house down.
**Cass:** Released Oct '83, on Motown by BMG Records (UK). Catalogue no: **CSTML 12194**
**Album:** Released Oct '83, on Motown by BMG Records (UK). Catalogue no: **STML 12194**

**BLOW THE HOUSE DOWN (SINGLE)**
Tracks: / Blow the house down / Ball baby.
**12" Single:** Released Oct '83, on Motown by BMG Records (UK). Catalogue no: **TMGT 1318**
**7" Single:** Released Oct '83, on Motown by BMG Records (UK). Deleted '84. Catalogue no: **TMG 1318**

**COMPACT COMMAND PERFORMANCES (19 greatest hits) (Walker, Junior & The All Stars)**
Tracks: / Shotgun / Do the boomerang / Shake and fingerpop / Cleo's mood / Road runner, (I'm a) / How sweet it is to be loved by you / Money (that's what I want) / Pucker up buttercup / Shoot your shot / Come see about me / Hip city, part 2 / Home cookin' / What does it take (to win your love)? / These eyes / Gotta hold on to this feeling / Do you see my love (for you growing) / Take me girl, I'm ready / Way back home / Walk in the night.
**CD:** Released Mar '87, on Motown by BMG Records (UK). Catalogue no: **WD 72511**

**GREATEST HITS: JUNIOR WALKER (Walker, Junior & The All Stars)**
**Cass:** Released '86, on Motown by BMG Records (UK). Catalogue no: **WK 72097**
**Album:** Released '86, on Motown by BMG Records (UK). Catalogue no: **WL 72097**
**CD:** Released 6 Aug '88, on Motown by BMG Records (UK). Catalogue no: **WD 72097**

**HOW SWEET IT IS (Walker, Junior & The All Stars)**
Tracks: / How sweet it is to be loved by you.
**7" Single:** Released Apr '88, on Motown by BMG Records (UK). Catalogue no: **ZB 41935**
**7" Single:** Released Aug '66, on Tamla Motown by Motown Records (UK). Deleted '69. Catalogue no: **TMG 571**

**JUNIOR WALKER AND THE ALL STARS (Walker, Junior & The All Stars)**
Tracks: / Road runner / Take me girl I'm ready / Walk in the night / What does it take to win your love.
Note: 4 track cassette.
**Cass:** Released May '83, on Motown by BMG Records (UK). Catalogue no: **CTME 2026**

**JUNIOR WALKER'S GREATEST HITS**
Tracks: / Shotgun / How sweet it is to be loved by you / Road runner / Hip city part 1 / Cleo's mood / Money (that's what I want) / Shoot your shot / Picker up buttercup / Come see about me / What does it take to win your love / Shake and fingerpop / Home cookin' / Baby you know you ain't right / Anyway you wanna.
**Cass:** Released Mar '82, on Motown by BMG Records (UK). Catalogue no: **CSTMS 5054**
**Album:** Released Mar '82, on Motown by BMG Records (UK). Catalogue no: **STMS 5054**

**ROAD RUNNER (Walker, Junior & The All Stars)**
Tracks: / Road runner / Shotgun.
**7" Single:** Released Jun '83, on Motown by BMG Records (UK). Catalogue no: **TMG 691**

**SHAKE AND FINGERPOP**
Tracks: / Shotgun / How sweet it is to be loved by you / Homecookin' / Money / Pucker up buttercup / What does it take (to win your love) / Come see about me / Hip city / Cleo's mood / Shake and fingerpop / Shoot your shot.
**Album:** Released Apr '89, on Blue Moon (1) by Magnum Music Group. Catalogue no: **BMLP 072**
**CD:** Released Apr '89, on Blue Moon (1) by Magnum Music Group. Catalogue no: **CDBM 072**

**SHOTGUN AND ROADRUNNER (Walker, Junior & The All Stars)**
Tracks: / Cleo's mood / Do the boomerang / Shake and fingerpop / Shoot your shot / Tune up / Hot cha / Tally ho / Monkey jump / Tally ho / Cleo's back / Ain't that the truth / Road runner, (I'm a) / How sweet it is to be loved by you / Pucker up Buttercup / Money (that's what I want / Last call / Anyway you wanna / Baby you know you ain't right / Ame' cherie (Soul darling) / Twist lackawanna / San-ho-zay / Mutiny.
Note: 2 Classic albums.
**CD:** Released Dec '86, on Motown by BMG Records (UK). Catalogue no: **ZD 72487**

**TAKE ME GIRL I'M READY (Walker, Junior & The All Stars)**
Tracks: / Take me girl I'm ready.
**7" Single:** Released Jan '73, on Tamla Motown by Motown Records (UK). Deleted '76. Catalogue no: **TMG 840**

**WALK IN THE NIGHT (Walker, Junior & The All Stars)**
Tracks: / Walk in the night.
**7" Single:** Released Aug '72, on Tamla Motown by Motown Records (UK). Deleted '75. Catalogue no: **TMG 824**

**WAY BACK HOME (Walker, Junior & The All Stars)**
Tracks: / Way back home.
**7" Single:** Released Jun '73, on Tamla Motown by Motown Records (UK). Deleted '76. Catalogue no: **TMG 857**

**WHAT DOES IT TAKE ? (Walker, Junior & The All Stars)**
Tracks: / What does it take ? / Take me girl, I'm ready.
**7" Single:** Released Oct '80, on Tamla Motown by Motown Records (UK). Deleted Oct '83. Catalogue no: **TMG 962**
**7" Single:** Released Oct '69, on Tamla Motown by Motown Records (UK). Deleted '72. Catalogue no: **TMG 712**

**WHOPPER BOPPER SHOW STOPPER**
Tracks: / Whopper bopper show stopper / You are the sunshine of my life / You're on fire / Leap and peep / Don't make no plans / I could never love another / I want you / Love ain't enough / My love.
**Album:** Released Jan '77, on Motown by BMG Records (UK). Deleted '81. Catalogue no: **STML 12048**

## Walker, Philip

**BLUES**
Tracks: / How many more years / 90 proof / What'd you hope to gain / Don't be afraid of the dark / Big rear window / Her own keys / Talk to that man / Sometime girl / I had a dream.
**CD:** Released Oct '88, on Demon by Demon Records. Catalogue no: **FIENDCD 128**
**Album:** Released Oct '88, on Demon by Demon Records. Catalogue no: **FIEND 128**

**BOTTOM OF THE TOP, THE**
**CD:** Released Feb '90, on Demon by Demon Records. Catalogue no: **FIENDCD 158**
**Album:** Released Feb '90, on Demon by Demon Records. Catalogue no: **FIEND 158**

**SOMEDAY YOU'LL HAVE THE BLUES**
Tracks: / Someday you'll have these blues / Beaumont blues / Breakin' up somebody's home / Mama's gone / When it needs gettin' done / Sure is cold / Part time love / El Paso blues / Don't tell me / If we can find it.
Note: Texas blues and hot guitar - that's what Philip Walker and this record are all

about. Texas has been a breeding ground for great blues guitarists ever since the days of Blind Lemon Jefferson. The real ground for great blues picking have almost been Texas men. Philip Walker is in the third generation of Texan blues guitar wizards, alongside Albert Collins and Johnny Guitar Watson. (Alligator catalogue 7/88)
**Album:** Released May '80, on Alligator (Sonet) by Alligator Records (USA). Catalogue no: **SNTF 831**

### TOUGH AS I WANT TO BE
**Album:** Released '88, on Rounder (USA) by Rounder Records (USA). Catalogue no: **ROUNDER 2038**
**Cass:** Released '88, on Rounder (USA) by Rounder Records (USA). Catalogue no: **ROUNDER 2038C**
**Album:** Released Jan '85, on Black & Blue (1) by Black & Blue Records. Catalogue no: **33 588**

## Walker, T-Bone

**Biographical details:** Guitarist, singer and songwriter Walker was born Aaron Thibeaux Walker in Texas in 1910 and died in California in 1975. A teenage friend was Charlie Christian and Walker had as great an influence in the blues as Christian had in jazz. He was responsible for a generation taking up electric guitar. After his win in a Cab Calloway amateur contest in 1930 he toured heavily and worked hard the rest of his life. He played at the Monterey Jazz Festival in '67. His song *Call it stormy Monday* was covered by the Allman Brothers. His 1968 LP *Good feelin'* was made in Paris with Manu Dibango and won a Grammy. (Donald Clarke, March 1988.).

### BLUESWAY SESSIONS
Tracks: / Goin to funky town / Party girl / Why my baby (keep on bothering me) / Jealous woman / Going to build me a playhouse / Long skirt baby blues / Struggling blues / I'm in an awful mood / I wish my baby (would come home at night) / I'm gonna stop this nite life / Little girl don't you know / Every night I have to cry / I'm still in love with you / Cold hearted woman / Treat me so low down / Stormy Monday / Confusion blues / I gotta break away / Flower blues.
**Cass:** Released Oct '88, on Charly by Charly Records. Catalogue no: **TCCDX 31**
**2 LP Set:** Released Oct '88, on Charly by Charly Records. Catalogue no: **CDX 31**

### COLLECTION: T-BONE WALKER
Tracks: / T-Bone jumps again / Sun went down, The / Call it stormy Monday / I got the blues / Railroad station blues / Hypin' woman blues / Hustle, The / I'm still in love with you / Blues is a woman / Born to be good / T-Bone shuffle / Baby you broke my heart / Bye bye, baby / I'm about to lose my mind / First love blues / I wish you were mine / Travellin' blues / Evil-hearted woman / Bobby sox blues / Blues for my baby.
**Cass:** Released Nov '85, on Deja Vu Catalogue no: **DVMC 2047**
**Album:** Released Nov '85, on Deja Vu Catalogue no: **DVLP 2047**

### GOOD FEELIN'
**Album:** Released Oct '82, on Polydor (France) by Polydor Ltd. Catalogue no: **2393 007**

### HIS ORIGINAL 45-50 PERFORMANCES
**Album:** Released '83, on Capitol (import) Catalogue no: **2C 068 86523**

### HOT LEFTOVERS
**Album:** Released Apr '85, on Pathe Marconi (France) Catalogue no: **PM 1561451**

### I DON'T BE JIVIN'
Tracks: / T-Bone's back on the scene / I used to be a good boy / I ain't your fool no more / Baby she's a hit / Reconsider baby (hate to see you go) / Don't let your heartache catch you / Sometimes I wonder / I don't be jivin' / T-Bone's jam / I ain't your fool no more / I wonder why / Further up the road / All night long / How long blues (that evening train) / Louisiana bayou drive.
**Album:** Released Sep '87, on Bear Family by Bear Family Records (Germany). Catalogue no: **BFX 15277**

### I GET SO WEARY
**Album:** Released Apr '85, on Pathe Marconi (France) Catalogue no: **PM 156 144 1**

### I WANT A LITTLE GIRL
**Album:** Released Dec '88, on Delmark (USA) by Delmark Records (USA). Catalogue no: **DL 633**

### INVENTOR OF THE ELECTRIC GUITAR BLUES, THE
Tracks: / Wichita falls blues / Sail on boogie / I'm still in love with you / T-Bone boogie / Mean old world blues / That's better for me / Hard pain blues / Hustle is on, The / Baby broke my heart / I walked away / No reason / My baby is now on my mind / Pony tail / When the sun goes down.
**Album:** Released Aug '87, on Blues Boy (Sweden) Catalogue no: **BB 304**

### LOW DOWN BLUES
Tracks: / Don't leave me baby / I'm gonna find my baby / It's a lowdown dirty deal / I know your wig has gone / T-Bone jumps again / Call it stormy monday / She's my old time used to be / Midnight blues / Long skirt baby blues / Too much trouble blues / Hypin' woman blues / Natural blues, The / That's better for me / Lonesome woman blues / Inspiration blues / T-Bone shuffle / That feeling is gone / I wish you were mine / She's the no sleepin'est woman / Plain old down home blues / Go back to the one you love / You're my best poker hand.
**CD:** Released Feb '86, on Charly by Charly Records. Catalogue no: **CDCHARLY 7**

### NATURAL BLUES, THE (18 tracks recorded 1946-48)
Tracks: / Lone some woman blues / Vacation blues / She had to let me down / Don't give me the runaround / Hard pain blues / So blue blues / I'm waiting for your call / Natural blues, The / That's better for me / Inspiration blues / Description blues / I want a little girl / Time seems so long, The / Home town blues / Misfortune blues / I'm still in love with you / She's the no sleepinest woman / I'm gonna move you out and let somebody else.
**Album:** Released Aug '83, on Charly R&B by Charly Records. Catalogue no: **CRB 1057**

### PLAIN OLE BLUES
Tracks: / I'm gonna find my baby / Don't leave me baby / No worry blues / It's a lowdown dirty deal / I'm in a awful mood / Long skirt baby blues / Goodbye blues / Plain old down home blues / That old feeling is gone.
**Album:** Released Mar '82, on Charly R&B by Charly Records. Catalogue no: **CRB 1037**

### STORMY MONDAY
Tracks: / Stormy Monday blues / All night long / My patience keeps running out / Glamour girl / T-Bones's way / That evening train / Louisiana bayou drive / When we were schoolmates / Don't go back to New Orleans / Got to cross the deep blue sea / You'll never find anyone to be a slave like me / Left home / When I was a kid.
**CD:** Released Feb '90, on Instant (2) by Charly Records. Catalogue no: **CDINS 5022**
**Album:** Released Feb '90, on Instant (2) by Charly Records. Catalogue no: **INS 5022**
**Album:** Released Sep '78, on Charly by Charly Records. Catalogue no: **CR 30144**
**Cass:** Released Feb '90, on Instant (2) by Charly Records. Catalogue no: **TCINS 5022**

### T-BONE BLUES
**Album:** Released Jun '88, on Atlantic by WEA Records. Catalogue no: **SD8258**

### T-BONE JUMPS AGAIN
Tracks: / Hypin' woman blues / Too much trouble blues / I got a break baby / Mean old woman / Bobby sox blues / I know your wig has gone / T-Bone jumps again / Call it stormy monday / You're my best poker hand / First love blues / She's my old time used to be / On your way blues / I wish you were mine / Wise man blues / Born to be no good / T-Bone shuffle.
**Cass:** Released '85, on Charly R&B by Charly Records. Catalogue no: **TCCRB 1019**
**Album:** Released '85, on Charly R&B by Charly Records. Catalogue no: **CRB 1019**

## Walking Blues

### WALKING BLUES (Various artists)
Note: Mono recording. Superlative 1941-42 country blues.
**Album:** Released Feb '79, on Flyright

by Interstate Music. Catalogue no: **FLY 541**

## Wallace, Bennie

**ART OF THE SAXOPHONE, THE**
Tracks: / Edith Head / You go to my head / Rhythm head / Monroe County moon / Thangs / All too soon / Chester leaps in / Prelude to a kiss / Prince Charles.
Note: Personnel: Bennie Wallace (Tenor sax), Harold Ashby, Jerry Bergonzi, Lew Tabackin (Tenor saxes), Oliver Lake (Alto sax), John Scofield (Guitar), Eddie Gomez (Bass), Dannie Richmond (Drums).
**CD:** Released Oct '88, on Denon Catalogue no: **CY 1648**
**Cass:** Released Oct '88, on Denon Catalogue no: **CC 16**

**BENNIE WALLACE PLAYS MONK**
**Album:** Released Jan '82, on Enja (Germany) by Enja Records (West Germany). Catalogue no: **ENJA 3091**

**BORDER TOWN**
Tracks: / Skanctified / Stormy weather / East 9 / Bordertown / Bon-a-rue / Seven sisters / Carolina moon / Dance with a dolly (with a hole in her stocking) / It's only a paper moon.
**Album:** Released Jul '89, on Blue Note by EMI Records. Catalogue no: **748 014 1**
**Album:** Released Jul '89, on Blue Note by EMI Records. Catalogue no: **B1 48014**
**CD:** Released Nov '88, on Blue Note by EMI Records. Catalogue no: **CDP 748 014 2**
**CD:** Released Nov '88, on Blue Note by EMI Records. Catalogue no: **BNZ 122**

**BRILLIANT CORNERS (Wallace, Bennie with Yosuke Yamashita)**
Tracks: / It don't mean a thing / Light blue / P.S. I love you / Night in Tunisia / Brilliant corners / Blues Yamashita / My ideal / Rhythn-a-ning / Another beauty.
Note: Bennie Wallace's highly-individual tenor-sax is supported splendidly by another first rate rhythm section. Bassist Jay Anderson & drummer Jeff Hieshfield are merely excellent; leading Japanese Yosuke Yamashita is constantly superb throughout. The Wallace-Yamashita duets ("It don't mean a thing", "Light blue", "P.S. I love you") are particularly ear-catching performances in that context. But the remaining half-dozen tracks by the full quartet (including superior versions of "A Night in Tunisia" & two other Monk classics, like the title tune) lose absolutely nothing in comparison.
**CD:** Released Sep '88, on Denon Catalogue no: **CY-30003**
**Cass:** Released Feb '89, on Denon Catalogue no: **CC-26**

**FOURTEEN BAR BLUES**
**Album:** Released Jan '82, on Enja (Germany) by Enja Records (West Germany). Catalogue no: **ENJA 3029**

**FREE WILL**
**Album:** Released Jan '82, on Enja (Germany) by Enja Records (West Germany). Catalogue no: **ENJA 3063**

**LIVE AT THE PUBLIC THEATRE**
**Album:** Released Jan '82, on Enja (Germany) by Enja Records (West Germany). Catalogue no: **ENJA 3045**

**SWEEPING THROUGH THE CITY**
**Album:** Released Nov '84, on Enja (Germany) by Enja Records (West Germany). Catalogue no: **ENJA 4078**

**TWILIGHT TIME**
Tracks: / All night dance / Is it true what they say about Dixie? / Sainte fragile / Tennessee waltz / Fresh out / Willie Mae / Trouble in mind / Saint expedito / Twilight time.
**CD:** Released Jul '89, on Blue Note by EMI Records. Catalogue no: **CDP 746 293 2**
**CD:** Released Jul '89, on Blue Note by EMI Records. Catalogue no: **BNZ 220**
**Album:** Released Jul '89, on Blue Note by EMI Records. Catalogue no: **BT 85107**

## Wallace, Sippie

**SINGS THE BLUES**
**Album:** Released Jan '88, on Storyville by Storyville Records AB. Catalogue no: **SLP 4017**

**SIPPIE WALLACE**
Tracks: / Women be wise / Up the country blues / I'm a mighty tight woman / Won't you come to my house / You've been a good old wagon / Man that don't want me / You got to know how / Suitcase blues / Say it isn't so / Everybody loves my baby / Mama's gone, goodbye.
**Album:** Released Oct '82, on Atlantic by WEA Records. Deleted Oct '87. Catalogue no: **SD 19350**

## Waller, Fats

**Biographical details:** Thomas Wright Waller was born in New York in 1904 and died of pneumonia in 1943: he lived very fast and his body just couldn't keep up. He was one of the most popular entertainers ever but he was also a great jazz pianist and a great songwriter, who sold some of his biggest hits for pocket money. As a teenager he played the organ in a cinema and gave lessons to Bill -- later Count -- Basie. With James P. Johnson as a teacher he became a master of the East Coast "stride" style, descended directly from ragtime, which requires a strong left hand for playing tenths in the bass while the right hand never forgets the melody. He collaborated with lyricist Andy Razaf on hit shows, including *Keep Shufflin'* and *Hot Chocolates* in 1928-29 and *Early To Bed* in '43. Waller's best-known songs include *Keepin' Out Of Mischief Now, Ain't Misbehavin'* (written while in jail for non-payment of alimony), *Black and Blue, I've Got A Feelin' I'm Fallin', I'm Crazy 'Bout My Baby and Honeysuckle Rose* (which began as a piano variation of *Tea For Two*). He began making piano rolls around 1920, records in 1922. He accompanied blues singers Sara Martin, Rosa Henderson (as Mamie Harris) and others, recorded for Victor 1926-29 and included piano and pipe organ solos and small-group classics as Fats & His Buddies. He recorded with Fletcher Henderson, McKinney's Cotton Pickers, Jack Teagarden and others, starred on radio in the early 30's and in '34 began making small-group records as Fats Waller & His Rhythm, his excellent voice and inspired clowning -- as well, of course, as great jazz -- racking up more than 60 hits. (Donald Clarke, March 1988.).

**20 GOLDEN PIECES: FATS WALLER**
Tracks: / Ain't misbehavin' / Your feets too big / Honeysuckle Rose / I'm gonna sit right down and write myself a letter / I've got my fingers crossed / Joint is jumpin', The / Sweet Sue / Nagasaki / Lonesome me / Hallelujah / Handful of keys / Christopher Columbus / It's a sin to tell a lie / Until the real thing comes along / Crazy 'bout my baby / Things look rosy now / Thousand dreams of you, A / Old Grandad / Dark eyes / Jingle bells.
**Album:** Released Jul '82, on Bulldog Records by President Records. Catalogue no: **BDL 2004**
**Cass:** Released Jul '82, on Bulldog Records by President Records. Catalogue no: **BDC 2004**

**1939: FATS WALLER**
**Album:** Released Apr '81, on Joker (USA) by Lifetime Records (USA). Catalogue no: **SM 3086**

**1943**
**Album:** Released Apr '81, on Jazz Live (Italy) Catalogue no: **BLJ 8031**

**1927-29 (Waller, Fats & Morriss Hot Babies) (See panel on next page)**
Tracks: / Fats Waller Stomp / Savannah blues / Won't you take me home / I ain't got nobody / Digah's stomp, The / Red hot Dan / Geechee / Please take me out of jail / Minor drag, The / Harlem fuss / Lookin' good but feelin bad / I someone like you / Lookin' for another sweetie / Ridin' but walkin' / Won't you get off it, please ? / When I'm alone.
Note: Thomas Wright 'Fats' Waller who became a legend in his own lifetime was a fun loving, hard drinking genius of the piano, completely at home in the wild prohibition days of New York in the 1920's. However, the years 1927 to 1929 were probably the most turbulent in his all too brief 39 years. Following the death of his mother in 1920 Fats almost immediately married young Edith Hatchett but the union was marred by his participation in Harlem's high life. The unhappiness, which should have been resolved when their son was born, soured and within a few years the marriage was over with Fats agreeing to twenty dollars a week maintenance payment. But in spite of regular work piano roll and recording dates, arranging and composing commitments, Fats did not meet his responsibility. Edith sought recourse to the law but a bitter and resentful Fats refused to comply with numerous Court orders and spent brief periods in jail. Undettered by his first

**Fats Waller - 1927-29 (Swaggie)**

experience Waller married 16 year old Anita Rutherford in late 1926. Although young, she had a strong influence on the exuberence Waller who modified his lifestyle. This time the marriage was a success.

Thomas Waller's first recordings for the Victor Talking Machine Company were organ solos made in November 1926 and were arranged by Ralph Peer their race records executive, who was also President and General Manager of Southern Music, a Victor subsidiary. Victor's main New York recording studio was a converted Camden, New Jersey church, complete with original organ, Steinway grand piano and console organ. The arrangement suited Waller as recordings prove and he made further solo organ sides in January and May 1927. Thomas Waller, with Anita, went to Chicago in March 1927 for an eight week engagement playing organ at the Vendome movie theatre on State Street. Waller with Erskine Tate and His Vendome Syncopators provided the daily specialities on stage. South Side Chicago was alive with jazz and it has been recalled that Fats Waller regularly took part in the all night musical activities. In the book *Ain't misbehavin'* Ed Kirkeby states that Waller was arrested in Chicago and taken back to New York to face another charge of failing to pay Edith's alimony. Anita, and their newly born son were rescued by her mother and followed on to New York. After more promises Fats was dismissed with a strong warning. On his return to New York in May 1927 Thomas Waller recorded with Fletcher Henderson's Orchestra. During 1926 Thomas Morris had established himself in the Victor catalogue with the release of ten sides using the *Hot babies* name. Little is known about Thomas Morris, other than his 1923 band recordings (SWAGGIE 805) with Clarence Williams Blue Five, his five Victor titles, and numerous but rare, accompaniments on blues records. He retired from music in the 1930s and John Chilton reports that Morris was a redcap at New York's Grand Central Station before joining Father Divine's religious sect.

Thomas Waller and the Morris Hot Babies re-entered Victor's Camden studio in December 1927 to record four more sides including an aptly titled *Please take me out of jail* plus the two pipe organ solos on side A. Early in 1928 Waller with his mentor, James P Johnson, contributed music to the popular show. *Shuffle along* and their intermission piano duets allegedly kept the audience in their seats. The pit orchestra led by Joe Jordan, comprised four brass, clarinet, oboe, two violins, flute, two pianos, cello and rhythm and in March 1928 a quartet from this band recorded four of the show tunes for Victor using James P Johnson, piano; Waller, organ; Garvin Bushell, reeds; and Jabbo Smith, trumpet. The titles released under the *Louisiana sugar babes* name, are available on SWAGGIE 849. After a short tour with *Shuffle along* Waller left in June to play engagements at the Royal Grand Theatre in Philadelphia and the Regal Theatre in Chicago, returning to New York in August.

The alimony arrears had again built up and the Court jailed Fats for six months. Variety reported the details in September 1928. This time the efforts of friends were unsuccessful and he was literally out of action until about February 1929. It was not until Ed Kirkeby began to manage Waller's affairs in the 1930s that his financial worries were finally resolved. Within weeks of his release from jail Fats Waller, a new father once again, entered Victor's Liederkranz Hall studio in New York to record two piano solos and two band sides with a pick up group which included banjoist Eddie Condon, Charlie Gaines and Arville Harris from Leroy Smith's Connie's Inn Orchestra and Charlie Irvis who at the time was with Charlie Johnson's band at Small's Paradise. Eddie Condon's account of this first Waller 'Buddies' session is now jazz legend. He had been given the task of rehearsing Waller and getting him to the studio on time and sober. The tunes were composed in a cab on the way to the session and the management, believing Condon had achieved the impossible, were delighted with the results which open Side B. The full story is related in Condon's autobiography *We called it music* where he claims that Victor issued the titles, *The minor drag* and *Harlem fuss* reversed. We have left them the way they were originally released for we are not about to challenge history.

Fats Waller put little value on his musical compositions. He was a prolific tunesmith and during the 1920's frivously sold or swapped countless items to music publishers and band leaders for as little as ten dollars, hamburgers or illicit gin. However, on 17th July 1929, due no doubt to his continued commitment to Edith, he sold the rights to 21 compositions outright to Irving Mills including the future classics *Ain't misbehavin', Black and blue, Sweet Savannah Sue, Jungle jamboree, Snake hip dance* and *Rhythm man.* The total sum recieved has been claimed to be a mere five hundred dollars but this may have been a final payment exclusive of earlier royalties. In August and September 1929 Fats Waller recorded more piano and organ solos and took part in a Little Chocolate Dandies session. Perhaps the success of the first Buddies' date impressed Victor, for two more dates were contracted and conclude the remainder of Side B. Both sessions featured a large band with black and white musicians. The titles were competently arranged and have the feeling of tunes from an as yet unidentified show. For years the full personnel of the September and December 1929 Waller Buddies sessions has intrigued collectors and although there have been numerous attempts at a definitive listing, none are quite convincing. Notwithstanding The Great Depression in October 1929 Fats

Waller was riding high. He had work, less financial problems and band work was frequent. The 1930's were even better and included trips to Europe, and an exclusive Victor contract. But the energetic, fast living Fats did not look after himself and died on 15th December 1943 on board the Santa Fe Chief train on his way back to New York from Los Angeles. Fortunately Fats Waller left a legacy of hundreds of recordings and the formative recordings from the years 1927-29, featured on this album are among the best. (Bill Haesler, Feb 1987)
**Album:** Released Sep '87, on Swaggie (Australia) Catalogue no: **S 850**

**1934-1941**
**Album:** Released '88, on Joker (USA) by Lifetime Records (USA). Catalogue no: **SM 4022**
**Cass:** Released '88, on Joker (USA) by Lifetime Records (USA). Catalogue no: **MC 4022**

**AFRICAN RIPPLES**
Tracks: / You look good to me / Something tells me / African ripples / In the gloaming / If I were you / Shame shame (everybody knows your game) / My fate is in your hands / Every day's holiday / Patty cake baker man / Hold my hand / Fair and square / I love to whistle / Tell me with your kisses / Let's break the good news / Baby oh where can you be / Yacht club swing.
**Album:** Released Jan '82, on RCA International by BMG Records (UK). Deleted Jan '87. Catalogue no: **INTS 5095**
**Cass:** Released '84, on RCA International by BMG Records (UK). Catalogue no: **NK 89008**
**Album:** Released '84, on RCA International by BMG Records (UK). Catalogue no: **NL 89008**

**AIN'T MISBEHAVIN' (Waller, Fats & His Rhythm)**
Tracks: / Honeysuckle rose / Ain't misbehavin' / I can't give you anything but love baby / Two sleepy people / I'm gonna sit right down / It's a sin to tell a lie / Minor drag / Joint is jumpin' / Hold tight / Your feet's too big / Until the real thing comes along / Tea for two.
**Album:** Released Apr '80, on RCA by BMG Records (UK). Catalogue no: **INTS 5009**
**CD:** Released Jan '89, on RCA by BMG Records (UK). Catalogue no: **2 RCA 2965.2**
**Album:** Released '84, on RCA International by BMG Records (UK). Catalogue no: **NL 89087**
**Cass:** Released '84, on RCA International by BMG Records (UK). Catalogue no: **NK 89087**

**ARMFUL O' SWEETNESS (Waller, Fats and His Rhythm)**
Tracks: / Porter's love song to a chambermaid, A / I wish I were twins / Armful o' sweetness / Do me a favour / Georgia May / Then I'll be tired of you / Don't let it bother you / Have a little dream on me / Serenade for a wealthy widow / How can you face me / Sweetie pie / Mandy / Lets pretend there's a moon / You're not the only oyster in the stew / I'm growing fonder of you / If it isn't love / Breakin' the ice.
Note: Mono recording
**Album:** Released Feb '87, on Saville by Conifer Records. Catalogue no: **SVL 182**
**Cass:** Released Feb '87, on Saville by Conifer Records. Catalogue no: **CSVL 182**

**BEST OF FATS WALLER**
Tracks: / Sweet Sue / Nagasaki / Crazy 'bout my baby / It's a sin to tell a lie / Lonesome me / Handful of keys / Honeysuckle rose / Ain't misbehavin / I've got my fingers crossed / Solitude / Hallelujah / Sometimes I feel like a motherless child / Two sleepy people.
**Album:** Released Apr '81, on Joker (USA) by Lifetime Records (USA). Catalogue no: **SM 3110**

**BOUNCIN' ON A V DISC**
**Album:** Released Jan '83, on Swaggie (Australia) Catalogue no: **S 1227**

**CHRONOLOGICAL VOL.1 (Waller, Fats & His Rhythm)**
**Album:** Released Sep '86, on JSP by JSP Records. Catalogue no: **JSP 1106**

**COMPLETE EARLY BAND WORKS 1927-9**
Note: Tracks include: *Fats Waller stomp, Savannah blues, Won't you take me home, Minor drag, Harlem fuss, Lookin' good but feelin' bad*, etc..
**Album:** Released Sep '87, on Halcyon (USA) by Submarine Records. Catalogue no: **HDL 115**
**Cass:** Released Sep '87, on Halcyon (USA) by Submarine Records. Catalogue no: **CHDL 115**

**DIAMOND SERIES: FATS WALLER**
Tracks: / I'm on a seesaw / Have a little dream on me / You meet the nicest people in your dreams / Carolina shout / Lulu's back in town / My very good friend the milkman / Do me a favour / Us on a bus / Porter's love song to a chambermaid, A / Then I'll be tired of you / There's honey on the moon tonight / Georgia on my mind / I'm crazy 'bout my baby / Lost and found / Meanest thing you ever did was kiss me / I'm gonna put you in your place.
**CD:** Released Apr '88, on Diamond Series by RCA Records. Catalogue no: **CD 90117**

**DUST OFF THAT OLD PIANNA (Waller, Fats & His Rhythm)**
Tracks: / I'm a hundred per cent for you / Baby Brown / Night wind / Because of once upon a time / I believe in miracles / You fit into the picture / Louisiana fairy tale / I ain't got nobody (and nobody cares for me) / Whose honey are you? / Rosetta / Pardon my love / What's the reason (I'm not pleasin' you)? / Cinders / (Oh Suzanna) dust off that old pianna / Lulu's back in town / Sweet and slow / You've been taking lessons in love (from somebody new) / You're the cutest one / I'm gonna sit right down and write myself a letter / Hate to talk about myself.
**Cass:** Released '88, on Saville by Conifer Records. Catalogue no: **CSVL 189**
**Album:** Released Sep '87, on Saville by Conifer Records. Catalogue no: **SVL 189**

**FASCINATIN' FATS**
**CD:** Released Aug '89, on Starline (Jazz) Catalogue no: **CDSG 401**

**FATS AT THE ORGAN**
Tracks: / Eighteenth Street strut / I'm coming, Virginia / If I could be with you one hour tonight / Laughin' cryin' blues / Midnight blues / Papa better watch your step / T'aint nobody's business if I do / Your time now will be mine after a while / Nobody but my baby is getting my love / Do it, mister so-and-so / Clearing house blues / You can't do what my last man did / Don't try to take my loving man away / Squeeze me.
Note: Stereo recording from 1923/7 Piano Rolls.
**Album:** Released Apr '81, on Living Era by Academy Sound & Vision Records. Catalogue no: **AJA 5007**
**CD:** Released Oct '88, on Living Era by Academy Sound & Vision Records. Catalogue no: **CD AJA 5007**
**Cass:** Released Apr '81, on Living Era by Academy Sound & Vision Records. Catalogue no: **ZC AJA 5007**

**FATS WALLER**
Tracks: / My very good friend the milkman / Don't let it bother you / You're not the only oyster in the stew / Dinah / It's a sing to tell a lie / Hold tight / Honeysuckle rose / I'm gonna sit right down & write myself a / When somebody thinks you're wonderful / You're not the kind / Joint is jumpin', The / Two sleepy people / Your feet's too big / Sheik of Araby, The / Until the real thing comes along / Ain't misbehavin'.
**Album:** Released '88, on Joker (USA) by Lifetime Records (USA). Catalogue no: **SM 4022**
**Album:** Released Sep '87, on Giants of Jazz by Hasmick Promotions. Catalogue no: **LPJT 2**
**Album:** Released '79, on RCA by BMG Records (UK). Deleted '84. Catalogue no: **LSA 3112**
**Album:** Released Mar '87, on Jazz Treasury Catalogue no: **JT 1001**

**FATS WALLER 1935 & 43**
**Album:** Released '88, on Collector's Classics Catalogue no: **CC 19**

**FATS WALLER COLLECTION**
**CD:** Released Oct '89, on Collection by K-Tel Records. Catalogue no: **OR 0078**
**Cass:** Released May '86, on Deja Vu Catalogue no: **DVMC 2059**
**Album:** Released May '86, on Deja Vu Catalogue no: **DVLP 2059**

**FATS WALLER AND HIS RHYTHM (Vol.1 - 1934)**
Tracks: / Lulu's back in town / Whose honey are you / It's a sin to tell a lie / Somebody stole my gal / Christopher

Columbus / If it isn't love / Pianna / To pay / Swingin' them jingle bells / Curse of an aching heart / Bye bye baby / Dream man / Oh Susannah / There's going to be the devil / Take it easy / Big chief de sota / Have a little dream on me.
**CD:** Released Oct '88, on BBC by BBC Records & Tapes. Catalogue no: **BBC CD 684**
**Cass:** Released Oct '88, on BBC by BBC Records & Tapes. Catalogue no: **ZCF 684**
**Album:** Released Oct '88, on BBC by BBC Records & Tapes. Catalogue no: **REB 684**
**Album:** Released Apr '88, on Swaggie (Australia) Catalogue no: **S 851**

**FATS WALLER IN LONDON**
**2 LP Set:** Released '88, on DRG (USA) by DRG Records (USA). Catalogue no: **SW 84423**
**CD:** Released '88, on DRG (USA) by DRG Records (USA). Catalogue no: **CDXP 8442**
**Album:** Released Jun '85, on Retrospect by EMI Records. Deleted Jan '88. Catalogue no: **EG 2604421**
**Cass:** Released Jun '85, on Retrospect by EMI Records. Deleted Jun '89. Catalogue no: **EG 2604424**

**FATS WALLER AND MORRIS HOT BABIES**
**Album:** Released Jul '81, on Joker (USA) by Lifetime Records (USA). Catalogue no: **SM 3080**

**FATS WALLER - PIANO AND RHYTHM**
**CD:** Released Oct '88, on Vogue by Vogue Records. Catalogue no: **VGCD 600 185**

**FINE ARABIAN STUFF**
**Album:** Released Apr '81, on Deluxe (1) Catalogue no: **DE 601**

**FRIENDS OF FATS VOL. 2**
**Album:** Released Feb '87, on Collectors Items Catalogue no: **CI 017**

**FROM THE BEGINNING, VOL. 2**
**Album:** Released Aug '87, on JSP by JSP Records. Catalogue no: **JSP 1108**

**FROM THE BEGINNING VOL. 3 (Waller, Fats & his Rhythm)**
**Album:** Released Jan '88, on JSP by JSP Records. Catalogue no: **JSP 1113**

**HALLELUJAH, I'M A BUM**
**Cass:** Released Jun '88, on Starline (Jazz) Catalogue no: **SLC 61011**

**HANDFUL OF KEYS**
Tracks: / Handful of keys / You're not the only oyster in the stew / Valentino stomp / Honeysuckle rose / St. Louis blues / I'm crazy 'bout my baby / Alligator crawl / Blue turning grey over you / Viper's drag / Your feet's too big / Carolina shout / Ain't misbehavin'.
Note: MONO recording.
**Album:** Released Jul '86, on RCA by BMG Records (UK). Deleted Jul '89. Catalogue no: **CL 89805**
**Cass:** Released Jul '86, on RCA by BMG Records (UK). Catalogue no: **CK 89805**

**HIS PIANO AND HIS RHYTHM VOL. 3**
**Album:** Released Jan '85, on Vogue by Vogue Records. Catalogue no: **502011**

**HONEY ON THE MOON**
Tracks: / Dinah / Alligator crawl / Honey hush / There's honey on the moon tonight / You look good to me / Old grand dad / Swinging them jingle bells / You're not the only oyster in the stew / Pantin' in the panther room / What a pretty miss / Last night a miracle happened / You've been reading my mail.
**Album:** Released Apr '86, on Meteor by Magnum Music Group. Catalogue no: **MTM 009**

**HONEYSUCKLE ROSE**
Tracks: / Let's pretend there's a moon / Honeysuckle rose / Serenade for a wealthy widow / How can you face me / Don't let it bother you / Have a little dream on me / My feelings are hurt / Sweetie pie / African ripples / Mandy / Handful of keys / Do me a favour / You're not the only oyster in the stew / Ridin' but walking / Alligator crawl / Viper's drag / Dream man / Smashin' thirds.
**CD:** Released Jun '88, on Compact Selection Catalogue no: **TQ 139**
**Album:** Released Apr '85, on Recollections (Decca) by Decca Records. Catalogue no: **RAL 509**

**INDISPENSABLE FATS WALLER VOLS. 1 & 2**
**2 LP Set:** Released '86, on RCA by BMG Records (UK). Deleted Jul '89. Catalogue no: **NL 89742**
**2 LP Set:** Released '83, on RCA (France) by BMG Records (France). Catalogue no: **PM 43686**

**INDISPENSABLE FATS WALLER VOLS. 3 & 4 (1926-1935)**
**2 LP Set:** Released '83, on RCA (France) by BMG Records (France). Catalogue no: **PM 43696**
**2 LP Set:** Released '86, on RCA by BMG Records (UK). Deleted Jul '89. Catalogue no: **NL 89819**

**INDISPENSABLE FATS WALLER VOLS. 5 & 6**
Tracks: / S' posin' / Hallelujah / Cryin' mood / Boo hoo / Honeysuckle rose / Smarty / Bat it out / How ya baby / Neglected / Florido flo / Skrontch / Sheik of Araby, The / T'aint good.
**2 LP Set:** Released Aug '86, on RCA by BMG Records (UK). Deleted Jul '89. Catalogue no: **NL 89745**
**Cass set:** Released Aug '86, on RCA by BMG Records (UK). Deleted May '89. Catalogue no: **NK 89745**

**INDISPENSABLE FATS WALLER VOL. 7 & 8**
Tracks: / Hold my hand / If I were you / Two sleepy people / Good man is hard to find / Hold tight / 'Taint what you do / Your feet's too big / Darktown strutters ball / I can't hive you anything but love / Cheatin' on me / Dry bones.
**2 LP Set:** Released '87, on RCA by BMG Records (UK). Deleted Jul '89. Catalogue no: **NL 89273**
**Cass:** Released '87, on RCA by BMG Records (UK). Deleted May '89. Catalogue no: **NK 89273**

**INDISPENSABLE FATS WALLER VOLS. 9 & 10**
Tracks: / My mommie sent me to the store / Fats Waller's original E-flat blues / Hey stop kissing my sister / Everybody loves my baby / T'aint nobody's business if I do / Abercrombie had a zombie / Scram / My melancholy baby / Mamacita / Pantin' in the panther room / Shortnin' bread / Pan-pan / I wanna hear swing songs / All that meat and no potatoes / Carolina shout / Twenty four robbers / Sad sap sucker am I / Chant off the groove / Come and get it / Rump steak serenade / Buck jumpin' / Winter weather / Cash for your trash / Don't give me that jive / Your socks don't match / Really fine / Jitterbug waltz / By the light of the silvery moon / Swing out to victory / Moppin' and boppin' / Ain't misbehavin'.
**Cass:** Released Sep '87, on RCA by BMG Records (UK). Deleted Jul '89. Catalogue no: **NK 89971**
**Album:** Released Sep '87, on RCA by BMG Records (UK). Deleted Jul '89. Catalogue no: **NL 89971**

**JAZZ TIME VOL.17**
**Album:** Released '88, on Vogue (France) by Vogue Records. Catalogue no: **502717**

**JOINT IS JUMPIN' (BLUEBIRD)**
Tracks: / Handful of keys / Minor drag / Numb fumblin' / Ain't misbehavin' / Smashing thirds / African ripples / Alligator crawl / Viper's drag / Lulu's back in town / Crazy 'bout my baby / S'posin' / Blues / Tea for two / I ain't got nobody / Joint is jumpin', The / Sheik of Araby, The / Yacht club swing / Squeeze me / Your feet's too big / Carolina shout / Honeysuckle rose.
**CD:** Released Apr '88, on Bluebird (2) by BMG Records (UK). Catalogue no: **ND 86288**

**JOINT IS JUMPIN' (TOPLINE)**
Tracks: / Ain't misbehavin' / Crazy'bout my baby / Handful of keys / Nagasaki / Joint is jumpin', The / Sweet Sue / Just you / Honeysuckle rose / I'm gonna sit right down & write myself a letter / It's a sin to tell a lie / Until the real thing comes along / Christopher Columbus / Your feet's too big.
**Album:** Released May '86, on Topline by Charly Records. Catalogue no: **TOP 139**
**Cass:** Released May '86, on Topline by Charly Records. Catalogue no: **KTOP 139**

**JUGGLING JIVE OF FATS WALLER (Live)**
**Cass:** Released Oct '86, on Giants of Jazz by Hasmick Promotions. Catalogue no: **GOJC 1041**
**Album:** Released Oct '86, on Giants of Jazz by Hasmick Promotions. Catalogue no: **GOJ 1041**

**LAST YEARS, THE (1940-1943)**
Tracks: / Old grand dad / Fat and greasy

/ Little curly hair in a high chair / (You're a) square from Delaware / You run your mouth / I'll run by business / Too tired / Send me Jackson / Epe, ipe, wanna piece of pie / Stop pretending / I'll never smile again / My mommie sent me to the store / Dry bones / Fats Waller's original E flat blues / Stayin' at home / Hey - stop kissing my sister / Everybody loves my baby / I'm gonna salt away some sugar / Tain't nobody's biz-ness if I do / Abercrombie had a zombie / Blue eyes / Scram / My melancholy baby / Mamacita / Liver lip Jones / Buckin' the dice / Pantin' in the Panther room / Come down to earth, my angel / Shortnin' break / I repent / Do you have to got pan-pan / I wanna hear swing songs / You're gonna be sotty / All that meat and no potatoes / Let's get away from it all / Twenty four robbers / I understand / Sad sap sucker am I / Headlines in the news / Chant of the groove / Come and get it / Rump steak serenade / Ain't nothin' to it / Oh baby, sweet baby / Buck jumpin' / That gets it Mr. Joe / Bells of San Raquel, The / Bessie, Bessie, Bessie / Clarinet marmalade / Winter weather / Cash for your trash / Don't give me that jive / Your socks don't match / We need a little love / You must be losing your mind / Really fine / Jitterbug waltz, The / By the light of the silvery moon / Swing out to victory / Up jumped you with love / Romance a la mode / Moppin' and boppin' / Ain't misbehavin'.

**CD Set:** Released Dec '89, on Bluebird (2) by BMG Records (UK). Catalogue no: **ND 90411**

**Cass set:** Released Dec '89, on Bluebird (2) by BMG Records (UK). Catalogue no: **NK 90411**

**LP Set:** Released Dec '89, on Bluebird (2) by BMG Records (UK). Catalogue no: **NL 90411**

## LEGENDARY PERFORMER

Tracks: / Ain't misbehavin' / I'm gonna sit right down / Handful of keys / Jitterbug waltz / How ya baby? / Joint is jumpin' / Honeysuckle rose / Viper's drag / Your feet's too big / I've got a feeling I'm falling / Yacht club swing / Keepin' out of mischief now / Lounging at the Waldorf.

**Album:** Released '79, on RCA by BMG Records (UK). Deleted '84. Catalogue no: **PL 12904**

## LIVE AT THE YACHT CLUB

Tracks: / Yacht Club swing / Hold my hand / Pent-up in a penthouse / Honeysuckle rose / You look good to me / Hallelujah / St. Louis blues / Flat foot floogie / After you've gone / You can't be mine (and someone else's too) / Monday mornin' / What do you know about love? / I had to do it.

**Album:** Released Jul '84, on Giants of Jazz by Hasmick Promotions. Catalogue no: **GOJ 1029**

**Cass:** Released Jul '84, on Giants of Jazz by Hasmick Promotions. Catalogue no: **GOJC 1029**

## LIVE: FATS WALLER, VOL.2

Tracks: / Lila Lou / Frenesi / So you're the one / Dark eyes / Perfidia / When you and I were young, Maggie / Hold my hand / Stop beatin' around the mulberry bush / What's the matter with you? / Hallelujah / What's your name? / What-cha know, Joe? / I give my word.

**Album:** Released Jan '85, on Giants of Jazz by Hasmick Promotions. Catalogue no: **GOJ 1035**

**Cass:** Released Oct '86, on Giants of Jazz by Hasmick Promotions. Catalogue no: **GOJC 1035**

## MAGIC MOMENTS

**Cass:** Released May '86, on RCA by BMG Records (UK). Catalogue no: **NK 89897**

## MASTERS OF JAZZ

**Album:** Released '83, on RCA (Germany) Catalogue no: **CL 42343**

## MOST IMPORTANT RECORDINGS OF FATS WALLER, THE

Tracks: / Birmingham blues / Henderson stomp / St Louis blues / Thou swell / Handful of keys / Minor drag, The / Numb fumbling / Valentine stomp / Lookin' good but feelin' bad / I'm crazy about my baby / You're not the only oyster in the stew / Alligator crawl / Viper's drag / Baby brown / Lulu's back in town / I'm gonna sit down and write myself a letter / Sweet Sue / I got rhythm / It's a sin to tell a lie / Swingin' them jingle bells / Meanest thing you ever did was kiss me, The / Honeysuckle rose / Keepin' out of mischief now / Joint is jumpin', The / Two sleepy people / Hold tight / Spider and the fly, The / You feet's too big / Darktown strutter's ball / Carolina shout / Ain't misbehavin' / Waller jive / Hallelujah.

**LP Set:** Released May '89, on Official by Official Records. Catalogue no: **OFF 3030-2**

**CD:** Released May '89, on Official by Official Records. Catalogue no: **OFF 83030-2**

## MY VERY GOOD FRIEND THE MILKMAN (Waller, Fats & his Rhythm)

Tracks: / I'm gonna sit right down and write myself a letter / Dinah / My very good friend the milkman / Baby brown / Whose honey are you / Blue because of you / 12th Street rag / You've been taking lessons in love / Somebody stole my gal / Breakin' the ice / I ain't got nobody / Just as long as the world goes round & round / I'm on a see-saw / I got rhythm / Sweet Sue / Rhythm & romance / Sweet thing / Serenade for a wealthy widow.

Note: Mono recording. All vocals by Fats Waller.

**Album:** Released Sep '86, on President by President Records. Catalogue no: **PLE 525**

## OH MERCY, LOOKA HERE

**Album:** Released '88, on Honeysuckle Rose (USA) Catalogue no: **HR 5000-3**

## ON THE AIR

**Album:** Released '88, on Collector's Classics Catalogue no: **CC 10**

## OUR VERY GOOD FRIEND, FATS

**Album:** Released Jun '88, on Dance Band Days by Prism Leisure. Catalogue no: **DBD 16**

**CD:** Released Jul '89, on Dance Band Days by Prism Leisure. Catalogue no: **DBCD 16**

**Cass:** Released Jun '88, on Dance Band Days by Prism Leisure. Catalogue no: **DBDC 16**

## PIANO SOLOS (1929-1941)

Tracks: / Blue black bottom / Handful of keys / Numb fumblin' / Ain't misbehavin' / Sweet savannah Sue / I've got a feeling i'm falling / Love me or leave me / Gladyse / Valentine stomp / Waiting at the end of the road / Baby, oh where can you be / Goin' about / My feelin's are hurt / Smashing thirds / My fate is in your hands / Turn on the heat / St. Louis blues / After you've gone / African ripples / Clothes line ballet / Alligator crawl / Viper's drag / Down home blues / E flat blues / Zonky / Keepin' out of mischief now / Stardust / Basin Street blues / Tea for two / I ain't got nobody / Georgia on my mind / Rockin' chair / Carolina shout / Honeysuckle rose / Ring dem bells.

Note: MONO recording.

**Cass set:** Released Sep '86, on Jazz Tribune by BMG Records (UK). Deleted May '89. Catalogue no: **NK 89741**

**2 LP Set:** Released '83, on RCA (France) by BMG Records (France). Catalogue no: **PM 43270**

**2 LP Set:** Released Sep '86, on Jazz Tribune by BMG Records (UK). Deleted Jul '89. Catalogue no: **NL 89741**

## RAGTIME PIANO ENTERTAINER

**CD:** Released 10 Jul '89, on Vogue by Vogue Records. Catalogue no: **VG 670219**

## RARE FATS WALLER (1927-42)

**Album:** Released Jan '83, on Swaggie (Australia) Catalogue no: **S 1243**

## RARE PIANO BOOGIE

**Cass:** Released Jun '84, on Pathe Marconi (France) Catalogue no: **PM 1648674**

**Album:** Released Jun '84, on Pathe Marconi (France) Catalogue no: **PM 1648671**

## SPREADIN' RHYTHM AROUND (Waller, Fats & his Rhythm)

Tracks: / Sweet beginning like this, A / Got a bran' new suit / I'm on a see-saw / Thief in the night / When somebody thinks you're wonderful / I've got my fingers crossed / Spreadin' rhythm around / Little bit independent, A / You stayed away too long / Sweet thing / Panic is on, The / Sugar rose / Oooh look-a there / Ain't she pretty / Moon rose / West wind / That never-to-be-forgotten night / Sing an old fashioned song / Garbo green / All my life / Christopher Columbus.

**Album:** Released Jul '89, on Saville by Conifer Records. Catalogue no: **SVL 204**

**Cass:** Released Jul '89, on Saville by

Conifer Records. Catalogue no: **CSVL 204**

**TAKE IT EASY (Waller, Fats & his Rhythm)**
Tracks: / Dinah / Take it easy / You're the picture (I'm the frame) / My very good friend the milkman / Blue because of you / There's going to be the devil to pay / 12th Street rag / There'll be some changes made / Somebody stole my gal / Sweet Sue - just you / Truckin' / Sugar blues / As long as the world goes 'round and 'round / Georgia rockin' chair / Brother, see and ye shall find / Girl I left behind me, The / You're so darn charming / Woe is me / Rhythm and romance / Loafin' time.
**Album:** Released '88, on Saville by Conifer Records. Catalogue no: **SVL 194**
**Cass:** Released '88, on Saville by Conifer Records. Catalogue no: **CSVL 194**

**THAT OLD FEELING**
**Album:** Released Jan '83, on Swaggie (Australia) Catalogue no: **S 1246**

**THAT'S FATS**
**CD:** Released Dec '86, on Vogue by Vogue Records. Catalogue no: **VGCD 600097**

**THOMAS 'FATS' WALLER RARE EARLY PIANO SOLOS 1923-1927 (Waller, Fats)**
Tracks: / New kind of man with a new kind of love, A / 18th Street stomp / Snake hips.
**CD:** Released Mar '88, on Delta (1) by Delta Records. Catalogue no: **20 801**

**THOMAS 'FATS' WALLER VOL.1 (Waller, Fats)**
**Album:** Released '88, on Vogue (France) by Vogue Records. Catalogue no: **502003**

**THOMAS 'FATS' WALLER VOL.2 (Waller, Thomas Fats)**
**Album:** Released '88, on Vogue (France) by Vogue Records. Catalogue no: **502006**

**VOCAL FATS, THE**
Tracks: / My very good friend the milkman / Don't let it bother you / You're not the only oyster in the stew / Dinah / It's a sin to tell a lie / Hold tight / Honey suckle rose / I'm gonna sit right down and write myself a letter / When somebody thinks you're wonderful / You're not the kind / Joint is jumpin', The / Two sleepy people / Your feet's too big / Sheik of Araby, The / Until the real thing comes along / Ain't misbehavin'.
**Cass:** Released Mar '86, on RCA by BMG Records (UK). Catalogue no: **NK 89574**
**Album:** Released Mar '86, on RCA by BMG Records (UK). Catalogue no: **NL 89574**

**YOU RASCAL, YOU**
Tracks: / Georgia May / I'm crazy 'bout my baby / Breakin' the ice / Baby, oh where can you be? / If it isn't love / Won't you get off it, please? / I wish I were twins / Numb fumblin' / You rascal, you / Ain't misbehavin' / Porter's love song to a chambermaid, A / Draggin' my heart around / Minor drag, The / My fate is in your hands / That's what I like about you / Harlem fuss / Believe it, beloved / Honeysuckle rose.
**Album:** Released Mar '86, on Living Era by Academy Sound & Vision Records. Catalogue no: **AJA 5040**
**Cass:** Released Mar '86, on Living Era by Academy Sound & Vision Records. Catalogue no: **ZC AJA 5040**
**CD:** Released Oct '88, on Living Era by Academy Sound & Vision Records. Catalogue no: **CD AJA 5040**

**YOUNG FATS WALLER**
**Album:** Released Apr '81, on Joker (USA) by Lifetime Records (USA). Catalogue no: **SM 3093**

## Wallgren, Jan

**LAVORO INCORSO (Wallgren, Jan Edvard/Swedish Radio Jazz Group)**
**Album:** Released '86, on Dragon by Dragon Records. Catalogue no: **DRLP 89**

## Wallington, George

**AT THE CAFE BOHEMIA (Wallington, George Quintet)**
**Album:** Released Jun '86, on Progressive (USA) by Jazzology Records (USA). Catalogue no: **PRO 7001**

**JAZZ FOR THE CARRIAGE TRADE (Wallington, George Quintet)**
Note: With Phil Woods,Donald Byrd etc.
**CD:** Released May '87, on JVC/Fantasy Catalogue no: **VDJ 1505**

**SYMPHONY OF A JAZZ PIANO**
Tracks: / Jack finding his Jill / Moment we fancy each other, The / Lovely things we see / Posthumous glory / Delusion / Soap bubbles / Mother wit / Love notes and ringlets / Spring of life, The / Two lovers / Goodness of heart / Billie, I must leave you now.
**CD:** Released '88, on Denon Deleted '88. Catalogue no: **C38 7825**

**VIRTUOSO**
Tracks: / Moon flower / Clearness of view / Beautiful eyes / Melody / Virtuoso / Temporal / Beautiful to behold / Heart of hearts / One foolish leaf / Sociability.
**CD:** Released '88, on Denon Catalogue no: **C38-7248**

## Wallis, Bob

**COME ALONG PLEASE (Wallis, Bob Storyville Jazz Men)**
Tracks: / Come along please.
**7" Single:** Released Jan '62, on Pye Jazz Today Deleted '65. Catalogue no: **7 NJ 2048**

**DOCTOR JAZZ**
**Album:** Released Jan '88, on Storyville by Storyville Records AB. Catalogue no: **SLP 256**

**EVERYBODY LOVES SATURDAY NIGHT (Wallis, Bob & His Storyville Jazz Men)**
**Album:** Released Jun '60, on Top Rank (1) Deleted '65. Catalogue no: **BUY 023**

**I'M SHY MARY ELLEN I'M SHY**
Tracks: / I'm shy Mary Ellen.
**7" Single:** Released Jul '61, on Pye Jazz Today Deleted '64. Catalogue no: **7 NJ 2043**

**LIVE: BOB WALLIS (Wallis, Bob Storyville Jazz Men)**
**Album:** Released Jun '86, on Storyville by Storyville Records AB. Catalogue no: **SLP 247**

## Walrath, Jack

**JACK WALRATH AND SPIRIT LEVEL (Walrath, Jack & Spirit Level)**
**Album:** Released '88, on Spotlite by Spotlite Records. Catalogue no: **SPJ LP25**

**MASTER OF SUSPENSE**
Tracks: / Meat / Children / No mystery / Study in porcine / Bouquet of roses / Lord's calypso, The / I'm so lonesome I could cry / Monk on the moon / Hymn for the discontented, A.
**Album:** Released Aug '87, on Blue Note by EMI Records. Deleted '88. Catalogue no: **BLJ 46905**
**CD:** Released Sep '87, on Blue Note by EMI Records. Deleted Jun '89. Catalogue no: **CDP 746 905 2**
**CD:** Released Sep '87, on Blue Note by EMI Records. Deleted Jun '89. Catalogue no: **BNZ 103**

**NEOHIPPUS**
Tracks: / Village of the darned / Watch your head / Fright night / Annie Lee / England / Beer / Future reference (CD only) / Smell of the blues, The (CD only).
**CD:** Released May '89, on Blue Note by EMI Records. Deleted Aug '89. Catalogue no: **CDP 791 101 2**
**CD:** Released May '89, on Blue Note by EMI Records. Deleted Aug '89. Catalogue no: **CDB1 91101**
**Album:** Released May '89, on Blue Note by EMI Records. Catalogue no: **B1 91101**

**PLEA FOR SANITY, A**
Tracks: / Jinx / Ballad for old time's sake / Li'l stinker / Free fall / Mucene the genie / Plea for sanity, A / St. Home in Rome.
**Album:** Released Jan '83, on Stash (USA) Catalogue no: **ST 223**

**REVENGE OF THE FAT PEOPLE (Walrath, Jack Group)**
**Album:** Released Aug '88, on Stash (USA) Catalogue no: **ST 221**

## Walton, Cedar

**Biographical details:** Pianist and composer Cedar Walton, who worked with everybody who was anybody in jazz in the late 1950's, including Art Blakey's Jazz Messengers, also made many albums of his own on Prestige. He was born in Texas in 1934 and since 1970 has spent a lot of time in Europe. (Donald Clarke, March 1988.).

**ANIMATION**
Tracks: / Animation / Jacob's ladder /

Charmed circle / Another star / Precious mountain / March of the fisherman / If it could happen / Ala Eduardo.
**Album:** Released '79, on CBS by CBS Records. Deleted '84. Catalogue no: **CBS 83504**

**BLUESVILLE TIME (Walton, Cedar Quartet)**
**Album:** Released '88, on Criss Cross Catalogue no: **CRISS 1017**

**BREAKTHROUGH (Walton, Cedar & Hank Mobley)**
**Album:** Released Apr '81, on Muse by Black & Blue Records. Catalogue no: **MR 5132**

**CEDAR BLUES (Live) (Walton, Cedar Quintet)**
**Album:** Released '88, on R.E.D. Catalogue no: **VPA 179**

**CEDAR WALTON**
Note: Cedar Walton / David Williams / Billy Higgins
**Album:** Released Oct '86, on Timeless by Timeless Records. Catalogue no: **SJP 223**

**CEDAR WALTON PLAYS (featuring Ron Carter & Billy Higgins)**
**CD:** Released '88, on Delos (USA) Catalogue no: **DCD 4008**

**EASTERN REBELLION (Walton, Cedar Quartet)**
Tracks: / Bolivia / 5/4 thing / Mode for Joe / Naima / Bittersweet.
Note: Recorded December 1975, New York. Personnel: Cedar Walton (piano), George Coleman (tenor), Sam Jones (bass), Billy Higgins (drums).
**CD:** Released Jun '89, on Timeless by Timeless Records. Catalogue no: **CDSJP 101**
**Cass:** Released Sep '86, on Timeless (Import) by Timeless Records. Catalogue no: **SJP 1101**
**Album:** Released Sep '86, on Timeless by Timeless Records. Catalogue no: **SJP 101**

**EASTERN REBELLION VOL.2 (With Bob Berg,Sam jones & Billy Higgins)**
**Album:** Released Apr '81, on Timeless (Import) by Timeless Records. Catalogue no: **SJP 106**

**EASTERN REBELLION VOL.3 (With Curtis Fuller,Bob Berg,Sam jones & Billy Higgins)**
**Album:** Released Apr '81, on Timeless by Timeless Records. Catalogue no: **SJP 143**

**FIRM ROOTS**
**Album:** Released Apr '81, on Muse by Black & Blue Records. Catalogue no: **MR 5059**

**FIRST SET**
**CD:** Released Jul '88, on Steeplechase (USA) Catalogue no: **SCCD 31085**
**Album:** Released Jul '88, on Steeplechase (USA) Catalogue no: **SCS 1085**

**LOVE...**
Note: with BillyHiggins, David Williams, Steve Grossman.
**Album:** Released Jan '87, on Red (Italy) Catalogue no: **VPA 189**

**NIGHT AT BOOMERS VOL. 1, A**
**Album:** Released Apr '81, on Muse by Black & Blue Records. Catalogue no: **MR 5010**

**NIGHT AT BOOMERS VOL. 2, A**
**Album:** Released Apr '81, on Muse by Black & Blue Records. Catalogue no: **MR 5022**

**PLAYS**
**CD:** Released Mar '90, on Delos Catalogue no: **JJCD54**

**SECOND SET (Walton, Cedar Quartet)**
**Album:** Released Sep '79, on Steeplechase (USA) Catalogue no: **SCS 1113**

**TRIO, THE (Walton,Cedar/David Williams / Billy Higgins)**
**Album:** Released Sep '86, on Red Pepper by Interstate Music. Catalogue no: **VPA 192**

**WILLOW WEEP FOR ME**
Tracks: / Willow weep for me / Book's bossa.
**CD 3":** Released '88, on Delos (USA) Catalogue no: **D/PC 2101**

## Walton, Mercy Dee

**MERCY DEE WALTON AND HIS PIANO**
**Album:** Released May '81, on Arhoolie (USA) by Arhoolie Records (USA). Catalogue no: **ARHOOLIE 1007**

## Ward, Clara

**GOSPEL CONCERT**
**CD:** Released Oct '88, on Vogue by Vogue Records. Catalogue no: **VGCD 600 167**

## Waring, Fred

**Biographical details:** Bandleader Fred Waring (1900-83) was also a songwriter and arranger. In his early years he played violin and banjo and he formed his first band while at college. Later Fred Waring's Collegians became the Pennsylvanians, based in Detroit. Hits on Victor in the 20's were very commercial, with some being jazz-influenced. In the 30's the band played in Broadway shows and then became even more squarely aimed at middle America with a glee-club style. Waring also invented, in 1937, the Waring blender, forerunner of today's kitchen mixing machines. He did a lot of radio work, published band and choral arrangements and the monthly Music Journal and became very rich. His last public appearance was at President Reagan's 1981 inauguration. (Donald Clarke, March 1988.).

**MEMORIAL ALBUM**
**Album:** Released Feb '85, on Stash (USA) Catalogue no: **ST 126**

## Warner's Seven Aces

**1923-1927 (White Jazz And Hot Dance From Atlanta)**
Tracks: / Lovesome lovesick blues / Mean eyes / Ace of spades / Bessie couldn't help it / When my sugar walks down the street / Blues have got me / Go get 'em Caroline / Breakin' the leg / Hangin' around / Who'd be blue / You've got those 'wanna go back again' blues / So is your old lady / That's my hap-hap-happiness / There's everything nice about you / When Jennie does her low down dance.
Note: Mono recording
**Album:** Released Jan '86, on Harlequin by Interstate Music. Catalogue no: **HQ 2030**

## Wash House Stompers

**THERE'LL BE SOME CHANGES MADE**
Tracks: / There'll be some changes made / I want a little girl / As long as I live / Lazy river / Swinging the blues / Some of these days / Original Dixieland one-step / Special one / Since you first came my way / Someday you'll be sorry / New Orleans / Shine.
**Album:** Released Jul '88, on Black Lion Catalogue no: **BLM 51110**

## Washboard Doc

**EARLY MORNING BLUES**
Note: With Washboard Doc, Lucky & Flash
**Album:** Released '88, on L&R Catalogue no: **LR 42.010**

## Washboard Rhythm Boys

**1933**
**Album:** Released '88, on WRB Catalogue no: **WRB 4014**

## Washboard Sam

**1935-47, VOLUME 1**
Note: Featuring Broonzy, Nelson, Black Bob, Morland etc.
**Album:** Released Sep '87, on Document Catalogue no: **DLP 507**

**I'M NOT THE LAD**
**Album:** Released Jun '88, on Bluetime (Denmark) by Contact Records (Denmark). Catalogue no: **BT 2012**

**WASHBOARD SAM 1936-42**
**Album:** Released '88, on Best Of Blues (USA) by Blue Island Records (USA). Catalogue no: **BOB 1**

**WASHBOARD SAM 1935-1941**
**Album:** Released '88, on Blues Classics(USA) by Arhoolie Records (USA). Catalogue no: **BC 10**

## Washboard Willie

**MOTOR TOWN BOOGIE**
Tracks: / C.C. Rider / Move after hours / Summit ridge drive / Dupree blues / Struttin' that stuff / 10.20 special / Calvin's blues / Shake your money maker / No name blues / Fool on a mule.
**Album:** Released Jul '82, on JSP by JSP Records. Catalogue no: **JSP 1036**

## Washington, Dinah

**Biographical details:** A singer whose gutsy style, unique phrasing, gospel background and feeling for the blues transcended category, Dinah Washington (1924-63) won a talent contest, toured with the Sallie Martin Gospel Singers, changed her name and sang with Lionel Hampton's band from 1943 to 1946. The first session under her own name was produced by Leonard Feather in '43 with Hampton sidesmen, and Feather's songs *Evil Man* and *Salty Papa* became eternally associated with her. Washington subsequently recorded for Mercury and nearly 30 rhythm-and-blues hits from 1949-61 began with Feather's *Baby Get Lost*, a No 1 hit. More than 20 singles also made the pop chart, including good standards like *What A Difference A Day Makes, It Could Happen To You, Our Love Is Here To Stay* and *For All We Know*. She also had hit duets with Brook Benton. (Donald Clarke, March 1988.)

This American singer, born Ruth Jones in Alabama in 1924, grew up singing and playing piano in church choirs. In 1943 she became vocalist with Lionel Hampton's noted jazz band. Upon leaving Hampton in '45, she began to record in a wide variety of styles, including pop, blues and country; but jazz remained her musical base. In 1959 Washington was suddenly in the pop spotlight. *What a difference a day makes*, a catchy, jazzy, blues-tinged single, took her to No.8 on the American charts. I was followed by *Unforgettable*, a US No.17 hit. These pop successes led to her duetting with a Mercury Records labelmate, Brook Benton. He was establishing himself as one of America's top pop singers, and this 1960 recording partnership caused cries of 'sell-out' by some of His Washington fans; but she was attracted by his smoky vocals, and the combination worked. It gave Washington the two biggest hits of her career - *Baby (you've got what it takes) reached the US No.5 slot and, later in 1960, A rockin' good way (to mess around and fall in love)* hit No.7. Both were lightweight conversational duets.

While Benton's career continued to flourish, Washington's diminished a little. Her singles continued to reach the American Top 40, but did not climb into the Top 20. Both singers, however, experienced a lack of British recognition - Washington's only charted record in the UK was 1961's *September in the rain*, which peaked at No.35. Her final Stateside Top 40 success was *Where are you*, which reached No.36 in the summer of '62. She died of an overdose of sleeping pills in December 1963, at the age of 39. Though Britons were largely unaware of Washington's vocal talents during her lifetime, two of her US successes received Top 10 action in the UK in later eras: *What a difference a day makes* was a No.6 hit for jazz-blues singer Esther Phillips in 1975, and *A rockin' good way* gave Shakin' Stevens & Bonnie Tyler a No.5 success in 1984. (Bob MacDonald, 26th April 1985).

## BACK TO THE BLUES

**Album:** Released Dec '87, on Fresh Sounds (Spain) by Fresh Sounds Records (Spain). Catalogue no: **FS 295**

## BESSIE SMITH SONGBOOK

Tracks: / After you've gone / Send me to the 'lectric chair / Jailhouse blues / Trombone butter / You've been a good old wagon / Careless love / Back water blues / If I could be with you one hour tonight / Me and my gin / Fine fat daddy.

Note: Dinah Washington, who died in 1963, combined the power of Bessie Smith with the emotion of Billie Holiday. Whether performing R & B, jazz or popular songs, the blues were never far away, indeed she was called the Queen of the Blues. This moving tribute to Bessie Smith was recorded between December 57-January 58 and originally released as *Bessie Smith Blues*. Digitally remastered from the original mono tapes.

**Cass:** Released Nov '86, on Polydor by Polydor Ltd. Catalogue no: **826 663-4**

**CD:** Released '86, on Mercury by Phonogram Ltd. Deleted Feb '88. Catalogue no: **826 663-2**

**Album:** Released Nov '86, on Polydor by Polydor Ltd. Catalogue no: **826 631-1**

## BEST OF DINAH WASHINGTON (Compact / Walkman jazz)

Tracks: / No hard feelings / Your nobody till somebody loves you / He's my guy / Good life / Do nothing till you hear from me / I wanna be around / Destination moon / If it's the last thing I do / Call me irresponsible / Don't say nothing at all / What kind of fool am I / For all we know / Unforgettable / Easy living / Backwater blues / If I were a bell / Teach me tonight / Keepin' out of mischief now / All of me / This bitter earth / What a difference a day made / If I could write a book / Make me a present of you / Smoke gets in your eyes / I wanna be loved / Manhattan / I've got you under my skin / I remember Clifford.

**CD:** Released May '87, on Mercury by Phonogram Ltd. Catalogue no: **830 700-2**

**Cass:** Released May '87, on Mercury by Phonogram Ltd. Catalogue no: **830 700-4**

**CD:** Released Jul '87, on Phonogram by Phonogram Ltd. Deleted Jan '89. Catalogue no: **831 700-2**

**Cass:** Released Jul '87, on Phonogram by Phonogram Ltd. Catalogue no: **831 700-4**

## COMPLETE DINAH WASHINGTON, VOL. 1 (1943-1945)

Tracks: / Evil gal blues / I know how to do it / Salty papa blues / Homeward bound / Blow top blues / Wise woman blues / Walking blues / No voot no boot / Chewin' mama blues / My lovin' papa / Rich man's blues / All or nothing / Beggin' mama blues / Mellow mama blues / My voot is really vout / Blues for a day / Pacific coast blues.

**CD:** Released Dec '88, on Official by Official Records. Catalogue no: **OFF 83004**

**Album:** Released May '88, on Official by Official Records. Catalogue no: **OFF 3004**

**Cass:** Released May '88, on Official by Official Records. Catalogue no: **OFF 43004**

## COMPLETE DINAH WASHINGTON, VOL. 2

Tracks: / Embraceable you / I can't get started with you / When a woman loves a man / Joy juice / Oo-wee walkie talkie / Man I love, The / You didn't want me then / Slick chick, A / Postman blues / That's why a woman loves a heel / Mean and evil blues / Stairway to the stars / I want to be loved / You satisfy / Fool that I am / There's got to be a change.

**Cass:** Released Dec '88, on Official by Official Records. Catalogue no: **OFF 43005**

**CD:** Released Dec '88, on Official by Official Records. Catalogue no: **OFF 83005**

**Album:** Released Dec '88, on Official by Official Records. Catalogue no: **OFF 3005**

## COMPLETE DINAH WASHINGTON, VOL. 3

Tracks: / Mean and evil blues / Since I fell for you / West side baby / You can depend on me / Early in the morning / I'm afraid of you / I love you, yes I do / Don't come knocking at my door / I wish I knew the name of the boy / No more lonely gal blues / Walkin' and talkin' / Ain't misbehavin' / What can I say after I say I'm sorry / Teel me so / I can't face the music / Pete.

**Cass:** Released Aug '88, on Official by Official Records. Catalogue no: **OFF 43007**

**CD:** Released Aug '88, on Official by Official Records. Catalogue no: **OFF 83007**

**Album:** Released Aug '88, on Official by Official Records. Catalogue no: **OFF 3007**

## COMPLETE DINAH WASHINGTON, VOL. 4

Tracks: / Am I asking too much ? / I'm getting old before my time / Record ban blues / Resolution blues / I want to cry / Long John blues / In the rain / I sold my heart to the junkman / I'll wait / It's too soon to know / Why can't you behave ? / It's funny / Laughing boy / Am I really sorry ? / How deep is the ocean ? / New York, Chicago and Los Angeles.

**Cass:** Released Dec '88, on Official by Official Records. Catalogue no: **OFF 43008**

**Album:** Released Dec '88, on Official by Official Records. Catalogue no: **OFF 3008**

**CD:** Released Dec '88, on Official by Official Records. Catalogue no: **OFF 83008**

## COMPLETE DINAH WASHINGTON, VOL. 5

Tracks: / Give me back my tears / Good daddy blues / Baby get lost / I only know / Drummer man / I challenge your kiss / Fast movin' mama / Juice head man of mine / Shuckin' and jivin' / Richest guy in the graveyard / Journey's end / It isn't fair / My kind of man / If I loved you / Why

don't you think things over / Big deal.
**Album:** Released '88, on Official by Official Records. Catalogue no: **OFF 3012**
**CD:** Released '88, on Official by Official Records. Catalogue no: **OFF 83012**
**Cass:** Released '88, on Official by Official Records. Catalogue no: **OFF 43012**

### COMPLETE DINAH WASHINGTON, VOL. 6
Tracks: / I'll never be free / I wanna be loved / Love (me) with misery / Harbor lights / I cross my fingers / Time out for tears / Only a moment ago / Fine fine daddy / Please send me someone to love / Ain't nobody's business but my own / I'm so lonely I could cry / My heart cries for you / I apologize / I won't cry anymore / Don't say you're sorry again / Mixed emotions.
**Album:** Released Dec '88, on Official by Official Records. Catalogue no: **OFF 3013**
**Cass:** Released Dec '88, on Official by Official Records. Catalogue no: **OFF 43013**
**CD:** Released Dec '88, on Official by Official Records. Catalogue no: **OFF 83013**

### COMPLETE DINAH WASHINGTON, VOL. 7 (1951-52)
Tracks: / Cold, cold heart / Baby, did you hear / New blowtop blues / What's the matter with you baby / Don't hold it against me / Be fair to me / Just one more chance / Saturday night / If you don't think I'm leavin' / I'm a fool to want you / I'm crying / Out in the cold again / Hey, good looking / Wheel of fortune / Tell me why / Trouble in mind.
**Album:** Released '88, on Official by Official Records. Catalogue no: **OFF 3018**
**CD:** Released '88, on Official by Official Records. Catalogue no: **OFF 83018**
**Cass:** Released '88, on Official by Official Records. Catalogue no: **OFF 43018**

### COMPLETE DINAH WASHINGTON, VOL. 8
Tracks: / When the sun goes down / I thought about you / Mad about the boy / I can't face the music / Stormy weather / My devotion / Make believe dreams / Pilloe blues / No caviar / Double dealing daddy / My song / Half as much / I cried for you / Gambler's blues / You let my love grow cold / Suprise party.
**Album:** Released '88, on Official by Official Records. Catalogue no: **OFF 3021**
**Cass:** Released '88, on Official by Official Records. Catalogue no: **OFF 43021**
**CD:** Released '88, on Official by Official Records. Catalogue no: **OFF 83021**

### COMPLETE DINAH WASHINGTON, VOL. 9
Tracks: / Don't get around much anymore / Ain't nothing good / Fat daddy / Go pretty daddy / TV is the thing / Feel like I wanna cry / Lean baby / Never, never / I ain't gonna cry no more / Am I blue / Pennies from heaven / Set me free / Since my man has gone and went / Silent night / Lord's prayer / My man's an undertaker.
**CD:** Released '88, on Official by Official Records. Catalogue no: **OFF 83025**
**Cass:** Released '88, on Official by Official Records. Catalogue no: **OFF 43025**
**Album:** Released '88, on Official by Official Records. Catalogue no: **OFF 3025**

### COMPLETE DINAH WASHINGTON, VOL. 10
Tracks: / Mean and evil / Short John / Old man's darlin' / Love for sale / Our love is here to stay / Such a night / Until sunrise / One Arabian night / I let a song go out of my heart / Foggy day, A / Bye bye blues.
**CD:** Released May '89, on Official by Official Records. Catalogue no: **OFF 83028**
**Album:** Released May '89, on Official by Official Records. Catalogue no: **OFF 3028**
**Cass:** Released May '89, on Official by Official Records. Catalogue no: **OFF 43028**

### COMPLETE DINAH WASHINGTON, VOL. 11
Tracks: / Blues skies / You can't love two / What a great sensation / Raindrops / Big long slidin' thing / Dream / I don't hurt anymore / Soft winds / If it's the last thing I do / Introduction / I've got you under my skin / No more / Darn that dream.
**Album:** Released '89, on Official by Official Records. Catalogue no: **OFF 3036**
**Cass:** Released '89, on Official by Official Records. Catalogue no: **OFF 43036**

### COMPLETE DINAH WASHINGTON, VOL. 12
Tracks: / You go to my head / Lover come back to me / Come rain or come shine / Crazy he calls me / There is no greater love / I'll remember April.
**Album:** Released '89, on Official by Official Records. Catalogue no: **OFF 3040**
**Cass:** Released '89, on Official by Official Records. Catalogue no: **OFF 43040**

### COMPLETE DINAH WASHINGTON, VOL. 13
**Cass:** Released Oct '89, on Official by Official Records. Catalogue no: **OFF 43051**
**Album:** Released Oct '89, on Official by Official Records. Catalogue no: **OFF 3051**

### DINAH JAMS
Tracks: / Lover come back to me / Alone together / Summertime / Come rain or come shine / No more / I've got you under my skin / There is no greater love / You go to my head.
Note: Artists include: Dinah washington, Clifford Brown, Max Roach.
**CD:** Released '84, on Phonogram (Import) Catalogue no: **814 639 2**

### DINAH WASHINGTON
**CD:** Released Oct '88, on Vogue by Vogue Records. Catalogue no: **VGCD 600 183**
**CD:** Released '88, on Mercury by Phonogram Ltd. Catalogue no: **832 573 2**
**Cass:** Released '88, on Mercury by Phonogram Ltd. Catalogue no: **832 573 4**

### DINAH WASHINGTON: HER TOP TEN HITS
**Cass:** Released '88, on Timeless Treasures Catalogue no: **MC 827**

### DINAH WASHINGTON SINGS VOL.1
Tracks: / After you've gone / Send me to the 'lectric chair / Jailhouse blues / Trombone butter / You've been a good ole wagon / Careless love / Back water blues / If I could be with you one hour tonight / Me and my girl / Fine fat daddy.
**Album:** Released Jan '82, on Jazz Reactivation Catalogue no: **JR 117**

### DINAH WASHINGTON SINGS VOL.2
Tracks: / Coquette / Love is the sweetest thing / I didn't know about you / Our love / These foolish things / Make someone happy / I'll close my eyes / Miss you / I left my heart in San Francisco / What kind of fool am I / Handful of stars / Good life / What's new / That Sunday that summer / Red sails in the sunset.
**Album:** Released May '83, on Jazz Reactivation Catalogue no: **JR 135**

### DINAH WASHINGTON AND BROOK BENTON (Washington, Dinah & Brook Benton)
Tracks: / There goes my heart / Call me / Baby (you've got what it takes) / Love walked in / Not one step behind / Rockin' good way, A / Someone to believe in / This I promise you / I do / Because of everything / Again / I believe.
**Cass:** Released Jun '83, on Mercury by Phonogram Ltd. Catalogue no: **7145 181**
**Album:** Released Jun '83, on Mercury by Phonogram Ltd. Catalogue no: **6463 181**

### DRINKING AGAIN
Tracks: / Drinking again / Just friends / I'm gonna laugh you out of my life / I'll be around / Lament (love, I found you gone) / I don't know you anymore / Baby won't you please come home / Lover man (oh, where can you be) / Man that got away, The / For all we know / Say it isn't so / On the street of regret.
**Album:** Released Oct '89, on Roulette (EMI) by EMI Records. Catalogue no: **793 270 1**
**CD:** Released Oct '89, on Roulette (EMI) by EMI Records. Catalogue no: **CDP 793 270 2**
**CD:** Released Oct '89, on Roulette (EMI) by EMI Records. Catalogue no: **CZ 234**
**Album:** Released Oct '89, on Roulette (EMI) by EMI Records. Catalogue no: **ROU 1002**

### FATS WALLER SONGBOOK
Tracks: / Christopher columbus / T'aint nobody's business if I do / Jitterbug waltz / Someone's rocking my dreamboat / Ain't cha glad / Squeeze me / Ain't misbehavin' / Black and blue / Everybody loves my baby / I've got a feeling I'm falling / Honeysuckle rose / Keeping out of mischief.
**Album:** Released Feb '85, on Emarcy Catalogue no: **818 930 1**
**Cass:** Released Feb '85, on Emarcy Catalogue no: **818 930 4**
**CD:** Released Apr '85, on Emarcy Catalogue no: **818 930 2**

**IF YOU DON'T BELIEVE I'M LEAVING**
**Album:** Released Apr '86, on Jukebox Lil (Sweden) Catalogue no: **JB 1102**

**IMMORTAL**
Tracks: / My devotion / Me & the one I love / That (that summer) / Something's got to give / I'm glad for your sake / I'll never stop loving you / To forget about you / Somebody else is taking my place / Don't say nothing at all / Love is the sweetest thing.
**Album:** Released Feb '83, on Carosello Catalogue no: **JLP 1056**

**IN THE LAND OF HI-FI**
**CD:** Released Jul '87, on Philips by Phonogram Ltd. Deleted Nov '88. Catalogue no: **826 453-2**

**JAZZ SIDES THE**
Tracks: / I could write a book / Make the man love me / Blue gardenia / You don't know what love is / My old flame / Blue skies / Lover come back to me / Crazy love / Backwater blues / All of me / Easy living / I get a kick out of you / This can't be love / If I had you / I let a song go out of my heart / Soggy day, A / Bye bye blues.
**Album:** Released Oct '83, on Mercury (USA) by PolyGram Rec.Inc.(USA). Catalogue no: **6641573**

**QUEEN OF THE BLUES (Original Soul Sister, The)**
Tracks: / Look to the rainbow / Ill wind / Cottage for sale / All of me / More than you know / There'll be some changes made / Goodbye / Willow weep for me / Make me a present of you / Smoke gets in your eyes / I could have told you / Accent on youth.
**Album:** Released Jun '88, on Memoir by Memoir Records. Catalogue no: **MOIR 131**
**Cass:** Released Nov '89, on Memoir by Memoir Records. Catalogue no: **CMOIR 131**

**ROCKIN' GOOD WAY (Washington, Dinah & Brook Benton)**
Tracks: / Rockin' good way.
**7" Single:** Released Jul '77, on Mercury by Phonogram Ltd. Catalogue no: **6198 160**

**SEPTEMBER IN THE RAIN**
Tracks: / September in the rain.
**7" Single:** Released Nov '61, on Mercury (EMI) Deleted '64. Catalogue no: **AMT 1162**

**STRANGER ON EARTH, A**
**Album:** Released Jun '88, on Fresh Sounds (Spain) by Fresh Sounds Records (Spain). Catalogue no: **FS 319**

**TWO OF US, THE (Washington, Dinah & Brook Benton)**
Tracks: / Two of us, The / Again / Baby / Because of everything / Call me / I believe / I do / Love walked in / Not one step behind / Rockin' good way, A / Someone to believe in / There goes my heart / This I promise you / Passing strangers / Alexander's ragtime band / All of my life / Always / Cheek to cheek / Easter parade / Girl that I marry, The / Isn't this a lovely day / I've got my love to keep me warm / Now it can be told / Remember / You're just in love.
**2 LP Set:** Released '78, on Mercury by Phonogram Ltd. Catalogue no: **6641 868**
**Cass set:** Released '78, on Mercury by Phonogram Ltd. Catalogue no: **7599 366**

**VERY BEST, THE**
Tracks: / September in the rain / This better Earth / It isn't fair / What a difference a day made / I wanna be loved / I don't hurt anymore / Unforgettable / Dream / Teach me tonight / Baby get lost / Trouble in mind / Make me a present of you / I'll never be free / There is no greater love / Salty papa blues / Tell love hello.
Note: This contains a medley.
**Cass:** Released Jul '84, on Philips (Timeless) by PolyGram UK Ltd. Catalogue no: **TIMEC 05**
**Album:** Released Jul '84, on Philips (Timeless) by PolyGram UK Ltd. Catalogue no: **TIME 05**

**WHAT A DIFFERENCE A DAY MADE**
Tracks: / I remember you / I thought about you / That's all there is to that / I'm through with love / Cry me a river / What a difference a day made / Nothing in the world (could make me love you more than I do) / Manhattan / Time after time / Its magic / Sunday kind of love, A / I won't cry anymore.
**CD:** Released Oct '84, on Mercury by Phonogram Ltd. Catalogue no: **818 815 2**

## Washington, Grover Jr

**Biographical details:** This American saxophonist began to make waves in the early Seventies. After scoring successes on the US jazz charts, he achieved a major Top 10 pop crossover album with 1975's *Feels so good*, which logged 30 weeks on the US album chart. This led him to become one of the most in-demand guest players on albums by such talents as Eric Gale, Bob James, and Ralph Macdonald. After a brief spell with Motown Records, Washington found his biggest success with Elektra Records in 1981. His *Winelight* album was one of the all time best sellers on the Billboard jazz listings, and reached the Top 10 of the US pop album chart. The LP was fuelled by its smash single *Just the two of us*, which featured the vocal prowess of Bill Withers; this laid back single, a sleek jazz-soul fusion, cruised to No.2 in America. In Britain, *Just the two of us* and *Winelight* peaked at No.34 on their respective charts - in each case, this represented the saxman's first foray into the UK listings.

Having reached the pinnacle of his career with *Winelight*, Washington's crossover appeal gradually lessened. His follow up albums, *Come morning* and *The best is yet to come* (the latter featured vocals by Patti Labelle), saw this classy instrumentalist veering dangerously towards the realms of supermarket muzak. (Bob MacDonald, 5th May 1985)

Washington, Grover Jr was born in 1943 in Bufallo, New York. Saxophonist, playing all the reeds; began in a jazz style, becoming more MoR with much commercial success. He worked with organ trios and rock bands, played on Randy Weston's *Blue Moses*; his own LPs began to chart in 1972 with *Inner City Blues*, reaching top 10 with *Mister Magic* and *Feels So Good* in 1975; double *Live At The Bijou* in 1978 was a hit; biggest was *Winelight*, number 5 LP with smooth vocals by Bill Withers(*Just The Two of Us*, number 2 USA single in 1981). (Donald Clarke 21/5/88).

**ALL THE KING'S HORSES**
Tracks: / No tears / In the end / All the king's horses / Where is the love? / Body and soul / Lean on me / Lover man / Interlude No. 2 / Love song 1700.
**Cass:** Released Mar '82, on Motown by BMG Records (UK). Catalogue no: **CSTMS 5056**
**Album:** Released Mar '82, on Motown by BMG Records (UK). Catalogue no: **STMS 5056**

**ANTHOLOGY (ELEKTRA): GROVER WASHINGTON JR.**
Tracks: / Best is yet to come, The / East River drive / Be mine tonight / Can you dig it? / In the name of love / Just the two of us / Jammin' / Little black samba / Jet stream / Let it flow.
**Album:** Released Nov '85, on Elektra by Elektra Records (UK). Catalogue no: **EKT 17**
**Cass:** Released Nov '85, on Elektra by Elektra Records (UK). Catalogue no: **EKT 17C**
**CD:** Released '89, on Elektra by Elektra Records (UK). Catalogue no: **960 415 2**

**ANTHOLOGY (MOTOWN): GROVER WASHINGTON JR.**
Tracks: / Inner city blues / Mercy mercy me / Where is the love? / Mr. Magic / It feels so good / Secret place / Masterpiece / Trouble man / Summer song / Santa Cruzin' / Snake eyes.
**Album:** Released Sep '82, on Motown by BMG Records (UK). Catalogue no: **TMSP 6015**
**Album:** Released '86, on Motown by BMG Records (UK). Catalogue no: **ZL 72168**
**Cass:** Released Sep '82, on Motown by BMG Records (UK). Catalogue no: **CTMSP 6015**

**AT HIS BEST**
Tracks: / It feels so good / Mister magic / Do dat / Summer song / Secret place / Ain't no sunshine / Masterpiece.
**CD:** Released Apr '85, on Motown by BMG Records (UK). Catalogue no: **WD 72366**

**BADDEST**
Tracks: / Black frost / Do dat / Summer song / Secret place / Ain't no sunshine / Mercy mercy me / It feels so good / Mr. Magic / No tears in the end / Inner city

blues / Lean on me / Masterpiece.
**Album:** Released Oct '81, on Motown by BMG Records (UK). Catalogue no: **TMSP 6011**
**Cass:** Released Oct '81, on Motown by BMG Records (UK). Catalogue no: **CTSMP 6011**

**BE MINE**
Tracks: / Be mine / Little black samba.
**7" Single:** Released Feb '82, on Elektra by Elektra Records (UK). Catalogue no: **K 12600**

**BEST IS YET TO COME**
Tracks: / Can you dig it? / Best is yet to come, The / More than meets the eye / Things are getting better / Mixed emotions / Brazilian memories / I'll be with you / Cassie's theme.
**Album:** Released Jan '83, on Elektra by Elektra Records (UK). Catalogue no: **E 0215**
**CD:** Released Feb '87, on Elektra by Elektra Records (UK). Catalogue no: **960 215-2**
**Cass:** Released Jan '83, on Elektra by Elektra Records (UK). Catalogue no: **E 02154**

**COME MORNING**
Tracks: / East River drive / Come morning / Be mine (tonight) / Reaching out / Jamming / Little black samba / Making love to you / I'm all yours.
**Album:** Released Nov '81, on Elektra by Elektra Records (UK). Catalogue no: **K 52337**
**CD:** Released Apr '84, on Elektra by Elektra Records (UK). Catalogue no: **252 337**
**Cass:** Released Nov '81, on Elektra by Elektra Records (UK). Catalogue no: **K4 52337**

**DO DAT**
Tracks: / Do dat / Reed seed.
**7" Single:** Released Jan '79, on Motown by BMG Records (UK). Deleted '83. Catalogue no: **TMG 1131**

**FEELS SO GOOD**
Tracks: / Sea lion / Knucklehead / Moonstreams / Feels so good / Hydra.
**Album:** Released Aug '88, on Motown by BMG Records (UK). Deleted Jun '89. Catalogue no: **WL 72080**
**Album:** Released Oct '81, on Motown by BMG Records (UK). Deleted '86. Catalogue no: **STMS 5028**
**CD:** Released Aug '88, on Motown by BMG Records (UK). Catalogue no: **WD 72080**
**Cass:** Released Oct '81, on Motown by BMG Records (UK). Deleted '86. Catalogue no: **CSTMS 5028**

**GREATEST PERFORMANCES**
Tracks: / Mr. Magic / It feels so good / Secret place / Do dat / Lean on me.
**Cass:** Released Jun '83, on Motown by BMG Records (UK). Catalogue no: **CSTMS 5099**
**Album:** Released Jun '83, on Motown by BMG Records (UK). Catalogue no: **STMS 5099**
**Cass:** Released '86, on Motown by BMG Records (UK). Catalogue no: **WK 72125**
**Album:** Released '86, on Motown by BMG Records (UK). Catalogue no: **WL 72125**

**INNER CITY BLUES**
Tracks: / Inner city blues / Georgia on my mind / Mercy mercy me / Ain't no sunshine / Better days / Until it's time for you to go / I loves you, Porgy.
**Album:** Released Feb '88, on Motown by BMG Records (UK). Catalogue no: **WL 72098**
**Cass:** Released Feb '88, on Motown by BMG Records (UK). Catalogue no: **WK 72098**
**CD:** Released Feb '88, on Motown by BMG Records (UK). Catalogue no: **WD 72098**
**Album:** Released Mar '82, on Motown by BMG Records (UK). Catalogue no: **STMS 5055**
**Cass:** Released Mar '82, on Motown by BMG Records (UK). Catalogue no: **CSTMS 5055**

**INSIDE MOVES**
Tracks: / Inside moves / Dawn song / Watching you watching me / Secret sounds / Jet stream / When I look at you / Sassy stew.
**Album:** Released Oct '84, on Elektra by Elektra Records (UK). Catalogue no: **960 318-1**
**Cass:** Released Oct '84, on Elektra by Elektra Records (UK). Deleted Aug '87. Catalogue no: **960 318-4**
**CD:** Released Feb '87, on Elektra by Elektra Records (UK). Catalogue no: **960 318-2**

**JAMMING**
Tracks: / Jamming / East River drive.
**7" Single:** Released Apr '82, on Elektra by Elektra Records (UK). Catalogue no: **K 13161**

**JUST THE TWO OF US**
Tracks: / Just the two of us / Make me a memory.
**7" Single:** Released May '81, on Elektra by Elektra Records (UK). Deleted '84. Catalogue no: **K 12514**

**JUST THE WAY YOU ARE**
Tracks: / Just the way you are / Lorans dance.
**7" Single:** Released Oct '81, on Motown by BMG Records (UK). Catalogue no: **TMG 1153**

**LET IT FLOW (FOR DR J)**
Tracks: / Let it flow / Winelight.
**12" Single:** Released Dec '80, on Asylum by WEA Records. Catalogue no: **K 12495T**
**7" Single:** Released Dec '80, on Asylum by WEA Records. Catalogue no: **K 12495**

**LIVE AT THE BIJOU**
Tracks: / On the cusp / You make me dance / Lock it in the pocket / Sausalito / Funkfoot / Summer song / Juffure / Days in our lives / Mr. Magic.
**Cass set:** Released Jun '86, on Motown by BMG Records (UK). Catalogue no: **WK 72267**
**2 LP Set:** Released Jun '86, on Motown by BMG Records (UK). Catalogue no: **WL 72267**

**MISTER MAGIC**
Tracks: / Earth tones / Passion flower / Mister magic / Black frost.
**Cass:** Released Oct '81, on Motown by BMG Records (UK). Catalogue no: **CSTMS 5027**
**Album:** Released Oct '81, on Motown by BMG Records (UK). Catalogue no: **STMS 5027**

**MISTER MAGIC/FEELS SO GOOD (2 classic albums)**
Tracks: / Earth tones / Passion flower / Mister Magic / Black frost / Sea lion, The / Moonstreams / Knucklehead / It feels so good / Hydra.
**CD:** Released Nov '86, on Motown by BMG Records (UK). Catalogue no: **ZD 72452**

**MISTER MAGIC (SINGLE)**
Tracks: / Mister Magic / Sausalito.
**7" Single:** Released Oct '80, on Kudu Deleted Oct '83. Catalogue no: **KUDUX 100**

**PARADISE**
Tracks: / Paradise / Icey / Answer in your eyes, The / Asia's theme / Shana / Tell me about it / Feel it comin'.
**CD:** Released Jul '87, on Elektra by Elektra Records (UK). Catalogue no: **K 252 130**
**Album:** Released Jun '79, on Elektra by Elektra Records (UK). Catalogue no: **K 52 130**

**PLAYBOY JAZZ FESTIVAL (Washington Grover, Jr & Weather Report)**
**Album:** Released May '84, on Elektra by Elektra Records (UK). Catalogue no: **960298-1**

**REED SEED**
Tracks: / Do dat / Step 'n' thru / Reed seed / Maracas beach / Santa Cruzin' / Just the way you are / Loran's dance.
**Cass:** Released '86, on Motown by BMG Records (UK). Catalogue no: **WK 72106**
**Album:** Released '86, on Motown by BMG Records (UK). Catalogue no: **WL 72106**
**Cass:** Released Jun '82, on Motown by BMG Records (UK). Catalogue no: **CSTMS 5072**
**Album:** Released Jun '82, on Motown by BMG Records (UK). Catalogue no: **STMS 5072**

**SECRET PLACE, A**
Tracks: / Secret place / Dolphine dance / Not yet / Love makes it better.
**Cass:** Released Oct '81, on Motown by BMG Records (UK). Deleted '86. Catalogue no: **CSTMS 5029**
**Album:** Released '86, on Motown by BMG Records (UK). Deleted Jun '89. Catalogue no: **WL 70281**
**Album:** Released Oct '81, on Motown by BMG Records (UK). Deleted '86. Catalogue no: **STMS 5029**

**SECRET PLACE, A/ALL THE KING'S HORSES (2 Classic albums)**
Tracks: / Secret place / Dolphin dance / Not yet / Love makes it better / No tears, in the end / All the king's horses / Where is the love / Body and soul / Lean on me / Lover man / Love song 1700.
**CD:** Released Jan '87, on Motown by BMG Records (UK). Catalogue no: **ZD 72494**

**SKYLARKIN'**
Tracks: / Easy loving you / Bright moments / Snake eyes / I can't help it / Love / Open up your mind.
**Album:** Released Apr '80, on Motown by BMG Records (UK). Catalogue no: **STML 12131**
**Album:** Released Sep '82, on Motown by BMG Records (UK). Deleted Jan '88. Catalogue no: **STMS 5072**
**Cass:** Released Apr '84, on Motown by BMG Records (UK). Catalogue no: **WK 72107**
**Album:** Released Apr '84, on Motown by BMG Records (UK). Catalogue no: **WL 72107**

**STRAWBERRY MOON**
Tracks: / Strawberry moon / Look of love, The / Shivaree Ride / Caught a touch of your love / Maddie's Blues / I will be here for you / Keep in touch / Summer nights.
**Cass:** Released Aug '87, on CBS by CBS Records. Catalogue no: **450464 4**
**CD:** Released Sep '87, on CBS by CBS Records. Catalogue no: **450 464 2**
**Album:** Released Aug '87, on CBS by CBS Records. Deleted Jan '90. Catalogue no: **450464 1**

**THEN AND NOW**
Tracks: / Blues for D.P. / Just enough / French connections / Something borrowed, something blue / Lullaby for Shana Bly / In a sentimental mood / Stella by starlight.
**CD:** Released Oct '88, on CBS by CBS Records. Catalogue no: **462516 2**
**Cass:** Released Oct '88, on CBS by CBS Records. Catalogue no: **462516 4**
**Album:** Released Oct '88, on CBS by CBS Records. Catalogue no: **462516 1**
**Album:** Released Jul '88, on CBS by CBS Records. Catalogue no: **OC 44256**

**TIME OUT OF MIND**
**CD:** Released Oct '89, on CBS by CBS Records. Catalogue no: **465 526 2**
**Cass:** Released Oct '89, on CBS by CBS Records. Catalogue no: **465 526 4**
**Album:** Released ct '89, on CBS by CBS Records. Catalogue no: **465 526 1**

**WINELIGHT**
Tracks: / Winelight / Let it flow / In the name of love / Take me there / Just the two of us / Make me a memory (sad samba).
**Album:** Released Nov '80, on Asylum by WEA Records. Catalogue no: **K 52262**
**CD:** Released Nov '80, on Asylum by WEA Records. Catalogue no: **252 262**

**WINELIGHT/PARADISE**
**Cass:** Released Oct '82, on Elektra by Elektra Records (UK). Deleted Sep '87. Catalogue no: **K4 62039**

## Watanabe, Kazumi

**BEST PERFORMANCE, THE**
Tracks: / Unicorn / Village in bubbles / Kylyn / Talk you all night / Olive's step / Lonesome cat / To Chi Ka / Please don't bundle me.
Note: Japanese guitarist, Kazumi Watanbe is able in this recording - one of many from Denon - to display not only his prowess on the instrumental but also his creativity as a composer and clearly demonstrates his diverse styles in numbers such as *(Village in bubbles)* and *(To chi ka)*. (Denon 10/88)
**Cass:** Released Oct '88, on Denon Catalogue no: **CC 19**
**CD:** Released Oct '88, on Denon Catalogue no: **C38 7581**

**KILOWATT**
Tracks: / 100 mega / Capri / No one / Jive / Papyrus / Sunspin / Pretty soon / Bernard / Dolphin dance / Good night machines.
**Cass:** Released Mar '90, on Gramavision Catalogue no: **794 154**
**Album:** Released Mar '90, on Gramavision Catalogue no: **794 151**
**CD:** Released Mar '90, on Gramavision Catalogue no: **794 152**

**KYLYN**
Tracks: / 199X / Sonic boom / Water ways flow backward again / Milestones / E-day project / Project / Akasaka moon / Kylyn / I'll be there / Mother Terra.
Note: Personnel: Kazumi Watanabe (Guitar), Ryuichi Sakamoto (Keyboard) and others.
**CD:** Released '88, on Denon Catalogue no: **C38-7135**

**LONESOME CAT**
Tracks: / Somebody, somebody / Mirrors / Aqua beauty / Blackstone / Moving nozzle / Lonesome cat.
Note: Recorded at Sound Ideas Studio, New York City, 14th December 1977. Personnel: Kazumi Watanabe (Guitar), George Cabels (Piano / Electric Piano), Cecil McBee (Bass), Lenny White (Drums).
**CD:** Released Feb '82, on Denon Catalogue no: **C38 7017**
**Album:** Released Feb '82, on Denon Deleted '88. Catalogue no: **YX 7525**

**MOBO 1**
Tracks: / Walk, don't run / Half blood / Yenshu tsubame gaeshi / American shorthair / Mobo 2.
Note: Kazumi Watanabe, electric, acoustic guitar, synthesizer, fake log drums, percussion; Michael Brecker, tenor sax; Don Grolnick, organ, synthesizer; Kei Akagi, piano, fake marimba; Robbie Shakespere, Marcus Miller, bass; Sly Dunbar, Omar Hakim, Steve Jordan, drums.
**Cass:** Released Oct '84, on Gramavision Catalogue no: **GRC 8404**
**Album:** Released Oct '84, on Gramavision Catalogue no: **GR 8404**

**MOBO 2**
Tracks: / Voyage / Yatokesa / Alicia / Shang hi / All beets are coming.
Note: Kazumi Watanabe, guitars, synthesizer, drums; Michael Brecker, tenor sax; Don Grolnick, organ, synthesizer; Kei Akagi, piano, fake marimba; Robbie Shakespere, Marcus Miller, bass; Sly Dunbar, Omar Hakim, Steve Jordan, drums.
**CD:** Released May '85, on Gramavision Catalogue no: **GRCD 8406**
**Album:** Released Feb '85, on Gramavision Catalogue no: **GR 8406**

**MOBO CLUB**
**CD:** Released May '89, on Gaia (UK) by Gaia Records (UK). Catalogue no: **188 506 2**
**Cass:** Released May '89, on Gaia (UK) by Gaia Records (UK). Catalogue no: **188 506 4**
**Album:** Released May '89, on Gaia (UK) by Gaia Records (UK). Catalogue no: **188 506 1**

**MOBO SPLASH**
**Cass:** Released May '89, on Gaia (UK) by Gaia Records (UK). Catalogue no: **188 602 4**
**Album:** Released May '89, on Gaia (UK) by Gaia Records (UK). Catalogue no: **188 602 1**
**CD:** Released May '89, on Gaia (UK) by Gaia Records (UK). Catalogue no: **188 602 2**

**SPICE OF LIFE**
**CD:** Released 30 Apr '88, on Sonet by Sonet Records. Catalogue no: **SNTCD 995**

**SPICE OF LIFE TOO**
Tracks: / Andre / Fu bu ki / Small wonder / Kaimon / We planet / Rain / Concrete cows / Men and angels.
**Cass:** Released Dec '88, on Gramavision Catalogue no: **1888104**
**Album:** Released Dec '88, on Gramavision Catalogue no: **1888101**
**CD:** Released Dec '88, on Gramavision Catalogue no: **1888102**

**TO CHI KA**
Tracks: / Liquid fingers / Black canal / To chi ka / Cokumo island / Unicorn / Don't be silly / Sayonara / Manhattan flu dance.
Note: Personnel: Kazumi Watanabe (Guitar), Mike Mainieri (Vibe), Peter Earskin (Drums), Steve Jordan (Drums), Marcus Miller (Bass), and others.
**CD:** Released '88, on Denon Catalogue no: **C38-7136**

## Watanabe, Sadao

**BOSSA NOVA CONCERT**
Tracks: / Feliciadade / Meditation / Song of Jet, The / Bonita / Train samba / Doralici / O grande amor / You and I / Girl from Ipanema, The / Agua de beber / Raza / Corcovado feliciadade / Music break / Mais que nada / I might as well as spring / Samba de orfe / So danco samba / Falicidade.
**CD:** Released Oct '89, on Denon Cata-

logue no: **DC 8556**

**CALIFORNIA SHOWER**
**Album:** Released Jun '79, on Miracle by Gull Records. Deleted '88. Catalogue no: **MLP 3005**

**DEDICATED TO CHARLIE PARKER**
Tracks: / Parker's mood / Song for Bird, A / Everything happens to me / I can't get started / Au privave / If I should lose you.
Note: Personnel: Sadao Watanabe (Alto sax), Kazuo Yashiro (Piano), Masanaga Harada (Bass), Fumio Watanabe (Drums), Terumasa Hino (Trumpet). Recorded during concert performance in Tokyo, 1969.
**CD:** Released Oct '89, on Denon Catalogue no: **DC 8558**
**CD:** Released '88, on Denon Catalogue no: **C38 7689**

**DUO CREATURES**
Tracks: / Duo creatures / Turning pages of wind.
**7" Single:** Released Oct '79, on Miracle by Gull Records. Deleted '88. Catalogue no: **M 12**

**FILL UP THE NIGHT**
**Album:** Released Mar '84, on WEA by WEA Records. Catalogue no: **250161 1**

**GOOD TIME FOR LOVE**
Tracks: / Good time for love / Love birds whisper in my ear / When we make a home / Step out on the street / I love to say your name / Pogo / All the way / Loving you is easy.
**Album:** Released Aug '86, on WEA by WEA Records. Catalogue no: **253037 1**
**CD:** Released Aug '86, on WEA by WEA Records. Catalogue no: **253037 2**
**Cass:** Released Aug '86, on WEA by WEA Records. Catalogue no: **253037 4**

**IF I'M STILL AROUND TOMORROW**
Tracks: / If I'm still around tomorrow / Maravelle.
**7" Single:** Released Oct '84, on WEA (International) by WEA Records. Catalogue no: **U 9261**
**12" Single:** Released Oct '84, on WEA (International) by WEA Records. Catalogue no: **U 9261 T**

**JAZZ AND BOSSA**
Tracks: / America / Taboo / In the wee small hours of the morning / I mean you / Van music break, Theme from / Raza / Song of the jet / Felicidade / Cupid's song / Forgive me if I'm late / Morning of the carnival.
Note: Personnel: Sadao Watanabe (Alto sax / Flute), Masabumi Kikuchi (Piano), Sadanori Nakamura (Guitar), Eijiro Hagiwara (Bass), Masahiko Togashi (Drums), Hideo Miyata.
**CD:** Released May '86, on Denon Deleted '88. Catalogue no: **C38-7870**

**LIVE AT THE BUDOKAN**
Tracks: / Up country / Mzuri / Tsumagoi / All about love / Nice shot / Seeing you / No problem / Boa noite / Sun dance / M & M Studio / My dear life.
**Album:** Released Jan '81, on CBS by CBS Records. Catalogue no: **CBS 22081**

**MAISHA**
Tracks: / What's now? / Men and women / Road song / Times we shared / Good news / Desert ride / Tip away / Stray birds / Maisha / Paysages.
**Album:** Released Jul '85, on WEA by WEA Records. Deleted Aug '87. Catalogue no: **252194 1**

**MODERN JAZZ ALBUM**
Tracks: / Going home / My favourite things / From Russia with love / And I love / There's no business like show business / Days of wine and roses / Emily / Shadow of your smile / I feel pretty / I could have danced all night.
Note: Personnel: Sadao Watanabe (Alto sax), Toshiyuki Miyama & His New Herd, Kazuo Yashiro & His Trio.
**CD:** Released '88, on Denon Catalogue no: **CY-1386**

**NO PROBLEM**
Tracks: / No problem / All about love.
**7" Single:** Released Nov '80, on CBS by CBS Records. Deleted Nov '83. Catalogue no: **CBS 9348**

**ORANGE EXPRESS**
Tracks: / Orange express / Ride on / Call me / Good for all night / Bagamoyo / Zanzibar / Straight to the top / Mbla I Africa.
**Album:** Released Nov '81, on CBS by CBS Records. Deleted Nov '86. Catalogue no: **CBS 85304**

**PLAYS BALLADS**
Tracks: / Here's that rainy day / My foolish heart / I thought about you / Old folks / Spring is here / Little girl blue / That's all / They say it's wonderful / My romance / Nightingale sang in Berkley Square / It's easy to remember.
Note: Personnel: Sadao Watanabe (Alto sax), Masabumi Kikuchi (Piano), Masanaga Harada (Bass), Masahiko Togashi (Drums).
**CD:** Released '88, on Denon Catalogue no: **CY-1381**
**CD:** Released Oct '89, on Denon Catalogue no: **DC 8555**

**RENDEZVOUS**
**Album:** Released Sep '84, on WEA by WEA Records. Deleted Aug '87. Catalogue no: **250804 1**

**SADAO MEETS BRAZILIAN FRIENDS**
Tracks: / Bim bom / E nada mais / Jequibau / Eu e a brisa / Barquinho diferente / Ritmo / Tristeza / Carolina / Bossa na praia / Mostra morena / Muito a vontade.
Note: Sadao Watanabe (Alto sax) plus Brazilian 8. Recorded in Sao-Paulo, in July 1968.
**CD:** Released Oct '89, on Denon Catalogue no: **DC 8557**
**CD:** Released '88, on Denon Deleted '88. Catalogue no: **C38-7871**

## Waters, Benny

**ON THE SUNNY SIDE OF THE STREET**
**Album:** Released Sep '81, on JSP by JSP Records. Catalogue no: **JSP 1027**

**TRUE SIDE OF**
**Album:** Released '88, on Kenneth Catalogue no: **KS 2041**

## Waters, Ethel

**Biographical details:** Ethel Waters (1900-77) was a much-loved actress and singer who became typed as a blues singer but eventually had an influence much wider than that. Twenty-five hits between 1921 and 1934 included many show songs, and *Stormy Weather*, in '33, hit No 1. She appeared in many shows and films, and won awards as a straight actress though usually forced, as a black woman, to play maids. She was said to be the first black woman to star in a network radio show in 1933 and to appear on television in 1939. Her 1951 autobiography, His Eye Is On The Sparrow, was a best-seller. (Donald Clarke, March 1988.).

**1938-39 (The Complete Bluebird Sessions)**
Note: Mono
**Album:** Released Oct '86, on Rosetta (USA) Catalogue no: **RR 1314**

**ETHEL WATERS**
**Album:** Released Mar '79, on Monmouth Evergreen Catalogue no: **MES 6812**

**ETHEL WATERS (GLENDALE)**
Tracks: / Cabin in the sky / Dinah / Summertime blues / Am I blue?.
Note: Tracks include those listed above.
**Album:** Released Jul '88, on Glendale (USA) by Glendale Records (USA). Catalogue no: **GL 9011**

**FOREMOTHERS VOL. 6**
**Cass:** Released Dec '86, on Rosetta (USA) Catalogue no: **RC 1314**

**NO-ONE CAN LOVE ME**
Note: Mono
**Cass:** Released Jul '86, on Emporium Cassettes Catalogue no: **041**

**STAGE AND SCREEN 1925-1940**
**Album:** Released Jan '89, on Silva Screen by Silva Screen Records. Catalogue no: **CCL 2792**

**WATERS, ETHEL: ON THE AIR**
Tracks: / Taking your time / Darkies never dream / Them green pastures / There'll be some changes made / Stormy weather / Woman without a man, A / Dinah / St Louis blues / Smoke gets in your eyes / Summertime / Can't help lovin' dat man / Sometimes I feel like a motherless child / Happiness is just a thing called Joe.
**Album:** Released Oct '86, on Totem Catalogue no: **TOTEM 1041**

**WHO SAID BLACKBIRDS ARE BLUE ?**
**Album:** Released Jan '89, on Silva Screen by Silva Screen Records. Catalogue no: **SH 2060**

## Waters, Muddy

**Biographical details:** Born McKinley Morganfield in Mississippi in 1915,

Muddy Waters was, by the time he died in 1983, in Chicago, the greatest and most influential bluesman between the classic era of Robert Johnson and the later success of B.B. King. A singer, guitarist and composer, he got his nickname from playing in a muddy creek as a child. He was recorded by John Lomax at Stovall's Plantation in 1941-42, moving to Chicago in 1943. A master of slide guitar, he switched to electric guitar the following year. He played clubs and party nights, worked in a paper mill and drove a truck. He first recorded for Okeh in '46 (unreleased until the anthology,*Okeh Chicago Blues*, in '81) then, also in '46, for Aristocrat, which became Chess two years later. Waters never had all that many R & B chart entries: his classics --*I Love The Life I Live,Rock Me,Got My Mojo Working,She's Got It,She's Nineteen Years Old*-- all came in 1957,*Baby Please Don't Go*in '58, but none charted. His music was too tough and uncompromising at a time when rhythm-and-blues was becoming slicker. He first visited Britain in 1958 and discovered his international fame. He was the king of an important new genre: Chicago blues, amplified to cut through the din in South Side taverns, was directly descended from the classic era of the rural south and was a huge influence on the rock of the 60's. White American kids heard these strange records on the radio and were enchanted by a mysterious world they could never hope to enter, but English youngsters were bolder, if only out of naivety. The Rolling Stones named themselves after a 1950 R & B hit and Waters later said: "They stole my music but they gave me my name". Early Muddy Waters classics were all on Chess, reissued by PRT and Vogue. From his middle period Electric Mud was widely considered a disaster, but the double Fathers And Sons in '69 was much better, with Otis Spann on piano, Sam Lay on drums, young white acolytes Paul Butterfield, Michael Bloomfield, Donald "Duck" Dunn and other guests. *Mud In Your Ear*from '67 on Muse included a classic line-up;*They Call Me Muddy Waters*('71) won the first of several Grammies; The London Muddy Waters Sessions in '72 was highly rated. He left Chess in the mid-70's and made several fine albums on Blue Sky. (Donald Clarke, March 1988.).

**20 BLUES CLASSICS**

**CD:** Released Jan '90, on Mainline (2) by Mainline Records. Catalogue no: **265 223 2**

**Album:** Released Jan '90, on Mainline (2) by Mainline Records. Catalogue no: **265 233 1**

**Cass:** Released Jan '90, on Mainline (2) by Mainline Records. Catalogue no: **265 233 4**

**AT NEWPORT 1960**

**Album:** Released '88, on Blues Rock Project Catalogue no: **BRP 2026**

**BACK IN THE EARLY DAYS VOL.1 AND 2**

Tracks: / I feel like going home / Mean red spider / You're gonna miss me / Muddy jumps one / Streamline women / Evan shuffle / Country boy / All night long / Baby please don't go / My fault / Gone to main street / Please have mercy / She's all / Who's gonna be your sweet man / Sad sad day / Lovin' man / I'm a natural born lover / Blow wind blow / Oh yeah / She's so pretty / I don't know why / Ooh wee / Young fashioned ways / Clouds in my heart / I want to be loved / My eyes keep me in trouble / I got to find my baby / Sugar sweet.

**2 LP Set:** Released Sep '82, on Syndicate Chapter Deleted Jun '89. Catalogue no: **SC 001/2**

**BEST OF MUDDY WATERS**

Tracks: / I just want to make love to you / Long distance call / Louisiana blues / Honey bee / Rollin' stone / I'm ready / Hoochie coochie / She moves me / I want you to love me / Standing around crying / Still a fool / I can't be satisfied.

**CD:** Released Jun '88, on MCA (USA) by MCA Records (USA). Catalogue no: **31268**

**Album:** Released Oct '87, on Chess by Vogue Records. Catalogue no: **GCH 8044**

**Cass:** Released Oct '87, on Chess by Vogue Records. Catalogue no: **GCHK 78044**

**BEST OF MUDDY WATERS (VOGUE)**

**Album:** Released Jul '84, on Vogue (France) by Vogue Records. Catalogue no: **515038**

**CAN'T GET NO GRINDIN'**

Tracks: / Can't get no grindin' / Mothers bad luck / Funky butt / Sad letter / Someday I'm gonna ketch you / Love weapon / Garbage man / After hours / Whiskey ain't no good / Muddy Waters' shuffle.

**Album:** Released '89, on Chess by Vogue Records. Catalogue no: **LPM 7002**

**CHESS MASTERS: MUDDY WATERS**

Tracks: / I just wanna love make to you / Rollin' stone / I'm ready / Hoochie coochie / Just to be with you / Gypsy woman / Louisiana blues / Mannish boy / Long distance call / Same thing / Rollin' and a tumblin' / She loves me / 40 days and 40 nights / Canary bird.

**Cass:** Released 19 Mar '88, on Stylus by Stylus Music Records. Catalogue no: **SMC 850**

**Album:** Released 19 Mar '88, on Stylus by Stylus Music Records. Catalogue no: **SMR 850**

**CD:** Released '88, on Stylus by Stylus Music Records. Catalogue no: **SMD 850**

**CHESS MASTERS - MUDDY WATERS 1**

**2 LP Set:** Released Apr '81, on Checker (USA) Catalogue no: **CXMD 4000**

**CHESS MASTERS - MUDDY WATERS 2**

Tracks: / Sad letter / Gonna need my help / Whiskey blues / Down South blues / Train fare blues / Kind hearted woman / Hello little girl / Early morning blues / Too young to know / She's all right / Landlady / Baby please don't go / I feel like going home / You're gonna miss me / Mean red spider / Burying around / Stuff you gotta watch / Where's my woman been / Lonesome day / Who's gonna be your sweet man / Gone to main street / Iodine in my coffee / Flood / Last time I fool around with you.

**2 LP Set:** Released Apr '82, on Chess (USA) Catalogue no: **CXMD 4006**

**CHESS MASTERS - MUDDY WATERS 3**

Tracks: / My fault / They call me Muddy Waters / All night long / Please have mercy / Sad sad day / Blow wind blow / She's so pretty / Oh yeah / I don't know why / I'm a natural born lover / Ooh wee / Young fashioned ways / I want to be loved / All aboard / Don't go no further / I love the life I live / Got my mojo working / Nineteen years old / Close to you / I wanna put a tiger in your tank / Meanest woman / You shook me / You need love / Five long years.

**Album:** Released May '83, on Chess (USA) Catalogue no: **CXMD 4015**

**CHICAGO BLUES**

Tracks: / Rollin' stone / Louisiana blues / Long distance call / Honey bee / I want you to love me / I just want to make love to you / I'm your hoochie coochie man / Mannish boy / I'm ready / Forty days and forty nights / She's alright / Walkin' blues / She moves me / Still a fool.

**Album:** Released Jul '89, on Instant (2) by Charly Records. Catalogue no: **INS 5003**

**CD:** Released Jul '89, on Instant (2) by Charly Records. Catalogue no: **CDINS 5003**

**Cass:** Released Jul '89, on Instant (2) by Charly Records. Catalogue no: **TCINS 5003**

**CHICAGO GOLDEN YEARS VOL.1**

**2 LP Set:** Released Oct '88, on Vogue by Vogue Records. Catalogue no: **427005**

**CHICAGO GOLDEN YEARS VOL.2**

**2 LP Set:** Released Oct '88, on Vogue by Vogue Records. Catalogue no: **427015**

**COLLECTION: MUDDY WATERS (20 blues greats)**

Tracks: / Baby please don't go / Got my mojo working / Rollin' stone / Mean mistreater / Rock me / Mean red spider / Forty days and forty nights / Stuff you gotta watch / All aboard / Lonesome room blues / Please have mercy / She's alright / Iodine in my coffee / Rollin' and tumblin' / I'm ready / You gonna miss me / Sad sad day / Oh yeah / I can't call her Sugar / I feel so good.

**Album:** Released Nov '85, on Deja Vu Catalogue no: **DVLP 2034**

**Cass:** Released Aug '85, on Deja Vu Catalogue no: **DVMC 2034**

**CD:** Released Aug '87, on Deja Vu Catalogue no: **DVCD 2034**

**DOWN ON STOVALL'S PLANTATION**
**Album:** Released May '86, on Testament Catalogue no: **T 2210**

**FATHERS AND SONS (CHARLY) (Waters, Muddy & Michael Bloomfield)**
**CD:** Released May '89, on Charly by Charly Records. Catalogue no: **CDRED 9**

**FATHERS AND SONS (CHESS) (Waters, Muddy & Michael Bloomfield)**
Tracks: / All aboard / Mean disposition / Blow wind blow / Can't lose what you ain't never had / Walkin' through the park / Forty days and forty nights / Standin' round crying / I'm ready / Twenty four hours / Sugar sweet / Long distance call / Baby please don't go / Honey bee / Same thing, The / Got my Mojo working (Part 1) / Got my Mojo working (Part 2).
Note: A star-studded live spectacular from the late sixties, featuring Buddy Mills, Phil Upchurch and Paul Butterfield, to name but three.
**CD:** Released Sep '88, on Chess by Vogue Records. Catalogue no: **CDRED 8**
**2 LP Set:** Released Dec '85, on Chess (PRT) Deleted '88. Catalogue no: **6 28593**

**FATHERS AND SONS (VOGUE) (Waters, Muddy & Michael Bloomfield)**
**CD:** Released Feb '89, on Vogue by Vogue Records. Catalogue no: **VGCD 600134**

**FOLK SINGER**
**Album:** Released Oct '88, on Vogue (France) by Vogue Records. Catalogue no: **515016**

**FOLK SINGERS**
Tracks: / My home is in the delta / Long distance / My captain / Good morning little schoolgirl / Your gonna need my help / Cold weather blues / Beg leg woman / Country boy / Feel like going home.
**Album:** Released Oct '87, on Chess by Vogue Records. Catalogue no: **GCH 8040**
**Cass:** Released Oct '87, on Chess by Vogue Records. Catalogue no: **GCHK 78040**

**GOOD NEWS VOL.3**
Tracks: / Trouble no more / Don't go no further / Diamonds at your feet / Evil / All aboard / I love the life I live / Mean mistreater / Recipe for love / Good news / Come home baby / I won't go / She's got it / Close to you.
**Album:** Released Sep '82, on Syndicate Chapter Deleted Jun '89. Catalogue no: **SC 002**

**HARD AGAIN**
Tracks: / Mannish boy / Bus driver / I want to be loved / Jealous-hearted man / I can't be satisfied / Blues had a baby and they named it rock 'n' roll / Deep down in Florida / Cross-eyed cat / Little girl.
**Album:** Released Sep '83, on Blue Sky Catalogue no: **SKY 32357**
**Cass:** Released Sep '83, on Blue Sky Catalogue no: **40 32357**

**HOOCHIE COOCHIE MAN (BLUE SKY)**
**Cass:** Released Jul '83, on Blue Sky Catalogue no: **40 25565**
**Album:** Released Jul '83, on Blue Sky Deleted Aug '87. Catalogue no: **SKY 25565**

**HOOCHIE COOCHIE MAN (EPIC)**
Tracks: / Mannish boy / I'm ready / Champagne and reefer / Baby please don't go / I want to be loved / Sad sad day / I'm a king bee / Blues had a baby and they named it rock 'n' roll / She's 19 years old / I can't be satisfied / Screamin' and cryin' / I'm your hoochie coochie man.
**Cass:** Released Aug '88, on Epic by CBS Records. Catalogue no: **461186 4**
**CD:** Released Aug '88, on Epic by CBS Records. Catalogue no: **461186 2**
**Album:** Released Aug '88, on Epic by CBS Records. Catalogue no: **461186 1**

**HOOCHIE COOCHIE MAN (MASTERS)**
**Cass:** Released '88, on Masters (Holland) Catalogue no: **CLMS 930683**
**Album:** Released '88, on Masters (Holland) Catalogue no: **CL 30683**

**I CAN'T BE SATISFIED**
Tracks: / I can't call her sugar / You can't lose what you ain't never had / Sad letter / I can't be satisfied / Baby please don't go / Walkin' thru the park / Trainfare blues / Sittin' here drinkin' / I got a rich man's woman / Mean mistreater.
**Cass:** Released Apr '86, on Castle Showcase by Castle Communications Records. Catalogue no: **SHTC 141**
**Album:** Released '88, on Castle Showcase by Castle Communications Records. Catalogue no: **SHLP 141**

**IN MEMORIAM**
Note: German pressings of some of the gems such as 'I'm Your Hoochie Coohie Man' and 'Got My Mojo Workin'.
**2 LP Set:** Released Dec '85, on Chess (PRT) Deleted '88. Catalogue no: **6 28622**

**KING BEE**
Tracks: / I'm a king bee / Too young to know / Mean old Frisco blues / Forever lonely / I feel like going home / Champagne and reefer / Sad sad day / Keep me in trouble / Deep down in Florida 2 / No escape from the blues.
**Album:** Released May '81, on Blue Sky Catalogue no: **SKY 84918**

**LIVE 65-68**
Tracks: / Blow wind blow / Hoochie coochie man / Sunrise blues / Honey Bee / Baby please don't go / All night long / Goodbye baby.
**Album:** Released Aug '87, on Onsala International by Onsala International. Catalogue no: **CFPC 401**
**Album:** Released Jun '88, on C P Records Catalogue no: **CPFC 401**

**LIVE AT MR KELL'S**
**Album:** Released Mar '84, on Vogue (France) by Vogue Records. Catalogue no: **515037**

**LIVE AT NEWPORT 1960**
**Album:** Released Jul '84, on Vogue (France) by Vogue Records. Catalogue no: **515039**

**LIVE IN ANTIBES 1974**
Tracks: / Honky tonk women / Blow wind blow / Off the wall / Can't get no grindin' / Trouble no more / Garbage man / I'm your hoochie coochie man / Baby, please don't go / Mannish boy / Everything gonna be alright / Got my mojo working.
**Album:** Released Jun '88, on France's Concert Catalogue no: **FC 116**
**CD:** Released Jun '88, on France's Concert Catalogue no: **FCD 116**

**LIVE IN PARIS 1968**
**CD:** Released Jun '89, on France's Concert Catalogue no: **FCD 121**
**Album:** Released Jun '89, on France's Concert Catalogue no: **FC 121**

**LONDON MUDDY WATERS SESSIONS THE**
**Album:** Released Apr '82, on Chess (USA) Catalogue no: **CXMP 2005**

**MANNISH BOY**
Tracks: / Mannish boy / I'm your hoochie coochie man / Blues had a baby and they named it rock 'n' roll (Available on 12" only.) / Little girl (Available on 12" version only.).
**7" Single:** Released Jul '88, on Epic by CBS Records. Catalogue no: **BRMT 016**
**12" Single:** Released Jul '88, on Epic by CBS Records. Deleted Jan '89. Catalogue no: **MUDT 1**
**7" Single:** Released Jul '88, on Epic by CBS Records. Deleted Jan '89. Catalogue no: **MUD 1**

**MISSISSIPPI**
**Cass:** Released '88, on Masters (Holland) Catalogue no: **CLMC 914983**
**Album:** Released '88, on Masters (Holland) Catalogue no: **CL 914983**

**MISSISSIPPI ROLLIN' STONE (BLUE MOON)**
**Album:** Released Sep '84, on Blue Moon (1) by Magnum Music Group. Catalogue no: **BMLP 1014**
**CD:** Released Jul '89, on Blue Moon (1) by Magnum Music Group. Catalogue no: **CDBM 1014**
**Album:** Released Jul '83, on Blue Moon (1) by Magnum Music Group. Catalogue no: **BMLP 1006**
**CD:** Released Jan '89, on Blue Moon (1) by Magnum Music Group. Catalogue no: **CDBM 1006**

**MISSISSIPPI ROLLIN' STONE (CHESS)**
**CD:** Released Oct '88, on Chess by Vogue Records. Catalogue no: **CDRED 1**

**MORE REAL FOLK BLUES**
**Album:** Released Oct '88, on Vogue (France) by Vogue Records. Catalogue

no: **515020**

**MUD IN YOUR EAR**
Tracks: / Diggin' my potatoes / Watchdog / Sting it / Why d'you do me? / Natural wig / Mud in your ear / Excuse me baby / Sad day uptown / Top of the boogaloo / Long distance call.
Note: Muddy Waters, Luther Johnson, Sammy Langhorne, guitars; George "Mojo" Burford, harmonica; Otis Spann, piano; Francis Clay, drums. Recorded 1973.
**Album:** Released Jul '83, on Happy Bird (Germany) Catalogue no: **B 90077**
**Album:** Released Apr '81, on Muse by Black & Blue Records. Catalogue no: **MR 5008**

**MUDDY MISSISSIPPI WATERS (LIVE)**
Tracks: / Mannish boy / She's nineteen years old / Nine below zero / Streamline woman / Howling wolf / Baby please don't go / Deep down in Florida.
**Album:** Released Jan '79, on Blue Sky Deleted '88. Catalogue no: **SKY 83422**

**MUDDY WATERS**
**CD:** Released Mar '90, on Roots Catalogue no: **RTS 33018**

**MUDDY WATERS AT NEWPORT**
Tracks: / I got my brand on you / Baby, please don't go / Soon forgotten / Tiger in your tank / I feel so good / I've got my mojo working / I've got my mojo working, part 2 / Goodbye Newport blues.
**Cass:** Released Apr '87, on Chess by Vogue Records. Catalogue no: **GCHK 78022**
**Album:** Released Apr '87, on Chess by Vogue Records. Catalogue no: **GCH 8022**

**MUDDY WATERS BOX SET**
**LP Set:** Released Nov '89, on Charly by Charly Records. Catalogue no: **BOX 259**
**Cass set:** Released Nov '89, on Charly by Charly Records. Catalogue no: **TCBOX 259**
**CD Set:** Released Nov '89, on Charly by Charly Records. Catalogue no: **CDBOX 259**

**MUDDY WATERS LIVE 1958**
**Album:** Released '88, on Krazy Kat by Interstate Music. Catalogue no: **KK 7405**

**MUDDY WATERS - VOL. 2**
Note: From the 'Blues Roots' catalogue, here we have 13 great tracks, including 'Tiger In Your Tank' and 'Country Boy' (live recording 1971.
**Album:** Released Dec '85, on Chess (PRT) Deleted '88. Catalogue no: **6 24801**

**NEWPORT**
**CD:** Released Jun '88, on MCA (USA) by MCA Records (USA). Catalogue no: **31269**

**ON CHESS VOL. 1 (1948-51)**
**CD:** Released Dec '85, on Vogue by Vogue Records. Catalogue no: **VGCD 600052**

**ON CHESS VOL. 2 (1951-59)**
**CD:** Released Dec '85, on Vogue by Vogue Records. Catalogue no: **VG 600 059**

**ORIGINAL HOOCHIE COOCHIE**
**Album:** Released Nov '84, on Astan (USA) Catalogue no: **20028**
**Cass:** Released Nov '84, on Astan (USA) Catalogue no: **40028**

**ORIGINAL HOOCHIE COOCHIE MAN**
Tracks: / Stuff you gotta watch / Iodine in my coffee / Close to you / You gonna miss me / Mean red spider / Diamonds at your feet / You gonna need my help / She's alright / So glad I'm living / One more mile.
**Album:** Released May '85, on Blue Moon (1) by Magnum Music Group. Catalogue no: **BMLP 1023**

**PROFILE: MUDDY WATERS**
**Album:** Released Apr '84, on Teldec (1) by ASV (Academy Sound & Vision). Catalogue no: **6.24474**

**RARE AND UNISSUED**
Tracks: / Little Annie May / Mean disposition / Feel like going home / You're gonna miss me / Stand here trembling / Last time I fool around with you / Where's my woman been / Gal you gotta watch / Lonesome day / Iodine in my coffee / Smokestack lightning / Let me hang around / Born lover / Down in my heart.
**Cass:** Released Aug '86, on Chess by Vogue Records. Catalogue no: **GCHK 78010**
**Album:** Released Aug '86, on Chess by Vogue Records. Catalogue no: **GCH 8010**
**Album:** Released Oct '88, on Vogue (France) by Vogue Records. Catalogue no: **515040**
**Album:** Released Mar '85, on Chess (PRT) Deleted '88. Catalogue no: **CXMP 2057**

**REAL FOLK BLUES**
**Album:** Released Oct '88, on Vogue (France) by Vogue Records. Catalogue no: **515008**

**ROCK ME**
**Cass:** Released Apr '87, on Masters (Holland) Catalogue no: **CL 00915983**
**Album:** Released Apr '87, on Masters (Holland) Catalogue no: **CL 915983**

**SINGS BIG BILL BROONZY**
Tracks: / Tell me baby / Southbound train / When I get to thinking / Just a dream (on my mind) / Double trouble / I feel so good / I done got wise / Moppers blues / Lonesome road blues / Hey hey.
**Cass:** Released Apr '87, on Chess by Vogue Records. Catalogue no: **GCHK 78029**
**Album:** Released Oct '88, on Vogue (France) by Vogue Records. Catalogue no: **515029**
**Album:** Released Apr '87, on Chess by Vogue Records. Catalogue no: **GCH 8029**

**SWEET HOME CHICAGO**
**Album:** Released Nov '84, on Astan (USA) Catalogue no: **20027**
**Cass:** Released Nov '84, on Astan (USA) Catalogue no: **40027**

**THEY CALL ME MUDDY WATERS**
Tracks: / When the eagle flies / Crawlin' kingsnake / County jail / It's all over / Bird nest on the ground / They call me Muddy Waters / Find yourself another fool / Kinfolk's blues / Making friends / Blind man / Howling wolf / Two steps forward.
**Cass:** Released '89, on Chess by Vogue Records. Catalogue no: **GCHK 78109**
**Album:** Released '89, on Chess by Vogue Records. Catalogue no: **GCH 8109**
**Album:** Released Mar '84, on Vogue (France) by Vogue Records. Catalogue no: **515036**

**TROUBLE NO MORE**
Tracks: / Sugar sweet / Trouble no more / All aboard / Don't go further / I love the life I live, I live... / Rock me / Got my mojo working / She's got it / Close to you / Mean mistreater.
**CD:** Released Feb '90, on Emarcy Catalogue no: **CHD 9291**

**'UNK' IN FUNK**
Tracks: / Rollin' and tumblin' / Just to be with you / Electric man / Trouble no more / 'unk' in funk / Drive my blues away / Katie / Waterboy waterboy / Everything gonna be alright.
**Album:** Released '89, on Chess by Vogue Records. Catalogue no: **GCH 8115**
**Cass:** Released '89, on Chess by Vogue Records. Catalogue no: **GCHK 78115**

**WARSAW SESSIONS, 1976, VOL 1 (Waters, Muddy Blues Band)**
**Album:** Released Oct '87, on Poljazz Catalogue no: **PSJ 79**

**WARSAW SESSIONS, 1976, VOL 2 (Waters, Muddy Blues Band)**
**Album:** Released Oct '87, on Poljazz Catalogue no: **PSJ 80**

## Watkiss, Cleveland

**GREEN CHIMNEYS**
Tracks: / Green chimneys II / Iswahdis / Sea the sky, The / Song for you / Incandescent dreams / Newborn / To a songstress / Puss in boots / Seeds of sin II.
**Cass:** Released Aug '89, on Polydor by Polydor Ltd. Catalogue no: **839 722-4**
**CD:** Released Aug '89, on Polydor by Polydor Ltd. Catalogue no: **839 722-2**
**Album:** Released Aug '89, on Polydor by Polydor Ltd. Catalogue no: **839 722-1**

**SPEND SOME TIME**
Tracks: / Spend some time / Spend some time (version).
**12" Single:** Released Apr '89, on Urban by Polydor Ltd. Deleted Dec '89. Catalogue no: **URBX 40**
**CD Single:** Released Apr '89, on Urban by Polydor Ltd. Catalogue no: **URBCD 40**
**7" Single:** Released Apr '89, on Urban

by Polydor Ltd. Deleted Dec '89. Catalogue no: **URB 40**

## Watrous, Bill

### LIVE AT THE PIZZA EXPRESS 1982

Tracks: / Straight, no chaser / When your lover has gone / Diane / Falling in love with love / There is no greater love / Dearly beloved / I should care.
**Album:** Released Jul '83, on Mole Catalogue no: **MOLE 7**
**CD:** Released Jul '83, on Mole Catalogue no: **MOLECD 7**

## Watson, Bobby

**Biographical details:** Bobby Watson, born in Lawrence, Kansas, in 1953, plays alto and soprano sax and other instruments and is also a composer-arranger. He began by arranging music for a high school concert band then he organised a dance band and wrote all the music. He played with and was musical director of Art Blakey's Jazz Messengers from 1977-81 and has been a popular jazzman ever since. He plays with the 29th Street Saxophone Quartet, with Ed Jackson on alto, Rich Rothenberg on tenor and Jim Hartog on baritone. (Donald Clarke, March 1988.).

### INVENTOR, THE

Tracks: / Heckle and jeckle / Inventor, The / P.D. on Great Jones Street / Sun, The / For children of all ages / Dreams so real / Shaw of Newark, The / Homemade blues (CD only.) / Long way home.
**CD:** Released Feb '90, on Blue Note by EMI Records. Catalogue no: **CDP 791 915 2**
**Album:** Released Feb '90, on Blue Note by EMI Records. Catalogue no: **B1 91915**
**CD:** Released Feb '90, on Blue Note by EMI Records. Catalogue no: **CDB1 91915**
**Album:** Released Feb '90, on Blue Note by EMI Records. Catalogue no: **791 915 1**

### NO QUESTION ABOUT IT

Tracks: / Country corn flakes / Forty acres and a mule / What can I do for you / Blood count / No question about it / Moonrise / And then again.
**Album:** Released Jul '89, on Blue Note by EMI Records. Catalogue no: **B1 90262**
**Album:** Released Jul '89, on Blue Note by EMI Records. Catalogue no: **790 262 1**
**CD:** Released Jul '89, on Blue Note by EMI Records. Catalogue no: **CDP 790 262 2**

## Watson, Leo

### SCAT MAN 1937-1946, THE (Watson, Leo & His Orchestra)

**Album:** Released Dec '88, on Syndicate Chapter Catalogue no: **SC 1026**

### SCAT MAN, THE

**Album:** Released '88, on Swingtime by Contact Records (Denmark). Catalogue no: **ST 1026**

## Watters, Lu

**Biographical details:** Trumpet player and bandleader Lu Watters, born in California in 1911, formed his first band in 1925 -- his 1939 residency at the Dawn Club launched the first jazz "revival", re-creating the classic New Orleans style. His band was soon called the Yerba Buena Jazz Band, recording until 1950 with such stars as of the revival genre as Turk Murphy, Bob Scobey and Clancy Hayes passing through. He reformed briefly in the early 50's, then left music. The album *Yerba Buena Days* includes tracks made between 1942 and 1949. (See also entry for Bunk Johnson.) (Donald Clarke, March 1988.).

### 50'S RECORDINGS VOL 1 (Watters, Lu & The Yerba Buena Jazz Band)

**Album:** Released Jun '79, on Dawn Club by Cadillac Music. Catalogue no: **DC 12010**

### 50'S RECORDINGS VOL 2 (Watters, Lu & The Yerba Buena Jazz Band)

**Album:** Released Jun '79, on Dawn Club by Cadillac Music. Catalogue no: **DC 12011**

### AIR SHOTS FROM THE DAWN CLUB 1941 (Yerba Buena Jazz Band)

**Album:** Released Jun '88, on Homespun (Ireland) by Outlet Records. Catalogue no: **H 107**

### LU WATTERS' YERBA BUENA JAZZ BAND (Watters, Lu & The Yerba Buena Jazz Band)

**Album:** Released Nov '88, on Homespun (USA) Catalogue no: **HS 104**

### YERBA BUENA JAZZ BAND VOL.1

Note: Vocals Clancy Hayes
**Album:** Released Jun '88, on Homespun (Ireland) by Outlet Records. Catalogue no: **H 101**

### YERBA BUENA JAZZ BAND VOL.2

Note: Vocals Clancy Hayes
**Album:** Released Jun '88, on Homespun (Ireland) by Outlet Records. Catalogue no: **H 102**

## Watts, Charlie

### LIVE AT FULHAM TOWN HALL (Watts, Charlie & His Orchestra)

Tracks: / Stompin' at the Savoy / Lester leaps in / Moonglow / Robbins nest / Scrapple from the apple / Flying home.
**Album:** Released Dec '86, on CBS by CBS Records. Catalogue no: **450253 1**
**Cass:** Released Dec '86, on CBS by CBS Records. Catalogue no: **450253 4**

## Watts, Ernie

### CHARIOTS OF FIRE

Tracks: / Chariots of fire / Hold on / Lady / Gigolo / Valdez in the country / Abraham's theme / Five circles.
**Album:** Released Feb '82, on Qwest (USA) by Qwest Records (USA). Catalogue no: **K 56982**

### CHARIOTS OF FIRE (SINGLE)

Tracks: / Chariots of fire.
**7" Single:** Released Jun '82, on Warner Bros. by WEA Records. Deleted Jun '85. Catalogue no: **K 17958**

### ERNIE WATTS QUARTET (Watts, Ernie Quartet)

Note: On this stunning JVC showcase, Ernie Watts is joined by Joel diBartolo on bass, Bob Leatherbarrow on drums and Pat Coil on piano. A collection of new compositions and well loved standards. CD contains 3 extra tracks.
**Cass:** Released Sep '88, on JVC Catalogue no: **JC 3309**
**Album:** Released Feb '89, on JVC Catalogue no: **JLP 3309**
**CD:** Released Sep '88, on JVC Catalogue no: **JD 3309**

### JUST HOLDIN' ON

Tracks: / Just holdin' on / Look in your heart.
**7" Single:** Released Dec '80, on Elektra by Elektra Records (UK). Catalogue no: **K 12489**

### LOOK IN YOUR HEART

Tracks: / Look in your heart / Just holdin' on / Dance music, makin' music / Let's sail away / Beyond the cosmic void suite (starship outness) / Love in transit / Marching to cretonia.
**Album:** Released Oct '80, on Elektra by Elektra Records (UK). Catalogue no: **E 6285**

### MUSICIAN

Tracks: / Music prayer for peace / Where the spirit lives / Rock camping / One love / Red dress / Looking glass / Don't you know / Urban renewal / Keepin' on.
**Album:** Released Aug '85, on Qwest (USA) by Qwest Records (USA). Deleted Aug '87. Catalogue no: **925283 1**

## Watts, Trevor

### CLOSER TO YOU

Tracks: / Ye Dublin ting / South of nowhere / Keep right / Dear Roland.
**Album:** Released May '79, on Ogun by Cadillac Music. Catalogue no: **OG 528**

### CYNOSURE

**Album:** Released Feb '79, on Ogun by Cadillac Music. Deleted Feb '84. Catalogue no: **OG 526**

### MOIRE MUSIC (Watts, Trevor Moire Music)

Note: Featuring Lol Coxhill/Simon Pickard / Peter Knight/Verian Winters/Paul Roger / Liam Genochey.
**Album:** Released Oct '86, on Arc Catalogue no: **ARC 02**

### MOIRE MUSIC SEXTET

Tracks: / Saalfelden encore / Don't stop now.
**Album:** Released Jan '88, on Cadillac by Cadillac Music. Catalogue no: **SGC 1015**

## We Love Ellington

### WE LOVE ELLINGTON (Various artists)

Tracks: / Johnny come lately: *Various artists* / Solitude: *Various artists* / Me and you: *Various artists* / Just a sittin and a rockin: *Various artists* / It don't mean a thing: *Various artists* / Mood indigo: *Various artists* / Do nothing till you hear from me: *Various artists* / I got it bad and that ain't good: *Various artists* / Caravan: *Various artists* / C jam blues: *Various artists*.

Note: Featuring Bosse Broberg, trumpet; Nisse Sandstrom, tenor sax; Ove Lind, clarinet; Knud Jorgensen, piano; Lasse Pettersson, bass; Robert Edman, drums.

**Album:** Released '82, on Phontastic (Sweden) Catalogue no: **PHONT 7520**

## Weather Report

**Biographical details:** One of the most popular fusion bands, Weather Report was co-led by Joe Zawinul on Keyboards and Wayne Shorter on sax. The band was formed in 1971 after Zawinul had worked with Cannonball Adderley, Shorter with Art Blakey and both with Miles Davis. All their 15 albums charted in the Top Two Hundred American LPs but their sales had an arc from the first at No 191 up to the Top Forty and down to No 195 with the last: they made as much as possible with very little and by 1986 each needed to do something else. (Donald Clarke, March 1988.)

At the time of their greatest success, this American jazz group consisted of Alejandro Acuno, Manolo Badrena, Jaco Pastorius, Wayne Shorter and Joe Zawinul. Weather Report were formed in 1971 by keyboards player/producer Zawinul and saxophonist Shorter. They have remained the nucleus of the band ever since, with Zawinul gradually assuming an increasingly dominant role; the other personnel have changed at frequent intervals, but the above-named quintet were responsible for the group's acclaimed 1977 album *Heavy weather*. Like many jazz greats of the Seventies and Eighties, Zawinul and Shorter (both nearly 40 years old by the time of the band's formation) had gained valuable experience by playing with the legendary trumpeter Miles Davis. The former had also worked closely with ace saxman Cannonball Adderley; the latter had played with the famous jazz drummer, Art Blakey. Thus, Weather Report began life with a superb pedigree and quickly headway in the jazz market. Their debut eponymous LP was released in 1971, and was followed by 1972's *I sing the body electric*. These albums set the standard for the band's future work - a tightly played but eclectic fusion of jazz and rock, always subtly progressive. Their accent on melody opened doors for pop and rock audiences who were normally alienated by jazz. Weather Report's first UK album was 1977's *Heavy Weather*. This reached No.43, and was fuelled by its dynamic opening track *Birdland*, which garnered substantial airplay as a bright, catchy, summery single. 1978's *Mr Gone*, also attained a British Top 50 placing. The band have continued to release albums on a regular basis; their Eighties LP's such as *Night passage* (1980) and *Domino theory* (1984), have sustained their international jazz following. (Bob MacDonald, 6th May 1986).

### 8.30

Tracks: / Black market / Scarlet woman / Teen town / Remark you made / Slang / In a silent way / Birdland / Thanks for the memory / Badia / Boogie woogie waltz medley / 8.30 / Brown Street / Orphan / Sightseeing.

**2 LP Set:** on CBS by CBS Records. Catalogue no: **22134**

**2 LP Set:** Released Nov '79, on CBS by CBS Records. Deleted '84. Catalogue no: **CBS 88455**

### BIRDLAND

Tracks: / Birdland / Remark you made / River people (Only on 12" single.).

**7" Single:** Released Jul '79, on CBS by CBS Records. Deleted '82. Catalogue no: **CBS 7701**

**12" Single:** Released Jul '79, on CBS by CBS Records. Deleted '82. Catalogue no: **CBS 137701**

### BLACK MARKET

**Album:** Released '87, on CBS by CBS Records. Deleted Jan '89. Catalogue no: **CBS 32226**

**CD:** Released May '87, on CBS by CBS Records. Deleted Jul '89. Catalogue no: **CD 81325**

### DOMINO THEORY

Tracks: / Can it be done / D flat waltz / Peasant, The / Predator / Blue soundnote / Swamp cabbage / Domino theory.

**Album:** Released Feb '84, on CBS by CBS Records. Catalogue no: **CBS 25839**

**Cass:** Released Feb '84, on CBS by CBS Records. Deleted '87. Catalogue no: **40 25839**

**CD:** Released Feb '84, on CBS by CBS Records. Deleted Jan '89. Catalogue no: **CD 25839**

### HEAVY WEATHER

Tracks: / Birdland / Remark you made, A / Teen town / Harlequin / Rumba mama / Palladium / Juggler, The / Havona.

**Album:** Released Sep '83, on CBS by CBS Records. Catalogue no: **CBS 32358**

**CD:** Released Nov '87, on CBS by CBS Records. Catalogue no: **CD 81775**

**Cass:** Released Sep '83, on CBS by CBS Records. Catalogue no: **40 32358**

**Album:** Released Apr '77, on CBS by CBS Records. Deleted '82. Catalogue no: **CBS 81775**

### I SING THE BODY ELECTRIC

**Album:** Released Oct '82, on CBS by CBS Records. Deleted Oct '87. Catalogue no: **CBS 32062**

### JAPAN DOMINO THEORY

Note: Running time: 61 mins.

**VHS:** Released '88, on Castle Hendring Video by Castle Communications Records. Catalogue no: **HEN 2 030 G**

### MR GONE

Tracks: / Pursuit of the woman in the feathered hat / River people / Young and fine / Elders, The / Mr. Gone / Punk jazz / Pinocchio / And then.

**Album:** Released Nov '78, on CBS by CBS Records. Deleted '83. Catalogue no: **CBS 82775**

**Album:** Released Sep '86, on Prix D'Ami (France) Catalogue no: **32790**

**Cass:** Released Sep '86, on Prix D'Ami (France) Catalogue no: **40 32790**

### MYSTERIOUS TRAVELLER

**CD:** Deleted 10 Jul '89. Catalogue no: **CD 80027**

### NEW ALBUM

**CD:** Released '88, on CBS by CBS Records. Deleted Jan '89. Catalogue no: **CD 26367**

### NIGHT PASSAGE

Tracks: / Dream clock / Port of entry / Forlorn / Rockin' in rhythm / Fast city / Night passage / Three views of a secret / Madagascar.

**CD:** Released '83, on CBS by CBS Records. Deleted Jan '89. Catalogue no: **CD 84597**

**Album:** Released '83, on CBS by CBS Records. Catalogue no: **CBS 84597**

### PROCESSION

Tracks: / Procession / Plaza real / Two lines / Where the moon goes / Well, The / Molasses run.

Note: A Weather Report album is always a special event but this one more so than most as it features Wayne Shorter and Josef Zawinul fronting a completely new Weather Report.

**CD:** Released Feb '83, on CBS by CBS Records. Catalogue no: **CD 25241**

**Album:** Released Feb '83, on CBS by CBS Records. Catalogue no: **CBS 25241**

**Cass:** Released Feb '83, on CBS by CBS Records. Catalogue no: **40 25241**

### SPORTIN' LIFE

Tracks: / Corner pocket / Indiscretions / Hot cargo / Confians / Pearl on the half-shell / What's going on? / Face on the bar room floor, The / Icepick Willy.

**Cass:** Released Jun '85, on CBS by CBS Records. Deleted Aug '87. Catalogue no: **40 26367**

**Album:** Released Jun '85, on CBS by CBS Records. Catalogue no: **CBS 26367**

### THIS IS THIS

Tracks: / This is this / Face the fire / I'll never forget you / Jungle stuff (part 1) / Man with the copper fingers / Consequently / Update / China blues.

**Album:** Released Jul '86, on CBS by CBS Records. Catalogue no: **CBS 57052**

**Cass:** Released Jul '86, on CBS by CBS Records. Deleted Nov '87. Catalogue no: **40 57052**

**WEATHER REPORT**
Tracks: / Volcano for hire / Current affairs / N.Y.C. / Dara factor one / When it was now / Speechless.
**Album:** Released Feb '82, on CBS by CBS Records. Deleted '87. Catalogue no: **CBS 85326**
**Album:** Released Mar '81, on CBS by CBS Records. Catalogue no: **CBS 32024**

## Weatherbird Jazzband

**FIREWORKS**
**Album:** Released '88, on Stomp Off (USA) Catalogue no: **SOS 1034**

## Weatherburn, Ron

**AFTER THE BALL**
**Album:** Released Oct '86, on Stomp Off (USA) Catalogue no: **SOS 1107**

## Webb, Chick

**Biographical details:** Bandleader Chick Webb (1909-39) was one of the finest jazz drummers of all time: Buddy Rich said of him, "Every beat was like a bell". A hunchback, he died of TB of the spine. During the 30's his band included Edgar Sampson, who wrote swing era classics*Blue Lou,Stompin' At The Savoy*and*Don't Be That Way*. Webb discovered Ella Fitzgerald, had hits with her -- including the No 1*A Tisket, A Tasket*-- and adopted her when her mother died. From 1931 his band was resident at the Savoy Ballroom: visiting bands had to do battle, and most lost. The Affinity album is a classic compilation. (Donald Clarke, March 1988.).

**CHICK WEBB VOL.1**
**Album:** Released Aug '81, on Kings Of Jazz Catalogue no: **KLJ 20017**

**FOR RADIO ONLY RECORDINGS 1939**
**CD:** Released Aug '89, on Tax Catalogue no: **TAXCD 3706-2**

**IN THE GROOVE (Big Band Bounce & Boogie)**
Tracks: / Don't be that way / What a shuffle / Blue Lou / Go Harlem / You'll have to swing it / Strictly jive / Rock it for me / Squeeze me / If dreams come true / Tisket a tasket, A / Azure / Spinnin' the web / Liza / Undecided / T'aint what you do (it's the way that you do it) / In the groove at the Groove.
Note: Featuring the young Ella Fitzgerald on early hits like A tisket a tasket, If dreams come true and You'll have to swing it, better known today as Mr Paganini. Drummer Webb was always a great bandleader and others on this album include Taft Jordan, Mario Bauza, Bobby Stark (trumpets), Wayman Carver (tenor sax, flute), Hilton Jefferson (alto sax), John Kirby (bass).
**Album:** Released Sep '83, on Affinity by Charly Records. Catalogue no: **AFS 1007**

**RHYTHM MAN**
**Album:** Released '88, on Hep Jazz by Hep Records. Catalogue no: **HEP 1023**

**STOMPIN' AT THE SAVOY (Webb, Chick Orchestra & Ella Fitzgerald)**
**Album:** Released '88, on Collector's Classics Catalogue no: **CC 17**

**STOMPIN' AT THE SAVOY 1936 (Webb, Chick & His orchestra)**
Note: With Ella F.
**Album:** Released Jun '86, on Circle (USA) by Jazzology Records (USA). Catalogue no: **CLP 81**

## Webb, George

**GEORGE WEBB'S DIXIELANDERS (Webb, George & His Dixielanders)**
**Album:** Released Jun '88, on Jazzology (USA) by Jazzology Records (USA). Catalogue no: **J 122**

## Weber, Eberhard

**COLOURS OF CHLOE, THE**
Note: With Rainer Bruninghaus, Peter Giger, Ralf Hubner, Ack Van Rooyen and the cellos of the Sudfunk Symphony Orchestra.
**CD:** Released Jul '88, on ECM Catalogue no: **833 331 2**
**Album:** Released '75, on ECM Catalogue no: **ECM 1042**

**FOLLOWING MORNING, THE**
Tracks: / T on a white horse / Moana I / Following morning, The / Moana II.
Note: Personnel: Rainer Bruninghaus-piano / Eberhard Weber - bass / Oslo Philharmonic Orchestra.
**Album:** Released Feb '77, on ECM Catalogue no: **ECM 1084**
**CD:** Released Jun '86, on ECM Catalogue no: **829 116 2**

**LATER THAT EVENING**
**Album:** Released Oct '82, on ECM Catalogue no: **ECM 1231**

**ORCHESTRA SOLO BASS (Weber, Eberhard Orchestra)**
Note: 'Orchestra' eshibits Eberhard's versatility on his instrument and is a run through of different musical styles and playing techniques. Although this is a collection of solo performances, two compositions have been recorded with a brass section to add depth and colour.
**Album:** Released Feb '89, on ECM Catalogue no: **ECM 1374**
**CD:** Released Feb '89, on ECM Catalogue no: **837 343-2**

**SILENT FEET (Weber, Eberhard Colours)**
**Album:** Released '78, on ECM Catalogue no: **ECM 1107**
**CD:** Released Sep '88, on ECM Catalogue no: **835 017-2**

**WORKS: EBERHARD WEBER**
Tracks: / Sand / Dark spell, A / More colours / Touch / Eyes that can see in the dark / Moana II.
Note: Personnel: Eberhard Weber, Ralph Towner, Jan Garbarek, Charlie Mariano, Rainer Bruninghaus, John Marshall, Jon Christensen, Oslo Philharmonic.
**Album:** Released Jun '89, on ECM Catalogue no: **825 429-1**
**CD:** Released Jun '89, on ECM Catalogue no: **825 429-2**

**Eberhard Weber**

## Weber, Hajo

**WINTEREISE (A Winter Journey) (Weber, Hajo & Ulrich Ingenbold)**
**Album:** Released Sep '82, on ECM Catalogue no: **ECM 1235**

## Webster, Ben

**Biographical details:** The greatest tenor saxist of the swing era after Coleman Hawkins, Ben Webster was born in Kansas City in 1909 and died in Amsterdam in 1973. He was the first and finest tenor star in Duke Ellington's band, becoming famous in 1940-42 with solos such as the controlled explosion on Cotton Tail. He was no Hawkins accolyte: he combined powerful swing with breathy sensuality on ballads and was a mainstream player compared with Hawkins' more scientific approach. He toured with Norman Grantz's Jazz at the Philharmonic, moved to Copenhagen in 1964 and spent the rest of his life in Europe. (Donald Clarke, March 1988.).

**AT THE NUWAY CLUB**
Tracks: / Dancing on the ceiling / Indiana / Ow / I remember you / Exactly like you / Man I love, The / Ad lib blues.
**Album:** Released Oct '82, on Nostalgia by Mainline Records. Catalogue no: **NOST 7630**

**AT THE RENAISSANCE**
Tracks: / Georgia on my mind / Caravan / Ole Miss blues / Stardust.
**Album:** Released 2 May '89, on Contemporary by Ace Records. Catalogue no: **COP 026**
**CD:** Released Apr '87, on Carrere (France) Catalogue no: **98626**

**ATMOSPHERE FOR LOVERS AND THIEVES**
Tracks: / Blue light / Stardust / What's new? / Autumn leaves / Easy to love / My romance / Yesterdays / Days of wine and roses.
**Album:** Released Jan '85, on Black Lion Catalogue no: **BLP 30105**

**BALLADS**
**2 LP Set:** Released Jan '75, on Verve Catalogue no: **2683 049**

**BALLADS AND BLUES**
**CD:** Released Sep '87, on Compact Collection Catalogue no: **15014**

**BEN AT THE NUWAY CLUB (Webster, Ben Quartet)**
**Album:** Released Sep '79, on Pumpkin Catalogue no: **1011**

**BEN AND SWEETS (Webster, Ben & Harry Sweets Edison)**
Tracks: / Better Go / How long has this been going on / Kitty / My Romance / Did you call her today / Embraceable you.
**Album:** Released Apr '88, on CBS (import) by CBS Records. Catalogue no: **4606 131**

**BEN WEBSTER**
**Album:** Released Dec '84, on Commodore Class Catalogue no: **AG6 24058**
**Album:** Released 10 Jul '89, on Black Lion Catalogue no: **BLP 60141**

**BEN WEBSTER AND ASSOCIATES**
**Album:** Released Dec '81, on Verve Catalogue no: **2304 221**

**BEN WEBSTER AND FRIENDS**
**Album:** Released Jun '77, on Verve Catalogue no: **2332 086**

**BEN WEBSTER IN EUROPE VOL.2**
Tracks: / Ben's bounce / Sunday / I got it bad and that ain't good / Cottontail / For all we know / That's all / You'd be so nice to come home to / I got rhythm.
**Album:** Released Apr '81, on Rarities Catalogue no: **RARITIES 55**

**BEN WEBSTER AND JOE ZAWINUL (Webster, Ben & Joe Zawinul)**
Tracks: / Travellin' light / Like someone in love / Too late now / Come Sunday / Frog legs / Soulmate / Governor / Evol deklaw ni / Where are you now / In a mellow tone / I surrender dear / Crazy rhythm.
**2 LP Set:** Released Oct '80, on Milestone (USA) by Fantasy Inc (USA). Deleted Oct '85. Catalogue no: **M 47056**

**BEN WEBSTER MEETS DON BYAS (Webster, Ben & Don Byas)**
Tracks: / Blues for Dottie Mae / Lullaby for Dottie Mae / Sundae / Perdido / When Ash mees Henry / Caravan.
Note: Personnel: Don Byas-tenor sax/Ben Webster-tenor sax/Tete Monoliu-piano/Peter Trunk-bass/Al 'Tootie' Heath-drums. Tenor giants Ben Webster and Don Byas are two of the handful of great tenor saxophonists in the melodic/harmonic tradition established before and during the swing era. Recorded 1968.
**CD:** Released Jun '86, on ECM Catalogue no: **827 920-2**

**BEN WEBSTER MEETS OSCAR PETERSON**
Tracks: / Touch of your lips / When your lover has gone / Bye bye blackbird / How deep is the ocean / In the wee small hours / Sunday / This can't be love.
**Album:** Released May '84, on Verve Deleted Jan '89. Catalogue no: **VRV 1**
**CD:** Released Aug '86, on Polydor by Polydor Ltd. Deleted Oct '88. Catalogue no: **829 167-2**
**Album:** Released Apr '81, on Verve Catalogue no: **2304 455**

**BEN WEBSTER PLAYS DUKE ELLINGTON**
**Album:** Released May '89, on Storyville by Storyville Records AB. Catalogue no: **SLP 4133**

**BEN WEBSTER (SMALL GROUPS)**
Note: Mono
**Album:** Released Jul '86, on Jazz Archives (USA) by Jazz Archives Inc.(USA). Catalogue no: **JA 35**

**BIG BEN TIME**
Tracks: / Just a sittin' and a rockin' / Exactly like you / How deep is the ocean / My one and only love / Honeysuckle rose / Jeep is jumpin' / Where or when / Wrap your troubles in dreams / Solitude / Remember.
**CD:** Released Sep '84, on Verve (USA) by Polydor Ltd. Catalogue no: **814 410-2**

**BLUE LIGHT**
Tracks: / Autumn leaves / Blue light / Stardust / What's new / Easy to love / My romance / Yesterdays / Days of wine and roses.
**Album:** Released Apr '84, on Polydor (Holland) by Polydor Ltd. Catalogue no: **2340 004**

**DAYS OF WINE AND ROSES**
**CD:** Released May '88, on Jazz Life Catalogue no: **247 351 2**
**Cass:** Released May '88, on Jazz Life Catalogue no: **2173512**
**Album:** Released May '88, on Jazz Life Catalogue no: **2273512**

**DID YOU CALL**
**Album:** Released Mar '79, on Nessa Deleted '83. Catalogue no: **N 8**

**DUKE'S IN BED**
Tracks: / What's I'm gotchere / Close your eyes / There is no greater love / Brother John's blues / Stompy Jones / Nancy with the laughing face / I got it bad and that ain't good / Duke's in bed.
**Album:** Released Apr '85, on Black Lion Catalogue no: **BLP 30137**

**FOR THE GUV'NOR**
Tracks: / I got it bad and that ain't good / Drop me off in Harlem / One for the guv'nor / Prelude to a kiss / In a sentimental mood / John Brown's body / Work song / Preacher, The / Straight no chaser / Rockin' in rhythm.
Note: An EMI-Holland recording. Produced by Joop Visser. Engineered by Klass Leyen.
**CD:** Released May '87, on Charly by Charly Records. Catalogue no: **CDCHARLY 15**
**2 LP Set:** Released Oct '79, on Affinity by Charly Records. Catalogue no: **AFFD 40**

**HORN 1944, THE (Webster, Ben and His Orchestra)**
**Album:** Released Jun '86, on Circle (USA) by Jazzology Records (USA). Catalogue no: **CLP 41**

**HORN AND HIS ORCHESTRA, THE**
**Album:** Released '88, on Circle (USA) by Jazzology Records (USA). Catalogue no: **CLP 42**

**KING OF THE TENORS**
Tracks: / Tenderly / Jive at six / Don't get around much any more / That's all / Bounce blues / Pennies from heaven / Cottontail / Danny boy.
**Album:** Released Jan '90, on Verve Catalogue no: **837 431 1**

**LIVE AT PIO'S**
**Album:** Released Jan '82, on Enja (Germany) by Enja Records (West Germany). Catalogue no: **ENJA 2038**

**LIVE IN AMSTERDAM**
Tracks: / Johnny come lately / Indiana / Blues in F / Perdido / Sunday / Come Sunday / How long has this been going on? / Old folks / For all we know.
Note: Recorded January 24th, 1969 at

the Lurelei Theatre, Amsterdam. Featuring Ben Webster (tenor sax), Cees Slinger (piano), Rob Langereis (bass), Peter Ypma (drums). Although I have not seen him for many years I shall be eternally grateful to a friend, Alan Hughes, for introducing me to so much wonderful music on record at the end of the Forties. High on the list was my first experience of Ben Webster, on an HMV 78 by Duke Ellington And His Famous Orchestra. Ben rendered me temporarily speechless as he oozed his way through a half chorus solo on *What am I here for*, a record which still sends shivers up my spine every time I here it. That solo turned me into a Ben Webster fan some forty years ago, and the love affair still continues.

Affinity's Joop Visser and I share so many musical likes that he knew I would be as excited as he was at the prospect of issuing a previously unreleased album of latterday Ben, taped one day in an Amsterdam theatre when the great tenor saxist was coming up for his 60th birthday. The facts relating to this singular man should be generally well-known by now; born in Kansas City, Missouri, on 27th March, 1909 he started out on piano, switched to tenor before he was 20 and during the Thirties played with just about every big band. He joined Duke Ellington's orchestra in February, 1940 and remained with the famous orchestra for three and a half years (although he had made guest appearances with Duke on record in the middle Thirties). For the rest of his life he worked as a featured soloist with jazz at the philharmonic or with the local rhythm sections. In 1964 he packed up his tenor and his record collection and headed for Europe where he used Holland as a base for some time, later moving on to Copenhagen. He was a familiar figure in European jazz clubs and at festivals and he was mourned by many when he passed away, in Amsterdam, on 20th September, 1973.

His move to Europe, comparatively late in his life, brought about a new facet to his playing. Whereas before he had been known as a hard, driving soloist, who only occasionally turned in a ballad, he now mellowed and the balance was reversed. His friend and colleague Rex Stuart, in a fine pen portrait of the man known as Frog to his intimates, wrote "there are some parallels between Ben's playing and his personal life. Over the years, his style has undergone a complete turnabout, which is obvious to a discerning listener. During his early period, he blew with unrestrained savagery, buzzing and growling through chord changes like a prehistoric monster challenging a foe. With the passage of time, this fire has given way to tender, introspective declamations of such maturity and reflective beauty that he has acquired a large number of new fans all over the world." (That was written in 1967 and appeared first in "Down Beat" magazine.)

In Europe he quickly became a legend in his own time. Some of the stories may well be apocryphal but no matter, they capture the very essence of this big, lovable, frustrating, fallible and gentle man. I know for a fact that he fell down between the platform and the train which had just brought him into Victoria and had to be wheeled off on a luggage barrow, protesting that the shock had robbed him of his mobility. Having just one taste too many with friends prior to appearing at Ronnie Scott's one evening he got as far as the entrance before passing out and I treasure a copy of a tape he sent Nat Pierce who had asked him why he no longer played stride piano. "Hello Nat Pierce, you old mother!" he says at the beginning, before plunging into an energetic keyboard version of *Moten Swing*. "That's all" he proclaims at the end, no other message, the music said it all.

Ben never seemed to have any difficulty in getting his message accross to his accompanists, as witness the remarkable transcription of a rehearsal with the Danish Radio Big Band ("*No fool, no fun*", Spotlite records). With his Dutch friends at the Lurelei Theatre he obviously felt at home, having worked with such men as Cees (pronounced "Case") Slinger and Rob Langereis on several occasions. The result is some of the best of his quartet work in Europe as he plays his way through some of his favourite songs. Listen to the masterly way he turns on the pressure during *For all we know*, commencing with a most graceful, tender theme chorus then bouncing increasingly powerful phrases off Langereis's strong bass line. Ben liked a positive, inventive bass line; after all, he had worked with the great Jimmy Blanton during his years with the Duke. And he remembered one of the greatest of all Ellington fans, collecting every recorded Ducal performance he could. On this release he plays a superb version of Billy Strayhorn's mysterious and slightly sinister *Johnny come lately*, re-examines Juan Tizol's *Perdido* and lavishes nothing but tender love on *Come Sunday* from Duke's "Black, brown and beige". Ben had left the band when Ellington wrote this extended work but it sounds as if it might almost have been written with Webster in mind. (In fact the featured voice on the original record was Ray Nance's violin.) *Blues in F* is a functional title for a twelve bar in the key of F minor and what we hear is probably part of a longer performance. No matter, those four choruses by Ben tell the whole story of the blues.

Here then is one of the most individual sounds in the entire history of jazz, recorded under relaxed conditions with no pressures, no trapeze artists or empire builders in the supporting band, just friends, as the song said. If you have never heard Ben Webster before then I envy you because your life is about to change, for the better. And if, like me, you have loved his music for more years than you care to remember then here, after 20 years in the vaults, are some classic performances by the master. (Alun Morgan, December, 1988)

**Cass:** Released Feb '89, on Affinity by Charly Records. Catalogue no: **TCAFF 202**

**Album:** Released Feb '89, on Affinity by Charly Records. Catalogue no: **AFF 202**

**CD:** Released Feb '89, on Affinity by Charly Records. Catalogue no: **CDCHARLY 168**

**LIVE IN PARIS, 1972**

**Album:** Released '89, on France's Concert Catalogue no: **FC 131**

**CD:** Released '89, on France's Concert Catalogue no: **FCD 131**

**MAKIN WHOOPEE (Webster, Ben Quartet)**

Tracks: / Prelude to a kiss / Johnny come lately / Autumn leaves / I want a little girl / Makin' whoopee / You better go now / Ash's cap / Hal's blues.

**Album:** Released '83, on Spotlite by Spotlite Records. Catalogue no: **SPJ LP 9**

**MASTERS OF JAZZ VOL 5**

**Album:** Released May '86, on Storyville by Storyville Records AB. Catalogue no: **SLP 4105**

**CD:** Released Feb '89, on Storyville by Storyville Records AB. Catalogue no: **STCD 4105**

**MIDNIGHT AT THE MONTMARTRE**

Tracks: / Friskin' the frog / Stormy weather / Teach me tonight / Perdido / Yesterdays / I'm gonna sit right down and write myself a letter / Set call.

**Album:** Released Sep '87, on Black Lion Catalogue no: **BLP 30173**

**MPS JAZZ TIME VOL.9**

Tracks: / Blues for Dottie Mae / Lullaby to Dottie Mae / Sundae / Perdido / When Ash meets Henry / Caravan.

**Album:** Released Jun '79, on MPS Jazz (France) Catalogue no: **5C 064 60412**

**NO FOOL, NO FUN**

Tracks: / Did you call her today / Cottontail / Old folks / Please don't talk about me when I'm gone / Impromptu / Song is ended, The / Baby, it's cold outside.

**Album:** Released '83, on Spotlite by Spotlite Records. Catalogue no: **SPJ 142**

**PLAYS BALLADS**

**Album:** Released Feb '90, on Storyville by Storyville Records AB. Catalogue no: **SLP 4118**

**SATURDAY NIGHT AT THE MONTMARTRE**

Tracks: / Our love is here to stay / My romance / Blues for Herluf / Londonderry air / Mck the knife / I can't get started / Theme.

**Album:** Released Sep '85, on Black Lion Catalogue no: **BLP 30155**

**SCANDINAVIAN DAYS**

**Album:** Released Apr '81, on Rarities Catalogue no: **RARITIES 45**

**SEE YOU AT THE FAIR**

Tracks: / See you at the fair / Over the rainbow / Our love is here to stay / In a mellow tone.

**Cass:** Released Aug '82, on Jasmine by Hasmick Promotions. Catalogue no: **JAS C33**
**Album:** Released Aug '82, on Jasmine by Hasmick Promotions. Catalogue no: **JAS 33**

### SOULMATES
**Album:** Released Aug '84, on Riverside (USA) by Fantasy Inc (USA). Catalogue no: **OJC 109**

### SOULVILLE
**Album:** Released Mar '81, on Verve Catalogue no: **2304 314**

### STORMY WEATHER
**CD:** Released Dec '88, on Black Lion Catalogue no: **BLCD 760108**
**Album:** Released Aug '89, on Black Lion Catalogue no: **BLP 60108**

### SUNDAY MORNING AT THE MONTMARTRE
Tracks: / Sunday / That's all / Gone with the wind / Over the rainbow / Indiana / Misty / Set call.
**Album:** Released Sep '87, on Black Lion Catalogue no: **BLP 30182**

### WARM MOODS, THE (Webster, Ben With Strings)
Tracks: / Stella by starlight / But beautiful / There's no you / I'm beginning to see the light / Time after time / Nancy.
Note: Arranged and conducted by Johnny Richards.
**Cass:** Released '88, on Discovery (USA) by Discovery Records (USA). Catalogue no: **DSC 818**
**Album:** Released '88, on Discovery (USA) by Discovery Records (USA). Catalogue no: **DS 818**

### WEBSTER'S DICTIONARY
Tracks: / Love is here to stay / Where are you / Willow weep for me / For all we know / That's all / Someone to watch over me / Shadow of your smile / Come Sunday / For heaven's sake / Old folks.
**Album:** Released Nov '79, on Pye Deleted '84. Catalogue no: **N 112**

## Weed, Buddy

### FEBRUARY 4TH AND 6TH, 1958 (Weed, Buddy Septet)
Tracks: / Five o'clock rush / I'm gonna flag that train / Mr. Imagination / Honky-tonk mama / Blue boy / Rajah's spree / Sweet reminiscence / Jackpot rag / Brazilian serenade / Minor swing.
**Album:** Released Oct '80, on From The Jazz Vault by Damont Audio Ltd.. Catalogue no: **JV 115**

## Weeks, Anson

**Biographical details:** Anson Weeks (1896-1969) was one of America's most popular hotel bandleaders, dispensing strict-tempo music. He had a few hit records in the mid-30's but was more popular on the radio and in the ballroom. (Donald Clarke, March 1988.).

### ANSON WEEKS, 1932
Tracks: / Let's fly away / You do something to me / I can't give anything but love / With a song in my heart / Who's your little who's zis / Dancing on the ceiling / You're my everything / When it's sleepy time down South / Was that the human thing to do / Fine and dandy / You're blase / Rain, rain, go away / Say it isn't so / Sweet and lowdown / I guess I'll have to change my plans / Georgia on my mind / On the Alamo / My ideal / I'll get by / Egyptian shimmy.
Note: This was the Weeks orchestra thst played the Mark Hopkins for a 4-year straight run prior to 1932. The LP consists of two complete broadcasts of songs, pop then, but which later turned out to be standards, and the orchestra featured such sidemen as Griff Williams, Jimmy Walsh, etc. Complete with announcements, including several short interviews with Weeks himself. Superb liner notes by Jack Bethards who knew the history of the Weeks band intimately as well as knowing all the surviving members. Outstanding quality, in view of the early year, 1932. Produced by Wally Heider. (Hindsight Catalogue - 1989)
**Album:** Released '88, on Hindsight Catalogue no: **HSR 146**

### ANSON WEEKS AND HIS ORCHESTRA, 1932
Tracks: / Let's fly away / You do something to me / I can't give you anything but love / With a song in my heart / Who's your little whozis / Dancing on the ceiling / You're my everything / When it's sleepy time down South / Was that the human thing to do / Fine and dandy / You're blase / Rain rain go away / Say it isn't so / Sweet and low down / I guess I'll have to change my plan / Georgia on my mind / On the Alamo / My ideal / I'll get by / Egyptian shimmy.
**Album:** Released Apr '80, on London Records by London Records Ltd. Catalogue no: **HMA 5070**

## Weems, Ted

**Biographical details:** Ted Weems (1901-63) was a popular American bandleader, with occasional semi-hot and novelty styles. His band was notable for Elmo Tanner, who sang and whistled, and for a young baritone who joined in 1936 -- Perry Como. Weems had more than 30 hits between 1922 and 1948. *Heartaches*was recorded in '33 with Tanner's whistling and didn't chart, but it was reissued in '47 and reached No 1. *I Wonder Who's Kissing Her Now*, with Perry Como, was recorded in 1939 and reached No 2 also in 1947: there was a Musicians' Union strike that year and so few new records. (Donald Clarke, March 1988.).

### HEARTACHES 1933 - 51 (Weems, Ted & His orchestra)
**Album:** Released Jun '88, on Bandstand Catalogue no: **BS 7141**
**Cass:** Released Jun '88, on Bandstand Catalogue no: **BS 7141C**

### MARVELLOUS (Weems, Ted & His orchestra)
Tracks: / Marvellous / Oh, if I only had you / From Saturday night to Sunday morning / She'll never find a fellow like me / Chick, chick, chick, chick, chicken / Cobblestones / You're the cream in my coffee / My troubles are over / Piccolo Pete / Man from the south, The / Come on, baby / Harmonica Harry / Mysterious Mose / Slappin' the bass / Washing dishes with my sweetie / Egyptian Ella / Jig time / Play that hot guitar / Oh Mo'nah / My favourite band.
**Cass:** Released 1 May '84, on Living Era by Academy Sound & Vision Records. Catalogue no: **ZC AJA 5029**
**Album:** Released 1 May '84, on Living Era by Academy Sound & Vision Records. Catalogue no: **AJA 5029**

### TED WEEMS BAND 1940/1 (BEAT THE BAND SHOWS)
**Album:** Released Jun '79, on Fanfare by Captain Billy's Music. Catalogue no: **FANFARE 31 131**

## Weisberg, Steve

### I CAN'T STAND ANOTHER NIGHT ALONE (IN BED WITHOUT YOU)
Tracks: / Table for one / Walking home alone / Waking up alone / Trapped in true love / You can't have anything.
Note: EMC's last release for 86 and the first album on Carla Bley and Michael Mantler's new label "Xtra Watt", a side label to Watt. This new label is dedicated to theWatt family musicians. Music composed and arranged by Steve Weisberg. Featured Soloists - Lew Soloff - trumpet (on Trapped) / Baikida Carroll-trumpet (on Table) / Gary Valente-trombone / John Clark-french horn / Wolfgang Puschnig - alto sax, flute / Howard Johnson - baritone sax, contrabass-clarinet, tuba / Hiram Bullock - guitar Steve Weisberg-piano,synthesiser, organ (on Table and You can't) / Steve Swallow - bass / Victor Lewis - drums(on I can't stand) / Anton Fier drums(on Table and Trapped)
**Album:** Released Jan '87, on Xtra Watt Catalogue no: **XW 01**

## Weiss, Harold

### DRUM WHISPERS
**Album:** Released Apr '83, on ECM Catalogue no: **ECM 1249**

## Weiss, Michael

### MICHAEL WEISS QUINTET
Note: Tom Kirkpatrick / R. Lalama / R. Drummond
**Album:** Released Jan '87, on Criss Cross Catalogue no: **CRISS 1022**

## Weldon, Casey Bill

### 1935-37
**Album:** Released '89, on Document Catalogue no: **DLP 565**
**Album:** Released Jan '88, on Old Tramp Catalogue no: **OT 1206**

## Welk, Lawrence

### 22 ALL TIME BIG BAND FAVOURITES
**CD:** Released May '89, on Ranwood Catalogue no: **RCD 7023**

**22 ALL TIME FAVOURITE WALTZES**
**CD:** Released May '89, on Ranwood Catalogue no: **RCD 7028**

**22 GREAT SONGS FOR DANCING**
**Album:** Released May '89, on Ranwood Catalogue no: **RCD 7009**

**22 OF THE GREATEST WALTZES**
**CD:** Released May '89, on Ranwood Catalogue no: **RCD 7004**

**BEST OF LAWRENCE WELK, THE**
**CD:** Released May '89, on Ranwood Catalogue no: **RCD 8226**

**DANCE TO THE BIG BAND SOUNDS**
**CD:** Released May '89, on Ranwood Catalogue no: **RCD 8228**

## Weller, Don

**COMMIT NO NUISANCE (Weller, Don Spring Quartet)**
**Album:** Released Jan '81, on Affinity by Charly Records. Deleted '88. Catalogue no: **AFF 44**

**DON WELLER**
**Album:** Released Oct '79, on Affinity by Charly Records. Deleted '88. Catalogue no: **AFF 43**

## Wells, Dicky

**Biographical details:** One of the most influential trombonists of the swing era, Dicky Wells (1907-85) worked in various bands, including Fletcher Henderson's, and played on sessions made by Spike Hughes in 1933 for British distribution.

He recorded in Paris in 1937 and became famous with Count Basie from 1938-45: for Basie he wrote *After Theatre Jump* and others, but the famous Dickie's Dream was written, for him, by Lester Young. In the 50's and 60's he toured with, among others, Jimmy Rushing and Buck Clayton. (Donald Clarke, March 1988.).

**BONES FOR THE KING**
**CD:** Released Jan '88, on London by London Records Ltd. Catalogue no: **820 601-2**
**Album:** Released Dec '86, on Affinity by Charly Records. Catalogue no: **AFF 164**

**LONESOME ROAD**
**Album:** Released Dec '82, on Uptown (USA) Catalogue no: **UP 27 07**

**TROMBONE FOUR IN HAND**
Tracks: / Blue moon / Airlift / It's all over now / Wine O junction / Heavy duty / Short, tall, fat and small / Girl hunt.
**Album:** Released Oct '86, on Affinity by Charly Records. Catalogue no: **AFF 168**

## Wells, Junior

**Biographical details:** Born Amos Blackmore in Memphis in 1934, blues singer and harmonica player Junior Wells often works with singer-guitarist Buddy Guy. He moved to Chicago in 1946 and played with Muddy Waters and others. Albums include *Hoodoo Man Blues*, with Guy, containing *Snatch It Back And Hold It* and *Good Morning Little Schoolgirl*. (Donald Clarke, March 1988.).

Don Weller

**BLUES HIT BIG TOWN**
**Album:** Released Dec '88, on Delmark (USA) by Delmark Records (USA). Catalogue no: **DL 640**

**CHIEFLY WELLS (Wells, Junior & Magic Sam)**
Tracks: / Two headed woman / Cha cha cha in blues / Lovey dovey lovey one / I'm a stranger / Things i'd do for you / I need me a car / I'll get you too / One day / Calling all blues / Love me / Galloping horses a lazy mule / Magic sam:you don't have to work / Mr. Charlie / My love is your love / She belongs to me / Shakey jake:respect me baby / Hard road.
**Album:** Released Oct '86, on Flyright by Interstate Music. Catalogue no: **FLY 605**

**HOODOO MAN BLUES**
**Album:** Released '74, on Delmark (USA) by Delmark Records (USA). Catalogue no: **DL 612**

**IN MY YOUNGER DAYS**
**Album:** Released Sep '82, on Red Lightnin' by Red Lightning Records. Catalogue no: **RL 007**

**IT'S MY LIFE BABY**
Tracks: / It's my life baby / Country girl / Stormy Monday blues / Checking on my baby / I got a stomach ache / Slow, slow / It's so sad to be lonely / You lied to me / Shake it baby / Early in the morning / Look how baby / Everything's going to be alright.
**CD:** Released Jul '89, on Start by Start Records Ltd.. Catalogue no: **VMCD 7311**
**Cass:** Released Jul '89, on Start by Start Records Ltd.. Catalogue no: **VMTC 6311**
**Album:** Released Jul '89, on Start by Start Records Ltd.. Catalogue no: **VMLP 5311**

**MESSIN' WITH THE KID**
Tracks: / Messin' with the kid / I'm a stranger / Come on in this house / Little by little / Cha cha cha in blues / Prison bars all round me / Love me / It hurts me too / Things I'd do for you / I could cry / So tired / Lovey dovey lovely one / I need me a car / You sure look good to me / You don't care / Two headed woman.
**Album:** Released Oct '86, on Charly R&B by Charly Records. Catalogue no: **CRB 1133**

**MESSIN' WITH THE KID (1957/63)**
**CD:** Released '89, on Flyright by Interstate Music. Catalogue no: **FLY CD 03**

**ON TAP**
**Album:** Released Dec '88, on Delmark (USA) by Delmark Records (USA). Catalogue no: **DL 635**
**Album:** Released '75, on Delmark (USA) by Delmark Records (USA). Catalogue no: **DS 635**

**SOUTHSIDE BLUES JAM**
**Album:** Released Dec '88, on Delmark (USA) by Delmark Records (USA). Catalogue no: **DL 628**
**Album:** Released '74, on Delmark (USA) by Delmark Records (USA).

Catalogue no: **DS 628**

**UNIVERSAL ROCK**
**Album:** Released Oct '86, on Flyright by Interstate Music. Catalogue no: **FLY 588**

## Wellstood, Dick

**Biographical details:** Pianist Dick Wellstood (1927-87), born in Connecticut, played traditional jazz before becoming a highly-rated interpreter of the classic songs of Fats Waller and others of that era. Musicians he played with included Sidney Bechet, Rex Stewart and Kenny Davern. (Donald Clarke, March 1988.).

**ALONE**
**Album:** Released Jun '88, on Jazzology (USA) by Jazzology Records (USA). Catalogue no: **JCE 73**

**CAFE DES COPAINS - AFTER YOU'VE GONE**
**Album:** Released '88, on Unisson (Canada) Catalogue no: **DDA 1008**

**IN A MELLOW ROLL (Wellstood, Dick / Kenny Davern Quartet)**
**Album:** Released Apr '79, on Black Eagle Catalogue no: **BE 1**

**LIVE AT THE CAFE DES COPAINS**
**Album:** Released Sep '87, on Unisson (Canada) Catalogue no: **DDA 1003**

**PIANO SOLOS**
**Album:** Released '88, on Eighty-Eight Upright Catalogue no: **88 UR 005**

**SOME HEFTY CATS**
Tracks: / China boy / Save it pretty mama / Carolina shout / Gone with the wind / Snowy morning blues / Monday date / Red rides again / Sweet Lorraine / Don't get around much anymore / 'S wonderful / Blues at the Copely / Bounce it.
**Album:** Released May '77, on Hefty Jazz Catalogue no: **HJ 100**

**THIS IS THE ONE**
**Album:** Released Aug '88, on Audiophile (USA) by Jazzology Records (USA). Catalogue no: **AP 120**

## Welsh, Alex

**Biographical details:** This British trumpeteer, one of the jazz market's national institutions, enjoyed one minor UK chart single in August 1961. *Tansy* reached No.45, and occurred during the middle of the trad jazz boom. That era helped to bring Welsh's band to greater prominence in concert halls and clubs and, after its demise, ensured that he was never out of work. (Bob MacDonald, 12th May 1985).

**ALEX WELSH SHOWCASE VOLUME 2**
Tracks: / You were meant for me / This is all I ask / Fascinating rhythm / Minor lament / Critics choice / What is this thing called love / You are the sunshine of my life / Recado / Limehouse blues.
**Album:** on Black Lion Catalogue no: **BLP 12121**

**AT HOME: ALEX WELSH**
Note: Recorded 1967. With Roy Williams / Johnny Barnes / Al Gay / Fred Hunt / Ronnie Rae / Jim Douglas / Lennie Hastings. Tracks include: It don't mean a thing / Just one more chance / Just squeeze me / Please / Shadow of your smile, etc..
**Album:** Released Sep '87, on Dormouse Catalogue no: **DM 16**

**DIXIELAND TO DUKE**
**Album:** Released Nov '86, on Dormouse Catalogue no: **DM 7**

**EVENING WITH ALEX WELSH, PART 1**
**Album:** Released '74, on Polydor by Polydor Ltd. Catalogue no: **2460 179**

**IN A PARTY MOOD (Welsh, Alex Band)**
**Album:** Released Nov '77, on One-Up by EMI Records. Catalogue no: **OU 2196**

**LIVE AT ROYAL FESTIVAL HALL 1954-5 (Welsh, Alex/George Melley)**
Tracks: / Panama rag / Memphis blues / Clarinet marmalade / Clark & Randolph blues / New Orleans function / Maryland my Maryland / Wild man blues / New Orleans stomp / Maple rag / Mississippi mud / Mama don't allow/When the saints.
**Album:** Released Apr '88, on Lake by Lake Records. Catalogue no: **LA 5008**
**Cass:** Released Apr '88, on Lake by Lake Records. Catalogue no: **LA 5008C**

**SALUTE TO SATCHMO**
Tracks: / Hear me talkin' to ya / Georgia on my mind / Basin street blues / Muskrat ramble / Ory's creole trombone / Rockin' chair / Wild man blues / I double dare you / That's my home / Ain't misbehavin' / Way down yonder in New Orleans / Royal Garden blues / St. James infirmary / When you're smiling / When it's sleepy time down South.
Note: Welsh, Alex / Humphrey Lyttleton / Bruce Turner / George Chisholm
**2 LP Set:** Released '79, on Black Lion Catalogue no: **BLPX 12161/2**

**TANSY**
Tracks: / Tansy.
**7" Single:** Released Aug '61, on Columbia by EMI Records. Deleted '64. Catalogue no: **DB 4686**

## Werner, Lasse

**TRIPLE PLAY JAZZ PIANO**
Note: Werner, Lasse/Jan Wallgren / Bobo Stenson
**Album:** Released Jun '86, on Dragon by Dragon Records. Catalogue no: **DRLP 12**

## Wess, Frank

**FLUTE JUICE**
Tracks: / Lover come back to me / Spring is here / Riled up / There is no greater love / Nada Mas / Battle royal.
Note: With Tommy Flanagan, Chuck Wayne, George Mraz, Ben Riley. Recorded 8 April 1981.
**Album:** Released Aug '82, on Progressive (USA) by Jazzology Records (USA). Catalogue no: **PRO 7057**

**I HEAR YA TALKIN'**
Note: For some unknown reason, this album was never released by Savoy when first recorded in 1959, and, in fact, this is its first release and a real gem too! When Wess recorded this he was 37 years old and a member of the Count Basie Orchestra, which he joined in 1953. The Basie influence is there, of course, added to the fact that trumpeter Thad Jones also appears here- he, too, was part of the Basie Orchestra at the time. Artists include: Frank Wess (flute, tener, alto sax)/Thad Jones (trumpet) / Curtis Fuller (trombone) / Charlie Fowlkes (baritone saxophone) / Hank Jone (piano) / Eddie Jones (bass) / Gus Johnson (drums). Recorded in New Jersey 1959.
**Album:** Released Dec '85, on Savoy (France) Deleted May '89. Catalogue no: **WL 70503**

**TWO AT THE TOP (Wess, Frank / Johnny Coles)**
**Album:** Released Nov '86, on Uptown (USA) Catalogue no: **UP 27 14**

**WESS OF THE MOON**
**Album:** Released '87, on Commodore Class Catalogue no: **6.25897**

## West Coast Jazz

**WEST COAST JAZZ VOL. 1 1922-31 (Various artists)**
**Album:** Released Apr '79, on Arcadia Catalogue no: **ARCADIA 2001**

**WEST COAST JAZZ VOL. 2 1925-31 (Various artists)**
**Album:** Released Apr '79, on Arcadia Catalogue no: **ARCADIA 2002**

## West Coast Scene

**WEST COAST SCENE (Various artists)**
**Cass set:** Released May '83, on Vogue Jazz (France) by Vogue Records. Catalogue no: **ZCVJD 536**

**WEST COAST SCENE VOL 2 (Various artists)**
Tracks: / Bernie's tune: *Various artists* / My old flame: *Various artists* / I'll remember April: *Various artists* / Neil's blues: *Various artists* / Champ, (The): *Various artists* / Chooch: *Various artists* / Nearness of you, (The): *Various artists* / Whippet: *Various artists* / Milt's tune: *Various artists* / Get happy: *Various artists* / Lost in a fugue: *Various artists* / Tone poem: *Various artists* / I only have eyes for you: *Various artists* / Frantastic: *Various artists* / Frankly speaking: *Various artists* / Illusion: *Various artists* / Caleta: *Various artists* / Crazy quilt: *Vari-*

*ous artists* / Varsity drag: *Various artists* / Swing house: *Various artists* / Love me or leave me: *Various artists* / Half Nelson: *Various artists* / Speak now: *Various artists* / Ladybird: *Various artists.*
**Cass set:** Released May '83, on Vogue Jazz (France) by Vogue Records. Catalogue no: **ZC VJD 570**
**2 LP Set:** Released May '83, on Vogue Jazz (France) by Vogue Records. Catalogue no: **VJD 570**

**WEST COAST SCENE VOL 3 (Various artists)**
Tracks: / Jazz wave: *Flory, Med & His Orchestra* / Davy Jones: *Flory, Med & His Orchestra* / Occasional man, An: *Flory, Med & His Orchestra* / I cover the waterfront: *Flory, Med & His Orchestra* / Between the Devil and the deep blue sea: *Flory, Med & His Orchestra* / Nightmare: *Geller, Herb Quintet* / Cool day, A: *Geller, Herb Quintet* / Princess, The: *Geller, Herb Quintet* / Little girl: *Levy, Lou Trio* / I'll never smile again: *Levy, Lou Trio* / Undecided: *Levy, Lou Trio* / Lover man: *Levy, Lou Trio* / Gypsy, The: *Levy, Lou Trio* / Sunday kind of love, A: *Levy, Lou Trio* / S'Pacific view: *Geller, Herb Sextet* / Jitterbug waltz: *Geller, Herb Sextet* / Fruit, The: *Geller, Herb Sextet.*
Note: Featuring such musicians as Al Porcino, Conte Candoli, Ray Triscariri, Kenny Dorman (trumpets), Bill Holman, Harold Land (tenor saxes), Med Flory, Herb Geller (alto saxes), Russ Freeman, Lou Levy (pianos), Leroy Vinnegar, Ray Brown (basses), Victor Feldman (vibes), Mel Lewis, Hus Johnson (drums). Recorded by Roulette in Los Angeles during 1957-58.
**2 LP Set:** Released Apr '82, on Vogue Jazz (France) by Vogue Records. Catalogue no: **VJD 578**

## West Coast All Stars

**TV JAZZ THEMES**
**Album:** Released Feb '88, on Fresh Sounds (Spain) by Fresh Sounds Records (Spain). Catalogue no: **FS 164**

## West End Jazz Band

**RED HOT CHICAGO**
**Album:** Released '88, on Stomp Off (USA) Catalogue no: **SOS 1042**

**WEST END JAZZ BAND VOL. 2**
**Album:** Released Jun '86, on Stomp Off (USA) Catalogue no: **SOS 1085**

## West End Stompers

**AIN'T YOU GLAD?**
Tracks: / Stevedore stomp / Louisiana / Shout 'em Aunt Tillie / Texas moaner / Ace in the hole / Tuxedo rag / Working man blues / Stockyards strut / Ain't you glad? / Marchand de poissons / Bei mir bist du schon.
**Album:** Released May '81, on Sweet Folk All by Sweet Folk All Records. Catalogue no: **SFA 113**

**TOO BUSY**
Tracks: / Wa, wa, wa / Nothing blues / Thriller rag / Mood indigo / Wild cat blues / Gatemouth / Grandpa's spells / Too busy / Come back, sweet Papa / Storyville blues / Carry me back to old Virginny / Preacher, The.
**Album:** Released May '81, on Sweet Folk All by Sweet Folk All Records. Catalogue no: **SFA 083**

## West Side Blues

**CHICAGO BLUES SESSION 7**
**Album:** Released Sep '87, on Wolf Catalogue no: **WOLF 120 853**

## Westbrook, Mike

**Biographical details:** Mike Westbrook is a bandleader and composer who plays tuba and piano; he was born in 1936 in High Wycombe, Bucks. Influenced by Monk, Duke Ellington, Charles Mignus, he has combined poetry, theatre etc. with jazz inspiration in large-scale works. He formed a jazz workshop in Plymouth Art Centre in 1960, a concert band '66; co-led multimedia group Cosmic Circus 1970-2; formed rock orientated Solid Gold Cadillac 1971-4, Brass Band in 1973 for cabaret on TV and in theatre. Kate Westbrook joined the Brass band in 1974; she plays several instruments, adapts and sings texts in several languages. He formed his Mike Westbrook Orchestra in 1979, she joined in 1981; they formed a trio in 1982 with Cris Biscoe on reeds, Westbrook Theatre Music in 1984. (Donald Clarke).

**CORTEGE**
**2 LP Set:** Released Jul '82, on Original Catalogue no: **ORA 309**

**DANCE BAND, THE**
Tracks: / Parade of the Pierides / Terpsichore: dance / Calliope: epic / Polyhymnia: sacred song / Eurerpe: erotic music / Thalia: lindy hop / Thalia: pastoral festival / Melpomene: tragedy / Erato: love / Erato-boogie / Urania: astronomy / Clio: history.
**CD:** Released Feb '89, on Line by Line Records (W.Germany). Catalogue no: **COCD9.00377**

**GOOSE SAUCE**
**Album:** Released '80, on Original Catalogue no: **ORA 001**

**HUMAN ABSTRACT**
Tracks: / Human abstract / Human abstract (part 2).
**7" Single:** Released Dec '82, on Original Catalogue no: **ABO 8**

**I SEE THY FORM**
Tracks: / I see thy form / Poison tree, A.
**7" Single:** Released Jan '83, on Original Catalogue no: **ABO 3**

**LITTLE WESTBROOK MUSIC, A (Westbrook, Kate & Mike & Chris Biscoe)**
**Album:** Released Oct '83, on Original Catalogue no: **LWM 1**
**Cass:** Released Oct '83, on Original Catalogue no: **ZCLWM 1**

**LONDON BRIDGE IS BROKEN DOWN**
Tracks: / London bridge is broken down / Wenceslas Square / Nahe des geliebten (Part 1 of Berlin Wall) / B.V.B.W. (Belle-vue Berlin Wall) (Part 2 of Berlin Wall) / Traurig aber falsch (Part 3 of Berlin Wall) / Ein vogel / Viennese waltz / Fur sie / Blighters / Les morts / Picardie three / Picardie four / Une fenetre / Picardie six / Aucassin et Nicolette.
**CD Set:** Released Jul '88, on Venture (2) by Virgin Records. Catalogue no: **CDVEB 13**
**Cass set:** Released Jul '88, on Venture (2) by Virgin Records. Catalogue no: **TCVEB 13**
**LP Set:** Released Jul '88, on Venture (2) by Virgin Records. Catalogue no: **VEB 13**

**MAMA CHICAGO**
Tracks: / Mama / Train boogie / Virgins of Illinois / Jackie-ing / Corkscrew / Prohibition / Slaughterhouse / Voyage / Seascape / Prisoners' hymn / Prelude / Preconceived ideas / Heart in heart, hand in hand / Goin' to Chicago / Apple pie / Mama Chicago (part 4) / Mama Chicago (part 5) / Windy City / Titanic song / Concrete / Shipwrecked sailor.
**2 LP Set:** Released Oct '79, on RCA by BMG Records (UK). Catalogue no: **PL 25252**

**ON DUKE'S BIRTHDAY (Westbrook, Mike Orchestra)**
**CD:** Released '88, on Hat Hut Catalogue no: **ARTCD 6021**

**PARIS ALBUM, THE**
**2 LP Set:** Released Dec '81, on Polydor by Polydor Ltd. Catalogue no: **2655 008**

**PIANO**
**Album:** Released '80, on Original Catalogue no: **ORA 002**

**PIER RIDES**
**Album:** Released May '86, on Westbrook Records Catalogue no: **WMLP 1**

**WESTBROOK BLAKE BRIGHT AS A FIRE, THE (Setting Of William Blake)**
Tracks: / Fields, The / I see thy form / London songs / Poison tree, A / Holy Thursday / Let the slave / Price of experience, The.
**Album:** Released Sep '81, on Original Catalogue no: **ORA 203**

**WESTBROOK - ROSSINI**
**CD:** Released Jul '88, on Hat Art Catalogue no: **ARTCD 6002**

## Weston, Randy

**Biographical details:** Randy Weston is a pianist, composer and teacher born in 1926 in Brooklyn NY. He has a unique voice, influenced by Thelonious Monk and by his own interest in African and West Indian music. He worked with Art Blakey in the late 1940s and has led his own trios and quartets since 1955, playing many colleges, museums and festivals; he visited Nigeria in the early '60s, ran a club in Tangeria in 1970 and was back in the USA in 1972. (Donald Clarke).

**BERKSHIRE BLUES**
Tracks: / Three blind mice / Perdido / Purple gazelle / Berkshire blues / Lagos

/ Sweet meat / Ifran.
**Album:** Released Mar '79, on Freedom Catalogue no: **FLP 41026**

**BLUES TO AFRICA**
Tracks: / African village / Bedford stuyvesant / Tangier Bay / Blues to Africa / Kasbah kids / Uhuru Kwanza / Call, The / Kucheza blues / Sahel.
**CD:** Released Dec '87, on Freedom Catalogue no: **FCD 41014**
**Album:** Released Sep '87, on Freedom Catalogue no: **FLP 41014**

**CARNIVAL**
Tracks: / Carnival / Tribute to Duke Ellington / Mystery of love.
**Album:** Released Sep '87, on Freedom Catalogue no: **FLP 41004**
**CD:** Released Sep '87, on Freedom Catalogue no: **FCD 41004**

**HOW HIGH THE MOON**
Tracks: / Loose wig / Run Joe / Theme for Teddy, A / In a little Spanish town / Don't blame me / JK blues / Well you needn't / How high the moon.
**Album:** Released Jul '89, on Meteor by Magnum Music Group. Catalogue no: **MTLP 018**

**MODERN ART OF JAZZ, THE**
**Album:** Released Feb '88, on Fresh Sounds (Spain) by Fresh Sounds Records (Spain). Catalogue no: **FS 284**

**NUIT AFRICAINE**
**Album:** Released Jan '82, on Enja (Germany) by Enja Records (West Germany). Catalogue no: **ENJA 2086**

**PERSPECTIVE (Weston, Randy & Vishnu Wood Duo)**
Tracks: / Blues to be there / Body and soul / Hi fly / Khadesha / African cookbook.
**CD:** Released Jun '89, on Denon Catalogue no: **DC 8554**

**UHURU, AFRICA**
**Album:** Released '88, on Vogue by Vogue Records. Catalogue no: **VG DRY21006**

## Wettling, George

**GEORGE WETTLING JAZZ BAND (Wettling, George Jazz Band)**
Note: Jonah Jones, Bud Freeman, M. Hinton, G. Barnes.
**Album:** Released Feb '87, on JSP by JSP Records. Catalogue no: **JSP 1103**

**GEORGE WETTLING**
Note: With Pee Wee Russell / Lou McGarity / Wild Bill
**Cass:** Released Jun '86, on Holmia Cassettes Catalogue no: **HM 03**

## What More D'Ya Want

**WHAT MORE D'YA WANT (Gospel Rarities 1926-1930) (Various artists)**
**Album:** Released May '89, on Eden by Balaclava Records. Catalogue no: **ELE 5-200**

## Wheatstraw, Peetie

**DEVILS SON IN LAW, THE (1937-41)**
**Album:** Released May '89, on Best Of Blues (USA) by Blue Island Records (USA). Catalogue no: **BOB 10**
**Album:** Released Dec '88, on Old Tramp Catalogue no: **OT 1200**

**PEETIE WHEATSTRAW 1930-41**
**Album:** Released '88, on Earl Archives Catalogue no: **BD 2011**

**PEETIE WHEATSTRAW AND KOKOMO**
**Album:** Released '88, on Blues Classics(USA) by Arhoolie Records (USA). Catalogue no: **BC 4**

## Wheeler, Kenny

**Biographical details:** Kenny Wheeler was born in 1930 in Canada; he plays trumpet, cornet and flugelhorn and is a composer. He studied at Toronto Conservatory, came to UK in 1952; played in big bands, then with John Dankworth '59-65; with Ronnie Scott, Joe Harriott, Tubby Hayes, Clarke-Boland Big Band. With complete mastery over trumpet range and turning to 'free' jazz, he worked with John Stevens' Spontaneous Music Ensemble, Globe Unity Orchestra, Anthony Braxton Quartet, other groups; co-founder of trio Azimuth in 1977, played in Dave Holland Quartet since 1983. He composes for groups of all sizes. Unlike most brass players he keeps getting better as he gets older and is emerging as a giant. Pianist John Taylor, Stan Sulzmann on reeds made a lovely duo LP of Wheeler tunes *Everybody's Song But My Own* in 1987 on Loose Tubes label. See also entries for *Azimuth* and *Dave Holland*. (Donald Clarke)..

**DEER WAN**
**Album:** Released Jan '78, on ECM Catalogue no: **ECM 1102**

**DOUBLE DOUBLE YOU**
Tracks: / Foxy trot / Ma bel / W. W. / Three for D'reen / Blue for Lou / Mark time.
Note: Kenny Wheeler: trumpet, flugelhorn. Mike Brecker: tenor saxophone. John Taylor: piano. David Holland: bass. Jack DeJohnette: drums. Recorded New York, May 1983.
**Album:** Released Feb '84, on ECM Catalogue no: **ECM 1262**
**CD:** Released Jan '90, on ECM Catalogue no: **815 675 2**

**GNU HIGH**
Tracks: / Heyoke / Smatter / Gnu suite.
**Album:** Released Mar '76, on ECM Catalogue no: **ECM 1069**
**CD:** Released Aug '85, on ECM Catalogue no: **825 591-2**

**SONG FOR SOMEONE**
**Album:** Released Jan '74, on Incus by Incus Records. Catalogue no: **INCUS 10**

## When Malindy Sings

**WHEN MALINDY SINGS (JAZZ VOCALISTS 1938 - 1961) (Various artists)**
Tracks: / Can't get started: *Holiday, Billie & Her Orchestra* / I left my baby: *Rushing, Jimmy / Count Basie & his Or chestra* / Piney Brown blues: *Turner, Joe & His Flying Cats* / Careless love: *Turner, Joe/ Willie the lion Smith* / Ja da *Watson, Leo & His Orchestra* / It's the tune that counts: *Watson, Leo & His Orchestra* / Robbins nest: *Thompson Sir Charles / Illinois Jacquet* / Blowtop blues: *Washington, Dinah/ Lionel Hampton & His Septet* / Key largo: *Vaughan Sarah* / Moonlight in Vermont: *Carter Better* / Thou swell: *Carter, Better* / Can' we be friends: *Carter, Better* / Misty *Connor, Chris* / Love: *Connor, Chris* When Malindy sings: *Lincoln, Abbey* End of the love affair, The: *Holiday, Billie & Ray Ellis & His Orchestra.*
**Album:** Released Aug '86, on New World (USA) by New World Records (USA). Catalogue no: **MW 295**

## White, Bukka

**Biographical details:** Blues singer and guitarist White was born Booker T Washington White in 1906 in Mississipp and died in 1977 in Memphis, Tennessee. He made some of the most powerfu and effective blues records, including 14 sides in 1930 -- as Washington White - two in 1937 (including *Shake 'Em On Down*) and 12 more in 1940, includin *Parchman Farm Blues*: while servin there he was recorded by John Loma for the Library of Congress. White wa rediscovered in '63, with much of his power intact, by John Fahey and Ed Denson, who recorded him that year in Memphis (*Legacy of the blues, Vol 1.* on Sonet). He made several more albums but the 1937-40 sides are essential (Donald Clarke, March 1988.).

**ABERDEEN MISSISSIPPI BLUES 1937-40**
Tracks: / Pine bluff arkansas / Shake 'em on down / Black train blues / Strange places blues / Where I change m clothes / Sleepy man blues / Parchman farm blues / Good gin blues / High feve blues / District attorney blues / Fixin' to die / Aberdeen Mississippi Blues Bukka's jitterbug swing / Special stream line.
**Album:** Released Sep '85, on Travelin Man by Interstate Music. Catalogue no **TM 806**

**BIG DADDY**
Tracks: / Black cats bones blues / 193 triggertoe / Cryin' Holy unto the Lord Shake my hand blues / Sic 'Em Dogs O / Gibson Hill / Mama Don' Low / Hc springs Arkansas / Jelly Roll working Black crepe blues / Glory bound train Aberdeen Mississippi blues.
**Album:** Released Apr '87, on Blue Moo (1) by Magnum Music Group. Catalogue no: **BMLP 1039**

**LEGACY OF THE BLUES-1**
Tracks: / Aberdeen Mississippi / Bab please don't go / New Orleans stream line / Parchman Farm blues / Poor boy Remembrance of Charlie Patton / Shak 'em on down / I am the heavenly way Atlanta special, The / Drunk man blues Army blues.

**Album:** Released '74, on Sonet by Sonet Records. Catalogue no: **SNTF 609**
**Album:** Released May '89, on GNP Crescendo (USA) by GNP Crescendo Records (USA). Catalogue no: **GNPS 10011**
**CD:** Released '74, on Sonet by Sonet Records. Catalogue no: **SNTCD 609**

**SKY SONGS VOL.1**
**Album:** Released May '81, on Arhoolie (USA) by Arhoolie Records (USA). Catalogue no: **ARHOOLIE 1019**

**SKY SONGS VOL.2**
**Album:** Released May '81, on Arhoolie (USA) by Arhoolie Records (USA). Catalogue no: **ARHOOLIE 1020**

## White Hot Jazz

**WHITE HOT JAZZ VOL.1 (Various artists)**
**Album:** Released Mar '84, on Broadway (USA) Catalogue no: **BR 115**

## White, Josh

**Biographical details:** Josh White (1908-69) came from Mississippi to become a folk/blues artist popular among the smart set in New York cabarets, long before the blues revival of the 1960's: he was derided by purists but at least he never had to be rediscovered. His left-wing views should have got him into trouble in the early 50's, the peak of his fame (albums on Elektra). But he was a black folk artist, so the professional anti-Communist brigade left him pretty much alone, as unimportant. He remained a popular concert artist until his death. His son, Josh White Jr, born in 1940, began as a child actor in '47 and is also a well-known singer and composer. (Donald Clarke, March 1988.).

**BLUES AND SPIRITUALS (White, Josh & The Ronnie Sisters)**
**Album:** Released Apr '81, on Joker (USA) by Lifetime Records (USA). Catalogue no: **SM 3512**

**JOSH WHITE JUNIOR**
**Album:** Released May '78, on Vogue by Vogue Records. Catalogue no: **VSD 79406**

**JOSH WHITE, VOL.2 1929-35**
**Album:** Released Oct '89, on Earl Archives Catalogue no: **BD 619**

**JOSHUA WHITE 1936-41 (White, Josh & His Carolinians)**
**Album:** Released May '89, on Best Of Blues (USA) by Blue Island Records (USA). Catalogue no: **BOB 11**

**LEGEND OF LEADBELLY (White, Josh/Sonny Terry)**
**Album:** Released '88, on Joker (USA) by Lifetime Records (USA). Catalogue no: **SM 3964**

**WORLD OF JOSH WHITE, THE**
**Album:** Released '69, on Decca by Decca International. Deleted '8. Catalogue no: **SPA 44**

## Whitehead, Annie

**ALIEN STYLE**

Tim Whitehead

Tracks: / Alien style / Star Wars style.
**7" Single:** Released Mar '85, on Paladin Catalogue no: **PALS 100**
**12" Single:** Released Mar '85, on Paladin Catalogue no: **PALS 100 12**

**MIX UP**
Tracks: / Alien style (12") / Pigeon post / Mozambique / Freedom marching / Time change / Badger, The / Rainy daze / Mambo III / Alien style.
**Cass:** Released Jun '85, on Paladin Catalogue no: **PALC 6**
**Album:** Released Jun '85, on Paladin Catalogue no: **PAL 6**

## Whitehead, Tim

**DECISION (Whitehead, Tim Band)**
Tracks: / Varao / Out / Early days / You and I / Chackpoint Charlie / Jiggery pokery / When I fall in love / Decision.
**Album:** Released Oct '88, on Editions EG Catalogue no: **EGED 58**
**Cass:** Released Oct '88, on Editions EG Catalogue no: **EGEDC 58**
**CD:** Released Oct '88, on Editions EG Catalogue no: **EGECD 58**

**ENGLISH PEOPLE (Whithead's, Tim Borderline)**
Tracks: / Little flower / Yellow hill / Rip rap / I want to talk to about you / Diggin' the parch / English people / Impossible question, The.
**Album:** Released '83, on Spotlite Catalogue no: **SPJ 523**

## Whiteman, Paul

**Biographical details:** Bandleader Whiteman (1890-1967) employed such top talent as Bix Beiderbecke, Jack Teagarden, Joe Venuti and Eddie Lang. He was also the first to hire a singer and his vocal trio the Rhythm Boys included the young Bing Crosby. Whiteman was the second-biggest record seller of the entire first half of the century, after Crosby himself: he had well over 200 hits through 1936, seeing off the sentimental songs and corny comedy that had dominated the recording industry in its early years. He commissioned George Gershwin's *Rhapsody In Blue* and his band recorded its most familiar arrangement. He and his arrangers deserve more credit than they are usually given for inventing the modern big band, which could then be adapted by black bandleaders into a vehicle for jazz-based arrangements, touching off the swing era which, ironically, made Whiteman sound old-fashioned. (Donald Clarke).

**1938 (Whiteman, Paul & His Orchestra)**
**Album:** Released Apr '81, on Solid Sender Catalogue no: **SOL 516**

**BIRTH OF RHAPSODY IN BLUE, THE**
Note: Historic Aeolian Hall concert in 1924.
**LP Set:** Released Jan '89, on Music Masters by Music Masters Records. Catalogue no: **MMD 20113X/14T**
**Cass set:** Released Jan '89, on Music Masters by Music Masters Records. Catalogue no: **MMD 40113W/14M**
**CD Set:** Released Jan '89, on Music Masters by Music Masters Records. Catalogue no: **MMD 60113 T**

**FOREVER POPS**
**Album:** Released Mar '90, on Sounds Rare Catalogue no: **SR5001**

**IN CONCERT AT QUEEN ELIZABETH HALL (Whiteman, Paul & His Orchestra)**
**Album:** Released Apr '79, on Wave by Wave Records. Catalogue no: **WAVE LP 27**

**JAZZ A LA KING 1920-1936**
Tracks: / Wang wang blues / Whispering / Everybody step / Hot lips / Way down yonder in New Orleans / Nuthin' but / Charleston / Footloose / Red hot Henry Brown / Milenberg joys / Charlestonette / Bell hoppin' blues / St. Louis blues / Wistful and blue / Muddy waters / I'm coming Virginia / Side by side / Magnolia / Sensation stomp / Five step / Lonely melody / Mississippi mud / From Monday on / Stop the Sun, stop the Moon / Rockin' chair / G. blues / Itchola / Serenade for a wealthy widow / Nobody's sweetheart / Farewell blues / Announcer's blues / Saddle your blues to a wild mustang.
**2 LP Set:** Released '83, on RCA (France) by BMG Records (France). Catalogue no: **PM 42413**

**LEGENDARY, THE**
**Cass:** Released Mar '90, on Silva Screen by Silva Screen Records. Catalogue no: **MRT 40032**

**MUSIC OF THE ROARING 20'S (Whiteman, Paul & His Orchestra)**
**Album:** Released Dec '77, on Wave by Wave Records. Catalogue no: **WAVE LP 27**

**NEW PAUL WHITEMAN ORCHESTRA, THE (Whiteman, Paul & His Orchestra)**
**Album:** Released Mar '79, on Monmouth Evergreen Catalogue no: **MES 7078**

**PAUL WHITEMAN COLLECTION (20 golden greats)**
Tracks: / Song of India / Japanese sandman / What'll I do? / Whispering / Hot lips / Coquette / When / Lovable / Is it gonna be long? / Oh, have you no idea? / Anytime, anyday, anywhere / My man / Love nest, The / I'll build a stairway to Paradise / Three o'clock in the morning / Felix the cat / Tain't so, honey, tain't so / I'd rather cry over you / Georgie Porgie / Out-of-town girl.
**Album:** Released Dec '87, on Deja Vu Catalogue no: **DVLP 2110**
**Cass:** Released Dec '87, on Deja Vu Catalogue no: **DVMC 2110**

**SHAKING THE BLUES AWAY 1920-1927 (Whiteman, Paul & His Orchestra)**
Tracks: / Wang wang blues / On the gin gin ginny shore / Stumbling / Hot lips / I'll build a stairway to paradise / Everything is K.O. in K.Y. / If I can't have the sweetie I want / Shake your feet / Steppin' out / Lazy / Charleston / Ukelele lady / Steppin' in society / Footloose / Got no time / No foolin' Manhattan / Sweet and low down / Birth of the blues / Shakin' the blues away.
**Album:** Released Mar '83, on Halcyon (USA) by Submarine Records. Catalogue no: **HAL 21**

**WANG WANG BLUES**
**Cass:** Released Jun '86, on Astan (USA) Catalogue no: **40184**

**WHITEMAN STOMP 1923-36**
**Album:** Released Dec '87, on Halcyon (USA) by Submarine Records. Catalogue no: **HDL 116**
**Cass:** Released Dec '87, on Halcyon (USA) by Submarine Records. Catalogue no: **CHDL 116**

## Whiting, Margaret

**Biographical details:** The daughter of top songwriter Richard Whiting (1891-1938), Margaret Whiting was born in Detroit in 1924. She began singing on the radio in 1941 with Johnny Mercer, sang with several bands and had more than 40 American hits on Capitol from 1946 to '54, including duets with country singer Jimmy Wakely: they had a smash with *Slippin' Around* in '49. She toured in the 70's with a nostalgia show, *Cavalcade of Bands*. (Donald Clarke, March 1988.).

**COME A LITTLE CLOSER**
**Album:** Released Aug '88, on Audiophile (USA) by Jazzology Records (USA). Catalogue no: **AP 173**

**GOIN' PLACES**
Tracks: / Gypsy in my soul / Sentimental journey / Anyplace I hang my hat is home / I'm gonna move to the outskirts of town / Gone with the wind / Runnin' wild / Between the devil and the deep blue sea / Over the rainbow / Hit the road to dreamland / East of the sun / Song of the wanderer / Home.
**Album:** Released Mar '85, on Jasmine by Hasmick Promotions. Catalogue no: **JASM 1514**

**JEROME KERN SONGBOOK, THE**
Tracks: / Fine romance, a / Song is you, The / I'm old fashioned / Yesterday / Look for the silver lining / I won't dance / Long ago and far away / Smoke gets in your eyes / You couldn't be cuter / Way you look tonight / Dearly beloved / Bill / She didn't say yes / All the things you are.
**Cass:** Released Nov '89, on Memoir by Memoir Records. Catalogue no: **CMOIR 125**
**Album:** Released Sep '87, on Memoir by Memoir Records. Catalogue no: **MOIR 125**

**LADY'S IN LOVE WITH YOU, THE**
**Album:** Released Jun '86, on Audiophile (USA) by Jazzology Records (USA). Catalogue no: **AP 207**

**LOVE SONGS BY MARGARET WHITING**
Tracks: / My ideal / Moonlight in Vermont / Bill / You're an old smoothie / Younger than Springtime / I've never been in love before / It might as well be spring / Tree in the meadow, A / He's funny that way / Wonderful guy / Come rain or come shine / If I had you.
**Album:** Released Jun '85, on Capitol by EMI Records. Deleted Aug '89. Catalogue no: **ED 2604221**

**Tommy Whittle - More Waxing with Whittle (Esquire)**

**Cass:** Released Jun '85, on Capitol by EMI Recc ds. Deleted Jun '88. Catalogue no: **ED 2604224**

### TOO MARVELLOUS FOR WORDS

**Album:** Released Aug '88, on Audiophile (USA) by Jazzology Records (USA). Catalogue no: **AP 152**

## Whittle, Tommy

### JIG SAW (Whittle, Tommy Quartet)

**Album:** Released Jun '79, on Alamo Deleted '88. Catalogue no: **AJ 4501**

### MORE WAXING WITH WHITTLE

Tracks: / Archer's treat / Pyramid / Willow weep for me / Crazy rhythm / Tenbar gait / Finisher, The / Someone to watch over me / Harry's blues / Flamingo / (I don't stand) a ghost of a chance(with you) / I'll remember April / You've done something to my heart / Stars fell on Alabama.

Note: "Tommy Whittle" wrote Digby Fairweather in Jazz, The Essential Companion (Grafton Books) "is a shining exception to the view that years of studio work dull the edges of jazz creativity." The truth of that opinion is manifest in every performance here on this second volume of the recordings which Tommy made for Esquire in the studios (as opposed to the occasion in February, 1954 when Carlo Krahmer and Peter Newbrook took their recording gear to the Royal Festival Hall to capture Tommy in full flight at a concert put on by the National Jazz Federation). The first volume in this series will be found on Esquire 305 with comprehensive coverage of Tommy's early career by Brian Davis. The band heard throughout this album is the one which Tommy formed in the summer of 1954 and took into the Studio 51 club. It was, virtually, an amalgamation of the Dill Jones Trio and the Whittle-Klein two-sax team. Tommy and Dill had known each other for years and had been members of the Medway Towns jazz circles in the middle Forties; Tommy was living in Gillingham in those days and playing with a local band led by Claude Giddings while Dill was in the Royal Navy and stationed at Chatham. The five and a half years which Tommy spent with the Ted Heath orchestra and his subsequent work with the short-lived BBC Show Band prepared Whittle for his task as a group leader in his own right and the quintet with Harry Klein gave him the opportunity to sketch out arranged ensemble passages as opposed to busked theme-solos-theme routines with a quartet.

The growing stature of Tommy Whittle may be judged from the fact that, by October 1956, he was selected to play in the United States as part of an exchange deal involving a visit to Britain by Sydney Bechet. (The following April Tommy took a quartet accross the Atlantic, this time in exchange for a visit to Britain by the Gerry Mulligan Quartet.) This album focuses our attention on the growing confidence which is manifest in Whittle's work and a subtle shift in emphasis from the Lester Young influence on the earlier dates to the more forceful, extrovert approach of Zoot Sims on the later recordings. The first session opens with a tune by drummer Eddie Taylor, the title of which is a play on words. *Archer Street*, between Piccadilly Circus and Cambridge Circus, was the London thoroughfare which used to be the musicians unofficial "labour exchange". It was here that bookers could "fix" bands from the musicians who congregated in the street each day. The music is swift moving and makes use of drum breaks. *Pyramid* brings to mind Duke Jordans *Jor-du* and has a very Lester-like, relaxed tenor solo from Tommy. The three chorus *Willow Weep For Me* is beautiful and makes use of the saxophone lines intertwining to masterly effect. This particular version has never previously been issued and was, in fact, a studio run-through, too long for issue as a 78 RPM record. By contrast *Crazy Rhythm* is fast and furious with solos from everyone. By the following March the book had been expanded and included more originals by Tommy and Harry. *Ten-Bar Gait* makes use of two separate lines in the theme statement and despite Tommy's graceful bow in the direction of Lester Young during his three chorus solo, the group is close to the conception of the Gerry Mulligan Quartet. Eddie Taylor plays maraccas behind Tommy at the beginning of *The Finisher*, a Whittle original which commences with three fine choruses from the late Dill Jones. *Someone To Watch Over Me* comprises just one and a half choruses at slow ballad tempo but the grace of the playing, the delicate and Teddy Wilson-like piano and the skilful harmonising of the saxophones is memorable. *Harry's Blues* turns out to be a showcase not for the composer but for pianist Dill Jones. Dill did not recognise stylistic barriers but simply loved good music. His death in 1984 at the age of 60 was a sad blow to those of us who had been privileged to know him and his music.

By the time the Quintet celebrated its first birthday Dave Willis had taken over grom Joe Muddell and this was the band which Esquire put in the studio to record a six-title ten inch LP. Five of the titles are included here; the sixth, *Cherokee*, will be on the third volume in this series. *Flamingo* has a Latin-American feel at the outset but by the time the solos start the rhythm has reverted to commomn time. Tommy's solo here is very much in the Zoot Sims vein. *Ghost of a chance* is another chorus and a half ballad with Whittle launching himself straight into his imptovisations and Klein's baritone continuing the mood from the mid point of the chorus. *I'll remember April* is a tune which tenor players love and Tommy is no exception. The Zoot Sims influence is apparent again as Whittleattacks his solo chorus. Noel Gay was a song-writer whose work has seldom attracted the attention of jazzmen, (Gay wrote *The Lambeth Walk* and *Run Rabbit Run* for example). However, *You've Done Something To Me* turned out to be intriguing; it has a 40 bar chorus and some quite unexpected chord changes which Whittle, Klein and Jones use to considerable advantage. Finally, *Stars Fell On Alabama*, another graceful ballad performance, supremely relaxed and with Tommy using terminal vibrato at the ends of his phrases. Here then are 13 pieces by a fine little band which, without the foresight of Esquire Records, might have been forgotten. Tommy can be proud of the music to be heard here for the years have dealt kindly with this excellent unit. Alun Morgan 1988.

**Album:** Released Dec '87, on Esquire by Titan Int. Prod.. Catalogue no: **ESQ 334**

### STRAIGHT EIGHT (Whittle, Tommy & Alan Barnes)

Tracks: / Stgraight eight / Con Alma / Joking / Pelppercorn / Note 8.7 / Goodbye / That's all / Early / Stablemates.

**Album:** Released May '86, on Miles Music by Miles Music Records. Catalogue no: **MM 001**

### WAXING WITH WHITTLE

**Album:** Released Apr '79, on Esquire by Titan Int. Prod.. Catalogue no: **ESQ 305**

### WHY NOT ? (Whittle, Tommy Quartet)

**Album:** Released Apr '79, on JAM (USA) by JAM Records (USA). Catalogue no: **JAM 648**

## Widespread Jazz

### PARIS BLUES

**Cass:** Released Oct '85, on CBS (import) by CBS Records. Catalogue no: **40 26561**

**Album:** Released Oct '85, on CBS (import) by CBS Records. Catalogue no: **26561**

### SWING IS THE THING

**Album:** Released '88, on Echo by Echo Records. Deleted Jun '89. Catalogue no: **ECJ 403**

## Wiggins, Gerald

### KING AND I, THE (Wiggins, Gerald Trio)

**Album:** Released Feb '88, on Fresh Sounds (Spain) by Fresh Sounds Records (Spain). Catalogue no: **FS 56**

## Wiggs, Johnny

### CONGO SQUARE (Wiggs, Johnny & Maxine Sullivan)

**Album:** Released '88, on New Orleans Catalogue no: **NOR 7206**

## Wilber, Bob

**Biographical details:** Bob Wilber was born in 1928 in New York City. The clarinettist and soprano saxophonist studied with the great Sidney Bechet and has been typed as a traditionalist, but he actually plays anything he wants, feeling strongly that the home of jazz is in mainstream of popular music. His co-operative group The Six in the mid-'50s was an attempt to create a music neither old-fashioned nor self-conciously modern. He played with The World's Greatest Jazz Band, which had begun as a recording group founded by Yank Lawson and Bob Haggart (alumni of the Bob Crosby band), was renamed in 1968 at the Colorado Jazz Festival and made many albums in the '70s. Wilber left in 1973 and formed Soprano Summit with Kenny Davern, Marty Grosz on banjo and guitar, George Duvivier on bass, various drummers. He toured in a trio with his wife, vocalist Joanne Horton and Dave McKenna on piano; he formed sextet Bechet Legacy in 1981; he has transcribed the music of Jelly Roll Morton and King Oliver and recreated the Duke Ellington Cotton Club sound for the film of that name. He has survived decades of critical lusting after the new to become one of the most popular musicians in the present age of repertory music, as has Davern (born 1935 in Long Island, NY); after Soprano Summit, Wilber returned to clarinet, on which he is very highly regarded. (Donald Clarke)..

**BOB WILBER**
**Album:** Released '88, on Phontastic (Sweden) Catalogue no: **PHON 50-14**

**BOB WILBER AND THE BECHET LEGACY**
Tracks: / Down in Honky Tonk Town / Si tu vois ma mere / Stop shimmying sister / Lazy blues / If I let you get away with it / Roses of Picardy / Petite fleur / Rue des Champes Elysees / Chant in the night / I'm a little blackbird / Kansas City man / China boy.
**Album:** Released May '81, on Bodeswell by Cadillac Music. Deleted '86. Catalogue no: **BW 103**

**BOB WILBER AND HIS FAMOUS JAZZ BAND (Wilber, Bob & His Famous Jazz Band)**
Note: Guest Star: Sidney Bechet.
**Album:** Released Jun '86, on Jazzology (USA) by Jazzology Records (USA). Catalogue no: **J 44**

**DIZZY FINGERS (Wilber, Bob Sextet)**
Tracks: / Dizzy fingers / Poor butterfly / Airmail special / Foolin' myself / Soft winds / Jumpin' at the Woodside / Clarinade / Rose room / Royal Garden blues / What a little moonlight can do / Memories of you / World is waiting for the sunrise, The.
Note: With Lars Erstrand, Mark Shane, Chris Flory, Phil Flanagan, Chuck Riggs.
**Album:** Released May '81, on Bodeswell by Cadillac Music. Deleted '86. Catalogue no: **BW 101**
**Album:** Released Aug '88, on Audiophile (USA) by Jazzology Records (USA). Catalogue no: **AP 187**

**DUET (Wilber, Bob & Dick Wellstood)**
**Album:** Released Jul '88, on Parkwood Catalogue no: **PARKWOOD 103**

**GROOVIN' AT THE GRUNEWALD**
Tracks: / My blue Heaven / Did I remember? / Love, your magic spell is everywhere / Please be kind / End of a beautiful friendship / Everywhere you go / Groovin' at the Grunewald / June night / Someone to watch over me / I'm beginning to see the light / Lotus blossom / Best thing for you, The.
Note: With Dave McKenna and Pug Horton.
**Album:** Released '82, on Phontastic (Sweden) Catalogue no: **PHONT 7414**

**IN THE MOOD FOR SWING**
Tracks: / I'm in the mood for swing / Talk of the town / Dinah / I'm confessin' / When lights are low / Ring dem bells / Memories of you / Bei mir bist du schon / Yours and mine / Chinatown.
Note: Featuring the American All Stars, with Lars Erstrand, Hank Jones, Frank Wess, Jimmy Maxwell, Al Klink, Buck Pizzarelli.
**Album:** Released '82, on Phontastic (Sweden) Catalogue no: **PHONT 7526**
**CD:** Released Apr '88, on Phontastic (Sweden) Catalogue no: **PHONTCD 7526**

**MOZART K581, K498**
**Album:** Released Feb '81, on Artemis Catalogue no: **ARTE 7109**

**MUSIC OF HOAGY CARMICHAEL (Wilber, Bob & Kenny Davern)**
**Album:** Released May '79, on Monmouth Evergreen Catalogue no: **MFS 6917**

**MUSIC OF KING OLIVER'S CREOLE (Wilber, Bob Ensemble)**
**Album:** Released '89, on GHB by Jazzology Records (USA). Catalogue no: **GHB 201**

**MUSIC OF KING OLIVER-VOL 1, THE (Wilber, Bob Jazz Repertory Orchestra)**
**Album:** Released Oct '84, on Bodeswell by Cadillac Music. Catalogue no: **BW 107**

**ODE TO BECHET (Wilber, Bob & The Bechet Legacy)**
Tracks: / Margie / Blues in the air / I can't believe that you're in love with me / I get the blues when it rains / Mooche, The / I ain't gonna give nobody none of this jelly-roll / When my dreamboat comes home / Ode to Bechet / Quincy Street stomp / Sailboat in the moonlight / High society / Bechet's fantasy / Shake it and break it.
**Cass:** Released Jul '83, on Bodeswell by Cadillac Music. Catalogue no: **BWC 104**
**Album:** Released Jul '83, on Bodeswell by Cadillac Music. Catalogue no: **BW 104**

**ON THE ROAD (Wilber, Bob & The Bechet Legacy)**
Tracks: / Lady be good / Georgia cabin / What a dream / I keep calling your name / Polka dot stomp / Egyptian fantasy / Ghost of the blues / Summertime / Love for sale / Santa Claus blues / Indian summer / Dans la rue d'antibes.
**Cass:** Released Jul '83, on Bodeswell by Cadillac Music. Catalogue no: **BWC 105**
**Album:** Released Jul '83, on Bodeswell by Cadillac Music. Catalogue no: **BW 105**

**ORIGINAL WILBER**
Tracks: / Movin' 'n' groovin' / BG / Treasure / Land of the midnight sun / Don't go away / Windsong / Wequaset Wall / I've loved you all my life / Hymn: In memory of Joe Oliver / I can't forget you now / Crawfish shuffle.
Note: With Dave McKenna and Pug Horton.
**Album:** Released '82, on Phontastic (Sweden) Catalogue no: **PHONT 7519**

**RAPTUROUS REEDS**
Tracks: / Jumping at the Woodside / Chloe / Sherman shuffle / Sultry summer day / Stompin' at the Savoy / You are my lucky star / I've loved you all my life / I double dare you / Alone together / Linger awhile / Yours is my heart alone.
Note: Bob Wilber, clarinet, alto sax, soprano sax; Arne Domerus, clarinet, alto sax; Bengt Hallberg, piano; Rune Gustafsson, guitar, Sture Nordin, bass; Rune Carlsson, drums.
**CD:** Released Feb '89, on Phontastic (Sweden) Catalogue no: **PHONTCD 7517**
**Album:** Released '82, on Phontastic (Sweden) Catalogue no: **PHONT 7517**

**REFLECTIONS (Wilber, Bob & The Bodeswell Strings)**
**Album:** Released Oct '84, on Circle (USA) by Jazzology Records (USA). Catalogue no: **BW 106**
**Album:** Released Aug '88, on Circle (USA) by Jazzology Records (USA). Catalogue no: **CLP 98**

**SOPRANO SUMMIT (Wilber, Bob & Kenny Davern)**
Tracks: / Swing parade / Song of songs / Meet me tonight in dreamland / Penny rag / Mooche, The / Oh sister ain't that hot / Steal away / Egyptian fantasy / Fish vendor, The / Johnny was there / Please clarify / Where are we.
**Album:** Released Apr '81, on World Jazz Catalogue no: **WJLPS 5**

**SOPRANO SUMMIT 2 (Wilber, Bob & Kenny Davern)**
Tracks: / Frog-I-more rag / Solace 1 / Tango a la Caprice / If you went away / Lincoln garden stomp / Solace 2 / Sidewalk blues / Creole nights / Rialto ripples / Sunflower slow drag.
**Album:** Released Apr '81, on World Jazz Catalogue no: **WJLPS 13**

**SOPRANO SUMMIT CONCERTO (Wilber, Bob & Kenny Davern)**
**Album:** Released Jun '77, on Concord Jazz by Concord Jazz Records (USA). Catalogue no: **CJ 129**

**SWINGIN' FOR THE KING**
Tracks: / Let's dance / It's been so long / Changes / Goodnight my love / Best things in life are free, The / I had to do it / Bach goes to town / By myself / Silhouetted in the moonlight / Jubilee / Why do I love you? / Seven come eleven / Jersey bounce / Deep night / All the

things you are / We'll meet again / Keep your sunny side up / Rachel's dream / Lullaby in rhythm / Miss my lovin' time / Someone else is taking my place / Lovely to look at / Stealin' apples / Goodbye.
Note: Featuring the Phontastic Swing Band -- Arne Domerus, Ove Lind, Anders Ohman, Lars Erstrand, Lars Siosten, Karl Erik Holgren, Arne Wilhemsson, Rune Carlsson, Pug Horton.
**2 LP Set:** Released '82, on Phontastic (Sweden) Catalogue no: **PHONT 7406/07**

**VITAL WILBER**
**Album:** Released '88, on Phontastic (Sweden) Catalogue no: **PHON 7**

## Wildflowers.....

**WILDFLOWERS (NEW YORK LOFT JAZZ SESSIONS 1976) VOL.1(Various artists)**
**Album:** Released Jun '77, on Douglas (USA) Deleted '87. Catalogue no: **NBLP 7045**

**WILDFLOWERS (NEW YORK LOFT JAZZ SESSIONS 1976) VOL.2 (Various artists)**
**Album:** Released Jun '77, on Douglas (USA) Deleted '87. Catalogue no: **NBLP 7046**

**WILDFLOWERS (NEW YORK LOFT JAZZ SESSIONS 1976) VOL.3 (Various artists)**
**Album:** Released Jun '77, on Douglas (USA) Deleted '87. Catalogue no: **NBLP 7047**

**WILDFLOWERS (NEW YORK LOFT JAZZ SESSIONS 1976 VOL.4 (Various artists)**
**Album:** Released Jun '77, on Douglas (USA) Deleted '87. Catalogue no: **NBLP 7048**

**WILDFLOWERS (NEW YORK LOFT JAZZ SESSIONS 1976 VOL.5 (Various artists)**
**Album:** Released Jun '77, on Douglas (USA) Deleted '87. Catalogue no: **NBLP 7049**

## Wilen, Barney

**UN TEMOIN DANS LA VILLE / JAZZ SUR**
Tracks: / Temoin dans la ville / La pendaison / Melodie pour les radio-taxis / Poursuite et metro / Ambiance pourpre / Premeditation dans l'appartement / La vie n'est qu'une lutte / Complainte du chauffeur / Sur l'antenne / S.O.S. radio-taxis / Final au jardin d'acclimatation / Swing 39 / Vamp menilmontant / John's groove / B. B. B. (Bag's Barney blues') / Swingin' Parisian rhythm / J'ai ta main / Nuages / La route enchantee / Que rest et il de nos amours / Minor's swing / Epistrophy.
Note: Original jazz soundtrack to the film Un Temoin Dans La Villé produced by Edouard Molinaro plus 1958 recording titles Jazz Sur Seine featuring Barney Wilen original compositions as well as pieces by Django Reinhardt and Thelonious Monk.
**CD:** Released Mar '88, on ECM Catalogue no: **832 658 2**

## Wiley, Lee

**Biographical details:** Lee Wiley (1915-75) was a highly-regarded American jazz singer with a breathy, little girl sound, distinctive vibrato, intimate warmth and great respect for lyrics. She sang with various bands and made classic albums in the days of 78s with the best available musicians in studio pick-up groups. She was married to pianist Jess Stacy and toured with him in the mid-40's, continuing to use the best freelance back-up on the occasional album, like *Night In Manhattan* (early 50's), *A Touch Of The Blues* ('58) and *Back Home Again* ('71). She was also a lyricist, adding words to Victor Young's music for *Got The South In My Soul* and *Anytime, Anyday, Anywhere.* (Donald Clarke, March 1988.).

**BACK HOME AGAIN**
**Album:** Released Mar '79, on Monmouth Evergreen Catalogue no: **MES 7041**

**DUOLOGUE 1954 (Wiley, Lee & Ellis Larkins)**
**Album:** Released Nov '88, on Black Lion Catalogue no: **BLP 60911**
**CD:** Released Jun '88, on Black Lion Catalogue no: **BLCD 760911**

**LEE WILEY AND BUNNY BERIGAN (1940) (Wiley, Lee & Bunny Berigan)**
**Album:** Released Nov '88, on Blu-Disc (USA) Catalogue no: **T 1013**

**LEE WILEY: ON THE AIR VOLUME 1**
Tracks: / You came to my rescue / Three little words / You turned the tables on me / Here's love in your eyes / South in my soul, The / I'm coming Virginia / Thousand goodnights, A / Funny little world / Sometimes I feel like a motherless child / If I love again / Little things you used to do, The / Robins and roses / When I'm with you / Crosspatch.
**Album:** Released Feb '88, on Totem Catalogue no: **TOTEM 1021**

**LEE WILEY: ON THE AIR VOLUME 2**
Tracks: / I've got a crush on you / Sweet and low down / You're lucky to me / On the sunny side of the street / Sugar / Don't blame me / When your lover has gone / How long has this been going on? / Ghost of a chance / I can't get started / Someone to watch over me / Any old time / Man I love, The / Down with love.
**Album:** Released May '79, on Totem Catalogue no: **TOTEM 1033**

**LEE WILEY RARITIES**
**CD:** Released Aug '89, on Jass Catalogue no: **JASSCD 15**

**LEE WILEY SINGS**
**Album:** Released Jun '88, on Audiophile (USA) by Jazzology Records (USA). Catalogue no: **AP 10**

**LEE WILEY SINGS GERSHWIN AND COLE PORTER**
**Album:** Released Mar '79, on Monmouth Evergreen Catalogue no: **MES 7034**

**LEE WILEY SINGS RODGERS AND HART AND HAROLD ARLEN**
**Album:** Released Mar '79, on Monmouth Evergreen Catalogue no: **MES 6807**

**LEGENDARY - COLLECTORS ITEMS.**
**Album:** Released Mar '90, on Tono Catalogue no: **TJ6004**

**SINGS THE SONGS OF GEORGE AND IRA GERSHWIN AND COLE PORTER**
**Album:** Released Jun '86, on Audiophile (USA) by Jazzology Records (USA). Catalogue no: **AP 1**

**SWEET AND LOWDOWN**
Tracks: / 'S wonderful / But not for me / Easy to love / Let's do it.
Note: Gershwin and Porter songs recorded in 1939 and 1940, featuring Fats Waller, Pee Wee Russell, Max Kaminsky and others. Tracks include those listed above.
**Album:** Released Dec '82, on Halcyon (USA) by Submarine Records. Catalogue no: **HAL 6**

**TOUCH OF THE BLUES, A**
Tracks: / Memphis blues, The / From the land of the sky blue water / Ace in the hole, The / Someday you'll be sorry / My melancholy baby / Hundred years from today / Blues in my heart / Maybe you'll be there / Between the devil and the deep blue sea / I don't want to walk without you / Make believe / Touch of the blues, A.
**Album:** Released Jun '87, on RCA by BMG Records (UK). Deleted Jul '89. Catalogue no: **NL 90041**
**Cass:** Released Jun '87, on RCA by BMG Records (UK). Deleted Jul '89. Catalogue no: **NK 90041**

**YOU LEAVE ME BREATHLESS**
Note: Broadcasts and rarities.
**Album:** Released Jun '88, on Jass Catalogue no: **JASS 15**

## Wilkerson, Don

**PREACH BROTHER**
**Album:** Released Sep '84, on Blue Note by EMI Records. Deleted '87. Catalogue no: **BST 84107**

**TEXAS TWISTER, THE**
**Album:** Released Feb '88, on Riverside (USA) by Fantasy Inc (USA). Catalogue no: **RSLP 332**

## Wilkins, Ernie

**BIG NEW BAND OF THE 60'S, THE (Wilkins, Ernie Orchestra)**
**Album:** Released Feb '88, on Fresh Sounds (Spain) by Fresh Sounds Records (Spain). Catalogue no: **FS 199**

**ERNIE WILKINS ALMOST BIG BAND**
**Album:** Released Dec '82, on Matrix (Denmark) Catalogue no: **MTX-29203**

**WILKINS, ERNIE AND THE ALMOST BIG BAND (Wilkins, Ernie**

**& The Almost Big Band)**
Note: With Kenny Drew & Ed Thigpen
**Album:** Released Sep '86, on Storyville by Storyville Records AB. Catalogue no: **SLP 4051**

## Williams, Big Joe

**Biographical details:** 'Big' Joe Williams (1903-82) was a blues singer and guitarist, aka Po' Joe Williams; not to be confused with the jazz singer Joe Williams; there were two or three more blues singers named Joe Williams, one recording before WWII, at least two younger men who recorded after the war. Big Joe had a distinctive sound on a nine-string guitar. Big Joé was one of 16 children; he made himself a one-string instrument and began singing as a small child; worked in railroad gangs, lumber camps; his records for Bluebird in 1935-41 are compiled on *Baby, Please Don't Go* on Charly; later LPs are on Sonet, Delmark and Arhoolie. (Donald Clarke)..

**BABY PLEASE DON'T GO**
**Album:** Released Sep '87, on Bluetime (Denmark) by Contact Records (Denmark). Catalogue no: **BT 2007**

**BIG JOE AND SONNY BOY WILLIAMSON (Williams, Big Joe & Sonny Boy Williamson)**
**Album:** Released '88, on Blues Classics(USA) by Arhoolie Records (USA). Catalogue no: **BC 21**

**BIG JOE WILLIAMS**
**Album:** Released '88, on Arhoolie (USA) by Arhoolie Records (USA). Catalogue no: **F 1053**
**Album:** Released '88, on Storyville by Storyville Records AB. Catalogue no: **SLP 224**

**BIG JOE WILLIAMS 1974**
**Album:** Released Feb '89, on Wolf Catalogue no: **120 918**

**FIELD RECORDINGS. 1973-80**
**Album:** Released '88, on L&R Catalogue no: **LR 42.047**

**LEGACY OF THE BLUES-6**
Tracks: / I've been wrong but I'll be right / Black gal you're sure looking warm / When I first left home / Little Annie May / Levee break blues / Hang it up on the wall / Lone wolf / This heavy stuff of mine / Tell my mother / Big fat mama / Back on my feet / Jefferson and Franklin blues.
**Album:** Released May '74, on Sonet by Sonet Records. Catalogue no: **SNTF 635**
**Album:** Released May '89, on GNP Crescendo (USA) by GNP Crescendo Records (USA). Catalogue no: **GNPS 10016**
**CD:** Released May '74, on Sonet by Sonet Records. Catalogue no: **SNTCD 635**

**MALVINA MY SWEET WOMAN**
**Album:** Released '88, on Oldie Blues Catalogue no: **OL 2804**

**NINE STRING GUITAR BLUES**
**Album:** Released May '74, on Delmark (USA) by Delmark Records (USA). Catalogue no: **DS 627**

**PINEY WOOD BLUES**
**Album:** Released May '74, on Delmark (USA) by Delmark Records (USA). Catalogue no: **DL 602**

**THINKING OF WHAT THEY DID**
**Album:** Released May '81, on Arhoolie (USA) by Arhoolie Records (USA). Catalogue no: **ARHOOLIE 1053**

**TOUGH TIMES**
**Album:** Released May '81, on Arhoolie (USA) by Arhoolie Records (USA). Catalogue no: **ARHOOLIE 1002**

## Williams, Clarence

**Biographical details:** Clarence Williams was one of the first superstars of the record industry, as a songwriter, pianist, record producer, music publisher, also an occasional vocalist. He was born in 1893 in Louisiana and died in 1965 in New York. He ran away from home at the age of 12 to work in a minstrel show and was 'Race Records' director for Okeh in the 1920s; he made nearly 300 sides under his own name 1921-38 including the famous Blue Five sessions of the mid-20's, with musicians like Louis Armstrong and Sidney Bechet backing vocalists, probably the best example we have of how an early jazz band sounded in the taverns of New Orleans. He wrote words and/or music for *Baby Won't You Please Come Home, Royal Garden Blues, Cake Walking Babies From Home, Gulf Coast Blues, Michigan Water Blues, Swing Brother Swing, The Stuff Is Here (And It's Mellow), Wild Cat Blues, West End Blues, West Indies Blues* and many, many more often working with Spencer Williams (no relation). He sold his publishing catalogue to Decca in 1943 and did very well out of his royalties for the rest of his life. (Donald Clarke)..

**1929-1931 (Williams, Clarence Jazz Kings)**
Tracks: / Breeze / Mountain city blues / In our cottage of love / Them things got me / Whoop it up / I'm not worrying / Pane in the glass / Freeze out / Nervous breakdown / Railroad rhythm / Zonky / You've got to be modernistic / High society blues / Lazy levee loungers / Shout sister shout / Papa de da da / Baby won't you please come home.
Note: Mono.
**Album:** Released '86, on VJM (Vintage Jazz Music) by Vintage Jazz Music Society(VJM). Catalogue no: **VLP 47**

**1933-1935 VOL. 1 (Williams, Clarence & His Washboard Band)**
Tracks: / Mississippi basin / I like to go back in the evening / Black eyed Susan Brown / Mama stayed out all night long / Beer garden blues / Right key but the wrong keyhole / Dispossin me / She's just got a little bit left / After tonight / Bimbo / Chocolate Avenue / Harlem rhythm dance.
**Album:** Released '88, on Classic Jazz Masters Catalogue no: **CJM 14**

**1933-1935 VOL 2 (Williams, Clarence & His Washboard Band)**
Tracks: / Way down home / For sale (Hanna Johnson's big jack ass) / Swaller

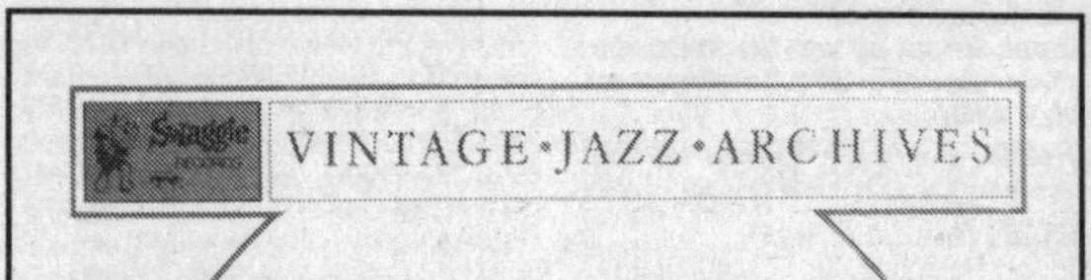

**Clarence Williams - 1933 - 35 Vol.2 (Swaggie (Australia)**

tail coat / Looka there ain't she pretty / St. Louis blues / How can I get it? / On the sunny side of the street / Won't you come over and say 'hello' / Old street sweeper / I'm gonna wash my sins away / Jimmy had a nickel / He's a colonel from Kentucky / Pretty baby, is it yes or no / Mister, will you serenade.
Note: Clarence Williams was born in Plaquemine, Louisiana, USA on 8th October 1893, although his death certificate indicates 1898. The Williams were a poor family; Clarence left Grammar School at an early age and his first job was as a water boy on his father's railroad gang. Subsequently he became a bus boy and errand boy. When only 10 years old he was working at Silver Brothers as second cook. Music influenced Clarence early in his life, and from the age of eight he had an ambition to become a pianist. While at the hotel he sang with a small band which also played around the streets for extra money. In about 1906, while Clarence was working in a tailor's shop, a minstrel troupe, thought to be Billy Kersand's show, passed through Plaquemine and lured him into the world of the travelling theatre. The show finished in New Orleans after several tours and young Clarence settled there taking tailoring, shoe shine and other jobs while playing and studying piano. He visited the bars and tonks on Canal Street, absorbing the styles of the house piano players, untutored until it became apparent that to succeed he should take lessons. Mrs. Ophelia Gould Smith was his first teacher and Clarence soon became a capable sight reader.
Clarence kept up with the latest sheet music releases and once claimed that he was 'way ahead of all the other piano players, introducing all the new songs to New Orleans'. In 1913 he became manager of a cabaret on South Rampart Street, a tough railroad establishment which he claims to have gradually transformed into a respectable place, employing the best musicians available, including King Oliver and Sidney Bechet. During this period Clarence claims to have managed the now famous Pete Lala's Cafe and to have toured with King Oliver as a black face comedian and entertainer with the accompanying show. In 1915 Clarence Williams and Armand J. Piron opened the first black music publishing house in New Orleans with only moderate success, until a New York publisher bought *You're some pretty doll*, said to have been a Ziegfeld Follies hit of 1917, although I have been unable to find evidence of this in the 1916-1917 Follies' songs listing. About the same time Columbia recorded and paid a large royalty for *Brown skin who you for*. The now successful young publisher composer moved to Chicago about 1918 and opened two music stores, expanding his publishing business under the name Williams and Piron, even though his partner remained in New Orleans concentrating on the activities of his popular orchestra. While in Chicago Clarence met Irene Gibbons, a Harlem dancer - better known as Eva Taylor - at a time when his latest songs *Royal Garden blues* and *I ain't gonna give you none of my Jelly Roll* were becoming popular. The prospects for publishing music in New York eventually drew Clarence Williams to that centre in 1920, although he appears to have maintained his Chicago outlet until he moved to New York permanently in 1921. In November 1921 Clarence Williams and Irene Gibbons were married in St. Benedict's Church on New York's 53rd Street and almost immediately became jointly involved in stage performances. In May 1922 Clarence opened his New York office at the same time that his wife Eva Taylor was a member of the Shuffle Along revue. Both appeared together several months later with the variety show *Step on it*, touring the Eastern States.
Throughout 1922 and 1923 Williams continued to arrange and accompany singers, using his own published titles whenever possible. The list of artists was impressive and included Bessie Smith, Sarah Martin, Eva Taylor and Mamie Smith. In May 1923 the first of the Clarence Williams Blue Five recordings were made. Using Eva Taylor as vocalist on many of the sides the group continued recording right through to December 1925 and included among its personnel at various times Sidney Bechet, Louis Armstrong and Buster Bailey. The group broadcast regularly over station WHN, backed various singers and made stage, department and music store appearances. Piron took his orchestra to New York late in 1923 and recorded several historic sides, broadcast, and made club appearances, all apparently booked through Williams' New York office. It was about this time that the firm was registered as Clarence Williams Music Publishing Company, following a severing of the connection with Piron. In January 1926 Clarence arranged a recording session for the Dixie Washboard Band which was to set a pattern for future groups and began an association with two musicians who dominated and remained with his recording stable for well over a decade - Ed Allen and Cyrus St. Clair was with Charlie Johnson's Band. The Dixie Washboard Band used other members from the Jordan group, which had been touring with the burlesque company 'Rarin' to go'. In March 1927 Clarence Williams again opened an office in Chicago, but the big event of the year was the musical comedy *Bottomland* with book, music and lyrics by Clarence Williams. The show received good reviews; apart from Williams as producer, pianist and actor the cast included Eva Taylor, Sarah Martin, Clarence's niece Katherine Henderson and a band directed by Joe Jordan. Except for occasional lapses, usually without too much publicity, Clarence recorded under an exclusive arrangement with Okeh from August 1923 until late 1928, and the association seems to have been profitable for both. The many advertisements in the black press enhanced Williams' already established reputation and his musical connections gave Okeh a catalogue of top artists.
Clarence Williams recorded his first sides for Victor in 1929 but the advent of the Depression, talking pictures and radio had a slowing effect on record sales, although late in 1930 and again early in 1931 Clarence used the Bingie Madison Band for several recording sessions. Both Clarence and Eva continued to broadcast and the CWMPC continued to make radio and personal appearances and it was not until the Vocalion contract, which produced the music reissued on this five volume Swaggie series, that their luck turned. Using titles taken mainly from Williams' own publishing company, the contract resulted in 79 available sides recorded between 15 May 1933 and 14 May 1935 and involving 19 separate sessions. The five volume Swaggie series also includes 11 titles, unissued by Vocation, taken from tests, four of which have now been issued for the first time ever. Only 36 recorded titles were made by Clarence Williams in the 11 years after the Vocation sessions and although he was busy, his life continued uneventfully. In 1943 Clarence Williams sold the music publishing company to Decca, but kept the name, a one third interest in the business and a half share in his own compositions. The transfer allowed Clarence the opportunity to give full time attention to his Harlem antiques shop, which soon became a Mecca for record collectors; but his health was not good and towards the end of his life he suffered several apaplectic strokes, became blind from diabetes and was knocked down by a taxi cab in 1952. Clarence Williams remained enthusiastic to the end, and in the last years prior to his death on 6th November 1964 he was playing and composing at home and talking about re-forming a recording group with his friend Ed Allen. (Bill Haesler, Nov 1982)
**Album:** Released '88, on Swaggie (Australia) Catalogue no: **SWAGGIE 812**

## CLARENCE WILLIAMS AND HIS ORCHESTRA

**Cass:** Released '88, on Classic Jazz Masters Catalogue no: **42025**
**Album:** Released '88, on Classic Jazz Masters Catalogue no: **22025**

## CLARENCE WILLIAMS AND HISWASHBOARD BAND VOL. 4 (Williams, Clarence & His Washboard Band)

**Album:** Released Aug '87, on Classic Jazz Masters Catalogue no: **CJM 17**

## CLARENCE WILLIAMS JAZZ KINGS 1927/9

**Album:** Released Apr '79, on VJM (Vintage Jazz Music) by Vintage Jazz Music Society(VJM). Catalogue no: **VLP 37**

## CLARENCE WILLIAMS JUG BANDS 1929-34

**Album:** Released '88, on Swaggie (Australia) Catalogue no: **S 827**

**CLARENCE WILLIAMS JUG AND WASBOARD BANDS**
Note: Fourteen rare sides, 11 on an album for the first time.
**Album:** Released May '88, on Right Keyhole Catalogue no: **RK 2001**

**CLARENCE WILLIAMS AND THE WASHBOARD BAND VOL. 1 (Williams, Clarence & The Washboard Band)**
**Album:** Released '88, on Swaggie (Australia) Catalogue no: **S 811**

**CLARENCE WILLIAMS AND THE WASHBOARD BAND VOL. 2 (Williams, Clarence & The Washboard Band)**
Tracks: / Way down home / For sale (Hanna Johnson's big jack ass) / Swaller-tail coat / Looka there, ain't ahe pretty / St. Louis blues / How can I get it ? / How can I get it ? (take 2) / On thew sunny side of the street / On the sunny side of the street (unissued) / Won't you come over and say hello / Old street sweeper / I'm gonna wash my sins away / Jimmy had a nickel / He's a Colonel from Kentucky / Pretty baby, is it Yes or No ? / Mister, will you serenade. ?
**Album:** Released '88, on Swaggie (Australia) Catalogue no: **S 812**

**CLARENCE WILLIAMS AND THE WASHBOARD BAND VOL. 3 (Williams, Clarence & The Washboard Band)**
**Album:** Released '88, on Swaggie (Australia) Catalogue no: **S 813**

**CLARENCE WILLIAMS AND THE WASHBOARD BAND VOL. 4 (Williams, Clarence & The Washboard Band)**
**Album:** Released '88, on Swaggie (Australia) Catalogue no: **S 814**

**CLARENCE WILLIAMS AND THE WASHBOARD BAND VOL. 5 (Williams, Clarence & The Washboard Band)**
**Album:** Released '88, on Swaggie (Australia) Catalogue no: **S 815**

**CLARENCE WILLIAMS VOL. 2 1924-30**
**Album:** Released Dec '88, on Swaggie (Australia) Catalogue no: **S 854**

**CLARENCE WILLIAMS AND EVA TAYLOR 1925-26 (Williams, Clarence & Eva Taylor)**
**Album:** Released Jan '88, on Swaggie (Australia) Catalogue no: **S 835**

**JAZZ CLASSIC' S IN DIGITAL STEREO**
Tracks: / Candy lips / I can't beat you doin' what you're doin' to me / Chizzlin' Sam / Log cabin blues / You're bound to look like a monkey when you ge / Pain in the glass, A / Walk that broad / Trouble / You ain't too old / Close fit blues / Lazy mama / He wouldn't stop doin' it / Worn out blues / Chocolate avenue / Have you ever felt that way / Organ grinder blues.
**CD:** Released Feb '89, on BBC by BBC Records & Tapes. Catalogue no: **BBC CD 721**
**Album:** Released Feb '89, on BBC by BBC Records & Tapes. Catalogue no: **REB 721**
**Cass:** Released Feb '89, on BBC by BBC Records & Tapes. Catalogue no: **ZCF 721**

**PIANO ALBUM**
**Album:** Released '88, on Meritt (USA) Catalogue no: **MERITT 4**

**RARE SELECTION VOL.1 1927-30**
**Album:** Released Oct '89, on Swaggie (Australia) Catalogue no: **S 853**

**WILD CAT BLUES (Williams, Clarence Blue Five (1923-1935))**
Note: Mono
**Album:** Released Jan '87, on Rhapsody by President Records. Catalogue no: **RHA 6031**

**WNYC JAZZ FESTIVAL (Williams, Clarence Jazz Kings)**
**Album:** Released Dec '86, on Jazz Unlimited Catalogue no: **JU-3**

## Williams, Claude

**KANSAS CITY GIANTS (See panel below)**
Tracks: / One for the count / Kansas city / Fiddler, The / Teach me tonight / Little bit of country / 51st and swope / Them there eyes / That certain someone / Texicana / Hundred years from today.
**Album:** Released May '82, on Big Bear Catalogue no: **BEAR 25**

## Williams, Cootie

**Biographical details:** Cootie Williams was born Charles Melvin Williams in 1908; he died in 1985. He joined Duke Ellington in 1929 and his muted growling trumpet was an important sound in the band during its great years; Duke wrote *Concerto For Cootie* for him, which became *Do Nothing Till You Hear From Me* when words were written for it. Cootie also played on scores of beautiful small-group dates with Duke, Billie Hiliday, Lionel Hampton and others. The music world was astonished when he left Duke to go with Benny Goodman in 1940, but Goodman paid more and Cootie loved playing with the Sextet; later he led his own band, never terribly successful but always making good music; he was the first to record Thelonious Monk's *Epistrophy*. Still later he was an honoured guest with the Ellington band. (Donald Clarke)..

**AND HIS SAVOY BALLROOM ORCHESTRA**
**Album:** Released Feb '88, on Fresh Sounds (Spain) by Fresh Sounds Records (Spain). Catalogue no: **FS 210**

**ART FORD'S JAZZ PARTY (August 1958)**
Note: With Buck Clayton, Roland Hanna, Connee Boswell/Georgie Auld / Hank D'amico/Roy Burns/Vinnie Burke, etc..
**Album:** Released Oct '87, on Jazz Connoisseur by Spotlite Records. Catalogue no: **AFJP 4**

**BOYS FROM HARLEM 1937-40**
**Album:** Released Jan '83, on Swaggie (Australia) Catalogue no: **S 1333**

**BOYS FROM HARLEM VOL.2**

Claude Williams - Kansas City Giants (Big Bear)

**1937-39**
**Album:** Released Jan '83, on Swaggie (Australia) Catalogue no: **S 1359**

**COOTIE WILLIAMS AND HIS ORCHESTRA**
**Album:** Released Jul '81, on Storyville by Storyville Records AB. Catalogue no: **SLP 803**

**COOTIE WILLIAMS AND HIS RUG CUTTERS (Williams, Cootie & His Rug Cutters)**
**Album:** Released '88, on Tax Catalogue no: **TAX 8011**

**COOTIE WILLIAMS AND THE BOYS FROM HARLEM (Williams, Cootie & The Boys From Harlem)**
**Album:** Released '88, on Tax Catalogue no: **TAX 8005**
**Album:** Released '88, on Tax Catalogue no: **M 8005**

**ECHOES OF HARLEM (Williams, Cootie and His Orchestra)**
Tracks: / Echoes of Harlem / Things ain't what they used to be / Tess 'torch song / You talk a little trash / Sweet Lorraine / Cherry red blues / Round midnight / Is you is or is you ain't my baby / Blue garden blues / Floogie boo / I don't know / Gotta do some work / My old flame / Now i know / Somebody's got to go / Honeysuckle rose.
**Album:** Released Jul '86, on Affinity by Charly Records. Catalogue no: **AFS 1031**

**FROM FILMS 1944-46 (Williams, Cootie & Billy Eckstine)**
Tracks: / Wild fire / Things ain't what they used to be / Go 'long mule / Keep on jumping / Second balcony jump / Rhythm in a riff / You call it madness / Lonesome lover blues / Taps Miller / I cried for you / I want to talk about you / Our delight / Prisoner of love.
Note: With Cleanhead Vinson, Laurel Watson, Bud Powell, Gene Ammons.
**Album:** Released '88, on Harlequin by Interstate Music. Catalogue no: **HQ 2068**

**MEMORIAL**
**Album:** Released Feb '86, on RCA by BMG Records (UK). Catalogue no: **NL 89811**
**Cass:** Released Feb '86, on RCA by BMG Records (UK). Catalogue no: **NK 89811**

**RHYTHM AND JAZZ IN THE MID FORTIES**
Tracks: / Blue Gordon blues / Is you is, or is you ain't / Somebody's gotta go / Juice head baby / Salt Lake City bounce / House of joy / When my baby left me / Everything but you / Stingy blues / Echoes of harlem / That's the lick / Wrong neighbourhood / I may be easy, but I ain't no fool / Let's do the whole thing or nothing at all / Ain't got no blues today / Bring 'em down front.
**Album:** Released Dec '88, on Official by Official Records. Catalogue no: **OFF 3014**

**ROLL 'EM**
**Cass:** Released Sep '89, on Big Band Era Catalogue no: **40182**

**SEXTET AND ORCHESTRA**
**Album:** Released Apr '81, on Phoenix (USA) by All Star Talent Inc.(USA). Catalogue no: **LP 1**

**THINGS AIN'T WHAT THEY USED TO BE (Williams, Cootie and His Orchestra)**
Tracks: / Echoes of Harlem / 'Gator lady / Lady be good / Across the alley from the Alamo / I shoulda been thinkin' instead of drinkin' / Let 'em roll / Wrong neighbourhood / Soft winds.
**Album:** Released Aug '89, on Jukebox Lil (Sweden) Catalogue no: **JB 623**

**TYPHOON**
**Album:** Released Jan '86, on Swingtime by Contact Records (Denmark). Deleted Jun '89. Catalogue no: **ST 1003**

## Williams, Fess

**FESS WILLIAMS AND HIS ROYLE FLUSH ORCHESTRA (Williams, Fess & His Royle Flush Orchestra)**
**Album:** Released Jul '78, on Fountain by Retrieval Records. Catalogue no: **FJ 116**

**FESS WILLIAMS VOL. 1 (1929)**
Tracks: / Here 'tis / Few riffs / Hot town / Friction / Kentucky blues / Do shuffle / Snag nasty / Big shot / Sell it / Betsy Brown / Sweet Savannah Sue / Ain't misbehavin' / Buttons / Musical camp meeting / Goin' to getcha / Slide, Mr. Jelly.
**Album:** Released Nov '85, on Harlequin by Interstate Music. Catalogue no: **HQ 2039**

**FESS WILLIAMS VOL. 2 (Complete Sessions 1929-30)**
Tracks: / Do shuffle (2 takes) / Betsy Brown / She's still dizzy / Hot mama / 11.30 Saturday night / I'm feelin devilish / Al for grits and gravy / Playing my saxophone (2 takes) / You can't go wrong / Ida, sweet as apple cider / Everything's OK with me / Dinah / Just to be with you.
Note: Mono
**Album:** Released Dec '86, on Harlequin by Interstate Music. Catalogue no: **HQ 2040**

**FESS WILLIAMS VOL.3 (Rare Masters)**
**Album:** Released '89, on Harlequin by Interstate Music. Catalogue no: **HQ 2062**

## Williams, G.O.

**BACK TO BOOGIE WOOGIE (Williams, G.O. & Dave Collett)**
Tracks: / Boogie elbow oogie / Lingerin' boogie / If I can help somebody / Cut and run boogie / Night train / Steam shovel boogie / Goofy stuff / Casablanca / Blue room / Freight train / Song of India / Mainline boogie.
**Album:** Released Oct '82, on Black Lion Catalogue no: **BLM 51012**

## Williams, James

**ALTER EGO**
Tracks: / Black scholars / Alter ego / Havana days / Fourplay / Touching affair, A / Waltz and monk / Beauty within.
**Album:** Released Jan '86, on Sunnyside Jazz(USA) Catalogue no: **SSC 1007**

**ARIOSO TOUCH, THE (Williams, James Trio)**
**Album:** Released Sep '82, on Concord Jazz by Concord Jazz Records (USA). Catalogue no: **CJ 192**

**FLYING COLOURS (Williams, James & Slide Hampton)**
**Album:** Released Apr '81, on Zim (USA) Catalogue no: **ZMS 2005**

**IMAGES OF THINGS TO COME**
**Album:** Released Mar '81, on Concord by Concord Jazz Records (USA). Catalogue no: **CJ 140**

**IN YOUR EYES**
Tracks: / In your eyes / Order in the house / With all my heart / If you knew what I know / Shadow of another love / Runner / Curious / Child of love / Diamond in the night / My friend / Smile.
**CD:** Released Oct '88, on CBS by CBS Records. Catalogue no: **461046 2**
**Album:** Released Oct '88, on CBS by CBS Records. Catalogue no: **461046 1**
**Cass:** Released Oct '88, on CBS by CBS Records. Deleted Jan '90. Catalogue no: **461046 4**

**JAMES WILLIAMS MAGICAL TRIO**
**CD:** Released Feb '90, on Emarcy Catalogue no: **832 859 2**

**MIRACLES OF THE HEART (Williams, James 'D Train')**
Tracks: / You are everything / Oh how I love you (girl) / Miracle of the heart / Misunderstandings / Let me love you / Ice melts into rain / I got your number / Stand up and fight.
**Album:** Released Sep '86, on CBS by CBS Records. Catalogue no: **450066 1**
**Cass:** Released Sep '86, on CBS by CBS Records. Deleted Nov '87. Catalogue no: **450066 4**

**MISUNDERSTANDING (Williams, James 'D Train')**
Tracks: / Misunderstanding.
**12" Single:** Released Feb '87, on CBS by CBS Records. Catalogue no: **650431 7**
**7" Single:** Released Feb '87, on CBS by CBS Records. Deleted Aug '87. Catalogue no: **650431 7**

**PROGRESS REPORT (Williams, James Sextet) (See panel on next page)**
Tracks: / Progress report / Episode from a village dance / Affaire d'amour / Mr. Day's dream / Unconscious behaviour / Renaissance lovers.

**James Williams - Progress Report (Sunnyside)**

Note: Personnel: James Williams - accoustic piano / Bill Easley - Alto saxophone, flute, clarinet / Kevin Eubanks - Electric guitar / Billy Pierce - Tenor saxophone and soprano saxophone / Tony Reedus - Drums / Rufus Reid - Accoustic bass / Jerry Gonzales - Congas, added on ' Episode from a Village Dance' only. All compositions except *'Unconscious Behaviour'* are published by Second Floor Music, BMI. *'Episode from a Village Dance'* is dedicated to Bobby Hutcherson and *'Affaire d'Amour'* is dedicated to the memory of Edward Kennedy and 'Duke' Ellington.
**Album:** Released Feb '86, on Sunnyside Jazz(USA) Catalogue no: **SSC 1012**
**CD:** Released Feb '86, on Sunnyside Jazz(USA) Catalogue no: **SSC 1012D**

### RUNNER
Tracks: / Runner / Runner (accapella) / Runner (12" version) (Only on 12", 12" picture bag & CD single.) / Runner (dub mix) (Only on 12" & CD single.) / In your eyes (12" version) (Only on 12" & CD single.) / Misunderstanding (Only on 12" picture bag version.) / You are everything (Only on 12" picture bag version.).
**CD Single:** Released Oct '88, on CBS by CBS Records. Deleted 17 Apr '89. Catalogue no: **653116 2**
**7" Single:** Released Oct '88, on CBS by CBS Records. Deleted 17 Apr '89. Catalogue no: **653116 7**
**12" Single:** Released Oct '88, on CBS by CBS Records. Deleted 17 Apr '89. Catalogue no: **653116 6**
**12" Single:** Released Nov '88, on CBS by CBS Records. Deleted 17 Apr '89. Catalogue no: **653116 8**

## Williams, Joe

**Biographical details:** Joe Williams was born Joseph Goreed in Georgia in 1918; the blues / ballad / pop singer with a big beautiful voice suffered prejudice among black bandleaders and club-owners in his early career because he was too dark, but he has now been popular for well over 30 years. He first worked with Count Basie in 1950, first recorded *Every Day (I Have The Blues)* in 1951 with the King Kolax Band, joined Basie 1954-60 and became famous: the album *Count Basie Swings--Joe Williams Sings* from '55 is a masterpiece, with *Every Day*, period pop ballad *Teach Me Tonight* and many other riches. He toured solo, expanding his repertoire of songs, worked with a Harry Edistone quintet, then his own trios with Chicago pianist Junior Mance, then Norman Simmons. He has recorded for RCA and many other labels including Concord Jazz (with the Capp-Pierce Juggernaut, and excellent big band). *Nothin' But The Blues* in 1983 got rave reviews and won a Grammy; *Every Night* on Verve in 1987 was made live at the Vine Street Bar and Grill in Hollywood with Simmons. Recently he has been seen on TV playing Bill Cosby's father-in-law in the sitcom. (Donald Clarke)..

### CHAINS OF LOVE
**Album:** Released Dec '87, on Jass Catalogue no: **JASS 6**

### COME BACK
Tracks: / Comeback / Hold it right there / Sent for you yesterday / Yesterday / Who she do.
**CD 3":** Released '88, on Delos (USA) Catalogue no: **D/PC 2102**

### EVERY NIGHT
**Album:** on Polydor by Polydor Ltd. Deleted 31 Aug '88. Catalogue no: **833 236 1**
**CD:** Released '87, on Polydor by Polydor Ltd. Deleted 30 May '89. Catalogue no: **833 234 2**

### EVERY DAY I HAVE THE BLUES
**Album:** Released Mar '85, on Savoy Jazz (USA) by Malaco Records (USA). Catalogue no: **SJL 1140**

### HAVING THE BLUES...
Tracks: / Don't get around much anymore / Satin doll / Experiment / Gee baby ain't I good to you / Early in the morning / Nobody know the way I feel this morning / What a difference a day made / Goin' to Chicago / Everyday I have the blues / All right, okay, you win / Evenin' / Roll 'em Pete / One o'clock jump.
Note: Joe Williams with The Count Basie Orchestra and others.
**Cass:** Released Apr '89, on Denon Catalogue no: **MC 7684**
**CD:** Released Apr '89, on Denon Catalogue no: **DC 8535**
**CD:** Released '88, on Denon Catalogue no: **C38-7684**

### I JUST WANT TO SING (Williams, Joe & Friends)
**CD:** Released '88, on Delos (USA) Catalogue no: **DCD 4004**
**CD:** Released Mar '90, on Delos Catalogue no: **JJCD56**

### IN GOOD COMPANY
Tracks: / Just friends / Baby you got what it takes / How deep is the ocean / Ain't got nothing but the blues / Love without money / Between the... / Is you is or is you ain't (my baby) / Too good to be true / Embraceable you / Please don't talk about me.
**Album:** Released Feb '90, on Polydor by Polydor Ltd. Catalogue no: **837 932 1**
**CD:** Released Feb '90, on Polydor by Polydor Ltd. Catalogue no: **837 932 2**
**Cass:** Released Feb '90, on Polydor by Polydor Ltd. Catalogue no: **837 932 4**

### JOE WILLIAMS AND COUNT BASIE (Williams,Joe/Count Basie)
**Album:** Released May '83, on Vogue Jazz (France) by Vogue Records. Catalogue no: **VJD 553**

### LIVE AT BIRDLAND
Tracks: / September in the rain / Come back baby / 5 o'clock in the morning / By the river Sainte Marie / This can't be love / Teach me tonight / I was telling her about you / Have you met Miss Jones? / Well oh well.
**Album:** Released Feb '88, on Fresh Sounds (Spain) by Fresh Sounds Records (Spain). Catalogue no: **FS 297**

### MAN AIN'T SUPPOSED TO CRY, A
Tracks: / What's new / It's the talk of the

town / I'll never smile again / I'm thru' with love / Where are you / I've only myself to blame / Say it isn't so / What will I tell my heart / You've got me grying again / Can't we talk it over / I laugh to keep from cryin' / Man ain't supposed to cry, A.
**Album:** Released Oct '89, on Roulette (EMI) by EMI Records. Catalogue no: **ROU 1001**
**CD:** Released Oct '89, on Roulette (EMI) by EMI Records. Catalogue no: **CZ 233**
**Album:** Released Oct '89, on Roulette (EMI) by EMI Records. Catalogue no: **793 269 1**
**CD:** Released Oct '89, on Roulette (EMI) by EMI Records. Catalogue no: **CDP 793 269 2**

**NOTHIN' BUT THE BLUES**
**CD:** Released Mar '90, on delos Catalogue no: **JJCD55**
**CD:** Released Jul '86, on DMS (USA) Catalogue no: **DCD 4001**
**Album:** Released Jul '86, on DMS (USA) Catalogue no: **DMS 4001**

**OVERWHELMING JOE WILLIAMS, THE**
Tracks: / Everyday / Come back baby / All God's chillun got rhythm / Do you wanna jump children / April in Paris / In the evening when the sun goes down / Just a sittin' and a rockin' / Wrap your troubles in dreams / Jump for joy / Every night / Rocks in my bed / Early in the morning / Kansas city / Prelude to a kiss / On the sunny side of the street.
**CD:** Released May '89, on Bluebird (2) by BMG Records (UK). Catalogue no: **ND 86464**
**Album:** Released May '89, on Bluebird (2) by BMG Records (UK). Catalogue no: **NL 86464**
**Cass:** Released May '89, on Bluebird (2) by BMG Records (UK). Catalogue no: **NK 86464**

**TOGETHER (Williams, Joe & Harry Edison)**
**Album:** Released Dec '87, on Fresh Sounds (Spain) by Fresh Sounds Records (Spain). Catalogue no: **FS 296**

**WAR NO MORE**
Tracks: / War no more / What a difference a day made / After you're gone / All the things you are.
**CD 3":** Released '88, on Delos (USA) Catalogue no: **D/PC 2103**

## Williams, Mary Lou

**Biographical details:** Mary Lou Williams was born Mary Elfrieda Scruggs in 1910 in Atlanta, Georgia; she died in 1981. The talented pianist, composer and arranger grew up in Pittsburgh, married reedman John Williams and worked with him Andy Kirk's band from 1929, where she developed her skill at composing and arranging. She led her own band in the '40s, with her second husband trumpeter Shorty Baker; she left music for a while, joined the Catholic church and started a foundation to help musicians with personal problems, leaving music for a while, but came back at the 1957 Newport Jazz Festival with Dizzy Gillespie. She was a fine pianist who never stopped learning. She wrote arrangements for Benny Goodman and Duke Ellington, among others; she also wrote religious music, some of which was commissioned by the Church. The two-piano duo *Embraced* in 1977 with Cecil Taylor was probably a failure, but typical of her interesting ideas. (Donald Clarke)..

**BEST OF MARY LOU WILLIAMS**
**Album:** Released '82, on Pablo Jazz (USA) by Pablo Records (USA). Catalogue no: **2310 856**
**Cass:** Released '82, on Pablo Jazz (USA) by Pablo Records (USA). Catalogue no: **K10 856**

**DON BYAS**
**Album:** Released '88, on GNP Crescendo (USA) by GNP Crescendo Records (USA). Catalogue no: **GNPS 9030**
**Cass:** Released '88, on GNP Crescendo (USA) by GNP Crescendo Records (USA). Catalogue no: **GNP5 9030**

**EMBRACED (Williams, Mary Lou & Cecil Taylor)**
**Cass:** Released Apr '78, on Pablo Jazz (USA) by Pablo Records (USA). Catalogue no: **K20 108**
**Album:** Released Apr '78, on Pablo Jazz (USA) by Pablo Records (USA). Catalogue no: **2620 108**

**FIRST LADY OF PIANO**
Note: Featuring Coleman Hawkins, Bill Coleman, Edmund Hall, Don Byas
**Album:** Released Sep '87, on Giants of Jazz by Hasmick Promotions. Catalogue no: **LPJT 20**
**Album:** Released Oct '88, on Vogue by Vogue Records. Catalogue no: **500078**

**FREE SPIRITS**
**CD:** Released Jul '88, on Steeplechase (USA) Catalogue no: **SCCD 31043**
**Album:** Released Jul '88, on Steeplechase (USA) Catalogue no: **SCS 1043**

**MARY LOU WILLIAMS IN LONDON**
**Album:** Released '88, on GNP Crescendo (USA) by GNP Crescendo Records (USA). Catalogue no: **GNPS 9029**

**MY MAMA PINNED A ROSE ON ME**
Tracks: / Blues / N.G. blues / Dirge blues / Baby bear boogie / Turtle speed blues / Blues for Peter / My mama pinned a rose on me / Prelude to prism / What's your story morning glory / Prelude to love roots / Rhythmic pattern / J.B's waltz / No title blues.
**Cass:** Released '82, on Pablo Jazz (USA) by Pablo Records (USA). Catalogue no: **K10 819**
**Album:** Released '82, on Pablo Jazz (USA) by Pablo Records (USA). Catalogue no: **231 0819**

**ROLL EM' (Williams, Mary Lou & Teddy Wilson Trio)**
Note: 1944 hitherto unknown titles
**Album:** Released Oct '88, on Audiophile (USA) by Jazzology Records (USA). Catalogue no: **AP 8**

**SOLO RECITAL MONTREUX JAZZ**
Tracks: / Over the rainbow / Offertory meditation / Tea for two / Concerto alone at Montreux / Little Joe from Chicago / Man I love / What's your story morning glory / Honeysuckle rose.
**Cass:** Released '82, on Pablo Jazz (USA) by Pablo Records (USA). Catalogue no: **K 08 218**
**Album:** Released '82, on Pablo Jazz (USA) by Pablo Records (USA). Catalogue no: **2308 218**

**WALKIN' AND SWINGIN'**
**Album:** Released Sep '85, on Saar Giants Of Jazz (Italy) Catalogue no: **MCJT 20**
**Album:** Released Sep '85, on Saar Giants Of Jazz (Italy) Catalogue no: **LPJT 20**

## Williams, Robert Pete

**LEGACY OF THE BLUES-9**
Tracks: / Woman you ain't no good / Come here sit down on my knee / Angola patience blues / Late night boogie / I'm going to have myself a ball / Poor girl out on the mountain / Graveyard blues / You're my all day steady and my midnight dream / Keep your bad dog off me.
**Album:** Released May '89, on GNP Crescendo (USA) by GNP Crescendo Records (USA). Catalogue no: **GNPS 10019**
**Album:** Released '73, on Sonet by Sonet Records. Catalogue no: **SNTF 649**
**CD:** Released '73, on Sonet by Sonet Records. Catalogue no: **SNTCD 649**

**ROBERT PETE WILLIAMS AND ROOSEVELT SKYES (Williams, Robert Pete & Roosevelt Sykes)**
**Album:** Released Jul '88, on 77 by 77 Records. Catalogue no: **77 LEU 12/50**

**ROBERT PETE WILLIAMS WITH BIG JOE WILLIAMS**
**Album:** Released Jan '88, on Storyville by Storyville Records AB. Catalogue no: **SLP 225**

**ROBERT PETE WILLIAMS LIVE**
**Album:** Released '88, on Wolf Catalogue no: **120 919**

**THOSE PRISON BLUES**
**Album:** Released May '81, on Arhoolie (USA) by Arhoolie Records (USA). Catalogue no: **ARHOOLIE 2015**

## Williams, Tony

**Biographical details:** Tony Williams was born in Chicago in 1945. The drummer and composer became famous on joining Miles Davis in 1963; the Davis rhythm section with Herbie Hancock on piano and Ron Carter on bass is regarded as one of the most important of the era. he made his own LPs beginning with *Life Time* on Blue Note in 1965; he left Davis to form a jazz-rock fusion group called Lifetime with John McLaughlin, Jack Bruce and Larry Young on organ; it suffered many personnel changes and was never as successful commercially as it was influential: its free playing over a rock beat soon became a cliche. He toured and recorded as V.S.O.P., re-creating the Davis group with Hancock, Carter, Wayne Shorter and Freddie Hubbard replacing Davis; he played on other people's albums and came back as a leader on Blue Note in 1985. (Donald Clarke)..

**ANGEL STREET**
Tracks: / Angel Street / Touch me / Red mask / Kiss me / Dreamland / Only with you / Pee wee / Thrill me / Obsession.
Note: All songs composed by Tony Williams. Producer/Arranger? Tony Williams and Jason Corsaro.
**Cass:** Released Jan '89, on Blue Note by EMI Records. Catalogue no: **TCB1 48494**
**CD:** Released Jan '89, on Blue Note by EMI Records. Catalogue no: **CDP 748 494 2**
**Album:** Released Jan '89, on Blue Note by EMI Records. Catalogue no: **B1 48494**

**CIVILIZATION**
Tracks: / Geo rose / Warrior / Ancient eyes / Soweto nights / Slump, The / Civilization / Mutants on the beach / Citadel.
Note: Master drummer Tony Williams returned to his own recording career, after five years playing only on other people's projects, in 1985 with "*Foreign Intrigue*". Although Tony was one of the innovators of both avant garde and fusion, that album brought him solidly into the contemporary jazz mainstream. The enthusiastic reputation of "*Foreign Intrigue*" prompted Williams to form a working group using many of the same musicians from the album. Throughout 1986, the Tony Williams Quintet with Bill Pierce on sax, Wallace Roney on trumpet, Mulgrew Miller on piano and another Blue Note recording artist Charnette Moffett on bass toured various cities in the US as well as South America and Europe. The results of that close-knit ensemble are now heard on "*Civilization*", recorded at the end of the band's most recent tour. The eight new Williams originals include the haunting beauty of "*Soweto Nights*", "*The Slump*" with it's humorous, catchy bass line turnarounds, the soaring, contemporary sound of "*Mutants On The Beach*" and the lovely title tune ballad. (EMI release sheet, May 1987)
**CD:** Released Jun '87, on Blue Note by EMI Records. Catalogue no: **BNZ 105**
**Album:** Released Jun '87, on Blue Note by EMI Records. Catalogue no: **BT 85138**
**CD:** Released Jun '87, on Blue Note by EMI Records. Catalogue no: **CDP 746 757 2**

**CIVILIZATION (SINGLE)**
Tracks: / Civilization / Girl like you.
**7" Single:** Released Jun '84, on Capitol by EMI Records. Deleted '88. Catalogue no: **CL 333**

**FOREIGN INTRIGUE**
Tracks: / Foreign intrigue / My Michelle / Life of the party / Takin' my time / Clearways / Sister Cheryl / Aboretum.
**CD:** Released Jul '89, on Blue Note by EMI Records. Catalogue no: **BNZ 221**
**CD:** Released Jul '89, on Blue Note by EMI Records. Catalogue no: **CDP 746 289 2**
**Album:** Released Jul '89, on Blue Note by EMI Records. Catalogue no: **BT 85119**

**JOY OF FLYING**
Tracks: / Going far / Hip skip / Hittin' on 6 / Open fire / Tony / Eris / Coming back home / Morgan's motion.
**Album:** Released '79, on CBS by CBS Records. Deleted '84. Catalogue no: **CBS 83338**

**MONEY**
Tracks: / Money.
**12" Single:** Released Aug '88, on Master Funk Catalogue no: **TWD 1956**

**NATIVE HEART**
**Album:** Released Mar '90, on Blue Note by EMI Records. Catalogue no: **B1 93170**
**CD:** Released Mar '90, on Blue Note by EMI Records. Catalogue no: **CDB1 93170**
**CD:** Released Mar '90, on Blue Note by EMI Records. Catalogue no: **793 170 2**
**Album:** Released Mar '90, on Blue Note by EMI Records. Catalogue no: **793 170 1**

**SPRING**
Tracks: / Extras / Echo / From before / Love song / Tee.
**CD:** Released Jul '87, on Blue Note by EMI Records. Deleted Feb '90. Catalogue no: **CDP 746 135 2**
**Album:** Released Jul '89, on Blue Note by EMI Records. Catalogue no: **BST 84216**
**CD:** Released Jul '87, on Blue Note by EMI Records. Catalogue no: **BNZ 104**

## Williamson, Claude

**BLUES IN FRONT + NEW DEPARTURE**
**CD:** Released Feb '90, on Storyville by Storyville Records AB. Catalogue no: **STCD4163**

**FABULOUS CLAUDE WILLIAMSON TRIO, THE (Williamson, Claude Trio)**
**Album:** Released Feb '88, on Fresh Sounds (Spain) by Fresh Sounds Records (Spain). Catalogue no: **FS 192**

**HOLOGRAPHY**
**Album:** Released Sep '79, on Interplay (USA) by Interplay Records (USA). Catalogue no: **IP 7708**

**KEYS WEST (Williamson, Claude Trio)**
**Album:** Released Apr '81, on Affinity by Charly Records. Deleted '88. Catalogue no: **AFF 62**

**LA FIESTA (Williamson, Claude Trio)**
Tracks: / Nica's dream / In your quiet place / La fiesta / Love of a child / First trip / Black forest.
Note: Claude Williamson - piano, Sam Jones - bass, Roy Haynes - drums.
**Cass:** Released Apr '90, on Tumi by Tumi Records. Catalogue no: **TUMIC 012**
**Album:** Released Sep '83, on Discovery (USA) by Discovery Records (USA). Catalogue no: **DS 862**
**Album:** Released Aug '79, on Interplay (USA) by Interplay Records (USA). Catalogue no: **IP-7727**

**MULLS THE MULLIGAN SCENE**
**Album:** Released Feb '88, on Fresh Sounds (Spain) by Fresh Sounds Records (Spain). Catalogue no: **FS 191**

**NEW DEPARTURE**
**Album:** Released Aug '79, on Interplay (USA) by Interplay Records (USA). Catalogue no: **IP 7717**

**SALUTE TO BUD (Williamson, Claude Trio)**
Tracks: / Salute to Bud / Bouncing with Bud / Penny / Thou swell / Woody 'n' you / Obsession / Indiana / Over the rainbow / Curtistan / Claudehopper / All God's chillun got rhythm.
**Album:** Released Sep '82, on Affinity by Charly Records. Deleted '88. Catalogue no: **AFF 72**

**SERMON, THE**
**Album:** Released Feb '88, on Fresh Sounds (Spain) by Fresh Sounds Records (Spain). Catalogue no: **FS 299**

**THEATRE PARTY**
**Album:** Released Feb '88, on Fresh Sounds (Spain) by Fresh Sounds Records (Spain). Catalogue no: **FS 220**

## Williamson, Sonny Boy (1)

Sonny Boy Mk 1, born John Lee Williamson in Tennessee in 1914, relocated to Chicago in 1937. He helped to make that city the No.1 blues capital, thanks to such influential tracks such as *Sugar Mama* and *Good Morning, Little Schoolgirl*. During the forties, he became one of the first blues artists to embellish his sound with a backing band; many of the city's talents later followed him in this respect, thus breaking away from the genre's traditionally sparse style. He died in Chicago in June 1948 at the age of 34, falling victim to a merciless attack and robbery.
John Lee Williamson (Sonny Boy Mk 1) was born in 1914 in Tennessee; he was a profoundly influencial blues singer and harmonica player by the time he was murdered by a mugger in Chicago in 1948. He recorded about 120 sides for Bluebird/Victor from 1937, accompanists on his dates incuded Big Bill Broonzy, Big Joe Williams, Speckled Red and others; he backed Williams on Columbia (CBS/USA) in 1947. His songs such as *Good morning little schoolgirl* became blues standards; his harmonica was a direct influence on Little Walter, Big Walter Horton etc. Compilations include *Bluebird blues* on Charly and several volumes of blues classics on Arhoolie. (Donald Clarke, May 1988)

**BLUEBIRD BLUES (Williamson, John Lee 'Sonny Boy')**
**Album:** Released Sep '87, on Bluetime

(Denmark) by Contact Records (Denmark). Catalogue no: **BT 2006**

**HARMONICA ACE, 1937-45**
**Album:** Released Aug '87, on Old Tramp Catalogue no: **OT 1205**

**KING BISCUIT TIME (Williamson, John Lee 'Sonny Boy')**
**Album:** Released May '81, on Arhoolie (USA) by Arhoolie Records (USA). Catalogue no: **ARHOOLIE 2020**

**RARE SONNY BOY**
Tracks: / Sugar mama blues / Skinny woman / Worried me blues / Black gal blues / Frigidaire blues / Suzanna blues / Early in the morning / My little Cornelius / Decoration blues / You can lead me baby / Miss Louisa blues / Sunnyland / I'm tired trucking my blues away / Beauty parlour / My baby I've been your slave / Doggin' my love around / Little low woman blues / Sugar mama blues No.2 / Good gravy / Good gal blues / I'm not pleasing you / Tell me, baby / Honey bee blues / I'm gonna catch you soon / Blues that made me drunk / Elevator woman / Mellow chick swing / Lacey belle / Apple tree swing / Sugar gal / No friend blues / I love you for myself / Bring another half a pint / Southern dream / Better cut that out.
**Album:** Released 14 Aug '88, on RCA (France) by BMG Records (France). Catalogue no: **NL 90027**

**SONNY BOY WILLIAMSON 1940-42**
**Album:** Released '89, on Wolf Catalogue no: **WSE 135**

**SONNY BOY WILLIAMSON 1937-1941**
**Album:** Released '88, on Blues Classics(USA) by Arhoolie Records (USA). Catalogue no: **BC 3**

**THROW A BOOGIE WOOGIE (Williamson, Sonny Boy/Big Joe Williams)**
Tracks: / Good morning school girl / Sugar mama blues / Got the bottle up and gone / Early in the morning / Black gal blues / Moonshine / Whiskey headed blues / You give an account / Rootin' ground hog / Brother James / Peach orchard mama / Crawlin' king snake / Highway 49 / Please don't go / North wind blues / Throw a boogie woogie.
**CD:** Released Feb '90, on RCA by BMG Records (UK). Catalogue no: **ND 90320**
**Cass:** Released Feb '90, on RCA by BMG Records (UK). Catalogue no: **NK 90320**
**Album:** Released Feb '90, on RCA by BMG Records (UK). Catalogue no: **NL 90320**

**WORK WITH ME**
Tracks: / Good evening everybody / You killing me / Work with me / I wonder why / Don't lose your eye / This is my apartment / Like Wolf / Dissatisfied / '99 / She got next to me / Keep your hand out of my pocket / Open road / I can't do without you / Down child / Too young to die / She's my baby / Stop right now / Hunt, The / Too old to think / That's all I want / Got to move / My younger days / Stop crying / Close to me.
**CD:** Released Sep '89, on Charly by Charly Records. Catalogue no: **CDRED 14**

## Williamson, Sonny Boy (2)

Sonny Boy Mk 2 was, in fact, born many years before his predecessor, but his career got off to a later start. Born in Mississippi in 1897, he first attracted attention in the early forties via an influential daily radio show in Arkanas, 'King Biscuit Time'. Although his real name was Rice Miller, he changed his name to that of his Chicago idol at about this time. In addition, he actually claimed to be the Sonny Boy; monstrous though this ploy was, it got Miller the necessary popularity and attention. By the time he was rumbled, he had sufficiently proved his musical worth to be able to survive solely on talent. In 1951, three years after the death of Sonny Boy Mk 1, Sonny Boy Mk 2 began making records. Now based in Chicago, he signed with the city's Chess label in 1955 and consolidated upon his ever growing status as a blues master. His best songs were the ones which displayed his prowess as a writer of engaging lyrics - *One Way Out, Nine Below Zero* (which later gave its name to a British R&B band) and *Fattening Frogs for Snakes* were among the finest examples. During 1963-4, he suddenly became a regular visitor to Europe and particularly Britain, where the burgeoning blues boom was winning him many new admirers. He played live with two of the UK's most important up and coming groups, the Animals and the Yardbirds - both collaborations yielded live albums, which did not make the charts but were nonetheless intriguing transatlantic and transgeneration projects. Sonny Boy's only entry into the British charts occured in June 1964, when Down and out Blues reached No. 20 on the LP lists. He passed away lesss than a year later - Sonny Boy Mk 2 died in Arkansas in May 1965 at the age of 68. (Bob Macdonald June 1985)
Rice Miller Williamson (Sonny Boy Mk 2) Was born Aleck Ford in Mississippi in 1899, but became known as Rice Miller from a childhood nickname and his stepfather's surname. He died in Arkansas in 1965. It is thought that both Rice Miller and John Lee (the original Sonny Boy) worked with Sunnyland Slim in the early '30s; Miller later worked with Elmore James, Big Boy Crudup, Robert Johnson and Howlin' Wolf; he appeared on the radio show King Biscuit Time in 1941-5, billed as Sonny Boy Williamson, and after John Lee was murdered he claimed to be the original: his talent justified the arrogance. He had R&B hits in the mid 1950s on Chess and Checker and toured Europe in the '60s, becoming one of the most direct influences on UK R&B and recording with The Animals, The Yardbirds and Brian Auger: Albums now on Charly include *Jam session* with Auger and Jimmy Page, and *Newcastle December 1963* with The Animals. See also the entry for The Yardbirds. (Donald Clarke, May '88).

**BEST OF SONNY BOY WILLIAMSON**
Tracks: / Don't start me to talkin' / All my love in vain / Let me explain / Keep it to yourself / Key (to your door), The / Fattening frogs for snakes / Cross my heart / Born blind / Ninety nine / Your funeral and my trial / Let your conscience be your guide / Goat, The / It's sad to be alone / Checkin' up on my baby / Lonesome cabin / Trust my baby / Too close together / Nine below zero / Help me / Bring it on home / Decoration day / One way out.
**CD:** Released Dec '86, on Greenline by Charly Records. Catalogue no: **CD CHESS 35**

**BLUES OF SONNY BOY WILLIAMSON, THE**
Note: Recorded in Copenhagen, Nov 1st 1963, Ivar Rosenberg. Tracks include: Why are you crying, Girl friends, I', so glad, Movin' out, On my way back home, Once upon a time, etc.
**Album:** Released Jun '87, on Storyville by Storyville Records AB. Catalogue no: **SLP 4062**
**CD:** Released Jun '87, on Storyville by Storyville Records AB. Catalogue no: **STCD 4062**

**CHESS MASTERS - SONNY BOY**
**Album:** Released Apr '81, on Checker (USA) Catalogue no: **CXMD 4001**
**2 LP Set:** Released Apr '83, on Chess (PRT) Deleted '88. Catalogue no: **CXMD 4012**

**CHESS YEARS, THE**
Tracks: / Good evening everybody / All my love in vain / Don't start me to talkin' / You killin' me (on my feet) / Work with me / Let me explain / I know what love is all about / Your imagination / I wonder why / Don't lose your eye / Keep it to yourself / Key, The (to your door) / Have you ever been in love / Please forgive / Fattening frogs for snakes / Hurts me so much / I don't know / This is my apartment / Like wolf / Cross my heart / Unseen eye / Ninety nine / Dissatisfied / Born blind / Little village / Wake up baby / She got next to me / Your funeral my trial / Let your consience be your guide / Unseeing eye / Keep your hand out of my pocket / Cool diposition / Goat,The / I never do wrong / Santa Claus / I'ts sad to be alone / I can't do without you / Open road / Checkin' up on my baby / Peach tree / Lonesome cabin / Temperature 110 / Down child / Trust my baby / Somebody help me / This old life / Too young to die / She's my baby / Stop right now / That's all I want / Too close together / Hunt,The / Too old to think / Nine below zero / One way out / Bye bye bird / Got to move / Help me / One way out / Bring it on home / My younger days / Stop cryin' / Trying to get back on my feet / Understand my life / Decoration

day / One way out / Close to me (I want you) / Don't make a mistake / Find another woman / I can't be alone / My name is Sonny Boy / Key,The (to your door) / Hurts me so much / Cool disposition / Dissatisfied / Cross my heart / She got next to me / Fattening frogs for snakes / Your funeral my trial / Cool disposition / Goat,The / Ninetynine.
**LP Set:** Released '87, on Chess by Vogue Records. Catalogue no: **BOX 1**

**CHICAGO GOLDEN YEARS**
**2 LP Set:** Released Oct '88, on Vogue by Vogue Records. Catalogue no: **427004**

**COLLECTION: SONNY BOY WILLIAMSON (20 Blues Greats)**
Tracks: / Mister Downchild / I don't care no more / Out on the water coast / Baby don't you worry / Nine below zero / Eyesight to the blind / I cross my heart / West Memphis blues / Do it if you wanna / Crazy about you baby / Pontiac blues / My babe / I'm gonna put you down / Night time is the right time / Cool cool blues / Come on back home / Mighty long time / Sonny Boy's Christmas blues / Stop now, baby / She brought life back to the dead.
**Cass:** Released Aug '86, on Deja Vu Catalogue no: **DVMC 2074**
**Album:** Released Aug '86, on Deja Vu Catalogue no: **DVLP 2074**

**DOWN AND OUT BLUES**
**CD:** Released Jun '88, on MCA (USA) by MCA Records (USA). Catalogue no: **31272**
**Album:** Released Jun '64, on Pye Deleted '69. Catalogue no: **NPL 28036**

**MORE REAL FOLK BLUES**
**Album:** Released Oct '88, on Vogue (France) by Vogue Records. Catalogue no: **515018**

**ONE WAY OUT**
Tracks: / Born blind / Work with me / You killing me / Keep it to yourself / Don't lose your eye / Good evening everybody / Too close together / Let you consience be your guide / I wonder why / This is my apartment / One way out / Like wolf / Have you ever been in love / Cool disposition / I know what love is all about.
**Album:** Released Oct '88, on Vogue (France) by Vogue Records. Catalogue no: **515015**
**Album:** Released Aug '86, on Chess by Vogue Records. Catalogue no: **GCH 8006**
**Album:** Released '88, on Blues Rock Project Catalogue no: **BRP 2015**
**Cass:** Released Aug '86, on Chess by Vogue Records. Catalogue no: **GCHK 78006**

**PORTRAIT IN BLUES, A**
**Album:** Released May '86, on Storyville by Storyville Records AB. Catalogue no: **SLP 4016**

**REAL FOLK BLUES**
**Album:** Released Oct '88, on Vogue (France) by Vogue Records. Catalogue no: **515010**

**SONNY BOY WILLIAMSON**
**Album:** Released Oct '89, on Chess Masters Catalogue no: **CHXT 108**
**Cass:** Released '88, on Arhoolie (USA) by Arhoolie Records (USA). Catalogue no: **C 216**

**SONNY BOY WILLIAMSON AND MEMPHIS IN PARIS (Williamson, Sonny Boy & Memphis Slim)**
**Album:** Released May '89, on GNP Crescendo (USA) by GNP Crescendo Records (USA). Catalogue no: **GNPS 10003**

**SONNY BOY WILLIAMSON STORY, THE**
Tracks: / Crazy about you baby / Mr. Downchild / Stop crying / Eyesight to the blind / Sonny Boy's Christmas blues / Cool cool blues / Take it easy baby / Bye bye bird / Pontiac blues / She brought life back to the dead / Do it if you wanna / I cross my heart / Come on back home / Out on the water coast / Nine below zero / Western Arizona / West Memphis blues / Stop now baby / Hours too long / I don't care no more / Lost care, A / Mighty long time.
**Cass:** Released May '89, on Deja Vu Catalogue no: **DVREMC 25**
**CD:** Released May '89, on Deja Vu Catalogue no: **DVRECD 25**

**SONNY BOY WILLIAMSON VOL. 2 1937-1946**
**Album:** Released '88, on Blues Classics(USA) by Arhoolie Records (USA). Catalogue no: **BC 20**

**SONNY BOY WILLIAMSON VOL.3**
**Album:** Released '88, on Blues Classics(USA) by Arhoolie Records (USA). Catalogue no: **BC 24**

**SONNY BOY WILLIAMSON AND YARDBIRDS 1963 (With Eric Clapton) (Williamson, Sonny Boy & The Yardbirds)**
**CD:** Released Aug '87, on L&R Catalogue no: **CDLR 42.020**
**Album:** Released '88, on L&R Catalogue no: **LR 42.020**

**TAKE IT EASY BABY**
Tracks: / Bye Bye Bird / I don't care no more / Baby don't worry / Twenty three hours too long / Take it easy baby.
Note: Live set recorded in London with the Yardbirds and Eric Clapton in support.
**7" EP:** Released Jul '87, on Blue Moon (1) by Magnum Music Group. Catalogue no: **BMEP 001**

**THE BLUES OF......**
**Album:** Released Feb '90, on Storyville by Storyville Records AB. Catalogue no: **STLP 4062**
**CD:** Released Feb '90, on Storyville by Storyville Records AB. Catalogue no: **STCD 4062**

## Willis, Jack

**ORLEANS STREET SHUFFLE (Willis, Jack & His New Orleans Band)**
**Cass:** Released Sep '86, on 504 Catalogue no: **TCS 5**
**Album:** Released Sep '86, on 504 Catalogue no: **LPS 5**

## Wilson, Clive

**ORIGINAL CAMELIA JAZZ BAND OF NEW ORLEANS (Wilson, Clive & Trevor Richards)**
**Album:** Released '88, on GHB by Jazzology Records (USA). Catalogue no: **GHB 244**

**PLAYS NEW ORLEANS JAZZ**
**Album:** Released Sep '86, on New Orleans Catalogue no: **NOR 7210**

## Wilson, Edith

**EDITH WILSON WITH JOHNNY DUNN'S JAZZ HOUNDS**
**Album:** Released Apr '79, on Fountain by Retrieval Records. Catalogue no: **FB 302**

## Wilson, Garland

**Biographical details:** Garland Wilson was born in 1909 in West Virginia, he died in Paris in 1954. He was a pianist, influenced by Earl Hines and highly regarded in the blues. He first went to Europe in 1932 with vocalist Nina Mae McKinney; he spent most of the rest of his life there. (Donald Clarke)..

**WAY I FEEL, THE**
Note: Artists also include: Nat Gonella / Nina Mae McKinney.
**Album:** Released Jul '86, on Collectors Items Catalogue no: **CI 016**

## Wilson, Gerald

**Biographical details:** Gerald Wilson was born in 1918 in Mississippi. He is an excellent trumpet player who rarely solos, a bandleader and composer underrated except by his fellow musicians. He played in the Jimmie Lunceford band in 1939-42 (he wrote *Hi Spook*; co-wrote *Yard Dog Mazurka*); he settled on the West Coast and freelanced, working in various bands and doing studio work. He first led his own big band in Los Angeles in the mid-40's; his wife Melba Liston is a trombonist who played with Dizzie Gillespie: Wilson wrote *Katy, Dizzier & Dizzier* for Gillespie. Wilson's various big bands have always included excellent sidemen such as Joe Pass and Harold Land. He also led bands on albums by vocalists Johnny Hartman, Nancy Wilson, Ella Fitzgerald, Al Hibbler, Bobby Darin, Julie London and others. Ella sang his *Imagine My Frustration* on LP *Ella At Duke's Place* with Ellington on Verve. He played trumpet solos on *Leroy Walks* by bassist Leroy Vinnegar on Contemporary; did film work, wrote for sym|pbony orchestra, had popular radio interview show on Los Angeles radio. His tune *Viva Tirado* was a top 30 hit in 1970 for L.A. band *El Chicano*. (Donald Clarke)..

**CALAFIA (Wilson's, Gerald Orchestra Of The Eighties)**
Tracks: / Prince Albert / Calafia / Eloy /

Red fox, The / 3/4 for Mayor Tom / Viva tirado '85 / Polygon / Jessica / Blues bones and bobby.
Note: Featuring - Ernie Watts, Harold Land, Milcho Leviev, Al Aarons, Anthony Wilson, Oscar Brashear, Rick Baptists, Garnett Brown, George (Buster) Cooper, Stanley Gibert, Anthony Ortega.
**CD:** Released Sep '86, on Trend (USA) by Trend Records (USA). Catalogue no: **TRCD 537**

**GERALD WILSON ALL STAR ORCHESTRA (VIDEO) (Wilson, Gerald All Star Orchestra)**
**VHS:** Released '88, on Kay Jazz (video) by Kay Jazz. Catalogue no: **KJ 042**

**GOLDEN SWORD, THE (Wilson, Gerald & His Orchestra)**
**Album:** Released Feb '84, on Discovery (USA) by Discovery Records (USA). Catalogue no: **DS 901**
**Cass:** Released '88, on Discovery (USA) by Discovery Records (USA). Catalogue no: **DSC 901**

**GROOVIN' HIGH**
Note: Wilson, Gerald, Wilbert Baranco and Jimmy Mundy
**Album:** Released Apr '81, on Hep Jazz by Hep Records. Catalogue no: **HEP 15**

**JESSICA (Wilson, Gerald & His Orchestra)**
Tracks: / Jessica / Love you madly / Blues, bones and Bobby / Getaway / Sophisticated lady / Don't get around much more.
**Cass:** Released Jan '84, on Trend (USA) by Trend Records (USA). Catalogue no: **TRC 531**
**Album:** Released Jan '84, on Trend (USA) by Trend Records (USA). Catalogue no: **TR 531**

**LOMELIN (Wilson, Gerald Orchestra Of The Eighties)**
Note: All music composed by Gerald Wilson. Featuring Harold Land, Oscar Brashear, Ernie Watts, Robert Conti, Mike Wofford, Bobby Bryant, Jerome Richardson, Buddy Collette, Jack Nimitz, Jimmy Cleveland.
**Cass:** Released '88, on Discovery (USA) by Discovery Records (USA). Catalogue no: **DSC 833**
**Album:** Released '88, on Discovery (USA) by Discovery Records (USA). Catalogue no: **DS 833**

**LOVE YOU MADLY (Wilson, Gerald & His Orchestra)**
**CD:** Released '88, on Discovery (USA) by Discovery Records (USA). Catalogue no: **DSCD 947**

**MOMENT OF TRUTH**
Tracks: / Viva tirado / Moment of truth / Patterns / Teri / Nancy Jo / Milestones / Latino / Josephina / Emerge.
**CD:** Released Jan '90, on Pacific Jazz by EMI Records. Catalogue no: **CZ 255**
**CD:** Released Jan '90, on Pacific Jazz by EMI Records. Catalogue no: **792 928 2**

## Wilson, Joe Lee

**SECRETS FROM THE SUN**
**Album:** Released Apr '79, on Inner City Catalogue no: **INNER CITY 1042**

**WITHOUT A SONG**
**Album:** Released Apr '79, on Inner City Catalogue no: **INNER CITY 1064**

## Wilson, Nancy

**Biographical details:** Nancy Wilson was born in 1937 in Ohio. She is a perennially popular pop singer handling all kinds of material with strong jazz qualities of phrasing, feeling, good intonation. She has recorded with Cannonball Adderley, George Searing, Gerald Wilson, many others; she had several Capitol LPs in the USA album chart almost every year from 1962 through the '70s. *Lush Life* in 1967 had arrangements by Billy May, Oliver Nelson and Sid Feller. *The Two Of Us* in 1984 featured Ramsey Lewis. (Donald Clarke)..

**BUT BEAUTIFUL**
Tracks: / Prelude to a kiss / For heaven's sake / Happiness is a thing called Joe / I'll walk alone / Supper time / Oh look at me now / Glad to be unhappy / In a sentimental mood / I thought about you / Easy living / Do it again / Darn that dream.
**CD:** Released Apr '90, on Pacific Jazz by EMI Records. Catalogue no: **CZ 275**
**CD:** Released Apr '90, on Pacific Jazz by EMI Records. Catalogue no: **CDP 792 868 2**

**GODSEND**
Tracks: / Feel like makin' love / Dindi / It's all been said / Loneliness / Godsend / Ribbon in the sky / Heart to heart / How could I have know / I believe in you / Another place in time.
**CD:** Released Dec '84, on Denon Deleted '88. Catalogue no: **C38 7188**

**LIFE, LOVE AND HARMONY**
Tracks: / Life, love and harmony / Here's to us / This is our song / Sunshine / You're the one / Open up your heart / Wrapped up in the comfort of your love / Best of the woman in me / Heaven.
**Album:** Released '79, on Capitol by EMI Records. Deleted '84. Catalogue no: **EST 11943**

**LUSH LIFE**
Tracks: / Free again / Midnight sun / Only the young / When the world was young / Right to love / Lush life / Over the weekend / You've changed / River shallow / Sunny / I stayed too long at the fair.
**Cass:** Released Apr '84, on Capitol by EMI Records. Deleted Jul '87. Catalogue no: **TCCAPS 2600064**
**Album:** Released Apr '84, on Capitol by EMI Records. Deleted Jun '89. Catalogue no: **CAPS 2600061**

**NANCY WILSON'S GREATEST HITS**
Tracks: / How glad I am / Face it girl it's over / Can't take my eyes off you / Uptight / Peace of mind / Now I'm a woman / Tell me the truth / I want to be with you / Don't come running back to me.
**Cass:** Released Dec '88, on Capitol (Specials) Catalogue no: **4XL 9449**

**TWO OF US, THE**
Tracks: / Ram / Midnight rendezvous / Breaker beat / Slippin' away / Two of us / Quiet storm / Never wanna say goodnight / Closer than close / Song without words.
**Cass:** Released Sep '84, on CBS by CBS Records. Deleted '87. Catalogue no: **40 25976**
**Album:** Released Sep '84, on CBS by CBS Records. Deleted '87. Catalogue no: **CBS 25976**

## Wilson, Teddy

**Biographical details:** Teddy Wilson was born in 1912 in Texas; he died in 1986 in New Britain, Connecticut. The pianist recorded with Benny Goodman and Gene Krupa in 1935, toured with Goodman in the trio, which became a quartet when Lionel Hampton joined, they helped to make history as the first integrated group in the Swing era. By this time his style of single note lines, influenced by Earl Hines and Art Tatum, but immensely sophisticated in its understated way, made him the most influential pianist since Hines; but eschewing obvious flash caused later to be underrated. He led scores of small-group record dates 1935-42 for Brunswick, including instrumentals and famous vocals by Ella Fitzgerald, Lena Horne, Helen Ward and others, but the most famous were with Billie Holiday: her finest records, some issued under his name on Brunswick, others hers on Vocalion. Made cheaply for Juke Boxes, using the best sideman in town for each date, the records employ nearly all the best jazzmen alive at the time; about 50 were hits 1935-38. Nearly all were made in NYC, but West Coast dates in 1937 yielded a number one hit instrumental *You Can't Stop Me From Dreaming.* He left Goodman in '39 and led his own fine big band for a year which was not recorded, writing some arrangements for himself; lived in New York for the rest of his life, teaching, broadcasting, occasionally recording, playing in clubs, touring overseas. (Donald Clarke)..

**2ND TIME AROUND**
**Cass:** Released May '88, on Jazz Life Catalogue no: **2173222**
**CD:** Released May '88, on Jazz Life Catalogue no: **247 322 2**
**Album:** Released May '88, on Jazz Life Catalogue no: **2273222**

**AIR MAIL SPECIAL**
**Album:** Released Feb '89, on Black Lion Catalogue no: **BLP 60115**

**AMERICAN DANCES BROADCASTS-1939**
**Album:** Released '88, on Jasmine by Hasmick Promotions. Catalogue no: **JASM 2519**
**Cass:** Released Jan '89, on Jasmine by

Hasmick Promotions. Catalogue no: **JASMC 2519**

**AS TIME GOES BY (Wilson, Teddy & Kay Penton)**
Tracks: / After you've gone / How high the moon / Isn't it romantic / These foolish things / It's the talk of the town / Rose room.
Note: Featuring Charlie Shavers, Red Norvo, Billy Taylor.
**Album:** Released '88, on Musicraft (USA) by Discovery Records (USA). Catalogue no: **MVS 2007**

**BODY AND SOUL**
**2 LP Set:** Released Jul '77, on Vogue by Vogue Records. Catalogue no: **VJD 535**

**COLE PORTER CLASSICS**
Tracks: / Get out of town / Just one of those things / I get a kick out of you / It's all right with me / Why shouldn't I? / Love for sale.
**Album:** Released Jul '84, on Black Lion Catalogue no: **BLM 51505**

**DEAR TEDDY (Wilson, Teddy Sextet) (See panel below)**
Tracks: / China boy / (I'm) confessin' / Rose room / After you've gone / How high the moon / I surrender dear / Whispering / Stompin' at the Savoy / I know that you know / Sheik of Araby, The / Body and soul / Dinah / Flying home / Sweet Georgia Brown / It's the talk of the town / Undecided / Speculation / Central Avenue blues.
Note: Charlie Shavers (trumpet), Red Norvo (vibraharp), Teddy Wilson (piano), Remo Palmieri (guitar), Al Hall (bass), Gordon 'Specs' Powell (drums). It is custom and practice - almost obligatory one might say - to commence the programme notes for a record with a fairly detailed biography of the artist. However, when the artist is well known, as indeed is Teddy Wilson, then the preamble is unnecessary. He has recorded so prolifically that his early days have been chronicled many times. However, there is one event in Teddy Wilson's life which marked the real turning point in his career. This was in 1933 when the late John Hammond loaned band leader Benny Carter 150 dollars to bring Teddy from Chicago to New York, initially to play piano on some Carter recordings under the name of the The Chocolate Dandies for the English Columbia label. From this point on, he never looked back and principally under Hammond's guidance, he emerged in the mid-thirties as a major jazz pianist whose original style would influence other pianists for years to come. Much has been written about the origins of Wilson's style, most writers seem to feel that the lineage is out of Earl Hines via Art Tatum. I am not sure that I agree with this theory. I am more inclined to think that Wilson like Hines, Tatum and certainly Count Basie, was a true original and developed his own style. Unlike Hines and Tatum, his playing was easily assimilated by the public, his left hand playing rhythmic tenths generated an easy swing and his right played single note linear runs like a horn. This style stood Wilson in great stead to the end of his life, being always in demand as a club or concert attraction usually in a trio format with bass and drums. To return to the thirties, it was John Hammond who paired off Wilson and Red Norvo in a septet which included Artie Shaw, Charlie Barnet and Jack Jenney, all of whom would become leaders in their own right. One of the tunes, recorded with this group was *I surrender dear* which became a standard in Norvo's repertoire and is reprised in this collection. Hammond certainly introduced Teddy to Benny Goodman, initially as an intermission pianist and later as a regular member of the Goodman Trio and Quartet. I have always thought that Benny would have been content to have Teddy as his pianist for ever - he always said to me that he felt comfortable with Teddy - nothing ever went wrong and there were never any musical gaffes. I am not sure that the feeling was always mutual and after Gene Krupa and Harry James left the Goodman fold, Teddy was only too happy to leave and go his own way, sadly not always financially successful. Thereafter he was often to return to Goodman in a variety of small groups.
To complete the catalogue of Hammond inspired work, the recordings made with Billie Holiday either under Billie's or Teddy's names are the quintessential examples of small group jazz, the only other equivalents are the sides made by Lionel Hampton for Victor during the four years when he too was in the Goodman small groups. The Wilson/Holiday records and the Goodman Trios and Quartets assure Teddy of a permanent place in the Jazz Hall Of Fame. In the ten year period from 1935, Teddy was rarely out of the recording studios and in the twelve months from June 1944 he appears on more than 150 titles under his own name or as a sideman. In retrospect this must have been one of the most productive times of his life. He was a member of the Paul Baron Orchestra and Sextet which accompanied Mildred Bailey on her regular weekly CBS broadcast, he was recording and gigging with Goodman, subsequently appearing in Billy Rose's revue *The seven lively arts* and when Mildred's series ended in February 1945, he as well as Red Norvo joined Benny on a full time basis remaining until Mel Powell was discharged from the Services in August 1945. Red Norvo (real name Kenneth Norville) born 31st March, 1908 was the first to play jazz on the xylophone and later the marimba. Married initially to Mildred Bailey he came to prominence with Paul Whiteman and then formed his own band with outstanding arrangements by Eddie Sauter. He had flirted briefly with the vibraharp in 1937 during the course of some recordings with Wilson and Harry James and in 1943 he finally abandoned the wooden bars for metallic ones. Much of his work on this record betrays his xylophonic background and it was a couple of years until the transition was complete. In the years since, he has

**Teddy Wilson - Dear Teddy (Esquire)**

often returned to B.G. for tours, recording and personal appearances. Charlie Shavers born 3rd August 1917 was a musical chameleon. He had an extraordinary technique which enabled him to play anything and whereas Red Norvo never displayed anything other than good taste, Charlie would let his emotions and his showmanship take over to produce some really excrutiating high note work. There is some evidence of that side of his persona on some tracks of this record, his worst excesses were exhibited during his sojurn with the Tommy Dorsey Orchestra and later with the Jazz At The Philharmonic groups, organised by Norman Granz. His best work appears on the John Kirby Sextet sessions which also showcase his abilities as a composer and arranger. He died of a heart attack in 1971. Remo Palmieri, the youngest of the musicians on this record was born on 29th March 1923. A Charlie Christian devotee, he started gigging in New York City in 1942 and like the others became a member of Paul Baron's CBS Orchestra. He stayed with the network for many years and is still active, recording for Concord and is now known as Remo Palmier.

Bassist Al Hall was born on the 18th March 1915. He started on cello, moved to the brass bass then to the stringed version in 1932. He played with Billy Hicks and 'Skeets' Tolbert before joining Teddy Wilson's ill fated big band in 1939. He also became a staff musician at CBS and his strong bass lines have always been in demand on countless disc dates and he has played in many pit bands for the top Broadway shows. He ran his own record label WAX and the records were released in the U.K. on the Esquire label. The last member of the sextet is drummer 'Specs' Powell born on the 5th June, 1922. His first jobs were with Edgar Hayes, Eddie South, John Kirby and Benny Carter. He joined Red Norvo's small group when Red finaly switched from marimba to vibes. A permanent studio percussionist, he played on Arthur Godfrey's radio and television shows and is still currently active. Many of the tunes played on this record had been featured on the weekly Mildred Bailey radio show and were thus well rehearsed. Most of the titles are real standards and played at jam sessions all over the world - they became the staple repertoire of Teddy's club and concert appearances. One might say that they form the basis of any buskers handbook and Teddy's little group does them full justice. Teddy Wilson was born on the 24th November 1912 and died on the 31st July 1986 at his home in Connecticut after a long battle with cancer. He left a lifetime of recorded music for us to enjoy for ever. Dear Teddy for this we thank you. (Peter Newbrook, 1987)

**Album:** Released Dec '87, on Esquire by Titan Int. Prod.. Catalogue no: **ESQ 335**

**D.S.C.B. MEETS TEDDY WILSON (Wilson, Teddy & Dutch Swing College Band)**

**Album:** Released Oct '86, on Timeless by Timeless Records. Catalogue no: **TTD 525**

**ELEGANT PIANO (Wilson, Teddy & Marion McPartland)**

**Album:** Released Jan '83, on Swaggie (Australia) Catalogue no: **S 1330**

**HOW HIGH THE MOON**

**Album:** Released Apr '81, on Kings Of Jazz Catalogue no: **KLJ 20011**

**I GOT RHYTHM**

**2 LP Set:** Released May '83, on Vogue Jazz (France) by Vogue Records. Catalogue no: **VJD 544**

**I LOVE A PIANO (Wilson, Teddy Trio & Mary Lou Williams Quartet)**

**Album:** Released Apr '79, on Esquire by Titan Int. Prod.. Catalogue no: **ESQ 304**

**IMPECCABLE MR WILSON, THE**

**Album:** Released Dec '81, on Verve Catalogue no: **2304 513**

**IN TOKYO**

**Album:** Released Apr '81, on Sackville by Spotlite Records. Catalogue no: **2005**

**JUMPIN' FOR JOY (Wilson, Teddy, His Orchestra & Billie Holiday)**

Tracks: / Somebody loves me / Blues in C sharp minor / Why do I lie to myself about you? / Way you look tonight / Sailin' / Why was I born? / I've found a new baby / You can't stop me from dreaming / Just a mood / Don't blame me / More than you know / Jumpin' for joy / Jumpin' on the blacks and whites / Wham (re-bop-boom-bam) / 711 / China boy / Fine and dandy.

**Album:** Released Sep '87, on Affinity by Charly Records. Catalogue no: **AFS 1044**

**LIVE AT SANTA TECLA**

**Album:** Released Feb '83, on Carosello Catalogue no: **CLE 21032**

**MASTERS OF JAZZ VOL. 11 (Wilson, Teddy Sextet)**

**Album:** Released May '86, on Storyville by Storyville Records AB. Catalogue no: **SLP 4111**

**MEETS E.KITAMURA**

**CD:** Released Feb '90, on Storyville by Storyville Records AB. Catalogue no: **STCD 4152**

**MOONGLOW**

Tracks: / Moonglow / Flying home / As time goes by / Ain't misbehavin' / I'm through with love / Airmail special.

Note: Tracks include those listed above.

**Album:** Released Apr '85, on Black Lion Catalogue no: **BLP 30133**

**MR WILSON AND MR GERSHWIN**

**Cass:** Released May '85, on CBS (import) by CBS Records. Catalogue no: **40-21125**

**Album:** Released May '85, on CBS (import) by CBS Records. Catalogue no: **21125**

**NOBLE ART OF TEDDY WILSON, THE (See panel below)**

Tracks: / My silent love / You brought a new kind of love to me / Paradise / My heart stood still / Serenata / Indiana / April in Paris / 'Deed I do / Autumn in New York / Ain't misbehavin' / Serenade in

Teddy Wilson - Noble Art of Teddy Wilson (Storyville)

blue / It's all right to me.
Note: With Niels-Henning Orsted on bass & Bjarne Rostvold on drums. Recorded at Metronome Studio, Copenhagen December 12th, 1968. What the world needs is another record by Teddy Wilson and here it is. Truly one of the greatest this gifted jazz pianist has shown impeccable taste and skill ever since his first tremendous solo on record *Once upon a time* with Benny Carter's Chocolate Dandies in 1933. Everthing Teddy plays is in perfect balance and order; he plays with warmth and enormous drive and a dazzling technique. This man is a master of melodic and logical improvisation ... his style is timeless - has never aged; he is like a Louis Armstrong, a Benny Carter, or a Johnny Hodges. He plays everything with clarity, and his sound is gentle. Teddy Wilson has given also a lot of singers the best accompaniment they ever had; notably and above all the great 'Lady Day' Billie Holiday. Surely Tedd's accompaniment to her had a great deal to do with her success. When you listen to Teddy you can hear traces of Fats Waller, Art Tatum and Earl Hines; of course, these great players inspired him, but above all you hear Teddy's own delicate creation. Teddy Wilson was born in Austin, Texas, on November 24th 1912. He studied piano and violin from childhood and took up theory of music at Talladega College. Teddy moved to Detroit in 1929, started playing with local bandsin 1929, moved on to Toledo where he met Art Tatum, who was to be his greatest inspiration. In 1930 he joined Milton Seniors Band in Toledo. From 1931 to 1933 he played in Chicago with Jimmy Noone, Erskine Tate and Louis Armstrong with whom he made several records for RCA Victor.
IN 1933 he came to New York, joined Benny Carter's band in 1934 and made several unforgettable records with Benny. Willie Bryant took over the Benny Carter band in 1934. Teddy stayed with him for a while; then accompanied The Charioteers for a while. John Hammond, the music critic who at the time was a talent scout for Brunswick Records, arranged for Teddy to do a long series of records with a small pick up band, featuring all the greatest jazz stars - among others Benny Goodman, Red Allen, Johnny Hodges, Chu Berry, Ben Webster and as a vocalist on most of these records Billie Holiday. Around this period Teddy played also for Mildred Bailey and many other singers. The the real big thing happened to Teddy: at a party at Mildred Bailey's and Red Norvo's house the Benny Goodman Trio was formed; and starting in July, 1935 together with Benny and Gene Krupa, Teddy made a series of records that became classics. Also, this was the first inter racial group. Teddy stayed with Benny Goodman until 1939 and made records and played for the public with the trio, the quartet (including Lionel Hampton) and with the big band as well. After this Teddy organized his own big band for the Golden Gate Ballroom in Harlem. This was surely one of the greatest and most musical bands Harlem had ever seen or heard. Teddy himself arranged and played the piano, and he featured many great soloists like Ben Webster, Harold 'Shorty' Baker, Doc Cheatham and others. From 1940 and the next five years Teddy worked with a sextet at the Cafe Society in New York.
At the same time, Teddy was teaching piano at the Juilliard in New York, appeared frequently as soloist or leader of a trio over different radio stations, made many records under his own name and, in 1952, he made a tour of Europe - played in Scandinavia and in 1953, in England. During the later years Teddy has worked with a trio around New York or on tours using the Swedish drummer Bertil Dahlander or Jo Jones and Arwell Shaw and many others on bass. Most of his latest recordings appeared on the Verve label. In November and December 1968 Teddy played at Timme's Club in Copenhagen - to the delight of the Danish jazz fans; and on the 12th of December 1968, we persuaded him to go to the Metronome studios to prove once again that there is only one Teddy Wilson. These trio recordings are, if possible even better than anything Teddy has done ever before - and that means a great deal. With Teddy on this date are the fine Danish bass player Niels Henning Orsted Pedersen and an equally fine flexible swinging drummer Bjarne Rostvold. (Timme Rosenkrantz 1985)
**Album:** Released May '86, on Storyville by Storyville Records AB. Catalogue no: **SLP 4086**

### PRESS AND TEDDY (Wilson, Teddy & Lester Young)
Tracks: / All of me / Prisoner of love / Louise / Pres returns / Love me or leave me / Taking a chance on love / Love is here to stay.
**Album:** Released Apr '83, on Verve (Import) Deleted Jan '88. Catalogue no: **2304 213**

### RAREST..., THE
**Album:** Released '89, on Everybody's (Sweden) Catalogue no: **E 1003**

### REVISITS THE GOODMAN YEARS (1980 - Copenhagen) (Wilson, Teddy Trio)
Note: With Ed Thigpen / J. Lundgard.
**Album:** Released May '86, on Storyville by Storyville Records AB. Catalogue no: **SLP 4046**
**CD:** Released Feb '89, on Storyville by Storyville Records AB. Catalogue no: **STCD 4046**

### RUNNIN' WILD
Tracks: / One o'clock jump / Mood indigo / Take the 'A' train / Satin doll / Smoke gets in your eyes / Runnin' wild / St. James' Infirmary blues / After you've gone.
**Album:** Released Sep '85, on Black Lion Catalogue no: **BLP 30149**

### SCHOOL FOR PIANIST
**Album:** Released '88, on Meritt (USA) Catalogue no: **MERITT 23**

### STOMPING AT THE SAVOY
Tracks: / I can't get started / Sometimes I'm happy / Body and soul / I'll never be the same / Easy living.
Note: Tracks include those listed above.
**Album:** Released Jan '85, on Black Lion Catalogue no: **BLP 30114**

### STRIDING AFTER FATS
Tracks: / Striding after Fats / Blue turning grey over you / I've got a feeling I'm falling / Handful of keys.
Note: Tracks include those listed above.
**Album:** Released Apr '84, on Carrere (France) Catalogue no: **65108**
**Cass:** Released Sep '85, on Black Lion Catalogue no: **BLP 30156C**
**Album:** Released Sep '85, on Black Lion Catalogue no: **BLP 30156**

### SUNDAY MORNING
Tracks: / I've got the world on a string / Fine and dandy / Why shouldn't I? / All of me / Long ago and far away / Cheek to cheek / Ain't misbehavin' / You're my favourite memory / I'm yours / Living in dreams / You took advantage of me.
**Album:** Released '88, on Musicraft (USA) by Discovery Records (USA). Catalogue no: **MVS 2008**

### TEDDY WILSON
**CD:** Released Jul '89, on Cleo Catalogue no: **CLCD 5023**
**Album:** Released '88, on GNP Crescendo (USA) by GNP Crescendo Records (USA). Catalogue no: **GNPS 9014**
**Album:** Released 10 Jul '89, on Black Lion Catalogue no: **BLP 60131**

### TEDDY WILSON 1936 / 37
Tracks: / Breaking in a pair of shoes / Remember me / Hour of parting, The / All my life / Mary had a little lamb / Coquette / Ain't misbehavin' / Blues in C sharp minor / Just a mood / Honeysuckle rose / Between the devil and the deep blue sea / I'm comin', Virginia.
**Cass:** Released Sep '89, on Neovox by Neovox Records. Catalogue no: **NEO 848**

### TEDDY WILSON, BENNY GOODMAN AND HARRY JAMES
**Album:** Released '88, on Meritt (USA) Catalogue no: **MERITT 3**

### TEDDY WILSON AND BIG BAND 1939-40 (Wilson, Teddy & Big Band)
**Album:** Released '88, on Tax Catalogue no: **TAX 8018**

### TEDDY WILSON COLLECTION (20 Golden Greats)
Tracks: / Sweet Lorraine / Sugar plum / What a little moonlight can do / Sunbonnet blue / Yankee Doodle never went to town / Miss Brown to you / I wished on the moon / What a night, what a moon / Eeny meeny miney mo / After you've gone / Who? / China boy / Lady be good / Nobody's sweetheart / Dinah / Moonglow / Stompin' at the Savoy / Sweet Sue / Whispering.
**Cass:** Released Dec '87, on Deja Vu

Catalogue no: **DVMC 2111**
**Album:** Released Dec '87, on Deja Vu Catalogue no: **DVLP 2111**

**TEDDY WILSON AND HIS ALL STARS VOL. 1**
**Album:** Released Apr '79, on Musicraft (USA) by Discovery Records (USA). Catalogue no: **MVS 502**

**TEDDY WILSON AND THE OVE LIND SWING GROUP**
**Album:** Released Jun '88, on Sonet by Sonet Records. Catalogue no: **SNTF 618**

**TEDDY WILSON, VOL 1**
Tracks: / I got rhythm / When your lover has gone / Sweet Georgia Brown / Too late / Limehouse blues / On the sunny side of the street / Smiles / My love is yours / As time goes by.
**Album:** Released Jan '82, on Jazz Reactivation Catalogue no: **JR 108**

**TEDDY WILSON, VOL 2**
Tracks: / Rose room / Just one of those things / Shiny stockings / Body and soul / Sweet Lorraine / Moonglow / But not for me / Nice work if you can get it / It had to be you / Someone to watch over me.
**Album:** Released May '83, on Jazz Reactivation Catalogue no: **JR 127**
**Album:** Released Jul '86, on Jazz Archives (USA) by Jazz Archives Inc.(USA). Catalogue no: **JA 36**

**TEDDY WILSON WITH BILLIE HOLIDAY (Wilson, Teddy & Billie Holiday)**
Tracks: / Nice work if you can get it / Where the lazy river goes by / If you were mine / My last love affair / Why do I lie to myself about you? / Mood that I'm in, The / I'm coming, Virginia / Easy living / How am I to know? / Hour of parting / Coquette / You let me down / I've found a new baby / All my life / Mary had a little lamb / Miss Brown to you / What a little moonlight can do / I wished on the moon.
Note: Recordings from 1935-37. Musicians and singers on the album - Ella Fitzgerald, Benny Goodman, Lester Young, Red Allen, Buster Bailey, Chu Berry, Buck Clayton, Roy Eldridge, Johnny Hodges, Harry James, Gene Krupa, Ben Webster.
**CD:** Released Oct '88, on Living Era by Academy Sound & Vision Records. Catalogue no: **CD AJA 5053**
**Album:** Released Jun '88, on Living Era by Academy Sound & Vision Records. Catalogue no: **AJA 5053**
**Cass:** Released Jun '88, on Living Era by Academy Sound & Vision Records. Catalogue no: **ZC AJA 5053**

**TEDDY WILSON AND BILLIE HOLIDAY VOL. 2 (Wilson, Teddy & Billie Holiday)**
**Album:** Released Jan '88, on Hep Jazz by Hep Records. Catalogue no: **HEP 1014**

**TEDDY'S CHOICE**
**Album:** Released '89, on Jazzology (USA) by Jazzology Records (USA). Catalogue no: **JCE 86**

**TOO HOT FOR WORDS (Wilson, Teddy, His orchestra & Billie Holiday)**
**Album:** Released May '86, on Hep Jazz by Hep Records. Catalogue no: **HEP 1012**
**CD:** Released Mar '90, on Hep Jazz by Hep Records. Catalogue no: **HEPCD 1012**

**TWO GOOD MEN (Wilson, Teddy & Jess Stacy)**
**Album:** Released Jun '86, on Esquire by Titan Int. Prod.. Catalogue no: **ESQ 314**

**WITH THEE I SWING (Wilson, Teddy & his orchestra)**
**Album:** Released '88, on Hep Jazz by Hep Records. Catalogue no: **HEP 1020**

## Winding, Kai

**Biographical details:** Kai Winding was born in 1922 in Denmark, emigrating to the USA at the age of 12; he died in 1983. He played first-class trombone in the bands of Stan Kenton, Charlie Ventura, Tadd Dameron; on the Miles David *Birth Of The Cool* session in 1948, and co-led a quintet with J.J. Johnson 1954-6 which was one of the most popular jazz acts of the decade, helping to restore the trombone to its rightful place after some neglect in the early modern jazz. (Donald Clarke)..

**GIANTS BONES 80**
Tracks: / Love 4 rent / Sweetness / I fall in love too easy / Scrapple from the apple / Corriente / Nu groove / Never never land / Hola.
**Album:** Released Jun '80, on Sonet by Sonet Records. Catalogue no: **SNTF 834**

**JANUARY 31ST & FEBRUARY 15th, 1963 (Winding, Kai,Trombones)**
Tracks: / Don't panic / Waltz on the wild side / Paul finks out / Thirteenth instant / Samba dis / Rotten blues / Raven / Blues for Indian Jim / Rum and bossa nova / Button up your lip / I knew Dana / That's where it is.
**Album:** Released Oct '80, on From The Jazz Vault by Damont Audio Ltd.. Catalogue no: **JV 107**

**KAI AND JAY (Winding, Kai & Jay Jay Johnson)**
Tracks: / Out of this world / Thous sweet / Lover / Lope city / Stolen bass / It's alright with me / Mad about the boy / Yes sir, that's my baby / That's how I feel about you / Gong rock.
**Cass:** Released Sep '86, on Affinity by Charly Records. Catalogue no: **TCAFF 161**
**Album:** Released Oct '86, on Affinity by Charly Records. Catalogue no: **AFF 161**

**KAI WINDING**
**CD:** Released Jul '89, on Cleo Catalogue no: **CLCD 5028**

**TROMBOMANIA (Winding, Kai / Frank Rosolino / Jay Jay Johnson)**
Tracks: / Out of this world / Thou swell / Lover / Lope city / Stolen bass / It's alright with me / Mad about the boy / Yes sir, that's my baby / That's how I feel about you / Gong rock / I may be wrong / Things we did last summer, The / Frieda / My de luxe / Flamingo.
**CD:** Released '89, on Charly by Charly Records. Catalogue no: **CDAFF 761**

## Windy City Blues

**WINDY CITY BLUES 1935-1953 (Various artists)**
Note: Featuring: Robert Lockwood, Johnny Shines, Pinetop Perkins etc.
**Album:** Released Dec '86, on Nighthawk by Nighthawk Records (USA). Catalogue no: **NH 101**

## Winstone, Norma

**SOMEWHERE CALLED HOME**
Tracks: / Cafe / Somewhere called home / Sea lady / Some time ago / Prologue / Celeste / Hi lili hi lo / Out of this world / Tea for two.
Note: After four albums with the trio Azimuth, British singer Norma winstone comes up with a highly individual statement in *Somewhere Called Home*. Supported by John Taylor, pianist with Azimuth and Tony Coe on tenor sax & clarinet, the programme features compositions by Egberto Gismonti, Ralph Towner, Pat Smythe, Kenny Wheeler & Bill Evans. Norma has written lyrics for several of the songs and interprets them as ballads. Personnel: Norma Winstone-voice / John Taylor - piano / Tony Coe-clarinet, tenor sax.
**Album:** Released Feb '87, on ECM Catalogue no: **ECM 1337**

## Witherspoon, Jimmy

**Biographical details:** Born in 1923 in Arkansas, Jimmy Witherspoon is a singer with a big, deep voice, characterised as a bluesman but with all-round skills. While he was serving in the Merchant Marine in the early 1940s he sang with Teddy Weatherford's band in Calcutta and from 1944-48 he was with Jay McShann. He had rhythm-and-blues hit singles between 1949 and 1952 on Supreme and Modern labels and began making LPs in 1958, recording for many labels, including Prestige. During the 1960s Jimmy Witherspoon regularly visited prisons, to sing for the inmates, and once a year he toured Europe. A compilation of early tracks, *Who's Been Jivin' You?*, is on Ace. (Donald Clarke, March 1988.).

**AIN'T NOBODY'S BUSINESS**
Tracks: / Ain't nobody's business / In the evening / Frog-I-more rag / McShann bounce / How long blues / Money's getting cheaper / Skid Row blues / Spoon calls Hootie / Backwater blues / Jumpin' with Louis / Destruction blues.
**Album:** Released Sep '85, on Black Lion Catalogue no: **BLP 30147**

**AT THE MONTEREY JAZZ FESTIVAL**
Tracks: / No rollin blues / Good rockin' tonight / Big fine girl / Ain't nobody's

**Jimmy Witherspoon - Jimmy Witherspoon Meets The Jazz Giants (Affinity)**

business / When I been drinking / Times gettin' tougher than tough / How long / Corrine, Corrina / See see rider / Roll em Pete / Everyday / (I'm gonna move to the) outskirts of town / Kansas City / Trouble in mind / St. Louis blues.
**CD:** Released Jan '88, on Charly by Charly Records. Catalogue no: **CD CHARLY 169**
**Album:** Released Jan '88, on Affinity by Charly Records. Catalogue no: **AFF 182**

**BEN WEBSTER AND JIMMY WITHERSPOON (That's Jazz Series) (Witherspoon, Jimmy & Ben Webster)**
**Album:** Released Mar '77, on Warner Bros. by WEA Records. Catalogue no: **K 56295**

**BIG BLUES**
**Album:** Released Aug '81, on JSP by JSP Records. Catalogue no: **JSP 1032**
**CD:** Released Sep '87, on JSP by JSP Records. Catalogue no: **JSP CD 205**

**COLLECTION: JIMMY WITHERSPOON (20 Blues Greats)**
Tracks: / Ain't nobody's business / How long blues / In the evening / Going to Kansas City / Skid Row blues / Money's getting cheaper / Frog-I-more rag / Backwater blues / Corina Corina / Blowin' the blues / I make a lot of money / Spoon calls Hootie / Good rockin' tonight / Time's gettin' tougher than tough / St. Louis blues / Everyday / Outskirts of town / Destruction blues / Trouble in mind / Gee baby ain't I good to you.
**Cass:** Released Dec '87, on Deja Vu Catalogue no: **DVMC 2113**
**Album:** Released Dec '87, on Deja Vu Catalogue no: **DVLP 2113**

**CRY THE BLUES (Witherspoon, Jimmy & Groove Holmes)**
**Album:** Released Jul '82, on Bulldog Records by President Records. Catalogue no: **BDL 1012**

**EVENIN' BLUES**
**Album:** Released Jan '88, on OBC Catalogue no: **OBC 511**

**FEDERAL SESSIONS, THE**
Tracks: / Lucille / Two little girls / One fine gal / Corn whiskey / Day is dawning, The / Jay's blues (part 1) / Jay's blues (part 2) / Miss Miss Mistreater / Back home / It / Back door blues / Fast woman - slow gin / Just for you / Move my baby / 'Cause I love you / Oh boy.
**Album:** Released '88, on Sing Catalogue no: **SING 1162**

**HEY, MR. LANDLORD**
**Album:** Released Oct '86, on Route 66 (Sweden) Catalogue no: **KIX 31**

**JIMMY WITHERSPOON MEETS THE JAZZ**
Tracks: / Good rockin' tonight / Big fine girl / Ain't nobody's business / How long / See see rider / Everyday / Kansas City / St Louis blues / When I been drinking / No rollin' blues / Times gettin' tougher than tough / Corina Corina / Roll 'em Pete / Outskirts of town (I'm gonna move) / Trouble in mind.
Note: Recorded live at the Monterey Jazz Festival and the Renaissance Club 1959. Featuring Ben Webster, Gerry Milligan, Roy Eldridge, Woody Herman, Coleman Hawkins, Earl Hines. In retrospect 1959 was the year for Jimmy Witherspoon. Not that he hasn't had lots of good years since then, but 1959 was in most ways the best year of his career so far. It might not have been so obvious at the time and, from the perspective of the end of the '50s, other earlier years may have seemed equally or more significant to Spoon himself. Three in particular would have come to mind. 1943 for instance, was the year he first stepped onto a professional bandstand, sitting in with the former Chicago pianist Teddy Weatherford. At the time Witherspoon was a merchant seaman, urged on by his shipmates, while Weatherfod was leading a hotel band in Calcutta. 1945, the year of Spoon's demobilisation found him presenting himself to pianist Jay McShann, also recently at liberty and missing his popular vocalist Walter Brown who, during the war, had gone off to front his own group - not only did Spoon walk straight into Brown's job, but soon after he made a large number of recordings, both with McShann and his drummer Al Wichard and guesting with a Basie unit led by Buddy Tate. Then in 1949 one of this group records, the double sided *Ain't nobody's business*, hit the black (i.e. rhythm and blues) charts and remained there for 34 weeks.

With post 1959 hindsight, however, many of these events appear to be false starts. To be sure, Jimmy gained much valuable experience to be false starts. To be sure, Jimmy gained much valuable experience with McShann (and nearly 30 years later enthusiastically recognised all the musicians in a band photograph) but bands such as this were then less in the limelight and like many other leader, Jay had been forced to cut down to a 7 piece. Yet, despite this move, as mcShann sideman Benny Bailey told me the very day I started to write these notes, 'Nobody had any money then, (mcShann) didn't have any money himself'. In addition, the first Spoon records were not only for small labels but most of them were made in a rush in the late 1947, in order for the companies concerned to try and beat the impending musicians' union ban on recording with the releases being spread over a considerable period and precluding the necessity for regular follow-up sessions, still less a planned recording career. Finally, of course, the disc which made such a big splash and helped to establish his solo career had, like all the others he was to make for some time to come, been done for a flat fee instead of a royalty agreement. So, to capitalise on his hit (and a couple more, one of them from a *Just jazz* concert recording), Spoon had to start what Ralph Gleason described as 'a decade of singing in dingy nightclubs and Jim Crow bars all over the country'.

1959 was the year that began a different kind of buzz about Witherspoon. He had always got on well with jazz-based musicians, from Charlie Parker to the sort of horn players who worked in R&B bands but had a feel for bop and swing. He admired their expressiveness and saw the links with his own mode of music making, while they dug his rhythmic flexibility and his updating of the 'Joe Turner' style ('Joe always was my idol', he told me and a thousand other interviewers). He had already recorded three jazz-orientated albums in the three preceding years (for Atlantic, RCA Victor and World Pacific), but the autumn of 1959 was the first time anyone had thought of putting him on at a jazz festival. Reports vary as to where Spoon's work all over the country had taken him but Jimmy Lyons, the disc-jocket and producer of the Monterey Festival, has this possibly picturesque version: 'He was at some drinking dive in Kentucky, just across the border from Ohio ... He said he'd home if he had enough money to buy a used car and drive to L.A. I wired him 250 dollars to buy himself a clunker and get out of that town.

Suffice it to say that his success at monterey benefitted Spoon's career almost as much as Ellington's at Newport in 1956. Coming on at the close of the first night of the festival (which had been opened by Chris Barber, plugging his hit single of *Petite fleur* Jimmy followed a trio performace by the then San Francisco-based Earl Hines with his bassist Vernon Alley plus L.A. based Mel Lewis; to them were then added Spoon's buddy Ben Webster, the visiting duo of Coleman Hawkins and Roy Eldridge, and Woody Herman who had been rehearsing his alumni big band for the following afternoon and evening. (Discographies state that it was Herman sideman Urbie Green who also sat in with Hines and is briefly audible behind Witherspoon, while Jimmy Lyons says it was Bob Brookmeyer - who I doubt was even thereplus J.J. Johnson, who certainly was). After the climatic addition of the singer, everyone else stayed on stage, but it was Spoon who took charge in no uncertain manner. The fact that the set has now been programmed for the first time ever in actual performance order tends to underline how completely unrehearsed the whole thing was, and how both vocalist and accompanist gain in confidence and rapport as the music progresses. As well as calling the keys and setting the tempos, Spoon brings in solos by Ben, Hawk, Woody and Roy before moving front and centre for a reprise of his *Just Jazz* hit *No rollin' blues* with Roy's squeals mirroring those of the audience. In fact, the atmosphere becomes so compelling, it hardly matters that the closing *Ain't nobody's business* suddenly finds both pianist and bassist at a loss for a second chord of the vocal chorus; fortunately, Ben offers his verbal counsel, 'We're in A flat? Then it's C next,' before joining in to help everyone along.

Not only did Spoon's appearance at the Monterey Festival raise his profile to the extent that he could now work in the top jazz clubs and tour overseas, but he was a regular returnee to Montery, until the year he had to turn down the offer with the words, 'The King of Siam called me. He's having a party and wants me to sing there.' One of the most immediate consequences, however, was his booking two months later at Hollywood's Renaissance Club - a renaissance for Spoon's nightclub career and, by all accounts, for the club itself. Dave Axelrod, who also produced Jimmy's World Pacific and later some of his Prestige albums had already recorded Monterey set for the Hifijazz label and hastened to catch Spoon on location again. And Gerry Mulligan, performing opposite him with a specially assembled quintet, took advantage of the non-exclusive nature of his Verve recording contract to accompany Jimmy on the stand and on the record.

The result is a splendid occasion which combined the informality of that magical moment at Monterey with the organised looseness that a few nights' collaboration brings. Mulligan shows his great ability to be a sympathetic supporter and full of ideas at the same time, but then so does Webster; while the other holdover from Monterey, drummer Mel Lewis underscores everything without drawing attention to himself (as he still does today). Jimmy Rowles and Leroy Vinnegar get little solo space, but their accompaniments are just sufficently unconventional to put a shame more hard-headed blues backings. And the programme is an amazing anthology of blues classics not just for the sake of it, but because all of them were in Spoon's regular working repertoire. Less well known except to Spoon fans in the ever-timely *Times getting*, originally recorded at the same session as the hit version of *Ain't nobody's business* but credited (under another title) to some publishing executive to whom Jimmy signed away his composing royalties, thereby illustrating perhaps the theme of the lyrics.

The all star personnel and the live situation bring out all that is elemental and essential in Witherspoon's conribution to the field of jazz and blues. The immediate impact of his performance is so vivid that you can almost touch it here, and anyone who's ever seen him in action will recall not only his electrifying presence but his ability to dominate a band. (In my youth I played behind him for one unforgettable set, and experienced him at first hand dictating the arrangement with his whole body and especially his foot. He needn't have worried, for drummer Spike Wells knew this record by heart - indeed he introduced me to it.)

It's not for nostalgic reasons, though that I'm inclined to say this may well be the album for Jimmy Witherspoon. There are great ones from both before and since, but, if you only wanted one Spoon on a platter, this is the one to get. (Brian Priestley)

**CD:** Released Apr '89, on Charly by Charly Records. Catalogue no: **CD CHARLY 169**

## JIMMY WITHERSPOON & JIMMY RUSHING

**CD:** Released Oct '87, on Vogue by Vogue Records. Catalogue no: **VG 600 161**

## LIVE AT MONTEREY

**CD:** Released Feb '88, on Fresh Sounds (Spain) by Fresh Sounds Records (Spain). Catalogue no: **M&MJ 421**

## MEAN OLD FRISCO

Tracks: / Mean old Frisco blues / Bad bad whiskey / One scotch one bourbon one beer / Blues and trouble / I'll go on living / It's a lonesome old world / Rocks in my bed / Baby baby baby / Lonely boy blues / Endless sleep / I can't hardly see.

**Album:** Released Nov '88, on Prestige Catalogue no: **PR 7855**

## MIDNIGHT LADY CALLED THE BLUES

Tracks: / New York City blues / Barber / Blinded by love / Happy hard times / Something rotten in East St Louis / Midnight lady called the blues / Blues hall of fame.

**Album:** Released Feb '87, on Muse (USA) by Muse Records (USA). Catalogue no: **MRC 5327**

## NEVER KNEW THIS KIND OF HURT BEFORE (The Bluesway Sessions)

Tracks: / Never knew hurt like this before / I made a lot of mistakes / Pillar to post / You can't do a thing when you're drunk / Parcel post blues / Bags under my eyes / Bug to put 'n' you' ear / Thoughts of home / I don't know / Evenin' / No rolling blues / Pay the consequences / Going down slow / Testifying / Nobody wants to hear nobody's troubles / Blow wind blow / Look at granny run run / Just a dream / Handbags and gladrags / Night they drove old Dixie down, The.

**2 LP Set:** Released Jan '89, on Charly by Charly Records. Catalogue no: **CDX 32**

## NEW ORLEANS BLUES (Witherspoon, Jimmy & Wilbur De Paris)

Tracks: / Lotus blossom / Trouble in mind / Big fine girl / How long blues / Good rollin' blues / Careless love / Tain't nobody's business If I do / St Louis blues / When the sun goes down / See see rider.

**Album:** on Official by Official Records. Catalogue no: **OFF 6046**

## OLYMPIA CONCERT

**Album:** Released '88, on Vogue by Vogue Records. Catalogue no: **500091**

## ON CONSTELLATION, 1961-62 (Witherspoon, Jimmy & Groove Holmes)

**Album:** Released May '88, on Fresh Sounds (Spain) by Fresh Sounds Records (Spain). Catalogue no: **FS 314**

## SINGS THE BLUES WITH PANAMA

Tracks: / Sent for you yesterday / I want a little girl / Don't you miss your baby / Goodmorning blues / Goin' to Chicago /

Sometimes I feel like a motherless child / Boogie woogie (I may be wrong) / Rain keeps falling down / Gee baby ain't I good to you.
**Album:** Released Feb '83, on Muse by Black & Blue Records. Catalogue no: **MR 5288**

**SPIRITUALS**
**Album:** Released May '88, on Fresh Sounds (Spain) by Fresh Sounds Records (Spain). Catalogue no: **FS 313**

**THEME FROM CHARLIE**
Tracks: / Theme from Charlie / Charlies blues.
**7" Single:** Released '84, on Towerbell Deleted '87. Catalogue no: **TOW 40**

**WHO'S BEEN JIVIN' YOU**
Tracks: / Jump children / Connie Lee / Take me back baby / Big fine girl / Same old blues / Your red wagon / Who's been jivin' with you / I'll be right on down / Oh mother, dear mother / Don't ever move a woman in to your house / Real ugly woman / Baby baby / Slow your speed / Doctor blues.
**Album:** Released Jan '84, on Ace by Ace Records. Deleted Jun '88. Catalogue no: **CH 92**

## Wolverines Orchestra

**WOLVERINES ORCHESTRA 1924, THE**
**Album:** Released Jan '83, on Swaggie (Australia) Catalogue no: **802**
**Album:** Released Apr '79, on Fountain by Retrieval Records. Catalogue no: **FJ 114**

## Women In Jazz

**WOMEN IN JAZZ: ALL WOMEN GROUPS (Various artists)**
**Album:** Released Apr '81, on Stash (USA) Catalogue no: **ST 111**

**WOMEN IN JAZZ: PIANISTS (Various artists)**
**Album:** Released Apr '81, on Stash (USA) Catalogue no: **ST 112**

**WOMEN IN JAZZ: SWINGTIME TO MODERN (Various artists)**
**Album:** Released Apr '81, on Stash (USA) Catalogue no: **ST 113**

## Women, Whisky & Wailin'

**WOMEN, WHISKY AND WAILIN' (Various artists)**
Tracks: / Bloodshot eyes: *Harris, Wynonie* / Good morning judge: *Harris, Wynonie* / Sittin' on it all the time: *Harris, Wynonie* / Boogie at midnight: *Brown, Roy* / My girl from Kokomo: *Brown, Roy* / Fannie Brown got married: *Brown, Roy* / My gal: *Moonglows* / Pedal pushin' papa: *Dominoes* / My baby's 3-D: *Dominoes* / South Shore drive: *Watts, Nobie* / Just a gigolo: *Prima, Louis* / I ain't got nobody: *Prima, Louis* / Jump, jive and wail: *Prima, Louis* / Buona sera: *Prima, Louis* / Hucklebuck with Jimmy: *Five Keys* / Too much boogie: *Pomus, Doc* / Ain't that just like a woman: *Flowers, Pat*
**Album:** Released Oct '86, on Charly R&B by Charly Records. Catalogue no: **CRB 1141**

## Wood, Scott

**SCOTT WOOD AND HIS SIX SWINGERS**
**Album:** Released Oct '77, on Retrospect by EMI Records. Catalogue no: **SH 249**

## Woods, Jimmy

**CONFLICT (Woods, Jimmy Sextet)**
Tracks: / Apart together / Look to your heart / Pazmuerte / Aim / Conflict / Coming home.
**Album:** Released Jun '85, on Boplicity by Ace Records. Deleted '88. Catalogue no: **COP 005**

## Woods, Phil

**AT THE VILLAGE VANGUARD (Woods, Phil Quartet)**
**CD:** Released '86, on Polystar (Japan) Catalogue no: **J33D 20003**

**BIRDS OF A FEATHER (Woods, Phil Quartet)**
**CD:** Released '86, on Polystar (Japan) Catalogue no: **J33D 20004**

**BOP STEW (Woods, Phil Quintet)**
Tracks: / Dreamsville / Bop stew / Poor Butterfly / Ys, There Is A C O Y A.
Note: First album for Concord from top alto player Woods, with Tom Harrell (trumpet), Hall Galper (piano), Steve Gilmore (bass) and Bill Goodwin (drums). Recorded at the Concord Jazz Festival in Japan, 1987. Sleeve notes by Leonard Feather. CD version has one extra track.
**Cass:** Released Jul '88, on Concord Jazz by Concord Jazz Records (USA). Catalogue no: **CJ 345 C**
**CD:** Released Jul '88, on Concord Jazz by Concord Jazz Records (USA). Catalogue no: **CCD 4345**
**Album:** Released Jul '88, on Concord Jazz by Concord Jazz Records (USA). Catalogue no: **CJ 345**

**BOUQUET (Live at the Fujitsu Concord Jazz Festival) (Woods, Phil Quintet)**
Note: The name Phil Woods has become synonymous with hard driging red hot jazz and with good reason. Bouquet, Woods most recent recording on Concord confirms this bebop master's uncompromising commitment to presenting quality and innovative music. Personnel: Phil Woods (alto sax & clarinet), Tom Harrell (trumpet and flugelhorn), Hal Galper (piano), Steve Gilmore (bass), Bill Goodwin (drums).
**CD:** Released May '89, on Concord Jazz by Concord Jazz Records (USA). Catalogue no: **CCD 4377**
**Cass:** Released May '89, on Concord Jazz by Concord Jazz Records (USA). Catalogue no: **CJ 377 C**
**Album:** Released May '89, on Concord Jazz by Concord Jazz Records (USA). Catalogue no: **CJ 377**

**CHROMATIC BANANA**
Tracks: / Chromatic banana / Ultimate choice / Sans melodie / Look back / Day when the world comes alive.
**Album:** Released Mar '83, on Affinity by Charly Records. Deleted '88. Catalogue no: **AFF 84**

**CRAZY HORSE (Woods, Phil & Chris Swansen)**
**Album:** Released Nov '88, on Sea Breeze Catalogue no: **SB 2008**

**EUROPEAN TOUR, LIVE**
**Album:** Released Sep '86, on Red Pepper by Interstate Music. Catalogue no: **VPA 163**

**EVOLUTION (Woods Phil, Little Big Band)**
Tracks: / Alvin G / Black flag / Hal mallet / Miles ahead (Only on CD.) / Rain go away (Only on CD.) / Song for Sisyphus / Thaddeus / Which way is uptown.
Note: Bop master and one of the all time great alto saxophonists, Phil Woods was voted the number one alto player in the 36th Annual Down Beat Critics Poll. On this, his second release on Concord, Woods is blazing new trails with an augmented ensemble he calls his 'Little Big Band'. Phil Woods, alto sax & clarinet, Tom Harrell, trumpet & flugelhorn, Nick Brignola, baritone sax, Hal Crook, trombone, Nelson Hill, tenor sax, Hal Galper, piano, Steve Gilmore, bass and Bill Goodwin, drums. (New Note, Nov 1988)
**Cass:** Released Nov '88, on Concord by Concord Jazz Records (USA). Catalogue no: **CJ 361 C**
**CD:** Released Nov '88, on Concord by Concord Jazz Records (USA). Catalogue no: **CCD 4361**
**Album:** Released Nov '88, on Concord by Concord Jazz Records (USA). Catalogue no: **CJ 361**

**FLASH (Woods, Phil Quintet Plus One)**
Tracks: / Journey to the center / Autumn nocturne / Dr Dunk / Flash / Misirlou / Ebullition / Weaver (Available on CD only) / Rado (Available on CD only) / Bradley's revenge (Available on CD only).
**Cass:** Released Mar '90, on Concord by Concord Jazz Records (USA). Catalogue no: **CJ 408C**
**CD:** Released Mar '90, on Concord by Concord Jazz Records (USA). Catalogue no: **CCD 4408**

**GRATITUDE (Woods, Phil Quartet)**
Tracks: / 111-444 / Another Jones /

Gratitude / My azure / Serenade in blue / Tenor of the times / Times mirror / Ya know.
Note: There is no doubt that Phil Woods remains one of the absolute masters of the alto-sax and this recording substantiates this claim. Apart from the awesome standard of solo contributions the most outstanding aspect of the exceptional release is the rapport sustained by the band throughout. (Denon 10/88). Personnel: Phil Woods (Alto sax / Clarinet), Tom Harrell (Trumpet / Flugelhorn), Hal Galper (Piano), Steve Gilmore (Bass), Bill Goodwin (drums).
**Cass:** Released Oct '88, on Denon Catalogue no: **CC 14**
**CD:** Released Oct '88, on Denon Catalogue no: **CY 1316**

**HEAVEN (Woods, Phil Quintet)**
Tracks: / I'm getting sentimental over you / Heaven / Duke, The / Azure / 222 / Occurrence.
Note: Phil Woods (alto saxophone), Tom Harrell (trumpet, flugelhorn), Hal Galper (piano), Steve Gilmore (bass), Bill Goodwin (drums)
**Cass:** Released Sep '86, on Black Hawk (USA) by Blackhawk Records (USA). Catalogue no: **BKHMC 50401**
**Album:** Released Sep '86, on Black Hawk (USA) by Blackhawk Records (USA). Catalogue no: **BKH 50401**

**INTEGRITY (Woods, Phil Quintet)**
Note: The new Phil Woods Quintet live.
**2 LP Set:** Released Jan '87, on Red (Italy) Catalogue no: **VPA 177**

**LITTLE BIG BAND**
**CD:** Released Jan '89, on Concord by Concord Jazz Records (USA). Catalogue no: **CCD 4361**
**Album:** Released Jan '89, on Concord by Concord Jazz Records (USA). Catalogue no: **CJ 361**
**Cass:** Released Jan '89, on Concord by Concord Jazz Records (USA). Catalogue no: **CJ 361 C**

**LIVE AT ARMADILLO (Woods, Phil Quartet)**
**Album:** Released '88, on Echo by Echo Records. Deleted Jun '89. Catalogue no: **ECJ 401**

**MUSIQUE DU BOIS**
**Album:** Released Apr '81, on Muse by Black & Blue Records. Catalogue no: **MR 5037**

**PAIRING OFF**
**Album:** Released Aug '84, on Prestige (USA) by Fantasy Inc (USA). Catalogue no: **OJC 092**

**PHIL AND QUILL WITH PRESTIGE (Woods, Phil/Gene Quill quintet)**
**Album:** Released Apr '86, on Original Jazz Classics (USA) by Fantasy Inc (USA). Catalogue no: **OJC 215**

**PHIL WOODS SIX, THE**
Tracks: / Sleepin' bee, A / Rain danse / Bye bye baby / Django's castle / I'm late / Superwoman (where were you when I needed you) / High clouds / How's your mama (Phil's theme) / Cheek to cheek / Lady J / Little Niles / Little peace, A / Brazilian affair / Prelude (preludio) / Love song (Cancao de amor) / Wedding dance / Joy (alegria).
**Album:** Released '79, on RCA by BMG Records (UK). Deleted '84. Catalogue no: **PL 02202**

**PIPER AT THE GATES OF DAWN (Woods, Phil & Chris Swansen)**
**Album:** Released Nov '88, on Sea Breeze Catalogue no: **SB 2019**

**RIGHTS OF SWING**
Tracks: / Prelude and part 1 / Part 2 (ballad) / Part 2 (waltz) / Part 4 (scherzo) / Part 5 (presto).
**CD:** Released Sep '88, on Candid Catalogue no: **CCD 9016**
**Album:** Released Jun '86, on Candid Catalogue no: **CS 9016**

**SONG FOR SISYPHUS (Woods, Phil Quintet)**
Tracks: / Song for Sisyphus / Last night when we were young / Nuages / Change partners / Monking business / Summer afternoon / When my dreams come true / Shaw 'nuff.
**Album:** Released Feb '79, on RCA by BMG Records (UK). Catalogue no: **PL 25179**

**THREE FOR ALL (Woods, Phil, Tommy Flanagan & Red Mitchell)**
**Album:** Released Jan '82, on Enja (Germany) by Enja Records (West Germany). Catalogue no: **ENJA 3081**

**WOODS NOTES (Woods, Phil & European Rhythm Machine)**
**Album:** Released Sep '87, on Lotus Catalogue no: **LOP 14 083**

## Workman, Reggie

**WORKS OF WORKMAN, THE**
**Album:** Released Mar '82, on Denon Deleted '88. Catalogue no: **YX 7539**

## World Rhythm Band

**IBEX (World Rhythm Band & Jeff Pressing Quintet)**
Tracks: / less Trocanter / Huseybi saz demaisi / Ibex / Flight / Home and mind / Stumbling along.
Note: A group from Australia performing unusual interpretations of Afro-jazz compositions.
**Album:** Released '88, on Discovery (USA) by Discovery Records (USA). Catalogue no: **DS 865**

## World Saxophone

**Biographical details:** World Saxophone Quartet comprised saxophonists Hamiet Bluiett, Julius Hemphill, Oliver Lake and David Murray, who was replaced in 1986 by John Stubblefield. Unlike the UK's Itchy Fingers they play without accompaniment and on records with an excess of production. See entries for individuals. (Donald Clarke 21 May 1988).

**DANCES AND BALLADS**
**Album:** Released '88, on Nonesuch Catalogue no: **979164 1**
**Cass:** Released '88, on Nonesuch Catalogue no: **979164 4**
**CD:** Released Jun '88, on Nonesuch Catalogue no: **979164 2**

**LIVE IN ZURICH**
Tracks: / Funny paper / Touchic / My first winter / Border town / Steppin' / Stick / Hattie wall.
**CD:** Released '86, on Black Saint (Italy) Catalogue no: **BSR 0077**

**PLAYS DUKE ELLINGTON**
**Cass:** Released Sep '87, on Nonesuch (USA) by Nonesuch Records (USA). Catalogue no: **K 979137 4**
**Album:** Released Sep '87, on Nonesuch (USA) by Nonesuch Records (USA). Catalogue no: **K 979137 1**

**STEPPIN'**
**CD:** Released '86, on Black Saint (Italy) Catalogue no: **BSR 0027**

**WORLD SAXAPHONE QUARTET**
**CD:** Released Oct '87, on Nonesuch Catalogue no: **979 137 2**

## Worlds Greatest Dixie Band

**SONGS THAT LOST THE WAR**
Tracks: / Lou-easy-an-i-a: *Various artists* / West End blues: *Various artists* / Dardanella: *Various artists* / Over the rainbow: *Various artists* / Weary blues: *Various artists* / Tuxedo rag: *Various artists* / At a Georgia camp meeting: *Various artists* / Trick or treat boogie: *Various artists* / It don't mean a thing: *Various artists.*
**Album:** Released Apr '79, on Jazz Connoisseur by Spotlite Records. Catalogue no: **JAZZ CASS 002**

## World's Greatest Jazz

**CENTURY PLAZA (Featuring Yank Lawson & Bob Haggart)**
**Album:** Released Apr '79, on World Jazz Catalogue no: **WJLPS 1**

**HARK THE HERALD ANGELS SWING (Featuring Yank Lawson & Bob Haggart)**
**Album:** Released Apr '79, on World Jazz Catalogue no: **WJLPS 2**

**IN CONCERT AT MASSEY HALL, VOL. 1 (Featuring Yank Lawson & Bob Haggart)**
Tracks: / Original dixieland one-step / Crawfish shuffle / I want to be happy / Do you know what it means (to Miss New Orleans) / California here I come / Fidgety feet / South / Lover come back to me / If you knew Susie / St. Louis Blues.
**Album:** Released Apr '81, on World Jazz Catalogue no: **WJLPS 3**

**IN CONCERT AT CARNEGIE HALL, VOL. 2**
Tracks: / At the jazz band ball / Just a closer walk with thee / Walk with thee / I've found a new baby / Hundred years from today / Lady is a tramp, The / Sweet Georgia Brown / Muskrat ramble / When your lover has gone / I gotta right to sing the blues / Keeping out of mischief / Chicago / Swing that music.
**Album:** Released Apr '81, on World Jazz Catalogue no: **WJLPS 4**

**ON TOUR**
Tracks: / Sheik of Araby, The / Basin street blues / Wrap your troubles in dreams / Just one of those things / Do you know what it means to Miss New Orleans / St. Louis blues / Mandy make up your mind / Stardust / Limehouse blues / Dear old Southland / When the saints go marching in / Stumbling / Poor butterfly / Caravan / Running wild / Big butter and egg man / I've got the world on a string / Too marvellous / Squeeze me / Hindustan.
**2 LP Set:** Released Apr '81, on World Jazz Catalogue no: **WJLPS 8/10**

**WORLD'S GREATEST JAZZ BAND PLAYS COLE PORTER**
Tracks: / Love for sale / All of you / It's alright with me / Let's do it / I concentrate on you / Just one of those things / Anything goes / It's de - lovely / Rosalie / So in love / You'd be so nice to come home to / From this moment on.
**Album:** Released Apr '81, on World Jazz Catalogue no: **WJLPS 6**

**WORLD'S GREATEST JAZZ BAND PLAYS DUKE ELLINGTON**
Tracks: / Take the 'A' train / Mood indigo / Just squeeze me / I got it bad and that ain't good / Perdido / Satin doll / Prelude to a kiss / In a mellow tone / Do nothing till you hear from me / Rockin' in rhythm.
**Album:** Released Apr '81, on World Jazz Catalogue no: **WJLPS 9**

**WORLD'S GREATEST JAZZ BAND PLAYS GEORGE GERSHWIN**
Tracks: / I've got a crush on you / But not for me / How long has this been going on / Embraceble you / Strike up the band / Who cares / Maybe / Fascinating rhythm / Soon / 'S wonderful.
**Album:** Released Apr '81, on World Jazz Catalogue no: **WJLPS 11**

**WORLD'S GREATEST JAZZ BAND PLAYS RODGERS AND HART**
Tracks: / Mountain greenery / Have you met Miss Jones / Isn't it romantic / M funny valentine / Blue room / You toc advantage of me / Lady is a tramp, Th / Dancing on the ceiling / Where or whe / Bewitched / Thou swell / Lover.
**Album:** Released Apr '81, on Wor Jazz Catalogue no: **WJLPS 7**

## Wrencher, John Big

**BIG JOHN'S BOOGIE**
Tracks: / Honeydripper / Third degree Now darling / Where did you stay la night / Trouble makin' woman / Lon some in my cabin / How many mo years / Come on over / Telephone blu / Runnin' wild.
**Album:** Released '82, on Big Bear b Big Bear Records. Deleted '88. Cat logue no: **BEAR 4**

## Wyands, Richard

**THEN, HERE AND NOW**
**Album:** Released Jan '88, on Storyvi by Storyville Records AB. Catalogue n **SLP 4083**

# Y

The following information was taken from the Music Matser database on April 14th, 1990.

## Yacht Club Jazz Band

**YACHT CLUB JAZZ BAND, THE**
**Album:** Released Jan '83, on Swaggie (Australia) Catalogue no: **S 1375**

## Yamamoto, Tsuyoshi

**ZEPHYR**
Tracks: / Just in time / Moonlight in Vermont / I got rhythm / Waters of March / You go to my head / Satin doll / Shade of love, A / Smokehouse blues / Solitude.
Note: Tsuyoshi Yamamoto: piano. Concord House musicians - Bob Maize: bass. Jeff Hamilton: drums. Jeff Clayton: tenor, alto flute, oboe.
**Album:** Released Jun '83, on Concord Jazz by Concord Jazz Records (USA). Catalogue no: **CJ 218**

## Yamashita, Yosuke

**BANSLIKANA**
**Album:** Released Jan '82, on Enja (Germany) by Enja Records (West Germany). Catalogue no: **ENJA 2080**

**CLAY (Yamashita, Yosuke trio)**
**Album:** Released Jan '82, on Enja (Germany) by Enja Records (West Germany). Catalogue no: **ENJA 2052**

**INNER SPACE**
**Album:** Released Jan '82, on Enja (Germany) by Enja Records (West Germany). Catalogue no: **ENJA 3001**

**KODO VERSUS YOSUKE YAMASHITA IN LIVE (Yamashita, Yosuke & Kodo...)**
Tracks: / Bolero / Monochrome / Sunayama / Secret of basement room, The / Sing sing sing / Gezan Beyashi.
Note: Kodo Wadaiko Percussion Group / Yosuke Yamashita (Piano) / Panja Ensemble. This is a live recording.
**CD:** Released '88, on Denon Catalogue no: **C38-7900**

**TRIBUTE TO MAL WALDRON**
**Album:** Released Jan '82, on Enja (Germany) by Enja Records (West Germany)..Catalogue no: **ENJA 3057**

## Yancey, Jimmy

**Biographical details:** Jimmy Yancey (1898-1951) spent his whole life in Chicago, much of it as a groundkeeper at a baseball park; he was one of the finest exponents of boogie-woogie piano in its original manifestation as a blues form rather than a fad. Sometimes worked with his wife, blues singer Estella 'Mama' Yancey (1896-1986). (Donald Clarke 14.5.88).

**IMMORTAL JIMMY YANCEY, THE**
**Album:** Released Feb '77, on Oldie Blues Catalogue no: **OL 2813**

**JIMMY YANCEY VOL.1 (Immortal, The)**
**Album:** Released '88, on Oldie Blues Catalogue no: **OL 2802**

**PIANO BLUES OF 1939-40**
**Album:** Released '88, on Swaggie (Australia) Catalogue no: **S824**

**PIANO SOLOS 1939**
Tracks: / Jimmy's stuff / Rolling the stone / Steady rock blues / P.I.K. special / South side stuff / Yancey's gateway / La salle street breakdown / Two o'clock blues / Janie's joys / Lean bacon / Big bear train / Lucile's lament.
**Album:** Released Apr '81, on Joker (USA) by Lifetime Records (USA). Catalogue no: **SM 3101**

**PITCHIN' BOOGIE**
**Album:** Released Jan '83, on Swaggie (Australia) Catalogue no: **S 1235**

**YANCEY - LOFTON SESSION. VOL. 1 (Yancey, Jimmy & Cripple Clarence Lofton)**
**Album:** Released Feb '90, on Storyville by Storyville Records AB. Catalogue no: **SLP 238**

**YANCEY - LOFTON SESSION VOL.2 (Yancey, Jimmy & Cripple Clarence Lofton)**
Note: Mono.
**Album:** Released '86, on Storyville by Storyville Records AB. Catalogue no: **SLP 239**

## Yankee Brass Band

**YANKEE BRASS BAND, THE**
Tracks: / Arizona quickstep / Bond's serenade / No one to love / Blondinette polka / Mabel waltz / Helene Schottisch / American hymn, An / Red stocking quickstep / Mockingbird quickstep / Memories of home-waltz / Schottische / Moon is above us / Brin d'amour polka / Goodnight my angel / Firemen's polka.
Note: Full title: Yankee Brass Band, The music from mid-nineteenth century America. Featuring the American Brass Quintet Brass Band and the American Brass Quintett.
**Album:** Released Mar '87, on New World (USA) by New World Records (USA). Catalogue no: **NW 312**

## Yarra Yarra Jazzband

**ON TOUR VOL 1**
**Album:** Released Jun '88, on GHB by Jazzology Records (USA). Catalogue no: **GHB 78**

## Yeah Jazz

**JULIE & THE SEALIONS**
**Special:** Released Jun '84, on Distinctive by Distinctive Records. Catalogue no: **YEAH 4**
**Special:** Released Jun '84, on Distinctive by Distinctive Records. Catalogue no: **YEAH 7**

**MORNING O' GRADY**
Tracks: / Morning O'Grady.
**12" Single:** Released Oct '88, on Cherry Red by Cherry Red Records. Catalogue no: **12 CHERRY 101**

**SHARON**
Tracks: / Sharon / Girl the years were kind to, The / This is not love (On 12" single only.).
**12" Single:** Released Nov '87, on Cherry Red by Cherry Red Records. Catalogue no: **12 CHERRY 100**
**7" Single:** Released Nov '87, on Cherry Red by Cherry Red Records. Catalogue no: **CHERRY 100**

**SHE SAID**
Tracks: / She said / Rain / Travel Scrabble (Available on 12" version only).
**12" Single:** Released '86, on Upright by Upright Records. Catalogue no: **UPT 18**
**7" Single:** Released '86, on Upright by Upright Records. Catalogue no: **UP 18**

**SIX LANE ENDS**
Tracks: / Sharon / Stones / Lee Marvin / All of my days / Freeland / Step into the light / Heaven / Girl the years were kind to, The / Dirty windows / Make a fist / Stranger than fiction / All the stars.
**Album:** Released Feb '88, on Cherry Red by Cherry Red Records. Catalogue no: **BRED 82**

**THIS IS NOT LOVE**
Tracks: / This is not love / Any day / Childish games / Bob's song.
**12" Single:** Released '86, on Upright by Upright Records. Catalogue no: **UPT 14**
**7" Single:** Released '86, on Upright by Upright Records. Catalogue no: **UP 14**

## Yorkshire Jazz Band

**KING TUBA**
Note: Features Yorkshire Tuba player Bob Barclay.
**Album:** Released Dec '87, on Esquire by Titan Int. Prod.. Catalogue no: **ESQ 338**

## Young, Johnny

**CHICAGO BLUES BAND**
**Album:** Released May '81, on Arhoolie (USA) by Arhoolie Records (USA). Catalogue no: **ARHOOLIE 1029**

**JOHNNY YOUNG AND BIG WAL-**

**TER (Young, Johnny/Big Walter)**
**Album:** Released '81, on Arhoolie (USA) by Arhoolie Records (USA). Catalogue no: **ARHOOLIE 1037**

## Young, Larry

**UNITY**
Tracks: / Zolitah / Monk's dream / If / Moontrane, The / Softly as a morning sunsrise / Beyond all limits.
Note: Produced by Alfred Lion.(P) 1986 Manhattan Records,a division of Capitol Records Inc.Larry Young was a superb organist who could play with the best of Jimmy Smith's disciples in the Blues and Funk groove.But he chose to go one step further and introduce to the organ the more progressive school of Modern Jazz. With a stunning cast of Trumpeter Peter Woody Shaw,Tenor Saxophonist Joe Henderson and Drummer Elvin Jones.Young hits his zenith with this album,which has become an underground classic among proffesional musicians who understand the influence that it had on the music of the day.Highlights include Woody Shaw's 'The Moontrane',Henderson's 'If' and a magnificent organ-drums duet on Thelonius Monk's 'Monk's Dream'.
**Album:** Released Jul '89, on Blue Note by EMI Records. Catalogue no: **BST 84221**

## Young, Lester

**Biographical details:** Lester Young was born in 1909 in Mississippi and died in 1959 in New York; he is one of the most influencial stylists of all time on the tenor saxophone. He said he was influenced by Frankie Trumbauer, who played C-melody sax on Bix Beiderbecke's records. He played in the Young family band, then with territory bands all over the South and the Midwest, joining Count Basie in Kansas City just before Basie hit the big time: his first recordings were made with a Basie small group in 1936 called Smith-Jones Incorporated, in order to make them some money after Basie had signed a bad contract with Decca (now MCA): they are still incandescent, and could be regarded as the first modern jazz records. He played with a high, light tone, as though on an alto instead of a tenor; his improvisation was lyrical and linear, presenting an alternative to the dominant big, rich chordal style of Coleman Hawkins. His swing was the most astonishing since that of Louis Armstrong's in 1925; he floated over the bar lines, usually behind the beat rather than pushing it like Hawkins; he brought a fresh rhythmic freedom to jazz, and above all he always pretty, remembering the words to a song as he improvised on it. He was a star of the classic Basie band and made small group records on Commodore (where he played outstanding clarinet) and with Teddy Wilson and Billie Holiday: he named her Lady Day, she named him Prez, and their recordings together are outstandingly beautiful. He was a shy, intelligent, sensitive man who was nearly destroyed by the US Army, which put him in a racist stockade and gave a dishonourable discharge to a man who never did anything dishonourable in his life. The orthodox critical opinion was that his post-war work was somehow inferior, but that is not true: he always knew what he was doing on his horn and played well until the mid-'50s, but he no longer sounded so astonishing, because half of the saxophonists in the business were imitating him. (Donald Clarke 14.5.88).

**1939-40 (Young, Lester & Charlie Christian)**
**Album:** Released '88, on Jass Catalogue no: **JA 42**

**ALTERNATIVE LESTER, THE**
**Album:** Released '88, on Tax Catalogue no: **M 8000**

**COMPLETE SAVOY SESSIONS**
**Cass:** Released Oct '85, on RCA by BMG Records (UK). Deleted May '89. Catalogue no: **WK 70505**
**2 LP Set:** Released Oct '85, on RCA by BMG Records (UK). Deleted Nov '89. Catalogue no: **WL 70505**

**GENIUS OF LESTER YOUNG, THE**
**2 LP Set:** Released Jun '75, on Verve Catalogue no: **2683 058**

**HISTORICAL PREZ LESTER YOUNG 1940-44**
**Album:** Released '88, on Everybody's (USA) Catalogue no: **EV 3001**

**IN PARIS**
**Album:** Released Aug '81, on Polydor by Polydor Ltd. Catalogue no: **2034 489**

**IN WASHINGTON D.C. 1956**
Tracks: / Foggy day / Whin you're smiling / I can't get started / Fast Bob blues / D.B. blues / Tea for two / Jeepers creepers.
**Album:** Released '82, on Pablo Jazz (USA) by Pablo Records (USA). Catalogue no: **230 8219**
**Cass:** Released '82, on Pablo Jazz (USA) by Pablo Records (USA). Catalogue no: **K 08 219**

**IN WASHINGTON D.C. - VOL.2**
**Cass:** Released '82, on Pablo Jazz (USA) by Pablo Records (USA). Catalogue no: **K 08 225**
**Album:** Released '82, on Pablo Jazz (USA) by Pablo Records (USA). Catalogue no: **230 8225**

**IN WASHINGTON D.C. - VOL.3**
Tracks: / Just you, just me / Sometimes I'm happy / Up 'n Adam / Indiana / G['s if you please / There'll never be another you.
**Cass:** Released '82, on Pablo Jazz (USA) by Pablo Records (USA). Catalogue no: **K 08 228**
**Album:** Released '82, on Pablo Jazz (USA) by Pablo Records (USA). Catalogue no: **230 8228**

**IN WASHINGTON D.C. - VOL.4**
Tracks: / Talk of the town / I cover the waterfront / Pennies from heaven / G's, if you please / Almost like being in love / D.B. blues / I'm confessin'.
**Album:** Released '82, on Pablo Jazz (USA) by Pablo Records (USA). Catalogue no: **230 8230**
**Cass:** Released '82, on Pablo Jazz (USA) by Pablo Records (USA). Catalogue no: **K 08 230**

**JAMMIN' THE BLUES 1944/46**
**CD:** Released Oct '89, on Jazz Anthology by Musidisc Records (France). Catalogue no: **550092**

**JAZZ GIANTS, THE**
**CD:** Released Aug '86, on Polydor by Polydor Ltd. Deleted Jul '88. Catalogue no: **825 672-2**

**LESTER -- AMADEUS (with Count Basie)**
Tracks: / Moten swing / Shout and feel it / You and me that used to be, The / Count steps in, The / They can't take that away from me / I'll always be in love with you / Swing, brother, swing / Bugle blues / I got rhythm / Allez oop / Blues with Helen / I ain't got nobody / Don't be that way / Song of the wanderer / Mortgage stomp.
**Album:** Released Oct '82, on Nostalgia by Mainline Records. Catalogue no: **NOST 7639**
**CD:** Released Oct '82, on Nostalgia by Mainline Records. Catalogue no: **CDNOST 7639**

**LESTER LEAPS**
Tracks: / Saxy blues / I cover the waterfront / These foolish things / Lester leaps in / Lovers leap / Leap frog.
**Cass:** Released Apr '86, on Star Jazz (USA) by Charly Records. Catalogue no: **SJAZZC 10**
**Album:** Released Apr '86, on Star Jazz (USA) by Charly Records. Catalogue no: **SJAZZ 10**

**LESTER LEAPS AGAIN**
Tracks: / Up 'n' at 'em / Indiana / Too marvellous for words / Mean to me / Sweet Georgia Brown / I'm confessin' / Neenah / I cover the waterfront / Lester leaps in / I don't stand a ghost of a chance / How high the moon / Bebop boogie / D.B. blues / Lavender blues / These foolish things / Just you, just me / Lester leaps again.
Note: Live recordings from Birdland in the late 1940s.
**2 LP Set:** Released Feb '82, on Affinity by Charly Records. Catalogue no: **AFFD 80**

**LESTER LEAPS IN**
**Album:** Released Apr '81, on Jazz Live (Italy) Catalogue no: **BLJ 8021**

**LESTER MEETS MILES, M.J.O. & JACK TEAGARDEN ALL STARS**
**Album:** Released Apr '81, on Unique Jazz by Spotlite Records. Catalogue no: **UJ 04**

**LESTER YOUNG**
**Album:** Released Sep '87, on Giants of Jazz by Hasmick Promotions. Catalogue no: **LPJT 9**

**LESTER YOUNG COLLECTION (Retrospective)**
Tracks: / Blue Lester / Jump, Lester,

jump / Back home again in Indiana / Improvisation / Too marvellous for words / Pennies from Heaven / These foolish things / Polka dots and moonbeams / Three little words / Jumpin' with Symphony Sid / Up 'n' at 'em / Neenah / Ghost of a chance.
**Album:** Released Jun '88, on Deja Vu Catalogue no: **DVLP 2126**
**Cass:** Released Jun '88, on Deja Vu Catalogue no: **DVMC 2126**
**CD:** Released Aug '88, on Deja Vu Catalogue no: **DVCD 2126**

**LESTER YOUNG STORY - VOL.5**
Tracks: / Louisiana / Easy does it / Let me see / Blow top / I'm pulling through / Laughing at life / Time on my hands / Evenin' / World is mad / What's your number? / Five o'clock whistle / Broadway / All of me.
**Album:** Released Sep '80, on CBS by CBS Records. Catalogue no: **CBS 88493**

**LESTER YOUNG & THE PIANO GIANTS (Compact / Walkman jazz) (Young, Lester & The Piano Giants)**
Tracks: / This year's kisses / September in the rain / Red boy blues / I want to be happy / Up 'n Adam / Press returns / Just you, just me / Too marvellous for words / Three little words / I guess I'll have to change my plans / Man I love, The.
**Cass:** Released 15 Aug '88, on Verve Catalogue no: **835 316-4**
**CD:** Released Aug '88, on Verve Catalogue no: **835 316-2**

**LESTER YOUNG - VOL.1**
Tracks: / Pennies from Heaven / Stardust / Mean to me / On the sunny side of the street / Three little words.
**Album:** Released Jan '82, on Jazz Reactivation Catalogue no: **JR 111**

**LESTER YOUNG VOL. 2**
Tracks: / Bebop boogie / These foolish things / DB blues / Just you just me / I cover the waterfront / How high the moon / Sunday.
**Album:** Released Jul '83, on Jazz Reactivation Catalogue no: **JR 130**

**LESTER YOUNG - VOL.3**
Tracks: / Blues tree / I cover the waterfront / These foolish things / Lester leaps in / Sunday / Destination moon.
**Album:** Released May '83, on Jazz Reactivation Catalogue no: **JR 143**

**MASTERS OF JAZZ VOL.7**
**Album:** Released May '86, on Storyville by Storyville Records AB. Catalogue no: **SLP 4107**

**MOST IMPORTANT RECORDINGS OF LESTER YOUNG, THE**
Tracks: / Shoe shine boy / Shoe shine boy 2 / Oh, lady be good / This year's kisses / Sailboat in the moonlight, A / Every tub / Doggin' around / Jumpin' at the woodside / I can't get started / Shorty George / Taxi war dance / Dickie's dream / Lester leaps in / Tickle toe / I never knew / All of me / Body and soul / Hello babe / Just you, just me / Lester leaps again / I got rhythm / Exercise in swing / Blue Lester / Midnight symphony / D.B. blues / These foolish things / Lover come back to me / She's funny that way / Jumpin' with symphony Sid / Something to remember you by / St Louis blues II / Fine and mellow.
**LP Set:** on Official by Official Records. Catalogue no: **OFF 3035-2**

**ON THE AIR**
**Album:** Released Apr '81, on Queendisc (Italy) Catalogue no: **QU 001**

**PREZ AND FRIENDS (Young,Lester & The Kansas City Six)**
**Album:** Released May '87, on Commodore Class Catalogue no: **6.24292**

**PREZ AT HIS VERY BEST**
Tracks: / Just you just me / I never knew / Afternoon of a basie-ite / Sometimes i'm happy / Ater theatre jump / Six cats and a prince / Lester leaps again / Destination k.c..
**Album:** Released Oct '83, on Philips by Phonogram Ltd. Catalogue no: **6336 346**

**PREZ & COMPLETE SAVOY RECORDS**
Tracks: / Circus in rhythm / Poor little plaything / Tush / These foolish things / Exercise in swing / Salute to fats / Basie english / Blue Lester / I don't stand a ghost of a chance / Indiana / Jump Lester jump / Crazy over J-Z / Ding dong / Blues'n'bells / June bug.
**Album:** Released Sep '78, on Savoy Jazz (USA) by Malaco Records (USA). Catalogue no: **SJL 2202**

**PREZ CONFERENCE**
**Album:** Released '88, on GNP Crescendo (USA) by GNP Crescendo Records (USA). Catalogue no: **GNPS 2122**
**Cass:** Released '88, on GNP Crescendo (USA) by GNP Crescendo Records (USA). Catalogue no: **GNP5 2122**

**PREZ CONFERENCES**
**CD:** Released Mar '90, on Jass Catalogue no: **JASS CD 18**

**PREZ & FRIENDS**
Tracks: / Three little words / Jo-jo / I got rhythm / Four o' clock drag.
**Album:** Released Jul '82, on Commodore Class Catalogue no: **AG6 24292**

**PREZ LIVES**
**Album:** Released Oct '85, on Savoy (France) Catalogue no: **WL 70528**

**PREZ'S HAT, VOL 1**
Note: Paris 1952, 3, 6, 9/NY Blue Room May 10 & 17 1944.
**Album:** Released May '88, on Philology Catalogue no: **214W 6**

**PREZ'S HAT, VOL 2**
**Album:** Released May '88, on Philology Catalogue no: **214W 7**

**PREZ'S HAT, VOL 3**
Note: NY Birdland Apr 15 1953 & Aug 7 1956/NY Blue Room May 27 1944
**Album:** Released May '88, on Philology Catalogue no: **214W 8**

**PREZ'S HAT, VOL 4**
Note: NY Birdland Sept 5 1956/NY Blue Room May 27 1944
**Album:** Released May '88, on Philology Catalogue no: **214W 9**

**PREZ, THE**
Note: Featuring Buddy Rich, Nat King Cole, Oscar Peterson, Vic Dickenson.
**Album:** Released Sep '87, on Giants of Jazz by Hasmick Promotions. Catalogue no: **LPJT 67**
**Album:** Released Sep '84, on Audio Fidelity(USA) by Audio Fidelity (USA). Catalogue no: **CP 504**

**SAVOY RECORDINGS**
Tracks: / Circus in rhythm / Poor little plaything / These foolish things / Exercise in swing / Salute to Fats / Basie English / Blue Lester / I don't stand a ghost of a chance / Indiana / Crazy over J-Z / Jump Lester jump / Ding dong / Blues'n'bells / June bug.
**CD:** Released Nov '86, on RCA by BMG Records (UK). Deleted Nov '89. Catalogue no: **ZD 70819**

**SWEET GEORGIA BROWN**
**Album:** Released Feb '87, on Pathe Marconi (France) Catalogue no: **2600221**

**SWINGIN' SAX**
Tracks: / Saxy blues / I cover the waterfront / These foolish things / Lester leaps in / Younger than sax time / Prophet / Lovers leap / Leap frog.
**Album:** Released Jul '80, on Manhattan Records by President Records. Catalogue no: **MAN 5035**

**TOO MARVELLOUS FOR WORDS**
**Cass:** Released '82, on Jazz Bird Catalogue no: **ZCJAZ 2004**
**Album:** Released '82, on Jazz Bird Catalogue no: **JAZ 2004**

**TOP BOX, VOLS. 1-3**
Tracks: / Sweet Georgia Brown / Lester leaps in / Oh lady be good / Ghost of a chance / I got rhythm / Just you, just me / How high the moon / Jumpin' with Symphony Sid.
Note: Part of CD boxed set presented in chronological order. Live recordings. Each set contains a booklet giving detailed information on recordings and personnel.
**CD Set:** Released '89, on Jazz-Up Catalogue no: **JUTB 3019**

**TOP BOX, VOLS. 4-6**
Tracks: / On the sunny side of the street / Mean to me / Three little words / Up 'n Adam / Deed I do / Almost like being in love / One o'clock jump.
Note: Part of CD boxed set presented in chronological order. Each set contains a booklet giving detailed information on the live recordings and personnel.
**CD Set:** Released '89, on Jazz-Up Catalogue no: **JUTB 3022**

**TOP BOX, VOLS. 7-9**
Tracks: / Indiana / Ghost of a chance, A / How high the moon / Tea for two / Lester leaps in.
Note: Part of CD boxed set presented in chronological order. Each set contains a booklet giving detailed information on the live recordings and personnel.
**CD Set:** Released '89, on Jazz-Up Catalogue no: **JUTB 3025**

**TOP BOX, VOLS. 10-12**
**CD Set:** Released Mar '90, on Jazz-Up Catalogue no: **JUTB 3028**

**TOP BOX, VOLS. 13-15**
**CD Set:** Released Mar '90, on Jazz-Up Catalogue no: **JUTB 3031**

## Young Man With A Horn

**YOUNG MAN WITH A HORN (Original soundtrack) (Various artists)**
Note: Starring Doris Day and Harry James.
**Album:** Released Jan '89, on Silva Screen by Silva Screen Records. Catalogue no: **ACL 582**
**Cass:** Released Jan '89, on Silva Screen by Silva Screen Records. Catalogue no: **BT 582**

## Young, Mighty Joe

**BLUES WITH A TOUCH OF SOUL**
**Album:** Released Dec '88, on Delmark (USA) by Delmark Records (USA). Catalogue no: **DL 629**

**LEGACY OF THE BLUES-4**
**CD:** Released Jun '88, on Sonet by Sonet Records. Catalogue no: **SNTCD 633**
**Album:** Released Jun '88, on Sonet by Sonet Records. Catalogue no: **SNTF 633**
**Album:** Released May '89, on GNP Crescendo (USA) by GNP Crescendo Records (USA). Catalogue no: **GNPS 10014**

## Young, Trummy

**STRUTTIN' WITH SOME BARBECUE (Young, Trummy & Barney Bigard)**
**Album:** Released '88, on Zodiac by Delta Records. Catalogue no: **ZR 1017**

## Young Tuxedo Brass

**NEW ORLEANS**
**Album:** Released Sep '86, on 504 Catalogue no: **LPS 10**
**Cass:** Released Sep '86, on 504 Catalogue no: **TCS 10**

**SOUNDS OF NEW ORLEANS STREET**
Tracks: / Lead me saviour / Eternal peace / Medley of hymns / Just a closer walk with thee / Bourbon Street parade / Lord Lord Lord / Just a little while to stay here / Panama / It feels so good / Joe Avery's piece / John Cashmir's whoopin' blues.
**Album:** Released '77, on Atlantic by WEA Records. Deleted '82. Catalogue no: **K 50404**

## Young, Webster

**WEBSTER YOUNG PLAYS THE MILES DAVIS SONGBOOK, THE VOL. 1**
**Album:** Released '81, on VGM (Import) Catalogue no: **VGM 0004**

**WEBSTER YOUNG PLAYS THE MILES DAVIS SONGBOOK, THE VOL. 2**
**Album:** Released '81, on VGM (Import) Catalogue no: **VGM 0005**

**WEBSTER YOUNG PLAYS THE MILES DAVIS SONGBOOK, THE VOL. 3**
**Album:** Released '81, on VGM (Import) Catalogue no: **VGM 0006**

# Z

The following information was taken from the Music Master database on April 14th, 1990.

## Zawinul, Joe

**Biographical details:** Joe Zawinal was born in Vienna in 1932. The keyboardist and composer went to the USA in 1959; he accompanied Dinah Washington, joined Cannonball Adderley in 1961 and was a key member of that popular group, writing arrangements including Grammy winner *Mercy mercy mercy*, Adderley's biggest hit. he also recorded with Ben Webster, others. He began playing electronic keyboards and miscellaneous instruments, made important albums with Miles Davis (1969-70) including *In A Silent Way* and *Bitches Brew* and formed Weather Report in 1971 with Wayne Shorter, which they co-led until 1985. It was the most successful electronic jazz-rock fusion band, but most of its stuff sounds very much of the 1970's, twinkling and winking away to little effect. *Dialects* in 1986 is a solo disc, all synthesisers with no over-dubbing; in that year he formed a quintet with guitarist John Scofield and three Weather Report vetrans. (Donald Clarke 14.3.88).

### DIALECTS
Tracks: / Harvest, The / Waiting for the rain / Zeebop / Great empire,The / Carnavalito / 6 a.m. / Walking on the Nile / Peace.
**Album:** Released Mar '86, on CBS by CBS Records. Deleted Aug '87. Catalogue no: **CBS 26813**
**Cass:** Released Mar '86, on CBS by CBS Records. Deleted Aug '87. Catalogue no: **40 26813**

### ZAWINUL
Tracks: / Doctor Honoris Causa / In a silent way / His last journey / Double image / Arrival in New York.
**Album:** Released '74, on Atlantic by WEA Records. Catalogue no: **K 40349**

## Zeitlin, Denny

**Biographical details:** Denny Zeitlin was born in Chicago in 1938; he is a qualified and practicing psychiatrist as well as a composer, keyboardist, bassist and leader. He studied harmony with George Russell and began recording with flautist Jeremy Steig in 1963. He appeared at Monterey and Newport jazz festivals, retired in 1968 to study electronics, keyboards and the possibilities of fusion while maintaining his private psychiatric practice, came back to music in the '70s but has never recorded prolifically. (Donald Clarke 14.3.88).

### TIDAL WAVE
**Album:** Released Jan '85, on Palo Alto Catalogue no: **PA 8044**

### TIME REMEMBERS ONE TIME ONCE (Zeitlin, Denny & Charlie Haden)
**Album:** Released Mar '83, on ECM Catalogue no: **ECM 1239**

## Zenter, Si

### GREAT BAND WITH GREAT VOICES (The great voices of the great bands) (Zenter, Si & His Orchestra/Johnny Mann Singers)
Tracks: / Mississippi mud / Marie / Chattanooga choo choo / At last / On the sunny side of the street / Undecided / Paper doll / If I didn't care / Hut sut song, The / It happened in Monterey / I'll never smile again / Rum and coca cola.
Note: Full title: Si Zenter & His Orchestra with The Johnny Mann Singers."Great band with great voices swing..The great voices of the great bands".Quite a mouthful of title and quite an earful of swinging sound! This album, one of a pair released by this line up,has been re-issued due to public demand and radio interest-a substantial demand is anticipated.Contains lots of well loved tunes from the swing era including *Chattanooga Choo Choo* , *On the Sunny Side of the Street* , *If I didn't care* & *It Happened in Monterey.*
**Cass:** Released May '86, on Liberty by EMI Records. Deleted Jan '88. Catalogue no: **TC EMS 1164**
**Album:** Released May '86, on Liberty by EMI Records. Deleted Jun '88. Catalogue no: **EMS 1164**

## Zorn, John

**Biographical details:** John Zorn was born in 1953 in New York City; he plays alto and soprano saxes, clarinet, keyboards and duck calls and he is an avant-garde composer. He played hard-edged alto in the Sonny Clark Memorial Quartet (album *Voodoo* on Black Saint, with Wayne Horvitz on piano, Bobby Previte on drums, Ray Drummond on bass), tribute to late pianist; he has reccorded with the rock group The Golden Paliminos, with Derek Bailey and George Lewis and many others; he contributed to tribute sets *That's The Way I Feel Now* (Thelonious Monk) and *Lost In The Stars* (Kurt Weil), both on A&M. His own albums on small American labels and now on Nonesuch reveal a composer of aural works of art compared to the paintings of Jackson Pollock, a chameleon crawling through a paint box or an elephant trapped in barbed wire, but no description does his work justice: he is influenced by Stockhausen, Anthony Braxton and the cartoon anarchy of Bugs Bunny. (Donald Clarke 14.3.88).

### BIG GUNDOWN
Note: John Zorn plays the music of Ennio Morricone.
**Cass:** Released Jan '87, on Nonesuch (USA) by Nonesuch Records (USA). Catalogue no: **9791394**
**CD:** Released Jan '87, on Nonesuch (USA) by Nonesuch Records (USA). Catalogue no: **979 139 2**
**Album:** Released Jan '87, on Nonesuch (USA) by Nonesuch Records (USA). Deleted Jan '90. Catalogue no: **9791391**

### NEWS FOR LULU (Zorn, John/Bill Frisell / George Lewis)
**CD:** Released Jul '88, on Hat Art Catalogue no: **ARTCD 6005**

### SPILLANE
**Cass:** Released Mar '88, on Nonesuch Catalogue no: **K 979172 4**
**CD:** Released Mar '88, on Nonesuch Catalogue no: **K 979172 2**
**Album:** Released Mar '88, on Nonesuch Catalogue no: **K 979172 1**

### SPY VS SPY - THE MUSIC OF ORNETTE COLEMAN
**Album:** Released Aug '89, on Nonesuch Catalogue no: **K 960 844 1**
**Cass:** Released Aug '89, on Nonesuch Catalogue no: **K 960 844 4**
**CD:** Released Aug '89, on Nonesuch Catalogue no: **K 960 844 2**

## Zottola, Glenn

### CHRISTMAS IN JAZZTIME
**Album:** Released Dec '86, on Dreamstreet (USA) by Dreamstreet Records (USA). Catalogue no: **DR 110**

## Zurke, Bob

### BOB ZURKE & DELTA RHYTHM BAND (Zurke, Bob & Delta Rhythm Band)
**Album:** Released '88, on Meritt (USA) Catalogue no: **MERITT 16**

## Zwerin, Mike

### NOT MUCH NOISE
**Album:** Released May '83, on Spotlite by Spotlite Records. Catalogue no: **SPJ LP19**

## Zwingerberger, Axel

### BOOGIE WOOGIE LIVE
**Album:** Released Dec '86, on Calligraph Catalogue no: **CLGLP 011**

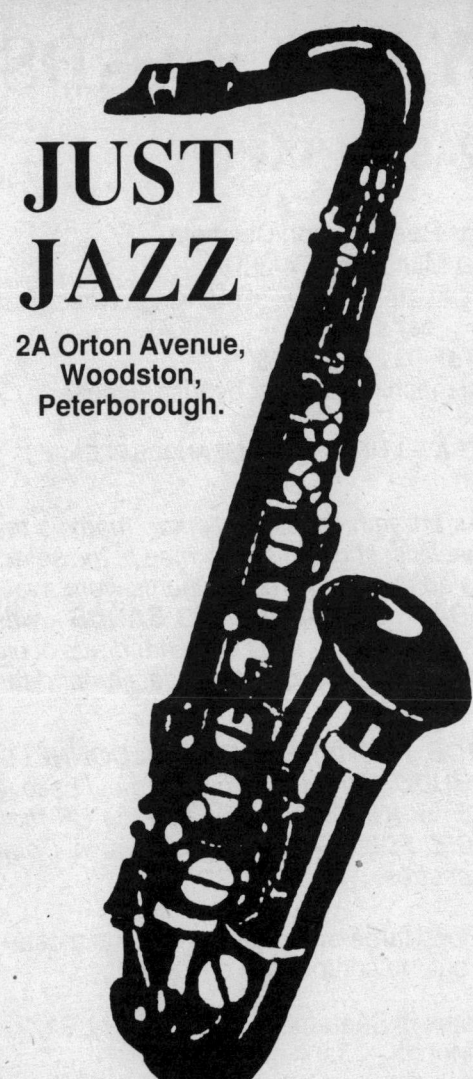